RECORD COLLECT

RARE
RECORD
PRICE
GUIDE
1994

Published in the United Kingdom 1994
by Diamond Publishing Group Limited,
45 St. Mary's Road, Ealing, London W5 5RQ

Printed in England

ISBN No. 0 9515553 4 0

RECORD COLLECTOR

RARE RECORD PRICE GUIDE 1994

PUBLISHED BY
RECORD COLLECTOR MAGAZINE
THE WORLD'S LEADING PUBLICATION FOR
COLLECTORS OF RARE RECORDS AND MEMORABILIA

PUBLISHER
Sean O'Mahony

MANAGING EDITOR
Johnny Dean

EDITOR
Peter Doggett

RESEARCH EDITOR
John Reed

ASSISTANT RESEARCH EDITOR
Andy Davis

ADDITIONAL RESEARCH
Mark Paytress
Pat Gilbert

PRODUCTION
Nicholas Barfield

ART DIRECTOR
Ian Gray

CONSULTANTS:
Laurence Cane-Honeysett, Malcolm Galloway, Ian Jones,
Eamonn Leightley, Paul Pelletier, Laurence Prangle (Soul Brother),
Pete Smith, Phil Spelman, Bob Thomas, Julian Thomas (Esprit),
Deke Wheeler, Dave Wilson.

ADDITIONAL INFORMATION:
K.E. Allen, Mike Atherton, Justin Beaney, Ben's Collectors Records, Paul Bird,
Owen Carne, Nick Chennells, Pete Chick, Dave Couldridge, Mark Dormon,
Phil Edwards, R. Edwards, Trev Faull, 58 Dean Street, Joe Geesin, Mark Griffiths,
George Richard Groom-White, Andy Halstead, Jason Hobbs, Jason Hodgson,
Keith Hunt, Noel Jones, Duncan Kennedy, Derek E. Leach, Bob Lusty,
Kevin McNulty, Lorne Murdoch, Andy Neill, Frank Prendergast, Brian Renforth,
Mick Reynolds, Rock of Ages, Howard Ross, John Seth, Neil Slater, Graham Spiers,
B.A. Sharp, N.M. Shiner, Duncan Smith, Ron Tabor, Steve Webb, David Wells,
Mike Weston, Andrew Whiteside & Rob Caiger, Barry Winton, Mark Woodroff.

CONTENTS

INTRODUCTION

Congratulations! You're reading the biggest, most comprehensive and most accurate Rare Record Price Guide ever published. Within the 1152 pages of this book, you'll be able to find the value of every collectable pop and rock record ever issued in Britain.

That's not all. Besides the detailed guide to soul, punk, indie, heavy metal, folk, reggae, funk, R&B and rock'n'roll that you would expect from the publishers of *Record Collector*, the world's best-selling magazine in the field, the 1994 edition of the *Rare Record Price Guide* has been enlarged, updated and fully revised. This new edition includes rare and valuable 78s for the first time, plus expanded coverage of blues, jazz, easy listening and film soundtracks.

The *Rare Record Price Guide 1994* now lists full descriptions and values of more than 70,000 singles and albums — covering every format from pre-war blues 78s to the latest digital technology of compact discs and digital audio tapes.

You'll find full details on how to use the *Rare Record Price Guide* on pages 12-15, plus a list of important abbreviations and specialist terms on page 19.

'RECORD COLLECTOR' MAGAZINE

Record Collector magazine was first published in 1979, and over the last 15 years it has become established as the bible of the pop and rock scene. When the magazine was born, record collecting was a small, disorganised business, which wasn't making much effort to encourage new people to get involved.

From the start, *Record Collector* set out to provide the information that collectors needed, whether they'd been buying and selling records for years, or were just starting to build up a collection. There were two vital things they wanted to know: what records had been released by their favourite artists, and how much were they worth?

Every issue of *Record Collector* has provided complete discographies (lists of records) for an amazing variety of performers, from pre-rock stars like Frank Sinatra to the latest arrivals. Our in-depth features have provided the essential information to help readers get the most out of their music — explaining the history of the artists and the records, and guiding people through the complicated business of telling rare items from common ones.

PRICING RECORDS

There is no fixed price for any second-hand record. The price is determined by what the buyer is prepared to pay, and what the seller will accept. In these recession-hit times, people quickly discover if they're overpricing their records.

THE BEATLES

MADONNA

The values listed in the *Rare Record Price Guide* are for items in Mint condition (see page 1150 for our Grading System). They are a guide, of course, not a hard-and-fast rule. But with our experience of the market, we've been able to work out the fairest possible price for each release.

One very important thing to remember: if you're selling to a shop or dealer, don't expect to get more than 50% of the price listed here. That's a standard mark-up that applies right across the collecting scene. Professional dealers have their overheads to cover and a profit margin to make. If you want the top price, sell privately to another collector, through the pages of *Record Collector*.

THE HISTORY OF THE PRICE GUIDE

In 1987, we published our first price guide — a slim volume designed as a quick and easy reference source to records by 2,000 important artists.

That was only the beginning, though. We soon began work on the first edition of the book you're holding. Published in late 1992, the first *Rare Record Price Guide* filled 960 pages and listed 60,000 rare and collectable records.

The response to that book was tremendous, but we soon realised that the collecting market was changing so quickly that we couldn't rest on our laurels. Every year, thousands of new records reach the shops, in a bewildering variety of formats — everything from 7" singles and cassettes to expensive multi-CD boxed sets, some of which retail at beyond the £100 mark.

A small but sizeable proportion of these new releases become instant collector's items. Over the last ten years, it's been very common for record companies to issue special limited editions — anything from a few hundred to a few thousand copies — which sell out in a few days. The most sought-after of these records soon begin to circulate on the collector's market, sometimes tripling or quadrupling their original retail price within a matter of weeks.

At the same time, interest in vinyl from the past continues to grow. As collectors track down all the records they want in a particular genre, they start to broaden their horizons. As a result, obscure items from the 50s, 60s and 70s suddenly become much-wanted treasures on the collector's market — and their prices soon rise to reflect the new demand.

THE BIRTH OF COLLECTING

When the collecting scene was in its infancy in the 1970s, the market was focused on very small areas, and it was quite simple for one person to know which records were collectable and which weren't.

All the early attention was concentrated on 1950s rock'n'roll, and 1960s beat music. In addition, major artists like the Beatles, the Rolling Stones, Elvis Presley and David Bowie began to attract specialist collectors, who wanted to track down a complete set of their recordings.

LIMITED EDITIONS

In the late 1970s, the arrival of punk and new wave spawned scores of new, independent record labels, who had fresh views about the way to market their releases. It became common for singles to appear in picture sleeves, as they had done overseas since the 1960s. Records also began to appear on coloured vinyl or as picture discs, in an attempt to attract more buyers. Never slow to cash in on a marketing trend, the major record companies soon joined in. By the early 1980s, they were issuing a bewildering variety of editions of the same record in slightly different formats.

This sudden change in marketing techniques helped to trigger an entirely new development on the collecting scene. For the first time, records were becoming instant collector's items. A limited edition single could be released one week, and sell for twice its retail price a fortnight later.

That opened the floodgates. No longer were 1950s and 1960s records the only things you'd find in the collector's shops. Now, it was open season, for anything and everything from Elvis Presley to Frankie Goes To Hollywood. The punk and new wave scene was the centre of a collecting boom, which soon spread into many other areas — psychedelic rock from the 60s, progressive rock from the 70s, and much more besides.

CDs AND VINYL

The arrival of compact discs (CDs) in the mid-1980s was greeted with doom and gloom in some quarters. But some CDs have actually helped increase the market for old vinyl releases. So many vintage recordings are available on CD that record-buyers today have a wider musical choice than ever before.

If you grew up in the 1960s, you probably remember that it was very difficult to find the records that had been hits only a few years earlier. Now, you can go into any record store and buy compilations of music from every era of pop and rock history. As a result, thousands of collectors are now keen to track down the original releases of music made before they were born.

What's more, CDs themselves have become collector's items. Only a small minority of full-length CD albums have acquired much second-hand value as yet, but CD singles have been popular with collectors for several years.

THE STATE OF THE MARKET

Over the last year, there have been several very noticeable trends in the collecting market — with some areas seeing increasing prices, while a few have shown a decline in demand.

Prices are still rising fast for original 1950s rock'n'roll and R&B singles on labels like London and Vogue. Any of these items in Mint condition will almost certainly continue rising in price in 1994, so you may have to pay more than we have indicated. Likewise, original 1960s albums by artists like the Beatles and the Stones, U.S. psychedelic bands, and those issued by cult record companies like 'orange label' Elektra and 'pink label' Island, are also going up in value all the time.

Also booming are British jazz LPs, by artists like Tubby Hayes; 1960s soundtrack LPs and film and TV spin-offs; 1970s and early 1980s black music, from funk to jazz-fusion and soul; reggae, ska and rocksteady from before 1973; and artists from the late 1970s/early 1980s 'New Wave Of British Heavy Metal'.

That last category illustrates an interesting point. Like many of the rarest progressive rock albums, these 'New Wave Of British Heavy Metal' releases are mainly selling to collectors in Europe and Japan. British collectors would be unlikely to pay equivalent prices — which means that an increasing number of these records are leaving the country for good. It remains to be seen what effect this will have on the U.K. market in future.

In the areas where the market has been booming, the key word is 'Mint' — i.e. top prices are only being paid for records in perfect condition. This particularly applies when the records in question are also available on CD. One thing the compact disc revolution certainly has done is to remind buyers that they don't have to listen to music through a layer of crackles and hiss!

The collecting market is changing all the time, as interest in some records and artists increases, and other items become less sought-after. But one thing is certain. The *Rare Record Price Guide 1994* is the best possible guide to the record collecting scene in the U.K. You can use it to value your own collection,

AXL ROSE of GUNS N' ROSES

to work out what you'll have to pay for the records you want, and to spot the thousands of bargains which are still out there, waiting to be found. Whatever your collecting interest, have fun!

Many thanks to all the collectors and dealers who helped us compile this new edition of the *Rare Record Price Guide*. Many readers have written to us, suggesting records that they thought deserved to be included. There isn't room to mention all those people here, but their help, assistance and enthusiasm has been invaluable in putting this book together.

HOW TO USE THE GUIDE

PRICING YOUR RECORDS

Although the *Rare Record Price Guide 1994* contains a comprehensive listing of collectable U.K. releases, it does NOT list all the recordings made by the artists we've included. Complete discographies of important artists can be found every month in *Record Collector* magazine.

MINIMUM VALUES FOR INCLUSION

ONLY THOSE RELEASES WHICH ARE CURRENTLY SOLD AT THE MINIMUM VALUES LISTED BELOW HAVE BEEN INCLUDED.
Any other releases obviously sell for less than these prices.

> 7" SINGLES, MAXI-SINGLES, CASSETTE SINGLES,
>   DOUBLE PACKS & FLEXIDISCS: £4
> 78s: £5
> 10" SINGLES: £5
> EPs, 12" SINGLES, CASSETTE EPs AND CD SINGLES: £7
> LPs: £10
> DOUBLE-LPs: £14
> CD ALBUMS: £15

NOTE: Unlike EPs from the 1950s and 1960s, which sold at around twice the retail price of a 7" single, many so-called EPs released since 1976 have actually been singles, which have been issued at normal 7" prices. These EPs have been included if they are worth £4 or more.

78rpm RELEASES

The market for 78rpm singles has been undergoing something of a revival in recent years, although they're still only sought-after by a small number of collectors. The common misconception about 78s is that they are more valuable than 7" singles. In fact, the complete opposite is true in most cases, as far more 78s were sold in the 1950s than 45rpm 7" singles.

The last batches of 78s issued in 1959 and 1960 are the main exception to this rule. As these were often only available by special order, they can prove to be much harder to find than their 45rpm equivalents.

All these collectable 78s from the 1950s have been added to this edition of the *Rare Record Price Guide*, along with earlier releases (some dating back as far as the 1920s) which are also of interest to modern pop and rock collectors. Almost all of these are by blues artists. The vast majority of 78s, however, are worth less than £5.

CURRENT MINT VALUES

The prices listed in this book are for the original issues of records, cassettes and CDs in MINT condition. To find out the value of any item which is in less than Mint condition, consult our Grading System on page 1150, and the Ready Reckoner on page 1151.

PACKAGING AND INSERTS

All prices refer to records with all their original packaging and inserts (where applicable) intact. Wherever possible, we have provided details of inserts and special items of packaging for each entry — pointing out gatefold sleeves, lyric sheets and other bonus items like posters, for example.

Any record with some or all of these additional items missing will obviously be worth less than the values listed here. The level of depreciation depends on the missing items: in some cases, an album can be almost worthless without its collectable booklet, while in others, it is the record itself that is desirable, and the insert is only of secondary importance.

DOUBLE PRICES: PICTURE SLEEVES

Since 1978, all U.K. 7", 10" and 12" singles have normally been issued in picture sleeves. Before 1978, however, picture covers were definitely the exception rather than the rule.

All singles that originally appeared in a picture sleeve are listed with the abbreviation '(p/s)'. In many cases, there are two prices listed for these items: the first refers to the record *with* its picture sleeve, the second *without*. If only one price is listed, then the single has to have its picture sleeve intact and in Mint condition to quality for this value.

Most singles from the 1950s, 1960s and early 1970s were issued in 'company' sleeves, carrying the name and logo of the label which issued the record. The prices listed in this guide are for singles with their company sleeves intact, and in Mint condition, like the records themselves. Many collectors are not concerned about company sleeves, but some of the more obscure sleeves can be worth nearly as much as the record.

For example, an original Kinks single from 1966, valued at £4, may only be worth £3.50 without its company sleeve. At the other extreme, no rock'n'roll collector is going to be bothered if a copy of a rarity like Bobby Charles' "See You Later Alligator", valued at £1,200, comes in a plain sleeve, or indeed, no sleeve at all — what matters here is that the record is in Mint condition.

DOUBLE PRICES: FREEBIES & INSERTS

Two prices have been listed for many items which were available in more than one form. 'Freebie' singles given away with newspapers and magazines have two values: the first for the record *with* the publication, the second for the disc itself. Records which were issued only briefly with an insert, like a poster or lyric sheet, are often priced both with *and* without the extra packaging.

DOUBLE PRICES: CHANGES IN DESIGN

Two or more prices have also been given for records which were released more than once with the same catalogue number, but in slightly different form — with a change of label colour or sleeve design (for instance, the substitution of triangular centres by round centres on late 1950s singles), or the manufacture of more recent singles in a variety of different coloured vinyls.

These variations of packaging and presentation can make an enormous difference to the price of a record, which is why we have documented them here. They help collectors identify the first pressing or edition of each release, which is almost always more sought-after than later issues of the same record. One notable example is the first edition of the Beatles' "Please Please Me" LP, which featured the gold-and-black Parlophone label for a few weeks, before the introduction of the more modern-looking yellow-and-black label. Gold-and-black copies of the stereo version of this LP are worth £700, as against £25 for the yellow-and-black edition issued a few weeks later.

Occasionally, second pressings can be worth more than the originals, as is the case with early Shadows and Cliff Richard singles. Green label copies of these 45s sold in their millions, while later re-pressings on black labels are much scarcer. So always check which pressing of any record you are buying before parting with your money.

MONO AND STEREO

In the case of EPs and LPs from the 1950s and 1960s, mono and stereo releases often have different values — and different catalogue numbers. Both prices are listed, together with the separate catalogue numbers for the two versions of each release (mono first, then stereo). Where the mono and stereo editions are worth the same amount, only one price has been listed.

U.K. RELEASES AND EXPORT ISSUES

Only U.K. releases are included in the *Rare Record Price Guide*, not overseas issues. The only exceptions to this rule are a handful of U2 singles from the Irish Republic which were heavily imported into Britain, but not officially issued here; and a number of 'Export Releases' by major artists, manufactured in the U.K. in the 1950s and 1960s by companies like EMI and Decca for distribution to countries which didn't have their own pressing plants. Export records by artists like the Beatles and the Rolling Stones are often worth many times the values of similar items destined for the U.K.

U.K. RELEASES MADE OVERSEAS

Although the great majority of the records we've listed were manufactured in the U.K., not all U.K. releases were made in this country — or vice versa. For example, a large proportion of the Rolling Stones' U.S. singles on the London label in the 1960s were actually manufactured in Britain. More recently, many British releases by major labels — notably WEA — have been made in Europe, and sent in identical form to Britain and many other countries. In these cases, the record sleeves often carry many different catalogue numbers, to cater for every country where the records are being distributed.

The problem of identifying the country where a particular record has been issued has grown more difficult with the advent of CDs. Many of the compact discs issued in Britain over the last ten years were actually made in Europe, or sometimes even in Japan. In these cases, it is the packaging that helps you identify the origin of a particular CD, rather than the disc itself.

COMMERCIAL RELEASES, NOT PROMOS

In general, this Guide only includes records which were manufactured for commercial release, or for distribution in some way to the public — as a freebie with a magazine, for example.

Promotional records, demos, acetates and test pressings have not been included, apart from exceptional cases where these items actually reached the public, or where (as with artists like Blinky & Edwin Starr) one promo single has become so famous among collectors that it would have been misleading for it not to be mentioned.

Full details of the values of non-commercial rarities like promos, demos, acetates and test pressings can be found in the articles and discographies in *Record Collector* every month. They were also documented in the 'Special Pressings' series published in the magazine (see page 1149 for more details).

ALPHABETICAL ORDER

The artists in this Guide are listed in alphabetical order, from A to Z. After the alphabetical listings, there is a section of Various Artists compilation releases, divided into four sections covering singles and EPs, LPs, film soundtrack LPs and original cast recordings from theatrical shows.

The alphabetical order within the Guide has been determined by the first letter of a group name or an artist's surname. The word 'the' has not been included when placing artists in alphabetical order; for instance, 'the Beatles' are listed under 'B', rather than 'T'.

The order follows the usual alphabetical principle of 'reading through' an artist's name or title, so that (for example) 'Peter Gabriel' is listed before 'Gabriel's Angels', and 'Generation X' is listed before 'Gen X'. Names and titles which include numbers appear as if the number was spelt out in full; e.g. the band '2.3' are listed as if their name was 'Two.Three'.

CHRONOLOGICAL ORDER

Within each artist entry, records are listed in chronological order of release. Singles (including 7", 10", 12", CD, cassette, and double packs) are listed first; then EPs; and finally LPs (including cassette and CD albums).

In the case of long entries by major artists like the Beatles and the Rolling Stones, export singles and Christmas Fan Club 45s have also been grouped together to make them easier to find.

IMPORTANT NOTE

Every effort has been taken to ensure that the information contained in this Price Guide is as accurate and up-to-date as possible. However, the publishers cannot take any responsibility for any errors or omissions; nor can they be held responsible or liable for any loss or damage to any person acting on the information in this Guide. The publishers welcome any corrections or additions to the Guide, which will be considered for future editions.

THE WORLD'S LEADING AUTHORITY

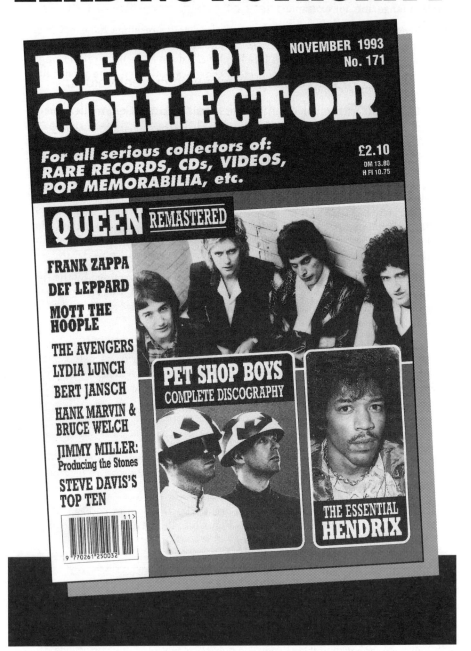

NOVEMBER 1993
No. 171

RECORD COLLECTOR

For all serious collectors of:
RARE RECORDS, CDs, VIDEOS,
POP MEMORABILIA, etc.

£2.10
DM 13.80
H FI 10.75

QUEEN REMASTERED

FRANK ZAPPA

DEF LEPPARD

MOTT THE HOOPLE

THE AVENGERS

LYDIA LUNCH

BERT JANSCH

HANK MARVIN & BRUCE WELCH

JIMMY MILLER: Producing the Stones

STEVE DAVIS'S TOP TEN

PET SHOP BOYS
COMPLETE DISCOGRAPHY

THE ESSENTIAL HENDRIX

Every month **RECORD COLLECTOR** provides detailed features on a wide variety of artists from the last 40 years of popular music.

PLUS:

- Complete Discographies with current values.

- Reviews of all the latest reissue and compilation CDs, music videos, rock books and fanzines.

- Up-to-the-minute news from the collecting scene.

- Over 50,000 records and CDs for sale & wanted.

DON'T MISS OUT – BUY

RECORD COLLECTOR

EVERY MONTH

USING THE GUIDE
A BRIEF SUMMARY

ALL PRICES REFER TO RECORDS
AND PACKAGING IN MINT CONDITION
(See pages 1150/1151 for Grading System and Ready Reckoner)

ARTISTS AND GROUPS are listed in alphabetical order.
Numerical names (e.g. 2.3) are listed as if the numbers are spelt in full.

ALL RECORDS LISTED ARE
U.K. COMMERCIAL RELEASES
with the following exceptions:

(1) Records pressed in the U.K. for export overseas.

(2) Important one-off demo or promo releases that are the only major collectable items by minor artists.

(3) Records or flexidiscs included as freebies with magazines, books and other records.

PROMOS & DEMOS ARE NOT INCLUDED

EACH ENTRY includes:

SINGLES (7" 45s & cassettes) worth £4 or more

78s and 10" singles worth £5 or more

EPs, 12" singles & CD singles worth £7 or more

LPs worth £10 or more

DOUBLE-LPs worth £14 or more

CD ALBUMS worth £15 or more

Records worth less than these prices have not been included.

WITHIN EACH ENTRY, records are listed in chronological order of release, within each of the following three categories:

(1st) SINGLES; (2nd) EPs; (3rd) LPs, ALBUMS & CDs

Where TWO PRICES are listed for a single item, they refer to

(a) the record with and without a special insert or piece of packaging

(b) mono and stereo editions of EPs and LPs

(c) pressings of the same record with different label or sleeve designs.

ABBREVIATIONS
USED IN THIS GUIDE

alt.	alternative	no.	number
b&w	black and white	no'd	numbered
cass.	cassette	p/s	picture sleeve
cat. no.	catalogue number	pic disc	picture disc
CD	compact disc	pt(s)	part(s)
co.	company	stkr	sticker
d/pack	double pack	sl.	sleeve
dble.	double	st.	stereo
diff.	different	t/p	test pressing
edn.	edition	vers.	version
ext.	extended	vol.	volume
flexi	flexidisc	w/	with
g/f(old)	gatefold sleeve	w/l	white label
intl.	international	2-CD	double CD
m/s	mono/stereo	2-LP	double LP
mag.	magazine	3-LP	triple LP

OTHER IMPORTANT TERMS

company sleeve	standard non-picture cover bearing the company name or logo, used by a label for its single releases
demo	demonstration record not commercially available to the public
die-cut sleeve	sleeve with circular hole cut into the centre
double pack	two singles issued together as one package
gatefold sleeve	double-size sleeve that opens out like a book
private pressing	record issued and distributed by private individuals rather than a company
promo	promotional record or item sent out to the media to publicise a new release
stickered	record issued with a small sticker on the cover, sleeve or wrapping
test pressing	manufacturer's sample record, pressed for quality control purposes
tri-centre	push-out triangular centre found on some 1950s singles and EPs
tri-fold	triple fold-out sleeve
withdrawn	record deliberately removed from sale by its manufacturer

AARDVARK
70	Deram Nova SDN 17	AARDVARK (LP)	60

LEE AARON
85	Roadrunner RR 5488	Barely Holding On/Danger Zone (p/s)	4
85	Roadrunner 12 RR 5488	Barely Holding On/Danger Zone/Call Of The Wild (12", p/s)	7
85	Roadrunner 12 RR 5495	Rock Me All Over/Line Of Fire/Evil Game (12", p/s)	7

ABACUS
71	Polydor 2371 215	ABACUS (LP)	35

ABBA
73	Epic EPC 1793	Ring Ring/Rock'N'Roll Band	35
74	Epic EPC 2452	Ring Ring (second version)/Rock'N'Roll Band	5
74	Epic EPC 2848	So Long/I've Been Waiting For You	12
75	Epic EPC 3229	I Do I Do I Do I Do I Do/Rock Me (yellow label)	5
79	Epic EPC 8088	I Have A Dream/Take A Chance On Me (live) (gatefold p/s)	7
80	Epic EPC 8835	The Winner Takes It All/Elaine (12", gatefold pop-up p/s)	30
81	Epic EPCA 11-1740	One Of Us/Should I Laugh Or Cry (picture disc)	4
82	Epic EPCA 11-2971	Under Attack/You Owe Me One (picture disc)	7
82	Lyntone LYN 2570/1	Happy Xmas Greetings (with other artists, flexidisc with 'Smash Hits' mag)	4
82	Epic EPCA 2618	GREATEST ORIGINAL HITS (EP)	4
82	Epic EPCA 2618	GREATEST ORIGINAL HITS (EP, cassette)	4
83	Epic A 38914	Thank You For The Music/Our Last Summer (poster p/s)	5
83	Epic WA 38914	Thank You For The Music/Our Last Summer (shaped picture disc)	12
84	Kelloggs KELL 1	I Have A Dream/SHAKIN' STEVENS: Oh Julie ('Rice Krispies' premium)	10
84	Epic ABBA 26	ANNIVERSARY BOXED SET (26 x blue vinyl 7", 2,000 only, numbered)	80
74	Epic EPC 32009	WATERLOO (LP, yellow label)	10
75	Epic EPC 80835	ABBA (LP, yellow label)	10
76	Epic EPC 69218	GREATEST HITS (LP, yellow label with "Fernando" sticker)	12
86	Epic EPC 11-86086	VOULEZ VOUS (LP, picture disc)	60
80	Epic PACH BH22/ABBOX 1	SUPER TROUPER (LP, box set with booklet & poster)	30
81	Epic EPC 86123	GRACIAS POR LA MUSICA (LP)	10
83	Epic ABBOX 2/ABBA 10	THE SINGLES — THE FIRST TEN YEARS (2-LP, picture discs, with poster, ticket & book in box)	50
83	Epic CDEPC 10022	SUPER TROUPER (CD, original issue)	15
83	Epic CDEPC 10032	THE VISITORS (CD, original issue)	15
86	Readers Digest GABA 112	THE BEST OF ABBA (5-LP box set)	25
86	Readers Digest GABC 112	THE BEST OF ABBA (5-cassette box set)	50

(see also Hep Stars, Hootenanny Singers, Northern Lights, Agnetha Faltskog, Frida)

ABBEY ROAD
73	Parlophone R 5989	Clunk-Click/Catamaran	10

BILLY ABBOTT & JEWELS
63	Cameo Parkway P 874	Groovy Baby/Come On And Dance With Me	12

ABC
83	Lyntone	"Beauty Stab" flexi sampler (yellow vinyl)	4
84	Neutron NTP 106	S.O.S./United Kingdom (picture disc)	4
85	Neutron NTD 108	Be Near To Me/A To Z//Poison Arrow (U.S. Remix)/The Look Of Love (U.S. Remix) (double pack, gatefold PVC sleeve with sticker)	4
85	Neutron NTP 109	Vanity Kills/Judy's Jewels (cartoon-shaped picture disc, PVC sleeve)	6
85	Neutron NTD 110	Ocean Blue/Tower Of London//All Of My Heart/The Look Of Love (double pack, stickered PVC gatefold p/s)	6
85	Neutron NT 110/NT 102	Ocean Blue/Tower Of London//Poison Arrow/Theme From "Mantrap" (p/s, shrinkwrapped double pack)	4
87	Neutron NTXG 113	King Without A Crown (Monarchy Mix)/The Look Of Love (live)/ Poison Arrow (live) (12", 'gold' p/s)	7
87	Neutron NTXRG 113	King Without A Crown (The Mendelson Mix)/The Look Of Love (live)/ Poison Arrow (live)/All Of My Heart (live) (12", 'gold' p/s)	7

(see also Vice Versa)

PAULA ABDUL
88	Siren SRNP 92	Knocked Out/Knocked Out (instrumental) (poster p/s)	4
88	Siren SRNS 92	Knocked Out/Knocked Out (instrumental) (shaped picture disc)	5
88	Siren SRNTX 101	(It's Just) The Way That You Love Me (U.S. Remix)/(It's Just) The Way That You Love Me (Drums All The Way Mix) (12", p/s)	7
88	Siren SRNCX 101	(It's Just) The Way That You Love Me (U.S. Remix)/(It's Just) The Way That You Love Me (Drums All The Way Mix) (CD)	8
89	Siren SRNP 111	Straight Up/Cold Heart (poster sleeve)	4
90	Siren SRNB 124	Opposites Attract/One Or The Other (in bag with 2 postcards & badge)	4

SHIRLEY ABICAIR
56	Parlophone MSP 6224	Willie Can/Happy Trails	8
57	Parlophone R 4347	Bimini/Where The Sun Always Shines (with Humphrey Lyttleton)	5
64	Piccadilly 7N 35364	I Will Be There/Am I Losing You	8
57	Parlophone GEP 8612	FAIR DINKUM (EP)	7

MICK ABRAHAMS (BAND)
71	Chrysalis ILPS 9147	A MUSICAL EVENING WITH THE MICK ABRAHAMS BAND (LP, g/fold sleeve)	15
72	Chrysalis CHR 1005	AT LAST (LP, circular foldout sleeve)	25

75	SRT SRTM 73313	HAVE FUN LEARNING THE GUITAR WITH MICK ABRAHAMS (LP) 15

(see also Blodwyn Pig, Jethro Tull)

ABRASIVE WHEELS
81	Abrasive ABW 1	Army Song/Juvenile/So Slow (p/s) 6
82	Riot City RIOT 4	VICIOUS CIRCLE (EP) 4
82	Riot City RIOT 9	Army Song/Juvenile/So Slow (p/s, reissue, red vinyl) 4
82	Riot City RIOT 16	Burn The Schools/Urban Rebels/Burn 'Em Down (p/s) 4

MIKE ABSALOM
60s	Sportsdisc ILP 1081	THE MIGHTY ABSALOM SINGS BATHROOM BLUES (LP) 15
69	Saydisc SDL 162	SAVE THE LAST GHERKIN FOR ME (LP) 25
71	Vertigo 6360 053	MIKE ABSALOM (LP, spiral label, poster sleeve) 60
73	Philips 6308 131	HECTOR AND OTHER PECCADILLOS (LP) 15

ABSOLUTE ELSEWHERE
76	Warner Bros K 16697	Earthbound/Gold Of The Gods 4
76	Warner Bros K 56192	IN SEARCH OF THE ANCIENT GODS (LP, with booklet) 10

ABYSSINIAN BAPTIST CHOIR
63	Philips 847095 BY	ABYSSINIAN BAPTIST CHOIR (LP) 40

ABYSSINIANS
73	Harry J HJ 6652	Yim Mas Gan/JOHN CROW GENERATION: Crank Shaft 5

ACADEMY
69	Morgan Bluetown BTS 2	Rachel's Dream/Munching The Candy 10
69	Morgan Bluetown BT 5001	POP-LORE ACCORDING TO THE ACADEMY (LP) 80

(see also Polly Perkins)

ACCELERATORS
81	Spiv ACCEL EP	POPGUNS AND GREEN LANTERNS (12" EP) 7

ACCENT
67	Decca F 12679	Red Sky At Night/Wind Of Change 70

(see also Rick Hayward)

ACCENTS
59	Coral Q 72351	Wiggle, Wiggle/Dreamin' And Schemin' 15
59	Coral Q 72351	Wiggle, Wiggle/Dreamin' And Schemin' (78) 18

ACCIDENTS
80	H. Line 'n' Sinker HOOK 1	Blood Spattered With Guitars/Curtains For You (p/s) 8
80	Hook Line 'n' Sinker	KISS ME ON THE APOCALYPSE (LP, unreleased; test pressings only, some with sleeves) 100/50

ACCIDENTS ON EAST LANCS.
81	Roach RR 1	The Back End Of Nowhere/Rat Race (p/s) 5
81	Roach SPLIFF 001	Tell Me What You Want/We Want It Legalised (p/s) 4

ACCOLADE
70	Columbia DB 8688	Natural Day/Prelude To A Dawn 7
70	Columbia SCX 6405	ACCOLADE (LP) 20
71	Regal Zono. SLRZ 1024	ACCOLADE 2 (LP) 25

(see also Gordon Giltrap)

ACCURSED
70s	Wrek 'Em ACC 3	Going Down (p/s) 4

AC/DC
76	Atlantic K 10745	It's A Long Way To The Top (If You Wanna Rock'N'Roll)/Can I Sit Next To You, Girl? 12
76	Atlantic K 10805	Jailbreak/Fling Thing (original issue, no p/s, dark label, heavy print) 12
76	Atlantic K 10860	High Voltage/Live Wire (some in p/s) 40/4
77	Atlantic K 10899	Dirty Deeds Done Dirt Cheap/Big Balls/The Jack (maxi-single, p/s) 25
77	Atlantic K 11018	Let There Be Rock/Problem Child 5
78	Atlantic K 11142	Rock'N'Roll Damnation/Sin City (no p/s) 4
78	Atlantic K 11142T	Rock'N'Roll Damnation/Sin City (12", p/s) 12
78	Atlantic K 11207	Whole Lotta Rosie (live)/Hell Ain't A Bad Place To Be (live) 4
78	Atlantic K 11207T	Whole Lotta Rosie (live)/Hell Ain't A Bad Place To Be (live) (12") 10
79	Atlantic K 11321	Highway To Hell/If You Want Blood, You've Got It ('1979' on p/s) 5
79	Atlantic K 11406	Girl's Got Rhythm/Get It Hot (p/s) 5
79	Atlantic K 11406E	Girl's Got Rhythm/If You Want Blood, You've Got It/Hell Ain't A Bad Place To Be (live)/Rock'N'Roll Damnation (p/s) 8
80	Atlantic K 11435	Touch Too Much/Live Wire (live)/Shot Down In Flames (live) (p/s) 5
80	Atlantic K 11435	Touch Too Much/Live Wire (live)/Shot Down In Flames (live) (p/s, misprinted back-to-front) 7
80	Atlantic K 10805	Jailbreak/Fling Thing (p/s, reissue, light label, fine print) 12
80	Atlantic K 11018	Let There Be Rock/Problem Child (reissue) 10
80	Atlantic K 11142	Rock'N'Roll Damnation/Sin City (p/s, reissue) 5
80	Atlantic K 11321	Highway To Hell/If You Want Blood, You've Got It (repressing,'1980' on p/s) 5
80	Atlantic HM 1	High Voltage/Live Wire (p/s) 4
80	Atlantic HM 2	Dirty Deeds Done Dirt Cheap/Big Balls/The Jack (reissue, p/s) 4
80	Atlantic HM 3	It's A Long Way To The Top (If You Wanna Rock'N'Roll)/Can I Sit Next To You (p/s, reissue) 4
80	Atlantic HM 4	Whole Lotta Rosie (live)/Hell Ain't A Bad Place To Be (live) (p/s, reissue) 4
80	Atlantic K 11600	You Shook Me All Night Long/Have A Drink With Me (p/s) 5
80	Atlantic K 11600	Shake A Leg/Have A Drink With Me (p/s, mispress) 50
80	Atlantic K 11630	Rock'N'Roll Ain't Noise Pollution/Hells Bells (p/s) 4
80	Atlantic K 11630T	Rock'N'Roll Ain't Noise Pollution/Hells Bells (12", p/s, some with badge) 10/7
82	Atlantic K 11706	Let's Get It Up/Back In Black (live) (p/s) 4
82	Atlantic K 11706T	Let's Get It Up/TNT (live)/Back In Black (live) (12", p/s) 7
82	Atlantic K 11721	For Those About To Rock (We Salute You)/Let There Be Rock (live) (p/s) 4

82	Atlantic K 11721T	For Those About To Rock (We Salute You)/Let There Be Rock (extended live) (12", p/s) 7
83	Atlantic A 9774	Guns For Hire/Landslide (p/s) 4
83	Atlantic A 9774P	Guns For Hire/Landslide (logo-shaped picture disc) 15
84	Atlantic A 9651	Nervous Shakedown/Rock'N'Roll Ain't Noise Pollution (live) (p/s) 4
84	Atlantic A 9651T	Nervous Shakedown/Rock'N'Roll Ain't Noise Pollution (live)/Sin City (live)/This House Of Fire (live) (12", p/s) 7
84	Atlantic A 9651P	Nervous Shakedown/Rock'N'Roll Ain't Noise Pollution (shaped picture disc) ... 15
84	Atlantic A 9651C	Nervous Shakedown/Rock'N'Roll Ain't Noise Pollution (live)/Sin City (live)/This House Of Fire (live) (cassette) 4
85	Atlantic A 9532W	Danger/Back In Business (poster p/s) 7
85	Atlantic A 9532P	Danger/Back In Business (fly-shaped picture disc) 15
86	Atlantic A 9474C	Shake Your Foundations/Stand Up ('calendar' poster p/s) 6
86	Atlantic A 9474P	Shake Your Foundations/Stand Up (Angus-shaped picture disc) 15
86	Atlantic A 9425T	Who Made Who (Collectors Mix)/Guns For Hire (live) (12", p/s, with poster) 12
86	Atlantic A 9425P	Who Made Who/Guns For Hire (live) (shaped picture disc) 12
86	Atlantic A 9377G	You Shook Me All Night Long/She's Got Balls (live) (gatefold p/s) 5
86	Atlantic A 9377P	You Shook Me All Night Long/She's Got Balls (live) (shaped picture disc) 10
88	Atlantic A 9098TP	That's The Way I Wanna Rock'N'Roll/Kissin' Dynamite/Borrowed Time (12", picture disc) 7
88	Atlantic A 9136TP	Heat Seeker/Go Zone/Snake High (12", picture disc) 10

(see also Geordie)

BUDDY ACE
| 68 | Action ACT 4504 | Got To Get Myself Together/Darling Depend On Me .... 5 |
| 64 | Vocalion VEP 1-70164 | BUDDY ACE (EP) .... 35 |

CHARLIE ACE
70	High Note HS 051	Creation (Version)/GAYTONES: Creation (Version Three) 5
70	Punch PH 49	Silver And Gold/PHILL PRATT ALLSTARS: Bump And Bore 4
70	Punch PH 53	Book Of Books/WINSTON HARRIS: Musical Dove 4
70	Punch PH 62	Love (You) I Madly/Especially For You 4
70	Punch PH 67	Do Something/MAYTONES: Run Babylon 4
71	Upsetter US 359	The Creeper/UPSETTERS: The Creeper (Version) 6
71	Smash SMA 2325	Need No Whip/Grine Grine 4
71	G.G. GG 4507	Ontarius Version/G.G. ALL STARS: Ontarius Version 2 4
71	G.G. GG 4518	Do Something/MAYTONES: Groove Me 4

(see also Charles & Melodians, Charles Paulette & Gee)

JOHNNY ACE
61	Vogue V 9180	Pledging My Love/Anymore 30
62	Vogue VE 1-70150	JOHNNY ACE (EP) 40
61	Vocalion VA 160177	THE MEMORIAL ALBUM (LP) 50

MARTIN ACE
| 70s | CJ's CJS 1 | Sad Party/Eating .... 6 |

(see also Man, Motors)

RICHARD ACE (& SOUND DIMENSIONS)
67	Coxsone CS 7031	Don't Let The Sun Catch You Crying/VICEROYS: Magadown 15
67	Studio One SO 2022	I Need You/SOUL VENDORS: Cool Shade 15
69	Studio One SO 2072	More Reggae (with Sound Dimensions)/GLADIATORS: Hello Carol 15
69	Studio One SO 2073	Love To Cherish (with Sound Dimensions)/KEN BOOTHE: You're On My Mind .. 15
69	Trojan TR 654	Hang 'Em High (with Sound Dimensions)/BLACK & GEORGE: Candy Lady 5
67	Coxsone SCE 1	CHRISTMAS REGGAE (EP) 45

ACE LANE
| 83 | Expulsion | SEE YOU IN HEAVEN (LP) .... 10 |

A CERTAIN RATIO
79	Factory FAC 5	All Night Party/The Thin Boys (p/s, 5,000 only, 1,000 with sticker) 10/7
82	Factory FAC 62	Knife Slits Water/Tumba Rumba (p/s) 4
85	Factory FAC 128C	Wild Party/Sounds Like Something Dirty (cassette, with extra tracks) 5
90	A&M ACRY 540	Won't Stop Loving You (Summer Mix)/Won't Stop Loving You (Cook Mix)/Won't Stop Loving You (Instrumental) (12", promo only, p/s) 7
79	Factory FAC 16C	THE GRAVEYARD AND THE BALLROOM (cassette, in 1 of 4 different coloured plastic bags) 10
85	private cassette	LIVE IN AMERICA (cassette, live, sold at gigs) 12
86	Factory FACT 135	THE OLD AND THE NEW (LP, with free 7" "Shack Up"/"The Thin Boys") 10

(see also Sir Horatio)

ACES
| 63 | Parlophone R 5094 | Wait Until Tomorrow/The Last One .... 5 |
| 64 | Parlophone R 5108 | I Count The Tears/But Say It Isn't So .... 5 |

ACES
| 82 | Etc ETC 01 | One Way Street/Why Should It Be Mine (p/s) .... 18 |

(see also Menace)

ACHES & PAINS
| 66 | Page One POF 008 | There's No Other Like Your Mother/Again And Again .... 4 |

ACHOR
| 76 | Cedar | END OF MY DAY (LP) .... 60 |

ACID ANGELS
| 88 | Product Inc. FUEL 1 | Speed Speed Ecstasy (Rev Mix 2)/Top Fuel Eliminator (7", promo only, plain stickered sleeve) .... 4 |

(see also Jesus & Mary Chain)

ACID GALLERY
| 69 | CBS 4608 | Dance Around The Maypole/Right Toe Blues .... 25 |

(see also Epics)

David ACKLES

MINT VALUE £

DAVID ACKLES

68	Elektra EKSN 45039	La Route A Chicago/Down River	4
69	Elektra EKSN 45054	Laissez Faire/Blue Ribbons	4
69	Elektra EKSN 45079	Subway To The Country/That's No Reason To Cry	4
68	Elektra EKL 4022	DAVID ACKLES (LP, orange label, also stereo EKS 74022)	16
70	Elektra EKS 74060	SUBWAY TO THE COUNTRY (LP, orange label)	14
72	Elektra EKS 75032	AMERICAN GOTHIC (LP)	10

BARBARA ACKLIN

68	MCA MU 1038	Love Makes A Woman/Come And See Me Baby	6
69	MCA MU 1071	Am I The Same Girl/Be By My Side	6
69	MCA MU 1102	Love Makes A Woman/Come And See Me Baby (reissue)	4
69	MCA MU 1103	Am I The Same Girl/Be By My Side (reissue)	4
75	Brunswick BR 26	Love Makes A Woman/Am I The Same Girl	4
70	MCA MUP 5416	SOMEONE ELSE'S ARMS (LP)	10

(see also Gene Chandler & Barbara Acklin)

A.C. MARIAS (A.C.)

81	Dome DOM 45 1	Drop/So (as A.C. Marias A.C., plain black sleeve)	8
87	Mute MUTE 50	Just Talk/Just Talk (No Talk Instrumental) (7", DJ-only)	6
90	Mute MUTE 105	One Of Our Girls Is Missing/(same) (7", DJ-only, stickered plain sleeve)	5

(see also Dome, Gilbert & Lewis, Po)

A CRAZE

83	Respond KOB 706	Wearing Your Jumper/She Is So (p/s)	4
83	Respond KOBX 706	Wearing Your Jumper/She Is So/Dub, But Not Mute (12", p/s)	7

SEPH ACRE & PETS

58	Pye Intl. 7N 25001	Rock And Roll Cha Cha/You Are My Love	6
58	Pye Intl. 7N 25001	Rock And Roll Cha Cha/You Are My Love (78)	5

(see also Pets)

ACT

67	Columbia DB 8179	Cobbled Streets/One Heart	15
67	Columbia DB 8261	Here Come Those Tears Again/Without You	15
68	Columbia DB 8331	Just A Little Bit/The Remedies Of Doctor Brohnicoy	25

ACT

67	Oak (no cat. no.)	ACT (EP, plain white sleeve)	75

ACT

87	ZTT 12 ZTAS 28	Snobbery And Decay (That's Entertainment)/Poison/I'd Be Surprisingly Good For You (12", p/s)	10
87	ZTT 12 ZACT 28	Snobbery And Decay (That's Entertainment)/Poison/I'd Be Surprisingly Good For You (12", gatefold p/s)	8
87	ZTT 12 XACT 28	Snobbery And Decay (Naked Civil Remix)/Strong Poison/Theme From Snobbery And Decay (12", different p/s, some with poster)	16/12
87	ZTT CTIS 28	SNOBBERY AND DECAY CABARET CASSETTE (cassette EP)	7
87	ZTT ZCID 28	Snobbery And Decay (Stephanie Beecham Extended Mix)/I'd Be Surprisingly Good For You/Poison/Theme From Snobbery And Decay (CD)	12
87	ZTT VIMM 1	Absolutely Immune 2/Bloodrush/States Of Logic (12", p/s)	16
87	ZTT CD IMM 2	I Can't Escape From You (Love And Hate)/Heaven Knows I'm Miserable Now/Dear Life/I Can't Escape From You (CD)	12
88	ZTT BET 1	Chance/Winner '88 (p/s, withdrawn)	40
88	ZTT BETT 1	Chance (12 To 1 Mix)/Winner '88/Chance (We Give You Another Chance) (12", p/s, withdrawn)	70
88	ZTT BETCD 1	Chance (12 To 1 Mix)/Winner '88/Chance (We Give You Another Chance) (CD, withdrawn)	100
88	ZTT ZQCD 1	LAUGHTER, TEARS AND RAGE (CD)	16

(see also Propaganda, Glenn Gregory & Claudia Brücken, Thomas Leer)

ACT

81	Hannibal HNS 701	Too Late At Twenty/Protection (p/s)	4

(see also Dream Academy)

ACTION

65	Parlophone R 5354	Land Of 1000 Dances/In My Lonely Room	25
66	Parlophone R 5410	I'll Keep On Holding On/Hey Sah-Lo-Ney	25
66	Parlophone R 5474	Baby You've Got It/Since I Lost My Baby	25
67	Parlophone R 5572	Never Ever/Twenty Four Hours	25
67	Parlophone R 5610	Shadows And Reflections/Something Has Hit Me	30
81	Edsel E 5001	I'll Keep On Holding On/Wasn't It You? (p/s)	4
81	Edsel E 5002	Since I Lost My Baby/Never Ever/Wasn't It You (p/s)	4
82	Edsel E 5003	Shadows And Reflections/Something Has Hit Me (p/s)	4
84	Edsel E 5008	Hey Sah-Lo-Ney/Come On, Come With Me (p/s)	4

(see also [Sandra Barry &] Boys, Mighty Baby, Reg King, Sandra Brown & Boyfriends)

ACTION PACT

81	Subversive ANARCHO 1	HEATHROW TOUCHDOWN (EP, 1 side by Dead Man's Shadow)	6
82	Fallout FALL 003	Suicide Bag/Stanwell/Blue Blood (p/s)	4
83	Fallout FALL 010	People/Times Must Change/Sixties Flix (p/s)	4

ACTIVE RESTRAINT

83	Sticky PEEL OFF 3	Terror In My Home/Turns Out Roses (p/s)	10

(see also Mighty Lemon Drops)

ACTIVES

84	Quiet QS 001	RIOT (EP)	4

ACTRESS

69	CBS 4016	It's What You Give/Good Job With Prospects	40

MINT VALUE £

ROY ACUFF & SMOKY MOUNTAIN BOYS

57	Brunswick 05635	I Like Mountain Music/It's Hard To Love (And Not To Be In Love)	6

ADAM & ANTS

78	Decca F 13803	Young Parisians/Lady (p/s, original with paper labels)	6
79	Do It DUN 8	Zerox/Whip In My Valise (p/s)	4
79	Do It DUN 8	Zerox/Whip In My Valise (p/s, mispress, B-side plays "Physical [You're So]")	7
81	Lyntone LYN 9285	A.N.T.S. (1-sided blue flexidisc free with 'Flexipop' magazine issue 4)	6/4
81	CBS A 1065	Stand And Deliver/Beat My Guest (poster sleeve)	4
81	CBS A 1408	Prince Charming/Christian D'Or (normal p/s)	4
81	CBS A11 1738	Ant Rap/Friends (picture disc)	4
82	Editions EG EGO 5	Deutscher Girls/Plastic Surgery (p/s)	4
82	Editions EG EGO 5	Deutscher Girls/Plastic Surgery (mispress, allegedly plays "Rockford Files" theme)	12
82	Do It DUNIT 20	THE ANT MUSIC EP (12")	8
89	Damaged Goods FNARR 7	Young Parisians/Lady/(interview) (12", white vinyl, p/s, 2,000 with no'd fanzine)	7
89	Damaged Goods FNARR 7	Young Parisians/Lady/(interview) (12", picture disc, with postcard)	8
79	Do It RIDE 3	DIRK WEARS WHITE SOX (LP, original with black labels & inner sleeve)	10
79	Do It RIDE 3	DIRK WEARS WHITE SOX (cassette)	10
80	CBS 84549	KINGS OF THE WILD FRONTIER (LP, with different version of "Antmusic" & different matrix number, with booklet)	10
83	CBS 25361	DIRK WEARS WHITE SOX (LP, different sleeve & tracks with inner sleeve)	10
83	CBS 40-25361	DIRK WEARS WHITE SOX (cassette, different sleeve & tracks)	10

(see also Adam Ant, Maneaters, Models)

ADAM, MIKE & TIM

66	Columbia DB 7902	A Most Peculiar Man/Wedding Day	4

(see also Mike Sedgewick)

ADAMO

64	Columbia DB 7273	Another Love Affair/Make Tonite Last Forever	4
64	Columbia DB 7329	She Was An Angel/The Stars Will Shine (Vous Permettez Monsieur)	4
67	HMV POP 1601	Inch Allah (God Willing)/The Tramp With A Beard	4
67	HMV POP 1609	Let's Stop The World From Turning/Hitch Hiker	4
63	HMV 7EG 8860	BELGIUM'S TOP RECORDING STAR ADAMO (EP)	7
66	HMV CLP 3601	THE HITS OF ADAMO (LP)	10
67	HMV CLP 3635	THE SENSATIONAL ADAMO (LP)	10
68	Columbia SCX 6254	SALVATORE ADAMO (LP)	10

ALICIA ADAMS

61	Capitol CL 15195	Love Bandit/Oom Dooby Doom Lovey Dovey Sh' Boom	4

ARTHUR K. ADAMS

68	Blue Horizon 57-3136	She Drives Me Out Of My Mind/Gimme Some Of Your Lovin'	15

BILLY ADAMS

60	Capitol CL 15107	Count Every Star/Peggy's Party	15

BILLY ADAMS

69	London HL 10258	Why Don't You Believe Me/I Need Your Love	5

BRYAN ADAMS

79	A&M AMS 7460	Let Me Take You Dancing/Don't Turn Me Away (p/s)	12
79	A&M AMSP 7460	Let Me Take You Dancing (Extended)/Don't Turn Me Away (12", p/s)	20
80	A&M AMS 7520	Hidin' From Love/Wait And See (p/s)	20
81	A&M AMS 8183	Lonely Nights/Don't Look Now (p/s)	5
83	A&M AM 103	Straight From The Heart/Lonely Nights (p/s)	4
83	A&M AMX 103	Straight From The Heart/Lonely Nights (12", p/s)	7
83	A&M AM 129	Cuts Like A Knife/Fits Ya Good (p/s)	4
83	A&M AMP 129	Cuts Like A Knife/Fits Ya Good/Hidin' From Love (12", p/s)	7
84	A&M AM 170	One Good Reason (withdrawn, any pressed?)	100
84	A&M AM 224	Run To You/I'm Ready/Cuts Like A Knife/Lonely Nights (p/s, double pack)	6
84	A&M AMY 224	Run To You/I'm Ready/Cuts Like A Knife (12", poster p/s)	8
85	A&M AMP 236	Somebody/Long Gone (picture disc)	8
85	A&M AMY 236	Somebody/Long Gone (12", p/s, with tour poster)	8
85	A&M AMS 256/FREE 3	Heaven/Diana//Straight From The Heart/You Want It, You Got It (double pack, stickered p/s)	5
85	A&M AM 285	It's Only Love (with Tina Turner)/The Best Was Yet To Come//Somebody/Long Gone (p/s, double pack)	8
85	A&M AM 297	Christmas Time/Reggae Christmas (p/s)	4
85	A&M AMY 297	Christmas Time/Reggae Christmas (12", p/s)	8
86	A&M AMS 322	Straight From The Heart/Fits Ya Good//Run To You/Somebody (p/s, double pack)	4
87	A&M ADAM 3	Hearts On Fire/Run To You (red vinyl, stickered p/s)	5
87	A&M ADAM 312	Hearts On Fire/Run To You/Native Sun (12", p/s)	7
87	A&M AMF 407	Victim Of Love/Heat Of The Night (live) (box set with postcards & patch)	4
80	A&M AMLH 64800	BRYAN ADAMS (LP)	12
81	A&M AMLH 64864	YOU WANT IT, YOU GOT IT (LP, original issue)	10
83	A&M CDA 4919	CUTS LIKE A KNIFE (CD, original issue)	15
83	A&M CDA 3152	YOU WANT IT, YOU GOT IT (CD, original issue)	15
83	A&M CDA 3100	BRYAN ADAMS (CD, original issue)	15

CLIFF ADAMS ORCHESTRA

60	Pye Intl. 7N 25056	The Lonely Man Theme/Trigger Happy	4

EDITH ADAMS

55	Brunswick 05406	Ohio (with Rosalind Russell)/A Little Bit In Love	4

FAYE ADAMS

56	London HLU 8339	I'll Be True/Happiness To My Soul	400
56	London HLU 8339	I'll Be True/Happiness To My Soul (78)	40

GLADSTON ADAMS
69	Trojan TR 659	Dollars And Cents/TOMMY McCOOK: Popcorn Regay	8

GLEN ADAMS
67	Island WI 3072	Silent Lover/I Remember	12
67	Island WI 3083	She/SONNY BURKE: Some Other Time	12
67	Island WI 3099	Grab A Girl/DELROY WILSON: This Heart Of Mine	12
67	Island WI 3100	Hold Down Miss Winey/VINCENT GORDON: Sounds And Soul	12
67	Island WI 3106	That New Girl/UNIQUES: Speak No Evil	10
67	Island WI 3120	She's So Fine/ROY SHIRLEY: Girl	10
68	Blue Cat BS 126	She Is Leaving/UNIQUES: Girls Like Dirt	10
68	Duke DU 58	My Girl/GLADIATORS: You Were To Be	5
68	Trojan TR 621	Rent Too High/Every Time	10
68	Bullet BU 414	Cat Woman/PETER TOUCH: Selassie Serenade (B-side actually by Peter Tosh)	7
68	Collins Downbeat CR 006	Cool Cool Rocksteady (actually by D. Tony Lee)/OWEN GRAY: Girl I Will Be Leaving	8
69	Amalgamated AMG 837	She's So Fine/ERNEST WILSON: Private Number	6
70	Gas GAS 141	Leaving On A Jet Plane/REGGAE BOYS: Phrases	4
	(see also Glen Amams)		

JOHNNY ADAMS (& GONDOLIERS)
59	Top Rank JAR 192	Come On/Nowhere To Go (as Johnny Adams & Gondoliers)	7
69	Polydor 56775	Reconsider Me/If I Could See You One More Time	10
72	Atlantic K 10245	I Wish It Would Rain/You're A Lady	6

LLOYD ADAMS
65	Blue Beat BB 366	I Wish Your Picture Was You/CREEPERS: Beat Of My Soul	10

MARIE ADAMS
59	Capitol CL 14963	A Fool In Love/What Do You Want To Make Those Eyes At Me For	20
	(see also Johnny Otis)		

RAY ADAMS
61	Pye Intl. 7N 25099	You Belong To My Heart/Hear My Song, Violetta	4
62	Decca F 11507	Venus In Blue Jeans/He's Got My Sympathy	4

RITCHIE ADAMS
60	London HLU 9200	Back To School/Don't Go My Love, Don't Go	18

RUSH ADAMS
54	Parlophone MSP 6101	I'm Sorry Dear/No One To Cry To	4
56	MGM SP 1162	Love Plays The Strings Of My Banjo/Kiss! Kiss! Kiss!	4
56	MGM SP 1176	The Birds And The Bees (with Loulie Jean Norman)/My Buddy's Girl	4
	(see also David Rose)		

WOODROW ADAMS
65	Blue Horizon BH 1001	Baby You Just Don't Know/Wine Head Woman	35

ADAM'S APPLES
77	Brunswick BR 42	Don't Take It Out On This World/Don't You Want To Take Me Home	5

AD CONSPIRACY
79	Diamond	AD CONSPIRACY (LP)	20

CANNONBALL ADDERLEY
67	Capitol CL 15489	Mercy Mercy Mercy/Games	5
67	Capitol CL 15500	Why (Am I Treated So Bad)/I'm On My Way	6
62	Riverside RLP 12-311	THE CANNONBALL ADDERLEY QUINTET IN SAN FRANCISCO (LP)	15
65	Fontana FJL 107	WOW! (LP)	10
	(see also Nancy Wilson, Miles Davis)		

ADDIX
79	Zig Zag ZZ 22002	Too Blind To See/(No Such Thing As A) Bad Boy (p/s)	4

ADDRISSI BROTHERS
59	London HL 8922	Cherrystone/Lillies Grow High	6
59	London HL 8922	Cherrystone/Lillies Grow High (78)	10
59	London HL 8973	Un Jarro/Saving My Kisses	6
59	London HL 8973	Un Jarro/Saving My Kisses (78)	10
59	Columbia DB 4370	Back To The Old Salt Mine/It's Love	8

ADDICTS
64	Decca F 11902	That's My Girl/Here She Comes	12

BOBBY ADENO
66	Vocalion V 9279	The Hands Of Time/It's A Sad World	20

ADICTS
81	Dining Out TUX 1	LUNCH WITH THE ADICTS (EP, with insert)	12
82	Fall Out FALL 002	Viva La Revolution/Steamroller (p/s)	5
82	Razor RZS 101	Chinese Takeaway/You'll Never Walk Alone (p/s)	4
83	Razor RZS 104	Bad Boy/Shake, Rattle, Bang Your Head (p/s)	4
83	Razor RZLP 104	Bad Boy/Shake, Rattle, Bang Your Head (picture disc)	6

BETH ADLAM with BUZZ & BOYS
60	Starlite ST45 024	Seventeen/I'll Walk Into The Sea	7

LARRY ADLER
56	Columbia SCM 5217	Rififi/Malaguena	4

ADLIBS (U.K.)
65	Fontana TF 584	Neighbour Neighbour/Lovely Ladies	30

AD-LIBS (U.S.)
66	Red Bird RB 10-102	The Boy From New York City/Kicked Around	20
70	Deep Soul DS 9102	Giving Up/Appreciation	10

MINT VALUE £

| 75 | Contempo CS 9029 | The Boy From New York City/Johnny My Boy | 6 |
| 79 | Inferno HEAT 1 | New York In The Dark/The Boy From New York City (p/s, coloured vinyl) | 4 |

ADMIRALS
| 65 | Fontana TF 597 | Promised Land/Palisades Park | 30 |

AD NAUSEUM
| 83 | Flicknife FLS 12 | BRAINSTORM (EP) | 4 |

A.D. 1984
| 79 | Voyage VOY 005 | The Russians Are Coming/New Moon Falling | 4 |

ADULT NET
85	Beggars Banquet BEG 137	Incense And Peppermints/Searching For The Now (p/s)	4
85	B. Banquet BEGT 137	Incense And Peppermints/Searching For The Now (12", p/s)	7
89	Fontana BRX 110	Take Me/Sea Of Rain/Incense And Peppermints/Going Nowhere (10", numbered p/s, blue vinyl with poster)	5
89	Fontana BRX 210	Where Were You/Over The River (10", no'd p/s, white vinyl with poster)	5

(see also Fall)

ADVENTURERS
| 60 | Capitol CL 15108 | Trail Blazer/Rip Van Winkle | 4 |

ADVENTURES
| 84 | Chrysalis CHSD 2000 | Another Silent Day/(version)//Nowhere Near Me/Token (double pack, g/fold p/s) | 4 |
| 84 | Chrysalis CHSP 2001 | Send My Heart/These Children (picture disc, printed PVC sleeve) | 4 |

ADVERTISING
| 77 | EMI EMI 2710 | Lipstick/Lonely Guys | 4 |
| 78 | EMI EMI 2754 | Stolen Love/Suspender Fun (p/s) | 4 |

(see also Secret Affair, Innocents)

ADVERTS
77	Stiff BUY 13	One Chord Wonders/Quickstep (p/s, 1st pressing with push-out centre)	7
77	Stiff BUY 13	One Chord Wonders/Quickstep (p/s, re-pressings with solid centres)	4-5
77	Anchor ANC 1043	Gary Gilmore's Eyes/Bored Teenagers (p/s, some with blanked-out eyes on label, white or pink lettering on p/s, push-out or solid centre)	5-6
77	Anchor ANC 1047	Safety In Numbers/We Who Wait (p/s)	4
78	Bright BR 1	No Time To Be 21/New Day Dawning (p/s)	4
78	RCA PB 5128	Television's Over/Back From The Dead (p/s)	5
79	RCA PB 5160	My Place/New Church (live) (p/s)	5
79	RCA PB 5191	Cast Of Thousands/I Will Walk You Home (p/s)	5
83	Bright BULB 1	Gary Gilmore's Eyes/We Who Wait/New Day Dawning (p/s)	4
78	Bright BRL 201	CROSSING THE RED SEA WITH THE ADVERTS (LP, 5000 on red vinyl)	18/10
81	Butt/Bright ALSO 002	CROSSING THE RED SEA WITH THE ADVERTS (LP, reissue, red vinyl)	10

(see also TV Smith)

ADVOCATES
| 73 | Dovetail DOVE 7 | HERE I REST MY CASE (LP) | 10 |

AEROSMITH
73	CBS 1898	Dream On/Somebody	8
76	CBS 4000	Dream On/Somebody (reissue)	4
76	CBS 4452	Last Child/Combination	5
77	CBS 4878	Walk This Way/Uncle Salty	5
77	CBS S AR 2	Draw The Line/Bright, Light, Fright (p/s)	6
78	CBS 6584	Come Together/Kings And Queens	4
80	CBS 8220	Remember (Walking In The Sand)/Bone To Bone (p/s)	5
87	Geffen GEF 29TP	Dude (Looks Like A Lady)/Simoriah/Once Is Enough (12" picture disc)	10
88	Geffen GEF 34TP	Angel/Girl Keeps Coming Apart (12" picture disc)	10
89	Geffen GEF 63	Love In An Elevator/Young Lust (p/s, with patch)	4
89	Geffen GEF 63TP	Love In An Elevator/Young Lust/Ain't Enough (10" picture disc)	7
89	Geffen GEF 68P	Janie's Got A Gun/Voodoo Medicine Man (shaped picture disc)	7
90	Geffen GEF 72P	Dude (Looks Like A Lady)/Monkey On My Back (shaped picture disc)	4
89	CBS 4607038	GREATEST HITS (LP, 'European Tour' picture disc)	10

A FAIR SET
| 65 | Decca F 12168 | Honey And Wine/Runaround | 8 |

AFEX
| 67 | King KG 1058 | She Got The Time/I Never Knew Love Was Like This | 30 |

AFFINITY
| 70 | Vertigo 6059 018 | Eli's Coming/United States Of Mind | 8 |
| 70 | Vertigo 6360 004 | AFFINITY (LP, gatefold sleeve, spiral label) | 65 |

(see also Linda Hoyle)

AFFLICTED
81	Bonk AFF 1	I'm Afflicted/Be Aware (rubber-stamped white labels, plain sleeve)	10
82	Bonk AFF 2	All Right Boy/Who Can Tell (p/s, stamped white labels)	10
82	Bonk AFF 4	AFFLICTED (untitled single in stamped striped bag)	8
82	Bonk AFF 3	THE AFFLICTED MAN'S MUSICAL BAG (LP, stamped white label in stamped bag sleeve)	12
82	Bonk AFF 6	HIGH SPEED AND THE AFFLICTED MAN — GET STONED (LP)	10

(see also Tontrix)

A FLOCK OF SEAGULLS
81	Cocteau COQ 3	It's Not Me Talking/Factory Music (p/s)	4
82	Jive JIVEP 14	I Ran/Pick Me Up/Messages (picture disc)	4
82	Jive JIVEP 17	Space Age Love Song/Windows (picture disc)	4
83	Jive JIVEP 33	Nightmares/Rosen Montag (picture disc)	4
83	Jive JIVEP 41	Transfer Affection/I Ran (picture disc)	4
84	Jive JIVEP 62	The More You Live The More You Love/Lost Control (square picture disc)	5
85	Jive AFOS 1	COLLECTION (10 x 7" pack)	12

85	Jive AFLOCK 1	COLLECTION (10 x 12" pack) 15
83	Jive HOPX 201	A FLOCK OF SEAGULLS (LP, picture disc) 10
83	Jive HIPX 4	LISTEN (LP, picture disc) 10

AFRICAN BEAVERS
| 65 | RCA RCA 1447 | Find My Baby/Jungle Fever ....4 |

AFRICAN MUSIC MACHINE
72	Mojo 2092 046	Black Water Gold (Pearl)/Making Nassau Fruit Drink 8
73	Contempo C13	Tropical/The Girl In France 5
73	Contempo C25	Never Name A Baby/Dapp 5
74	Contempo CS 2025	Mr Brown/Camel Time 5

AFRIQUE
| 73 | Pye International 7N 25616 | Soul Makossa/Hot Mud ....5 |

AFRO RHYTHM KINGS
| 54 | Lyragon J 732 | Skokiaan/Bantu Boogie (78) ....6 |

AFROTONES
69	Trojan TR 655	Things I Love/ERIC FATTER: Since You've Been Gone 8
69	Duke DU 19	Freedom Sound/BOYS: Easy Sound 7
69	High Note HS 023	All For One/BELTONES: Broken Heart 6

AFTER DARK
81	After Dark AD 001	Evil Woman/Johnny — Lucy 20
83	Lazer PROMO 1	Deathbringer/Call Of The Wild (picture disc, promotional only) 6
81	SRT	AFTER DARK (LP) 10

AFTER TEA
| 68 | Ace Of Clubs SCL-R 1251 | AFTER TEA (LP) ....20 |
| | *(see also Ray Fenwick)* | |

AFTER THE FIRE
79	CBS 7025	One Rule For You/Joy (p/s, red vinyl) 4
79	CBS 7769	Laser Love/Your Love Is Alive (p/s, red vinyl) 4
80	Epic EPC 8394	Love Will Always Make You Cry/Every Mother's Son (p/s, withdrawn) 8
78	Rapid RR 001	SIGNS OF CHANGE (LP, with insert) 35
80	Epic EPC 84545	80-F (LP, unreleased, only on cassette with white labels) 20
82	Epic EPC 85135	BATTERIES NOT INCLUDED (LP, withdrawn version with different sleeve) 10
	(see also Narnia, Waiting For The Sun)	

AGENTS
| 79 | Grapevine GRP 142 | Trouble/The Love I Hold ....4 |

AGE OF CHANCE
85	Riot Bible RIOT 1	Motor City/Everlasting Yeah! (p/s) 5
86	Riot Bible RIOT 2	Bible Of The Beats/The Liquid Jungle (p/s) 4
86	Riot Bible BIBLE 001	THE TWILIGHT WORLD OF SONIC DISCO (12" EP, pink or yellow vinyl, with insert) 7
86	Fon AGE 5	Kiss/Crash Conscious (orange or green vinyl, p/s in corresponding colours) 4
86	Fon AGE 5M	CRASH COLLISION (double pack) 6

AGGROVATORS
| 70 | Jackpot JP 751 | Sex Machine/You Left Me And Gone (both act. by Dave Barker & Aggrovators) ...4 |
| | *(see also Dave Barker)* | |

AGINCOURT
| 70 | Merlin HF 3 | FLY AWAY (LP, with insert) ....450 |
| | *(see also Ithaca, Alice Through The Looking Glass, Tomorrow Come Someday)* | |

AGNES STRANGE
| 75 | Birdsnest BN 1 | Give Yourself A Chance/Clever Fool ....10 |
| 75 | Birdsnest BRL 9000 | STRANGE FLAVOUR (LP) ....100 |

AGONY BAG
| 80 | Monza MON 2 | Rabies Is A Killer/Never Never (p/s) ....4 |
| | *(see also Pesky Gee, Black Widow)* | |

A-HA
84	Warner Bros W 9146	Take On Me/And You Tell Me (silver/blue p/s) 30
84	Warner Bros W 9146T	Take On Me (Extended)/And You Tell Me/Stop And Make Your Mind Up (12", silver/blue p/s, some with poster and stickers, p/s) 70/45
85	Warner Bros W 9006	Take On Me/Love Is The Reason (black & white p/s) 8
85	Warner Bros W 9006T	Take On Me/Love Is The Reason (12", black & white p/s) ...15
85	Warner Bros W 9006	Take On Me/Love Is The Reason (reissue, colour p/s with gatefold booklet) 10
86	Warner Bros W 8846P	The Sun Always Shines On T.V./Driftwood (shaped picture disc) 15
86	Lyntone	The Sun Always Shines On T.V. (U.S. Remix) (square picture flexidisc free with 'No. 1' magazine) 5/4
86	Warner Bros W 8846T	The Sun Always Shines On T.V. (Extended Remix)/Driftwood (12", p/s) 7
86	Warner Bros W 8736T	Train Of Thought (Extended)/(7" Remix)/And You Tell Me (12" p/s, with poster) .7
86	Warner Bros W 8736P	Train Of Thought (Remix)/And You Tell Me (train-shaped picture disc) 12
86	Warner Bros W 8663TP	Hunting High And Low (Extended)/Hunting High And Low (Remix)/The Blue Sky (Demo) (12" picture disc) 10
86	Warner Bros W 8663T	Hunting High And Low (Extended)/Hunting High And Low (Remix)/The Blue Sky (Demo) (12", p/s, with poster) 10
86	Warner Bros W 8594T	I've Been Losing You (Extended Remix)/I've Been Losing You (Dub)/This Alone Is Love (12", p/s, with poster) 10
86	Warner Bros W 8500V	Cry Wolf/Maybe Maybe (foldout p/s) 4
86	Warner Bros W 8500TP	Cry Wolf (Extended)/Cry Wolf (7" Version)/Maybe Maybe (12" picture disc) 10
87	Warner Bros W 8405W	Manhattan Skyline/We're Looking For The Whales (p/s) 5
87	Warner Bros W 8405T	Manhattan Skyline (Extended Remix)/Manhattan Skyline (LP Version)/We're Looking For The Whales (12", p/s, with poster) 10

MINT VALUE £

87	Warner Bros W 8405TP	Manhattan Skyline (Extended Remix)/Manhattan Skyline (LP Version)/ We're Looking For The Whales (12", picture disc)	12
87	Warner Bros W 8305V	The Living Daylights/(Instrumental) (gatefold 'bullet hole' p/s)	4
87	Warner Bros W 8305 TP	The Living Daylights (Extended)/(7" remix)/(Instrumental) (12" picture disc)	10
88	Warner Bros W 7936 T	Stay On These Roads (Extended Remix)/Soft Rains Of April (Original Mix) (12", p/s with poster)	7
88	Warner Bros W 7936 TP	Stay On These Roads (Extended Remix)/Soft Rains Of April (Original Mix) (12", picture disc)	8
88	Warner Bros W 7840 W	The Blood That Moves The Body/There's Never A Forever Thing (pack of 3 postcards in cardboard wallet)	4
88	Warner Bros W 7840 T	The Blood That Moves The Body (Extended)/The Blood That Moves The Body (LP Version)/There's Never A Forever Thing (12", p/s with poster)	7
88	Warner Bros W 7840 TP	The Blood That Moves The Body (Extended)/The Blood That Moves The Body (LP Version)/There's Never A Forever Thing (12", picture disc)	7
88	Warner Bros W 7749 W	Touchy!/Hurry Home (felt p/s)	4
88	Warner Bros W 7749 WW	Touchy!/Hurry Home ('liquid' poster p/s)	7
88	Warner Bros W 7636 V	You Are The One (Remix)/Out Of Blue Comes Green (Xmas card pack)	4
88	Warner Bros W 7636 TP	You Are The One (12" Remix)/You Are The One (Instrumental)/ Out Of Blue Comes Green (12", picture disc)	8
90	Warner Bros W 9547EP	CRYING IN THE RAIN (EP, p/s)	6
88	Warner Bros 925 616-2	STAY ON THESE ROADS (CD, picture disc)	15

(see also Phenomena)

AHAB
| 82 | Chicken Jazz JAZZ 5 | Party Girl/Don't Give Up On Us (p/s) .... | 8 |

(see also Another Pretty Face, Waterboys)

A HOUSE
87	Rip ARIP 1	Kick Me Again Jesus/I Want You (p/s)	5
87	Rip ARIPT 1	Kick Me Again Jesus/I Want You/When I Change (12", p/s)	10
87	Rip ARIP 2	Snowball Down/Y.O.U. (p/s)	5
87	Rip ARIPT 3	Kick Me Again Jesus/I Want You/When I Change/Snowball Down/Y.O.U. (12", p/s)	8
92	Setanta CAO 003	Kick Me Again Jesus/When I Change/Y.O.U./Snowball Down (gig freebie, die-cut company sleeve)	6

ALYN AINSWORTH
| 59 | Parlophone R 4533 | Bedtime For Drums/The Cobbler's Song (with His Orchestra) .... | 4 |
| 59 | Parlophone R 4594 | 18th-Century Rock/Hells Bells (with Rock-A-Fellas) .... | 4 |

AIRMAIL
| 83 | Grafitti GIT 001 | No Human Feeling/In A Moment (p/s) .... | 4 |

AIRPORT & DEAN
| 81 | Polydor POSP 312 | Lost In Space/Window In The Sky (p/s) .... | 4 |

(see also X-Ray Spex)

AIRTO
73	CTI CTS 4003	Do It Again/Branches (as Deodato-Airto)	4
72	Polydor 2318 040	SEEDS TO THE GROUND — THE NATURAL SOUNDS OF AIRTO (LP)	12
73	CTI CTI 18	FINGERS (LP)	10
74	CTI CTI 21	IN CONCERT (LP, with Deodato)	10
74	CTI CTI 23	VIRGIN LAND (LP)	10

(see also Deodato)

AIR TRAFFIC CONTROL
| 77 | Epic EPC 5665 | Gotta Get A Message Back To You/Move On Up .... | 4 |

BOBBY AITKEN (& CARIBBEATS)
62	Blue Beat BB 93	Never Leave (South Virginia)/Isabella	12
62	Blue Beat BB 146	Don't Leave Me/Mom And Dad (both with Tinse)	12
62	Island WI 028	Baby Baby (with Patsy)/Lonely Boy	12
63	Rio R 14	I've Told You/Please Go Back	10
63	Rio R 15	It Takes A Friend/LAUREL AITKEN: Sunshine	10
64	Rio R 34	Rolling Stone/LESTER STERLING'S GROUP: Man About Town	10
64	Rio R 40	Garden Of Eden/Whiplash	10
64	Rio R 50	Little Girl/Together	10
65	Rio R 52	Rain Came Tumbling Down/SHENLEY LUNAN: Something Is On Your Mind	10
65	Rio R 64	Mr Judge/BINZ: Times Have Changed	8
65	Blue Beat BB 369	Shame And Scandal/Coconut Woman	12
65	Black Swan WI 441	Jericho/LESTER STERLING: Lunchtime	10
66	Ska Beat JB 252	Thunderball/ORIGINATORS: Chelip Chelip	8
67	Doctor Bird DB 1071	Keep On Pushing/You Won't Regret It	10
67	Doctor Bird DB 1072	Let Them Have A Home/Temptation (with Caribbeats)	10
67	Doctor Bird DB 1077	Sweets For My Sweet/How Sweet It Is (with Caribbeats)	10
67	Island WI 3028	Kiss Bam Bam/CYNTHIA RICHARDS: How Could I	10
67	Giant GN 11	What A Fool/Curfew (with Caribbeats)	7

(see also Caribbeats)

LAUREL AITKEN (& BLUE BEATS)
60	Kalypso XX 15	Sweet Chariot/Nebuchnezer	10
60	Kalypso XX 16	Aitken's Boogie/Cherrie	10
60	Kalypso XX 19	Baba Kill Me Goat/Tribute To Collie Smith	10
60	Starlite ST45 011	Boogie In My Bones/Little Sheila	15
60	Starlite ST45 014	Honey Girl (with Caribs)/Drinkin' Whisky (with Bluebeats)	15
60	Melodisc M 1570	Mary Lee/Lonesome Lover (with Bluebeats)	15
60	Blue Beat BB 1	Boogie Rock/Heavenly Angel	18
61	Starlite ST45 034	Love Me Baby/Stars Were Made	15
61	Blue Beat BB 10	Jeannie Is Back/If It's Money You Need	12
61	Blue Beat BB 14	Judgment Day/Yea Yea Baby	12
61	Blue Beat BB 22	Railroad Track/Tell Me Darling	12
61	Blue Beat BB 25	More Whisky/LLOYD CLARKE: Parapinto Boogie	12

MINT VALUE £

61	Blue Beat BB 40	Bartender/Mash Potato Boogie	10
61	Blue Beat BB 52	Bouncing Woman/Nursery Rhyme Boogie (with Blue Beats)	8
61	Blue Beat BB 70	Mighty Redeemer/Please Don't Leave Me	8
61	Blue Beat BB 84	Brother David/Back To New Orleans (with Blue Beats)	8
62	Blue Beat BB 109	Lucille/I Love You More Everyday	8
62	Blue Beat BB 120	Sixty Days And Sixty Nights/Going To Kansas	8
62	Blue Beat BB 142	Weary Wanderer/BANDITS: Jenny Jenny	8
62	Blue Beat BB 149	She's Going To Napoli/Have Mercy Mr Percy (with Owen Gray)	8
62	Blue Beat BB 164	Zion/Swing Low Sweet Chariot	8
62	Dice CC 1	Mabel/You Got Me Rocking (with Hyacinth)	12
63	Dice CC 13	Sweet Jamaica/Bossa Nova Hop	10
63	Blue Beat BB 194	Little Girl/Daniel Saw The Stone	8
63	Duke DK 1002	Low Down Dirty Girl/Pink Lane Shuffle	8
63	Island WI 092	I Shall Remove/We've Got To Move	12
63	Island WI 095	What A Weeping/Zion City Wall	12
63	Island WI 099	In My Soul/One More River To Cross	12
63	Rio R 11	Adam & Eve/BOBBY AITKEN: Devil Woman	12
63	Rio R 12	Mary/Hometown	12
63	Rio R 13	Bad Minded Woman/Life	12
63	Rio R 17	Devil Or Angel/Fire	12
63	Rio R 18	Freedom Train/Peace Perfect Peace	12
64	Rio R 35	Rock Of Ages/The Mule	10
64	Rio R 36	Leave Me Standing/Bug A Boo	10
64	Rio R 37	John Saw Them Coming/Jericho	10
64	R&B JB 167	Yes Indeed/You Can't Stop Me From Loving You	12
64	R&B JB 170	Pick Up Your Bundle And Go/Let My People Go	12
64	R&B JB 171	Bachelor Life/You Was Up	12
64	Columbia DB 7280	Be Mine/Don't Stay Out Late	7
64	Blue Beat BB 249	This Great Day/I May Never See My Baby	7
64	Black Swan WI 401	Remember My Darling (with Cynthia Richards)/Lion Of Judah	12
64	Black Swan WI 411	The Saint/Go Gal Go	12
64	Dice CC 28	Jamaica/I Don't Want No More	10
65	Dice CC 31	We Shall Overcome/You Left Me Standing	10
65	Rio R 53	Mary Don't You Weep/I Believe	10
65	Rio R 54	Mary Lou/Jump And Shout	10
65	Rio R 56	One More Time/Ring Don't Mean A Thing	10
65	Rio R 65	Let's Be Lovers/I Need You	10
65	Blue Beat BB 340	Clementine/Bongo Jerk	7
65	Island WI 198	Boogie In My Bones/Little Sheila	10
65	Island WI 252	How Can I Forget You/Weeping And Crying	10
66	Ska Beat JB 232	Jumbie Jamboree/Looking For My Baby	10
66	Ska Beat JB 236	Propaganda/Shake	10
66	Ska Beat JB 239	Green Banana/Darling	10
66	Rio R 91	How Can I Forget You/I've Been Weeping And Crying	8
66	Rio R 92	Baby Don't Do It/That Girl	8
66	Rio R 97	We Shall Overcome/Street Of Glory	8
66	Rio R 99	Clap Your Hands/Revival	8
66	Rainbow RAI 101	Don't Break Your Promises/Last Night (with Soulmen)	10
66	Rainbow RAI 106	Voodoo Woman/Bewildered And Blue	10
67	Rainbow RAI 111	Sweet Precious Love/I Want To Love You Forever (with Carols)	10
67	Columbia Blue Beat DB 102	Rock Steady/Blowin' In The Wind	7
67	Columbia Blue Beat DB 106	I'm Still In Love With You Girl/Blue Rhythm	7
67	Fab FAB 5	Never You Hurt/I Need You Baby	7
68	Fab FAB 45	For Sentimental Reasons/Last Waltz (with Rainbows)	7
68	Doctor Bird DB 1160	Mr Lee/Birmingham Girl	8
68	Doctor Bird DB 1161	La La La (Means I Love You)/DETOURS: Sunnyside	8
69	Doctor Bird DB 1187	Fire In Your Wire/Quando Quando	8
69	Doctor Bird DB 1190	Rice And Peas/CLASSICS: Worried Over Me	8
69	Doctor Bird DB 1196	Reggae Prayer/Deliverance Will Come	8
69	Doctor Bird/J.J. DB 1197	The Rise And Fall (Of Laurel)/If You're Not Black	8
69	Doctor Bird DB 1202	Haile Haile (The Lion)/SEVEN LETTERS: Call Collect	7
69	Doctor Bird DB 1203	Carolina/Kingston Town	7
69	Junior JR 105	Think Me No Know/RECO: Trombone Man	8
69	Nu Beat NB 024	Woppi King/Mr Soul	5
69	Nu Beat NB 025	Suffering Still (with Girlie)/Reggae '69	5
69	Nu Beat NB 032	Haile Selassie/Blues Dance	5
69	Nu Beat NB 033	Lawd Doctor (with Girlie)/Big Fight In Hell Stadium	5
69	Nu Beat NB 035	Run Powell Run/RICO RODRIGUEZ: A Message To You	5
69	Nu Beat NB 035	Run Powell Run/RICO RODRIGUES: Message To You	4
69	Nu Beat NB 039	Save The Last Dance/Walk Right Back	4
69	Nu Beat NB 040	Don't Be Cruel/John B.	4
69	Nu Beat NB 043	Shoo Be Doo/Babylon Gone	4
69	Nu Beat NB 044	Landlords And Tenants/Everybody Sufferin'	5
69	Nu Beat NB 045	Jesse James/Freedom	5
69	Nu Beat NB 046	Pussy Price Gone Up/Gimme Back Me Dollar	5
69	Nu Beat NB 047	Skinhead Train/Kent People	7
70	Nu Beat NB 048	Skinhead Invasion/Benwood Dick (unissued, blank white label demos only)	10
70	Nu Beat NB 048	Mr Popcorn/GRUVY BEATS: Share Your Popcorn	4
70	Nu Beat NB 049	I've Got Your Love/GRUVY BEATS: Blue Mink	4
70	Nu Beat NB 050	Scandal In Brixton Market/Soul Grinder (both sides with Girlie)	4
70	New Beat NB 054	Nobody But Me/Baby Please Don't Go	4
70	New Beat NB 056	I'll Never Love Any Girl/The Best I Can	4
70	New Beat NB 057	Reggae Popcorn/Take Me Back	4
70	New Beat NB 063	Baby I Need Your Loving/Think It Over	4
70	New Beat NB 065	Sex Machine/Since You Left	4
70	New Beat NB 072	Pachanga/Version	4

Laurel AITKEN

70	Ackee ACK 104	Pussy Got Thirteen Life/Single Man	6
70	Ackee ACK 106	Sin Pon You/Everynight	6
70	Bamboo BAM 16	Moon Rock/Cut Up Munno	6
70	Pama PM 818	Mary's Boy Child/RUPIE EDWARDS ALLSTARS: Version	4
70	Pama Supreme PS 300	Why Can't I Touch You/Can't Turn Your Back On Me	4
71	Trojan TR 7826	It's Too Late/AITKEN'S BAND: Slow Rock	4
71	New Beat NB 078	True Love/The Best I Can	4
71	New Beat NB 089	I Can't Stop Loving You/El Paso	4
71	Black Swan BW 1408	If It's Hell Down Below/Just A Little Bit Of Love	4
72	Camel CA 90	Africa Arise/GI GINGRI: Holy Mount Zion	4
75	Camel CA 2007	La Vien Rose/Spanish Eyes	4
66	Rio LR 1	SKA WITH LAUREL (LP)	120
67	Doctor Bird DLM 5012	SAYS FIRE (LP)	80
69	Pama PSP 1012	THE HIGH PRIEST OF REGGAE (LP)	40
69	Pama ECO 8	SCANDAL IN BRIXTON MARKET (LP, with Girlie)	30
69	J.J.	RISE AND FALL (LP)	70

A-JAES
| 64 | Oak RGJ 132 | I'm Leaving You/Kansas City | 175 |

AKA & CHARLATANS
| 78 | Vanity VANE 1 | Heroes Are Losers/Lady Of The Night/Perhaps One Day (12", screen-printed die-cut p/s) | 12 |

JEWEL AKENS
65	London HLN 9954	The Birds And The Bees/Tic Tac Toe	5
65	London HLN 9969	Georgie Peorgie/Around The Corner	4
66	Ember EMB S 219	Dancin' Jenny/A Wee Bit More of Your Lovin'	8
65	London HA-N 8234	THE BIRDS AND THE BEES (LP)	10

AK 47
| 81 | Output ORR 202 | Stop! Dance!/Autobiography/Hilversum-Ao (p/s) | 5 |

(see also AK Process, File Under Pop, I Start Counting)

JAN AKKERMAN
| 73 | Harvest HAR 8069 | Blue Boy/Minstrel-Farmers Dance | 4 |
| 78 | CBS 81843 | ARUNJUEZ (LP) | 10 |

(see also Hunters, Brainbox, Focus)

AK PROCESS
| 80s | Output | ELECTRONIC MUSIC (EP, p/s) | 5 |
| 80s | Output/Ch. Red OPR 101 | All Love/Post Town (p/s) | 4 |

AKRYLYKZ
80	Double R RED 2	Spyderman/Smart Boy (p/s)	7
80	Polydor POSP 128	Spyderman/Smart Boy (reissue, p/s)	5
80	Polydor 2059 253	J.D./Ska'd For Life (p/s)	6

(see also Fine Young Cannibals)

AL & VIBRATORS
67	Doctor Bird DB 1085	Move Up/Lone Lover	10
69	High Note HS 005	Check Up/I'll Come Back	6
69	High Note HS 007	Move Up Calypso/PATSY: Fire In Your Wire	6

ALABAMA FOUR
| 31 | Piccadilly 569 | His Troubles Was Hard/Jerusalem Mornin' (78) | 40 |

ALABAMA JUG BAND
| 55 | Brunswick OE 9161 | ALABAMA JUG BAND (EP) | 12 |

STEVE ALAIMO
62	Pye International 7N 25161	My Friends/Going Back To Marty	4
63	Pye International 7N 25174	Every Day I Have To Cry/Little Girl	20
63	Pye International 7N 25199	It's A Long Long Way To Happiness/A Lifetime Of Loneliness	4
66	HMV POP 1531	So Much Love/Truer Than True	8
68	Atlantic 588 227	Watching The Trains Go By/Thank You For The Sunshine Days	4

ALARM
81	White Cross W 3/4	Unsafe Buildings/Up For Murder (gatefold p/s)	60
82	Illegal ILS 0032	Marching On/Across The Border/Lie Of The Land (p/s)	20
83	IRS PFP 1014	The Stand/Third Light (p/s)	6
83	IRS PFPX 1014	The Stand/For Freedom/Reason 41 (12", p/s)	8
83	IRS PFPC 1023	68 Guns Pts 1 & 2 (p/s)	4
83	IRS PFPX 1023	68 Guns (Full Length Version)/Thoughts Of A Young Man (12", p/s)	7
83	IRS PFPC 1023	68 Guns Pts 1 & 2 (p/s, with free cassette: "The Stand"/"Across The Border"/"Marching On"/"Lie Of The Land"/"For Freedom" (all live) [CS 70504])	8
84	IRS IRS 101	Where Were You Hiding When The Storm Broke/Pavilion Steps (p/s)	4
84	IRS IRSX 101	Where Were You Hiding When The Storm Broke/Pavilion Steps/What Kind Of Hell (12", p/s)	7
84	IRS IRS 103	The Deceiver/Reason 41 (p/s, some on clear vinyl)	8/4
84	IRS IRS 103	The Deceiver/Reason 41 (p/s, mispress on mustard vinyl)	60
84	IRS IRSD 103/103A	The Deceiver/Reason 41//Lie Of The Land/Legal Matter (double pack, gatefold p/s)	15
84	IRS IRSX 103	The Deceiver/Reason 41/Second Generation (12", p/s)	7
84	IRS IRS 114	The Chant Has Just Begun/The Bells Of Rhymney (p/s)	4
84	IRS IRSY 114	The Chant Has Just Begun (remix)/The Bells Of Rhymney/The Stand (extended version) (12", p/s)	7
85	IRS ALARMD 1	Absolute Reality/Blaze Of Glory//Room At The Top/Reason 36 (double pack, gatefold p/s)	5
85	IRS IPM 104	Strength/Majority (poster sleeve)	4
86	IRS IRMTD 109	Spirit of '76/Where Were You Hiding When The Storm Broke (live)/Deeside (live)//Knockin' On Heaven's Door (live)/68 Guns (live) (12" dbl pack, p/s)	8

86	IRS IRMSP 112	Knife Edge (edit)/Caroline Isenberg (poppy-shaped picture disc) 6
86	IRS IRMG 112	Knife Edge/Caroline Isenberg (gatefold p/s) 5
87	IRS IRM 144	Rain/In The Summertime (with sticker & 5 postcards in signed stickered pack) . . . 4
87	IRS DIRM 144	Rain In The Summertime/Rescue Me/Presence Of Love/
		Eye Of The Hurricane (CD, promo only) 7
87	IRS IRMBV 150	Rescue Me/My Land Your Land (p/s, blue vinyl) 4
87	IRS IRM 150	Rescue Me/My Land Your Land (poster pack) 4
88	IRS IRMP 155	Presence Of Love (Laugherne)/Knife Edge (picture disc) 4
89	IRS EIRSP 123	Sold Me Down The River/Gwethoch Fi I Lawr Yr Afon (with 2 b&w photos
		in PVC foldout sleeve) 4
89	IRS EIRS10 123	Sold Me Down The River/Gwethoch Fi I Lawr Yr Afon/Firing Line (10", p/s) 5
89	IRS WIRSB 129	Hwylio Dros Y Mor/Y Graig (gatefold p/s with booklet) 4
89	IRS EIRSTEN 129	A New South Wales/The Rock (Long Version)/Rivers To Cross
		(New Version)/Working Class Hero (10", p/s, white vinyl) 5
90	IRS EIRSPD 134	Love Don't Come Easy/Croesi'r Afon/Change II (Radio Version) (10" picture disc) 5
80s	Lyntone	flexidisc with tour magazine (red vinyl) 10

(see also Seventeen)

BILLY ALBERT "THE KID"
| 56 | Vogue Coral Q 72214 | Black Jack/The Golden Touch .... 4 |

EDDIE ALBERT
| 55 | London HL 8136 | I'm In Favour Of Friendship/Come Pretty Little Girl .... 25 |
| 56 | London HLU 8241 | Little Child (Daddy Dear) (with Sondra Lee)/Jenny Kissed Me .... 18 |

MEL ALBERT
| 59 | Top Rank JAR 178 | Sugar Plum/Never Let Me Go .... 4 |

ALBERTO Y LOS TRIOS PARANOIAS
76	Big T BIG 541	Dread Jaws/De Version 6
77	Stiff LAST 2	SNUFF ROCK (EP, p/s) 5
78	Logo GO(D) 323	DEAD MEAT EP (double pack, gatefold p/s) 4
82	New Hormones ORG 30	Cruisin' With Santa (p/s) 5
76	Transatlantic TRA 316	ALBERTO Y LOS TRIOS PARANOIAS (LP) 10
77	Transatlantic TRA 349	ITALIANS FROM OUTER SPACE (LP) 10
78	Logo LOGO 1009	SKITE (LP) 10

AL ALBERTS
58	Coral Q 72344	Things I Didn't Say/God's Greatest Gift 4
59	Coral Q 72352	Willingly/My Love 4
59	Coral Q 72363	How Soon? (Will I Be Seeing You)/Taking A Chance On Love 4

(see also Four Aces)

ALBION COUNTRY BAND
| 76 | Island HELP 25 | BATTLE OF THE FIELD (LP) .... 12 |

(see also Shirley & Dolly Collins)

DENNIS ALCAPONE
70	Explosion EX 2039	Revelation Version/Marka Version 5
70	Supreme SUP 214	You Must Believe Me (with Niney)/RUPIE EDWARDS ALLSTARS:
		Funk The Funk 4
71	Treasure Isle TI 7069	The Great Woggie/TOMMY McCOOK & SUPERSONICS: Buttercup Version 10
71	Treasure Isle TI 7074	Wake Up Jamaica (with Joya)/TOMMY McCOOK/SUPERSONICS: Version 10
71	Big Shot BI 565	Shades Of Hudson/Spanish Amigo 7
71	Banana BA 328	Duppy Serenade/Sunshine Version 6
71	Banana BA 341	(Love Me) Forever Version/I Don't Want To See You Cry 8
71	Ackee ACK 146	Power Version/BLUESBLASTERS: Martie 6
71	Upsetter US 373	Well Dread/UPSETTERS: Dread Version 7
71	Upsetter US 377	Alpha And Omega/JUNIOR BYLES: Beat Down Babylon 7
71	Duke DU 125	Medley Version/Version Two 5
71	Prince Buster PB 8	Sons Of Zion/ANSELL COLLINS: Short Circuit 5
71	Prince Buster PB 12	Let It Roll (with Max Romeo)/ANSELL COLLINS: Clear Blue
		(unissued, blank white label demos only) 7
71	Jackpot JP 773	Jumping Jack (with John Holt)/AGGROVATORS: King Of The Track 5
71	Jackpot JP 775	Togetherness (Black & White) (with John Holt)/DELROY WILSON: Live Good 5
71	Dynamic DYN 421	Horse And Buggy/ROLAND ALPHONSO & DENZIL LAING: Buggy And Horse ... 4
71	Dynamic DYN 422	Ripe Cherry/INNER CIRCLE: Red Cherry 4
71	Dynamic DYN 427	Alcapones Guns Don't Bark/Alcapones Guns Don't Bark Version 4
71	Camel CA 74	This A Butter/PHIL PRATT ALLSTARS: Version 4
71	Tropical AL 003	False Prophet/MAX ROMEO: Rude Medley 4
72	Tropical AL 019	Worldwide Love (with Twinkle Brothers)/CARL MASTERS: Gable Up 4
72	Upsetter US 381	Wonderman (with Dave Parker, actually Dave Barker)/
		Place Called Africa (with Parker & Junior Byles) 7
72	Upsetter US 388	Master Key/UPSETTERS: Keyhole 7
72	Grape GR 3035	Rasta Dub/UPSETTERS: Rasta Version 6
72	Attack ATT 8027	Fine Style/WINSTON SCOTLAND: On The Track 6
72	Duke DU 131	The Sky's The Limit/HUDSON'S ALLSTARS: Limit Version 5
72	Duke DU 147	Get In The Groove (with Dennis Brown)/DYNAMITES: Version 5
72	Techniques TE 918	Look Into Yourself/TECHNIQUES ALLSTARS: Yourself Version 5
72	Green Door GD 4041	Rub Up A Daughter/TONY'S ALLSTARS: Daughter Version 5
72	Jackpot JP 808	Cassius Clay/SLIM SMITH: Love And Affection 4
72	Downtown DT 508	You Don't Say/TONY'S ALLSTARS: Version 4
72	Bullet BU 509	Dub Up A Daughter/PRINCE TONY'S ALL STARS: Version 4
73	Bread BR 1121	Musical Liquidator/Lorna Banana (B-side with Prince Jazzbo) 4
71	Trojan TRL 187	GUNS DON'T ARGUE (LP) 15
73	Magnet MGT 001	KING OF THE TRACK (LP) 15

(see also El Paso, Dennis & Lizzy, Mad Roy, D. Smith)

CRAIG ALDEN
| 60 | London HLW 9224 | Crazy Little Horn/Goggle-Eye'd .... 4 |

STEVE ALDO (& CHALLENGERS)
64	Decca F 12041	Can I Get A Witness/Baby What You Want Me To Do (with Challengers)	25
66	Parlophone R 5432	Everybody Has To Cry/You're Absolutely Right (solo)	25

RONNIE ALDRICH
54	Decca F 10248	Coach Call Boogie/Donegal Cradle Song	10
54	Decca F 10274	Wolf On The Prowl/Mudhopper	10
55	Decca F 10494	Ko Ko Mo (I Love You So)/Rock Love (with Squads)	15
55	Decca F 10544	Rock Candy/Boom, Boom Boomerang (with Squads)	15
55	Decca F 10564	Rhythm 'N Blues/Where Ya Gone, Baby? (with Squads)	15
57	Columbia DB 3882	Right Now, Right Now/Rock And Roll Boogie (with Squadronaires)	18
57	Columbia DB 3882	Right Now, Right Now/Rock And Roll Boogie (with Squadronaires) (78)	8
57	Columbia DB 3945	Crazy Bear/The Big Band Beat (with Squadronaires)	10
60	Decca F 11283	Friendly Persuasion/Our Concerto (with Dreamers)	4
60	Decca F 11310	The Singer Not The Song/Pepe (with Dreamers)	4
69	Decca F 12909	Ride My See-Saw/Romance On The North Sea (with London Festival Orchestra)	5
60	Ace Of Clubs ACL 1020	ALL TIME HITS OF JAZZ (LP)	10

(see also Squadronaires, Joan Regan)

ALEANNA
70s	Inchrecronin	ALEANNA (LP, private pressing)	30

DON ALESSI
66	Salvo SLO 5521-LP	GUITAR SPECTACULAR! (LP)	12

ARTHUR ALEXANDER
62	London HLD 9523	You Better Move On/A Shot Of Rhythm And Blues	20
63	London HLD 9566	Where Have You Been/Soldiers Of Love	22
63	London HLD 9641	Anna/I Hang My Head And Cry	20
63	London HLD 9667	Go Home Girl/You're The Reason	20
64	London HLD 9899	Black Knight/Ole John Amos	15
66	London HLU 10023	(Baby) For You/The Other Woman	12
76	Buddah BDS 439	Everyday I Have To Cry/Everybody Needs Somebody To Love	5
63	London RED 1364	ALEXANDER THE GREAT (EP)	60
63	London RED 1401	SOLDIERS OF LOVE (EP)	60
62	London HA-D 2457	YOU BETTER MOVE ON (LP)	90

DAVID ALEXANDER
74	Rare Earth RES 112	Love Love Love/Missy	4

JEFF ALEXANDER & HIS ORCHESTRA
58	London HA-P 2130	ALFRED HITCHCOCK PRESENTS — MUSIC TO BE MURDERED BY (LP)	10

TEXAS ALEXANDER
61	Fontana 467 136TE	TREASURES OF NORTH AMERICAN NEGRO MUSIC VOLUME 7 (EP)	15

ALFI & HARRY
56	London HLU 8242	Trouble With Harry/A Little Beauty	20
56	London HLU 8242	Trouble With Harry/A Little Beauty (78)	5
57	London HLU 8494	Closing Time/Safari	10
57	London HLU 8494	Closing Time/Safari (78)	5

(see also David Seville)

CLEM ALFORD
74	Columbia SCX 6571	MIRROR IMAGE — THE ELECTRONIC SITAR OF CLEM ALFORD (LP)	40
75	KPM	MUSIC LIBRARY ALBUM (LP)	40

(see also Sagram, Magic Carpet)

SANDRA ALFRED
58	Oriole CB 1408	Rocket And Roll/Six Day Rock	25
58	Oriole CB 1408	Rocket And Roll/Six Day Rock (78)	30

ALFRED & MELMOTH
68	Island WI 3130	I Want Someone/ALFRED BROWN: One Scotch One Bourbon One Beer	10

ALICE COOPER
(see under C)

ALICE THROUGH THE LOOKING GLASS
69	SNP (no cat. no.)	ALICE THROUGH THE LOOKING GLASS (LP, private pressing)	500

(see also Ithaca, Agincourt, Tomorrow Come Someday)

ALIENS
70s	Alien ALI 001	When The River Runs Dry	4

ALIEN SEX FIEND
83	Anagram ANA 11	Ignore The Machine/The Gurl At The End Of My Gun (p/s, green or pink print on sleeve)	6/5
83	Anagram 12 ANA 11	Ignore The Machine/The Gurl At The End Of My Gun/ Under The Thunder (12", p/s)	8
83	Anagram ANA 15	Lips Can't Go/Drive My Rocket Uranus (p/s)	4
83	Anagram 12 ANA 15	Lips Can't Go/Drive My Rocket Uranus/Toytown Mix/Second Coma (12", p/s)	7
84	Anagram ANA 18	R.I.P./New Christian Music (p/s)	4
84	Anagram ANA 18	R.I.P./New Christian Music (cream & black p/s & red vinyl or b&w poster p/s)	6/7
84	Anagram 10 ANA 18	R.I.P./New Christian Music/Crazee (10", p/s)	7
84	Anagram 12 ANA 18	R.I.P./New Christian Music/Crazee (12", p/s)	7
84	Anagram ANA 23	Dead And Buried/Attack (p/s, some on red vinyl)	5/4
84	Anagram PANA 23	Dead And Buried/Attack (picture disc)	6
84	Anagram ANA 25	E.S.T. (Trip To The Moon)/Boneshaker Baby (p/s)	4
84	Anagram 11 ANA 25	E.S.T. (Trip To The Moon)/Boneshaker Baby/I Am A Product (live) (11", PVC sleeve with insert)	10
85	Anagram PANA 11	Ignore The Machine/The Gurl At The End Of My Gun (picture disc)	5

85	Anagram S ANA 11	Ignore The Machine (Special Electro Mix)/The Gurl At The End Of My Gun/ Ignore The Dub (12", p/s) 8
86	Flicknife DLEP 106	I Walk The Line/School's Out/Here She Comes/Can't Stop Smoking (double pack, gatefold p/s) 5
87	Anagram ANA 40	Stuff The Turkey/They Call Me Crazee (p/s, red or green vinyl) 5
88	Flexi FLX 730	So Much To Do, So Little Time (flexidisc) 4
87	Anagram CD GRAM 25	THE FIRST ALIEN SEX FIEND COMPACT DISC (CD, with poster) 15
90	Windsong 02	ASF BOX (box set, export issue, 4,000 only, with 3 coloured vinyl singles [12", 11"& 10"], poster, T-shirt & imitation dog turd) 25

(see also Demon Preacher, Demons)

ALKATRAZ
| 76 | Rockfield UAS 30001 | DOING A MOONLIGHT (LP) .... 10 |

(see also Man)

ALKATRAZZ
82	RCA RCA 183	Think It Over/Halfway There (picture disc) 4
81	RCA RCALP 5023	YOUNG BLOOD (LP) 10
82	RCA RCALP 3066	RADIO 5 (LP) 10

ALL ABOUT EVE
85	Eden EDEN 1	D For Desire/Don't Follow Me (12", p/s) 45
86	Eden EDEN 2	In The Clouds/End Of The Day/Love Leads Nowhere (12", p/s, some with poster) 30/25
87	Eden EVEN 3	Our Summer/Lady Moonlight (p/s) 7
87	Eden EVENX 3	Our Summer (extended)/Lady Moonlight/Shelter From The Rain (12", p/s) 15
87	Eden EVEN 4	Flowers In Our Hair/Paradise (p/s) 6
87	Eden EVENX 4	Flowers In Our Hair/Paradise/Devil Woman (12", p/s) 12
87	Mercury EVEN 5	In The Clouds/She Moves Through The Fair (p/s) 4
87	Mercury EVENP 5	In The Clouds/She Moves Through The Fair (envelope sleeve with poster) 7
87	Mercury EVENX 5	In The Clouds/Calling Your Name/She Moves Through The Fair (12", p/s) 8
88	Mercury EVENX 6	Wild-Hearted Woman (extended)/Apple Tree Man/Like Emily (12", p/s) 7
88	Mercury EVENX 622	Wild-Hearted Woman (extended)/Apple Tree Man/Like Emily/ What Kind Of Fool (live) (12" in box with enamel badge) 7
88	Mercury EVENM 6	Wild-Hearted Woman/Appletree Man/Like Emily/Our Summer (cassette) 6
88	Mercury EVNCD 6	Wild-Hearted Woman/Appletree Man/Like Emily/In The Clouds (CD) 8
88	Mercury EVENG 7	Every Angel/Wild Flowers (gatefold foldout p/s) 5
88	Mercury EVEN 710	Every Angel (extended)/Candy Tree/Wild Flowers/More Than This Hour (10", numbered envelope sleeve with poster) 7
88	Mercury EVNCD 7	Every Angel/Candy Tree/Wild Flowers/More Than This Hour (CD) 7
88	Mercury EVNXB 8	Martha's Harbour/Another Door/In The Clouds/Shelter From The Rain (live) (12" p/s, numbered pack with poster, 2,000 autographed) 10/7
88	Mercury EVENM 8	Martha's Harbour/Another Door/Never Promise (live)/In The Meadow (live) (boxed cassette with postcards) 5
88	Mercury EVNCD 8	Martha's Harbour/Wild Flowers/She Moves Through The Fair (CD, initially with gatefold sleeve) 10/7
88	Mercury EVNXB 9	What Kind Of Fool/Gold And Silver/The Garden Of Jane Delawney (12", envelope pack with poster) 7
88	Mercury EVENX 99	What Kind Of Fool (Synthesis Mix)/Gold And Silver/What Kind Of Fool (Autumn Rhapsody)/The Garden Of Jane Delawney (12", p/s, withdrawn) 8
88	Mercury EVNCD 99	What Kind Of Fool/Gold And Silver/The Garden Of Jane Delawney/What Kind Of Fool (Autumn Rhapsody) (CD in envelope pack with postcards) 7
88	Mercury EVEN 910	What Kind Of Fool/Gold And Silver/Every Angel (live) (10", gatefold p/s, with booklet) 7
89	Mercury EVENX 10	Road To Your Soul (extended)/Pieces Of Our Heart/Hard Spaniard (12", p/s, with cover print, 5,000 only) 7
89	Mercury EVCDX 10	Road To Your Soul/Pieces Of Our Heart/Hard Spaniard (picture CD in gold wallet) 7
89	Mercury EVENP 11	December/Drowning/Paradise ('89 remix) (picture disc, some numbered) 5/4
89	Mercury EVENB 11	December (Narnia Mix)/Drowning/Paradise ('89 remix) (10" box with poster) 7
89	Mercury EVEMC 11	December/Drowning/The Witches Promise (boxed cassette with badge) 6
90	Mercury EVENXL 12	Scarlet/Our Summer/Candy Tree/Tuesday Child (live gatefold 12" with poster) 7
91	Mercury EVCDX 13	In The Clouds/Never Promise Anyone Forever/Scarlet/More Than The Blues/Road To Your Soul (CD, live picture disc) 7
91	Mercury EVCX 13	In The Clouds/Never Promise Anyone Forever/Scarlet/More Than The Blues/Road To Your Soul (live cassette distributed by fan club, some copies also include "She Moves Through The Fair") 12/7
80s	fan club	LIVE AT THE BRIXTON ACADEMY (live cassette) 20

JOHNNIE ALLAN
| 74 | Oval 1000 | Promised Land/SHELTON DUNAWAY: Betty And Dupree .... 5 |
| 78 | Oval/Stiff LOT 1 | Promised Land/PETE FOWLER: One Heart One Song .... 4 |

RICHARD ALLAN/ALLEN
60	Parlophone R 4634	As Time Goes By/Only Love 5
60	Parlophone R 4673	Everyday/Doctor In Love (as Richard Allen) 4
60	Parlophone R 4711	Don't Ever Say You're Gonna Leave Me/Poetry In Motion 4

ALL DAY
| 73 | private pressing | YORK POP MUSIC PROJECT (LP) .... 350 |

ANNISTEEN ALLEN
55	Capitol CL 14264	Fujiyama Mama/Wheels Of Love 40
57	Brunswick 05639	Don't Nobody Move/The Money Tree 12
57	Brunswick 05639	Don't Nobody Move/The Money Tree (78) 8

BARBARA ALLEN
| 59 | Felsted AF 115 | Tommy's Song/Never Let Me Go .... 4 |

BOBBY ALLEN (& COMMANCHES)
| 62 | Fontana 267252 TF | I'll Forget About You/Your Cheatin' Heart .... 5 |

Bobby ALLEN

| 63 | Fontana TF 401 | Here Comes The Bride/Nothing's Impossible | 4 |
| 64 | Fontana TF 429 | Half As Much As You/So In Love With You (with Commanches) | 4 |

(see also Commanches)

CLAY ALLEN
62	Starlite ST45 086	This Time It's Really Goodbye/Broken Home	8
63	Starlite ST45 096	I Can't Stop The Blues From Moving/You've Got The Cleanest Mind	8
63	Starlite ST45 106	Crazy Crazy World/Just A Stone's Throw Away	8

DAEVID ALLEN
82	Charly CYX 202	Opium For The People/Stone Innocent Frankenstein (10", p/s)	6
82	Charly CYX 203	Jungle Window/Much Too Old (10", p/s)	6
75	Caroline C 1512	BANANA MOON (LP)	10
76	Virgin V 5024	GOOD MORNING (LP)	12

(see also Gong, Dashiell Hedayat)

DAVE ALLEN
| 69 | Philips BF 1748 | The Good Earth/A Way Of Life | 4 |

DEAN ALLEN
| 58 | London HLM 8698 | Rock Me To Sleep/Ooh-Ooh Baby Baby | 22 |
| 58 | London HLM 8698 | Rock Me To Sleep/Ooh-Ooh Baby Baby (78) | 8 |

JERRY ALLEN & HIS TRIO
| 54 | Decca F 10248 | S'Posin'/When I Needed You Most | 4 |
| 55 | Decca F 10443 | Kind/Delaunay's Dilemma | 4 |

LEE ALLEN (& HIS BAND)
58	HMV POP 452	Walkin' With Mr. Lee/Promenade	25
58	HMV POP 452	Walkin' With Mr. Lee/Promenade (78)	20
59	Top Rank JAR 265	Cat Walk/Creole Alley	8
82	NoLa 4	Zabo/Walking With Mr Lee	4
59	Top Rank JKR 8020	WALKIN' WITH MR LEE (EP)	15
78	NoLa LP 16	DOWN ON BOURBON STREET (LP)	10

MAURICE ALLEN
| 58 | Pye 7N 15128 | Ooh Baby/Rockhearted | 8 |

RANCE ALLEN GROUP
| 73 | Stax 2025 152 | (There's Gonna Be) A Showdown/That Will Be Good Enough For Me | 4 |
| 75 | Truth TRS 4207 | SOULFUL EXPERIENCE (LP) | 10 |

REX ALLEN
54	Brunswick 05341	This Ole House/They Were Doin' The Mambo (with Tex Williams)	12
57	Brunswick 05675	The Little White Horses/Drango	5
57	Brunswick 05677	Wringle Wrangle/Westward Ho The Wagons	5
57	Brunswick 05699	Flower Of San Antone/Money, Marbles And Chalk	5
59	Top Rank JAR 188	One More Sunrise/The Little Old Church In The Valley	4
57	Brunswick OE 9317	WESTWARD HO THE WAGONS (EP)	7
64	Mercury 10011MCE	COUNTRY AND WESTERN ACES (EP)	7

(see also Tex Williams)

RODNEY ALLEN
88	Subway Organisation SUBWAY 18T	Circle Line/Will It Rain Tomorrow?/Julianne (New Version)/Picture/Sometimes (12", p/s)	7
87	Subway Org. SUBORG 002	HAPPY SAD (LP)	10
80s	Fire	flexidisc	4

(see also Blue Aeroplanes)

STEVE ALLEN (& HIS ORCHESTRA)
56	Vogue Coral Q 72118	The Ballad Of Davy Crockett/Very Square Dance	7
56	Vogue Coral Q 72126	Memories Of You/What Is A Wife?	6
56	Vogue Coral Q 72136	Goodbye/Let's Dance	4
56	Vogue Coral Q 72155	What Is A Husband? (with Jayne Meadows)/What Is A Free Man?	5
56	Vogue Coral Q 72184	Lola's Theme/Conversation (On The Telephone)	4
58	Vogue Coral Q 72310	Pretend You Don't See Her/But I Haven't Got Him	4
58	London HLD 8742	Almost In Your Arms (Love Song From "Houseboat")/Hula Hoop	4

(see also George Cates)

TONY ALLEN
| 62 | Philips BBE 12522 | TIME TO SWING (EP) | 8 |

VERNON ALLEN
| 64 | R&B JB 169 | Fari Come/Babylon | 7 |

VERNON ALLEN & MILTON HAMILTON
| 66 | Blue Beat BB 348 | It Is I/Baby What's More | 12 |
| 66 | Blue Beat BB 353 | You're The Angel/Someone Like You | 12 |

WOODY ALLEN
64	Colpix PX 775	Spot Floyd/The Bullet	6
64	Colpix PXL 488	VOLUME 2 (LP)	12
65	Colpix PXL 518	WOODY ALLEN (LP)	12

ALLEY CATS
| 59 | Vogue V 9155 | Last Night/Snap-Crackle And Pop | 15 |
| 59 | Vogue V 9155 | Last Night/Snap-Crackle And Pop (78) | 10 |

ALLIES
| 80 | Harp HSP 1025 | Plush Living/Computer (p/s) | 4 |

CLAY ALLISON
| 80s | Bucketfull Of Brains SR 1 | Fell From The Sun/All Souls (free with 'Bucketfull Of Brains' magazine) | 5 |

GENE ALLISON
| 58 | London HLU 8605 | Hey, Hey, I Love You/You Can Make It If You Try | 60 |

| 58 | London HLU 8605 | Hey, Hey, I Love You/You Can Make It If You Try (78) | 30 |

JERRY ALLISON & CRICKETS
| 65 | Liberty LIB 10196 | Now Hear This/Everybody's Got A Little Problem | 10 |

(see also Crickets, Ivan)

LUTHER ALLISON
| 69 | Delmark DS 625 | LOVE ME MAMA (LP, blue label) | 12 |

LYNN ALLISON
| 57 | Columbia DB 3867 | Mama From The Train (A Kiss, A Kiss)/Song Of The Sparrow | 4 |
| 57 | Columbia DB 3906 | If Only/The Sky | 4 |

MOSE ALLISON
61	Fontana H 292	Baby Please Don't Go/Deed I Do	10
64	Columbia DB 7330	I Love The Life I Live/Life Is Suicide	10
59	Esquire EP 214	PARCHMAN FARM (EP)	20
59	Esquire EP 221	BACK COUNTRY SUITE (EP)	20
60	Esquire EP 224	BLUEBERRY HILL (EP)	20
61	Esquire EP 231	THAT MAN MOSE AGAIN (EP)	30
64	Columbia SEG 8353	ALLISON SINGS THE BLUES (EP)	20
60	Esquire 32-094	CREEK BANK (LP)	20
63	London HA-K 8083	SWINGIN' MACHINE (LP, as Mose Allison Jazz Group)	20
64	Columbia SX 6058	V-8 FORD (LP)	25
64	Stateside SL 10106	MOSE ALLISON SINGS (LP)	20
66	Atlantic 587/588 007	MOSE ALIVE (LP)	12
66	CBS Realm RM(S) 52318	I LOVE THE LIFE I LIVE (LP)	35
66	Atlantic 587/588 031	WILD MAN ON THE LOOSE (LP)	15
67	Transatlantic PR 7189	AUTUMN SONG (LP)	15
68	Transatlantic PR 7279	MOSE ALLISON (LP)	10

ALLISONS (U.K.)
61	Fontana H 294	Are You Sure/There's One Thing More (as the Allisons [Bob & John])	4
61	Fontana H 304	Words/Blue Tears	4
61	Fontana H 336	What A Mess!/Lorraine	4
61	Fontana H 362	Lesson In Love/Oh, My Love	4
62	Fontana 267 231TF	Sweet And Lovely/Sugar Love	4
62	Fontana 267 255TF	I'll Cross My Fingers/You Should Be Sorry	4
69	Fontana TF 1021	Are You Sure/There's One Thing More (reissue)	4
61	Fontana TFE 17339	THE ALLISONS (EP)	15
61	Fontana TFL 5135	ARE YOU SURE (LP, also stereo STFL 558)	18/25

ALLISONS (U.S.)
| 64 | Stateside SS 289 | Surfer Street/Money | 7 |

ALLMAN BROTHERS BAND
70	Atco 226 013	Black Hearted Woman/Every Hungry Woman	4
70	Atco 2091 040	Revival (Love Is Everywhere)/Leave My Blues At Home	4
71	Atco 2091 070	Midnight Rider/Whipping Post	4
69	Atco 228 033	THE ALLMAN BROTHERS BAND (LP)	10
70	Atco 2400 032	IDLEWILD SOUTH (LP)	10

(see also Duane Allman, Gregg Allman, Dickie Betts Band, Allman Joys, Hourglass)

DUANE ALLMAN
| 72 | Capricorn K 67502 | AN ANTHOLOGY (2-LP) | 14 |

GREGG ALLMAN
| 73 | Capricorn K 47508 | LAID BACK (LP) | 10 |

ALLMAN JOYS
| 73 | Mercury 6398 005 | ALLMAN JOYS (LP) | 15 |

ALLNIGHT BAND
| 79 | Casino Classics CC 5/6-12 | The Wigan Joker/Six By Six/RON GRAINER ORCHESTRA: A Touch Of Velvet — A Sting Of Brass/Theme From "Joe 90" (12", p/s, crimson vinyl, Disco DJ Version) | 7 |

TOMMY ALLSUP
| 65 | London HA-U 8218 | BUDDY HOLLY SONG BOOK (LP) | 20 |

LAURINDO ALMEIDA QUARTET
| 56 | Vogue V 2382 | Atabaque/Inquietacao | 4 |

ALMIGHTY
89	Polydor PO 60	Destroyed/Blood, Fire And Love (p/s)	4
89	Polydor PZ 60	Destroyed/Blood, Fire And Love (12", p/s)	8
89	Polydor PZP 60	Destroyed/Blood, Fire And Love (12", picture disc)	10
90	Polydor PZP 66	Power/Detroit/Wild And Wonderful (live)/Lay Down The Law (12", picture disc)	7

JOHNNY ALMOND MUSIC MACHINE
69	Deram DM 266	Solar Level/To R.K.	5
69	Deram DML/SML 1043	PATENT PENDING (LP)	25
70	Deram SML 1057	HOLLYWOOD BLUES (LP)	20

(see also John Mayall & Blues Breakers, Mark-Almond)

MARC ALMOND
82	Lyntone LYN 12505	Discipline (as 'Marc Almond & Friends', clear flexidisc with 'Flexipop' 23)	10/8
84	Some Bizzare BZS 23	The Boy Who Came Back/Joey Demento (p/s)	5
84	Some Bizzare BZS 2312	The Boy Who Came Back (Extended)/Joey Demento (Extended) (12", p/s)	7
84	Some Bizzare BZS 2310	The Boy Who Came Back (Extended)/Joey Demento (Extended) (10", p/s)	12
84	Some Bizzare BZS 24	You Have/Split Lip (p/s)	4
84	Some Bizzare BZS 2412	You Have/Split Lip (Extended)/Joey Demento (12", p/s)	7
84	Some Bizzare BZS 2410	You Have/Split Lip/Black Mountain Blues (10", p/s with lyric sheet)	12
84	Some Bizzare BZS 25	Tenderness Is A Weakness/Love For Sale (p/s)	4

Marc ALMOND

84	Some Bizzare BZS 2510	Tenderness Is A Weakness (Extended)/Love For Sale/Pink Shack Blues (live)/The Heel (live) (10", p/s)	12
85	Some Bizzare BONK 1	Stories Of Johnny/Stories Of Johnny (with choir) (p/s)	4
85	Some Bizzare BONKD 1	Stories Of Johnny/Stories Of Johnny (with choir)/Blond Boy/Take My Heart (double pack, gatefold p/s)	5
85	Some Bizzare BONK 1-10	Stories Of Johnny/(with choir)/Blond Boy/Take My Heart (10", p/s)	8
85	Some Bizzare BONK 112	Stories Of Johnny/(with choir)/Blond Boy/Take My Heart (12", p/s)	7
85	Some Bizzare BONK P2	Love Letter/Love Letter (with choir) (p/s, with poster insert)	4
85	Some Bizzare BONK 2-10	Love Letter (Special Cabaret Voltaire Mix)/Love Letter (with choir) (10" p/s)	8
85	Some Bizzare BONK 212	Love Letter (12" Mix)/Love Letter (with choir) (12", p/s)	7
85	Some Bizzare GLOW 1	The House Is Haunted (By The Echo Of Your Last Goodbye)/Broken Bracelets (promo only)	10
85	Some Bizzare GLOWD 1	The House Is Haunted (By The Echo Of Your Last Goodbye)/Broken Bracelets//Cara A Cara/Medley (double pack, gatefold p/s)	6
86	Some Bizzare GLOWY 210	A Woman's Story/The Heel/A Salty Dog/The Plague/The Little White Cloud That Cried/For One Moment/Just Good Friends (10" picture disc, stickered PVC sleeve)	10
86	Some Bizzare TGLOW 212	A Woman's Story/For One Moment/The Heel/A Salty Dog/The Plague/The Little White Cloud That Cried/Just Good Friends (cassette)	5
86	Some Bizzare GLOW 313	Ruby Red (Re-recorded Extended Dance Mix)/(instrumental) (12", p/s)	7
86	Some Bizzare GLOW 313	Ruby Red (Remastered & Rethought Mix)/(instrumental) (12" p/s, with stickered sleeve)	7
87	Some Bizzare GLOWD 4	Melancholy Rose/Gyp The Blood//Surabaya Johnny/Pirate Jenny (double pack, gatefold p/s)	4
87	Some Bizzare GLOW 5	Mother Fist/Two Sailors On The Beach (promo only)	10
88	Parlophone RX 6186	Tears Run Rings/Everything I Want Love To Be (box with booklet, cards & badge)	4
90	Parlophone RPD 6229	A Lover Spurned (Full Length)/Exotica Rose (shaped picture disc, printed PVC sleeve)	4
92	Some Bizzare YZ 638T	The Days Of Pearly Spencer (12", 3-track, withdrawn, 300 only)	12
88	Parlophone PSR 500	Kept Boy (1-sided etched, withdrawn)	12
80s	MM Vinyl Conflict 1	Oily Black Limousine (b/w 3 songs by others, free with 'Melody Maker')	5/4
80s	Gutterhearts	Your Aura (fan club flexidisc)	12
80s	Gutterhearts LYN 14210	My Death (fan club flexidisc)	12
84	Some Bizzare BIZL 8	VERMIN IN ERMINE (LP, with inner bag & lyric sheet)	10
85	Some Bizzare FAITH 1	STORIES OF JOHNNY (LP, with special lyric book)	10

(see also Soft Cell, Marc & Mambas, Burmoe Brothers, Vicious Pink Phenomena, Flesh Volcano)

MARC ALMOND & GENE PITNEY

89	Parlophone RX 6201	Something's Gotten Hold Of My Heart/MARC ALMOND: Something's... (numbered box with 2 postcards, foldout discography, badge & sticker)	4

ALMOND LETTUCE

68	Columbia DB 8442	The Tree Dog Song/To Henry With Hope	4
69	Philips BF 1764	Magic Circle/Twenty Weary Miles	10

ALONE AGAIN OR

84	All One ALG 1	Drum The Beat (In My Soul)/Smartie Edit (p/s)	12
85	Polydor ALG 2	Dream Come True/Smarter Than The Average Bear (p/s)	6
85	Polydor ALGX 2	Dream Come True (Splintered Version)/Smarter Than The Average Bear (Ursa Major)/Drum The Beat (Shall We Dance?) (12", p/s)	8

(see also Shamen)

HERB ALPERT (& TIJUANA BRASS)

67	Pye International 7N 25419	Casino Royale/Wall Street Rag	4
68	A&M AMS 700	Casino Royale/Wall Street Rag (reissue, p/s)	5
69	A&M AMS 755	Without Her/Sandbox (p/s)	4
80	A&M AMSP 7500	Rotation/Behind The Rain (12")	7
63	Stateside SL 10027	THE LONELY BULL (LP)	10
64	Stateside SL 10072	HERB ALPERT'S TIJUANA BRASS (VOL. 2) (LP)	10

ALPHAVILLE

86	WEA X 8643T	Universal Daddy (Aquarian Dance Mix)/Next Generation (12", p/s)	8

CARLTON ALPHONSO

67	Pama PM 700	Where In This World/Peacemakers	10
69	Grape GR 3000	Belittle Me/Keep Your Love	5

CLYDE ALPHONSO

69	Studio One SO 2076	Good Enough/Let The Music Play	12

ORVILLE ALPHONSO

65	Caribou CRC 1	Belly Lick/Inspiration	7

ROLAND ALPHONSO (alias ROLAND AL)

62	Blue Beat BB 112	Four Corners Of The World (with Alley Cats)/SHINERS: Romantic Shuffle	12
65	Blue Beat BB 356	Just A Closer Walk/Jericho Train (Joshua)	10
65	Island WI 217	El Pussy Cat Ska/LORD BRYNNER: Tiger In Your Tank	12
65	Ska Beat JB 210	Numble Foot/ANDY & JOEY: Love Is Stronger	12
65	Ska Beat JB 216	Nuclear Weapon (& Baba Brooks)/STRANGER COLE: Love Thy Neighbour	10
65	Rio R 58	Jazz Ska/HYACINTH: Oh Gee	12
66	Island WI 259	James Bond/LEE PERRY: Just Keep It Up	12
66	Doctor Bird DB 1010	From Russia With Love/Cleopatra (with Soul Brothers)	12
66	Doctor Bird DB 1011	Sufferer's Choice (with Soul Brothers)/SOULETTES: I Want To Be	12
66	Doctor Bird DB 1017	Sugar And Spice/Get Out Of My Life (with Soul Brothers)	12
66	Doctor Bird DB 1020	Phoenix City(with Soul Brothers)/DEACONS: Men Alone	12
66	Doctor Bird DB 1023	Doctor Ring-A-Ding/FREDDIE & HEARTACHES: Here Is My Heart	12
66	Ska Beat JB 231	Rinky Dink (So Good) (with Studio One Orchestra)/SCRATCH & DYNAMITES: Deacon Johnson	10
67	Pyramid PYR 6005	Women Of The World (& Beverley's Allstars)/SPANISHTONIANS: Kisses	12
67	Pyramid PYR 6006	On The Move (& Beverley's Allstars)/DESMOND DEKKER & ACES: It's A Shame	10

67	Pyramid PYR 6007	Jungle Bit (& Beverley's Allstars)/NORMAN GRANT: Somebody Please Help Me 12
67	Pyramid PYR 6009	Guantanamera Ska (& Beverley's Allstars)/SPANISHTONIANS: Suffer Me Not 10
67	Pyramid PYR 6018	Sock It To Me (& Beverley's Allstars)/SPANISHTONIANS: Rudie Gets Plenty 10
68	Pyramid PYR 6022	Whiter Shade Of Pale/On The Move 10
68	Coxsone CS 7077	Reggae In The Grass/ROY RICHARDS: Get Smart 15
69	Gas GAS 112	A Thousand Tons Of Megaton (actually with Derrick Morgan)/Musical Resurrection 4
70	Punch PH 39	Roll On (& Upsetters)/CARL DAWKINS: True Love 5
71	Banana BA 340	Mellow Mood (Way To My Heart)/MAYTALS: Marching On 6

ALQUIN

73	Polydor 2480 152	MARKS (LP) 10
74	Polydor 2480 179	THE MOUNTAIN QUEEN (LP) 10
75	Polydor 2480 262	NOBODY CAN WAIT FOREVER (LP) 10

ALTECS

| 61 | London HLU 9387 | Easy/Recess ....6 |

ALTERED IMAGES

81	Epic EPC A 1023	Dead Pop Stars/Sentimental (p/s) 5
81	Epic EPC 40-A1023	Dead Pop Stars/Sentimental/Leave Me Alone (cassette) 6
81	Epic EPC A 1167	A Day's Wait/Who Cares? (p/s) 4
81	Epic A 11 1834	I Could Be Happy/Insects (picture disc) 4
82	Epic A 2617	Happy Birthday/I Could Be Happy/Dead Pop Stars/A Day's Wait (EP) 4
82	Epic A 112198	See Those Eyes/How About That Then (picture disc) 4
82	Epic A 4226	Pinky Blue/Think That It Might (Dance Mix) (pink vinyl, PVC sleeve) 4
83	Epic WA 3083	Don't Talk To Me About Love/Last Goodbye (picture disc) 4
83	Epic WA 3398	Bring Me Closer/Surprise Me (picture disc) 4
83	Epic WTA 3398	Bring Me Closer (Extended Mix)/Surprise Me (12" picture disc) 7
83	Lyntone LYN 10795	Happy New Year/Real Toys/Leave Me Alone (red vinyl flexidisc free with 'Flexipop' 14) 5/4
83	Lyntone LYN 10795	Happy New Year/Real Toys/Leave Me Alone (hard vinyl test pressing) 15

ALTERNATIVE TV

77	Sniffing Glue SG 12	Love Lies Limp (1-sided flexidisc free with 'Sniffing Glue' magazine issue 12) .10/6
77	Deptford Fun City DFC 02	How Much Longer/You Bastard (p/s) 5
77	Deptford Fun City DFC 02	How Much Longer/You Bastard (p/s, labelled 'alternate versions') 8
78	Deptford Fun City DFC 04	Life After Life/Life After Dub (p/s) 4
78	Deptford Fun City DFC 05	Life/Love Lies Limp (p/s) 4
78	Deptford Fun City DLP 01	THE IMAGE HAS CRACKED (LP) 10
78	Deptford Fun City DLP 02	WHAT YOU SEE IS ... WHAT YOU ARE (LP, 1 side by Here & Now) 12
78	Deptford Fun City DLP 03	VIBING UP THE SENILE MAN (LP) 10
79	Crystal CLP 01	LIVE AT THE RAT CLUB '77 (LP) 15
80	Deptford Fun City DLP 05	ACTION TIME VISION (LP) 10
81	International SP 70023	STRANGE KICKS (LP) 10
81	Conventional CON 14	AN YE AS WELL (cassette) 10

(see also Mark Perry, Good Missionaries, The Door & The Window, Reflections)

ALTERNATORS

| 78 | Energy NRG 001 | No Answers/The Lad Don't Know (no p/s) ....5 |

ALTERNOMEN UNLIMITED

| 79 | Object OM 06 | Facade/Connections (p/s) ....4 |

(see also Spherical Objects)

ALTON (Ellis) & EDDY

| 61 | Blue Beat BB 17 | Muriel/CLUE J. & HIS BLUES BLASTERS: Silky ....12 |
| 62 | Island WI 009 | My Love Divine/Let Me Dream ....12 |

(see also Alton Ellis)

ALTON & FLAMES

(see under Alton Ellis)

ALVARO

77	Squeaky Shoes SSRM 1	DRINKING MY OWN SPERM (LP) 18
79	Squeaky Shoes SSRM 2	MUM'S MILK NOT POWDER (LP) 15
81	Squeaky Shoes SSRM 3	THE WORKING CLASS (LP) 15

(see also 101'ers)

ALVYN

| 69 | Morgan Bluetown MR 18S | You've Gotta Have An Image/Mind The Gap ....5 |

AMALGAM

69	Transatlantic TRA 196	A PRAYER FOR PEACE (LP) 40
73	A Records A 002	PLAY BLACKWELL & HIGGINS (LP) 15
77	Vinyl VS 100	ANOTHER TIME (LP) 10
77	Vinyl VS 104	SAMANNA (LP, with T. Watts) 10
70s	Vinyl VS	DEEP (LP) 10
79	Tangent TGS 121	INNOVATION (LP) 10

GLEN AMAMS

| 69 | Escort ES 804 | Rich In Love/WOODPECKERS: Zumbelly ....4 |

(see also Glen Adams)

AMAZIAH

| 70s | Sunrise SR 001 | STRAIGHT TALKER (LP, private pressing) ....175 |

AMAZING BLONDEL

72	Island WIP 6153	Alleluia (Cantus Firmus To Counterpoint)/Safety In God Alone 4
70	Bell SBLL 131	THE AMAZING BLONDEL AND A FEW FACES (LP) 100
70	Island ILPS 9136	EVENSONG (LP, gatefold sleeve) 12

MINT VALUE £

71	Island ILPS 9156	FANTASIA LINDUM (LP)	12
72	Island ILPS 9205	ENGLAND '72 (LP, gatefold sleeve)	12
73	Island ILPS 9257	BLONDEL (LP, gatefold sleeve)	12
76	DJM DJF 20442	MULGRAVE STREET (LP)	10
76	DJM DJF 20446	INSPIRATION (LP)	10

(see also Methuselah)

AMAZING DANCE BAND
| 68 | Verve VS 567 | Deep Blue Train/Simon Smith & His Amazing Dancing Bear | 15 |

AMAZING FRIENDLY APPLE
| 69 | Decca F 12887 | Water Woman/Magician | 25 |

AMBERGRIS
| 70 | Paramount PAS 5014 | AMBERGRIS (LP) | 10 |

AMBER SQUAD
| 80 | Sound Of Leicester ST 1 | (I Can't) Put My Finger On You/Tell You A Lie (p/s) | 12 |
| 80 | Dead Good DEAD 17 | Can We Go Dancing?/You Should See (What I Do To You In My Dreams) (p/s) | 10 |

(AMERICAN) AMBOY DUKES
68	Fontana TF 971	Let's Go Get Stoned/It's Not True	12
68	Fontana (S)TL 5468	THE AMBOY DUKES (LP)	35
68	London HA-T/SH-T 8378	JOURNEY TO THE CENTER OF THE MIND (LP, as American Amboy Dukes)	30
69	London HA-T/SH-T 8392	MIGRATION (LP, as American Amboy Dukes)	25

(see also Ted Nugent)

AMBOY DUKES (U.K.)
66	Polydor 56149	Turn Back To Me/I Never Complain About You	4
67	Polydor 56172	All I Need/Doing The Best I Can	6
67	Polydor 56190	High Life In Whitley Wood Pts 1 & 2	4
68	Polydor 56228	Judy In Disguise/Who's Foolin' Who	4
68	Polydor 56243	Simon Says/The Marquis	4
68	Polydor 56281	He Came To See Me Yesterday/Easy Going Me	4

AMBROSE & HIS ORCHESTRA
| 56 | MGM SP 1151 | Lilacs In The Rain/Deep Purple | 4 |

SAMMY AMBROSE
| 65 | Stateside SS 385 | This Diamond Ring/Bad Night | 45 |
| 65 | Stateside SS 399 | Monkey See Monkey Do/Welcome To Dreamsville | 50 |

AMBROSE SLADE
69	Fontana TF 1015	Genesis/Roach Daddy	125
69	Fontana STL 5492	BEGINNINGS (LP, glossy cover & black label with silver print)	250
75	Contour 6870 678	BEGINNINGS OF SLADE (LP, withdrawn reissue, different cover)	50

(see also Slade, In-Be-Tweens)

AMBROSIA
75	20th Century BTC 2207	Holdin' On To Yesterday/Make Us All Aware	4
82	Warner Bros K 17933	How Can You Love Me/Fool Like Me (picture disc)	4
75	20th Century BT 434	AMBROSIA (LP)	15
76	20th Century BT 519	SOMEWHERE I'VE NEVER TRAVELLED (LP)	15
78	Warner Bros K 56252	LIFE BEYOND L.A. (LP)	12
80	Warner Bros K 56811	ONE EIGHTY (LP)	12
82	Warner Bros K 56968	ROAD ISLAND (LP)	10

AMEBIX
| 82 | Spiderleg SDL 6 | The Enemy/Carnage/No Gods No Masters (p/s) | 5 |
| 83 | Spiderleg SDL 10 | Winter/Beginning Of The End (p/s) | 4 |

LOLA AMECHE
| 53 | Oriole CB 1143 | Rock The Joint/Don't Let The Stars Get In Your Eyes (78) | 8 |

AMEN CORNER
67	Deram DM 136	Gin House Blues/I Know	5
67	Deram DM 151	The World Of Broken Hearts/Nema	4
68	Deram DM 172	Bend Me Shape Me/Satisnek The Job's Worth	4
68	Deram DM 197	High In The Sky/Run, Run, Run	4
69	Deram DM 228	The World Of Broken Hearts/Gin House Blues	4
69	Immediate IM 073	(If Paradise Is) Half As Nice/Hey Hey Girl	4
69	Immediate IM 081	Hello Susie/Evil Man's Gonna Win	4
69	Immediate IM 084	Get Back/Farewell To The Real Magnificent Seven	4
68	Deram DML/SML 1021	ROUND AMEN CORNER (LP)	12
69	Immediate IMSP 023	NATIONAL WELSH COAST LIVE (LP)	10
69	Immediate IMSP 028	FAREWELL TO THE REAL MAGNIFICENT SEVEN (LP)	10

(see also Andy Fairweather-Low, Fairweather, Mayfield's Mule, Gary Pickford-Hopkins & Friends)

AMERICAN BREED
67	CBS 2888	Step Out Of Your Mind/The Same Old Thing	7
67	CBS 2972	Step Out Of Your Mind/The Same Old Thing (reissue)	5
68	Stateside SS 2078	Bend Me Shape Me/Mindrocker	4
68	Dot DOT 101	Green Light/Don't It Make You Cry	4
68	Dot DOT 106	Ready, Willing And Able/Take Me If You Want Me	4
67	Dot DOLP 255	AMERICAN BREED (LP)	10
68	Dot (S)LPD 502	BEND ME, SHAPE ME (LP)	10
68	Dot (S)LPD 507	NO WAY TO TREAT A LADY (LP, soundtrack)	10
68	Dot (S)LPD 518	PUMPKIN, POWDER, SCARLET AND GREEN (LP)	10
69	Dot (S)LPD 526	THE LONELY SIDE OF THE CITY (LP)	10

AMERICAN EXPRESS
| 79 | Mercury 6007 212 | Exodisco/Kickback | 4 |
| 79 | Mercury 9198 168 | Exodisco/Kickback (12") | 7 |

(see also Clover, Huey Lewis & News)

AMERICAN GYPSY
75	BTM BTM 1001GG	AMERICAN GYPSY (LP)	25

(AMERICAN) POETS
66	London HLC 10037	She Blew A Good Thing/Out To Lunch	35
71	United Artists UP 35308	She Blew A Good Thing/Out To Lunch (reissue, as Poets)	4

AMERICAN SPRING
72	United Artists UP 35376	Good Time/Sweet Mountain	4
72	United Artists UP 35421	Mama Said/Tennessee Waltz	4
73	CBS 1590	Shyin' Away/Falling In Love	6
72	United Artists UAG 29363	AMERICAN SPRING (LP)	15

(see also Beach Boys)

AMERICAN YOUTH CHOIR
71	Polydor 2066 013	Together We Can Make It/Keep Your Fine Self Near Me	12

EDDIE AMES
57	HMV POP 311	The Bean Song (Which Way To...)/I'd Give You The World	4

NANCY AMES
66	Columbia DB 7809	Friends And Lovers Forever/I've Got A Lot Of Love	8
66	Columbia DB 8039	Cry Softly/I Don't Want To Talk About It	40

AMES BROTHERS
53	HMV 7M 153	You, You, You/My Life, My Love, My Happiness	10
54	HMV 7M 179	I Can't Believe That You're In Love/Boogie Woogie Maxine	8
54	HMV 7M 209	The Man With The Banjo/Man, Man, Is For The Woman Made	6
54	HMV 7M 253	Hopelessly/One More Time	6
55	HMV 7M 281	The Naughty Lady Of Shady Lane/Addio	18
55	HMV 7M 310	Sweet Brown-Eyed Baby/Sympathetic Eyes	6
55	HMV 7M 322	Wrong Again/Merci Beaucoup	6
55	HMV 7M 331	So Will I/My Bonnie Lassie	6
56	HMV 7M 410	My Love, Your Love/If You Wanna See Me Tonight	6
56	HMV 7MC 46	If You Wanna See Mamie Tonight/It Only Hurts For A little While (export issue)	6
56	HMV POP 242	I'm Gonna Hurt You/It Only Hurts For A little While	8
56	HMV POP 264	49 Shades Of Green/Summer Sweetheart	4
57	RCA RCA 1015	Rocking Shoes/B-Side	8
57	RCA RCA 1015	Rocking Shoes/B-Side (78)	5
57	RCA RCA 1021	Melodie D'Amour/So Little Time	4
58	RCA RCA 1049	A Very Precious Love/In Love	4
58	RCA RCA 1091	No One But You (In My Heart)/Pussy Cat	4
58	RCA RCA 1091	No One But You (In My Heart)/Pussy Cat (78)	5
59	RCA RCA 1104	Red River Rose/When The Summer Comes	4
59	RCA RCA 1118	(Yes, I Need) Only Your Love/Dancin' In The Streets	4
59	RCA RCA 1135	Someone To Come To/Mason-Dixon Line	4
59	RCA RCA 1135	Someone To Come To/Mason-Dixon Line (78)	5
57	HMV 7EG 8237	EXACTLY LIKE YOU (EP)	9
59	RCA RCX 1047	BEST OF THE AMES BROTHERS (EP)	9
56	Coral LVA 9071	THE SOUNDS OF CHRISTMAS HARMONY (LP)	10

IDI AMIN
73	Transatlantic BIG 527	Amazin' Man/Findin' De Lady	4

AMM
66	Incus EP 1	AT THE ROUNDHOUSE (EP)	100
67	Elektra EUKS 7256	AMM MUSIC (LP)	80

ALBERT AMMONS
40s	Brunswick 02187	Boogie Woogie Stomp/Nagasaki (78)	10
40s	Brunswick 02336	Early Mornin' Blues/Mile-Or-Mo Bird Rag (78)	10
40s	Parlophone R 2902	Shout For Joy/MEADE LUX LEWIS: Bear Cat Crawl (78)	8
52	Vogue V 2109	Boogie Woogie Stomp/Boogie Woogie Blues (78)	5
53	Vogue V 2213	Suitcase Blues/Bass Goin' Crazy (78)	5
55	Vogue EPV 1071	ALBERT AMMONS (EP)	40
57	Brunswick OE 9325	BOOGIE WOOGIE STOMP (EP)	15
54	Mercury MG 25012	ALBERT AMMONS (10" LP)	20
62	Storyville SLP 184	BOOGIE WOOGIE TRIO (LP)	12

ALBERT AMMONS & PETE JOHNSON
40s	HMV B 3325	Sixth Avenue Express/Pine Creek (78)	8
40s	HMV B 9251	BH Boogie/Cuttin' Boogie (78)	8
55	HMV DLP 1011	EIGHT TO THE BAR (10" LP)	20

ALBERT AMMONS, PETE JOHNSON & MEADE 'LUX' LEWIS
40s	Parlophone R 2649	Boogie Woogie Prayer Pts 1 & 2 (78)	10
55	Columbia SEG 7528	ALBERT AMMONS, PETE JOHNSON & MEADE 'LUX' LEWIS (EP)	20
63	Riverside RLP 12-106	GIANTS OF BOOGIE WOOGIE (LP)	15

(see also Pete Johnson, Meade 'Lux' Lewis)

GENE AMMONS (BAND)
60	Starlite ST45 017	Echo Chamber Blues/Ammons' Boogie	25
63	Starlite ST45 097	Anna/Cae' Cae'	8
62	Esquire EP 249	BOSSA NOVA BY THE BOSS (EP)	8
60	Esquire 32-097	JAMMIN' WITH GENE (LP)	15
73	Prestige PR 10019	YOU TALK THAT TALK (LP)	10
73	Prestige PR 10021	BROTHER JUG (LP)	10
73	Prestige PR 24021	JUG & DODO (LP)	10
74	Prestige PR 24036	JUGANTHOLOGY VOL. 1 (LP)	10

AMON DÜÜL II
69	Liberty LBS 83279	PHALLUS DEI (LP)	20

AMON DÜÜL II

70	Liberty LBS 83359	YETI (2-LP, gatefold sleeve)	20
71	United Artists UAD60003/4	DANCE OF THE LEMMINGS (2-LP, gatefold sleeve)	16
72	United Artists UAG 23927	CARNIVAL IN BABYLON (LP)	12
72	Sunset SLS 50257	PHALLUS DEI (LP, reissue)	10
72	United Artists UAG 29406	WOLF CITY (LP, gatefold sleeve)	12
73	United Artists USP 102	LIVE IN LONDON (LP)	10
73	United Artists UAS 29504	VIVE LA TRANCE (LP)	10
82	Illuminated JAMS 024	HAWK MEETS PENGUIN (LP)	10
84	Illuminated JAMS 27	MEETING WITH MEN MACHINES (LP, as Amon Düül [UK])	10

(see also Utopia)

TORI AMOS

91	East West YZ 618	Silent All These Years/Me And A Gun (p/s)	8
91	East West YZ 618T	Silent All These Years/Me And A Gun + 2 (12", p/s)	12
91	East West YZ 618CD	Silent All These Years/Me And A Gun + 2 (CD)	15
91	East West	Silent All These Years/Ode To A Banana King/Song For Eric/Happy Phantom (live) (CD, digipak)	8
92	East West A 7504 CDX	Winter/Angie/Smells Like Teen Spirit/Thank You (CD, foldout digipak)	10
92	Atlantic A 7479CD	Crucify (CD box)	7

AMOS & SARA

81	private cassette	THE PRIVATE WORLD OF AMOS (cassette)	8
82	It's War Boys £9	Go Home Soldier/Enough Is Enough/Surveillance O.H.M.S. (12", screen-printed p/s)	7

(see also Homosexuals)

MOREY AMSTERDAM

54	MGM SP 1086	Somebody Bad Stole De Wedding Cake/I Wish I Was A Peanut	4

ANAN

68	Pye 7N 17571	Haze Woman/I Wonder Where My Sister's Gone	18
68	Pye 7N 17642	Madena/Standing Still	15

ANCIENT GREASE

70	Mercury 6338 033	WOMAN AND CHILDREN FIRST (LP)	40

(see also Eyes Of Blue, Big Sleep, Man, Gary Pickford-Hopkins)

AND ALSO THE TREES

84	Reflex RE 3	The Secret Sea/Secrecy (p/s)	12
84	Reflex 12 RE 6	The Secret Sea/Secrecy/There Were No Bounds/The Tease The Tear/Midnight Garden/Wallpaper Dying (12", p/s)	10
84	Reflex FS 9	Shantell/Wallpaper Dying (p/s)	12
85	Reflex 12 RE 8	A Room Lives In Lucy/There Was A Man Of Double Deed/Scarlet Aran (12", p/s)	8
87	Reflex 12 RE 12	The Critical Distance/Scythe And Spade/The Renegade (12", p/s)	8
87	Reflex 12 RE 13	Shaletown/Needle Street/L'Unica Strada (12", p/s)	7
80s	Reflex	12" box set	25
84	Reflex LEX 1	AND ALSO THE TREES (LP)	10

ERIC ANDERSEN

65	Fontana TFL 6061	TODAY IS THE HIGHWAY (LP)	16
68	Fontana STFL 6068	'BOUT CHANGES AND THINGS TAKE 2 (LP)	14
73	CBS 65571	BLUE RIVER (LP)	10

CAROL ANDERSON

79	Grapevine GRP 133	Sad Girl/I'll Get Off At The Next Stop	4

ERNESTINE ANDERSON

59	Mercury AMT 1035	Be Mine/I Don't See Me In Your Eyes Any More	5
59	Mercury AMT 1073	My Love Will Last/Call Me Darling	4
60	Mercury AMT 1082	There Are Such Times/You, You, You	4
60	Mercury AMT 1103	A Kiss To Build A Dream On/Come On, Baby, Let's Go	4
61	Mercury AMT 1137	A Lover's Question/That's All I Want From You	4
64	Sue WI 309	Keep An Eye On Love/Continental Mind	18
65	Stateside SS 455	Somebody Told You/How Many Times	8
65	Mercury MF 912	Jerk & Twine/You Can't Buy Love	8
60	Mercury ZEP 10057	RUNNING WILD (EP)	10
60	Mercury ZEP 10089	WELCOME TO THE CLUB (EP)	10
61	Mercury ZEP 10105	AZURE-TE (EP)	8
61	Mercury ZEP 10124	JUST A SWINGIN' (EP)	8
64	Mercury 10007 MCE	ERNESTINE ANDERSON (EP)	10
58	Pye Nixa NPT 19025	BY SPECIAL REQUEST (LP)	15
59	Mercury MMC 14016	RUNNIN' WILD (LP)	20
60	Mercury MMC 14037	THE FASCINATING ERNESTINE (LP)	15
61	Mercury MMC 14062	MOANIN' (LP)	15
64	Sue ILP 911	THE NEW SOUND OF ERNESTINE ANDERSON (LP, unissued, test pressings only)	50+
67	Columbia S(C)X 6145	ERNESTINE ANDERSON (LP)	12

GLADSTONE ANDERSON (& FOLLOWERS)

69	Blue Cat BS 172	Judas/The World Come To An End (with Followers)	4
73	Ashanti SHAN 103	IT MAY SOUND SILLY (LP, solo)	10

(see also Stranger & Gladdy)

IAN ANDERSON

83	Chrysalis CHS 2746	Fly By Night/End Game (p/s)	4

(see also Jethro Tull)

IAN (A.) ANDERSON

71	Village Thing VTSX 1002	One More Chance/Policeman's ball	15
69	Saydisc EP SD 134	ALMOST THE COUNTRY BLUES (EP, with Elliot Jackson)	15
68	Saydisc Matchbox SDM 159	THE INVERTED WORLD (LP, with Mike Cooper)	40

69	Liberty LBS 83242E	STEREO DEATH BREAKDOWN (LP, as Ian Anderson Country Blues Band) 35
70	Fontana STL 5542	BOOK OF CHANGES (LP) 20
70	Village Thing VTS 3	ROYAL YORK CRESCENT (LP) 15
71	Village Thing VTS 9	A VULTURE IS NOT A BIRD YOU CAN TRUST (LP) 15
72	Village Thing VTS 18	SINGER SLEEPS ON AS BLAZE RAGES (LP) 12

(see also Mike Cooper, Anderson Jones Jackson)

JON ANDERSON
| 76 | Atlantic K 10840 | Flight Of The Moorglade/To The Runner . . . . 4 |
| 76 | Atlantic K 50261 | OLIAS OF SUNHILLOW (LP, gatefold sleeve with page & inner sleeve) . . . . 10 |

(see also Yes, Jon & Vangelis, Hans Christian, Warriors, Mike Oldfield, Anderson Bruford Wakeman & Howe)

LEROY ANDERSON & HIS "POPS" CONCERT ORCHESTRA
| 55 | Brunswick 05375 | Song Of The Bells/Sandpaper Ballet . . . . 4 |
| 55 | Brunswick 05485 | Forgotten Dreams/The Last Rose Of Summer . . . . 6 |

MILLER ANDERSON
| 71 | Deram DM 337 | Bright City/Another Time, Another Place . . . . 5 |
| 71 | Deram SDL 3 | BRIGHT CITY (LP) . . . . 35 |

(see also Voice, At Last The 1958 Rock'n'Roll Show, Hemlock, Keef Hartley Band, Dog Soldier)

REUBEN ANDERSON
| 66 | Doctor Bird DB 1045 | Christmas Time Again/DESMOND TUCKER: Oh Holy Night . . . . 6 |

ROSHELL ANDERSON
| 75 | Contempo CS 2035 | The Grapevine Will Lie Sometimes/Such A Beautiful Thing . . . . 4 |

SONNY ANDERSON
| 60 | London HLP 9036 | Lonely Lonely Train/Yes, I'm Gonna Love You . . . . 35 |

VICKI ANDERSON
71	Polydor 2001 150	Super Good/Super Good (Version) 7
73	Mojo 2093 005	I'm Too Tough For Mr Big Stuff/Sound Funky 6
74	Mojo 2093 028	Don't Throw Your Love In The Garbage Can/Land Of Milk And Honey/
		BOBBY BYRD: Sayin' It And Doin' It Are Two Different Things 5

(see also Bobby Byrd)

ANDERSON, BRUFORD, WAKEMAN & HOWE
89	Arista 612 379	Brother Of Mine/Themes: Sound (gatefold p/s) 5
89	Arista 260 018	Brother Of Mine/Vultures In The City (10", p/s with free print) 5
89	Arista 662 379	Brother Of Mine/Themes: Sound/Attention/Soul Warrior (CD, picture disc) 7
89	Arista 612 618	Order Of The Universe (Long Edit)/Fist Of Fire/Order Of The Universe
		(Short Edit) (12", gatefold p/s) 7
91	Arista 209 970	ANDERSON, BRUFORD, WAKEMAN & HOWE (LP, gatefold sleeve with print) . . . 10

(see also Yes, Asia, Jon Anderson, Steve Howe)

ANDERSON, HARLEY & BATT
88	Epic PEEPS 1	Whatever You Believe/Whatever You Believe (live) (p/s) 15
88	Epic PEEPS 12P 1	Whatever You Believe/Whatever You Believe (live)/R.A.F. BAND:
		Morning Has Broken (12", p/s) 10

(see also Steve Harley, Mike Batt)

ANDERSON, JONES, JACKSON
| 68 | Saydisc 33 SD 125 | ANDERSON, JONES, JACKSON (EP) . . . . 18 |

(see also Ian A. Anderson, Al Jones)

ANDERSON'S ALLSTARS
| 68 | Blue Cat BS 133 | Intensified Girls/Jump And Shout . . . . 12 |

BARRY ANDREWS
79	Virgin VS 260	TOWN AND COUNTRY (EP) 5
80	Virgin VS 378	Rossmore Road (NW1)/Win A Night Out With A Well Known Paranoiac (p/s) 7
81	Virgin VS 428	Rossmore Road (NW1)/Pages Of My Love (p/s) 5

(see also XTC, Shriekback)

BIG SISTER ANDREWS
| 50 | Capitol CL 13139 | Muddy Water/The Hucklebuck (78) . . . . 20 |

EAMONN ANDREWS
| 56 | Parlophone R 4234 | High Wind/The Legend Of Wyatt Earp . . . . 4 |
| 57 | Parlophone R 4318 | The Ship That Never Sailed/The Magic Tree . . . . 4 |

ERNIE ANDREWS
60	Vogue V 9166	'Round Midnight/Lover Come Back To Me 8
65	Capitol CL 15407	Where Were You/What Do I See In The Girl 15
76	Capitol CL 15873	Fine Young Girl/Then I'll Know 5

HARVEY ANDREWS
65	Transatlantic TRAEP 133	HARVEY ANDREWS (EP) 15
70	Decca Nova SDN 9	PLACES AND FACES (LP) 20
72	Cube HIFLY 10	WRITER OF SONGS (LP) 10
73	Fly HIFLY 15	FRIENDS OF MINE (LP) 12
75	Transatlantic TRA 298	FANTASIES FROM A CORNER SEAT (LP) 10
76	Transatlantic TRA 329	SOME DAY (LP) 12

INEZ ANDREWS & ANDREWETTES
| 65 | Vogue EDVP 1283 | INEZ ANDREWS & ANDREWETTES (EP) . . . . 20 |

JOHN ANDREWS & LONELY ONES
| 66 | Parlophone R 5455 | A Rose Growing In The Ruins/It's Just Love . . . . 25 |

(see also Supertramp)

JULIE ANDREWS
| 58 | Philips PB 846 | I Could Have Danced All Night (with Philippa Bevans)/Without You . . . . 4 |
| 60 | Decca F 11230 | Tom Pillibi/Lazy Afternoon . . . . 4 |

LEE ANDREWS (& HEARTS)

57	London HL 7031	Teardrops/Girl Around The Corner (solo, export issue)	80
58	London HLM 8546	Teardrops/Girl Around The Corner (solo)	200
58	London HLM 8546	Teardrops/Girl Around The Corner (solo) (78)	35
58	London HLU 8661	Try The Impossible/Nobody's Home (as Lee Andrews & Hearts)	250
58	London HLU 8661	Try The Impossible/Nobody's Home (as Lee Andrews & Hearts) (78)	45

Mrs NOEL ANDREWS & GUY TYNEGATE-SMITH

| 58 | Oriole CB 1448 | How To Dance The Kwela Jive Pts 1 & 2 | 4 |

PATTY ANDREWS

| 55 | Capitol CL 14324 | Without Love/Where To My Love? | 10 |
| 55 | Capitol CL 14374 | Suddenly There's A Valley/Booga Da Woog | 10 |

(see also Bing Crosby, Jimmy Durante)

RUBY ANDREWS

| 76 | ABC ABC 4156 | I Got A Bone To Pick With You/I Don't Know How To Love You | 5 |

TIM ANDREWS

67	Parlophone R 5656	Sad Simon Lives Again/You Won't Be Seeing Me Anymore	5
68	Parlophone R 5695	Your Tea Is Strong/(Something About) Suburbia	4
70	Parlophone R 5824	Tiny Goddess/Josephine	4

TIM ANDREWS & PAUL KORDA

68	Parlophone R 5714	Smile If You Want To/Makin' Love To Him	4
68	Parlophone R 5746	Angel Face/Waiter Get Me A Drink	4
69	Parlophone R 5769	Discovery/How Many More Hearts Must Be Broke	4

(see also Paul Korda)

ANDREWS SISTERS

57	Capitol CL 14705	Rum And Coca-Cola/No, Baby	6
57	Capitol CL 14807	I'm Goin' Home/By His Word	4
58	Capitol CL 14826	One Mistake/Melancholy Moon	4
58	Capitol CL 14878	Torero/Sunshine	4
59	Brunswick 05782	I'll Be With You In Apple Blossom Time/Oh! Johnny	4
59	Capitol CL 14998	I've Got An Invitation To A Dance/My Love Is A Kitten	4
60	Capitol CL 15170	Rum And Coca-Cola/I'll Be With You In Apple Blossom Time	4

ANDROIDS OF MU

| 80 | Fuck Off FLP 001 | BLOOD ROBOTS (LP) | 15 |

ANDROMEDA

69	RCA RCA 1854	Go Your Way/Keep Out 'Cos I'm Dying	15
69	RCA SF 8031	ANDROMEDA (LP)	100
90s	Reflection MM 06	SEVEN LONELY STREET (LP, 500 only, numbered)	25

(see Attack, Five Day Week Straw People, Hard Stuff, Atomic Rooster)

AND THE NATIVE HIPSTERS

| 80 | Heater Volume H.V.R. 003 | There Goes Concorde Again.../Stands, Still The Building.../ I Wanna Be Around (foldaround p/s with insert in poly bag) | 4 |

ANDWELLA('S DREAM)

69	CBS 4301	Midday Sun/Sunday (as Andwella's Dream)	25
69	CBS 4469	Mrs. Man/Felix (as Andwella's Dream)	15
69	CBS 4634	Mister Sunshine/Shades Of Grey (as Andwella's Dream)	15
70	Reflection RS 1	Every Little Minute/Michael Fitzhenry (as Andwella's Dream)	5
70	Reflection RS 6	Are You Ready/People's People (as Andwella)	5
69	CBS 63673	LOVE AND POETRY (LP, as Andwella's Dream)	250
71	Reflection REF 1010	PEOPLE'S PEOPLE (LP, as Andwella)	15
70	Reflection REFL 10	WORLD'S END (LP, as Andwella, with poster)	15

(see also David Lewis, David Parker, David Baxter)

BOB ANDY

67	Island WI 3040	I've Got To Get Back Home/SONNY BURKE: Rudy Girl	12
68	Studio One SO 2063	Too Experienced/Let Them Stay	15
68	Coxsone CS 7074	Born A Man/MARCIA GRIFFITHS: Mark My Word	15
69	Doctor Bird DB 1183	The Way I Feel/ETHIOPIANS: Long Time Now	10
69	Studio One SO 2075	I'm Going Home/SOUND DIMENSION: Straight Flush	15
71	London HLJ 7127	Games People Play/GAYLETTES: Son Of A Preacher Man (export issue)	5
72	Green Door GD 4047	Life/Medley	5
73	Green Door GD 4059	You Don't Know/The Border Song	4

(see also Bob & Marcia)

HORACE ANDY

| 72 | Trojan TBL 197 | YOU ARE MY ANGEL (LP) | 15 |

ANDY & CLYDE

65	Rio R 62	Never Be A Slave/Magic Is Love	10
65	Rio R 69	I'm So Lonesome/WINSTON STEWART: Day After Day	10
65	Rio R 71	We All Have To Part/UPSETTERS: Scandalizing	10

ANDY & JOEY

62	Island WI 056	Have You Ever/Cross My Heart	10
64	Port-O-Jam PJ 4009	I Want To Know/My Love Has Gone	10
64	Ska Beat JB 162	You're Wondering Now/You'll Never	10

ANGEL

| 74 | Cube BUG 41 | Good Time Fanny/Who D'Ya Think You're Foolin' | 6 |
| 74 | Cube BUG 51 | Little Boy Blue/Tragedy Queen | 10 |

ANGEL

76	Casablanca CBX 514	On And On/Angel Theme	5
76	Casablanca CBX 522	Feelings/Angel Theme	5
77	Casablanca CAN 104	That Magic Touch/Big Boy (Let's Do It Again)	4

77	Casablanca CAN 113	Winter Song/You Can Feel It	4
78	Casablanca CAN 125	Ain't Gonna Eat Out My Heart/Flying With Broken Wings	4
80	Casablanca CAN 193	20th Century Foxes/Can You Feel It	4
76	Casablanca CBC 4007	ANGEL (LP)	25
76	Casablanca CBC 4010	HELLUVA BAND (LP)	15
77	Casablanca CAL 2002	ON EARTH AS IT IS IN HEAVEN (LP, with poster)	12
78	Casablanca CSL 2023	WHITE HOT (LP)	10
79	Casablanca CAL 2046	SINFUL (LP)	10
80	Casablanca NBLP 7203	LIVE — WITHOUT A NET (2-LP)	15

JOHNNY ANGEL

60	Parlophone R 4642	Chinese Butterfly/My Very Good Friend The Milkman	4
60	Parlophone R 4679	Too Young To Go Steady/You're Thrilling	4
61	Parlophone R 4750	What Happens To Love/Luna Luna Luna Lu	4
61	Parlophone R 4795	Trocadero-Double-Nine-One-O/Web Of Love	4
62	Parlophone R 4874	Look, Look Little Angel/Jenny From Missouri	4
62	Parlophone R 4948	Better Luck Next Time/The Power Of You	4
63	Parlophone R 5026	A Touch Of Venus/The Two Together	4

MARIAN ANGEL

65	Columbia DB 7537	It's Gonna Be Alright/Tomorrow's Fool	8

ANGELA & FANS

66	Pye 7N 17108	Love Ya Illya/I Know You	12
	(see also Alma Cogan)		

ANGELIC UPSTARTS

78	Dead IS/AU/1024	Murder Of Liddle Towers/Police Oppression (p/s, 1,000 only)	20
79	Rough Trade RT/SW 001	Murder Of Liddle Towers/Police Oppression (reissue, p/s)	6
79	Warner Bros K 17354	I'm An Upstart/Leave Me Alone (p/s)	4
79	Warner Bros K 17354	I'm An Upstart/Leave Me Alone (green vinyl, no p/s)	5
79	Warner Bros K 17354T	I'm An Upstart/Leave Me Alone (12", p/s)	8
79	Warner Bros K 17426	Teenage Warning/The Young Ones (p/s)	4
79	Warner Bros K 17426C	Teenage Warning/The Young Ones (red vinyl, no p/s)	5
79	Warner Bros	cassette single	6
85	Gas GM 3010	Brighton Bomb/Thin Red Line/Soldier (12", banned 'Maggie Thatcher' p/s)	10
80	Regal Zono. Z 12	England/Stick's Diary (p/s)	10
81	Regal Zono. ZEM 102	LIVE (LP, with free flexidisc "We're Gonna Take The World"/"Leave Me Alone"/"The Young Ones"/"White Riot")	10

BOBBY ANGELO & TUXEDOS

61	HMV POP 892	Baby Sitting/Skinny Lizzie	15
61	HMV POP 982	Don't Stop/I Gotta Have You	15

JERRY ANGELO

59	Parlophone R 4548	Crush Me/Mary Lou	4
59	Parlophone R 4561	If You Change Your Mind/I Love You My Love	4
60	Parlophone R 4656	Maria Elena/Old Man River	5
62	Palette PG 9031	Lonely Hill/Make Her Mine	4
62	Palette PG 9034	Innocent Angel/The Boy Who Walks Alone	4

MICHAEL ANGELO & HIS ORCHESTRA

61	Columbia DB 4705	Rocco's Theme/Spinneree	5
62	Columbia DB 4800	Tears/The Roman Spring Of Mrs Stone	8
	(see also John Barry)		

MAYA ANGELOU

57	London HA-U 2062	MISS CALYPSO (LP)	12

ANGEL PAVEMENT

69	Fontana TF 1059	Baby You've Gotta Stay/Green Mello Hill	7
70	Fontana TF 1072	Tell Me What I've Got To Do/When Will I See June Again	6

ANGELS

62	Pye International 7N 25150	Everybody Loves A Lover/Blow Joe	5
63	Mercury AMT 1211	My Boyfriend's Back/Now	4
63	Mercury AMT 1215	I Adore Him/Thank You And Goodnight	6
64	Philips BF 1312	Wow Wee Wee/Snowflakes And Teardrops	4

ANGEL STREET

79	Motor MTR 003	Midnight Man/Running Away (blue vinyl, no p/s)	4

ANGELWITCH

80	EMI EMI 5064	Sweet Danger/Flight Nineteen (p/s)	8
80	EMI 12EMI 5064	Sweet Danger/Flight Nineteen/Hades Paradise (12", p/s)	15
80	Bronze BRO 108	Angel Witch/Gorgon (p/s)	8
81	Bronze BRO 121	Loser/Suffer/Dr Phibes (p/s)	8
80	Bronze BRON 532	ANGELWITCH (LP)	10

ANGIE

79	Stiff BUY 51	Peppermint Lump/ANGIE'S ORCHESTRA: Breakfast In Naples (p/s)	4
	(see also Pete Townshend)		

ANGLETRAX

79	Ariola AHA 554	Things To Make And Do/Nuclear Power (die-cut plain orange sleeve)	4

ANGLIANS

67	CBS 202489	A Friend Of Mine/Daytime Lover	8
	(see also Moving Finger)		

ANGLOS

65	Brit WI 004	Incense/You're Fooling Me	20
65	Fontana TF 561	Incense/You're Fooling Me (unissued)	
65	Fontana TF 589	Incense/You're Fooling Me (reissue)	15

67	Sue WI 4033	Incense/You're Fooling Me (unissued)	
69	Island WIP 6061	Incense/You're Fooling Me (2nd reissue)	7

(see also Stevie Winwood)

ANIMALS

64	Columbia DB 7247	Baby Let Me Take You Home/Gonna Send You Back To Walker	4
64	Columbia DB 7301	The House Of The Rising Sun/Talkin' 'Bout You	4
64	Columbia DB 7354	I'm Crying/Take It Easy	4
65	Columbia DB 7445	Don't Let Me Be Misunderstood/Club-A-Go Go (standard issue, matrix: '2N')	4
65	Columbia DB 7445	Don't Let Me Be Misunderstood/Club-A-Go Go (mispress, with 'demo' version of A-side, matrix: '1N')	50
65	Columbia DB 7539	Bring It On Home To Me/For Miss Caulker	4
65	Columbia DB 7639	We've Gotta Get Out Of This Place/I Can't Believe It	5
65	Columbia DB 7741	It's My Life/I'm Going To Change The World	4
66	Decca F 12332	Inside Looking Out/Outcast	5
66	Decca F 12407	Don't Bring Me Down/Cheating	5
63	Graphic Sound ALO 10867	I JUST WANNA MAKE LOVE TO YOU (1-sided 12" EP, 99 only, private pressing, blank white cover, typed details on label)	250
64	Columbia SEG 8374	THE ANIMALS IS HERE (EP)	12
65	Columbia SEG 8400	THE ANIMALS (EP)	15
65	Columbia SEG 8439	THE ANIMALS No. 2 (EP)	15
65	Columbia SEG 8452	THE ANIMALS ARE BACK (EP)	12
65	Decca DFE 8643	IN THE BEGINNING THERE WAS EARLY ANIMALS (EP, reissue of Graphic Sound EP tracks)	20
66	Columbia SEG 8499	ANIMAL TRACKS (EP)	20
64	Columbia 33SX 1669	THE ANIMALS (LP)	18
65	Columbia 33SX 1708	ANIMAL TRACKS (LP)	22
66	Columbia SX 6035	MOST OF THE ANIMALS (LP)	15
66	Decca LK 4797	ANIMALISMS (LP)	22
60s	EMI Regal SREG 104	THE ANIMALS (LP, export issue)	15

(see also Eric Burdon & Animals, Alan Price)

ANIMALS & MEN

80	Strange Days DAYS 1	The Terraplane Fixation/Shell Shock (p/s)	4
80	TW HIT 101	Don't Misbehave In The New Age/Machines (p/s)	4

ANIMATED EGG

69	Marble Arch MAL 890	ANIMATED EGG (LP)	15

PAUL ANKA

57	Columbia DB 3980	Diana/Don't Gamble With Love (mauve label)	6
57	Columbia DB 3980	Diana/Don't Gamble With Love (re-pressings on green or black label)	12
57	Columbia DB 3980	Diana/Don't Gamble With Love (78)	5
57	Columbia DB 4022	I Love You, Baby/Tell Me That You Love Me (mauve or green label)	6/7
57	Columbia DB 4022	I Love You, Baby/Tell Me That You Love Me (78)	5
58	Columbia DB 4063	You Are My Destiny/When I Stop Loving You (mauve or green label)	6/7
58	Columbia DB 4063	You Are My Destiny/When I Stop Loving You (78)	5
58	Columbia DB 4110	Crazy Love/Let The Bells Keep Ringing (green label)	6
58	Columbia DB 4110	Crazy Love/Let The Bells Keep Ringing (78)	5
58	Columbia DB 4172	Verboten! (Forbidden)/Midnight	4
58	Columbia DB 4172	Verboten! (Forbidden)/Midnight (78)	5
58	Columbia DB 4199	Just Young/So It's Goodbye	4
58	Columbia DB 4199	Just Young/So It's Goodbye (78)	5
59	Columbia DB 4241	(All Of A Sudden) My Heart Sings/That's Love	4
59	Columbia DB 4241	(All Of A Sudden) My Heart Sings/That's Love (78)	6
59	Columbia DB 4286	I Miss You So/Late Last Night	6
59	Columbia DB 4286	I Miss You So/Late Last Night (78)	7
59	Columbia DB 4324	Lonely Boy/Your Love	6
59	Columbia DB 4324	Lonely Boy/Your Love (78)	15
59	Columbia DB 4355	Put Your Head On My Shoulder/Don't Ever Leave Me	5
59	Columbia DB 4355	Put Your Head On My Shoulder/Don't Ever Leave Me (78)	15
60	Columbia DB 4390	It's Time To Cry/Something Has Changed Me	4
60	Columbia DB 4390	It's Time To Cry/Something Has Changed Me (78)	15
60	Columbia DB 4434	Puppy Love/Adam And Eve	5
60	Columbia DB 4472	My Home Town/Waiting For You	4
60	Columbia DB 4504	I Love You In The Same Old Way/Hello Young Lovers	4
60	Columbia DB 4524	Summer's Gone/I'd Have To Share	4
61	Columbia DB 4582	The Story Of My Love/Don't Say You're Sorry	4
61	Columbia DB 4629	Tonight My Love, Tonight/I'm Just A Fool Anyway	4
61	Columbia DB 4669	I Talked To You (On The Telephone)/Dance On Little Girl	4
61	Columbia DB 4702	Cinderella/Kissin' On The Phone	4
62	Columbia DB 4772	The Bells At My Wedding/Loveland	4
62	RCA RCA 1276	Love Me Warm And Tender/I'd Like To Know	4
62	RCA RCA 1318	Eso Beso/Give Me Back My Heart	4
65	RCA RCA 1434	To Wait For Love/Behind My Smile (p/s)	7
67	RCA RCA 1567	I Don't Wanna Catch Him Round You Anymore/Sunrise, Sunset	4
68	RCA RCA 1676	Can't Get You Out Of My Mind/When We Get There	25
57	Columbia SEG 7747	DIANA (EP)	15
58	Columbia SEG 7801	ANKA AGAIN (EP)	12
59	Columbia SEG 7890	SING SING SING (EP)	12
60	Columbia SEG 7985	SINGS SONGS FROM 'GIRLS' TOWN' AND OTHER SUCCESSES (EP)	12
64	RCA RCX 7127	FLY ME TO THE MOON (EP)	10
64	RCA RCX 7152	FOUR GOLDEN HITS (EP)	10
64	RCA RCX 7170	SYLVIE (EP)	10
58	Columbia 33SX 1092	PAUL ANKA (LP, green label)	22
59	Columbia 33SX 1196	MY HEART SINGS (LP)	20
60	Columbia 33SX 1268	ANKA SWINGS FOR YOUNG LOVERS (LP)	20
60	Columbia 33SX 1282	PAUL ANKA SINGS HIS BIG 15 (LP)	16

MINT VALUE £

60	Columbia 33SX 1287	IT'S CHRISTMAS EVERYWHERE (LP)	22
61	Columbia 33SX 1395	PAUL ANKA SINGS HIS BIG 15 VOL. 2 (LP)	15
62	Columbia 33SX 1432	PAUL ANKA SINGS HIS BIG 15 VOL. 3 (LP)	15
62	RCA RD 27257/SF 5129	YOUNG ALIVE AND IN LOVE (LP)	12
62	RCA RD/SF 7533	LET'S SIT THIS ONE OUT (LP)	12
63	RCA RD/SF 7547	OUR MAN AROUND THE WORLD (LP)	12
63	RCA RD/SF 7573	ANKA'S 21 GOLDEN HITS (LP)	14
63	RCA RD/SF 7613	SONGS I WISH I'D WRITTEN (LP)	14
64	RCA RD 7700	EXCITEMENT ON PARK AVENUE — LIVE AT THE WALDORF ASTORIA (LP)	14
68	RCA RD/SF 7956	TIMELESS (LP)	12

(see also Micki Marlo & Paul Anka)

ANNETTE (& AFTERBEATS)

59	Top Rank JAR 137	Wild Willie/Lonely Guitar	8
59	Top Rank JAR 233	First Name Initial/My Heart Became Of Age (with Afterbeats)	8
60	Top Rank JAR 343	It Took Dreams/O Dio Mio	8
60	Pye Intl. 7N 25061	Pineapple Princess/Luan Cha Cha Cha (with Afterbeats)	7
64	HMV POP 1270	Muscle Beach Party/I Dream About Frankie	8
64	HMV POP 1322	Scrambled Egghead/Merlin Jones	7
65	HMV POP 1447	The Monkey's Uncle (with Beach Boys)/How Will I Know My Love	15
60s	Gala 45XP 1046	TALL PAUL (EP)	15
64	HMV CLP 1782	BEACH PARTY (LP)	30
60s	Buena Vista BV 3305	DANCE ANNETTE (LP)	10

ANNETTE & KEYMEN

| 64 | King KG 1006 | Look Who's Blue/How Can I Tell Him | 6 |

ANNIS

| 79 | GTO GT 266 | Don't Play Your Games/After Me | 8 |

ANN-MARGRET

61	RCA RCA 1245	I Just Don't Understand/I Don't Hurt Anymore	5
61	RCA RCA 1267	It Do Me So Good/Gimme Love	5
64	RCA RCA 1396	Man's Favourite Sport/Hey Little Star	5
64	RCA RCX 7148	THE VIVACIOUS ONE (EP)	25
62	RCA RD 27239/SF 5020	AND HERE SHE IS (LP, mono/stereo)	18/20
62	RCA Victor RD/SF 7503	ON THE WAY UP (LP, mono/stereo)	16/18
63	RCA Victor RD/SF 7580	BYE BYE BIRDIE (LP, mono/stereo)	15/17
64	RCA Victor RD/SF 7632	BEAUTY AND THE BEARD (LP, mono/stereo, with Al Hirt)	14/16
64	RCA Victor RD/SF 7649	BACHELORS' PARADISE (LP, mono/stereo)	15/17
64	RCA Victor RD/SF 7591	"ANNE MARGARET" (LP, mono/stereo)	14/16

ANNO DOMINI

| 71 | Deram SML-R 1085 | ON THIS NEW DAY (LP) | 90 |

ANONYMES

| 80s | Irradiated | 3986/No One Feels (p/s) | 4 |

(see also Mute Drivers)

ANOTHER DREAM

| 80s | Sticky PEEL OFF 2 | Forever In Darkness/Human Life (p/s) | 8 |

(see also Mighty Lemon Drops)

ANOTHER PRETTY FACE

79	New Pleasures Z1	All The Boys Love Carrie/That's Not Enough (green & white foldout p/s)	22
79	New Pleasures Z1	All The Boys Love Carrie/That's Not Enough (red & white p/s)	12
80	Virgin VS 320	Whatever Happened To The West?/Goodbye 1970's (p/s)	10
80	Chicken Jazz JAZZ 1	Only Heroes Live Forever/Heaven Gets Closer Everyday (poster p/s)	18
81	Chicken Jazz JAZZ 2	I'M SORRY THAT I BEAT YOU, I'M SORRY THAT I SCREAMED FOR A MOMENT THERE I REALLY LOST CONTROL (8-track cassette, badge, minizine, some with extra tracks)	60/80
81	Chicken Jazz JAZZ 3	Soul To Soul/A Woman's Place/God On The Screen (foldout p/s)	20

(see also DNV, Funhouse, Waterboys)

ANOTHER SUNNY DAY

| 88 | Sarah SARAH 004 | Anorak City (5³/₄" flexidisc free with 'Are You Scared To Get Happy' fanzine, 1,500 only) | 20 |
| 88 | Sarah SARAH 007 | I'm In Love With A Girl Who Doesn't Know I Exist/Things Will Be Nice/The Centre Of My Little World (14" x 10" foldout poster p/s) | 7 |

ANSELL (Collins) & ELAINE

| 72 | Camel CA 98 | Presenting Cheater/RON WILSON: Official Trombone | 4 |

ANSWERS

| 66 | Columbia DB 7847 | It's Just A Fear/You've Gotta Believe Me | 60 |
| 66 | Columbia DB 7953 | That's What You're Doing To Me/Got A Letter From My Baby | 12 |

(see also Misunderstood, High Tide)

ADAM ANT

82	CBS A11 2367	Goody Two Shoes/Red Scab (p/s, credited to 'Adam & the Ants')	15
82	CBS A 2367	Goody Two Shoes/Red Scab (poster p/s)	4
82	CBS A11 2367	Goody Two Shoes/Red Scab (picture disc)	4
82	CBS A11 2736	Friend Or Foe/Juanito The Bandito (picture disc)	4
82	CBS A 2892	Desperate But Not Serious/Why Do Girls Love Horses? (non-gatefold p/s)	20
82	CBS A11 2892	Desperate But Not Serious/Why Do Girls Love Horses? (picture disc)	4
84	CBS WA 3614	Puss 'N' Boots/Kiss The Drummer (picture disc)	6
84	CBS A 3589	Strip/Yours, Yours, Yours ('calendar' poster p/s)	4
84	CBS WA 3589	Strip/Yours, Yours, Yours (picture disc)	7
84	CBS TA 4719	Apollo 9 (Splashdown Remix)/B Side Baby (12", p/s)	15
85	CBS A 6367	Vive Le Rock/Greta X (p/s, mispress, both sides play "Vive Le Rock")	4
90	MCA MCAR 1387	Room At The Top/Bruce Lee (poster p/s)	4
90	MCA MCAX 1387	Room At The Top (U.S. Remix)/Bruce Lee (12", p/s)	7

MINT VALUE £

| 90 | MCA MCA 1404 | Can't Set Rules About Love /(Version) (p/s) | 4 |

(see also Adam & Ants, Maneaters)

ANTEEKS

| 66 | Philips BF 1471 | I Don't Want You/Ball And Chain | 50 |

PAUL ANTELL

| 65 | Pye International 7N 25329 | The Times They Are A-Changin'/Yesterday And Tomorrow | 4 |

BILLIE ANTHONY

54	Columbia SCM 5143	This Ole House/Oh, What A Dream	25
54	Columbia DB 3519	This Ole House/Oh, What A Dream (78)	5
54	Columbia SCM 5155	Teach Me Tonight/Don't Let The Kiddygeddin	18
55	Columbia SCM 5164	Butterscotch Hop/No More	12
55	Columbia SCM 5174	Tweedlee Dee/Shake The Hand Of A Stranger	15
55	Columbia DB 3592	Tweedlee Dee/Shake The Hand Of A Stranger (78)	5
55	Columbia SCM 5184	Something's Gotta Give/Boom Boom Boomerang	12
55	Columbia SCM 5191	The Banjo's Back In Town (with Big Ben Banjo Band)/Ten Little Kisses	10
55	Columbia SCM 5210	Bring Me A Bluebird/The Old Pi-anna Rag	10
56	Columbia SCM 5286	A Sweet Old Fashioned Girl/The Treasure Of Love	12
56	Columbia DB 3818	Lay Down Your Arms/One Finger Piano	10
57	Columbia DB 3874	I Dreamed/The Charge Of The Light Brigade (B-side with ex-R.S.M. Brittain)	8
57	Columbia DB 3935	Rock-A-Billy/A Needle And Thread	15
57	Columbia DB 3935	Rock-A-Billy/A Needle And Thread (78)	5
57	Columbia DB 3970	One/It's Fun Finding Out About London (with Big Ben Banjo Band)	4
57	Columbia DB 4021	Love And Kisses/Everybody's Buddy	4
58	Columbia DB 4141	Careful, Careful (Handle Me With Care)/You	4
59	Columbia DB 4279	Too Late Now/Yes, We Have No Bananas	4
60	Columbia DB 4394	Sure Fire Love/A Handful Of Gold	4

(see also Big Ben Banjo Band)

DAVE ANTHONY'S MOODS

| 66 | Parlophone R 5438 | New Directions/Give It A Chance | 18 |

DAVID ANTHONY

| 68 | Island WI 3148 | All Night/Out Of My Mind | 10 |

LITTLE JOHN ANTHONY

| 60 | Ember EMB 3302 | TEENAGE DANCE PARTY (LP) | 10 |

RAY ANTHONY

55	Capitol CL 14205	I Don't Hurt Anymore/Woman's World	8
55	Capitol CL 14243	Juke Box Special/Heat Wave	12
55	Capitol CL 14275	Baby You/Happy Hornblowers (with Dick Stabile Orchestra)	8
55	Capitol CL 14306	Sluefoot/Something's Gotta Give	8
55	Capitol CL 14321	Learnin' The Blues/Mmmm Mamie	10
55	Capitol CL 14345	Pete Kelly's Blues/DC-7	8
55	Capitol CL 14354	Hernando's Hideaway/The Bunny Hop	12
56	Capitol CL 14525	Flip-Flop/Hurricane Anthony	12
56	Capitol CL 14553	Cry Me A River/Bullfighter's Lament	5
56	Capitol CL 14567	Rockin' Through Dixie/Madeira	6
56	Capitol CL 14588	The Sleep Walker/Braziliera (Mexican Storm Song)	5
56	Capitol CL 14648	I Love You, Samantha/I Am In Love	5
56	Capitol CL 14670	Love Is Just Around The Corner/Dancing Lovers	5
57	Capitol CL 14689	Rock Around The Rock Pile/The Girl Can't Help It	12
57	Capitol CL 14689	Rock Around The Rock Pile/The Girl Can't Help It (78)	10
57	Capitol CL 14703	Plymouth Rock/Calypso Dance	6
57	Capitol CL 14740	The Incredible Shrinking Man/This Could Be The Night	4
57	Capitol CL 14752	The Lonely Trumpet/Cello-phane	4
57	Capitol CL 14769	The Bunny Hop/The Hokey Pokey	6
57	Capitol CL 14775	Drive-In/Show Me The Way To Go Home	4
58	Capitol CL 14929	Peter Gunn/Tango For Two (Mmm Shall We Dance?)	4
59	Capitol CL 15019	The Bunny Hop Rock/Walkin' To Mother's	5
57	Capitol EAP 1-823	THE GIRL CAN'T HELP IT (EP)	20
57	Capitol EAP 1-958	ROCK AND ROLL WITH RAY ANTHONY (EP)	12
57	Capitol EAP 1008	THE LONGEST WALK (EP)	7
53	Capitol LC 6570	RAY ANTHONY'S ORCHESTRA (10" LP)	15
53	Capitol LC 6615	SWEET AND LOVELY (10" LP)	12
53	Capitol LC 6617	HOUSE PARTY (10" LP)	15
54	Capitol LC 6653	I REMEMBER GLENN MILLER (10" LP)	12
55	Capitol LC 6692	ARTHUR MURRAY SWING FOXTROTS (10" LP)	15
57	Capitol T 831	STAR DANCING (LP)	10
57	Capitol T 866	YOUNG IDEAS (LP)	10
58	Capitol T 786	DANCES IN LOVE (LP)	10
59	Capitol (S)T 1028	DANCING OVER THE WAVES (LP, mono/stereo)	10/12
59	Capitol T 1086	ANTHONY PLAYS ALLEN (LP)	10
60	Capitol (S)T 1200	SOUND SPECTACULAR (LP, mono/stereo)	10/12

(see also Gordon MacRae & Ray Anthony)

RAYBURN ANTHONY

| 60 | London HLS 9167 | There's No Tomorrow/Who's Gonna Shoe Your Pretty Little Feet | 10 |

SHEILA ANTHONY

| 75 | Route RT 13 | Livin' In Love/Woman To Woman | 4 |

VAL ANTHONY

| 53 | Columbia SCM 5079 | Walk With The Wind/No Tears, No Regrets | 4 |
| 54 | Columbia SCM 5103 | The Heart Of A Fool/The Portuguese Fishermen | 4 |

ANTHRAX

| 86 | Island 12ISP 285 | Madhouse/Air/God Save The Queen (12" picture disc) | 8 |
| 86 | Island 12IS 285 | Madhouse/Air/God Save The Queen (12", p/s with patch) | 8 |

87	Megaforce MRS 05P	ARMED AND DANGEROUS (12" EP, import picture disc) 15
87	Island LAWP 1	I Am The Law/Bud E. Luvbomb And Satan's Lounge Band (picture disc) 6
87	Island ISX 316	I Am The Law (live)/Bud E. Luvbomb And Satan's Lounge Band/
		Madhouse (live) (p/s, red vinyl) 4
87	Island 12IS 316	I Am The Law/Bud E. Luvbomb And Satan's Lounge Band (12" poster p/s) .. 8
87	Island ISP 325	Indians/Sabbath Bloody Sabbath (picture disc with sticker) 7
87	Island IS 325	Indians/Sabbath Bloody Sabbath (p/s, orange vinyl) 5
87	Island IS 325	Indians/Sabbath Bloody Sabbath (p/s, orange vinyl, mispress) 9
87	Island 12IS 325	Indians/Sabbath Bloody Sabbath/Taint (12" poster p/s) 8
87	Island 12ISP 325	Indians/Sabbath Bloody Sabbath/Taint (12" picture disc) 7
87	Island ISP 338	I'm The Man/Caught In The Mash (logo-shaped picture disc) 8
88	Island IS 379	Make Me Laugh(live)/Anti Social(live) (p/s, yellow vinyl) 4
86	Music For Nations 62P	SPREADING THE DISEASE (LP, picture disc) 10
87	Music For Nations 14P	FISTFUL OF METAL (LP, picture disc) 10
87	Island PILPS 9865	AMONG THE LIVING (LP, picture disc) 10
88	Island PILPS 9916	STATEOF EUPHORIA (LP, picture disc, die-cut sleeve) 10

ANTI ESTABLISHMENT
| 80 | Charnel House CADAV 1 | 1980/Mechanical Man (p/s) .... 4 |

ANTI GROUP
85	Sweatbox SOX09	Zulu/Ha (12", die-cut white embossed sleeve, 2,000 with 8-page booklet) 10/8
86	Sweatbox SOX 010	ShT (EP, black die-cut embossed sleeve) 8
87	Sweatbox OX 011	Big Sex/The Ocean (printed plastic sleeve, 2,000 only) 8
87	Sweatbox SOX 011	Big Sex/The Ocean/Big Sex (12", red embossed die-cut sleeve) 8
86	Sweatbox SOX 012	DIGITARIA (LP, with inner sleeve) 10
88	Sweatbox SACD 012	DIGITARIA (CD) 15

(see also Clock DVA)

ANTI NOWHERE LEAGUE
82	WXYZ ABCD 1	So What/Streets Of London (p/s, withdrawn) 6
82	WXYZ ABCD 1T	So What/Streets Of London (12", p/s, withdrawn) 8
82	WXYZ ABCD 2	I Hate ... People/Let's Break The Law (p/s) 4
82	WXYZ ABCD 4	Woman/Rocker (picture disc) 5
83	WXYZ ABCD 6	For You/Ballad Of J.J. Decay (p/s) 4
84	WXYZ ABCS 004P	Out On The Wasteland/We Will Survive (picture disc) 4
82	Lyntone LYN 12647	World War III/DEFECTS: Dance/METEORS: Mutant Rock (Instrumental)
		(red flexidisc free with 'Flexipop' magazine, issue 26) 6/5

ANTI PASTI
80	Rondelet ROUND 2	FORE SORE POINTS (EP) 4
81	Rondelet ROUND 5	Let Them Free/Another Dead Soldier (p/s, red or black vinyl) 4
81	Rondelet ROUND 10	Six Guns/Now's The Time/Call the Army (p/s) 4
82	Rondelet ROUND 18	East To The West/Burn In Your Own Flames (p/s) 4
82	Rondelet ROUND 26	Caution To The Wind/Last Train (p/s) 4

ANTISOCIAL
| 78 | Dynamite DRO 1 | Traffic Lights/Teacher Teacher .... 8 |

ANTISOCIAL
82	Lightbeat SOCIAL 1	MADE IN ENGLAND (EP) 6
82	Beat The System BTS 2	Battle Scarred Skinheads/Sewer Rat/Official Hooligan (p/s) 6
82	Lightbeat	THE NEW PUNKS EP (cassette) 6

ANTI SYSTEM
| 83 | Paragon/Pax PAX 11 | DEFENCE OF THE REALM (EP) .... 4 |

ANTOINE
66	Vogue VRS 7009	Les Elucubrations D'Antoine/J'ai Oublié La Nuit 4
66	Vogue VRS 7017	Before The Good Thing/Elephants Looking At Me 4
66	Vogue VRS 7022	Ma Fete Forraine/Only These Few Snowflakes 4
68	Vogue VRS 7028	La Tramontana/10 Voglic Andaré In Guerra 4
68	Vogue VRS 7031	The Football Match/Where Did Everyone Go To 4
68	Vogue VRL 3032	ANTOINE (LP) 10

ANTOINETTE
| 66 | Piccadilly 35310 | Lullaby Of Love/I'm For You .... 6 |
| 66 | Piccadilly 7N 35293 | Why Don't I Run Away From You/There's No-One In The Whole World .... 6 |

REY ANTON
62	Oriole CB 1771	Hey Good Looking/Mary Lou 5
63	Oriole CB 1811	Peppermint Man/Can't Say More Than That (with Batons) 5
64	Parlophone R 5132	You Can't Judge A Book By The Cover/It's Cold Outside (with Peppermint Men) 20
64	Parlophone R 5172	Heard It All Before/I Want You (with Peppermint Men) 12
65	Parlophone R 5245	Wishbone/Kingsway (with Peppermint Men) 12
65	Parlophone R 5274	Girl You Don't Know Me/Don't Treat Me Bad (with Peppermint Men) 12
65	Parlophone R 5310	Nothing Comes Easy/Breakout (with Peppermint Men) 12
65	Parlophone R 5358	Premeditation/Now That It's Over (with Pro Formula) 12
66	Parlophone R 5420	Don't You Worry Boy/Hold It Babe (with Pro Formula) 12
66	Parlophone R 5487	Things Get Better/Newsboy (with Pro Formula) 12

ANTHONY ANTONIO
| 82 | Elite DAZZ 15 | Lifeline/Vibeline (12", p/s) .... 7 |

DAVE ANTONY
| 68 | Mercury MF 1031 | Race With The Wind/Hide And Seek .... 12 |

ANTS
| 63 | Parlophone R 5082 | Christmas Star/Wandering .... 5 |

ANVIL FLUTES & CAPRICORN VOICES
| 68 | Deram DM 208 | April Showers/Jolie Gendarme .... 6 |
| 68 | Deram DML/SML 1026 | SOMETHING NEW IS COMING (LP) .... 15 |

MINT VALUE £

ANY TROUBLE
79	Pennine PSS 165	Yesterday's Love/(Where Are All The) Nice Girls (p/s)	15
80	Stiff TRUBZ 1	LIVE AT THE VENUE (LP)	15

(see also Tickawinda)

APARTMENT
80	Heartbeat PULSE 7	The Car/Winter (p/s)	4

APARTMENT 1
70	Pink Elephant	OPEN HOUSE (LP)	15

APEX RHYTHM & BLUES ALLSTARS
68	John Lever	APEX RHYTHM & BLUES ALLSTARS (EP)	200

(see also Ian Hunter)

APHRODITE'S CHILD
68	Mercury MF 1039	Rain & Tears/Don't Try To Catch A River	5
69	Mercury MF 1079	The End Of The World/You Always Stand In My Way	4
69	Polydor 56769	I Want To Live/Magic Mirror	5
69	Polydor 56785	Let Me Love Let Me Live/Marie Jolie	5
70	Polydor 56791	It's Five O'Clock/Funky Mary	4
69	Mercury SMCL 20140	END OF THE WORLD (LP)	12
72	Vertigo 6673 001	666 (2-LP, spiral label)	18

APOLLOS
60	Mercury AMT 1096	Rockin' Horse/Just Dreaming	8

A POPULAR HISTORY OF SIGNS
80	Melodia M 1	Justice Not Vengeance/Possession (p/s, with insert)	4
81	Melodia M 2	Crowds/Crossing The Border (stamped p/s with insert)	4
82	Melodia M 4	Dancing With Ideas (p/s)	4

APPALACHIANS
63	HMV POP 1158	Bony Maronie/It Takes A Man	7
65	Mercury MF 930	Look Away/My Broken Heart	4

APOSTOLIC INTERVENTION
67	Immediate IM 043	(Tell Me) Have You Ever Seen Me/Madame Garcia	65

DAVE APPELL (& APPLEJACKS)
55	Brunswick 05396	Smarter/My Heart Will Wait For You (as Dave Appell & Applejacks)	20
55	Brunswick 05396	Smarter/My Heart Will Wait For You (as Dave Appell & Applejacks) (78)	6
57	Columbia DB 3894	Applejack/Country Dance (as Dave Appell & Applejacks)	30
57	Columbia DB 3894	Applejack/Country Dance (as Dave Appell & Applejacks) (78)	15
62	Columbia DB 4763	Noivous/Happy Jose (as Dave Appell & Orchestra)	8

(see also Applejacks [U.S.])

APPLE
68	Page One POF 101	Let's Take A Trip Down The Rhine/Buffalo Billy Can	40
68	Page One POF 110	Doctor Rock/The Other Side	50
68	Page One POLS 016	AN APPLE A DAY (LP, with booklet)	600

APPLE BOUTIQUE
88	Creation CRE 052T	Love Resistance/I Don't Even Believe In You/The Ballad Of Jet Harris (12", p/s)	7

APPLEJACKS (U.S.)
58	London HLU 8753	Mexican Hat Rock/Stop, Stop Red Light	12
58	London HLU 8753	Mexican Hat Rock/Stop, Stop Red Light (78)	7
58	London HL 7063	Mexican Hat Rock/Stop, Stop Red Light (export issue)	8
59	London HLU 8806	Rocka-Conga/Am I Blue	12
59	London HLU 8806	Rocka-Conga/Am I Blue (78)	7
60	Top Rank JAR 273	Circle Dance/Love Scene	6

(see also Dave Appell)

APPLEJACKS (U.K.)
64	Decca F 11833	Tell Me When/Baby Jane	4
64	Decca F 11916	Like Dreamers Do/Everybody Fall Down	4
64	Decca F 11981	Three Little Words/You're The One For Me	4
65	Decca F 12050	Chim Chim Chiree/It's Not A Game Anymore (export, probably unissued)	100+
65	Decca F 12106	It's Not A Game Anymore/Bye Bye Girl	8
65	Decca F 12216	I Go To Sleep/Make Up Or Break Up	12
65	Decca F 12301	I'm Through/We Gotta Get Together	7
67	CBS 202615	You've Been Cheating/Love Was In My Eyes	12
64	Decca LK 4635	THE APPLEJACKS (LP)	80

APPLETREE THEATRE
68	MGM 2353 051	THE PLAYBACK (LP)	20

CHARLIE APPLEWHITE
54	Brunswick 05358	No One But You/Parade	4
55	Brunswick 05411	Prize Of Gold/Mister Publisher (Have I Got A Song For You)	5
55	Brunswick 05416	Blue Star/A Prayer Was Born	8

APRIL WINE
76	London HLU 10544	Child's Garden/The Whole World's Goin' Crazy	6
77	London HLU 10549	You Won't Dance With Me/Shot Down	6
81	Capitol CL 16184	Just Between You And Me/Big City Girls (poster p/s)	4
76	London SH-U 8503	THE WHOLE WORLD'S GOIN' CRAZY (LP)	12
77	London SH-U 8510	LIVE AT THE EL MOCAMBO (LP)	10

A PRIMARY INDUSTRY
85	Sweatbox SOX 007	Sicatrice/Obeah/Biting Back/Bled Dry (12", stamped p/s)	8
86	Temps Modernes CSBTVV	At Gunpoint/Perversion (p/s)	12

AQUARIAN AGE
68   Parlophone R 5700   10,000 Words In A Cardboard Box/Good Wizard Meets Naughty Wizard 50
(see also Twink, Tomorrow, Clem Cattini, Nicky Hopkins)

AQUARIAN DREAM
77   Buddah BDS 455   Phoenix/Once Again 4

AQUARIANS
71   Ackee ACK 135   Circy Cap/Circy Version 4
71   Ackee ACK 137   Rebel/Invasion Version 4

AQUATONES
58   London HLO 8631   You/She's The One For Me 30
58   London HLO 8631   You/She's The One For Me (78) 20

AQUILA
70   RCA SF 8126   THE AQUILA SUITE (LP, gatefold sleeve) 50

ARANBEE POP SYMPHONY
66   Immediate IMLP/IMSP 003   TODAY'S POP SYMPHONY (LP) 100
(see also Andrew Oldham Orchestra, Keith Richard[s])

ARBORS
68   CBS 3221   Valley Of The Dolls/You Are The Music 4

ARC
71   Decca SKL-R 5077   AT THIS (LP) 40
(see also Heavy Jelly, Skip Bifferty)

ARCADIA
85   EMI NSR 1   Election Day/She's Moody And Grey (gatefold p/s) 5
85   EMI 12 NSR 1   Election Day (Consensus Mix)/Election Day/She's Moody And Grey She's
                     Mean And She's Restless (12", p/s) 7
85   EMI 12 NSRA 1   Election Day (Cryptic Cut No Voice Mix)/(7" Mix)/(Consensus Mix) (12", p/s) 12
86   EMI 12 NSR 2   The Promise/Rose Arcana/The Promise (7" Mix)
                     (12", stickered gold p/s with poster) 10
86   EMI 12 NSR 2   The Promise/Rose Arcana/The Promise (7" Mix) (12", blue p/s) 7
86   EMI 12 NSR 3   Flame (Extended Remix)/Flame Game (Yo Homeboy Mix)/
                     Election Day (Early Rough Mix) (12", p/s) 8
85   Parlophone PCSD 101   SO RED THE ROSE (LP, with inner sleeve & lyric insert) 10
(see also Duran Duran)

ARCADIUM
69   Middle Earth MDS 102   Sing My Song/Riding Alone 25
69   Middle Earth MDLS 302   BREATH AWHILE (LP) 250

ARCHIES
69   RCA RD/SF 8073   SUGAR SUGAR (LP) 10

ARCHITECTS OF DISASTER
82   Neuter NEU 1   Cucumber Sandwich/Friendly Fire (no p/s, 6" x 6" insert in poly bag) 8
(see also Orange Disaster, Perfect Disaster)

TONI ARDEN
55   HMV 7M 314   Beware/I'll Step Aside 4
57   Brunswick 05645   Little By Little/Without Love (There Is Nothing) 6
57   Brunswick 05679   My Empty Heart/Like A Baby 4
58   Brunswick 05745   Padre/All At Once 4

NEIL ARDLEY
65   Decca SKL 4690   WESTERN UNION (LP) 80
69   Verve SVLP 9236   DEJEUNER SUR L'HERBE (LP) 100
70   Columbia SCX 6414   GREEK VARIATIONS (LP, with Ian Carr & Don Rendell) 70
72   Regal Zono. SLRZ 1028   A SYMPHONY OF AMARANTHS (LP) 80
74   Argo ZDA 164/5   WILL POWER (2-LP, with Ian Carr, Stan Tracey & Mike Gibbs) 70
75   Gull GULP 1018   KALEIDOSCOPE OF RAINBOWS (LP) 10
78   Decca TXS-R 133   HARMONY OF THE SPHERES (LP, featuring John Martyn) 10
(see also Ian Carr, Don Rendell)

AREA CODE 615
70   Polydor 56546   Ruby/Southern Comfort 4
69   Polydor 583 572   AREA CODE 615 (LP) 10
70   Polydor 2425 023   A TRIP IN THE COUNTRY (LP) 10

ARENA TWINS
59   London HL 7071   Mama, Care Mama/Little Pig (export issue) 10

ARGENT
71   Epic S EPC 9135   Hold Your Head Up/Closer To Heaven/Keep On Rollin (p/s) 5
70   CBS 63781   ARGENT (LP) 10
71   Epic EPC 64190   RING OF HANDS (LP) 10
72   Epic EPC 64962   ALL TOGETHER NOW (LP, with booklet) 10
74   Epic EQ 32195/Q 65475   IN DEEP (LP, quadrophonic) 14
74   Epic EPC 88063   ENCORE (2-LP) 14
(see also Zombies, Unit 4 + 2, John Verity Band)

ARGONAUTS
85   Lyntone LYN 18249/50   Apeman/Under My Thumb (signed white label, no p/s) 10
(see also Madness)

ARGOSY
69   DJM DJS 214   Mr. Boyd/Imagine 4

A RIOT OF COLOUR
86   Lyntone LYN 17114/GIVE 1   Skink/Newtown (p/s, flexidisc free with various fanzines) 8/6

A RIOT OF COLOUR

87	Dreamworld DREAM 009	Skink/Country/House/Newtown (12", p/s)	8

ARIZONA BOYS' CHOIR
56	Columbia SCM 5215	Ballad Of Davy Crockett/Blue Shadows On The Trail	4

ARIZONA SWAMP COMPANY
70	Parlophone R 5841	Train Keeps Rollin'/Tennessee Woman	15

A.R. KANE
87	4AD BAD 704	Lolita/Sado-Masochism Is A Must/Butterfly Collector (12", p/s)	7
88	Rough Trade RT 201	Baby Milk Snatcher/W.O.G.S. (promo-only, plain black stickered sleeve)	6

WILLIAM ARKLE
80s	The Stand WAM 1	THE MUSIC OF WILLIAM ARKLE (cassette)	10

(see also Robert John Godfrey)

DEE ARLEN
59	Philips PB 950	Stay/Why Should We Wait Any Longer	4
59	Philips PB 950	Stay/Why Should We Wait Any Longer (78)	8

STEVE ARLEN
58	Melodisc M 1458	That's Love/Easy 'N' Free	10
58	Melodisc M 1458	That's Love/Easy 'N' Free (78)	8
60	HMV POP 835	Suddenly I'm In Love/Happy Days	4

DEKE ARLON & OFFBEATS
64	HMV POP 1340	I Need You/I Must Go And Tell Her	15
64	Columbia DB 7194	I'm Just A Boy/Can't Make Up My Mind	20
65	Columbia DB 7487	If I Didn't Have A Dime/Gotta Little Girl	7
65	Columbia DB 7753	Little Piece Of Paper/I've Been Away (solo)	5
66	Columbia DB 7841	Hard Times For Young Lovers/Little Boy (solo)	5

ARMAGEDDON
75	A&M AMLH 64513	ARMAGEDDON (LP)	30

JOAN ARMATRADING
73	Cube BUG 31	Lonely Lady/Together In Words And Music	6
75	A&M AMS 7181	Back To The Night/So Good	4
76	Cube BUG 74	Alice/All The Kings' Gardens	5
78	A&M AMS 7365	Flight Of The Wild Geese/No Way Out	4
72	Cube HIFLY 12	WHATEVER'S FOR US (LP, original issue, gatefold sleeve)	10

ARMED FORCE
80	Armed Force AF 1	Pop Star/Attack (p/s)	5

KAY ARMEN
55	MGM SP 1146	He/Suddenly There's A Valley	4
58	Brunswick 05729	Ha! Ha! Ha! (Chella Lla!)/Till	4

ARMENIAN JAZZ QUARTET
57	London HLR 8454	Harem Dance/Pretty Girl	6

RUSSELL ARMS
57	London HLB 8406	Cinco Robes (Five Oaks)/The World Is Made Of Lisa	6
57	London HL 7018	Cinco Robes (Five Oaks)/The World Is Made Of Lisa (export issue)	4

ARMS & LEGS
76	MAM MAM 140	Janice/She'll Surprise You	8
76	MAM MAM 147	Heat Of The Night/Good Times	8
77	MAM MAM 156	Is There Anymore Wine/She'll Surprise You	8

(see also Joe Jackson)

FRANKIE ARMSTRONG
72	Topic 12TS 216	LOVELY ON THE WATER (LP)	12
75	Topic 12TS 273	SONGS AND BALLADS (LP)	10

LOUIS ARMSTRONG
50	Brunswick 04627	Life Is So Peculiar/You Rascal You (78, with Louis Jordan)	5
52	Brunswick 04995	Takes Two To Tango/That's My Desire (78, B-side with Velma Middleton)	5
53	Columbia SCM 5061	King Of The Zulus/Lonesome Blues	6
54	Columbia SCM 5118	Chicago Breakdown/Twelfth Street Rag	6
54	Columbia SCM 5142	I'm Not Rough/Put 'Em Down Blues	6
54	Brunswick 05303	Basin Street Blues Pts 1 & 2	6
54	Brunswick 05332	Skokiaan Pts 1 & 2	6
54	Brunswick 05347	Muskrat Ramble/Someday You'll Be Sorry (B-side with Commanders)	6
55	Brunswick 05364	Trees/Spooks	6
55	Brunswick 05400	Ko Ko Mo (I Love You So)/Struttin' With Some Barbecue (with Gary Crosby)	12
55	Brunswick 05415	Pledging My Love/Sincerely	6
55	Brunswick 05460	Pretty Little Missy/Bye And Bye	6
55	Brunswick 05505	Christmas Night In Harlem/Christmas In New Orleans	6
56	Brunswick 05512	Only You (And You Alone)/Moments To Remember	6
56	Brunswick 05574	Easy Street/Lazybones (with Gary Crosby)	4
56	Capitol CL 14643	Now You Has Jazz (with Bing Crosby)/High Society Calypso	6
57	Brunswick 05649	This Younger Generation/In Pursuit Of Happiness	4
59	Brunswick 05772	The Mardi Gras March/I Love Jazz	4
59	MGM MGM 1035	The Beat Generation/Someday You'll Be Sorry	4
59	Philips PB 967	Mack The Knife/The Faithful Hussar	4
59	Pye Intl. 7N 25043	The Formula For Love (with Nina & Frederick)/Struttin' With Some Barbecue (with Velma Middleton)	4
60	Philips JAZ 108	Mahogany Hall Blues Stomp/On The Sunny Side Of The ...	4
60	Philips JAZ 112	Way Down Yonder In New Orleans/Do You Know What It Means To ...	4
60	MGM MGM 1107	Muskrat Ramble/Dardanella	4
69	United Artists UP 35059	We Have All The Time In The World/Pretty Little Missy	20
69	United Artists UA 3172	We Have All The Time In The World/Pretty Little Missy (reissue, p/s)	30

Rare Record Price Guide

69	United Artists JB 001	We Have All The Time In The World (1-sided)	20
51	Brunswick LA 8528	LOUIS ARMSTRONG CLASSICS (10" LP)	15
51	Brunswick LA 8534	JAZZ CONCERT (10" LP)	15
52	Brunswick LA 8537	NEW ORLEANS DAYS (10" LP)	15
52	Brunswick LAT 8017	SATCHMO AT SYMPHONY HALL (LP)	15
52	Brunswick LAT 8018	SATCHMO AT SYMPHONY HALL (LP)	15
52	Brunswick LAT 8019	SATCHMO AT PASADENA (LP)	15
53	Brunswick LA 8597	LOUIS ARMSTRONG JAZZ — CLASSICS (10" LP)	15
53	London AL 3501	PLAYS THE BLUES (10" LP)	25
53	Columbia 33S 1007	JAZZIN' WITH ARMSTRONG (10" LP)	15
53	HMV DLP 1015	NEW YORK TOWN HALL CONCERT 1947 (10" LP)	15
54	Columbia 33SX 1029	LOUIS ARMSTRONG AND HIS HOT FIVE (LP)	15
54	HMV DLP 1036	LAUGHIN' LOUIS (10" LP)	15
54	Columbia 33S 1041	LOUIS ARMSTRONG AND HIS HOT SEVEN (10" LP)	15
54	Brunswick LA 8679	SATCHMO SERENADES (10" LP)	15
54	Brunswick LA 8681	LOUIS ARMSTRONG AND THE MILLS BROTHERS (10" LP)	15
54	Brunswick LA 8691	BASIN STREET BLUES (10" LP)	15
55	Columbia 33S 1058	RENDEZVOUS AT THE SUNSET CAFE (10" LP)	15
55	Columbia 33S 1069	LOUIS ARMSTRONG (10" LP)	15
55	HMV DLP 1105	SATCHMO SESSION (10" LP)	15
55	Philips BBL 7017	SATCHMO PLAYS W.C. HANDY (LP)	12
55	Philips BBL 7046	LOUIS ARMSTRONG AND EARL HINES (LP)	12
55	Brunswick LA 8698	LOUIS' HOT FIVES AND SEVENS (10" LP)	15
55	Brunswick LA 8700	BLUEBERRY HILL (10" LP)	15
56	Philips BBL 7064	SATCH PLAYS FATS (LP)	12
56	Philips BBL 7091	AMBASSADOR SATCH (LP)	12
56	Brunswick LAT 8084	LOUIS ARMSTRONG AT THE CRESCENDO VOL. 1 (LP)	10
56	Brunswick LAT 8085	LOUIS ARMSTRONG AT THE CRESCENDO VOL. 2 (LP)	10
57	Philips BBL 7134	LOUIS ARMSTRONG STORY VOL. 1 (LP)	10
57	Philips BBL 7189	LOUIS ARMSTRONG STORY VOL. 2 (LP)	10
57	Brunswick LAT 8210	LOUIS AND THE ANGELS (LP)	10
57	Brunswick LAT 8211	SATCHMO — A MUSICAL AUTOBIOGRAPHY (LP)	10
57	Brunswick LAT 8212	SATCHMO — A MUSICAL AUTOBIOGRAPHY (LP)	10
57	Brunswick LAT 8213	SATCHMO — A MUSICAL AUTOBIOGRAPHY (LP)	10
57	Brunswick LAT 8214	SATCHMO — A MUSICAL AUTOBIOGRAPHY (LP)	10
58	Philips BBL 7202	LOUIS ARMSTRONG STORY VOL. 3 (LP, with Earl Hines)	10
58	Fontana TFR 6003	LOUIS ARMSTRONG AND HIS HOT FIVE (10" LP)	12
58	Philips BBL 7216	SATCHMO THE GREAT (LP, soundtrack)	12
58	Philips BBL 7218	LOUIS ARMSTRONG STORY VOL. 4 (LP)	10
58	Brunswick LAT 8243	SATCHMO SINGS (LP)	10
58	Brunswick LAT 8270	LOUIS AND THE GOOD BOOK (LP)	10
60	HMV CLP 1328	LOUIS ARMSTRONG MEETS OSCAR PETERSON (LP)	10
60	HMV CLP 1388/CSD 1317	I'VE GOT THE WORLD ON A STRING (LP)	10/12
60	Parlophone PMC 1140	HIS GREATEST YEARS VOL. 1 (LP)	10
60	Parlophone PMC 1142	HIS GREATEST YEARS VOL. 2 (LP)	10
60	Audio Fidelity AFLP 1930	SATCHMO PLAYS KING OLIVER (LP, also stereo AFSD 5930)	10/12
61	Philips BBL 7445	SATCHMO PLAYS W.C. HANDY (LP, reissue)	10
62	Riverside 12-101	YOUNG LOUIS ARMSTRONG (LP)	10
65	Fontana FJL 116	YEAH! (LP)	10

(see also Danny Kaye, Ella Fitzgerald & Louis Armstrong)

ARMY OF LOVERS

88	Ton Son Ton SON 7	Love Me Like A Loaded Gun/Love Me Like A Loaded Gun (Version) (p/s)	7
88	Ton Son Ton SONL 7	Love Me Like A Loaded Gun (Vietcong Audience House Mix)/ Dub Me Like A Loaded Gun (12", p/s)	12
90	Ton Son Ton SON 12	Ride The Bullet/Mondo Trasho (p/s)	5
90	Ton Son Ton SONL12	Ride The Bullet/Mondo Trasho (12", p/s)	8
91	Ton Son Ton SON 13	My Army Of Lovers/Scorpio Rising (p/s)	4
91	Ton Son Ton SONL 13	My Army Of Lovers/Scorpio Rising (12", p/s)	7

B.J. ARNAU

73	RCA RCA 2365	Live And Let Die/In One Night	8

GINNY ARNELL

60	Brunswick 05836	Carnival/We	4

CHICO ARNEZ & HIS LATIN AMERICAN ORCHESTRA

59	Pye 7N 15196	Yashmak/Ain't She Sweet	20

(see also Jackie Davies)

ARNIE'S LOVE

83	Streetwave WAVE 9	I'm Out Of Your Life/I'm Out Of Your Life (Instrumental) (p/s)	5
83	Streetwave WAVE 9T	I'm Out Of Your Life/I'm Out Of Your Life (Instrumental) (12", p/s)	10

CALVIN ARNOLD

68	MGM MGM 1378	Snatchin' Back/Funky Way	5
68	MGM MGM 1449	Mama In Law/Mini Skirt	4

EDDY ARNOLD

54	HMV 7MC 10	Prayer/Robe Of Calvary (export issue)	10
54	HMV 7MC 16	Free Home Demonstrations/If I Never Get To Heaven (export issue)	10
54	HMV 7MC 19	Second Fling/My Everything (export issue)	10
54	HMV 7MC 22	Hep Cat Baby/This Is The Thanks I Get (For Loving You) (export issue)	10
55	HMV 7MC 32	In Time/Two Kinds Of Love (export issue)	10
55	HMV 7M 339	I Walked Alone Last Night/The Richest Man (In The World)	7
57	RCA RCA 1008	Little Bit/Gonna Find Me A Bluebird	6
57	RCA RCA 1008	Little Bit/Gonna Find Me A Bluebird (78)	5
57	RCA RCA 1017	Scarlet Ribbons/Bayou Baby (A Cajun Lullaby)	4
57	RCA RCA 1017	Scarlet Ribbons/Bayou Baby (A Cajun Lullaby) (78)	5
58	RCA RCA 1057	Little Miss Sunbeam/My Darling, My Darling	5

Eddy ARNOLD

58	RCA RCA 1057	Little Miss Sunbeam/My Darling, My Darling (78)	5
59	RCA RCA 1138	Tennessee Stud/What's The Good (Of All This Love)	6
59	RCA RCA 1138	Tennessee Stud/What's The Good (Of All This Love) (78)	7
60	RCA RCA 1212	Just Out Of Reach/Before This Day Ends	4
54	HMV 7EG 8020	EDDY ARNOLD (EP)	8
55	HMV 7EG 8080	CHAPEL ON THE HILL (EP)	8
59	RCA Camden CDN 133	EDDY ARNOLD (LP)	10
60	RCA RD 27155	THEREBY HANGS A TALE (LP)	12
62	RCA Victor RD 7796	I WANT TO GO WITH YOU (LP)	10
63	RCA Victor RD 7804	CATTLE CALL (LP)	10

KOKOMO ARNOLD
69	S/disc Matchbox SDR 163	KOKOMO ARNOLD (LP)	12

P.P. ARNOLD
66	Immediate IM 040	Everything's Gonna Be Alright/Life Is But Nothin'	60
67	Immediate IM 047	The First Cut Is The Deepest/Speak To Me	7
67	Immediate IM 055	The Time Has Come/If You See What I Mean	5
68	Immediate IM 061	(If You Think You're) Groovy/Though It Hurts Me Badly	5
68	Immediate IM 067	Angel Of The Morning/Life Is But Nothin'	5
69	Immediate IM 079	The First Cut Is The Deepest/The Time Has Come	4
69	Polydor 56350	Bury Me Down The River/Give A Hand To Take A Hand	4
76	Virgin/NEMS SV 103	Angel Of The Morning/Everything's Gonna Be Alright/The First Cut Is The Deepest/(If You Think You're) Groovy/The Time Has Come (double pack, gatefold p/s)	5
67	Immediate IMLP/IMSP 011	THE FIRST LADY OF IMMEDIATE (LP)	18
68	Immediate IMSP 017	KAFUNTA (LP, gatefold sleeve)	15
	(see also Nice, Small Faces)		

ARRIVALS
69	Pye 7N 17756	Scooby Doo/She's About A Mover	4

ARROWS (U.S.)
65	Capitol CL 15386	Apache '65/Blue Guitar	5

ARROWS (U.K.)
69	Pye 7N 17756	Mercy/See Saw	4

ARS NOVA
68	Elektra EKSN 45029	Zoroaster/Pavan For My Lady	5
68	Elektra EKSN 45034	Fields Of People/Song To The City	5
68	Elektra EKS 74020	ARS NOVA (LP, orange label, gatefold sleeve)	12
69	Atlantic 588 196	SUNSHINE AND SHADOWS (LP)	10

ART
67	Island WIP 6019	What's That Sound (For What It's Worth)/Rome Take Away Three	12
75	Island WIP 6224	What's That Sound (For What It's Worth)/Flying Anchors	4
68	Island ILP 967	SUPERNATURAL FAIRY TALES (LP, pink label, laminated sleeve)	35
75	Island ILP 967	SUPERNATURAL FAIRY TALES (LP, reissue, matt sleeve, 'palm tree' label)	15
	(see also VIP's, Spooky Tooth)		

ART & LANGUAGE/RED CRAYOLA
80	Rough Trade RT 054	Born In Flames/Sword Of God (p/s)	4
81	Rough Trade ROUGH 19	KANGAROO (LP)	10
81	Rough Trade COPY 005	KANGAROO (cassette, with 2 extra tracks)	10
	(see also Red Crayola)		

ART ATTACKS
78	Albatross TIT 1	I'm A Dalek/Neutron Bomb (p/s)	10
79	Fresh FRESH 3	Punk Rock Stars/Rat City/First And Last (p/s)	8
	(see also Monochrome Set, Tagmemics, Kray Cherubs)		

ART BEARS
81	Recommended RE 6622	CODA TO "MAN & BOY" (EP, live, 1-sided clear vinyl, silk-screened p/s, 1,750 only, 500 signed & numbered for magazine subscribers)	12/10
78	Recommended REC 2188	HOPES AND FEARS (LP, gatefold sleeve with poster & booklet)	12
79	Recommended REC 0618	WINTER SONGS (LP, with booklet)	12
	(see also Henry Cow)		

ARTERY
79	Limited Edition TAKE 1	Mother Moon/Pretends/Heinz (p/s)	12
80	Aardvark STEAL 3	Unbalanced/The Slide (p/s, some with EP [Perhaps/Turtle/Toytown/Heinz])	8/5
81	Aardvark AARD 5	Cars In Motion/Life And Death (p/s)	4
81	Armageddon AS 026	Afterwards/Into The Garden (p/s)	4
82	Red Flame RF 704	The Clown/?? (p/s)	4
82	Red Flame RFM 4	OCEANS (LP, with insert)	10
	(see also Mission)		

ARTFUL DODGER
80	Ariola ARL 5061	RAVE ON (LP)	10

DAVID & TONI ARTHUR
70	Trailer LER 1	Bushes And Briars/Lazio Feher	4
69	Topic 12T 190	THE LARK IN THE MORNING (LP)	30
81	Leader LER 2017	HEARKEN TO THE WITCHES' RUNE (LP)	10
	(see also Strollers)		

ARTHUR COMICS
77	XS	Isgodaman? (unissued)	

ANDY ARTHURS
78	Radar ADA 7	I Can Detect You For 1,000,000 Miles/I Am A Machine (p/s)	12
78	TDS TDS 3	I Can Detect You For 1,000,000 Miles/I Am A Machine (p/s)	4
79	TDS TDS 6	I Feel Flat (p/s)	4

ARTICLE 58
81	Rational RATE 4	Echoes/Lost And Found/Events To Come (folded p/s in zip lock bag) 4

ARTISTICS
66	Coral Q 72488	I'm Gonna Miss You/Hope We Have 15
67	Coral Q 72492	Girl I Need You/I'm Glad I Met You 20
70	MCA MU 1117	I'm Gonna Miss You/Hope We Have (reissue) 5
76	Brunswick BR 39	I'm Gonna Miss You/GENE CHANDLER: There Was A Time 6

ART MOVEMENT
68	Decca F 12768	I Love Being In Love With You/The Game Of Love 6
68	Decca F 12836	Loving Touch/Happy Song 5
69	Columbia DB 8602	Yes Sir . . . No Sir/Sally Goes Round The Moon 4
70	Columbia DB 8651	For As Long As You Need Me/Nice 'n' Easy 4
70	Columbia DB 8697	The Sooner I Get To You/Morning Girl 4

ART NOUVEAUX
64	Fontana TF 483	Extra Terrestrial Visitations/The Way To Play It 12

ART OBJECTS
80	Heartbeat PULSE 10	Showing Off To Impress The Girls/Our Silver Sister (live) (p/s) 6
81	Fried Egg EGG 007	Hard Objects/Bibliotheque/Fit Of Pique (p/s) 5
81	Heartbeat HB 5	BAGPIPE MUSIC (LP) 12
(see also Blue Aeroplanes)		

ART OF NOISE
83	ZTT ZTIS 100	INTO BATTLE WITH THE ART OF NOISE (12" EP) 7
83	ZTT CTIS 100	INTO BATTLE WITH THE ART OF NOISE (EP, cassette) 10
84	ZTT P ZTPS 01	Close (To The Edit)/A Time To Hear (Who's Listening) (picture disc) 4
84	ZTT 12 P ZTPS 01	Edited/A Time To Clear (It Up) (12" picture disc) 7
85	ZTT 12 ZTPS 01	Close Up/Close Up (Hop) (12", p/s, matrix: 01 A 1U) 8
85	ZTT 12 ZTPS 01	Close Up/Close Up (Hop)/Close (To The Edit) (12", p/s) 7
85	ZTT 12 ZTPS 01	Closely Closely (Enough's Enough)/Close Up (Hop)/
		A Time To Hear (Who's Listening) (12", p/s) 7
85	ZTT 12 ZTPS 01	Closely Closely (Enough's Enough)/Moment In Love/
		The Time To Hear (You're Listening) (12", p/s, matrix: 01 A 4U) 7
85	ZTT 12 ZTPS 1	CLOSE TO THE EDIT (12", unreleased, stamped green label) 10
85	ZTT CTIS 106	CLOSE (TO THE EDIT) (cassette) 6
85	ZTT P ZTPS 02	Moments In Love/Beatbox (tortoise-shaped picture disc) 6
85	ZTT CTIS 109	Moments In Love (cassette) 8
85	ZTT ZTAS 108	Beatbox (Diversions 1 & 2) (12", p/s) 7
85	China WOKR 5	Legs (Last Leg Mix)/Legs/Hoops & Mallets (12", p/s) 8

ART OF NOISE & MAX HEADROOM
86	China WOKD 9	Paranoimia/Why Me?//Legs/Hoops And Mallets (double pack, gatefold p/s) .. 6
86	China WOKP 9	Paranoimia/Why Me? (shaped picture disc) 4
86	China WOKR 9	Paranoimia (Paranoid remix)/Why Me?/A Nation Rejects (12", p/s) 7

ART OF NOISE WITH DUANE EDDY
86	China WOKP 6	Peter Gunn/Something Always Happens (shaped picture disc) 4
86	China WOKR 6	Peter Gunn (Twang Mix)/Peter Gunn/Something Always Happens (12", p/s) 7
(see also Duane Eddy)		

ARTWOODS
64	Decca F 12015	Sweet Mary/If I Ever Get My Hands On You 30
65	Decca F 12091	Oh My Love/Big City 30
65	Decca F 12206	Goodbye Sisters/She Knows What To Do 30
66	Decca F 12384	I Take What I Want/I'm Looking For A Saxophonist Doubling French
		Horn Wearing Size 37 Boots 30
66	Decca F 12465	I Feel Good/Molly Anderson's Cookery Book 30
67	Parlophone R 5590	What Shall I Do/In The Deep End 60
66	Decca DFE 8654	JAZZ IN JEANS (EP) 200
66	Decca LK 4830	ART GALLERY (LP) 140
73	Spark SRLM 2006	THE ARTWOODS (LP) 25
74	Decca Eclipse ECS 2025	ART GALLERY (LP, reissue in different sleeve) 45
(see also St. Valentine's Day Massacre, Keef Hartley Band, Jon Lord, Dog Soldier, Lucas & Mike Cotton Sound)		

ARZACHEL
69	Evolution Z 1003	ARZACHEL (LP) 250
(see also Egg, Steve Hillage, Khan)		

A.S.A.P.
(see under Adrian Smith & Project)		

ASGARD
72	Threshold TH 10	Friends/Children Of A New Born Age 5
73	Threshold TH 15	In The Realm Of Asgard/Town Cryer 5
72	Threshold THS 6	IN THE REALM OF ASGARD (LP, gatefold sleeve) 40

VIC ASH QUARTET
56	Tempo A 135	Blue Lou/Doxy 4
56	Tempo A 137	Early Morning/Just One Of Those Things 4

ASHBURY-STABBINS DUO
77	Bead BEAD 4	FIRE WITHOUT BRICKS (LP) 10

IRVING ASHBY & HIS COMBO
58	London HLP 8578	Big Guitar/Motatin' 15
58	London HLP 8578	Big Guitar/Motatin' (78) 8

JOHNNY ASHCROFT
59	Felsted AF 118	A Pub With No Beer/Bouquet For The Pride 4
60	HMV POP 759	Little Boy Lost/My Love Is A River 4

MINT VALUE £

ASHFORD & SIMPSON
74	Warner Brothers K 16373	Have You Ever Tried It?/Time	4

ASHKAN
70	Decca Nova (S)DN-R 1	IN FROM THE COLD (LP)	45

TYRONE ASHLEY
76	Pye International 7N 25710	Nothing Short Of A Miracle/Miracle Worker	5

ASH RA (TEMPLE)
77	Virgin V 2080	NEW AGE OF EARTH (LP)	10
77	Virgin V 2091	BLACKOUTS (LP)	10
79	Virgin V 2117	CORRELATIONS (LP)	10

BUD ASHTON
61	Embassy WEP 1058	SWINGING GUITARS (EP)	7
63	Embassy WEP 1088	MORE SWINGING GUITARS (EP)	7

(Tony) ASHTON & (Jon) LORD
74	Purple PUR 121	We're Gonna Make It/Band Of The Salvation Army Band	6
74	Purple TPS 3507	FIRST OF THE BIG BANDS (LP)	10

(see also Ashton Gardner & Dyke, Paice Ashton & Lord, Jon Lord, Deep Purple)

ASHTON, GARDNER & DYKE
69	Polydor 56306	Maiden Voyage/See The Sun In My Eyes	4
69	Polydor 583 081	ASHTON, GARDNER & DYKE (LP)	10
71	Capitol EST 563	THE WORST OF ASHTON, GARDNER AND DYKE (LP)	10
72	Capitol EST 862	WHAT A BLOODY LONG DAY IT'S BEEN (LP)	10

(see also Ashton & Lord, Remo Four, Creation, Birds, Mike Hurst & Method, Badger, Medicine Head, Family)

ASIA
82	Geffen GEF A 2228	Only Time Will Tell/Ride Easy (p/s)	4
82	Geffen GEF A 11-2228	Only Time Will Tell/Ride Easy (picture disc)	7
82	Geffen GEF WA 3580	Don't Cry/True Colours (logo-shaped picture disc)	6
83	Geffen GEF TA 3836	The Smile Has Left Your Eyes/Lying To Yourself/Midnight Sun (12", p/s, red vinyl)	7
85	Geffen TA 6737	Go (Remix)/Go (Instrumental)/After The War (12", p/s)	10
92	Musidisc 108521/MU 111	Who Will Stop The Rain/Aqua Pt. 1/Heart Of Gold (10", picture disc)	8
92	Musidisc 109526	Who Will Stop The Rain/Aqua Pt. 1/Heart Of Gold (12", p/s)	7
92	Musidisc 109522	Who Will Stop The Rain/Aqua Pt. 1/Heart Of Gold/Obsession (CD)	7
82	Geffen GEF 11-85577	ASIA (LP, picture disc)	12

(see also Yes, Emerson Lake & Palmer, Steve Howe, Anderson Bruford Wakeman & Howe)

ARTHUR ASKEY
57	Oriole MG 20017	HELLO! PLAYMATES (LP)	10

ASLAN
76	Profile 6	ASLAN (LP)	40

MONICA ASPELUND
77	RCA PB 9044	Lapponia/La-La, Sing A Song	8

VERA ASPEY
77	Topic 12TS 356	THE BLACKBIRD (LP)	10

VERA & GAE ORY ASPEY
75	Topic 12TS 255	FROM THE NORTH (LP)	10
76	Topic 12TS 299	A TASTE HOTPOT (LP)	10

ASSAGAI
71	Vertigo 6059 034	Telephone Girl/I'll Wait For You	5
71	Vertigo 6360 030	ASSAGAI (LP, gatefold sleeve, spiral label)	18
72	Philips 6308 079	ZIMBABWE (LP)	15

LYS ASSIA
54	Decca F 10097	O Mein Papa/Ponylied	4
54	Decca F 10278	The Glow Of The Candle/My Love, My Life, My Own	4
55	Decca F 10516	Apples, Peaches And Cherries (with Johnston Brothers)/Words Of Love	4
56	Decca F 10675	My Love/Someone	4
57	Decca F 10930	Through The Eyes Of Love/Scusami	4

ASSOCIATES
80	Double Hip DHR 1	Boys Keep Swinging/Mona Property Girl (no p/s, 500 only)	50
80	MCA MCA 537	Boys Keep Swinging/Mona Property Girl (no p/s, demos more common, £25)	30
80	Fiction FICS 11	The Affectionate Punch/You Were Wrong (p/s)	7
80	Fiction FICS 13	A/Would I ... Bounce Back (p/s)	4
80	Fiction FICSX 13	A/Would I ... Bounce Back (12", p/s)	7
81	Situation 2 SIT 4	Q Quarters/Kissed (p/s)	4
81	Situation 2 SIT 4T	Q Quarters/Kissed/Q Quarters (Original) (12", p/s)	7
81	RSO RSO 78	A Girl Named Property/39 LION ST.: Kites (p/s)	6
81	RSO RSOX 78	A Girl Named Property/39 LION ST.: Kites (12", p/s)	8
82	Lyntone LYN 11649	Even Dogs In The Wild (clear 1-sided flexi free with 'Flexipop' mag, issue 20)	6/4
82	Lyntone LYN 11649	Even Dogs In The Wild (hard vinyl test pressing)	25
84	Beggars Banquet BEG 86	Tell Me Easter's On Friday (unreleased, white labels only)	20
84	WEA YZ 16T	Waiting For The Loveboat (Extended Version)/(John Peel Session Version)/Schampout (Extended Version) (12", stickered p/s)	8
85	WEA YZ 28P	Breakfast/Breakfast Alone (picture disc, stickered PVC sleeve)	4
85	WEA YX 47TE	Take Me To The Girl/Perhaps/God Bless The Child (live)/Dogs In The Wild (live)/The Boy That Santa Claus Forgot (live) (10", p/s)	8
88	WEA YZ 310 TX	Heart Of Glass (The Temperament Mix)/Heart Of Glass/Her Only Wish/Heavens Blue (12", 3-D p/s shrink-wrapped with 3-D glasses)	15
88	WEA YZ 329T	Country Boy/Heart Of Glass (Dub Mix)/Just Can't Say Goodbye (12" Mix) (12", p/s, unissued, white labels only)	60

88	WEA YZ 329CD	Country Boy/Just Can't Say Goodbye (12" Mix)/Take Me To The Girl/	
		Heart Of Glass (Dub Mix) (3" CD with adaptor, jewel case, unissued)	50
90	Circa BILLY 1	WILD AND LONELY (12" sampler)	8
90	Circa BILLY 1	WILD AND LONELY (cassette sampler)	6
90	Circa BILLY 1	WILD AND LONELY (CD sampler, printed PVC sleeve)	8
84	Beggars Banquet BEGA 43	FOURTH DRAWER DOWN (LP, gatefold sleeve with poster)	10

(see also Orbidöig, Jih, Sensation Creed, Yello)

ASSOCIATION

66	London HLT 10054	Along Comes Mary/Your Own Love	5
66	London HLT 10074	Cherish/Don't Blame It On Me	4
66	London HLT 10098	Pandora's Golden Heebie Jeebies/Standing Still	6
67	London HLT 10118	No Fair At All/Looking Glass	5
67	London HLT 10140	Windy/Sometime	4
67	London HLT 10157	Never My Love/Requiem For The Masses	4
68	Warner Bros WB 7163	Everything That Touches You/We Love Us	4
68	Warner Bros WB 7195	Time For Livin'/Birthday Morning	4
68	Warner Bros WB 7229	Six Man Band/Like Always	4
69	Warner Bros WB 7267	Goodbye Columbus/The Time It Is Today	4
70	Warner Bros WB 7372	Just About The Same/Look At Me, Look At You	4
66	London HA-T 8305	AND THEN . . . ALONG COMES THE ASSOCIATION (LP)	12
67	London HA-T 8313	RENAISSANCE (LP)	12
67	London HA-T/SH-T 8342	INSIGHT OUT (LP)	12
68	Warner Bros W(S) 1733	BIRTHDAY (LP)	10
69	Warner Bros W(S) 1767	GREATEST HITS (LP)	10
69	Warner Bros W(S) 1786	GOODBYE COLUMBUS (LP, soundtrack)	10
69	Warner Bros W(S) 1800	THE ASSOCIATION (LP)	10

FRED ASTAIRE

57	HMV POP 337	Funny Face/AUDREY HEPBURN: How Long Has This Been Going On	7
57	MGM MGM 963	Paris Loves Lovers (with Cyd Charisse & Carol Richards)/All Of You	5
57	MGM MGM 964	The Ritz Roll And Rock/JANIS PAIGE: Satin And Silk	12
57	MGM MGM 964	The Ritz Roll And Rock/JANIS PAIGE: Satin And Silk (78)	5

(see also Judy Garland)

EDWIN ASTLEY ORCHESTRA

65	RCA RCA 1492	Danger Man Theme/Saint Theme	15

RICK ASTLEY

87	RCA PB 41447P	Never Gonna Give You Up/(Instrumental) (poster p/s)	4
87	RCA PT 41448R	Never Gonna Give You Up (Escape From Newton Mix)/Never Gonna Give	
		You Up (Escape To New York Mix) (12" remix, p/s)	7
87	RCA PB 41567P	Whenever You Need Somebody/Just Good Friends (picture disc)	4
87	RCA PB 41568R	Whenever You Need Somebody (Rick Sets It Off Mix)/Whenever You Need	
		Somebody (Instrumental)/Just Good Friends (12" remix, p/s)	7
87	RCA PB 41683	When I Fall In Love/My Arms Keep Missing You (poster p/s)	4
88	RCA 41817PB	Together Forever (Lover's Leap Remix)/I'll Never Set You Free (poster p/s)	4
88	RCA PT 41818R	Together Forever (House Of Love Mix)/I'll Never Set You Free (12", p/s)	8
88	RCA PT 42190R	She Wants To Dance With Me (Bordering On A Collie Mix)/She Wants To	
		Dance With Me (Instrumental) (12", p/s)	7
88	RCA PV 42190	She Wants To Dance With Me (Extended)/(Instrumental)/It Would Take A	
		Strong Man (Matt's Jazzy Guitar Mix) (boxed cassette with poster)	4
87	RCA PL 71529	WHENEVER YOU NEED SOMEBODY (LP, with free 7" picture disc)	10

VIRGINIA ASTLEY

82	Why Fi WHYD 8	4 BAU A QU (10" EP, p/s; also 7" demos £12)	10
83	Why Fi WFI 001	Love Is A Lonely Place To Be/Soaring (p/s)	4
83	Why Fi WFIT 001	Love Is A Lonely Place To Be/Soaring/A Summer Long Since Passed/	
		It's Too Hot To Sleep (12", p/s)	7
84	Rough Trade RTT 158	MELT THE SNOW (12" EP, label also listed as Happy Valley HA 002)	7
85	Elektra EKR 21	Tender/A Long Time Ago (p/s)	5
85	Elektra EKR 21T	Tender (6.02)/Mindless Days/Tender (Instrumental)/A Long Time Ago (12", p/s)	8
85	Elektra YZ 53	Darkness Has Reached Its End/The End Of Time (p/s)	4
85	Elektra YZ 53T	Darkness Has Reached Its End/The End Of Time/Shadows Will Fall Behind	
		(12", p/s)	7
87	WEA YZ 107	Some Small Hope/A Summer Long Since Passed (p/s, with David Sylvian)	4
87	WEA YZ 107T	Some Small Hope/A Summer Long Since Passed/So Like Dorian	
		(Instrumental) (12", p/s, with David Sylvian)	7

(see also Victims Of Pleasure, David Sylvian)

ASTON & YEN

66	Doctor Bird DB 1064	Skillamy/BABA BROOKS & BAND: Party Time	10

ASTORS

65	Atlantic AT 4037	Candy/I Found Out	25
69	Atlantic 584245	Candy/I Found Out (reissue)	7

ASTRAL NAVIGATIONS

71	Holyground HG 114	ASTRAL NAVIGATIONS (LP, actually by Lightyears Away & Thundermother,	
		poster cover & booklet, 250 copies only, some numbered)	200
89	Magic Mixture MM 2	ASTRAL NAVIGATIONS (LP, reissue with booklet, 425 copies only)	25

(see also Bill Nelson, Gagalactyca)

ASTRONAUTS

66	Hala Gala HG 9	Before You Leave/Syncopate	10
67	Island WI 3065	Before You Leave/Syncopate (reissue)	8

ASTRONAUTS

79	Bugle BLAST 1	All Night Party/Back Soon/Everything Stops The Baby/Survivors (p/s)	12
80	Bugle BLAST 5	PRANKSTERS IN REVOLT (EP)	8
81	Bugle GENIUS 001	PETER PAN HITS THE SUBURBS (LP)	40

ASTRONAUTS

82	Bugle	IT'S ALL DONE BY MIRRORS (LP) 35
86	All The Madmen MAD 5	IT'S ALL DONE BY MIRRORS (LP, reissue) 10

(see also Syndicate, Restricted Hours)

A SUDDEN SWAY
(see under Sudden Sway)

ASYLUM CHOIR
68	Mercury SMCL 21041	A LOOK INSIDE THE ASYLUM CHOIR (LP) 10

(see also Leon Russell)

ATACAMA
71	Charisma CAS 1039	ATACAMA (LP) 15
72	Charisma CAS 1060	THE SUN BURNS UP ABOVE (LP) 15

ATHENIANS
64	ESC ESC 1	You Tell Me/Little Queenie (some in custom sleeve) 50/25
64	Waverley SLP 532	I've Got Love If You Want It/I'm A Lover Not A Fighter (some in p/s) 60/30
65	Waverley SLP 533	Thinking Of Your Love/Mercy Mercy (some in custom sleeve) 40/20

GLENN ATHENS & TROJANS
65	Spot 7E 1018	GLENN ATHENS & TROJANS (EP) 250

PETE ATKIN
70	Philips 6006 050	Be Careful When They Offer You/Master Of The Revels 4
70	Fontana 6309 011	BEWARE THE BEAUTIFUL STRANGER (LP) 12
71	Philips 6308 070	DOWN THROUGH MYTHICAL AMERICA (LP) 10

BENNY ATKINS
60	Mercury AMT 1113	Lipstick On Your Lips/I'm Following You 6

CHET ATKINS
59	RCA Victor RCA 1153	Boo Boo Stick Beat/Django's Castle 5
59	RCA Victor RCA 1153	Boo Boo Stick Beat/Django's Castle (78) 12
60	RCA Victor RCA 1174	Teensville/One Mint Julep 5
60	RCA Victor RCA 1174	Teensville/One Mint Julep (78) 25
60	RCA Victor RCA 1209	"The Dark At The Top Of The Stairs" Theme/Hocus Pocus 4
65	RCA Victor RCA 1464	Yakety Axe/Letter Edged In Black 4
63	RCA Victor RCX 7118	GUITAR GENIUS (EP) 7
60	RCA Victor RD 27168	TEENSVILLE (LP) 15
60	RCA Victor RD 27194	THE OTHER CHET ATKINS (LP) 12
60	RCA Victor RD 27214	CHET ATKINS' WORKSHOP (LP) 12
62	RCA Victor RD 7519	CARIBBEAN GUITAR (LP) 10
62	RCA Camden CDN 160	AND HIS GUITAR (LP) 10
62	RCA Camden CDN 165	DOWN HOME (LP) 10
63	RCA Victor RD/SF 7529	OUR MAN IN NASHVILLE (LP, mono/stereo) 10/12
63	RCA Victor RD 7557	TRAVELIN' (LP) 10
63	RCA Victor RD/SF 7602	TEENSCENE (LP, mono/stereo) 10/12
63	RCA Victor RD 7664	BEST OF CHET ATKINS (LP) 10
64	RCA Victor RD 7691	REMINISCING (LP, with Hank Snow) 10
65	RCA Victor RD 7710	MY FAVOURITE GUITARS (LP) 10
65	RCA Victor RD 7763	GUITAR COUNTRY (LP) 10
66	RCA Victor RD/SF 7813	PICKS ON THE BEATLES (LP, mono/stereo) 12/15
67	RCA Victor RD 7838	FROM NASHVILLE WITH LOVE (LP) 10
67	RCA Victor RD 7882	IT'S A GUITAR WORLD (LP) 10
68	RCA Victor RD/SF 7934	SOLO FLIGHTS (LP) 10
70	RCA Victor SF 8092	SOLD GOLD 70 (LP) 10
70	RCA Victor SF 8130	YESTERGROOVIN' (LP) 10

(see also Country Hams)

SWEETPEA ATKINSON
82	Ze ILPS 7018	DON'T WALK AWAY (LP, with lyric inner sleeve) 12

(see also Was [Not Was])

ATLANTA DISCO BAND
76	Ariola AA 103	Do What You Feel/I Am Trying 4

ATLANTIC BRIDGE
71	Dawn DNX 2507	I Can't Lie To You/Hilary Dickson/Childhood Room 4
70	Dawn DNLS 3014	ATLANTIC BRIDGE (LP, gatefold sleeve) 18

ATLANTIS
73	Vertigo 6360 609	ATLANTIS (LP, spiral label) 12
74	Vertigo 6360 614	IT'S GETTING BETTER (LP, 'spaceship' label) 10

ATLAS
78	Emerging WIL 001	AGAINST ALL ODDS (LP) 25

AT LAST THE 1958 ROCK & ROLL SHOW
68	CBS 3349	I Can't Drive/Working On The Railroad 10

(see also Ian Hunter, Mott The Hoople, Freddie 'Fingers' Lee, Miller Anderson, Charles Wolfe)

ATMOSFEAR
79	Elite DAZZ 4	Journey To The Powerline/LEVEL 42: Sandstorm (12", white label test pressing)125
79	Elite	Dancing In Outer Space/Dancing In Outer Space (Version) (12") 12
79	MCA 12 MCA 543	Dancing In Outer Space/Dancing In Outer Space (Version) (12", co. sleeve) 10
80	Elite DAZZ 2	Motivation/Extract (12", p/s) 8
83	Elite DAZZ 23	What Do We Do? (Club Mix)/What Do We Do?/Xtra Special (12", p/s) 8
81	MCA MCF 3110	ENTRANCE (LP) 15

(see also Level 42)

ATMOSPHERES
59	London HLW 8977	Kabalo/The Fickle Chicken 15
59	London HLW 8977	Kabalo/The Fickle Chicken (78) 15

60	London HLW 9091	Telegraph/Caravan	12

A TO AUSTR

70	Holy Ground HG 113	A TO AUSTR (LP, with booklet, 99 copies only)	450
89	Magic Mixture MM 1	A TO AUSTR (LP, reissue, 425 only)	25

ATOMIC ROOSTER

70	B&C CB 121	Friday The 13th/Banstead (initial copies in p/s)	8/4
70	B&C CB 131	Tomorrow Night/Play The Game	4
72	Dawn DNS 1027	Stand By Me/Never To Lose	4
72	Dawn DNS 1029	Save Me/Close Your Eyes	4
74	Decca FR 13503	Tell Your Story (Sing Your Song)/O.D. (as Vincent Crane's Atomic Rooster)	8
80	EMI EMI 5084	Do You Know Who's Looking For You/Throw Your Life Away (p/s)	4
80	EMI 12 EMI 5084	Do You Know Who's Looking For You (Ext.)/Throw Your Life Away (12", p/s)	7
81	Polydor POSP 334	Play It Again/Start To Live (p/s)	4
81	Polydor POSPX 334	Play It Again/Start To Live/Devil's Answer (live) (p/s)	4
82	Polydor POSP 408	End Of The Day/Living Underground (p/s)	4
82	Polydor POSPX 408	End Of The Day/Living Underground/Tomorrow Night (live) (12", p/s)	7
70	B&C CAS 1010	ATOMIC ROOSTER (LP)	15
70	B&C CAS 1026	DEATH WALKS BEHIND YOU (LP, gatefold sleeve)	15
71	Pegasus PEG 1	IN HEARING OF ATOMIC ROOSTER (LP, gatefold sleeve)	10
72	Dawn DNLS 3038	MADE IN ENGLAND (LP, some in limited 'denim' cover)	35/12
73	Dawn DNLS 3049	NICE'N'GREASY (LP)	30

(see also Vincent Crane & Chris Farlowe, Chris Farlowe, Crazy World Of Arthur Brown, Hard Stuff, Leaf Hound, Andromeda)

ATOMS

79	Rinka R 23	Max Bygraves Killed My Mothger/Beatles jacket (colour-silkscreened p/s in poly bag with inserts)	4

A II Z

81	Polydor POSP 243	No Fun After Midnight/Treason (p/s)	7
81	Polydor POSPX 243	No Fun After Midnight/Treason/Valhalla's Force (12", p/s, red vinyl)	12
81	Polydor POSP 314	I'm The One Who Loves You/Ringside Seat (p/s)	7
80	Polydor 2383 587	THE WITCH OF BERKELEY (LP)	10

ATTACK (U.S.)

67	Philips BF 1585	Washington Square/Please Mr Spector	15

ATTACK (U.K.)

67	Decca F 12550	Try It/We Don't Know	35
67	Decca F 12578	Hi-Ho Silver Lining/Any More Than I Do	20
67	Decca F 12631	Created By Clive/Colour Of My Mind	20
68	Decca F 12725	Neville Thumbcatch/Lady Orange Peel	35

(see also Andromeda, Five Day Week Straw People, Nice)

ATTAK

82	No Future OI 17	TODAY'S GENERATION (EP)	4

ATTEMPTED MOUSTACHE

78	Skeleton SKL 003	Superman/No Way Out (folded p/s)	5

(see also Half Man Half Biscuit)

ATTIC

79	Attic ATT 1	Yes I Want To/We're At War (white labels, stamped plain sleeve with insert)	6
80	Brain Booster BB 003	ALL PLANS EXIST (EP, stickered white labels)	4

ATTILA THE STOCKBROKER

81	No Wonder E 1	PHAZING OUT CAPITALISM (EP)	5
82	Cherry Red CHERRY 46	COCKTAILS (EP)	4

ATTITUDES

76	Dark Horse AMS 5504	Ain't Love Enough/The Whole World's Crazy	4
76	Dark Horse AMS 5508	Sweet Summer Music/If We Want To	4
75	Dark Horse AMLH 22008	THE ATTITUDES (LP)	10

ATTRACTION

66	Columbia DB 7936	Stupid Girl/Please Tell Me	25
66	Columbia DB 8010	Party Line/She's A Girl	30

ATTRACTIONS

80	F-Beat XXLP 8	MAD ABOUT THE WRONG BOY (LP, with free EP [COMB 1])	10

(see also Elvis Costello)

ATTRITION

81	Sound For Industry SFI 671/A.R.R. 002	Fear/Devoid (flexidisc, p/s, some with 'Adventures In Reality' fanzine issue 5)	20/8
84	Uniton Recordings 1984-1	MONKEY IN A BIN (12" EP, poster p/s, split with Schamanen Circel)	15
84	Third Mind TMS 03	THE VOICE OF GOD (12" EP)	12
85	Third Mind TMS 04	Shrinkwrap/Pendulum Turns (12", p/s with insert)	12
87	Hamster HAM 18	DEATH HOUSE (mini-LP)	10
87	Hamster HAM 18	DEATH HOUSE (cassette)	10

ATTRIX

78	Attrix RB 01	Lost Lenore/Hard Times (p/s, stamped white labels)	6
81	Scoff DT 011	Procession/11th Hour (p/s)	4

WINIFRED ATWELL

55	Decca F 10448	Song Of The Sea/The Black Mask Waltz	4
55	Decca F 10476	Big Ben Boogie/Winnie's Waltzing Rag	6
55	Decca F 10496	17th Century Boogie/Stranger In Paradise	6
55	Decca F 10634	"Let's Have A Ding-Dong" Medley	5
56	Decca F 10681	Poor People Of Paris (Poor John)/Piano Tuners Boogie	8
56	Decca F 10730	Port-Au-Prince/Startime	5
56	Decca F 10762	Left Bank (C'est A Hambourg)/Rampart Street Rock	5

Winifred ATWELL

56	Decca F 10785	Bumble Boogie/St. Louis Blues	6
56	Decca F 10796	Make It A Party (medley, both sides)	5
56	Decca F 10825	The Garden Of Eden/Moonlight Gambler	4
57	Decca F 10852	Let's Rock 'N' Roll (medley, both sides)	8
57	Decca F 10886	Spaceship Boogie/Jane Street	7
57	Decca F 10956	"Let's Have A Ball" Medley	4
58	Decca F 10987	Raunchy/Dugga Dugga Boom Boom	4
55	Decca DFE 6099	BOOGIE WITH WINIFRED ATWELL (EP)	7
50s	Decca	10" LPs	10

AUBREY SMALL
71	Polydor 2383 048	AUBREY SMALL (LP, with insert)	50

AUDIENCE
71	Charisma CB 126	Belladonna Moonshine/The Big Spell	4
71	Charisma CB 141	Indian Summer/It Brings A Tear/Princess (p/s)	7
71	Charisma CB 156	You're Not Smiling/Eye To Eye	4
72	Charisma CB 1845	Stand By The Door/Thunder And Lightnin'	4
69	Polydor 583 065	AUDIENCE (LP)	70
70	Charisma CAS 1012	FRIEND'S FRIEND'S FRIEND (LP)	15
71	Charisma CAS 1032	THE HOUSE ON THE HILL (LP, gatefold sleeve)	12
72	Charisma CAS 1054	LUNCH (LP, gatefold sleeve)	10

AUDREY
69	Downtown DT 414	Love Me Tonight/BROTHER DAN ALLSTARS: Show Them Amigo	5
69	Downtown DT 418	Lover's Concerto/BROTHER DAN ALLSTARS: Along Came Roy	5
69	Downtown DT 436	You'll Lose A Good Thing/DESMOND RILEY: If I Had Wings	5
69	Downtown DT 452	Sweeter Than Sugar/The Way You Move	5
69	Downtown DT 454	Oh I Was Wrong/Let's Try It Again (B-side with Dandy)	5
69	Downtown DT 457	Someday We'll Be Together/MUSIC DOCTORS: Sunset Rock	4
70	Trend 6099 006	Getting Ready For A Heartache/M Y O B Leave Me Alone	5

BRIAN AUGER (&) TRINITY
65	Columbia DB 7590	Fool Killer/Let's Do It Tonight (as Brian Auger Trinity)	15
65	Columbia DB 7715	Green Onions '65/Kiko (as Brian Auger Trinity)	12
67	Columbia DB 8163	Tiger/Oh Baby, Won't You Come Back Home To Croydon, Where	
		Everybody Beedle's And Bo's (solo)	20
67	Marmalade 598 003	Red Beans And Rice Pts 1 & 2	8
68	Marmalade 598 006	I Don't Know Where You Are/A Kind Of Love In (with Julie Driscoll)	6
69	Marmalade 598 015	What You Gonna Do/Bumpin' On Sunset	4
70	RCA RCA 1947	I Want To Take You Higher/Just Me Just You	4
68	Marmalade 607 003	DEFINITELY WHAT! (LP)	16
68	Marmalade 608 004	DON'T SEND ME NO FLOWERS (LP, with Jimmy Page	
		& Sonny Boy Williamson)	30
70	RCA SF 8101	BEFOUR (LP)	10
70	Polydor 2334 004	THE BEST OF BRIAN AUGER & THE TRINITY (LP)	10
71	RCA SF 8170	OBLIVION EXPRESS (LP)	12
71	Polydor 2383 062	BETTER LAND (LP)	10
72	Polydor 2383 104	SECOND WIND (LP)	10
73	CBS 65625	CLOSER TO IT (LP)	10
74	CBS 80058	STRAIGHT AHEAD (LP)	10

(see also Julie Driscoll Brian Auger & Trinity, Shotgun Express, Jimmy Page, Sonny Boy Williamson)

AU-GO-GO SINGERS
65	Columbia DB 7493	San Francisco Bay Blues/Pink Polemoniums	7
64	Columbia 33SX 1696	THEY CALL US AU GO-GO SINGERS (LP)	50

(see also Buffalo Springfield, Stephen Stills, Poco)

GEORGIE AULD
54	Vogue Coral Q 2002	Manhattan/Solitaire	6
60	Top Rank JAR 281	Hawaiian War Chant/Sleepy Lagoon	4

(see also Lancers, Modernaires)

AUM
69	London HA-K/SH-K 8401	BLUESVIBES (LP)	20

CLIFF AUNGIER
68	Polydor 56250	Time/Fisherboy	4
68	RCA RCA 1730	My Love And I/Abigail	4
69	Pye 7N 17753	Lady From Baltimore/Back On The Road Again	4
69	Pye NSPL 18294	LADY FROM BALTIMORE (LP)	10

(see also Boyd Rivers & Cliff Aungier)

AUNTIEPUS
80s	Septic AUNT 1	Half-Way To Venezuela/Marmalade Freak (p/s)	6

(see also Damned)

AUNT FORTESCUE'S BLUESROCKERS
76	Vole VOLE 01	Not Getting Caught Again/Cannards Grave	4

(see also Graham Larkbey)

AU PAIRS
80	021 OTO 2	You/Domestic Departure/Kerb Crawler (p/s, with lyric insert)	4
81	Human HUMAN 1	PLAYING WITH A DIFFERENT SEX (LP)	10
82	Kamera KAM 010	SENSE AND SENSUALITY (LP)	10
83	AKA AKA 6	LIVE IN BERLIN (LP)	10

AURAL EXCITERS
79	Ze ZE 700	Spooks In Space '4'/Spooks In Space (die-cut p/s, luminous vinyl)	4

BURNER-LEE AUSTIN
73	Mojo 2093 027	Gimme Your Hand/Real Woman	5

GENE AUSTIN
| 51 | London L 567 | Ace In The Hole (with Les Paul Trio)/I'm Crying Just For You (78) | 5 |

PATTI AUSTIN
69	United Artists UP 35018	Family Tree/Magical Boy	4
71	CBS 7180	Now That I Know What Love Is/Are We Ready For Love	8
74	Probe PRO 608	Music To My Heart/Love 'Em And Leave 'Em Kind Of Love	4

PETER AUSTIN
| 68 | Caltone TONE 125 | Your Love/Time Is Getting Harder | 8 |

REG AUSTIN
| 65 | Pye 7N 15885 | My Saddest Day/I'll Find Her | 30 |

SIL AUSTIN
57	Mercury MT 132	Slow Walk/Wildwood (78)	12
58	Mercury MT 189	Fall Green/Green Blazer (78)	10
58	Mercury 7MT 220	Don't You Just Know It/Rainstorm	12
58	Mercury MT 220	Don't You Just Know It/Rainstorm (78)	7
58	Mercury 7MT 225	Hey, Eula/The Last Time	12
58	Mercury MT 225	Hey, Eula/The Last Time (78)	7
58	Mercury MEP 9540	THE BAND WITH THE BEAT (EP)	20
58	Mercury MEP 9541	GO SIL GO (EP)	20
58	Mercury MPL 6534	SLOW WALK ROCK (LP)	30

AUSTRALIAN PLAYBOYS
| 67 | Immediate IM 054 | Black Sheep R.I.P./Sad | 125 |

AUTOMATIC FINE TUNING
| 76 | Charisma CAS 1122 | AUTOMATIC FINE TUNING (LP) | 10 |

AUTOMATIC DLAMINI
86	D For Drum DLAM 1	THE CRAZY SUPPER EP (p/s)	5
87	D For Drum DLAM 2	I Don't Know You But... (p/s)/I've Never Been That Colour Anywhere Before (w/ insert)	4
87	Idea IDEA 009	Me And My Conscience (p/s)	4
87	Idea IDEAT 009	Me And My Conscience (12", p/s)	7
87	Idea IDEALP 001	"THE D IS FOR DRUM" (LP)	10
(see also P.J. Harvey)			

AUTOMATICS
| 78 | Island WIP 6433 | Wakin' With The Radio On/Watch Her Now (unissued) | |
| 78 | Island WIP 6439 | When Tanks Roll Over Poland/Watch Her Now (p/s) | 4 |

GENE AUTRY
| 58 | London HLU 9001 | Nine Little Reindeer/Buon Natale | 4 |

AUTUMN VINE
| 70 | Evolution E 2447 | He Ain't No Superman/Maxi Baby | 5 |

FRANKIE AVALON
58	HMV POP 453	Dede Dinah/Ooh-La-La	12
58	HMV POP 453	Dede Dinah/Ooh-La-La (78)	8
58	London HL 8636	You Excite Me/Darlin'	25
58	London HL 8636	You Excite Me/Darlin' (78)	10
58	HMV POP 517	Ginger Bread/Blue Betty	8
58	HMV POP 517	Ginger Bread/Blue Betty (78)	8
59	HMV POP 569	I'll Wait For You/What Little Girl?	6
59	HMV POP 603	Venus/I'm Broke	6
59	HMV POP 636	Bobby Sox To Stockings/A Boy Without A Girl	6
59	HMV POP 658	Just Ask Your Heart/Two Fools	5
60	HMV POP 688	Why/Swinging On A Rainbow	6
60	HMV POP 727	Don't Throw Away All Those Teardrops/Talk, Talk, Talk	5
60	HMV POP 742	The Faithful Kind/Gee Whizz — Whilikins — Golly Gee	4
60	HMV POP 766	Where Are You/Tuxedo Junction	4
60	HMV POP 794	Togetherness/Don't Let Love Pass Me By	4
60	HMV POP 816	Green Leaves Of Summer/Here's To The Ladies	4
58	HMV 7EG 8471	FRANKIE AVALON (EP)	12
58	HMV 7EG 8482	FRANKIE AVALON NO. 2 (EP)	12
58	HMV 7EG 8507	FRANKIE AVALON NO. 3 (EP)	12
60	HMV 7EG 8632	SONGS OF THE ALAMO (EP)	8
59	HMV CLP 1346	SWINGIN' ON A RAINBOW (LP)	10
60	HMV CLP 1423	SUMMER SCENE (LP)	10
60	HMV CLP 1440/CSD 1358	YOUNG AND IN LOVE (LP, mono/stereo)	10/12
64	United Artists ULP 1078	MUSCLE BEACH PARTY (LP)	12

AVALONS
| 76 | Island WI 263 | Everyday/I Love You | 7 |

AVANT-GARDE
| 68 | CBS 3704 | Naturally Stoned/Honey And Gall | 7 |

AVANT GARDENER
| 77 | Virgin VEP 1003 | GOTTA TURN BACK (EP) | 4 |

AVENGER
| 83 | Neat NEAT 31 | Too Wild To Tame/On The Rocks (p/s) | 4 |

AVENGERS
| 68 | Parlophone R 5661 | Everyone's Gonna Wonder/Take My Hand | 6 |

AVERAGE WHITE BAND
| 74 | Atlantic K 10489 | Pick Up The Pieces/You Got It | 4 |
| (see also Dream Police) | | | |

MINT VALUE £

AVIATOR
79	Harvest HAR 5180	Time Traveller/Rocking Chair (p/s)	4

AVIATOR
87	RCA PL 89934	AVIATOR (LP)	10

AVO-8
80s	Stroppo STROP 1	Gone Wrong/Target One/No Hesitation (p/s)	10

ALAN AVON & TOY SHOP
74	Concord CONC 005	A Night To Remember	12

AVON CITIES' JAZZ BAND
56	Tempo A 151	Shim-Me-Sha-Wabble/Hawaiian War Chant	4
60	Tempo A 169	Upper Set/American Patrol	4

AVONS
59	Columbia DB 4236	Jerri-Lee (I Love Him So)/Baby-O	5
59	Columbia DB 4363	Seven Little Girls Sitting In The Back Seat/Alone At Eight	5
59	Columbia DB 4363	Seven Little Girls Sitting In The Back Seat/Alone At Eight (78)	5
60	Columbia DB 4413	Pickin' Petals/We Fell In Love	5
60	Columbia DB 4461	We're Only Young Once/I Keep Dreaming	4
60	Columbia DB 4522	Four Little Heels/This Was Meant To Be	4

(see also Novas)

AVON SISTERS
59	Columbia DB 4236	Jerri-Lee (I Love Him So)/Baby-O	4

AWAY FROM THE SAND
70s	Beaujangle DB 0003	AWAY FROM THE SAND (LP)	70

(see also Bev Pegg, Dave Cartwright, Brindley Brae)

A WITNESS
85	Ron Johnson ZRON 15	LOUDHAILER SONGS (12" EP)	7

DAVID AXELROD
68	Capitol ST 2982	SONGS OF INNOCENCE (LP)	12

AXIS
81	Metal Minded AX 1047	Lady/Messiah (p/s)	5
81	Axis	When You Hold Me	8
81	Neat NEAT 13	You Got It/One Step Ahead (p/s)	4

HOYT AXTON
64	Stateside SL 10082	GREENBACK DOLLAR (LP)	14
64	Stateside SL 10096	THUNDER N' LIGHTNIN' (LP)	12
66	London HA-F/SH-F 8276	THE BEST OF HOYT AXTON (LP)	10

KEVIN AYERS (& WHOLE WORLD)
70	Harvest HAR 5011	Singing A Song In The Morning/Eleanor's Cake Which Ate Her	10
70	Harvest HAR 5027	Butterfly Dance/Puis-Je? (with Whole World)	7
71	Harvest HAR 5042	Stranger In Blue Suede Shoes/Stars (with Whole World)	5
72	Harvest HAR 5064	Oh! Wot A Dream/Connie On A Rubber Band	5
73	Harvest HAR 5071	Caribbean Moon/Take Me To Tahiti (some in p/s)	10/4
74	Island WIP 6194	The Up Song/Everybody's Sometimes & Some People's All The Time Blues	4
74	Island WIP 6201	After The Show/Thank You Very Much	4
75	Harvest HAR 5100	Caribbean Moon/Take Me To Tahiti	4
76	Island WIP 6271	Falling In Love Again/Everyone Knows The Song	4
76	Harvest HAR 5107	Stranger In Blue Suede Shoes/Fake Mexican Tourist Blues (some in p/s)	4
76	Harvest HAR 5109	Caribbean Moon/Take Me To Tahiti (reissue, some in different p/s)	10/4
77	Harvest HAR 5124	Star/The Owl	4
80	Harvest HAR 5198	Money, Money, Money/Stranger In Blue Suede Shoes (p/s)	4
83	Charly/Celluloid CYZ 7107	Champagne & Valium/My Speeding Heart (p/s)	4
86	Illuminated LEV 71	Stepping Out/Only Heaven Knows (1-sided, promo-only)	7
70	Harvest SHVL 763	JOY OF A TOY (LP, gatefold sleeve)	20
71	Harvest SHSP 4005	SHOOTING AT THE MOON (LP, with Whole World)	15
73	Harvest SHVL 800	WHATEVERSHEBRINGSWESING (LP, gatefold sleeve)	12
73	Harvest SHVL 807	BANANAMOUR (LP, gatefold sleeve, some with booklet)	25/12
74	Island ILPS 9263	THE CONFESSIONS OF DR. DREAM AND OTHER STORIES (LP)	10
75	Island ILPS 9322	SWEET DECEIVER (LP, with inner sleeve)	10
76	Harvest SHSP 2005	ODD DITTIES (LP)	10
76	Harvest SHSP 4057	YES WE HAVE NO MANANAS (LP, with inner sleeve)	10
78	Harvest SHSP 4085	RAINBOW TAKEAWAY (LP)	10
80	Harvest SHSP 4106	THAT'S WHAT YOU GET BABE (LP, with inner sleeve)	10
86	Illuminated AMA 25	AS CLOSE AS YOU THINK (LP)	15

(see also Soft Machine, Lady June, Lol Coxhill, David Bedford, Mike Oldfield, Bridget St. John)

AYERS, CALE, NICO & ENO
74	Island ILPS 9291	JUNE 1ST, 1974 (LP)	10

(see also Kevin Ayers, John Cale, Nico, Brian Eno)

ROY AYERS (UBIQUITY)
76	Polydor 2066 671	Evolution/Mystique Voyage (as Roy Ayers' Ubiquity)	7
77	Polydor 2066 842	Running Away/Cincinnati Growl (as Roy Ayers' Ubiquity)	5
78	Polydor 2066 896	Freaky Dee Jay/You Came Into My Life	4
78	Polydor 2066 930	Let's Do It/Melody Maker	4
78	Polydor 2066 982/AYERS 7	Get On Up Get On Down/And Don't Say No	4
78	Polydor AYERS 12	Get On Up Get On Down/And Don't Say No (12")	8
79	Polydor PB 16	Heat Of The Beat/No Deposit, No Return	4
79	Polydor POSP 53	Fever/Is It Too Late To Try	4
79	Polydor POSPX 53	Fever/Is It Too Late To Try (12")	8
80	Polydor STEP 9	Don't Stop The Feeling	4
80	Polydor STEPX 9	Don't Stop The Feeling (12")	7

80	Polydor POSP 135	Running Away/Can't You See Me	4
80	Polydor POSPX 135	Running Away/Can't You See Me (12")	10
80	Polydor POSPX 186	Sometimes, Believe In Yourself (12")	8
82	Polydor POSP 427	Turn Me Loose/Ooh	4
82	Polydor POSP 474	Let's Stay Together/Knock Knock (p/s)	4
83	Polydor UM 1T	Silver Vibrations/Fast Money (12")	7
77	Muse MR 5101	CRYSTAL REFLECTION (LP, with B. Williams)	12
77	Polydor 2391 256	VIBRATIONS (LP, as Roy Ayers' Ubiquity)	12
77	Polydor 2391 292	LIFELINE (LP, as Roy Ayers' Ubiquity)	10
78	Polydor 2391 365	YOU SEND ME (LP)	10
78	Polydor 2391 380	STEP INTO OUR LIFE (LP, with Wayne Henderson)	10
78	Polydor 2490 145	LET'S DO IT (LP)	10
79	Polydor 2391 396	FEVER (LP)	10
79	Polydor 2391 429	LOVE FANTASY — THE BEST OF ROY AYERS (LP)	10
82	Polydor 2391 539	FEELIN' GOOD (LP)	35
83	Uno Melodic UMLP 2	DRIVIN' ON UP (LP)	10
88	Urban UMID 1	EVERYBODY LOVES THE SUNSHINE (LP)	12
	(see also Jack Wilson Quartet)		

AYSHEA

65	Fontana TF 627	Eeny Meeny/Peep My Love	6
68	Polydor 56276	Only Love Can Save Me Now/Celebration Of The Year	12
69	Polydor 56302	Another Night/Taking The Sun From My Eyes	4
73	Harvest HAR 5073	Farewell/The Best Years Of My Life	4
74	DJM DJLPS 445	LIFT OFF WITH AYSHEA (LP)	15

AZTEC CAMERA

81	Postcard 81-3	Just Like Gold/We Could Send Letters (die-cut sleeve, some with card)	15/12
81	Postcard 81-8	Mattress Of Wire/Lost Outside The Tunnel (p/s)	15
82	Rough Trade RT 112	Pillar To Post/Queen's Tattoos (p/s)	6
82	Rough Trade RT 112P	Pillar To Post/Queen's Tattoos (picture disc)	10
83	Rough Trade RT 122	Oblivious/Orchid Girl (p/s)	4
83	Rough Trade RT 122T	Oblivious/Orchid Girl/Haywire (12", p/s)	7
83	Rainhill ACFC 1	Oblivious (Langer/Winstanley Remix)/(Colin Fairley Remix) (fan club issue)	15
83	WEA AZTEC 1	Oblivious/Orchid Girl//We Could Send Letters (live)/Back On Board (live) (double pack, numbered gatefold p/s, 10,000 only)	6
84	WEA AC 1T	All I Need Is Everything (Remix)/Jump (Loaded Version) (12", p/s with insert)	7
84	WEA AC 1T	All I Need Is Everything (Latin Mix)/Jump (Loaded Version) (12", stickered p/s)	7
84	WEA AC 2P	Still On Fire/Walk Out To Winter (live) (camera-shaped picture disc)	8
84	WEA AC 2	Still On Fire/Walk Out To Winter/The Boy Wonder (live)/Mattress Of Wire (live)/The Bugle Sounds (live) (12" with poster)	7

AZYMUTH

79	Milestone MRC 101	Jazz Carnival/Fly Over The Horizon (12")	7
78	ECM ECM 1130	THE TOUCHSTONE (LP)	10
80	ECM ECM 1163	DEPART (LP, with Ralph Towner)	10
80	Milestone M 9097	OUTUBRO (LP)	10

BOB AZZAM & HIS ORCHESTRA

| 60 | Decca F 21235 | Mustapha/Tintarella Di Luna | 5 |

THE ANIMALS

IKE B & CRYSTALS
68   Island WI 3151   Try A Little Merriness/Patricia 10

B's
74   private pressing   IN YOUR BONNET (LP) 150

MEHA BABA
70   Universal Spiritual   HAPPY BIRTHDAY (LP, with inserts,
      League 1   100 only, 6 Pete Townshend tracks) 60
70   Univ'l Spiritual League 2 I AM (LP, with inserts, features 5 Pete Townshend tracks) 50
76   Univ'l Spiritual League 3 WITH LOVE (LP, features 3 Pete Townshend tracks) 35
70s MBO MBO 1   STAR OF THE SILENT SCREEN ,. . . MEHA BABA (LP,
                       reissue of "Happy Birthday" without insert) 20
70s MBO MBO 2   I AM (LP, reissue, without inserts) 20
    (see also Pete Townshend)

BABE RUTH
76   Capitol CL 15689   Elusive/Say No More 5
72   Harvest SHSP 4022   FIRST BASE (LP) 12
73   Harvest SHVL 812   AMAR CABALLERO (LP) 12
75   Harvest SHSP 4038   BABE RUTH (LP) 12
75   Capitol E-ST 11451   STEALIN' HOME (LP) 10
    (see also Jenne Haan)

MONTY BABSON
59   London HLJ 8877   All Night Long/The Things Money Cannot Buy 4

BABY
75   Mercury   BABY (LP) 12
77   Chelsea CHL 517   WHERE DID ALL THE MONEY GO (LP) 12

BABY DOLLS
60   Warner Bros WB 16   Quiet!/Hey, Baby! 4

BABY LEMONADE
87   Narodnik NRK 004   The Secret Goldfish/Real World (p/s) 7
87   Sha La La 003   Jiffy Neckware Creation/BACHELOR PAD: Girl Of Your Dreams (p/s) (flexidisc) ..6

BABYLON
69   Polydor 56356   Into The Promised Land/Nobody's Fault But Mine (some in p/s) 10/4

BABYS
77   Chrysalis CHR 1129   BABYS (LP) 10
78   Chrysalis CHR 1150   BROKEN HEARTS (LP) 10
79   Chrysalis CHR 1195   HEAD FIRST (LP) 10
79   Chrysalis CHR 1267   UNION JACKS (LP) 10
80   Chrysalis CHR 1305   ON THE EDGE (LP) 10
82   NEMS   OFFICIAL UNOFFICIAL LP (LP) 15

BABY SUNSHINE
75   Deroy DER 1301   BABY SUNSHINE (LP, with insert) 80
    (see also Fairy's Moke)

BURT BACHARACH ORCHESTRA
65   London HLR 9983   What's New Pussycat/My Little Red Book (B-side with Tony Middleton) 15
69   A&M AMS 702   Bond Street/Alfie 15
    (see also Tony Middleton)

BACHDENKEL
77   Initial IRL 001   LEMMINGS (LP, some with free EP) 25/12
77   Initial IRL 002   STALINGRAD (LP) 15

JOHNNY BACHELOR
60   London HLN 9074   Mumbles/Arabella Jean 40

BACHELORS
58   Parlophone R 4454   Platter Party/Love Is A Two Way Street 12
58   Parlophone R 4454   Platter Party/Love Is A Two Way Street (78) 5
59   Parlophone R 4547   Please Don't Touch/Ding Dong 12

BACHELORS
60   Decca F 11300   Lovin' Babe/Why Can't It Be Me 5
72   Decca F 13248   Diamonds Are Forever/Where There's A Heartache 6

BACH TWO BACH
70s Mushroom 100 MR 10 BACH TWO BACH (LP) 120

BACK ALLEY CHOIR
72   York SYK 517   Smile Born Of Courtesy/Why Are You Here 18
72   York FYK 406   BACK ALLEY CHOIR (LP) 175

BACKBEAT PHILHARMONIC
61   Top Rank JAR 576   Rock And Roll Symphony Pts 1 & 2 7

BACK DOOR
72   Blakey BLP 5989   BACK DOOR (LP, sold at gigs) 30
73   Warner Bros K 46231 BACK DOOR (LP) 10

BACK PORCH MAJORITY
65	Columbia DB 7627	Ramblin' Man/Good Time Joe	4

BACK STREET CRAWLER
75	Atlantic K 50173	THE BAND PLAYS ON (LP)	10
76	Atlantic K 50267	SECOND STREET (LP)	10

(see also Paul Kossoff)

BACK TO ZERO
79	Fiction FICS 004	Your Side Of Heaven/Back To Back (p/s)	5

JIM BACKUS (& FRIEND)
58	London HLJ 8674	Delicious (The Laughing Song) (as Jim Backus & Friend)/I Need A Vacation	6

BACKYARD HEAVIES
73	Action ACT 4616	Just Keep On Truckin'/Never Can Say Goodbye	4

GAR BACON
58	Felsted AF 107	Mary Jane/Chains Of Love	10
58	Felsted AF 107	Mary Jane/Chains Of Love (78)	25
59	Fontana H 196	Marshal, Marshal/Too Young To Love	25
59	Fontana H 196	Marshal, Marshal/Too Young To Love (78)	18

BACON FAT
70	Blue Horizon 57-3171	Nobody But You/Small's On 53rd	8
71	Blue Horizon 57-3181	Evil/Blues Feeling	8
70	Blue Horizon 7-63858	GREASE ONE FOR ME (LP)	40
71	Blue Horizon 2431 001	TOUGH DUDE (LP)	45

(see also Dirty Blues Band)

BAD BRAINS
82	Alt. Tentacles VIRUS 13	I Luv Jah/Sailin' On/Big Takeover (12", p/s)	7
83	Food For Thought YUMT 101	I And I Survive/Destroy Babylon (12", p/s)	7

BAD COMPANY
76	Island WIP 6263	Run With The Pack/Do Right By Your Woman	4
77	Island WIP 6381	Everything I Need/Too Bad	4
79	Swan Song SSK 19416	Rock'n'Roll Fantasy/Crazy Circles (p/s)	4

(see also Free, Firm)

BADFINGER
70	Apple APPLE 20	Come And Get It/Rock Of All Ages (some with p/s)	8/4
70	Apple APPLE 31	No Matter What/Better Days (some with p/s)	15/4
72	Apple APPLE 35	Name Of The Game/Suitcase (unreleased)	
72	Apple APPLE 40	Day After Day/Sweet Tuesday Morning (some with p/s)	12/4
72	Apple APPLE 42	Baby Blue/Flying (unreleased in U.K.)	
74	Apple APPLE 49	Apple Of My Eye/Blind Owl	12
70	Apple SAPCOR 12	MAGIC CHRISTIAN MUSIC (LP)	35
70	Apple SAPCOR 16	NO DICE (LP, gatefold sleeve)	35
72	Apple SAPCOR 19	STRAIGHT UP (LP)	40
73	Warner Bros K 56023	BADFINGER (LP, with insert)	12
74	Apple SAPCOR 27	ASS (LP, with inner sleeve)	30
74	Warner Bros K 56076	WISH YOU WERE HERE (LP, withdrawn)	30

(see also Iveys, Masterminds, Gary Walker & Rain, Natural Gas, Blue Goose)

BADGE
81	Metal Minded MM 2	Silver Woman/Something I've Lost (p/s)	20

BADGER
74	Epic EPC 2326	White Lady/Don't Pull The Trigger	4
73	Atlantic K 40473	ONE LIVE BADGER (LP, gatefold pop-up sleeve)	20
74	Epic EPC 80009	WHITE LADY (LP)	10

(see also Ashton, Gardner & Dyke, Jackie Lomax)

BADGER'S MATE
70s	Cottage COT 521	BRIGHTER THAN USUAL (LP)	25

BAD MANNERS
80	Magnet MAG 180	Special Brew/Ivor The Engine (picture disc)	4
81	Flexipop 005	Just Pretendin'/No Respect (blue flexidisc free with 'Flexipop', issue 5)	5/4

HENRY BADOWSKI
79	Deptford Fun City DFC 11	Baby, Sign Here With Me/Making Love With My Wife (gold die-cut p/s with insert)	6
79	A&M AMS 7478	Baby, Sign Here With Me/Making Love With My Wife (reissue, gold die-cut p/s)	4

(see also Good Missionaries)

JOAN BAEZ
65	Fontana TF 604	It's All Over Now Baby Blue/Daddy You've Been On My Mind	4
65	Fontana TF 639	Farewell Angelina/Queen Of Hearts	4
66	Vanguard VA 2	Love Minus Zero/Love Is Just A Four-Letter Word	4
63	Fontana TE 18012	WITH GOD ON OUR SIDE (EP)	7
60	Fontana (S)TFL 6002	JOAN BAEZ (LP)	10
61	Fontana (S)TFL 6025	JOAN BAEZ 2 (LP)	10
62	Fontana (S)TFL 6035	IN CONCERT 2 (LP)	10
64	Fontana (S)TFL 6043	JOAN BAEZ 5 (LP)	10
65	Fontana (S)TFL 6058	FAREWELL ANGELINA (LP)	10
66	Fontana (S)TFL 6078	NOEL (LP)	10
67	Fontana (S)TFL 6082	JOAN (LP)	10
68	Vanguard SVRL 19000	BAPTISM (LP)	10

(see also Pete Seeger & Joan Baez)

DOC BAGBY
58	Fontana H 106	Dumplin's/Sylvia's Calling (78)	8

MINT VALUE £

BURR BAILEY (& SIX SHOOTERS)
63	Decca F 11686	San Francisco Bay/Like A Bird Without Feathers (with Six Shooters)	8
64	Decca F 11846	Chahawki/You Made Me Cry	14

CLIVE BAILEY & RICO'S GROUP
61	Blue Beat BB 92	Evening Train/Going Home	10

DAVE BAILEY SEXTET
69	Fontana SFJL 919	MODERN MAINSTREAM (LP)	10

DEREK BAILEY & TRISTAN HOSINGER
70s	Incus INCUS 2	DUO (LP, private pressing)	25

JIM BAILEY
75	United Artists UAG 29470	JIM BAILEY (LP)	10

MILDRED BAILEY
50s	Parlophone GEP 8600	MILDRED BAILEY AND HER ALLEY CATS (EP)	12
50s	Brunswick LA 8692	THE ROCKIN' CHAIR LADY (10" LP)	20

PEARL BAILEY
54	Vogue Coral Q 2026	She's Something Spanish/What Happened To The Hair	5
56	HMV POP 244	Tired/Go Back Where You Stayed Last Night	5
56	London HLN 8354	That Certain Feeling/Hit The Road To Dreamland	15
56	London REU 1104	THAT CERTAIN FEELING (EP)	8

ROY BAILEY
71	Trailer LER 3021	ROY BAILEY (LP)	10

ZEDDIE BAILEY
73	Grape GR 3037	Babylon Gone/TONY KING: Speak No Evil	5

ALY BAIN & MIKE WHELLANS
70s	Trailer LER 2022	ALY BAIN & MIKE WHELLANS (LP)	10

BOB BAIN & HIS MUSIC
58	Capitol CL 14912	Wagon Wheels/Strollin' Home	4

ARTHUR BAIRD SKIFFLE GROUP
56	Beltona BL 2669	Union Train/Union Maid	5

BINKY BAKER & PIT ORCHESTRA
78	Stiff BUY 41	Toe Knee Black Burn/Rainy Day In Brighton (p/s)	4

CHET BAKER (QUARTET)
56	Vogue V 2377	My Funny Valentine/But Not For Me	5
56	Vogue V 2381	Just Friends/Daybreak	5
56	Vogue V 2232	Winter Wonderland/This Time The Dream's On Me	5
56	Vogue V 2309	Long Ago And Far Away/Bea's Flat	5
54	Vogue EPV 1007	CHET BAKER QUARTET (EP)	8
55	Vogue EPV 1032	THE FABULOUS CHET BAKER QUARTET (EP)	8
56	Vogue EPV 1121	CHET BAKER SEXTET (EP)	8
56	Vogue EPV 1131	CHET BAKER ENSEMBLE VOL. 1 (EP)	8
56	Vogue EPV 1132	CHET BAKER ENSEMBLE VOL. 2 (EP)	8
56	Vogue EPV 1137	CHET BAKER SINGS AND PLAYS (EP)	8
56	Vogue EPV 1138	CHET BAKER SINGS AND PLAYS (EP)	8
57	Vogue EPV 1186	CHET BAKER AND HIS CREW (EP)	8
57	Felsted ESD 3034	MYTH (EP)	8
59	Felsted ESD 3069	CHET BAKER PLAYS STANDARDS (EP)	8
54	Vogue LDE 045	CHET BAKER QUARTET (10" LP)	18
55	Philips BBL 7022	CHET BAKER AND STRINGS (LP)	15
55	Vogue LDE 116	CHET BAKER QUARTET (10" LP)	18
56	Vogue LAE 12018	CHET BAKER SINGS (LP)	15
56	Vogue LDE 159	CHET BAKER SEXTET (10" LP)	18
56	Vogue LDE 163	CHET BAKER ENSEMBLE (10" LP)	18
56	Vogue LDE 182	CHET BAKER SINGS (10" LP)	18
56	Felsted PDL 85008	CHET BAKER QUARTET VOL. 1 (LP)	15
56	Felsted PDL 85013	CHET BAKER QUARTET VOL. 2 (LP)	15
57	Felsted PDL 85036	I GET CHET (LP, as Chet Baker & His Combo)	15
57	Vogue LAE 12044	CHET BAKER QUARTET AT ANN ARBOR (LP)	15
57	Vogue LAE 12076	CHET BAKER AND HIS CREW (LP, mono)	15
58	Vogue LAE 12109	CHET BAKER BIG BAND — PHIL'S BLUES (LP)	15
59	Vogue SEA 5005	CHET BAKER AND HIS CREW (LP, stereo)	18
59	Vogue LAE 12164	CHET BAKER SINGS (LP)	12
59	Vogue LAE 12183	CHET BAKER AND ART PEPPER SEXTET — PLAYBOYS! (LP)	12
66	Fontana TL 5326	MICHELLE (LP, with Bud Shank)	10

(see also Art Pepper)

GINGER BAKER('S AIRFORCE)
70	Polydor BM 53680	Man Of Constant Sorrow/Doin' It	4
72	Polydor 2058 107	Atunde! (We Are Here)/Part 2 (as Ginger Baker Drum Choir)	4
70	Polydor 2662 001	GINGER BAKER'S AIRFORCE (2-LP, gatefold sleeve)	14
70	Polydor 2383 029	AIRFORCE II (LP, gatefold sleeve, with insert)	10
72	Polydor 2383 133	STRATAVARIOUS (LP)	10
72	Regal Zono. SLRZ 1023	FELI RANSOME-KUTI & THE AFRICA '70 WITH GINGER BAKER LIVE! (LP)	15

(see also Cream, Graham Bond Organisation, Blind Faith)

GLEN BAKER
85	The Stand STAND 3	BRIEF ENCOUNTER (LP)	20

(see also Enid)

HYLDA BAKER
59	Decca F 11186	She Knows Y'Know/Makin' Love	4

JEANETTE BAKER
59	Vogue POP V 9143	Everything Reminds Me Of You/JEANETTE & DECKY: Crazy With You	60
59	Vogue POP V 9143	Everything Reminds Me Of You/JEANETTE & DECKY: Crazy With You (78)	45

KENNY BAKER
53	Parlophone MSP 6019	Round About Midnight/Afternoon In Paris	4
53	Parlophone MSP 6057	Hayfoot, Strawfoot/The Continental	4
54	Parlophone MSP 6062	Trumpet Fantasy/Melancholy Baby	4
54	Parlophone MSP 6082	That's My Desire/Stompin' At The Savoy	4
54	Parlophone MSP 6114	I Speak To The Stars/Wanted	4
54	Parlophone MSP 6121	Peg O' My Heart/The Other Side	4

LAVERN BAKER (& GLIDERS)
55	Columbia SCM 5172	Tweedle Dee/Tomorrow Night (with Gliders)	125
55	Columbia DB 3591	Tweedle Dee/Tomorrow Night (with Gliders) (78)	25
55	London HLA 8199	That Old Lucky Sun/Play It Fair (with Gliders)	125
55	London HLA 8199	That Old Lucky Sun/Play It Fair (with Gliders) (78)	15
56	London HLE 8260	Get Up! Get Up! (You Sleepy Head)/My Happiness Forever (with Gliders)	100
56	London HLE 8260	Get Up! Get Up! (You Sleepy Head)/My Happiness Forever (with Gliders) (78)	15
57	Columbia DB 3879	Jim Dandy/Tra La La (with Gliders)	125
57	Columbia DB 3879	Jim Dandy/Tra La La (with Gliders) (78)	25
57	London HLE 8396	I Can't Love You Enough/Still	80
57	London HLE 8396	I Can't Love You Enough/Still (78)	15
57	London HLE 8442	Game Of Love/Jim Dandy Got Married	100
57	London HLE 8442	Game Of Love/Jim Dandy Got Married (78)	15
57	London HLE 8524	Humpty Dumpty Heart/Love Me Right	50
57	London HLE 8524	Humpty Dumpty Heart/Love Me Right (78)	15
58	London HLE 8638	Learning To Love/Substitute	40
58	London HLE 8638	Learning To Love/Substitute (78)	15
58	London HLE 8672	Whipper Snapper/Harbour Lights	35
58	London HLE 8672	Whipper Snapper/Harbour Lights (78)	15
59	London HLE 8790	I Cried A Tear/St. Louis Blues	30
59	London HLE 8790	I Cried A Tear/St. Louis Blues (78)	15
59	London HLE 8871	I Waited Too Long/You're Teasing Me	30
59	London HLE 8871	I Waited Too Long/You're Teasing Me (78)	15
59	London HLE 8945	So High So Low/If You Love Me (I Won't Care)	25
59	London HLE 8945	So High So Low/If You Love Me (I Won't Care) (78)	15
60	London HLE 9023	Tiny Tim/For Love Of You	25
60	London HLE 9252	Bumble Bee/My Time Will Come	20
61	London HLE 9300	You're The Boss/I'll Never Be Free (with Jimmy Ricks)	15
61	London HLK 9343	Saved/Don Juan	20
61	London HLK 9468	Hey, Memphis/Voodoo Voodoo	40
63	London HLK 9649	See See Rider/The Story Of My Love (I Had A Dream)	20
65	Atlantic AET 6009	THE BEST OF LAVERN BAKER (EP)	30
58	London HA-E 2107	ROCK 'N' ROLL WITH LAVERN BAKER (LP)	175
58	London Jazz LTZK 15139	SINGS BESSIE SMITH (LP)	45
61	London HA-K 2422	SAVED (LP)	55
63	London HA-K 8074	SEE SEE RIDER (LP)	45
64	Atlantic ATL 5002	THE BEST OF LAVERN BAKER (LP, plum label)	60
68	Atlantic 587/588 133	SEE SEE RIDER (LP)	20

MICKEY BAKER
70	Major Minor SMLP 67	IN BLUNDERLAND (LP)	12
(see also Mighty Flea)			

SAM BAKER
68	Monument MON 1009	I Believe In You/I'm Number One	10

TWO-TON BAKER
55	London HL 8121	Clink, Clank (In My Piggy Bank)/Mr. Froggie (Went A Courtin')	60
55	London HL 8121	Clink, Clank (In My Piggy Bank)/Mr. Froggie (Went A Courtin') (78)	10

BAKERLOO
69	Harvest HAR 5004	Driving Backwards/Once Upon A Time	30
69	Harvest SHVL 762	BAKERLOO (LP)	65

BALAAM & THE ANGEL
84	Chapter 22 22-001	World Of Light/For More Than A Day/The Darklands/A New Dawn (12", p/s)	7
85	Chapter 22 22-002	Love Me/The Thought Behind It All/Family And Friends/15th Floor (12", p/s)	7
85	Chapter 22 CHAP 3/7	Day And Night/Isabella's Eyes (p/s, with sticker)	4

BALANCE
73	Incus INCUS 11	BALANCE (LP)	25
73	private pressing	IN FOR THE COUNT (LP)	20

BALANCE
81	Portrait PRTA 1477	Breaking Away/It's So Strange	4
81	Portrait	BALANCE (LP)	10
82	Portrait	IN FOR THE COUNT (LP)	10

BALCONY
82	Praxis TM 2	Surprise After Surprise/The Lizard Hunt (p/s)	4

BALDHEAD GROWLER
67	Jump Up JU 531	Sausage/Bingo Woman	6

CHRIS BALDO
68	Vogue VRS 7029	Living For Your Love/Arretez Vous A Saint Michel	15

LONG JOHN BALDRY
64	United Artists UP 1056	Up Above My Head (I Hear Music In The Air)/You'll Be Mine (with Rod Stewart)	18

Long John BALDRY

65	United Artists UP 1078	I'm On To You Baby/Goodbye Baby	6
65	United Artists UP 1107	How Long Will It Last/House Next Door	25
66	United Artists UP 1124	Unseen Hands/Turn On Your Lovelight	8
66	United Artists UP 1136	The Drifter/Only A Fool Breaks His Own Heart	18
66	United Artists UP 1158	Cuckoo/Bring My Baby Back To Me	4
67	United Artists UP 1204	Only A Fool Breaks His Own Heart/Let Him Go (And Let Me Love You)	6
67	Pye 7N 17385	Let The Heartaches Begin/Annabella (Who Flies To Me When She's Lonely)	4
68	Pye 7N 17455	Hold Back The Daybreak/Since I Lost You Baby	4
68	Pye 7N 17563	Mexico/We're Together	4
68	Pye 7N 17593	When The Sun Comes Shining Thru'/Wise To The Ways Of The World	4
69	Pye 7N 17664	It's Too Late Now/Long And Lonely Nights	4
69	Pye 7N 17815	Wait For Me/Don't Pity Me	4
70	Pye 7N 17921	Well I Did/Setting The Tail Of A Fox On Fire	4
70	Pye 7N 45007	When The World Is Over/Where Are My Eyes?	4
72	Warner Bros K 16175	Iko Iko/Mother Ain't Dead	5
65	United Artists UEP 1013	LONG JOHN'S BLUES (EP, with Hoochie Coochie Men)	15
64	United Artists ULP 1081	LONG JOHN'S BLUES (LP, with Hoochie Coochie Men)	45
66	Utd. Artists (S)ULP 1146	LOOKING AT LONG JOHN (LP)	16
67	Pye N(S)PL 18208	LET THE HEARTACHES BEGIN (LP)	10
68	Pye N(S)PL 18228	LET THERE BE LONG JOHN (LP)	10
71	Warner Bros K 46088	IT AIN'T EASY (LP)	10
72	Warner Bros K 46160	EVERYTHING STOPS FOR TEA (LP, Rod Stewart duets on 1 track)	10

(see also Rod Stewart)

BALDWIN
67	Decca F 22624	The Land At Rainbow's End/Beautiful Butterfly	4

KEITH BALFOUR
69	Studio One SO 2079	Dreaming/Tired Of Waiting	12

DAVE BALL
83	Some Bizzare BIZL 5	IN STRICT TEMPO (LP)	12
83	Some Bizzare BIZLC 5	IN STRICT TEMPO (cassette)	10

(see also Soft Cell, Grid)

KENNY BALL & HIS (JAZZ) BAND
59	Collector JDN 101	Waterloo/Wabash Cannonball	15
60	Pye 7N 15272	Teddy Bears' Picnic/Waltzing Matilda	4

BALLADEERS
59	Columbia DB 4364	Tom Gets The Last Laugh/Morning Star	4

DAVE BALLANTYNE
66	Columbia DB 7807	I Can't Express It/Ginger Eyes	4
66	Columbia DB 7896	Love Around The World/Wonder Full Of Women	4

(see also Just Plain Jones, Esprit De Corps)

BALLARAT Y.W.C.A CHOIR
60	Starlite ST45 010	The Happy Wanderer/You'll Never Walk Alone	4

FLORENCE BALLARD
68	Stateside SS 2113	It Doesn't Matter How I Say It (It's What I Say That Matters)/Goin' Out Of My Head	20

(see also Supremes)

HANK BALLARD & THE MIDNIGHTERS
59	Parlophone R 4558	The Twist/Kansas City	30
60	Parlophone R 4682	Finger Poppin' Time/I Love You, I Love You So-O-O	15
60	Parlophone R 4688	The Twist/Teardrops On Your Letter	20
60	Parlophone R 4707	Let's Go, Let's Go, Let's Go/If You'd Forgive Me	15
60	Parlophone R 4728	The Hoochie Coochie Coo/LITTLE WILLIE JOHN: Walk Slow	15
61	Parlophone R 4762	Let's Go Again/Deep Blue Sea	8
61	Parlophone R 4771	The Continental Walk/What Is This I See	8
74	Mojo 2093 010	Annie Had A Baby/Teardrops On Your Letter	4
80s	Urban	From The Loveside (12")	10
61	Parlophone PMC 1158	SPOTLIGHT ON HANK BALLARD (LP)	30
63	London HA 8101	THE JUMPIN' HANK BALLARD (LP)	30

KAYE BALLARD
55	Brunswick 05376	Triumph Of Love/Where Were You Last Night?	4
55	Brunswick 05436	Don't You Tell Pa/In Love And Out Again	4

BALLOON FARM
68	London HLP 10185	A Question Of Temperature/Hurtin' For Your Love	45

BALLOONS
80	Earwacks WAK 002	Jean-Paul's Wife/The Slope (p/s)	4
80	Earwacks WAK 003	(LOVE RUNS) THROUGH YOUR ELBOW (LP)	10

BALLS
73	Wizard WIZ 101	Fight For My Country/Janie Slow Down	8

(see also Denny Laine, Lemon Tree, Trevor Burton, Uglys, Wizzard)

LORI BALMER
68	Polydor 56293	Treacle Brown/Four Faces West	4

BALTIMORE & OHIO MARCHING BAND
67	Stateside SS 2065	Lapland/Condition Red	70
68	Stateside (S)SL 10231	LAPLAND (LP)	30

BAMA WINDS
69	Island ILPS 9096	WINDY (LP)	15

BAMBIS
64	Oriole CB 1965	Not Wrong/Handle With Care	15

| 65 | CBS 201778 | Baby Blue/If This Is Love .... 12 |

BAMBOO SHOOT
| 68 | Columbia DB 8370 | The Fox Has Gone To Ground/There And Back Again .... 70 |

BANANAMEN
| 83 | Big Beat NS 88 | The Crusher/Love Me/Surfin' Bird (p/s) .... 5 |

BANANARAMA
81	Demon D 1010	Aie A Mwana/Dubwana (p/s) 10
81	Deram DM 446	Aie A Mwana/Dubwana (p/s, reissue) 8
81	Deram DMX 446	Aie A Mwana (Extended)/Dubwana (Extended) (12", p/s) 12
82	Deram NANA 1	Really Saying Something/Give Us Back Our Cheap Fares (poster p/s) 4
82	London NANA 2	Shy Boy/Don't Call Us (p/s, in carrier bag) 4
82	London NANPD 2	Shy Boy/Don't Call Us (picture disc) 5
82	London NAN DP 3	Cheers Then/Girls About Town//Aie A Mwana/Dubwana (double pack, gatefold p/s) 5
83	London NANA 5	Cruel Summer/Summer Dub//Cheers Then/Girls About Town (double pack, gatefold p/s) 5
83	London NANPD 6	Robert De Niro's Waiting/Push (picture disc, 3 different designs) .... each 4-5
83	London NANX 6	Robert De Niro's Waiting/Push (3 x 12", coloured vinyl with different labels) 15
84	London NANAJ 8	Hotline To Heaven/State I'm In (p/s, with jigsaw) 6
85	London NANPD 9	Do Not Disturb/Ghost (picture disc, 3 different shaped designs) .... each 4-5
86	London NANPD 10	Venus/White Train (picture disc) 4
86	London NANA 11	More Than Physical/Scarlett (poster p/s, 3 different designs) .... each 4
86	London NANDP 11	More Than Physical (Alternate Mix)/Scarlett//Venus/White Train (double pack, gatefold p/s) 5
86	London NANPD 11	More Than Physical (Alternate Mix)/Scarlett (picture disc) 4
87	London NANPD 12	Trick Of The Night/Tricky Mix (picture disc) 4
87	London NANPP 12	Trick Of The Night/Tricky Mix (p/s, with free poster) 4
87	London NANDP 12	Trick Of The Night/Tricky Mix//Venus/White Train (double pack, gatefold p/s) 4
87	London NANM 14	Love In The First Degree/Mr Sleeze ('mobile' pack) 5
87	London NANPD 14	Love In The First Degree/Mr Sleeze (picture disc, 2 different designs) ...... each 4
87	London NANA 15	I Can't Help It/Ecstacy (gatefold p/s with poster) 4
88	London NANB 17	Love, Truth And Honesty/Strike It Rich (box set with postcards & sticker) 5
89	London NANEX 19	Cruel Summer '89 Dubs (12", 3-track remix) 7

(see also Shakespear's Sister)

BANBARRA
| 76 | United Artists UP 36113 | Shack Up Pts 1 & 2 .... 4 |

BAND
68	Capitol CL 15559	The Weight/I Shall Be Released 4
69	Capitol CL 15613	Up On Cripple Creek/The Night They Drove Old Dixie Down 4
72	Capitol CL 15737	Don't Do It/Rag Mama Rag 4
73	Capitol CL 15767	Ain't Got No Home/Get Up Jake 4
68	Capitol T/ST 2955	MUSIC FROM BIG PINK (LP) 10

(see also Levon & Hawks, Bob Dylan, Ronnie Hawkins)

BAND AID
| 85 | Mercury FEEDP 1 | Do They Know It's Christmas?/Feed The World (shaped picture disc) .... 8 |

BAND OF ANGELS
64	United Artists UP 1049	Not True As Yet/Me 15
64	United Artists UP 1066	Gonna Make A Woman Of You/She'll Never Be You 15
66	Piccadilly 7N 35279	Leave It To Me/Too Late My Love 15
66	Piccadilly 7N 35292	Invitation/Cheat And Lie 15

(see also Mike D'Abo)

BAND OF MERCY & SALVATION
| 69 | Duke DU 20 | Suffering Stink/WINSTON FRANCIS: The Break .... 5 |

BAND OF SUSANS
| 88 | Furthur FU-2-7 | Hope Against Hope (Radio Edit) (white label) .... 5 |

BANDWAGON
(see under Johnny Johnson & Bandwagon)

HONEY BANE
| 81 | Crass 521984/1 | YOU CAN BE YOU (EP, stapled gatefold p/s) .... 4 |
| 81 | Zonophone Z 15 | Turn Me On Turn Me Off/In Dreams//'Tain't Nobody's Business/Negative Exposure (double pack, gatefold p/s) .... 4 |

(see also Fatal Microbes)

ED BANGER
78	EMI INTERNATIONAL 571	Kinnel Tommy/Baby Was A Baby (numbered p/s) 4
81	Spiv DIV 1	I've Just Had My Car Nicked/P.C. Plod/Sponge (p/s, with photo insert) 6
83	Cloud Nine CNS 01	Poor People/Vicars In The Dark (P/S) 5

(see also Nosebleeds, Slaughter & Dogs)

BANGLES
85	CBS A 4527	Hero Takes A Fall/Where Were You When I Needed You? (p/s) 4
85	CBS DA 4914	Going Down To Liverpool/Dover Beach//Hero Takes A Fall/Where Were You When I Needed You? (shrinkwrapped double pack, p/s) 6
85	CBS TX 4914	Going Down To Liverpool/Dover Beach/The Real World/I'm In Line/How Is The Air Up Here? (12", p/s) 7
86	CBS QA 6796	Manic Monday/In A Different Light (poster p/s) 6
86	CBS DA 7062	If She Knew What She Wants/Angels Don't Fall In Love//Hero Takes A Fall (Remix)/James (double pack, gatefold p/s) 5
86	CBS WA 7062	If She Knew What She Wants/Angels Don't Fall In Love (shaped picture disc) 5

BANGLES

86	CBS A 7255	Going Down To Liverpool/Let It Go (p/s, with postcard) 4
86	CBS 650071-0	Walk Like An Egyptian/Not Like You (poster p/s) 4
86	CBS 650071-8	Walk Like An Egyptian/Not Like You//Manic Monday/In A Different Light (shrinkwrapped double pack, bonus 7" without p/s) 6
87	CBS BANGS D1	Walking Down Your Street (Remix)/Return Post//Walk Like An Egyptian/ Not Like You (double pack, gatefold p/s) 4
87	CBS BANGSD 2	Following/Dover Beach (p/s, with 4 badges) 8
87	CBS BANGSQ 2	Following/Dover Beach (poster p/s) 4
88	Def Jam BANGSQ 3	Hazy Shade Of Winter/JOAN JETT: She's Lost You (poster p/s) 4
88	Def Jam BANGSP 3	Hazy Shade Of Winter/JOAN JETT: She's Lost You (picture disc) 5
88	CBS BANGSQ 4	In Your Room/Bell Jar (poster p/s) 4
88	CBS BANGSP 4	In Your Room (12" Remix)/In Your Room (Instrumental)/Bell Jar (12" pic disc) ...7
89	CBS BANGSP 6	Be With You/Let It Go (shaped picture disc) 4
89	CBS BANGSD 6	Be With You/Manic Monday (California Remix)/In Your Room (Extended Remix) (CD, picture disc) 7

BANGOR FLYING CIRCUS
| 70 | Stateside SSL 5022 | BANGOR FLYING CIRCUS (LP) .... 12 |

BANJO BOYS
| 55 | Capitol CL 14298 | Hey, Mr. Banjo/Kvi-vi-vi-vi-vitt .... 6 |

BANKROBBERS
| 79 | Good Vibrations GOT 18 | On My Mind/All Night (p/s) .... 5 |
| 84 | Good Vibrations TUBE 1 | Jenny/The Interview/Over The Edge (p/s, special 'Tube' issue) .... 6 |

BESSIE BANKS
64	Red Bird BC 106	Go Now/Sounds Like My Baby 20
67	Verve VS 563	I Can't Make It Without You Baby/Need You 15
68	Soul City SC 105	Go Now/Sounds Like My Baby (reissue) 8

DARRELL BANKS
66	London HL 10070	Open The Door To Your Heart/Our Love (Is In The Pocket) (demos only) 200
66	Stateside SS 536	Open The Door To Your Heart/Our Love (Is In The Pocket) (reissue) 15
67	Atlantic 584 120	Angel Baby (Don't You Ever Leave Me)/Look Into The Eyes Of A Fool 20
69	Stax STAX 124	Just Because Your Love Is Gone/I'm The One Who Loves You 15
77	Atlantic K 10879	Angel Baby (Don't You Ever Leave Me)/Look Into The Eyes Of A Fool (reissue) .. 5
78	Contempo CS 8005	Open The Door To Your Heart/Angel Baby (Don't You Ever Leave Me) 4
69	Stax SXATS 1011	HERE TO STAY (LP) 15

HOMER BANKS
66	Liberty LIB 12028	A Lot Of Love/Fighting To Win 18
67	Liberty LIB 12047	60 Minutes Of Your Love/Do You Know What 15
67	Liberty LIB 12060	Hooked By Love/Lady Of Stone 12
68	Minit MLF 11004	Round The Clock Lover Man/Foolish Hearts Break Fast 8
68	Minit MLF 11007	60 Minutes Of Your Love/A Lot Of Love 7
69	Minit MLF 11015	Me Or Your Mama/I Know You Know I Know You Know 8
70	Liberty LIB 15392	60 Minutes Of Your Love/I Know You Know I Know You Know 8
72	United Artists UP 35360	Hooked By Love/Lady Of Stone (reissue) 4

LARRY BANKS
| 67 | Stateside SS 579 | I Don't Wanna Do It/I'm Coming Home .... 10 |

LLOYD BANKS
| 66 | Reaction 591 008 | We'll Meet Again/Look Out Girl .... 8 |

PETER BANKS
| 73 | Sovereign SNVA 7256 | PETER BANKS (LP, gatefold sleeve) .... 20 |

(see also Syndicats, Syn, Neat Change, Yes, Flash, Jan Akkerman, Phil Collins, Steve Hackett)

RON BANKS & DRAMATICS
| 75 | ABC ABC 4052 | Trying To Get Over Losing You/How Do You Feel .... 4 |
| 75 | ABC ABC 4090 | (I'm Going By) The Stars In Your Eyes/Me Myself And I .... 4 |

ROSIE BANKS
| 76 | Tamla Motown TMG 1037 | Darling Baby/Whole New Thing .... 6 |

(see also Sly & Family Stone)

TONY BANKS
79	Charisma CB 344	For A While/From The Undertow 4
80	Charisma CB 365	For A While (Remix)/A Curious Feeling (p/s) 4
86	Charisma CB 426	Short Cut To Somewhere/Smilin' Jack Casey (p/s, with Fish) 4
86	Charisma CB 426-12	Short Cut To Somewhere/Smilin' Jack Casey/K2 (12", p/s, with Fish) 7

(see also Genesis, Fish)

BANNED
77	Can't Eat EAT 1 UP	Little Girl/CPGJ's (no p/s, stamped white labels) 10
77	Harvest HAR 5145	Little Girl/CPGJ's (reissue, p/s) 4
78	Harvest HAR 5149	Him Or Me/You Dirty Rat (p/s) 4

AL BANO & ROMINA POWER
| 76 | Epic S EPC 4218 | We'll Live It All Again/Na Na Na .... 4 |

BANSHEES
64	Columbia DB 7361	Don't Say Goodnight And Mean Goodbye/I Got A Woman 20
65	Columbia DB 7530	Big Buildin'/Mockingbird 15
65	Columbia DB 7752	I'm Gonna Keep On Loving You/Yes Indeed 15

(this group does NOT include Bryan Ferry)

BARBARA & BRENDA
| 68 | Direction 58-3799 | Never Love A Robin/Sally's Party .... 8 |

BARBARIANS
| 65 | Stateside SS 449 | Are You A Boy Or Are You A Girl/Take It Or Leave It .... 15 |
| 66 | Stateside SS 497 | Moulty/I'll Keep On Seeing You .... 10 |

Paul BARBARIN/Punch MILLER

MINT VALUE £

PAUL BARBARIN & BAND/PUNCH MILLER & BAND
64	London HA-K/SH-K 8164	JAZZ AT PRESERVATION HALL VOL. 4 (LP, with George Lewis)	10

LUCA BARBAROSSA
| 88 | CBS 651 593 7 | Ti Scrivo/Da Grande (p/s) | 4 |

BARBECUE BOB
| 67 | Kokomo K 1002 | GEORGIA BLUES NO. 1 (LP) | 50 |

JOHN HENRY BARBEE
| 65 | Storyville 670 171 | PORTRAITS IN BLUES VOLUME 9 (LP) | 12 |

CHRIS BARBER'S JAZZ BAND
51	Esquire 12-013	Oh, Didn't He Ramble/CRANE RIVER JAZZ BAND: Eh La Bas! (78)	7
54	Decca F 10417	Chimes Blues/Merrydown Rag	5
55	Decca F 10492	Bobby Shafto/The Martinique	5
55	Decca F 10666	It's Tight Like That/All The Girls Go Crazy About The Way I Walk	5
56	Decca FJ 10724	The World Is Waiting For The Sunrise/St. Louis Blues	5
56	Decca FJ 10790	I Never Knew Just What A Girl Could Do/Storyville Blues	5
56	Tempo A 116	Tiger Rag/Precious Lord, Lead Me On (B-side with Lonnie Donegan)	5
56	Tempo A 132	Saratoga Swing/Ice Cream	5
57	Tempo A 160	Ice Cream/Down By The Riverside	5
58	Pye Jazz 7NJ 2011	Whistlin' Rufus/Hushabye	5
58	Pye Jazz 7NJ 2004	Tuxedo Rag/Brown Skin Mama	5
58	Pye Jazz 7NJ 2007	High Society/Papa De-Da-Da	5
58	Pye Jazz 7NJ 2023	When The Saints Go Marching In (both sides)	4
59	Pye Jazz 7NJ 2026	Petite Fleur/Bugle Boy March	5
59	Columbia DB 4333	Lonesome (with Monty Sunshine)/There'll Be A Hot Time In The Old Town Tonight (with Ottilie Patterson)	5
60	Pye Jazz 7NJ 2030	Bill Bailey Won't You Please Come Home/Wild Cat Blues	4
60	Columbia DB 4501	Bohemia Rag/Swanee River	4
60	Columbia DB 4531	The Mountains Of Mourne/Real Old Mountain Dew (with Ottilie Patterson)	4
56	Polygon Jazz JTE 103	PLUS/MINUS 1 (EP)	8
54	Decca LF 1198	NEW ORLEANS JOYS (10" LP, with Lonnie Donegan's Skiffle Group)	25
55	Nixa Jazz Today NJL 1	ECHOES OF HARLEM (LP, with Ottilie Patterson)	15
55	Polygon Jazz Today JTL 3	CHRIS BARBER PLAYS VOL. 1 (10" LP)	25
56	Nixa Jazz Today NJT 500	CHRIS BARBER PLAYS VOL. 1 (10" LP, reissue)	15
56	Nixa Jazz Today NJT 502	CHRIS BARBER PLAYS VOL. 2 (10" LP)	15
57	Nixa Jazz Today NJT 505	CHRIS BARBER PLAYS VOL. 3 (10" LP)	15
57	Nixa Jazz Today NJT 508	CHRIS BARBER PLAYS VOL. 4 (10" LP)	15
57	Columbia 33S 1112	JAZZ SACRED AND SECULAR (10" LP, with Lonnie Donegan)	25
57	Nixa Jazz Today NJL 6	CHRIS BARBER IN CONCERT (LP, with Ottilie Patterson)	12
58	Pye Nixa Jazz NJL 15	CHRIS BARBER IN CONCERT VOL. 2 (LP, with Ottilie Patterson)	12
58	Pye Nixa Jazz NJL 17	CHRIS BARBER IN CONCERT VOL. 3 (LP, with Ottilie Patterson)	12
58	Decca LK 4246	BARBER'S BEST (LP)	12
59	Columbia 33SX 1158	BAND BOX VOL. 1 (LP)	12
59	Columbia 33SX 1189	BARBER IN BERLIN VOL. 1 (LP, with Ottilie Patterson)	12
59	Columbia 33SX	BARBER IN BERLIN VOL. 2 (LP, with Ottilie Patterson)	12
60	Columbia 33SX 1245	BAND BOX VOL. 2 — ELITE SYNCOPATIONS (LP, stereo SCX 3319)	12/14
60	Ace Of Clubs ACL 1037	THE BEST OF CHRIS BARBER (LP, with Ottilie Patterson & Lonnie Donegan)	10
61	Columbia 33SX 1274	BARBER IN COPENHAGEN (LP, also stereo SCX 3342)	10/12
61	Columbia 33SX 1321	CHRIS BARBER'S AMERICAN JAZZ BAND (LP, also stereo SCX 3376)	10/12
61	Columbia 33SX 1333	CHRIS BARBER'S BLUES BOOK (LP, with Ottilie Patterson, also stereo SCX 3384)	10/12

(see also Ottilie Patterson, Lonnie Donegan, Sonny Terry & Brownie McGhee, Kenneth Washington & Chris Barber)

CHRIS BARBER'S SKIFFLE GROUP
51	Esquire 10-180	Everybody Loves My Baby/Whoop It Up (78, with Washboard Wonders)	7
58	Pye Jazz 7NJ 2014	Doin' My Time/Where Could I Go? (with Johnny Duncan)	5
58	Pye Jazz 7NJ 2017	Can't You Line 'Em/Gipsy Dave (with Dickie Bishop)	5
57	Pye Jazz NJE 1025	CHRIS BARBER SKIFFLE GROUP (EP)	15

(see also Lonnie Donegan)

CHRIS BARBER'S BAND
| 67 | Marmalade 598 005 | Catcall/Mercy Mercy Mercy | 35 |
| 69 | Marmalade 608 009 | BATTERSEA RAIN DANCE (LP, as Chris Barber & His Band) | 25 |

CHRIS BARBER SOUL BAND
| 65 | Columbia DB 7461 | Finishing Straight/Morning Train | 20 |

(see also Louis Jordan & Chris Barber)

FRANK BARBER ORCHESTRA
| 62 | Ember JBS 709 | Flyover/Golden Shadows | 4 |

DAVE BARBOUR & HIS ORCHESTRA
| 59 | Oriole CB 1507 | Tough/Bu Bam | 5 |

EDDIE BARCLAY & HIS ORCHESTRA
| 57 | Felsted ESD 3041 | JAMES DEAN — MUSIC FROM HIS FILMS (EP) | 7 |

RUE BARCLAY & PEGGY DUNCAN
| 54 | London HL 8033 | Tongue Tied Boy/River Of Tears | 20 |

BARCLAY JAMES HARVEST
68	Parlophone R 5693	Early Morning/Mr. Sunshine	12
69	Harvest HAR 5003	Brother Thrush/Poor Wages	8
70	Harvest HAR 5025	Taking Some Time On/The Iron Maiden	5
71	Harvest HAR 5034	Mocking Bird/Vanessa Simmons	5
72	Harvest HAR 5051	I'm Over You/Child Of Man	5
72	Harvest HAR 5058	Thank You/Medicine Man	5
73	Harvest HAR 5068	Rock And Roll Woman/The Joker (BJH logo p/s)	6
74	Polydor 2058 474	Poor Boy Blues/Crazy City	4

BARCLAY JAMES HARVEST

75	Polydor 2058 660	Titles/Song For You 4
77	Polydor 2229 198	LIVE (EP, p/s) 5
77	Polydor 2058 904	Hymn/Our Kid's Kid (p/s) 4
78	Polydor POSP 012	Loving Is Easy/Polk Street Rag (blue or black vinyl) 4/5
79	Polydor POSP 097	Love On The Line/Alright Get Down Boogie (Mu Ala Rusic) (p/s) 4
79	SH 01041/2	Negative Earth/RARE BIRD: Diamonds (33rpm flexidisc free with 'Sounds') 5/4
80	Polydor POSP 140	Capricorn/Berlin (p/s) 4
83	Polydor POPPX 585	Just A Day Away/Looking From The Outside (shaped picture disc) 6
84	Polydor POSPP 674	Victims Of Circumstance/(instrumental) (shaped picture disc) 6
70	Harvest SHVL 770	BARCLAY JAMES HARVEST (LP) 10
71	Harvest Q4SHVL 788	ONCE AGAIN (LP, quadrophonic) 15
71	Harvest SHVL 794	AND OTHER SHORT STORIES (LP) 10

(see also Bombadil, John Lees, Wooly Wolstenholme)

KENNY BARDELL
| 58 | Oriole CB 1420 | Salty Salty Is The Sea/My Darling, My Darling ....4 |

PETER BARDENS
| 70 | Transatlantic TRA 222 | THE ANSWER (LP) ....12 |
| 71 | Transatlantic TRA 243 | PETER BARDENS (LP, gatefold sleeve) ....15 |

(see also Cheynes, Peter B's, Shotgun Express, Them, Village, Camel)

BARDO
| 82 | Epic EPC A 11-2265 | One Step Further/Lady Of The Night (picture disc) ....4 |

BRIGITTE BARDOT
| 66 | Vogue VRS 7018 | Mister Sun/Gang Gang (some in p/s) ....10/5 |
| 68 | Pye International 7N 25450 | Harley-Davidson/Contact ....6 |

BOBBY BARE
60	Top Rank JAR 310	I'm Hanging Up My Rifle/That's Where I Want To Be 10
63	RCA RCA 1352	Detroit City/Heart Of Ice 4
63	RCA RCA 1366	500 Miles Away From Home/It All Depends On Linda 4
64	RCA RCX 7139	DETROIT CITY (EP) 7
66	RCA RD 7783	CONSTANT SORROW (LP) 12

(see also Bill Parsons, Skeeter Davis & Bobby Bare)

MINOUCHE BARELLI
| 67 | CBS 2806 | Boum Badaboum/Let Me Take You ....20 |

MARK BARKAN
| 67 | Stateside SS 2064 | Pity The Woman/A Great Day For The Clown ....10 |

BAR-KAYS
67	Stax 601 014	Soul Finger/Knucklehead 6
68	Stax 601 036	A Hard Day's Night/I Want Someone 4
69	Atlantic 584 244	Soul Finger/Knucklehead (reissue) 5
69	Atco 228 030	SOUL FINGER (LP) 15
69	Stax STATS 1009	GOTTA GROOVE (LP) 12
71	Stax 2362 003	BLACK ROCK (LP) 15
72	Stax 2325 087	DO YOU SEE WHAT I SEE? (LP) 10
76	Stax STX 1033	COLD BLOODED (LP) 10
78	Mercury 9100 048	FLYING HIGH ON YOUR LOVE (LP) 10
79	Stax STX 3023	MONEY TALKS (LP) 10

(see also Otis Redding)

BUTCH BARKER
| 75 | Creole CR 113 | The Joker/Juicie Brucie ....4 |

BLUE LU BARKER
| 49 | Capitol CL 13033 | A Little Bird Told Me/What Did You Do To Me? (78) ....12 |

DAVE BARKER
70	Upsetter US 331	Shocks Of Mighty/Set Me Free (with Upsetters) 6
70	Upsetter US 344	Some Sympathy/UNTOUCHABLES: Tender Love 6
70	Punch PH 20	Prisoner Of Love/BUSTY & UPSETTERS: Soul Juice 6
70	Punch PH 22	You Betray Me/Will You Still Love Me Tomorrow? 6
70	Punch PH 25	Shocks Of Mighty Pts 1 & 2 6
70	Punch PH 42	Reggae Meeting/MARTIN ALL STARS: Soul Bone 5
70	Ackee ACK 113	Johnny Dollar/Version 5
70	Ackee ACK 119	Life Of A Millionaire/Version 5
70	Jackpot JP 736	The Fastest Man Alive/NORMAN GRANT: Bloodshot Eyes 5
70	Jackpot JP 742	Wet Version/I Got To Get Away 5
70	Jackpot JP 746	Girl Of My Dreams/On Broadway 5
71	Upsetter US 347	Sound Underground/Don't Let The Sun Catch You Crying 5
71	Upsetter US 358	Shocks '71/HURRICANES: You've Got To Be Mine 5
71	Upsetter US 362	Groove Me/UPSETTERS: Screwdriver 5
71	Upsetter US 364	What Confusion/UPSETTERS: Confusion Version 5
71	Punch PH 69	What A Confusion/BOB MARLEY: Small Axe 15
71	Supreme SUP 228	Double Heavy/Johnny Dollar 4
72	Jackpot JP 803	You'll Be Sorry/Green Grow The Lilacs 4
72	Fab FAB 25	Green Grow The Lilacs/JIMMY RILEY: Keep An Eye (On Your Closest Friend) (white label) 4
76	Trojan TRL 127	PRISONER OF LOVE (LP) 18

(see also Glen & Dave, Dave & Ansell Collins, Bobby & Dave, Aggrovators, David Crooks)

BARNEY J. BARNES & INTRO.
| 67 | Decca F 12662 | It Must Be Love/Can't Stand The Pain ....4 |

BENNY BARNES
| 60 | Mercury AMT 1094 | Token Of Love/That-A-Boy Willie ....4 |

DENA BARNES
79	Grapevine GRP 141	If You Ever Walked Out Of My Life/Who Am I	4

J.J. BARNES
67	Polydor 56722	Day Tripper/Deeper In Love	10
69	Stax STAX 130	Baby Please Come Back Home/Easy Living	12
73	Tamla Motown TMG 870	Real Humdinger/Please Let Me In/I Ain't Gonna Do It	6
74	Contempo CS 2009	To An Early Grave/To An Early Grave (Instrumental Version)	4
69	Stax SXATS 1012	RARE STAMPS (LP, with Steve Mancha)	25
75	Contempo CLP 520	THE GROOVESVILLE MASTERS (LP)	10
77	Contempo CLP 604	SARA SMILE (LP)	10

LLOYD BARNES
64	Blue Beat BB 235	Time Is Hard/BUSTER'S ALLSTARS: Reincarnation	12
65	Blue Beat BB 287	Time Is Hard/LASCELLES PERKINS: Wear And Tear	12

MYRA BARNES
88	Urban	Message For The Soul Sisters/(Bobby Byrd track) (12")	10

RICHARD BARNES
68	Columbia DB 8436	Woman, Woman/The Princess And The Soldier	4
68	Columbia DB 8507	Look Away/Mr In Between	4
70	Philips BF 1840	Take To The Mountains/But It's Now I Need Your Love	4

SIDNEY BARNES
76	Charly CYS 1007	I Hurt On The Other Side/Good Lovin'	4

ERIC BARNET(T)
68	Gas GAS 100	The Horse (actually by Theo Beckford & Group)/Action Line (actually by Versatiles)	6
69	Gas GAS 106	Te Ta Toe (actually by Theo Beckford & Group)/MILTON BOOTHE: Lonely And Blue	6
69	Crab CRAB 37	Quaker City/Double Up (both actually by Theo Beckford & Group)	5
70	Gas GAS 130	Pink Shark/Swing Free (both actually by Theo Beckford & Group)	4
70	Gas GAS 147	Bumper To Bumper/Fat Turkey (both actually by Theo Beckford & Group)	4
	(see also Theo Beckford)		

BARRY BARNETT
58	HMV POP 487	The Book Of Love/All I Have To Do Is Dream	5
58	HMV POP 487	The Book Of Love/All I Have To Do Is Dream (78)	5
58	HMV POP 511	When/Secretly	5
58	HMV POP 511	When/Secretly (78)	5
58	HMV POP 521	My Lucky Love/Too Young To Love	5
58	HMV POP 521	My Lucky Love/Too Young To Love (78)	5
58	HMV POP 532	Susie Darlin'/Just A Dream	5
58	HMV POP 532	Susie Darlin'/Just A Dream (78)	5
59	HMV POP 579	The Diary/Only One Memory	4
59	HMV POP 627	Cuckoo Girl/I'll String Along With You	4

BARNSTORMERS SPASM BAND
58	Parlophone R 4416	Whistling Rufus/Won't You Come Home, Bill Bailey?	4
59	Tempo A 168	Stormin' The Barn/That's All There Is (There Ain't No ...)	4

H.B. BARNUM
61	Fontana H 299	Lost Love/Hallelujah	7
65	Capitol CL 15391	The Record (Baby I Love You)/I'm A Man	15
76	Capitol CL 15851	Heartbreaker/Searchin' For My Soul	4
79	Capitol CL 16067	Heartbreaker/BOBBY PARIS: I Walked Away	7
64	RCA RCX 7147	THE GREAT H.B. BARNUM (EP)	75
62	RCA Victor RD/SF 7500	THE BIG VOICE OF BARNUM . . . H.B., THAT IS (LP, mono/stereo)	12/15
63	RCA Victor RD/SF 7543	EVERYBODY LOVES H.B. (LP, mono/stereo)	12/15

BAROCK & ROLL ENSEMBLE
65	HMV 7EG 8887	EINE KLEINE BEATLEMUSIK (EP)	7

CARL BARON & CHEETAHS
63	Columbia DB 7162	This Is Only The Beginning/Beg Borrow Or Steal	8

RIKKY BARON
60	Parlophone R 4706	Angry Young Man/My Lonely Heart	4

BARON & HIS POUNDING PIANO
65	Sue WI 398	Is A Bluebird Blue?/In The Mood	15

BARONS (U.S.)
57	London HLP 8391	Don't Walk Out/Once In A Lifetime	500
57	London HLP 8391	Don't Walk Out/Once In A Lifetime (78)	50

BARONS (U.K.)
61	Oriole CB 1608	Cossack/Summertime	8
61	Oriole CB 1620	Samurai/Whirlwind	8

BARRABAS
76	Atlantic K 10716	Checkmate/Four Seasons Woman	4

BARRACUDAS
79	Cells CELLOUT 1	I Want My Woody Back/Subway Surfin' (p/s)	12
80	Zonophone Z 5	Summer Fun/Chevy Baby (p/s, initially with stickers)	10/6
80	Zonophone Z 8	His Last Summer/Barracuda Waver/Surfers Are Back (p/s)	8
80	Zonophone Z 11	(I Wish It Could Be) 1965 Again/Rendezvous (p/s)	8
81	Zonophone Z 17	I Can't Pretend/The KGB (Made A Man Out Of Me) (p/s)	8
82	Flicknife FLS 207	Inside Mind/Hour Of Degradation (p/s)	5
83	Lyntone BOB 7	Very Last Day/There's A World Out There (flexi with 'Bucketfull Of Brains')	5/4
81	Zonophone ZONO 103	DROP OUT WITH THE BARRACUDAS (LP)	10

BARRACUDAS

89 Shakin' Street YEAHHUP 6 GARBAGE DUMP TAPES (LP, blue vinyl with family tree) .10

DICKIE BARRETT
58 MGM MGM 976 Smoke Gets In Your Eyes/Remember Me 4

JOE BARRETT
55 Brunswick 05432 I'm Sincere/Why Did You Break My Heart? 4

RICHARD BARRETT & CHANTELS
59 HMV POP 609 Come Softly To Me/Walking Through Dreamland 8
(see also Chantels)

RITCHIE BARRETT
62 London HLK 9552 Some Other Guy/Tricky Dicky 25

'SWEET EMMA' BARRETT
60s Riverside RLP 364 THE BELL GAL AND HER DIXIELAND BOYS (LP) 10

SYD BARRETT
69 Harvest HAR 5009 Octopus/Golden Hair 60
70 Harvest SHVL 765 THE MADCAP LAUGHS (LP, gatefold sleeve) 15
70 Harvest SHSP 4007 BARRETT (LP, laminated or textured sleeve) 15
(see also Pink Floyd)

RAY BARRETTO
63 Columbia DB 7051 El Watusi/Ritmo Sabroso 12
65 Columbia DB 7684 El Watusi/Swingin' Shepherd Blues 8
69 London HL 10262 Acid/Mercy Mercy Baby 7
67 Island ILP 946 EL WATUSI (LP) 30
69 London HA/SH 8383 ACID (LP) 20

BARRIER
68 Eyemark EMS 1013 Georgie Brown/Dawn Breaks Through 50
68 Philips BF 1692 The Tide Is Turning/Place In Your Heart 5
68 Philips BF 1731 Spot The Lights/Uh 20

BARRINO BROTHERS
72 Invictus INV 523 I Shall Not Be Moved/When Love Was A Child 6

BARRON KNIGHTS
62 Fontana H 368 Let's Face It/Never Miss A Chance 6
63 Columbia DB 7108 Jo-Anne/That's My Girl 4
64 Columbia DB 7188 Comin' Home Baby/Peanut Butter 4
64 Columbia SEG 8424 GUYING THE TOP POPS (EP) 7
66 Columbia SEG 8526 THOSE VERSATILE BARRON KNIGHTS (EP) 7
64 Columbia 33SX 1648 CALL UP THE GROUPS (LP) 15
66 Columbia SX 6007 BARRON KNIGHTS (LP) 12
67 Columbia S(C)X 6176 SCRIBED (LP) 12

BARROW POETS
68 Fontana TF 939 Letter In A Bottle (Music "Sleepy Lagoon")/Dynamite Barbee
  (Music "Barbee Song") 6
70 RCA SF 8110 JOKER (LP) 20
72 Argo ZSW 508 OUTPATIENTS (LP) 25
72 Argo ZSW 511 MAGIC EGG (LP) 25

DAVE BARRY
60 London HA-G 2313 LAUGHS FOR LOSERS (LP) 10

DAVE BARRY & SARA BERNER
56 London HLU 8324 Out Of This World With Flying Saucers Pts 1 & 2 .50
56 London HLU 8324 Out Of This World With Flying Saucers Pts 1 & 2 (78) 8

JOE BARRY
61 Mercury AMT 1149 I'm A Fool To Care/I Got A Feeling 6
68 Stateside SS 2127 I Started Loving You Again/California Bound 6
62 Mercury ZEP 10130 A FOOL TO CARE (EP) 50

JOHN BARRY (SEVEN)
57 Parlophone R 4363 Zip Zip/Three Little Fishes (as John Barry & The Seven) 25
57 Parlophone R 4363 Zip Zip/Three Little Fishes (as John Barry & The Seven) (78) 15
58 Parlophone R 4394 Every Which Way/You've Gotta Way (as John Barry Seven) 22
58 Parlophone R 4394 Every Which Way/You've Gotta Way (as John Barry Seven) (78) 8
58 Parlophone R 4418 Big Guitar/Rodeo (as John Barry Seven) 20
58 Parlophone R 4418 Big Guitar/Rodeo (as John Barry Seven) (78) 8
58 Parlophone R 4453 Pancho/Hideaway (as John Barry Seven) 8
58 Parlophone R 4453 Pancho/Hideaway (as John Barry Seven) (78) 5
58 Parlophone R 4488 Farrago/Bee's Knees (as John Barry Seven) 5
58 Parlophone R 4488 Farrago/Bee's Knees (as John Barry Seven) (78) 5
59 Parlophone R 4530 Long John/Snap 'n' Whistle 7
59 Parlophone R 4530 Long John/Snap 'n' Whistle (78) 5
59 Parlophone R 4560 Little John/For Pete's Sake 7
59 Parlophone R 4560 Little John/For Pete's Sake (78) 5
59 Parlophone R 4582 Twelfth Street Rag/Christella 15
60 Columbia DB 4414 Hit And Miss/Rockin' Already 5
60 Columbia DB 4446 Beat For Beatniks/Big Fella (with Orchestra) 5
60 Columbia DB 4480 Blueberry Hill/Never Let Go (with Orchestra) 6
60 Columbia DB 4505 Walk Don't Run/I'm Movin' On 5
60 Columbia DB 4554 Black Stockings/Get Lost Jack Frost 5
61 Columbia DB 4598 The Magnificent Seven/Skid Row 4
61 Columbia DB 4659 The Menace/Rodeo (with Orchestra) 4
61 Columbia DB 4699 Starfire/A Matter Of Who 4
61 Columbia DB 4746 Watch Your Step/Twist It 4
62 Columbia DB 4806 Cutty Sark/Lost Patrol (with Orchestra) 4

62	Columbia DB 4898	The James Bond Theme/The Blacksmith Blues (with Orchestra) (green or black label) 4/5
62	Columbia DB 4941	The Lolly Theme/March Of The Mandarins 8
63	Columbia DB 7003	The Human Jungle/Onward, Christian Spacemen (some in p/s) 12/5
63	Ember EMB S 178	Kinky/Fancy Dance 5
63	Ember EMB S 181	007/From Russia With Love 6
63	Ember EMB S 183	Elizabeth/The London Theme 6
63	Ember EMB S 185	Zulu Stamp/Monkey Feathers (mauve/grey or red/yellow label; some in p/s) 10/4
64	Columbia DB 7414	Twenty-Four Hours Ago/Seven Faces 20
64	United Artists UP 1060	Seance On A Wet Afternoon/Oublie Ca 20
64	United Artists UP 1068	Goldfinger/Troubador 7
64	Stateside SS 296	Barney's Blues/Theme From The Film "Man In The Middle" (No More) 15
65	CBS 201747	Man Alone (Ipcress File Theme)/Barbra's Theme 10
65	CBS 201822	The Syndicate/What A Question 15
66	CBS 202390	Vendetta/The Danny Scipio Theme 5
67	CBS 202451	Wednesday's Child (Quiller Memorandum)/Sleep Well My Darling 10
67	Ember EMB S 243	007/The Loneliness Of Autumn (some in p/s) 8/4
67	CBS 2825	You Only Live Twice/The Girl With The Sun In Her Hair 10
68	CBS Special Prod. WB 730	James Bond Theme/RAY CONNIFF: Love Is Blue (p/s) 8
69	CBS 3935	Lion In Winter Pts 1 & 2 20
69	CBS 4468	Midnight Cowboy/Fun City 5
69	CBS 4680	On Her Majesty's Secret Service/We Have All The Time In The World 12
60s	Lyntone LYN 378	Theme Music From The Ingersoll Trendsetters T.V. Commercial (flexidisc) 15
72	Polydor 2058 216	This Way Mary/Diamonds Are Forever 10
72	Polydor 2058 275	The Adventurer/Follow Follow 5
58	Parlophone GEP 8737	THE BIG BEAT (EP) 30
61	Columbia SEG 8069	THE JOHN BARRY SOUND (EP) 20
62	Columbia SEG 8138	BEAT GIRL (EP, with Adam Faith) 30
63	Columbia SEG 8255	THEME SUCCESSES (EP) 15
63	United Artists UEP 1011	FROM RUSSIA WITH LOVE (EP, soundtrack) 18
64	Ember EMB EP 4544	LONELINESS OF AUTUMN (EP) 15
64	United Artists UEP 1012	GOLDFINGER (EP, soundtrack) 18
65	Ember EMB EP 4551	JAMES BOND IS BACK (EP) 15
65	United Artists UEP 1015	THUNDERBALL (EP, soundtrack) 15
60	Columbia 33SX 1225	BEAT GIRL (LP, soundtrack, with Adam Faith) 30
61	Columbia 33SX 1358	STRINGBEAT (LP, also stereo SCX 3401) 30/35
63	United Artists (S)ULP 1052	FROM RUSSIA WITH LOVE (LP, soundtrack, mono/stereo) 15/18
64	Ember NR 5012	ZULU (LP, soundtrack) 15
64	Stateside S(S)L 10087	MAN IN THE MIDDLE (LP, soundtrack, with Lionel Bart) 30
64	United Artists (S)ULP 1076	GOLDFINGER (LP, soundtrack, mono/stereo) 12/15
65	Ember NR 5025	JOHN BARRY PLAYS 007 (LP) 25
65	Ember NR 5032	JOHN BARRY MEETS CHAD & JEREMY (LP) 20
66	CBS BPG 62530	THE IPCRESS FILE (LP, soundtrack) 25
66	CBS (S)BPG 62402	THE GREAT MOVIE SOUNDS OF JOHN BARRY (LP) 10
66	CBS (S)BPG 62665	THE CHASE (LP, soundtrack) 15
67	CBS SS 63038	JOHN BARRY CONDUCTS HIS GREATEST MOVIE HITS (LP) 10
68	CBS 70049	THE LION IN WINTER (LP, soundtrack) 15
68	Stateside S(S)L 10263	DEADFALL (LP, soundtrack, Shirley Bassey on 1 track) 15
69	MCA MUPS 360	BOOM (LP, soundtrack, with Georgie Fame) 80
70	CBS 63952	READY WHEN YOU ARE, JB (LP) 15
71	Ember SE 8008	JOHN BARRY REVISITED (LP, fold out sleeve) 20
71	CBS 64816	THE PERSUADERS (LP) 10
71	Polydor 2383 156	THE CONCERT JOHN BARRY (LP) 15
71	Probe SPB 1027	THE LAST VALLEY (LP, soundtrack, with insert) 35/30
73	United Artists UAS 29021	THE BEST OF BOND (LP) 10
73	Utd. Artists UAD 60027/8	THE JAMES BOND COLLECTION (2-LP) 20
74	WEA K 56009	ALICE IN WONDERLAND (2-LP) 14
74	Polydor 2383 300	PLAY IT AGAIN (LP) 15
76	CBS 22014	THE MUSIC OF JOHN BARRY (2-LP) 20
76	Polydor 2383 405	AMERICANS (LP) 20

(see also Alan Bown, Chad & Jeremy, Adam Faith, Michael Angelo & His Orchestra, Elizabeth Taylor, Desmond Lane)

LEN BARRY

65	Cameo Parkway P 969	Hearts Are Trump/Little White House 12
65	Brunswick 05942	1-2-3/Bullseye 4
66	Brunswick 05949	Like A Baby/Happiness 5
66	Brunswick 05955	Somewhere/It's A Crying Shame 6
66	Brunswick 05962	It's That Time Of The Year/Happily Ever After 6
66	Brunswick 05966	I Struck It Rich/Love Is 6
67	RCA RCA 1588	The Moving Finger Writes/Our Love 8
68	Bell BLL 1022	4-5-6 Now I'm Alone/Funky Night 4
73	Paramount PARA 3031	Heaven And Earth/I'm Marching To The Music 4
73	Paramount PARA 3039	It's Time To Fall In Love/Touching Holding Feeling 4
70s	Now! NOW 1003	Now I'm Alone/Funky Night (p/s) 4
66	Cameo Parkway CPE 556	LEN BARRY (EP) 12
66	Cameo Parkway C 1082	LEN BARRY AND THE DOVELLS (LP) 14
69	RCA Intl. INTS 1027	MY KIND OF SOUL (LP) 10

(see also Dovells)

SANDRA BARRY (& BOYS)

64	Decca F 11851	Really Gonna Shake/When We Get Married (as Sandra Barry & Boys) 15
65	Pye 7N 15753	The End Of The Line/We Were Lovers 5
65	Pye 7N 15840	Question/You Can Take It From Me 5
66	Pye 7N 17102	Stop! Thief/I Won't Try To Change Your Mind 5

(see also Boys, Sandra Brown & Boyfriends)

BARRY SISTERS (U.S.)

56	London HLA 8248	Cha Cha Joe/Baby Come A Little Closer	20
56	London HLA 8304	Till You Come Back To Me/Intrigue	20
56	Columbia DB 3843	Sing Me A Sentimental Love Song/The Italian Theme	4
58	Columbia DB 4215	I Hear Bells/I Get Up Ev'ry Morning	4
60	Columbia DB 4562	Misty/Why Don't You Do Right?	4
60	Columbia 33SX 1309	SIDE BY SIDE (LP)	10

LIONEL BART

67	Deram DML/SML 1028	ISN'T THIS WHERE WE CAME IN (LP)	15

CHRIS BARTLEY

62	Cameo Parkway P 101	The Sweetest Thing This Side Of Heaven/Love Me Baby	45
68	Bell BLL 1031	I Found A Goodie/Be Mine Forever	8
75	Right On RO 105	I See Your Name/I See Your Name (Instrumental)	4

BARTOK

82	On ON 1	Insanity/I Am The Bomb (p/s)	8

EVA BARTOK

67	Philips BF 1589	Broken Blossoms/Wait For Summer	4

EILEEN BARTON

55	Vogue Coral Q 72060	The Year We Fell In Love/I Don't Want To Mambo Polka	8
55	Vogue Coral Q 72075	Fujiyama Mama/I'd've Baked A Cake	25
56	Vogue Coral Q 72122	Cry Me A River/Come Home	12
56	Vogue Coral Q 72122	Cry Me A River/Come Home (78)	6
56	Vogue Coral Q 72148	Teenage Heart/My Social Hot Dog	7
56	Vogue Coral Q 72205	Spring It Was/I Have To Tell You	6
57	Vogue Coral Q 72250	Too Close For Comfort/Here I Am In Love Again	6
57	Vogue Coral Q 72270	Without Love/The Scene Of The Crime	6

BASHFUL ALLEY

81	Ellie Jay/Graffiti	Running Blind (p/s)	20

COUNT BASIE & HIS ORCHESTRA

59	Columbia DB 4262	The Late Late Show/The M Squad Theme	4
59	Columbia SCD 2116	April In Paris/Party Blues (with Joe Williams)	4
60	HMV POP 733	April In Paris/The Midgets	4
60	Philips JAZ 109	The Golden Bullet/Bluebeard Blues	4
67	Coral Q 72497	Green Onions/Hang On Sloopy	4
68	MCA MCA 1014	For Your Precious Love/Uptight (with Jackie Wilson)	5
68	Decca AD 1008	For Your Precious Love/Uptight (with Jackie Wilson, export issue)	12
53	Brunswick LA 8589	BASIE'S BEST (10" LP)	15
54	Oriole/Mercury MG 25015	COUNT BASIE/LESTER YOUNG (10" LP, 1 side each)	15
55	Columbia 33S 1054	THE COUNT (10" LP)	12
55	Philips BBR 8036	THE OLD AND THE NEW COUNT (10" LP)	12
55	Columbia Clef 33C 9010	THE COUNT BASIE SEXTET (10" LP)	12
55	Columbia Clef 33CX 10007	COUNT BASIE DANCE SESSION (LP)	10
56	Columbia Clef 33CX 10026	COUNT BASIE SWINGS AND JOE WILLIAMS SINGS (LP)	10
56	Columbia Clef 33CX 10044	COUNT BASIE DANCE SESSION NO. 2 (LP)	10
57	Columbia Clef 33CX 10065	BASIE (LP)	10
57	Columbia Clef 33CX 10088	APRIL IN PARIS (LP)	10
57	Vanguard PPL 11005	A NIGHT AT COUNT BASIE'S (LP, with Joe Williams)	10
57	Philips BBL 7141	BASIE'S BACK IN TOWN (LP)	10
57	Philips BBL 7190	BLUES BY BASIE (LP)	10
58	Columbia Clef 33CX 10110	AT NEWPORT (LP)	10
58	Columbia 33SX 1084	THE ATOMIC MR. BASIE (LP, also stereo SCX 3265)	10
58	Columbia 33SX 1135	BASIE PLATS HEFTI (LP)	10
59	Columbia 33SX 1151	SING ALONG WITH BASIE (LP)	10
59	Columbia 33SX 1174	COUNT BASIE SWINGS — TONY BENNETT SWINGS (LP, stereo SCX 3278)	10
59	Columbia 33SX 1175	MEMORIES AD-LIB (LP, also stereo SCX 3280)	10
59	Columbia 33SX 1183	BASIE (ONE MORE TIME) (LP, also stereo SCX 3284)	10
59	Fontana TFL 5046	ONE O'CLOCK JUMP (LP)	10
60	Fontana TFL 5077	COUNT BASIE CLASSICS (LP, with Jimmy Rushing)	10
60	Columbia 33SX 1209	BREAKFAST DANCE AND BARBECUE (LP, also stereo SCX 3294)	10
60	Columbia 33SX 1224	CHAIRMAN OF THE BOARD (LP, also stereo SCX 3304)	10
60	Columbia 33SX 1264	DANCE ALONG WITH BASIE (LP, also stereo SCX 3333)	10
61	Columbia 33SX 1293	NOT NOW, I'LL TELL YOU WHEN (LP, also stereo SCX 3356)	10
61	HMV CLP 1428	THE BAND OF DISTINCTION (LP)	10
61	Columbia 33SX 1316	THE COUNT BASIE STORY (VOL. 1) (LP, also stereo SCX 3372)	10
61	Columbia 33SX 1317	THE COUNT BASIE STORY (VOL. 2) (LP, also stereo SCX 3373)	10
61	Columbia 33SX 1326	JUST THE BLUES (LP, with Joe Williams, also stereo SCX 3380)	10

(see also Joe Williams, Jackie Wilson, Tony Bennett)

BASIES

67	Coxsone CS 7030	River Jordan/SOUL VENDORS: Swing Easy	15

ALFIE BASS

60	Pye 7N 15286	Villikens And His Dinah/Rat Catcher's Daughter	4

BILLY BASS

69	Pama PM 761	I'm Coming Too/I Need Your Love So Bad	12

FONTELLA BASS

65	Chess CRS 8007	Don't Mess Up A Good Thing/Baby What You Want Me To Do (as Fontella Bass & Bobby McClure)	12
65	Chess CRS 8007	Don't Mess Up A Good Thing/OLIVER SAIN: Jerk Loose	15
65	Chess CRS 8023	Rescue Me/Soul Of The Man	6
66	Chess CRS 8027	Recovery/Leave It In The Hands Of Love	6

MINT VALUE £

66	Chess CRS 8032	I Can't Rest/Surrender	8
66	Chess CRS 8042	Safe And Sound/You'll Never Know	7
69	Chess CRS 8090	Rescue Me/I Can't Rest	4
72	Mojo 2092 045	I Want Everyone To Know/I Want To Be Loved	4
74	Contempo CS 2004	Now That I've Found A Good Thing/Home Wrecker	4
66	Chess CRE 6015	FONTELLA'S HITS (EP)	12
66	Chess CRE 6020	I CAN'T REST (EP)	12
66	Chess CRE 6025	FONTELLA BASS AND BOBBY McCLURE (EP)	15
66	Chess CRL 4517	THE NEW LOOK (LP)	15
72	Mojo 2916 018	FREE (LP)	10

(see also Bobby McClure)

SHIRLEY BASSEY

57	Philips JK 1006	The Banana Boat Song/Tra La La (jukebox edition)	12
57	Philips JK 1018	If I Had A Needle And Thread/Tonight My Heart She Is Crying (jukebox edition)	10
57	Philips JK 1034	Puh-leeze! Mister Brown/Take My Love, Take My Love (jukebox edition)	10
58	Philips PB 845	As I Love You/Hands Across The Sea	4
58	Philips PB 860	Kiss Me, Honey Honey, Kiss Me/There's Never Been A Night	5
59	Philips PB 917	Love For Sale/Crazy Rhythm	4
59	Philips PB 919	My Funny Valentine/How About You?	4
59	Philips PB 975	Night And Day/The Gypsy In My Soul	4
59	Columbia DB 4344	If You Love Me/Count On Me	4
64	Columbia DB 7360	Goldfinger/Strange How Love Can Be	6
66	United Artists UP 1134	Don't Take The Lovers From The World/Takeaway	8
67	United Artists UP 1192	Big Spender/Dangerous Game	4
68	United Artists UP 2254	To Give/My Love Has Two Faces	10
72	United Artists UP 35293	Diamonds Are Forever/Pieces Of Dreams	4
59	Philips BBE 12232	BLUES BY SHIRLEY BASSEY (EP)	7
58	Philips BBR 8130	BORN TO SING THE BLUES (10" LP)	12
60	Columbia 33SX 1286	SHIRLEY (LP, also stereo SCX 3352)	10

BAS-SHEVA

55	Capitol CL 14218	Flame Of Love/I Just Wanna Be Your Loving Baby	5

JOE BATAAN

75	RCA RCA 2457	Latin Strut/Peace, Friendship And Solidarity	5
75	RCA RCA 2553	The Bottle/When You're Down	6
76	Epic EPC 3818	The Bottle (La Botella)/When You're Down (reissue)	4
69	London HA/SH 8386	RIOT! (LP)	15

JUNE BATEMAN

64	Sue WI 347	I Don't Wanna/NOBLE 'THIN MAN' WATTS & HIS BAND: Noble's Theme	20

COLLIN BATES TRIO

68	Fontana SFJ 2913	BREW (LP)	15

JON BATES

65	CBS 201818	Where Were You Last Night/If Anything Goes Wrong	4

MARTYN BATES

82	Cherry Red TRED 38	LETTERS WRITTEN (10" EP)	10

(see also Eyeless In Gaza)

BATFISH BOYS

84	Batfish Inc. BF 102	Swamp Liquor/Hand Of Death (p/s)	5
84	Batfish Inc. USS 101	Swamp Liquor/Hand Of Death/Hot Dog (12", p/s)	7
86	Batfish Inc. USS 107	Justine/Amoeba Rock (p/s, 1,000 only)	4
89	GWR GWPD 7	Another One Bites The Dust/The Bomb Song (Echo Logy Mix)/Born To Be Wild (live) (12", picture disc, PVC sleeve with sticker)	7

(see also March Violets)

STIV BATORS

79	London/Bomp HLZ 10575	It's Cold Outside/The Last Year (p/s)	7

(see also Dead Boys, Lords Of The New Church, Wanderers)

BATS

64	Columbia DB 7429	Accept It/Lovers Lie Sleeping	6
66	Decca F 22534	Listen To My Heart/Stop Don't Do It	6
67	Decca F 22568	You Will Now, Won't You?/You Look Good Together	6
67	Decca F 22616	Hard To Get Up In The Morning/Take Me As I Am	6

MIKE BATT

68	Liberty LBF 15093	Mister Poem/Fading Yellow	6
68	Liberty LBF 15122	I See Wonderful Things In You/Mary Goes Round	4
69	Liberty LBF 15210	Your Mother Should Know/Suddenly	4

(see also Phase 4, Anderson Harley & Batt)

BATTERED ORNAMENTS

69	Harvest HAR 5013	Goodbye We Loved You (Madly)/CHRIS SPEDDING: Rock'n'Roll Band	10
69	Harvest SHVL 758	MANTEL PIECE (LP)	60

(see also Pete Brown & His Battered Ornaments, Chris Spedding)

SKIP BATTIN

73	Signpost SGP 756	Central Park/St. Louis Browns	4
72	Signpost SG 4255	SKIP (LP)	12

(see also Skip & Flip, Byrds, Flying Burrito Brothers, Evergreen Blueshoes)

BATTLEAXE

82	Guardian	Burn This Town (no p/s)	4

BAUHAUS

79	Small Wonder TEENY 2	Bela Lugosi's Dead/Boys/Dark Entries (12", p/s, black vinyl)	7
79	Small Wonder TEENY 2	Bela Lugosi's Dead/Boys/Dark Entries (12", p/s, white vinyl)	15

MINT VALUE £

80s	Small Wonder TEENY 2	Bela Lugosi's Dead/Boys/Dark Entries (12", p/s, green or blue vinyl) 10
80s	Small Wonder TEENY 2P	Bela Lugosi's Dead/Boys/Dark Entries (12", picture disc) 8
80	Axis AXIS 3	Dark Entries/Untitled (p/s) 18
80	4AD AD 3	Dark Entries/Untitled (p/s) 8
80	4AD AD 3	Dark Entries/Untitled (p/s, with BEG 37 label stuck on top of 4AD labels) 12
80	Beggars Banquet BEG 37	Dark Entries/Untitled (p/s, on Beggars Banquet) 15
80	4AD AD 7	Terror Couple Kill Colonel/Scopes/Terror Couple Kill Colonel II (p/s) 7
80	4AD AD 7	Terror Couple Kill Colonel (Remix)/Scopes/Terror Couple Kill Colonel II (p/s) ...14
80	4AD AD 17	Telegram Sam/Crowds (p/s) 6
80	4AD AD 17T	Telegram Sam/Rosegarden/Funeral Of Sores/Crowds (12", p/s) 10
81	Beggars Banquet BEG 54	Kick In The Eye/Satori (p/s) 4
81	Beggars Banquet BEG 54T	Kick In The Eye/Satori (12", p/s, white or Beggars labels) 15/10
81	Beggars Banquet BEG 59	The Passion Of Lovers/David J: Peter Murphy: Kevin Haskins: Daniel Ash (p/s, with lyric insert) 5
82	Beggars Banquet BEG 74	Kick In The Eye/Harry/Earwax (p/s) 4
82	Beggars Banquet BEG 74T	Kick In The Eye/In Fear Of Dub/Harry/Earwax (12", p/s) 7
82	B. Banquet BEG 74TA1	Kick In The Eye/Poison Pen/Harry/Earwax (12" mispress, p/s) 30
82	Beggars Banquet BEG 79	Spirit/Terror Couple Kill Colonel (live) (p/s, with Beggars labels) 4
82	Beggars Banquet BEG 79	Terror Couple Kill Colonel (live)/GARY NUMAN: We Take Mystery (p/s, mispress) 10
82	Beggars Banquet BEG 79P	Spirit/Terror Couple Kill Colonel (live) (picture disc in printed PVC sleeve) 8
82	Beggars Banquet BEG 83	Ziggy Stardust/Third Uncle (p/s) 4
82	Beggars Banquet BEG 83	Ziggy Stardust/Third Uncle (poster p/s) 10
82	Beggars Banquet BEG 83T	Ziggy Stardust/Party Of The First Part/Third Uncle/Waiting For The Man (12", p/s) 7
82	Lyntone LYN 12106	A God In An Alcove (New Version) (blue flexidisc with 'Flexipop', issue 23) 8/6
82	Lyntone LYN 12106	A God In An Alcove (New Version) (hard vinyl test pressing) 40
83	Lyntone LYN 13777/8	The Sanity Assassin/Spirit In The Sky (fan club freebie, about 250 only) 120
83	Beggars Banquet BEG 88	Lagartija Nick/Paranoia! Paranoia! (p/s) 4
83	Beggars Banquet BEG 88T	Lagartija Nick/Watch That Grandad Go/Paranoia! Paranoia!/In The Flat Field (live) (12", p/s) 7
84	Beggars Banquet BEG 91P	She's In Parties/Departure (picture disc in PVC sleeve) 8
80s	Bauhaus 1	THE INTERVIEW SITUATION (picture disc) 5
82	Beggars Banquet BEGA 42	THE SKY'S GONE OUT (LP, with free LP "Press The Eject And Give Me The Tape" [BEGA 38] & inner sleeves) 12
82	Beggars Banquet BEGA 38	PRESS THE EJECT AND GIVE ME THE TAPE (LP, with free 45 "Satori In Paris" [BH 1] & poster) 12
83	Beggars Banquet BEGA 45P	BURNING FROM THE INSIDE (LP, picture disc) 15
85	Beggars Banquet BEGA 64	1979-1983 (LP, with numbered inserts) 10

(see also Sinister Ducks, Peter Murphy, Tones On Tail, David J., Love & Rockets)

ART BAXTER

56	Philips PB 652	Jingle Rock/Rock And Roll Rag (78) 10
57	Philips PB 666	Don't Knock The Rock/Rock Rock Rock (78) 10
57	Philips BBR 8107	ROCK YOU SINNERS (10" LP) 75

DAVID BAXTER

| 70 | Reflection REFL 9 | GOODBYE DAVE (LP) ....45 |

(see also David Lewis)

LES BAXTER & HIS ORCHESTRA

54	Capitol CL 14166	I Love Paris/Manhattan 8
54	Capitol CL 14173	Midnight On The Cliffs/Dream Rhapsody (with Leonard Pennario) 8
55	Capitol CL 14217	When You're In Love/Romantic Rio 8
55	Capitol CL 14237	Cheery Pink And Apple Blossom White/Play Me Hearts And Flowers 8
55	Capitol CL 14239	Earth Angel/Happy Baby (as Les Baxter & Bombers) 15
55	Capitol CL 14239	Earth Angel/Happy Baby (as Les Baxter & Bombers) (78) 5
55	Capitol CL 14249	I Ain't Mad At You (with Bombers)/Blue Mirage 8
55	Capitol CL 14257	Unchained Melody/Blue Star (The Medic Theme) 12
55	Capitol CL 14344	Wake The Town And Tell The World/I'll Never Stop Loving You 8
55	Capitol CL 14351	The Strike/The Toy Tiger 7
55	Capitol CL 14358	Take My Love/If You've Forgotten Me 7
56	Capitol CL 14533	Poor John/"Helen Of Troy" Theme 6
56	Capitol CL 14546	The Trouble With Harry/Havana 5
56	Capitol CL 14589	Tango Of The Drums/If You Can Dream 5
57	Capitol CL 14677	Giant/There's Never Been Anyone Else But You 4
59	Capitol CL 15055	Sabre Dance/Milord 4
60	Capitol CL 15140	Ooch-I-Baba/Boomada (as Les Baxter Drums) 4
66	Pye International 7N 25351	Michelle/Little Girl Lonely 4
60	Capitol (S)T 1355	TEEN DRUMS (LP) 10

RONNIE BAXTER

| 60 | Top Rank JAR 293 | I Finally Found You/Is It Because? ....6 |

BAY CITY ROLLERS

72	Bell BLL 1220	We Can Make Music/Jenny 6
72	Bell BLL 1262	Manana/Because I Love You 4
73	Bell BLL 1319	Saturday Night/Het C B 4
77	Arista ARIST 127	You Made Me Believe In Magic/Are You Cuckoo/Dedication (p/s) 10

BAYTOWN SINGERS

| 65 | Decca F 12160 | Walkin' Down The Line/Let My Feet Fall On The Ground ....5 |

B.B. BLUNDER

71	United Artists UP 35203	Sticky Living/Rocky Yagbag 5
71	United Artists UP 35204	Little Boy/10,000 Miles 6
71	United Artists UAG 20196	WORKERS' PLAYTIME (LP) 25

(see also Julie Driscoll, Brian Auger & Trinity)

BBC RADIOPHONIC WORKSHOP
64	Decca F 11837	Doctor Who/BRENDA & JOHNNY: This Can't Be Love	12
74	BBC RESL 11	Doctor Who/Reg	5

BEA & DEE
59	Capitol CL 15066	Jerry/Wishing Time	4

BEACH BOYS
62	Capitol CL 15273	Surfin' Safari/409	15
63	Capitol CL 15285	Ten Little Indians/County Fair	30
63	Capitol CL 15305	Surfin' USA/Shut Down	12
64	Capitol CL 15339	Fun, Fun, Fun/Why Do Fools Fall In Love	15
64	Capitol CL 15350	I Get Around/Don't Worry Baby	6
64	Capitol CL 15361	When I Grow Up (To Be A Man)/She Knows Me Too Well	6
65	Capitol CL 15370	Dance, Dance, Dance/The Warmth Of The Sun	6
65	Capitol CL 15384	All Summer Long/Do You Wanna Dance	6
65	Capitol CL 15392	Help Me Rhonda/Kiss Me Baby	5
65	Capitol CL 15409	California Girls/Let Him Run Wild	4
65	Capitol CL 15425	The Little Girl I Once Knew/There's No Other (Like My Baby)	5
66	Capitol CL 15432	Barbara Ann/Girl Don't Tell Me	4
66	Capitol CL 15441	Sloop John B/You're So Good To Me	4
66	Capitol CL 15459	God Only Knows/Wouldn't It Be Nice	4
66	Capitol CL 15475	Good Vibrations/Wendy	4
67	Capitol CL 15502	Then I Kissed Her/Mountain Of Love	4
67	Capitol CL 15510	Heroes And Villains/You're Welcome	4
67	Capitol CL 15521	Wild Honey/Wind Chimes	5
68	Capitol CL 15527	Darlin'/Country Air	4
68	Capitol CL 15545	Friends/Little Bird	5
69	Capitol CL 15598	Break Away/Celebrate The News	4
70	Capitol CL 15640	Cottonfields/The Nearest Faraway Place (black label)	5
70	Stateside SS 2181	Tears In The Morning/It's About Time	5
71	Stateside SS 2190	Long Promised Road/Deirdre	5
71	Stateside SS 2194	Don't Go Near The Water/Student Demonstration Time (demos in p/s £15)	5
72	Reprise K 14173	You Need A Mess Of Help To Stand Alone/Cuddle Up (p/s)	8
72	Capitol CMS 1	Wouldn't It Be Nice/Fun Fun Fun/California Girls (in special bag)	5
72	Capitol CMS 2	Barbara Ann/Dance Dance Dance/You're So Good To Me (in special bag)	5
74	Reprise K 14346	California Saga: California/Sail On Sailor/Marcella/I'm The Pied Piper (in special bag)	4
76	Reprise K 14411	Child Of Winter/Susie Cincinnati (withdrawn)	35
76	Reprise K 14440	Rock And Roll Music/The T.M. Song (p/s)	4
77	Reprise K 14481	Mona/Rock And Roll Music/Sail On Sailor/Marcella (p/s)	4
78	Capitol CL 15969	Little Deuce Coupe/SUNRAYS: I Live For The Sun/SUPERSTOCKS: Hot Rod High (p/s)	4
79	Caribou 12-7204	Here Comes The Night/(Disco Version)/Baby Blue (12", p/s, blue vinyl)	7
79	Capitol BBP 26	SINGLES COLLECTION (26 x 7" box set)	55
63	Capitol EAP 1-20540	SURFIN' USA (EP)	12
64	Capitol EAP 1-20603	FUN, FUN, FUN (EP)	12
64	Capitol EAP 5267	FOUR BY THE BEACH BOYS (EP)	10
64	Capitol EAP 4-2198	BEACH BOYS CONCERT (EP)	12
64	Capitol EAP 1-20781	THE BEACH BOYS HITS (EP)	10
67	Capitol EAP 6-2458	GOD ONLY KNOWS (EP)	10
62	Capitol T 1808	SURFIN' SAFARI (LP)	25
63	Capitol (S)T 1890	SURFIN' USA (LP, mono/stereo)	15/16
63	Capitol (S)T 1998	LITTLE DEUCE COUPE (LP, mono/stereo)	15/16
63	Capitol (S)T 2027	SHUT DOWN VOLUME 2 (LP, mono/stereo)	15/16
64	Capitol (S)T 2164	THE BEACH BOYS' CHRISTMAS ALBUM (LP, mono/stereo)	22/25
64	Capitol (S)T 2198	BEACH BOYS CONCERT (LP, mono/stereo)	14/15
64	Capitol (S)T 2110	ALL SUMMER LONG (LP, mono/stereo)	18/20
65	Capitol (S)T 2398	BEACH BOYS' PARTY! (LP, mono/stereo)	12/10
65	Capitol (S)T 2269	BEACH BOYS TODAY! (LP)	12
65	Capitol (S)T 2354	SUMMER DAYS (AND SUMMER NIGHTS!!) (LP)	10
66	Capitol (S)T 2458	PET SOUNDS (LP)	10
66	Capitol (S)T 20856	THE BEST OF THE BEACH BOYS (LP)	10
67	Capitol (S)T 1981	SURFER GIRL (LP)	10
67	Capitol (S)T 20956	THE BEST OF THE BEACH BOYS VOL. 2 (LP)	10
67	Capitol (S)T 9001	SMILEY SMILE (LP)	10
68	Capitol (S)T 2859	WILD HONEY (LP, mono/stereo)	12/10
68	Capitol (S)T 2895	FRIENDS (LP, mono/stereo)	12/10
69	Capitol (S)T 21142	THE BEST OF THE BEACH BOYS VOL. 3 (LP)	10
69	Capitol E T/ST 133	20-20 (LP, mono/stereo, gatefold sleeve)	12/10
70	Stateside SSLA 8251	SUNFLOWER (LP, gatefold sleeve)	10
71	Stateside SSL 10313	SURF'S UP (LP, original pressing)	10
73	Reprise K 54008	HOLLAND (LP, with free EP "Mount Vernon And Fairway")	10
77	EMI EMTV 1	20 GOLDEN GREATS (LP, blue vinyl)	10
79	Caribou CRB 11-86081	L.A. (LIGHT ALBUM) (LP, picture disc)	15
81	World Rec Club SM 651-657	THE CAPITOL YEARS (7-LP box set)	45

(see also Brian Wilson, Dennis Wilson, Bruce Johnston, California Music, Legendary Masked Surfers, American Spring, Annette)

BEACHCOMBERS
63	Columbia DB 7124	Mad Goose/You Can't Sit Down	12
64	Columbia DB 7200	Night Train/The Keel Row	12

BEACH NUTS
65	London HL 9988	Out In The Sun (Hey-O)/Someday Soon	6

BEACON STREET UNION
68	MGM MGM 1416	Blue Suede Shoes/Four Hundred And Five	6

George BEAN

68	MGM C 8069	THE EYES OF THE BEACON STREET UNION (LP)	18

BEALE STREET BUSKERS
60	Ember EMB S 107	'Fraidy Cat/Dusty	4

GEORGE BEAN
63	Decca F 11762	Secret Love/Lonely Weekends	6
64	Decca F 11808	Will You Be My Lover Tonight?/It Should Be You	7
64	Decca F 11922	A Sad Story/Er Um Er	10
65	Decca F 12228	She Belongs To Me/Why Must They Criticise?	5
67	CBS 2801	The Candy Shop Is Closed/Smile From Sequin	5
68	CBS 3374	Bring Back Lovin'/Floatin'	4

BEAN & LOOPY'S LOT
66	Parlophone R 5458	A Stitch In Time/Haywire	10

BEANS
62	Starlite ST45 071	Jumping Beans/Salute To Fitz	7
62	Starlite ST45 076	Hey Janey/Crazy Dog	7

BEAR
68	Verve FTS 3059	GREETINGS CHILDREN OF PARADISE (LP)	12

DEAN BEARD & CREW CATS
57	London HLE 8463	Rakin' And Scrapin'/On My Mind Again	175
57	London HLE 8463	Rakin' And Scrapin'/On My Mind Again (78)	30

BEARS
81	Waldo's JS 001	On Me/Wot's Up Mate (p/s, various designs, with insert)	4

BEARS
79	Good Vibrations Intl. GVI 1	Insane/Decisions (p/s)	4

BEARZ
80	Axis AXIS 2	She's My Girl/Girls Will Do (p/s)	10
84	Occult OCC 1	Darwin/Julie (p/s)	4

BEAS
68	Pama PM 744	Where Do I Go From You/Dr. Goodfoot And His Bikini Machine	20

BEASTIE BOYS
82	Rat Cage MOTR 21	POLLY WOG STEW (EP)	8
87	Def Jam BEASTP 1	No Sleep Till Brooklyn/Posse In Effect (shaped picture disc)	4

BEAT
79	2-Tone TT 6	Tears Of A Clown/Ranking Full Stop (paper label, 2-Tone sleeve)	4
81	Go Feet FEET 16	I Confess/Sole Salvation//Door To Your Heart/Save It For Later/Mirror In The Bathroom (double pack, gatefold p/s)	5
83	Go Feet BEAT 6	WHAT IS BEAT (LP, with free 12" remixes LP)	10

(see also Fine Young Cannibals, General Public)

BEAT BOYS
63	Decca F 11730	That's My Plan/Third Time Lucky	15

(see also Rats, Al Torino)

BEAT BROTHERS
63	Polydor NH 52185	Nick Nack Hully Gully/Lantern Hully Gully	25

(see also Tony Sheridan & Beat Brothers, Bobby Patrick Big Six)

BEAT CHICS
64	Decca F 12016	Skinny Minnie/Now I Know	6

BEATHOVEN
88	CBS 651 626 7	Socrates/Socrates (withdrawn)	30

BEATLES
62	Parlophone R 4949	Love Me Do/P.S. I Love You (original red label)	35
63	Parlophone R 4949	Love Me Do/P.S. I Love You (original black label)	50
63	Parlophone R 4983	Please Please Me/Ask Me Why (original red label)	35
63	Parlophone R 4983	Please Please Me/Ask Me Why (original black label)	6
63	Parlophone R 5015	From Me To You/Thank You Girl	4
63	Parlophone R 5055	She Loves You/I'll Get You	4
63	Parlophone R 5084	I Want To Hold Your Hand/This Boy	4
64	Polydor NH 52317	Ain't She Sweet/TONY SHERIDAN & BEATLES: If You Love Me Baby	35

(for other Polydor recordings see under Tony Sheridan & Beatles)

64	Parlophone R 5114	Can't Buy Me Love/You Can't Do That	4
64	Parlophone R 5160	A Hard Day's Night/Things We Said Today	4
64	Parlophone R 5200	I Feel Fine/She's A Woman	4
65	Parlophone R 5265	Ticket To Ride/Yes It Is	4
65	Parlophone R 5305	Help!/I'm Down	4
65	Parlophone R 5389	We Can Work It Out/Day Tripper	4
66	Parlophone R 5452	Paperback Writer/Rain	4
66	Parlophone R 5493	Yellow Submarine/Eleanor Rigby	4
67	Parlophone R 5570	Penny Lane/Strawberry Fields Forever (original p/s)	18
67	Parlophone R 5570	Penny Lane/Strawberry Fields Forever	4
67	Parlophone R 5620	All You Need Is Love/Baby You're A Rich Man (without label reference to "Our World" TV show)	15
67	Parlophone R 5620	All You Need Is Love/Baby You're A Rich Man	4
67	Parlophone R 5655	Hello, Goodbye/I Am The Walrus	4
68	Parlophone R 5675	Lady Madonna/The Inner Light	4
68	Apple (no cat. no.)	OUR FIRST FOUR (4 x 7" promo presentation pack of "Hey Jude" [R 5722] & singles by other artists [APPLE 2, 3 & 4], 4 inserts; card or plastic box)	850
60s	Apple	other singles (1968-1969)	3-4
70	Apple R 5833	Let It Be/You Know My Name (Look Up The Number) (p/s)	8
76	Parlophone R 6016	Back In The U.S.S.R./Twist And Shout (p/s, black cross on reverse)	5

77	Lingasong NB 1	Twist And Shout/Falling In Love Again	10
78	Parlophone R 6022	Sgt. Pepper's Lonely Hearts Club Band/With A Little Help From My Friends/A Day In The Life (p/s)	4
82	AFE AFS 1	Searching/Twist And Shout/Till There Was You (p/s)	10
82	Parlophone R 4949	Love Me Do/P.S. I Love You (p/s, red label reissue, with publishing credited to "Ardmore & Beechwood" instead of "MPL")	20
82	Parlophone RP 4949	Love Me Do/P.S. I Love You (picture disc, with publishing miscredit)	20
82	Parlophone RP 4949	Love Me Do/P.S. I Love You (picture disc)	7
82	Parlophone 12R 4949	Love Me Do/P.S. I Love You/Love Me Do (Original Single Version) (12", p/s)	8
83	Parlophone RP 4983	Please Please Me/Ask Me Why (picture disc)	7
83	Parlophone RP 5015	From Me To You/Thank You Girl (picture disc)	15
83	Parlophone RP 5015	From Me To You/Thank You Girl (picture disc, with "Souvenir From Abbey Road Studios" sticker)	18
83	Parlophone RP 5055	She Loves You/I'll Get You (picture disc)	18
83	Parlophone RP 5084	I Want To Hold Your Hand/This Boy (picture disc)	6
84	Parlophone RP 5114	Can't Buy Me Love/You Can't Do That (picture disc)	6
84	Parlophone RP 5160	A Hard Day's Night/Things We Said Today (picture disc)	6
84	Parlophone RP 5200	I Feel Fine/She's A Woman (picture disc)	6
85	Parlophone RP 5265	Ticket To Ride/Yes It Is (picture disc)	5
85	Parlophone RP 5305	Help!/I'm Down (picture disc)	5
85	Parlophone RP 5389	We Can Work It Out/Day Tripper (picture disc)	5
86	Parlophone RP 5452	Paperback Writer/Rain (picture disc)	4
86	Parlophone RP 5493	Yellow Submarine/Eleanor Rigby (picture disc)	4
87	Parlophone RP 5570	Penny Lane/Strawberry Fields Forever (picture disc)	4
87	Parlophone RP 5620	All You Need Is Love/Baby You're A Rich Man (picture disc)	4
87	Parlophone RP 5655	Hello, Goodbye/I Am The Walrus (picture disc)	4
88	Parlophone RP 5675	Lady Madonna/The Inner Light (picture disc)	4
88	Apple RP 5722	Hey Jude/Revolution (picture disc, with insert)	4
88	Apple 12RP 5722	Hey Jude/Revolution (12" picture disc, with insert)	7
89	Apple RP 5777	Get Back/Don't Let Me Down (picture disc, with insert)	6
89	Apple RP 5786	The Ballad Of John And Yoko/Old Brown Shoe (picture disc, with insert)	6
89	Apple RP 5814	Something/Come Together (picture disc)	7
90	Apple RP 5833	Let It Be/You Know My Name (Look Up The Number) (picture disc)	8

(the DP & P-R singles below are export issues, manufactured in the U.K.)

64	Parlophone DP 562	If I Fell/Tell Me Why	25
65	Parlophone DP 563	Yesterday/Dizzy Miss Lizzy	60
66	Parlophone DP 564	Michelle/Drive My Car	60
68	Parlophone DP 570	Hey Jude/Revolution (some with Swedish p/s)	50/20
70	Parlophone P-R 5833	Let It Be/You Know My Name (Look Up The Number) (no p/s)	50
70	Apple P-R 5833	Let It Be/You Know My Name (Look Up The Number) (no p/s)	75
63	Lyntone LYN 492	The Beatles' Christmas Record (fan club flexidisc, gatefold p/s)	75
64	Lyntone LYN 757	Another Beatles Christmas Record (fan club flexidisc, p/s with gatefold insert)	45
65	Lyntone LYN 948	The Beatles' Third Christmas Record (fan club flexidisc, p/s with gatefold insert)	50
66	Lyntone LYN 1145	Pantomime: Everywhere It's Christmas (fan club flexidisc, p/s with insert)	50
67	Lyntone LYN 1360	Christmas Time (Is Here Again) (fan club flexidisc, p/s with insert)	50
68	Lyntone LYN 1743/4	The Beatles' Sixth Christmas Record (fan club flexidisc, p/s with 'poster ad' insert)	50
69	Lyntone LYN 1970/1-IL	The Beatles' Seventh Christmas Record (fan club flexidisc, p/s, some with 2 x A4 fan club literature)	50

(fan club flexidiscs without newsletters are worth around £10 less, and without picture sleeves a third of these values)

77	Sound For Industry SFI 291	The Beatles' Singles Collection (flexidisc sampler for box set, with poster)	18
78	Sound For Industry SFI 65	The Beatles' Collection (flexidisc sampler for box set, with poster)	10
78	Lyntone LYN 9657	The Beatles' Collection (U.K. sampler flexidisc for French LP box set)	5
80	World Record Club	The Beatles 1962-1966/1967-1970 (sampler flexidisc)	10
80	Lyntone LYN 8982	World Records Presents The Music Of The Beatles (flexidisc sampler for WRC box set [SM 701/708])	10

(all the singles below are known mispressings)

78	Apple R 5777	Get Back/Don't Let Me Down (re-pressing, mispressed, B-side plays Wings' "I've Had Enough", p/s)	15
82	Parlophone RP 4949	Love Me Do/P.S. I Love You (mispressed picture disc, plays "Love Me Do" both sides)	25
82	Parlophone RP 4983	Please Please Me/Ask Me Why (mispressed picture disc, A-side plays "From Me To You")	20
82	United Artists UPP 35381	HAWKWIND: Silver Machine/Seven By Seven (mispressed picture disc, B-side plays "Ask Me Why")	15
85	Parlophone RP 5265	Ticket To Ride/Yes It Is (mispressed picture disc, B-side plays Power Station's "Some Like It Hot")	18
86	Parlophone RP 5452	Paperback Writer/Rain (mispressed picture disc, A-side plays Queen's "Friends Will Be Friends")	25
76	Parlophone/Apple BS 24	THE BEATLES' SINGLES COLLECTION, 1962-1970 (24 x 7" green & white box set)	40
76	Parlophone/Apple/ World Record Club	THE BEATLES' COLLECTION (24 x 7" mail order black box set; later copies with "Sgt. Pepper's Lonely Hearts Club Band" [R 6022])	40/45
78	Parlophone/Apple BSC 1	THE BEATLES' SINGLES COLLECTION (26 x 7" blue box set, with insert; some copies include mispress of "Get Back" [Apple R 5777])	45/55
82	Parlophone/Apple BSCP 1	THE BEATLES' SINGLES COLLECTION (27 x 7" blue box set, export issue, with bonus picture disc, "Love Me Do")	50
82	Parlophone/Apple BSCP 1	THE BEATLES' SINGLES COLLECTION (27 x 7" blue box set, export issue, with mispressed picture disc, "Love Me Do"/"Love Me Do")	70
88	Baktabak TABOKS 1001	THE BEATLES 1962 (15-single box set, withdrawn)	40
89	Baktabak BAKPAK 1004	THE BEATLES CONQUER AMERICA (4 x 7" interview pack)	12
63	Parlophone GEP 8882	TWIST AND SHOUT (EP)	7
63	Parlophone GEP 8880	THE BEATLES' HITS (EP)	8/7
63	Parlophone GEP 8883	THE BEATLES (No. 1) (EP)	7

Year	Catalogue	Description	Value
64	Polydor H 21-610	MY BONNIE (EP, as Tony Sheridan & Beatles)	40
64	Parlophone GEP 8891	ALL MY LOVING (EP)	7
64	Parlophone GEP 8899	GOLDEN DISCS (EP, unreleased)	
64	Parlophone GEP 8913	LONG TALL SALLY (EP)	8
64	Parlophone GEP 8920	EXTRACTS FROM THE FILM "A HARD DAY'S NIGHT" (EP)	7
64	Parlophone GEP 8924	EXTRACTS FROM THE ALBUM "A HARD DAY'S NIGHT" (EP)	15
65	Parlophone GEP 8931	BEATLES FOR SALE (EP)	7
65	Parlophone GEP 8938	BEATLES FOR SALE (NO. 2) (EP)	15
65	Parlophone GEP 8946	THE BEATLES' MILLION SELLERS (EP, early copies with 'Beatles *Golden* Hits' on label)	each 15
66	Parlophone GEP 8948	YESTERDAY (EP)	18
66	Parlophone GEP 8952	NOWHERE MAN (EP)	20
67	Parlophone (S)MMT-1	MAGICAL MYSTERY TOUR (2-EP, gatefold p/s, with booklet & blue lyric sheet, mono/stereo)	18/15
70s	Parlophone SMMT-1	MAGICAL MYSTERY TOUR (2-EP reissue, gatefold p/s, with booklet & yellow lyric sheet)	7
67	Parlophone MMT-1	MAGICAL MYSTERY TOUR (2-EP, gatefold p/s, with booklet & blue lyric sheet, mispressed with Beach Boys' "Darling" on flip of "I Am The Walrus")	30
81	Parlophone BEP 14	THE BEATLES EP COLLECTION (14-EP box set, including bonus EP: "The Beatles")	40
63	Parlophone PMC 1202	PLEASE PLEASE ME (LP, gold/black label, mono)	150
63	Parlophone PCS 3042	PLEASE PLEASE ME (LP, gold/black label, stereo)	700
63	Parlophone PMC 1202	PLEASE PLEASE ME (LP, yellow/black label, mono)	20
63	Parlophone PCS 3042	PLEASE PLEASE ME (LP, yellow/black label, stereo)	25
63	Parlophone PMC 1206	WITH THE BEATLES (LP, yellow/black label, mono)	20
63	Parlophone PCS 3045	WITH THE BEATLES (LP, yellow/black label, stereo)	25
64	Polydor Special 236 201	THE BEATLES' FIRST (LP, as Tony Sheridan & Beatles, original with rough red label)	50
64	Parlophone PMC 1230	A HARD DAY'S NIGHT (LP, yellow/black label, mono)	20
64	Parlophone PCS 3058	A HARD DAY'S NIGHT (LP, yellow/black label, stereo)	25
64	Parlophone PMC 1240	BEATLES FOR SALE (LP, gatefold sleeve, yellow/black label, mono)	20
64	Parlophone PCS 3062	BEATLES FOR SALE (LP, gatefold sleeve, yellow/black label, stereo)	25
65	Parlophone PMC 1255	HELP! (LP, yellow/black label, mono)	20
65	Parlophone PCS 3071	HELP! (LP, yellow/black label, stereo)	22
66	Parlophone PMC 1267	RUBBER SOUL (LP, yellow/black label, mono)	20
66	Parlophone PCS 3075	RUBBER SOUL (LP, yellow/black label, stereo)	22
66	Parl. PMC/PCS 7009	REVOLVER (LP, yellow/black label, mono/stereo)	20/22
67	Polydor Special 236 201	THE BEATLES' FIRST (LP, as Tony Sheridan & Beatles, reissue, with smooth red label)	35
67	Parl. PMC/PCS 7016	A COLLECTION OF BEATLES OLDIES (LP, yellow/black, mono/stereo)	20/22
67	Parlophone PMC/PCS 7027	SGT. PEPPER'S LONELY HEARTS CLUB BAND (LP, yellow/black label, gatefold sleeve, with red & white inner & cut-out insert, mono/stereo)	30/20

(all the above Parlophone LPs [except PMC 1240] come with flipback sleeves & 'use Emitex' tracing paper-lined inners)

Year	Catalogue	Description	Value
68	Apple PMC/PCS 7067/8	THE BEATLES (2-LP, numbered, top opening gatefold sleeve with dark inners, poster & 4 colour prints, mono/stereo)	50/35
69	Apple PMC/PCS 7070	YELLOW SUBMARINE (LP, mono/stereo, flipback sleeve with black inner)	35/18
69	Apple PCS 7088	ABBEY ROAD (LP, 1st press with laminated sleeve, black inner & dark green label)	10
70	Apple PXS 1/PCS 7096	LET IT BE (LP, box set with "Get Back" book held in cardboard support, orange-red Apple logo on LP back cover ['PXS 1' not listed on package!])	180
70	Apple PCS 7096	LET IT BE (LP, orange-red Apple logo on back cover)	10
70	Apple/Lyntone LYN 2154	FROM THEN TO YOU (The Beatles' Christmas Album) (LP, fan club issue, mail-order only)	250
76	Polydor 2683 068	THE BEATLES TAPES (2-LP, interview, gatefold sleeve with booklet)	15
78	Apple PCSPR 717	THE BEATLES 1962-1966 (2-LP, reissue, red vinyl, gatefold stickered sleeve with lyric inners)	20
78	Apple PCSPB 718	THE BEATLES 1967-1970 (2-LP, reissue, blue vinyl, gatefold stickered sleeve with lyric inners)	20
79	Parlophone PHO 7027	SGT. PEPPER'S LONELY HEARTS CLUB BAND (LP, picture disc, die-cut sleeve)	18
78	Parlophone BC 13	THE BEATLES COLLECTION (13-LP box set, stereo)	110
82	Parlophone BMC 10	THE BEATLES MONO COLLECTION (10-LP red box set, mono)	120
82	Parlophone PMC 7027	SGT. PEPPER'S LONELY HEARTS CLUB BAND (LP, from the 'Mono Collection', mispressed with stereo B-side)	15
80	WRC SM 701/708	THE BEATLES' BOX (8-LP box set, mail-order only)	70
82	Parlophone EMTVS 34	THE BEATLES' GREATEST HITS (2-LP, unreleased)	
84	St Michael 1361/5701	THEIR GREATEST HITS (cassette with 64-page book in 12" box set)	25
84	Orbis HRL 026	THE HISTORY OF ROCK VOL. 26 (2-LP)	18
86	EMI SMMC 151	ONLY THE BEATLES (mail-order 'Heineken' cassette, withdrawn)	15
87	HMV BEACD 25/1	PLEASE PLEASE ME/WITH THE BEATLES/A HARD DAY'S NIGHT/BEATLES FOR SALE (4 CDs in numbered 12" black box set with 'Book Of Beatles Lists' paperback book)	175
87	HMV BEACD 25/2	HELP!/RUBBER SOUL/REVOLVER (3 CDs in numbered 12" red box set with insert & reprint of 'Beatles Monthly', issue 12)	55
87	HMV BEACD 25/3	SGT. PEPPER'S LONELY HEARTS CLUB BAND (CD in numbered 12" box set with booklet, cut-outs & badge)	20
87	HMV BEACD 25/4	THE BEATLES (2-CD in numbered 12" box set with booklet & badge)	25
87	HMV BEACD 25/5	YELLOW SUBMARINE (CD in numbered 12" box set with insert, cut-outs & badge)	60
87	HMV BEACD 25/6	MAGICAL MYSTERY TOUR (CD in numbered 12" box set with booklet, poster & badge)	25
87	HMV BEACD 25/7	ABBEY ROAD (CD in numbered 12" box set with 2 posters, booklet & badge)	20
87	HMV BEACD 25/8	LET IT BE (CD in numbered 12" box set with booklet & badge)	20
88	HMV BEACD 25/9	PAST MASTERS VOL. 1 (CD in numbered 12" box set with booklet & badge)	15
88	HMV BEACD 25/10	PAST MASTERS VOL. 2 (CD in numbered 12" box set with booklet & badge)	15

(all CPCS and P-PCS series LPs listed below are stereo export issues, manufactured in U.K.)

65	Parlophone CPCS 101	SOMETHING NEW (LP, yellow/black label)	500
66	Parlophone CPCS 103	THE BEATLES' SECOND ALBUM (LP, yellow/black label)	500
66	Parlophone CPCS 104	BEATLES VI (LP, yellow/black label)	500
68	Parlophone P-PCS 7067/8	THE BEATLES (2-LP, yellow/black label, numbered, with black inners, poster & 4 colour prints)	800
68	Parlophone P-PCS 7067/8	THE BEATLES (2-LP, reissue, silver/black label, numbered, with black inner sleeves, poster & 4 colour prints)	400
69	Parlophone P-PCS 7070	YELLOW SUBMARINE (LP, yellow/black label)	600
69	Odeon P-PCS 7070	YELLOW SUBMARINE (LP)	500
69	Parlophone P-PCS 7070	YELLOW SUBMARINE (LP, reissue, silver/black label)	300
69	Parlophone P-PCS 7088	ABBEY ROAD (LP, yellow/black label)	600
69	Parlophone P-PCS 7088	ABBEY ROAD (LP, reissue, silver/black label)	300
69	Parlophone CPCS 101	SOMETHING NEW (LP, silver/black label, reissue)	250
69	Parlophone CPCS 103	THE BEATLES' SECOND ALBUM (LP, silver/black label, reissue)	250
69	Parlophone CPCS 104	BEATLES VI (LP, silver/black label, reissue)	250
70	Parlophone CPCS 106	HEY JUDE! (LP, silver/black label)	300
70s	Parl./Apple (P-)CPCS 106	HEY JUDE! (LP, reissue, Apple label [CPCS 106] in Parlophone sleeve)	30
70s	Apple CPCS 106	HEY JUDE! (LP, reissue, initially with dark green label)	50/25
70	Parlophone P-PCS 7096	LET IT BE (LP, yellow/black label)	600
70	Parlophone P-PCS 7096	LET IT BE (LP, reissue, silver/black label)	300
70	Parl./Apple (P-)PCS 7096	LET IT BE (LP, reissue, Apple label [PCS 7096] in Parlophone sleeve)	25

(the four coloured vinyl LPs listed below are export issues, manufactured in the U.K.)

78	Parlophone PCTC 255	MAGICAL MYSTERY TOUR (LP, transparent yellow vinyl)	40
78	Apple PCS 7067/8	THE BEATLES (2-LP, white vinyl, gatefold sleeve)	70
78	Apple PCS 7088	ABBEY ROAD (LP, green vinyl)	65
78	Apple PCS 7096	LET IT BE (LP, white vinyl)	55

(see John Lennon, Paul McCartney/Wings, George Harrison, Ringo Starr, Pete Best Four, George Martin)

BEATMEN
64	Pye 7N 15659	You Can't Sit Down/Come On Pretty Baby	8
65	Pye 7N 15792	Now The Sun Has Gone/Please Believe	5

BEAT MERCHANTS
64	Columbia DB 7367	Pretty Face/Messin' With The Man	25
65	Columbia DB 7492	So Fine/She Said Yeah	25

BEAT SIX
64	Decca F 12011	Bernadine/The River And I	6

BEATSTALKERS
65	Decca F 12259	Ev'rybody's Talking 'Bout My Baby/Mr. Disappointed	8
66	Decca F 12352	Left Right Left/You'd Better Get A Better Hold On	12
66	Decca F 12460	A Love Like Yours/Base Line	15
67	CBS 2732	My One Chance To Make It/Ain't Got No Soul (Left In These Old Shoes)	18
67	CBS 3105	Silver Treetop School For Boys/Sugar Coated Man	25
68	CBS 3557	Rain Coloured Roses/Everything Is For You	15
69	CBS 3936	When I'm Five/Little Boy	15

PAUL BEATTIE
57	Parlophone R 4385	I'm Comin' Home/Nothing So Strange	5
58	Parlophone R 4429	Me, Please Me/Wanderlust	4
58	Parlophone R 4468	Banana/A House, A Car, And A Wedding Ring	4

E.C. BEATTY
59	Felsted AF 127	Ski King/I'm A Lucky Man	12

BEAU
70	Dandelion S 4403	1917 Revolution/Sleeping Town	4
69	Dandelion S 63751	BEAU (LP)	20
71	Dandelion DAN 8006	CREATION (LP)	20

BEAU BRUMMEL
82	Moonlight MNS 004	Hot George/Oscar (p/s)	6

(see also Paul Roland)

BEAU BRUMMELS
65	Pye International 7N 25293	Laugh Laugh/Still In Love With You Baby	7
65	Pye International 7N 25306	Just A Little/They'll Make You Cry	7
65	Pye International 7N 25318	You Tell Me Why/I Want You	7
65	Pye International 7N 25333	Don't Talk To Strangers/In Good Time	7
65	Pye International NPL 28062	INTRODUCING THE BEAU BRUMMELS (LP)	30

BEAU-MARKS
60	Top Rank JAR 377	Clap Your Hands/Daddy Said	10

JIMMY BEAUMONT
66	London HLZ 10059	You Got Too Much Going For You/I Never Loved Her Anyway	35

BEAVER & KRAUSE
71	Warner Bros K 46130	GANDHARVA (LP)	10
72	Warner Bros K 46184	ALL GOOD MEN (LP)	10

BEAVERS
58	Capitol CL 14909	Road To Happiness/Low As I Can Be	4

JACKIE BEAVERS
75	Buddah BDS 423	Mr Bump Man/Somebody Help The Bigger Man	4
76	Jay Boy BOY 102	Trying To Get Back To You Girl/Trying To Get Back To You Girl (Version)	5

BEAZERS
64	Decca F 11827	The Blue Beat/I Wanna Shout	18

(see also Chris Farlowe, Little Joe Cook)

MINT VALUE £

BE-BOP DELUXE

72	Smile LAFS 001	Teenage Archangel/Jets At Dawn	20
74	Harvest HAR 5081	Jet Silver (And The Dolls Of Venus)/Third Floor Heaven	8
75	Harvest HAR 5091	Between The Worlds/Lights (withdrawn)	40
75	Harvest HAR 5098	Maid In Heaven/Lights	4
76	Harvest HAR 5104	Ships In The Night/Crying To The Sky	4
76	Harvest HAR 5110	Kiss Of The Light/FUNKY PHASER UNEARTHLY MERCHANDISE: Shine	4
77	Harvest HAR 5135	Japan/Futuristic Manifesto	4
78	Harvest HAR 5147	Panic In The World/Blue As A Jewel	4
78	Harvest HAR 5158	Electrical Language/Surreal Estate (p/s)	4
77	Harvest SHVL 816	LIVE IN THE AIR AGE (LP, with free EP "Live! In The Air Age" [PSR 412])	10

(see also Bill Nelson)

BE-BOP PRESERVATION SOCIETY

71	Dawn DNLS 3027	THE BE-BOP PRESERVATION SOCIETY (LP, gatefold sleeve with insert)	12

GILBERT BECAUD

59	HMV POP 574	The Day The Rains Came/Les Marches De Provence	4

SIDNEY BECHET

59	Vogue V 9141	Petit Fleur/Dans Les Rue D'Antibes (78)	5

GORDON BECK (QUARTET)

68	Morgan MJ 1	GYROSCOPE (LP)	50
69	M. Minor MMLP/SMLP 21	EXPERIMENTS WITH POPS (LP, as Gordon Beck Quartet)	20
69	M. Minor MMLP/SMLP 22	HALF A JAZZ SIXPENCE (LP)	20
69	Major Minor SMLP 88	DR. DOOLITTLE LOVES JAZZ (LP)	20
72	Dire FO 341	BECK-MATTHEWSON-HUMAIR TRIO (LP)	25

JEFF BECK

67	Columbia DB 8151	Hi-Ho Silver Lining/Beck's Bolero	6
67	Columbia DB 8227	Tallyman/Rock My Plimsoul	10
68	Columbia DB 8359	Love Is Blue (L'Amour Est Bleu)/I've Been Drinking	4
72	Epic EPC 7720	Got The Feeling/Situation	4
82	RAK RRP 3	Hi Ho Silver Lining/Beck's Bolero/Rock My Plimsoul (picture disc)	5
68	Columbia SCX 6293	TRUTH (LP, blue/black labels)	15
69	Columbia SCX 6351	BECK-OLA (LP, blue/black labels)	15
74	Epic Q 64619	ROUGH AND READY (LP, quadrophonic)	15
74	CBS Q 31331	JEFF BECK GROUP (LP, quadrophonic)	15

(see also Yardbirds, Beck Bogert Appice, Rod Stewart)

BECK, BOGERT, APPICE

73	Epic EPC 7720	Got The Feeling/Situation	4
73	CBS EPC 22001	BECK, BOGERT, APPICE (LP)	10
75	CBS EQ 32140/Q 65455	BECK, BOGERT, APPICE (LP, quadrophonic)	15

(see also Jeff Beck, Vanilla Fudge, Cactus)

BECKETT

74	Raft RA 48502	BECKETT (LP, with lyric insert)	10

HAROLD BECKETT

71	Philips 6308 026	FLARE UP (LP)	15
72	RCA SF 8225	WARM SMILES (LP)	15
73	RCA SF 8264	THEME FOR FEGA (LP)	15
75	Cadillac SGC 1004	JOY UNLIMITED (LP)	12

(see also Graham Collier)

K. BECKFORD

73	Big Shot BI 521	Suzie Wong/SWINGING KINGS: Deebo	5

(see also Lynn Beckford)

LYN BECKFORD

68	Island WI 3144	Combination/Hey Little Girl (actually by Keeling Beckford)	8
69	Jackpot JP 707	Kiss Me Quick/MR. MILLER: Feel It	5

THEO(PHILUS) BECKFORD

61	Blue Beat BB 15	Easy Snappin'/Goin' Home (as Theophilus Beckford)	12
61	Blue Beat BB 33	Jack And Jill Shiffle/Little Lady (as Theophilus Beckford)	12
61	Blue Beat BB 50	Georgie And The Old Shoe/That's Me	10
61	Blue Beat BB 87	Walking Down King Street/SIR DEE'S GROUP: The Clock	10
62	Blue Beat BB 132	Bringing In The Sheaves/Run Away	10
62	Island WI 026	I Don't Want You/Seven Long Years	10
63	Island WI 106	Daphney/Boller Man A Come	10
64	Blue Beat BB 250	She's Gone/Old Flame (as Cotheo Beckford, B-side actually Frederick Hibbert)	10
64	Blue Beat BB 257	Don't Worry To Cry/Love Me Or Leave Me (as Theophilus Beckford, B-side actually by Lloyd Clarke)	10
64	Blue Beat BB 287	On Your Knees/Now You're Gone (with Yvonne Harrison)	10
64	Blue Beat BB 303	Dig The Dig/Don't Let Me Cry Anymore	10
65	Black Swan WI 452	Take Your Time/STRANGER COLE: Happy Go Lucky	10
65	Island WI 238	Trenchtown People/PIONEERS: Sometime	10
65	Island WI 243	You Are The One Girl/Grateful People	10
65	Island WI 246	If Life Was A Thing/LLOYD CLARKE: Parro Saw The Light	10
65	Island WI 248	What A Woe/Bejan Girl	10
68	Nu Beat NB 009	Easy Snappin'/ERIC MORRIS: My Lonely Days	6
69	Crab CRAB 25	Brother Ram Goat (as T. Beckford)/STARLIGHTS: What A Condition	4

(see also Eric Barnet[t])

BOB BECKHAM

59	Brunswick 05808	Just As Much As Ever/Your Sweet Love	4
60	Brunswick 05822	Crazy Arms/Beloved	4
60	Brunswick 05835	Mais Oui/Only The Broken Hearted	4
60	Brunswick 05837	Nothing Is Forever/Two Wrongs Don't Make A Right	4

DAVID BEDFORD

70	Argo ZRG 638	MUSIC FOR ALBION MOONLIGHT (LP, 1 side by Elizabeth Lutyens)	20
72	Dandelion 2310 165	NURSE'S SONG WITH ELEPHANTS (LP, gatefold sleeve)	20
74	Virgin V 2020	STARS END (LP)	10
75	Virgin V 2026	ORCHESTRAL TUBULAR BELLS (LP)	10
75	Virgin V 2038	RIME OF THE ANCIENT MARINER (LP)	10
76	Virgin V 2070	THE ODYSSEY (LP)	10

(see also Coxhill/Bedford Trio, Kevin Ayers & Whole World, Mike Oldfield)

BEDLAM

73	Chrysalis CHR 1048	BEDLAM (LP)	12

(see also Cozy Powell)

EDWIN BEE

68	Decca F 12781	I've Been Loving You/Call For My Baby	6

MOLLY BEE

57	London HLD 8400	Since I Met You, Baby/I'll Be Waiting For You	12
57	London HLD 8400	Since I Met You, Baby/I'll Be Waiting For You (78)	8
58	Capitol CL 14849	Going Steady (With A Dream)/Magic Mirror	5
58	Capitol CL 14880	Don't Look Back/Please Don't Talk About Me When I'm Gone	5
58	Capitol CL 14949	After You've Gone/Five Points Of A Star	5
65	MGM MGM 1280	Single Girl Again/Keep It A Secret	4

BEEFEATERS

64	Pye International 7N 25277	Please Let Me Love You/Don't Be Long	50
70	Elektra 2101 007	Please Let Me Love You/Don't Be Long (reissue)	15

(see also Byrds)

BEE GEES

67	Polydor 56727	Spicks And Specks/I Am The World	5
67	Polydor 56161	New York Mining Disaster 1941/I Can't See Nobody	4
67	Polydor 56178	To Love Somebody/Close Another Door	4
60s	Polydor	other 45s	3-4
67	Polydor 582/583 012	BEE GEES FIRST (LP)	10
68	Polydor 582/583 020	HORIZONTAL (LP)	10
68	Polydor 236 221	RARE PRECIOUS AND BEAUTIFUL (LP)	12
68	Polydor 236 513	RARE PRECIOUS AND BEAUTIFUL VOL. 2 (LP)	12
68	Polydor 236 556	RARE PRECIOUS AND BEAUTIFUL VOL. 3 (LP)	12
68	Polydor 582/583 036	IDEA (LP)	10
69	Polydor 582 049/050	ODESSA (2-LP, felt cover)	20
70	Polydor 2383 010	CUCUMBER CASTLE (LP)	10
70	Polydor 2310 069	TWO YEARS ON (LP)	10
71	Polydor 2383 052	TRAFALGAR (LP)	10
72	Polydor 2383 139	TO WHOM IT MAY CONCERN (LP)	10

(see also Barry Gibb, Robin Gibb, Maurice Gibb, Humpy Bong, Fut)

MARK BEER

80	Waste WAS 001	ISOLATIONS (EP, with printed info sheet)	5
81	My China TAO 001	DUST ON THE ROAD (LP)	25

BEES

67	Blue Beat BB 386	Jesse James Rides Again/The Girl In My Dreams	7
67	Columbia Blue Beat DB 101	Jesse James Rides Again/The Girl In My Dreams	6
68	Columbia Blue Beat DB 111	The Prisoner From Alcatraz/The Ska's The Limit	6

BEES MAKE HONEY

73	EMI EMI 2078	Knee Trembler/Caldonia	5
72	EMI EMC 3013	MUSIC EVERY NIGHT (LP)	18

BEE VAMP

81	Monsters In Orbit TVEYE 2	Valium Girls/Lucky Grills/Without Barry In Bengal (p/s)	5

B.E.F. (British Electric Foundation)

91	Ten/Flexi (no cat. no.)	Excerpts From The Album Music Of Quality And Distinction Vol. II (promo-only flexidisc)	4
82	Virgin VV 2219	MUSIC OF QUALITY & DISTINCTION VOL. 1 (5 x 7" box set & insert)	10
88	Virgin BEF 1	MUSIC FOR LISTENING TO (LP, export issue)	10

(see also Heaven 17)

BEGGARS FARM

84	White Rabbit WR 1001	THE DEPTH OF A DREAM (LP)	45

BEGGARS HILL

76	Moonshine MS 60	BEGGARS HILL (LP, private pressing)	250

BEGGARS OPERA

70	Vertigo 6059 026	Sarabande/Think	8
70	Vertigo 6059 060	Hobo/Pathfinder	4
73	Vertigo 6059 088	Two Timing Woman/Lady Of Hell Fire	4
74	Vertigo 6059 105	Classical Gas/Sweet Blossom Woman	5
70	Vertigo 6360 018	ACT ONE (LP, spiral label, gatefold sleeve)	20
71	Vertigo 6360 054	WATERS OF CHANGE (LP, spiral label, gatefold sleeve)	25
72	Vertigo 6360 073	PATHFINDER (LP, spiral label, foldout poster cover)	20
73	Vertigo 6360 090	GET YOUR DOG OFF ME! (LP, 'spaceship' label)	10

BEGINNING OF THE END

71	Atlantic 2091 097	Funky Nassau Pts 1 & 2	4
71	Atlantic K 40304	FUNKY NASSAU (LP)	18

BRENDAN BEHAN

60	Argo RG 239	THE HOSTAGE (LP)	10

MINT VALUE £

DOMINIC BEHAN

59	Decca F 11147	The Bells Of Hell/The Captains And The Kings	4
60	Topic 12T 35	DOWN RY TYE LIFERSIDE — IRISH STREET BALLADS (LP)	10
61	Topic 12T 44	EASTER WEEK AND AFTER — SONGS OF "THE TROUBLES" (LP)	10
66	Pye NPL 18134	IRELAND SINGS (LP)	10

BIX BEIDERBECKE & HIS GANG

60	Philips JAZ 116	Since My Best Gal Turned Me Down/At The Jazz Band Ball	4
55	Columbia SEG 7523	BIX BEIDERBECKE AND HIS ORCHESTRA (EP)	12
56	Columbia SEG 7577	BIX BEIDERBECKE (EP)	12
55	Columbia 33SL 1035	THE GREAT BIX (10" LP)	20

(HARRY) BELAFONTE

54	HMV 7M 202	Hold 'Em Joe/Suzanne (Every Night When The Sun Goes Down)	6
54	HMV 7M 224	I'm Just A Country Boy/Pretty As A Rainbow	6
55	Capitol CL 14312	Close Your Eyes/I Still Get A Thrill (Thinking Of You)	6
57	HMV POP 308	Banana Boat Song (Day-O)/Jamaica Farewell	8
57	HMV POP 339	Mama Looka Boo Boo/Don't Ever Love Me	6
57	HMV POP 360	Scarlet Ribbons (For Her Hair)/Hold 'Em Joe	8
57	RCA RCA 1007	Island In The Sun/Coconut Woman	5
57	RCA RCA 1022	Mary's Boy Child/Eden Was Just Like This	5
58	RCA RCA 1033	Judy Drowned/Lucy's Door	4
58	RCA RCA 1035	Lead Man Holler/Haiti Cherie	4
56	Capitol EAP1 619	CLOSE YOUR EYES (EP)	7
57	HMV 7EG 8211	CALYPSO (EP)	7
57	HMV 7EG 8259	MATHILDA MATHILDA (EP)	7
57	HMV DLP 1147	THE VERSATILE MR. BELAFONTE (10" LP)	15
57	HMV CLP 1122	MARK TWAIN AND OTHER FOLK FAVOURITES (LP)	12
57	RCA RC 24005	BELAFONTE SINGS OF THE CARIBBEAN (10" LP)	12
57	RCA RD 27001	AN EVENING WITH BELAFONTE (LP)	10
58	RCA RD 27092	TO WISH YOU A MERRY CHRISTMAS (LP)	10
59	RCA RD 27093	BELAFONTE SINGS THE BLUES (LP)	10
59	RCA RD 27107	CALYPSO (LP)	10
59	RCA RD 27116	LOVE IS A GENTLE THING (LP)	10
59	RCA RD 27129	PORGY AND BESS (LP, with Lena Horne)	12
59	RCA RD 27151/SF 5050	BELAFONTE AT CARNEGIE HALL (LP, mono/stereo)	10/12
60	RCA RD 27170/SF 5058	MY LORD, WHAT A MORNIN'! (LP, mono/stereo)	10/12
61	RCA RD 27172/SF 5061	SWING DAT HAMMER (LP)	10/12
61	RCA RD 27205/SF 5088	BELAFONTE RETURNS TO CARNEGIE HALL (LP)	10/12

(see also Lena Horne)

BEL CANTO'S

65	R&B MRB 5003	Feel Aw Right Pts 1 & 2	10

BELFAST GYPSIES

66	Island WI 3007	Gloria's Dream/Secret Police	15

(see also Them)

ED 'TEX' BELIN

63	Starlite STEP 39	ED 'TEX' BELIN (EP)	12
67	Starlite GRK 509	ED 'TEX' BELIN (EP, reissue)	8

ALEXANDER BELL

67	CBS 2977	Alexander Bell Believes/Hymn ... With Love	7

ARCHIE BELL & DRELLS

68	Atlantic 584 185	Tighten Up/Dog Eat Dog	6
68	Atlantic 584 217	I Can't Stop Dancing/You're Such A Beautiful Child	5
71	Atlantic 2091 156	Tighten Up/I Can't Stop Dancing/(There's Gonna Be A) Showdown	5
72	Atlantic K 10210	Here I Go Again/A World Without Music	4
68	Atlantic	TIGHTEN UP (LP)	18
72	Atlantic K 40454	HERE I GO AGAIN (LP)	10
76	Phil. Intl. PIR 81567	WHERE WILL WE GO WHEN THE PARTY'S OVER (LP)	10

BELINDA BELL

73	Columbia SCXA 9255	STONE VALLEY (LP, gatefold sleeve)	30
73	One Up OU 2009	MUSIC OF W. GULGOWSKI (LP)	10

BENNY BELL & BLOCK BUSTERS

57	Parlophone R 4372	The Sack Dress/Dr. Jazz	7

CHARLES BELL & CONTEMPORARY JAZZ QUARTET

63	London HA-K/SH-K 8095	ANOTHER DIMENSION (LP)	10

FREDDIE BELL & BELLBOYS

56	Mercury MT 122	Giddy-Up-A Ding Dong/I Said It And I'm Glad (78)	10
57	Mercury MT 141	Hucklebuck/Rompin' And Stompin' (78)	10
57	Mercury MT 146	Teach You To Rock/Take The First Train Out Of Town (78)	10
57	Mercury MT 149	Big Bad Wolf/Rockin' The Polonaise (78)	10
57	Mercury MT 159	Rockin' Is My Business/You're Gonna Be Sorry (78)	10
56	Mercury MEP 9508	ROCK WITH THE BELL BOYS (EP)	30
57	Mercury MEP 9512	ROCK WITH THE BELL BOYS VOL. 2 (EP)	40

FREDRICK BELL

68	Nu Beat NB 004	Rocksteady Cool/CARLTON ALPHONSO: I Have Changed	5

GRAHAM BELL

66	Polydor 56067	How Can I Say I Don't Love You/If You're Gonna Go	6

(see also Heavy Jelly, Griffin, Every Which Way, Skip Bifferty)

MADELINE BELL

63	HMV POP 1215	I Long For Your Love/Because You Didn't Care	8
64	Columbia DB 7257	You Don't Love Me No More/Don't Cross Over To My Side Of The Street	5

65	Columbia DB 7512	Daytime/Don't Cry My Heart Out 5
65	Philips BF 1448	What The World Needs Now Is Love/I Can't Wait To See My Baby's Face 12
66	Philips BF 1501	Don't Come Running To Me/I Got Carried Away 6
66	Philips BF 1526	One Step At A Time/You Won't See Me 5
67	Philips BF 1611	Picture Me Gone/Go Ahead On 12
68	Philips BF 1656	I'm Gonna Make You Love Me/I'm Gonna Leave You 6
68	Philips BF 1688	Thinkin'/Don't Give Your Love Away 4
67	Philips (S)BL 7818	BELLS A POPPIN' (LP) 10
68	Philips SBL 7865	DOIN' THINGS (LP) 10

(see also Seven Ages Of Man, Blue Mink)

MAGGIE BELL

| 73 | Polydor 2383 239 | QUEEN OF THE NIGHT (LP) .... 10 |
| 75 | Polydor 2383 313 | SUICIDE SAL (LP) .... 10 |

(see also Stone The Crows)

WILLIAM BELL

67	Atlantic 584 076	Never Like This Before/Soldier's Goodbye 5
69	Atlantic 584 259	Everyday Will Be Like A Holiday/Ain't Got No Girl 4
67	Stax 601 019	Eloise (Hang On In There)/One Plus One 5
68	Stax 601 038	A Tribute To A King/Every Man Oughta Have A Woman 4
69	Stax STAX 110	I Forgot How To Be Your Lover/Bring The Curtain Down 4
69	Stax STAX 128	Happy/Johnny I Love You 8
68	Atco 228 003	TRIBUTE TO A KING (LP) 12
69	Stax SXATS 1016	BOUND TO HAPPEN (LP) 10
73	Stax 2362 027	PHASES OF REALITY (LP) 10

(see also Judy Clay & William Bell)

GEORGE BELLAMY

| 65 | Parlophone R 5282 | Where I'm Bound/How Could I Ever .... 8 |

(see also Tornados)

PETER BELLAMY

68	Argo	MAINLY NORFOLK (LP) 20
69	Topic 12T 200	THE FOX JUMPS OVER THE PARSON'S GATE (LP) 10
70	Argo ZFB 11	OAK, ASH AND THORN (LP) 20
71	Argo ZFB 37	WON'T YOU GO MY WAY (LP) 15
72	Argo ZFB 81	MERLIN'S ISLE OF GRAMARYE (LP) 15
74	Trailer LER 2089	PETER BELLAMY (LP) 10
83	Fellside FE 032	PETER BELLAMY WITH FRIENDS: KEEP ON KIPLING (LP) 15

(see also Young Tradition)

BELL & ARC

| 71 | Charisma CAS 1053 | BELL & ARC (LP) .... 10 |

(see also Skip Bifferty)

BELL BROTHERS

| 68 | Action ACT 4510 | Tell Him No/Throw Away The Key .... 6 |

BELLES

| 70 | President PT 311 | Don't Pretend/Words Can't Explain .... 5 |

BELLE STARS

81	Stiff PBUY 117	Hiawatha/Big Blonde (picture disc) 4
82	Stiff PBUY 155	The Clapping Song/Blame (picture disc) 4
82	Stiff PBUY 167	Sign Of The Times/Madness (picture disc) 4

(see also Bodysnatchers)

BELL NOTES

59	Top Rank JAR 102	I've Had It/Be Mine 5
59	Top Rank JAR 147	Old Spanish Town/She Went That-a-way 5
59	Top Rank JAR 201	That's Right/Betty Dear 5

BELLS OF JOY

| 55 | Vogue V 2357 | I'm Gonna Press On/How Sweet It Is (78) .... 12 |

BELL SOUNDS

| 59 | HMV POP 685 | Marching Guitars/Chloe .... 5 |

LOUIS BELLSON

| 50s | Columbia Clef SEG 10030 | BOOGIE WOOGIE PIANO AND DRUMS NO. 1 (EP) .... 7 |
| 50s | Columbia Clef SEG 10052 | BOOGIE WOOGIE PIANO AND DRUMS NO. 2 (EP) .... 7 |

TONY BELLUS

| 59 | London HL 8933 | Robbin' The Cradle/Valentine Girl .... 25 |

BELMONTS

| 61 | Pye International 7N 25094 | Tell Me Why/Smoke From Your Cigarette .... 8 |
| 62 | Stateside SS 128 | Come On Little Angel/How About Me? .... 6 |

(see also Dion & Belmonts)

BELOUIS SOME

| 85 | Parlophone RD 6134 | Jerusalem (Remix)/Target Practice//Round And Round/Stand Down
(double pack, gatefold p/s) .... 4 |

BELOVED

86	Flim Flam HARP 2	A Hundred Words (Radio Mix)/Slow Drowning (freebie) 6
86	Flim Flam HARP 2T	A Hundred Words/Slow Drowning/In Trouble And Shame (12", p/s) ... 10
86	Flim Flam HARP 3	This Means War/If Only (p/s) 5
86	Flim Flam HARP 3T	This Means War/Let It Begin/Saints Preserve Us (12", p/s) 8
87	Flim Flam HARP 7	Forever Dancing/Surprise Me (p/s) 5
87	Flim Flam HARP 7ET	Forever Dancing (Remix) (12", p/s) 12
89	WEA YZ 311W	Loving Feeling/Acid Love (poster p/s) 4
89	WEA YZ 311CD	Loving Feeling/Acid Love (CD in picture case) 15

89	WEA YZ 357TX	Your Love Takes Me Higher (Angelic Mix)/Paradise (My Darling, My Angel) (12", p/s)	8
89	WEA YZ 414T	The Sun Rising/The Sun Rising (Gentle Night)/The Sun Rising (Eurovisionary)/The Sun Rising (Deeply Satisfying) (12")	7
89	WEA YZ 414TP	The Sun Rising/The Sun Rising (Version) (12", picture disc)	7
90	WEA YZ 426T	Hello (Honky Tonk)/Hello/Hello (Uncle Arthur) (12", p/s)	7
90	WEA YZ 426TX	Hello ('Ello 'Ello)/Hello (What's All This Then?) (12", stickered p/s)	8
90	WEA YZ 463P	Your Love Takes Me Higher/Paradise (reissue, shaped picture disc)	6
90	WEA YZ 482X	Time After Time/Time After Time (Through The Round Window) (picture disc, 3-D flip pack)	7

BELT & BRACES ROADSHOW BAND
| 70s | Belt & Braces Roadshow | BELT & BRACES ROADSHOW BAND (LP, with lyric sheet) | 15 |

BELTONES
68	Trojan TR 628	No More Heartaches/I'll Follow You	7
69	Duke DU 17	Home Without You/Why Pretend	7
69	High Note HS 017	Mary Mary/Going Away	8
69	High Note HS 023	A Broken Heart	6
72	Ackee ACK 150	Wrapped Up In Love/SOUND DIMENSION: Pasero	5
(see Bop & Beltones)

JESSE BELVIN
| 59 | RCA RCA 1119 | Guess Who/Funny | 8 |
| 59 | RCA RCA 1119 | Guess Who/Funny (78) | 8 |

BEN
| 71 | Vertigo 6360 052 | BEN (LP, gatefold sleeve, spiral label) | 125 |

PAT BENATAR
79	Chrysalis CHS 2373	If You Think You Know How To Love Me/So Sincere (p/s)	7
79	Chrysalis CHS 2395	Heartbreaker/My Clone/Sleeps Alone (p/s)	4
80	Chrysalis CHS 2403	We Live For Love/I Need A Lover (p/s)	4
80	Chrysalis CHS 2474	Hit Me With Your Best Shot/You Better Run/Heartbreaker/We Live For Love (p/s, red vinyl)	5
81	Chrysalis CHS 2511	Treat Me Right/Hell Is For Children (p/s, clear vinyl)	8
81	Sounds FREEBIE No. 1	Promises In The Dark (Edit)/MICHAEL SCHENKER GROUP: Let Sleeping Dogs Lie (flexidisc in red printed sleeve, free with 'Sounds' magazine)	5/4
81	Chrysalis CHS 2529	Fire And Ice/Hard To Believe (p/s, clear vinyl)	6
81	Chrysalis CHSP 2529	Fire And Ice/Hard To Believe (picture disc)	5
83	Chrysalis CHSP 2662	Shadows Of The Night/The Victim (shaped picture disc)	8
83	Chrysalis CHS 12 2662	Shadows Of The Night/The Victim (12", p/s, blue vinyl)	7
84	Chrysalis CHSP 2747	Love Is A Battlefield/Hell Is For Children (live) (picture disc)	5
84	Chrysalis CHSP 2821	We Belong/Suburban King (picture disc)	4
85	Chrysalis PATP 2	Shadows Of The Night/Hit Me With Your Best Shot (shaped pic disc, with plinth)	6
82	Chrysalis PCHR 1396	GET NERVOUS (LP, picture disc)	10
84	Chrysalis CHRP 1451	LIVE FROM EARTH (LP, picture disc)	10

RALF BENDIX & LITTLE ELIZABETH
| 65 | Columbia DB 7774 | Sag Mir Deine Sorgen/Baby Sittin' Boogie | 6 |

TEX BENEKE & HIS ORCHESTRA
| 56 | MGM SP 1158 | 'S Wonderful/Singin' In The Rain | 4 |

ROGER BENNET
| 67 | Polydor NH 56724 | Night Flight To Tokyo/Memories | 4 |

BOBBY BENNETT (U.K.)
67	CBS 202511	Just Say Goodbye/She Believes In Me	8
68	Columbia DB 8435	All My Life Is You/To Give (The Reason I Live)	6
69	Columbia DB 8532	Music Mother Made/You're Ready Now	25

BOBBY BENNETT (U.S.)
| 69 | London HL 10274 | Big New York/Baby, Try Me | 8 |

BOYD BENNETT & HIS ROCKETS
55	Parlophone MSP 6161	Everlovin'/Boogie At Midnight (with Big Moe)	150
55	Parlophone R 4002	Everlovin'/Boogie At Midnight (78) (with Big Moe)	25
55	Parlophone MSP 6180	Seventeen/Little Ole You-All	150
55	Parlophone R 4063	Seventeen/Little Ole You-All (78)	15
56	Parlophone MSP 6203	My Boy — Flat Top/Banjo Rock And Roll	150
56	Parlophone R 4121	My Boy — Flat Top/Banjo Rock And Roll (78)	15
56	Parlophone MSP 6233	Blue Suede Shoes/Oo-Oo-Oo (with Big Moe)	110
56	Parlophone R 4167	Blue Suede Shoes/Oo-Oo-Oo (with Big Moe) (78)	18
58	Parlophone R 4423	Click Clack/Move	100
58	Parlophone R 4423	Click Clack/Move (78)	25
59	Mercury AMT 1031	Tear It Up/Tight Tights (as Big Moe & His Orchestra)	40
59	Mercury AMT 1031	Tear It Up/Tight Tights (as Big Moe & His Orchestra) (78)	25
(see also Big Moe & Boyd Bennett, Moon Mullican)

BRIAN BENNETT
67	Columbia DB 8294	Canvas/Slippery Jim De Grize	12
74	Fontana 6007 040	Chase Side Shoot-Up/Pegasus	10
76	DJM DJS 10714	Thunderbolt/Clearing Skies (promos in p/s)	8/4
77	DJM DJS 10756	Saturday Night Special/Farewell To A Friend (promos in p/s)	8/4
77	DJM DJS 10791	Girls Back Home/Jony Jump	4
78	DJM DJS 10843	Pendulum Force/Ocean Glide	4
82	DJM DJS 10981	Top Of The World/Soul Ice	4
68	Columbia S(C)X 6144	CHANGE OF DIRECTION (LP)	25
69	Col. Studio Two TWO 268	ILLUSTRATED LONDON NOISE (LP)	50
77	DJM DJF 20499	ROCK DREAMS (LP)	10
(see also Shadows, Thunder Company, Wasp, Marty Wilde & Wildcats, Krewcats, Collage, Alan Skidmore, Big Jim Sullivan)

CAROLE BENNETT
56	Capitol CL 14652	The Little Magician/I Was Your Only Love	4
57	Capitol CL 14692	Play The Music/Miser's Gold	4
57	Capitol CL 14725	Haunted Lover/Let The Chips Fall (Where They May)	4

CLIFF BENNETT & REBEL ROUSERS
61	Parlophone R 4793	You've Got What I Like/I'm In Love With You	15
61	Parlophone R 4836	When I Get Paid/That's What I Said	15
62	Parlophone R 4895	Hurtin' Inside/Poor Joe	15
63	Parlophone R 5046	My Old Stand-By/Everybody Loves A Lover	5
63	Parlophone R 5080	You Really Got A Hold On Me/Alright	5
64	Parlophone R 5119	Got My Mojo Working/Beautiful Dreamer	5
64	Parlophone R 5173	One Way Love/Slow Down	4
65	Parlophone R 5229	I'll Take You Home/Do You Love Him?	4
65	Parlophone R 5259	Three Rooms Of Running Water/If Only You'd Reply	5
65	Parlophone R 5317	I Have Cried My Last Tear/As Long As She Looks Like You	5
66	Parlophone R 5406	You Can't Love 'Em All/Need Your Loving Tonight	4
66	Parlophone R 5466	Eyes For You/Hold On I'm Coming	4
66	Parlophone R 5534	Never Knew Lovin' Could Be So Doggone Good/Don't Help Me Out	4
67	Parlophone R 5565	I'm Sorry/I'll Take Good Care Of You	6
67	Parlophone R 5598	I'll Be There/Use Me	4
68	Parlophone R 5666	Take Your Time/House Of A Thousand Dolls (by Cliff Bennett Band)	5
68	Parlophone R 5691	You're Breaking Me Up (And I'm Wasting Away)/I Hear Her Voice (by Cliff Bennett Band)	4
68	Parlophone R 5711	Lonely Weekends/Good Times (by Cliff Bennett Band)	4
68	Parlophone R 5728	One More Heartache/Nobody Runs Forever	6
68	Parlophone R 5749	Back In The USSR/This Man (by Cliff Bennett Band)	4
64	Parlophone GEP 8923	CLIFF BENNETT AND THE REBEL ROUSERS (EP)	25
65	Parlophone GEP 8936	TRY IT BABY (EP)	22
66	Parlophone GEP 8955	WE'RE GONNA MAKE IT (EP)	50
64	Parlophone PMC 1242	CLIFF BENNETT AND THE REBEL ROUSERS (LP)	35
66	M. For Pleasure MFP 1121	DRIVIN' YOU WILD (LP)	10
66	EMI Regal REG 1039	CLIFF BENNETT (LP, export issue)	15
67	Parlophone PCS 7017	GOT TO GET YOU INTO OUR LIVES (LP)	35
68	Parlophone PMC/PCS 7054	BRANCHES OUT (LP, as Cliff Bennett & His Band)	30

(see also Charles Hodges, Rebel Rousers, Toefat)

DICKIE BENNETT
55	Decca F 10595	There, But For The Grace Of God Go I/Stars Shine In Your Eyes	4
56	Decca F 10697	Dungaree Doll/Can't We Be Partners (After The Dance)	6
56	Decca F 10782	You Don't Know Me/Cry Upon My Shoulder	4

DUSTER BENNETT
68	Blue Horizon 57-3141	It's A Man Down There/Things Are Changing	10
68	Blue Horizon 57-3148	Raining In My Heart/Jumpin' For Joy	12
69	Blue Horizon 57-3154	Bright Lights, Big City/Fresh Country Jam	10
69	Blue Horizon 57-3164	I'm Gonna Wind Up Endin' Up Or I'm Gonna End Up Windin' Up With You/Rock Of Ages, Cleft For Me	15
70	Blue Horizon 57-3173	I Chose To Sing The Blues/If You Could Hang Your Washing Like You Hang Your Lines	8
70	Blue Horizon 57-3179	Act Nice And Gentle/I Want You To Love Me	8
74	Rak RAK 177	Comin' Home/Pretty Little Thing	12
68	Blue Horizon 7-63208	SMILING LIKE I'M HAPPY (LP, with His House Band, i.e. Fleetwood Mac)	30
69	Blue Horizon 7-63221	BRIGHT LIGHTS... (LP, gatefold sleeve)	45
70	Blue Horizon 7-63868	12 DB's (LP)	25

(see also Fleetwood Mac)

JOE BENNETT & SPARKLETONES
57	HMV POP 399	Black Slacks/Boppin' Rock Boogie	100
57	HMV POP 399	Black Slacks/Boppin' Rock Boogie (78)	18
58	HMV POP 445	Rocket/Penny Loafers And Bobby Socks	80
58	HMV POP 445	Rocket/Penny Loafers And Bobby Socks (78)	30

JO JO BENNETT
67	Doctor Bird DB 1097	The Lecture/Cantelope Rock (with Fugitives)	10
67	Doctor Bird DB 1117	Rocksteady/Real Gone Loser (with Fugitives)	10
70	Explosion EX 2029	Groovy Jo Jo/Ten Steps To Soul (both actually by Mudie's All Stars)	4
70	Trojan TR 7774	Leaving Rome/In The Nude	5
70	Trojan TBL 133	GROOVY JO JO (LP, with Mudies Allstars)	16

KIM BENNETT
55	Decca F 10449	Softly Softly/ROLAND SHAW ORCHESTRA: Trumpeters Lullaby	6
55	Decca F 10460	Melody Of Love/Ding Dong	6
55	Decca F 10599	The Kentuckian Song/Overnight	4
56	Decca F 10706	No, Not Much/You Can't Keep Running	4

LEE BENNETT & SUNLINERS
64	Decca F 12024	Poor Bachelor Boy/Fool, Fool, Fool	5

NICKY BENNETT
60	Columbia DB 4516	You Understand Me/Mr. Lonely	4

PETER E. BENNETT
71	RCA SF 8190	THE BALLAD OF GALDWAIN (LP)	10

RAY BENNETT
62	Decca DFE 8516	INTRODUCING RAY BENNETT (EP)	12

RUDI BENNETT
68	Decca F 12741	I'm So Proud/WHISTLING JACK SMITH: Havah Nagilah	4

(see also Whistling Jack Smith)

MINT VALUE £

TONY BENNETT

53	Columbia SCM 5048	Congratulations To Someone/Take Me	5
57	Philips JK 1008	Whatever Lola Wants/Heart (jukebox edition)	8
58	Philips PB 831	Young And Warm And Wonderful/Now I Lay Me Down To Sleep	4
58	Philips PB 855	Firefly/The Night That Heaven Fell	4
59	Philips PB 907	Being True To One Another/It's So Peaceful In The Country	4
59	Philips PB 961	Smile (Theme From "Modern Times")/You Can't Love 'Em All	4
60	Philips PB 996	Love Look Away/The Cool School	4
60	Philips PB 1008	Ask Me (I Know)/I'll Bring You A Rainbow	4
60	Philips PB 1079	Till/Ask Anyone In Love	4
60	Philips PB 1089	Marriage-Go-Round/Somebody	4
55	Philips BBE 12009	STRANGER IN PARADISE (EP)	7
60	Philips SBBL 542	IN PERSON (LP, with Count Basie Orchestra)	10
61	Philips BBL 7413	TO MY WONDERFUL ONE (LP)	10
61	Philips BBL 7455	SINGS A STRING OF HAROLD ARLEN (LP, also stereo SBBL 609)	10

VAL BENNETT

68	Island WI 3113	Jumping With Mr. Lee/ROY SHIRLEY: Keep Your Eyes On The Road	10
68	Island WI 3146	The Russians Are Coming (Take Five)/LESTER STERLING: Sir Lee's Whip	10
68	Trojan TR 611	Spanish Harlem/ROY SHIRLEY: If I Did Know	10
68	Trojan TR 640	Baby Baby/Barbara	8
69	Crab CRAB 6	Reggae City/CANNON KING: Mellow Trumpet (B-side actually by Carl 'King Cannon Ball' Bryan)	5
69	Camel CA 24	Midnight Spin/SOUL CATS: Money Money	4

JOHNNY BENNINGS & HIS RHYTHM & BLUES BAND

54	Esquire 10-376	Third Degree Blues/Timber (78)	25

BENNY & TINA

69	Mercury MF 1133	This Love Is Real/Over My Dead Body	8

BENNY PROFANE

88	Ediesta CALC 7048	Parasite/Kamikaze Drinking (DJ-only, no p/s)	5
90	Imaginary RED ONE	Hey Waste Of Space (1-sided, promo only)	4
	(see also Room)		

BARRY BENSON

66	Parlophone R 5446	Stay A Little While/That's For Sure	18
67	Parlophone R 5578	Cousin Jane/Meet Jacqueline	5
67	Page One POF 034	I Can't Wait/Oh No	5

BOBBIE BENSON & HIS COMBO

58	Philips PB 854	Taxi Driver, I Don't Care/Gentleman Bobby	4

GEORGE BENSON (QUARTET)

66	CBS (S)BPG 62817	IT'S UPTOWN (LP, as George Benson Quartet)	10
68	CBS 63533	WILLOW WEEP FOR ME (LP)	10
72	CTI CTL 6	WHITE RABBIT (LP)	10
74	CTI CTL 20	BODY TALK (LP)	10

HOAGY BENSON

68	CBM CBM 003	Kangaroo/Turn Me On	4

MARIE BENSON & LONDONAIRES

55	Decca F 10452	Mambo Italiano/Mobile	6

MICHAEL BENTINE

62	Parlophone PMC 1179	IT'S A SQUARE WORLD (LP, also stereo PCS 3031)	15
67	RCA RD 7885	SQUARE BASHING (LP)	10
	(see also Goons)		

BRIAN BENTLEY & BACHELORS

60	Philips PB 1085	Wishing Well/Please Make Up Your Mind	4
60	Philips PB 1086	First Flight East/Sunday Break	4
62	Salvo SLO 1813	Caramba/Nellie Dean	8

BENTLEY BROTHERS

59	Top Rank JAR 208	Ma (She's Making Eyes At Me)/Yes, We Have No Bananas	4

BROOK BENTON

56	Philips PB 639	Give Me A Sign/Love Made Me Your Fool (78)	5
58	RCA RCA 1044	A Million Miles From Nowhere/Devoted	5
58	RCA RCA 1044	A Million Miles From Nowhere/Devoted (78)	8
58	Mercury AMT 1014	It's Just A Matter Of Time/Hurtin' Inside	5
58	Mercury AMT 1014	It's Just A Matter Of Time/Hurtin' Inside (78)	15
59	Mercury AMT 1043	Endlessly/So Close	5
59	Mercury AMT 1043	Endlessly/So Close (78)	15
59	Mercury AMT 1061	Thank You Pretty Baby/With All Of My Heart	4
59	Mercury AMT 1068	So Many Ways/I Want You Forever	4
60	Mercury AMT 1097	The Ties That Bind/Hither And Thither And Yon	4
60	Mercury AMT 1109	Kiddio/The Same One	5
60	Mercury AMT 1121	Fools Rush In/Somebody You'll Want Me To Want You	4
61	Mercury AMT 1134	For My Baby/Think Twice	4
61	Mercury AMT 1148	Your Eyes/The Boll Weevil Song	4
61	Mercury AMT 1157	Frankie And Johnny/It's Just A House Without You	4
65	Mercury MF 863	Love Me Now/Asleep At The Foot Of The Bed	4
69	Mercury MF 1100	Rockin' Good Way/I Do	4
69	Atlantic 584 266	Touch 'Em With Love/She Knows What To Do For Me	4
58	Mercury MMC 14015	IT'S JUST A MATTER OF TIME (LP)	12
59	Mercury MMC 14022	ENDLESSLY (LP)	12
59	RCA Camden CDN 143	BROOK BENTON (LP)	10
60	Mercury MMC 14042	I LOVE YOU IN SO MANY WAYS (LP)	12

MINT VALUE £

60	Mercury MMC 14060	SONGS I LOVE TO SING (LP, also stereo CMS 18041)	12/14
61	Mercury MMC 14090	THE BOLL WEEVIL SONG (LP, also stereo CMS 18060)	12/14
61	Mercury MMC 14108	THERE GOES THAT SONG AGAIN (LP, also stereo CMS 18068)	12/14
62	Mercury MMC 14124	GOLDEN HITS (LP)	10
62	Mercury 20024 MCL	BORN TO SING THE BLUES (LP)	10
63	Mercury 20040 MCL	IT'S JUST A MATTER OF TIME (LP)	10
63	Mercury 20053 MCL	THIS BITTER EARTH (LP)	12

BROOK BENTON & DINAH WASHINGTON

60	Mercury AMT 1083	Baby (You've Got What It Takes)/I Do	7
60	Mercury AMT 1099	A Rockin' Good Way/I Believe	12
61	Mercury ZEP 10120	A ROCKING GOOD WAY (EP, also stereo SEZ 19022)	12/18
64	Mercury 20069 MCL	THE TWO OF US (LP)	10

BERETS

| 70s | Avant Garde AVS 116 | THE MASS FOR PEACE (LP, with insert) | 10 |

BERKELEY KITES

| 68 | Polydor 56742 | Hang Up City/Mary-Go-Round | 4 |
| 69 | Polydor 56770 | Alice In Wonderland/What Goes Up Must Come Down | 4 |

MILTON BERLE

| 56 | Vogue Coral Q 72197 | In The Middle Of The House/Buffalo | 10 |

BERLIN

| 80 | Charisma CB 351 | Over 21/Waiting For The Future (p/s) | 4 |

BERLIN BLONDES

| 80 | EMI EMI 5031 | Science/Mannequin (p/s) | 5 |
| 80 | Scratch SCR 005 | Marseille/The Poet (p/s) | 4 |

SHELLEY BERMAN

| 60 | HMV POP 732 | 'On The Phone': Hold On/Nephew Trouble | 4 |

BERMUDAS

| 64 | London HLN 9894 | Donnie/Chu Sen Ling | 4 |

KENNY BERNARD (& WRANGLERS)

65	Pye 7N 15920	The Tracker/You Gotta Give (with Wranglers)	10
66	Pye 7N 17131	Nothing Can Change This Love/What Love Brings	15
67	Pye 7N 17233	Ain't No Soul (Left In These Old Shoes)/Hey Woman	22
67	CBS 2936	Somebody/Pity My Feet	40
68	CBS 3860	Victim Of Perfume And Lace/A Change Is Gonna Come	40

ROD BERNARD

59	London HLM 8849	This Should Go On Forever/Pardon, Mr. Gordon	30
59	London HLM 8849	This Should Go On Forever/Pardon, Mr. Gordon (78)	35
59	Mercury AMT 1070	One More Chance/Shedding Teardrops Over You	8

BERNIE & BUZZ BAND

| 68 | Decca F 22829 | The House That Jack Built/PETE KELLY'S SOULUTION: Midnight Confessions (export issue) | 6 |
| 68 | Deram DM 181 | When Something's Wrong With My Baby/Don't Knock It | 5 |

(see also Pete Kelly's Soulution)

ELMER BERNSTEIN

59	Capitol CL 15101	Staccato's Theme/The Jazz At Waldo's	5
63	MGM MGM 1238	Rat Race/Saints & Sinners	10
66	United Artists UP 1163	The Magnificent Seven/Return Of The Seven	4
60	Capitol EAP1 1287	STACCATO (EP)	7

CHUCK BERRY

56	London HLU 8275	No Money Down/Down Bound Train (gold label, probably doesn't exist!)	500+
56	London HLU 8275	No Money Down/Down Bound Train (silver label, tri or round centre)	175/125
56	London HLU 8275	No Money Down/Down Bound Train (78)	50
57	London HLN 8375	You Can't Catch Me/Havana Moon (gold label, later on silver label)	175/125
57	London HLN 8375	You Can't Catch Me/Havana Moon (78)	40
57	London HLU 8428	Roll Over Beethoven/Drifting Heart	70
57	London HLU 8428	Roll Over Beethoven/Drifting Heart (78)	25
57	Columbia DB 3951	School Day (Ring! Ring! Goes The Bell)/Blue Feeling	120
57	Columbia DB 3951	School Day (Ring! Ring! Goes The Bell)/Blue Feeling (78)	15
57	London HLM 8531	Rock And Roll Music/Blue Feeling	45
57	London HLM 8531	Rock And Roll Music/Blue Feeling (78)	25
58	London HLM 8585	Sweet Little Sixteen/Reelin' And Rockin'	25
58	London HLM 8585	Sweet Little Sixteen/Reelin' And Rockin' (78)	20
58	London HLM 8629	Johnny B. Goode/Around And Around	18
58	London HLM 8629	Johnny B. Goode/Around And Around (78)	25
58	London HL 8677	Beautiful Delilah/Vacation Time	25
58	London HL 8677	Beautiful Delilah/Vacation Time (78)	25
58	London HL 8712	Carol/Hey Pedro	30
58	London HL 8712	Carol/Hey Pedro (78)	25
58	London HL 7055	Carol/Hey Pedro (export issue)	30
58	London HLM 8767	Sweet Little Rock And Roller/Joe Joe Gun	20
58	London HLM 8767	Sweet Little Rock And Roller/Joe Joe Gun (78)	25
59	London HLM 8853	Almost Grown/Little Queenie	20
59	London HLM 8853	Almost Grown/Little Queenie (78)	40
59	London HLM 8921	Back In The U.S.A./Memphis, Tennessee	15
59	London HLM 8921	Back In The U.S.A./Memphis, Tennessee (78)	70

(some of the above 45s were reissued with silver top labels & round centres, which are worth half to two-thirds the value)

60	London HLM 9069	Let It Rock/Too Pooped To Pop	15
60	London HLM 9159	Bye Bye Johnny/Mad Lad	15
61	Pye International 7N 25100	I'm Talkin' 'Bout You/Little Star (blue label)	12
63	Pye International 7N 25209	Go Go Go/Come On	5

Chuck BERRY

63	Pye International 7N 25218	Memphis, Tennessee/Let It Rock	5
63	Pye International 7N 25228	Run Rudolph Run/Johnny B. Goode	6
64	Pye International 7N 25236	Nadine (Is It You?)/O Rangutang	5
64	Pye International 7N 25242	No Particular Place To Go/Liverpool Drive	5
64	Pye International 7N 25257	You Never Can Tell/Brenda Lee	5
64	Pye International 7N 25271	Little Marie/Go Bobby Soxer	7
65	Pye International 7N 25285	The Promised Land/The Things I Used To Do	5
65	Chess CRS 8006	Lonely School Days/I Got A Booking	6
65	Chess CRS 8012	Dear Dad/My Little Lovelight	6
65	Chess CRS 8022	It Wasn't Me/It's My Own Business	6
66	Chess CRS 8037	Ramona Say Yes/Lonely School Days	6
66	Mercury MF 958	Club Nitty Gritty/Laugh And Cry	4
67	Mercury MF 994	Back To Memphis/I Do Really Love You	4
68	Chess CRS 8075	Johnny B. Goode/Sweet Little Sixteen	5
69	Chess CRS 8089	No Particular Place To Go/It Wasn't Me	5
72	Chess 6145 007	Rock And Roll Music/Johnny B. Goode/School Days	4
56	London REU 1053	RHYTHM AND BLUES WITH CHUCK BERRY (EP, maroon/gold label, triangular centre)	80
56	London REU 1053	RHYTHM AND BLUES WITH . . . (EP, maroon/silver label, round centre)	50
60	London REM 1188	REELIN' AND ROCKIN' (EP, maroon/silver label, triangular or round centre)	80/50
63	Pye International NEP 44011	CHUCK BERRY (EP)	10
63	Pye International NEP 44013	THIS IS CHUCK BERRY (EP)	10
64	Pye International NEP 44018	THE BEST OF CHUCK BERRY (EP)	10
64	Pye International NEP 44028	CHUCK BERRY HITS (EP)	10
64	Pye International NEP 44033	BLUE MOOD (EP)	10
65	Chess CRE 6002	THE PROMISED LAND (EP)	20
65	Chess CRE 6005	COME ON (EP)	20
66	Chess CRE 6012	I GOT A BOOKING (EP)	20
66	Chess CRE 6016	YOU CAME A LONG WAY FROM ST. LOUIS (EP)	20
58	London HA-M 2132	ONE DOZEN BERRYS (LP)	75
62	Pye International NPL 28019	NEW JUKE BOX HITS (LP)	25
63	Pye International NPL 28024	CHUCK BERRY (LP)	15
63	Pye International NPL 28027	CHUCK BERRY ON STAGE (LP)	12
63	Pye International NPL 28028	MORE CHUCK BERRY (LP)	10
64	Pye International NPL 28031	THE LATEST AND THE GREATEST (LP)	15
64	Pye International NPL 28039	YOU NEVER CAN TELL (LP)	15
65	Chess CRL 4005	CHUCK BERRY IN LONDON (LP)	14
65	Chess CRL 4506	FRESH BERRYS (LP)	14
66	Golden Guinea GGL 0352	CHUCK BERRY (LP)	10
67	Mercury 20110 (S)MCL	CHUCK BERRY IN MEMPHIS (LP)	10
67	Mercury 20112 (S)MCL	LIVE AT THE FILLMORE AUDITORIUM — SAN FRANCISCO (LP)	10
69	Mercury 20162 SMCL	CONCERTO IN B. GOODE (LP)	12
72	Chess 6641 018	GOLDEN DECADE (2-LP, gatefold sleeve)	14
73	Driving Wheel LP 1001	SIX TWO FIVE (LP)	25

CHUCK BERRY/BO DIDDLEY

63	Pye International NEP 44009	CHUCK AND BO (EP)	10
63	Pye International NEP 44012	CHUCK AND BO, VOL. 2 (EP)	10
64	Pye International NEP 44017	CHUCK AND BO, VOL. 3 (EP)	10
64	Pye International NPL 28047	TWO GREAT GUITARS (LP)	20

(see also Bo Diddley)

DAVE BERRY (& CRUISERS)

63	Decca F 11734	Memphis/Tossin' & Turnin' (with Cruisers)	5
63	Decca F 11803	My Baby Left Me/Hoochie Coochie Man (B-side with Cruisers)	5
65	Decca F 12103	Little Things/I've Got A Tiger By The Tail	4
65	Decca F 12188	This Strange Effect/Now	5
65	Decca F 12258	I'm Gonna Take You There/Just Don't Know	4
66	Decca F 12337	If You Wait For Love/Hidden	4
66	Decca F 12435	Mama/Walk, Walk, Talk	4
66	Decca F 12513	Picture Me Gone/Ann	5
67	Decca F 12579	Stranger/Stick By The Book	4
67	Decca F 12651	Forever/And I Have Learned To Dream	4
68	Decca F 12739	Just As Much As Ever/I Got A Feeling	4
68	Decca F 12771	(Do I Figure) In Your Life/Latisha	4
69	Decca F 12905	Oh What A Life/Huma Luma (by Dave Berry & Sponge)	4
70	Decca F 13080	Chaplin House/Trees (with involvement of Kevin Godley & Lol Creme)	4
64	Decca DFE 8601	DAVE BERRY (EP)	12
65	Decca DFE 8625	CAN I GET IT FROM YOU (EP)	10
64	Decca LK 4653	DAVE BERRY (LP)	30
66	Decca LK 4823	THE SPECIAL SOUND OF DAVE BERRY (LP)	25
66	Ace Of Clubs ACL/SCL 1218	ONE DOZEN BERRIES (LP)	15
68	Decca LK/SKL 4932	DAVE BERRY '68 (LP)	18

(see also Cruisers)

MIKE BERRY (& OUTLAWS)

61	Decca F 11314	Will You Love Me Tomorrow/My Baby Doll (with Outlaws)	12
61	HMV POP 912	Tribute To Buddy Holly/What's The Matter (with Outlaws)	8
62	HMV POP 979	It's Just A Matter Of Time/Little Boy Blue (backing group miscredited as Admirals, actually Outlaws)	8
62	HMV POP 1042	Every Little Kiss/How Many Times	8
62	HMV POP 1105	Don't You Think It's Time/Loneliness (with Outlaws)	8
63	HMV POP 1142	My Little Baby/You'll Do It, You'll Fall In Love	8
63	HMV POP 1194	It Really Doesn't Matter/Try A Little Bit Harder	8
64	HMV POP 1257	This Little Girl/On My Mind	8
64	HMV POP 1284	Lovesick/Letter Of Love	8
64	HMV POP 1314	Who Will It Be/Talk (with Innocents)	8
64	HMV POP 1362	Don't Try To Stand In My Way/Two Lovers	5

MINT VALUE £

65	HMV POP 1449	That's All I Ever Wanted From You/She Didn't Care	5
65	HMV POP 1494	It Comes And Goes/Gonna Fall In Love	5
66	HMV POP 1530	Warm Baby/Just Thought I'd 'Phone	5
67	Polydor 56182	Raining In My Heart/Eyes	5
63	HMV 7EG 8793	IT'S TIME FOR MIKE BERRY (EP, with Outlaws)	20
63	HMV 7EG 8808	A TRIBUTE TO BUDDY HOLLY (EP)	25

(see also Outlaws)

RICHARD BERRY & PHARAOHS
| 64 | Ember EMB EP 4527 | RHYTHM AND BLUES VOL. 3 (EP) | 100 |

BERRY STREET STATION
| 75 | Crystal CR 7024 | Chocolate Sugar/All I Want Is You | 8 |

JON BEST
| 65 | Decca F 12077 | Young Boy Blues/Living Without Love | 10 |

PETE BEST FOUR
| 64 | Decca F 11929 | I'm Gonna Knock On Your Door/Why Did I Fall In Love With You | 30 |

(see also Lee Curtis & Allstars)

BETHNAL
77	Bethnal VIOL 1	The Fiddler/Just Another Love Story (p/s)	7
78	Vertigo BET 1	We've Gotta Get Out Of This Place/Outcome (p/s)	4
78	Vertigo BET 2	Don't Do It/Where Do We Stand (p/s)	4
78	Vertigo BET 12	Don't Do It/Where Do We Stand (12", p/s)	7
78	Vertigo 6059 213	Nothing New/Summer Wine (p/s, blue vinyl)	4

BETHNAL
| 76 | DJM DJS 10656 | Yes I Would/Katie's Calender | 4 |
| 79 | Magic Moon MACH 7 | Morning Child | 4 |

BET LYNCH'S LEGS
| 80 | Absurd ABSURD 10 | Riders In The Sky/High Noon (p/s) | 4 |
| 80 | Absurd ABSURD 11 | Some Like It Hot/Some Don't (p/s) | 4 |

BETTERDAYS
65	Polydor BM 56024	Don't Want That/Here 'Tis	100
91	N.T.B. 001	HOWL OF THE STREETS (EP, numbered p/s)	8
92	N.T.B. 1002	DOWN ON THE WATERFRONT (EP, numbered p/s)	8

HAROLD BETTERS
| 65 | Sue WI 378 | Do Anything You Wanna Pts 1 & 2 | 12 |

DICKIE BETTS BAND
| 75 | Capricorn 2429 117 | HIGHWAY CALL (LP) | 10 |

(see also Allman Brothers)

BEVERLEY
| 66 | Deram DM 101 | Happy New Year/Where The Good Times Are | 12 |
| 67 | Deram DM 137 | Museum/DENNY CORDELL ENSEMBLE: A Quick One For Sanity | 8 |

(see also John & Beverley Martyn)

BEVERLEY SISTERS
55	Decca F 10539	I Remember Mama/I've Been Thinking	5
55	Decca F 10603	Humming Bird/Have You Ever Been Lonely?	5
55	Decca F 10641	My Heart Goes A-Sailing/Teddy Bear	5
56	Decca F 10705	Willie Can/I've Started Courtin'	8
56	Decca F 10729	Rickshaw Boy/You Ought To Have A Wife	4
56	Decca F 10770	Born To Be With You/It's Easy	6
56	Decca F 10813	Come Home To My Arms/Doodle-Doo-Doo	4
57	Decca F 10832	I Dreamed/Mama From The Train (A Kiss, A Kiss)	5
57	Decca F 10853	Greensleeves/I'll See You In My Dreams	4
57	Decca F 10893	Mr. Wonderful/Blow The Wind Southerly	4
57	Decca F 10909	Bye, Bye Love/It's Illegal, It's Immoral, Or It Makes You Fat	6
57	Decca F 10943	Riding Down From Bangor/The Young Cavaliero	4
58	Decca F 10971	Without You/Long Black Nylons	8
58	Decca F 10999	Always And Forever/Siesta	4
58	Decca F 11042	Left Right Out Of My Heart/I Would (Climb The Highest Mountain)	4
59	Decca F 11107	The Little Drummer Boy/Strawberry Fair	4
59	Decca F 11172	Little Donkey/And Kings Come A-Calling	4
56	Columbia SEG 7602	THREE'S COMPANY (EP)	7
56	Decca DFE 6307	THE BEVERLEY SISTERS (EP)	7
57	Decca DFE 6401	THE BEVERLEY SISTERS NO. 2 (EP)	8
58	Decca DFE 6512	THE BEVERLEY SISTERS NO. 4 (EP)	7
55	Philips BBR 8052	A DATE WITH THE BEVS (10" LP)	15
60	Columbia 33SX 1285	THE ENCHANTING BEVERLEY SISTERS (LP)	10
60	Ace Of Clubs ACL 1048	THOSE BEVERLEY SISTERS (LP)	10

BEVERLEY'S ALLSTARS
| 65 | Black Swan WI 449 | Go Home/THEO BECKFORD: Ungrateful People | 10 |
| 69 | Trojan TR 683 | Double Shot/Gimme Gimme Gal (B-side actually "Banana Water" by Mellotones) | 5 |

BEVIS FROND
88	Freakbeat/Lyntone	African Violets (flexidisc free with 'Freakbeat' fanzine)	8/6
88	Bucketfull Of Brains BOB 21	High In A Flat/DREAM SYNDICATE: Blind Willie McTell (free with 'Bucketfull Of Brains' issue 27, 33rpm, yellow die-cut sleeve)	7/5
90	Clawfist PIS 1	Sexorcist/WALKINGSEEDS: Reflection In A Tall Mirror (p/s, mail-order only)	6
87	Woronzow WOO 3	MIASMA (LP)	15
87	Woronzow WOO 4	INNER MARSHLAND (LP)	15
87	Woronzow WOO 5 1/2	BEVIS THROUGH THE LOOKING GLASS (2-LP, heavily counterfeited)	60
88	Woronzow WOO 8	TRIPTYCH (LP)	15

(see also Von Trap Family, Room 13)

MINT VALUE £

RODNEY BEWES
69	Revolution REV 1003	Remember When/Dear Mother Love Albert	6
70	Revolution Pop REVP 1001	Dear Mother Love Albert/Meter Maid	6

BEYOND
82	MJB MEL 001	My Father's Name Was Dad/Grey (p/s)	4

B-52s
79	Island WIP 6527	6060-842/Hero Worship (p/s)	4
80	Island PWIP 6551	Planet Claire/There's A Moon In The Sky (Called The Moon) (picture disc)	6
80	Island WIP 6579	Give Me Back My Man/Give Me Back My Man (Version) (p/s, mispressed B-side plays "Strobe Light")	8
80	Island WIP 6685	Strobe Light/Dirty Back Road (in blue/black plastic bag)	6
83	Island ISD 107	Future Generation/Future Generation (Instrumental)//Planet Claire/There's A Moon In The Sky (Called The Moon) (double pack, gatefold p/s)	6
86	Island BFTD 1	Rock Lobster/Planet Claire//Song For A Future Generation/52 Girls (double pack)	5
86	Island BFTR/BFTL/BFTP 1	Rock Lobster/Planet Claire (set of 3 x 10" x 7" picture discs ['rock'/'lobster'/'planet'], each with same tracks, in printed PVC folder)	15
79	Island ILPS 9580	THE B-52s (LP, with free single "Rock Lobster"/"52 Girls" [PSR 438])	12
80	Island ILPS 9622	WILD PLANET (LP, in plastic bag with badge)	10

MAURICIO BIANCHI
81	Sterile SR 2	SYMPATHY FOR A GENOCIDE (LP, 200 only)	70

GENE BIANCO GROUP
53	London L 1209	Limehouse Boogie/Harpin' Boogie (78)	5
60	Vogue V 9167	Alarm Clock Rock/Harp Rock Boogie	15

BIBBY
65	Blue Beat BB 289	Rub It Down/Wicked Man	10

(see also B.B. Seaton)

BIBLE
86	Backs NCH 109	Graceland/Sweetness (black p/s)	5
86	Backs NCH 111	Mahalia/Spend Spend Spend (p/s)	4
86	Backs NCH 111	Mahalia/Spend Spend Spend/Sweetness (12", p/s)	7
86	Chrysalis BIBG 1	Graceland (Remix)/Glorybound (live)//Mahalia/Spend Spend Spend (double pack, gatefold p/s)	4

(see also Great Divide)

BIDDLE UNIVERSITY QUINTET
25	Actuelle 11225	Ezekiel Saw De Wheel/I've Got A Home In That Rock (78)	40
25	Actuelle 11226	Heaven/Who'll Be A Witness (78)	40

BIDDU
67	Regal Zonophone RZ 3002	Daughter Of Love/Look Out Here I Come	5
69	Polydor 56323	Started Me Thinking/Where In The World	4

(see also Headbangers)

BIELERFELDER KINDERCHOR
66	Parlophone CPCS 105	A GERMAN CHRISTMAS (LP, export issue, yellow/black label)	10

BIFF BANG POW!
84	Creation CRE 003	Fifty Years Of Fun/Then When I Scream (foldaround sprayed p/s in poly bag)	8
84	Creation CRE 007	There Must Be A Better Life/The Chocolate Elephant Man (in foldaround p/s in poly bag)	15
90s	Caff CAFF 13	Sleep/TIMES: Extase (p/s, with insert)	20
89	Creation CRELP 046	THE ACID HOUSE ALBUM (LP, hand-sprayed sleeve)	10

(see also Laughing Apple)

BIG AUDIO DYNAMITE
85	CBS TA 6963/QTA 6591	E=MC² (Extended Remix)/This Is Big Audio Dynamite//The Bottom Line (U.S. Remix)/B.A.D. (12" double pack, shrink-wrapped with sticker)	8
85	CBS DTA 7181	Medicine Show/A Party/E=MC² (70mm Wide Screen Remix)//Albert Einstein Meets The Human Beatbox (12" double pack, gatefold p/s)	10
86	CNS 650 147-8/XPR 1320	C'mon Every Beatbox (Extended Vocal Version)/Bedrock City/Beatbox's At Dawn//The Bottom Line (Rick Rubin Remix) (12", with free 1-sided white label stickered 12")	8

(see also Clash, Don Letts & Jah Wobble)

BIG BARON
60	Top Rank JAR 404	Swinging Bells (Oberon Jump)/Romance	4

BIG BEN ACCORDIAN BAND
56	Columbia DB 3835	"Rock 'N' Roll (No. 1)" Medley (both sides)	8
56	Columbia DB 3856	"Rock 'N' Roll (No. 2)" Medley (both sides)	8

BIG BEN BANJO BAND
66	Columbia DB 8069	Beatle Medley For Mums And Pops Pts 1 & 2	4

(see also Billie Anthony)

BIG BERTHA
69	Atlantic 584 298	This World's An Apple/Gravy Booby Jam (with Ace Kefford)	15

(see also Cozy Powell, Ace Kefford Stand)

BIG BLACK
86	Homestead HMS 042	Il Duce/Big Money (p/s)	6
87	Blast First BFFP 24	He's A Whore/The Model (p/s)	4
85	Homestead HMS 007	RACER-X (12" EP, with insert)	8
87	Blast First BFFP 14T	HEADACHE (12" p/s, 1,000 only in black vinyl bag, dark red vinyl, 12-page booklet, fold-out poster & free 45, "Heartbeat"/"Things To Do Today"/"I Can't Believe", sealed with gold medallion, Blast First logo on back)	50
87	Blast First BFFP 14C	HEADACHE (cassette EP)	8

87	NOT 2 (BUT 1)	SOUND OF IMPACT (LP, 1,000 only, numbered with 8-page booklet)	60
87	NOT 2 (BUT 1)	SOUND OF IMPACT (LP, re-pressing numbered from 1001 to 1500)	45
90	NOT 2 (BUT 1)	SOUND OF IMPACT (LP, 500 only with booklet; 'unofficial' reissue)	50
92	Touch & Go TG 81	PIGPILE (LP, boxed set with video & T-shirt with insert)	20

BIG BOB

| 59 | Top Rank JAR 185 | Your Line Was Busy/What Am I | 20 |

BIG BOPPER

58	Mercury AMT 1002	Chantilly Lace/Purple People Eater Meets Witchdoctor	10
59	Mercury AMT 1017	Big Bopper's Wedding/Little Red Riding Hood	15
59	Mercury AMT 1046	It's The Truth, Ruth/That's What I Am Talking About	18
59	Mercury ZEP 10004	THE BIG BOPPER (EP)	80
59	Mercury ZEP 10027	PINK PETTICOATS (EP)	90
58	Mercury MMC 14008	CHANTILLY LACE (LP)	160
74	Contour 6870 531	CHANTILLY LACE (LP)	10

BIG BORIS

| 72 | RCA RCA 2197 | Big Country/Devil's Drive | 6 |

BIG BOY PETE

| 68 | Camp 602005 | Cold Turkey/My Love Is Like A Spaceship | 60 |
| | (see also Miller) | | |

BIG BROTHER & HOLDING COMPANY

67	Fontana TF 881	Bye Bye Baby/All Is Loneliness	10
68	CBS 3683	Piece Of My Heart/Turtle Blues (some in p/s)	15/5
68	London HLT 10226	Down On Me/Call On Me	7
67	Fontana (S)TL 5457	BIG BROTHER & THE HOLDING COMPANY (LP, with Janis Joplin)	22
68	CBS 63392	CHEAP THRILLS (LP, with Janis Joplin)	12
68	London HA-T/SH-T 8377	BIG BROTHER & THE HOLDING COMPANY (LP, reissue, with Janis Joplin)	10
71	CBS 64118	BE A BROTHER (LP)	10
	(see also Janis Joplin, Nick Gravenites)		

BIG CARROT

| 73 | EMI EMI 2047 | Blackjack/Squint Eye Mangle | 20 |
| | (see also Marc Bolan/T. Rex) | | |

BIG COUNTRY

82	Mercury COUNT 1	Harvest Home/Balcony (p/s)	4
82	Mercury COUNT 12	Harvest Home/Balcony/Flag Of Nations (Swimming) (12", p/s)	7
82	Mercury COUNX 1	Harvest Home/Balcony/Flag Of Nations (Swimming) (12" p/s, clear vinyl)	15
83	Mercury COUP 2	Fields Of Fire/Angle Park/Harvest Home (Scotland-shaped picture disc)	12
83	Mercury COUNT 212	Fields Of Fire/Angle Park/Fields Of Fire (Alternative Mix) (12", p/s)	7
83	Mercury COUNX 212	Fields Of Fire/Angle Park/Fields Of Fire (Alternative Mix) (12", p/s, clear vinyl)	15
83	Mercury COUNT 3	In A Big Country/All Of Us (p/s)	4
83	Mercury COUNT 313	In A Big Country (Pure Mix)/Heart And Soul/In A Big Country/All Of Us (12", red p/s)	12
83	Mercury COUNT 4	Chance/The Tracks Of My Tears (live) (p/s, with card photo insert)	4
84	Mercury COUP 4	Chance/The Tracks Of My Tears (live)/The Crossing (12", picture disc)	15
84	Mercury COUNT 5/55	Wonderland/Giant//Lost Patrol (live) (Pts 1 & 2) (double pack with booklet)	6
84	Mercury COUNX 5	Wonderland (Extended Mix)/Wonderland/Giant (12" p/s, clear vinyl)	8
84	Mercury MERP 175	East Of Eden/Prairie Rose (poster p/s)	4
84	Mercury MERXP 175	East Of Eden/Prairie Rose (12" poster p/s)	7
84	Mercury MERD 185	Where The Rose Is Sown/Belief In The Small Man//Wonderland/In A Big Country/Auld Lang Syne (double pack, gatefold p/s)	12
84	Mercury MERX 185	Where The Rose Is Sown (Extended Remix)/Where The Rose Is Sewn/Bass Dance/Belief In The Small Man (12", p/s)	7
86	Mercury BIGCD 1	Look Away/Restless Natives//Margo's Theme/Highland Scenery (double pack, gatefold p/s)	7
86	Mercury BIGCX 11	Look Away (Outlaw Mix)/(12" Mix)/Restless Natives (12", p/s)	8
86	Mercury BIGCP 1	Look Away/Restless Natives (shaped picture disc)	10
86	Mercury BIGCX 2	The Teacher (Mystery Mix)/Restless Natives (Soundtrack Part Two) (12", p/s)	7
86	Mercury BIGCD/E 3	One Great Thing/Song Of The South//Wonderland (live)/Chance (live) (double pack, blue or green p/s)	6/8
86	Mercury BIGCG 3	One Great Thing/Song Of The South (p/s, with inserts)	4
86	Mercury BIGCX 3	One Great Thing (Boston Mix)/Song Of The South (12", gatefold p/s with almanac & discography)	8
86	Mercury BIGCM 3	One Great Thing (Big Baad Country Mix)/Song Of The South/In A Big Country (Pure Mix)/Fields Of Fire (live) (cassette)	5
86	Mercury BIGCX 44	Hold The Heart/Honky Tonk Woman (live)/Interview Pts 1 & 2 (12", gatefold p/s)	7
88	Mercury BIGCR 612	Broken Heart (Thirteen Valleys)/Soapy Soutar Strikes Back/When A Drum Beats/On The Shore (12", p/s with poster, some on red vinyl)	8/7
89	Mercury MIGCP 7	Peace In Our Time/Promised Land (The R.E.L. Tapes) (shrinkwrapped stickered p/s with 2 postcards)	4
89	Mercury BIGCR 712	Peace In Our Time/Promised Land (The R.E.L. Tapes) (12", gatefold p/s)	7
89	Mercury BIGCD 7	Peace In Our Time/Chance/The Longest Day/Promised Land (CD)	7
83	Mercury MERS 27	THE CROSSING (LP, with red sleeve)	10
83	Mercury MERS 27	THE CROSSING (LP, with white sleeve)	12
	(see also Skids)		

BIG DAVE (Cavanaugh) & HIS ORCHESTRA

54	Capitol CL 14156	Rock, Roll, Ball And Wall/The Big Goof (78)	12
54	Capitol CL 14195	Loosely With Feeling/The Cat From Coos Bay (tri centre)	12
54	Capitol CL 14195	Loosely With Feeling/The Cat From Coos Bay (78)	5
55	Capitol CL 14245	Rock And Roll Party/Your Kind Of Love (tri centre)	20
55	Capitol CL 14245	Rock And Roll Party/Your Kind Of Love (78)	5

MINT VALUE £

BIG FLAME
84	Laughing Gun PLAQUE 001	Sink/The Illness/Sometimes (p/s, with insert)	15
85	Ron Johnson ZRON 3	RIGOUR (EP, with insert)	8
85	Ron Johnson ZRON 4	TOUGH! (EP, with insert)	7
86	Ron Johnson ZRON 7	Why Pop Stars Can't Dance/!Chanel Samba!/Breath Of A Nation (p/s, with insert)	7
86	Ron Johnson RERON 8	TWO KAN GURU EP (10", p/s, coloured vinyl)	8
87	Ron Johnson ZRON 13	Cubist Pop Manifesto (p/s, pink vinyl)	6

(see also Great Leap Forward)

BIG IN JAPAN
77	Eric's 0001	Big In Japan/CHUDDIE NUDDIES: Do The Chud (p/s)	10
78	Zoo CAGE 001	FROM Y TO Z AND NEVER AGAIN (EP, foldout p/s)	12

(see also Pink Industry/Military, Jane, Holly, Yachts, Bill Drummond, Creatures/Siouxsie & Banshees)

BIG MAYBELLE
57	London HLC 8447	I Don't Want To Cry/All Of Me	25
57	London HLC 8447	I Don't Want To Cry/All Of Me (78)	8
59	London HLC 8854	Baby, Won't You Please Come Home/Say It Isn't So	15
59	London HLC 8854	Baby, Won't You Please Come Home/Say It Isn't So (78)	8
65	London HL 9941	Careless Love/My Mother's Eyes	10
67	CBS 2735	Turn The World Around The Other Way/I Can't Wait Any Longer	18
67	CBS 2926	Mama (He Treats Your Daughter Mean)/Keep That Man	7
68	Direction 58-3312	Quittin' Time/I Can't Wait Any Longer	15
67	CBS 62999	THE PURE SOUL OF BIG MAYBELLE (LP)	20

BIG MOE with BOYD BENNETT & ROCKETS
56	Parlophone R 4214	The Groovy Age/Hit That Jive, Jack	125
56	Parlophone R 4214	The Groovy Age/Hit That Jive, Jack (78)	20
56	Parlophone R 4252	The Most/Rockin' Up A Storm	100
56	Parlophone R 4252	The Most/Rockin' Up A Storm (78)	25

(see also Boyd Bennett)

BIGROUP
70s	Peer Intl. Library PIL 009	BIG HAMMER (LP)	150

BIG SLEEP
71	Pegasus PEG 4	BLUEBELL WOOD (LP, gatefold sleeve)	45

(see also Eyes Of Blue , Ancient Grease, Man, Ritchie Francis)

BIG SOUND AUTHORITY
85	MCA BSAD 1	This House/I Miss My Baby//Soul Man (live)/In The Hands Of Love (live) (double pack, gatefold p/s)	4
85	Lyntone	fan club flexidisc (mail order only)	5

(see also Directions)

BIG STAR
78	Stax STAX 504	September Gurls/Mod Lang	5
78	Aura AUS 103	Kizza Me/Dream Lover	4
78	Aura AUS 107	Jesus Christ/Big Black Car	4
78	Stax SXSP 302	RADIO CITY/BIG STAR (2-LP)	15
78	Aura AUL 703	THIRD ALBUM (LP)	10

(see also Alex Chilton, Box Tops)

BIG STICK
86	Blast First BFFP 6	Shoot The President/Drag Racing/I Look Like Shit/Hell On Earth/Jesus Was Born (On An Indian Reservation) (12", p/s with inner)	8
80s	Sonic Life SL 002	Black Cow/Joe Turner Blues (mail order only, no p/s)	5

BIG THREE
63	Decca F 11614	Some Other Guy/Let True Love Begin	10
63	Decca F 11689	By The Way/Cavern Stomp	6
63	Decca F 11752	I'm With You/Peanut Butter	10
64	Decca F 11927	If You Ever Change Your Mind/You've Got To Keep Her Under Hand	10
73	Polydor 2058 343	Some Other Guy/Let It Rock/If You Gotta Make A Fool Of Somebody	5
63	Decca DFE 8552	AT THE CAVERN (EP)	18
73	Polydor 2383 199	RESURRECTION (LP)	20

(see also Escorts, Paddy, Klaus & Gibson, Johnny Gustafson)

BIG THREE
68	Roulette RCP 5002	THE BIG THREE FEATURING MAMA CASS (LP)	15

(see also Mama Cass [Elliot], Mamas & Papas)

BIG YOUTH
69	Gayfeet CS 206	Medicine Doctor/Facts Of Life	5
72	Blue Beat BB 424	Chi Chi Run/JOHN HOLT: OK Fred	7
72	Downtown DT 497	Dock Of The Bay/CRYSTALITES: Bass And Drums (Version)	6
73	Prince Buster PB 46	Chi Chi Run/Drums And Bass (Version)	6
73	Prince Buster PB 48	Leggo Beast/Leave Your Skeng	6
73	Prince Buster PB 50	Cane And Abel/Cane And Abel (Version)	6
73	Grape GR 3040	Foreman Versus Frazier/Foreman Versus Frazier Round Two	5
73	Grape GR 3044	Ja To UK/Ja To UK (Version)	5
73	Grape GR 3051	Opportunity Rock/Double Attack	5
73	Grape GR 3061	Concrete Jungle/Screaming Tonight	5
73	Green Door GD 4051	Cool Breeze/CRYSTALITES: Windstorm	6
73	Summit SUM 8542	A So We Say/WINSTON SCOTLAND: Scarface	6
74	Harry J HJ 6682	Ride On Ride On/Wild Goose Chase (both with Dennis Brown)	4
72	Fab MS 8	CHI CHI RUN (LP)	18
73	Trojan TRLS 61	SCREAMING TARGET (LP)	15
76	Trojan TRLS 123	NATTY CULTURAL DREAD (LP)	10
76	Trojan TRLS 137	HIT THE ROAD JACK (LP)	10

BIG YOUTH & KEITH HUDSON
73 Pyramid PYR 7055   Can You Keep A Secret/HORACE ANDY & EARL FLUTE: Peter And Judas 5
(see also Keith Hudson)

BIKINIS
58 Columbia DB 4149   Bikini/Boogie Rock And Roll 10
58 Columbia DB 4149   Bikini/Boogie Rock And Roll (78) 8

(Mr.) ACKER BILK (& HIS PARAMOUNT JAZZ BAND)
56 Tempo A 134   Dippermouth Blues/Where The River Shannon Flows 4
59 Pye 7NJ 2029   Marching Through Georgia/Delia Gone 4
60 Melodisc 1547   Goodnight Sweet Prince/East Coast Trot 5
60 Pye 7NJ 2033   The C.R.E. March (Wings)/Willie The Weeper 4
61 Columbia SCD 2155   Stars And Stripes Forever/Creole Jazz (p/s) 4
62 Columbia SCD 2176   Gotta See Baby Tonight/If You Were The Only Girl In The World (p/s) 4
58 Pye Nixa NJT 513   ACKER BILK REQUESTS (10" LP) 10

BILLIE & EDDIE
59 Top Rank JAR 249   The King Is Coming Back/Come Back, Baby 10

BILLIE & ESSENTIALS
63 London HLW 9657   Over The Weekend/Maybe You'll Be There 20

BILLION DOLLAR BABIES
77 Polydor 2391 273   BATTLE AXES (LP) 10

TREVOR BILLMUSS
70 Charisma CAS 1017   FAMILY APOLOGY (LP) 12

BILLY & LILLIE (& Billy Ford & Thunderbirds)
58 London HLU 8564   La Dee Dah/BILLY FORD'S THUNDERBIRDS: The Monster 25
58 London HLU 8564   La Dee Dah/BILLY FORD'S THUNDERBIRDS: The Monster (78) 5
58 London HLU 8630   Creepin', Crawlin', Cryin'/Happiness (with Billy Ford & Thunderbirds) 25
58 London HLU 8630   Creepin', Crawlin', Cryin'/Happiness (with Billy Ford & Thunderbirds) (78) 5
58 London HLU 8689   The Greasy Spoon/Hangin' On To You (with Billy Ford & Thunderbirds) 15
58 London HLU 8689   The Greasy Spoon/Hangin' On To You (with Billy Ford & Thunderbirds) (78) 7
59 London HLU 8795   Lucky Ladybug/I Promise You 15
59 London HLU 8795   Lucky Ladybug/I Promise You (78) 5
59 Top Rank JAR 157   Bells, Bells, Bells/Honeymoonin' 6
59 Top Rank JAR 157   Bells, Bells, Bells/Honeymoonin' (78) 5

BIM & BAM
70 Crab CRAB 48   The Pill (with Clover)/TOMMY McCOOK: Spring Fever 4
70 Crab CRAB 49   Immigrant Plight (with Clover)/PETER AUSTIN & HORTENSE:
    Bang Shangalang 4
73 Gayfeet GS 201   Fatty/Landlord 5

UMBERTO BINDI & HIS ORCHESTRA
60 Oriole CB 1577   Il Nostro Concerto/Un Giorno, Un Mese, Un Anno 5

RONALDE BINGE & HIS ORCHESTRA
54 Decca F 10410   September In The Rain/Holiday For Bells 4

SONNY BINNS (& RUDIES)
69 Downtown DT 420   The Untouchables/Lazy Boy 4
69 Downtown DT 424   Wheels/Night Train 4
70 Escort ES 818   Boss A Moon (as S. Binns)/BUNNY LEE ALLSTARS: Brotherly Love 4
(see also Rudies)

BIONIC BOOGIE
(see under Gregg Diamond)

IVOR BIRD
78 RSO 2090 270   Over The Wall We Go/Beauty Queen 7
(see also Oscar)

STANLEY & JEFFREY BIRD
60 HMV POP 702   Johnny At The Crossheads/Betty, Betty (Go Steady With Me) 5

BIRDHOUSE
80s Strychnine STR 01   New Race (live)/MONKS: You Took Me By Surprise (33rpm flexi disc,
    free with 'Strychnine' magazine) 4

BIRDLAND
89 Lazy LAZY 13   Hollow Heart/Sugar Blood (p/s) 5
89 Lazy LAZY 13T   Hollow Heart/Crystal/Gotta Get Away/Sugar Blood
    (12", p/s in various colours) 7
89 Lazy LAZY 14T   Paradise/White/Rage/Stay (12", p/s, mispress with extra track) 8
89 Lazy LAZY 17L   Sleep With Me/Wanted/Hollow Heart (Acoustic)/Sleep With Me (Acoustic)
    (mailer pack, some mispressed with 2 tracks by French artist) 4/6
89 Lazy LAZY 24L   Everybody Needs Somebody/Don't Hang On/Twin Sons/Exit (Acoustic)
    (numbered mailer p/s) 4
89 Lazy LAZY 20   Rock'n'Roll Nigger (12", white label only) 7
89 Lazy LAZY 16T   LIVE (LP, 1-sided, plain sleeve, gig freebie) 10
(see also Zodiac Motel)

BIRD LEGS & PAULINE
66 Sue WI 4014   Spring/In So Many Ways 10

BIRDS
64 Decca F 12031   You're On My Mind/You Don't Love Me (You Don't Care) 60
65 Decca F 12140   Leaving Here/Next In Line 40
65 Decca F 12257   No Good Without You Baby/How Can It Be 40
(see also Bird's Birds, Ron Wood, Faces, Creation)

MINT VALUE £

BIRDS BIRDS
66　Reaction 591 005　　　　Say Those Magic Words/Daddy Daddy 150
　(see also Birds)

BIRDS OF A FEATHER
69　Page One POF 156　　　Blacksmith Blues/Sing My Song And Pray 6
70　Page One POF 179　　　All God's Children Got Soul/Get It Together 6
70　Page One POLS 027　　BIRDS OF A FEATHER (LP) 60
　(see also Chanters, Chanter Sisters)

BIRDS WITH EARS
83　Laughing Man BONK 1　Mr Sneed/Doggy (p/s) 4

JANE BIRKIN & SERGE GAINSBOURG
69　Fontana TF 1042　　　Je T'Aime Moi Non Plus/Jane B (initially with p/s) 8/5
69　Major Minor MM 645　Je T'Aime Moi Non Plus/Jane B (reissue) 4
74　Antic K 11511　　　　Je T'Aime Moi Non Plus/Jane B (2nd reissue, 'nude' p/s) 8
69　Fontana STL 5493　　JANE BIRKIN AND SERGE GAINSBOURG (LP) 10

BIRMINGHAM
71　Grosvenor GRS 1011　BIRMINGHAM (LP) 150
　(see also Dave Peace Quartet)

BIRTH CONTROL
71　Charisma CAS 1036　　BIRTH CONTROL (LP) 15

BIRTHDAY PARTY
80　4AD AD 12　　　　　　The Friend Catcher/Waving My Arms/Cat Man (p/s) 8
81　4AD AD 111　　　　　Release The Bats/Blast Off (p/s) 7
81　4AD AD 114　　　　　Mr. Clarinet/Happy Birthday (p/s) 8
82　Masterbag BAG 005　Dead Joe (flexi disc free with 'Masterbag' issue 15) 8/6
　(see also Nick Cave & Bad Seeds, Roland S. Howard & Lydia Lunch)

DICKIE BISHOP & SIDEKICKS
57　Decca F 10869　　　Cumberland Gap/No Other Baby 8
57　Decca F 10959　　　The Prisoner's Song/Please Remember Me 6
58　Decca F 10981　　　Skip To My Lou/No Other Baby 7
58　Decca F 11028　　　They Can't Take That Away From Me/Jumpin' Judy 7
　(see also Chris Barber's Skiffle Group)

TOMMY BISHOP'S RICOCHETS
65　Decca F 12238　　　I Should Have Known/On The Other Hand 5

BISHOPS
　(see under Count Bishops)

BITCH
79　Hurricane FIRE 5　　Big City/Wild Lads (p/s) 4
81　Rutland RX 101　　　First Bite/Maggie (p/s) 6

BITCHES SIN
81　Neat NEAT 09　　　Always Ready (For Love) (p/s) 5
83　Quiet QT 001　　　No More Chances/Overnight/Ice Angels (12", p/s) 7
83　Terminal TCAS 21　OUT OF MY MIND (cassette EP, 6-track) 4
82　Heavy Metal HMRLP 4　PREDATOR (LP) 15

BITING TONGUES
87　Factory FAC 188　　Compressor/Compressor (7", promo-only) 5
85　Factory FACT 105　FEVERHOUSE (LP) 12
　(see also 808 State)

BIZET BOYS
89　Parlophone RIDE 1　Ride 'Em Cowboy/Ride 'Em Cowboy (Speechless) (p/s) 4
89　Parlophone 12RIDE 1　Ride 'Em Cowboy (A Classic Mix)/Ride 'Em Cowboy (Opera House Mix)/
　　　　　　　　　　　　Ride 'Em Cowboy (3 M's Much More Mix) (12", p/s) 10

BLAB HAPPY
80s　Wisdom WIZ 1　　IT'S TURNED OUT NICE AGAIN (EP, p/s in bag, white labels) 4

BLACK
81　Rox ROX 17　　　　Human Features/Electric Church (p/s) 25
82　Wonderful World Of WW 3　More Than The Sun/Jump (p/s) 8
84　Eternal JF 3　　　Hey Presto/Stephen (p/s) 4
84　Eternal JF 3T　　Hey Presto/Stephen/Liquid Dream (12", p/s) 7
85　WEA BLACK 1　　More Than The Sun/Butterfly Man (p/s) 4
85　WEA BLACK 1T　More Than The Sun/Butterfly Man/I Could Kill You/
　　　　　　　　　　Wide Mouth/Stephen (12", p/s) 7
86　Ugly Man JACK 71　Wonderful Life/Birthday Night (p/s) 4
86　Ugly Man JACK 71D　Wonderful Life/Birthday Night//Sometimes For The Asking/
　　　　　　　　　　　Everything's Coming Up Roses (double pack, gatefold p/s) 6
86　Ugly Man JACK 1　Wonderful Life/Birthday Night/Everything's Coming Up Roses (12", p/s) 7
87　A&M AM 388　　　Everything's Coming Up Roses/Ravel In The Rain (p/s, white vinyl,
　　　　　　　　　　with 4-page booklet) 4

BILL BLACK'S COMBO
59　Felsted AF 129　　Smokie Pts 1 & 2 8
59　Felsted AF 129　　Smokie Pts 1 & 2 (78) 30
60　London HLU 9090　White Silver Sands/The Wheel 5
60　London HLU 9156　Josephine/Dry Bones 5
60　London HLU 9212　Don't Be Cruel/Rollin' 5
61　London HLU 9267　Blue Tango/Willie 6
61　London HLU 9306　Hearts Of Stone/Royal Blue 6
61　London HLU 9383　Ole Buttermilk Sky/Yogi 6
61　London HLU 9436　Movin'/Honky Train 8

61	London HLU 9479	Twist-Her/My Girl Josephine	6
62	London HLU 9594	So What/Blues For The Red Boy	4
62	London HLU 9645	Joey's Song/Hot Taco	4
63	London HLU 9721	Do It — Rat Now/Little Jasper	4
63	London HLU 9788	Monkey-Shine/Long Gone	5
64	London HLU 9855	Comin' On/Soft Winds	4
64	London HLU 9903	Tequila/Raunchy	6
64	London HLU 9925	Little Queenie/Boo-Ray	20
68	London HLU 10216	Turn On Your Love Light/Ribbon Of Darkness	4
60	London REU 1277	BILL BLACK'S COMBO (EP)	12
63	London REU 1369	THE UNTOUCHABLE SOUND OF BILL BLACK (EP)	12
62	London HA-U 2310	SOLID AND RAUNCHY (LP)	25
62	London HA-U 2427	LET'S TWIST (LP, also stereo SAH-U 6222)	16/18
62	London HA-U 2433	MOVIN' (LP)	18
63	London HA-U 8080	THE UNTOUCHABLE SOUND OF BILL BLACK (LP)	16
63	London HA-U 8113	GREATEST HITS (LP)	12
64	London HA-U 8187	PLAYS CHUCK BERRY (LP)	20
68	London HA-U/SH-U 8367	BILL BLACK'S BEAT GOES ON (LP)	12
69	London HA-U/SH-U 8373	TURN ON YOUR LOVE LIGHT (LP)	10
69	London HA-U/SH-U 8389	SOULIN' THE BLUES (LP)	10

(see also Elvis Presley)

CILLA BLACK

63	Parlophone R 5065	Love Of The Loved/Shy Of You	5
66	Parlophone R 5162	It's For You/He Won't Ask Me	4
60s	Parlophone	other 45s	4
64	Parlophone GEP 8901	ANYONE WHO HAD A HEART (EP)	7
64	Parlophone GEP 8916	IT'S FOR YOU (EP)	8
66	Parlophone GEP 8954	CILLA'S HITS (EP)	8
67	Parlophone GEP 8967	TIME FOR CILLA (EP)	12
65	Parlophone PMC 1243	CILLA (LP, yellow/black label, also stereo PCS 3063)	10/12
66	Parlophone PMC/PCS 7004	SINGS A RAINBOW (LP, mono/stereo, yellow/black label)	10/12
68	Parlophone PMC/PCS 7041	SHER-OO! (LP, yellow/black label)	10
69	Parlophone PMC/PCS 7079	SURROUND YOURSELF WITH CILLA (LP, yellow/black label)	10

'FLIP' BLACK & BOYS UPSTAIRS

| 59 | Capitol CL 15037 | For You My Lover/Tell Her Mister Moon | 4 |

JEANNE BLACK

| 60 | Capitol CL 15131 | He'll Have To Stay/JEANNE & JANIE: Under Your Spell Again | 5 |

(see also Janie, Jeanne & Janie)

MATT BLACK & DOODLEBUGS

| 77 | Punk BCS 0005 | Punky Xmas/Nightmare (no p/s) | 6 |

STANLEY BLACK & HIS PIANO ORCHESTRA

| 63 | Decca F 11624 | Hand In Hand/Lullaby Of The Stars | 6 |

BLACK ABBOTTS

| 70 | Chapter One CH 123 | She Looked Away/I Don't Mind | 5 |
| 71 | Evolution E 3004 | Love Is Alive/The Painter | 15 |

BLACK ACE

| 61 | XX MIN 701 | BLACK ACE (EP) | 8 |
| 62 | Heritage HLP 1006 | BLACK ACE (LP) | 30 |

BLACK AXE

| 80 | Metal MELT 1 | Highway Rider/Red Lights (no p/s) | 8 |

BLACKBIRDS

| 68 | Saga OPP 3 | No Destination/Space (company sleeve, possibly promo-only) | 20 |
| 68 | Saga FID 2113 | NO DESTINATION (LP) | 30 |

TONY BLACKBURN

65	Fontana TF 562	Don't Get Off That Train/Just To Be With You Again	6
65	Fontana TF 601	Is There Another Way To Love You/Here Today Gone Tomorrow	4
66	Fontana TF 729	Green Light/Winter Is Through	4
67	MGM MGM 1375	So Much Love/In The Night	4
68	MGM MGM 1394	She's My Girl/Closer To A Dream	4
69	MGM MGM 1467	It's Only Love/Janie	4
69	Polydor 56360	Blessed Are The Lonely/Wait For Me	4
66	Fontana SFL 13161	TONY BLACKBURN MEETS MATT MONRO (LP)	10
68	MGM C(S) 8062	TONY BLACKBURN SINGS (LP)	10

BLACKBYRDS

74	Fantasy FTC 113	Do It Fluid/Summer Love	5
75	Fantasy FTC 114	Walking In Rhythm/Baby	4
75	Fantasy FTC 117	I Need You/All I Ask	4
76	Fantasy FTC 122	Rock Creek Park/Flying High	4
76	Fantasy FTC 129	Happy Music/Love So Fine	4
85	Streetwave SWAVE 3	Rock Creek Park/Walking In Rhythm (12")	8
75	Fantasy FT 9444	BLACKBYRDS (LP)	15
75	Fantasy FT 522	FLYING START (LP)	15
76	Fantasy FTA 3003	CITY LIFE (LP)	12
77	Fantasy FT 534	ACTION (LP)	12
79	Fantasy FT 555	NIGHT GROOVES — THE BEST OF THE BLACKBYRDS (LP)	12

(see also Donald Byrd)

BLACK CAT BONES

| 70 | Decca Nova SDN 15 | BARBED WIRE SANDWICH (LP) | 75 |

(see also Leaf Hound, Brian Short)

BLACK CROWES

90	Def American DEFA 4	Jealous Again/Thick'n'Thin (p/s)	5
90	Def American DEFA 412	Jealous Again/Thick'n'Thin/Waitin' Guilty (12", p/s)	8
90	Def American DEFAC 4	Jealous Again/Thick'n'Thin/Waitin' Guilty (CD)	10
90	Def American DEFAP 412	Jealous Again/Thick'n'Thin/Waitin' Guilty (12" picture disc)	12
90	Def American DEFA 6	Hard To Handle/Jealous Again (Acoustic) (p/s)	4
90	Def American DEFAM 6	Hard To Handle/Jealous Again (Acoustic) (cassette)	4
90	Def American DEFA 612	Hard To Handle/Jealous Again (Acoustic)/Twice As Hard (live) (12", p/s)	7
90	Def American DEFA 612	Hard To Handle/Jealous Again (Acoustic)/Twice As Hard (live) (12", crow-shaped picture disc)	10
90	Def American DEFAC 6	Hard To Handle/Jealous Again (Acoustic)/Twice As Hard (Remix) (CD)	8
91	Def American DEFA 7	Twice As Hard/Jealous Again (live) (p/s)	4
91	Def American DEFAM 7	Twice As Hard/Jealous Again (live) (cassette)	4
91	Def American DEFA 712	Twice As Hard/Jealous Again (live)/Jealous Guy (live) (12", poster p/s)	10
91	Def American DEFAP 712	Twice As Hard/Jealous Again (live)/Could I've Been So Blind (live) (12", picture disc with insert)	10
91	Def American DEFAC 712	Twice As Hard/Jealous Again (live)/Jealous Guy (live) (CD)	8
91	Def American DEFA 812	Jealous Again/She Talks To Angels/She Talks To Angels (live) (12", p/s, with patch)	8
91	Def American DEFAC 812	Jealous Again/She Talks To Angels (live)/Could I've Been So Blind (live) (CD)	7
91	Def American DEFAP 10	Hard To Handle/Stare It Cold (live) (shaped picture disc)	6
91	Def American DEFAG 1312	Seeing Things/Could I've Been So Blind (live)/She Talks To Angels (live)/Sister Luck (live) (12", gatefold p/s)	7
92	Def American DEFA 1612	Remedy/Darling Of The Underground Press/Time Will Tell (12", in tin)	7

BLACK DYKE MILLS BAND

68	Apple APPLE 4	Thingumybob/Yellow Submarine	30

BLACK DYNAMITES

60	Top Rank JAR 319	Lonely Cissy/Brush Those Tears	20

BLACK FLAG

81	Alt. Tentacles VIRUS 9	SIX PACK (EP)	5
84	SST 12001	Slip It In/Family Man/I Won't Stick Any Of You Unless And Until I Can Stick All Of You (12", p/s)	7

J.D. BLACKFOOT

70	Mercury 6338 031	THE ULTIMATE PROPHECY (LP)	35

BLACKFOOT SUE

73	Jam JAL 104	NOTHING TO HIDE (LP)	10
75	DJM DJLPS 455	GUN RUNNING (LP, withdrawn)	45

BLACK IVORY

74	Kwanza K 19500	What Goes Around Comes Around/No One Else Will Do	4

BLACKJACK

80	Polydor POSP 76	Without Your Love/Heart Of Mine (p/s)	10
79	Polydor 2391 411	BLACKJACK (LP)	10
80	Polydor	WORLDS APART (LP)	12

BLACKJACKS

63	Pye 7N 15586	Woo Hoo/Red Dragon	10
	(see also Pat Harris & Blackjacks)		

BLACK KNIGHTS

65	Columbia DB 7443	I Gotta Woman/Angel Of Love	10

BLACK MAMBAZO

58	Columbia DB 4135	Fuzzy Night/Matshutshu	4

HONOR BLACKMAN

68	CBS 3896	Before Today/I'll Always Be Loving You	7
	(see also Patrick MacNee & Honor Blackman)		

RITCHIE BLACKMORE

65	Oriole CB 314	Getaway/Little Brown Jug	250
	(see also Outlaws, Deep Purple, [Ritchie Blackmore's] Rainbow, Neil Christian & Crusaders)		

BLACK NASTY

80	Grapevine GRP 140	Cut Your Motor Off/Keep On Stepping	4

BLACK ROSE

82	Teesbeat TB 5	No Point Running/Sucker For You	5
83	Bullet BOLT 6	WE GONNA ROCK YOU (12" EP)	7
85	Neat NEAT 4812	Nightmare/Need A Lot Of Lovin'/Rock Me Hard (12", p/s)	7
84	Bullet BULP 3	BOYS WILL BE BOYS (LP)	10
87	Neat NEAT 1034	WALK IT LIKE YOU TALK IT (LP)	10

BLACK SABBATH

70	Fontana TF 1067	Evil Woman (Don't Play Your Games With Me)/Wicked World	50
70	Vertigo V2	Evil Woman (Don't Play Your Games With Me)/Wicked World (reissue)	15
70	Vertigo 6059 010	Paranoid/The Wizard	5
72	Vertigo 6059 061	Tomorrow's Dream/Laguna Sunrise	8
73	WWA WWS 002	Sabbath Bloody Sabbath/Changes	5
76	NEMS 6165 300	Am I Going Insane? (Radio)/Hole In The Sky	5
78	Vertigo SAB 001	Never Say Die/She's Gone (p/s)	5
78	Vertigo SAB 002	Hard Road/Symptom Of The Universe (no p/s, purple vinyl)	5
80	Vertigo SAB 3	Neon Nights/Children Of The Sea (p/s)	4
80	Vertigo SAB 4	Die Young/Heaven And Hell (p/s)	4
80	Vertigo SAB 412	Die Young/Heaven And Hell (full version) (12", p/s)	8
81	Vertigo SAB 5	Mob Rules/Die Young (live) (p/s)	4

MINT VALUE £

81	Vertigo SAB 512	Mob Rules/Die Young (live) (12", p/s)	8
82	Vertigo SABP 6	Turn Up The Night/Lonely Is The Word (picture disc)	5
82	Vertigo SABP 612	Turn Up The Night/Lonely Is The Word (12", picture disc)	8
82	NEMS NEP 1	Paranoid/Iron Man (picture disc)	5
82	NEMS 12 NEX 01	Paranoid/War Pigs/Iron Man/Fairies Wear Boots (12", p/s, clear vinyl)	8
89	IRS EIRSPD 115	Devil And Daughter (1-sided picture disc)	4
89	IRS EIRSB 115	Devil And Daughter (box set, 1-sided disc with stencil, memo & postcards)	4
70	Vertigo VO 6	BLACK SABBATH (LP, gatefold sleeve, spiral label)	12
70	Vertigo 6360 011	PARANOID (LP, gatefold sleeve, spiral label)	10
71	Vertigo 6360 050	MASTERS OF REALITY (LP in box cover, spiral label, some with poster)	18/10
72	Vertigo 6360 071	BLACK SABBATH VOL. 4 (LP, gatefold sleeve with booklet, initially spiral label, also rare re-pressing with 'spaceship' label)	10/15
85	NEMS NEP 6003	PARANOID (LP, reissue, picture disc)	10
85	NEMS NEP 6009	GREATEST HITS (LP, picture disc)	10
89	IRS EIRSAPD 1002	HEADLESS CROSS (LP, picture disc)	10

(see also Ozzy Osborne, Dio, Elf, Gillan)

BLACKTHORN

77	WHM 1921	BLACKTHORN (LP)	80
70s	WHM 1923	BLACKTHORN II (LP)	80

BLACK VELVET

69	Beacon BEA 129	African Velvet/Whatcha Gonna Do About It	4
69	Beacon BEA 137	Peace And Love Is The Message/Clown	4
70	Beacon BEA 151	Please Let Me In/Clown	4
70	Beacon BEA 162	What Am I To Do/Coal Mine	4
70	Beacon BEA 170	Thought I Had Me A Good Thing Going/Loves Makes The World Go Round	4
70	Pye 7N 45183	So Good To See You/Velvet Funk	4
73	Pye 7N 45228	There Must Be A Way/Domestic Man	4
73	Seven Sun SSUN 4	Groove Along/Can You Feel It	5
74	Seven Sun SSUN 6	There Goes My heart Again/Cindy Cindy	4
71	Beacon BEAS 16	THIS IS BLACK VELVET (LP)	30
72	Pye NSPL 18392	PEOPLE OF THE WORLD (LP)	40
73	Seven Sun SUNLP 1	CAN YOU FEEL IT (LP)	50

CHARLES BLACKWELL ORCHESTRA

61	HMV POP 977	Taboo/Midnight In Luxembourg	15
62	Columbia DB 4839	Supercar/Persian Theme	12
62	Columbia DB 4919	Freight Train/Death Valley	7
63	Columbia DB 4994	High Noon/For Me And My Gal	5
63	Columbia DB 7066	El Toro/Hawaiian War Chant	4
63	Columbia DB 7139	The Hokey Croakey/Lost Patrol	4
65	Columbia DB 7501	Meditation/La Bamba	4

OTIS BLACKWELL

58	London HLE 8616	Make Ready For Love/When You're Around	30
58	London HLE 8616	Make Ready For Love/When You're Around (78)	20

RORY BLACKWELL & HIS BLACKJACKS

57	Parlophone R 4326	Bye Bye Love/Such A Shame	15
57	Parlophone R 4326	Bye Bye Love/Such A Shame (78)	5
70s	Rory SJP 763	Daddy Don't You Walk So Fast/Drum Rhapsody	4

SCRAPPER BLACKWELL

67	Collector JEN 7	SCRAPPER BLACKWELL (EP)	8
63	'77' LA 12/4	BLUES BEFORE SUNRISE (LP)	20
60s	Xtra XTRA 5011	MR SCRAPPER'S BLUES (LP)	15

BLACKWELLS (U.S.)

60	London HLW 9135	Unchained Melody/Mansion On The Hill	6
61	London HLW 9334	Love Or Money/Big Daddy And The Cat	8

BLACKWELLS (U.K.)

65	Columbia DB 7442	Why Don't You Love Me/All I Want Is Your Love	20

BLACK WIDOW

70	CBS 5031	Come To The Sabbat/Way To Power	25
71	CBS 7596	Wish You Would/Accident	6
70	CBS 63948	SACRIFICE (LP, gatefold sleeve)	20
70	CBS 64133	BLACK WIDOW — MAYBE NOW (LP)	20
71	CBS 64562	BLACK WIDOW III (LP)	25

(see also Pesky Gee, Agony Bag)

BLADE RUNNER

85	Ebony EBON 26	Back Street Lady/Too Far Too Late (p/s)	4

BLADES

80	Energy NRG 3	Hot For You/The Reunion	6
81	Energy NRG 5	Ghost Of A Chance/Real Emotion	5

BLADES OF GRASS

68	Stateside SS 2101	Charlie And Fred/You Won't Find That Girl	4

BLAH BLAH BLAH

79	Absurd ABSURD 1	In The Army/Why Diddle? (p/s)	4
81	Some Bizzare	BLAH BLAH BLAH (LP, unreleased, stickered sleeve, w/l test pressings only)	40

HAL BLAINE

64	RCA RCA 1379	Gear Stripper/Challenger II	10
64	RCA RD 7624	DEUCES, T'S, ROADSTERS AND DRUMS (LP)	25

BLAIR

79	Miracle M4	Night Life/Virgo Princess (12")	10

BEVERLEY BLAIR
| 58 | Mercury 7MT 209 | With Love We Live/Tony | 4 |

SALLY BLAIR
| 58 | MGM MGM 1000 | Whatever Lola Wants (Lola Gets)/Daddy | 4 |

ERIC BLAKE
| 80 | Carrere CAR 141 | Sin City/Zero 6 | 8 |
| 81 | Carrere CAR 179 | Born To Be Special/80's Girl/Give Generously | 4 |

GARRY BLAKE
| 66 | Columbia DB 7977 | Wait Until Dark/Jungle Juice | 4 |
| 66 | Columbia DB 8074 | The Danny Scipio Theme/Celebration Day | 5 |

KARL BLAKE
80s	Daark Inc.	THE NEW POLLUTION (C-60 cassette)	10
80s	Daark Inc.	TANK DEATH (C-60 cassette)	10
83	Glass GLASS 013	THE PREHENSILE TALES (LP)	10

(see also Lemon Kittens, Shock Headed Peters, Underneath)

KEITH BLAKE
| 68 | Blue Cat BS 102 | Musically/I'm Moving On | 10 |

SONNY BLAKE
| 80 | Rooster R 706 | HARMONICA BLUES (EP) | 8 |

TIM BLAKE
| 78 | Barclay Towers CLAY 7005 | BLAKE'S NEW JERUSALEM (LP) | 10 |

(see also Gong, Hawkwind)

ART BLAKEY JAZZ MESSENGERS
61	Blue Note 45-1796	Night In Tunisia Pts 1 & 2	6
62	Blue Note 45-1735	Moanin' Pts 1 & 2	6
64	Blue Note 45-1626	Message From Kenya/Nothing But The Soul	5
60	Fontana TFE 17257	BLUES MARCH (EP)	8
61	Fontana TFE 17337	I REMEMBER CLIFFORD (EP)	8
61	Fontana TFE 17364	ARE YOU REAL (EP, with Lee Morgan & Benny Golson)	8
61	Fontana TFL 5116	OLYMPIA CONCERT (LP)	15
62	Blue Note BLP 4049	A NIGHT IN TUNISIA (LP)	15
62	HMV CLP 1532	ART BLAKEY JAZZ MESSENGERS (LP, also stereoCSD 1423)	12/15
62	Blue Note BLP 4090	MOSAIC (LP)	15
62	Blue Note BLP 1554	ORGY IN RHYTHM VOL. 1 (LP)	15
62	Fontana TFL 5184	DANGEROUS FRIENDSHIPS (LP, soundtrack)	15
63	Utd. Artists (S)ULP 1017	THREE BLIND MICE (LP, mono/stereo)	12/15
63	Blue Note (B)BLP 4003	MOANIN' (LP)	15
63	Blue Note (B)BLP 4104	BUHAINA'S DELIGHT (LP)	15
64	Riverside RLP 438	CARAVAN (LP)	12
64	Blue Note (B)BLP 1521	A NIGHT AT BIRDLAND VOL. 1 (LP)	15
64	Blue Note (B)BLP 1522	A NIGHT AT BIRDLAND VOL. 2 (LP)	15
64	HMV CLP 1760	A JAZZ MESSAGE (LP)	12
64	Blue Note (B)BLP 4156	FREEDOM RIDER (LP)	15
64	Riverside RLP 464	UGETSU (LP)	12
65	Blue Note (B)BLP 1555	ORGY IN RHYTHM VOL. 2 (LP)	15
65	Limelight (S)LML 4000	'S MAKE IT (LP)	10
66	Limelight (S)LML 4012	SOUL FINGER (LP)	10
66	Blue Note (B)BLP 4170	FREE FOR ALL (LP)	15
66	Limelight (S)LML 4021	BUTTERCORN LADY (LP)	10
67	Limelight (S)LML 4023	HOLD ON, I'M COMIN' (LP)	10
67	Atlantic 590 009	BLUE MONK (LP, with Thelonious Monk)	12
67	Blue Note BLP 4245	LIKE SOMEONE IN LOVE (LP, also stereo BST 84245)	15
69	Storyville 673 013	KYOTO (LP)	10
70	Blue Note BST 84258	WITCH DOCTOR (LP)	10
70	Polydor 545 116	RIGHT DOWN FRONT (LP)	10
74	Prestige PR 10047	CHILD'S DANCE (LP)	10
74	Milestone ML 47008	THERMO (LP)	10
70s	Blue Note BST 84383	GREATEST HITS (LP)	10
70s	Blue Note BST 84003	MOANIN' (LP, reissue)	10
70s	Blue Note BST 84004	HOLIDAY FOR SKINS VOL. 1 (LP)	10
70s	Blue Note BST 84005	HOLIDAY FOR SKINS VOL. 2 (LP)	10
70s	Blue Note BST 84015	MEET YOU AT THE JAZZ CORNER OF THE WORLD 1 (LP)	10
70s	Blue Note BST 84016	MEET YOU AT THE JAZZ CORNER OF THE WORLD 2 (LP)	10
70s	Blue Note BST 84029	THE BIG BEAT (LP)	10
70s	Blue Note BST 84049	A NIGHT IN TUNISIA (LP, reissue)	10
70s	Blue Note BST 84090	MOSAIC (LP, reissue)	10
70s	Blue Note BST 84097	AFRICAN BEAT (LP)	10
70s	Blue Note BST 84104	BUHAINA'S DELIGHT (LP, reissue)	10
70s	Blue Note BST 84156	FREEDOM RIDER (LP, reissue)	10
70s	Blue Note BST 84170	FREE FOR ALL (LP)	10
70s	Blue Note BST 84347	ROOTS AND HERBS (LP)	10
70s	Blue Note BST 81507	AT CAFE BOHEMIA VOL. 1 (LP)	10
70s	Blue Note BST 81508	AT CAFE BOHEMIA VOL. 2 (LP)	10
70s	Blue Note BST 81521	A NIGHT AT BIRDLAND VOL. 1 (LP, reissue)	10
70s	Blue Note BST 81522	A NIGHT AT BIRDLAND VOL. 2 (LP, reissue)	10
70s	Blue Note BST 81554	ORGY IN RHYTHM VOL. 1 (LP, reissue)	10
70s	Blue Note BST 81555	ORGY IN RHYTHM VOL. 2 (LP, reissue)	10

(see also Thelonious Monk)

MEL BLANC
| 58 | Capitol CL 14950 | I Taut I Taw A Puddy Cat/K-K-K-Katy | 8 |
| 60 | Warner Bros WB 26 | Tweety's Twistmas Twouble/I Keep Hearing Those Bells | 4 |

BURT BLANCA
60	Zodiac ZR 004	Texas Rider/Shamash	12

BLANCMANGE
79	Blaah Music MFT-1	IRENE AND MAVIS (EP, gatefold p/s)	12
82	Lyntone LYN 1183/84	Living On The Ceiling/Sad Day (excerpt)/PASSAGE: Born Every Minute (33rpm clear black flexidisc free with 'Melody Maker' magazine)	5/4
82	London BLAPD 2	Feel Me/Feel Me (Instrumental) (picture disc)	4
84	London BLAPD 6	That's Love That It Is/Vishnu (picture disc)	4
84	London BLAPD 8	The Day Before You Came/All Things Are Nice (picture disc)	4
84	London BLAPX 8	The Day Before You Came/Feel Me/All Things Are Nice (12", picture disc)	7
82	London SHPD 8552	HAPPY FAMILIES (LP, picture disc)	10
84	London SHPD 8554	MANGE TOUT (LP, picture disc)	10

BILLY BLAND
60	London HL 9096	Let The Little Girl Dance/Sweet Thing	10

BOBBY BLAND
61	Vogue V 9178	Cry Cry Cry/I've Been Wrong So Long	18
61	Vogue V 9182	Lead Me On/Hold Me Tenderly	18
61	Vogue V 9188	Don't Cry No More/St. James Infirmary	15
62	Vogue V 9190	You're The One (That I Need)/Turn On Your Love Light	15
62	Vogue V 9192	Blue Moon/Who Will The Next Fool Be?	15
64	Vocalion VP 9222	Ain't Nothing You Can Do/Honey Child	12
64	Vocalion VP 9229	After It's Too Late/Share Your Love With Me	12
65	Vocalion VP 9232	Yield Not To Temptation/How Does A Cheating Woman Feel?	10
65	Vocalion VP 9251	These Hands (Small But Mighty)/Today	12
66	Vocalion VP 9262	I'm Too Far Gone (To Turn Around)/If You Could Read My Mind	10
66	Vocalion VP 9273	Good Time Charlie/Good Time Charlie (Working His Groove Bag)	12
68	Sue WI 4044	That Did It/A Touch Of The Blues	18
69	Action ACT 4524	Rockin' In The Same Old Boat/Wouldn't You Rather Have Me?	10
69	Action ACT 4538	Gotta Get To Know You/Baby I'm On My Way	15
69	Action ACT 4548	Share Your Love With Me/Honey Child	10
69	Action ACT 4553	Chains Of Love/Ask Me 'Bout Nothing But The Blues	10
74	ABC ABC 4014	Ain't No Love In The Heart Of The City/Twenty Four Blues	5
75	ABC ABC 4030	I Wouldn't Treat A Dog (The Way You Treat Me)/I Ain't Gonna Be The First To Cry	8
77	ABC ABC 4186	The Soul Of A Man/If I Weren't A Gambler	4
63	Vocalion VEP 170153	YIELD NOT INTO TEMPTATION (EP)	35
64	Vocalion VEP 170157	BOBBY BLAND (EP)	35
61	Vogue VAP 160183	TWO STEPS FROM THE BLUES (LP)	35
64	Vocalion VAP 8027	AIN'T NOTHING YOU CAN DO (LP)	35
65	Vocalion VAP 8034	CALL ON ME/THAT'S THE WAY LOVE IS (LP)	35
66	Vocalion VAP 8041	HERE'S THE MAN (LP)	35
68	Island ILP 974	A TOUCH OF THE BLUES (LP)	30
69	Action ACLP 6006	A PIECE OF GOLD (LP)	25
73	ABC ABCL 5044	HIS CALIFORNIA ALBUM (LP)	10
74	ABC ABCL 5053	DREAMER (LP)	10
74	Polydor 2383 257	BLUES FOR MR. CRUMP (LP, with tracks by Junior Parker & Howlin' Wolf)	15
75	ABC ABCL 5139	GET ON DOWN WITH BOBBY BLAND (LP)	10

BOBBY BLAND & B.B. KING
74	ABC ABCD 605	TOGETHER FOR THE FIRST TIME (2-LP)	14

(see also B.B. King)

MARCIE BLANE
62	London HLU 9599	Bobby's Girl/A Time To Dream	10
63	London HLU 9673	What Does A Girl Do/How Can I Tell Him	5
63	London HLU 9744	Little Miss Fool/Ragtime Sound	5
63	London HLU 9787	You Gave My Number To Billy/Told You So	5
63	London REU 1393	MARCIE BLANE (EP)	40

VIVIAN BLANE
54	Parlophone MSP 6070	Changing Partners/Lonely	4

BLANKS
79	Void SRTS/79/CUS/560	The Northern Ripper/Understand (p/s)	15

(see also Destructors)

BLAZER, BLAZER
78	Logo GO 362	Cecil B. Devine/Warsaw/Six O'Clock In The Morning (p/s)	4

BLAZERS
58	Fontana TFR 6010	ROCK AND ROLL (10" LP)	30

BLAZING SONS
83	Cool Ghoul COOL 002	Chant Down The National Front/N.F. Dub (no p/s)	10

(see also Phantom)

BLEACH BOYS
78	Tramp THF 002	Chloroform/You've Got Nothing (no p/s)	6

BLEAKHOUSE
82	Buzzard BUZZ 2	CHASE THE WIND (EP, p/s with insert)	35

BLEECHERS
69	Trojan TR 679	Ease Up/You're Gonna Feel It	6
69	Upsetter US 314	Come Into My Parlour/MELOTONES: Dry Up Your Tears	5
70	Columbia Blue Beat DB 118	Send Me The Pillow (That You Dream On)/Adam And Eve	6
71	Duke DU 118	Put It Good/J.J. ALLSTARS: Good Good Version	4

PETER BLEGVAD
80   Recommended RRA 5.75   Alcohol (p/s, 1-sided, other side etched) 4
(see also Slapp Happy)

BLENDELLS
64   Reprise RS 20291   La La La La La La/Huggies Bunnies 8
64   Reprise RS 20340   Dance With Me/Get Your Baby 10

CARLA BLEY
72   JCOA EOTH 3   ESCALATOR OVER THE HILL (3-LP set) 20

PAUL BLEY TRIO
69   Fontana SFJL 929   TOUCHING (LP) 25
(see also Bley-Peacock Synthesizer Show, Annette Peacock)

ARCHIE BLEYER & HIS ORCHESTRA
54   London HL 8035   Amber/Julie's Jump 20
54   London HL 8111   The Naughty Lady Of Shady Lane/While The Vesper Bells Were Ringing 18
55   London HLA 8176   Hernando's Hideaway/S'il Vous Plait 18
56   London HLA 8243   Nothin' To Do/JANET BLEYER: 'Cause You're My Lover 15
56   London HLA 8243   Nothin' To Do/JANET BLEYER: 'Cause You're My Lover (78) 5
56   London HLA 8263   Bridge Of Happiness/You Tell Me Your Dream, I'll Tell You Mine 15

BLEY-PEACOCK SYNTHESIZER SHOW
72   Polydor 2425 043   REVENGE (LP) 50
(see also Annette Peacock, Paul Bley)

BLIND BLAKE
50   Tempo R 23   Hey Hey Daddy Blues/Brownskin Mama Blues (78) 8
50   Tempo R 40   Southern Rag/CC Pill Blues (78) 6
54   Jazz Collector L 97   Hot Potatoes/Southbound Rag (78) 5
58   Ristic LP 18   THE LEGENDARY BLIND BLAKE (10" LP) 40
50s   Jazz Collector JLP 2001   THE LEGENDARY BLIND BLAKE (10" LP, reissue) 30
67   Riverside RLP 8804   BLUES IN CHICAGO (LP) 20
60s   Whoopee 101   BLIND BLAKE 1927-30 (LP) 15

BLIND BLAKE/CHARLIE JACKSON
50s   Heritage HLP 1011   BLIND BLAKE AND CHARLIE JACKSON (LP) 30

BLIND BLAKE/RAMBLIN' THOMAS
60s   Jazz Collector JEL 4   THE MALE BLUES VOLUME 3 (EP) 8

BLIND FAITH
69   Island (no cat. no.)   Change Of Address From June 23rd 1969 (promo single) 50
69   Polydor 583 059   BLIND FAITH (LP, gatefold sleeve) 10
(see also Stevie Winwood, Ginger Baker, Eric Clapton)

BLINKERS
69   Pye 7N 17752   Original Sin/Dreams Secondhand 40

BLINKY & EDWIN STARR
69   Tamla Motown TMG 720   Oh How Happy/Ooo Baby Baby (demo only) 100
70   Tamla Motown TMG 748   Oh How Happy/Ooo Baby Baby 4
70   T. Motown (S)TML 11131   JUST WE TWO (LP) 12
(see also Edwin Starr)

BLISS
69   Chapter One CH 107   Castles In Castille/Lifetime 4

MELVIN BLISS
77   Contempo CS 2013   Reward/Synthetic Substitute 4

BLITZ
82   No Future OI 1   ALL OUT ATTACK (EP) 7
82   No Future OI 6   Never Surrender/Razor In The Night (p/s) 6
82   No Future OI 16   Warriors/Youth (p/s) 5
83   Future 12 FS 6   Solar (Extended Remix)/Husk (Dance Mix) (12", p/s) 7

BLITZ BOYS
81   Told You So TYS 001   Eddy's New Shoes/Eddie's Friend/She Told My Friends (foldover p/s) 12

BLITZKRIEG
82   No Future OI 8   LEST WE FORGET (EP) 4
83   Sexual Phonograph SPH 3   CONSCIOUS PRAYER (EP) 4

BLITZKRIEG
81   Neat NEAT 10   Buried Alive/Blitzkrieg (p/s) 6
85   Neat NEAT 1023   A TIME FOR CHANGES (LP) 10

BLITZKRIEG BOP
77   Mortonsound
      MTN 3172/3   Let's Go/Nine Till Five/Bugger Off 15
77   Lightning GTL 504   Let's Go/Life Is Just A So So/Mental Case 6
78   Lightning GTL 543   U.F.O./Bobby Joe 5

BLOATED TOADS
79   Shattered SHAT 4   Why/Essential In Some Form/Happy Home/Yankee TV Victim (p/s, with insert) ...4

BLODWYN PIG
69   Island WIP 6059   Dear Jill/Sweet Caroline 8
69   Island WIP 6069   Walk On The Water/Summer Day 8
69   Island WIP 6078   Same Old Story/Slow Down 8
69   Island ILPS 9101   AHEAD RINGS OUT (LP, pink label, gatefold sleeve; pink & white label £10) 18
70   Chrysalis ILPS 9122   GETTING TO THIS (LP, gatefold sleeve) 15
(see also Mick Abrahams)

BLOND
69	Fontana TF 1040	(I Will Bring You) Flowers In The Morning/I Wake Up And Call	10
69	Fontana STL 5515	LILAC YEARS (LP)	100

BLONDE ON BLONDE
68	Pye 7N 17637	All Day All Night/Country Life	40
70	Ember EMB S 279	Castles In The Sky/Circles (some in p/s)	12/6
69	Pye NSPL 18288	CONTRASTS (LP, gatefold sleeve)	40
70	Ember NR 5049	REBIRTH (LP, gatefold sleeve)	30
71	Ember NR 5058	REFLECTIONS ON A LIFE (LP, gatefold sleeve)	30

BLONDIE
77	Private Stock PVT 90	X Offender/In The Sun (unissued, no p/s, copies supposedly exist)	£100+
77	Private Stock PVT 105	In The Flesh/X Offender (no p/s)	20
77	Chrysalis CHS 2180	Rip Her To Shreds/In The Flesh/X Offender (p/s)	8
77	Chrysalis CHS 2180-12	Rip Her To Shreds/In The Flesh/X Offender (12", green labels & '75p' in corner)	8
78	Chrysalis CHS 2204	Denis (Denee)/Contact In Red Square (red p/s)	4
78	Chrysalis CHS 2242	Picture This/Fade Away (And Radiate) (p/s, yellow vinyl)	5
80	Flexi FLX 146	Auto-American Interview (Blondie Fan Club flexidisc)	8
82	Lyntone LYN 10840/1	Yuletown Throwdown (Rapture) (with Freddie)/BRATTLES: The Christmas Song/ SNUKY TATE: Santa's Agent (33rpm blue vinyl flexi with 'Flexipop' 15)	6/5
82	Chrysalis CHSP 2608	Island Of Lost Souls/Dragonfly (picture disc)	5
82	Chrysalis CHSP 2624	War Child/Little Caesar (picture disc)	5
76	Private Stock PVLP 1017	BLONDIE (LP)	15
82	Chrysalis PCDL 1384	THE HUNTER (LP, picture disc)	10

(see also Debbie Harry, New York Blondes, Wind In The Willows, Jimi Destri)

BLOOD
83	No Future OI 22	Megalomania/Parasite In Paradise (p/s)	5
83	Noise NOY 1	Stark Raving Normal/Mesrine (p/s)	4

BLOOD
85	Conquest QUEST 3	SE PARARE NEX (LP)	20

BLOODROCK
69	Capitol	BLOODROCK (LP)	10
70	Capitol	BLOODROCK 2 (LP)	10
71	Capitol EST 765	BLOODROCK 3 (LP)	10

BLOODS
84	Exit Intl./021 OTO 9	Button Up/Raumen	5

BLOODSTONE
73	Decca F 13382	Natural High/This Thing Is Heavy	4
72	Decca TXS 110	BLOODSTONE (LP)	12
73	Decca SKL 5150	NATURAL HIGH (LP)	10
74	Decca SKL 5156	UNREAL (LP)	10
74	Decca SKL 5185	I NEED TIME (LP)	10
75	Decca SKL 5202	RIDDLE OF THE SPHINX (LP, with insert)	10

BLOOD, SWEAT & TEARS
68	CBS 3563	I Can't Quit Her/House In The Country	5
68	CBS 63296	CHILD IS THE FATHER TO THE MAN (LP)	10
73	CBS CQ 31170/Q 64803	GREATEST HITS (LP, quadrophonic)	10

(see also Al Kooper)

BLOOD UNCLES
86	Drastic Plastic DRASTIC 1	PETROL (12" EP)	7

ROGER BLOOM'S HAMMER
67	CBS 202654	Out Of The Blue/Life's A Gamble	10
67	CBS 2848	Polly Pan/Fifteen Degree Temperature Rise	5

MIKE BLOOMFIELD
69	CBS 63652	IT'S NOT KILLING ME (LP)	10

MIKE BLOOMFIELD & AL KOOPER
69	CBS 66216	THE LIVE ADVENTURES OF MIKE BLOOMFIELD AND AL KOOPER (2-LP)	15

(see also Al Kooper, Paul Butterfield Blues Band, Electric Flag)

BLOOMSBURY SET
80	Graduate GRAD 13	This Year Next Year/The Other Side Of You (p/s)	4
83	Stiletto STL 13	Hangin' Around With The Big Boys/Getting Away From It All (p/s)	4
83	Stiletto STL 15	Dress Parade/Serenade (p/s)	5

BLOSSOMS
58	Capitol CL 14833	Move On/He Promised Me	15
58	Capitol CL 14856	Little Louie/Have Faith In Me	15
58	Capitol CL 14947	No Other Love/Baby Daddy-O	15

BLOSSOMS
68	MGM MGM 1435	Tweedle Dee/You Got Me Hummin'	4
71	Pama PM 814	Stand By/Soul And Inspiration	15

BLOSSOM TOES
67	Marmalade 598 002	What On Earth/Mrs Murphy's Budgerigar/Look At Me I'm You (some in p/s)	30/12
68	Marmalade 598 009	I'll Be Your Baby Tonight/Love Is	12
68	Marmalade 598 012	Postcard/Everyone's Leaving Me Now	8
69	Marmalade 598 014	Peace Loving Man/Up Above My Hobby Horse's Head	8
67	Marmalade 607/608 001	WE ARE EVER SO CLEAN (LP)	45
68	Marmalade 608 010	IF ONLY FOR A MOMENT (LP)	65

(see also B.B. Blunder, Stud)

MICHAEL BLOUNT

72	York FYK 401	SOUVENIRS (LP)	15
73	York FYK 414	FANTASIES (LP)	12
70	CBS 64230	PATCHWORK (LP)	20

BLOW MONKEYS

80	Parasol PAR 1	Live Today Love Tomorrow/In Cold Blood (no p/s)	12
84	RCA RCA 398	Go Public/Rub-A-Dub Shanka (p/s)	5
84	RCA RCAT 398	Go Public/Rub-A-Dub Shanka (12", p/s)	8
84	RCA RCA 418	The Man From Russia/Resurrection Love (p/s)	5
84	RCA RCAT 418	The Man From Russia/Resurrection Love/Slither (12", p/s)	8
84	RCA RCA 444	Atomic Lullaby/My Twisty Jewel (p/s)	5
84	RCA RCAT 444	Atomic Lullaby (Extended Mix)/Kill The Pig/My Twisty Jewel (12", p/s)	8
85	RCA RCA 477	Wild Flower/Waiting For Mr. Moonlight (live) (p/s)	5
85	RCA RCAT 477	Wild Flower/It's Not Unusual (live)/Waiting For Mr Moonlight (live)/Trashtown Incident (live) (12", p/s)	8
85	RCA PB 40331	Forbidden Fruit/My America (p/s)	4
85	RCA PB 40332	Forbidden Fruit/My America/The Optimist (12", p/s)	7
85	RCA PT 40334	Forbidden Fruit/My America//Sweet Murder (Eek-A-Mix)/Kill The Pig (Pig Mix) (12", double pack in stickered gatefold p/s)	10
86	RCA MONKY 1	Digging Your Scene (Remix)/I Backed A Winner (In You)/Digging Your Scene (Instrumental)/The Man From Russia (Remix) (10", p/s)	6
86	RCA PB 40600	Digging Your Scene (Long)/Backed A Winner (In You)/Digging Your Scene (Short)/Digging Your Scene (Longer) (12", die-cut p/s)	7
86	RCA MONKD 2	Wicked Ways/Walking The Blue Beat//Digging Your Scene (Scat Mix)/Automatic Lullaby (double pack, gatefold p/s)	8
86	RCA MONKTG 2	Wicked Ways (Long)/Wildflower/Wicked Ways (Instrumental)/Walking The Blue Beat (12", p/s, double-groove edition)	7
86	RCA MONKTX 3	Don't Be Scared Of Me (Mix)/Superfly/Digging Your Scene (Scat Mix)/Wildflower/He's Shedding Skin (12", poster p/s)	7
87	RCA MONK 5P	Out With Her/The Grantham Grizzler/The Grantham Groover (12", poster p/s)	7
87	RCA MONK 5D	Out With Her/The Grantham Grizzler//Digging Your Scene/It Doesn't Have To Be This Way (12", double pack, gatefold p/s)	7
87	RCA MONKX 6	Celebrate (The Remix)/It's Not Unusual (live)/Beautiful Child/The Smile On Your Face (Sweet Murder) (10", p/s, with Curtis Mayfield)	5
87	RCA MONKX 6	(Celebrate) The Day After You (Election Mix)/It's Not Unusual (live)/Beautiful Child/The Smile On Your Face (Sweet Murder) (10", withdrawn 'Thatcher' p/s, 'General Election Party Edition')	25
87	RCA MONKB 7	Some Kind Of Wonderful/Sweet Obsession (p/s, shrinkwrapped with badge & stickered front)	4
87	RCA MONKS 7	Some Kind Of Wonderful/Sweet Obsession/Huckleberry (12", gatefold p/s with catalogue)	7
88	RCA PT 42150R	This Is Your House/This Is Your Life (Short)/This Day Today (12", numbered gatefold p/s with 'sash')	7
88	RCA PT 42232R	It Pays To Be Twelve/This Is Your House/Digging Your Remix (12", die-cut sleeve)	12
84	RCA PL 70395	LIMPING FOR A GENERATION (LP, original sleeve with lyric inner bag)	10

(see also Curtis Mayfield)

BABBITY BLUE

65	Decca F 12053	Don't Make Me/I Remembered How To Cry	5
65	Decca F 12149	Don't Hurt Me/Question	5

DAVID BLUE

67	Elektra EKL 4003	DAVID BLUE (LP, red label)	20
72	Asylum SYL 9001	STORIES (LP)	10
73	Asylum SYL 9009	NICE BABY AND THE ANGEL (LP)	10
75	Asylum SYL 9025	COMIN' BACK FOR MORE (LP)	10
76	Asylum K 53056	CUPID'S ARROW (LP)	10

PAMELA BLUE

63	Decca F 11761	My Friend Bobby/Hey There Stranger	30

BLUE ACES

64	Pye 7N 15672	Land Of Love/Love Song Of The Waterfall	6
65	Columbia DB 7755	Tell Me What You're Gonna Do/All I Want	20
66	Columbia DB 7954	That's All Right/Talk About My Baby	50

(see also Riot Squad)

BLUE AEROPLANES

86	Fire BLAZE 12T	TOLERANCE (12" EP)	7

(see also Art Objects, Exploding Seagulls)

BLUE & FERRIS

68	Blue Cat BS 147	You Stole My Money/Tell Me The Reason	7

BLUE ANGEL

80	Polydor POSP 212	I'm Gonna Be Strong/Anna Blue (no p/s)	18
81	Polydor POSP 241	I Had A Love/Can't Blame Me	18
84	Polydor POSP 212	I'm Gonna Be Strong/Anna Blue (p/s, reissue)	10
80	Polydor 2391 486	BLUE ANGEL (LP)	20

(see also Cyndi Lauper)

BLUEBEARD

70s	Ember LT 7004	BLUEBEARD (LP, test pressings only)	500

BLUEBEATS

64	Ember EMB EP 4525	THE FABULOUS BLUEBEATS VOL. 1 (EP)	40
64	Ember EMB EP 4526	THE FABULOUS BLUEBEATS VOL. 2 (EP)	40

BLUE-BELLES
62	HMV POP 1029	I Sold My Heart To The Junkman/Itty Bitty Twist	12

(see also Patti LaBelle & Blue Belles, Labelle)

BLUEBELLS
82	London LON(F) 14/	Forevermore/Aim In Life (p/s, with free 33rpm clear vinyl flexidisc	
	Lyntone LYN 12361	"Everybody's Somebody's Fool")	6
83	London LON 20	Cath/All I Ever Said (p/s)	4
83	London LON 27	Sugar Bridge (It Will Stand)/Patriot's Game//Some Sweet Game/	
		Happy Birthday (p/s, double pack)	4
84	London LON 49	Young At Heart/Tender Mercy (p/s)	4
84	London LON 49	Young At Heart/Tender Mercy (blue bell-shaped disc)	6

(see also McClusky Brothers)

BLUEBERRIES
65	Mercury MF 894	It's Gonna Work Out Fine/Please Don't Let Me Know	25

BLUE BLOOD
70	Sonet SNTF 615	BLUE BLOOD (LP)	15

BLUE CHEER
68	Philips BF 1646	Summertime Blues/Out Of Focus	8
68	Philips BF 1684	Just A Little Bit/Gypsy Ball	6
68	Philips BF 1711	Feathers From Your Tree/Sun Cycle	6
69	Philips BF 1778	West Coast Child Of Sunshine/When It All Gets Old	7
71	Philips 6051 010	Pilot/Babaji	7
68	Philips (S)BL 7839	VINCEBUS ERUPTUM (LP)	15
68	Philips SBL 7860	OUTSIDEINSIDE (LP, gatefold sleeve)	20
69	Philips SBL 7896	NEW! IMPROVED! (LP)	15
69	Philips 6336 001	BLUE CHEER (LP)	18
70	Philips 6336 004	ORIGINAL HUMAN BEING (LP)	25

(see also Leigh Stephens)

BLUE CHIPS
65	Pye 7N 15970	I'm On The Right Side/You're Good To Me	20
66	Pye 7N 17111	Some Kind Of Lovin'/I Know A Boy	20
66	Pye 7N 17155	Tell Her/Good Lovin' Never Hurt	20

BLUE DANUBE
80	EMI EMI 5070	You Are A Song/Du Bist Music/Let Me Hear That Song Again	5

BLUE DIAMONDS
60	Decca F 21292	Ramona/All Of Me	4
60	Decca DFE 6675	I'M FOREVER BLOWING BUBBLES (EP)	7

BLUE EPITAPH
74	Holyground HG 117	ODE (LP)	350

(see also Magus)

BLUE FLAMES
(see under Georgie Fame & Blue Flames)

BLUE GOOSE
79	Anchor ANC 1015	Loretta/Call On Me	4
79	Anchor ANCL 2005	BLUE GOOSE (LP)	10

(see also Badfinger)

BLUE JEANS
69	Columbia DB 8555	Hey Mrs. Housewife/Sandfly	15

(see also Swinging Blue Jeans, Ray Ennis & Blue Jeans)

BLUE MAGIC
74	Atlantic K 10494	Sideshow/Just Don't Want To Be Lonely	4
75	Atlantic K 10553	Three Ring Circus/Spell	5

(see also Margie Joseph)

BLUE MEN
60	Triumph RGXST 5000	I HEAR A NEW WORLD (PART ONE) (EP)	200
60	Triumph TRX ST 9000	I HEAR A NEW WORLD (LP, unreleased, demo only)	600

(see also Joe Meek, Peter Jay & Blue Men)

BLUE MINK
72	Regal Zono. SLRZ 1029	LIVE AT THE TALK OF THE TOWN (LP)	10

(see also Madeline Bell)

BLUE MOUNTAIN BOYS
62	Oriole CB 1774	Drop Me Gently/One Small Photograph Of You	4

BLUE NILE
81	RSO RSO 84	I Love This Life/The Second Act (p/s)	15
80s	Linn LKS 1	Stay/Saddle The Horses (white p/s)	8
80s	Linn LKS 1-12	Stay/Saddle The Horses (12", p/s)	12
84	Linn LKS 1	Stay (Remix)/Saddle The Horses (p/s)	4
84	Linn LKSD 1	Stay (Remix)/Saddle The Horses//Tinsel Town In The Rain/Heatwave	
		(Instrumental) (p/s, double pack)	8
84	Linn LKS 1-12	Stay (Extended Remix)/Saddle The Horses (12", p/s)	8
84	Linn LKS 2	Tinsel Town In The Rain/Heatwave (Instrumental) (p/s)	4
84	Linn LKS 2-12	Tinsel Town In The Rain (Extended)/Regret/Heatwave (Instrumental) (12", p/s)	8
80s	Linn	flexidisc (demonstration disc)	20

BLUENOTES
60	Top Rank JAR 291	I Don't Know What It Is/You Can't Get Away From Love	4

BLUE ORCHIDS
81	Rough Trade RT 065	Disney Boys/The Flood (p/s)	4

BLUE ORCHIDS

81	Rough Trade RT 067	Work/The House That Faded Out (p/s)	4
82	Rough Trade RT 117T	AGENTS OF CHANGE (12" EP, in carrier bag)	7
84	Rough Trade ROUGH 37	GREATEST HITS (LP, in plastic bag)	10

(see also Nosebleeds, Fall)

BLUE OYSTER CULT

76	CBS 4483	(Don't Fear) The Reaper/Tattoo Vampire (promos with different B-side)	10
76	CBS 4483	(Don't Fear) The Reaper/R U Ready 2 Rock	5
78	CBS 5689	Going Through The Motions/Searching For The Celine	4
78	CBS 12-6333	(Don't Fear) The Reaper (12")	8
79	CBS 7763	Mirrors/Lonely Teardrops (clear vinyl)	4
81	CBS A 1453	Burnin' For You/Heavy Metal (p/s)	4
81	CBS A 13 1453	Burnin' For You/Heavy Metal/The Black & Silver (12", p/s)	7
83	CBS A 3937	Take Me Away/Feel The Thunder (p/s)	4
83	CBS TA 3937	Take Me Away/Feel The Thunder/Burnin' For You/ Doctor Music (12", p/s)	7
84	CBS A 4117	Shooting Shark/Dragon Lady (p/s)	4
84	CBS TA 4117	Shooting Shark/Dragon Lady (12", p/s)	7
73	CBS 64904	BLUE OYSTER CULT (LP)	10
80	CBS 86120	CULTOSAURUS ERECTUS (LP, initially with poster)	10

BLUE PHANTOM

72	Kaleidoscope KAL 101	DISTORTIONS (LP)	70

BLUE RIDGE RANGERS

73	Fantasy FTC 105	Hearts Of Stone/Somewhere Listening For My Name	4
73	Fantasy FTC 110	You Don't Own Me/Back In The Hills	4
73	Fantasy FT 511	BLUE RIDGE RANGERS (LP)	10

(see also John Fogerty, Creedence Clearwater Revival)

BLUE RIVERS & MAROONS

67	Columbia Blue Beat DB 103	Witchcraft Man/Searching For You Baby	6
68	Columbia SX 6192	BLUE BEAT IN MY SOUL (LP)	18

BLUE RONDOS

64	Pye 7N 15734	Little Baby/Baby I Go For You	40
65	Pye 7N 15833	Don't Want Your Lovin' No More/What Can I Do	30

BLUES BAND

80	Arista BBBP 101	OFFICIAL BOOTLEG ALBUM (LP, with autographs)	10

(see also Paul Jones)

BLUESBREAKERS

(see under John Mayall['s Bluesbreakers])

BLUES BUSTERS

60	Limbo XL 101	Little Vilma/Early In The Morning	12
61	Starlite ST 031	The Spiritual/Lost My Baby	12
61	Starlite ST 053	Your Love/You Send Me Crazy	12
61	Blue Beat BB 55	Donna/You're Driving Me Crazy	12
61	Blue Beat BB 73	There's Always Sunshine/You Had It Wrong	12
62	Blue Beat BB 102	Tell Me Why/I've Done You Wrong	12
62	Island WI 023	Behold/Oh, Baby	12
65	Island WI 214	How Sweet It Is/I Had A Dream	8
65	Island WI 222	Wings Of A Dove/BYRON LEE & DRAGONAIRES: Dan Is The Man	8
66	Doctor Bird DB 1030	I've Been Trying/Pretty Girls	8
67	Doctor Bird DB 1078	There's Always Sunshine/Lover's Reward	8
65	Island ILP 923	BEHOLD! (LP)	80
66	Doctor Bird DLM 5008	THE BLUES BUSTERS (LP)	50

BLUES BY FIVE

64	Decca F 12029	Boom Boom/I Cried	40

BLUES COUNCIL

65	Parlophone R 5264	Baby Don't Look Down/What Will I Do	50

BLUES IMAGE

70	Atlantic 2091 009	Ride Captain Ride/Pay My Dues	4
71	Atlantic 2400 120	RED, WHITE AND BLUES IMAGE (LP)	10

BLUES INCORPORATED

(see under Alexis Korner)

BLUES MAGOOS

66	Mercury MF 954	(We Ain't Got) Nothin' Yet/Gotta Get Away	25
67	Fontana TF 848	One By One/Love Seems Doomed	15
66	Fontana (S)TL 5402	BLUES MAGOOS (LP, mono/stereo)	30/35

BLUESOLOGY

65	Fontana TF 594	Come Back Baby/Time's Getting Tougher Than Tough	150
66	Fontana TF 668	Mister Frantic/Everyday (I Have The Blues)	150

(see also Stu Brown & Bluesology, Elton John, Elton Dean)

BLUES PROJECT

67	Verve Forecast VS 1505	I Can't Keep From Crying/The Way My Baby Walks	15
67	Verve (S)VLP 6004	PROJECTIONS (LP)	15
72	Capitol EST 11017	THE BLUES PROJECT (LP)	10

(see also Al Kooper, Tommy Flanders, Seatrain)

BLUE STARS

65	Decca F 12303	Please Be A Little Kind/I Can Take It	80

BLUE STEAM

78	Rip Off RIP 5	Lizard King/Cortina Cowboys (p/s)	5

BLUE TRAIN
87   Dreamworld DREAM 007T   LAND OF GOLD (12" EP) 8

BLUE VELVET BAND
69   Warner Bros WB 7320   Hitch Hiker/Sittin' On Top Of The World 4

BLUEWATER FOLK
70s   Folk Heritage   BLUEWATER FOLK (LP) 40
70s   Moonraker MOO 1   BUGS, BLACK PUDDINGS AND CLOGS (LP, with insert) 10
70s   Moonraker MOO 2   A LANCASHIRE LIFE (LP, with insert) 10

BLUE ZONE
88   Arista RHCD 115   Thinking About His Baby/Big Thing (Extended Version) (3" CD) 7
(see also Lisa Stansfield)

COLIN BLUNSTONE
71   Epic EPC 7520   Caroline Goodbye/Though You Are Far Away 4
(see also Zombies, Neil McArthur)

BLUNT INSTRUMENT
78   Diesel DCL 01   No Excuse/Interrogation (p/s) 5

BLUR
90   Food FOOD 26   She's So High/I Know (p/s) 4
90   Food 12 FOOD 26   She's So High (Definitive)/Sing/I Know (Extended) (12", p/s) 8
91   Food 12 FOODDX 29   There's No Other Way (12" Remix)/Won't Do It/Day Upon Day (live) (12", p/s) ...8
90s   Food/Parlophone BLUR 6   The Wassailing Song (1-sided promo/freebie, p/s) 10

BLURT
80   Test Pressing TP 1   My Mother Was A Friend Of An Enemy Of The People/Get (p/s) 4
81   Armageddon AS 013   The Fish Needs A Bike/This Is My Royal Wedding Souvenir (p/s) 4

JIMMY BLYTHE
54   London AL 3527   SOUTH SIDE BLUE PIANO (10" LP) 25
54   London AL 3529   SOUTH SIDE CHICAGO JAZZ (10" LP) 25

BLYTH POWER
86   All The Madmen MAD 12   The Junction Signal/Bind Their Kings In Chains And The Nobles With
Links Of Iron 4

B-MOVIE
80   Dead Good DEAD 9   TAKE THREE (EP) 20
80   Dead Good BIG DEAD 12   NOWHERE GIRL (12" EP, with insert) 25
81   Deram DM 437   Remembrance Day/Institution Walls (Remix)
(p/s, brown paper or red plastic labels) 5
81   Deram DMX 437   Remembrance Day/Institution Walls (Remix) (12", plain brown sleeve) 8
81   Lyntone LYN 10410   Remembrance Day/SOFT CELL: Metro Mr X (coloured flexidisc with 'Flexipop'
mag issue 12; mag also included 2nd flexi by Weapon Of Peace) 8/6
81   Deram DM 443   Marilyn Dreams/Film Music (Part 1) (p/s) 5
81   Deram DMX 443   Marilyn Dreams/Film Music (Part 1) (12", p/s) 8
82   Some Bizzare BZZ 8   Nowhere Girl/Scare Some Life Into Me (p/s, b&w picture or moulded labels) 4
82   Some Bizzare BZZX 8   Nowhere Girl/Nowhere Girl (Version)/Scare Some Life Into Me (12", p/s) 7
88   Wax 12 WAX 3   Nowhere Girl/Remembrance Day (12", p/s, 250 only on orange vinyl, numbered) 12
88   Wax 12 WAX 3   Nowhere Girl/Remembrance Day (12", p/s, pink or black vinyl, numbered) 10/7
88   Wax 12 WAX 4   Polar Opposites/Taxi Driver (12", clear vinyl or picture disc) 7/8
88   Wax WAXLP 1P   THE DEAD GOOD TAPES (LP, picture disc) 10
88   Wax WAXCD 1   THE DEAD GOOD TAPES (CD) 15
91   Dead Good GOOD 3   REMEMBRANCE DAYS (LP, with 7" "The Fool"/"Swinging Lights" [CHEAP 1]) ..12

BMX BANDITS
86   53rd & 3rd AGARR 3   Sad?/E102 (p/s, some with comic) 6/4
86   53rd & 3rd AGARR 312   Sad?/E102/The Cat From Outer Space (live)/Strawberry Sunday (live)/
Groovy Good Luck Friend (live) (12", p/s) 8
87   53rd & 3rd AGARR 6   What A Wonderful World/The Day Before Tomorrow (p/s) 4
87   53rd & 3rd AGARR 612   What A Wonderful World/The Day Before Tomorrow/Johnny Alucard/Sad?/
Sandy's Wallet (12", p/s) 7
(see also Soup Dragons, Boy Hairdressers)

EDDIE BO
73   Action ACT 4609   Check Your Bucket Pts 1 & 2 6

BO & PEEP
64   Decca F 11968   Young Love/The Rise Of The Brighton Surf 18
(see also Andrew Oldham Orchestra)

BOB
88   Sombrero TWO   Kirsty/The Hippy Goes Fishing/Banwell Blues (No. 2)/Times Like These
(12", p/s) 8
88   House Of Teeth   Prune (Your Tree)/Groove/Brian Wilson's Bed (flexidisc, p/s) 8
89   House Of Teeth HOT 003   Esmerelda Brooklyn/I Don't Know (unreleased, stickered white card sleeve) ... 10

BOB (Relf) & EARL (Nelson)
65   Sue WI 374   Harlem Shuffle/I'll Keep Running Back 12
65   Sue WI 393   Baby I'm Satisfied/The Sissy 15
67   Sue WI 4030   Don't Ever Leave Me/Fancy Free 15
69   Island WI 6053   Harlem Shuffle/I'll Keep Running Back (reissue) 4
69   B&C CB 102   Dancin' Everywhere/Baby It's Over 4
69   Warner Bros WB 6059   Everybody Jerk/He's A Playbrother 5
70   Uni UN 519   Pickin' Up Love's Vibrations/Uh Uh Naw Naw Naw 4
73   Jay Boy BOY 72   I Can't Get Away/I'll Keep Running Back 4
73   Jay Boy BOY 73   My Little Girl/His & Her Shuffle (as Bob & Earl Band) 4
73   Contempo C 4   Harlem Shuffle/Harlem Shuffle (Instrumental Version) 4
67   Sue ILP 951   HARLEM SHUFFLE (LP) 35

BOB & EARL

69	Joy JOYS 199	TOGETHER (LP)	10
69	B&C BCB 1	BOB AND EARL (LP)	10
71	Jay Boy JSX 2004	HARLEM SHUFFLE (LP)	10

(see also Bob Relf, Jackie Lee, Earl Nelson, Hollywood Flames)

BOB & JERRY
58	Pye International 7N 25003	Ghost Satellite/Nothin'	8
58	Pye International 7N 25003	Ghost Satellite/Nothin' (78)	8
61	Philips PB 1205	Dreamy Eyes/We're The Guys	6

BOB (Andy) & MARCIA (Griffiths)
70	Bamboo BAM 40	Really Together/BOB ANDY: Desperate Lover	7
70	Trojan TBL 122	YOUNG, GIFTED & BLACK (LP)	15
71	Trojan TRLS 26	PIED PIPER (LP)	12

(see also Bob Andy, Marcia Griffiths)

BOB & TYRONE
69	Coxsone CS 7086	I Don't Care/LASCELLES PERKINS: Little Green Apples	12

BOBBEJAAN
60	Palette PG 9009	I'm Cryin' In My Beer/A Little Bit Of Heaven	4

BOBBETTES
57	London HLE 8477	Mr. Lee/Look At The Stars	35
57	London HLE 8477	Mr. Lee/Look At The Stars (78)	15
58	London HLE 8597	Come-A Come-A/Speedy	35
58	London HLE 8597	Come-A Come-A/Speedy (78)	15
60	London HLE 9173	I Shot Mr. Lee/Untrue Love	25
60	London HLE 9248	Have Mercy Baby/Dance With Me Georgie	20
60	Pye International 7N 25060	I Shot Mr. Lee/Billy (as Bobettes)	20
72	Action ACT 4603	That's A Bad Thing To Know/All In Your Mind	10

BOBBSEY TWINS
57	London HLA 8474	A Change Of Heart/Part-Time Gal	10
57	London HLA 8474	A Change Of Heart/Part-Time Gal (78)	6

BOBBY & DAVE
70	Ackee ACK 116	Build My World Around You/LIZZY & TONY BOP: Sammy Version	5

(see also Dave Barker)

BOBBY & JIM
58	Capitol CL 14877	Carry My Books/A Lover Can Tell	4

BOBBY & LAURIE
66	Parlophone R 5480	Hitch Hiker/You'll Come 'Round	6

BOBCATS
67	Pye 7N 17242	Can't See For Looking/Let Me Get By	12

FRIDA BOCCARA
69	Philips BF 1765	Through The Eyes Of A Child/So Fair	15

BOCKY & VISIONS
65	Atlantic AT 4049	I Go Crazy/Good Good Lovin'	12

BODAST
82	Cherry Red BRED 12	THE BODAST TAPES FEATURING STEVE HOWE (LP)	10

(see also Steve Howe)

J.P. BODDY
73	Columbia DB 8989	Stop Me Spinning (Like A Top)/Song Without A Word	5

BODIES
79	Waldo's HS 007	Art Nouveau/Machinery (poster p/s, 5 different colours)	5
79	Waldo's HS 007	Art Nouveau/Machinery (re-pressing, different p/s)	4

BODINES
85	Creation CRE 016	God Bless/Paradise (wraparound p/s with poly bag)	8
86	Creation CRE 028	Therese/I Feel (p/s)	4
86	Creation CRE 028T	Therese/Scar Tissue/I Feel (12", p/s)	7
86	Creation CRE 030	Heard It All/Clear (12", p/s)	4
86	Creation CRE 030T	Heard It All/William Shatner/Clear (12", p/s)	7
87	Magnet BODT 1	Therese (4.20 Extended Wear Mix)/Heard It All/Therese (Original 7" Mix) (12", p/s, with free 7" "Canadian Bootleg")	7

BODKIN
72	West CSA 104	BODKIN (LP, private pressing in posthumously-designed sleeve)	350

BODY
81	Recession	THE BODY ALBUM (LP, private pressing with booklet)	50

BODYSNATCHERS
80	2-Tone CHS TT 9	Let's Do Rocksteady/Ruder Than You (paper label, company sleeve)	4
80	2-Tone CHS TT 12	Easy Life/Too Experienced (paper label, company sleeve)	5

BOFFALONGO
70	United Artists UAG 29130	BEYOND YOUR HEAD (LP)	12

LUCILLE BOGAN
57	Jazz Collector L 90	Sweet Man, Sweet Man/Down In Boogie Alley (78)	5

DIRK BOGARDE
65	Fontana TF 615	Darling/MOVIE SOUNDS: Pavanne For Diane	4
60	Decca LK 4373	LYRICS FOR LOVERS (LP)	10

BOGDON
81	Black Label GB 3	Oh Eddie/Reet Petite (p/s)	6
81	Brilliant HIT 1	Who Do You Think You Are?/Take Me Back (p/s)	6

BOHANNON

75	Brunswick BR 16	South African Man/Have A Good Day	4
75	Brunswick BR 19	Disco Stomp/Disco Stomp (demo only)	5
76	Brunswick BR 33	Bohannon's Beat/Bohannon's Beat (demo only)	4
78	Mercury 6167 700	Let's Start The Dance/I Wonder Why	4
78	Mercury 9199 830	Let's Start The Dance/I Wonder Why (12")	7
75	Brunswick BRLS 3013	SOUTH AFRICAN MAN (LP)	10

HOUSTON BOINES

66	Blue Horizon 45 BH 1006	Superintendent Blues/Monkey Motion	45

MARC BOLAN

65	Decca F 12288	The Wizard/Beyond The Rising Sun	160
66	Decca F 12413	The Third Degree/San Francisco Poet	225
66	Parlophone R 5539	Hippy Gumbo/Misfit	250
74	Track 2094 013	Jasper C. Debussy/Hippy Gumbo/The Perfumed Garden Of Gulliver Smith (p/s)	20
81	Cherry Red CHERRY 29	You Scare Me To Death/The Perfumed Garden Of Gulliver Smith (initial copies with free flexi disc [Lyntone LYN 10086])	7
81	Cherry Red CHERRY P29	You Scare Me To Death/The Perfumed Garden Of Gulliver Smith (picture disc)	6
81	Cherry Red CHERRY 32	Cat Black/Jasper C. Debussy (p/s)	5
82	Cherry Red CHERRY 39	The Wizard/Beyond The Rising Sun/Rings Of Fortune (p/s)	5
90	Archive Jive TOBY 1	The Road I'm On (Gloria) (p/s, mail order issue, 1,500 only)	10
74	Track 2410 201	THE BEGINNING OF DOVES (LP)	20
81	Cherry Red PERED 20	YOU SCARE ME TO DEATH (LP, picture disc)	12
81	Cherry Red ERED 20	YOU SCARE ME TO DEATH (LP, gatefold sleeve with booklet)	10
89	Media Motion MEDIA 2	THE BEGINNING OF DOVES (LP, reissue, 750 only, withdrawn)	10

MARC BOLAN & GLORIA JONES

77	EMI EMI 2572	To Know Him Is To Love Him/City Port	6

(see also Gloria Jones)

MARC BOLAN/T. REX

70	Octopus OCTO 1	Ride A White Swan/Summertime Blues/Jewel (unreleased, handwritten white label test pressings only)	750
70	Fly BUG 1	Ride A White Swan/Is It Love/Summertime Blues (p/s, 1st pressing had purple labels, later ones had mustard labels)	15/7
71	Fly BUG 6	Hot Love/Woodland Rock/King Of The Mountain Cometh (1st pressing had mustard labels, later ones had 'fly' design)	6/5
71	Fly BUG 10	Get It On/There Was A Time/Raw Ramp (p/s, with silver 'fly' label, later with silver 'fly' & then silver 'fly' labels in capitals)	12/4/4
71	Fly GRUB 1A	Electric Warrior Preview Single: Jeepster/Life's A Gas (2 label designs, originally in pink sleeve)	150/90
71	Fly BUG 16	Jeepster/Life's A Gas (white 'fly' label, rarer without 'GRUB 1A' on label)	5/4
72	EMI T REX 101	Telegram Sam/Cadillac/Baby Strange	5
72	EMI MARC 1	Metal Guru/Thunderwing/Lady	4
72	EMI MARC 2	Children Of The Revolution/Jitterbug Love/Sunken Rags	4
72	EMI MARC 3	Solid Gold Easy Action/Born To Boogie	4
72	EMI MARC 3	Solid Gold Easy Action/(5th Dimension track) (mispress)	15
72	EMI MARC 3	Solid Gold Easy Action/(Partridge Family track) (mispress)	15
72	fan club	Christmas Time/Wanna Spend My Christmas With You/Christmas/Everybody Knows It's Christmas (flexidisc with letter in brown envelope)	5
73	EMI MARC 4	20th Century Boy/Free Angel	4
73	EMI MARC 5	The Groover/Midnight	4
73	EMI MARC 6	Truck On (Tyke)/Sitting Here	4
74	EMI MARC 7	Teenage Dream/Satisfaction Pony (credited to 'Marc Bolan & T. Rex' or 'Marc Bolan')	5/4
74	EMI MARC 8	Light Of Love/Explosive Mouth	4
74	EMI MARC 9	Zip Gun Boogie/Space Boss	5
75	EMI MARC 10	New York City/Chrome Sitar	4
75	EMI MARC 11	Dreamy Lady/Do You Wanna Dance?/Dock Of The Bay (as T. Rex Dance Party)	4
75	EMI MARC 12	Christmas Bop/Telegram Sam/Metal Guru (unreleased)	
76	EMI MARC 13	London Boys/Soul Baby	5
76	Cube BUG 66	Hot Love/Get It On	5
76	EMI MARC 14	I Love To Boogie/Baby Boomerang	4
76	EMI MARC 15	Laser Love/Life's An Elevator	4
77	EMI MARC 16	The Soul Of My Suit/All Alone	5
77	EMI MARC 17	Dandy In The Underworld/Groove A Little/Tame My Tiger (p/s)	6
77	EMI MARC 18	Celebrate Summer/Ride My Wheels (p/s)	7
78	EMI MARC 19	Crimson Moon/Jason B. Sad (p/s)	4
77	Cube ANT 1	BOLAN'S BEST PLUS ONE (EP)	4
78	Cube ANT 2	Hot Love/Raw Ramp/Lean Woman Blues (p/s, misprinted "Raw Amp")	4
78	Cube BINT 1	Steve Dixon Interview (free to early buyers of HIFLD 1 compilation LP)	7
79	Cube ANTS 001	Life's A Gas/Find A Little Wood/Once Upon The Seas Of Abyssinia/Blessed Wild Apple Girl (12", p/s)	12
81	Rarn MBFS 001C	Sing Me A Song/Endless Sleep (Extended Version)/The Lilac Hand Of Menthol Dan (12", p/s, clear vinyl, handwritten labels)	8
81	Rarn MBFS 001P	Sing Me A Song/Endless Sleep (Extended Version)/The Lilac Hand Of Menthol Dan (12" picture disc, misprinted with black rim; also white rim)	15/7
81	Rarn MBFS 001P	Sing Me A Song/Endless Sleep (Extended Version)/The Lilac Hand Of Menthol Dan (12", picture disc misprinted back-to-front)	20
81	Cube/Dakota	Christmas Jingle/Sailors Of The Highway (free MBFS flexidisc)	4
82	Rarn MBFS RAP 1	Life's A Gas/Find A Little Wood/Once Upon The Seas Of Abyssinia/Blessed Wild Apple Girl (12", p/s, reissue)	7
82	Marc ABOLAN 2	THE CHILDREN OF RARN (10", p/s, 10" EP, 33rpm, with 12-page lyric book)	20
82	Marc SBOLAN 13	Mellow Love/Foxy Box/Lunacy's Back (p/s blue vinyl)	4
82	Rarn MBFS RAP 2	Deep Summer/Oh Baby/One Inch Rock (New Version) (12", blue vinyl)	7

Marc BOLAN/T. REX

82	Old Gold OG 9234	Debora/One Inch Rock (1,000 mispressed with "Beltane Walk" on B-side) 4
82	Marc SBOLAN 12EP	CHRISTMAS BOP EP (12", p/s, MBFS only, extra tracks: acoustic versions of "King Of The Rumbling Spires" & "Savage Beethoven") 7
82	Marc SBOLAN 14PD	Think Zinc/Magical Moon/Till Dawn (picture disc) 4
85	Marc PTANX 1	Megarex 2/Tame My Tiger/Chrome Sitar/Solid Baby (shaped picture disc) 7
85	Marc STANX 1	Megarex 3/Tame My Tiger/Chrome Sitar/Solid Baby (12", picture disc) 7
70	Fly HIFLY 2	T. REX (LP, in semi-gatefold sleeve) 10
71	Fly HIFLY 6	ELECTRIC WARRIOR (LP, with poster & inner sleeve) 14
72	Fly HIFLY 8	BOLAN BOOGIE (LP) 10
72	EMI BLN 5001	THE SLIDER (LP, with lyric inner sleeve) 10
72	EMI BLN 5002	TANX (LP, with poster & inner sleeve) 14
73	EMI BLN 5003	GREAT HITS (LP, with poster) 12
74	EMI BNLA 7751	ZINC ALLOY (LP, 1st 1,000 with 3-way foldout numbered sleeve & inner sleeve) 150
74	EMI BNLA 7751	ZINC ALLOY (LP, gatefold sleeve & inner) 14
75	EMI BNLA 7752	BOLAN'S ZIP GUN (LP, diamond-cut sleeve & inner) 18
76	EMI BLNA 5004	FUTURISTIC DRAGON (LP, with inner lyric) 12
77	EMI BLNA 5005	DANDY IN THE UNDERWORLD (LP) 10
78	Cube HIFLY 1	MARC: THE WORDS AND MUSIC OF MARC BOLAN 1947-1977 (2-LP, gatefold sleeve, with free single, BINT 1) 20
81	Marc ABOLAN 1P	T. REX IN CONCERT (LP, picture disc, 2 designs 10
82	Cube/Dakota ICSX 1004	ACROSS THE AIRWAVES (LP, picture disc) 10
82	Marc ABOLAN 3P	ELECTRIC WARRIOR (LP, picture disc) 10
84	Marc ABOLAN 5	T. REXTASY (LP & 12" "Jam (live)"/"Elemental Child (live)" [ABOLAN 5F]) 12
86	M. On Wax WARRIOR 1/4	HISTORY OF T. REX (4-LP, numbered picture disc set) 20

(see also Tyrannosaurus Rex, Dib Cochran & Earwigs, John's Children, Big Carrot)

TOMMY BOLIN
76	Nemperor K 10730/NE 4	The Grind/Homeward Strut 4
75	Atlantic K 50208	TEASER (LP) 10

(see also James Gang, Deep Purple)

SIMON BOLIVAR ORCHESTRA
56	London HLG 8245	Merengue Holiday/Shy 15

BOLSHOI
85	Situation 2 SIT 38	Sob Story/Ports Of Amsterdam (p/s) 5
85	Situation 2 SIT 38T	Sob Story/Ports Of Amsterdam/Crosstown Traffic (12", p/s) 8
85	Situation 2 SIT 40	Happy Boy/Boxes (p/s) 4
85	Situation 2 SIT 40T	Happy Boy/Boxes/Holiday By The Sea (12", p/s) 7

BOMBADIL
72	Harvest HAR 5056	Breathless/When The City Sleeps 5
75	Harvest HAR 5095	Breathless/When The City Sleeps (reissue) 5

(see also Barclay James Harvest)

BOMBAY DUCKS
80	Complete Control CON 1	Sympathy For The Devil/1-0-6-9 (p/s) 8
80s	United Dairies UP 05	DANCE MUSIC (LP) 20
80s	Erasehead C-60	ANYONE CAN BE ENO (cassette) 10
80s	Erasehead C-30	A RETROSPECTIVE LOOK AT THE BOMBAY DUCKS (cassette with mask) 10

BOMBERS
77	The Label TLR 006	I'm A Liar, Baby/2230 A.D. (p/s) 4

BOMB PARTY
85	Abstract 12 ABS 032	RAY GUN (12" EP) 7
85	Abstract ABS 035	THE NEW MESSIAH (EP) 5
85	Abstract ABS 038	Life's A Bitch/Get So Down/New Messiah (p/s) 5
87	Workers Playtime WPCS1	Pretty Face/These Are Your Rights (numbered, die-cut p/s) 4

BOMB THE BASS
88	Rhythm King	BOX SET (3 x 3" CD singles) 10

BON-BONS
55	London HL 8139	That's The Way Love Goes/Make My Dreams Come True 22
55	London HL 8139	That's The Way Love Goes/Make My Dreams Come True (78) 5
56	London HLU 8262	Circle/Frog On A Log 18
56	London HLU 8262	Circle/Frog On A Log (78) 5

BOBBY BOND
61	Pye Intl. 7N 25081	You're A Livin' Doll/Sweet Love 8
69	Warner Bros WB 7292	One More Mile, One More Town/If You're Leaving Me 4

BRIGITTE BOND
64	Blue Beat BB 212	Oh Yeah Baby/Blue Beat Baby 8

GRAHAM BOND (ORGANISATION)
64	Decca F 11909	Long Tall Shorty/Long Legged Baby (as Graham Bond Organization) 30
65	Columbia DB 7471	Wade In The Water/Tammy (as Graham Bond Organisation) 25
65	Columbia DB 7528	Tell Me (I'm Gonna Love Again)/Love Come Shining Through (as Graham Bond Organisation) 20
65	Columbia DB 7647	Lease On Love/My Heart's In Little Pieces (as Graham Bond Organisation) 20
66	Columbia DB 7838	St. James' Infirmary/Soul Tango (as Graham Bond Organisation) 20
67	Page One POF 014	You've Gotta Have Love Babe/I Love You 25
70	Warner Bros WB 8004	Walking In The Park/Springtime In The City (solo) 8
65	Columbia SX 1711	THE SOUND OF '65 (LP) 60
66	Columbia SX 1750	THERE'S A BOND BETWEEN US (LP) 60
70	Warner Bros WS 3001	SOLID BOND (2-LP, solo) 25
71	Vertigo 6360 021	HOLY MAGICK (LP, gatefold sleeve, spiral label, as Graham Bond & Magick) ...18
71	Vertigo 6360 042	WE PUT OUR MAGICK ON YOU (LP, gatefold sleeve, spiral label, as Graham Bond With Magick) 18

| 71 | Philips 6499 200/1 | BOND IN AMERICA (2-LP, solo) | 20 |
| 72 | Philips 6382 010 | THIS IS GRAHAM BOND (LP, solo) | 10 |

(see also Jack Bruce, Dick Heckstall-Smith, Ginger Baker, Duffy Power, Who, Don Rendell)

GRAHAM BOND & PETE BROWN

| 72 | Greenwich G 55104 | LOST TRIBE (EP) | 15 |
| 72 | Chapter One CHSR 813 | TWO HEADS ARE BETTER THAN ONE (LP) | 70 |

(see also Pete Brown)

JACKI BOND

| 66 | Strike JH 302 | Tell Him To Go Away/Don't You Worry ('Bout Me) | 4 |
| 66 | Strike JH 320 | He Say/Why Can't I Love Him | 20 |

JANE BOND & UNDERCOVER MEN

| 86 | Dreamworld BIG DREAM 1 | POLITICALLY CORRECT (LP) | 10 |

JOHNNY BOND

50s	MGM MGM 262	Music Music Music (Put Another Nickel In) (with Orchestra)/ ENSEMBLE & ROSEMARY CALVIN: Rag Mop (78)	5
60	London HLU 9189	Hot Rod Jalopy/Five-Minute Love Affair	12
60	London HL 7100	Hot Rod Lincoln/Five-Minute Love Affair (export issue)	12
65	London HLB 9957	Ten Little Bottles/Eleven More Months And Ten More Days (B-side with Cowboy Copas)	6
62	Stateside SL 10008	THAT WILD, WICKED BUT WONDERFUL WEST (LP)	12
63	London HA-B 8098	LIVE IT UP (LP, as Johnny Bond & His Friends On Stage)	15
65	London HA-B 8228	THE SONGS THAT MADE HIM FAMOUS (LP)	20

JOYCE BOND

67	Airborne NBP 0011	It's Alright/Mrs. Soul	12
66	Island WI 3019	Tell Me What It's All About/Tell Me Right Now	7
67	Island WIP 6010	Do The Teasy/Sugar	6
67	Island WIP 6018	This Train/Not So With Me	6
68	Island WIP 6051	Ob-La-Di, Ob-La-Da/Robin Hood Rides Again	5
68	Pama PM 718	Back To School/They Wish	6
69	Pama PM 770	Mr. Pitiful/Let's Get Married	6
70	Upfront UPF 5	Wind Of Change/First In Line	4
68	Island ILP 968	SOUL AND SKA (LP)	60

MARGARET BOND

55	Decca F 10506	You'll Always Be My Lifetime Sweetheart/Where Is The One For Me	5
55	Decca F 10555	My Love's A Gentle Man/Mirror, Mirror	5
55	Decca F 10632	There's Always A First Time/Dancing In My Socks	5
57	Parlophone R 4283	Your Love Is My Love/Goodnight My Love, Pleasant Dreams	7
57	Parlophone R 4312	The Wind In The Willow/Young And In Love	4

OLIVER BOND

| 66 | Parlophone R 5476 | I Saw You All Alone/Let Me Love You | 10 |

(see also Oliver Bone)

RONNIE BOND

| 69 | Page One POF 123 | Anything For You/Carolyn | 20 |

(see also Troggs)

(GARY) 'U.S.' BONDS

60	Top Rank JAR 527	New Orleans/Please Forgive Me (as U.S. Bonds)	7
61	Top Rank JAR 566	Not Me/Give Me One More Chance (as U.S. Bonds)	7
61	Top Rank JAR 575	Quarter To Three/Time Ole Story (as U.S. Bonds)	6
61	Top Rank JAR 581	School Is Out/One Million Tears	7
61	Top Rank JAR 595	School Is In/Trip To The Moon	7
62	Top Rank JAR 602	Dear Lady Twist/Havin' So Much Fun	6
62	Top Rank JAR 615	Twist Twist Senora/Food Of Love	6
62	Stateside SS 111	Seven Day Weekend/Gettin' A Groove	5
62	Stateside SS 125	Copy Cat/I'll Change That Too	5
63	Stateside SS 144	Mixed Up Faculty/I Dig This Station	5
63	Stateside SS 179	Where Did That Naughty Little Girl Go?/Do The Limbo With Me	6
63	Stateside SS 219	What A Dream/I Don't Wanta Wait	5
64	Stateside SS 271	New Orleans/Quarter To Three	5
64	Stateside SS 308	My Sweet Baby Rose/Ella Is Yella	6
67	Stateside SS 2025	Send Her To Me/Workin' For My Baby	12
61	Top Rank 35/114	DANCE 'TIL QUARTER TO THREE WITH U.S. BONDS (LP)	30
62	Stateside SL 10001	TWIST UP CALYPSO (LP)	20
63	Stateside SL 10037	THE GREATEST HITS OF GARY (U.S.) BONDS (LP)	20

OLIVER BONE & SOUNDS MAXIMUM

| 66 | Parlophone R 5527 | Knock On Wood/Jugger Tea | 8 |

(see also Oliver Bond)

BROTHER BONES & HIS SHADOWS

| 60 | Oriole CB 1030 | Sweet Georgia Brown/Margie | 4 |

BONEY M

| 76 | Creole CR 119 | Baby Do You Wanna Bump Pts 1 & 2 | 4 |
| 79 | Atlantic K 11279 | Hooray Hooray It's A Holi Holiday/Ribbons Of Blue (picture disc) | 4 |

BONGOS

80	Fetish FET 003	Telephoto Lens/Glow In The Dark (p/s)	6
81	Fetish FET 005	In The Congo/Mambo Sun (p/s)	6
81	Fetish FET 009	The Bulrushes/Automatic Doors (p/s)	5
82	Fetish FE 17	Zebra Club/Certain Harbours (p/s)	4
82	Fetish FE 18	Mambo Sun/Hunting (p/s)	4
82	Fetish FET 18	Mambo Sun/Hunting (12", p/s)	7
81	Fetish FR 2004	BONGOS (LP)	10
82	Fetish FM 2009	TIME AND THE RIVER (mini-LP)	8

BON JOVI

84	Vertigo VER 11	She Don't Know Me/Breakout (p/s)	15
84	Vertigo VERX 11	She Don't Know Me/Breakout (12", p/s)	25
84	Vertigo VER 14	Runaway/Breakout (live) (p/s)	15
84	Vertigo VERX 14	Runaway/Breakout (live)/Runaway (live) (12", p/s)	20
85	Vertigo VER 19	In And Out Of Love/Roulette (live) (p/s)	10
85	Vertigo VERP 19	In And Out Of Love/Roulette (live) (picture disc)	18
85	Vertigo VERX 19	In And Out Of Love/Roulette (live)/Shot Through The Heart (live) (12", p/s)	12
85	Vertigo VER 22	The Hardest Part Is The Night/Always Run To You (p/s)	8
85	Vertigo VERDP 22	The Hardest Part Is The Night/Always Run To You//Tokyo Road (live)/ Shot Through The Heart (live) (double pack, gatefold p/s)	12
85	Vertigo VERX 22	The Hardest Part Is The Night/Always Run To You/Tokyo Road (live) (12", p/s)	12
85	Vertigo VERXR 22	Red Hot And Two Parts Live: The Hardest Part Is The Night/Tokyo Road (live)/In And Out Of Love (live) (12", p/s, red vinyl)	18
86	Vertigo VER 26	You Give Love A Bad Name/Let It Rock (p/s)	5
86	Vertigo VERP 26	You Give Love A Bad Name/Let It Rock (10" shaped picture disc)	15
86	Vertigo VERX 26	You Give Love A Bad Name/Let It Rock (12", with poster)	10
86	Vertigo VERXR 26	You Give Love A Bad Name/Let It Rock/Hardest Part Is The Night (live)/Burning For Love (12", p/s, blue vinyl)	12
86	Vertigo VER 28	Livin' On A Prayer/Wild In The Streets (p/s)	4
86	Vertigo VERPA 28	Livin' On A Prayer/Wild In The Streets (p/s, with patch)	7
86	Vertigo VERP 28	Livin' On A Prayer/Wild In The Streets (picture disc)	12
86	Vertigo VERXR 28	Livin' On A Prayer/Wild In The Streets/Edge Of A Broken Heart (12", p/s, green vinyl)	12
86	Vertigo VERXG 28	Livin' On A Prayer/Wild In The Streets/Only Lonely (live)/Runaway (live) (12", gatefold p/s)	12
87	Vertigo JOVS 1	Wanted Dead Or Alive/Shot Through The Heart (p/s, with metal stickers)	5
87	Vertigo JOVPB 112	Wanted Dead Or Alive/Shot Through The Heart/Social Disease (12", poster p/s)	8
87	Vertigo JOVR 112	Wanted Dead Or Alive/Shot Through The Heart/Social Disease/ Get Ready (live) (12", p/s, silver vinyl)	10
87	Vertigo JOVCD 1	Wanted Dead Or Alive (Full Version)/(Radio Edit)/(Acoustic) (CD)	8
87	Vertigo JOVR 212	Never Say Goodbye/Raise Your Hands/Wanted Dead Or Alive (Acoustic Version) (12", yellow vinyl, PVC sleeve)	5
88	Vertigo JOVS 3	Bad Medicine/99 In The Shade (in special p/s)	5
88	Vertigo JOVR 312	Bad Medicine/You Give Love A Bad Name/Livin' On A Prayer (live) (12", embossed p/s)	7
88	Vertigo JOVCD 3	Bad Medicine/Lay Your Hands On Me/99 In The Shade (CD)	7
88	Vertigo JOVS 4	Born To Be My Baby/Love For Sale (gold 'calendar' card envelope pack)	4
88	Vertigo JOVP 412	Born To Be My Baby/Love For Sale/Wanted Dead Or Alive (live) (12", picture disc)	8
88	Vertigo JOVR 412	Born To be My Baby/Love For Sale/Wanted Dead Or Alive (live) (12", gatefold p/s)	7
89	Vertigo JOVPB 5	I'll Be There For You/Homebound Train (p/s, with poster)	4
89	Vertigo JOVS 661	Lay Your Hands On Me/Bad Medicine (live) (3 x 7" red vinyl pack)	6
89	Vertigo JOVP 610	Lay Your Hands On Me/Bad Medicine (live)/Blood On Blood (10", picture disc with card insert)	6
89	Vertigo JOVG 612	Lay Your Hands On Me/Blood On Blood (live)/Born To Be My Baby (Acoustic) (12", gatefold p/s)	7
90	Vertigo JOVR 712	Living In Sin/Love Is War/Ride Cowboy Ride/Stick To Your Guns (12", silver/white vinyl with card insert)	7
90	Vertigo JOVCD 7	Living In Sin/Love Is War/Ride Cowboy Ride/Stick To Your Guns (CD, boxed)	7
88	Vertigo VERHP 38	SLIPPERY WHEN WET (LP, picture discwith poster)	12
88	Vertigo VERHP 62	NEW JERSEY (LP, picture disc)	10

JUKE BOY BONNER

69	Blue Horizon 57-3163	Runnin' Shoes/Jackin' In My Plans	18
60s	Jan & Dil JR 451	MORE DOWN HOME BLUES (EP)	8
68	Flyright LP 3501	THE ONE MAN TRIO (LP)	25
69	Liberty LBS 83319	THINGS AIN'T RIGHT (LP)	12

GRAHAM BONNET

72	RCA RCA 2230	Rare Specimen/Whisper In The Night	5
73	RCA RCA 2380	Trying To Say Goodbye/Castles In The Air	5
74	DJM DJS 328	Back Row In The Stalls/Ghost Writer In My Eye	5
77	Ring O' 2017 015	It's All Over Now, Baby Blue/Heroes On My Picture Wall (company sleeve)	4
77	Ring O' 2017 106	Danny/Rock Island Line (generic p/s)	5
77	Ring O' 2017 110	Goodnight And Goodmorning/Wino Song (company sleeve)	4
78	Ring O' 2017 114/POSP 2	Warm Ride/10/12 Observation (company sleeve)	4
78	Ring O' POSP 002	Warm Ride/10/12 Observation (12", company sleeve)	7
81	Lyntone LYN 10138/9	Night Games/POLECATS: We Say Yeah/THIN LIZZY: Song For Jimmy/WAY OF THE WEST: Monkey Time (orange flexi with 'Flexipop' mag, issue 10)	5/4
77	Ring O' 2320 103	GRAHAM BONNET (LP)	15

(see also Marbles, Rainbow)

GRAHAM BONNEY

65	Columbia DB 7773	My Little World Is All Blue/Why Can't We Be Friends	4
66	Columbia DB 7843	Super Girl/Hill Of Lovin'	6
66	Columbia DB 7934	Baby's Gone/Later Tonight	4
66	Columbia DB 8005	No One Knows/Mixed Up Baby Girl	7
67	Columbia DB 8111	Thank You Baby/Briony	4
67	Columbia DB 8142	Happy Together/That Bad Day	4
67	Columbia DB 8283	Papa Joe/My Jenny	4
68	Columbia DB 8338	By The Way I Love You/Devil's Child	4
68	Columbia DB 8382	I'll Be Your Baby Tonight/Back From Baltimore	4
68	Columbia DB 8464	Frenzy/Something I've Got To Tell You	4
69	Columbia DB 8531	Get Ready/Fly Me High Lorelei	7
69	Columbia DB 8592	Leander Angeline/Mixing The Wine	4

MINT VALUE £

70	Columbia DB 8648	Sign On The Dotted Line/Words We Said	7
66	Columbia SX 6052	SUPER GIRL (LP)	12

(see also Riot Squad)

BONNIE & TREASURES
65	London HLU 9998	Home Of The Brave/Our Song	20

BONZO DOG (DOO-DAH) BAND
66	Parlophone R 5430	My Brother Makes The Noises For The Talkies/I'm Gonna Bring A Watermelon To My Gal Tonight	20
66	Parlophone R 5499	Alley Oop/Button Up Your Overcoat	20
67	Liberty LBF 15040	Equestrian Statue/The Intro And Outro	7
69	Liberty LBF 15201	Mister Apollo/Ready Mades	5
69	Liberty LBF 15273	I Want To Be With You/We Were Wrong	6
70	Liberty LBF 15314	You Done My Brain In/Mr Slater's Parrot	5
67	Liberty LBL/LBS 83056	GORILLA (LP, some with booklet)	18/14
68	Liberty LBL/LBS 83158E	THE DOUGHNUT IN GRANNY'S GREENHOUSE (LP, gatefold sleeve, some with booklet)	20/15
69	Liberty LBS 83257	TADPOLES (LP, die-cut sleeve, some with insert)	18/15
69	Liberty LBS 83290	KEYNSHAM (LP, gatefold sleeve)	15
72	United Artists UAS 29288	LET'S MAKE UP AND BE FRIENDLY (LP)	10

(see also Vivian Stanshall, Neil Innes, Grimms, Roger Ruskin Spear)

BETTY BOO (U.S.)
79	Grapevine GRP 125	Say It Isn't So/Say It Isn't So (Instrumental)	4

JAMES BOOKER
61	Vogue V 9177	Cool Turkey/Gonzo	12
63	Vocalion VEP 170154	GONZO (EP)	40

BOOKER T. & M.G.'s
62	London HLK 9595	Green Onions/Behave Yourself	8
63	London HLK 9670	Jelly Bread/Aw' Mercy	8
63	London HLK 9784	Chinese Checkers/Plum Nellie	8
65	Atlantic AT 4033	Boot-Leg/Outrage	8
66	Atlantic AT 4063	Be My Lady/Red Beans And Rice	8
66	Atlantic 584 044	My Sweet Potato/Booker Loo	6
66	Atlantic 584 060	Jingle Bells/Winter Wonderland	7
67	Atlantic 584 088	Green Onions/Boot-Leg	5
67	Stax 601 009	Hip Hug Her/Summertime (initially dark blue label; later light blue)	7/4
67	Stax 601 018	Slim Jenkins' Place/Groovin'	6
67	Stax 601 026	Chinese Checkers/Plum Nellie	5
68	Stax STAX 102	Soul Limbo/Heads Or Tails	4
69	Stax STAX 119	Time Is Tight/Hang 'Em High	4
69	Stax STAX 127	Soul Clap '69/Mrs. Robinson	4
63	London REK 1367	R&B WITH BOOKER T (EP)	12
64	Atlantic AET 6002	R&B WITH BOOKER T VOL. 2 (EP)	12
64	London HA-K 8182	GREEN ONIONS (LP)	15
65	Atlantic ATL 5027	SOUL DRESSING (LP)	15
66	Atlantic 587/588 033	GREEN ONIONS (LP, reissue)	10
67	Atlantic 587 047	SOUL DRESSING (LP, reissue)	10
67	Stax 589 002	AND NOW! (LP)	12
68	Stax 589 013	SOUL CHRISTMAS (LP)	12
69	Stax 230 002/231 002	DOIN' OUR THING (LP)	12
69	Stax (S)XATS 1001	SOUL LIMBO (LP)	12
69	Atco 228 004	GET READY (LP)	12
69	Stax (S)XATS 1005	UPTIGHT (LP, soundtrack)	12
70	Stax (S)XATS 1015	THE BOOKER T. SET (LP)	12
70	Stax (S)XATS 1031	McLEMORE AVENUE (LP)	12
71	Stax 2325 030	MELTING POT (LP)	10
71	Stax 2362 002	GREATEST HITS (LP)	10
71	Stax 2362 012	THE BOOKER T. SET (LP, reissue)	10
71	Stax 2362 016	McLEMORE AVENUE (LP, reissue)	10
75	Stax STX 1037	MEMPHIS SOUND (LP)	10

(see also Mar-kays)

BOOMERANGS
64	Fontana TF 507	Rockin' Robin/Don't Let Her Be Your Baby	20
65	Fontana TF 555	Another Tear Falls/Fun Fun Fun	15

BOOMERANGS
66	Pye 7N 17049	Dream World/Upgraded	8

BOOMTOWN RATS
78	Ensign	RAT PACK (6 singles in plastic wallet)	12
81	Flexipop 003	Dun Laoghaire (clear, green, yellow or red 1-sided flexi with 'Flexipop' issue 3)	4-5
82	Mercury MER 106	Charmed Lives/No Hiding Place//Nothing Happened Today/Storm Breaks (double pack)	5
84	Mercury MER 179	Dave/Hard Times (picture disc)	4

(see also Kirsty MacColl)

PAT BOONE
55	London HLD 8172	Ain't That A Shame/Tennessee Saturday Night (gold label)	25
55	London HLD 8172	Ain't That A Shame/Tennessee Saturday Night (78)	5
55	London HLD 8197	No Arms Can Ever Hold You/At My Front Door (gold label)	25
55	London HLD 8197	No Arms Can Ever Hold You/At My Front Door (78)	5
56	London HLD 8233	Gee Whittakers/Take The Time (gold label)	15
56	London HLD 8233	Gee Whittakers/Take The Time (78)	5
56	London HLD 8253	I'll Be Home/Tutti Frutti (gold label)	15
56	London HLD 8253	I'll Be Home/Tutti Frutti (78)	5

Pat BOONE

56	London HLD 8291	Long Tall Sally/Just As Long As I'm With You (gold label)	15
56	London HLD 8291	Long Tall Sally/Just As Long As I'm With You (78)	5
56	London HLD 8303	I Almost Lost My Mind/I'm In Love With You (gold label)	12
56	London HLD 8316	Rich In Love/Two Hearts, Two Kisses (gold label, later on silver)	12/8
56	London HLD 8346	Friendly Persuasion (Thee I Love)/Chains Of Love (gold or silver label)	12/8
57	London HLD 8370	Don't Forbid Me/Anastasia (gold label, later on silver)	12/8
57	London HLD 8404	Why Baby Why/I'm Just Waiting For You (gold label, later on silver)	12/8
57	London HLD 8445	Love Letters In The Sand/Bernadine	5
57	London HLD 8479	Remember You're Mine/There's A Goldmine In The Sky	5
57	London HLD 8512	April Love/When The Swallows Come Back To Capistrano	5
57	London HLD 8520	White Christmas/Jingle Bells	6
58	London HLD 8574	A Wonderful Time Up There/It's Too Soon To Know	5
58	London HLD 8640	Sugar Moon/Cherie, I Love You	5
58	London HLD 8675	If Dreams Came True/That's How Much I Love You	5
58	London HLD 8739	Gee, But It's Lonely/For My Good Fortune	5
59	London HLD 8775	I'll Remember Tonight/The Mardi Gras March	4
59	London HLD 8824	With The Wind And The Rain In Your Hair/There's Good Rockin' Tonight	6
59	London HLD 8855	For A Penny/Wang Dang Taffy-Apple Tango	4
59	London HLD 8910	Twixt Twelve And Twenty/Rock Boll Weevil	4
59	London HLD 8910	Twixt Twelve And Twenty/Rock Boll Weevil (78)	8
59	London HLD 8974	A Fool's Hall Of Fame/Brightest Wishing Star	4
59	London HLD 8974	A Fool's Hall Of Fame/Brightest Wishing Star (78)	8
60	London HLD 9029	Beyond The Sunset/The Faithful Heart	4
60	London HLD 9029	Beyond The Sunset/The Faithful Heart (78)	10
60	London HLD 9067	(Welcome) New Lovers/Words	4
60	London HLD 9067	(Welcome) New Lovers/Words (78)	10
60	London HLD 9138	Walking The Floor Over You/Spring Rain	4
60	London HLD 9184	Delia Gone/Candy Sweet	4
60	London HLD 9184	Delia Gone/Candy Sweet (78)	20
60	London HLD 9238	Dear John/Alabam	4
61	London HLD 9299	The Exodus Song/There's A Moon Out Tonight	4
61	London HLD 9350	Moody River/A Thousand Years	5
61	London HLD 9420	Big Cold Wind/That's My Desire	4
61	London HLD 9461	Johnny Will/(If I'm Dreaming) Just Let My Dream	4
62	London HLD 9504	I'll See You In My Dreams/Pictures In The Fire	4
64	Dot DS 16658	Beach Girl/Little Honda	5
67	Dot DS 26752	As Tears Go By/Something About You	4
69	Polydor 56763	July, You're Just A Woman/Break My Mind	4

(the singles below are all export issues)

56	London HL 7007	I'll Be Home/Tutti Frutti	5
56	London HL 7010	Long Tall Sally/Just As Long As I'm With You	5
56	London HL 7012	I Almost Lost My Mind/I'm In Love With You	5
56	London HL 7015	Friendly Persuasion (Thee I Love)/Chains Of Love	5
57	London HL 7019	Love Letters In The Sand/Bernadine	4
58	London HL 7033	A Wonderful Time Up There/It's Too Soon To Know	4
58	London HL 7041	Sugar Moon/Cherie, I Love You	4
58	London HL 7051	If Dreams Came True/That's How Much I Love You	4
58	London HL 7059	Gee, But It's Lonely/For My Good Fortune	4
59	London HL 7070	With The Wind And The Rain In Your Hair/There's Good Rocking Tonight	4
59	London SLD 4002	For A Penny/Wang Dang Taffy-Apple Tango (both tracks stereo)	20
61	London HLD 7112	Moody River/The Exodus Song	4
63	London HL 7118	Send Me The Pillow You Dream On/(You've Got) Personality	8
63	London HLD 7121	Mexican Joe/In The Room	10
56	London RED 1063	PAT BOONE SINGS THE HITS (EP)	9
57	London RED 1086	PAT BOONE SINGS THE HITS NO. 2 (EP)	9
57	London RED 1109	PAT BOONE SINGS THE HITS NO. 3 (EP)	9
58	London RED 1132	PAT PART ONE (EP)	9
58	London RED 1133	PAT PART TWO (EP)	8
61	London RED 1294	ALL HANDS ON DECK (EP)	7
62	London RED 1335	PAT BOONE'S LATEST AND GREATEST NO. 2 (EP)	8
63	London RED 1384	ALWAYS YOU AND ME (EP)	8
63	London RED 1391	PAT SINGS MOVIE THEMES (EP)	8
57	London HA-D 2024	PAT'S BIG HITS (LP)	15
57	London HA-D 2030	HOWDY! (LP)	12
57	London HA-D 2049	PAT! (LP)	12
58	London HA-D 2078	APRIL LOVE (LP, soundtrack, with Shirley Jones & Lionel Newman Orchestra)	12
58	London HA-D 2082	SINGS IRVING BERLIN (LP, also stereo SAH-D 6038)	10/12
58	London HA-D 2098	PAT'S BIG HITS, VOL. 2 (LP)	14
58	London HA-D 2127	STARDUST (LP, also stereo SAH-D 6001)	10/12
59	London HA-D 2144	YES INDEED! (LP, also stereo SAH-D 6010)	10/12
59	London HA-D 2161	PAT SINGS (LP, stereo edition SAH-D 6013 unissued)	10
60	London HA-D 2204	TENDERLY (LP, also stereo SAH-D 6053)	10/12
60	London HA-D 2210	SIDE BY SIDE (LP, with Shirley Boone, also stereo SAH-D 6057)	10/12
60	London HA-D 2265	MOONGLOW (LP, also stereo SAH-D 6085)	12
61	London HA-D 2305	THIS AND THAT (LP)	12
61	London HA-D 2354	THE GREAT GREAT GREAT PAT BOONE (LP, also stereo cat no. SAH-D 6155)	10
61	London HA-D 2382	MOODY RIVER (LP, also stereo SAH-D 6182)	12
62	London HA-D 2452	I'LL SEE YOU IN MY DREAMS (LP, also stereo SAH-D 6240)	12
62	London HA-D/SH-D 8031	PAT BOONE'S GOLDEN HITS (LP)	10
63	London HA-D/SH-D 8053	I LOVE YOU TRULY (LP, with Shirley Boone)	12
63	London HA-D/SH-D 8073	DAYS OF WINE AND ROSES (LP)	12
63	London HA-D/SH-D 8109	SINGS ... GUESS WHO? (LP)	30
64	London HA-D/SH-D 8153	THE TOUCH OF YOUR LIPS (LP)	12
65	Dot (D)DLP 3594	BOSS BEAT (LP)	12
66	Dot (D)DLP 3650	MY TENTH ANNIVERSARY WITH DOT RECORDS (LP)	10

(see also Fontane Sisters)

BOO RADLEYS
90	Rough Trade R2757E	Everybird (Radio Edit) (DJ-only)	7
92	Imaginary FREE 004	Smile Fades Fast/SCORPIO RISING: Watermelon (12" promo, free with "Seconds Out, Round One" LP [ILLUSION 034])	7
90s	Own Label	Ichabod And I (LP)	15

ANTHONY BOOTH
69	Tangerine DP 0008	Till Death Do Us Part/September Days	4

KEN BOOTHE
66	Island WI 3020	The Train Is Coming/This Is Me	12
66	Island WI 3035	I Don't Want To See You Cry/WAILERS: Baby I Need You	25
66	Ska Beat JB 248	You're No Good/SOULETTES: Don't Care What The People Say	10
67	Doctor Bird DB 1110	Say You/LYN TAITT & JETS: Smokey Places	10
67	Coxsone CS 7006	Lonely Teardrops/Oowee Baby	15
67	Coxsone CS 7020	Home Home Home/SOUL BROTHERS: Windell	15
67	Caltone TONE 107	The One I Love/You Left The Water Running	8
67	Studio One SO 2000	Feel Good/Mustang Sally	15
67	Studio One SO 2012	Puppet On A String/ROLAND ALPHONSO: Look Away	12
67	Studio One SO 2014	Fatty Fatty (actually Heptones)/Mother Word (actually by Delroy Wilson)	12
67	Studio One SO 2026	Why Did You Leave (actually by Leroy Sibbles)/Don't Try To Reach Me (actually by Gaylads)	15
68	Studio One SO 2039	When I Fall In Love/HEPTONES: Christmas Time	15
68	Studio One SO 2041	The Girl I Left Behind/TERMITES: My Last Love	15
68	Studio One SO 2053	Tomorrow/Movin' Away	12
68	Fab FAB 63	I Remember Someone/Can't You See?	8
68	Coxsone CS 7041	Everybody Knows/GAYLADS: I'm Free	12
69	Coxsone CS 7094	Sherry/I've Got You	12
69	Studio One SO 2073	You're On My Mind/RICHARD ACE: Love To Cherish	12
69	High Note HS 003	Lady With The Starlight/LESLIE BUTLER & COUNT OSSIE: Gay Drums	6
69	Bamboo BAM 4	Pleading/SOUND DIMENSION: Call 1143	7
69	Bamboo BAM 8	Be Yourself/SOUND DIMENSION: Rathid	7
69	Trojan TR 7716	Why, Baby Why/Keep My Love From Fading	4
70	Trojan TR 7756	Freedom Street/BEVERLEY'S ALLSTARS: Version	4
70	Trojan TR 7772	It's Gonna Take A Miracle/Now I Know	4
70	Trojan TR 7780	Drums Of Freedom/BEVERLEY'S ALLSTARS: Version	4
70	Punch PH 30	Artibella/PRATT ALLSTARS: Version Of Artibella	4
70	Punch PH 33	Morning/Morning (Version)	4
70	Gas GAS 169	Give To Me/Why	4
70	Jackpot JP 748	You Left The Water Running/PHIL PRATT ALL STARS: Cut Throat	4
71	Banana BA 352	Original Six Pts 1 & 2	6
71	Summit SUM 8518	I Wish It Could Be Peaceful Again/BEVERLEY'S ALLSTARS: Peaceful Version	4
71	Summit SUM 8519	Your Feeling And Mine/BEVERLEY'S ALLSTARS: Your Feeling Version	4
73	Green Door GD 4053	Silver Words/Rasta God Version	5
67	Studio One SOL 9001	MR. ROCK STEADY (LP)	80

(see also Stranger & Ken, Keith Hudson, Gaylads)

BOOTLES
64	Vocalion VN 9216	I'll Let You Hold My Hand/Never Till Now	8

BOOTS
68	CBS 3550	Even The Bad Times Are Good/The Animal In Me	10
68	CBS 3833	Keep Your Lovelight Burning/Give Me One More Chance	12

DAVE BOOTS
60s	Solent SM 013	GREEN SATIN AND GOLD (LP)	100

BOOTSY'S RUBBER BAND
77	Warner Bros K 16964T	Pinocchio Theory/Psychoticbumpschool/What's A Telephone (12")	7
78	Warner Bros K 17196T	Bootzilla/Hollywood Squares (12", p/s)	7
76	Warner Bros K 56200	STRETCHIN' OUT IN BOOTSY'S RUBBER BAND (LP)	10
77	Warner Bros K 56302	AHH ... THE NAME IS BOOTSY, BABY! (LP)	10
78	Warner Bros K 56424	BOOTSY? PLAYER OF THE YEAR (LP)	10
79	Warner Bros K 56615	THE BOOT IS MADE FOR FONK-N (LP)	10
81	Warner Bros K 56998	THE ONE GIVETH, THE COUNT TAKETH AWAY (LP)	10

(see also Parliament, Funkadelic)

BOP & BELTONES
67	Coxsone CS 7012	Treat Me Good/PETER TOUCH & WAILERS: Dancing Time (both actually by Bop & Beltones)	15

(see also Beltones)

BILLY BORLYNN
60	Philips PB 1031	Baby Listens/Liebelei	4
60	Philips PB 1057	Every Step Of The Way/It Takes Time	4

BOSS GUITARS
65	London HA-R/SH-R 8237	PLAY THE WINNERS (LP)	10

EARL BOSTIC (ORCHESTRA)
53	Parlophone R 3782	Memories/The Very Thought Of You (78)	8
54	Parlophone MSP 6075	Off Shore/What! No Pearls	12
54	Parlophone R 3818	Off Shore/What! No Pearls (78)	5
54	Parlophone MSP 6089	Deep Purple/Smoke Rings	12
54	Parlophone R 3838	Deep Purple/Smoke Rings (78)	5
54	Parlophone MSP 6105	Melancholy Serenade/Don't You Do It	10
54	Parlophone R 3878	Melancholy Serenade/Don't You Do It (78)	5
54	Parlophone MSP 6110	Jungle Drums/Danube Waves	10
54	Parlophone R 3881	Jungle Drums/Danube Waves (78)	5

Earl BOSTIC

54	Parlophone MSP 6119	Mambolino/Blue Skies	10
54	Parlophone R 3892	Mambolino/Blue Skies (78)	5
54	Parlophone MSP 6131	These Foolish Things/Mambostic	12
54	Parlophone R 3932	These Foolish Things/Mambostic (78)	8
55	Parlophone MSP 6162	Melody Of Love/Sweet Lorraine	10
55	Parlophone R 4003	Melody Of Love/Sweet Lorraine (78)	5
55	Parlophone R 3976	Cracked Ice/The Sheik Of Araby (78)	8
55	Parlophone R 3991	Liebestraume No. 3 (Liszt)/Song Of The Islands (78)	6
55	Parlophone R 4028	Embraceable You/Night And Day (78)	6
55	Parlophone R 4049	Remember/Cherry Bean (78)	6
55	Parlophone R 4104	Cocktails For Two/When Your Lover Has Gone (78)	5
56	Vogue V 2145	Flamingo/Sleep	12
56	Vogue V 2148	Moonglow/Ain't Misbehaving	12
56	Parlophone R 4169	Ubangi Stomp/Time On My Hands (78)	7
56	Parlophone R 4187	Steamwhistle Jump/The Hour Of Parting (78)	8
56	Parlophone R 4208	Mean To Me/The Bo-Do Rock (with Bill Doggett)	8
56	Parlophone R 4208	Mean To Me/The Bo-Do Rock (with Bill Doggett) (78)	5
56	Parlophone R 4232	Beyond The Blue Horizon/For All We Know	7
57	Parlophone R 4263	I Hear A Rhapsody/Harlem Nocturne	7
57	Parlophone R 4278	Bubbins Rock/Indiana (with Bill Doggett)	8
57	Parlophone R 4278	Bubbins Rock/Indiana (with Bill Doggett) (78)	5
57	Parlophone R 4305	Avalon/Too Fine For Crying (B-side with Bill Jones)	7
57	Parlophone R 4370	Temptation/September Song	5
58	Parlophone R 4460	Twilight Time/Over The Waves Rock	8
62	Ember JBS 708	Tuxedo Junction/Air Mail Special	10
66	Island WI 271	Honeymoon Night/PATSY COLE: Disappointed Bride	10
54	Parlophone GEP 8506	FLAMINGO (EP)	10
55	Parlophone GEP 8513	LINGER AWHILE (EP)	8
55	Parlophone GEP 8520	EARL BOSTIC AND HIS ALTO SAX (EP)	10
55	Vogue EPV 1010	EARL BOSTIC (EP)	15
56	Vogue EPV 1111	VELVET SUNSET (EP)	7
56	Parlophone GEP 8539	WRAP IT UP (EP)	8
56	Parlophone GEP 8548	EARL'S IMAGINATION (EP)	7
56	Parlophone GEP 8565	ALTO SAX AND MAMBO STRINGS (EP)	7
56	Parlophone GEP 8571	MUSIC A LA BOSTIC NO. 1 (EP)	7
56	Parlophone GEP 8574	MUSIC A LA BOSTIC NO. 2 (EP)	8
57	Parlophone GEP 8603	MUSIC A LA BOSTIC NO. 3 (EP)	8
57	Parlophone GEP 8637	BOSTIC IN HARLEM (EP)	7
58	Parlophone GEP 8701	BOSTIC BEAT (EP)	7
58	Parlophone GEP 8741	ROCKING WITH BOSTIC (EP)	8
58	Parlophone GEP 8754	ALTO MAGIC (EP)	8
54	Vogue LDE 100	EARL BOSTIC AND HIS ORCHESTRA (10" LP)	20
54	Parlophone PMD 1016	EARL BOSTIC AND HIS ALTO SAX (10" LP)	20
56	Parlophone PMD 1040	EARL BOSTIC AND HIS ALTO SAX NO. 2 (10" LP)	20
58	Parlophone PMD 1054	BOSTIC MEETS DOGGETT (10", with Bill Doggett)	25
58	Parlophone PMD 1068	BOSTIC ROCKS (10" LP)	25
59	Parlophone PMD 1071	BOSTIC SHOWCASE OF SWINGING DANCE HITS (10" LP)	18
59	Parlophone PMD 1074	SWEET TUNES OF THE FANTASTIC FIFTIES (10" LP)	18

(see also Bill Doggett)

BOSTON

79	Epic EPC 7888	Don't Look Back/More Than A Feeling/Smokin' (p/s)	4
76	Epic EPCH 81611	BOSTON (LP, audiophile pressing)	10
76	Epic EPC 81611	BOSTON (LP, picture disc)	12
86	MCA MCGP 6017	THIRD STAGE (LP, picture disc)	10

BOSTON CRABS

65	Columbia DB 7586	Down In Mexico/Who?	10
65	Columbia DB 7679	As Long As I Have You/Alley Oop	10
66	Columbia DB 7830	Gin House/You Didn't Have To Be So Nice	8

BOSTON DEXTERS

64	Contemporary CR 101	Matchbox/La Bamba	25
64	Contemporary CR 102	You've Been Talking About Me/Nothing's Gonna Change Me	25
64	Contemporary CR 103	What Kind Of Girl Are You/I've Got Troubles Of My Own	25
65	Columbia DB 7498	I Believe To My Soul/I've Got Something To Tell You	15
65	Columbia DB 7641	Try Hard/No More Tears	15

BOSTON POPS ORCHESTRA

68	RCA RCA 1683	And I Love Her/A Hard Day's Night	5

BO STREET RUNNERS

64	Decca F 11986	Bo Street Runner/Tell Me	30
65	Columbia DB 7488	Tell Me What You're Gonna Do/And I Do Just What I Want	50
65	Columbia DB 7640	Baby Never Say Goodbye/Get Out Of My Way	25
66	Columbia DB 7901	Drive My Car/So Very Woman (featuring Mike [Too Much] Patto)	25
64	Oak RGJ 131	BO STREET RUNNERS (EP)	500

(see also [Mike] Patto, Fleetwood Mac)

CONNIE BOSWELL

54	Brunswick 05319	T-E-N-N-E-S-S-E-E (Spells ...)/If I Give My Heart To You	7
55	Brunswick 05397	How Important Can It Be?/Fill My Heart With Happiness	5

EVE BOSWELL

50	Parlophone R 3277	I Can Dream, Can't I/Mamma Knows Best (78)	5
50	Parlophone R 3297	If I Loved You/Bewitched (78)	5
50	Parlophone R 3311	Your Heart And My Heart/I Remember The Cornfields (78)	5
50	Parlophone R 3343	Beloved Be Faithful/Yes! I'll Be There (78)	5
51	Parlophone R 3372	My Heart Cries For You/All My Life (78)	5
51	Parlophone R 3394	Transatlantic Lullaby/Broken Heart (78)	5

MINT VALUE £

51	Parlophone R 3421	Would You/I'm In Love Again (78)	5
51	Parlophone R 3455	I'll Be Around/The Way That The Wind Blows (78)	5
52	Parlophone R 3479	I Was Never Loved By Anyone Else/While We're Young (78)	5
52	Parlophone R 3501	We Won't Live In A Castle/Paradise (78)	5
52	Parlophone R 3517	Please Mr. Sun/Love's Last Word Is Spoken (78)	5
52	Parlophone R 3549	Dance Me Loose/Just For Old Times (with Derek Roy) (78)	5
52	Parlophone R 3561	Sugar Bush/I'm Yours (78)	5
52	Parlophone R 3584	I Ain't Gonna Marry/Here In My Heart (78)	5
52	Parlophone R 3599	Moon Above Malaya (China Nights)/Oh My Love, Oh My Heart (78)	5
53	Parlophone MSP 6006	Sugar Bush/Moon Above Malaya (China Nights)	18
55	Parlophone MSP 6158	Ready, Willing And Able/Pam-Poo-Dey	15
55	Parlophone MSP 6160	The Heart You Break (May Be Your Own)/Tika Tika Tok	15
56	Parlophone MSP 6208	Young And Foolish/Where You Are	15
56	Parlophone MSP 6220	Cookie/It's Almost Tomorrow	15
56	Parlophone MSP 6245	Keeping Cool With Lemonade/Down By The Sugar Cane	10
56	Parlophone MSP 6250	Saries Marias/Come Back My Love	10
56	Parlophone R 4230	True Love/Where In The World Is Billy?	10
57	Parlophone R 4275	Rock Bobbin' Boats/Tra La La	12
57	Parlophone R 4299	Chantez, Chantez/She Said (Aunt Magnolia)	10
57	Parlophone R 4328	With All My Heart/Sugar Candy	8
57	Parlophone R 4341	The Gypsy In My Soul/Stop Whistlin' Wolf	8
57	Parlophone R 4362	Swedish Polka (Chickadee)/Tell My Love	6
58	Parlophone R 4401	(I Love You) For Sentimental Reasons/Bobby	6
58	Parlophone R 4414	I Do/Love Me Again	6
58	Parlophone R 4455	Left Right Out Of Your Heart/Voom-Ba-Voom	6
58	Parlophone R 4479	More Than Ever (Come Prima)/I Know Why	5
58	Parlophone R 4492	Christmas Lullaby/The Christmas Tree	5
59	Parlophone R 4517	If I Had A Talking Picture Of You/Piccaninny	5
59	Parlophone R 4544	Wimoweh Cha Cha/Boegoeberg Se Dam	5
59	Parlophone R 4555	Once Again/You Are Never Far Away From Me	4
60	Parlophone R 4618	Misty/Turnabout Heart	4
69	Morgan MRS 19	This Is My Love/Lonely In A Crowd	4
57	Parlophone GEP 8601	THE ENCHANTING EVE (EP)	12
58	Parlophone GEP 8690	EVE BOSWELL'S SHOWCASE (EP)	12
58	Parlophone GEP 8717	EVE BOSWELL'S SHOWCASE NO. 2 (EP)	12
56	Parlophone PMD 1039	SUGAR AND SPICE (10" LP)	25
57	Parlophone PMC 1038	SENTIMENTAL EVE (LP)	20
59	Parlophone PMC 1105	FOLLOWING THE SUN AROUND (LP)	16

SIMON BOSWELL

| 75 | Transatlantic TRA 307 | MIND PARASITES (LP) | 10 |

BOTANY 500

| 86 | Supreme Intl. Eds. 86-12 | Bully Beef/My Silent Love/Chillshake (12", p/s) | 7 |

PERRY BOTKIN

| 60 | Brunswick 05838 | The Executioner Theme/Waltz Of The Hunter | 4 |

BOW BELLS

| 66 | Parlophone R 5520 | Belinda/When You're In | 4 |
| 65 | Polydor 56030 | Not To Be Taken/I'll Try Not To Hold It Against You | 4 |

JIMMY BOWEN

57	Columbia DB 3915	Ever Lovin' Fingers/I'm Stickin' With You	40
57	Columbia DB 3915	Ever Lovin' Fingers/I'm Stickin' With You (78)	10
57	Columbia DB 3984	Warm Up To Me, Baby/I Trusted You	35
57	Columbia DB 3984	Warm Up To Me, Baby/I Trusted You (78)	10
57	Columbia DB 4027	Cross Over/It's Shameful	20
57	Columbia DB 4027	Cross Over/It's Shameful (78)	10
58	Columbia DB 4184	The Two Step/By The Light Of The Silvery Moon	15
58	Columbia DB 4184	The Two Step/By The Light Of The Silvery Moon (78)	10
65	Reprise RS 23043	Spanish Cricket/The Eagle (demos list "The Golden Eagle" on B-side)	40
67	Reprise RS 20592	Raunchy (with Chorus & Orchestra)/It's Such A Pretty World Today (w/ Singers)	4
58	Columbia SEG 7757	MEET JIMMY BOWEN (EP)	60
58	Columbia SEG 7793	MEET JIMMY BOWEN NO. 2 (EP)	60

BEN BOWERS

55	Columbia SCM 5192	The Kentuckian Song/The Man From Laramie	10
56	Columbia SCM 5260	To You, My Love/I'm Still A King To You	5
57	Parlophone R 4317	Rum And Coconut Water (Rum And Coca-Cola)/Country Boy (with His Royal Jamaicans)	6
57	Pye Jazz NJE 1001	BIG BEN BLUES (EP, with His Bluesicians)	8
58	Pye NEP 24069	KINGS OF CALYPSO VOL. 4 (EP)	7

DAVID BOWIE

66	Pye 7N 17020	Can't Help Thinking About Me/And I Say To Myself (with Lower Third)	80
66	Pye 7N 17079	Do Anything You Say/Good Morning Girl	100
66	Pye 7N 17157	I Dig Everything/I'm Not Losing Sleep	100
66	Deram DM 107	Rubber Band/The London Boy's	90
67	Deram DM 123	The Laughing Gnome/The Gospel According To Tony Day (inverted matrix no.)	50
67	Deram DM 135	Love You Till Tuesday/Did You Ever Have A Dream	70
69	Philips BF 1801	Space Oddity/Wild Eyed Boy From Freecloud (mono or stereo)	8/10
70	Mercury MF 1135	The Prettiest Star/Conversation Piece	80
70	Mercury 6052 026	Memory Of A Free Festival Parts 1 & 2	80
71	Mercury 6052 049	Holy Holy/Black Country Rock	80
72	RCA RCA 2160	Changes/Andy Warhol	5
72	RCA RCA 2199	Starman/Suffragette City (some in p/s)	40/4
72	RCA RCA 2263	John, I'm Only Dancing (Alternate Sax Version)/Hang Onto Yourself	5
72	Pye 7NX 8002	Do Anything You Say/I Dig Everything/I Can't Help Thinking About Me/I'm Not Losing Sleep (p/s)	10

MINT VALUE £

73	RCA RCA 2352	Drive-In Saturday/Round And Round	4
73	RCA RCA 2316	Life On Mars/The Man Who Sold The World (some in p/s)	10/4
73	Deram DM 123	The Laughing Gnome/The Gospel According To Tony Day (reissue, matrix number correct way up on label)	4
74	RCA LPBO 5009	Rebel Rebel/Queen Bitch	4
74	RCA LPBO 5021	Rock'N'Roll Suicide/Quicksand	4
74	RCA APBO 0293	Diamond Dogs/Holy Holy	4
74	Lyntone LYN 2929/ RCA/Mainman	Bowie's Greatest Hits (excerpts from Knock On Wood/Space Oddity/The Man Who Sold The World/Life On Mars/Starman/Jean Genie/Sorrow/Diamond Dogs) (33rpm 1-sided flexidisc with 'Record Mirror'/'Popswop' magazine)	7/5
75	Decca F 13579	The London Boys/Love You Till Tuesday	4
75	RCA RCA 2593	Space Oddity/Changes/Velvet Goldmine (p/s)	8
76	RCA RCA 2726	Suffragette City/Stay (p/s)	12
77	RCA PB 1121	Heroes/V-2 Schneider	4
78	RCA PB 1190	Beauty And The Beast/Sense Of Doubt (p/s)	6
79	RCA BOW 2	Boys Keep Swinging/Fantastic Voyage (p/s)	4
79	RCA BOW 3	DJ/Repetition (p/s, some on green vinyl)	20/4
79	RCA BOW 4	John, I'm Only Dancing (Again)/John, I'm Only Dancing (p/s)	4
79	RCA BOW 12-4	John, I'm Only Dancing (Again) (Extended)/John, I'm Only Dancing (12", p/s)	7
80	RCA BOW 5	Alabama Song/Space Oddity (poster p/s)	5
80	RCA BOW 6	Ashes To Ashes/Move On (12 different sleeves, with sheet of 9 stamps)	each 5
81	RCA BOW 8	Scary Monsters/Because You're Young (p/s)	4
81	RCA BOWC 8	Scary Monsters/Because You're Young (cassette)	8
81	RCA BOW 9	Up The Hill Backwards/Crystal Japan (p/s)	4
81	RCA BOWC 9	Up The Hill Backwards/Crystal Japan (cassette)	8
82	RCA BOW 11	IN BERTHOLT BRECHT'S "BAAL" (EP in foldout p/s)	4
83	EMI America EAP 157	China Girl/Shake It (picture disc)	5
83	EMI America 12 EA 158	Modern Love/Modern Love (Live) (12", p/s, with poster)	8
84	EMI America EA 187	Tonight/Tumble And Twirl (poster p/s)	4
85	EMI America EAP 195	Loving The Alien (Remixed Version)/Don't Look Down (Remixed Version) (shaped picture disc)	6
85	EMI America 12 EAG 195	Loving The Alien (Extended Dance Mix)/Don't Look Down (Extended Dance Mix)/Loving The Alien (Extended Dub Mix) (12", gatefold p/s with poster)	7
86	Virgin VSS 838	Absolute Beginners/Absolute Beginners (Dub Mix) (square picture disc)	6
86	EMI America EAP 216	Underground (Edited Version)/Underground (Instrumental) (shaped picture disc)	8
86	Virgin VSS 906	When The Wind Blows/When The Wind Blows (Instrumental) (shaped pic disc)	5
87	EMI America 12 EAX 230	Day-In Day-Out (Remix)/(Extended Dub Mix)/Julie (12", stickered black p/s)	7
87	EMI America EAP 237	Time Will Crawl/Girls (poster p/s)	4
87	EMI America 12 EAX 237	Time Will Crawl (Dance Crew Mix)/(Dub)/Girls (Japanese Version) (12", p/s)	7
87	EMI America EAP 239	Never Let Me Down/'87 And Cry (picture disc)	4
82	RCA BOW 100	FASHIONS (10 x 7" picture discs in plastic wallet [BOWP 101-110], each £4)	40
67	Deram DML/SML 1007	DAVID BOWIE (LP, mono/stereo)	125/175
69	Philips SBL 7912	DAVID BOWIE (LP, gatefold sleeve)	125
70	Decca PA 58	THE WORLD OF DAVID BOWIE (LP, mono)	20
72	Decca SPA 58	THE WORLD OF DAVID BOWIE (LP, stereo, 'curly hair' cover)	10
71	Mercury 6338 041	THE MAN WHO SOLD THE WORLD (LP, with 'dress' cover)	180
71	Mercury 6338 041	THE MAN WHO SOLD THE WORLD (cassette, with 'dress' cover)	20
71	RCA SF 8244	HUNKY DORY (LP, orange label with lyric sheet)	10
72	RCA SF 8267	THE RISE AND FALL OF ZIGGY STARDUST AND THE SPIDERS FROM MARS (LP, orange label with lyric inner sleeve)	10
72	RCA LSP 4813	SPACE ODDITY (LP, orange label with lyric inner sleeve & poster)	12
72	RCA LSP 4816	THE MAN WHO SOLD THE WORLD (LP, orange label with inner sleeve & poster)	12
73	RCA RS 1001	ALADDIN SANE (LP, orange label, gatefold sleeve & lyric inner sleeve & poster, some with fan club membership card)	15/10
74	RCA APL 1-0576	DIAMOND DOGS (LP, orange label, gatefold sleeve)	10
74	RCA APL 2-0771	DAVID LIVE (2-LP, gatefold sleeve, orange label, photos on inners)	18
76	RCA APLI 1327	STATION TO STATION (LP, with original colour proof sleeve)	500
76	RCA RS 1055	CHANGESONEBOWIE (LP, with 'sax' version of "John I'm Only Dancing")	25
78	RCA PL 02913	STAGE (2-LP, gatefold sleeve, yellow vinyl)	20
80	RCA BOW LP 2	SCARY MONSTERS (AND SUPER CREEPS) (LP, purple vinyl)	200+
83	EMI America AMLP 3029	LET'S DANCE (LP, picture disc)	10
84	RCA BOPIC 1	ALADDIN SANE (LP, picture disc with numbered insert)	15
84	RCA BOPIC 2	HUNKY DORY (LP, picture disc with numbered insert)	15
84	RCA BOPIC 3	ZIGGY STARDUST (LP, picture disc with numbered insert)	15
84	RCA BOPIC 4	PIN-UPS (LP, picture disc with numbered insert)	15
84	RCA BOPIC 5	DIAMOND DOGS (LP, picture disc with numbered insert)	15
84	Deram 800 087-2	DAVID BOWIE (CD, withdrawn with white title)	70
85	RCA PD 84623	HUNKY DORY (CD, withdrawn)	30
85	RCA PD 84654	THE MAN WHO SOLD THE WORLD (CD, withdrawn)	35
85	RCA PD 84702	THE RISE AND FALL OF ZIGGY STARDUST AND THE SPIDERS FROM MARS (CD, withdrawn)	35
85	RCA PD 84813	SPACE ODDITY (CD, withdrawn)	30
85	RCA PD 84653	PIN-UPS (CD, withdrawn)	30
85	RCA PD 83890	ALADDIN SANE (CD, withdrawn)	30
85	RCA PD 80998	YOUNG AMERICANS (CD, withdrawn)	30
85	RCA PD 81327	STATION TO STATION (CD, withdrawn)	40
85	RCA PD 81732	CHANGESONEBOWIE (CD, withdrawn)	30
85	RCA PD 83856	LOW (CD, withdrawn)	25
85	RCA PD 82743	HEROES (CD, withdrawn)	20
85	RCA PD 82743	PETER AND THE WOLF (CD, withdrawn)	20
85	RCA PD 89002	STAGE (CD, withdrawn)	50
85	RCA PD 84234	LODGER (CD, withdrawn)	20
85	RCA PD 83647	SCARY MONSTERS (AND SUPER CREEPS) (CD, withdrawn)	40
85	RCA PD 84202	CHANGESTWOBOWIE (CD, withdrawn)	30
85	RCA PD 94792	GOLDEN YEARS (CD, withdrawn)	20

| 85 | RCA PD 84919 | FAME AND FASHION (ALL TIME GREATEST HITS) (CD, withdrawn) | 70 |

(see also King Bees, Lower Third, Manish Boys, Arnold Corns, Spiders From Mars, Mick Ronson, Tin Machine, Queen)

DAVID BOWIE & BING CROSBY

| 82 | RCA BOWT 12 | Peace On Earth/Little Drummer Boy/Fantastic Voyage (12", p/s, picture labels) | 8 |

ALAN BOWN (SET)

65	Pye 7N 15934	Can't Let Her Go/I'm The One	10
66	Pye 7N 17084	Baby Don't Push Me/Everything's Gonna Be Alright	12
66	Pye 7N 17148	Headline News/Mister Pleasure	8
66	Pye 7N 17192	Emergency 999/Settle Down	12
67	Pye 7N 17256	Gonna Fix You Good (Everytime You're Bad)/I Really Really Care	15
67	Music Factory CUB 1	We Can Help You/Magic Handkerchief	6
67	MGM MGM 1355	Toyland/Technicolour Dream	5
68	MGM MGM 1387	Story Book/Little Lesley	5
69	Deram DM 259	Still As Stone/Wrong Idea	5
69	Deram DM 278	Gypsy Girl/All I Can	5
70	Island WIP 6091	Pyramid/Crash Landing	5
67	Music Factory CUB LM/LS 1	OUTWARD BOWN (LP)	18
69	Deram DML/SML 1049	THE ALAN BOWN! (LP)	15
70	Island ILPS 9131	LISTEN (LP)	10

(see also Robert Palmer, John Barry Seven, Bronco)

ALAN BOWN/JIMMY JAMES & VAGABONDS

| 68 | Pye N(S)PL 18156 | LONDON SWINGS — LIVE AT THE MARQUEE CLUB (LP, 1 side each) | 20 |

(see also Jimmy James & Vagabonds)

BOW WOW

| 83 | Heavy Metal Intl. HMINT 2 | You're Mine/Don't Cry Baby (live) (p/s) | 7 |
| 83 | Heavy Metal Intl. HMILP 5 | WARNING FROM STARDUST (LP) | 10 |

BOW WOW WOW

80	EMI EMI 5088	C-30 C-60 C-90 Go!/Sun Sea And Piracy (cassettes, some in promo 'dog food' can with inserts)	5
81	EMI TCEMI 5153	W.O.R.K./C-30 ... Anda! (cassette)	5
81	RCA RCA 100	Prince Of Darkness/Orang Utang (poster p/s)	4
81	Tour D'Eiffel TE 001	The Mile High Club/C-30 C-60 C-90 Go! (plain white sleeve)	8
82	RCA RCA 238	I Want Candy (p/s, 1-sided, etched B-side)	5
82	RCA RCA 238	I Want Candy/King Kong (p/s)	5
82	RCA RCXK 004	I Want Candy/See Jungle/Go Wild In The Country/Chihuahua (cassette)	5
82	RCA RCA 263	Louis Quatorze (re-recorded)/Mile High Club (p/s)	5
82	Lyntone LYN 11358	Elimination Dancing (New Version)/King Kong (New Version) (green or clear 1-sided 33rpm flexidisc free with 'Flexipop' issue 18; with/without mag)	5/4
83	RCA RCA 314	Do You Wanna Hold Me?/What's The Time (Hey Buddy) (picture disc)	5
80	EMI WOW 1	BOW WOW WOW — YOUR CASSETTE PET (cassette, mini-LP)	7

BRENDAN BOWYER (& ROYALS)

65	HMV POP 1481	The Wonder Of You/Fun Fun Fun	4
66	HMV POP 1521	The Fly/Answer Me	4
67	King KG 1059	Sitting In The Sun/Da Doo Ron Ron (as Brendan Bowyer & Royals)	4
68	King KG 1078	Woman Woman/Lady Willpower (as Brendan Bowyer & Royals)	4

DAVID BOX

| 64 | London HLU 9874 | If You Can't Say Something Nice/Sweet Sweet Day | 8 |
| 64 | London HLU 9924 | Little Lonely Summer Girl/No One Will Ever Know | 8 |

BOXER

| 75 | Virgin V 2049 | BELOW THE BELT (LP, with uncensored full-frontal back cover) | 10 |
| 76 | Virgin V 2073 | BLOODLETTING (LP, withdrawn) | 80 |

(see also Patto, Timebox)

BOXEROS

| 61 | Palette PG 9023 | El Senior Ping Pong/Y Viva El Cha Cha | 4 |

BOX TOPS

67	Stateside SS 2044	The Letter/Happy Times	5
67	Stateside SS 2070	Neon Rainbow/She Knows How	5
68	Bell BLL 1001	Cry Like A Baby/The Door You Closed To Me	4
68	Bell BLL 1017	Choo Choo Train/Fields Of Clover	4
68	Bell BLL 1035	I Met Her In Church/People Gonna Talk	4
68	Bell BLL 1045	Sandman/Sweet Cream Ladies, Forward March	4
69	Bell BLL 1063	I Shall Be Released/I Must Be The Devil	4
69	Bell BLL 1068	Soul Deep/The Happy Song	4
69	Bell BLL 1084	Turn On A Dream/Together	4
70	Bell BLL 1097	You Keep Tightening Up On Me/Come On Honey	4
73	London HLU 10402	Sugar Creek Woman/It's All Over	4
68	Stateside (S)SL 10218	THE LETTER/NEON RAINBOW (LP)	15
68	Bell MBLL/SBLL 105	CRY LIKE A BABY (LP)	10
68	Bell MBLL/SBLL 108	NON-STOP (LP)	10
69	Bell SBLL 120	DIMENSIONS (LP)	10
70	Bell BELLS 149	BOX TOPS (LP)	10

(see also Big Star, Alex Chilton)

EL BOY

| 57 | Columbia DB 3927 | Jack, Jack, Jack/Tonight My Heart She Is Crying | 4 |

DENNIS BOYCE & HIS ORCHESTRA/RHYTHM

| 57 | Oriole CB 1358 | One Man Went To Rock/Thunderstorm (78) | 8 |
| 58 | Oriole CB 1458 | Bad Boy/When Your Hair Has Turned To Silver | 4 |

TOMMY BOYCE

| 65 | MGM MGM 1287 | Pretty Thing/I Don't Have To Worry 'Bout You | 5 |

TOMMY BOYCE & BOBBY HART
67	A&M AMS 705	Out And About/My Little Chickadee	4
67	A&M AMS 710	Sometimes She's A Little Girl/Love Every Day	4
68	A&M AMS 714	I Wonder What She's Doing Tonight?/Ambushers	4
68	A&M AMS 722	Goodbye Baby/Where Angels Go Trouble Follows	4
68	A&M AMS 729	Alice Long (You're Still My Favourite Girlfriend)/P.O. Box 9847	4
67	A&M AML 907	TEST PATTERNS (LP)	10

(see also Monkees, Tommy Boyce)

EDDIE BOYD
66	Blue Horizon 45 BH 1009	It's So Miserable To Be Alone/Empty Arms	50
67	Blue Horizon 57-3137	The Big Boat/Sent For You Yesterday (with Fleetwood Mac)	10
62	Esquire EP 247	BOYD'S BLUES (EP, as Eddie Boyd Blues Combo)	10
67	Decca LK/SKL 4872	EDDIE BOYD AND HIS BLUES BAND FEATURING PETER GREEN (LP)	70
65	Fontana STJL 905	FIVE LONG YEARS (LP)	15
68	Blue Horizon 7-63202	7936 SOUTH RHODES (LP)	55
68	Storyville SLP 4054	IN CONCERT (LP)	10

(see also Fleetwood Mac)

EDDIE BOYD/BUDDY GUY
66	Chess CRE 6009	WITH THE BLUES (EP, 2 tracks each)	15

(see also Buddy Guy)

JIMMY BOYD
53	Columbia SCM 5072	I Saw Mommy Kissing Santa Claus/Little Train A-Chuggin'	30

JACQUELINE BOYER
60	Columbia DB 4452	Tom Pillibi/FRANCOIS DEGUELT: Ce Soir-La	5

BOY HAIRDRESSERS
88	53rd & 3rd AGARR T12	Golden Showers/Tidalwive/The Assumption As An Elevator (12", p/s)	15

(see also Teenage Fanclub, BMX Bandits)

BILLY BOYLE
62	Decca F 11503	My Baby's Crazy 'Bout Elvis/Held For Questioning	15
63	Decca F 11709	I'm Coming Home/Sunday's Child	4
63	Columbia DB 7111	Lovers Hill/She's New To You	4
63	Columbia DB 7127	Hootin' In The Kitchen/Lover's Hill	4
64	Columbia DB 7294	Walk, Walk, Walkin'/My Baby Tonight (with Le Roys)	6

(see also Le Roys)

BOYS (U.K.)
63	Parlophone R 5027	Polaris/Jumping	15

BOYS (U.K.)
64	Pye 7N 15726	It Ain't Fair/I Want You	35

(see also Sandra Barry & Boys, Sandra Brown & Boyfriends, Action)

BOYS (Jamaica)
69	Duke DU 19	Easy Sound/AFROTONES: Freedom Sound	6

(see also Harry J. Allstars)

BOYS (U.K.)
77	NEMS NES 102	I Don't Care/Soda Pressing	5
77	NEMS NES 111	First Time/Whatcha Gonna Do/Turning Grey	5
78	NEMS NES 116	Brickfield Nights/Teacher's Pet (p/s)	5
79	Safari SAFE 21	Kamikaze/Bad Days (p/s, some with booklet)	7/5
80	Safari SAFE 23	Terminal Love/I Love Me (p/s)	4
80	Safari SAFE 27	You Better Move On/Schoolgirls (p/s)	4
80	Safari SAFE 31	Weekend/Cool (p/s)	4
80	Safari SAFE 33	Let It Rain/Lucy (p/s)	6
77	NEMS NES 6001	TH E BOYS (LP)	10
78	NEMS NEL 6015	ALTERNATIVE CHARTBUSTERS (LP)	10
79	Safari 1-2 BOYS	TO HELL WITH THE BOYS (LP, with free songbook)	10

(see also Yobs, Cockney 'N' Westerns, Rowdies)

BOYS BLUE
65	HMV POP 1427	You Got What I Want/Take A Heart	50

BOYS WONDER
87	Sire W 8195	Shine On Me/Stop It (p/s)	4
87	Sire W 8195T	Shine On Me/Stop It/Shine On It (Extended) (12", p/s)	7
87	Sire W 8293	Now What Earthman/TenMillionTonHeadache (p/s)	4
87	Sire W 8293T	Now What Earthman (Extended Remix)/TenMillionTonHeadache/Now What Earthman (Alternative Mix) (12", p/s)	7

BOZ
66	Columbia DB 7832	You're Just The Kind Of Girl I Want/Isn't That So	5
66	Columbia DB 7889	Meeting Time/No (Ah) Body Knows The Blues	6
66	Columbia DB 7941	Pinnochio/Stay As You Are	4
66	Columbia DB 7972	The Baby Song/Carry On Screaming	4
68	Columbia DB 8406	I Shall Be Released/Down In The Flood	4
68	Columbia DB 8468	Light My Fire/Back Against The Wall	4

JANET BRACE
55	Brunswick 05272	Teach Me Tonight/My Old Familiar Heartache	6

BRACKEN
79	Look LKLP 6438	PRINCE OF THE NORTHLANDS (LP, private pressing with insert)	125

KIM & KELLY BRADEN
67	Columbia DB 8312	You're Leaving, She's Laughing/Didn't I	4
68	Columbia DB 8421	Happiness Is/Sing A Rainbow	4

BRADFORD

88	Village VILS 101	Skin Storm/Gatling Gun (white title sleeve, 'old man' p/s)	10/5
88	Village VILT 101	Skin Storm/Gatling Gun/Dodging Around In Cars(12", 'old man' p/s)	7
88	Village VILSD 101	Skin Storm/Gatling Gun/Lust Roulette (CD, white sleeve)	8

PROF. ALEX BRADFORD

63	Stateside SL 10047	ONE STEP (LP)	12

(see also Bradford Singers)

BRADFORD SINGERS

64	Stateside SL 10083	ANGEL ON VACATION (LP)	12

(see also Prof. Alex Bradford)

GEORGE BRADLEY & HIS BAND

65	HMV POP 1459	Breakout/Vendetta	4

JAN BRADLEY

63	Pye International 7N 25182	Mama Didn't Lie/Lovers Like Me	12

OWEN BRADLEY

56	Brunswick 05528	Theme From "The Threepenny Opera"/Lights Of Vienna (with Orchestra)	4
57	Brunswick 05700	White Silver Sands/Midnight Blues (as Owen Bradley Quintet)	5
58	Brunswick 05736	Big Guitar/Sentimental Dream (as Owen Bradley Quintet)	10
58	Brunswick 05736	Big Guitar/Sentimental Dream (as Owen Bradley Quintet) (78)	10
60	Brunswick LAT 8327	THE BIG GUITAR (LP)	10

BUDDY BRADSHAW

59	Capitol CL 15036	Nothing You Can Say/Tonight I Walk Alone	4

TINY BRADSHAW & HIS ORCHESTRA

52	Vogue V 2146	Breaking Up The House/Walk That Mess (78)	8
54	Parlophone MSP 6118	The Gypsy/Spider Web	8
54	Parlophone R 3894	The Gypsy/Spider Web (78)	8
55	Parlophone MSP 6145	Overflow/Don't Worry 'Bout Me	12
55	Parlophone MSP 6145	Overflow/Don't Worry 'Bout Me (78)	10
55	Parlophone R 4062	Cat Nap/Stomping Room Only (78)	5
55	Parlophone R 4084	Pompton Turnpike/Come On (78)	5
54	Parlophone GEP 8507	TRAIN KEPT A ROLLING (EP)	20
56	Parlophone GEP 8552	POMPTON TURNPIKE (EP)	15

TINY BRADSHAW ORCHESTRA/WYNONIE HARRIS

70	Polydor 623 273	KINGS OF RHYTHM AND BLUES (LP, 1 side each)	15

(see also Wynonie Harris)

BOB BRADY & CON CHORDS

68	Bell BLL 1025	Everybody's Goin' To The Love-In/It's Been A Long Time Between Kisses	8

BILLY BRAGG

80s	Go! Discs/Flexi FLX 418	Back To Basics Audio Aid/Play In A Day The Billy Bragg Way (square flexidisc free with book 'Back To Basics')	8/'4

(see also Riff Raff)

AL 'TNT' BRAGGS

66	Vocalion VP 9278	Earthquake/How Long (Do You Hold On)	10
68	Action ACT 4506	Earthquake/How Long (Do You Hold On) (reissue)	8
69	Action ACT 4526	I'm A Good Man/I Like What You Do To Me	6
65	Vocalion VEP 170163	AL 'TNT' BRAGGS (EP)	22

ERNEL BRAHAM

66	Rio R 79	Musical Fight/EDWARDS ALLSTARS: Pipeline	8

BRAIN

67	Parlophone R 5595	Nightmares In Red/Kick The Donkey	60
87	Bam Caruso OPRA 63	Nightmares In Red/SRC: Black Sheep (jukebox edition, die-cut company sleeve)	4

(see also Giles Giles & Fripp, Trendsetters Ltd)

BRAINBOX

69	Parlophone R 5775	Woman's Gone/Down Man	8
70	Parlophone R 5842	So Helpless/To You	5
70	Parlophone PCS 7094	BRAINBOX (LP)	25

(see also Jan Akkerman, Hunters, Focus)

BRAINCHILD

70	A&M AMLS 979	HEALING OF THE LUNATIC OWL (LP)	35

BRAINIAC 5

80	Roach RR 5002	Working/Feel (p/s)	10
78	Roach RREP 5001	MUSHY DOUBT (EP, 33rpm, p/s)	12

BRAINSTORM

77	RCA PB 0811	Wake Up And Be Somebody/We Know A Place	4

DELANEY BRAMLETT

64	Vocalion VP 9227	Heartbreak Hotel/You Never Looked Sweeter	10
65	Vocalion VP 9237	Liverpool Lou/You Have No Choice	20

(see also Delaney & Bonnie, King Curtis with Delaney & Friends)

BRAM STOKER

72	Windmill WMD 117	HEAVY ROCK SPECTACULAR (LP)	50

BILL BRAMWELL

58	Starlite ST45 004	My Old Man/Shoutin' In That Amen Corner	5
60	Decca F 11309	Candid Camera Theme/Frederika	4

BRAND
| 64 | Piccadilly 7N 35216 | I'm A Lover Not A Fighter/Hear 'Em Talking (unissued) | |
| 64 | Piccadilly 7N 35216 | I'm A Lover Not A Fighter/Zulu Stomp | 75 |

BILL BRANDON
| 73 | Mercury 6052 186 | I Am Free Of Your Love/(Take Another Little) Piece Of My Heart | 5 |

JOHNNY BRANDON
56	Parlophone MSP 6238	Rock-A-Bye Baby/Lonely Lips	5
56	Parlophone R 4174	Rock-A-Bye Baby/Lonely Lips (78)	5
56	Parlophone R 4207	Shim Sham Shuffle/I Didn't Know	8
56	Decca F 10778	Glendora/Song For A Summer Night	5
57	Decca F 10858	Nothing Is Too Good For You/A Sort-Of-A-Feeling	5
59	Top Rank JAR 241	Santa Claus Jnr./I Heard A Bluebird Sing	4
55	Pye NEP 24003	JOHNNY BRANDON HITS (EP)	15

KIRK BRANDON & PACK OF LIES
| 87 | SS SS1N2/SS2N1 | KIRK BRANDON AND THE PACK OF LIES (EP) | 15 |

(see also Theatre Of Hate, Spear Of Destiny, Senate, Pack)

TONY BRANDON
| 68 | MGM MGM 1401 | Candy Kisses/Get Going Baby | 4 |

VERN BRANDON
| 62 | Decca F 11472 | Let Me Be The One/Gotta Know The Reason | 10 |

ANGELO BRANDUARDI
| 79 | Ariola ARL 5016 | HIGHDOWN FAIR (LP) | 12 |

BRANDY BOYS
| 65 | Columbia DB 7507 | Gale Winds/Don't Come Knocking At My Door | 10 |

BRANDY WINE BRIDGE
| 77 | Cottage COT 311 | THE GREY LADY (LP) | 25 |
| 78 | Cottage COT 321 | AN ENGLISH MEADOW (LP, hand-drawn sleeve with insert) | 25 |

JOHNNY BRANTLEY'S ALL STARS
| 58 | London HLU 8606 | The Place/Pot Luck | 12 |
| 58 | London HLU 8606 | The Place/Pot Luck (78) | 5 |

BRASS CONSTRUCTION
| 76 | United Artists UP 36090 | Movin'/Talkin' | 4 |
| 76 | United Artists UAS 2993 | BRASS CONSTRUCTION (LP) | 10 |

ANDRÉ BRASSEUR
| 65 | Pye International 7N 25332 | Early Bird Satellite/Special 230 | 8 |
| 67 | CBS 202 557 | Holiday/The Kid | 5 |

BRASS TACKS
| 68 | Big T BIG 110 | I'll Keep On Holding On/Let The Sunshine In | 5 |

BRATZ
| 80 | A Famous Record AFR 1 | The Bratz Are Coming/Coast To Coast/Everyone Wants To Be Elvis | 6 |

RICHARD BRAUTIGAN
| 69 | Zapple ZAPPLE 03 | LISTENING TO RICHARD BRAUTIGAN (LP, unreleased, acetates exist) | |

BRAVO
| 84 | CBS A 4486 | Lady Lady/Dime For Que | 4 |

PRISCILLA BRAZIER
| 74 | Dovetail DOVE 9 | PRISCILLA BRAZIER (LP) | 25 |
| 70s | Key KLO | SOMETHING BEAUTIFUL (LP) | 25 |

BREAD
| 69 | Elektra EKSN 45071 | London Bridge/Dismal Day | 4 |

BREAD & BEER BAND
69	Decca F 12891	Dick Barton Theme/Breakdown Blues	80
73	Decca F 13354	Dick Barton Theme/Breakdown Blues (reissue)	15
69	private pressing	THE BREAD AND BEER BAND (LP, only 1 copy known to exist)	1700

(see also Elton John, Caleb)

BREAD, LOVE & DREAMS
69	Decca F 12958	Virgin Kiss/Switch Out The Sun	7
69	Decca SKL 5008	BREAD, LOVE AND DREAMS (LP)	45
70	Decca SKL 5048	THE STRANGE TALE OF CAPTAIN SHANNON AND THE HUNCHBACK FROM GIGHA (LP)	45
71	Decca SKL 5081	AMARYLLIS (LP)	125

BREADWINNER
| 85 | Ninth Wand DOG 1 | BEST OF NINTH WAND RECORDS (private cassette with 'glitter' cover) | 20 |
| 90 | Ninth Wand DOG 2 | GIVE US A LIGHT, YOU BASTARD (LP, private pressing) | 50 |

(see also Mr Rubbish)

BREAKAWAYS
62	Pye 7N 15471	He's A Rebel/Wishing Star	6
63	Pye 7N 15585	That Boy Of Mine/Here She Comes	4
64	Pye 7N 15618	He Doesn't Love Me/That's How It Goes	4
65	Pye 7N 15973	Danny Boy/Your Kind Of Love	4

(see also Sharades)

BREAKDOWN
| 77 | private pressing | MEET ME ON THE HIGHWAY (LP, with insert) | 35 |

BREAKTHRU'
| 68 | Mercury MF 1066 | Ice Cream Tree/Julius Caesar | 10 |

BREAKWATER
86	Arista ARIST 12674	Say You Love Me Girl/Work It Out (12", p/s)	7

BRECKER BROTHERS
75	Arista ARTY 103	THE BRECKER BROTHERS (LP)	10

JIMMY BREEDLOVE
57	London HLE 8490	Over Somebody Else's Shoulder/That's My Baby	50
57	London HLE 8490	Over Somebody Else's Shoulder/That's My Baby (78)	15
62	Pye International 7N 25121	You're Following Me/Fabulous	8
75	Pye Disco Demand DDS 110	I Can't Help Loving You/I Saw You	4

(see also Cues)

BRELLO CABAL
67	CBS 3214	Margarine Flavoured Pineapple Chunk/Follow That	5

BEVERLY BREMMERS
72	Wand WN 18	Get Smart Girl/Don't Say You Don't Remember	10

BRENDA & TABULATIONS
67	London HL 10127	Dry Your Eyes/The Wash	12
67	London HL 10174	When You're Gone/Hey Boy	15
68	Direction 58-3678	Baby You're So Right For Me/To The One I Love	10
69	Action ACT 4541	That's In The Past/I Can't Get Over Her	20
69	Action ACLP 6003	DRY YOUR EYES (LP)	15

BUDDY BRENNAN QUARTET
60	London HLU 9049	Big River/The Chase	4

ROSE BRENNAN
55	HMV 7M 299	Ding Dong/Sincerely	12
55	HMV 7M 328	Wake The Town And Tell The People/Ten Little Kisses	10
56	HMV 7M 360	You Are My Love/My Dublin Bay	10
56	HMV 7M 383	Band Of Gold/My Believing Heart	12
56	HMV 7M 392	Coortin' In The Kitchen/Those Who Have Loved	6
57	HMV POP 302	Tra La La/Without Love (There Is Nothing)	8
58	HMV POP 548	Mean To Me/Treasure Of Your Love	5
59	Top Rank JAR 152	Johnny Let Me Go/My Summer Diary	4

WALTER BRENNAN
60	London HLD 9148	Dutchman's Gold/Back To The Farm	6
62	Liberty LIB 55436	Old Rivers/Epic Ride Of John H Glenn	4
62	Liberty LIB 55477	Houdini/The Old Kelly Place	4
63	Liberty LIB 55508	Mama Sang A Song/Who Will Take Gramma	4

BERNIE BRENT'S COMBO
60s	Honey Hit TB 4501	BERNIE BRENT'S COMBO (EP)	7

FRANKIE BRENT
57	Pye N 15102	Rockin' Shoes/I Ain't Never Gonna Do You No Good (78)	7
57	Pye N 15103	Be My Girl/Rang Dang Doo (78)	5

TONY BRENT
53	Columbia SCM 5042	Have You Heard?/Strange Love	20
53	Columbia SCM 5057	Which Way The Wind Blows/My One And Only Heart	18
54	Columbia SCM 5135	I Understand Just How You Feel/The Magic Tango	15
54	Columbia SCM 5146	Nicolette/Tell Me, Tell Me	12
55	Columbia SCM 5160	It's A Woman's World/Give Me The Right To Be Wrong	15
55	Columbia SCM 5170	Open Up Your Heart (with Anne Warren)/Hearts Of Stone (with Coronets)	18
55	Columbia SCM 5188	Mirror, Mirror/Love And Kisses	12
55	Columbia SCM 5200	With Your Love/On A Little Balcony In Spain	10
56	Columbia SCM 5245	Sooner Or Later (Love Comes Along)/Pick Yourself A Star	10
56	Columbia SCM 5272	My Little Angel/What A Heavenly Night For Love	10
56	Columbia DB 3844	Cindy, Oh Cindy/Two Innocent Hearts	10
57	Columbia DB 3884	Amore/If Wishes Were Horses	8
57	Columbia DB 3918	Butterfly/How Lonely Can One Be?	10
57	Columbia DB 3950	Dark Moon/The Game Of Love (A-One And A-Two)	8
57	Columbia DB 3987	Deep Within Me/Why Ask For The Moon	7
57	Columbia DB 4043	We Belong Together/Love By The Jukebox Light	7
58	Columbia DB 4066	Don't Save Your Love (For ...)/The Clouds Will Soon Roll By	5
58	Columbia DB 4128	Chanson D'Amour/Little Serenade	5
58	Columbia DB 4177	Girl Of My Dreams/Don't Play That Melody	5
59	Columbia DB 4238	Call Me/I Surrender, Dear	4
59	Columbia DB 4304	My Little Room/Why Should I Be Lonely?	5
59	Columbia DB 4357	Forever, My Darling (Pledging My Love)/Worried Mind	4
60	Columbia DB 4402	Oh, So Wunderbar/Just As Much As Ever	4
60	Columbia DB 4478	Your Cheatin' Heart/Come On In	4
60	Columbia DB 4514	I'm Alone Because ! Love You/Just A-Wearyin' For You	4
61	Columbia DB 4610	Until The Real Thing Comes Along/Ten Lonely Weekends	4
61	Columbia DB 4657	Is It Too Late?/You Made Me Care	4
58	Columbia SEG 7824	TONY CALLS THE TUNE (EP)	15
58	Columbia SEG 7869	TIME FOR TONY (EP)	15
59	Columbia SEG 8019	OFF STAGE (EP)	15
59	Columbia SEG 8040	OFF STAGE NO. 2 (EP)	15
58	Columbia 33S 1125	OFF STAGE (10" LP)	30
60	Columbia 33SX 1200	TONY TAKES FIVE (LP, also stereo SCX 3288)	20/25
60s	Columbia 33SX 5001	TONY'S BIG HITS (LP)	25

TONY BRENT & JULIE DAWN
53	Columbia SCM 5029	Ding Dong Boogie/When Are We Gonna Get Married?	25

(see also Julie Dawn)

MINT VALUE £

BRENT FORD & NYLONS
78	Brumbeat	19th Nervous Breakdown/Big Rock Candy Mountain (no p/s)	8

BRENTWOOD ROAD ALLSTARS
70	Bamboo BAM 23	Love At First Sight/MAYTALS: Life Could Be A Dream	6
70	Bamboo BAM 25	Soul Shake/Moon Ride	6

GERRY BRERETON
53	Parlophone MSP 6056	From Here To Eternity/If You've Never Been In Love	4
54	Parlophone MSP 6081	The Book/Somewhere Someone (Is Saying A Prayer)	4
55	Columbia SCM 5195	A Million Helping Hands/Fair Sets The Wind For Love	4

(see also Eddie Calvert)

BERNARD BRESSLAW
58	HMV POP 522	Mad Passionate Love/You Need Feet	5
59	HMV POP 599	Charlie Brown/The Teenager's Lament	5
59	HMV POP 669	Ivy Will Cling/I Found A Hole	4

PAUL BRETT('S SAGE)
71	Dawn DNX 2508	Reason For Askin'/Everlasting Butterfly/Savannah Ladies/To Everyman (p/s)	6
73	Bradley's BRAD 305	Summer Driftin'/Clocks (p/s)	4
70	Pye NSPL 18347	PAUL BRETT SAGE (LP)	15
71	Dawn DNLS 3021	JUBILATION FOUNDRY (LP, gatefold sleeve, as Paul Brett's Sage)	12
72	Dawn DNLS 3032	SCHIZOPHRENIA (LP, foldout sleeve, as Paul Brett's Sage)	15
75	PF private pressing	PHOENIX FUTURE (LP, 500 only)	12
70s	private pressing	MUSIC MANIFOLD (LP, library issue)	50

STEVE BRETT & MAVERICKS
65	Columbia DB 7470	Wishing/Anything That's Part Of You	70
65	Columbia DB 7581	Sad, Lonely And Blue/Candy	70
65	Columbia DB 7794	Sugar Shack/Chains On My Heart	70

(see also Slade)

TONY BREVETT
71	Supreme SUP 224	Don't Get Weary/BREVETT ALLSTARS: Version	4

(see also Melodians)

TERESA BREWER
49	London L 511	When The Train Comes In/A Man Wrote A Song (78)	6
50	London L 562	Copper Canyon/'Way Back Home (with Bobby Wayne) (78)	6
50	London L 563	Ol' Man Mose/I Beeped When I Shoulda Bopped! (78)	6
50	London L 604	Music! Music! Music!/Copenhagen (78)	5
50	London L 678	Choo'n Gum/Honky Tonkin' (78)	5
50	London L 696	The Picnic Song/Let's Have A Party (B-side with Snooky Lanson, Claire Hogan & Bobby Wayne) (78)	6
50	London L 768	Cincinnati Dancing Pig/Punky Punkin (78)	5
50	London L 873	The Thing/I Guess I'll Have To Dream The Rest (78)	5
51	London L 878	A Penny A Kiss — A Penny A Hug/Hello (with Snooky Lanson) (78)	6
51	London L 967	I've Got The Craziest Feeling/If You Want Some Lovin' (78)	5
51	London L 970	Counterfeit Kisses/Lonesome Gal (78)	5
51	London L 1069	The Wang Wang Blues/Longing For You (78)	5
51	London L 1085	I Wish I Wuz/If You Don't Marry Me (78)	5
54	Vogue Coral Q 2001	Jilted/Le Grand Tour De L'Amour (78)	8
54	Vogue Coral Q 2011	Skinny Minnie (Fishtail)/I Had Someone Else Before I Had You	18
54	Vogue Coral Q 2029	Au Revoir/Danger Signs	15
55	Vogue Coral Q 72043	Let Me Go, Lover (with Lancers)/Baby, Baby, Baby	18
55	Vogue Coral Q 72065	How Important Can It Be?/What More Is There To Say?	12
55	Vogue Coral Q 72066	Tweedlee Dee/Rock Love	18
55	Vogue Coral Q 72066	Tweedlee Dee/Rock Love (78)	5
55	Vogue Coral Q 72077	Pledging My Love/I Gotta Go Get My Baby	15
55	Vogue Coral Q 72083	You're Telling Our Secret/Time	12
55	Vogue Coral Q 72098	The Banjo's Back In Town/How To Be Very, Very Popular	10
56	Vogue Coral Q 72130	A Good Man Is Hard To Find/It's Siesta Time	10
56	Vogue Coral Q 72139	Rememb'ring/My Sweetie Went Away	12
56	Vogue Coral Q 72146	A Tear Fell/Bo Weevil	15
56	Vogue Coral Q 72172	A Sweet Old-Fashioned Girl/Goodbye, John	12
56	Vogue Coral Q 72199	Keep Your Cotton Pickin' Paddies Offa My Heart/So Doggone Lonely	7
56	Vogue Coral Q 72213	Crazy With Love/The Moon Is On Fire	8
57	Vogue Coral Q 72224	Nora Malone/When I Leave The World Behind	8
57	Vogue Coral Q 72239	I'm Drowning My Sorrows/How Lonely Can One Be	6
57	Vogue Coral Q 72251	Empty Arms/The Ricky-Tick Song	7
57	Vogue Coral Q 72278	Teardrops In My Heart/Lulu Rock-A-Hula	10
57	Vogue Coral Q 72292	You Send Me/Born To Love	8
58	Coral Q 72301	Mutual Admiration Society/Careless Caresses	6
58	Coral Q 72320	Saturday Dance/I Think The World Of You	6
58	Coral Q 72336	Pickle Up A Doodle/The Rain Falls On Ev'rybody	6
58	Coral Q 72340	The Hula Hoop Song/So Shy	6
58	Coral Q 72349	I Like Christmas/Jingle Bell Rock	6
59	Coral Q 72354	The One Rose (That's Left In My Heart)/Satellite	5
59	Coral Q 72364	Heavenly Lover/Fair Weather Sweetheart	6
59	Coral Q 72375	Bye Bye Baby Goodbye/Chain Of Friendship	6
59	Coral Q 72383	Mexicali Rose/Bill Bailey, Won't You Please Come Home	5
60	Coral Q 72386	Peace Of Mind/Venetian Sunset	5
60	Coral Q 72396	How Do You Know It's Love/If There Are Stars In My Eyes	5
60	Coral Q 72405	Anymore/That Piano Man	5
59	Coral FEP 2013	HULA HOOP TIME WITH TERESA BREWER (EP)	12
59	Coral FEP 2036	WHEN YOUR LOVER HAS GONE PART 1 (EP)	10
59	Coral FEP 2037	WHEN YOUR LOVER HAS GONE PART 2 (EP)	10
59	Coral FEP 2038	WHEN YOUR LOVER HAS GONE PART 3 (EP)	10

MINT VALUE £

60	Coral FEP 2047	TERESA BREWER AND THE DIXIELAND BAND PART 1 (EP)	10
60	Coral FEP 2048	TERESA BREWER AND THE DIXIELAND BAND PART 2 (EP)	10
60	Coral FEP 2061	HOW DO YOU KNOW IT'S LOVE (EP)	10
51	London H-APB 1006	SHOWCASE (10" LP)	30
57	Coral LVA 9020	MUSIC! MUSIC! MUSIC! (LP)	20
58	Coral LVA 9075	FOR TEENAGERS IN LOVE (LP)	20
58	Coral LVA 9091	AT CHRISTMAS TIME (LP)	20
59	Coral LVA 9095	TIME FOR TERESA BREWER (LP)	16
59	Coral LVA 9100	WHEN YOUR LOVER HAS GONE (LP, also stereo SVL 3003)	16/18
59	Coral LVA 9107	TERESA BREWER AND THE DIXIELAND BAND (LP)	15
60	Coral LVA 9129	RIDIN' HIGH (LP)	15
60	Coral LVA 9131	MY GOLDEN FAVOURITES (LP)	15
60	Coral LVA 9138	NAUGHTY NAUGHTY NAUGHTY (LP)	15
61	Coral LVA 9145	SONGS EVERYBODY KNOWS (LP)	15
62	Coral LVA 9152	ALOHA FROM TERESA (LP)	15
62	Coral LVA 9204	DON'T MESS AROUND WITH TESS (LP)	15
67	Wing WL 1157	TERRIFIC TERESA BREWER! (LP)	10

BREWER & SHIPLEY
| 69 | Kama Sutra 2361 005 | WEEDS (LP) | 10 |

BREWERS DROOP
| 72 | RCA RCA 2216 | Sweet Thing/Heart Of Stone/It Ain't The Meat — It's The Motion (p/s) | 5 |

BRIAR
| 82 | Happy Face MM 142 | Rainbow (To The Skies)/Crying In The Rain (p/s) | 6 |

BRIDES OF FUNKENSTEIN
| 78 | Atlantic K 50545 | FUNK OR WALK (LP) | 15 |

(see also Parliament, Funkadelic)

BRIDEWELL TAXIS
| 88 | Cubic Music | Lies/Just Good Friends (p/s, flexidisc) | 6 |
| 89 | Stolen BLAG 1 | Just Good Friends/Too Long/Wild Boar/Hold On (12", black p/s) | 7 |

BOBBY BRIDGER
| 69 | Beacon BEA BEA 149 | The World Is Turning On/Why Do I Love You | 4 |
| 69 | Beacon BEA 159 | Sugar Shaker/You're In Love | 4 |

(see also Errol Sobers)

MARC BRIERLEY
68	CBS 3857	Autograph Of Time/Hold On, Hold On, The Garden Sure Looks Good Spread On The Floor	6
69	CBS 4191	Stay A Little Longer Merry Ann/Flaxen Hair	5
69	CBS 4632	Lady Of The Light/Sunny Weather	5
70	CBS 5266	Be My Brother/If You Took The Bandage Off	4
67	CBS 63478	WELCOME TO THE CITADEL (LP)	20
69	CBS 63835	HELLO (LP)	15

BRIGANDAGE
| 86 | Gung Ho GHLP 001 | PRETTY FUNNY THING (LP) | 10 |

(see also VDU's)

ANN BRIGGS
63	Topic TOP 94	HAZARDS OF LOVE (EP)	20
71	CBS 64612	THE TIME HAS COME (LP)	70
71	Topic 12TS 207	ANN BRIGGS (LP)	65

BILLY BRIGGS
| 51 | Columbia DB 2938 | Chew Tobacco Rag (No. 2)/Alarm Clock Boogie (78) | 10 |

DUGGIE BRIGGS BAND
| 78 | It IT 3 | Punk Rockin' Granny/I'm A Flasher (p/s) | 4 |

LILLIAN BRIGGS
| 55 | Philips PB 522 | I Want You To Be My Baby/Give Me A Band And My Baby (78) | 5 |
| 60 | Coral Q 72408 | Not A Soul (Blanket Roll Blues)/Smile For The People | 5 |

BRILLIANT
81	Limelight LIME 7001	That's What Good Friends Are For/Push (p/s)	5
83	Rough Trade RTT 105	Colours/Colours (Monster Mix) (12", p/s)	7
85	Food FOOD 5	It's A Man's Man's Man's World/Crash The Car (picture disc)	4

(see also Youth, Killing Joke, J.A.M.s)

BRILLIANT CORNERS
84	SS20 SS21	She's Got Fever/Black Water (red or pink p/s)	20/25
84	SS20 SS22	Big Hip/Tangled Up In Blue (p/s)	8
84	SS20 SS23T	My Baby's In Black/Rope In My Hand/Sixteen Years (12", p/s)	12
86	SS20 SS25	FRUIT MACHINE (EP)	5
86	SS20 SS25T	FRUIT MACHINE (12" EP)	8
87	SS20 SS27	Brian Rix/Trudy Is A Squeal (p/s)	4
87	SS20 SS28	Delilah Sands/Is There Anybody Home? (p/s)	4
87	SS20 SS28T	Delilah Sands/Is There Anybody Home?/Please Please Please (12", p/s)	7

BRILLS
| 79 | Barclay Towers TB-1 | Gang Of One/What Is Done/Burst Of Old Flames (p/s) | 4 |

BRINDLEY BRAE
| 70s | Harmony DB 0002 | VILLAGE MUSIC (LP, private pressing with insert) | 50 |

(see also Bev Pegg, Away From The Sand)

BRINSLEY SCHWARZ
| 70 | United Artists UP 35118 | Shining Brightly/What Do You Suggest | 6 |
| 70 | Liberty LBY 15419 | Country Girl/Funk Angel | 7 |

BRINSLEY SCHWARZ

72	United Artists UP 35312	Country Girl/Funk Angel (reissue)	6
73	United Artists UP 35588	Speedo/I Worry	4
74	United Artists UP 35642	I've Cried My Last Tear/Bringdown	4
74	United Artists UP 35700	(What's So Funny 'Bout) Peace, Love And Understanding/ Ever Since You're Gone	4
75	United Artists UP 35768	Everybody/I Like You, I Don't Love You	4
75	United Artists UP 35812	There's A Cloud In My Heart/I Got The Real Thing	4
70	United Artists UAS 29111	BRINSLEY SCHWARZ (LP, gatefold sleeve)	15
70	Liberty LBG 83427	DESPITE IT ALL (LP, gatefold sleeve)	20
72	United Artists UAS 29217	SILVER PISTOL (LP, some with poster)	15/10
72	United Artists UAS 29374	NERVOUS ON THE ROAD (LP)	10
73	United Artists UAS 29489	PLEASE DON'T EVER CHANGE (LP)	18
74	United Artists UAS 29641	THE NEW FAVOURITES OF BRINSLEY SCHWARZ (LP)	10

(see also Kippington Lodge, Hitters, Knees, Limelight, Nick Lowe, Ernie Graham, Rumour)

JOHNNY BRISTOL
75	MGM 2006 505	Leave My World/All Goodbyes Aren't Gone	5
80	Ariola/Hansa AHA 567	Love No Longer Has A Hold On Me/Till I See You Again	4
80	Ariola/Hansa AHAD 567	Love No Longer Has A Hold On Me/Till I See You Again (12")	10

BRITISH ELECTRIC FOUNDATION
(see under B.E.F.)

BRITISH LIONS
78	Vertigo 6059 192	One More Chance To Run/Booster	4
78	Vertigo 6059 201	International Heroes/Eat The Rich	4
78	Vertigo 9102 019	BRITISH LIONS (LP)	10

(see also Mott The Hoople)

BRITISH WALKERS
65	Pye International 7N 25298	I Found You/Diddley Daddy	20

BRITT
66	Piccadilly 7N 35273	You Really Have Started Something/Leave My Baby Alone	6

MAY BRITT
59	Top Rank JAR 230	Falling In Love Again/Lola-Lola	4

TINA BRITT
65	London HLC 9974	The Real Thing/Teardrops Fell	20

BUDDY BRITTEN & REGENTS
62	Piccadilly 7N 35075	My Pride, My Joy/Long Gone Baby	6
62	Decca F 11435	Don't Spread It Around/The Beat Of My Heart	6
63	Oriole CB 1827	If You Gotta Make A Fool Of Somebody/Money	7
63	Oriole CB 1839	Hey There/I'll Cry No More	6
63	Oriole CB 1859	My Resistance Is Low/When I See You Smile	6
63	Oriole CB 1889	Money/Sorrow Tomorrow	6
64	Oriole CB 1911	I Guess I'm In The Way/Zip-A-Dee-Doo-Dah	7
65	Piccadilly 7N 35241	She's About A Mover/Since You've Gone	8
65	Piccadilly 7N 35257	Right Now/Jailer Bring Me Water	6

(see also Regents)

JON BRITTEN
68	Philips BF 1641	Once I Had A Dream/My Need For You	4

BOBBIE BRITTON
54	Decca F 10288	Wanted/Lost (as Bobbie Britton & Keynotes)	4
54	Decca F 10385	Always You/When	4
55	Decca F 10453	Could It Be/My Eyes Are Wide Open	4
55	Decca F 10563	Learnin' The Blues/Strange Lady In Town (with Ted Heath Music)	4
56	Decca F 10777	Autumn Concerto/The Fool Of The Year (with Ted Heath Music)	4
56	Decca F 10807	True Love/If You Don't Love Me (with Ted Heath Music)	4

CHRIS BRITTON
69	Page One POLS 022	AS I AM (LP)	75

(see also Troggs)

DAVE BROCK
83	Flicknife FLS 024	Social Alliance/Raping Robots In The Street (p/s)	4
83	Flicknife FLS 024P	Social Alliance/Raping Robots In The Street (picture disc)	6

(see also Dr. Technical & Machines, Hawkwind)

NORAH BROCKSTEDT
60	Top Rank JAR 353	Big Boy/Tell Me No Lies	10

BROKEN BONES
85	Fall Out FALL 020	Decapitated/Problem/Liquidated Brains (p/s)	4
85	Fall Out FALL 034P	Seeing Through My Eyes/The Point Of Agony/It's Like (picture disc)	4
85	Fall Out FALL 10034	Seeing Through My Eyes/The Point Of Agony/It's Like/Decapitated/ Part 2/Death Is Imminent (10", p/s)	5

BROKEN GLASS
75	Capitol E-ST 11510	BROKEN GLASS (LP)	10

JOHN BROMLEY
68	Polydor 56224	What A Woman Does/My My	4
68	Polydor 56287	And The Feeling Goes/Sweet Little Princess	4
69	Polydor 56305	Melody Fayre/Sugar Love	4
69	Polydor 56340	Hold Me Woman/Weather Man	4
69	Atlantic 584 289	Kick A Tin Can/Wonderland Avenue U.S.A.	5
69	Polydor 583 048	SING (LP)	10

(see also Fleur De Lys)

BRONCO
70	Island ILPS 9124	COUNTRY HOME (LP)	12
71	Island ILPS 9161	ACE OF SUNLIGHT (LP)	10

(see also Alan Bown)

BRONSKI BEAT
84	Forbidden Fruit BITPD 1	Smalltown Boy/Memories (shaped picture disc)	5
84	Forbidden Fruit BITEX 1	Smalltown Boy/Memories/Infatuation (12", logo p/s)	7
85	Forbidden Fruit BITEX 4	Medley: I Feel Love/Love To Love You Baby/Johnny Remember Me (Cake Mix)/(Instrumental Fruit Mix) (10", megamix, p/s, with Marc Almond)	5
85	Forbidden Fruit BITER 6	Hit That Perfect Beat (Instant Mix)/Gave You Everything (12", p/s)	7

(see also Communards, Jimmy Somerville, Marc Almond)

BRONX CHEER
70	Parlophone R 5865	Drive My Car/Foxtrot	5
71	Dawn DNX 2512	Barrel House Player/Surprising Find/Whether Or Not/Party For One (p/s)	5
72	Dawn DNLS 3004	GREATEST HITS VOLUME 3 (LP)	10

BRONZ
84	Bronze BRO 178	Send Down An Angel/Tiger (p/s)	4
84	Bronze BROX 178	Send Down An Angel/Tiger/Stranded (12", p/s)	7

PATTI BROOK (& DIAMONDS)
60	Pye 7N 15300	Since You've Been Gone/That's The Way It's Gonna Be (with Diamonds)	4
61	Pye 7N 15339	When The Red Red Robin/Look What You've Done To Me	4
62	Pye 7N 15422	I Love You, I Need You/Unloved, Unwanted	8

TONY BROOK & BREAKERS
64	Columbia DB 7279	Meanie Genie/Ooh Poo Pah Doo (some in p/s)	50/30
65	Columbia DB 7444	Love Dances On/I Won't Hurt You	8

BROOK BROTHERS
60	Pye 7N 15298	Say The Word/Everything But Love	5
61	Pye 7N 15333	Warpaint/Sometimes	6
61	Pye 7N 15352	Little Bitty Heart/Tell Her	5
61	Pye 7N 15369	Ain't Gonna Wash For A Week/One Last Kiss	6
61	Pye 7N 15387	Married/I Love Girls	5
62	Pye 7N 15409	He's Old Enough To Know Better/Win Or Lose	4
62	Pye 7N 15415	Too Scared/Tell Tale	4
62	Pye 7N 15441	Double Trouble/Just Another Fool	4
62	Pye 7N 15453	Welcome Home Baby/So Long	4
62	Pye 7N 15463	I Can't Make Up My Mind/Town Girl	4
63	Pye 7N 15498	Trouble Is My Middle Name/Let The Good Times Roll	4
63	Pye 7N 15527	I'm Not Jimmy/Side By Side (with RBQ)	4
63	Pye 7N 15570	Crosswords/Whistle To The Wind	4
61	Pye NEP 24140	BROOK BROTHERS HIT PARADE (EP)	12
61	Pye NEP 24148	BROOK BROTHERS HIT PARADE VOLUME 2 (EP)	12
62	Pye NEP 24155	BROOK BROTHERS (EP)	12
61	Pye NPL 18067	BROOK BROTHERS (LP)	35

(see also Brooks)

BROOKLYN
80	Rondelet ROUND 3	I Wanna Be A Detective (p/s)	7
81	Rondelet ROUND 6	Hollywood/Late Again (p/s)	7
80	Rondelet ABOUT 3	YOU NEVER KNOW WHAT YOU'LL FIND (LP)	10

BROOKLYN BRIDGE
68	Pye International 7N 25473	Little Red Boat By The River/From My Window I Can See	4
69	Buddah 201 029	The Worst That Could Happen/Your Kite My Kite	4

BROOKS
60	Top Rank JAR 349	Green Fields/How Will It End?	4
60	Top Rank JAR 409	Please Help Me, I'm Falling/When Will I Be Loved	5

(see also Brook Brothers)

BABA BROOKS
63	Island WI 078	Shock Resistance/Distant Drums	12
63	Island WI 096	Bank To Bank Pts 1 & 2	12
63	Island WI 127	Three Blind Mice/BILLY & BOBBY: We Ain't Got Nothing	10
63	R&B JB 125	Water Melon Man/STRANGER COLE: Things Come To Those Who Wait	12
64	Black Swan WI 412	Jelly Beans/ERIC MORRIS: Sampson	12
64	Black Swan WI 434	Spider/Melody Jamboree	10
64	Black Swan WI 438	Cork Foot/HERSANG COMBO: B.B.C. Channel Two	10
65	Black Swan WI 442	Musical Workshop/DUKE WHITE: Be Wise	10
65	Black Swan WI 451	Ethiopia/ARCHIBALD TROTT: Promised Land	10
65	Black Swan WI 466	Baby Elephant Walk/DON DRUMMOND: Don's Special	10
65	Ska Beat JB 220	One Eyed Giant (with His Band)/DYNAMITES: Walk Out On Me	10
65	Island WI 229	Guns Fever/DOTTY & BONNIE: Don't Do It	10
65	Island WI 233	Independent Ska/STRANGER & CLAUDETTE: Seven Days	10
65	Island WI 235	Duck Soup/ZODIACS: Renegade	10
65	Island WI 241	Teenage Ska/ALTON ELLIS: You're The One To Blame	10
65	Rio R 061	Skank J. Sheck (& Band)/SHENLEY & HIACYNTH: Set Me Free	10
66	Doctor Bird DB 1042	The Clock (& Band)/LYN TAITT & COMETS & SILVERTONES: Raindrops	10
66	Doctor Bird DB 1046	Jam Session (with His Band)/CONQUERORS: What A Agony	10
67	Ska Beat JB 268	One Eyed Giant (with His Band)/DYNAMITES: Walk Out On Me (reissue)	8

CHUCK BROOKS
70	Soul City SC 116	Black Sheep/I've Got To Get Myself Together	8

DALE BROOKS
66	Stateside SS 553	I Wanna Be Your Girl/Like Other Girls Do	5

MINT VALUE £

DONNIE BROOKS

60	London HLN 9168	Mission Bell/Do It For Me	4
60	London HLN 9168	Mission Bell/Do It For Me (78)	25
60	London HLN 9253	Doll House/Round Robin	4
61	London HLN 9361	That's Why/Memphis	4
62	London HLN 9572	Oh, You Beautiful Doll/Just A Bystander	4
61	London HA-N 2391	THE HAPPIEST DONNIE BROOKS (LP)	25

ELKIE BROOKS

64	Decca F 11928	Something's Got A Hold On Me/Hello Stranger	8
64	Decca F 11983	Nothing Left To Do But Cry/Strange Though It Seems	8
65	Decca F 12061	The Way You Do The Things You Do/Blue Tonight	10
65	HMV POP 1431	He's Gotta Love Me/When You Appear	10
65	HMV POP 1480	All My Life/Can't Stop Thinking Of You	8
66	HMV POP 1512	Baby Let Me Love You/Stop The Music	8
69	NEMS 56-4136	Come September/If You Should Go	4

(see also Dada, Vinegar Joe)

HADDA BROOKS

50	London L 684	I Hadn't Anyone 'Till You/Hadda's Boogie (78)	12
51	London L 865	man Plays A Horn/All I Need is You (78)	8
51	London L 859	Vanity/It Hadda B Brooks (78)	8
51	London L 796	Maggie's Boogie/A Rendezvous With The Blues (78)	8

JOEY BROOKS & BAROQUE FOLK

66	Decca F 12328	I Ain't Blamin' You/Nobody Waved Goodbye	4

NORMAN BROOKS & GO BOYS

54	London L 1166	Hello Sunshine/You're My Baby	25
54	London L 1202	You Shouldn't Have Kissed Me The First Time/Somebody Wonderful	25
54	London L 1228	A Sky-Blue Shirt And A Rainbow Tie/This Waltz With You	25
54	London HL 8015	I'd Like To Be In Your Shoes, Baby/I'm Kinda Crazy	20
54	London HL 8041	I Can't Give You Anything But Love (solo)/GO-BOYS:Johnny's Tune	20
54	London HL 8051	My 3-D Sweetie/Candy Moon	20
55	London HL 8115	Back In Circulation/Lou Lou Louisiana	20
54	London REP 1004	NORMAN BROOKS VOLUME 1 (EP)	15
55	London REP 1021	BABY MINE (EP)	15

BROOKS & JERRY

68	Direction 58-3267	I Got What It Takes Pts 1 & 2	4

BIG BILL BROONZY

51	Vogue V 2068	Back Water Blues/Lonesome Road Blues (78)	10
51	Vogue V 2073	In The Evenin'/Low Land Blues (78)	10
51	Vogue V 2074	John Henry/Blues In 1890 (78)	10
51	Vogue V 2075	Big Bill Blues/Hey Hey Baby (78)	10
51	Vogue V 2076	House Rent Stomp/The Moppin' Blues (78)	10
51	Vogue V 2077	Black, Brown And White/Feelin' Low Down (78)	10
52	Vogue V 2078	Make My Getaway/What I Used To Do (78)	10
52	Melodisc 1191	Keep Your Hands Off Her/Stump Blues (78)	12
52	Melodisc 1203	Five Foot Seven/Plough Hand Blues (78)	12
50s	private pressing	Keep Your Hand On Your Heart/T For Texas (78)	15
56	Pye Jazz NJ 2012	When Do I Get To Be Called A Man/Mindin' My Own Business (78)	8
57	Pye Jazz NJ 2016	Southbound Train/It Feels So Good (78)	8
58	Vogue V 2351	Guitar Shuffle/When Did You Leave Home	10
61	Storyville A 44053	Midnight Special/Black Brown And White	8
55	Vogue EPV 1024	HEY BUD BLUES (EP)	8
56	Vogue EPV 1074	SINGS THE BLUES (EP)	10
56	Vogue EPV 1107	GUITAR SHUFFLE (EP)	10
56	Pye Jazz NJE 1005	MISSISSIPPI BLUES VOLUME 1 (EP)	7
56	Pye Jazz NJE 1015	MISSISSIPPI BLUES VOLUME 2 (EP)	7
57	Pye Jazz NJE 1047	SOUTHERN SAGA (EP)	7
57	Columbia SEG 7674	BIG BILL BROONZY SINGS THE BLUES (EP)	10
57	Tempo EXA 61	BILL BAILEY WON'T YOU PLEASE COME HOME (EP)	7
58	Columbia SEG 7790	BIG BILL BROONZY SINGS THE BLUES NO. 2 (EP)	10
50s	Melodisc EPM7 65	KEEP YOUR HANDS OFF (EP)	7
60	Mercury ZEP 10065	WALKIN' DOWN A LONESOME ROAD (EP)	7
60	Mercury ZEP 10093	HOLLERIN' BLUES (EP)	7
62	Storyville SEP 383	BLUES ANTHOLOGY VOLUME 3 (EP)	7
64	Mercury 10003 MCE	BLUES-GOSPEL-SPIRITUAL (EP)	8
57	Vogue LAE 12009	BIG BILL BLUES (LP)	25
57	Philips BBL 7113	BIG BILL BROONZY (LP)	35
58	Vogue LAE 12063	THE BLUES (LP)	25
58	Pye Nixa Jazz NJL 16	TRIBUTE TO BIG BILL (LP)	25
59	Tempo TAP 23	AN EVENING WITH BIG BILL BROONZY (LP)	30
61	HMV CLP 1544	LAST SESSION PART 1 (LP)	15
62	HMV CLP 1551	LAST SESSION PART 2 (LP)	15
62	HMV CLP 1562	LAST SESSION PART 3 (LP)	15
65	Storyville SLP 143	AN EVENING WITH BROONZY (LP)	10
65	Fontana 688 206ZL	TROUBLE IN MIND (LP)	20
66	Mercury 20044 MCL	REMEMBERING BROONZY — THE GREATEST MINSTREL OF THE AUTHENTIC BLUES (LP)	10
66	Storyville SLP 188	BLUES IN EUROPE (LP)	10
67	Storyville 670 154	PORTRAITS IN BLUES VOLUME 2 (LP)	15
69	CBS Realm 52648	BIG BILL'S BLUES (LP)	10
60s	Xtra XTRA 1093	SINGS COUNTRY BLUES (LP)	10
78	Spotlite SPJ 900	TROUBLE IN MIND (LP, reissue)	10

(see also Chicago Bill)

BIG BILL BROONZY & PETE SEEGER
64	Xtra XTRA 1006	IN CONCERT (LP)	18
66	Verve Folkways VLP 5006	IN CONCERT (LP, reissue, also stereo SVLP 506)	15

(see also Pete Seeger)

BIG BILL BROONZY/SONNY BOY WILLIAMSON [I]
65	RCA Victor RD 7685	BIG BILL AND SONNY BOY (LP)	20

(see also Sonny Boy Williamson [I])

BIG BILL BROONZY, SONNY TERRY & BROWNIE McGHEE
64	Xtra XTRA 1004	BIG BILL BROONZY/SONNY TERRY/BROWNIE McGHEE (LP)	20

(see also Sonny Terry & Brownie McGhee)

BROS
87	CBS ATOM 1	I Owe You Nothing/I Owe You Nothing (The Voice) (white or black p/s)	6
87	CBS ATOM Q1	I Owe You Nothing/I Owe You Nothing (The Voice) (poster sleeve)	8
87	CBS ATOM T1	I Owe You Nothing (Shep Pettibone Mix)/(The Voice)/(7" Mix) (12", white p/s)	10
87	CBS ATOM T1	I Owe You Nothing (Shep Pettibone Mix)/(The Voice)/(7" Mix) (12", black p/s)	10
87	CBS ATOM C1	I Owe You Nothing (Shep Pettibone Mix)/(The Pettibeat)/(The Voice)/(7" Mix) (cassette)	5
87	CBS ATOM P2	When Will I Be Famous/Love To Hate You (picture disc)	7
87	CBS ATOM QT2	When Will I Be Famous (Infamous Mix)/I Owe You Nothing (Shep Pettibone Mix) Love To Hate You (12", poster p/s with calendar)	10
87	CBS ATOM S2	When Will I Be Famous/Love To Hate You (p/s, with badges)	6
88	CBS ATOM B3	Drop The Boy/The Boy Is Dropped (p/s, badge pack)	4
88	CBS ATOM P3	Drop The Boy/The Boy Is Dropped (poster p/s)	4
88	CBS ATOM W3	Drop The Boy/The Boy Is Dropped (shaped picture disc)	4
88	CBS ATOM QT 3	Drop The Boy (Art Mixing)/(Shep Pettibone Mix)/When Will I Be Famous/The Boy Is Dropped (12", p/s)	8
88	CBS ATOM QT 4	I Owe You Nothing (Club Mix)/(The Voice)/(The Beats)/(Over 18 Mix)/Nothing (12", p/s)	7
88	CBS ATOMP 5	I Quit/I Quit (Acid Drops) (shaped picture disc)	4
89	CBS ATOM W7	Too Much (Wembley Souvenir Mix)/Too Much/Astroglically (12", p/s, souvenir issue)	7
89	CBS CDATOM 9	Sister/I'll Count The Hours/Too Much (Remix) (CD)	7

BROTH
70	Mercury 6338 032	BROTH (LP)	15

BROTHER DAN ALLSTARS
68	Trojan TR 601	Donkey Returns/Tribute To Sir K.B.	8
68	Trojan TR 602	Eastern Organ/JIVERS: Our Love Will Last	8
68	Trojan TR 603	Hold Pon Them/OWEN GRAY: Answer Me	8
68	Trojan TR 607	Read Up/Gallop	8
68	Trojan TR 608	Another Saturday Night/Bee's Knees	8
68	Trojan TBL 101	LET'S CATCH THE BEAT (LP)	30
69	Trojan TRL 1	FOLLOW THAT DONKEY (LP)	18

BROTHERHOOD
69	Philips BF 1766	Paper Man/Give It To Me Now	8

BROTHERHOOD OF BREATH
74	Ogun OG 100	LIVE AT WILLISAU (LP, with Chris McGregor)	15

(see also Chris McGregor's Brotherhood Of Breath)

BROTHERHOOD OF MAN
69	Deram DM 276	Love One Another/A Little Bit Of Heaven	4
76	Pye 7N 45569	Save Your Kisses For Me/Let's Love Together (p/s)	4
70	Dawn DNLS 3063	GOOD THINGS HAPPENING (LP)	10

BROTHERS
67	London HLU 10158	Love Story/The Girl's Alright	5

BROTHERS
75	People PEO 118	In The Pocket/Everybody Loves A Winner	4
75	People PLEO 25	DISCO SOUL (LP)	25

BROTHERS & SISTERS (U.S.)
69	CBS 63746	DYLAN'S GOSPEL (LP)	10

BROTHERS & SISTERS (U.K.)
70s	private pressing	ARE WATCHING YOU (LP)	70

BROTHERS FOUR
60	Philips PB 1009	Greenfields/East Virginia	4

BROTHERS GRIMM
65	Decca F 12224	Lost Love/Make It Or Break It	5
66	Ember EMB 222	A Man Needs Love/Looky Looky	60

BROTHERS JOHNSON
76	A&M AMS 7237	I'll Be Good To You/Devil	4
76	A&M AMS 7251	Get The Funk Out Me Face/Tomorrow	4

BROTHERS KANE
66	Decca F 12448	Walking In The Sand/Won't You Stay Long	4

(see also Sarstedt Brothers, Peter Lincoln, Peter Sarstedt, Clive Sands, Wes Sands, Eden Kane)

BROTHERS TWO
68	Action ACT 4513	Here I Am, In Love Again/I'm Tired Of You Baby	8

BROTHERS WILLIAM
65	Parlophone R 5293	Linda Jane Blues/Honey Love	5

MINT VALUE £

EDGAR BROUGHTON BAND

69	Harvest HAR 5001	Evil/Death Of An Electric Citizen	5
70	Harvest HAR 5015	Out Demons Out/Momma's Reward	4
70	Harvest HAR 5032	Apache Drop Out/Freedom	4
72	Harvest HAR 5049	Gone Blue/Someone/Mr Crosby	4
69	Harvest SHVL 757	WASA WASA (LP, gatefold sleeve)	15
70	Harvest SHVL 772	SING BROTHER SING (LP, gatefold sleeve)	15
71	Harvest SHVL 791	THE EDGAR BROUGHTON BAND (LP, gatefold sleeve)	15
72	Harvest SHTC 252	IN SIDE OUT (LP, gatefold sleeve with lyric sheet)	18
73	Harvest SHVL 810	OORA (LP)	15
75	NEMS NEL 6006	BANDAGES (LP)	10

ADA BROWN

| 24 | Parlophone E 5260 | Evil Mama Blues/Break O'Day Blues (78) | 40 |

AL BROWN (Jamaica)

| 71 | Banana BA 360 | No Soul Today/RUFFIANS: Where Did I Go Wrong (B-side actually "Bang Shang Alang" by Peter Austin & Hortense Ellis) | 5 |

AL BROWN'S TUNETOPPERS (U.S.)

| 60 | Top Rank JAR 374 | The Madison/Mo' Madison | 4 |

(CRAZY WORLD OF) ARTHUR BROWN

65	Lyntone LYN 770/1	You Don't Know (as Arthur Brown & Diamonds)/DIAMONDS: You'll Be Mine (Reading University Rag Week flexidisc)	70
67	Track 604 008	Devil's Grip/Give Him A Flower	7
68	Track 604 022	Fire!/Rest Cure (push-out or large centre)	5/4
68	Track 604 026	Nightmare/What's Happening (some copies list "Music Man" as B-side)	6
74	Gull GULS 4	Gypsies/Dance	4
75	Gull GULS 13	We Gotta Get Out Of This Place/Here I Am	4
68	Track 612 005/613 005	THE CRAZY WORLD OF ARTHUR BROWN (LP)	15
70	Backtrack 2407 012	THE CRAZY WORLD OF ARTHUR BROWN (LP, reissue, different sleeve)	10
74	Gull GULP 1008	DANCE (LP, with insert)	10
77	Gull GUD 2003/4	THE LOST EARS (2-LP, gatefold sleeve, as Arthur Brown's Kingdom Come)	18
78	Gull GULP 1023	CHISHOLM IN MY BOSOM (LP)	10

(see also Kingdom Come, Nick Greenwood)

AMANDA BROWN (Viola McCoy)

| 24 | Actuelle 10693 | I've Got The World In A Jug/Do Right Blues (78) | 75 |

BEN BROWN

| 67 | Polydor 56198 | Ask The Lonely/Sidewinder | 20 |

BESSIE BROWN

| 30s | Brunswick 3761 | Chloe (Song Of The Swamp)/Someone Else May Be There While I'm Gone (78) | 40 |

BOOTS BROWN & HIS BLOCKBUSTERS

58	RCA RCA 1078	Cerveza/Juicy	5
58	RCA RCA 1078	Cerveza/Juicy (78)	5
59	RCA RCA 1102	Jim Twangy/Trollin'	5
59	RCA RCA 1102	Jim Twangy/Trollin' (78)	15

BUSTER BROWN

60	Melodisc 1559	Fannie Mae/Lost In A Dream	45
65	Sue WI 368	Fannie Mae/Lost In A Dream (reissue)	15
67	Island WI 3031	My Blue Heaven/Two Women	18
69	Blue Horizon 57-3147	Sugar Babe/I'm Going, But I'll Be Back	12
60s	XX MIN 713	B. AND BUSTER BROWN (EP, with B. Brown)	8

BUSTY BROWN

68	Doctor Bird DB 1158	Here Comes The Night/Don't Look Back	8
69	Upsetter US 304	What A Price/How Can I Forget?	6
69	Upsetter US 308	To Love Somebody/BLEECHERS: Farmer's In The Den	6
69	Punch PH 10	Broken Heart/Tribute To A King	4
70	Punch PH 38	Greatest Love/I Love You Madly	4
70	Escort ERT 845	Man Short (with Gaytones)/DAVE BARKER: She Want It	4
70	Gas GAS 154	I Love You Madly/Greatest Love	4
70	High Note HS 048	Man Short (with Gaytones)/GAYTONES: Another Version	4
71	Punch PH 72	You Inspire Me/UPSETTERS: Version	4

CHARLES BROWN (BAND)

56	Vogue V 9061	I'll Always Be In Love With You/Soothe Me	120
56	Vogue V 9061	I'll Always Be In Love With You/Soothe Me (78)	40
57	Vogue V 9065	Confidential/Trouble Blues	100
57	Vogue V 9065	Confidential/Trouble Blues (78)	40
61	Parlophone R 4848	It's Christmas All Year Round/Christmas Question	25

(see also Brown Brothers)

CLARENCE 'GATEMOUTH' BROWN

65	Vocalion VE 170161	CLARENCE 'GATEMOUTH' BROWN (EP)	50
72	Python PLP 26	CLARENCE 'GATEMOUTH' BROWN VOL. 1: 1948-1953 (LP)	25
72	Python PLP 27	CLARENCE 'GATEMOUTH' BROWN VOL. 2: 1956-1965 (LP)	25

CLIFFORD BROWN (& GROUP)

54	Vogue LDE 042	CLIFFORD "BROWNIE" BROWN QUARTET (10" LP)	15
56	Emarcy ERE 1501	SWEET CLIFFORD (EP, as Clifford Brown & Group)	8
58	Emarcy ERE 1565	STUDY IN BROWN VOL. 1 (EP, as Clifford Brown & Group)	7
58	Emarcy ERE 1566	STUDY IN BROWN VOL. 2 (EP, as Clifford Brown & Group)	7
58	Emarcy ERE 1572	CLIFFORD BROWN AND MAX ROACH (EP)	7
54	Esquire EP 3	CLIFFORD BROWN & ART FARMER WITH THE SWEDISH ALLSTARS (EP)	7
54	Esquire EP 4	AND ART FARMER WITH THE SWEDISH ALLSTARS VOL. 2 (EP)	7
55	Esquire EP 71	CLIFFORD BROWN WITH TADD DAMERON'S BAND (EP)	7

MINT VALUE £

55	Vogue EPV 1027	GIGI GRYCE — CLIFFORD BROWN ORCHESTRA (EP) 7
55	Vogue EPV 1041	CONCEPTION (EP) 7
56	Vogue EPV 1119	CLIFFORD BROWN ENSEMBLE (EP) 7
55	Vogue LDE 121	THE CLIFFORD BROWN SEXTET (10" LP) 15
58	Emarcy EJL 1278	STUDY IN BROWN (LP) 12
63	Blue Note (B)BLP1526	CLIFFORD BROWN MEMORIAL ALBUM (LP) 15

(see also Art Farmer, Tadd Dameron, Sonny Rollins, Max Roach)

DENNIS BROWN
70	Bamboo BAM 56	Love Grows/SOUND DIMENSION: Less Problem 7
70	Banana BA 309	No Man Is An Island/SOUL SISTERS: Another Night 7
71	Banana BA 336	Never Fall In Love/Make It With You 7
71	Ocean OC 001	Little Green Apples/SOUND DIMENSION: Version 6
72	Duke DU 139	What About The Half/What About The Half Version 4
72	Explosion EX 2068	Black Magic Woman/Version 4
72	Pressure Beat PB 5513	Money In My Pocket/JOE GIBBS ALLSTARS: Money Love 4
72	Randy's RAN 526	Cheater/TOMMY McCOOK & IMPACT ALLSTARS: Harvest In The East 4
72	Randy's RAN 528	Meet Me On The Corner (actually unknown instrumental)/ IMPACT ALLSTARS: Version 4
72	Songbird SB 1074	Silhouettes/CRYSTALITES: Version 4
73	Ashanti ASH 402	It's Too Late/Song My Mother Used To Sing 4
73	Jackpot JP 813	He Can't Spell/CRYSTALITES: Acid Version 4
73	Smash SMA 2327	Concentration/Version 4
73	Trojan TRLS 57	SUPER REGGAE & SOUL HITS (LP) 10

DUSTY BROWN
| 61 | Starlite ST45 058 | Please Don't Go/Well You Know ....25 |

ED BROWN
| 64 | London HA 8149 | THE JOHN FITZGERALD KENNEDY MEMORIAL ALBUM (LP, unissued) |

FAY BROWN
| 55 | Columbia SCM 5185 | Unchained Melody/I Was Wrong ....15 |

FRIDAY BROWN(E)
66	Parlophone R 5396	Getting Nowhere/And (To Me He Meant Everything) (as Friday Browne) 4
66	Fontana TF 736	32nd Love Affair/Born A Woman 4
67	Fontana TF 851	Ask Any Woman/Outdoor Seminar 4

(see also Marianne & Mike, High Society, Manchester Mob, Graham Gouldman)

GABRIEL BROWN
| 77 | Policy Wheel PW 4592 | GABRIEL BROWN AND HIS GUITAR (LP, withdrawn) ....15 |

GEORGIA BROWN
55	Decca F 10489	My Crazy L'il Mixed Up Heart/Before We Know It 4
55	Decca F 10551	I Love To Dance With You/That's All I Need 4
55	Decca F 10616	I Went To The Village/Wrong Again 4
71	Fly BUG 18	Turn Out The Light/I Scare Myself (p/s) 5

GERRY BROWN'S JAZZMEN
| 61 | Fontana TFL 5165 | IT'S TRAD TIME! (LP) ....20 |

GLEN BROWN
68	Blue Cat BS 131	Way Of Life (with Joe White & Trevor)/CARL BRYAN & LYN TAITT: I'm So Proud 8
70	Summit SUM 8502	Collie And Wine/BEVERLEY'S ALLSTARS: Version 4
70	Songbird SB 1021	Love I/CRYSTALITES: Heavy Load 5
72	Songbird SB 1081	Smokey Eyes (with Crystalites)/Smokey Eyes (Version) 5
73	Downtown DT 507	Two Wedding Skank/BARRY SIMPSON: Sugar Down Deh 5

(see also Lloyd & Glen, Glenmore Brown)

GLENMORE BROWN & HOPETON LEWIS
| 68 | Fab FAB 42 | Girl You're Cold/Soul Man ....5 |

(see also Hopeton Lewis & Glenmore Brown)

HENRY BROWN
50s	Signature 909	Henry Brown Blues/Twenty-First Street Blues (78) 10
50s	Jazz Collector L 15	Henry Brown Blues/Twenty-First Street Blues (78, reissue) 5
50s	Jazz Collector L 31	Blues Stomp/Blind Boy Blues (78) 5
50s	Jazz Collector L 55	It Hurts So Good/Screenin' The Blues (78) 5
50s	Jazz Collector L 70	Deep Morgan Blues/Eastern Chimes Blues (78) 5
61	'77' LA 12-5	HENRY BROWN BLUES (LP) 20

HYLO BROWN
| 59 | Capitol CL 15075 | You Can't Relive The Past/Thunder Clouds Of Love ....4 |
| 60 | Capitol CL 15139 | I've Waited As Long As I Can/Just Any Old Love ....4 |

IRVING BROWN
70	Bamboo BAM 36	Today/SOUND DIMENSION: Young Gifted And Black Version 7
70	Bamboo BAM 58	I'm Still Around/Run Come 7
71	Bamboo Now BN 1003	Now I'm Alone/Funky Night 6

JAMES BROWN (& FAMOUS FLAMES)
60	Parlophone R 4667	Think/You've Got The Power (with Famous Flames) 20
60	Fontana H 273	This Old Heart/Wonder When You're Coming Home 25
62	Parlophone R 4922	Why Does Everything Happen To Me/Night Train (with Famous Flames) 20
62	Parlophone R 4952	Shout And Shimmy/Come Over Here (with Famous Flames) 17
63	London HL 9730	Prisoner Of Love/Choo-Choo (Locomotion) 15
63	London HL 9775	These Foolish Things/(Can You) Feel It (Part 1) 15
64	Philips BF 1368	Out Of Sight/Maybe The Last Time 10
64	Sue WI 360	Night Train/Why Does Everything Happen To Me 15
65	London HL 9945	Have Mercy Baby/Just Won't Do Right (with Famous Flames) 12
65	London HL 9990	Papa's Got A Brand New Bag Pts 1 & 2 8

James BROWN

Year	Label	Title	Value
65	Ember EMB S 216	Tell Me What You're Gonna Do/Lost Someone	10
65	Philips BF 1458	Try Me/Papa's Got A Brand New Bag	7
66	Philips BF 1481	New Breed Pts 1 & 2	7
66	Pye International 7N 25350	I Got You (I Feel Good)/I Can't Help It (with Famous Flames)	8
66	Pye International 7N 25367	Ain't That A Groove Pts 1 & 2 (with Famous Flames)	6
66	Pye International 7N 25371	It's A Man's Man's Man's World/Is It Yes Or Is It No? (with Famous Flames)	6
66	Pye International 7N 25379	Money Won't Change You Pts 1 & 2 (with Famous Flames)	6
66	Pye International 7N 25394	Don't Be A Drop-Out/Tell Me That You Love Me (with Famous Flames)	6
67	Pye International 7N 25411	Bring It Up/Nobody Knows (with Famous Flames)	6
67	Pye International 7N 25418	Kansas City/Stone Fox (with Famous Flames)	6
67	Pye International 7N 25423	Let Yourself Go/Good Rockin' Tonight (with Famous Flames)	6
67	Pye International 7N 25430	Cold Sweat Pts 1 & 2 (with Famous Flames)	6
67	Pye International 7N 25441	Get It Together Pts 1 & 2 (with Famous Flames)	7
68	Polydor 56740	I Can't Stand Myself/There Was A Time	6
68	Polydor 56743	I Got The Feelin'/If I Ruled The World	6
68	Polydor 56744	Licking Stick, Licking Stick Pts 1 & 2	5
68	Polydor 56752	Say It Loud, I'm Black And I'm Proud Pts 1 & 2	7
68	Polydor 56540	Please, Please, Please/That's Life	5
68	Polydor 56541	Say It Loud, I'm Black And I'm Proud Pts 1 & 2 (reissue)	5
69	Polydor 56776	Mother Popcorn Pts 1 & 2	4
69	Polydor 56780	World Pts 1 & 2	4
69	Polydor 56783	Let A Man Come In And Do The Popcorn/Sometimes	5
70	Polydor 56787	There Was A Time/I Can't Stand Myself/When You Touch Me	5
70	Polydor 56793	Ain't It Funky Now Pts 1 & 2	4
70	Polydor 2001 018	It's A New Day/Georgia On My Mind	4
70	Polydor 2001 071	Get Up, I Feel Like Being A Sex Machine Pts 1 & 2 (paper or plastic label)	5/4
70	Polydor 2001 097	Call Me Super Bad Pts 1 & 2	4
71	Polydor 2001 163	Soul Power Pts 1, 2 & 3	4
71	Polydor 2001 190	I Cried/Get Up, Get Into It, Get Involved	4
71	Polydor 2001 213	Hot Pants (She Got To Use What She Got To Get What She Wants) Pts 1, 2 & 3	4
71	Polydor 2001 223	Make It Funky Pts 1 & 2	4
71	Mojo 2093 006	Hey America!/Brother Rapp Pt 1	4
71	Polydor 2066 153	I'm A Greedy Man Pts 1 & 2	4
72	Polydor 2066 185	King Heroin/Theme From King Heroin	4
72	Polydor 2066 210	There It Is Pts 1 & 2	4
72	Polydor 2066 216	Honky Tonk Pts 1 & 2	4
72	Polydor 2066 231	Get On The Good Foot Pts 1 & 2	4
72	Polydor 2066 283	What My Baby Needs Now Is A Little More Lovin'/This Guy's In Love With You (with Lyn Collins)	4
73	Polydor 2066 285	I've Got A Bag Of My Own/I Know It's True	4
73	Polydor 2141 008	Papa's Got A Brand New Bag/Out Of Sight/It's A Man's Man's Man's World (p/s)	4
73	Polydor 2066 296	I Got Ants In My Pants Pts 1, 15 & 16	4
73	Polydor 2066 329	Think/Something	4
73	Polydor 2066 370	Woman Pts 1 & 2	4
74	Polydor 2066 411	Stone To The Bone/Sexy, Sexy, Sexy	4
74	Polydor 2066 485	My Thing/The Payback	4
74	Polydor 2066 513	It's Hell/Papa Don't Take No Mess	6
75	Polydor 2066 520	Funky President (People It's Bad)/Cold Blooded	5
76	Polydor 2066 642	Hot (I Need To Be Loved, Loved, Loved)/Superbad, Superslick Part 1	4
76	Polydor 2066 687	Get Up Offa That Thing/Release The Pressure	4
77	Polydor 2066 763	Bodyheat Pts 1, 15 & 16	4
77	Polydor 2066 834	Honky Tonk/Brother Rapp	4
78	Polydor 2066 915	Eyesight/I Never, Never, Never Will Forget	4
78	Polydor 2066 984	Nature Pts 1 & 2	4
64	London RE 1410	JAMES BROWN AND THE FAMOUS FLAMES (EP)	15
64	Ember EMB EP 4549	I DO JUST WHAT I WANT (EP)	12
66	Pye Intl. NEP 44059	I GOT YOU (EP)	10
66	Pye Intl. NEP 44068	I'LL GO CRAZY (EP)	10
67	Pye Intl. NEP 44072	PRISONER OF LOVE (EP)	10
67	Pye Intl. NEP 44076	HOW LONG DARLING (EP)	10
67	Pye Intl. NEP 44088	BRING IT UP (EP)	10
70	Polydor 580 701	TURN IT LOOSE (EP)	12
64	London HA 8177	PURE DYNAMITE! (LP, as James Brown & Famous Flames)	25
64	London HA 8184	AT THE APOLLO (LP, as James Brown & Famous Flames)	30
64	Ember EMB 3357	TELL ME WHAT YOU'RE GONNA DO (LP)	20
64	Philips BL 7630	SHOWTIME (LP)	20
65	London HA 8203	UNBEATABLE 16 HITS (LP)	20
65	London HA 8231	PLEASE, PLEASE, PLEASE (LP, as James Brown & Famous Flames)	25
65	Philips BL 7664	GRITS AND SOUL (LP)	18
65	London HA 8240	JAMES BROWN TOURS THE U.S.A. (LP, with Famous Flames)	20
66	London HA 8262	PAPA'S GOT A BRAND NEW BAG (LP, as James Brown & Famous Flames)	25
66	Philips BL 7697	JAMES BROWN PLAYS JAMES BROWN TODAY AND YESTERDAY (LP)	18
66	Pye Intl. NPL 28074	I GOT YOU (I FEEL GOOD) (LP)	25
66	Philips BL 7718	JAMES BROWN PLAYS NEW BREED (LP)	15
66	Pye Intl. NPL 28079	IT'S A MAN'S MAN'S MAN'S WORLD (LP)	20
66	Pye Intl. NPL 28097	THE JAMES BROWN CHRISTMAS ALBUM (LP)	25
67	Pye Intl. NPL 28093	MIGHTY INSTRUMENTALS (LP)	18
67	Philips (S)BL 7761	HANDFUL OF SOUL (LP)	15
67	Pye Intl. NPL 28099	PAPA'S GOT A BRAND NEW BAG (LP, reissue)	15
67	Pye Intl. NPL 28100	MR. EXCITEMENT (LP)	15
67	Polydor 582 703	THE JAMES BROWN SHOW (LP)	15
67	Pye Intl. NPL 28103	SINGS RAW SOUL (LP)	15
67	Pye Intl. NPL 28104	LIVE AT THE GARDEN (LP)	25
68	Philips (S)BL 7823	JAMES BROWN PLAYS THE REAL THING (LP)	15
68	Polydor 623 017	JAMES BROWN'S GREATEST HITS (LP)	12
68	Polydor 623 032	MR. DYNAMITE (LP)	15

68	Polydor 184 100	MR. SOUL (LP)	15
68	Polydor 184 136	I CAN'T STAND MYSELF (LP)	25
69	Polydor 184 148	SOUL FIRE (LP)	18
69	Polydor 184 159	KING OF SOUL (LP)	15
69	Mercury 20133 SMCL	JAMES BROWN SINGS OUT OF SIGHT (LP)	15
69	Polydor 583 729/30	LIVE AT THE APOLLO VOLUME TWO (2-LP)	18
69	Polydor 583 741	SAY IT LOUD — I'M BLACK AND I'M PROUD (LP)	25
69	Polydor 583 765	THE BEST OF JAMES BROWN (LP)	10
69	Polydor 583 768	IT'S A MOTHER (LP)	30
69	Polydor 643 317	THIS IS JAMES BROWN (LP)	15
70	Polydor 583 742	GETTIN' DOWN TO IT (LP)	25
70	Polydor 184 319	THE POPCORN (LP)	35
70	Polydor 2343 010	AIN'T IT FUNKY (LP)	25
70	Polydor 2612 005	LIVE AT THE APOLLO VOLUME TWO (2-LP, reissue)	14
70	Polydor 2334 009	PAPA'S GOT A BRAND NEW BAG (LP)	12
71	Polydor 2625 004	SEX MACHINE (LP)	25
71	Polydor 2310 022	SOUL ON TOP (LP)	25
71	Polydor 2310 029	IT'S A NEW DAY (LP)	25
71	Polydor 2310 089	SUPER BAD (LP)	20
71	Polydor 2343 036	SOUL BROTHER, NUMBER ONE (LP)	10
71	Polydor 2425 086	HOT PANTS (LP)	15
72	Philips 6336 201	THIS IS ... JAMES BROWN (LP)	10
72	Polydor 2659 011	REVOLUTION OF THE MIND (2-LP)	30
72	Polydor 2391 033	THERE IT IS (LP)	30
73	Polydor 2659 018	GET ON THE GOOD FOOT (2-LP)	30
73	Polydor 2391 057	JAMES BROWN SOUL CLASSICS (LP)	15
73	Polydor 2490 117	BLACK CAESAR (LP)	30
73	Polydor 2391 084	SLAUGHTER'S BIG RIP-OFF (LP, soundtrack)	15
74	Polydor 2391 116	SOUL CLASSICS VOLUME TWO (LP)	15
74	Polydor 2659 030	THE PAYBACK (2-LP)	45
74	Polydor 2659 036	IT'S HELL (2-LP)	40
75	Polydor 2391 164	REALITY (LP)	15
75	Polydor 2391 166	SOUL CLASSICS VOLUME THREE (LP)	15
75	Polydor 2391 175	SEX MACHINE TODAY (LP)	15
75	Polydor 2482 184	LIVE AT THE APOLLO (LP)	10
75	Polydor 2391 197	EVERYBODY'S DOIN' THE HUSTLE AND DEAD ON THE DOUBLE BUMP(LP)	15
76	Polydor 2391 214	HOT (LP)	15
76	Polydor 2391 228	GET UP OFFA THAT THING (LP)	12
77	Polydor 2391 258	BODYHEAT (LP)	10
77	Polydor 2679 044	SOLID GOLD (LP)	10
77	Polydor 2391 300	MUTHA'S NATURE (LP)	15
78	Polydor 2391 342	JAM 1980s (LP)	10
79	Polydor 2391 384	TAKE A LOOK AT THOSE CAKES (LP)	10
79	Polydor 2391 412	THE ORIGINAL DISCO MAN (LP)	10
80	Polydor 2391 446	PEOPLE (LP)	10
80	Polydor 2683 085	LIVE/HOT ON THE ONE (LP)	12
80	RCA LP 5006	SOUL SYNDROME (LP)	10
81	Polydor POLS 1029	THE THIRD COMING (LP)	10
88	Urban URBLP 11	IN THE JUNGLE GROOVE (2-LP)	18

(see also Lyn Collins, JBs, Maceo & All King's Men)

JERICHO BROWN

| 60 | Warner Bros WB 14 | Don'tcha Know (That I Love You)/Look For A Star | 5 |
| 64 | Warner Bros WB 141 | I'm Watching You/Wisdom Of A Fool | 4 |

JIM EDWARD BROWN & MAXINE BROWN

55	London HL 8123	Itsy Witsy Bitsy Me/Why Am I Falling?	25
55	London HL 8123	Itsy Witsy Bitsy Me/Why Am I Falling? (78)	5
55	London HLU 8166	Your Love Is Wild As The West Wind/Draggin' Mainstreet	22
55	London HLU 8166	Your Love Is Wild As The West Wind/Draggin' Mainstreet ... (78)	8
55	London HLU 8200	You Thought I Thought/Here Today And Gone Tomorrow (B-side with Bonnie)	20
55	London HLU 8200	You Thought I Thought/Here Today And Gone Tomorrow (78)	5
55	London R-EP 1024	COUNTRY SONGS (EP)	15
55	London R-EU 1044	COUNTRY SONGS VOLUME 3 (EP)	15

(see also Browns)

JOE BROWN (& BRUVVERS)

59	Decca F 11185	People Gotta Talk/Comes The Day (solo, tri-centre)	10
59	Decca F 11185	People Gotta Talk/Comes The Day (78)	10
60	Decca F 11207	Darktown Strutter's Ball/Swagger (solo)	10
60	Decca F 11246	Jellied Eels/Dinah	8
60	Pye 7N 15322	Shine/The Switch	7
61	Piccadilly 7N 35000	Crazy Mixed Up Kid/Stick Around	4
61	Piccadilly 7N 35005	I'm Henery The Eighth I Am/Good Luck & Goodbye	4
62	Piccadilly 7N 35024	What A Crazy World We're Living In/Popcorn	4
62	Decca F 11496	Comes The Day/People Gotta Talk (reissue)	5
62	Piccadilly 7N 35058	Your Tender Look/The Other Side Of The Town	4
62	Piccadilly 7N 35082	It Only Took A Minute/All Things Bright And Beautiful	4
63	Piccadilly 7N 35106	That's What Love Will Do/Hava Nagila	4
63	Piccadilly 7N 35129	Nature's Time For Love/The Spanish Bit	5
63	Piccadilly 7N 35138	Sally Ann/There's Only One Of You	5
63	Piccadilly 7N 35150	Little Ukelele/Hercules Unchained	5
64	Piccadilly 7N 35163	You Do Things To Me/Everybody Calls Me Joe	5
64	Piccadilly 7N 35194	Don't/Just Like That	5
65	Pye 7N 15784	Teardrops In The Rain/Lonely Circus	4
65	Pye 7N 15888	Sicilian Tarantella/Thinkin' That I Loves You	4
65	Pye 7N 15983	Charlie Girl/My Favourite Occupation	4
66	Pye 7N 17074	Sea Of Heartbreak/Mrs O's Theme	5

Joe BROWN

66	Pye 7N 17135	Little Ray Of Sunshine/Your Loving Touch	4
66	Pye 7N 17184	A Satisfied Mind/Stay A Little While	7
67	Pye 7N 17339	With A Little Help From My Friends/Show Me Around	4
62	Decca DFE 8500	A PICTURE OF JOE BROWN (EP)	10
62	Piccadilly NEP 34025	JOE BROWN HIT PARADE (EP)	8
62	Piccadilly NEP 34026	ALL THINGS BRIGHT AND BEAUTIFUL (EP)	8
62	Ace Of Clubs ACL 1127	A PICTURE OF JOE BROWN (LP)	15
63	Piccadilly NPL 38006	JOE BROWN — LIVE! (LP)	16
65	Golden Guinea GGL 0146	A PICTURE OF YOU (LP)	12
67	Golden Guinea GGL 0231	HERE COMES JOE! (LP)	12
68	MCA MUPS 347	JOE BROWN (LP)	10
72	Bell BELLS 208	BROWN'S HOME BREW (LP)	10

JOE BROWN/MARK WYNTER

63	Piccadilly NEP 24167	JUST FOR FUN (EP, soundtrack, 2 tracks each)	7
64	Golden Guinea WO 1	BIG HITS OF JOE BROWN AND MARK WYNTER (EP)	7
66	Golden Guinea GGL 0179	JOE BROWN/MARK WYNTER (LP, 6 tracks each)	10

(see also Mark Wynter)

JOHNNY BROWN

61	Philips PB 1119	Walkin' Talkin' Kissin' Doll/Sundown	4

J.T. BROWN

75	Flyright LP 4712	ROCKIN' WITH J.T. (LP)	12

KAY BROWN

56	Brunswick 05595	Me 'N' You 'N' The Moon/What Do You Think It Does To Me?	4

KENT BROWN (& RAINBOWS)

61	Blue Beat BB 66	Hey Diddle Diddle/MOSSMAN & ZEDSIE: Pocket Money	10
68	Fab FAB 53	When You Going To Show Me How/Come Ya Come Ya (with Rainbows)	7

(see also Kent & Jeannie)

LENNOX BROWN

72	Green Door GD 4023	High School Serenade/WINSTON SCOTLAND: On The Track	4
72	Bullet BU 501	High School Serenade/WINSTON SCOTLAND: On The Track	4

LES BROWN & HIS BAND OF RENOWN

54	Vogue Coral Q 2034	Ramona/Hot Point	5
54	Vogue Coral Q 2042	St. Louis Blues Mambo/Moon Song	5
55	Vogue Coral Q 72049	The Man That Got Away/Doodle-Doo-Doo	5
55	Capitol CL 14331	Frenesi/Perfidia	6
55	Capitol CL 14350	He Needs Me/Simplicity	6
55	Vogue Coral Q 72107	Lullaby Of Birdland/Bernie's Tune	4
56	Vogue Coral Q 72123	Hong Kong Blues (with Hoagy Carmichael & Band of Renown)/It's All Right With Me	5
56	Vogue Coral Q 72215	Flamingo/Midnight Sun	4
56	Capitol CL 14512	Sincerely Yours/Take Back Your Mink	4
56	Capitol CL 14611	Hit The Roade To Dreamland/That Certain Feeling	4
56	Capitol CL 14631	Talk About A Party/Ancient History	5
57	Capitol CL 14675	Priscilla/The Best Years Of My Life	4
57	Capitol CL 14706	Original Joe/If I Had The Money	4
57	Vogue Coral Q 72242	Forty Cups Of Coffee/I'm Forever Blowing Bubbles	8
59	Coral Q 72367	Boola/Say It With Music	4
54	Vogue Coral LVC 10002	LES DANCE (10" LP)	10
55	Vogue Coral LVC 10017	INVITATION (10" LP)	10
55	Vogue Coral LVC 10033	LES BROWN (10" LP)	10

MAXINE BROWN

61	London HLU 9286	All In My Mind/Harry, Let's Marry	12
62	HMV POP 1102	Am I Falling In Love/Promise Me Anything	20
63	Stateside SS 188	Ask Me/Yesterday's Kisses	6
64	Pye Intl. 7N 25272	Oh No Not My Baby/You Upset My Soul	10
65	Pye Intl. 7N 25299	It's Gonna Be Alright/You Do Something To Me	8
65	Pye Intl. 7N 25317	One Step At A Time/Anything For A Laugh	8
67	Pye Intl. 7N 25410	I've Got A Lot Of Love Left In Me/Hold On (I'm Comin') (B-side withChuck Jackson)	8
67	Pye Intl. 7N 25434	Since I Found You/Gotta Find A Way	8
70	Major Minor MM 709	Reason To Believe/I Can't Get Along Without You	5
73	Avco 6105 022	Picked Up, Packed Up And Put Away/Bella And Me	4
75	Pye Disco Demand DDS 117	One In A Million/Let Me Give You My Lovin'	4

(see also Chuck Jackson & Maxine Brown)

NAPPY BROWN (& HIS BAND)

55	London HL 8145	Don't Be Angry/It's Really You	400
55	London HL 8145	Don't Be Angry/It's Really You (78)	40
55	London HLC 8182	Pitter Patter/There'll Come A Day	200
55	London HLC 8182	Pitter Patter/There'll Come A Day (78)	25
57	London HLC 8384	Little By Little/I'm Getting Lonesome (& His Band)	150
57	London HLC 8384	Little By Little/I'm Getting Lonesome (& His Band) (78)	15
58	London HLC 8760	It Don't Hurt No More/My Baby	50
58	London HLC 8760	It Don't Hurt No More/My Baby (78)	15

NOEL BROWN

68	Island WI 3149	Man's Temptation/Heartbreak Girl	10
69	Songbird SB 1012	By The Time I Get To Phoenix/Heartbreak Girl	5
70	Bullet BU 423	By The Time I Get To Phoenix/Heartbreak Girl (reissue)	5

OSCAR BROWN JNR

61	Philips PB 1097	But I Was Cool/Dat Dere	4
61	Philips BBL 7478	SIN AND SOUL (LP)	10

PETE BROWN

69	Parlophone R 5767	The Week Looked On Paper/Morning Call (& His Battered Ornaments; in promo p/s £40) 15
70	Harvest HAR 5008	Living Life Backwards/High Flying Electric Bird (as Pete Brown & Piblokto) 8
70	Harvest HAR 5023	Can't Get Off The Planet (& His Battered Ornaments) 8
70	Harvest HAR 5028	Flying Hero Sandwich (& His Battered Ornaments) 8
69	Harvest SHVL 752	A MEAL YOU CAN SHAKE HANDS WITH IN THE DARK(LP, & His Battered Ornaments) 50
70	Harvest SHVL 768	ART SCHOOL DANCE (LP, as Pete Brown & Piblokto) 55
70	Harvest SHVL 782	THOUSANDS ON A RAFT (LP, as Pete Brown & Piblokto) 55
73	Deram SML 1103	THE NOT FORGOTTEN ASSOCIATION (LP, with Graham Bond) 60
77	Harvest SHSM 2017	MY LAST BAND (LP, as Pete Brown & Piblokto) 15
70s	Discs Intl. INTLP 1	PARTY IN THE RAIN (LP, private pressing, with Ian Lynn) 50

(see also Battered Ornaments, Graham Bond & Pete Brown)

PITNEY BROWN

54	Esquire 10-330	That's Right Little Girl/EDDIE CHAMBLEE: Blues For Eddie (78) 15

RANDY BROWN

80	Casablanca CAL 2010	MIDNIGHT DESIRE (LP) 12

ROY BROWN

57	London HLP 8398	I'm Sticking With You/Party Doll 175
57	London HLP 8398	I'm Sticking With You/Party Doll (78) 30
57	London HLP 8448	Saturday Night/Everybody 400
57	London HLP 8448	Saturday Night/Everybody (78) 40

RUTH BROWN (& HER RHYTHMAKERS)

55	London HL 8153	Mambo Baby/Mama (He Treats Your Daughter Mean) (with Rhythmakers) 125
55	London HL 8153	Mambo Baby/Mama (He Treats Your Daughter Mean) (as Ruth Brown & Her Rhythmakers) (78) 20
55	London HLE 8210	As Long As I'm Moving/R.B. Blues (with Her Rhythmakers) 125
55	London HLE 8210	As Long As I'm Moving/R.B. Blues (78) (with Her Rhythmakers) 15
56	London HLE 8310	I Want To Do More/Sweet Baby Of Mine 90
56	London HLE 8310	I Want To Do More/Sweet Baby Of Mine (78) 10
57	London HLE 8401	Mom Oh Mom/I Want To Be Loved (But Only By You) 70
57	London HLE 8401	Mom Oh Mom/I Want To Be Loved (But Only By You) (78) 10
57	Columbia DB 3913	Lucky Lips/My Heart Is Breaking Over You 100
57	Columbia DB 3913	Lucky Lips/My Heart Is Breaking Over You (78) 30
57	London HLE 8483	One More Time/When I Get You Baby 40
57	London HLE 8483	One More Time/When I Get You Baby (78) 10
58	London HLE 8552	A New Love/Look Me Up 40
58	London HLE 8552	A New Love/Look Me Up (78) 10
58	London HLE 8645	Just Too Much/Book Of Lies 40
58	London HLE 8645	Just Too Much/Book Of Lies (78) 10
58	London HLE 8757	This Little Girl's Gone Rockin'/Why Me 40
58	London HL 7061	This Little Girl's Gone Rockin'/Why Me (export issue) 20
58	London HLE 8757	This Little Girl's Gone Rockin'/Why Me (78) 20
59	London HLE 8887	Jack O' Diamonds/I Can't Hear A Word You Say 35
59	London HLE 8887	Jack O' Diamonds/I Can't Hear A Word You Say (78) 20
59	London HLE 8946	I Don't Know/Papa Daddy 25
59	London HLE 8946	I Don't Know/Papa Daddy (78) 20
60	London HLE 9093	Don't Deceive Me/I Burned Your Letter 18
61	London HLK 9304	Sure 'Nuff/Here He Comes 20
64	Brunswick 05904	Yes Sir That's My Baby/What Happened To You 10
76	President PT 457	Sugar Babe/Stop Knocking 4
55	London REE 1038	THE QUEEN OF R&B (EP) 80
63	Philips BE 12537	GOSPEL TIME (EP) 12
60	London Jazz LTZ-K 15187	LAST DATE WITH RUTH BROWN (LP) 30
62	Philips 652 012 BL	ALONG COMES RUTH (LP) 25
63	Philips 652 020 BL	GOSPEL TIME (LP) 25
64	Atlantic ATL 5007	THE BEST OF RUTH BROWN (LP, plum label) 60
76	President PTLS 1067	SUGAR BABE (LP) 10

RUTH BROWN/JOE TURNER

56	London REE 1047	THE KING AND QUEEN OF R&B (EP, 2 tracks each) 120

SANDY BROWN('S JAZZ BAND)

58	Tempo A 124	African Queen/Special Delivery (as Sandy Brown's Jazz Band) 5
53	Esquire 20-022	SANDY BROWN (10" LP, with Bobby Mickleburgh) 20
56	Tempo TAP 3	SANDY'S SIDEMEN PLAYING COMPOSITIONS BY AL FAIRWEATHER (LP) 15
57	Nixa Jazz Today NJL 9	McJAZZ (LP) 15
50s	Columbia	THE INCREDIBLE MAC JAZZ VOL. 1 (LP) 25
50s	Columbia	THE INCREDIBLE MAC JAZZ VOL. 2 (LP) 25
50s	Columbia	THE INCREDIBLE MAC JAZZ VOL. 3 (LP) 25
69	Fontana SFJL 921	HAIR AT ITS HAIRIEST (LP) 12

(see also Wally Fawkes, Sandy & Teachers)

SHIRLEY BROWN

75	Stax STXS 2019	Woman To Woman/Yes Sir, Brother 5
75	Stax STXS 2032	I Can't Give You Up/It Ain't No Fun 4
77	Arista SPARTY 1017	SHIRLEY BROWN (LP) 10
75	Stax STX 1031	WOMAN TO WOMAN (LP) 10

STU BROWN & BLUESOLOGY

67	Polydor 56195	Since I Found You Baby/Just A Little Bit 150

(see also Bluesology, Elton John)

TINY BROWN

50	Capitol CL 13306	No More Blues/Slow-Motion Baby (78) 20

MINT VALUE £

VEDA BROWN
74 Stax STXS 2008   Short Stopping/I Can See Every Woman's Man But Mine 4

WATSON T. BROWN & EXPLOSIVE
68 President PT 207   Some Lovin'/Home Is Where Your Heart Lies 4
68 President PT 221   Crying All Night/I Close My Eyes 5
70 Bell BLL 1109   Will You Still Love Me Tomorrow/Save The Last Dance For Me 5

WILLIAM BROWN
71 Ackee ACK 128   I'm Alone/BELTONES: Soul People 5

BROWN BROTHERS
59 Vogue V 9131   Let The Good Times Roll/You're Right, I'm Left 75
59 Vogue V 9131   Let The Good Times Roll/You're Right, I'm Left (78) 30
(see also Charles Brown)

DUNCAN BROWNE
68 Immediate IM 070   On The Bombsite/Alfred Bell 8
78 Logo GO 329   Wild Places/Camino Real 4
68 Immediate IMSP 018   GIVE ME, TAKE YOU (LP) 30
73 RAK SRKA 6754   DUNCAN BROWNE (LP, gatefold sleeve) 15

GEORGE BROWNE
57 Columbia DB 3940   Sound Barrier/Te-Le-Le 4
(see also Humphrey Lyttleton)

JACKSON BROWNE
74 Asylum K2 43007   LATE FOR THE SKY (LP, quadrophonic) 12

SANDRA BROWNE (& BOYFRIENDS)
63 Columbia DB 4998   By Hook Or By Crook/Johnny Boy (as Sandra Browne & Boyfriends) 6
63 Columbia DB 7109   You'd Think He Didn't Know Me/Mama Never Told Me 6
65 Columbia DB 7465   Knock On Any Door/I Want Love 8
(see also Sandra Barry, Boys, Action)

TEDDY BROWNE
59 Capitol CL 15059   A Corner In Paradise/The Everglades 4
61 Starlite ST45 033   Pretty Little Baby/Genevieve 8

THOMAS F. BROWNE
72 Vertigo 6325 250   WEDNESDAY'S CHILD (LP, gatefold sleeve) 50

TOM BROWNE
80 Arista ARIST 12357   Funkin' For Jamaica (N.Y.)/Her Silent Smile (12") 8

DUKE BROWNER
79 Grapevine GRP 145   Crying Over You/Crying Over You (Instrumental) 4
(see also Kaddo Strings)

BROWNHILL'S STAMP DUTY
69 Columbia DB 8625   Maxwell's Silver Hammer/My Woman's Back 5

BROWNS
59 RCA RCA 1140   The Three Bells/Heaven Fell Last Night 4
59 RCA RCA 1140   The Three Bells/Heaven Fell Last Night (78) 7
59 RCA RCA 1157   Scarlet Ribbons (For Her Hair)/Blue Bells Ring 4
59 RCA RCA 1157   Scarlet Ribbons (For Her Hair)/Blue Bells Ring (78) 18
60 RCA RCA 1176   Teen-Ex/The Old Lamplighter 4
60 RCA RCA 1193   Margo (The Ninth Of May)/Lonely Little Robin 4
60 RCA RCA 1218   Send Me The Pillow You Dream On/You're So Much A Part Of Me 4
60 RCA RCX 587   IN THE COUNTRY (EP) 10
59 RCA RD 27153/SF 5052   SWEET SOUNDS BY THE BROWNS (LP, mono/stereo) 16/18
(see also Jim Edward & Maxine Brown)

BROWN SUGAR
70s Lovers Rock CJ 613   I'm In Love With A Dreadlocks/Version 4

ANNETTE (Reis) & VICTOR BROX
65 Fontana TF 536   I've Got The World In A Jug/Wake Me And Shake Me 4
74 Sonet SNTF 663   ROLLIN' BACK (LP) 15

DAVE BRUBECK (QUARTET)
53 Vogue 45-2156   A Foggy Day/Lyons Busy 8
53 Vogue 45-2157   Mam'selle/Me And My Shadow 8
53 Vogue 45-2158   Frenesi/At A Perfume Counter 8
53 Vogue 45-2159   Body And Soul/Let's Fall In Love 8
53 Vogue 45-2160   I'll Remember April/Singin' In The Rain 8
53 Vogue 45-2161   Lullaby In Rhythm/You Stepped Out Of A Dream 8
56 Vogue V 2171   Me And My Shadow/At A Perfume Counter 5
56 Vogue V 2206   Frenesi/Mam'selle 5
60 Philips JAZ 106   I'm In A Dancing Mood/Lover 4
61 Fontana H 339   Take Five/Blue Rondo A La Turk 4
54 Vogue LDE 090   DAVE BRUBECK TRIO (10" LP) 15
54 Vogue LDE 095   DAVE BRUBECK QUARTET (10" LP) 15
54 Vogue LDE 104   DAVE BRUBECK QUARTET VOL. 2 (10" LP) 15
55 Vogue LDE 114   DAVE BRUBECK QUARTET VOL. 3 (10" LP) 15
57 Fontana TFL 5017   DAVE DIGS DISNEY (LP) 10
59 Vogue LAE 12008   THE FABULOUS DAVE BRUBECK TRIO AND OCTET (LP) 12
59 Fontana TFL 5071   GONE WITH THE WIND (LP, also stereo STFL 501) 10
60 Vogue LAE 12114   DAVE BRUBECK QUARTET FEATURING PAUL DESMOND (LP) 12
60 Fontana TFL 5085   TIME OUT (LP, also stereo STFL 523) 10
60 Fontana TFL 5099   SOUTHERN SCENE (LP, also stereo STFL 530) 10
60 Fontana TFL 5101   THE RIDDLE (LP, also stereo STFL 532) 10
60 Fontana TFL 5114   BERNSTEIN PLAYS BRUBECK PLAYS BERNSTEIN (LP, also stereo STFL 542) .10

Dave BRUBECK

MINT VALUE £

60	Philips BBL 7447	JAZZ GOES TO COLLEGE (LP) 10
61	Fontana TFL 5126	BRUBECK AND RUSHING (LP, with Jimmy Rushing, also stereo STFL 550) 10
61	Fontana TFL 5136	THE BEST OF BRUBECK (LP) 10

(see also Paul Desmond, Jimmy Rushing, Carmen McRae)

JACK BRUCE

65	Polydor BM 56036	I'm Getting Tired (Of Drinking And Gambling)/Rootin' Tootin' 35
71	Polydor 2058 153	The Consul At Sunset/Letter Of Thanks 8
74	RSO 2090 141	Keep It Down/Golden Days 4
69	Polydor 583 058	SONGS FOR A TAILOR (LP, gatefold sleeve) 10
70	Polydor 2343 033	THINGS WE LIKE (LP) 10
71	Polydor 2310 107	HARMONY ROW (LP) 10

(see also Cream, Manfred Mann, Graham Bond Organisation, John Mayall & Blues Breakers, West Bruce & Laing)

JACK BRUCE & ROBIN TROWER

| 81 | Chrysalis CHS 2497 | What It Is/Into Money (p/s, clear vinyl) ....4 |

(see also Robin Trower)

LENNY BRUCE

| 69 | Transatlantic TRA 195 | BERKELEY CONCERT (2-LP) ....25 |

TOMMY BRUCE (& BRUISERS)

60	Columbia DB 4453	Ain't Misbehavin'/Got The Water Boilin' (with Bruisers) 5
60	Columbia DB 4498	Broken Doll/I'm On Fire (with Bruisers) 7
60	Columbia DB 4532	On The Sunny Side Of The Street/My Little Girl (with Bruisers) 5
61	Columbia DB 4581	You Make Love So Well/I'm Crazy 'Bout My Baby (with Bruisers) 5
61	Columbia DB 4682	Love, Honour And Oh! Baby/I'm Gonna Sit Right Down And Write 4
62	Columbia DB 4776	Babette/Honey Girl, You're Lonely 4
62	Columbia DB 4850	Horror Movies/It's You 4
62	Columbia DB 4927	Buttons And Bows/London Boys 4
63	Columbia DB 7025	Let's Do It, Let's Fall In Love/Two Feet Left 4
63	Columbia DB 7132	Lavender Blue/Sixteen Years Ago Tonight 4
64	Columbia DB 7241	Let It Be Me/No More 4
64	Columbia DB 7387	Over Suzanne/It's Drivin' Me Wild 5
65	Polydor BM 56006	Boom Boom/Can Your Monkey Do The Dog (with Bruisers) 10
66	RCA RCA 1535	Monster Gonzales/I Hate Getting Up In The Morning 5
68	CBS 3405	I've Been Around Too Long/Where The Colour Of The Soil Is Different 4
61	Columbia SEG 8077	KNOCKOUT (EP) 40

HEIDI BRÜHL

| 63 | Philips 345 579 BF | Marcel/Talk It Over With Someone ....12 |

BRUISERS

| 63 | Parlophone R 5042 | Blue Girl/Don't Cry ....5 |
| 63 | Parlophone R 5092 | Your Turn To Cry/Give It To Me ....5 |

(see also [Peter] Lee Stirling & Bruisers)

BRUMBEATS

| 64 | Decca F 11834 | Cry Little Girl, Cry/I Don't Understand ....15 |

(see also Norman Haines Band, Locomotive)

BEAU BRUMMEL ESQUIRE

65	Columbia DB 7447	I Know Know Know/Shoppin' Around 6
65	Columbia DB 7538	The Next Kiss/Come And Get Me 6
65	Columbia DB 7675	A Better Man Than I/Teardrops 6
66	Columbia DB 7878	You Don't Know What You've Got/Take Me Like I Am 5

BRUNNING (HALL) SUNFLOWER BLUES BAND

68	Saga FID 2118	BULLEN STREET BLUES (LP, as Brunning Sunflower Blues Band) 15
69	Saga EROS 8132	TRACKSIDE BLUES (LP) 35
69	Gemini GM 2010	THE BRUNNING/HALL SUNFLOWER BLUES BAND (LP) 60
70	Saga EROS 8150	I WISH YOU WOULD (LP, as Brunning Sunflower Blues Band) 40
71	Boulevard 4032	BULLEN STREET BLUES (LP, reissue) 10

(see also Five's Company, Fleetwood Mac, Leaf Hound)

BRUTE FORCE

| 69 | Apple APPLE 8 | King Of Fuh/Nobody Knows ....350 |

CARL BRYAN

69	Trojan TR 673	Red Ash/SILVERTONES: Bluebirds Flying Over 7
69	Duke DU 13	Soul Pipe/Overproof 6
69	Camel CA 22	Run For Your Life/TWO SPARKS: When We Were Young 4

(see also Cannon Ball, King Cannon)

DORA BRYAN

| 63 | Fontana TF 427 | All I Want For Christmas Is A Beatle/If I Were A Fairy ....4 |

FITZVAUGHN BRYAN'S ORCHESTRA

| 60 | Melodisc 45-1560 | Evening News/Hold Your Head Up And Smile (with Kentrick Patrick) ....8 |

RAD BRYAN

| 71 | Bullet BU 463 | Shock Attack/Cuban Waltz ....4 |

WES BRYAN

58	London HLU 8607	Lonesome Love/Tiny Spaceman 15
58	London HLU 8607	Lonesome Love/Tiny Spaceman (78) 15
59	London HLU 8978	Honey Baby/So Blue Over You 30
59	London HLU 8978	Honey Baby/So Blue Over You (78) 20

BRYAN & BRUNELLES

| 65 | HMV POP 1394 | Jacqueline/Louie Louie ....35 |

ANITA BRYANT

| 59 | London HLL 8983 | Six Boys And Seven Girls/The Blessings Of Love ....5 |

Anita BRYANT

60	London HLL 9075	Little George (Got The Hiccoughs)/Love Look Away	5
60	London HLL 9114	Paper Roses/Mixed Emotions	4
60	London HLL 9171	In My Little Corner Of The World/Just In Time	6
60	London HLL 9171	In My Little Corner Of The World/Anyone Would Love You (unissued)	
60	London HLL 9219	One Of the Lucky Ones/The Party's Over	5
60	London HLL 9247	Wonderland By Night/Pictures	5
61	London HLL 9281	Till There Was You/A Texan And A Girl From Mexico	5
61	London HLL 9353	Do-Re-Mi/An Angel Cried	5
61	Philips BF 1182	The Wedding/Seven Kinds Of Lonesome	4
66	CBS 202026	My Mind's Playing Tricks On Me Again/Another Year, Another Love	30
62	CBS AGG 20005	KISSES SWEETER THAN WINE (EP)	7
61	London HA-L 2381	IN MY LITTLE CORNER OF THE WORLD (LP)	25

BOOD & FILEECE (Boudleaux & Felice) BRYANT
| 51 | MGM MGM 452 | Overweight Blues/I Dreamed Of A Wedding (78) | 5 |

BOUDLEAUX BRYANT
| 60 | Polydor NH 66952 | Hot Spot/Touche (B-side with Sparks) | 4 |

(see also Bood & Felice Bryant)

DON BRYANT
| 70 | London HA-U/SH-U 8409 | PRECIOUS SOUL (LP) | 10 |

LAURA K. BRYANT
| 58 | London HLU 8551 | Bobby/Angel Tears | 10 |
| 58 | London HLU 8551 | Bobby/Angel Tears (78) | 10 |

MARIE BRYANT
52	Lyragon J 701	Tomato/Rhumboogie Anna (78)	5
61	Kalypso XX 27	Water Melon/Tomato	6
61	Kalypso XX 28	Don't Touch My Nylon/Little Boy	6
61	Kalypso XXEP 7	CALYPSOS TOO HOT TO HANDLE (EP)	12
60s	Melodisc MLP 132	DON'T TOUCH ME NYLONS (LP)	20

RAY BRYANT TRIO/COMBO
60	Pye Intl. 7N 25052	Little Susie Pts 2 & 4	4
60	Philips PB 1003	Little Susie Pts 1 & 3	4
60	Philips PB 1014	The Madison Time Pts 1 & 2	4

SANDRA BRYANT
| 67 | Major Minor MM 523 | Girl With Money/Golden Hours | 4 |
| 68 | Major Minor MM 553 | Out To Get You/There's No Lock Upon My Door | 8 |

CALUM BRYCE
| 68 | Condor PS 1001 | Love-Maker/I'm Glad | 40 |

BERYL BRYDEN'S BACK-ROOM SKIFFLE
| 56 | Decca F 10823 | Casey Jones/Kansas City Blues | 7 |

BETSY BRYE
| 59 | Columbia DB 4350 | Sleep Walk/Daddy Daddy (Gotta Get A Phone In My Room) | 6 |

B.T. EXPRESS
75	Pye International 7N 25674	Express Pts 1 & 2	4
75	Pye International 7N 25682	Once You Get It/This House Is Smokin'	4
75	Pye Intl. NSPL 28207	DO IT (TIL YOU'RE SATISFIED) (LP)	10
75	EMI International INA 1501	NON-STOP (LP)	10
76	EMI International INA 1502	ENERGY TO BURN (LP)	10
77	EMI International INS 3009	FUNCTION AT THE JUNCTION (LP)	10
78	EMI International INS 3016	SHOUT (SHOUT IT OUT) (LP)	10

BUBA & SHOP ASSISTANTS
| 85 | Villa 21 002 | Something To Do/Dreaming Backwards (p/s, with insert in poly bag) | 40 |

(see also Shop Assistants, Pastels)

BUBBLE GUM
| 68 | Philips BF 1677 | Little Red Bucket/With The Sun In Your Hair | 4 |

BUBBLEGUM SPLASH
| 87 | Subway Org. SUBWAY 13 | SPLASHDOWN (EP, foldaround p/s with insert in poly bag) | 4 |

BUBBLEMEN
| 88 | Beggars Banquet BULB 1 | The Bubblemen Are Coming/The B-Side (p/s, with comic) | 4 |
| 88 | Beggars Banquet BULB 1T | The Bubblemen Rap!/Dub Rap!/The Bubblemen Are Coming!/The B-Side (12", p/s) | 8 |

(see also Love & Rockets)

BUBBLES
| 63 | Duke DK 1001 | Bopping In The Barnyard/The Wasp | 8 |

BUCCA
| 82 | Plant Life | THE HOLE IN HARPERS HEAD (LP) | 12 |

BUCKINGHAM-NICKS
74	Polydor 2066 398	Don't Let Me Down Again/Races Are Run	8
76	Polydor 2066 700	Don't Let Me Down Again/Crystal	6
73	Polydor 2391 013	BUCKINGHAM-NICKS (LP, with insert, some with stickered sleeve)	40/35
81	Polydor 2482 378	BUCKINGHAM-NICKS (LP, reissue with insert)	25

(see also Stevie Nicks, Fleetwood Mac, Walter Egan)

BUCKINGHAMS (U.K.)
| 65 | Pye 7N 15848 | I'll Never Hurt You No More/She Lied | 6 |
| 65 | Pye 7N 15921 | To Be Or Not To Be/I Was Your First Guy | 5 |

BUCKINGHAMS (U.S.)
| 66 | Stateside SS 529 | I Call Your Name/Makin' Up And Breakin' Up | 5 |

Rare Record Price Guide

67	Stateside SS 588	Kind Of A Drag/You Make Me Feel So Good	5
67	Stateside SS 2011	Makin' Up And Breakin' Up/Lawdy Miss Clawdy	5
68	CBS 2640	Don't You Care/Why Don't You Love Me	12
67	CBS 2859	Mercy Mercy Mercy/You Are Gone	5
67	CBS 3195	Susan/Foreign Policy	5
68	CBS 3559	Back In Love Again/You Misunderstand Me	4

SEAN BUCKLEY & BREADCRUMBS
| 65 | Stateside SS 421 | It Hurts Me When I Cry/Everybody Knows | 50 |

TIM BUCKLEY
67	Elektra EKSN 45008	Aren't You The Girl/Strange Street Affair Under Blue	6
67	Elektra EKSN 45018	Morning Glory/Knight-Errant	5
68	Elektra EKSN 45023	Once I Was/Phantasmagoria In Two	5
68	Elektra EKSN 45031	Wings/I Can't See You	5
68	Elektra EKSN 45041	Pleasant Street/Carnival Song	5
70	Straight 4799	Happy Time/So Lonely	4
66	Elektra EKL/EKS 4004	TIM BUCKLEY (LP, orange label)	25
67	Elektra EKL/EKS 318	GOODBYE AND HELLO (LP, orange label, gatefold sleeve)	20
68	Elektra EKS 74045	HAPPY SAD (LP, orange label)	20
69	Straight STS 1060	BLUE AFTERNOON (LP)	20
70	Elektra 2410 005	LORCA (LP)	25
70	Straight STS 1064	STARSAILOR (LP)	20
72	Warner Bros K 46176	GREETINGS FROM L.A. (LP, gatefold sleeve)	12
74	Discreet K 49201	SEFRONIA (LP)	12
74	Discreet K 59204	LOOK AT THE FOOL (LP)	15

TEDDY BUCKNER & HIS BAND
56	Vogue V 2369	Oh, Didn't He Ramble/Battle Hymn Of The Republic	4
56	Vogue V 2375	When The Saints Go Marching In/West End Blues	4
57	Vogue V 2414	Sweet Georgia Brown/That's My Home	4

BUCKS FIZZ
82	RCA RCAP 241	Now Those Days Are Gone/Takin' Me Higher (picture disc)	4
82	RCA RCAP 300	If You Can't Stand The Heat/Stepping Out (picture disc)	4
82	RCA RCA 300	If You Can't Stand The Heat/Stepping Out (poster p/s)	4
83	RCA RCAP 342	When We Were Young/Where The Ending Starts (picture disc)	4
83	RCA RCAP 363	London Town/Identity (picture disc)	4
83	Lyntone LYN 12468	Christmas Medley (green vinyl flexidisc free with 'Flexipop' magazine issue 25)	4
83	RCA FIZP 1	Run For Your Life/Shot Me Through The Heart (picture disc)	4
84	RCA FIZEP 2	Talking In Your Sleep/Don't Think You're Fooling Me//20th Century Hero/Don't Pay The Ferryman (double pack)	4
84	RCA FIZP 3	Golden Days/Where Do I Go Now (picture disc)	4

BUCKY & STRINGS
| 62 | Salvo SLO 1807 | Lolita's On The Loose/Lonely Island | 7 |

BUD & HIS BUDDIES
| 58 | Starlite ST45 006 | June, July And August/Sing A Little Sweeter | 4 |

BUD & TRAVIS
59	London HLU 8965	Bonsoir Dame/Truly Do	4
60	London HLG 9211	The Ballad Of The Alamo/The Green Leaves Of Summer	4
61	London HA-G 2328	BUD AND TRAVIS IN CONCERT (LP, also stereo SAH-G 6128)	10

ROY BUDD
| 65 | Pye 7N 15807 | Birth Of the Budd/M'Ghee M'Ghee | 4 |
| 68 | Pye NPL 18212 | ROY BUDD AT NEWPORT (LP) | 10 |

BUDDY & JUNIORS
(see under Buddy Guy)

BUDGIE
71	MCA MK 5072	Crash Course In Brain Surgery/Nude Disintegrating Parachutist Woman	10
72	MCA MK 5085	Whisky River/Guts	6
74	MCA MCA 133	Zoom Club/Wondering What Everyone Knows	5
75	MCA MCA 175	I Ain't No Mountain/Honey	4
80	Active BUDGIE 1	If Swallowed Do Not Induce Vomiting (12", p/s)	10
80	Active BUDGIE 2	Crime Against The World/Hellbender (12", p/s)	10
81	RCA BUDGE 3	Keeping A Rendezvous/Apparatus (picture disc)	5
81	RCA BUDGE 4	I Turned To Stone/I Turned To Stone (Version) (p/s, orange vinyl)	5
82	RCA RCA 271	Bored With Russia/Don't Cry (p/s)	5
82	RCA RCAP 271	Bored With Russia/Don't Cry (picture disc)	5
71	MCA MKPS 2018	BUDGIE (LP)	18
72	MCA MKPS 2023	SQUAWK (LP)	15
73	MCA MDKS 8010	NEVER TURN YOUR BACK ON A FRIEND (LP, gatefold sleeve)	10
74	MCA MCF 2546	IN FOR THE KILL (LP)	10
75	MCA MCF 2723	BANDOLIER (LP)	10
75	MCA MCF 2766	THE BEST OF BUDGIE (LP)	10
76	A&M AMLH 68377	IF I WAS BRITANNIA I'D WAIVE THE RULES (LP)	10
78	A&M AMLH 64675	IMPECKABLE (LP)	10
80	Active ACTLP 1	POWER SUPPLY (LP)	10

DENNIS BUDIMAR
| 67 | Fontana TL 5307 | THE CREEPER (LP) | 10 |

BUENA VISTAS
| 66 | Stateside SS 525 | Hot Shot/T.N.T. | 15 |

BUFFALO
| 81 | Heavy Metal HEAVY 3 | Battle Torn Heroes (p/s) | 8 |
| 82 | Heavy Metal HEAVY 15 | Mean Machine/The Rumour (p/s) | 10 |

MINT VALUE £

BUFFALO SPRINGFIELD

67	Atlantic 584 077	For What It's Worth (Stop Hey What's That Sound)/Do I Have To Come Right Out And Say It 5
67	Atlantic 584 145	Rock'n'Roll Woman/A Child's Claim To Fame 5
68	Atlantic 584 165	Expecting To Fly/Everydays 6
68	Atlantic 584 189	Uno-Mundo/Merry-Go-Round 5
69	Atco 226 006	Pretty Girl Why/Questions 4
72	Atlantic K 10237	Bluebird/Mr Soul/Rock'n'Roll Woman/Expecting To Fly (p/s) 5
67	Atlantic 587/588 070	BUFFALO SPRINGFIELD (LP, "Baby Don't Scold Me", mono/stereo) 35/30
67	Atlantic 587/588 070	BUFFALO SPRINGFIELD (LP, plays "For What It's Worth", mono/stereo) 20/18
68	Atlantic 587/588 091	BUFFALO SPRINGFIELD AGAIN (LP) 16
69	Atco 228 024	LAST TIME AROUND (LP) 15

(see also Neil Young, Stephen Stills, Poco, Au-Go-Go Singers, Crosby Stills Nash & Young)

BUFFOONS

67	Columbia DB 8317	My World Fell Down/Tomorrow Is Another Day 6

BULAWAYO SWEET RHYTHMS BAND

54	Decca F 10350	Skokiaan/In The Mood 5

JOHN BULL BREED

66	Polydor BM 56065	Can't Chance A Breakup/I'm A Man 90

BULLDOG BREED

69	Deram DM 270	Portcullis Gate/Halo In My Hair 25
70	Deram Nova (S)DN 5	MADE IN ENGLAND (LP) 35

BULLDOGS

64	Mercury MF 808	John, Paul, George And Ringo/What Do I See 10

BULLET

71	Purple PUR 101	Hobo/Sinister Minister 8

BULLY WEE (BAND)

75	Folksound	BULLYWEE (LP) 18
76	Red Rag RRR 007	THE ENCHANTED LADY (LP) 15
70s	Red Rag RRR 017	SILVERMINES (LP, as Bullywee Band) 10
81	Red Rag	MADMEN OF GOTHAM (LP) 20

B. BUMBLE & STINGERS

61	Top Rank JAR 561	Bumble Boogie/School Day Blues 6
62	Top Rank JAR 611	Nut Rocker/Nautilus 4
62	Stateside SS 113	Apple Knocker/The Moon And The Sea 5
62	Stateside SS 131	Dawn Cracker/Scales 5
63	Stateside SS 192	Baby Mash/Night Time Madness 5
67	Mercury MF 977	Silent Movies/Twelfth Street Rag 5
72	Pye International 7N 25597	Down At Mother's Place/Manhattan Spiritual 4
62	Stateside SE 1001	THE PIANO STYLINGS OF B. BUMBLE (EP) 15

BUNCH

67	CBS 202506	We're Not What We Appear To Be/You Never Came Home 35
67	CBS 2740	Don't Come Back To Me/You Can't Do This 10
67	CBS 3060	Looking Glass Alice/Spare A Shilling 50
68	CBS 3692	Birthday/Still 12
68	CBS 3709	Birthday/Still (reissue) 10

BUNCH

72	Island WIP 6130	When Will I Be Loved/Willie And The Hand Jive 4
72	Island ILPS 9189	ROCK ON (LP, some with 1-sided flexidisc "Let There Be Drums" [WI 4002]) .25/12

(see also Sandy Denny, Richard & Linda Thompson)

BUNCH OF FIVES

66	Parlophone R 5494	Go Home Baby/At The Station 18

ROGER BUNN

71	Major Minor SMLP 70	PIECE OF MIND (LP) 12

BUNNIES

66	Decca F 12350	Thumper/Ja Da 5

BUNNY & RUDDY

68	Nu Beat NB 011	On The Town/MONTY MORRIS: Simple Simon 5

BOB BUNTING

68	Transatlantic TRA 166	YOU'VE GOT TO GO DOWN THIS WAY (LP) 30

VASHTI BUNYAN

70	Philips 6308 019	JUST ANOTHER DIAMOND DAY (LP) 250

(see also Vashti, Fairport Convention)

ERIC BURDON & ANIMALS

66	Decca F 12502	Mama Told Me Not To Come/See See Rider (unreleased, demos may exist) ....40+
66	Decca F 12502	Help Me Girl/See See Rider 5
67	MGM MGM 1340	When I Was Young/A Girl Named Sandoz 5
67	MGM MGM 1344	Good Times/Ain't That So 5
67	MGM MGM 1359	San Franciscan Nights/Gratefully Dead 6
68	MGM MGM 1373	Sky Pilot Pts 1 & 2 6
68	MGM MGM 1412	Monterey/Anything 6
69	MGM MGM 1461	Ring Of Fire/I'm An Animal 7
69	MGM MGM 1481	River Deep Mountain High/Help Me Girl 7
67	MGM C(S) 8052	WINDS OF CHANGE (LP) 12
68	MGM CS 8074	THE TWAIN SHALL MEET (LP) 12
68	MGM CS 8105	LOVE IS (LP) 12
71	MGM 2354 006/7	LOVE IS (2-LP) 18

73	MGM 2619 002	LOVE IS (2-LP, reissue)	14

(see also Animals, Stud)

ERIC BURDON & WAR

70	Polydor 2001 072	Spill The Wine/Magic Mountain	4
71	Liberty LBF 15434	They Can't Take Away Our Music/Home Cookin'	4
71	United Artists UP 35217	Paint It Black/Spirit	4
70	Polydor 2310 041	ERIC BURDON DECLARES WAR (LP)	10
70	Liberty LDS 8400	BLACKMAN'S BURDON (2-LP, some with banned track "P.C. 3")	18/14

(see also War)

ERIC BURDON & JIMMY WITHERSPOON

71	United Artists UAG 29251	GUILTY (LP, gatefold sleeve)	10

(see also Jimmy Witherspoon)

DAVE BURGESS (TRIO)

55	London HLB 8175	I Love Paris/Five Foot Two, Eyes Of Blue (Has Anybody Seen My Girl)	20
58	Oriole CB 1413	I'm Available/Who's Gonna Cry?	70

SONNY BURGESS

60	London HLS 9064	Sadie's Back In Town/A Kiss Goodnight	125

KENI BURKE

82	RCA RCAT 252	Risin' To The Top (Give It All You Got)/Hang Tight (12")	7
80s	RCA	CHANGES (LP)	10
81	RCA RCALP 5059	YOU'RE THE BEST (LP)	10

SOLOMON BURKE

61	London HLK 9454	Just Out Of Reach/Be Bop Grandma	18
62	London HLK 9512	Cry To Me/I Almost Lost My Mind	12
62	London HLK 9560	Down In The Valley/I'm Hanging Up My Heart For You	10
63	London HLK 9715	If You Need Me/You Can Make It If You Try	10
63	London HLK 9763	Can't Nobody Love You/Stupidity	10
64	London HLK 9849	He'll Have To Go/Rockin' Soul	10
64	London HLK 9887	Goodbye Baby (Baby Goodbye)/Someone To Love Me	10
64	Atlantic AT 4004	Everybody Needs Somebody To Love/Looking For My Baby	8
64	Atlantic AT 4014	The Price/More Rockin' Soul	8
65	Atlantic AT 4022	Got To Get You Off My Mind/Peepin'	7
65	Atlantic AT 4030	Maggie's Farm/Tonight's The Night	9
65	Atlantic AT 4044	Someone Is Watching/Dance, Dance, Dance	7
65	Atlantic AT 4061	Only Love (Can Save Me Now)/Little Girl That Loves Me	8
66	Atlantic AT 4073	Baby Come On Home/No, No, No, I Can't Stop Lovin' You Now	6
66	Atlantic 584 005	I Feel A Sin Comin' On/Mountain Of Pride	5
66	Atlantic 584 026	Keep Lookin'/Suddenly	5
67	Atlantic 584 100	Keep A Light In The Window Till I Come Home/Time Is A Thief	5
67	Atlantic 584 122	Take Me (Just As I Am)/I Stayed Away Too Long	5
68	Atlantic 584 191	I Wish I Knew (How It Would Feel To Be Free)/It's Just A Matter Of Time	5
68	Atlantic 584 204	Save It/Meet Me In Church	5
68	Bell BLL 1047	Uptight Good Woman/I Can't Stop (No No No)	5
69	Bell BLL 1062	Proud Mary/What Am I Living For	5
74	Anchor ABC 4002	Midnight And You/I Have A Dream	4
63	London REK 1379	TONIGHT MY HEART SHE IS CRYING (EP)	20
65	Atlantic AET 6008	ROCK'N'SOUL (EP)	15
63	London HA-K 8018	SOLOMON BURKE'S GREATEST (LP)	20
64	Atlantic ATL 5009	ROCK'N'SOUL (LP)	25
66	Atlantic 587/588 016	THE BEST OF SOLOMON BURKE (LP)	15
66	Atlantic 590 004	KING OF ROCK'N'SOUL (LP)	15
68	Atlantic 587 105	KING SOLOMON (LP)	15
68	Atlantic 587/588 117	I WISH I KNEW (LP)	15
69	Bell MBLL/SBLL 118	PROUD MARY (LP)	12
72	Polydor 2315 048	THE ELECTRONIC MAGNETISM (LP)	10

SONNY BURKE & HIS ORCHESTRA (U.S.)

55	Brunswick 05361	"Phffft" Mambo/Long Hair Mambo	4

SONNY BURKE (Jamaica)

65	Black Swan WI 469	Glad/Jeanie	8
65	Black Swan WI 470	Dance With Me/My Girl Can't Cook	8
65	Black Swan WI 471	Wicked People/Good Heaven Knows	8
66	Blue Beat BB 363	Blue Island/You Came And Left	7
67	Blue Beat BB 371	Look In Her Eyes/LLOYD CLARKE: Love Is Strange	7
68	Island ILP 972	THE SOUNDS OF SONNY BURKE (LP)	60

(see also Bob Andy)

SACHA BURLAND

61	Philips PB 1152	Gorilla Walk/Hole In My Soul	5

BURMOE BROTHERS

85	Wild Blue Yonder WBY 121	Skin/Leber Oder Lippenstift/Under The Blanket Of Love (12")	10

(see also Marc Almond, Nick Cave)

JEAN-JACQUES BURNEL

79	United Artists UP 36500	Freddie Laker (Concorde And Eurobus)/Ozymandias (p/s)	5
80	United Artists BP 351	Girl From The Snow Country/Ode To Joy (live)/Do The European (live) (p/s, unreleased)	250
88	Strangers Information Service S.I.S. 003	Goebbels, Mosley, God And Ingrams (fan club flexidisc, with issue 27 of 'Stranded' magazine)	5
79	United Artists UAG 30214	EUROMAN COMETH (LP)	10
88	Mau Mau P MAU 601	EUROMAN COMETH (LP, picture disc reissue)	12

(see also Stranglers)

Jean-Jacques BURNEL & Dave GREENFIELD

JEAN-JACQUES BURNEL & DAVE GREENFIELD
84   Epic EPCA 4076   Rain And Dole And Tea/Consequences (p/s) 4
(see also Stranglers)

FRANCES BURNETT
59   Coral Q 72374   Please Remember Me/How I Miss You So 4

REV. J.C. BURNETT/REV. GATES/REV. MOSELEY
60   Fontana TFE 17265   TREASURES OF NORTH AMERICAN NEGRO MUSIC VOLUME 6:
                             PREACHERS AND CONGREGATIONS (EP) 12

DORSEY BURNETTE
60   London HLN 9047   Juarez Town/(There Was A) Tall Oak Tree 12
60   London HLN 9160   Hey Little One/Big Rock Candy Mountain 12
61   London HLN 9365   (It's No) Sin/Hard Rock Mine 10
65   Tamla Motown TMG 534   Jimmy Brown/Everybody's Angel 40
69   Liberty LBF 15190   The Greatest Love/Thin Little Simple Little Plain Little Girl ..8
63   London RE-D 1402   DORSEY BURNETTE SINGS (EP) 30
63   London HA-D 8050   DORSEY BURNETTE (LP) 50

JOHNNY BURNETTE (TRIO)
56   Vogue Coral Q 72177   Tear It Up/You're Undecided (as Johnny Burnette & Rock'N'Roll Trio) ...250
56   Vogue Coral Q 72177   Tear It Up/You're Undecided (as Johnny Burnette & Rock'N'Roll Trio) (78) 75
57   Vogue Coral Q 72227   Honey Hush/Lonesome Train (as Johnny Burnette Trio) 175
57   Vogue Coral Q 72227   Honey Hush/Lonesome Train (as Johnny Burnette Trio) (78) 75
57   Vogue Coral Q 72283   Touch Me/Eager Beaver Baby (as Johnny Burnette Trio) 150
57   Vogue Coral Q 72283   Touch Me/Eager Beaver Baby (as Johnny Burnette Trio) (78) 50
60   London HLG 9172   Dreamin'/Cincinnati Fireball 5
60   London HLG 9172   Dreamin'/Cincinnati Fireball (78) 175
60   London HLG 9254   You're Sixteen/I Beg Your Pardon 5
60   London HLG 7104   You're Sixteen/Settin' The Woods On Fire (export issue) 20
61   London HLG 9315   Little Boy Sad/Pledge Of Love 5
61   London HL 7109   Little Boy Sad/I Go Down To The River (export issue) 25
61   London HLG 9388   Girls/I've Got A Lot Of Things To Do 6
61   London HLG 9453   God Country And My Baby/Honestly I Do 6
61   London HLG 9458   Settin' The Woods On Fire/I'm Still Dreaming 7
61   London HLG 9473   Big Big World/The Fool 8
62   Liberty LIB 55416   Clown Shoes/The Way I Am 5
62   Liberty LIB 55489   Damn The Defiant/Lonesome Waters 6
66   Liberty LIB 10235   Dreamin'/Little Boy Sad 6
62   Pye International 7N 25158 I Wanna Thank Your Folks/The Giant 6
63   Pye International 7N 25187 Remember Me/Time Is Not Enough 6
63   Capitol CL 15322   All Week Long/It Isn't There 10
64   Capitol CL 15347   Sweet Suzie/Walking Talking Doll 12
60   London RE-G 1263   DREAMING (EP) 40
61   London RE-G 1291   LITTLE BOY SAD (EP) 40
61   London RE-G 1309   BIG BIG WORLD (EP) 40
61   London RE-G 1327   GIRLS (EP) 40
63   Liberty LEP 2091   HIT AFTER HIT (EP) 20
64   Capitol EAP 20645   FOUR BY BURNETTE (EP) 40
56   Coral LVC 10041   ROCK AND ROLL TRIO (10" LP, as Johnny Burnette Trio) 400
61   London HA-G 2306   DREAMIN' (LP) 60
61   London HA-G 2349   YOU'RE SIXTEEN (LP) 60
61   London HA-G 2375   JOHNNY BURNETTE SINGS (LP, also stereo SAH-G 6175) 60/75
62   Liberty LBY 1006   BURNETTE'S HITS AND OTHER FAVOURITES (LP) 30
64   Liberty LBY 1231   THE JOHNNY BURNETTE STORY (LP) 45
66   Ace Of Hearts AH 120   ROCK AND ROLL TRIO (LP, reissue, as Johnny Burnette Trio, 2 diff. issues) ...20
68   Sunset SLS 50007E   DREAMIN' (LP) 12
68   Coral CP 10   TEAR IT UP (LP, as Johnny Burnette Trio) 15
71   Coral CP 61   ROCK AND ROLL TRIO (LP, 2nd reissue, as Johnny Burnette Trio) 12
74   United Artists UAS 29643 TENTH ANNIVERSARY ALBUM (LP) 10

JOHNNY & DORSEY BURNETTE
63   Reprise R 20153   Hey Sue/It Don't Matter Much 20
(see also Johnny Burnette, Dorsey Burnette)

SMILEY BURNETTE
50   Capitol CL 13388   Rudolph The Red-Nosed Reindeer/Grandaddy Frog (78) 8
54   London HL 8071   Lazy Locomotive/That Long White Line 50
54   London HL 8071   Lazy Locomotive/That Long White Line (78) 5
54   London HL 8085   Chuggin' On Down "66"/Mucho Gusto 50
54   London HL 8085   Chuggin' On Down "66"/Mucho Gusto (78) 5

BURNIN' RED IVANHOE
71   Warner Bros K 44062   BURNIN' RED IVANHOE (LP) 12
71   Dandelion 2310 145   W.W.W. (LP, gatefold sleeve) 18

JAN BURNNETTE
62   Oriole CB 1716   I Could Have Loved You So Well/The Miracle Of Life 5
62   Oriole CB 1742   All At Once/Does My Heartache Show? 5
62   Oriole CB 1761   Teddy/Trust In Me 5
63   Oriole CB 1807   The Boy I Used To Know/Unimportant Things 5
63   Oriole CB 1841   Till I Hear The Truth From You/Fall In Love 5
64   Oriole CB 1905   Let Me Make You Smile Again/No Regrets 5
64   Oriole CB 1920   Too Young/The Four Winds And The Seven Seas 5
64   Oriole CB 1949   Love, Let Me Not Hunger/The One I Love (Belongs To Somebody Else) 5

EDDIE 'GUITAR' BURNS
72   Action ACMP 100   BOTTLE UP AND GO (LP) 12
75   Big Bear BEAR 7   DETROIT BLACKBOTTOM (LP) 10

Rare Record Price Guide

JACKIE BURNS & BELLES
63 MGM MGM 1226   He's My Guy/I Do The Best I Can 60

JIMMY BURNS
79 Grapevine GRP 118   I Really Love You/I Love You Girl 4

RANDY BURNS
68 Fontana STL 5520   EVENING OF THE MAGICIAN (LP) 10

RAY BURNS
53 Columbia SCM 5077   Rags To Riches/Begorrah 5
54 Columbia SCM 5115   Helpless/The Homecoming Waltz 5
54 Columbia SCM 5153   I Can't Tell A Waltz From A Tango/Lonely Nightingale 5
55 Columbia SCM 5179   Why?/A Smile Is Worth A Million Tears 5
56 Columbia SCM 5224   Stealin'/'Cause I'm Sorry 5
56 Columbia SCM 5263   Wild Cherry/Give Me Another Chance 5
56 Columbia DB 3811   Condemned For Life (With A Rock And Roll Life)/The Mare Piccola 8
57 Columbia DB 3886   Whispering Heart/Nashville 4
57 Columbia DB 3966   Wonderful! Wonderful!/Bernadine 4
57 Columbia DB 3998   The Little Hut/Dapper Dan 4
58 Columbia DB 4107   Are You Sincere/The Best Dream Of All 4
58 Columbia DB 4157   The Better To Love You/Meanwhile, Back In My Arms 4
55 Columbia SEG 7594   RAY BURNS (EP) 10
(see also Ruby Murray, Ronnie Harris)

WILFRED BURNS
53 MGM SP 1059   There Was An Old Lady/Broken Horseshoe 4

KENNY BURRELL
61 Esquire 32-140   ALL NIGHT LONG (LP, as Kenny Burrell All Stars) 15
61 Blue Note (B)BLP 4021   BURRELL AT THE FIVE SPOT (LP; stereo version released in 1964) 15
64 Blue Note (B)BLP 4123   MIDNIGHT BLUE (LP) 15
64 Verve VLP 9058   BLUE BLASH (LP, with Jimmy Smith) 12
65 Verve VLP 9099   GUITAR FORMS (LP) 12
66 Stateside SL 10163   CRASH! (LP, with Brother Jack McDuff) 15
68 Verve (S)VLP 9217   BLUES, THE COMMON GROUND (LP) 12
70 Verve SVLP 9250   ASPHALT CANYON SUITE (LP) 10
73 CTI CTL 9   GOD BLESS THE CHILD (LP) 10
74 Polydor 2304 094   GUITAR (LP) 10
74 Checker 6467 310   COOL COOKIN' 1 (LP) 10
70s Blue Note BST 81523   INTRODUCING KENNY BURRELL (LP) 10
70s Blue Note BST 81543   KENNY BURRELL (LP) 10
70s Blue Note BST 81596   BLUE LIGHTS VOL. 1 (LP) 10
70s Blue Note BST 81597   BLUE LIGHTS VOL. 2 (LP) 10
70s Blue Note BST 84123   MIDNIGHT BLUE (LP, reissue) 10
(see also Brother Jack McDuff, Jimmy Smith)

BUDDY BURTON
(see under Dixie Four)

HAL BURTON
58 Embassy WB 308   Move It/Susie Darling 4

HAROLD BURRAGE
65 Sue WI 353   I'll Take One/A Longways Together 12
68 President PT 130   You Made Me So Happy/Take Me Now 5

GARY BURTON QUARTET
68 RCA Victor SF 7923   LOFTY FAKE ANAGRAM (LP) 10

JAMES BURTON
71 A&M AMLS 64293   THE GUITAR SOUNDS OF JAMES BURTON (LP) 40
(see also Jim & Joe, Shindogs)

TOMMY BURTON COMBO
64 Blue Beat BB 237   I'm Walking/Lavender Blue 7

TREVOR BURTON
71 Wizard WIZ 103   Fight For My Country/Janie Slow Down 5
(see also Uglys, Move, Balls, Denny Laine, Danny King's Mayfair Set)

LOU BUSCH & HIS ORCHESTRA
56 Capitol CL 14504   Zambesi/Rainbow's End 10
56 Capitol CL 14547   11th Hour Melody/The Charming Mademoiselle From Paris France 5
56 Capitol CL 14592   Tango Afrique/Jato 5
56 Capitol CL 14667   Friendly Persuasion/Portofino 5
57 Capitol CL 14730   The Wild Ones/Midnight Melody 6
57 Capitol CL 14751   Hot Cappuccino/Cayo Coco (Coconut Rock) 4
58 Capitol CL 14957   Cool/Street Scene '58 4
(see also Joe 'Fingers' Carr)

KATE BUSH
78 EMI EMI 2719   Wuthering Heights/Kite (some with p/s) 25/4
78 EMI EMI 2806   The Man With The Child In His Eyes/Moving (p/s) 12
78 EMI EMI 2887   Hammer Horror/Coffee Homeground (p/s) 7
'79 EMI EMI 2911   Wow/Fullhouse (p/s) 7
79 EMI PSR 442/3   KATE BUSH ON STAGE (EP, double pack, gatefold sleeve, promo only) 50
80 EMI EMI 5058   Breathing/The Empty Bullring (p/s) 5
80 EMI EMI 5085   Babooshka/Ran Tan Waltz (p/s) 4
80 EMI EMI 5106   Army Dreamers/Delius/Passing Through The Air (p/s) 5
80 EMI EMI 5121   December Will Be Magic Again/Warm And Soothing (p/s) 6
81 EMI EMI 5201   Sat In Your Lap/Lord Of The Reedy River (p/s) 5
82 EMI EMI 5296   The Dreaming/Dreamtime (Instrumental Version) (some in thick cord p/s) 7/4

Kate BUSH

82	EMI EMI 5350	There Goes A Tenner/Ne T'Enfuis Pas (some in thick cord, p/s) 7/4
84	EMI KBS 1	THE SINGLE FILE (13 x 7" box set with lyric booklet, some numbered) 100/80
85	EMI KB 1	Running Up That Hill (A Deal With God)/Under The Ivy (gatefold p/s) 6
85	EMI 12 KB 1	Running Up That Hill (A Deal With God) (Extended)/Under The Ivy/Running Up That Hill (Instrumental) (12", p/s) 7
85	EMI 12 KB 2	Cloudbusting (Orangon Mix)/Burning Bridges/My Lagan Love (12", p/s) 7
86	EMI KB 4P	The Big Sky (Single Mix)/Not This Time (picture disc) 12
89	EMI EMPD 119	This Woman's Work/Be Kind To My Mistakes (picture disc, with insert, PVC sl.) ..5
89	EMI EMPD 119	This Woman's Work/Be Kind To My Mistakes (poster p/s) 4
79	EMI EM LP 3223	THE KICK INSIDE (LP, picture disc) 45
79	EMI EM CP 3223	THE KICK INSIDE (LP, picture disc, second pressing with "manufactured in the U.K. by EMI Records Ltd" wording) 40
79	EMI EM CP 3223	THE KICK INSIDE (LP, picture disc, mispress with same picture both sides) ...120
90	EMI KBBX 1	THIS WOMAN'S WORK (LP, box set) 80
90	EMI CDKBBX 1	THIS WOMAN'S WORK (CD, box set) 100

(see also Peter Gabriel & Kate Bush)

RAY BUSH & AVON CITIES' SKIFFLE
56	Tempo A 146	Hey Hey Daddy Blues/Green Corn 5
56	Tempo A 149	Fisherman's Blues/This Little Light Of Mine 5
57	Tempo A 156	How Long, How Long, Blues/Julian Johnson 5
57	Tempo A 157	Lonesome Day Blues/I Don't Know 5
57	Tempo EXA 40	RAY BUSH & AVON CITIES' SKIFFLE (EP) 8
57	Tempo EXA 50	RAY BUSH & AVON CITIES' SKIFFLE NO. 2 (EP) 8

BUSH BOYS
| 59 | Capitol CL 15082 | A Broken Vow/Never Before ....4 |

BUSHIDO
| 84 | Third Mind TMS 02 | Among The Ruins/The First Cut/Beyond The Great Wall (12") ....8 |
| 85 | Third Mind TMS 05 | VOICES (12" EP) ....7 |

BUSH TETRAS
| 81 | Fetish FET 007 | Things That Go Boom In The Night/Das Ah Riot (p/s) ....5 |
| 82 | Fetish FET 16 | RITUALS (12" EP) ....7 |

BUSINESS
81	Secret SHH 123	Harry May/Employer's Blacklist (p/s) 5
82	Secret SHH 132	Smash The Disco/Disco Girls/Dayo (The Banana Boat Song) (p/s) 5
85	Wonderful World Of W121	Get Out Of My House/All Out Tonight/Foreign Girl/Outlaw (p/s) 6
85	Diamond DIA 11	Drinking And Driving/H-Bomb (p/s) 4

BUSKERS
| 73 | Rubber RUB 007 | LIFE OF A MAN (LP) ....15 |
| 75 | Hawk HALPX 142 | THE BUSKERS (LP) ....15 |

GEORGE HENRY BUSSEY/JIM BUNKLEY
| 78 | Revival RVS 1003 | GEORGE HENRY BUSSEY/JIM BUNKLEY (LP) ....15 |

EDDIE 'BUSTER' FOREHAND
| 68 | Action ACT 4519 | Forehand Young Boy Blues/You Were Meant For Me ....6 |

BUSTERS
| 63 | Stateside SS 231 | Bust Out/Astronauts ....6 |

BUSTER'S ALLSTARS
66	Blue Beat BB 342	Cincinnati Kid/Sammy Dead Medley 10
67	Blue Beat BB 372	Sounds And Pressure/My Darling (both actually by Hopeton Lewis) 10
67	Blue Beat BB 384	Take It Easy/Why Must I Cry (both actually by Hopeton Lewis) 10
67	Blue Beat BB 384	Take It Easy/Why Must I Cry (2nd issue, B-side actually by Hopeton Lewis) 10
69	Fab FAB 101	Pum Pum A Go Kill You/Oh Lady Oh 7

(see also Prince Buster)

BUSTER'S GROUP
| 61 | Starlite ST45 052 | Buster's Shack/ERIC MORRIS: Search The World ....10 |

(see also Prince Buster)

TONY BUTALA
| 62 | Salvo SLO 1801 | Long Black Stockings/Rumors ....12 |

SAM BUTERA (& WITNESSES)
58	HMV POP 476	Good Gracious Baby/It's Better Than Nothing At All 30
58	HMV POP 476	Good Gracious Baby/It's Better Than Nothing At All (78) 15
58	Capitol CL 14913	Bim Bam/Twinkle In Your Eye (as Sam Butera & Witnesses) 70
59	Capitol CL 14988	Handle With Care/French Poodle 15
64	Prima PR 1003	Skinnie Minnie/Little Liza Jane 5
56	HMV 7EG 8087	SAX SERENADE (EP) 25
60	London HA-D 2288	THE RAT RACE (LP, as Sam Butera & Witnesses) 15

(see also Louis Prima)

BILLY BUTLER
68	Soul City SC 113	The Right Track/Boston Monkey 12
74	Epic EPC 2508	The Right Track/Couldn't Live Without Her 4
60s	Soul City	THE RIGHT TRACK (LP) 25

CHAMP BUTLER
| 56 | Vogue Coral Q 72119 | Someone On Your Mind/I Want To Love You ....5 |
| 56 | Vogue Coral Q 72163 | The Joshua Tree/Down In Mexico ....5 |

JERRY BUTLER
58	London HL 8697	For Your Precious Love/Sweet Was The Wine (with Impressions) 100
58	London HL 8697	For Your Precious Love/Sweet Was The Wine (with Impressions) (78) 25
60	Top Rank JAR 389	I Found A Love/A Lonely Soldier 20
60	Top Rank JAR 531	He Will Break Your Heart/Thanks To You 30

MINT VALUE £

61	Top Rank JAR 562	Find Another Girl/When Trouble Calls	18
61	Columbia DB 4743	Moon River/Aware Of Love	12
62	Stateside SS 121	Make It Easy On Yourself/It's Too Late	12
63	Stateside SS 158	You Can Run But You Can't Hide/I'm The One	10
63	Stateside SS 170	You Go Right Through Me/The Wishing Star	10
63	Stateside SS 195	Whatever You Want/You Won't Be Sorry	10
64	Stateside SS 252	Need To Belong/Give Me Your Love	10
64	Stateside SS 300	Giving Up On Love/I've Been Trying	10
65	Fontana TF 553	Good Times/I've Grown Accustomed To Her Face	10
65	Fontana TF 588	I Can't Stand To See You Cry/Nobody Needs Your Love	7
65	Mercury MF 932	Love (Oh, How Sweet It Is)/Loneliness	5
66	Sue WI 4003	I Stand Accused/I Don't Want To Hear Anymore	20
66	Sue WI 4009	Just For You/Believe In Me	12
67	Mercury MF 964	I Dig You Baby/Some Kinda Magic	8
67	Mercury MF 1005	Mr. Dream Merchant/'Cause I Love You So	5
68	Mercury MF 1035	Never Give You Up/Beside You	4
68	Mercury MF 1058	Hey Mr Western Union Man/Just Can't Forget About You	8
69	Mercury MF 1078	Are You Happy/Strange I Still Love You	4
69	Mercury MF 1094	Only The Strong Survive/Just Because I Really Love You	5
69	Mercury MF 1122	Moody Woman/Go Away And Find Yourself	6
69	Mercury MF 1132	A Brand New Me/What's The Use Of Breaking Up	7
72	Mercury 6052 036	One Night Affair/What's So Good About It (You're My Baby)	4
63	Stateside SL 10032	HE WILL BREAK YOUR HEART (LP)	25
63	Stateside SL 10050	FOLK SONGS (LP)	18
68	Fontana (S)TL 5264	LOVE ME (LP)	15
68	Mercury 20118 SMCL	MR. DREAM MERCHANT (LP)	15
69	Mercury 20144 SMCL	SOUL GOES ON (LP)	15
69	Mercury 20154 SMCL	THE ICE MAN COMETH (LP)	15
72	Mercury 6338 102	SPICE OF LIFE (LP)	12
72	Mercury 6430 401	THE VERY BEST OF JERRY BUTLER (LP)	10

(see also Betty Everett & Jerry Butler, Impressions)

LESLIE BUTLER (& FUGITIVES)

67	Island WI 3069	Hornpipe Rocksteady/You Don't Have To Say You Love Me	8
67	Doctor Bird DB 1083	Winchester Rocksteady (with Fugitives)/ASTON CAMPBELL & CONQUERORS: Ramona	10
69	High Note HS 008	Top Cat/WEBBER SISTERS: Stars Above	7
69	High Note HS 009	Revival/GAYLADS: Over The Rainbow's End	8

BUTTERBEANS & SUZIE

27	Parlophone R 3255	Mama Stayed Out The Whole Night Long/ALBERTA HUNTER: If You Can't Hold The Man You Love (Don't Cry When He's Gone) (78)	40
30s	Parlophone R 8833	Times Is Hard (So I'm Savin' For A Rainy Day)/Elevator Papa, Switchboard Mama (78)	20
28	Parlophone R 113	Mama Why Do You Treat Me So?/That's When I'll Come Back To You (78)	25

BUTTERCUPS

| 68 | Pama PM 742 | If I Love You/Loving You | 15 |
| 69 | Pama PM 760 | Come Put My Life In Order/If I Love You | 10 |

BILLY BUTTERFIELD & HIS ORCHESTRA

| 51 | Capitol CL 13514 | Billy's Boogie/Stardust (78) | 5 |
| 55 | London HLF 8181 | The Magnificent Matador/Sugar Blues Mambo | 15 |

(PAUL) BUTTERFIELD BLUES BAND

66	London HLZ 10100	Come On In/I Got A Mind To Give Up Living	10
67	Elektra EKSN 45007	All These Blues/Never Say No	5
67	Elektra EKSN 45020	Run Out Of Time/One More Heartache	5
68	Elektra EKSN 45047	Get Yourself Together/Mine To Love	5
68	Elektra EKSN 45069	Where Did My Baby Go/In My Own Dream	5
65	Elektra EKL/EKS 294	PAUL BUTTERFIELD BLUES BAND (LP, orange label)	20
66	Elektra EKL/EKS 315	EAST — WEST (LP, orange label)	25
67	Elek. EKL 4015/EKS 74015	THE RESURRECTION OF PIGBOY CRABSHAW (LP, orange label)	15
68	Elektra EKL 4025	IN MY OWN DREAM (LP, orange label, also stereo EKS 74025)	15
69	Elektra EKS 74053	KEEP ON MOVIN' (LP)	10
70	Elektra EKD 2001	LIVE (2-LP)	14

(see also John Mayall's Bluesbreakers with Paul Butterfield, Mike Bloomfield)

BUTTERFLIES

| 68 | President PT 192 | Love Me Forever/He's Got Everything | 4 |

BUTTERFLYS

| 64 | Red Bird RB 10009 | Goodnight Baby/Swim | 15 |

(see also Ellie Greenwich)

BUTTERSCOTCH CABOOSE

| 68 | Bell BLL 1023 | Melinda/Let A Little Sunshine In | 4 |

BUTTHOLE SURFERS

| 84 | Alt. Tentacles VIRUS 22 | BUTTHOLE SURFERS (mini-LP, black & white sleeve) | 8 |
| 80s | LBV | DOUBLE LIVE (2-LP, with booklet) | 20 |

SHEILA BUXTON

55	Columbia SCM 5193	Thank You For The Waltz/Just Between Friends	6
57	Columbia DB 3887	Perfect Love/I Love You Baby (My Baby Loves Me)	7
57	Columbia DB 4051	Charm/The In-Between Age	7
59	Top Rank JAR 113	Li Per Li/Soldier, Won't You Marry Me?	4
59	Top Rank JAR 144	The Valley Of Love/The Wonder Of You	4
59	Top Rank JAR 240	All I Do Is Dream Of You/Shakedown	4
60	Top Rank JAR 356	Sixteen Reasons/Goodnight, God I Love You	4

BUZZ
66	Columbia DB 7887	You're Holding Me Down/I've Gotta Buzz	120

BUZZ & BUCKY
65	Stateside SS 428	Tiger A Go Go/Bay City	15

BUZZCOCKS
77	New Hormones ORG 1	SPIRAL SCRATCH (EP, plastic labels, p/s doesn't credit Howard Devoto)	15
77	United Artists UP 36316	Orgasm Addict/Whatever Happened To ...? (p/s)	5
78	United Artists UP 36348	What Do I Get?/Oh Shit (p/s)	4
78	United Artists UP 36386	I Don't Mind/Autonomy (p/s)	4
78	United Artists UP 36433	Love You More/Noise Annoys (p/s)	4
78	United Artists UP 36455	Ever Fallen In Love (With Someone You Shouldn't've?)/Just Lust (p/s)	4
78	United Artists UP 36455	Ever Fallen In Love (With Someone You Shouldn't've?)/Just Lust (p/s, mispressed with Gerry Rafferty track on B-side)	10
78	United Artists UP 36471	Promises/Lipstick (p/s)	4
79	United Artists UP 36499	Everybody's Happy Nowadays/Why Can't I Touch It? (3 different col'd sleeves)	4
79	United Artists UP 36541	Harmony In My Head/Something's Gone Wrong Again (blue p/s)	4
79	United Artists UP 36541	Harmony In My Head/Something's Gone Wrong Again (red p/s)	5
79	United Artists BP 316	You Say You Don't Love Me/Raison D'Etre (p/s)	4
80	United Artists BP 365	Why She's A Girl From The Chainstore/Are Everything (p/s)	5
80	United Artists BP 371	Strange Thing/Airwaves Dream (p/s)	5
80	United Artists BP 392	Running Free/What Do You Know (p/s)	5
79	New Hormones ORG 1	SPIRAL SCRATCH (EP, reissue, p/s credits Howard Devoto, paper label)	5
91	New Hormones ORG 1	SPIRAL SCRATCH (EP, 2nd reissue, promo only on 7")	10
78	United Artists UALP 15	Moving Away From The Pulsebeat (12", 1-sided, die-cut company sleeve	18
78	United Artists UAG 30159	ANOTHER MUSIC IN A DIFFERENT KITCHEN (LP, black inner sleeve, initially in printed carrier bag)	25/10
78	United Artists UAG 30197	LOVE BITES (LP, with embossed sleeve with inner)	10
79	United Artists UAG 30260	A DIFFERENT KIND OF TENSION (LP, with inner Sleeve)	10
91	Document DLP 2	TIME'S UP (LP, with free 33rpm interview single [FDLP 2])	10

(see also Magazine, Steve Diggle, Flag Of Convenience, Pete Shelley)

DON BYAS & HIS RHYTHM
56	Vogue V 2390	On The Way To Your Heart/The Portuguese Washerwomen	4

BYE LAWS
68	Pye 7N 17481	Then You Can Tell Me Goodbye/Come On Over To My Place	5
69	Pye 7N 17701	Run Baby Run/To Sir With Love	5

MAX BYGRAVES
53	HMV 7M 112	Cowpuncher's Cantata/True Loves And False Lovers	10
53	HMV 7M 113	Little Sir Echo/Bygraves Boogie	8
53	HMV 7M 114	The Travelling Salesman/Ten Bottles Of Gin	8
53	HMV 7M 134	Lovely Dollar Lolly (w/Peter Brough & Archie Andrews)/The Red Robin Cantata	8
53	HMV 7M 145	Time To Dream/The Queen Of Ev'ryone's Heart	8
53	HMV 7M 154	Big 'Ead/Say "Si Si" (B-side with Peter Brough & Archie Andrews)	8
54	HMV 7M 180	She Was A Good Girl (As Good Girls Go)/The Jones Boy	8
54	HMV 7M 194	(The Gang That Sang) Heart Of My Heart/Once She's Got You Up (B-side with Tanner Sisters)	10
54	HMV 7M 220	Friends And Neighbours (with Tanner Sisters)/Chip Chopper Charlie	8
54	HMV 7M 237	Gilly Gilly Ossenfeffer Katznellen.../Third Little Turning On The Right	8
54	HMV 7M 238	Bank Of Sunshine/Little Johnny Rainbow	8
56	HMV 7M 357	The Ballad Of Davy Crockett/A Good Idea — Son	8
56	HMV 7M 368	Out Of Town/Fingers Crossed	8
56	HMV 7M 388	Nothin' To Do/Lift Boy	8
56	HMV 7M 400	Seventeen Tons/Try Another Cherry Tree	8
60	Decca F 11214	Fings Ain't Wot They Used To Be/When The Thrill Has Gone	4
55	HMV 7EG 8061	PETER BROUGH, ARCHIE ANDREWS AND MAX BYGRAVES (EP)	7
55	HMV 7EG 8123	TOMORROW (EP)	7
56	HMV 7EG 8203	A GOOD IDEA SON (EP)	7
57	HMV 7EG 8271	SING WITH MAX (EP)	7

(see also Joan Regan)

MAX BYGRAVES & TED HEATH
59	Decca LK 4317/SKL 4068	THE HITS OF THE TWENTIES (LP)	10
60	Decca LK 4360/SKL 4106	THE HITS OF THE THIRTIES (LP)	10

(see also Ted Heath)

JUNIOR BYLES
71	Upsetter US 387	Festival Da Da/UPSETTERS: Version	6
71	Bullet BU 499	Beat Down Babylon/UPSETTERS: Version	5
72	Pama PM 857	Fever/GROOVERS: Soul Sister (B-side actually by Heptones)	6
72	Dynamic DYN 432	Pharaoh Hiding/Hail To Power	4
72	Randy's RAN 523	King Of Babylon/UPSETTERS: Nebuchadnezzer	5
73	Pama PM 878	Education Rock/KEN McKAY: Nobody Knows	4
74	Dip DL 5035	Curly Locks/Now Generation	5
74	Magnet MAG 27	Curly Locks/Now Generation	4
75	Ethnic ETH 26	Mumbling And Grumbling/King Size Mumble	4
72	Trojan TRL 52	BEAT DOWN BABYLON (LP)	12

JAMES BYNUM
79	Grapevine GRP 117	Time Passes By/Love You	4

BOBBY BYRD
71	Mojo 2001 118	I Need Help Pts 1 & 2	6
71	Mojo 2027 003	I Know You Got Soul/If You Don't Work You Can't Eat	8
73	Warner Bros K 16291	Try It Again/I'm On The Move	4
73	Mojo 2093 004	Hot Pants I'm Coming I'm Coming I'm Coming/Hang It Up	5
74	Mojo 2093 013	Keep On Doin' What You're Doin'/Let Me Know	4

MINT VALUE £

74	Mojo 2093 017	If You Got A Love/You've Got To Change Your Mind	4
74	Mojo 2093 020	Never Get Enough/My Concerto	4
75	Mojo 2093 028	Saying It And Doing It Are Two Different Things/VICKI ANDERSON: Don't Throw Your Love In Garbage/In The Land Of Milk And Honey	5
75	Seville SEV 1003	Back From The Dead/The Way To Get Down	7
75	Seville SEV 1005	Headquarters/Headquarters (Instrumental Version)	5
76	Contempo CS 7096	Here For The Party/Thank You For Your Love	4
87	Urban URBX 8	I Know You Got Soul/Hot Pants ... I'm Coming, I'm Coming, I'm Coming/ I Know You Got Soul (Version) (12", generic title die-cut sleeve)	10
72	Mojo 2918 002	I NEED HELP — LIVE (LP)	60

(see also JB's, James Brown, Anna King & Bobby Byrd, Vicki Anderson)

C. BYRD & SIR D.'s GROUP

| 60 | Blue Beat BB 49 | Baa Baa Black Sheep/LLOYD & CECIL: Come Over Here | 12 |

DONALD BYRD

62	Blue Note 45-1764	Fuego/Amen	6
66	Verve VS 532	Boom Boom/See See Rider	8
74	Blue Note 45-623	Flight Time/Blackbird	5
75	Blue Note BNXW 7001	Blackbird/Stop Jar Blues	6
76	Blue Note BNXW 7003	Changes (Makes You Want To Hustle) Pts 1 & 2	5
80	United Artists UP 622	Dominoes/Wind Parade	4
80	United Artists 12 UP 622	Dominoes/Wind Parade (12")	15
81	Elektra K 12559T	Love Has Come Around/Loving You (12")	8
50s	Esquire EP 139	DONALD BYRD'S JAZZ GROUP (EP)	8
50s	Esquire EP 149	DONALD BYRD JAZZ GROUP (EP)	8
59	Philips BBE 12274	DONALD BYRD & GIG GRYCE (EP)	8
61	Blue Note BLP 4026	FUEGO (LP)	15
62	Blue Note BLP 4060	BYRD AT THE HALF NOTE CAFE (LP)	15
62	Eros ERL 50067	AND THEN SOME (LP)	12
64	Blue Note (B)BLP 4075	THE CAT WALK (LP)	15
64	Blue Note (B)BLP 4124	A NEW PERSPECTIVE (LP)	15
65	Blue Note (B)BLP 4188	I'M TRYING TO GET HOME (LP)	15
65	Vintage Jazz VLP 9104	UP WITH BYRD (LP)	12
67	Polydor 423/623 224	CHILD'S PLAY (LP, with Johnny Coles)	10
69	Blue Note BST 84292	SLOW DRAG (LP)	12
70	Blue Note BST 84319	FANCY FREE (LP)	12
70s	Blue Note BST 84019	BYRD IN HAND (LP)	10
70s	Blue Note BST 84026	FUEGO (LP, reissue)	10
70s	Blue Note BST 84048	BYRD IN FLIGHT (LP)	10
70s	Blue Note BST 84060	JAZZ AT THE WATERFRONT 1 (LP)	10
70s	Blue Note BST 84061	JAZZ AT THE WATERFRONT 2 (LP?)	10
70s	Blue Note BST 84075	THE CAT WALK (LP, reissue)	10
70s	Blue Note BST 84101	ROYAL FLUSH (LP)	10
70s	Blue Note BST 84118	FREE FORM (LP)	10
70s	Blue Note BST 84188	I'M TRYIN' TO GET HOME (LP, reissue)	10
70s	Blue Note BST 84238	MUSTANG (LP)	10
70s	Blue Note BST 84259	BLACKJACK (LP)	10
70s	Blue Note BST 84349	ELECTRIC BYRD (LP)	10
70s	Blue Note BST 84380	ETHIOPIAN KNIGHTS (LP)	10
70s	Blue Note UAG 20001	PLACES AND SPACES (LP)	25
78	Blue Note UAG 20008	CARICATURES (LP)	10

(see also Blackbyrds)

MICHAEL BYRD & COMMERCIALS

| 81 | Another AN 002 | SELL OUT BEFORE THE FALL OUT (EP, gatefold p/s) | 4 |

RUSSELL BYRD

| 64 | Sue WI 305 | Hitch Hike Parts 1 & 2 | 20 |

BYRDS

65	CBS 201765	Mr. Tambourine Man/I Knew I'd Want You	5
65	CBS 201796	All I Really Want To Do/Feel A Whole Lot Better	5
65	CBS 202008	Turn! Turn! Turn! (To Everything There Is A Season)/She Don't Care About Time	5
66	CBS 202037	Set You Free This Time/It Won't Be Wrong	8
66	CBS 202067	Eight Miles High/Why	6
66	CBS 202259	5D (Fifth Dimension)/Captain Soul	5
66	CBS 202295	Mr Spaceman/What's Happening?!?!	6
67	CBS 202559	So You Want To Be A Rock'n'Roll Star/Everybody's Been Burned	6
67	CBS 2648	My Back Pages/Renaissance Fair	5
67	CBS 2924	Lady Friend/Don't Make Waves	12
67	CBS 3093	Goin' Back/Change Is Now	5
68	CBS 3411	You Ain't Goin' Nowhere/Artificial Energy	4
68	CBS 3752	I Am A Pilgrim/Pretty Boy Floyd	5
69	CBS 4055	Bad Night At The Whiskey/Drug Store Truck Drivin' Man	6
69	CBS 4284	Lay Lady Lay/Old Blue	6
69	CBS 4572	Wasn't Born To Follow/Child Of The Universe	4
70	CBS 4753	Jesus Is Just Alright/It's All Over Now Baby Blue	4
71	CBS 7253	I Trust/This Is My Destiny	4
72	CBS 7712	America's Great National Pastime/Farther Along (unreleased)	
73	Asylum AYM 516	Things Will Be Better/For Free (promos in p/s)	15/4
66	CBS EP 6069	THE TIMES THEY ARE A' CHANGIN' (EP)	12
66	CBS EP 6077	EIGHT MILES HIGH (EP)	15
65	CBS (S)BPG 62571	MR TAMBOURINE MAN (LP)	14
66	CBS (S)BPG 62652	TURN! TURN! TURN! (LP)	16
66	CBS (S)BPG 62783	FIFTH DIMENSION (LP)	14
67	CBS (S)BPG 62988	YOUNGER THAN YESTERDAY (LP)	14
68	CBS (S)BPG 63169	THE NOTORIOUS BYRD BROTHERS (LP)	12

(originals copies of the above LPs had rough textured labels & flipback sleeves, later copies are worth around £10)

MINT VALUE £

68	CBS 63353	SWEETHEART OF THE RODEO (LP, mono/stereo)	12/10
69	CBS 63545	DR BYRDS & MR HYDE (LP)	10
69	CBS 63795	THE BALLAD OF EASY RIDER (LP)	10
71	Bumble GEXP 8001	PRE-FLYTE (LP)	20
73	Asylum SYLA 8754	THE BYRDS (LP)	10

(see also Beefeaters, Roger McGuinn, David Crosby, Gene Clark, Gram Parsons, Gene Parsons, Skip Battin, Earl Scruggs)

BOBBY BYRNE & ALL STAR ORCHESTRA
| 59 | Top Rank TR 5011 | Rhapsody In Blue/Adios | 4 |

DAVID BYRNE
| 81 | Sire SIR 4054 | Big Blue Plymouth/Leg Bells (p/s) | 4 |

(see also Talking Heads, Dinosaur, Love Of Life Orchestra, Robert Fripp)

JERRY BYRNE
| 76 | Speciality SON 5011 | Lights Out/Honey Baby | 5 |

ED(WARD) BYRNES
60	Warner Bros WB 5	Kookie, Kookie (Lend Me Your Comb) (with Connie Stevens)/You're The Top	5
60	Warner Bros WB 27	Lonely Christmas/Yulesville (as Edd Byrnes)	4
60	Warner Bros WEP 6010	KOOKIE (EP, also stereo WSEP 2010)	10
63	Warner Bros W(S)EP 6108	KOOKIE VOLUME 2 (EP)	10
60s	Warner Bros	77 SUNSET STRIP (LP)	10

(see also Connie Stevens)

PAUL BYRON
| 60 | Decca F 11210 | Pale Moon/Year Ago Tonight | 8 |

BYSTANDERS
65	Pylot WD 501	That's The End/This Time	75
66	Piccadilly 7N 35330	(You're Gonna) Hurt Yourself/Have I Offended The Girl	15
66	Piccadilly 7N 35351	My Love — Come Home/If You Walk Away	18
67	Piccadilly 7N 35363	98.6/Stubborn Kind Of Fellow	10
67	Piccadilly 7N 35382	Royal Blue Summer Sunshine Day/Make Up Your Mind	18
67	Piccadilly 7N 35399	Pattern People/Green Grass	12
68	Pye 7N 17476	When Jezamine Goes/Cave Of Clear Light	25
68	Pye 7N 17540	This World Is My World/Painting The Time	15

(see also Man)

BYZANTIUM
73	A&M AMS 7064	What A Coincidence/My Seasons Changing With The Sun	6
72	private press	LIVE AND STUDIO ('BLACK AND WHITE') (LP)	90
72	A&M AMLH 68104	BYZANTIUM (LP, some with poster)	20/15
72	A&M AMLH 68163	SEASONS CHANGING (LP, with poster sleeve)	35

(see also Ora)

MARC BOLAN & MICKEY FINN OF T. REX

FANTASTIC JOHNNY C
67	London HL 10169	Boogaloo Down Broadway/Look What Love Can Make You Do	8
68	London HL 10212	Hitch It To The Horse/Cool Broadway	8
69	Action ACT 4543	Is There Anything Better Than Making Love/New Love	8
75	Island USA 8	Don't Depend On Me Pts 1 & 2	6
69	Action ACLP 6001	BOOGALOO DOWN BROADWAY (LP)	15

ROY C
66	Island WI 273	Shotgun Wedding/I'm Going To Make It	10
67	Ember EMB S 230	Twistin' Pneumonia/Tear Avenue	7
77	Island WI 273	Shotgun Wedding/High School Dropout	6
66	Ember NR 5055	THE SHOTGUN WEDDING MAN (LP)	15
75	Mercury 9100 017	SEX AND SOUL (LP)	10

CABARET VOLTAIRE
78	Rough Trade RT 003	EXTENDED PLAY (EP)	6
79	Rough Trade RT 018	"Nag, Nag, Nag"/Is That Me (Finding Someone At the Door Again?) (p/s)	5
80	Rough Trade RT 035	Silent Command/The Soundtrack For 'Chance Versus Causality' (p/s)	5
80	Rough Trade RT 038	THREE MANTRAS (12", p/s, 33rpm maxi-single)	8
80	Rough Trade RT 060	Seconds Too Late/Control Addict (p/s)	5
81	Rough Trade RT 096	Eddie's Out/Walls Of Jericho (12", p/s, initially with free 7" "Jazz The Glass"/"Burnt To The Ground" [pink die-cut sleeve, RT 095] in plastic wallet)	10/6
83	Factory FAC 82	Yashar (7.20)/Yashar (5.00) (12", die-cut stickered p/s)	7
82	Masterbag BAG 004	Gut Level (live) (flexidisc free with 'Masterbag' magazine)	7/5
85	Virgin CVM 1	DRINKING GASOLINE (12", p/s, double pack)	7
87	Doublevision DVR(P) 21	THE DRAIN TRAIN (12", p/s, double pack)	8
76	Cabaret Voltaire	LIMITED EDITION (private cassette)	50
80	Rough Trade ROUGH 7	LIVE Y.M.C.A. 27.10.79 (LP)	10
81	Industrial IRC 35	1974-76 (cassette)	10
82	Rough Trade ROUGH 45	2 X 45 (LP, as 2 x 12", in foldout envelope sleeve)	10
86	Some Bizzare CV 1	THE CRACKDOWN (LP, with free 12" "Doublevision" [CVDV 1] [stickered plain sleeve])	12
90	Parlophone PCSX 7338	GROOVY, LAIDBACK AND NASTY (LP, with free 12" [PCSX 73382])	10

(see also Richard H. Kirk, Peter Hope & Richard H. Kirk, Hafler Trio, Stephen Mallinder)

CABLES
68	Coxsone CS 7072	What Kind Of World?/My Broken Heart	15
68	Studio One SO 2060	Baby Why?/Be A Man	15
68	Studio One SO 2071	Love Is A Pleasure/Cheer Up	15
69	Studio One SO 2085	Got To Find Someone/ALEXANDER HENRY: Please Be True	15
69	Bamboo BAM 12	So Long/PRESSURE BOYS: More Love	6
70	Bamboo BAM 19	How Can I Trust You?/SOUND DIMENSIONS: How Can I Trust You? (Instrumental)	6

CACTUS
70	Atlantic 2400 020	CACTUS (LP)	12
71	Atlantic 2460 114	ONE WAY OR ANOTHER (LP)	10
72	Atlantic K 40307	RESTRICTIONS (LP)	10
72	Atlantic K 50013	'OT AND SWEATY (LP)	10

(see also Vanilla Fudge, Leaf Hound, Beck Bogert Appice)

CACTUS WORLD NEWS
85	Mother MUM 2	The Bridge/The Other Extreme (p/s)	4
85	Mother 12MUM 2	The Bridge/The Other Extreme/Frontiers (12", p/s)	7
80s	Rainbow CWN 1	Don't Let Me Down/Funny (no p/s)	4

BILL CADDICK
81	Leader LER 2097	SUNNY MEMORIES (LP)	10
81	Highway SHY 7006	REASONS BRIEFLY SET DOWN BY THE AUTHOR (LP)	10

ALAN CADDY
64	HMV POP 1286	Tornado/Workout	20

(see also Tornados)

CADETS
56	London HLU 8313	Stranded In The Jungle/I Want You (gold or silver lettering on label)	200/100
56	London HLU 8313	Stranded In The Jungle/I Want You (78)	30

CADETS
63	Decca F 11677	Hello Trouble/Our First Quarrel	5
64	Pye 7N 15693	Chapel Of Love/I Gave My Wedding Dress Away	5
65	Pye 7N 15769	Are You Teasing Me?/My Heart Skips A Beat	4
65	Pye 7N 15852	Right Or Wrong/Jealous Heart	4
65	Pye 7N 15947	Baby Roo/Raining In My Heart	4
66	Pye 7N 17024	If I Had My Life To Live Over/Best Of All	4
66	Pye 7N 17167	At The Close Of A Long Long Day/True Love	4
69	Pye 7N 17762	Dying Ranger/Storeen Bawn	4

CADILLAC
86	CBS A 7180	Valentino/Valentino (p/s)	8

EARL CADILLAC & HIS ORCHESTRA
59	Vogue V 9133	Zon, Zon, Zon/Il Suffit D'Une Melodie	4
59	Vogue V 9138	The Fish Seller/Tremendo Cha Cha Cha (Plegaria)	4

CADILLACS
59	London HLJ 8786	Peek-A-Boo/Oh, Oh, Lolita	25
59	London HLJ 8786	Peek-A-Boo/Oh, Oh, Lolita (78)	20

CAEDMON
78	private pressing	CAEDMON (LP, with free 7" "Beyond The Second Mile"/"Give Me Jesus")	300

CAESAR & CLEO
65	Reprise R 20419	Love Is Strange/Let The Good Times Roll	6
65	Reprise R 30056	CAESAR AND CLEO (EP, 2 tracks each by Caesar & Cleo and Sonny & Cher)	10
	(see also Sonny & Cher)		

CAESARS
65	Decca F 12251	On The Outside Looking In/Can You Blame Me?	10
66	Decca F 12462	Five In The Morning/It's Superman	8

CAFE SOCIETY
75	Konk KOS 5	Whitby Two-Step/Maybe It's Me	5
75	Konk KONK 102	CAFE SOCIETY (LP)	12
	(see also Tom Robinson Band)		

BUTCH CAGE
78	Flyright LP 545	RAISE A RUCKUS TONIGHT (LP)	12

BUTCH CAGE/MABEL LEE WILLIAMS
60s	Storyville SLP 129	COUNTRY BLUES (LP)	15

AUBREY CAGLE
62	Starlite ST45 082	Come Along Little Girl/Blue Lonely World	150

PATRICIA CAHILL
70	Deram Nova SDN 22	SUMMERS DAUGHTER (LP)	20

CAIN
68	Page One POF 054	Her Emotion/Take Me Back One Time	8

CAIN
80s	private pressing	CAIN (2-LP)	30

AL CAIOLA (ORCHESTRA)
56	London HLC 8285	Flamenco Love/From The Heart	20
56	London HLC 8285	Flamenco Love/From The Heart (78)	5
61	London HLT 9294	The Magnificent Seven/The Lonely Rebel	5
61	London HLT 9325	Bonanza/Bounty Hunter	12
61	HMV POP 884	Bonanza/Bounty Hunter (as Al Caiola Orchestra, reissue)	4
61	HMV POP 889	The Magnificent Seven/The Lonely Rebel (as Al Caiola Orchestra)	4
62	Oriole CB 1732	Mambo Jambo/Twistin' At The Woodchoppers Mill	4
66	United Artists UEP 1018	HIT T.V. THEMES (EP)	10
56	London HA-C 2017	DEEP IN A DREAM (LP)	10
57	London HA-C 2022	SERENADE IN BLUE (LP)	10
64	United Artists ULP 1090	TUFF GUITAR (LP)	12
66	United Artists (S)ULP 1115	SOUNDS FOR SPIES AND PRIVATE EYES (LP)	15

JOHN CAIRNEY
57	HMV POP 424	Two Strangers/A Certain Girl I Know (with Sammy San)	4
68	Waverley SLP 543	Please/Deep Purple	4

CAIRO
80	Absurd ABSURD 7	I Like Blue Beat/Version (p/s)	4
80	Absurd ASK 15	Movie Stars/Cuthbert's Birthday Treat (p/s)	4

CAKE
68	MCA MUPS 303	THE CAKE (LP)	10
69	MCA MUPS 390	A SLICE OF CAKE (LP)	12

J.J. CALE
66	Liberty LIB 55881	Outside Lookin' In/In Our Time	7
72	A&M AMS 7018	Cajun Moon/Starbound	4
72	A&M AMS 7022	After Midnight/Crazy Mama	4
79	Shelter ISA 5018	FIVE (LP, with free single "Katy Cool"/"Juan And Maria Juarez Blues" [JJ-1])	10
	(see also Leathercoated Minds)		

JOHN CALE
74	Island WIP 6202	The Man Who Couldn't Afford To Orgy/Sylvia Said	4
77	Illegal IL 006	Jack The Ripper In The Moulin Rouge/Memphis(unissued, 7" test pressings only)	12
71	CBS 64256	VINTAGE VIOLENCE (LP, orange label)	10
71	CBS 64259	CHURCH OF ANTHRAX (LP, with Terry Riley)	15
72	Reprise K 44212	ACADEMY OF PERIL (LP)	10
73	Reprise K 44239	PARIS 1919 (LP)	10
76	Island ILPS 9350	HELEN OF TROY (LP, includes "Coral Moon")	10
	(see also Velvet Underground, Nico, Terry Riley, Ayers Cale Nico & Eno)		

CALEB (Quaye)
67	Philips BF 1588	Baby Your Phrasing Is Bad/Woman Of Distinction	125
	(see also Mirage, Hookfoot, Bread & Beer Band)		

CALEDONIANS
69	Fab FAB 103	Funny Way Of Laughing/Don't Please	5
	(see also Clarendonians)		

RANDY CALIFORNIA
82	Beggars Banquet BEG 76	Hand Gun (Toy Guns)/This Is The End (p/s)	4
82	Beggars Banquet BEG 82	All Along The Watchtower/Radio Man (p/s)	5
	(see also Spirit, Kapt. Kopter & Fabulous Twirly Birds)		

CALIFORNIA IN-CROWD
66   Fontana TF 779   Questions And Answers/Happiness In My Heart 30

CALIFORNIA MUSIC
74   RCA RCA 2488   Don't Worry Baby/Ten Years Harmony 4
76   RCA RCA 2661   Jamaica Farewell/California Farewell 4
(see also Bruce Johnston, Beach Boys)

CALIFORNIANS
67   CBS 2263   Golden Apples/Little Ship With A Red Sail 20
67   Decca F 12678   Follow Me/What Love Can Do 8
67   Decca F 12712   Sunday Will Never Be The Same/Can't Get You Out Of My Mind 5
68   Decca F 12758   Congratulations/What Is Happy, Baby? 5
68   Decca F 12802   Out In The Sun/The Sound 5
69   Fontana TF 991   The Cooks Of Cakes And Kindness/Mandy 35
69   Fontana TF 1052   Sad Old Song/Weep No More 6

CALL
83   London LON 28   Walls Came Down/Upper Birth (p/s) 4

CALLAN & JOHN
69   CBS 4447   House Of Delight/Long Shadow Day 10

CALL GIRLS
88   53rd & 3rd AGAR 001   Primal World/VATICAN SHOTGUN SCARE: Thick Fat Heat Source (p/s) 10

(MISSISSIPPI) JOE CALLICOTT
68   Blue Horizon 7-63227   PRESENTING THE COUNTRY BLUES (LP) 35
72   Revival RVS 1002   DEAL GONE DOWN (LP, as Joe Callicott) 18

TERRY CALLIER
78   Elektra K 52096   FIRE ON ICE (LP) 10

CALLINAN-FLYNN
72   Mushroom 150 MR 18   FREEDOM'S LAMENT (LP) 200

JO CALLIS
81   Pop: Aural POP 12   Woah Yeah/Sinistrale/Dodo Boys (p/s) 4
(see also Rezillos, Shake, Human League)

CAB CALLOWAY
30s   Brunswick 01294   Six Or Seven Times/Black Rhythm (78) 15
30s   Brunswick 01339   Bugle Call Rag/Minnie The Moocher (78) 15
30s   Brunswick 0161   St James Infirmary/Nobody's Sweetheart (78) 15
30s   Brunswick 01673   St Louis Blues/Minnie The Moocher's Wedding Day (78) 15
30s   Parlophone R 2941   Willow Weep For Me/I Don't Stand A Ghost Of A Chance (78) 10
38   HMV B 8659   Jitterbug/Emaline (78) 10
40s   HMV X 4318   Kickin' The Gong Around/Magie (78, export issue) 12
40s   HMV B 6347   Evenin'/Harlem Hospitality (78) 12
40s   HMV B 6460   Harlem Camp Meeting/Zah Zuh Za (78) 12
40s   HMV B 6451   Father's Got His Glasses On/I Learned About Love From Her (78) ... 12
40s   HMV B 6465   The Scat Song/Cabin In The Cotton (78) 12
50   London L 657   La Mucura/Pero Que Jelenque (78) 8
52   Brunswick 05022   Minnie The Moocher/Kickin' The Gong Around (78) 7
66   Stateside SS 509   History Repeats Itself/After Taxes 4
58   Gala 45XP 1016   CAB CALLOWAY (EP) 8
60   Fontana TFE 17216   CAB CALLOWAY (EP) 20
70s   Vintage Jazz VEP 22   CABULOUS CALLOWAY (EP) 8
70s   Vintage Jazz VEP 35   CABULOUS CALLOWAY VOL. 2 (EP) 8

EDDIE CALVERT
53   Columbia SCM 5003   My Yiddishe Momme/Hora Staccato 6
53   Columbia SCM 5004   Ave Maria/Just A-Wearyin' For You (as Eddie Calvert Orchestra) 8
54   Columbia SCM 5084   Montparnasse/Tenderly 4
54   Columbia SCM 5097   Midnight/Margot's Minuet 4
54   Columbia SCM 5109   Donna/Faraway 4
54   Columbia SCM 5125   Caress/I Speak To The Stars 5
54   Columbia SCM 5129   My Son, My Son/Sherpa Song 8
55   Columbia SCM 5163   Open Your Heart/Waiting For You 5
55   Columbia SCM 5168   Cherry Pink And Apple Blossom White/Roses Of Picardy 10
55   Columbia SCM 5194   Love Is A Many Splendored Thing/Spellbound 5
56   Columbia SCM 5237   The Man With The Golden Arm/Memories Of You 8
56   Columbia SCM 5253   The Bells Of St. Mary's/You Above All (with Gerry Brereton) 5
56   Columbia SCM 5277   Moonglow & Theme From "Picnic"/If I Loved You 4
56   Columbia DB 3812   They Didn't Believe Me/Goodnight Mother, Goodnight 4
56   Columbia DB 3837   Jungle Moon/Beyond Mombasa 4
57   Columbia DB 3902   Trees/Let The Rest Of The World Go By (with Gerry Brereton) 5
57   Columbia DB 3917   Almost Paradise/Song Of Corsica 4
57   Columbia DB 3956   Mandy (La Panse)/Never Say Goodbye 5
57   Columbia DB 3975   Forgotten Dreams/Our Concerto 4
58   Melodisc EPM 7   MISERLOU (EP) 7
58   Columbia DB 4105   Little Serenade/Fanfare Tango (The Awakening) 5
50s   Columbia SEG series   EPs 4-6
50s   Columbia 33S(X) series   LPs 8-10

ROBERT CALVERT
73   United Artists UP 35543   Catch A Falling Starfighter/Ejection (as Captain Lockheed & Starfighters, p/s) .. 18
73   United Artists UP 35543   Catch A Falling Starfighter/Ejection (as Captain Lockheed & Starfighters, different mix of A-side, no p/s) 10
79   Wake Up WUR 5   Cricket Star (p/s, 33rpm flexidisc, as Robert Calvert & 1st XI) 6
80   Flicknife FLS 204   Lord Of The Hornets/The Greenfly & The Rose (purple print p/s) 4
81   Flicknife FLS 204   Lord Of The Hornets/The Greenfly & The Rose (reissue, black print p/s) 4

Robert CALVERT

74	United Artists UAG 29507	CAPTAIN LOCKHEED AND THE STARFIGHTERS (LP, gatefold sleeve, with inner sleeve, some with booklet)	25/18
75	United Artists UAG 29852	LUCKY LIEF AND THE LONGSHIPS (LP, gatefold sleeve)	25
81	A-Side IF 0311	HYPE (SONGS OF TOM MAHLER) (LP)	12
88	Harbour	ROBERT CALVERT READS THE EARTH RITUAL (cassette, unreleased?)	15+
88	Harbour	LIVE AT THE QUEEN ELIZABETH HALL (cassette, unreleased?)	15+
89	Clear BLACK 1	ROBERT CALVERT AT THE QUEEN ELIZABETH HALL (LP, mail order only, with badge, poster & T-shirt, gatefold sleeve)	25

(see also Hawkwind, Inner City Unit)

TABBY CALVIN & ROUNDERS
| 56 | Capitol CL 14640 | False Alarm/I Came Back To Say I'm Sorry | 6 |

CAMARATA
| 73 | Deram SML 1101 | THE VELVET GENTLEMAN: A TRIBUTE TO ERIK SATIE (LP) | 80 |

CAMEL
72	MCA MU 1177	Never Let Go/Curiosity	8
73	MCA MUPS 477	CAMEL (LP)	10
74	Deram SML 1107	MIRAGE (LP)	10

(see also Pete Bardens, Gong/Camel)

CAMEL DRIVERS
| 68 | Pye International 7N 25471 | Sunday Morning 6 O'Clock/Give It A Try | 5 |

CAMEO
77	Casablanca CAN 106	Rigor Mortis/Post Mortem	4
77	Casablanca CANL 106	Rigor Mortis/Post Mortem (12")	8
70s	Casablanca	Freaky Dancin' (12", double pack)	10
77	Casablanca CAL 2015	CARDIAC ARREST (LP)	15
78	Casablanca CAL 2026	WE ALL KNOW WHO WE ARE (LP)	12
79	Casablanca CAL 2038	UGLY EGO (LP)	10
81	Casablanca 6480 041	KNIGHTS OF THE SOUND TABLE (LP)	12

CAMEOS (U.K.)
| 63 | Columbia DB 7092 | Powercut/High Low And Lonesomely | 20 |
| 64 | Columbia DB 7201 | My Baby's Coming Home/Where E'er You Walk | 15 |

CAMEOS (U.S.)
| 67 | Toast TT 503 | A Pretty Shade Of Blue/You Didn't Have To Be So Nice | 4 |
| 68 | Toast TT 508 | The Love Of A Boy/On The Good Ship Lollipop | 4 |

ANDY CAMERAN
| 78 | Klub KLUB 03 | Ally's Tartan Army/I Want To Be A Punk Rocker (no p/s, different label colours) | 4 |

CAMERA OBSCURA
| 80 | Small Wonder SMALL 28 | Destitution/Race In Athens (p/s) | 4 |

DEBBIE CAMERON & TOMMY SEEBACH
| 81 | EMI EMI 5173 | Lord Have Mercy/Get Ready | 7 |

DION CAMERON & THREE TOPS
| 66 | Rio R 111 | Lord Have Mercy/Get Ready | 10 |

(see also Dion & Three Tops)

G.C. CAMERON
| 76 | Tamla Motown TMG 1033 | Me And My Life/Act Like A Shotgun | 5 |

(see also Detroit Spinners)

ISLA CAMERON
| 64 | Transatlantic TRAEP 109 | LOST LOVE (EP) | 10 |

JOHN CAMERON (QUARTET)
67	Columbia DB 8120	You Owe Me/Walk Small (solo)	5
69	Deram DM 256	Troublemaker/Off Centre	5
67	Columbia SCX 6116	COVER LOVER (LP)	25
69	Deram DML/SML 1044	OFF CENTRE (LP)	45

JOHNNY CAMERON
| 60 | Top Rank JAR 396 | I Double Dare You/Fantasy | 4 |

RAY CAMERON
| 67 | Island WIP 6003 | Doin' My Time/Getaway, Getaway Car | 6 |

ALEX CAMPBELL
65	Transatlantic TRASP 4	Been On The Road So Long/The Night Visiting Song (some in p/s)	7/4
68	Saga OPP 2	Victoria Dines Alone/Pack Up Your Sorrows	5
60s	Arc ARC 36	OUT WEST WITH ALEX CAMPBELL (EP)	7
67	Saga ERO 8021	ALEX CAMPBELL AND HIS FRIENDS (LP, with Sandy Denny)	12
76	Look LKLP 6043	NO REGRETS (LP)	10
70s	Ad-Rhythm/Tepee ARPS 2	THIS IS ALEX CAMPBELL VOL. 2 (LP)	12

(see also Sandy Denny)

CHOKER CAMPBELL'S BIG BAND
| 65 | Tamla Motown TMG 517 | Mickey's Monkey/Pride And Joy | 50 |
| 65 | Tamla Motown TML 11011 | HITS OF THE SIXTIES (LP) | 100 |

CHRISTINE CAMPBELL
66	Page One POF 11	Auld Lang Syne/All Through The Night	4
67	Page One POF 021	Sleep Little Boy/Nos Da	4
63	Parlophone GEP 8874	WHEREVER I GO (EP)	7

CORNELL CAMPBELL
| 62 | Island WI 039 | Rosahelle/Turn Down Date | 10 |
| 63 | Island WI 083 | Each Lonely Night/ROLAND ALPHONSO: Steamline | 8 |

64	Port-O-Jam PJ 4008	Jericho Road (with Dimple Hinds)/DON DRUMMOND & GROUP:	
		Roll On Sweet Don	10
64	Rio R 38	Gloria/I'll Be True	8
72	Trojan TBL 199	CORNELL CAMPBELL (LP)	15

DAVID CAMPBELL
| 67 | Transatlantic | YOUNG BLOOD (LP) .... | 30 |

DUGGIE CAMPBELL
| 79 | DinDisc DIN 3 | Enough To Make You Mine/Steamin' (p/s) .... | 7 |

ETHNA CAMPBELL
| 64 | Mercury MF 804 | What's Easy For Two Is Hard For One/Again .... | 12 |
| 64 | Mercury MF 816 | Girls Like Boys/Five Minutes More .... | 4 |

GLEN CAMPBELL
61	Top Rank JAR 596	Turn Around, Look At Me/Brenda	8
62	Capitol CL 15268	Too Late To Worry, Too Blue To Cry/How Do I Tell My Heart Not To Break?	4
62	Capitol CL 15278	Here I Am/Long Black Limousine	5
63	Capitol CL 15295	Prima Donna/Oh My Darling	4
68	Ember EMB S 252	I Wanna Live/Hey Little One	4
69	Ember EMB S 255	Dreams Of The Everyday Housewife/Combine	5
69	Ember EMB S 258	Straight Life/That's Not Home	4
69	Ember EMB S 261	Wichita Lineman/Back In The Race (p/s)	6
70	Speciality SPE 1002	Satisfied Mind/Can't You See I'm Trying	4
66	London HA-F/SH-F 8291	SWINGING 12-STRING (LP)	10

IAN CAMPBELL (FOLK) GROUP
64	Topic STOP 102	The Sun Is Burning/The Crow On The Cradle	5
64	Decca F 11802	Marilyn Monroe/The Bells Of Rhymney	5
65	Transatlantic TRASP 2	Kelly From Killane/Boys Of Wexford (with Boys From Wexford)	4
65	Transatlantic TRASP 5	The Times They Are A-Changin'/Across The Hills	5
66	Transatlantic TRASP 6	Come Kiss Me/The First Time I Ever Saw Your Face (some in p/s)	7/4
66	Transatlantic TRASP 7	Guantanamera/Mary Anne	4
66	Transatlantic TRASP 10	One Eyed Reilly/Snow Is Falling (solo)	4
67	Big T BIG 103	Lover Let Me In/Private Harold Harris (as Ian Campbell Four)	5
69	Major Minor MM 639	Break My Mind/Govan Cross Special (solo)	5
64	Decca DFE 8592	IAN CAMPBELL FOLK GROUP (EP)	10
65	Transatlantic EP 128	SAMPLER (EP)	7
63	Transatlantic TRA 110	THIS IS THE IAN CAMPBELL FOLK GROUP! (LP)	20
64	Transatlantic TRA 118	ACROSS THE HILLS (LP)	20
65	Transatlantic	COALDUST BALLADS (LP)	18
66	Transatlantic	CONTEMPORARY CAMPBELLS (LP)	20
68	Xtra XTRA 1074	TAM O'SHANTER (LP, as Ian Campbell & John Dunkerley)	10
68	Transatlantic TRA 163	THE CIRCLE GAME (LP)	18
69	Transatlantic TRASAM 4	THIS IS THE IAN CAMPBELL FOLK GROUP! (LP)	15
69	Transatlantic TRASAM 12	SAMPLER 2 (LP, as Ian Campbell Folk Four)	12
69	MFP SMFP 1349	IAN CAMPBELL & FOLK GROUP WITH DAVE SWARBRICK (LP)	10
70	Argo ZFB 13	THE SUN IS BURNING (LP)	20
72	Pye PKL 5506	SOMETHING TO SING ABOUT (LP)	10

(see also Farewell Nancy, Dave Swarbrick)

JIMMY CAMPBELL
69	Fontana TF 1009	On A Monday/Dear Marge	4
70	Fontana TF 1076	Lyanna/Frankie Joe	4
70	Fontana 6007 025	Don't Leave Me Now/So Lonely Without You	4
69	Fontana STL 5508	SON OF ANASTASIA (LP)	12
70	Vertigo 6360 010	HALF BAKED (LP, gatefold sleeve, spiral label)	12
72	Philips 6308 100	JIMMY CAMPBELL'S ALBUM (LP)	15

(see also Kirkbys, 23rd Turnoff)

JO-ANN CAMPBELL
58	London HLU 8536	Wait A Minute/It's True	30
58	London HLU 8536	Wait A Minute/It's True (78)	10
60	HMV POP 776	Bobby, Bobby, Bobby/A Kookie Little Paradise	6
61	HMV POP 873	Motorcycle Michael/Puka Puka Pants	6
62	HMV POP 1003	You Made Me Love You/I Changed My Mind Jack	6
62	Columbia DB 4889	Sloppy Joe/I'm The Girl From Wolverton Mountain	5
62	Cameo Parkway CP 237	Mr Fix It Man/Let Me Do It My Way	7
63	Cameo Parkway CP 249	Mother Please/Waiting For Love	7

JUNIOR CAMPBELL
| 74 | Deram SML 1106 | SECOND TIME AROUND (LP) .... | 10 |

(see also Marmalade)

ROY CAMPBELL & JAZZBO JASPERS
| 68 | Giant GN 41 | Another Saturday Night/Wonderful World .... | 5 |

PATRICK CAMPBELL-LYONS
73	Sovereign SOV 115	Everybody Should Fly A Kite/I Think I Want Him Too	12
73	Sovereign SOV 119	Out On The Road/Me And My Friend	12
77	Electric WOT 12	That's What My Guru Said Last Night/The Whistling Fiddler	4
73	Sovereign SVNA 7258	ME AND MY FRIEND (LP, gatefold sleeve)	120
81	Public PUBL 1	THE ELECTRIC PLOUGH (LP)	15

(see also Nirvana, Erewhon, Patrick O'Magick, Rock O'Doodle, Pica, Hat & Tie)

ROBERT CAMPBESS
| 77 | Decca SKL 5285 | LIVING IN THE SHADOW (LP) .... | 10 |

CAN
| 73 | United Artists UP 35506 | Spoon/I'm So Green .... | 6 |
| 73 | United Artists UP 35596 | Moonshake/Future Days (Edit) .... | 6 |

MINT VALUE £

74	United Artists UP 35749	Dizzy Dizzy (Edit)/Splash (Edit) 6
76	Virgin VS 153	I Want More/... And More 4
76	Virgin VS 166	Silent Night/Cascade Waltz 4
77	Virgin VS 172	Don't Say No/Return 4
78	Lightning LIG 545	Can-Can/Can Be 4
69	United Artists UAS 29094	MONSTER MOVIE (LP) 18
71	Utd Artists UAD 60009/10	TAGO MAGO (2-LP, flip-top sleeve) 18
70	United Artists UAS 29283	SOUNDTRACKS (LP) 15
72	United Artists UAS 29414	EGE BAMYASI (LP, with printed inner sleeve) 15
73	United Artists UAS 29505	FUTURE DAYS (LP) 12
74	United Artists UAG 29673	SOON OVER BABALUMA (LP, original silver sleeve) 12
75	Virgin V 2041	LANDED (LP) 10

CANAAN
73	Dovetail DOVE 3	CANAAN (LP) 60
70s	Myrrh	OUT OF THE WILDERNESS (LP) 40

CANDIDO
70s	Blue Note BST 84357	BEAUTIFUL (LP) 10
79	Salsoul SSLP 1517	DANCIN' AND PRANCIN' (LP) 10

CANDLE FACTORY
70s	CAVS	NIGHTSHIFT (LP, private pressing) 50

CANDLEMASS
86	7 AX 1	Samarithan/Solitude 4

CONTE CANDOLI
56	London Jazz LZ-N 14010	SINCERELY, CONTE (10" LP) 12
56	London Jazz LTZ-N 15036	TOOTS SWEET (LP) 10

PETER CANDOLI & HIS ORCHESTRA
56	Capitol CL 14615	St. Louis Blues — Boogie/The Big Top (Entry Of The ...) 8
60	Warner Bros WB 2	Sunset Strip Cha-Cha/DON RALKE: 77 Sunset Strip 4

PENNY CANDY
60	Top Rank JAR 328	Come On Over/They Said 4

CANDY & KISSES
65	Cameo Parkway C 336	The 81/Two Happy People 50
85	Kent TOWN 104	Mr Creator/CHUCK JACKSON: Hand It Over (withdrawn) 15

CANDY CHOIR
66	Parlophone R 5472	Silence Is Golden/Shake Hands (And Come Out Crying) 8
67	CBS 3061	Children And Flowers/Marianne 5
68	CBS 3305	Alexander's Ragtime Band/No Grey Skies 5

CANDYMEN
67	HMV POP 1612	Georgia Pines/Movies In My Mind 7

CANE
78	Lightning GIL 531	3 X 3 (EP) 8

CANNED HEAT
68	Liberty	Rollin' And Tumblin'/Bullfrog Blues (unreleased)
68	Liberty LBF 15090	On The Road Again/The World In A Jug 4
69	Liberty LBF 15169	Going Up The Country/One Kind Favour 4
69	Liberty LBF 15200	Time Was/Low Down 4
69	Liberty LBF 15255	Poor Moon/Sic 'Em Pigs 4
70	Liberty LBF 15350	Sugar Bee/Shake It And Break It 4
70	Pye International 7N 25513	Spoonful/Big Road Blues 6
70	Liberty LBF 15395	Future Blues/Skat 4
70	Liberty LBF 15429	Christmas Blues/Do Not Enter 4
71	Liberty LBF 15439	Wooly Bully/My Time Ain't Long 4
72	United Artists UP 35348	Rockin' With The King (with Little Richard)/I Don't Care What You Tell Me 4
67	Liberty LBL/LBS 83059E	CANNED HEAT (LP) 15
68	Liberty LBL/LBS 83103	BOOGIE WITH CANNED HEAT (LP, mono/stereo) 15/12
69	Liberty LDS 84001	LIVING THE BLUES (2-LP, gatefold sleeve) 20
69	Liberty LBS 83239	HALLELUJAH (LP, gatefold sleeve) 15
70	Pye Intl. NSPL 28129	VINTAGE HEAT (LP) 15
70	Liberty LBS 83333	CANNED HEAT '70: LIVE IN EUROPE (LP, gatefold sleeve) 12
71	Liberty LPS 103/4	HOOKER'N'HEAT (2-LP, gatefold sleeve, with John Lee Hooker) 20

CANNED ROCK
76	Barn 2014 104	Ho! Ho! It's Christmas/How Can It Be 4
79	Canned Rock CANS 3	This Town Ain't Big Enough/Star Wars 4
78	Canned Rock CAN 002	KINETIC ENERGY (LP) 20
79	Canned Rock CAN 003	LIVE (LP) 15

CANNIBAL & HEADHUNTERS
65	Stateside SS 403	Land Of A Thousand Dances/I'll Show You How To Love Me 15
67	CBS 62942	LAND OF A 1000 DANCES (LP) 12

CANNIBALS
78	Big Cock F-UK 1	Good Guys/Nothing Takes The Place Of You (printed paper bag sleeve) 8

(see also Count Bishops, Mike Spenser)

ACE CANNON
62	London HLU 9498	Tuff/Sittin' 5
62	London HLU 9546	Blues Stay Away From Me/Blues In My Heart 5
63	London HLU 9745	Cottonfields/Mildew 4
64	London HLU 9866	Searchin'/Love Letters In The Sand 5
67	London HLU 10105	Wonderland By Night/As Time Goes By 4
70	London HA-U/SH-U 8407	ACE OF SAX (LP) 10

FREDDY CANNON

59	Top Rank JAR 135	Tallahassee Lassie/You Know	6
59	Top Rank JAR 135	Tallahassee Lassie/You Know (78)	20
59	Top Rank JAR 207	Okefenokee/Kookie Hat	8
59	Top Rank JAR 247	Way Down Yonder In New Orleans/Fractured	5
60	Top Rank JAR 309	California, Here I Come/Indiana	6
60	Top Rank JAR 334	Chattanooga Shoeshine Boy/Boston (My Home Town)	6
60	Top Rank JAR 369	The Urge/Jump Over	6
60	Top Rank JAR 407	Happy Shades Of Blue/Guernavaca Choo Choo	5
60	Top Rank JAR 518	Humdinger/My Blue Heaven	6
61	Top Rank JAR 548	The Muskrat Rumble/Two Thousand 88	4
61	Top Rank JAR 568	Buzz Buzz A Diddle It/Opportunity	15
61	Top Rank JAR 579	Transistor Sister/Walk To The Moon	7
61	Top Rank JAR 592	From Me And My Gal/Blue Plate Special	5
62	Top Rank JAR 609	Teen Queen Of The Week/Wild Guy	6
62	Stateside SS 101	Palisades Park/June July And August	4
62	Stateside SS 118	What's Gonna Happen When Summer's Done/Broadway	4
62	Stateside SS 134	The Truth Ruth/If You Were A Rock & Roll Record	5
63	Stateside SS 155	Come On And Love Me/Four Letter Man	5
63	Stateside SS 183	The Ups And Downs Of Love/It's Been Nice	5
63	Stateside SS 201	Patty Baby/Betty Jean	8
63	Stateside SS 220	Everybody Monkey/Oh Gloria	5
64	Stateside SS 260	That's The Way Girls Are/Do What The Hippies Do	5
64	Warner Bros WB 123	Abagail Beecher/All American Girl	5
64	Warner Bros WB 298	Sweet Georgia Brown/What A Party	5
65	Warner Bros WB 5645	Action/Beechwood City	5
66	Warner Bros WB 5693	The Dedication Song/Come On Come On	4
69	London HLK 10252	Beautiful Downtown Burbank/If You Give Me A Title	4
60	Top Rank JKP 2058	THE EXPLOSIVE FREDDY CANNON (EP)	18
60	Top Rank JKP 2066	FOUR DIRECT HITS (EP)	15
61	Top Rank JKP 3010	ON TARGET (EP)	18
62	Stateside SE 1002	BLAST OFF WITH FREDDY CANNON (EP)	15
60	Top Rank 25/018	THE EXPLOSIVE FREDDY CANNON (LP)	25
61	Top Rank 35/106	HAPPY SHADES OF BLUE (LP)	30
61	Top Rank 35/113	FREDDY CANNON FAVOURITES (LP)	30
63	Stateside SL 10013	BANG ON (LP)	30
64	Stateside SL 10062	STEPS OUT (LP)	35
64	Warner Bros WM/WS 8153	FREDDIE CANNON (LP)	25

JUDY CANNON
| 65 | Pye 7N 15900 | The Very First Day I Met You/Hello Heartache | 15 |

SEAN CANNON
| 70s | Cottage COT 411 | THE ROVING JOURNEY MAN (LP) | 10 |

CANNONBALLS
| 61 | Coral Q 72428 | Cannonball Caboose/New Orleans Beat | 12 |
| 61 | Coral Q 72431 | Lullaby Of Birdland/Calliope Boogie | 12 |

CANNONS
| 60 | Decca F 11269 | I Didn't Know The Gun Was Loaded/My Guy's Come Back | 12 |
| 61 | Columbia DB 4724 | Bush Fire/Juicy | 12 |

CANNON'S JUG STOMPERS etc
| 66 | Tax LP 2 | CANNON'S JUG STOMPERS/CLIFFORD'S LOUISVILLE JUG BAND (LP, 1 side each) | 20 |

CANNY FETTLE
| 75 | Tradition TSR 023 | VARRY CANNY (LP) | 25 |

EDDIE CANTOR
| 61 | Capitol EAP1 20113 | MA HE'S MAKING EYES AT ME (EP) | 7 |

CAPABILITY BROWN
73	Charisma CB 207	Midnight Cruiser/Silent Sounds	4
70s	Charisma BCP 7	War (p/s)	5
72	Charisma CAS 1056	FROM SCRATCH (LP)	10
73	Charisma CAS 1068	VOICE (LP)	10
	(see also Unit 4+2, Tony Rivers & Castaways)		

JIM CAPALDI
| 77 | Island ILPS 9497 | PLAY IT BY EAR (LP) | 10 |
| | (see also Hellions, Traffic) | | |

CAPITOLS (U.K.)
| 66 | Pye 7N 17025 | Honey And Wine/Boulavogue | 8 |

CAPITOLS (U.S.)
66	Atlantic 584 004	Cool Jerk/Hello Stranger	8
76	Contempo CS 9030	Cool Jerk/Ain't That Terrible	4
	(see also Three Caps)		

ANDY CAPP
| 68 | Treasure Isle TI 7052 | Popatop/RICO: The Lion Speaks | 4 |
| 70 | Duke DU 69 | The Law Pts 1 & 2 | 4 |

AL CAPPS
| 73 | Stateside SS 2214 | Magician/Shangri La | 5 |

CAPREEZ
| 79 | Grapevine GRP 113 | How To Make A Sad Man Glad | 4 |

DANNY CAPRI
| 55 | Capitol CL 14265 | Desirable/I Do, I Do | 5 |
| 55 | Capitol CL 14302 | Don't Make A Liar Out Of Me/Angelica | 5 |

CAPRICORN
| 84 | private cassette | CAPRICORN (demo cassette, 2,000 only) | 20 |

(see also Mega City Four)

CAPRIS
| 61 | Columbia DB 4605 | There's A Moon Out Tonight/Indian Girl | 50 |

CAPTAIN BEEFHEART & HIS MAGIC BAND
68	Pye International 7N 25443	Yellow Brick Road/Abba Zabba	15
68	A&M AMS 726	Moonchild/Who Do You Think You're Fooling	20
73	Reprise K 14233	Too Much Time/My Head Is My Only House Unless It Rains	6
74	Virgin VS 110	Upon The My-Oh-My/Magic Be	5
78	Buddah BDS 466	Sure 'Nuff 'N Yes I Do/Electricity	6
78	MCA MCA 366	Hard Workin' Man (Jack Nitzsche featuring Captain Beefheart)/JACK NITZSCHE: Coke Machine	4
79	Virgin SIXPACK 1	SIXPACK (EP, picture disc, 5,000 only)	15
71	A&M AME 600	DIDDY WAH DIDDY (EP)	180
82	Virgin VS 534 12	LIGHT REFLECTED OFF THE OCEANDS OF THE MOON (12" EP)	7
68	Pye Intl. NPL 28110	SAFE AS MILK (LP, mono)	18
68	Liberty LBL/LBS 83172	STRICTLY PERSONAL (LP, gatefold sleeve)	20
68	Marble Arch MAL 1117	SAFE AS MILK (LP, mono reissue, 10 tracks only)	10
69	Straight STS 1053	TROUT MASK REPLICA (2-LP, gatefold sleeve)	20
70	Buddah 623 171	SAFE AS MILK (LP, stereo reissue)	12
70	Straight STS 1063	LICK MY DECALS OFF, BABY (LP)	15
71	Buddah 2365 002	MIRROR MAN (LP, gatefold sleeve)	12
71	Reprise K 44162	THE SPOTLIGHT KID (LP, with lyric card insert)	10
72	Reprise K 54007	CLEAR SPOT (LP, PVC sleeve with card insert)	12

(see also Mallard, Mu)

CAPTAIN BEYOND
| 72 | Capricorn K 47503 | CAPTAIN BEYOND (LP) | 15 |

(see also Deep Purple)

CAPTAIN NOAH & HIS FLOATING ZOO
| 72 | Argo ZDA 149 | HOLY MOSES (LP, with Kings Singers) | 10 |

CAPTAIN SCARLET
(see under Century 21)

CAPTAIN SENSIBLE
81	Crass 321984/5	THIS IS YOUR CAPTAIN SPEAKING (EP, foldout p/s)	4
82	Big Beat NS 77	Jet Boy, Jet Girl/SOFTIES: Children Of The Damned (p/s)	4
82	A&M CAPP 3	Croydon/Jimi Hendrix's Strat (picture disc)	4

(see also Damned, Magic Michael, Maxim's Trash)

C.A. QUINTET
| 83 | Psycho PSYCHO 12 | TRIP THROUGH HELL (LP, reissue of U.S. LP) | 20 |

CARAVAN
69	Verve VS 1518	A Place Of My Own/Ride	15
70	Decca F 13063	If I Could Do It All Over Again, I'd Do It All Over You/Hello, Hello	7
71	Decca F 23125	Love To Love You (And Tonight Pigs Will Fly)/Golf Girl	7
75	Decca FR 13599	Stuck In A Hole/Lover	4
76	BTM SBT 104	All The Way (With John Wayne's Single-Handed Liberation Of Paris)/Chiefs And Indians (p/s)	5
77	Arista ARIST 110	Better By Far/Silver Strings	4
80	Kingdom KV 8009	Heartbreaker/It's Never Too Late (p/s)	4
81	Kingdom KV 8014	Keepin' Up De Fences/Golden Mile (p/s)	4
68	Verve (S)VLP 6011	CARAVAN (LP, mono/stereo)	60
70	Decca SKL 5052	IF I COULD DO IT ALL OVER AGAIN, I'D DO IT ALL OVER YOU (LP)	12
71	Deram SDL-R 1	IN THE LAND OF GREY AND PINK (LP, gatefold sleeve)	12
72	Deram SDL 8	WATERLOO LILY (LP, gatefold sleeve)	12
72	MGM 2353 058	CARAVAN (LP, reissue)	20
73	Deram SDL 12	FOR GIRLS WHO GROW PLUMP IN THE NIGHT (LP)	12
74	Deram SML 1110	CARAVAN AND THE NEW SYMPHONIA (LIVE AT DRURY LANE) (LP)	10

(see also Gringo, Matching Mole)

CARAVELLES
63	Decca F 11697	You Don't Have To Be A Baby To Cry/The Last One To Know	4
63	Decca F 11758	I Really Don't Want To Know/I Was Wrong	4
64	Decca F 11816	Have You Ever Been Lonely?/Gonna Get Along Without Ya Now	4
64	Fontana TF 466	You Are Here/How Can I Be Sure?	4
64	Fontana TF 509	I Don't Care If The Sun Don't Shine/I Like A Man	4
64	Polydor NH 59034	True Love Never Runs Smooth/Georgia Boy	4
66	Polydor 56137	Hey Mamma You've Been On My Mind/New York	4
67	Polydor 56156	I Want To Love You Again/I Had To Walk Home Myself	4
68	Pye 7N 17654	The Other Side Of Love/I Hear A New Kind Of Music	4
63	Decca LK 4565	THE CARAVELLES (LP)	20

(see also Louise Cordet, Lois Lane)

GUY CARAWAN
| 58 | Pye 7N 15132 | Old Man Atom (Talking Atomic Blues)/Michael Row The Boat Ashore | 6 |

CARDIAC ARREST
| 79 | Tortch TOR 002 | A BUS FOR A BUS ON A BUS (EP) | 12 |

(see also Cardiacs)

CARDIAC ARREST
81   Another Record AN 1   Running In The Street/T.V. Friends (p/s) 8

CARDIACS
81   private label   TOY WORLD (cassette) 20
86   Alphabet ALPH 002   SEASIDE TREATS (12" EP) 10
87   Alphabet ALPH 005   LIVE AT READING '86 (LP) 10
(see also Cardiac Arrest)

CARDIGANS
58   Mercury AMT 1007   Poor Boy/Each Other 7
58   Mercury AMT 1007   Poor Boy/Each Other (78) 5

CARE
83   Arista KBIRD 2   Flaming Sword/Misericorde (picture disc) 5
(see also Wild Swans, Lotus Eaters, Lightning Seeds)

CAREFREES
63   Oriole CB 1916   We Love You Beatles/Hot Blooded Lover 8

CARETAKER RACE
88   Roustabout RST 004   Anywhere But Home/Gilda (unreleased, DJ-only) 4
(see also Loft)

BILL CAREY
55   Vogue Coral Q 72096   Heavenly Lover/My Fate Is In Your Hands 5
56   Vogue Coral Q 72151   Where Walks My True Love/Laughing Boy 5

DAVE CAREY (JAZZ BAND)
53   Columbia SCM 5030   Broken Wings/Oh, Happy Day (as David Carey) 6
56   Tempo A 122   Kater Street Rag/Kansas City Kitty 4
56   Tempo A 133   I've Found A New Baby/Brown Skin Mama 4
56   Tempo A 138   Sunset Cafe Stomp/Sweet Georgia Brown 4
56   Tempo A 150   Ida, Sweet As Apple Cider/Button Up Your Overcoat 4

HENSON CARGILL
68   Monument MON 1015   Skip A Rope/Very Well-Travelled Man 4

CARIBBEANS
69   Doctor Bird DB 1181   Let Me Walk By/AMBLINGS: Tell Me Why 10
69   Crab CR 14   Please Please/MATADORS: The Destroyer 4

CARIBBEATS
66   Ska Beat JB 246   The Bells Of St. Mary's/WINSTON RICHARDS: Loki 8
67   Double D DD 101   Highway 300/I Think Of You (actually by Merlene McKenzie) 10
67   Double D DD 103   I'll Try/If I Did Look 10
(see also Bobby Aitken)

CARIBS
60   Starlite ST45 012   Taboo/Mathilda Cha Cha Cha! 5

CARL & COMMANDERS
61   Columbia DB 4719   Farmer John/Cleanin' Up 8

CARLEW CHOIR
71   Spark SRL 1028   Huma Luma/Give A Hand To The Clown 4

BELINDA CARLISLE
86   IRS IRM 118   Mad About You/I Never Wanted A Rich Man (p/s) 4
86   IRS IRMT 118   Mad About You/(Extended Mix)/I Never Wanted A Rich Man (12", p/s) 8
88   IRS DIRM 118   Mad About You/I Never Wanted A Rich Man/Mad About You
   (Extended Mix) (3" CD) 25
87   Virgin VSCD 1036   Heaven Is A Place On Earth/We Can Change/Heaven Is A Place On Earth
   (Heavenly Version)/Heaven Is A Place On Earth (Acapella Version) (CD) 10
88   Virgin VSCD 1046   I Get Weak/Should I Let You In/I Get Weak (12" Version) (CD, picture disc) 15
88   Virgin VSTY 1074   Circle In The Sand/(Beach Party Mix)/(Seaside Groove Mix) (12", picture disc) ..15
88   Virgin VSCD 1074   Circle In The Sand/Circle In The Sand (Beach Party Mix)/
   Circle In The Sand (Seaside Groove Mix)/Circle In The Sand
   (Sandblast Multi-Mix) (CD) 8
88   Virgin VSX 1114   World Without You (Remix)/Nobody Owns Me (box set, with 2 cards &
   lyric sheet) 7
88   Virgin VSTP 1114   World Without You (Extended World-wide Mix)/World Without You
   (7" Remix)/Nobody Owns Me (12", poster p/s) 12
88   Virgin VSCD 1114   World Without You (Extended World-wide Mix)/World Without You
   (7" Remix)/World Without You (Panavision Mix) (CD) 10
88   Virgin VSCD 1150   Love Never Dies (Full Length Version)/I Feel Free (live)/Heaven Is A Place
   On Earth (live)/Circle In The Sand (live) (5" CD, with prints) 10
89   Virgin VSP 1210   Leave A Light On/Shades Of Michaelangelo/Leave A Light On (Extended Mix)
   (foldout poster p/s) 7
89   Virgin VSX 1230   La Luna/Whatever It Takes ('Xmas' pack) 6
89   Virgin VSCD 1230   La Luna/Whatever It Takes (3" CD) 7
89   Virgin VSCD 1230DJ   La Luna/Whatever It Takes (3" CD, promo-only picture disc) 50
(see also Go-Go's)

BILL CARLISLE & CARLISLES
59   Mercury AMT 1063   Down Boy/Union Suit 20
64   Hickory 45-1254   Shanghai Rooster/Big John Henry's Girl 4

CARLISLE BROTHERS
59   Parlophone GEP 8799   FRESH FROM THE COUNTRY (EP) 12

DAVE CARLSEN
73   Spark SRLP 110   A PALE HORSE (LP) 20

(LITTLE) CARL CARLTON
68	Action ACT 4501	Competition Ain't Nothin'/Three Way Love	20
68	Action ACT 4514	46 Drums 1 Guitar/Why Don't They Leave Us Alone	6
69	Action ACT 4537	Look At Mary Wonder/Bad For Each Other (as Carl Carlton)	8
75	ABC ABC 4040	Smokin' Room/Signed, Sealed, Delivered, I'm Yours (as Carl Carlton)	4

EDDIE CARLTON
76	Cream CRM 5001	It Will Be Done Pts 1 & 2	8

CARLTON & HIS SHOES
68	Coxsone CS 7065	Love Me Forever/Happy Land	15
68	Studio One SO 2062	This Feeling/You And Me (Love Is A Treasure)	15
70s	Studio One PSOL 003	LOVE ME FOREVER (LP)	12

CARMEL
82	Red Flame RF 701	Storm/I Can't Stand The Rain (p/s)	5
82	Red Flame RFM 9	CARMEL (mini-LP)	7
(see also Thunderboys)			

CARMEN
74	Regal Zonophone RZ 3086	Flamenco Fever/Lonely House	5
74	Regal Zonophone RZ 3090	Bulerias/Stepping Stone	5
73	R. Zonophone SRZA 8518	FANDANGOS IN SPACE (LP, gatefold sleeve)	15
75	R. Zonophone SLRZ 1040	DANCING ON A COLD WIND (LP, with inner sleeve)	25

HOAGY CARMICHAEL
55	Vogue Coral Q 72078	Crazy Otto Rag/Happy Hoagy's Medley	5
55	Vogue Coral Q 72095	Lazy River/I'm Just Wild About Mary	5
56	Vogue Coral Q 72123	Hong Kong Blues/LES BROWN: It's All Right With Me	5
56	Vogue Coral Q 72206	I Walk The Line/Flight To Hong Kong	5
58	Vogue VE 170113	HOAGY CARMICHAEL (EP)	10
54	Brunswick OE 9023	THE STARDUST ROAD (EP)	7

IAN CARMICHAEL
57	HMV POP 406	Lucky Jim (How I Envy Him)/Tomorrow, Tomorrow	4

CARMITA
58	Fontana H 160	The Crowd/Waterwagon Blues	4

JEAN CARN
77	Philadelphia Intl. PIR 5501	If You Wanna Go Back/You Are All I Need	4
80	Philadelphia Intl. PIR 8840	Was That All It Was/What's On Your Mind	6
80	Phil. Intl. PIR 13 8840	Was That All It Was/What's On Your Mind (12")	10
80s	Streetwave	Was That All It Was (12", reissue)	7
70s	Philadelphia Intl.	LPs	12

CARNABY
65	Piccadilly 7N 35272	Jump And Dance/My Love Will Stay	30

CARNABY STREET POP
69	Carnaby CNLS 6003	CARNABY STREET POP (LP)	60

CARNAGE
83	Creative Reality REAL 5	All The Sad People/Dismal 1984 (p/s)	4
84	Creative Reality REAL 6	Liars And Hypocrites/Vivisecting Bastards/Corrupt Youth (p/s)	4
85	Creative Reality REAL 10	Our Life In Their Hands/Land Of Make Believe/Every Six Seconds (p/s)	4

CARNATIONS
65	Blue Beat BB 285	Might Man/What Are You Selling	8

JUDY CARNE
68	Reprise RS 20680	Sock It To Me/Right Said Fred	4

CARNEGY HALL
68	Polydor 56224	The Bells Of San Francisco/Slightly Cracked	15

CARNIVAL
67	Columbia DB 8255	The Big Bright Green Pleasure Machine/Silver Dreams And Scarlet Memories	5
69	Liberty LBF 15252	Son Of A Preacher Man/Walk On By	4

CAROL & MEMORIES
66	CBS 202086	Tears On My Pillow/Crying My Eyes Out	8

BOBBI CAROL
63	Fontana 267 260TF	Will You Love Me Tomorrow/It Doesn't Matter	6

CAROLINA SLIM
72	Flyright LP 4702	CAROLINA BLUES AND BOOGIE (LP)	20

CAROLINES
65	Polydor BM 56027	Love Made A Fool Of Me/Believe In Me	4

CAROLLS
65	Polydor BM 56046	Give Me Time/Darling I Want You So Much	4
(see also Carrolls)			

RENATO CAROSONE & HIS QUARTET
57	Parlophone R 4366	Ricordate Marcellino!/Lazzarella	4
58	Parlophone R 4433	Torero — Cha Cha Cha/Il Piccolo Montanaro	5

CAROUSEL
89	Cosmic English Music CTA 102	Strawberry Fayre/Evergreen/Halfpennies And Farthings/September Come Again (12", p/s)	8
90	Cosmic English Music CTA 104	Sorrow Is The Way To Love/Hand Me Down Green/Locks And Bolts/No Ticket For The Train (12", p/s)	7
(see also Talulah Gosh)			

THELMA CARPENTER
| 61 | Coral Q 72422 | Yes, I'm Lonesome Tonight/Gimme A Little Kiss | 6 |
| 61 | Coral Q 72442 | Back Street/I Ought To Know | 6 |

WINGY CARPENTER & HIS WINGIES
| 44 | Brunswick 03453 | Put Me Back In The Alley/JAY McSHANN: Dexter Blues (78) | 10 |

CARPENTERS
71	A&M AMS 832	Love Is Surrender/For All We Know	6
71	A&M AMS 851	Rainy Days And Mondays/Saturday	4
71	A&M AMS 868	Merry Xmas Darling/Bless The Beasts And The Children	6
72	A&M AMS 885	Hurting Each Other/Maybe It's You	4
78	A&M AMS 7327	Sweet Sweet Smile/Two Sides	4
76	A&M CARP 1000	THE CARPENTERS (3-LP)	15
81	World Records ALBUM 92	THE BEST OF THE CARPENTERS (4-LP, mail-order only)	18

CARPET BAGGERS
| 67 | Spin SP 2006 | Flea Teacher/On Sunday | 8 |

CARPETTES
77	Small Wonder SMALL 3	RADIO WUNDERBAR (EP)	5
78	Small Wonder SMALL 9	Small Wonder?/2 Ne 1 (p/s)	5
80	Beggars Banquet BEG 32	Johnny Won't Hurt You/Frustration Paradise (double pack)	4

CATHY CARR
56	London HLH 8274	Ivory Tower/Please, Please Believe Me	30
56	Vogue Coral Q 72175	Heartbroken/I'll Cry At Your Wedding	5
59	Columbia DB 4270	First Anniversary/With Love	4
59	Columbia DB 4317	I'm Gonna Change Him/The Little Things You Do	4
60	Columbia DB 4408	Little Sister/Dark River	4
63	Stateside SS 147	Sailor Boy/The Next Time The Band Plays A Waltz	5

IAN CARR('S NUCLEUS)
60s	Columbia	CHANGE IS 2 (LP, with Don Rendell)	40
71	Vertigo 6360 039	SOLAR PLEXUS (LP, gatefold sleeve, spiral or 'spaceship' label)	18/10
72	Vertigo 6360 076	BELLADONNA (LP, gatefold sleeve, spiral or 'spaceship' label)	30/15
	(see also Nucleus, Don Rendell & Ian Carr Quintet, Neil Ardley)		

JAMES CARR
66	Stateside SS 507	You've Got My Mind Messed Up/That's What I Want To Know	25
66	Stateside SS 535	Love Attack/Coming Back To Me Baby	12
66	Stateside SS 545	You're Pouring Water On A Drowning Man/Forgetting You	8
67	Stateside SS 2001	The Dark End Of the Street/Loveable Girl	7
67	Stateside SS 2038	Let It Happen/A Losing Game	10
67	Stateside SS 2052	I'm A Fool For You/Gonna Send You Back To Georgia	6
68	Bell BLL 1004	A Man Needs A Woman/Stronger Than Love	5
69	B&C CB 101	Freedom Train/That's The Way Love Turned Out For Me	6
72	Mojo 2092 053	Freedom Train/That's What I Want To Know	4
67	Stateside SL 10205	YOU GOT MY MIND MESSED UP (LP)	40
69	Bell MBLL/SBLL 113	A MAN NEEDS A WOMAN (LP)	20

JOE 'FINGERS' CARR
54	Capitol CL 14169	Piccadilly Rag/Fiddle-A-Delphia	10
55	Capitol CL 14359	The Barky-roll Stomp/Deep In The Heart Of Texas (with Carr-Hops)	8
55	Capitol CL 14372	Give Me A Band And My Baby/Zig-A-Zig (with Joy-Riders)	6
56	Capitol CL 14520	Memories Of You/Henderson Stomp (with Carr-Hops)	6
56	Capitol CL 14535	Let Me Be Your Honey, Honey/Ragtime Cowboy Joe (with Carr-Hops)	6
56	Capitol CL 14587	The Portuguese Washerwoman/Stumbling	6
	(see also Lou Busch, Vicki Young)		

JOHNNY CARR (& CADILLACS)
64	Decca F 11854	Remember That Night/Respectable	10
65	Fontana TF 600	Do You Love That Girl?/Give Him A Little Time	8
66	Fontana TF 681	Then So Do I/I'm Just A Little Bit Shy (solo)	6
67	Fontana TF 823	Things Get Better/You Got Me Baby (solo)	15

LEROY CARR
53	Jazz Collector L 58	Alki Blues/HOKUMBAND: Easy Rider (78)	6
54	Jazz Collector L 92	Barrelhouse Woman No. 2/I Believe I'll Make A Change (78)	6
58	Fontana TFE 17051	TREASURES OF NORTH AMERICAN NEGRO MUSIC VOLUME 1 (EP)	15
64	RCA RCX 7168	R.C.A. VICTOR RACE SERIES VOL. 2 (EP)	12
63	CBS BPG 62206	BLUES BEFORE SUNRISE (LP)	25

LINDA CARR
| 67 | Stateside SS 2058 | Everytime/Trying To Be Good For You | 10 |

MIKE CARR
| 68 | Columbia SCX 6248 | UNDER PRESSURE (LP) | 10 |

ROMEY CARR
| 70 | Columbia DB 8710 | These Things Will Keep Me Loving You/Stand Up And Fight | 20 |

VALERIE CARR
58	Columbia DB 4083	You're The Greatest/Over The Rainbow	4
58	Columbia DB 4131	When The Boys Talk About The Girls/Padre	5
58	Columbia DB 4225	Bad Girl/Look Forward	4
59	Columbia DB 4365	The Way To My Heart/I'm Only Asking	4
61	Columbia 33SX 1228	EV'RY HOUR, EV'RY DAY OF MY LIFE (LP, also stereo SCX 3307)	10

WYNONA CARR
| 61 | Reprise R 20033 | I Gotta Stand Tall/My Faith | 15 |

ANDREA CARROLL
| 63 | London HLX 9772 | It Hurts To Be Sixteen/Why Am I So Shy | 5 |

Barbara CARROLL

BARBARA CARROLL
| 59 | London HLR 8981 | North By Northwest/Far Away | 6 |
| 59 | London HLR 8981 | North By Northwest/Far Away (78) | 5 |

BERNADETTE CARROLL
| 64 | Stateside SS 311 | Party Girl/I Don't Wanna Know | 6 |

BOB CARROLL
55	MGM SP 1132	I Love You So Much It Hurts/My Dearest, My Darling, My ...	6
56	London HLU 8299	Red Confetti, Pink Balloons And Tambourines/Handwriting On The Wall	20
58	London HLT 8724	Hi Yo Silver/Tonto The Brave	8
59	London HLT 8888	I Can't Get You Out Of My Heart/Since I'm Out Of Your Arms	6
59	London HLT 8888	I Can't Get You Out Of My Heart/Since I'm Out Of Your Arms (78)	5

DIAHANN CARROLL
| 59 | London HLT 8788 | The Big Country/Guiding Light | 6 |
| 59 | London HLT 8788 | The Big Country/Guiding Light (78) | 5 |

DON CARROLL
| 57 | Capitol CL 14812 | At Your Front Door/The Gods Were Angry With Me | 4 |
| 58 | Capitol CL 14823 | In My Arms/The Things I Might Have Been | 4 |

GINA CARROLL
| 65 | Decca F 12297 | Bye Bye Big Boy/Down The Street | 4 |

JOHNNY CARROLL & HOT ROCKS
56	Brunswick 05580	Corrine Corrina/Wild Wild Women	300
56	Brunswick 05580	Corrine Corrina/Wild Wild Women (78)	50
56	Brunswick 05603	Crazy, Crazy Lovin'/Hot Rock	300
56	Brunswick 05603	Crazy, Crazy Lovin'/Hot Rock (78)	50

PAT CARROLL
| 72 | Pye International 7N 25592 | To The Sun/Out Of My Mind | 15 |

RONNIE CARROLL
60	Philips PB 1004	Footsteps/Where My True Love Walks	4
62	Philips PB 1222	Ring-A-Ding Girl/The Girls In Their Summer Dresses	5
62	Philips 326550	If Only Tomorrow/Think Of Her (p/s)	4
56	Philips BBE 12074	WALK HAND IN HAND (EP)	8
62	Philips BL 7563	SOMETIMES I'M HAPPY, SOMETIMES I'M BLUE (LP)	10
62	Philips (S)BL 7591	MR AND MRS IS THE NAME (LP, with Millicent Martin)	10

TONI CARROLL
| 58 | MGM MGM 987 | Dreamsville/I've Never Felt This Way Before | 4 |

CARROLLS
| 66 | Polydor BM 56081 | Surrender Your Love/The Folk I Love | 8 |

(see also Carolls)

CARROLLS
68	CBS 3414	So Gently Falls The Rain/Nice To See You Darling	4
68	CBS 3710	Ever Since/Come On	5
69	CBS 4401	We're In This Thing Together/We Know Better	5

BEN CARRUTHERS & DEEP
| 65 | Parlophone R 5295 | Jack O' Diamonds/Right Behind You | 30 |

CARS
78	Elektra K 12301	My Best Friend's Girl/Living In Stereo (picture disc)	5
78	Elektra K 12312	Just What I Needed/I'm In Touch With Your World (withdrawn)	10
79	Elektra K 12312	Just What I Needed/I'm In Touch With Your World (picture disc)	5
79	Elektra K 12312T	Just What I Needed/I'm In Touch With Your World (12", plain sleeve)	7
79	Elektra K 12352	Good Times Roll/All Mixed Up (p/s, with free badge)	4
79	Elektra K 12385	Double Life/Got A Lot On My Head (picture disc, 1,000 only)	7
79	Elektra K 12371	Let's Go/That's It (picture disc)	5
81	Elektra K 12583	Shake It Up/Cruiser (picture disc, grey/pink or black/pink)	4
79	Elektra K 52148	CANDY O (LP, with no title on cover & handwritten, numbered note)	10

CHAD CARSON
| 63 | HMV POP 1156 | Stop Picking On Me/They Were Wrong | 15 |

DEL CARSON
| 59 | Decca F 11135 | Jean/I Told Myself A Lie | 4 |

JOHNNY CARSON
60	Fontana H 243	Fraulein/I Wish It Were You	4
60	Fontana H 259	The Train Of Love/First Proposal	4
60	Fontana H 277	You Talk Too Much/Now And Always	4
62	Ember EMB S 150	Teenage Bachelor/Are You Anyone's Girl?	4
63	Ember EMB S 161	The Tears Came Rolling Down/One Track Mind	4

KAY CARSON
| 56 | Capitol CL 14565 | Those Who Have Loved/The Fellow Over There | 5 |
| 56 | Capitol CL 14634 | There's A Shadow Between Us/This Man | 4 |

(see also Kit Carson)

KEN CARSON
| 55 | London HLF 8213 | Hawkeye/I've Been Working On The Railroad | 30 |
| 56 | London HLF 8237 | Let Her Go, Let Her Go/The Song Of Daniel Boone (The Daddy Of Them All) | 30 |

KIT CARSON
| 56 | Capitol CL 14524 | Band Of Gold/Cast Your Bread Upon The Waters | 8 |

MINDY CARSON
| 58 | Philips PB 822 | The Sentimental Touch/I Was Born | 4 |

MINDY CARSON & GUY MITCHELL
53   Columbia SCM 5022   That's A Why/Train Of Love 20
(see also Guy Mitchell)

VINCE CARSON
55   HMV 7M 313   Sweetie, Sweet, Sweet Sue/My Possession 4

ANITA CARTER
58   London HLA 8693   Blue Doll/Go Away Johnnie 6
60   London HLW 9102   Moon Girl/Mama Don't Cry At My Wedding 4

BENNY CARTER
54   HMV 7M 189   Blue Mountain/Sunday Afternoon 4
(see also Helen Humes)

BETTY CARTER
63   London HLK 9748   The Good Life/Nothing More To Look Forward To 5
(see also Ray Charles)

CAROLINE CARTER
65   Decca F 12239   The Ballad Of Possibilities/We Want Love 5

CAROLYN CARTER
65   London HL 9959   It Hurts/I'm Thru' 15

CHRIS CARTER
81   Industrial IRC 32   THE SPACE BETWEEN (cassette) 10
(see also Throbbing Gristle, Chris & Cosey)

CLARENCE CARTER
68   Atlantic 584 154   Thread The Needle/Don't Make My Baby Cry 7
68   Atlantic 584 176   Looking For A Fox/I Can't See Myself (Crying About You) 8
68   Atlantic 584 187   Funky Fever/Slip Away 6
68   Atlantic 584 223   Too Weak To Fight/Let Me Comfort You 5
69   Atlantic 584 248   Snatchin' It Back/Making Love (At The Dark End Of The Street) 4
69   Atlantic 584 272   The Feeling Is Right/You Can't Miss When You Can't Measure 4
70   Atlantic 584 309   Take It Off Him And Put It On Me/The Few Troubles I've Had 4
71   Atlantic 2091 045   It's All In Your Mind/Willie And Laura Mae Jones 4
71   Atlantic 2091 093   The Court Room/Getting The Bills 4
71   Atlantic 2091 139   Slipped, Tripped And Fell In Love/I Hate To Love And Run 4
75   ABC ABC 4037   Warning/On Your Way Down 4
68   Atlantic 588 152   THIS IS CLARENCE CARTER (LP) 10
68   Atlantic 588 172   THE DYNAMIC CLARENCE CARTER (LP) 10
69   Atlantic 588 191   TESTIFYIN' (LP) 10
70   Atlantic 2400 027   PATCHES (LP) 10

HAL CARTER
62   Oriole CB 1709   Twistin' Time Is Here/Come On And Twist 5

JEAN CARTER & CENTREPIECES
68   Stateside SS 2114   No Good Jim/And None 6
72   Stateside SS 2204   No Good Jim/And None (reissue) 4

MEL CARTER
63   Pye International 7N 25212   When A Boy Falls In Love/So Wonderful 7

SHEILA CARTER & EPISODE SIX
66   Pye 7N 17194   I Will Warm Your Heart/Incense 25
(see also Episode, Episode Six)

SONNY CARTER with EARL BOSTIC & HIS ORCHESTRA
55   Parlophone MSP 6167   There Is No Greater Love/Oh Baby 8
55   Parlophone R 4015   There Is No Greater Love/Oh Baby (78) 5
(see also Earl Bostic)

SYDNEY CARTER
66   Elektra EPK 801   LORD OF THE DANCE (EP) 7

CARTER FAMILY
55   Brunswick OE 9168   MOUNTAIN MUSIC VOL. 2 (EP) 7
62   RCA RCX 7100   ORIGINAL AND GREAT CARTER FAMILY VOL. 1 (EP) 7
62   RCA RCX 7101   ORIGINAL AND GREAT CARTER FAMILY VOL. 2 (EP) 7
62   RCA RCX 7102   ORIGINAL AND GREAT CARTER FAMILY VOL. 3 (EP) 7
63   RCA RCX 7109   ORIGINAL AND GREAT CARTER FAMILY VOL. 4 (EP) 7
63   RCA RCX 7110   ORIGINAL AND GREAT CARTER FAMILY VOL. 5 (EP) 7
63   RCA RCX 7111   ORIGINAL AND GREAT CARTER FAMILY VOL. 6 (EP) 7

CARTER-LEWIS & SOUTHERNERS
61   Piccadilly 7N 35004   So Much In Love/Back On The Scene 20
61   Ember EMB S 145   Two Timing Baby/Will It Happen To Me? 30
62   Piccadilly 7N 35085   Here's Hopin'/Poor Joe 25
62   Ember EMB S 165   Tell Me/My Broken Heart 30
63   Oriole CB 1835   Sweet And Tender Romance/Who Told You? 15
63   Oriole CB 1868   Your Momma's Out Of Town/Somebody Told My Girl 25
64   Oriole CB 1919   Skinnie Minnie/Easy To Cry 15
(see also Ivy League, Flowerpot Men, White Plains, Jimmy Page)

CARTER THE UNSTOPPABLE SEX MACHINE
88   Big Cat BBA 03   Sheltered Life/Is This The Only Way To Get Through To You?/
Granny Farming In The U.K. (12", p/s, original issue) 7
89   Big Cat ABB 100T   Sheriff Fatman/R.S.P.C.E./Twin Tub With Guitar/Everybody's Happy
Nowadays (12", p/s, 2,500 only) 8
90   Big Cat ABB 102T   Rubbish/Rent/Alternative Alf Garnet (12", p/s) 7
90   Big Cat ABB 102CD   Rubbish/Rent/Alternative Alf Garnet (CD) 7

MINT VALUE £

90	Rough Trade GIFT 1	Christmas Shoppers Paradise/G.I. Blues (gig freebie)	25
90	Big Cat ABB 103X	HANDBUILT FOR PERVERTS (mini-LP, export issue)	15
90	Big Cat ABB 103XCD	HANDBUILT FOR PERVERTS (mini-CD, export issue)	15

(see also Jamie Wednesday)

MARTIN CARTHY

60s	Topic STOP 7002	The Bonny Lass Of Anglesey/Palaces Of Gold	5
65	Fontana (S)TL 5269	MARTIN CARTHY (LP)	20
66	Fontana STL 5362	SECOND ALBUM (LP)	20
71	Philips 6308 049	LANDFALL (LP)	15
72	Philips 6282 022	THIS IS MARTIN CARTHY (LP)	10
73	Pegasus PEG 12	SHEARWATER (LP)	15
74	Deram SML 1111	SWEET WIVELSFIELD (LP)	12
75	Mooncrest CREST 25	SHEARWATER (LP, reissue)	10

MARTIN CARTHY & DAVE SWARBRICK

67	Fontana STL 5434	BYKER HILL (LP)	20
68	Fontana STL 5477	BUT TWO CAME BY (LP)	20
69	Fontana STL 5529	PRINCE HEATHEN (LP)	20
71	Pegasus PEG 6	SELECTIONS (LP, gatefold sleeve)	15

(see also Three City Four, Dave Swarbrick, Steeleye Span)

CARTOONE

| 69 | Atlantic 584 240 | Knick Knack Man/A Penny For The Sun | 7 |
| 69 | Atlantic 588 174 | CARTOONE (LP) | 25 |

(see also Jimmy Page)

DAVE CARTWRIGHT

70	Harmony DB 0001	MIDDLE OF THE ROAD (LP, private pressing with insert)	50
72	Transatlantic TRA 255	A LITTLE BIT OF GLORY (LP)	10
73	Transatlantic TRA 267	BACK TO THE GARDEN (LP)	10
75	Transatlantic TRA 284	DON'T LET YOUR FAMILY DOWN (LP)	10

(see also Bev Pegg, Away From The Sand, Clifford T. Ward)

DICK CARUSO

| 60 | MGM MGM 1077 | Two Long Years/Yes Sir, That's My Baby | 4 |
| 60 | MGM MGM 1099 | Pretty Little Dancin' Doll/We've Never Met | 4 |

MARIAN CARUSO

55	Brunswick 05398	The Dove/Before We Know It	4
55	Brunswick 05442	A Man called Peter/This Is The Thanks I Get	4
55	Brunswick 05462	The Boston Fancy/I Keep Telling Myself	4

MIKE CARVER

| 79 | Venom SRTS/79/CUS/396 | MURDER OF BLAIR PEACH (EP, 2 different sleeves) | 5 |

CASABLANCA

| 74 | Rocket PIGL 7 | CASABLANCA (LP, die-cut sleeve with inner lyric sleeve) | 12 |

(see also Trees)

CASCADES

63	Warner Bros WB 88	Rhythm Of The Rain/Let Me Be	4
63	Warner Bros WB 98	Shy Girl/The Last Leaf	5
63	Warner Bros WB 103	I Wanna Be Your Lover/My First Day Alone	5
63	RCA Victor RCA 1358	Cinderella/A Little Like Loving	4
64	RCA Victor RCA 1378	Jeannie/For Your Sweet Love	4
65	Liberty LIB 55822	I Bet You Won't Stay/She'll Love Again	6
66	Stateside SS 515	Cheryl's Goin' Home/Truly Julie's Blues	4
69	Uni UN 508	Maybe The Rain Will Fall/Naggin' Cries	4
63	Warner Bros WEP 6106	RHYTHM OF THE RAIN (EP)	15
63	Warner Bros WM 8127	RHYTHM OF THE RAIN (LP)	25

AL CASEY & K.C.ETTES

| 63 | Pye Intl. 7N 25215 | Surfin' Hootenanny/Easy Picking | 8 |

(see also Sanford Clark)

HOWIE CASEY & SENIORS

62	Fontana H 364	Double Twist/True Fine Mama	15
62	Fontana H 381	I Ain't Mad At You/Twist At The Top	12
63	Fontana TF 403	The Boll Weevil Song/Bony Moronie	12
62	Fontana TFL 5108	TWIST AT THE TOP (LP)	35
65	Wing WL 1022	LET'S TWIST (LP)	20

ALVIN CASH (& REGISTERS)

65	Stateside SS 386	Twine Time/The Bump (as Alvin Cash & Crawlers)	15
66	Stateside SS 543	Philly Freeze/No Deposits, No Returns (as Alvin Cash & Registers)	10
68	President PT 115	Philly Freeze/No Deposits, No Returns (as Alvin Cash & Registers) (reissue)	5
68	President PT 119	Alvin's Boo-Ga-Loo/Let's Do Some Good Timing (as Alvin Cash & Registers)	5
68	President PT 129	Doin' The Ali Shuffle/Feel So Good	5
68	President PT 147	Charge/Diff'rent Strokes For Diff'rent Folks	5
73	President PT 351	Twine Time/Twine Awhile	4
74	President PT 383	Barracuda Pts 1 & 2	4
66	President PTL 1000	THE PHILLY FREEZE (LP)	15

JOHNNY CASH (& TENNESSEE TWO)

57	London HL 8358	I Walk The Line/Get Rhythm (gold label, later silver)	80/40
57	London HL 8358	I Walk The Line/Get Rhythm (78)	15
57	London HLS 8427	Train Of Love/There You Go	35
57	London HLS 8427	Train Of Love/There You Go (78)	10
57	London HLS 8461	Next In Line/Don't Make Me Go	25
57	London HLS 8461	Next In Line/Don't Make Me Go (78)	10
57	London HLS 8514	Home Of The Blues/Give My Love To Rose	18
57	London HLS 8514	Home Of The Blues/Give My Love To Rose (78)	10

58	London HLS 8586	Ballad Of A Teenage Queen/Big River (with Tennessee Two) 15
58	London HLS 8586	Ballad Of A Teenage Queen/Big River (78) 15
58	London HLS 8656	Guess Things Happen That Way/Come In, Stranger (with Tennessee Two) 12
58	London HLS 8656	Guess Things Happen That Way/Come In, Stranger (78) 10
58	London HLS 8709	The Ways Of A Woman In Love/You're The Nearest Thing To Heaven
		(with Tennessee Two) 10
58	London HLS 8709	The Ways Of A Woman In Love/You're The Nearest Thing To Heaven (78) 10
58	Philips PB 874	All Over Again/What Do I Care 8
58	Philips PB 874	All Over Again/What Do I Care (78) 20
59	Philips PB 897	Don't Take Your Guns To Town/I Still Miss Someone 8
59	Philips PB 897	Don't Take Your Guns To Town/I Still Miss Someone (78) 20
59	London HLS 8789	It's Just About Time/I Just Thought You'd Like To Know
		(with Tennessee Two) 10
59	London HLS 8789	It's Just About Time/I Just Thought You'd Like To Know (78) 15
59	London HLS 8847	Luther Played The Boogie/Thanks A Lot 15
59	London HLS 8847	Luther Played The Boogie/Thanks A Lot (78) 20
59	Philips PB 928	Frankie's Man, Johnny/You Dreamer You 8
59	Philips PB 928	Frankie's Man, Johnny/You Dreamer You (78) 20
59	London HLS 8928	Katy Too/I Forgot To Remember To Forget 10
59	London HLS 8928	Katy Too/I Forgot To Remember To Forget (78) 20
59	Philips PB 953	I Got Stripes/Five Feet High And Rising 8
59	Philips PB 953	I Got Stripes/Five Feet High And Rising (78) 20
59	London HLS 8979	You Tell Me/Goodbye, Little Darlin', Goodbye 8
59	London HLS 8979	You Tell Me/Goodbye, Little Darlin', Goodbye (78) 20
59	Philips PB 979	The Little Drummer Boy/I'll Remember You 6
59	Philips PB 979	The Little Drummer Boy/I'll Remember You (78) 20
60	London HLS 9070	Straight A's In Love/I Love You Because 10
60	Philips PB 1017	Seasons Of My Heart/Smiling Bill McCall 6
60	London HLS 9182	Down The Street To 301/Story Of A Broken Heart 8
60	Philips PB 1075	Going To Memphis/Loading Coal 6
61	London HLS 9314	Oh Lonesome Me/Life Goes On 7
61	Philips PB 1148	The Rebel Theme/Forty Shades Of Green 6
61	Philips PB 1200	Tennessee Flat-Top Box/Tall Men 5
63	CBS AAG 159	Ring Of Fire/I'd Still Be There 4
63	CBS AAG 173	The Matador/Still In Town 4
65	CBS 201741	Orange Blossom Special/All God's Children Ain't Free 4
65	CBS 201760	It Ain't Me Babe/Time And Time Again 5
65	CBS 210809	Ring Of Fire/Streets Of Laredo 4
66	CBS 202046	The One On The Right Is The One On The Left/Cotton Pickin' Hands 4
66	CBS 202256	Everybody Loves A Nut/Austin Prison 4
67	CBS 202546	You Beat All I Ever Saw/Put The Sugar To Bed 4
67	CBS 3268	Rosanna's Going Wild/Long-Legged Guitar-Pickin' Man 4
68	CBS 3433	Certain Kind Of Hurtin'/Another Song To Sing 4
68	CBS 3549	Folsom Prison Blues/Folk Singer 4
68	CBS 3878	Daddy Sang Bass/He Turned The Water Into Wine 4
69	CBS 4460	A Boy Named Sue/San Quentin 4
69	CBS 4638	Blistered/See Ruby Fall 4

(the singles below are all export issues)

57	London HL 7020	Next In Line/Don't Make Me Go 15
57	London HL 7023	Home Of The Blues/Give My Love To Rose 15
58	London HL 7032	Ballad Of A Teenage Queen/Big River 12
58	London HL 7053	The Ways Of A Woman In Love/You're The Nearest Thing To Heaven 10
58	London RES 1120	JOHNNY CASH (EP, initially with triangular centre) 30/18
59	London RES 1193	JOHNNY CASH SINGS HANK WILLIAMS (EP, initially with triangular centre) .25/15
59	London RES 1212	COUNTRY BOY (EP, initially with triangular centre) 25/15
59	London RES 1230	JOHNNY CASH NO. 2 (EP, initially with triangular centre) 25/15
60	Philips BBE 12377	THE TROUBADOR (EP) 15
60	Philips BBE 12395	SONGS OF OUR SOIL (EP) 15
61	Philips BBE 12494	STRICTLY CASH (EP) 15
64	CBS AGG 20050	FORTY SHADES OF GREEN (EP) 15
65	CBS EP 6061	IT AIN'T ME BABE (EP) 12
66	CBS EP 6073	MEAN AS HELL (EP) 12
69	CBS EP 6601	FOLSOM PRISON BLUES (EP) 12
59	London HA-S 2157	SINGS THE SONGS THAT MADE HIM FAMOUS (LP) 25
59	London HA-S 2179	THE ROCK ISLAND LINE (LP) 20
59	Philips BBL 7298	THE FABULOUS JOHNNY CASH (LP, also stereo SBBL 554) 16/18
59	Philips BBL 7353	SONGS OF OUR SOIL (LP) 15
59	Philips BBL 7373	HYMNS BY JOHNNY CASH (LP) 12
60	Philips BBL 7358	NOW *THERE* WAS A SONG! (LP, also stereo SBBL 580) 14/16
60	Philips BBL 7417	RIDE THIS TRAIN (LP) 14
61	CBS (S)BPG 62042	THE FABULOUS JOHNNY CASH (LP) 12
62	CBS (S)BPG 62015	HYMNS FROM THE HEART (LP) 10
62	CBS (S)BPG 62073	THE SOUND OF JOHNNY CASH (LP) 12
63	CBS BPG 62119	BLOOD SWEAT AND TEARS (LP) 15
63	CBS (S)BPG 62171	RING OF FIRE (LP) 12
63	CBS (S)BPG 62284	THE CHRISTMAS SPIRIT (LP) 12
64	CBS (S)BPG 62371	I WALK THE LINE (LP) 12
64	CBS (S)BPG 62463	BITTER TEARS (LP) 12
65	CBS (S)BPG 62501	ORANGE BLOSSOM SPECIAL (LP) 10
65	Fontana FJS 301	JOHNNY CASH'S COUNTRY ROUND-UP (LP, 4 tracks only) 10
65	London HA-S 8220	THE ORIGINAL SUN SOUND OF JOHNNY CASH (LP) 18
65	CBS (S)BPG 62538	BALLADS OF THE TRUE WEST VOL. 1 (LP) 10
65	CBS (S)BPG 62575	RIDE THIS TRAIN (LP) 10
65	CBS (S)BPG 62591	BALLADS OF THE TRUE WEST VOL. 2 (LP) 10
66	London HA-S 8253	LONESOME ME (LP) 18
68	CBS 63316	OLD GOLDEN THROAT (LP) 10

Johnny CASH

68	CBS 63428	THE HOLY LAND (LP)	15
69	CBS 63521	MORE OF OLD GOLDEN THROAT (LP)	10
70	CBS 64089	THE JOHNNY CASH SHOW (LP)	10
71	CBS 64331	MAN IN BLACK (LP)	10
73	CBS Q 63629	LIVE AT SAN QUENTIN (LP, quadrophonic)	12
75	CBS 88153	RIDING THE RAILS (2-LP)	15

CASH PUSSIES
| 79 | The Label TLR 010 | 99% Is Shit/Cash Flow (p/s) | 5 |

(see also Sex Pistols)

CASINO ROYALES
| 67 | London HLU 10122 | When I Tell You That I Love You/Love In The Open Air | 4 |

CASINOS
67	Ember EMB S 241	That's The Way/Too Good To Be True	25
68	President PT 123	Then You Can Tell Me Goodbye/I Still Love You	10
68	President PT 140	To Be Loved/Tailor Made	4
68	President PT 156	When I Stop Dreaming/Please Love Me	4
68	President PTL 1007	THEN YOU CAN TELL ME GOODBYE (LP)	10

TONY CASO
| 68 | London HL 10178 | Shadow On The Ground/I Don't Care Who Knows It | 4 |

MAMA CASS

(see under Mama Cass Elliot, Mamas & Papas, Mugwumps, Big Three)

CASSANDRA COMPLEX
| 85 | Complex CXD 001 | March/Pickup (live)/Hcoma (12", p/s) | 7 |

DAVID CASSIDY
72	Bell BLL 1224	Could It Be Forever/Cherish (p/s)	4
85	Arista ARISD 89	The Last Kiss/The Letter (shaped picture disc)	4
85	Arista ARIST 589	The Last Kiss/The Letter (poster p/s)	4
85	Arista ARIST 12 589	The Last Kiss/The Letter (12", signed p/s)	7
85	Arista ARISD 620	Romance (Let Your Heart Go)/(Instrumental Mix) (picture disc)	4

(see also Partridge Family)

STEVE CASSIDY
| 63 | Ember EMB S 177 | Ecstasy/I'm A Worrying | 5 |

TED CASSIDY
| 65 | Capitol CL 15423 | The Lurch/Wesley | 15 |

CASTANARC
| 86 | Peninsula | JOURNEY TO THE EAST (LP, private pressing) | 30 |

CASTAWAYS
| 65 | London HL 10003 | Liar Liar/Sam | 15 |

CASTE
| 68 | President PT 211 | Don't Cast Aside/One Step Closer | 5 |

JOEY CASTELL
| 57 | Decca F 10966 | I'm Left, You're Right, She's Gone/Tryin' To Get To You | 50 |
| 57 | Decca F 10966 | I'm Left, You're Right, She's Gone/Tryin' To Get To You (78) | 20 |

CASTELLS
| 61 | London HLN 9392 | Sacred/I Get Dreamy | 15 |
| 62 | London HLN 9551 | So This Is Love/On The Street Of Tears | 15 |

LEE CASTLE & BARONS
| 64 | Parlophone R 5151 | Foolin'/A Love She Can Count On | 10 |

ROY CASTLE
60	Philips PB 1087	Little White Berry/Crazy Little Thorn	4
65	CBS 201736	Doctor Terror's House Of Horrors/Voodoo Girl	4
68	Olga OLE 12	Wonderful World/For All The World	4
61	Philips BBL 7457	CASTLEWISE (LP, also stereo SBBL 626)	10

CASTLE ROCK
| 73 | private pressing | NOTTINGHAM CASTLE FESTIVAL FRINGE (LP) | 200 |

CASTLE SISTERS (U.K.)
| 59 | Columbia DB 4335 | Drifting And Dreaming/Lucky Girl | 4 |

CASTLE SISTERS (Jamaica)
| 66 | Ska Beat JB 257 | Stop Your Lying/Don't Be A Fool | 8 |

CAST OF THOUSANDS
| 66 | Stateside SS 546 | My Jeannie Wears A Mini/Girl Do What You Gonna Do | 12 |

CASTON & MAJORS
| 75 | Tamla Motown TMG 938 | Child Of Love/No One Will Know | 4 |

JIMMY CASTOR (BUNCH)
67	Philips BF 1543	Hey Leroy, Your Mama's Callin'/Hamhock's Espanol	6
67	Philips BF 1590	Magic Saxophone/Just You Girl	20
71	Mercury 6052 110	Hey Leroy, Your Mama's Callin'/Hamhock's Espanol (reissue)	4
72	Mercury 6052 185	Bang Bang/Hey Willie	5
72	RCA Victor RCA 2226	Troglodyte/I Promise To Remember	4
73	RCA Victor APD1 0103	DIMENSION 3 (LP, quadrophonic)	10
74	Atlantic K 50052	THE EVERYTHING MAN (LP)	10
75	Atlantic K 50120	BUTT OF COURSE (LP)	10
75	Atlantic K 50190	SUPERSOUND (LP)	10
76	Atlantic K 50295	E-MAN GROOVIN' (LP)	10

FRANKIE CASTRO
56 Mercury MT 114   Goodbye, So Long, I'm Gone/Too Much (78) 18

CASUALS
65 Fontana TF 635   If You Walk Out/Please Don't Hide 6
68 Decca F 12737   Adios Amor (Goodbye My Love)/Don't Dream Of Yesterday 4
68 Decca F 22784   Jesamine/I've Got Something Too 4
68 Decca F 22852   Toy/Touched (some in p/s) 8/4
69 Decca SKL-R 5001   HOUR WORLD (LP) 15

CATAPILLA
71 Vertigo 6360 029   CATAPILLA (LP, gatefold sleeve, spiral label) 50
72 Vertigo 6360 074L   CHANGES (LP, gatefold sleeve, spiral label) 125

CATAPULT
88 September SEPT 6T   Sink Me/RAF/Undemocratic (12", p/s) 7

CATCH
77 Logo GO 103   Borderline/Black Blood (no p/s) 60
(see also Tourists, Eurythmics)

CATERAN
87 D.D.T. DISP 6   Last Big Lie/Difficult Days (p/s) 4
88 Imaginary MIRAGE 666   THE BLACK ALBUM (EP, 500 only, numbered, stickered black sleeve) 6
89 What Goes On PROGO 7   Cage (1-sided, promo-only, stickered plain black sleeve) 5

GEORGE CATES & HIS ORCHESTRA
55 Vogue Coral Q 72106   Autumn Leave (with Steve Allen)/High And Dry 4

CATFISH
70 CBS 64006   GET DOWN (LP) 10
71 Epic EPC 64408   LIVE CATFISH (LP) 10

RAY CATHODE (BBC RADIOPHONICS)
62 Parlophone R 4901   Time Beat/Waltz In Orbit 4

CAT IRON
69 Xtra XTRA 1087   CAT IRON (LP) 35

CAT MOTHER & ALL NIGHT NEWSBOYS
70 Polydor 56543   Good Old Rock'N'Roll/Bad News 8
69 Polydor 184 300   THE STREET GIVETH AND THE STREET TAKETH AWAY (LP) 15
70 Polydor 2425 021   ALBION DOO-WAH (LP) 15
72 United Artists UAG 29313   CAT MOTHER & ALL NIGHT NEWS BOYS (LP) 10
73 United Artists UAG 29381   LAST CHANCE DANCE (LP) 10

CATS
68 Baf BAF 1   Swan Lake/Swing Low 4
68 Baf BAF 2   My Girl/The Hog 4
68 Baf BAF 3   The Hig/Blues For Justice 4
68 Baf BAF 4   William Tell/Love Walk Right In 4

CATS
67 Parlophone R 5558   What A Crazy Life/Hopeless Try 4
68 Parlophone R 5663   What Is The World Coming To/How Could I Be So Blind? 4
69 Columbia DB 8524   I Gotta Know What's Going On/Lea 4
69 Columbia DB 8571   Why/Mandy, My Dear 4
70 Columbia DB 8655   Marian/Somewhere Up There 4
71 Columbia DB 8748   I Love You, I Do/Where Have I Been Wrong 4
71 Columbia DB 8816   One Way Mind/Country Woman 4
72 Columbia DB 8850   Dance, Dance, Dance/My Friend Joe 4
72 Columbia DB 8909   Let's Dance/I've Been In Love Before 4

CATS EYES
68 Deram DM 190   Smile Girl For Me/In A Fantasy World 6
68 Deram DM 209   I Thank You Marianne/Turn Around 4
69 Deram DM 251   Where Is She Now?/Tom Drum 15

CAT'S PYJAMAS
68 Direction 58-3235   Virginia Waters/Baby I Love You 15
68 Direction 58-3482   Camera Man/House For Sale 15
(see also Kenny Bernard)

CLEM CATTINI ORK
65 Decca F 12135   No Time To Think/Impact 15
(see also Tornados, Aquarian Age)

NADIA CATTOUSE
65 Parlophone R 5240   Port Mahon/A Little More Oil 5
66 Reality RE 503   Beautiful Barbados/Turn Around 7
66 Reality RY 1001   NADIA CATTOUSE (LP) 70
69 RCA Victor SF 8070   EARTH MOTHER (LP) 18

EDDIE CAVE & FYX
66 Pye 7N 17161   Fresh Out Of Tears/It's Almost Good 25

NICK CAVE
88 Mute MUTE 86   Oh Deanna/The Girl At The Bottom Of My Class (DJ-only) 4
90 Mute CDMUTE 118   The Weeping Song/Cocks 'n' Asses/Helpless (CD, with extra 4th track) 7
88 Mute STUMM 52   TENDER PREY (LP, with free 12" "And The Ass Saw The Angel") 10
90 Mute STUMM 76   THE GOOD SON (LP, with free acoustic 7" "The Mercy Seat"/"City Of Refuge"/"Deanna" [PSTUMM 76]) 10
(see also Birthday Party, Annie Hogan, Burmoe Brothers)

MINT VALUE £

ANDY CAVELL
62	HMV POP 1024	Hey There Cruel Heart/Lonely Soldier Boy	20
62	HMV POP 1080	Always On Saturday/Hey There, Senorita	20
63	Pye 7N 15539	Andy/There Was A Boy	20
64	Pye 7N 15610	Tell The Truth/Shut Up	20

JIMMY CAVELLO & HIS HOUSE ROCKERS
57	Vogue Coral Q 72226	Rock, Rock, Rock/The Big Beat	150
57	Vogue Coral Q 72226	Rock, Rock, Rock/The Big Beat (78)	20
57	Vogue Coral Q 72240	Foot Stompin'/Ooh-Wee	160
57	Vogue Coral Q 72240	Foot Stompin'/Ooh-Wee (78)	20

(see also Alan Freed)

CAVERN
| 82 | Kay Drum DRUM 2 | No Reason To Cry/Cry For You/Won't Let You Go (p/s) | 5 |

FRANCISCO CAVEZ
| 56 | Parlophone MSP 6205 | Arriverderci Roma/Ecuador | 5 |

MONTE CAZAZZA
79	Industrial IR 0005	To Mom On Mother's Day/Candy Man (p/s, with insert, 2,500 only)	12
80	Industrial IR 0010	SOMETHING FOR NOBODY (EP)	8
81	Industrial IRC 28	LIVE AT LEEDS FAN CLUB (cassette)	10

C.C.S.
| 70 | Rak SRKA 6751 | C.C.S. (LP) | 10 |
| 72 | Rak SRAK 503 | C.C.S. 2 (LP) | 10 |

(see also Alexis Korner)

CEDARS
68	Decca F 22720	For Your Information/Hide If You Want To Hide	25
68	Decca F 22772	I Like The Way/I Don't Know Why	25
68	Decca	THE CEDARS (EP)	100

(see also Seaders)

CELIA & MUTATIONS
77	United Artists UP 36262	Mony Mony/Mean To Me (p/s)	6
77	United Artists UP 36318	You Better Believe Me/Round And Around (p/s)	8
81	S.I.S./Liberty FREE 18	Mony Mony/Mean To Me (reissue, no p/s)	7

(see also Stranglers)

CELLOPHANE
(see under Selofane)

CELTIC FOLKWEAVE
| 70s | Polydor | CELTIC FOLKWEAVE (LP, original pressing, Irish only) | 40 |

CENOTAPH CORNER
| 76 | Cottage | UPS AND DOWNS (LP) | 20 |
| 79 | Cottage COT 031 | EVERY DAY BUT WEDNESDAY (LP) | 25 |

CENTIPEDE
| 71 | RCA Neon NE 9 | SEPTOBER ENERGY (2-LP) | 30 |
| 74 | RCA DPS 2054 | SEPTOBER ENERGY (2-LP, reissue, different cover) | 15 |

CENTURY 21 (Gerry Anderson TV spin-offs)
65	Century 21 MA 100	JOURNEY TO THE MOON (EP)	12
65	Century 21 MA 101	INTO ACTION WITH TROY TEMPEST (EP)	12
65	Century 21 MA 102	A TRIP TO MARINEVILLE (EP)	12
65	Century 21 MA 103	INTRODUCING THUNDERBIRDS (EP)	12
65	Century 21 MA 104	MARINA SPEAKS (EP)	10
65	Century 21 MA 105	TV CENTURY 21 THEMES (EP)	12
66	Century 21 MA 106	THE DALEKS (EP)	35
66	Century 21 MA 107	F.A.B. (EP)	15
66	Century 21 MA 108	THUNDERBIRD 1 (EP)	15
66	Century 21 MA 109	THUNDERBIRD 2 (EP)	15
66	Century 21 MA 110	THE STATELY HOME ROBBERIES (EP)	15
66	Century 21 MA 111	LADY PENELOPE & OTHER TV THEMES (EP)	15
66	Century 21 MA 112	THUNDERBIRD 3 (EP)	15
66	Century 21 MA 113	THUNDERBIRD 4 (EP)	15
66	Century 21 MA 114	THE PERILS OF PENELOPE (EP)	15
66	Century 21 MA 115	TOPO GIGIO IN LONDON (EP)	15
67	Century 21 MA 116	GREAT THEMES FROM GERRY ANDERSON'S THUNDERBIRDS (EP)	15
67	Century 21 MA 117	SPACE AGE NURSERY RHYMES (EP)	20
67	Century 21 MA 118	LADY PENELOPE AND PARKER (EP)	22
67	Century 21 MA 119	BRAINS AND TIN TIN (EP)	20
67	Century 21 MA 120	INTERNATIONAL RESCUE (EP)	18
67	Century 21 MA 121	THUNDERBIRDS (EP)	22
67	Century 21 MA 122	LADY PENELOPE (EP)	22
67	Century 21 MA 123	BRAINS (EP)	22
67	Century 21 MA 124	BRINK OF DISASTER (EP)	22
67	Century 21 MA 125	ATLANTIC INFERNO (EP)	22
67	Century 21 MA 126	RICOCHET (EP)	22
67	Century 21 MA 127	TINGHA & TUCKER & THE WOMBAVILLE BAND (EP)	25
67	Century 21 MA 128	ONE MOVE & YOU'RE DEAD (EP)	22
67	Century 21 MA 129	30 MINUTES AFTER NOON (EP)	22
67	Century 21 MA 130	TINGHA & TUCKER IN NURSERY RHYME TIME (EP)	20
67	Century 21 MA 131	INTRODUCING CAPTAIN SCARLET (EP)	20
67	Century 21 MA 132	CAPTAIN SCARLET AND THE MYSTERONS (EP)	20
67	Century 21 MA 133	CAPTAIN SCARLEY IS INDESTRUCTIBLE (EP)	20
67	Century 21 MA 134	CAPTAIN SCARLET OF SPECTRUM (EP)	20
67	Century 21 MA 135	CAPTAIN SCARLET VS. CAPTAIN BLACK (EP)	20

MINT VALUE £

67	Century 21 MA 136	THEMES FROM GERRY ANDERSON'S CAPTAIN SCARLET (EP)	18
80s	Fanderson MAF 1	MUSIC FROM THE 21st CENTURY (EP, 33rpm)	7
65	Century 21 LA 100	JOURNEY TO THE MOON (LP)	50
66	Century 21 LA 1	THE WORLD OF TOMORROW (LP)	30
66	Century 21 LA 2	LADY PENELOPE PRESENTS (LP)	30
66	Century 21 LA 3	JEFF TRACY INTRODUCES INTERNATIONAL RESCUE (LP)	30
66	Century 21 LA 4	LADY PENELOPE INVESTIGATES (LP)	30
66	Century 21 LA 5	THE TINGHA & TUCKER CLUB SONG BOOK (LP)	20
67	Century 21 LA 6	FAVOURITE TELEVISION THEMES (LP)	30
68	Marble Arch MAL 770	TV FAVOURITES VOL. 1 (LP)	20
68	Marble Arch MAL 771	TV FAVOURITES VOL. 2 (LP)	20
72	Hallmark HMA 227	THUNDERBIRDS AND CAPTAIN SCARLET (LP)	15

(see also Barry Gray)

CERRONE

78	Atlantic K 11089	Supernature/Give Me Love	4
78	Atlantic K 11089T	Supernature/Give Me Love (12")	8
77	Atlantic K 50334	LOVE IN 'C' MINOR (LP)	10
77	Atlantic K 50377	CERRONE'S PARADISE (LP)	10
78	Atlantic K 50431	SUPERNATURE (LP)	10

FRANK CHACKSFIELD & HIS ORCHESTRA

53	Parlophone MSP 6018	Quiet Rhythm Blues/Junior Miss	5
54	Decca F 10255	Song Of Canterbury/The Pied Piper	4
54	Decca F 10284	Fiddler's Boogie/Pizzicato Rag	5
54	Decca F 10354	Smile (Theme From "Modern Times")/Piper In The Heather	4
54	Decca F 10387	Sur Le Pave (Pavements Of Paris)/Lonely Nightingale	4
55	Decca F 10467	Blue Mirage/Lady From Luxembourg	4
56	Decca F 10689	In Old Lisbon (Lisboa Antigua)/Memories Of You	5
56	Decca F 10743	The Donkey Cart/The Banks Of The Seine	5
58	Decca F 11027	Rodeo/Souvenirs Of Love	4
59	Decca F 11146	Java Boogie/A Paris Valentine	4

CHAD (STUART) & JEREMY (CLYDE)

64	Ember EMB S 180	Yesterday's Gone/Lemon Tree (as Chad Stuart & Jeremy Clyde)	7
64	Ember EMB S 186	Early In The Morning/Like I Love You Today (as Chad Stuart & Jeremy Clyde)	7
64	United Artists UP 1062	Summer Song/No Tears For Johnnie (as Chad Stuart & Jeremy Clyde)	4
64	United Artists UP 1070	Willow Weep For Me/If She Was Mine	4
65	Ember EMB S 205	If I Loved You/No Tears For Johnnie	4
65	CBS 201769	Before And After/Evil-Hearted Me	10
65	CBS 201814	I Don't Want To Lose You/Pennies	4
66	Ember EMB S 217	What Do You Want With Me/Donna Donna	4
66	CBS 202035	Teenage Failure/Early Mornin' Rain	4
66	CBS 202279	Distant Shores/Last Night	4
66	CBS 202397	You Are She/I Won't Cry	4
64	Ember EMB EP 4543	YESTERDAY'S GONE (EP)	8
65	United Artists UEP 1008	CHAD STUART AND JEREMY CLYDE (EP)	7
65	Ember NR 5021	SING FOR YOU (LP)	12
66	Ember NR 5031	THE SECOND ALBUM (LP)	12
66	Ember (ST)NR 5036	THE BEST OF CHAD AND JEREMY (LP)	12
66	CBS 2671	OF CABBAGES AND KINGS (LP)	10

(see also John Barry, Jeremy Clyde)

ERNIE CHAFFIN

| 57 | London HLS 8409 | Lonesome For My Baby/Feelin' Low | 70 |
| 57 | London HLS 8409 | Lonesome For My Baby/Feelin' Low (78) | 20 |

CHAIN GANG

| 87 | Supreme International Editions EDITION 87-14 | Makin' Tracks/Creepy Crawlies (p/s) | 6 |

CHAINSAW

| 84 | Thunderbolt THBE 1006 | MASSACRE (12" EP) | 7 |

CHAIRMEN OF THE BOARD

70	Invictus INV 501	Give Me Just A Little More Time/Since The Days Of Pigtails	4
70	Invictus INV 504	You Got Me Dangling On A String/Tricked And Trapped	4
71	Invictus INV 507	Everything Is Tuesday/Bless You	4
71	Invictus INV 511	Pay To The Piper/When Will She Tell Me?	4
71	Invictus INV 516	Chairman Of The Board/Hanging On To A Memory	4
71	Invictus INV 516	Chairman Of The Board/When Will She Tell Me?	5
72	Invictus INV 519	Working On A Building Of Love/Try On My Love For Size	4
72	Invictus INV 524	Elmo James/Bittersweet	4
72	Invictus INV 527	I'm On My Way To A Better Place/So Glad You're Mine	4
73	Invictus INV 530	Finders Keepers/Finders Keepers (Instrumental)	4
70	Invictus SVT 1002	CHAIRMEN OF THE BOARD (LP)	18
71	Invictus SVT 1003	IN SESSION (LP)	18
72	Invictus SVT 1006	BITTERSWEET (LP)	12
73	Invictus SVT 1009	GREATEST HITS (LP)	10
74	Invictus 65868	SKIN I'M IN (LP)	12

(see also Showmen, General Johnson)

CHAKACHAS

| 72 | Polydor 2489 050 | JUNGLE FEVER (LP) | 15 |

GEORGE CHAKARIS

| 59 | Saga SAG 45-2905 | Cool/I Got Rhythm | 8 |
| 60 | Triumph RGM 1010 | I'm Always Chasing Rainbows/Heart Of A Teenage Girl | 20 |

CHAKK

| 85 | Fon FON 001 | You(edit)/They Say (edit) (p/s) | 4 |

BRYAN CHALKER

72	Chapter One CMS 1010	NEW FRONTIER (LP)	30
73	Chapter One CMS 1017	BRYAN CHALKER (LP)	15
74	Chapter One CMS 1020	DADDY SING ME A SONG (LP)	12
75	BBC REC 206	FROM WATERS OF THE MEDWAY (LP)	10
75	Sweet Folk & C. SFAO 20	EARLY DAYS (LP)	10
75	Sweet Folk & C. SFAO 25	SONGS AND BALLARDS WITH BRYAN CHALKER (LP)	10

CHALLENGERS (U.K.)

61	Parlophone R 4773	City Of The Wild Goose/Deadline	6

CHALLENGERS (U.S.)

63	Stateside SS 177	Torquay/Bulldog	5
65	Vocalion V 9253	The Man From U.N.C.L.E./The Streets Of London	12
66	Vocalion V 9270	Walk With Me/How Could I	5
63	Stateside SL 10030	SURFBEAT (LP)	20
67	Vocalion VA-N/SAV-N 8069	WIPE OUT (LP)	20

RICHARD CHAMBERLAIN

63	MGM MGM-EP 776	HITS (EP)	7
63	MGM C 923	SINGS (LP)	10
64	MGM C 1009	JOY IN THE MORNING (LP)	10

CHAMBER POP ENSEMBLE

68	Decca F 12789	Walk Away Renee/59th Street Bridge Song (Feeling Groovy)	4
68	Decca SKL 4933	CHAMBER POP ENSEMBLE (LP)	15

CHAMBERS BROTHERS

66	Vocalion VL 9267	Love Me Like The Rain/Pretty Girls Everywhere	7
66	Vocalion VL 9276	Call Me/Seventeen	7
67	CBS 202565	All Strung Out Over You/Falling In Love	5
68	Direction 58-3215	Up Town/Love Me Like The Rain	4
68	Direction 58-3671	Time Has Come Today/Dinah	4
68	Direction 58-3865	I Can't Turn You Loose/Do Your Thing	4
69	Direction 58-4098	Are You Ready/You Got The Power To Turn Me On	4
69	Direction 58-4318	People Get Ready/No No Don't Say Goodbye	4
69	Direction 58-4367	Wake Up/Everybody Needs Someone	4
70	Direction 58-4846	Love Peace And Happiness/If You Want Me To	4
70	Direction 58-5033	Let}s Do It/To Love Somebody	4
71	CBS 5389	Funky/Love Peace And Happiness	4
71	CBS 7689	By The Hair On My Chinny Chin Chin/Heaven	4
66	Vocalion VA-L/SAV-L 8058	PEOPLE GET READY (LP)	20
68	Direction 8-63407	THE TIME HAS COME (LP)	15
68	Direction 8-63451	A NEW TIME — A NEW DAY (LP)	15
70	Direction 8-66228	LOVE PEACE AND HAPPINESS (Live At Bill Graham's Fillmore West) (2-LP)	15
70	Liberty LBS 83276	FEELING THE BLUES (LP)	10
71	CBS 64156	A NEW GENERATION (LP)	10

EDDIE CHAMBLEE & HIS RHYTHM & BLUES BAND

53	Esquire 10-329	All Out/TOMMY DEAN R&B BAND: Scamon Boogie (78)	7
53	Esquire 10-330	Blues For Eddie/PINEY BROWN: That's Right, Little Girl (78)	15
53	Esquire 10-340	Cradle Rock/Back Street (78)	15

CHAMELEONS

82	Epic EPCA 2210	In Shreds/Less Than Human (p/s)	25
83	Statik STAT 30	As High As You Can Go/Pleasure And Pain (p/s)	10
83	Statik STAT 3012	As High As You Can Go/Pleasure And Pain/Paper Tigers (12", p/s)	15
83	Statik TAK 6	A Person Isn't Safe Anywhere These Days/Thursday's Child (p/s)	10
83	Statik TAK 6/12	A Person Isn't Safe Anywhere These Days/Thursday's Child/Prisoners Of The Sun (12", p/s)	15
85	Statik TAK 29	In Shreds/Nostalgia (p/s)	15
85	Statik TAK 29/12	In Shreds/Less Than Human/Nostalgia (12", p/s)	20
85	Statik TAK 35	Singing Rule Britannia (While The Walls Close In)/Singing Rule Britannia (Radio 1 'Saturday Live' Session Version) (p/s)	6
85	Statik TAK 35/12	Singing Rule Britannia (While The Walls Close In)/(Radio 1 'Saturday Live' Session Version) (12", p/s)	10
86	Geffen GEF 4	Tears/Paradiso (p/s)	6
86	Geffen GEF 4F/SAM 287	Tears/Paradiso//Swamp Thing/Inside Out (double pack, gatefold p/s)	12
86	Geffen GEF 10	Swamp Thing/John, I'm Only Dancing (p/s)	5
86	Geffen GEF 10T	Swamp Thing/John, I'm Only Dancing/Tears (Original Arrangement) (12", p/s)	8
85	Statik STATLP 22	WHAT DOES ANYTHING MEAN? BASICALLY (LP, gatefold sleeve)	10
90	Glass Pyramid EMC 1	TONY FLETCHER WALKED ON WATER (12" EP)	30
90	Glass Pyramid EMCD 1	TONY FLETCHER WALKED ON WATER (CD EP)	30
85	Statik STATLP 17	SCRIPT OF THE BRIDGE (LP, picture disc)	20
86	Hybrid CHAMLP 1	THE FAN AND THE BELLOWS (LP)	10

(see also Sun & Moon, Years)

TEDDY CHAMES

68	Blue Cat BS 141	I Want It Girl/She Is Gone (actually by Teddy Charmes)	5

CHAMPIONS

63	Oriole CB 1854	Circlorama/Pinky	7

CHAMPS (U.S.)

58	London HLU 8580	Tequila/Train To Nowhere	10
58	London HLU 8580	Tequila/Train To Nowhere (78)	5
58	London HL 8655	El Rancho Rock/Midnighter	12
58	London HL 8655	El Rancho Rock/Midnighter (78)	8
58	London HL 8715	Chariot Rock/Subway	10
58	London HL 8715	Chariot Rock/Subway (78)	15
59	London HLH 8811	Beatnik/Gone Train	8

MINT VALUE £

59	London HLH 8811	Beatnik/Gone Train (78)	20
59	London HLH 8864	Caramba/Moonlight Bay	8
59	London HLH 8864	Caramba/Moonlight Bay (78)	20
60	London HLH 9052	Too Much Tequila/Twenty Thousand Leagues	6
61	London HLH 9430	Cantina/Panic Button	5
62	London HLH 9506	Tequila Twist/Limbo Rock	5
62	London HLH 9539	Experiment In Terror/La Cucaracha	5
62	London HLH 9604	Limbo Dance/Latin Limbo	5
59	London RE 1176	Four By The Champs (EP)	20
59	London REH 1209	ANOTHER FOUR BY THE CHAMPS (EP)	20
59	London REH 1223	STILL MORE BY THE CHAMPS (EP)	20
61	London REH 1250	KNOCKOUTS! (EP)	20
58	London HA-H 2152	GO CHAMPS GO! (LP)	30
59	London HA-H 2184	EVERYBODY'S ROCKIN' WITH THE CHAMPS (LP)	30
62	London HA-H 2451	GREAT DANCE HITS (LP, early issues with flipback cover)	22/18
77	London ZGH 141	BEST OF THE CHAMPS (LP)	10

CHAMPS (Jamaica)
64	Blue Beat BB 267	Walk Between Your Enemies/Do What I Say	7

JACQUI CHAN
60	Pye 7N 15273	But No One Knows/Gentlemen Please!	4

ROB CHANCE & CHANCES-R
67	CBS 3130	At The End Of The Day/I've Got The Power	7

(see also Chances-R)

CHANCES ARE
67	Columbia DB 8144	Fragile Child/What Went Wrong	20

CHANCES-R
67	CBS 202614	Talking Out The Back Of My Head/I Aimed Too High	7
67	CBS 2940	Do It Yourself/Turn A New Leaf Over	7

(see also Ron Chance & Chances-R)

DANY CHANDELLE
65	Columbia DB 7540	Lying Awake/I Love You	15

BARBARA CHANDLER
63	London HLR 9823	Do You Really Love Me Too?/I Love To Love You	4
64	London HLR 9861	I'm Going Out With The Girls/Lonely New Year	4

GENE CHANDLER
62	Columbia DB 4793	Duke Of Earl/Kissing In The Kitchen	25
63	Stateside SS 185	Rainbow/You Threw A Lucky Punch	6
64	Stateside SS 331	Just Be True/A Song Called Soul	8
64	Stateside SS 364	Bless Our Love/London Town	6
65	Stateside SS 388	What Now/If You Can't Be True (Find A Part Time Love)	10
65	Stateside SS 401	You Can't Hurt Me No More/Everybody Let's Dance	8
65	Stateside SS 425	Nothing Can Stop Me/The Big Lie	20
65	Stateside SS 458	Good Times/No One Can Love You (Like I Do)	10
66	Stateside SS 500	(I'm Just A) Fool For You/Buddy Ain't It A Shame	8
66	Chess CRS 8047	I Fooled You This Time/Such A Pretty Thing	35
67	Coral Q 72490	The Girl Don't Care/My Love	18
68	Soul City SC 102	Nothing Can Stop Me/The Big Lie (reissue)	10
69	Action ACT 4551	I Can't Save It/I Can't Take Care Of Myself	18
69	President PT 234	Duke Of Earl/Stand By Me	5
71	Mercury 6052 033	Groovy Situation/Not The Marrying Kind	4
71	Mercury 6052 098	You're A Lady/Stone Cold Feeling	4
76	Brunswick BR 39	There Was A Time/ARTISTICS: I'm Gonna Miss You	6
65	Fontana TL 5247	DUKE OF EARL (LP)	30
68	MCA MUPS 367	THERE WAS A TIME (LP)	12
69	Action ACLP 6010	LIVE ON STAGE (LP)	15
74	Joy JOYS 136	A GENE CHANDLER ALBUM (LP)	10
70s	Chi-Sound T-578	GET DOWN (LP)	10

GENE CHANDLER & BARBARA ACKLIN
69	MCA Soul Bag BAG 1	Little Green Apples/Will I Find Love	4
74	Brunswick BR 30	From The Teacher To The Preacher/Little Green Apple	4

(see also Barbara Acklin)

GEORGE CHANDLER
76	RCA RCA 2720	One In A Million/Games Are For Children	4

JEFF CHANDLER
54	Brunswick 05264	I Should Care/More Than Anyone	8
55	Brunswick 05380	Everything Happens To Me/Always	8
55	Brunswick 05417	My Prayer/When Spring Comes	7
55	Brunswick 05441	Foxfire/Shaner Maidel	5
55	Brunswick 05465	A Little Love Can Go A Long, Long Way/Only The Very Young	5
57	London HLU 8484	Half Of My Heart/Hold Me	8
58	London HA-U 2100	JEFF CHANDLER SINGS TO YOU (LP)	10

KAREN CHANDLER
55	Vogue Coral Q 72091	The Price You Pay For Love/The Man In The Raincoat	4
56	Brunswick 05570	Love Is The $64,000 Question/(I'm Just A) Beginner	4
56	Brunswick 05596	Tonight You Belong To Me/Crazy Arms (with Jimmy Wakely)	5
57	Brunswick 05662	Your Wild Heart/It's An International Language	4
62	Salvo SLO 1803	My Own True Love/You Made Me Love You	6

KENNY CHANDLER
63	Stateside SS 166	Heart/Wait For Me	4
68	Stateside SS 2110	Beyond Love/Charity	35

Lorraine CHANDLER

LORRAINE CHANDLER
75	Black Magic BM 105	Love You Baby/What Can I Do	4

CHANDONS
68	RCA RCA 1704	Timber/Never Been Loved Before	4

CHANGIN' TIMES
68	Bell BLL 1009	When The Good Sun Shines/Show Me The Way To Go Home	4

BRUCE CHANNEL
62	Mercury AMT 1171	Hey! Baby/Dream Girl	4
62	Mercury AMT 1177	Number One Man/If Only I Had Known	4
62	Pye Intl. 7N 25137	Run Romance Run/Don't Leave Me	5
63	London HLU 9776	I Don't Wanna/Blue And Lonesome	5
64	London HLU 9841	Going Back To Louisiana/Forget Me Not	5
67	Stateside SS 2066	Mr. Bus Driver/It's Me	5
68	Bell BLL 1010	Keep On/Barbara Allen	4
68	Bell BLL 1038	Mr. Bus Driver/Trouble With Sam	4
62	Mercury MMC 14104	HEY! BABY! (LP)	18
69	Bell MBLL/SBLL 1110	KEEP ON (LP)	15
	(see also Two Smith Brothers)		

CHANNEL 4
79	Ripping RIP 1	Vampire/Channel 4 (numbered p/s with insert)	6

CHANNEL 3
82	No Future OI 11	I've Got A Gun/Manzanar/Mannequin (p/s)	5

CHANTAYS
63	London HLD 9696	Pipeline/Move It	7
64	King KG 1018	Beyond/I'll Be Back Someday	8
66	Dot DS 26757	Pipeline/Move It (reissue)	5
63	London RED 1397	PIPELINE (EP)	20
63	London HA-D/SH-D 8087	PIPELINE (LP, mono/stereo)	30/35

CHANTELLES
65	Parlophone R 5271	I Want That Boy/London My Home Town	10
65	Parlophone R 5303	The Secret Of My Success/Sticks And Stones	7
65	Parlophone R 5350	Gonna Get Burned/Gonna Give Him Some Love	8
66	Parlophone R 5431	I Think Of You/Please Don't Kiss Me	5
66	Polydor 56119	There's Something About You/Just Another Fool	8
67	CBS 2777	Blue Mood/Man I Love	6

CHANTELS
58	London HLU 8561	Maybe/Come My Little Baby	75
58	London HLU 8561	Maybe/Come My Little Baby (78)	30
62	London HLL 9428	Look In My Eyes/Glad To Be Back	18
62	London HLL 9480	Well I Told You/Still	15
62	London HLL 9532	Summertime/Here It Comes Again	15
63	Capitol CL 15297	Swamp Water/Eternally	8
69	Roulette RK 514	Maybe/He's Gone	5
	(see also Richard Barrett)		

IRENE CHANTER
75	Polydor 2058 608	Make Me Happy/Funky Music	5

CHANTERS
66	CBS 202454	Every Night (I Sit And Cry)/Where	5
67	CBS 202616	You Can't Fool Me/All Day Long	10
68	CBS 3400	What's Wrong With You/Right By Your Side	5
68	CBS 3668	My Love Is For You/Mississippi Paddleboat	7
	(see also Birds Of A Feather)		

CHANTS (U.S.)
58	Capitol CL 14876	Close Friends/Lost And Found	8

CHANTS (U.K.)
63	Pye 7N 15557	I Don't Care/Come Go With Me	6
64	Pye 7N 15591	I Could Write A Book/A Thousand Stars	6
64	Pye 7N 15643	She's Mine/Then I'll Be Home	6
64	Pye 7N 15691	Sweet Was The Wine/One Star	6
66	Fontana TF 716	Come Back And Get This Loving Baby/Love Light	8
67	Decca F 12650	A Lover's Story/Wearing A Smile	6
67	Page One POF 016	Ain't Nobody Home/For You	6
68	RCA RCA 1754	A Man Without A Face/Baby I Don't Need Your Love	25
69	RCA RCA 1823	I Get The Sweetest Feeling/Candy	15
76	Chipping Norton CHIP 2	I've Been Trying/Lucky Old Me	40
	(see also Real Thing)		

CHAOS U.K.
82	Riot City RIOT 6	BURNING BRITAIN (EP)	4
82	Riot City RIOT 12	LOUD, POLITICAL AND UNCOMPROMISING (EP)	4

CHAOTIC DISCHORD
82	Riot City RIOT 10	FUCK THE WORLD (EP)	4

PAUL CHAPLAIN & HIS EMERALDS
60	London HLU 9205	Shortnin' Bread/Nicotine	25

CHARLES CHAPLIN
57	HMV POP 370	The Spring Song/Mandolin Serenade	4

GENE CHAPMAN
63	Starlite ST45 102	Oklahoma Blues/Don't Come Crying	90

GRADY CHAPMAN
60	Mercury AMT 1107	Sweet Thing/I Know What I Want	4

MICHAEL CHAPMAN
69	Harvest HAR 5002	It Didn't Work Out/Mozart Lives Upstairs	4
69	Harvest SHVL 755	RAINMAKER (LP, gatefold sleeve)	18
69	Harvest SHVL 764	FULLY QUALIFIED SURVIVOR (LP, gatefold sleeve)	15
71	Harvest SHVL 798	WINDOW (LP, gatefold sleeve)	15
71	Harvest SHVL 786	WRECKED AGAIN (LP, gatefold sleeve)	15
73	Deram SML 1105	MILLSTONE GRIT (LP)	12
74	Deram SML 1114	DEAL GONE DOWN (LP)	12
76	Decca SKL-R 5242	SAVAGE AMUSEMENT (LP, with lyric sheet)	12
70s	Standard ESL 146	GUITARS (LP, library issue)	60

CHAPS
62	Parlophone R 4979	Poppin' Medley Pts 1 & 2	12

CHAPTER FIVE
66	CBS 202395	Anything That You Do/You Can't Mean It	150
67	CBS 2696	One In A Million/Hey Hey (unissued, demos only)	80

CHAPTER FOUR
66	United Artists UP 1143	In My Life/In Each Other's Arms	80

CHAPTERHOUSE
90	Dedicated STONE 001T	FREE FALL (12" EP)	10
90	Dedicated STONE 001CD	FREE FALL (CD EP)	12
90	Dedicated STONE 002	Something More/Rain (p/s)	6
90	Dedicated STONE 002T	SUNBURST (12" EP)	8
90s	Dedicated	GIG FREEBIE (no p/s, other tracks by 5:30 & Belltower)	10

CHAPTERS
65	Pye 7N 15815	Can't Stop Thinking About Her/Dance Little Lady	35

CHAPTER THREE
75	Pye International 7N 25680	I'll Never Be The Same Pts 1 & 2	4

CHAQUITO & HIS ORCHESTRA
60	Fontana H 265	Never On Sunday/Song Of Orpheus	4
	(see also Johnny Gregory)		

CHARGE
69	SRT private pressing	CHARGE (LP, 1 known copy)	900
92	Kissing Spell KSLP 9205	CHARGE (LP, reissue, new sleeve, 500 only)	20

CHARGE
81	Test Pressing TP 3	Kings Cross/Brave New World (p/s)	5
82	Kamera ERA 003	DESTROY THE YOUTH (EP)	4
82	Kamera ERA 007	Fashion/Ugly Shadows (p/s, red vinyl)	4
82	Kamera ERA 015	Luxury/Madman In The North (p/s)	4

MARK CHARIG
77	Ogun OG 710	PIPEDREAM (LP)	10

CHARLATANS (U.S.)
69	Philips SBL 7903	THE CHARLATANS (LP)	45
	(see also Mike Wilhelm)		

CHARLATANS (U.K.)
90	Dead Dead Good GOOD 1	Indian Rope/You Can Talk To Me/Who Wants To Know (12", p/s)	12
	(see also Electric Crayons)		

BOBBY CHARLES
56	London HLU 8247	See You Later, Alligator/On Bended Knee	1200
56	London HLU 8247	See You Later, Alligator/On Bended Knee (78)	100
73	Bearsville K 15508	Small Town Talk/Grown Too Old	4
73	Chess 6145 024	See You Later, Alligator/DIXIE CUPS: Iko Iko	4
72	Bearsville K 45516	BOBBY CHARLES (LP)	12

DON CHARLES
62	Decca F 11424	Walk With Me My Angel/Crazy Man, Crazy	12
62	Decca F 11464	The Hermit Of Misty Mountain/Moonlight Rendezvous	12
62	Decca F 11528	It's My Way Of Loving You/Guess That's The Way It Goes	12
63	Decca F 11602	Angel Of Love/Lucky Star	15
63	Decca F 11645	Heart's Cold Ice/Daybreak	20
63	HMV POP 1271	Tower Tall/Look Before You Love	5
64	HMV POP 1307	If You Don't Know I Ain't Gonna Tell Ya/Voice On The Phone	5
64	HMV POP 1332	Big Talk From A Little Man/She's Mine	12
65	HMV POP 1382	Forgetting Me, Loving Him/A Long Time Ago	4
65	HMV POP 1420	Dream On Little Dreamer/We Only Live Once	4
65	HMV POP 1478	I Could Conquer The World/Time Will Tell	4
66	HMV POP 1542	Out Of This Cold/From The Beginning	4
67	Parlophone R 5564	So Let It Be/Bring Your Love To Me	4
67	Parlophone R 5596	Have I Told You Lately/Time Waits For Nobody	4
68	Parlophone R 5659	(I've Got Everything) I've Got You/If I Had The Chance	4
68	Parlophone R 5688	The Drifter/Great To Be Livin'	20
68	Parlophone R 5712	Your Name Is On My Heart/How Can I	4
63	Decca DFE 8530	DON CHARLES (EP)	30

JIMMY CHARLES
60	London HLU 9206	A Million To One/Hop Scotch Hop	6

RAY CHARLES
58	London HLE 8768	Rockhouse Pts 1 & 2	20

Ray CHARLES

58	London HLE 8768	Rockhouse Pts 1 & 2 (78)	20
59	London HLE 8917	What'd I Say Pts 1 & 2	15
59	London HLE 8917	What'd I Say Pts 1 & 2 (78)	25
59	London HLE 9009	I'm Movin' On/I Believe To My Soul	8
59	London HLE 9009	I'm Movin' On/I Believe To My Soul (78)	30
60	London HLE 9058	Let The Good Times Roll/Don't Let The Sun Catch You Cryin'	8
60	HMV POP 774	Sticks And Stones/Worried Life Blues	6
60	London HLK 9181	Tell The Truth/You Be My Baby	8
60	HMV POP 792	Georgia On My Mind/Carry Be Back To Old Virginny	5
60	HMV POP 792	Georgia On My Mind/Carry Be Back To Old Virginny (78)	100
60	London HLK 9251	Come Rain Or Come Shine/Tell Me You'll Wait For Me	6
61	HMV POP 825	Ruby/Hard Hearted Hannah	5
61	HMV POP 838	Them That Got/I Wonder	5
61	London HLK 9364	Early In The Mornin'/A Bit Of Soul	7
61	HMV POP 862	One Mint Julep/Let's Go	6
61	HMV POP 935	Hit The Road Jack/The Danger Zone	5
61	London HLK 9435	I Wonder Who/Hard Times	7
62	HMV POP 969	Unchain My Heart/But On The Other Hand Baby	4
62	HMV POP 1017	Hide Nor Hair/At The Club	5
62	HMV POP 1034	I Can't Stop Loving You/Born To Lose	4
62	HMV POP 1064	You Don't Know Me/Careless Love	4
62	HMV POP 1099	Your Cheating Heart/You Are My Sunshine	4
63	HMV POP 1133	Don't Set Me Free/The Brightest Smile In Town	4
63	HMV POP 1161	Take These Chains From My Heart/No Letter Today	4
63	HMV POP 1202	No One/Without Love (There Is Nothing)	4
63	HMV POP 1221	Busted/Making Believe	6
64	HMV POP 1251	That Lucky Old Sun/Mississippi Mud	4
64	HMV POP 1272	Baby Don't You Cry/My Heart Cries For You	4
64	HMV POP 1315	My Baby Don't Dig Me/Something's Wrong	4
64	HMV POP 1333	No One To Cry To/A Tear Fell	4
64	HMV POP 1350	Smack Dab In The Middle/I Wake Up Crying	5
65	HMV POP 1383	Makin' Whoopee/Move It On Over	4
65	HMV POP 1392	Cry/Teardrops From My Eye	4
65	HMV POP 1414	Light Out Of Darkness/Please Forgive And Forget	4
65	HMV POP 1437	I Gotta Woman/Without A Song	5
65	HMV POP 1457	Love's Gonna Live Here/I'm A Fool To Care	4
65	HMV POP 1484	The Cincinnati Kid/That's All I Am To You	4
66	HMV POP 1502	Crying Time/When My Dreamboat Comes Home	4
66	HMV POP 1519	Together Again/You're Just About To Lose Your Clown	4
66	HMV POP 1537	Let's Go Get Stoned/The Train	5
66	HMV POP 1551	I Chose To Sing The Blues/Hopelessly	6
66	HMV POP 1566	Please Say You're Fooling/I Don't Need No Doctor	25
67	Atlantic 584 093	What'd I Say/I Got A Woman	4
67	HMV POP 1589	You Win Again/Bye Bye Love	4
67	HMV POP 1595	Somebody Oughta Write A Book About It/Here We Go Again	4
67	HMV POP 1607	In The Heat Of The Night/Something's Got To Change	5
72	Tangerine 6121 001	Booty Butt/Zig Zag	4
59	London Jazz EZK 19043	THE GREAT RAY CHARLES (EP)	12
59	London Jazz EZK 19048	SOUL BROTHERS (EP, with Milt Jackson)	12
61	London REK 1306	WHAT'D I SAY (EP)	10
61	London REK 1317	RAY CHARLES AT NEWPORT (EP)	10
62	HMV 7EG 8729	HIT THE ROAD JACK (EP)	8
62	HMV 7EG 8781	I CAN'T STOP LOVING YOU (EP)	7
63	HMV 7EG 8783	THE BALLAD STYLE OF RAY CHARLES (EP)	7
63	HMV 7EG 8801	THE SWINGING STYLE OF RAY CHARLES (EP)	7
63	HMV 7EG 8807	BABY IT'S COLD OUTSIDE (EP, with Betty Carter)	7
63	HMV 7EG 8812	TAKE THESE CHAINS FROM MY HEART (EP)	7
63	London REB 1407	THE ORIGINAL RAY CHARLES VOLUME ONE (EP)	12
63	London REB 1408	THE ORIGINAL RAY CHARLES VOLUME TWO (EP)	12
63	London REB 1409	THE ORIGINAL RAY CHARLES VOLUME THREE (EP)	12
64	HMV 7EG 8841	BUSTED (EP)	8
64	HMV 7EG 8861	RAY CHARLES SINGS (EP)	7
64	Realm REP 4001	THE YOUNG RAY CHARLES (EP)	10
66	HMV 7EG 8932	RAY CHARLES LIVE IN CONCERT (EP)	7
66	HMV 7EG 8951	RAY CHARLES SINGS SONGS OF BUCK OWENS (EP)	7
58	London Jazz LTZ-K 15134	THE GREAT RAY CHARLES (LP)	30
58	London Jazz LTZ-K 15149	RAY CHARLES AT NEWPORT (LP, also stereo SAH-K 6008)	20/22
58	London HA-E 2168	YES INDEED (LP)	15
59	London Jazz LTZ-K 15146	SOUL BROTHERS (LP with Milt Jackson, also stereo SAH-K 6030)	18/20
59	London HA-E 2226	WHAT'D I SAY (LP)	20
60	London Jazz LTZ-K 15190	THE GENIUS OF RAY CHARLES (LP)	25
60	HMV CLP 1387/CSD 1320	THE GENIUS HITS THE ROAD (LP, mono/stereo)	12/15
60	London HA-K 2284	RAY CHARLES IN PERSON (LP)	15
60	London LJZ-K 15238	THE GENIUS SINGS THE BLUES (LP)	15
61	HMV CLP 1449/CSD 1362	DEDICATED TO YOU (LP, mono/stereo)	12/15
61	HMV CLP 1475/CSD 1384	GENIUS + SOUL = JAZZ (LP, mono/stereo)	12/15
61	HMV CLP 1520/CSD 1414	RAY CHARLES AND BETTY CARTER (LP, mono/stereo)	12/15
61	HMV CLP 1580/CSD 1451	MODERN SOUNDS IN COUNTRY AND WESTERN (LP, mono/stereo)	18/20
62	London HA-K 8022	THE ORIGINAL RAY CHARLES (LP)	20
63	London HA-K 8023	THE RAY CHARLES STORY VOL. 1 (LP)	12
63	London HA-K 8024	THE RAY CHARLES STORY VOL. 2 (LP)	12
63	HMV CLP 1613/CSD 1477	MODERN SOUNDS IN COUNTRY AND WESTERN VOL. TWO (LP, mono/stereo)	12/14
63	London HA-K 8035	THE GENIUS AFTER HOURS (LP)	15
63	HMV CLP 1626/CSD 1482	GREATEST HITS (LP, mono/stereo)	12/14

63	HMV CLP 1678	INGREDIENTS IN A RECIPE FOR SOUL (LP) 12
64	London HA-K/SH-K 8045	SOUL MEETING (LP, with Milt Jackson) 15
64	HMV CLP 1728/CSD 1537	SWEET AND SOUR TEARS (LP, mono/stereo) 12/14
64	HMV CLP 1795/CSD 1566	HAVE A SMILE WITH ME (LP, mono/stereo) 12/14
65	HMV CLP 1872/CSD 1696	LIVE IN CONCERT (LP, mono/stereo) 12/14
65	HMV CLP 1914/CSD 1630	C&W MEETS R&B (LP, mono/stereo) 12/14
65	Concert Hall CJ 1250	THE AUTHENTIC RAY CHARLES (LP) 10
66	HMV CLP/CSD 3533	CRYIN' TIME (LP, with Raelets) 12
66	HMV CLP/CSD 3574	RAY'S MOODS (LP) 15
67	Atlantic 587/588 056	HALLELUJAH I LOVE HER SO (LP) 10
67	HMV CLP/CSD 3630	RAY CHARLES INVITES YOU TO LISTEN (LP) 12
68	Atlantic 590 014	YES INDEED (LP, reissue) 10
68	Stateside S(S)L 10241	GREATEST HITS (VOL. 2) (LP) 10
68	Atlantic 587/588 124	THE GREAT RAY CHARLES (LP, reissue) 10
69	Stateside S(S)L 10269	A PORTRAIT OF RAY (LP) 10
69	Atlantic 587/588 132	RAY CHARLES AT NEWPORT (LP, reissue) 10
69	Stateside S(S)L 10281	I'M ALL YOURS — BABY! (LP) 10
69	Atlantic 587/588 161	WHAT'D I SAY (LP, reissue) 10
69	Atlantic 587/588 164	RAY CHARLES IN PERSON (LP, reissue) 10
70	Stateside SSL 10293	DOING HIS THING (LP) 10
70	Probe SPB 1015	LOVE COUNTRY STYLE (LP) 10
71	Transatlantic XTRA 1103	RAY CHARLES (LP) 10
71	Tangerine 6495 001	MY KIND OF JAZZ (LP) 10
71	Probe SPB 1039	VOLCANIC ACTION OF MY SOUL (LP) 10
72	Atlantic 2659 009	SALUTE TO RAY CHARLES (LP) 12
73	Probe PBSP 108	ALL TIME GREAT C&W HITS (LP) 10
73	Atlantic K 50234	SOUL MEETING (LP, reissue, with Milt Jackson) 10

(see also Raelets, Milt Jackson)

SONNY CHARLES & CHECKMATES LTD

| 67 | Ember EMB S 240 | Mastered The Art Of Love/Please Don't Take My World Away ....15 |
| 69 | A&M AMS 752 | Black Pearl/Lazy Susan ....6 |

(see also Checkmates Ltd)

CHARLES, PAULETTE & GEE

| 71 | G.G. GG 4517 | Rock And Shake (Version 3) (actually "Lover's Affair" by Charlie Ace & Maytones)/ Roll On (Version 2) (actually "My Love And I" by Winston Wright) ....4 |

(see also Charlie Ace)

CHARLIE & MELODIANS

(see under Charlie Ace)

CHARLIE PARKAS

| 80 | Paranoid Plastics PPS 1 | The Ballad Of Robin Hood/Space Invaders (p/s) ....8 |

CHARLOTTES

| 88 | Molesworth HUNTS 5 | Are You Happy Now/How Can You Say (foldover p/s) ....6 |
| 90 | Subway Org. SUBWAY 27T | LOVE IN THE EMPTINESS (12" EP) ....7 |

CHARME

| 84 | RCA RCAT 484 | Georgy Porgy/Rock The Boat (12", p/s) ....7 |

CHARMERS (U.S.)

| 58 | Vogue V 9095 | He's Gone/Oh! Yes ....150 |
| 58 | Vogue V 9095 | He's Gone/Oh! Yes (78) ....30 |

CHARMERS (Jamaica)

61	Blue Beat BB 42	Lonely Boy/I Am Going Back Home 10
62	Blue Beat BB 114	Crying Over You/Now You Want To Cry 8
63	Blue Beat BB 157	Time After Time/Done Me Wrong 8
63	Blue Beat BB 204	I'm Back/It's A Dream 8
63	Blue Beat BB 238	Waiting For You/You Are My Sunshine 8
63	R&B JB 118	Angel Love/My Heart 10
63	R&B JB 121	Oh Why Baby/ROLAND ALPHONSO: Perhaps 10
64	R&B JB 151	What's The Use/I Am Through 8
64	R&B JB 156	In My Soul/Beware 8
64	Blue Beat BB 251	Dig The Prince/Girl Of My Dreams (as Charmer) 8
64	Blue Beat BB 256	Glamour Girl/PRINCE BUSTER'S ALLSTARS: Downbeat Funeral 8
64	Blue Beat BB 279	Nobody Takes My Baby Away From Me/BUSTER'S ALLSTARS: Mules Mules Mules 8
64	Blue Beat BB 315	Oh My Baby/SPANISHTONIANS: Stop That Train 8
66	Blue Beat BB 345	Oh My Baby/STRANGER COLE: When The Party Is Over 8
66	Ska Beat JB 237	Best Friend/MAYTALS: My Darling 8
66	Rio R 78	You Don't Know/CORNELL CAMPBELL & ROY PANTON: Sweetest Girl 8
68	Coxsone CS 7043	Things Going Wrong/KEN BOOTHE: You Keep Me Hanging On 15
68	Treasure Isle TI 7036	Keep On Going (actually by Lloyd Charmers)/SILVERTONES: Don't Say No 10
70	Duke DU 87	Colour Him Father/Version 4
70	Explosion EX 2026	Can I Get Next To You?/Big Five 4
70	Explosion EX 2035	Sweet Back/Music Talk (actually by Lloyd Charmers) 4
70	Explosion EX 2045	Skinhead Train/Everstrong (B-side with Tony Binns) 8
71	Supreme SUP 220	Just My Imagination/Gotta Get A Message To You (actually by Dave Barker) 4

LLOYD CHARMERS (alias Chalmers)

67	Coxsone CS 7023	Time Is Getting Hard/TONY GREGORY: I Sit By The Shore 10
69	Duke DU 15	Cooyah/UNIQUES: Forever 5
69	Duke DU 16	Follow This Sound/Why Pretend 5
69	Duke DU 36	Safari (Far East)/Last Laugh 5
69	Explosion EX 2001	Death A Come/Zylon 5
69	Song Bird SB 1007	Duckey Luckey/In The Spirit 5
70	Bullet BU 435	Dollars And Bonds/Sounds Familiar 4
70	Bullet BU 442	Reggae A Bye Bye/Doctor Jekyll 4

Lloyd CHARMERS

| 70 | Trojan TTL 25 | REGGAE IS TIGHT (LP) | 10 |
| 70 | Trojan TTL 30 | REGGAE CHARM (LP) | 10 |

(see also Charmers, Lloyd Tyrell/Terrel)

CHARMETTES
| 63 | London HLR 9820 | Please Don't Kiss Me Again/What Is A Tear | 5 |

CHARMS (U.S.)
| 55 | Parlophone MSP 6155 | Hearts Of Stone/Ko Ko Mo (I Love You So) | 150 |
| 55 | Parlophone R 3988 | Hearts Of Stone/Ko Ko Mo (I Love You So) (78) | 40 |

(see also Otis Williams & Charms, Tiny Topsy)

CHARMS (Jamaica)
| 64 | Island WI 154 | Carry Go Bring Home (actually Justin Hinds & Dominoes)/Hill And Gully | 8 |
| 66 | Rio R 98 | Everybody Say Yeah/This World Is Yours | 8 |

CHARTBUSTERS
| 64 | London HLU 9906 | She's The One/Slippin' Thru Your Fingers | 6 |
| 64 | London HLU 9934 | Why/Stop The Music | 6 |

CHASAR
| 85 | American Phono. APK 11 | CHASAR (LP) | 10 |

CHASE
| 71 | CBS EQ 30472 | CHASE (LP, quadrophonic) | 10 |

LINCOLN CHASE
57	London HLU 8495	Johnny Klingeringding/You're Driving Me Crazy (What Did I Do)	8
57	London HLU 8495	Johnny Klingeringding/You're Driving Me Crazy (What Did I Do) (78)	5
61	Philips PB 1103	Miss Orangutang/Walking Slowly	5

CHASERS
65	Decca F 12302	Hey Little Girl/That's What They Call Love (some in p/s)	50/30
66	Parlophone R 5451	Inspiration/She's Gone Away	60
67	Philips BF 1546	The Ways Of A Man/Summer Girl	12

ROBERT CHAUVIGNY
| 59 | Top Rank JAR 142 | The Bottle Theme/French Rockin' Waltz (Eux) | 4 |

CHEAP FLIGHTS
| 78 | Rough Notes RNS 001 | I'm Sorry/Scared (p/s) | 4 |

CHEAP TRICK
78	Epic S EPC 6199	So Good To See You/You're All Talk (withdrawn)	10
78	Epic S EPC 6427	California Man/Stiff Competition	5
79	Epic S EPC 7144	Voices/Surrender (withdrawn)	6
88	Epic 651 466-0	The Flame/Through The Night (shaped picture disc)	5
88	Epic 652 896-0	Don't Be Cruel/I Know What I Want (shaped picture disc)	5
78	Epic EPC 86083	AT BUDOKAN (LP, yellow vinyl)	10
79	Epic EPC 11-83522	DREAM POLICE (LP, picture disc)	10
82	Epic EPC 85740	ONE ON ONE (LP, red vinyl)	10
82	Epic EPC 11-85740	ONE ON ONE (LP, picture disc)	15

CHEATIN' HEARTS
| 66 | Columbia DB 8048 | Zip-Tease/The Bad Kind | 7 |

CHUBBY CHECKER
59	Top Rank JAR 154	The Class/Schooldays, Oh, Schooldays	25
59	Top Rank JAR 154	The Class/Schooldays, Oh, Schooldays (78)	20
60	Columbia DB 4503	The Twist/Toot	6
60	Columbia DB 4541	The Hucklebuck/Whole Lotta Shakin' Goin' On	10
61	Columbia DB 4591	Pony Time/Oh Susannah	6
61	Columbia DB 4652	Good Good Loving/Mess Around	7
61	Columbia DB 4691	Let's Twist Again/Everything's Gonna Be All Right	4
61	Columbia DB 4728	The Fly/That's The Way It Goes	5
62	Columbia DB 4808	Slow Twistin'/The Lose Your Inhibitions Twist	5
62	Columbia DB 4876	Dancin' Party/Gotta Get Myself Together	5
62	Pye Intl. 7N 25160	Dancin' Party/Gotta Get Myself Together (reissue)	5
62	Cameo Parkway P 806	What Do You Say/Something To Shout About	4
62	Cameo Parkway P 824	Let's Twist Again/The Twist	4
62	Cameo Parkway P 849	Limbo Rock/Hitch Hiker	4
63	Cameo Parkway P 862	Let's Limbo Some More/Twenty Miles	4
63	Cameo Parkway P 873	Black Cloud/Birdland	4
63	Cameo Parkway P 879	Twist It Up/Surf Party	4
64	Cameo Parkway P 890	Loddy Lo/Hooka Tooka	5
64	Cameo Parkway P 907	Hey Bobba Needle/Spread Joy	4
64	Cameo Parkway P 920	Lazy Elsie Molly/Rosie	5
65	Cameo Parkway P 936	Lovely, Lovely/The Weekend's Here	8
65	Cameo Parkway P 949	(At The) Discotheque/Do The Freddie	20
65	Cameo Parkway P 959	Everything's Wrong/Cu Ma La Be Stay	18
65	Cameo Parkway P 965	Two Hearts Make One Love/You Just Don't Know (What You Do To Me)	70
65	Cameo Parkway P 989	Hey You Little Boogaloo/Pussy Cat	15
69	Buddah 201045	Back In the U.S.S.R./Windy Cream	4
76	London HLU 10515	(At The) Discotheque/Show Me	4
78	London HLU 10557	You Just Don't Know (What You Do To Me)/Two Hearts Make One Love (reissue)	4
62	Columbia SEG 8155	KING OF THE TWIST (EP)	8
63	Cameo Parkway CPE 550	DANCING PARTY (EP)	8
61	Columbia 33SX 1315	TWIST WITH CHUBBY CHECKER (LP)	18
61	Columbia 33SX 1341	FOR TWISTERS ONLY (LP)	16
61	Columbia 33SX 1365	IT'S PONY TIME (LP)	15
62	Columbia 33SX 1445	TWIST ALONG WITH CHUBBY CHECKER (LP)	15
62	Golden Guinea GGL 0236	TWISTIN' ROUND THE WORLD (LP)	16

63	Cameo Parkway P 7014	ALL THE HITS (LP)	14
63	Cameo Parkway P 7020	LIMBO PARTY (LP)	12
63	Cameo Parkway P 7036	CHUBBY CHECKER (LP)	16

CHUBBY CHECKER & BOBBY RYDELL

62	Columbia DB 4802	Teach Me To Twist/Swingin' Together	5
62	Cameo Parkway C 205	Jingle Bell Rock/What Are You Doing New Year's Eve?	4
64	Cameo Parkway CPE 554	CHUBBY CHECKER AND BOBBY RYDELL IN LONDON (EP)	12
62	Columbia 335X 1424	"Checker And Rydell" (LP)	15

(see also Bobby Rydell)

CHECKMATES

61	Piccadilly 7N 35010	Rockin' Minstrel/Pompeii	8
63	Decca F 11603	Westpoint/You've Gotta Have A Gimmick Today	12
64	Decca F 11844	Sticks And Stones/Please Listen To Me	6
65	Decca F 12114	Around/I've Got To Know Now	10
65	Parlophone R 5337	Stop That Music/I've Been In Love Before	12
66	Parlophone R 5402	(You Got) The Gamma Goochie/It Ain't Right	15
66	Parlophone R 5495	Every Day Is Just The Same/I'll Be Keeping The Score	12
61	Pye NPL 18061	THE CHECKMATES (LP)	18

(see also Original Checkmates)

CHECKMATES LTD

67	Ember EMB S 235	Do The Walk (The Temptation Walk)/Glad For You	6
69	A&M AMS 747	Love Is All I Have To Give/I Never Should Have Lied	6
69	A&M AMS 769	Proud Mary/Spanish Harlem	4
70	A&M AMS 780	I Keep Forgetting/Do You Love Your Body	6
69	A&M AMLS 943	LOVE IS ALL I HAVE TO GIVE (LP)	12

(see also Sonny Charles & Checkmates Ltd)

CHEECH & CHONG

71	A&M AMLS 67010	CHEECH AND CHONG (LP)	10
72	A&M AMLH 67014	BIG BAMBU (LP, foldout sleeve)	10
73	Ode ODE 77019	LOS COCHINOS (LP)	10
74	Ode ODE 77025	WEDDING ALBUM (LP)	10
76	Ode ODE 77040	SLEEPING BEAUTY (LP)	10

JUDY CHEEKS

| 79 | Ariola ARO 164 | The Little Girl In Me/Kiss Me Baby (p/s) | 4 |

CHEERS

54	Capitol CL 14189	Bazoom (I Need Your Lovin')/Arriverderci	35
55	Capitol CL 14248	Bernie's Tune/Whodaya Want?	25
55	Capitol CL 14280	Blueberries/Can't We Be More Than Friends	25
55	Capitol CL 14337	I Must Be Dreaming/Fancy Meeting You Here	25
55	Capitol CL 14377	Black Denim Trousers And Motorcycle Boots/Some Night In Alaska	30
55	Capitol CL 14377	Black Denim Trousers And Motorcycle Boots/Some Night In Alaska (78)	5
56	Capitol CL 14561	Chicken/Don't Do Anything	18
56	Capitol CL 14601	Que Pasa Muchacha/BERT CONVY: Heaven On Earth	15
56	Capitol EAP1 584	THE CHEERS (EP)	30

(see also Bert Convy [& Thunderbirds])

CHEETAHS

64	Philips BF 1362	Mecca/Goodnight Kiss	7
65	Philips BF 1383	Soldier Boy/Johnny	7
65	Philips BF 1412	Goodbye Baby (Baby Goodbye)/That's How It Goes	7
65	Philips BF 1453	Whole Lotta Love/Party	6
66	Philips BF 1499	The Russian Boat Song/Gamble	7

CHEETER

| 79 | GTO GT 250 | Goodbye Baby/That's How It Goes | 4 |

(see also Wimple Winch)

CHELSEA

77	Step Forward SF 2	Right To Work/The Loser (p/s)	5
77	Step Forward SF 5	High Rise Living/No Admission (p/s)	5
78	Step Forward SF 8	Urban Kids/No Flowers (p/s)	4
80	Step Forward SF 14	No One's Coming Outside/What Would You Do (p/s)	4
80	Step Forward SF 15	Look At the Outside/Don't Get Me Wrong (p/s)	4
80	Step Forward SF 16	No Escape/Decide (p/s)	4
81	Step Forward SF 17	Rockin' Horse/Years Away (p/s)	4
81	Step Forward SF 18	Freemans/I.D. Parade/How Do You Know? (p/s)	4
81	Step Forward SF 20	Evacuate/New Era (p/s)	4
82	Step Forward SF 21	War Across The Nation/High Rise Living (Remix) (p/s)	4
82	Step Forward SF 22	Stand Out/Last Drink (p/s)	4
82	Step Forward SF 22	Stand Out/Last Drink (picture disc)	5
79	Step Forward SFLP 2	CHELSEA (LP, with inner sleeve)	15
81	Step Forward SFLP 5	ALTERNATIVE HITS (LP)	15
82	Step Forward SFLP 7	EVACUATE (LP)	12
84	Picasso PIK 003	LIVE AND WELL (LP)	10

(see also Gene October)

CLIFTON CHENIER

69	Action ACT 4550	Black Gal/Frogs Legs	6
70	Sonet SNTF 5012	BAYOU BLUES (LP)	10
70	Harvest MHSP 4002	CLIFTON CHENIER'S VERY BEST (LP)	20
79	Flyright FLY 539	ZYDECO BLUES (LP, with other artists)	10

CHER

65	Liberty LIB 66114	All I Really Want To Do/I'm Gonna Love You	4
66	Liberty LIB 66136	Where Do You Go/See See Rider	4
66	Liberty LIB 66160	Bang Bang (My Baby Shot Me Down)/Our Day Will Come	4

MINT VALUE £

67	Liberty LIB 12034	I Feel Something In The Air/Come To Your Window	4
67	Liberty LIB 12046	Mama (When My Dollies Have Babies)/Behind The Door	4
67	Liberty LBF 15038	You Better Sit Down Kids/Elusive Butterfly	4
69	Atlantic 584 278	Walk On Gilded Splinters/Tonight I'll Be Staying Here With You	4
69	Atco 226 003	For What It's Worth/Hangin' On	4
75	PSI 2010 006	A Love Like Yours (with Nilsson)/Hangin' On	4
76	PSI 2010 013	A Woman's Story/Baby I Love You	5
87	Geffen GEF 31P	I Found Someone/Dangerous Times (picture disc)	4
88	Geffen GEF 35TP	We All Sleep Alone (Remix) (12", 3-track picture disc)	7
66	Liberty LEP 4047	THE HITS OF CHER (EP)	7
65	Liberty LBY 3058	ALL I REALLY WANT TO DO (LP)	10
66	Liberty (S)LBY 3072	THE SONNY SIDE OF CHER (LP)	10
66	Liberty (S)LBY 3081	CHER (LP)	10
68	Liberty LBL/LBS 83051	WITH LOVE, CHER (LP)	10
70	Atco 226 026	3614 JACKSON HIGHWAY (LP, gatefold sleeve)	10

(see also Sonny & Cher, Caesar & Cleo, Nilsson)

CHEROKEES (U.S.)
| 61 | Pye Intl. 7N 25066 | Cherokee/Harlem Nocturne | 8 |

CHEROKEES (U.K.)
64	Decca F 11915	You've Done It Again Little Girl/Girl Girl Girl	6
64	Columbia DB 7341	Seven Daffodils/Are You Back In My World Now	4
65	Columbia DB 7473	Wondrous Place/Send Me All Your Love	5
65	Columbia DB 7704	I Will Never Turn My Back On You/Dig A Little Deeper	7
66	Columbia DB 7822	Land Of A 1000 Dances/Everybody's Needs	8

DON CHERRY
56	Philips PB 549	Band Of Gold/Rumble Boogie (78)	7
56	Brunswick 05538	Wanted Someone To Love/The Thrill Is Gone	6
57	Philips JK 1013	Don't You Worry/The Last Dance (jukebox edition)	8
58	Philips PB 816	Another Time, Another Place/The Golden Age	4
59	Philips PB 911	Hasty Heart/I Look For A Love	4
66	London HLU 10045	I Love You Drops/Don't Change	4

(see also John Coltrane)

CHERRY BOYS
81	Open Eye OE 5	Man To Man/So Much Confusion (embossed p/s)	4
82	Cherryosa CY 2001	Only Fools Die/Comes The Day (p/s)	4
83	Crash CRA 510	Kardomah Cafe/Airs And Graces (p/s)	4

CHERRY PEOPLE
68	MGM MGM 1438	And Suddenly/Imagination	25
69	MGM MGM 1472	Gotta Get Back/I'm The One Who Loves You	6
69	MGM MGM 1489	Light Of Love/On To Something New	6

CHERRY SMASH
67	Track 604 017	Sing Songs Of Love/Movie Star	8
68	Decca F 12838	Goodtime Sunshine/Little Old Country Home Town	12
69	Decca F 12884	Fade Away Maureen/Green Plant	12

PETE CHESTER
| 60 | Pye 7N 15305 | Ten Swinging Bottles/Whole Lotta Shakin' On The Range (with Consulates) | 15 |
| 61 | Pye Intl. 7N 25074 | Three Old Maids/Forest Fire (with Group) | 15 |

(see also Five Chesternuts)

VIC CHESTER
| 57 | Decca F 10882 | Rock-A-Billy/First Date, First Kiss, First Love | 12 |

CHESTERFIELDS
| 86 | Subway Org. SUBWAY 5 | A GUITAR IN YOUR BATH (EP, wraparound p/s in poly bag) | 7 |

MORRIS CHESTNUT
| 79 | Grapevine GRP 128 | Too Darn Soulful/You Don't Love Me Anymore | 4 |

MAURICE CHEVALIER
| 55 | Decca F 10429 | Mon P'tit Moustique/Deux Amoureux Sur Un Banc | 4 |

CHEVLONS
| 66 | Pye 7N 17145 | Too Long Alone/It's My Problem | 5 |

CHEVRONS
| 60 | Top Rank JAR 308 | Lullaby/Day After Forever | 7 |

CHEVY
80	Avatar AAA 104	Too Much Loving/See The Light	6
80	Avatar AAA 107	The Taker/Life On The Run (p/s)	10
81	Avatar AAA 114	Just Another Day (no p/s)	5
80	Avatar AALP 5001	THE TAKER (LP, with inner sleeve)	10

CHEYNES
63	Columbia DB 7153	Respectable/It's Gonna Happen To You	35
64	Columbia DB 7368	Going To The River/Cheyne-Re-La	40
65	Columbia DB 7464	Down And Out/Stop Running Around	35

(see also Peter Bardens, Fleetwood Mac, Mark Leeman Five)

CHEYNES
| 71 | Bell BLL 1144 | April Fool/Gotta Get Back | 4 |

CHICAGO
69	CBS 4381	Questions 67 And 68/Listen	4
69	CBS 4503	I'm A Man Pts 1 & 2 (withdrawn)	12
69	CBS 66221	CHICAGO TRANSIT AUTHORITY (2-LP)	14
71	CBS 66405	IV (AT CARNEGIE HALL) (4-LP)	20

CHICAGO BILL

51	Melodisc 1191	Keep Your Hands Off/Stump Blues (78)	8
52	Melodisc 1203	Five Foot Seven/Plough Hand Blues (78)	8

(see also Big Bill Broonzy)

CHICAGO LINE

66	Philips BF 1488	Jump Back/Shimmy Shimmy Ko Ko Bop	60

CHICAGO LOOP

66	Stateside SS 564	(When She Needs Good Lovin') She Comes To Me/This Must Be The Place	4

CHICANES

81	Dinosaur DD 003	Further Thoughts/Cry A Little (p/s)	5

CHICK with TED CAMERON & D.J.'s

60	Pye 7N 15292	Early In The Morning/Cool Water	15

CHICKEN OF SEA

72	Seaweed WEED 1	ROASTED WING (LP, private pressing, with flavoured insert & feather)	125

(see also Egg, Some Chicken, Atomic Rooster, Chicken Shack, Birds Of A Feather, Wild Turkey, Sparrow)

CHICKEN SHACK

67	Blue Horizon 57-3135	It's OK With Me Baby/When My Left Eye Jumps	8
68	Blue Horizon 57-3143	Worried About My Woman/Six Nights In Seven	8
68	Blue Horizon 57-3146	When The Train Comes Back/Hey Baby	5
69	Blue Horizon 57-3153	I'd Rather Go Blind/Night Life	5
69	Blue Horizon 57-3160	Tears In The Wind/The Tears You Put Me Through	5
70	Blue Horizon 57-3168	Maudie/Andalucian Blues	5
70	Blue Horizon 57-3176	Sad Clown/Tired Eyes	6
73	Deram DM 381	Time Goes Passing By/Poor Boy	4
73	Deram DM 396	You Know You Could Be Right/The Loser	4
68	Blue Horizon 7-63203	FORTY BLUE FINGERS FRESHLY PACKED AND READY TO SERVE (LP)	30
69	Blue Horizon 7-63209	O.K. KEN? (LP)	25
69	Blue Horizon 7-63218	100 TON CHICKEN (LP)	25
70	Blue Horizon 7-63861	ACCEPT CHICKEN SHACK (LP)	25
71	Deram SDL 5	IMAGINATION LADY (LP, gatefold sleeve)	20
73	Deram SML 1100	UNLUCKY BOY (LP)	15
74	Deram SDL 8008	GOODBYE CHICKEN SHACK (LP)	10

(see also Errol Dixon, Fleetwood Mac, Stan Webb, Christine Perfect)

CHICKEN SHED

77	Colby AJ 370	ALICE (LP)	120
78	Colby AJ 371	ROCK (LP)	20

CHICORY TIP

73	CBS S CBS 1866	I.O.U./Join Our Gang	6
75	Route RT 01	Survivor/Move On	6
73	CBS 64871	SON OF MY FATHER (LP)	10

CHIEFS

58	London HLU 8624	Apache/Dee's Dream	25
58	London HLU 8624	Apache/Dee's Dream (78)	15
58	London HLU 8720	Enchiladas!/Moments To Remember	15
58	London HLU 8720	Enchiladas!/Moments To Remember (78)	8

CHIEFTAINS

65	Claddagh CC 2	THE CHIEFTAINS (LP)	12
69	Claddagh CC 7	THE CHIEFTAINS VOL. 2 (LP)	10
71	Claddagh CC 10	THE CHIEFTAINS VOL. 3 (LP)	10
73	Claddagh CC 14	THE CHIEFTAINS VOL. 4 (LP)	10

CHIFFONS

63	Stateside SS 172	He's So Fine/Oh! My Lover	5
63	Stateside SS 202	One Fine Day/Why Am I So Shy	5
63	Stateside SS 230	A Love So Fine/Only My Friend	6
64	Stateside SS 254	I Have A Boyfriend/I'm Gonna Dry Your Eyes	7
64	Stateside SS 332	Sailor Boy/When Summer's Through	7
65	Stateside SS 437	Nobody Knows What's Going On (In My Mind But Me)/The Real Thing	15
66	Stateside SS 512	Sweet Talkin' Guy/Did You Ever Go Steady	5
66	Stateside SS 533	Out Of This World/Just A Boy	8
66	Stateside SS 559	Stop Look And Listen/March	8
67	Stateside SS 578	My Boyfriend's Back/I Got Plenty Of Nuttin'	12
64	Stateside SE 1012	THEY'RE SO FINE (EP)	30
63	Stateside SL 10040	THE CHIFFONS (LP)	40
66	Stateside S(S)L 10190	SWEET TALKIN' GUY (LP)	35

(see also Four Pennies)

SONY CHILDE (& T.N.T.)

65	Decca F 12218	Giving Up On Love/Mighty Nice	10
66	Polydor 56108	Two Lovers/Ain't That Good News	15
66	Polydor 56141	Heartbreak/I Still Love You (as Sonny Childe & T.N.T.)	15
66	Polydor 582 003	TO BE CONTINUED (LP)	12

BILLY CHILDISH

87	Hangman HANG 9-UP	THE 1982 CASSETTES (LP, pink and black sleeve)	15

(see also Milkshakes, Mighty Caesars)

DR. A.A. CHILDS & CONGREGATION

50s	Esquire 10-414	The Healing Prayer Pts 1 & 2 (78)	12
60	Starlite ST45 009	The Healing Prayer Pts 1 & 2	5

CHI-LITES

68	Beacon BEA 119	Pretty Girl/Love Bandit	10

CHI-LITES

70	MCA MU 1138	(For God's Sake) Give More Power To The People/Trouble's A-Comin'	4
72	Brunswick BR 1	We Need Order/Living In The Footsteps Of Another	4
73	Brunswick BR 2	A Letter To Myself/Sally	4
74	Brunswick BR 25	It's Time For Love/The Coldest Days Of My Life	4
70	MCA MUPS 397	GIVE IT AWAY (LP)	12
71	MCA MUPS 437	(FOR GOD'S SAKE) GIVE MORE POWER TO THE PEOPLE (LP)	12
72	MCA MUPS 457	A LONELY MAN (LP)	12
73	Brunswick BRLS 3017	A LETTER TO MYSELF (LP)	10
74	Brunswick BRLS 3009	THE CHI-LITES (LP)	10
74	Brunswick BRLS 3010	TOBY (LP)	10
75	Brunswick BRLS 3001	(FOR GOD'S SAKE) GIVE MORE POWER TO THE PEOPLE (LP, reissue)	10
75	Brunswick BRLS 3012	A LONELY MAN (LP, reissue)	10
75	Brunswick BRLS 3015	HALF A LOVE (LP)	10

(see also Jackie Wilson)

CHILLIWACK

71	London HLU 10327	Everyday/Sundown	4
71	London SH-U 8418	CHILLIWACK (LP)	10
75	Sire 9103 250	ROCKERBOX (LP)	10

CHILLI WILLI & RED HOT PEPPERS

75	Mooncrest MOON 40	Breathe A Little/Friday Song	4
72	Revelation REV 002	KINGS OF THE ROBOT RHYTHM (LP)	15
74	Mooncrest CREST 21	BONGOS OVER BALHAM (LP)	10

CHILLUM

| 71 | Mushroom 100 MR 11 | CHILLUM (LP, with photo insert) | 30 |

ALEX CHILTON

| 80 | Aura AUS 117 | Hey! Little Child/No More The Moon Shines Lorena | 4 |

(see also Box Tops, Big Star)

CHIMES (U.S.)

| 61 | London HLU 9283 | Once In A While/Summer Night | 15 |

CHIMES featuring DENISE (U.K.)

| 63 | Decca F 11783 | Say It Again/Can This Be Love? | 4 |
| 64 | Decca F 11885 | I'll Be Waiting, I'll Be Here/Hello Heartache | 4 |

CHINA CRISIS

82	Inevitable INEV 10	African And White/Red Sails (p/s)	4
83	Virgin VSP 562	Christian/Green Acre Bay/Performing Seals (picture disc)	4
84	Virgin VS 647	Wishful Thinking/This Occupation (p/s, red vinyl)	4
85	Virgin VSP 752	Black Man Ray/Animalistic (shaped picture disc)	5
85	Virgin VS 799	You Did Cut Me/(Version)//Christian/Seven Sports For All (live) (double pack)	4
85	Virgin VSP 799	You Did Cut Me/You Did Cut Me (Version) (shaped picture disc)	4

CHINA DOLLS

| 82 | Speed FIRED 1 | One Hit Wonder/Ain't Love Ain't Bad (p/s) | 20 |

(see also Slade)

CHINA STREET

| 78 | Criminal CRM 1 | You're A Ruin/(I Wanna Be) Your M.P. (foldout lyric p/s in poly bag & badge) | 4 |

CHINATOWN

| 81 | Airship AP 138 | Short And Sweet (p/s) | 25 |
| 80s | Airship | PLAY IT TO DEATH (LP) | 12 |

CHIN CHIN

| 88 | 53rd & 3rd AGAS 001 | Stop! Your Crying/Dark Days/Never Surrender/Cry In Vain/Revolution/ Stay With Me/My Guy/Jungle Of Fear (12") | 8 |

KES CHINS

| 62 | Starlite ST45 089 | Annie/Moody | 5 |

CHIPMUNKS

58	London HLU 8762	The Chipmunk Song/DAVID SEVILLE: Almost Good	5
60	London HLG 9243	Rudolph The Red-Nosed Reindeer/Lilly Of Laguna	4
64	Liberty LIB 10170	All My Loving/Please Please Me	7
64	Liberty LBY 1218	THE CHIPMUNKS SING THE BEATLES (LP)	10

(see also David Seville)

CHIPS

| 82 | CBS A 2366 | Day After Day/Good Morning | 4 |

GEORGE CHISHOLM & BLUENOTES

| 56 | Beltona BL 2671 | Honky Tonk/D.R. Rock (with Bert Weedon) | 7 |

(see also Bert Weedon)

CHITINIOUS ENSEMBLE

| 71 | Deram SML 1093 | CHITINIOUS ENSEMBLE (LP) | 75 |

CHOCOLATE FROG

| 68 | Atlantic 584 027 | Butchers And Bakers/I Forgive You | 15 |

CHOCOLATE MILK

75	RCA RCA 2592	Action Speaks Louder Than Words/Ain't Nothing But A Thing	6
75	RCA RCAT 2592	Action Speaks Louder Than Words/Ain't Nothing But A Thing (12")	8
77	RCA PL 11830	COMIN' (LP)	25

CHOCOLATE WATCH BAND (U.K.)

| 67 | Decca F 12649 | The Sound Of The Summer/The Only One In Sight | 15 |
| 67 | Decca F 12704 | Requiem/What's It To You | 20 |

CHOIR

| 68 | Major Minor MM 537 | It's Cold Outside/I'm Going Home | 30 |

68	Major Minor MM 557	When You Were With Me/Changin' My Mind	25

(see also Raspberries)

CHOPYN
75	Jet JET 751	In The Midnight Hour/Funky Lady	4
75	Jet JET 752	Wasting Time/If It Feels Good Do It	4
75	Jet LPO 8	GRAND SLAM (LP)	20

CHORDETTES
54	Columbia SCM 5158	Mr. Sandman/I Don't Wanna See You Cryin'	75
54	Columbia DB 3553	Mr. Sandman/I Don't Wanna See You Cryin' (78)	10
55	London HLA 8169	Humming Bird/Lonely Lips	30
56	London HLA 8217	Dudelsack Polka/I Told A Lie	25
56	London HLA 8264	Eddie My Love/Our Melody	30
56	London HLA 8264	Eddie My Love/Our Melody (78)	5
56	London HLA 8302	Born To Be With You/Love Never Changes	30
56	London HA 7011	Born To Be With You/Love Never Changes (export issue)	15
56	London HLA 8323	Lay Down Your Arms/Teenage Goodnight	25
57	London HLA 8473	Just Between You And Me/Echo Of Love	15
57	London HLA 8497	Like A Baby/Soft Sands	15
58	London HLA 8566	Baby Of Mine/Photographs	15
58	London HLA 8584	Lollipop/Baby, Come-A-Back-A	12
58	London HLA 8584	Lollipop/Baby, Come-A-Back-A (78)	5
58	London HLA 8654	Love Is A Two-Way Street/I Don't Know, I Don't Care	12
58	London HLA 8654	Love Is A Two-Way Street/I Don't Know, I Don't Care (78)	5
59	London HLA 8809	No Other Arms, No Other Lips/We Should Be Together	8
59	London HLA 8926	A Girl's Work Is Never Done/No Wheels (B-side with Jeff Crom & Jackie Ertel)	10
59	London HLA 8926	A Girl's Work Is Never Done/No Wheels (78)	15
61	London HLA 9400	Never On Sunday/Faraway Star	6
62	London HLA 9519	The White Rose Of Athens/Adios (Goodbye My Love)	5
60	London REA 1228	THE CHORDETTES (EP)	25
58	London HA-A 2088	THE CHORDETTES (LP)	30
62	London HA-A 2441	THE CHORDETTES SING (LP)	25

CHORDS (U.S.)
54	Columbia SCM 5133	Sh-Boom (Life Could Be A Dream)/Little Maiden	400
54	Columbia DB 3512	Sh-Boom (Life Could Be A Dream)/Little Maiden (78)	50

CHORDS (U.K.)
79	Polydor 2059 141	Now It's Gone/Don't Go Back (p/s)	4
80	Polydor POSP 101	Maybe Tomorrow/I Don't Wanna Know/Hey Girl (p/s)	4
80	Polydor POSP 146	Something's Missing/This Is What They Want (p/s)	4
80	Polydor 2059 258	The British Way Of Life/The Way It's Got To Be (p/s)	4
80	Polydor POSP 185	In My Street/I'll Keep On Holding On (p/s)	4
81	Polydor POSP 270	One More Minute/Who's Killing Who (p/s)	4
81	Polydor POSP 288	Turn Away Again/Turn Away Again (Again) (p/s)	5
80	Polydor Super POLS 1019	SO FAR AWAY (LP, with 7" "Now It's Gone"/"Things We Said" [KRODS 1])	10

CHORDS FIVE
67	Island WI 3044	I'm Only Dreaming/Universal Vagrant	20
68	Polydor 56261	Same Old Fat Man/Hold On To Everythin' You've Got	30
69	Jay Boy BOY 6	Some People/Battersea Fair	15

(see also Smoke)

CHORUS
85	Aaz AAZ 3	These Stones/Diamond Mine/The Verse (p/s)	6

CHOSEN FEW
73	Trojan TRLS 56	HIT AFTER HIT (LP)	10

CHOSEN FEW
74	Action ACT 4623	Funky Butter/Wondering	4
76	Polydor 2058 721	I Can Make Your Dreams Come True/Pretty Face	10
78	Polydor 2058 975	You Mean Everything To Me/It Won't Be Long	10

CHOU PAHROT
79	Klub KEP 101	Buzgo Tram Chorus/Gwizgweela Gwamhnoo/Lemons	8
79	Klub KLP 19	LIVE (LP, private pressing)	35

CHRIS & COSEY
81	Rough Trade RT 078	October (Love Song)/Little Houses (p/s)	5
81	Rough Trade RTT 078	October (Love Song)/Little Houses (12", p/s)	7
80s	Electronic Sound Maker	Sweet Surprise (magazine with free cassette)	20
84	Intl. One CTI 002	Conspiracy International/The Gift Of Tongues/The Need (p/s)	7
85	Rough Trade RTT 148	Sweet Surprise 1 (1984)/2 (1985) (12", p/s, with Annie Lennox & Dave Stewart)	3
91	World Serpent WS7 004	Passion (p/s, 1-sided, other side etched)	4
80s	Sinn And Form	City Of Spirit (cassette magazine)	10
81	Rough Trade ROUGH 34	HEARTBEAT (LP, with insert)	12
81	Rough Trade COPY 008	HEARTBEAT (cassette with 2 extra tracks "Pressure Drop" & "Tight Fit")	10
82	Rough Trade ROUGH 44	TRANCE (LP)	10

(see also Throbbing Gristle, Chris Carter, Eurythmics, Cosey Fanni Tutti)

CHRIS & STUDENTS
61	Parlophone R 4806	Ducks Away From My Fishin'/Lass Of Richmond Hill	15

PETER CHRIS & OUTCASTS
66	Columbia DB 7923	Over The Hill/The Right Girl For Me	20

BOBBY CHRISTIAN & HIS ORCHESTRA
57	Oriole CB 1384	Enough Man/Crickets On Parade (possibly unreleased on 7")	10+
57	Oriole CB 1384	Enough Man/Crickets On Parade (78)	10

MINT VALUE £

CHARLIE CHRISTIAN & ED HALL
64	Blue Note 45-1634	Profoundly Blue/IKE QUEBEC: Blue Harlem	8

HANS CHRISTIAN
68	Parlophone R 5676	All Of The Time/Never My Love	40
68	Parlophone R 5698	(The Autobiography Of) Mississippi Hobo/Sonata Of Love	40

(see also Yes, Jon Anderson)

LILLIE DELK CHRISTIAN
40s	Parlophone R 2234	Baby/I Must Have That Man (78)	35

LIZ CHRISTIAN
67	CBS 202520	Suddenly (You Find Love)/Make It Work Out	35
69	Spark SRL 1004	Call My Name/Think Of You Baby	5

MARIA CHRISTIAN
85	MCA MCA 974	Wait Until The Weekend Comes/(Instrumental) (p/s)	20/15

NEIL CHRISTIAN (& CRUSADERS)
62	Columbia DB 4938	The Road To Love/The Big Beat Drum	12
63	Columbia DB 7075	A Little Bit Of Someone Else/Get A Load Of This (Neil Christian & Crusaders)	8
66	Strike JH 301	That's Nice/She's Got The Action	6
66	Strike JH 313	Oops/She Said Yeah	5
66	Strike JH 319	Two At A Time/Wanna Lover	4
67	Pye 7N 17372	You're All Things Bright And Beautiful/I'm Gonna Love You Baby	8
66	Columbia SEG 8492	A LITTLE BIT OF SOMETHING ELSE (EP)	40

(see also Guy Hamilton, Jimmy Page, Ritchie Blackmore, Nicky Hopkins, Miki Dallon)

CHRISTIAN DEATH
83	No Future FL 2	ONLY THEATRE OF PAIN (LP, with insert)	25
86	Jungle NOS 006	OFFICIAL ANTHOLOGY OF LIVE BOOTLEGS (LP, black & yellow sleeve)	25
86	Jungle NOS 006	OFFICIAL ANTHOLOGY OF LIVE BOOTLEGS (LP, pink vinyl)	10

JOHN CHRISTIAN DEE
68	Pye 7N 17566	Take Me Along/The World Can Pack Their Bags	4
69	Decca F 12901	The World Can Pack Their Bags/Stick To Your Guns	4

CHRISTIAN'S CRUSADERS
64	Columbia DB 7289	Honey Hush/One For The Money	8

(see also Neil Christian & Crusaders)

DAVE CHRISTIE
68	Mercury MF 1028	Love And The Brass Band/Penelope Breedlove	4

JOHN CHRISTIE
74	Polydor 2058 496	4th Of July/Old Enough To Know Better (some in p/s)	20/10

LOU CHRISTIE
63	Columbia DB 4983	The Gypsy Cried/Red Sails In The Sunset	5
63	Columbia DB 7031	Two Faces Have I/All That Glitters Isn't Gold	5
63	Columbia DB 7096	How Many Teardrops/You And I	5
64	Colpix PX 735	Merry Go Round/Guitars And Bongos	5
66	MGM MGM 1297	Lightnin' Strikes/Cryin' In The Streets	5
66	MGM MGM 1308	Rhapsody In The Rain/Trapeze	4
66	MGM MGM 1325	Song Of Lita/If My Car Could Only Talk	4
67	CBS 2718	Shake Hands And Walk Away Cryin'/Escape	4
67	King KG 1036	All That Glitters Isn't Gold/Outside The Gates Of Heaven	6
69	Buddah 201 057	I'm Gonna Make You Mine/I'm Gonna Get Married	4
69	Buddah 201 073	She Sold Me Magic/Are You Gettin' Any Sunshine	4
70	MGM MGM 1492	Lightnin' Strikes/Cryin' In The Streets (reissue)	4
66	MGM C(S) 8008	LIGHTNIN' STRIKES (LP)	10
66	Colpix PXL 551	STRIKES AGAIN (LP)	10

TONY CHRISTIE (& TRACKERS)
66	CBS 202097	Life's Too Good To Waste/Just The Two Of Us	4
67	MGM MGM 1365	Turn Around/When Will I Ever Love Again?	4
68	MGM MGM 1386	I Don't Want To Hurt You Anymore/Say No More	4
68	MGM MGM 1440	My Prayer/I Need You	4

KEITH CHRISTMAS
69	RCA Victor SF 8059	STIMULUS (LP, with Mighty Baby)	40
70	B&C CAS 1015	FABLE OF THE WINGS (LP)	15
71	B&C CAS 1041	PIGMY (LP)	15

(see also Mighty Baby, Esperanto)

JUNE CHRISTY
55	Capitol CL 14355	Pete Kelly's Blues/Kicks	6
56	Capitol CL 14554	Look Out Up There/I Never Wanna Look Into Those Eyes Again	4
56	Capitol CL 14604	Intrigue/You Took Advantage Of Me	4
57	Capitol CL 14673	Sing Something Simple/Maybe You'll Be There	4
57	Capitol CL 14746	This Year's Kisses/The Best Thing For You	4
65	CBS 201738	Cool Elephant/Love's Not Only For The Young	4
55	Capitol EAP 516	SOMETHING COOL (EP)	7
54	Capitol LC 6682	SOMETHING COOL (10" LP)	12
56	Capitol T 725	JUNE CHRISTY (LP)	10
57	Capitol T 833	JUNE — FAIR AND WARMER (LP)	10
58	Capitol T 902	GONE FOR THE DAY (LP)	10
58	Capitol T 1006	JUNE CHRISTY (LP)	10
59	Capitol (S)T 1076	JUNE'S GOT RHYTHM (LP)	10
59	Capitol (S)T 1114	THE SONG IS JUNE (LP)	10
59	Capitol T 1202	JUNE CHRISTY RECALLS THOSE KENTON DAYS (LP)	10
60	Capitol (S)T 1308	BALLADS FOR NIGHT PEOPLE (LP)	10

61	Capitol (S)T 1398	COOL SCHOOL (LP, with Joe Castro Quartet) 10

(see also Stan Kenton)

CHROME
80	Siren/Red RS 12007	READ ONLY MEMORY (12" EP, some with poster) 12/8
80	Beggars Banquet BEG 36	New Age/Information (p/s) 7
81	D. F. O. T. Mountain Y3	INWORLDS (12" EP) 12
82	D. F. O. T. Mountain Z17	Firebomb/Shadows Of A Thousand Years (p/s) 8
80	Beggars Banquet BEGA 15	RED EXPOSURE (LP, with inner sleeve) 12
80	Beggars Banquet BEGA 18	HALF MACHINE LIP MOVES (LP, some with poster insert) 12/10
81	D. F. O. T. Mountain X6	BLOOD ON THE MOON (LP, with inner sleeve) 12
82	D. F. O. T. Mountain X18	3RD FROM THE SUN (LP, with insert) 12

CHRON GEN
81	Gargoyle GRGL 780	PUPPETS OF WAR (EP) 6
81	Gargoyle/Fresh GRGL 780	PUPPETS OF WAR (EP, reissue, silver & black label) 5
81	Step Forward SF 19	Reality/Subway Sadist (p/s) 4
82	Secret SEC 3	LIVING NEXT DOOR TO ALICE (EP, with 'Chronic Generation Oi' magazine No. 1) 7/4
82	Secret SHH 129	Jet Boy Jet Girl/Abortions/Subway Sadist (p/s) 4
82	Secret SHH 139	Outlaw/Behind Closed Doors/Disco (p/s) 4

CHRONICLE
78	private pressing	TWO SIDES OF CHRONICLE (LP) 15

CHUBBY & HONEYSUCKERS
66	Rio R 75	Emergency Ward/LEN & HONEYSUCKERS: One More River 7

CHUBUKOS
73	Mainstream MSS 303	Witch Doctor Bump/House Of The Rising Funk 4

CHUCK & BETTY
59	Brunswick 05815	Sissy Britches/Come Back Little Girl 18

CHUCK & DARBY
60	Blue Beat BB 19	Til The End Of Time/DUKE REID & HIS GROUP: What Makes Honey 10
60	Blue Beat BB 23	Cool School/DUKE REID & HIS GROUP: Joker 10

(see also Chuck & Dobby)

CHUCK & DOBBY
61	Starlite ST45 043	Sad Over You/Sweeter Than Honey 10
61	Starlite ST45 044	Lovey Dovey/Sitting Square 10
61	Blue Beat BB 59	Oh Fanny/Running Around 10

CHUCK & GARY
58	HMV POP 466	Can't Make Up My Mind/Teenie Weenie Jeanie 30
58	HMV POP 466	Can't Make Up My Mind/Teenie Weenie Jeanie (78) 12

CHUCK & GIDEON
63	Parlophone R 5011	Cherry Berry Lips/The Tender Touch 4

CHUCK (Josephs) & DOBBY (Dobson)
61	Blue Beat BB 39	Du Du Wap/I Love My Teacher (with Aubrey Adams & Du Droppers) 10

CHUCK & JOE WHITE
64	Ska Beat JB 180	Punch You Down/TOMMY McCOOK: Cotton Tree 8
65	Island WI 201	Low Minded People/Irene 10

(see also Joe White & Chuck)

CHUCKS
63	Decca F 11569	Loo Be Loo/Anytime Is The Right Time 4
63	Decca F 11617	Mulberry Bush/That's All I Needed 4
63	Decca F 11777	The Hitch Hiker/Humpty Dumpty 4
64	Decca DFE 8562	THE CHUCKS (EP) 10

CHURCH
82	Carrere CAR 212	Unguarded Moment/Busdriver (p/s) 10
82	Carrere CAR 247	Almost With You/Life Speeds Up (p/s) 8
82	Carrere CAR 257	Unguarded Moment/Interlude/Golden Dawn (p/s) 7
82	Carrere CAR EP 257	Unguarded Moment/Interlude/Golden Dawn/Sisters (10", p/s) 15
83	Carrere CHURCH 5	SING SONGS (12" EP) 20
83	Carrere CHURCH R5A	Different Man/I Am A Rock (p/s) 15
84	Carrere CAR 336	It's No Reason/Someone Special (p/s) 6
84	Carrere CART 336	It's No Reason/Someone Special/Autumn Soon (12", p/s) 10
86	B. Of Brains BOB 9	Warm Spell (flexidisc with 'Bucketfull Of Brains' magazine) 5/4
88	Arista 109 778	Under The Milky Way/Musk (gatefold p/s) 4
82	Carrere CAL 140	THE BLURRED CRUSADE (LP, gatefold sleeve) 12
88	Arista 208895	STARFISH (LP, with free 5-track numbered 12") 15

EUGENE CHURCH
59	London HL 8940	Miami/I Ain't Goin' For That 30
59	London HL 8940	Miami/I Ain't Goin' For That (78) 18

CHICK CHURCHILL
73	Chrysalis CHR 1051	YOU AND ME (LP) 10

(see also Ten Years After)

SAVANNAH CHURCHILL
53	Brunswick 05218	Shake A Hand/Shed A Tear (78) 20
61	London HLW 9273	I Want To Be Loved/Time Out For Tears 6

CHURCH OF RAISM
89	Creation CRELP 057	CHURCH OF RAISM (LP) 10

CIGARETTES
78	Dead Good KEVIN 1	THE CIGARETTES (EP, unreleased)

CIGARETTES

79	Company CIGCO 008	They're Back Again, Here They Come/I've Forgot My Number/All We Want Is Your Money (gatefold p/s, 1st pressing has burgundy label)	14/12
80	Dead Good DEAD 10	Can't Sleep At Night/It's The Only Way To Live (Die) (p/s)	10

CIMARRONS
70	Hot Rod HR 105	Grandfather Clock/Kick Me Or 1 Kick You	4
70	Reggae REG 3003	Bad Day At Black Rock (with Cimmaron Kid)/Fragile	8

CINDERELLAS
59	Brunswick 05794	Mister Dee-Jay/Yum Yum Yum	15
60	Philips PB 1012	The Trouble With Boys/Puppy Dog	12
64	Colpix PX 11026	Baby, Baby (I Still Love You)/Please Don't Wake Me	40

CINDERS
63	Warner Bros WB 86	The Cinnamon Cinder/C'mon Wobble	5

CINDY & BARBIE DOLLS
80	Not Major NOTEM 1	ISN'T SHOWBIZ WONDERFUL (EP, foldout poster p/s)	4

CINDY & BERT
74	BASF BA 1004	Our Summer Song Of Love/Spanish Guitars	8

CINDY & LINDY
57	HMV POP 409	Tell Me Something Sweet/The Language Of Love	4
59	Coral Q 72368	Saturday Night In Tia Juana/The Wonder That Is You	6

CINDYTALK
84	Midnight CHIME 00.065	CAMOUFLAGE HEART (LP, with inner sleeve)	10

CINNAMON QUILL
69	Morgan MRS 21	Candy/Hello, It's Me	4
69	Morgan TAKE 17	Girl On A Swing/Take It Or Leave It	4

CIRCLE JERKS
82	Step Forward SFLP 8	WILD IN THE STREETS (LP)	10

CIRCLES
66	Island WI 279	Take Your Time/Don't You Love Me No More	35

CIRCLES
79	Graduate GRAD 4	Opening Up/Billy (p/s)	6
80	Vertigo ANGRY 1	Angry Voices/Summer Nights (p/s)	6
80	Chrysalis CHS 2418	Opening Up/Billy (reissue) (p/s)	5
85	Graduate GRAD 17	Circles/Summer Nights (p/s)	7

CIRCUS
67	Parlophone R 5633	Sink Or Swim/Gone Are The Songs Of Yesterday	10
68	Parlophone R 5672	House Of Wood/Do You Dream	30
69	Transatlantic TRA 207	CIRCUS (LP, gatefold sleeve)	35
	(see also Philip Goodhand-Tait)		

CIRCUS MAXIMUS
67	Vanguard VSD 79260	CIRCUS MAXIMUS (LP)	18
68	Vanguard VSD 79274	NEVERLAND REVISITED (LP)	15

CIRKUS
70s	Guardian GRCA 4	Melissa/Amsterdam/Pick Up A Phone (EP)	50
73	RCB 1	CIRKUS ONE (LP, private pressing with gatefold sleeve)	125
77	Shock SHOCK 1	FUTURE SHOCK (LP)	175
86	Five Hours Back TOCK 1	CIRKUS ONE (LP, reissue, gatefold sleeve)	10

CITATIONS
63	Columbia DB 7068	Moon Race/Slippin' And Slidin'	10

CITY OF WESTMINSTER STRING BAND
68	Pye 7N 17620	A Touch Of Velvet And A Sting Of Brass/Tommy Tucker	6

CITY RAMBLERS SKIFFLE GROUP
57	Tempo A 158	Ella Speed/2.19 Blues	5
57	Tempo A 161	Mama Don't Allow/Tom Dooley	5
57	Tempo A 165	Delia's Gone/Boodle-Am Shake	5
50s	Storyville SEP 327	I WANT A GIRL (EP)	12
50s	Storyville SEP 345	I SHALL NOT BE MOVED (EP)	12
57	Tempo EXA 59	I WANT A GIRL (EP)	10
57	Tempo EXA 71	GOOD MORNING BLUES (EP)	10
50s	Tempo EXA 77	DELIA'S GONE (EP)	10

CITY SMOKE
66	Mercury MF 971	Sunday Morning/A Little Bit Of Love	4

CITY WAITES
74	EMI EMI 2149	The Fox/One Of My Aunts	7
74	EMI EMC 3027	A GORGEOUS GALLERY OF GALLANT INVENTIONS (LP)	70
76	Decca SKL 5264	THE CITY WAITES (LP)	60

C-JAM BLUES
66	Columbia DB 8064	Candy/Stay At Home Girl	12

CLAGUE
70	Dandelions 4493	Bottle Up And Go/Mandy Lee (with Kevin Coyne)	5
70	Dandelions 4494	The Stride/I Wonder Where (with Kevin Coyne)	5
	(see also Kevin Coyne, Siren)		

GARY CLAIL
86	World WR 009	Half Cut For Confidence/Half A Gram A Shout (12", p/s)	7

CLAIM
| 80s | Esurient PALE 7 | Losers Corner/Picking Up The Bitter Little Pieces (p/s) | 4 |

ALISDAIR CLAIRE
| 70s | Acorn | ADAM AND THE BEASTS (LP) | 30 |

JIMMY CLANTON
58	London HLS 8699	Just A Dream/You Aim To Please (as Jimmy Clanton & His Rockets)	15
58	London HLS 8699	Just A Dream/You Aim To Please (78)	12
58	London HL 7066	A Letter To An Angel/A Part Of Me (export issue)	12
59	London HLS 8779	A Letter To An Angel/A Part Of Me (as Jimmy Clanton & Aces)	25
59	London HLS 8779	A Letter To An Angel/A Part Of Me (78)	10
59	Top Rank JAR 189	My Own True Love/Little Boy In Love	7
59	Top Rank JAR 189	My Own True Love/Little Boy In Love (78)	20
60	Top Rank JAR 269	Go, Jimmy, Go/I Trusted You	6
60	Top Rank JAR 382	Another Sleepless Night/I'm Gonna Try	6
60	Top Rank JAR 509	Come Back (To Me)/Wait	7
61	Top Rank JAR 544	What Am I Gonna Do/If I	6
62	Stateside SS 120	Venus In Blue Jeans/Highway Bound	5
63	Stateside SS 159	Darkest Street In Town/Dreams Of A Fool	4
65	Stateside SS 410	Hurting Each Other/Don't Keep Your Friends Away	5
69	London HLP 10289	Curly/I'll Never Forget Your Love	4
59	London RES 1224	JUST A DREAM (EP)	40

CLAPHAM SOUTH ESCALATORS
| 81 | Upright UP YOUR 1 | Get Me To The World On Time/Leave Me Alone/Cardboard Cut Outs (p/s) | 5 |

(see also Meteors)

ERIC CLAPTON
66	Purdah 45-3502	Lonely Years/Bernard Jenkins (with John Mayall)	60
70	Polydor 2001 096	I Am Yours (withdrawn, any pressed?)	
70	Polydor 2001 096	After Midnight/Easy Now	4
71	Polydor 2058 035	Little Wing (withdrawn, any pressed?)	
74	RSO 2090 139	Willie And The Hand Jive/Mainline Florida (p/s)	5
76	RSO 2090 208	Hello Old Friend/All Our Pastimes (p/s)	5
83	Duck W 9701	The Shape You're In/Crosscut Saw (picture disc)	4
85	Duck W 8461F	Behind The Sun/Grand Illusion//Crossroads (live)/White Room (live) (double pack)	4
90	Duck W 2644B	Bad Love/Before You Accuse Me (box set	4
90	Duck W 9981B	No Alibis/Running On Faith (box set with 2 photos & metal badge)	4
70	Polydor 2383 021	ERIC CLAPTON (LP)	10
74	RSO QD 4801	461 OCEAN BOULEVARD (LP, quadrophonic)	15
73	RSO 2479 702	CLAPTON (LP, withdrawn)	15
82	RSO RSDX 3	TIME PIECES (2-LP, withdrawn in favour of single LP, any pressed?)	
82	RSO BOX 3	BACKLESS/461 OCEAN BOULEVARD/SLOWHAND (3-LP box set)	20

(see also Yardbirds, John Mayall (& Blues Breakers), Cream, Blind Faith, Delaney & Bonnie, Derek & Dominoes)

ALAN CLARE GROUP
62	Parlophone R 4938	Screwball/Love For Sale	4
65	Pye 7N 15764	Dog's Body/Mulligatawny	4
68	Decca SKL 4965	YOUNG GIRL (LP)	10

KENNY CLARE
| 67 | Columbia DB 8216 | If I Were A Buddy Rich Man/Hum-Drum | 4 |

KENNY CLARE & RONNIE STEPHENSON
| 67 | Studio Two TWO 146 | DRUM SPECTACULAR (LP; also in mono Columbia SX 6168) | 10 |

CLARENDONIANS
65	Ska Beat JB 219	Doing The Jerk/You Won't See Me	8
66	Ska Beat JB 261	My Friend/You Are A Fool	8
66	Island WI 284	Try Me One More Time/Can't Keep A Good Man Down	8
66	Island WI 295	Rude Boy Gonna Jail (as Desmond Baker & Clarendonians)/ SHARKS: Don't Fool Me	8
66	Island WI 3005	I'll Never Change/Rules Of Life	10
67	Island WI 3032	Shoo-Be-Doo-Be (I Love You)/Sweet Heart Of Beauty	10
67	Island WI 3041	You Can't Be Happy/Goodbye Forever	10
67	Studio One SO 2004	The Table's Going To Turn/I Can't Go On	15
67	Studio One SO 2007	He Who Laughs Last/GAYLADS: Just A Kiss From You	15
67	Studio One SO 2017	Love Me With All Your Heart/Love Don't Mean Much To Me	15
67	Rio R 112	Rudie Bam Bam/Be Bop Boy	8
67	Rio R 115	Musical Train/Lowdown Girl	8
68	Caltone TONE 114	Baby Baby/Bye Bye Bye	8
69	Duke DU 97	Come Along/Try To Be Happy	4
70	Trojan TR 7719	Baby Don't Do It/BEVERLEY'S ALLSTARS: Touch Down	4
70	Trojan TR 7714	Lick It Back/BEVERLEY'S ALLSTARS: Busy Bee	4

ALICE CLARK
| 69 | Action ACT 4520 | You Got A Deal/Say You'll Never | 12 |

CHRIS CLARK
67	Tamla Motown TMG 591	Love's Gone Bad/Put Yourself In My Place	35
67	Tamla Motown TMG 624	From Head To Toe/The Beginning Of The End	25
68	Tamla Motown TMG 638	I Want To Go Back There Again/I Love You	20
68	T. Motown (S)TML 11069	SOUL SOUNDS (LP)	40

CLAUDINE CLARK
62	Pye Intl. 7N 25157	Party Lights/Disappointed	6
63	Pye Intl. 7N 25186	Walk Me Home From The Party/Who Will You Hurt?	6
67	Sue WI 4039	The Strength To Be Strong/Moon Madness	12

DAVE CLARK FIVE

62	Ember EMBS 156	Chaquita/In Your Heart (grey/pink or yellow labels)	35/30
62	Piccadilly 7N 35088	First Love/I Walk The Line	30
62	Piccadilly 7N 35500	I Knew It All The Time/That's What I Said	30
63	Columbia DB 7011	The Mulberry Bush/Chaquita	20
63	Columbia DB 7112	Do You Love Me/Doo-Dah	5
63	Columbia DB 7154	Glad All Over/I Know You	4
64	Columbia DB 7210	Bits And Pieces/All Of The Time	4
64	Columbia DB 7291	Can't You See That She's Mine/Because	4
64	Columbia DB 7335	Thinking Of You Baby/Whenever You're Around	4
64	Columbia DB 7377	Any Way You Want It/Crying Over You	4
65	Columbia DB 7453	Everybody Knows/Say You Want Me	6
65	Columbia DB 7503	Reelin' And Rockin'/Little Bitty Pretty One	4
65	Columbia DB 7580	Come Home/Mighty Good Loving	4
65	Columbia DB 7625	Catch Us If You Can/Move On	4
65	Columbia DB 7744	Over And Over/I'll Be Yours	4
66	Columbia DB 7863	Try Too Hard/All Night Long	4
66	Columbia DB 7909	Look Before You Leap/Please Tell Me Why	4
66	Columbia DB 8028	Nineteen Days/I Need Love	4
67	Columbia DB 8152	You Got What It Takes/Sitting Here Baby	4
67	Columbia DB 8194	Tabatha Twitchit/Man In A Pin-Striped Suit	4
67	Columbia DB 8286	Everybody Knows/Concentration Baby	4
68	Columbia DB 8342	No One Can Break A Heart Like You/You Don't Want My Lovin'	4
68	Columbia DB 8465	The Red Balloon/Maze Of Love	4
68	Columbia DB 8505	Live In The Sky/Children	4
69	Columbia DB 8545	The Mulberry Tree/Small Talk	4
69	Columbia DB 8591	Get It On Now/Maze Of Life (unreleased, acetates exist)	100
69	Columbia DB 8624	Put A Little Love In Your Heart/34-06	4
69	Columbia DB 8638	Good Old Rock'N'Roll Medley Pts 1 & 2 (p/s)	6
70	Columbia DB 8660	Everybody Get Together/Darling I Love You	4
70	Columbia DB 8681	Julia/Five By Five	7
70	Columbia DB 8689	Here Comes Summer/Break Down And Cry	4
70	Columbia DB 8724	Play More Good Old Rock'N'Roll/Wild Weekend	4
71	Columbia DB 8749	Southern Man/If You Wanna See Me Cry	4
71	Columbia DB 8791	Won't You Be My Lady/Into Your Life	4
72	Columbia DB 8963	All Time Greats Medley/Wild Weekend (p/s)	7
75	EMI EMI 2307	Here Comes Summer/Break Down & Cry (reissue)	4
77	Polydor 2058 953	Everybody Knows/Always Me (p/s)	12/6
64	Columbia SEG 8289	THE DAVE CLARK FIVE (EP)	10
65	Columbia SEG 8381	THE HITS OF THE DAVE CLARK FIVE (EP)	16
65	Columbia SEG 8447	WILD WEEKEND (EP)	12
64	Columbia 33SX 1598	A SESSION WITH THE DAVE CLARK FIVE (LP)	20
64	Ember FA 2003	THE DAVE CLARK FIVE AND THE WASHINGTON DC'S (LP)	25
65	Regal REG 2017	IN SESSION (LP, export issue)	30
65	Columbia SX 1756	CATCH US IF YOU CAN (LP, soundtrack)	25
66	Columbia SX 6105	THE DAVE CLARK FIVE'S GREATEST HITS (LP)	14
68	Columbia SX 6207	EVERYBODY KNOWS (LP)	18
68	M. For Pleasure MFP 1260	A SESSION WITH THE DAVE CLARK FIVE (LP, reissue, different sleeve)	10
68	Columbia SX 6309	14 TITLES (5 BY 5 1964-69) (LP)	16
71	Columbia SCX 6437	IF SOMEBODY LOVES YOU (LP)	15
71	Starline SRS 5090	PLAYS GOOD OLD ROCK AND ROLL (LP)	10

(see also Dave Clark & Friends)

DAVE CLARK & FRIENDS

71	Columbia DB 8834	One Eyed, Blues Suited, Gun Totin' Man/Draggin' The Line	4
72	Columbia DB 8862	Think Of Me/Right Or Wrong	4
72	Columbia DB 8907	Rub It In/I'm Sorry Baby	4
73	EMI EMI 2013	Sweet City Woman/Love Comes But Once	4
73	EMI EMI 2082	Sha-Na-Na/I Don't Know	4
74	EMI EMI 2205	Rub It In/I'm Sorry Baby (reissue)	4
72	Columbia SCX 6494	DAVE CLARK AND FRIENDS (LP)	15

(see also Dave Clark Five)

DEE CLARK

59	London HL 8802	Nobody But You/When I Call On You	15
59	London HL 8802	Nobody But You/When I Call On You (78)	12
59	London HL 8915	Just Keep It Up (And See What Happens)/Whispering Grass (Don't Tell The Trees)	15
59	London HL 8915	Just Keep It Up (And See What Happens)/Whispering Grass (Don't Tell The Trees) (78)	18
59	Top Rank JAR 196	Hey, Little Girl/If It Wasn't For Love	15
59	Top Rank JAR 196	Hey, Little Girl/If It Wasn't For Love (78)	25
60	Top Rank JAR 284	How About That/Blues Get Off My Shoulder	10
60	Top Rank JAR 373	At My Front Door/Cling-A-Ling	18
60	Top Rank JAR 501	Gloria/You're Looking Good	6
61	Top Rank JAR 551	Your Friends/Because I Love You	6
61	Top Rank JAR 570	Raindrops/I Want To Love You	6
62	Columbia DB 4768	Don't Walk Away From Me/You're Telling Our Secrets	8
63	Stateside SS 180	I'm A Soldier Boy/Shook Up Over You	7
64	Stateside SS 355	Heartbreak/Warm Summer Breeze	7
65	Stateside SS 400	T.C.B./It's Impossible	15
70	Liberty LBF 15334	Where Did All The Good Times Go?/24 Hours Of Loneliness	5
60	Top Rank BUY 044	HOW ABOUT THAT! (LP)	25
70	Joy JOYS 130	YOU'RE LOOKING GOOD (LP)	10

DOTTY CLARK

61	London HLX 9418	It's Been A Long, Long Time/That's A Step In The Right Direction	4

GENE CLARK

67	CBS 202523	Echoes/I Found You	8
67	CBS 62934	GENE CLARK WITH THE GOSDIN BROTHERS (LP)	18
72	A&M AMLS 64297	WHITE LIGHT (LP)	10
74	Asylum SYL 9020	NO OTHER (LP)	10

(see also Byrds, Dillard & Clark)

GUY CLARK

75	RCA Victor APLI-130	OLD NO. 1 (LP)	10
76	RCA Victor RS 1097	TEXAS COOKIN' (LP)	10

JAMES CLARK + SOUNDS

68	Fontana TF 918	"A Man Of Our Times" T.V. Series Theme/Spring Bossa	4

JIMMY 'SOUL' CLARK

76	Black Magic BM 115	Sweet Darlin' Pts 1 & 2	4

LOUIS CLARK

79	Jet JET 151	Escape/Departure (p/s)	4
80	Jet JET 7031	Hooked On Christmas/Motif (p/s)	4
79	Jet JETLP 218	PER-SPEK-TIV (LP)	10

(see also E.L.O.)

MICHAEL CLARK

66	Liberty LIB 55893	None Of These Girls/Workout	10

PETULA CLARK

49	Columbia DB 2538	Put Your Shoes On Lucky/There's A House In The Sky (78)	8
49	Columbia DB 2551	I'll Always Love You/Clancy Lowered The Boom (78)	8
49	Decca F 9285	Two Lips (with Benny Lee)/Talkin' To The Horses (with Benny Lee) (78)	6
51	Polygon P 1002	You Are My True Love/You're The Sweetest In The Land (with Stargazers) (78)	6
51	Polygon P 1003	Be Loved, Be Faithful/Fly Away Peter, Fly Away Paul (78)	6
51	Polygon P 1004	Tennessee Waltz/Sleepy Eyes (78)	6
51	Polygon P 1005	Teasin'/Black Note Serenade (78)	6
51	Polygon P 1008	May Kway/Clickety Clack (78)	6
51	Polygon P 1009	Mariandl/Broken Heart (with Jimmy Young, 78)	6
52	Polygon P 1021	Cold Cold Heart/That's How A Love Song Is Born (78)	6
52	Polygon P 1022	Tell Me Truly/Song Of The Mermaid (78)	6
52	Polygon P 1043	It Had To Be Me/The Card (78)	6
52	Polygon P 1048	A Boy In Love/Fly Away Peter, Fly Away Paul (78)	6
52	Polygon P 1056	Where Did My Sunshine Go?/Anytime Is Teatime Now (78)	5
52	Polygon P 1057	Made In Heaven/Temptation Rag (78)	5
53	Polygon P 1063	My Love Is A Wonder/Take Care Of Yourself (78)	5
53	Polygon P 1072	Christopher Robin At Buckingham Palace/Three Little Kittens (78)	5
53	Polygon P 1082	Poppa Piccolino/The Who Is It Song (78)	5
54	Polygon P 1121	Meet Me In Battersea Park/A Long Way To Go (78)	5
54	Polygon P 1128	Smile/Somebody (78)	5
54	Polygon P 1135	Christmas Cards/Little Johnny Rainbow (78)	5
55	Polygon P 1169	Pendulum Song/Crazy Otto Rag (with Joe Henderson, 78)	5
55	Polygon P 1179	How Are Things With You/Tuna Puna Trinidad (78)	5
57	Pye Nixa 7N 15096	With All My Heart/Gonna Find Me A Bluebird	15
57	Pye Nixa 7N 15112	Alone/Long Before I Knew You	6
58	Pye Nixa 7N 15126	Baby Lover/The Little Blue Man	6
58	Pye Nixa 7N 15135	Love Me Again/In A Little Moment	5
58	Pye Nixa 7N 15152	Devotion/St. Tropez (Sur La Plage)	6
58	Pye Nixa 7N 15168	Fibbin'/I Wish I Knew	6
59	Pye Nixa 7N 15182	Ever Been In Love/Lucky Day	8
59	Pye Nixa 7N 15191	Watch Your Heart/Suddenly	6
59	Pye Nixa 7N 15208	Where Do I Go From Here?/Mama's Talking Soft	7
59	Pye Nixa 7N 15220	Adonis/If I Had My Way	5
59	Pye Nixa 7N 15203	Dear Daddy/Through The Livelong Day	5
60	Pye 7N 15244	I Love A Violin/Guitare Et Tambourin	6
60	Pye 7N 15281	Cinderella Jones/All Over Now	7
61	Pye 7N 15324	Sailor/My Heart	4
61	Pye 7N 15337	Something Missing/Isn't This A Lovely Day?	4
61	Pye 7N 15355	Welcome Home/Les Gens Diront	4
61	Pye 7N 15361	Romeo/You're Getting To Be A Habit With Me	4
61	Pye 7N 15389	My Friend The Sea/With All My Love	4
62	Pye 7N 15407	I'm Counting On You/Some Other World	4
62	Pye 7N 15437	Whistlin' For The Moon/Tender Love	6
62	Pye 7N 15448	Ya Ya Twist/Si C'est Oui, C'est Oui	4
62	Pye 7N 15456	Jumble Sale/Too Late	6
62	Pye 7N 15478	The Road/No Love, No Nothin'	6
63	Pye 7N 15495	I Will Follow Him/Darling Cheri	4
63	Pye 7N 15517	Valentino/Imagination	12
63	Pye 7N 15522	Chariot/Casanova	5
63	Pye 7N 15551	Let Me Tell You/Be Good To Me	4
63	Pye 7N 15573	Baby It's Me/This Is Goodbye	4
64	Pye 7N 15606	Thank You/Crying Through A Sleepless Night	4
64	Pye 7N 15639	In Love/Forgetting You (J'ai Tout Oublié)	4
65	Pye 7N 15991	You're The One/Gotta Tell The World	5
67	Pye 7N 17325	Don't Sleep In The Subway/Here Comes The Morning	4
68	Pye 7N 17646	I Want To Sing With Your Band/Look To The Sky	5
69	Pye 7N 17733	Happy Heart/Love Is The Only Thing	4
69	Pye 7N 17779	Look At Mine/You And I	5
70	Pye 7N 17973	Melody Man/Big Love Sale	5
73	Polydor 2058 413	Lead Me On/Taking It On (with Sacha Distel)	15
74	Polydor 2058 519	Let's Sing A Love Song/I'm The Woman You Need	8
75	Polydor 2058 560	I Am Your Song/Super Loving Lady	10

Petula CLARK

75	Pye 7N 45473	Wind Of Change (edit)/Memories Are Made Of This	4
75	Pye 7N 45506	What I Did For Love/I Believe In Love	5
76	Pye 7N 45650	Downtown (Disco Version)/Two Rivers	6
78	CBS S 6781	(Life Is) Just A Dance With Time/Don't Stop The Music	4
81	Epic EPC A 1475	Eidelweiss/Darkness	6
82	Scotti Bros SCTA 1645	Natural Love/Because I Love Him	4
82	Scotti Bros SCTA 2904	Dreamin' With My Eyes Wide Open/Afterglow	4
85	PRT 7P 323	Mr Orwell (English Language)/Glamoureuse	4
89	Legacy LGYCD 100	I Couldn't Live Without Your Love ('89 Mix — Extended)/(7" Version)/ (Original Version)/Come On Home/Call Me '89 ('65 vocal) (CD)	10
56	Pye Nixa NEP 24006	CHILDREN'S CHOICE (EP)	30
56	Pye Nixa NEP 24016	PETULA CLARK HIT PARADE (EP)	20
57	Pye Nixa NEP 24056	PETULA CLARK HIT PARADE NO. 2 (EP)	8
57	Pye Nixa NEP 24060	YOU ARE MY LUCKY STAR PART 1 (EP)	15
57	Pye Nixa NEP 24061	YOU ARE MY LUCKY STAR PART 2 (EP)	15
57	Pye Nixa NEP 24062	YOU ARE MY LUCKY STAR PART 3 (EP)	15
58	Pye Nixa NEP 24080	PETULA CLARK HIT PARADE NO. 3 (EP)	7
58	Pye Nixa NEP 24089	PETULA CLARK SINGS IN FRENCH (EP)	12
58	Pye Nixa NEP 24094	A CHRISTMAS CAROL (EP, also stereo NSEP 85001)	12/25
61	Pye NEP 24137	PETULA CLARK HIT PARADE 4 (EP)	12
61	Pye NEP 24150	PETULA CLARK HIT PARADE 5 (EP)	7
63	Pye NEP 24182	EN FRANÇAIS (EP)	10
64	Pye NEP 24189	ENCORE EN FRANÇAIS (EP)	8
64	Pye NEP 24194	PETULA SINGS 'HELLO DOLLY!' IN FRENCH (EP)	8
65	Pye NEP 24206	DOWNTOWN (EP)	7
65	Pye-Vogue VRE 5004	LES DISQUES D'OR DE LA CHANSON (EP)	7
65	Pye-Vogue VRE 5007	PETULA CLARK CHANTE EN ITALIEN (EP)	12
65	Pye NEP 24233	YOU'RE THE ONE (EP)	7
66	Pye NEP 24237	CALL ME (EP)	7
66	Pye NEP 24259	JUST SAY GOODBYE (EP)	8
66	Pye NEP 24266	I COULDN'T LIVE WITHOUT YOUR LOVE (EP)	8
66	Pye-Vogue VRE 5019	L'AGENT SECRET (EP)	10
66	Pye-Vogue VRE 5023	HELLO MISTER BROWN (EP)	10
67	Pye-Vogue VRE 5025	C'EST MA CHANSON (EP)	7
67	Pye NEP 24286	HERE, THERE AND EVERYWHERE (EP)	8
68	Pye-Vogue VRE 5026	L'AMOUR VIENDRA (EP)	8
68	Pye-Vogue VRE 5028	DIS-MOI AU REVOIR (EP)	8
68	Pye NEP 24301	DON'T GIVE UP (EP)	12
56	Pye Nixa NPT 19002	PETULA CLARK SINGS (10" LP)	75
56	Pye Nixa NPT 19014	A DATE WITH PET (10" LP)	75
57	Pye Nixa NPL 18007	YOU ARE MY LUCKY STAR (LP)	50
59	Pye Nixa NPL 18039	PETULA CLARK IN HOLLYWOOD (LP)	45
62	Pye NPL 18070	IN OTHER WORDS — PETULA CLARK (LP)	25
63	Pye NPL 18089	PETULA (LP)	15
64	Pye-Vogue VRL 3001	LES JAMES DEAN (LP)	15
65	Pye NPL 18114	DOWNTOWN (LP)	15
65	Pye N(S)PL 18118	THE NEW PETULA CLARK ALBUM (LP)	15
65	Pye NPL 18123	SINGS THE INTERNATIONAL HITS (LP)	15
65	Pye-Vogue VRL 3010	PETULA '65 (LP, in French)	25
66	Pye-Vogue VRL 3016	HELLO PARIS VOL. 1 (LP)	20
66	Pye-Vogue VRL 3019	HELLO PARIS VOL. 2 (LP)	15
66	Pye NPL 18141	MY LOVE (LP)	12
66	Pye N(S)PL 18148	I COULDN'T LIVE WITHOUT YOUR LOVE (LP)	12
66	Pye-Vogue VRL 3022	PETULA '66 (LP)	15
67	Pye N(S)PL 18159	PETULA CLARK'S HIT PARADE (LP)	10
67	Pye N(S)PL 18171	COLOUR MY WORLD (LP, original track listing, with "England Swings" & "Reach Out I'll Be There")	15
67	Pye N(S)PL 18171	COLOUR MY WORLD (LP, revised track listing, with "This Is My Song" & "The Show Is Over")	10
67	Pye-Vogue VRL 3030	C'EST MA CHANSON (LP)	12
67	Pye N(S)PL 18197	THESE ARE MY SONGS (LP)	10
68	Pye N(S)PL 18211	THE OTHER MAN'S GRASS IS ALWAYS GREENER (LP)	10
68	Warner Bros WF(S) 2550	FINIAN'S RAINBOW (LP, soundtrack)	18
68	Pye-Vogue VRLS 3035	PETULA CLARK A PARIS (LP	10
68	Pye N(S)PL 18235	PETULA (LP)	10
69	Pye N(S)PL 18282	PETULA CLARK'S HIT PARADE VOL. 2 (LP)	10
69	Pye NSPL 18292	PORTRAIT OF PETULA (LP)	10
69	MGM CS 8113	GOODBYE MR CHIPS (LP, soundtrack)	20
69	Pye NSPL 18325	JUST PET (LP)	10
69	Pye-Vogue VRLS 3039	PETULA CLARK (LP)	10
70	Pye NSPL 18345	MEMPHIS (LP)	10
71	Pye NSPL 18363	THE SONG OF MY LIFE (LP)	10
71	Pye Special PKL 5502	TODAY (LP)	12
71	Pye NSPL 18370	PETULA '71 (LP)	15
74	Pye 11PP 101	DEVOTION (4-LP set of previously released LPs)	25
74	Polydor 2383 279	COME ON HOME (LP)	12
74	Polydor 2383 303	LIVE IN LONDON (LP)	15
75	Polydor 2383 324	I'M THE WOMAN YOU NEED (LP)	18
75	Pet Projects PP 1	NOEL (LP, International Petula Clark Society issue)	15
76	Pet Projects PP 2	BEAUTIFUL SOUNDS (LP, International Petula Clark Society issue)	15

ROY CLARK

59	HMV POP 581	Please Mr. Mayor/Puddin'	40
59	HMV POP 581	Please Mr. Mayor/Puddin' (78)	45
63	Capitol CL 15288	In The Mood/Texas Twist	8
63	Capitol CL 15317	Tips Of My Fingers/Spooky Movies	6
69	Dot DOT 126	Yesterday When I Was Wrong/Just Another Man	4

69	Dot DOT 131	September Song/For The Life Of Me	4
62	Capitol (S)T 1780	THE LIGHTNING FINGERS OF ROY CLARK (LP)	12

SANFORD CLARK
56	London HLD 8320	The Fool/Lonesome For A Letter (with Al Casey)	80
56	London HL 7014	The Fool/Lonesome For A Letter (export issue, with Al Casey)	30
56	London HLD 8320	The Fool/Lonesome For A Letter (78)	10
59	London HLW 8959	Run, Boy Run/New Kind Of Fool	20
59	London HLW 8959	Run, Boy Run/New Kind Of Fool (78)	20
60	London HLW 9026	Son-Of-A-Gun/I Can't Help It (If I'm Still In Love With You)	12
60	London HLW 9095	Pledging My Love/Go On Home	12
68	Ember EMB S 250	Shades/Once Upon A Time	7
57	London RED 1105	PRESENTING SANFORD CLARK (EP)	50
60	London REW 1256	LOWDOWN BLUES (EP)	30
72	Ember CW 131	THEY CALL ME COUNTRY (LP)	10

(see also Al Casey)

ALLAN CLARKE
72	RCA SF 8283	MY REAL NAME IS 'AROLD (LP)	10

(see also Hollies)

JOHN COOPER CLARKE
78	Rabid TOSH 103	INNOCENTS (EP, orange p/s, green labels)	7
78	Rabid TOSH 103	INNOCENTS (EP, 2nd pressing, blue foldout p/s, blue labels)	5
78	CBS S CBS 6541	Post-War Glamour Girls/Kung Fu International (live) (p/s)	4
79	Epic S EPC 12 7009	¡Gimmix!/I Married A Monster From Outer Space (Third Version) (p/s, triangular, orange vinyl)	7
79	Epic S EPC 7982	Splat/Twat/Sleepwalk (double-grooved A-side, p/s, with Epic inner sleeve)	4
80	Epic S EPC 8655	It Man/36 Hours (no p/s)	4
80	CBS JCC 1	WALKING BACK TO HAPPINESS (10" mini-LP,clear vinyl stickered PVC sleeve)	8
80	Epic EPC 84083	SNAP, CRACKLE [&] BOP (LP, with 48-page book in sleeve pocket)	10

KENNY CLARKE
57	Columbia SEG 7830	KENNY CLARKE QT. (EP)	7
63	London HA-K 8085	JAZZ IS UNIVERSAL (LP, with Francy Boland Big Band)	12

LINDA CLARKE
68	Decca F 12787	Society's Child/Rain In My Heart	4

LLOYD CLARKE
62	Blue Beat BB 99	Good Morning/Now I Know A Reason	10
62	Blue Beat BB 104	Fool's Day/You're A Cheat	10
62	Island WI 007	Love You The Most/LLOYD ROBINSON: You Said You Loved Me	10
62	Island WI 045	Japanese Girl/He's Coming	10
63	Rio R 16	Love Me/Half As Much	8
64	Rio R 23	Stop Your Talking/A Penny	8
64	Rio R 24	Fellow Jamaican/PATRICK & GEORGE: My Love	8
68	Island WI 3116	Summertime/VAL BENNETT: Soul Survivor	10
68	Blue Cat BS 136	Young Love/UNTOUCHABLES: Wall Flower	6
70	Escort ERT 849	Chicken Thief/STRANGER COLE: Tomorrow	4

(see also Derrick & Lloyd)

TONY CLARKE
64	Pye Intl. 7N 25251	Ain't Love Good, Ain't Love Proud/Coming Back Strong	12
65	Chess CRS 8011	The Entertainer/This Heart Of Mine	15
69	Chess CRS 8091	The Entertainer/Ain't Love Good, Ain't Love Proud	10
74	Chess 6146 030	Landslide/The Entertainer	6

VINCE CLARKE & PAUL QUINN
85	Mute TAG 1	One Day/Song For (p/s)	4
85	Mute 12TAG 1	One Day (Extension)/Song For (Extension) (12", p/s)	8

(see also Erasure, Paul Quinn)

CLARK-HUTCHINSON
70	Decca Nova (S)DN-R 2	A = MH ^{2}(LP)	15
70	Deram SML 1076	RETRIBUTION (LP)	15
71	Deram SML 1090	GESTALT (LP)	18

(see also Upp)

CLARK SISTERS
59	London HLD 8791	Chicago/Opus 1	7
58	London RED 1198	SING, SING, SING (EP)	12
58	London HA-D 2128	SING, SING, SING (LP)	15
59	London HA-D 2177	THE CLARK SISTERS SWING AGAIN (LP, also stereo SAH-D 6025)	15

CLASH
77	CBS S CBS 5058	White Riot/1977 (p/s, 'The Clash' or 'The CLASH' on label)	5
77	CBS CL-1	CAPITAL RADIO (EP, 'NME' freebie)	30
77	CBS S CBS 5293	Remote Control/London's Burning (live) (p/s)	5
77	CBS S CBS 5664	Complete Control/The City Of The Dead (p/s)	5
78	CBS S CBS 5834	Clash City Rockers/Jail Guitar Doors (p/s)	5
78	CBS S CBS 6383	(White Man) In Hammersmith Palais/The Prisoner (initially green, then pink, blue or yellow die-cut sleeve)	5/4
78	CBS S CBS 6788	Tommy Gun/1, 2, Crush On You (p/s)	4
79	CBS S CBS 7082	English Civil War/Pressure Drop (p/s)	4
79	CBS S CBS 7324	THE COST OF LIVING (EP, gatefold red, green or yellow p/s & inner sleeve)	8
79	CBS S CBS 8087	London Calling/Armagideon Time (p/s)	4
79	CBS S CBS 12 8087	London Calling/Armagideon Time/Armagideon Time (Version): Justice Tonight (Version)/Kick It Over (Version) (12", p/s)	10
80	CBS S CBS 8323	Bankrobber/MIKEY DREAD: Rockers Galore (p/s)	4
80	CBS S CBS 9339	The Call Up/Stop The World (p/s)	4

MINT VALUE £

81	CBS S CBS 9480	Hitsville U.K./Radio One (special sleeve)	4
81	CBS A 1133	The Magnificent Seven/The Magnificent Dance (die-cut p/s)	4
81	CBS A12 1133	The Magnificent Seven/The Magnificent Dance (12", p/s, with sticker sheet)	7
81	CBS A 1797	This Is Radio Clash/Radio Clash (p/s)	4
81	CBS A12 1797	This Is Radio Clash/Radio Clash (12", p/s)	7
81	CBS S 2309	Know Your Rights/First Night Back In London (p/s, with sticker)	4
82	CBS A 2479	Rock The Casbah/Long Time Jerk (p/s, with stickers)	4
82	CBS A 11 2479	Rock The Casbah/Long Time Jerk (picture disc)	7
82	CBS A 12 2479	Rock The Casbah/Mustapha Dance (12", p/s)	7
82	CBS A 2646	Should I Stay Or Should I Go/Straight To Hell (p/s, with sticker)	4
82	CBS A 2646	Should I Stay Or Should I Go/Straight To Hell (p/s, laser-etched on 1 side)	5
82	CBS A 11 2646	Should I Stay Or Should I Go/Straight To Hell (picture disc)	7
82	CBS A 12 2646	Should I Stay Or Should I Go/Straight To Hell (12", p/s, with stencil)	7
85	CBS A 6122	This Is England/Do It Now (poster p/s)	4
88	CBS CLASHB 2	London Calling/Brand New Cadillac/Rudie Don't Fail (box set)	6
78	CBS 82431	GIVE 'EM ENOUGH ROPE (LP, with promo-only poster)	40

(all the early Clash singles were re-pressed in 1979 with p/s)
(see also 101'ers, Big Audio Dynamite, Topper Headon, Janie Jones & Lash, Tymon Dogg, Ellen Foley, Futura 2000)

CLASSICS
61	Mercury AMT 1152	Life Is But A Dream/That's The Way	30
63	Stateside SS 215	Till Then/Enie Minie Mo	8
66	Capitol CL 15470	Pollyanna/Cry Baby	8

CLASSICS
| 69 | Doctor Bird DB 1190 | Worried Over Me/LAUREL AITKEN: Rice And Peas | 6 |

CLASSICS IV
68	Liberty LBF 15051	Spooky/Poor People	6
69	Liberty LBF 15177	Stormy/Twenty Four Hours Of Loneliness	4
69	Liberty LBF 15196	Traces/Mary Mary Row Your Boat	4
69	Liberty LBF 15231	Everyday With You Girl/Sentimental Lady	5

CLASSIC SULLIVANS
| 74 | Kwanza K 19501 | Paint Yourself In The Corner/I Don't Want To Lose You | 6 |

CLASSIX NOUVEAUX
| 80 | ESP ES 1 | The Robots Dance/623 (p/s) | 4 |

(see also Sal Solo)

CLASSMATES
63	Decca F 11736	Let's Get Together Tonight/It's No Game	4
63	Decca F 11779	Go Tell It On The Mountain/Give Me A Girl	4
64	Decca F 11806	In Morocco/I Feel	4
64	Decca F 12047	Go Away/Pay Day	10

CLAUDETTE & CORPORATION
| 70 | Grape GR 3020 | Skinheads A Bash Them /CORPORATION: Walkin'Thru Jerusalem | 8 |

CASSIUS CLAY
| 64 | CBS AAG 190 | Stand By Me/I Am The Greatest | 15 |
| 66 | CBS 202190 | Stand By Me/I Am The Greatest (reissue) | 10 |

JEFFREY CLAY
55	Vogue Coral Q 72093	No Arms Can Ever Hold You/Come On Back, Come On Back	4
55	Vogue Coral Q 72113	Sweet Kentucky Rose/Unknown To Me	4
56	Vogue Coral Q 72143	These Hands/You'll Be Sorry (When Someone Else Is Glad)	4

JUDY CLAY
| 67 | Stax 601 022 | You Can't Run Away From Your Heart/It Takes A Lotta Good Love | 7 |

(see also Billy Vera & Judy Clay)

JUDY CLAY & WILLIAM BELL
| 68 | Stax STAX 101 | Private Number/Love Eye Tis | 4 |
| 69 | Stax STAX 115 | My Baby Specialises/Left Over Love | 4 |

(see also William Bell, Billy Vera & Judy Clay)

OTIS CLAY
67	President PT 121	It's Easier Said Than Done/Flame In Your Heart	5
68	President PT 132	I'm Satisfied/I Testify	5
68	President PT 148	That's How It Is/Show Place	5
68	President PT 176	A Lasting Love/Got To Find A Way	6
69	Atlantic 584 282	Baby Jane/You Hurt Me For The Last Time	5
72	London HLU 10397	Trying To Live My Life Without You/Let Me Be The One	4
74	London HLU 10467	You Did Something To Me/It Was Jealousy	4
73	London SH-U 8446	TRYING TO LIVE MY LIFE WITHOUT YOU (LP)	10

TOM CLAY
| 72 | Tamla Motown TMG 801 | What The World Needs Now/The Victors | 5 |

BUCK CLAYTON
| 68 | CBS Realm RM 52078 | A BUCK CLAYTON JAM SESSION (LP) | 10 |

BUCK CLAYTON & JOE TURNER
| 73 | Black Lion 2460 303 | FEEL SO FINE (LP) | 10 |

(see also Joe Turner)

DOCTOR CLAYTON
| 65 | RCA Victor RCX 7177 | RCA RACE SERIES VOLUME 6 (EP) | 15 |
| 70 | RCA International INTS1176 | PEARL HARBOUR BLUES (LP) | 12 |

MERRY CLAYTON
| 70 | A&M AMLS 995 | GIMME SHELTER (LP) | 10 |
| 71 | A&M AMLS 67012 | MERRY CLAYTON (LP) | 10 |

(see also Raelets)

PAUL CLAYTON
61	London HLU 9285	Wings Of A Dove/So Long (It's Been Good To Know You)	8
60	London REU 1276	PAUL CLAYTON (EP)	12

STEVE CLAYTON
56	Vogue Coral Q 72200	Two Different Worlds/It Happened Again	4
57	Vogue Coral Q 72253	The Boy With The Golden .../I Wanna Put My Arms Around ...	4
60	London HLU 9033	Let's Tell Them Now/They Say In Time	4

CLAYTON SQUARES
65	Decca F 12250	Come And Get It/And Tears Fell	15
66	Decca F 12456	There She Is/Imagination	35

(see also Liverpool Scene)

CLEANLINESS & GODLINESS SKIFFLE BAND
68	Vanguard SVRL 19043	GREATEST HITS (LP)	10

CLEAR BLUE SKY
71	Vertigo 6360 013	CLEAR BLUE SKY (LP, gatefold sleeve, spiral label)	60

CLEAR LIGHT
67	Elektra EKSN 45019	Black Roses/She's Ready To Be Free	6
68	Elektra EKSN 45027	Night Sounds Loud/How Many Days Have Passed	5
67	Elektra EKL/4011	CLEAR LIGHT (LP, orange label, also stereo EKS 7401)	20

CLEARLIGHT
75	Virgin V 2029	FOREVER BLOWING BUBBLES (LP)	15
75	Virgin V 2039	SYMPHONY (LP)	15

(see also Gong, Steve Hillage)

CLEARWAYS
64	Columbia DB 7333	I'll Be Here/I've Just Got A Letter	5

JOHN CLEESE & 1948 CHOIR
67	Pye 7N 17336	The Ferret Song — From 'At Last The 1948 Show'/The Rhubarb Tart Song	4

(see also Monty Python)

CLEFS
62	Salvo SLO 1010	Don't Cry/The Dream Train Special	15

CLEFTONES
56	Columbia DB 3801	You Baby, You/Little Girl Of Mine	200
56	Columbia DB 3801	You Baby, You/Little Girl Of Mine (78)	25
61	Columbia DB 4678	Heart And Soul/How Do You Feel	35
61	Columbia DB 4720	(I Love You) For Sentimental Reasons/Deed I Do	25
63	Columbia DB 4988	Lover Come Back To Me/There She Goes	16

JACK CLEMENT
58	London HLS 8691	Ten Years/Your Lover Boy	35
58	London HLS 8691	Ten Years/Your Lover Boy (78)	18

SOUL JOE CLEMENTS
68	Plexium PXM 10	Smoke And Ashes/Ever Ever	150

CLEO
64	Decca F 11817	To Know Him Is To Love Him/ANDREW OLDHAM ORCHESTRA: There Are But Five Rolling Stones	18

(see also Andrew Oldham Orchestra, This 'N' That)

CLERKS
80s	Rok ROK VIII/VII	No Good For Me/HAZARD: Gotta Change My Life (company sleeve)	6
80s	Ruddisc SRT8 KS 1538	Dancing With My Girl/On The Telephone/All I Want Is You (p/s)	5

DAISY CLIFF (Viola McCoy)
25	Guardsman 7002	It Makes No Difference Now/NELLY COLMAN: Afternoon Blues (78)	75
25	Guardsman 7003	West Indies Blues/LILA VIVIAN: You've Got Everything A Sweet Mama Needs (78)	75

(see also Viola McCoy [Daisy Cliff/Amanda Brown], Edna Hicks [Lila Vivian], Lena Wilson [Nelly Colman])

JIMMY CLIFF
62	Blue Beat BB 78	I'm Sorry/RED PRICE & BLUE BEATS: Roarin'	10
62	Island WI 012	Hurricane Hatty/Dearest Beverley	8
62	Island WI 016	Miss Jamaica/Gold Digger	8
62	Island WI 025	Since Lately/I'm Free	8
63	Island WI 062	My Lucky Day/One Eyed Jacks	8
63	Island WI 070	King Of Kings/SIR PERCY: Oh Yeah	8
63	Island WI 112	Miss Universe/The Prodigal	6
63	Black Swan WI 403	The Man/You Are Never Too Old	10
64	Stateside SS 342	One Eyed Jacks/King Of Kings	8
66	Fontana TF 641	Call On Me/Pride And Passion	8
67	Island WIP 6004	Aim And Ambition/Give And Take	4
67	Island WIP 6011	I Got A Feeling/Hard Road To Travel	4
67	Island WIP 6024	That's The Way Life Goes/Thank You	5
68	Island WIP 6039	Waterfall/Reward	8
68	Island ILP 962	HARD ROAD TO TRAVEL (LP)	25
69	Trojan TRLS 16	JIMMY CLIFF (LP)	10
71	Island ILPS 9159	ANOTHER CYCLE (LP)	10

(see also Jackie Edwards & Jimmy Cliff)

CLIFF & HANK
(see under Cliff Richard)

CLIFF DWELLERS
66	Polydor BM 56707	Hang On Stupid/I'm A Superman For You Baby	5

Buzz CLIFFORD

BUZZ CLIFFORD
61	Fontana H 297	Baby Sittin' Boogie/Driftwood	8
61	Fontana H 312	Three Little Fishes/Simply Because	5
62	Columbia DB 4903	More Dead Than Alive/Nobody Loves Me Like You	7

LINDA CLIFFORD
74	Paramount PARA 3051	After Loving You/Check Out Your Heart	6
78	Curtom K 17163	If My Friends Could See Me Now/Runaway Love	4
78	Curtom K 17163T	If My Friends Could See Me Now/Runaway Love (12")	7

CLIFFTERS
62	Philips PB 1242	Django/Amapola (Pretty Little Poppy)	7

BILL CLIFTON
60	Melodisc 1554	You Don't Think About Me/Mail Carrier's Warning	6
63	Decca F 11793	Beatle Crazy/Little Girl Dressed In Blue	7
58	Mercury MEP 9546	BILL CLIFTON AND THE DIXIE MOUNTAIN BOYS (EP)	8

BILL CLIFTON & JIM EANES
60s	Melodisc EPM 7102	BLUE RIVER HOEDOWN (EP)	10

CLIMACTICS
80s	Pulsebeat CINE 001	FAREWELL TO THE PLAYGROUND (EP, foldover p/s)	25

(see also Razorcuts)

CLIMAX (CHICAGO) BLUES BAND
69	Parlophone R 5809	Like Uncle Charlie/Loving Machine	7
69	Parl. PMC/PCS 7069	CLIMAX CHICAGO BLUES BAND (LP)	25
69	Parlophone PCS 7084	PLAYS ON (LP)	20
70	Harvest SHSP 4009	A LOT OF BOTTLE (LP)	12
71	Harvest SHSP 4015	TIGHTLY KNIT (LP)	10
72	Harvest SHSP 4024	RICH MAN (LP)	10

PATSY CLINE
57	Brunswick 05660	A Poor Man's Roses (Or A Rich Man's Gold)/Walkin' After Midnight	15
57	Brunswick 05660	A Poor Man's Roses (Or A Rich Man's Gold)/Walkin' After Midnight (78)	7
61	Brunswick 05855	I Fall To Pieces/Lovin' In Vain	10
61	Brunswick 05861	Crazy/Who Can I Count On	10
62	Brunswick 05866	She's Got You/Strange	6
62	Brunswick 05869	When I Get Through With You/Imagine That	6
62	Brunswick 05874	So Wrong/You're Stronger Than Me	6
62	Brunswick 05878	Heartaches/Why Can't He Be You	5
63	Brunswick 05883	Leavin' On Your Mind/Tra Le La Le La Triangle	6
63	Brunswick 05888	Sweet Dreams/Back In My Baby's Arms	6
62	Brunswick OE 9490	SWEET DREAMS (EP)	10
62	Brunswick LAT 8394	SHOWCASE (LP)	15
62	Brunswick LAT/STA 8510	SENTIMENTALLY YOURS (LP)	15
63	Brunswick LAT 8549	A TRIBUTE TO PATSY CLINE (LP)	15
64	Brunswick LAT/STA 8589	A PORTRAIT OF PATSY CLINE (LP)	15
65	Ember CW 16	IN MEMORIAM (LP)	10
65	Fontana FJL 302	TODAY TOMORROW AND FOREVER (LP)	10
66	Fontana FJL 309	I CAN'T FORGET YOU (LP)	10
68	MCA MUP 316	THE SOUND OF PATSY CLINE (LP)	10
68	MCA MUP(S) 326	HEARTACHES (LP)	10
69	MCA MUP(S) 350	ALWAYS (LP)	10

BUDDY CLINTON
60	Top Rank JAR 287	Across The Street From Your House/How My Prayers Have ...	4

GEORGE CLINTON
79	ABC ABC 4053	Please Don't Run From Me/Life And Breath	6

(DO NOT see also Parliament, Funkadelic)

LARRY CLINTON
79	Grapevine GRP 120	She's Wanted In Three States/If I Knew	4

CLIQUE (U.K.)
65	Pye 7N 15786	She Ain't No Good/Time Time Time	50
65	Pye 7N 15853	We Didn't Kiss, Didn't Love, But Now We Do/You've Been Unfair	125
60s	private pressing	THE CLIQUE (EP, no p/s)	500

(see also Hammersmith Gorillas)

CLIQUE (U.S.)
69	London HLU 10286	Sugar On Sunday/Superman	15

CLIVE & GLORIA
63	R&B JB 113	Change Of Plan/Little Gloria	7
64	R&B JB 173	Money Money Money/Have I Told You Lately	7
64	King KG 1004	Do The Ska/You Made Me Cry	10

CLIVE & NAOMI
65	Ska Beat JB 181	You Are Mine/Open The Door	8

CLOCK DVA
81	Fetish FET 008	Four Hours (Re-mixed)/Sensorium (p/s)	8
82	Polydor POSP 437	Passions Still Aflame: Sons Of Sons/Theme (I.M.D.) (p/s)	6
82	Polydor POSPX 437	PASSIONS STILL AFLAME (12" EP)	8
82	Polydor POSP 499	High Holy Disco Man/The Voice That Speaks From Within (Triumph Over Will) (p/s)	5
82	Polydor POSPX 499	High Holy Disco Man/High Holy Disco Man (Dance Macabre)/The Voice That Speaks From Within (Triumph Over Will) Part 1 (12", p/s)	8
83	Polydor POSP 578	Resistance/The Secret Life Of The Big Black Suit (Instrumental) (12", p/s)	5
83	Polydor POSPX 578	Resistance/The Secret Life Of The Big Black Suit (Instrumental)/The Suit Walks On (Size 12) (12", p/s)	8

83	Polydor POSP 627	Breakdown (Remix)/Black Angel's Death Song (p/s)	4
83	Polydor POSPX 627	Breakdown (Remix) (Extended Version)/Black Angel's Death Song (12", p/s)	7
85	Doublevision DVR 18	4 Hours (Remixed)/Sensorium (Remixed) (12", p/s)	8
90s	Anterior BIGSEX 0001	Hacker (Hacked) (Reprogrammed 1)/(Reprogrammed 1) (p/s)	6
80	private cassette	DEEP FLOOR (cassette)	12
80	private cassette	FRAGMENT DVATION (cassette)	12
81	Fetish FR 2002	THIRST (LP, with insert)	12
81	Industrial IRC 31	WHITE SOULS IN BLACK SUITS (cassette, some with booklet)	25/15
83	Polydor POLS 1082	ADVANTAGE (LP, with inner sleeve)	10
83	Polydor POLSC 1082	ADVANTAGE (cassette)	10

(see also Anti Group)

CLOCKWORK ORANGES
| 66 | Ember EMB S 227 | Ready Steady/After Tonight | 8 |

CLOCKWORK SOLDIERS
| 84 | Rot ASS 5 | Wet Dreams/Suicide/In The Name Of Science (p/s) | 4 |

BETTY CLOONEY
| 55 | HMV 7M 311 | I Love You A Mountain/Can't Do Without You | 5 |

(see also Rosemary Clooney)

ROSEMARY CLOONEY
51	Columbia DB 2895	Come On-A My House/Kentucky Waltz (78)	5
52	Columbia DB 3129	Half As Much/Botch-A-Me (Ba-Ba-Baciami Piccina) (78)	5
53	Columbia SCM 5019	Half As Much/Botch-A-Me (Ba-Ba-Baciami Piccina)	15
53	Columbia SCM 5027	If I Had A Penny/You're After My Own Heart	8
53	Columbia SCM 5028	On The First Warm Day/If Teardrops Were Pennies	10
53	Columbia SCM 5040	(Remember Me) I'm The One Who Loves You/Lover's Gold	7
53	Columbia SCM 5049	Blues In The Night/Who Kissed Me Last Night?	10
54	Columbia SCM 5093	I Still Feel The Same About You (with Betty Clooney)/Why Fight The Feeling	7
57	Philips JK 1010	Mangos/All The Pretty Little Horses	12
58	Philips PB 800	I Could Have Danced All Night/I've Grown Accustomed To ...	4
58	MGM MGM 990	The Loudenboomer Bird/It's A Boy	4
59	Philips PB 900	Tonight/Come Rain Or Come Shine	4
59	Coral Q 72357	Diga Me (Deega May-Tell Me)/A Touch Of The Blues	4
59	MGM MGM 1010	Love Eyes/Flattery (B-side with Jose Ferrer)	4
60	Coral Q 72388	Love, Love Away/I Wish I Were In Love Again	4
60	MGM MGM 1062	For You/I Wonder	4
60	RCA RCA 1203	Many A Wonderful Moment/Vaya, Vaya	4
54	Columbia SEG 7552	ROSEMARY CLOONEY AND HARRY JAMES (EP)	7
55	Philips BBE 12004	ROSEMARY CLOONEY (EP)	12
56	Philips BBE 12051	ROSEMARY CLOONEY (EP)	10
60	Coral FEP 2045	SWING AROUND ROSIE VOL. 1 (EP)	7
60	Coral FEP 2046	SWING AROUND ROSIE VOL. 2 (EP)	7
54	Philips BBR 8022	WHITE CHRISTMAS (10" LP)	25
55	Philips BBR 8047	ROSEMARY CLOONEY (10" LP)	20
56	Philips BBR 8073	AT THE LONDON PALLADIUM (10" LP)	20
56	Philips BBL 7090	HEY BABY (LP, with Duke Ellington)	15
57	Philips BBL 7156	RING AROUND ROSIE (LP, with Hi-Lo's)	15
57	Philips BBL 7191	CHILDREN'S FAVOURITES (LP)	15
59	Philips BBL 7301	SHOWCASE OF HITS (LP)	15
59	Coral LVA 9112	SWING AROUND ROSIE (LP)	12
61	RCA RD 27189	CLAP HANDS, HERE COMES ROSIE! (LP, also stereo SF 5075)	10
61	MGM C 838	SWINGS SOFTLY (LP)	10

ROSEMARY CLOONEY & MARLENE DIETRICH
| 53 | Columbia SCM 5010 | Too Old To Cut The Mustard/Good For Nothin' | 12 |

(see also Marlene Dietrich, Betty Clooney, Bob Hope & Rosemary Clooney)

CLAUDE CLOUD
57	MGM MGM 946	The Beat/Around The Horn (as Claude Cloud & His Orchestra)	8
55	MGM MGM-EP 517	LET'S GO CATSTATIC NO. 1 (EP, as Claude Cloud & Thunderclaps)	25
56	MGM MGM-D 142	ROCK 'N' ROLL (10" LP)	40

(see also Sonny Thompson)

| 55 | MGM MGM 820 | Cloudburst/One Bone (78, with Thunderclaps) | 20 |

CLOUDS
69	Island WIP 6055	Make No Bones About It/Heritage	7
69	Island WIP 6067	Scrapbook/Carpenter	7
69	Island ILPS 9100	SCRAPBOOK (LP, pink label)	20
71	Island ILPS 9151	WATERCOLOUR DAYS (LP, pink label, gatefold sleeve)	15

CLOUDS
86	Sha La La Ba Ba Ba 001	Throwaway/CLOUDS: Jenny Nowhere (p/s, flexi free with various fanzines)	8/6
88	Subway Org. SUBWAY 12	Tranquil/Get Out Of My Dream (p/s)	4
88	Subway Org. SUBWAY 12T	Tranquil/Get Out Of My Dream/Village Green (12", p/s)	7

(see also Boy Hairdressers, Teenage Fanclub)

CLOVEN HOOF
82	Cloven Hoof TOA 1402	OPENING RITUAL (EP)	12
84	Neat NEAT 1013	CLOVEN HOOF (LP)	10
88	Heavy Metal HMRLP 113	DOMINATOR (LP)	10

CLOVER
70	Liberty LBF 15341	Wade In The Water/Stealin'	7
76	Vertigo 6059 157	Chicken Funk/Show Me Your Love	4
77	Vertigo 6059 164	I Lie Away And Dream Of You/Take Another Look	4
77	Vertigo 6059 171	Love Love/Leavin' Is	4
77	Vertigo 6059 175	Chain Gang/Streets Of London	4
77	Vertigo 6059 188	Oh Senorita/Ain't Nobody	4

70	Liberty LBS 83340	CLOVER (LP)	15
71	Liberty LBS 83487	FORTY NINER (LP)	15
77	Vertigo 6360 145	UNAVAILABLE (LP)	10
77	Vertigo 6360 155	LOVE ON THE WIRE (LP)	10

(see also American Express, Huey Lewis & News)

CLOVERLEAFS

56	MGM MGM 933	Step Right Up And Say Howdy/With Plenty Of Money And You (Gold Digger's Lullaby)	6

(see also Art Mooney)

CLOVERS

56	London HLE 8229	Nip Sip/If I Could Be Loved By You (gold or silver label)	275/225
56	London HLE 8229	Nip Sip/If I Could Be Loved By You (78)	35
56	London HLE 8314	Love, Love, Love/Hey, Doll Baby	250
56	London HLE 8314	Love, Love, Love/Hey, Doll Baby (78)	30
56	London HLE 8334	From The Bottom Of My Heart/Your Tender Lips	225
56	London HLE 8334	From The Bottom Of My Heart/Your Tender Lips (78)	35
58	London HL 7048	Wishing For Your Love/All About You (export issue)	80
58	London HL 7048	Wishing For Your Love/All About You (78, export issue)	20
58	HMV POP 542	In The Good Old Summertime/Idaho	20
58	HMV POP 542	In The Good Old Summertime/Idaho (78)	50
59	London HLT 8949	Love Potion No. 9/Stay Awhile	30
59	London HLT 8949	Love Potion No. 9/Stay Awhile (78)	55
60	London HLT 9122	Lovey/One Mint Julep	30
60	London HLT 9154	Easy Lovin'/I'm Confessin' (That I Love You)	25
61	HMV POP 883	Honey Dripper/Have Gun	15
68	Atlantic 584 160	Your Cash Ain't Nothin' But Trash/I've Got My Eyes On You	10
69	Atlantic 587 162	LOVE BUG (LP)	30

JEREMY CLYDE

65	CBS 201823	I Love My Love/Anytime	4

(see also Chad & Jeremy)

CLYDE VALLEY STOMPERS

56	Beltona BL 2650	Old Time Religion/Pearly Gates (78)	5
57	Decca FJ 10897	Nilenberg Joys/Bill Bailey Won't You Please Come Home (with Mary McGowan)	4

(see also Ian Menzies)

C.M.J.

60s	Impression	I Can't Do It All By Myself/Nothing At All	10
60s	private press	C.M.J. (LP)	300

C.M.U. (CONTEMPORARY MUSIC UNIT)

72	Transatlantic BIG 508	Heart Of The Sun/Doctor Am I Normal?	8
71	Transatlantic TRA 237	OPEN SPACES (LP, gatefold sleeve)	50
72	Transatlantic TRA 259	SPACE CABARET (LP)	40

CNN

90s	On ON 4 01	3-track white label (mail order only, in printed PVC cover)	8

COACHMEN

59	Vogue V 9154	Those Brown Eyes/Bald Mountain	8
59	Vogue V 9154	Those Brown Eyes/Bald Mountain (78)	5
61	Vogue VAE 170149	HERE COME THE COACHMEN (EP)	10
60	Vogue VA 16062	HERE COME THE COACHMEN (LP)	12

COACHMEN

66	Columbia DB 8057	Gabrielle/Seasons In The Sun	5

COASTERS

57	London HLE 8450	Searchin'/Young Blood	30
57	London HL 7021	Searchin'/Young Blood (export issue)	15
57	London HLE 8450	Searchin'/Young Blood (78)	10
58	London HLE 8665	Yakety Yak/Zing! Went The Strings Of My Heart	15
58	London HLE 8665	Yakety Yak/Zing! Went The Strings Of My Heart (78)	15
58	London HLE 8729	The Shadow Knows/Sorry But I'm Gonna Have To Pass	20
58	London HLE 8729	The Shadow Knows/Sorry But I'm Gonna Have To Pass (78)	15
59	London HLE 8819	Charlie Brown/Three Cool Cats	8
59	London HLE 8819	Charlie Brown/Three Cool Cats (78)	15
59	London HL 7073	Charlie Brown/Three Cool Cats (export issue)	7
59	London HLE 8882	Along Came Jones/That Is Rock And Roll (silver top label)	12
59	London HLE 8882	Along Came Jones/That Is Rock And Roll (78)	20

(all the above 45s originally came with tri centres, later round centre reissues are worth half to two thirds the value)

59	London HLE 8938	Poison Ivy/I'm A Hog For You	8
59	London HLE 8938	Poison Ivy/I'm A Hog For You (78)	25
60	London HLE 9020	What About Us/Run Red Run	8
60	London HLE 9020	What About Us/Run Red Run (78)	30
60	London HLK 9111	Besame Mucho Pts 1 & 2	8
60	London HLK 9111	Besame Mucho Pts 1 & 2 (78)	40
60	London HLK 9151	Wake Me, Shake Me/Stewball	8
60	London HLK 9208	Shoppin' For Clothes/The Snake And The Bookworm	8
61	London HLK 9293	Wait A Minute/Thumbin' A Ride	7
61	London HLK 9349	Little Egypt/Keep On Rolling	6
61	London HLK 9413	Girls! Girls! Girls! Pts 1 & 2	6
62	London HLK 9493	(Ain't That) Just Like Me/Bad Blood	6
64	London HLK 9863	T'Ain't Nothin' To Me/Speedo's Back In Town	6
66	Atlantic 584 033	She's A Yum Yum/Saturday Night Fish Fry	6
67	Atlantic 584 087	Searchin'/Yakety Yak	5
67	CBS 2749	Soul Pad/Down Home Girl	8
68	Direction 58-3701	She Can/Everybody's Woman	5
72	Stateside SS 2201	Cool Jerk/Talkin' 'Bout A Woman (withdrawn)	10

MINT VALUE £

72	Parlophone R 5931	Love Potion No. 9/D.W. Washburn	4
74	London HLZ 10437	Love Potion No. 9/D.W. Washburn (reissue)	4
59	London REE 1203	THE COASTERS (EP)	50
60	London HA-E 2237	GREATEST HITS (LP)	30
63	London HA-K 8033	COASTIN' ALONG WITH THE COASTERS (LP)	35
66	Atlantic 588 134	COASTIN' ALONG WITH THE COASTERS (LP, reissue)	20
67	Atlantic 590 015	ALL TIME GREATEST HITS (LP)	20
74	London SHZ 8460	ON BROADWAY (LP)	12
74	Joy JOYS 189	HUNGRY (LP)	10

(see also Robins)

COAST ROAD DRIVE

74	Deram SML 1113	DELICIOUS AND REFRESHING (LP)	35

ODIA COATES

75	United Artists UP 35779	Showdown/Leave Me In The Morning	5

C.O.B. (CLIVE'S OWN BAND)

72	Polydor 2058 260	Blue Morning/Bones	15
71	CBS 69010	SPIRIT OF LOVE (LP)	45
72	Polydor 2383 161	MOYSHE McSTIFF AND THE TARTAN LANCERS OF THE SACRED HEART (LP)	125

(see also Famous Jug Band, Incredible String Band)

COBBLERS LAST

70s	Banshee BAN 1012	BOOT IN THE DOOR (LP)	75

COBBS

69	Amalgamated AMG 845	Hot Buttered Corn/COUNT MACHUKI: It Is I	5
69	Amalgamated AMG 849	Space Daughter/LLOYD & DEVON: Reggae Baby	5

JUNIE COBB'S HOMETOWN BAND

59	Collector JDL 38	Chicago Buzz/East Coast Trot	5

BILLY COBHAM

73	Atlantic K 40406	SPECTRUM (LP, gatefold sleeve)	10
74	Atlantic K 50098	TOTAL ECLIPSE (LP)	10
74	Atlantic K 50037	CROSSWINDS (LP)	10
75	Atlantic K 50147	SHABAZZ (LP)	10
75	Atlantic K 50185	A FUNKY SIDE OF THINGS (LP)	10

COBRA

78	Rip Off RIP 3	Graveyard Boogie/Looking For A Lady (p/s)	4

COCHISE

70	Liberty LBS 83428	SWALLOW TALES (LP)	10
71	United Artists UAS 29117	COCHISE (LP)	12
72	United Artists UAS 29286	SO FAR (LP)	10

(see also B.J. Cole, Mick Grabham)

DIB COCHRAN & EARWIGS

70	Bell BLL 1121	Oh Baby/Universal Love (3 different colours of label)	120

(see also Marc Bolan)

EDDIE COCHRAN

57	London HLU 8386	20 Flight Rock/Dark Lonely Street (silver tri-centre, later round centre)	90/30
57	London HLU 8386	20 Flight Rock/Dark Lonely Street (78)	25
57	London HLU 8433	Sittin' In The Balcony/Completely Sweet	200
57	London HLU 8433	Sittin' In The Balcony/Completely Sweet (78)	30
58	London HLU 8702	Summertime Blues/Love Again (tri-centre or black round centre)	18/12
58	London HLU 8702	Summertime Blues/Love Again (78)	30
59	London HLU 8792	C'mon Everybody/Don't Ever Let Me Go (black or silver-top tri centre)	18/14
59	London HLU 8792	C'mon Everybody/Don't Ever Let Me Go (78)	30
59	London HLU 8880	Teenage Heaven/I Remember	20
59	London HLU 8880	Teenage Heaven/I Remember (78)	50
59	London HL 7082	Teenage Heaven/Boll Weevil Song (export issue)	75
59	London HLU 8944	Somethin' Else/Boll Weevil Song (tri-centre or round centre)	45/20
59	London HLU 8944	Somethin' Else/Boll Weevil Song (78)	50

(the above singles originally had tri-centres, round centre reissues are worth around half the value unless stated otherwise)

60	London HLW 9022	Hallelujah, I Love Her So/Little Angel	12
60	London HLW 9022	Hallelujah, I Love Her So/Little Angel (78)	75
60	London HLG 9115	Three Steps To Heaven/Cut Across Shorty	12
60	London HLG 9115	Three Steps To Heaven/Cut Across Shorty (78)	125
60	London HLG 9196	Sweetie Pie/Lonely	15
61	London HLG 9362	Weekend/Cherished Memories	12
61	London HLG 9460	Jeannie, Jeannie, Jeannie/Pocketful Of Hearts	20
61	London HLG 9464	Pretty Girl/Teresa	25
61	London HLG 9467	Undying Love/Stockin's 'N' Shoes	25
62	Liberty LIB 10049	Never/Think Of Me	15
63	Liberty LIB 10088	My Way/Rock And Roll Blues	12
63	Liberty LIB 10108	Drive-In Show/I Almost Lost My Mind	20
64	Liberty LIB 10151	Skinny Jim/Nervous Breakdown	30
66	Liberty LIB 10233	C'mon Everybody/Summertime Blues (demo only)	20
66	Liberty LIB 10233	C'mon Everybody/Milk Cow Blues	15
66	Liberty LIB 10249	Three Stars/Somethin' Else	40
67	Liberty LIB 10276	Three Steps To Heaven/Eddie's Blues	35
68	Liberty LBF 15071	Summertime Blues/Let's Get Together	10
68	Liberty LBF 15109	Somethin' Else/Milk Cow Blues	10
70	Liberty LBF 15366	C'mon Everybody/Mean When I'm Mad	10
72	United Artists UP 35361	Somethin' Else/Three Steps To Heaven	4
72	United Artists UP 35408	Summertime Blues/Cotton Picker	5
59	London REU 1214	C'MON EVERYBODY (EP, orange sleeve, tri-centre or round centre)	60/50

Eddie COCHRAN

59	London REU 1214	C'MON EVERYBODY (EP, yellow sleeve, silver top round centre)	50
60	London REU 1239	SOMETHIN' ELSE (EP)	50
60	London REG 1262	EDDIE'S HITS (EP)	50
61	London REG 1301	CHERISHED MEMORIES OF EDDIE COCHRAN (EP)	50
62	Liberty LEP 2052	NEVER TO BE FORGOTTEN (EP)	25
63	Liberty LEP 2090	CHERISHED MEMORIES (VOL.1) (EP)	30
63	Liberty LEP 2111	C'MON EVERYBODY (EP, reissue)	20
63	Liberty LEP 2122	SOMETHIN' ELSE (EP, reissue)	25
63	Liberty LEP 2123	CHERISHED MEMORIES OF EDDIE COCHRAN (EP, reissue)	30
63	Liberty LEP 2124	EDDIE'S HITS (EP, reissue)	25
64	Liberty LEP 2165	C'MON AGAIN (EP)	40
64	Liberty LEP 2180	STOCKIN'S AND SHOES (EP)	25
58	London HA-U 2093	SINGIN' TO MY BABY (LP)	90
60	London HA-G 2267	THE EDDIE COCHRAN MEMORIAL ALBUM (LP)	50
62	Liberty LBY 1109	CHERISHED MEMORIES (LP)	20
63	Liberty LBY 1127	THE EDDIE COCHRAN MEMORIAL ALBUM (LP, reissue)	20
63	Liberty LBY 1158	SINGIN' TO MY BABY (LP, reissue)	25
64	Liberty LBY 1205	MY WAY (LP)	40
68	Liberty LBL/LBS 83009	THE EDDIE COCHRAN MEMORIAL ALBUM (LP, reissue)	10
68	Liberty LBL/LBS 83072E	CHERISHED MEMORIES (LP, reissue)	12
68	Liberty LBL 83104	MY WAY (LP, reissue in different sleeve)	12
68	Liberty LBL/LBS 83152	SINGIN' TO MY BABY (LP, 2nd reissue in different sleeve)	12
70	Liberty LBS 83337	THE VERY BEST OF EDDIE COCHRAN (LP)	10
71	United Artists UAS 29163	THE LEGENDARY EDDIE COCHRAN (LP)	10
72	United Artists UAD 60017	THE LEGENDARY MASTER SERIES (2-LP, with booklet)	18
72	United Artists UAS 29380	ON THE AIR (LP)	12
79	United Artists UAK 30244	THE SINGLES ALBUM (LP, w/ 7" "Pretty Girl"/"Think Of Me" [FREE 12] & poster)	12
80	United Artists UP ECSP 20	20TH ANNIVERSARY ALBUM (4-LP box set)	35

HANK COCHRAN

68	Monument LMO 5020	HEART OF HANK (LP)	10

HEAVY COCHRAN

78	Psycho P 2611	I've Got Big Balls/Well, Fairly Big	4

JACKIE LEE COCHRAN

57	Brunswick 05669	Mama Don't You Think I Know/Ruby Pearl (with Jimmy Pruett)	500
57	Brunswick 05669	Mama Don't You Think I Know/Ruby Pearl (78)	75

BRUCE COCKBURN

72	Epic EPC 65187	SUNWHEEL DANCE (LP)	12

JOE COCKER

64	Decca F 11974	I'll Cry Instead/Precious Words	30
67	Action ACT 002 EP	RAG GOES MAD AT THE MOJO (33rpm EP, 2 tracks by Joe Cocker's Blues Band, free with Sheffield University rag magazine 'Twikker')	50
68	Regal Zono. RZ 3006	Marjorine/New Age Of The Lily	5
68	Regal Zono. RZ 3013	With A Little Help From My Friends/Something's Coming On	4
69	Regal Zono. RZ 3024	Delta Lady/She's So Good To Me	4
70	Regal Zono. RZ 3027	The Letter/Space Captain	4
70	Fly BUG 3	Cry Me A River/Give Peace A Chance (p/s)	6
71	Fly BUG 9	High Time We Went/Black Eyed Blues	4
72	Magni Fly ECHO 103	With A Little Help From My Friends/Delta Lady/The Letter (p/s)	7
83	Island WIP 6818	Ruby Lee/Talking Back To The Night (export issue)	6
60s	Oak	JOE COCKER (EP)	150
69	Regal Zono. SLRZ 1006	WITH A LITTLE HELP FROM MY FRIENDS (LP)	12
69	Regal Zono. SLRZ 1011	JOE COCKER! (LP)	10
71	Fly HIFLY 3	COCKER HAPPY (LP)	10

(see also Grease Band)

COCKNEY REBEL

(see under Steve Harley/Cockney Rebel)

COCKNEY 'N' WESTERNS

80	Beggars Banquet BEG 39	She's No Angel/Had A Real Good Time (p/s)	5

(see also Boys, Rowdies)

COCKNEY REJECTS

79	Small Wonder SW 19	Flares'N'Slippers/Police Star/I Wanna Be A Star (p/s)	5
79	EMI EMI 5008	I'm Not A Fool/East End (p/s)	4
80	EMI EMI 5035	Bad Man!/The New Song (p/s)	4
80	Zonophone Z 2	The Greatest Cockney Rip-Off/Hate Of The City (p/s, yellow vinyl)	4
80	Zonophone Z 4	I'm Forever Blowing Bubbles/West Side Boys (p/s)	4
80	Zonophone Z 6	We Can Do Anything/15 Nights (p/s)	4
80	Zonophone Z 10	We Are The Firm/War On The Terraces (p/s)	4
81	Zonophone Z 20	Easy Life/Motorhead/Hang 'Em High (p/s)	4
81	Zonophone Z 21	On The Streets Again/London (p/s)	4
82	A.K.A. AKS 102	Till The End Of The Day/Rock'N'Roll Dream (p/s)	4
80	Zonophone ZONO 101	GREATEST HITS VOLUME 1 (LP)	10
81	Zonophone ZONO 102	GREATEST HITS VOLUME 2 (LP, with inner sleeve & poster)	10
82	Zonophone ZEM 101	GREATEST HITS VOLUME 3 (LIVE AND LOUD) (LP)	10

COCKNEYS

64	Philips BF 1303	After Tomorrow/I'll Cry Each Night	8
64	Philips BF 1338	After Tomorrow/I'll Cry Each Night (reissue)	8
64	Philips BF 1360	I Know You're Gonna Be Mine/Oh No You Won't	8

COCKSPARRER

77	Decca FR 13710	Runnin' Riot/Sister Suzie (no p/s; demos in p/s £40)	7
77	Decca FR 13732	We Love You/Chip On My Shoulder (no p/s)	7
77	Decca LFR 13732	We Love You/Chip On My Shoulder (12" p/s, with photo insert, 7,500 only)	10

82	Carrere CAR 255	England Belongs To Me/Argy Bargy (p/s)	10

(see also Little Roosters)

COCKTAIL CABINET
67	Page One POF 046	Puppet On A String/Breathalyse	15

COCTEAU TWINS
83	4AD AD 303	Peppermint Pig/Laugh Lines (p/s)	18
84	4AD AD 314	Sugar Hiccup (1-sided, promo-only)	15
84	4AD BAD 405	Pearly-Dewdrop's Drops/The Spangle Maker/Pepper-Tree (12", embossed p/s)	7
88	4AD CAD 807	BLUE BELL KNOLL (LP, tri-foldout sleeve)	10

(see also This Mortal Coil)

C.O.D.s
66	Stateside SS 489	Michael (The Lover)/Cry No More	15

JAMIE COE
59	Parlophone R 4600	Summertime Symphony/There's Gonna Be A Day	100
60	Parlophone R 4621	School Day Blues/I'll Go On Loving You	30
61	HMV POP 991	How Low Is Low/Little Dear Little Darling	12
63	London HLX 9713	The Fool/I've Got That Feeling Again	12

TONY COE QUINTET
60s	Philips B 10784L	SWINGIN' TILL THE GIRLS COME HOME (LP)	12

TONY COE & ROBERT FARNON
70	Chapter One CHS 804	POP MAKES PROGRESS (LP)	25

TONY COE & BRIAN LEMON TRIO
68	'77' SEU 12/41	TONY COE AND BRIAN LEMON TRIO (LP)	10

COFFEE SET
69	Mercury MF 1076	Dicky Boy/Georgia On My Mind	4
69	Mercury MF 1113	Happy Birthday	4

ALMA COGAN
53	HMV 7M 106	I Went To Your Wedding/You Belong To Me	25
53	HMV 7M 107	To Be Loved By You/The Homing Waltz (B-side with Larry Day)	25
53	HMV 7M 166	Over And Over Again/Isn't Life Wonderful (with Les Howard)	20
54	HMV 7M 173	Ricochet (Rick-O-Shay)/The Moon Is Blue	25
54	HMV 7M 188	Bell Bottom Blues/Love Me Again	25
54	HMV 7M 196	Make Love To Me/Said The Little Moment	20
54	HMV 7M 219	The Little Shoemaker/Chiqui-Chaqui (Chick-ee Chock-ee)	25
54	HMV 7M 228	Little Things Mean A Lot/Canoodlin' Rag	18
54	HMV 7M 239	What Am I Going To Do, Ma/Skinnie Minnie (Fishtail)	30
54	HMV 7M 269	This Ole House/Skokiaan	25
54	HMV 7M 271	I Can't Tell A Waltz From A Tango/Christmas Cards	20
55	HMV 7M 286	Paper Kisses/Softly, Softly	20
55	HMV 7M 293	Chee-Chee-Oo-Chee (Sang The Little Bird)/Tika Tika Tok	20
55	HMV B 10872	Dreamboat/(The Diddle-ee-i) Irish Mambo (78)	5
55	HMV B 10887	Where Will The Dimple Be?/Keep Me In Mind (78)	5
55	HMV 7M 301	More Than Ever Now/Tweedlee-Dee	20
55	HMV 7M 316	Got'n Idea/Give A Fool A Chance	20
55	HMV B 10917	Go On By/The Banjo's Back In Town (78)	5
55	HMV 7M 337	Never Do A Tango With An Eskimo/Twenty Tiny Fingers	20
56	HMV 7M 367	Love And Marriage/Sycamore Tree	20
56	HMV POP 187	Willie Can/Lizzie Borden (78)	5
56	HMV POP 189	Bluebell/Don't Ring-a Da Bell (Don't Knock at Da Door) (78)	5
56	HMV 7M 415	The Birds And The Bees/Why Do Fools Fall In Love	20
56	HMV POP 239	Mama Teach Me To Dance/I'm In Love Again	15
56	HMV POP 261	In The Middle Of The House/Two Innocent Hearts	25
57	HMV POP 284	You, Me And Us/Three Brothers	15
57	HMV POP 317	Whatever Lola Wants (Lola Gets)/Lucky Lips	15
57	HMV POP 336	Chantez, Chantez/Funny, Funny, Funny	12
57	HMV POP 367	Fabulous/Summer Love	15
57	HMV POP 392	That's Happiness/What You've Done To Me	10
57	HMV POP 415	Party Time/Please Mr. Brown (Mr. Jones, Mr. Smith)	10
58	HMV POP 433	The Story Of My Life/Love Is	12
58	HMV POP 450	Sugartime/Gettin' Ready For Freddy	15
58	HMV POP 482	Stairway Of Love/Comes Love	12
58	HMV POP 500	Fly Away Lovers/Sorry, Sorry, Sorry	6
58	HMV POP 531	There's Never Been A Night/If This Isn't Love	8
59	HMV POP 573	Last Night On The Back Porch/Mama Says	8
59	HMV POP 608	Pink Shoelaces/The Universe	8
59	HMV POP 670	We Got Love/I Don't Mind Being All Alone	6
60	HMV POP 728	O Dio Mio/Dream Talk	6
60	HMV POP 760	The Train Of Love/The 'I Love You' Bit	6
60	HMV POP 815	Must Be Santa/Just Couldn't Resist Her With Her Pocket Transistor	6
61	Columbia DB 4607	Cowboy Jimmy Joe/Don't Read This Letter	4
61	Columbia DB 4679	With You In Mind/Ja-Da	4
61	Columbia DB 4749	All Alone/Keep Me In Your Heart	5
62	Columbia DB 4794	She's Got You/In The Shade Of The Old Apple Tree	5
62	Columbia DB 4912	Goodbye Joe/I Can't Give You Anything But Love	5
63	Columbia DB 4965	Tell Him/Fly Me To The Moon	4
63	Columbia DB 7059	Hold Out Your Hand You Naughty Boy/Just Once More	5
64	Columbia DB 7233	The Tennessee Waltz/I Love You Too Much	6
64	Columbia DB 7390	It's You/I Knew Right Away	6
65	Columbia DB 7619	Love Is A Word/Now That I've Found You	6
65	Columbia DB 7652	Snakes, Snails And Puppy Dog Tails/How Many Days How Many Nights	6
	Columbia DB 7757	Let Her Go/Yesterday (unreleased)	

Alma COGAN

65	Columbia DB 7786	Eight Days A Week/Help!	4
55	HMV 7EG 8122	THE GIRL WITH A LAUGH IN HER VOICE (EP)	15
55	HMV 7EG 8151	THE GIRL WITH A LAUGH IN HER VOICE NO. 2 (EP)	12
56	HMV 7EG 8169	THE GIRL WITH A LAUGH IN HER VOICE NO. 3 (EP)	12
57	HMV 7EG 8352	THE HITS FROM 'MY FAIR LADY' (EP, 1 side by Ronnie Hilton)	8
57	HMV 7EG 8437	SHE LOVES TO SING (EP)	15
58	HMV CLP 1152	I LOVE TO SING (LP)	45
61	HMV CLP 1459	OLIVER! (LP, with others, also stereo CSD 1370)	40/50
61	Columbia 33SX 1345	ALMA SINGS WITH YOU IN MIND (LP)	50
62	Columbia 33SX 1465	HOW ABOUT LOVE! (LP)	45
67	Columbia SX 6130	ALMA (LP)	40
70	M For Pleasure MFP 1377	THE GIRL WITH THE LAUGH IN HER VOICE (LP)	10

(see also Ronnie Hilton, Angela & Fans, Billy Cotton)

ALMA COGAN & FRANKIE VAUGHAN

54	HMV 7M 226	Do, Do, Do, Do, Do, Do, Do It Again/Jilted	15

(see also Frankie Vaughan)

DON COGAN

58	MGM MGM 984	The Fountain Of Love/I'm Takin' Over	4

SHAYE COGAN

58	Columbia DB 4055	Billy Be Sure/Doodle Doodle Doo	4
60	MGM MGM 1063	Mean To Me/They Said It Couldn't Be Done	5

LEONARD COHEN

68	CBS 3337	Suzanne/So Long, Marianne	5
69	CBS 4245	Bird On The Wire/Seems So Long Ago, Nancy	5
71	CBS 7292	Joan Of Arc/Diamonds In The Mine	4
74	CBS 2494	Bird On The Wire (live)/Tonight Will Be Fine (live)	4
74	CBS 2699	Lover Lover Lover/Who By Fire	4
76	CBS 4306	Suzanne/Take This Longing	4
70	CBS 9162	McCABE AND MRS MILLER (EP)	7
68	CBS 63241	SONGS OF LEONARD COHEN (LP)	10
68	CBS 63587	SONGS FROM A ROOM (LP)	10
70	CBS 69004	SONGS OF LOVE AND HATE (LP, with booklet)	10

COIL

79	Northamp. Wood Hill HAV1	Motor Industry/Alcoholic Stork (p/s)	8

COIL

85	Force & Form/K.422 FFK 5.12	Panic/Tainted Love/Aqua Regis (12", red or black vinyl, 'hair'-textured p/s)	15/10
86	Force & Form/K.422 ROTA 121	The Anal Staircase/Blood From The Air/Ravenous (12", p/s, some on clear vinyl)	15/10
89	Shock SX 002	Scope/Wrong Eye (white p/s, 1,000 only, 26 lettered, others numbered)	25/15
89	Shock SX 002	Scope/Wrong Eye (green p/s, 3,000 only, numbered)	10
80s	Solar Lodge COIL 001	HELLRAISER (10" EP, with insert, clear or pink vinyl, also black vinyl)	10/8/6
87	Threshold ROTA 1	HORSE ROTORVATOR (LP, clear vinyl)	12
88	Threshold House LOCI 1	GOLD IS THE METAL (LP, red or clear vinyl; with inner sleeve, some with free 7" "The Wheal"/"Keel Hauler")	25/18
88	Threshold House LOCI 1	GOLD IS THE METAL (LP, box set)	55
88	Threshold House LOCI 1	GOLD IS THE METAL (LP, box set with 7", poster & booklet in black linen folder, embossed sleeve, 55 only)	250
88	Threshold House LOCI 1	GOLD IS THE METAL (CD, 1,000 only)	15
80s	Nekrophile	COIL/ZOS KIA LIVE (cassette)	12

(see also Psychic TV)

ALVADEAN COKER

55	London HLU 8191	Do Dee Oodle De Do I'm In Love/We're Gonna Bop	200
55	London HLU 8191	Do Dee Oodle De Do I'm In Love/We're Gonna Bop (78)	35

SANDY COKER & HIS BAND

54	London HL 8109	Meadowlark Melody/Toss Over	22

RIC COLBECK QUARTET

70	Fontana 6383 001	THE SUN IS COMING UP (LP)	25

MARION COLBY

58	Capitol CL 14959	A Man Could Be A Wonderful Thing/He Like It! She Like ...	4

COLD BLOOD

70	Atlantic 584 319	You Got Me Hummin'/If You Will	4
70	Atlantic 588 218	COLD BLOOD (LP)	15
71	Atlantic 2400 102	SISYPHUS (LP)	15
74	Warner Bros K 56047	LYDIA (LP)	15

BEN COLDER

64	MGM MGM-EP 791	MAKE THE WORLD GO BY (EP)	10

BILLY COLE

75	Power Exchange PX 104	Extra Careful/Bump All Night	5

B.J. COLE

72	United Artists UAS 29418	NEW HOVERING DOG (LP)	12

(see also Cochise)

BOBBY COLE

68	CBS 3626	Mister Bo Jangles/Bus 22 To Jerusalem	4

BUDDY COLE & WOOD SISTERS

55	Philips PB 464	Plantation Boogie/Foolishly (78)	5

CINDY COLE

65	Columbia DB 7519	A Love Like Yours/He's Sure The Boy I Love	5

Rare Record Price Guide

| 66 | Columbia DB 7973 | Just Being Your Baby (Turns Me On)/Lonely City Blue Boy .... 10 |

(see also Jeannie & Big Guys)

CLAY COLE
| 62 | London HLP 9499 | Twist Around The Clock/Don't Twist .... 5 |

COZY COLE
58	London HL 8750	Topsy Pts 1 & 2 8
58	London HL 7065	Topsy Pts 1 & 2 (export issue) 6
58	London HL 8750	Topsy Pts 1 & 2 (78) 5
59	Mercury AMT 1015	St. Louis Blues/Father Co-operates 6
59	Mercury AMT 1015	St. Louis Blues/Father Co-operates (78) 5
59	London HL 8843	Turvy Pts 1 & 2 6
59	London HL 8843	Turvy Pts 1 & 2 (78) 5
62	Coral Q 72457	Big Noise From Winnetka Pts 1 & 2 5
57	MGM MGM-EP 622	COZY COLE ALL STARS (EP) 10

DON COLE & ALLEYNE
| 65 | Fontana TF 522 | Gotta Find My Baby/Something's Gotta Hold Of Me .... 4 |

JERRY COLE
| 65 | Capitol CL 15397 | Every Window In The City/Come On Over To My Place .... 4 |

LLOYD COLE & COMMOTIONS
84	Welcome To L. Vegas LC 1	Are You Ready To Be Heartbroken?/Down At The Mission (withdrawn) (p/s) 50
84	Polydor COLEG 2	Forest Fire/Andy's Baby (gatefold p/s) 4
84	Polydor COLEX 2	Forest Fire/Andy's Baby (cassette) 4
85	Polydor COLET 5	Lost Weekend/Big World (10", p/s) 5
86	Polydor COLEG 6	Cut Me Down (Remix)/Are You Ready To Be Heartbroken? (live)//
		Perfect Blue (Instrumental)/Forest Fire (live) (double pack) 4
87	Polydor COLEG 8	Jennifer She Said/Perfect Blue (foldout p/s) 4

NATALIE COLE
| 75 | Capitol E-ST 11429 | INSEPARABLE (LP) .... 10 |

NAT 'KING' COLE
50	Capitol CL 13370	I Almost Lost My Mind/Bang Bang Boogie (78, as Nat 'King' Cole Trio) 8
52	Capitol CL 13722	(Get Your Kicks On) Route 66 (as Nat 'King' Cole Trio)/
		Wine, Women And Song (78) 6
52	Capitol CL 13774	Somewhere Along The Way/Walkin' My Baby Back Home (78) 5
52	Capitol CL 13811	Because You're Mine/Faith Can Move Mountains (78) 5
53	Capitol CL 13878	Pretend/Funny (Not Much) (78) 5
53	Capitol CL 13912	Mother Nature And Father Time/My Flaming Heart (78) 5
53	Capitol CL 13937	Can't I/Small Towns Are Smile Towns (78) 5
54	Capitol CL 14061	Tenderly/Why (78) 5
54	Vogue V 2214	Nat's Kicks Pts 1 & 2 (78, as Nat 'King' Cole Quintet) 6
54	Capitol CL 14149	Smile (Theme From 'Modern Times')/Make Her Mine 12
54	Capitol CL 14155	Unbelievable/Hajji Baba (Persian Lament) 10
54	Capitol CL 14172	I Am In Love/There Goes My Heart 10
54	Capitol CL 14203	If I Give My Heart To You/Hold My Hand 10
54	Capitol CL 14207	Papa Loves Mambo/Teach Me Tonight 12
55	Capitol CL 14215	Long Long Ago/Open Up The Doghouse (with Dean Martin) 15
55	Capitol CL 14235	A Blossom Fell/Alone Too Long 12
55	Capitol CL 14251	The Sand And The Sea/Darling, Je Vous Aime Beaucoup 10
55	Capitol CL 14295	If I May (with Four Knights)/I Envy 10
55	Capitol CL 14317	Annabelle/I'd Rather Have The Blues ('Kiss Me Deadly' Theme) 10
55	Capitol CL 14327	My One Sin/Don't Hurt The Girl 12
55	Capitol CL 14364	Love Is A Many-Splendoured Thing/Autumn Leaves 10
55	Capitol CL 14378	Someone You Love/Forgive My Heart 10

(all the above 45s originally came with triangular centres, later re-pressings are worth around half the value)

56	Capitol CL 14513	Dreams Can Tell A Lie/Ask Me 8
56	Capitol CL 14529	Nothing Ever Changes (My Love For You)/
		I'm Gonna Laugh You Out Of My Life 5
56	Capitol CL 14573	Too Young To Go Steady/Never Let Me Go 7
56	Capitol CL 14621	Love Me As Though There Were No Tomorrow/That's All There Is To That
		(as Nat 'King' Cole & Four Knights) 8
56	Capitol CL 14632	My Dream Sonata/I Just Found Out About Love 4
56	Capitol CL 14661	To The Ends Of The Earth/Toyland 4
57	Capitol CL 14678	Night Lights/Dame Crazy 4
57	Capitol CL 14688	You Are My First Love/Ballerina 4
57	Capitol CL 14709	When I Fall In Love/Calypso Blues 6
57	Capitol CL 14733	When Rock And Roll Came To Trinidad/It's All In The Game 7
57	Capitol CL 14765	My Personal Possession (as Nat 'King' Cole & Four Knights)/Send For Me . 5
57	Capitol CL 14787	Stardust/Love Letters 5
58	Capitol CL 14820	Angel Smile/Back In My Arms 4
58	Capitol CL 14853	With You On My Mind/The Song Of Raintree County 4
58	Capitol CL 14882	Looking Back/Just For The Fun Of It 4
58	Capitol CL 14898	Come Closer To Me/Nothing In The World 4
58	Capitol CL 14937	Non Dimenticar (Don't Forget)/Bend A Little My Way 4
59	Capitol CL 14987	Madrid/Give Me Your Love 4
59	Capitol CL 15017	You Made Me Love You/I Must Be Dreaming 4
59	Capitol CL 15056	Midnight Flyer/Sweet Bird Of Truth 4
59	Capitol CL 15087	Buon Natale/The Happiest Little Christmas Tree 4
59	Capitol CL 15111	Time And The River/Whatcha' Gonna Do 4
60	Capitol CL 15129	That's You/Is It Better To Have Loved And Lost 4
60	Capitol CL 15144	My Love/Steady (with Stan Kenton) 4
60	Capitol CL 15163	Just As Much As Ever/I Wish I Knew The Way To Your Heart 4
55	Capitol EAP 1-514	TENTH ANNIVERSARY ALBUM PART 1 (EP) 7
55	Capitol EAP 2-514	TENTH ANNIVERSARY ALBUM PART 2 (EP) 7
55	Capitol EAP 3-514	TENTH ANNIVERSARY ALBUM PART 3 (EP) 7
55	Capitol EAP 4-514	TENTH ANNIVERSARY ALBUM PART 4 (EP) 8

56	Capitol EAP 1-633	MOODS IN SONG (EP) 7
56	Capitol EAP 1010	LOVE IS A MANY-SPLENDORED THING (EP) 7
53	Capitol LC 6569	CAPITOL PRESENTS NAT KING COLE (10" LP) 20
53	Capitol LC 6587	CAPITOL PRESENTS NAT KING COLE AND HIS TRIO VOLUME 1 (10" LP) 15
53	Capitol LC 6593	CAPITOL PRESENTS NAT KING COLE AT THE PIANO (10" LP) 18
53	Capitol LC 6594	CAPITOL PRESENTS NAT KING COLE AND HIS TRIO VOLUME 2 (10" LP) 15
53	Capitol LC 6627	NAT KING COLE SINGS FOR TWO IN LOVE (10" LP) 15
54	Capitol LCT 6003	NAT KING COLE TENTH ANNIVERSARY ALBUM (LP) 17
56	Capitol LC 6818	BALLADS OF THE DAY (10" LP) 15
56	Capitol LC 6830	THE PIANO STYLE OF NAT KING COLE (10" LP) 15
56	Brunswick LAT 8123	IN THE BEGINNING (LP, as King Cole Trio) 18
57	Capitol (S)LCT 6129	LOVE IS THE THING (LP) 14
57	Capitol LCT 6133	AFTER MIDNIGHT (LP, as Nat King Cole & His Trio) 12
57	Capitol LCT 6142	THIS IS NAT KING COLE (LP) 12
58	Capitol (S)LCT 6149	JUST ONE OF THOSE THINGS (LP) 12
58	Capitol (S)LCT 6156	ST LOUIS BLUES — SONGS OF W.C. HANDY (LP) 10
58	Capitol LCT 6166	COLE ESPANOL (LP) 10
59	Capitol LCT 6167	EVERY TIME I FEEL THE SPIRIT (LP) 10
59	Capitol (S)LCT 6173	THE VERY THOUGHT OF YOU (LP) 10
59	Capitol (S)LCT 6176	WELCOME TO THE CLUB (LP) 10
59	Capitol (S)LCT 6182	TO WHOM IT MAY CONCERN (LP) 10

(see also Dean Martin)

STRANGER COLE

63	R&B JB 133	Out Of Many/Nothing Tried 8
63	Island WI 110	Stranger At The Door/Conqueror 8
63	Island WI 114	Last Love/STRANGER & KEN: Hush Baby 8
63	Island WI 126	We Are Rolling/Millie Maw 8
64	R&B JB 129	Morning Star/Beat Up Your Gum 8
64	Island WI 133	Til My Dying Days/STRANGER & PATSY: I Need You 8
64	Blue Beat BB 165	Rough And Tough/DUKE REID BAND: The Mood I Am In 10
64	Black Swan WI 413	Uno Dos Tres (actually with Ken Boothe)/Look Before You Leap
		(B-side actually by unknown artist) 8
64	Black Swan WI 415	Summer Day/Loving You Always 8
64	Black Swan WI 435	Little Boy Blue/ERIC MORRIS: Words Of Wisdom 8
65	Ska Beat JB 192	Pussy Cat/MAYTALS: Sweet Sweet Jenny 8
65	Island WI 169	Koo Koo Doo (with Owen & Leon)/GLORIA & DREAMLETTS:
		Stay Where You Are 8
65	Island WI 177	Run Joe/Make Believe 8
65	Blue Beat BB 322	When The Party Is Over/BUSTER'S ALLSTARS: Happy Independence '65 ..8
65	Blue Beat BB 333	Matilda (actually with Prince Buster)/When The Party Is Over 8
66	Doctor Bird DB 1025	We Shall Overcome/Do You Really Love Me (as Stranger Cole & Seraphines) 8
66	Doctor Bird DB 1040	Drop The Ratchet/Oh Yee Mahee (as Stranger Cole & Conquerors) 8
68	Island WI 3154	Jeboza Macoo/Now I Know 8
68	Amalgamated AMG 801	Just Like A River (as Stranger Cole & Gladdy)/LEADERS: Hope Someday 8
69	Amalgamated AMG 838	What Mama Na Want She Get/We Two 6
69	Duke DU 27	Glad You're Living/Help Wanted 4
69	Escort ES 810	Pretty Cottage/To Me 4
69	Escort ES 819	Leana Leana/Na Na Na 4
69	Escort ES 826	Loneliness/Remember 4
69	Unity UN 501	Last Flight To Reggae City (with Tommy McCook)/JUNIOR SMITH:
		Watch Dem Go 5
69	Unity UN 514	When I Get My Freedom/Life Can Be Beautiful 4
70	Pama PM 790	Come Dance With Me/Dance With Me 4
71	Camel CA 72	Crying Every Night/DENNIS ALCAPONE & DELROY WILSON: It Must Come 4
71	Escort ERT 849	Tomorrow/SONNY BURKE: Chicken Thief 4

(see also Stranger, Stranger & Glady, Stranger & Patsy, Stranger & Ken, Stranger & Claudette, Rob Walker)

BOBBY COLEMAN

| 66 | Pye Intl. 7N 25365 | (Baby) You Don't Have To Tell Me/Pleasure Girl ....60 |

ELLEN COLEMAN (HELEN BAXTER)

24	Edison 51200	Cruel Back Bitin' Blues (A Heart Aching Chant)/You've Got Ev'ry Thing
		A Sweet Man Needs (But Me) (78) 40
24	Edison 51242	She Walked Right Up And Took My Ma Away/(Ann Chandler track) (78) 40

FITZROY COLEMAN

| 61 | Starlite ST45 064 | Lucilla/Caribbean Sunset ....7 |

LONNIE COLEMAN & JESSE ROBERTSON

| 56 | London HLU 8335 | Dolores Diane/Oh Honey, Why Don'tcha ....30 |

ORNETTE COLEMAN

60	Contemporary LAC 12228	TOMORROW IS THE QUESTION (LP) 20
61	London Jazz LTZ-K 15199	CHANGE OF THE CENTURY (LP, also stereo SAH-K 5099) 18
61	London Jazz LTZ-K 15228	THIS IS OUR MUSIC (LP, also stereo SAH-K 6181) 18
62	London Jazz LTZ-K 15241	THE ORNETTE COLEMAN QUARTET (LP, also stereo, SAH-K 6235) ...18
66	Blue Note BLP 4224	AT THE GOLDEN CIRCLE, STOCKHOLM 1 (LP, also stereo BST 84224) 20
66	Blue Note BLP 4225	AT THE GOLDEN CIRCLE, STOCKHOLM 2 (LP, also stereo BST 84225) 20
67	CBS 66023	CHAPPAQUA SUITE (2-LP) 18
67	Blue Note BLP 4246	EMPTY FOXHOLE (LP, also stereo BST 84246) 20
68	Polydor 623 246/7	AN EVENING WITH ORNETTE COLEMAN (2-LP) 14
68	Atlantic 588 121	ORNETTE ON TENOR (LP) 12
69	Blue Note BST 84287	NEW YORK IS NOW (LP) 15
69	Impulse MIPL/SIPL 518	ORNETTE AT 12 (LP) 10
69	Fontana SFJL 923	TOWN HALL 1962 (LP) 10
70	RCA RD/SF 7944	THE MUSIC OF ORNETTE COLEMAN (LP, with Philadelphia Woodwind Quintet) 10
71	Atlantic 2400 109	THE ART OF THE IMPROVISERS (LP) 10
72	Atlantic K 40278	TWINS (LP) 10
72	Polydor 2383 090	ORNETTE COLEMAN IN EUROPE VOLUME 1 (LP) 10

72	Polydor 2383 091	ORNETTE COLEMAN IN EUROPE VOLUME 2 (LP) 10
72	CBS 64774	SCIENCE FICTION (LP) 10
72	CBS 65147	SKIES OF AMERICA (LP) 10
70s	Blue Note BST 84356	LOVE CALL (LP) 12

ROGER COLEMAN
60	Top Rank JAR 311	Nobody's Fool/Endlessly 4

COLENSO PARADE
84	Goliath SLING 01	Standing Up/Smoky Fingered Reminder (p/s) 4
	(see also House Of Love)	

COLLAGE
73	Studio Two TWO 410	MISTY (LP) 15
	(see also Brian Bennett)	

COLETTE & BANDITS
65	Stateside SS 416	A Ladies Man/Lost Love 6

COLLECTIVE HORIZONTAL
79	Dolmen DO 1	COLLECTIVE HORIZONTAL EP (gatefold p/s, stickered white labels) 4

COLLECTORS
70	London HLU 10304	I Must Have Been Blind/The Beginning 4
68	Warner Bros WS 1774	GRASS AND WILD STRAWBERRIES (LP) 20

COLLEGE BOYS
63	Blue Beat BB 202	Love Is A Treasure/Someone Will Be There 8

BUDDY COLLETTE & HERBIE MANN GROUP
59	Top Rank 25/015	PORGY AND BESS (10" LP) 10
	(see also Herbie Mann)	

GRAHAM COLLIER SEXTET/SEPTET
67	Deram DML/SML 1005	DEEP DARK BLUE CENTRE (2-LP) 40
69	Fontana SFJL 922	DOWN ANOTHER ROAD (LP) 35
70	Fontana 6309 006	SONGS FOR MY FATHER (LP, Graham Collier Music featuring Harry Beckett) 35
71	Philips 6308 051	MOSAICS (live LP, as Graham Collier Music featuring Harry Beckett) 40
72	Saydisc SDL 244	PORTRAITS (LP) 15
	(see also Harry Beckett)	

MITTY COLLIER
64	Pye Intl. 7N 25275	I Had A Talk With My Man/Free Girl 25

AL 'JAZZBO' COLLINS
56	Vogue Coral Q 72160	Max/Sam 4

ALBERT COLLINS
69	Liberty LBS 83238	LOVE CAN BE FOUND ANYWHERE (LP) 20
71	Tumbleweed TW 3501	THERE'S GOTTA BE A CHANGE (LP) 20

ANSELL COLLINS
69	Trojan TR 699	Night Of Love/DERRICK MORGAN: Copy Cat 4
	(see also Conquerors)	

BOOTSY COLLINS
	(see under Bootsy's Rubber Band)

DAVE & ANSELL COLLINS
71	Trojan TBL 162	DOUBLE BARREL (LP) 10

DONIE COLLINS SHOWBAND
68	Pye 7N 17682	Get Down With It/I Can't Help Myself (Sugar Pie Honey Bunch) 8

DOROTHY COLLINS
51	MGM MGM 354	Me And My Imagination/I'm Playing With Fire (78) 5
52	Brunswick 05010	So Madly In Love (with Gordon Jenkins Orchestra)/GORDON JENKINS, ORCHESTRA & CHORUS: Just Say The Word (78) 5
53	Brunswick 05042	Jump Back Honey/I Will Still Love You (with Snooky Lanson) (78) 10
53	Brunswick 05051	If'n/Puppy Love (with Raymond Scott Orchestra, 78) 5
55	Vogue Coral Q 72111	My Boy — Flat Top/In Love 20
55	Vogue Coral Q 72111	My Boy — Flat Top/In Love (78) 5
56	Vogue Coral Q 72116	Moments To Remember/Love And Marriage 10
56	Vogue Coral Q 72116	Moments To Remember/Love And Marriage (78) 5
56	Vogue Coral Q 72137	Seven Days/Manuello 12
56	Vogue Coral Q 72137	Seven Days/Manuello (78) 5
56	Vogue Coral Q 72173	Treasure Of Love/He's Got Me, Hook, Line And Sinker 15
56	Vogue Coral Q 72173	Treasure Of Love/He's Got Me, Hook, Line And Sinker (78) 5
56	Vogue Coral Q 72193	Love Me As Though There Were No Tomorrow/Rock And Roll Train 20
56	Vogue Coral Q 72193	Love Me As Though There Were No Tomorrow/Rock And Roll Train (78) 15
56	Vogue Coral Q 72198	The Italian Theme/Cool It, Baby 20
56	Vogue Coral Q 72198	The Italian Theme/Cool It, Baby (78) 15
56	Vogue Coral Q 72208	The Twelve Gifts Of Christmas/Mr. Santa 7
57	Vogue Coral Q 72232	Would You Ever/Baby Can Rock 12
57	Vogue Coral Q 72232	Would You Ever/Baby Can Rock (78) 15
57	Vogue Coral Q 72252	Mr. Wonderful/I Miss You Already 7
57	Vogue Coral Q 72262	Four Walls/Big Dreams 6
57	Vogue Coral Q 72262	Four Walls/Big Dreams (78) 5
57	Vogue Coral Q 72287	Soft Sands/Sing It, Children, Sing It 6
59	Top Rank JAR 259	Baciare, Baciare (Kissing ...)/Everything I Have Is Yours 4
60	Top Rank JAR 401	Banjo Boy/Tintarella Di Luna 4
60	Top Rank JAR 523	Unlock Those Chains/I'll Be Yours, You'll be mine 4
55	London REP 1025	DOROTHY COLLINS SINGS (EP) 15
57	Coral LVA 9058	AT HOME WITH DOROTHY AND RAYMOND (LP) 15

EDWYN COLLINS

87	Creation CRE 047T	Don't Shilly Shally (12", unreleased, white label test pressings only) 50
87	Elevation ACID 4T	Don't Shilly Shally/If Ever You're Ready/Queer Fish (12", p/s) 7
87	Elevation ACIDB 6	My Beloved Girl/50 Shades Of Blue (Acoustic Version)/Clouds (Fogging Up My Mind)/What's The Big Idea (box set with postcards) 6

(see also Orange Juice, Paul Quinn & Edwyn Collins)

GLENDA COLLINS

60	Decca F 11280	Take A Chance/Crazy Guy 6
61	Decca F 11321	Oh How I Miss You Tonight/Age For Love 6
61	Decca F 11417	Head Over Heels In Love/Find Another Fool 6
63	HMV POP 1163	I Lost My Heart In The Fairground/I Feel So Good 50
63	HMV POP 1233	If You've Got To Pick A Baby/In The First Place 15
64	HMV POP 1283	Baby It Hurts/Nice Wasn't It 15
64	HMV POP 1323	Lollipop/Everybody's Got To Fall In Love 15
65	HMV POP 1439	Johnny Loves Me/Paradise for Two 20
65	HMV POP 1475	Thou Shall Not Steal/Been Invited To A Party 12
66	Pye 7N 17044	Something I've Got To Tell You/My Heart Didn't Lie 15
66	Pye 7N 17150	It's Hard To Believe It/Don't Let It Rain On Sunday 15

JUDY COLLINS

66	London HLZ 10029	I'll Keep It With Mine/Thirsty Boots 5
67	Elektra EKSN 45011	In My Life/Hard Lovin' Loser 4
69	Elektra EKSN 45077	Turn Turn Turn/Mister Tambourine Man 4
68	Elektra EKL 4012	WILD FLOWERS (LP, orange label, also stereo 74012) 10
69	Elektra EKL 4033	WHO KNOWS WHERE THE TIME GOES (LP, orange label, also stereo EKS 74033) 10

KEANYA COLLINS

| 78 | Grapevine GRP 105 | Barnabus Collins — Love Bandit/I Call You Daddy ....4 |

LYN COLLINS

74	Polydor 2066 490	Rock Me Again And Again And Again/Wide Awake Dream 7
74	Mojo 2093 029	Think (About It)/Me And My Baby Got Our Own Thing Going 8
88	Urban URBX 15	Rock Me Again And Again And Again (12") 8
72	Polydor 2918 006	THINK (ABOUT IT) (LP) 40
88	Urban URBLP 7	LYN COLLINS (THE FEMALE PREACHER) (LP) 15

(see also James Brown)

PETER COLLINS

| 70 | Decca Nova SDN 21 | PETER COLLINS (LP) ....15 |

PHIL COLLINS

81	Virgin VSK 102	In The Air Tonight/The Roof Is Leaking (p/s, with 12-page cartoon booklet) 8
81	Virgin VS 423	If Leaving Me Is Easy/Drawing Board: In The Air Tonight/I Missed Again/ If Leaving Me Is Easy (p/s, with poster) 4
82	Virgin VSY 524	Thru' These Walls/Do You Know, Do You Care? (picture disc) 6
82	Virgin VSY 531	You Can't Hurry Love/I Cannot Believe It's True (picture disc) 8
84	Virgin VSY 674	Against All Odds/Making A Big Mistake (picture disc) 5
85	Virgin VSY 736 12	Sussudio (Extended)/Sussudio/The Man With The Horn (shaped pic. disc) 8
85	Virgin VSS 755	One More Night/I Like The Way (shaped picture disc with plinth) 8
85	Virgin VS 777/VS 674	Take Me Home/We Said Hello, Goodbye//Against All Odds/Making A Big Mistake (double pack) 4
85	Virgin VS 777 12	Take Me Home (Extended Remix)/Take Me Home/We Said Hello, Goodbye (12", p/s, with map) 7
88	Virgin VST 1141	Two Hearts/The Robbery (Full Length Version) (12", p/s, with postcards) 7

(see also Genesis, Flaming Youth, Peter Banks)

PHIL COLLINS & MARILYN MARTIN

| 85 | Virgin VSS 818 | Separate Lives/Only You Know And I Know (white vinyl & poster in wallet) .....4 |
| 85 | Virgin VSSD 818 | Separate Lives/Only You Know And I Know (2 x interlocking picture discs) .....12 |

(see also Marilyn Martin)

RODGER COLLINS

| 67 | Vocalion VF 9285 | She's Good Looking/I'm Serving Time ....10 |

SHIRLEY COLLINS

60	Collector JEB 1508	SHIRLEY COLLINS (EP) 25
60	Collector JEB 3	THE FOGGY DEW (EP) 25
60	Collector JEB 5	ENGLISH SONGS (EP) 25
64	Collector JEB 9	ENGLISH SONGS VOL. 2 (EP, with Robin Hall) 25
63	Topic TOP 95	HEROES IN LOVE (EP) 40
59	Folkways FG 3564	FALSE TRUE LOVERS (LP) 100
60	Argo RG 150	SWEET ENGLAND (LP) 100
64	Decca LK 4652	FOLK ROOTS, NEW ROUTES (LP, with Davy Graham) 80
67	Topic 12TS 170	THE SWEET PRIMEROSES (LP) 25
68	Polydor 583 025	THE POWER OF THE TRUE LOVE KNOT (LP) 60
74	Topic 12T 238	ADIEU TO OLD ENGLAND (LP) 30
75	Deram SML 1117	A FAVOURITE GARLAND (LP) 25
76	Harvest SHSM 2008	AMARANTH (LP) 15
78	Topic 12T 380	FOR AS MANY AS WILL (LP) 15

SHIRLEY & DOLLY COLLINS

69	Harvest SHVL 754	ANTHEMS IN EDEN (LP, gatefold sleeve) 45
70	Harvest SHVL 771	LOVE, DEATH AND THE LADY (LP, gatefold sleeve) 55
71	Pegasus PEG 7	NO ROSES (LP, gatefold sleeve, with Albion Country Band) 25
74	Mooncrest CREST 11	NO ROSES (LP, reissue in different sleeve) 12

(see also Davy Graham, Albion Country Band)

TERRY COLLINS

| 74 | Warner Bros K 16426 | I L.O.V.E. Y.O.U./Action Speaks Louder ....4 |

TOMMY COLLINS
58	Capitol CL 14838	Think It Over Boys/All Of The Monkeys Ain't In The Zoo 6
58	Capitol CL 14894	Let Down/It Tickles 6
59	Capitol CL 15076	Little June/A Hundred Years From Now 8
60	Capitol CL 15118	Wreck Of The Old '97/You Belong In My Arms 6
57	Capitol T 776	WORDS AND MUSIC COUNTRY STYLE (LP) 20
59	Capitol T 1196	THIS IS TOMMY COLLINS (LP) 20

HELEN COLMAN (LENA WILSON)
| 25 | Guardsman 7002 | Afternoon Blues/DAISY CLIFF: It Makes No Difference Now (78) ....75 |

(see also Lena Wilson [Helen Colman], Viola McCoy [Daisy Cliff])

COLONEL
| 75 | Ring O' 2017 104 | Cokey Cokey/Away In A Manger (company sleeve) ....4 |

COLONEL
| 80 | Virgin VS 380 | Too Many Cooks (In The Kitchen)/I Need Protection (p/s) ....6 |

(see also XTC)

JERRY COLONNA
54	Brunswick 05243	Ebb Tide/The Velvet Glove 12
54	Brunswick 05342	It Might As Well Be Spring/Ja-Da 10
55	Parlophone MSP 6165	Let Me Go, Lover/I Want To Love You, Cara Mia 7
55	London HL 8143	Chicago Style/Baffi 18
56	HMV 7M 369	The Shifting, Whispering Sands/Waltz Me Around 6
59	London HA-U 2190	LET'S ALL SING (LP) 15

COLORADOS
| 64 | Oriole CB 1972 | Lips Are Redder On You/Who You Gonna Hurt? ....8 |

COLORS OUT OF TIME
| 81 | Monsters In Orbit TVEYE 1 | Rock Section/Mambo Girls/Dancing With You (hand-made p/s) ....7 |
| 82 | Monsters In Orbit TVEYE 5 | She Spins/The Ocean (p/s) ....4 |

COLOSSEUM
69	Fontana TF 1029	Walking In The Park/Those About To Die 6
69	Fontana STL 5510	THOSE WHO ARE ABOUT TO DIE SALUTE YOU (LP, gatefold sleeve) 15
69	Vertigo VO 1	VALENTYNE SUITE (LP, gatefold sleeve, spiral label & inner bag) 15
70	Vertigo 6360 017	DAUGHTER OF TIME (LP, gatefold sleeve, some with spiral label & bag) 15/12

(see also Dick Heckstall-Smith, Chris Farlowe, Greenslade, John Mayall, Howard Riley Trio, Tempest)

COLOURBOX
82	4AD AD 215	Breakdown/Tarantula (p/s) 10
82	4AD BAD 215	Breakdown/Tarantula (12", p/s) 15
83	4AD AD 314	Breakdown (Second Version)/Tarantula (Second Version) (different p/s) 7
83	4AD BAD 314	Breakdown (Second Version)/Tarantula (Second Version) (12", different p/s) 7

(see also MARRS)

COLOURFIELD
| 84 | Chrysalis COLF D2 | Thinking Of You/Wild Flames//Little Things/Thinking Of You (double pack) ......4 |
| 85 | Chrysalis COLF D4 | Castles In The Air/Your Love Was Smashing//I Can't Get Enough Of You Baby/Castles In The Air (Instrumental Mix) (double pack, gatefold p/s) ....4 |

(see also Specials, Fun Boy Three)

COLOURFUL SEASONS
| 68 | MGM MGM 1433 | Out Of The Blue/It's Gonna Break My Heart ....4 |

COLO(U)RS OF LOVE
68	Page One POF 060	I'm A Train/Up On A Cotton Cloud 5
68	Page One POF 086	Just Another Fly/Twenty Ten 4
69	Page One POF 124	Mother Of Convention/Music Mother Made 4

CHRISTOPHER COLT
| 68 | Decca F 12726 | Virgin Sunrise/Girl In The Mirror ....15 |

TONY COLTON('S BIG BOSS BAND)
64	Decca F 11879	Lose My Mind/So Used To Loving You (solo) 10
65	Pye 7N 15886	I Stand Accused/Further On Down The Track (with Big Boss Band) 75
66	Pye 7N 17046	You're Wrong There Baby/Have You Lost Your Mind 20
66	Pye 7N 17117	I've Laid Some Down In My Time/Run Pony Rider 20
68	Columbia DB 8385	In The World Of Marnie Dreaming/Who Is She? (solo) 10

(see also Poet & One Man Band, Real McCoy)

JOHN COLTRANE
64	Blue Note 45-1718	A Moment's Notice Pts 1 & 2 10
60	Esquire EP 229	SOUL OF 'TRANE (EP) 10
61	Esquire EP 239	BASS BLUES (EP) 10
64	Fontana 469 203TE	WHILE MY LADY SLEEPS (EP) 10
58	Esquire 32-079	THE FIRST TRANE (LP) 18
58	Esquire 32-089	SOUL TRANE (LP) 18
59	Esquire 32-091	TRANEING IN (LP) 18
60	London Jazz LTZ-K 15197	GIANT STEPS (LP) 18
61	Esquire 32-129	LUSH LIFE (LP) 18
61	London Jazz LTZ-K 15219	COLTRANE JAZZ (LP, also stereo SAH-K 6162) 18
61	Blue Note BLP 1577	BLUE TRAIN (LP) 20
62	London Jazz LTZ-K 15232	BAGS AND TRANE (LP, also stereo SAH-K 6192) 18
62	Columbia 33SX 1399	THE BIRDLAND STORY VOL. 1: ECHOES OF AN ERA (LP) 15
62	London Jazz LTZ-K 15239	OLE COLTRANE (LP, also stereo SAH-K 6223) 18
62	HMV CLP 1548	AFRICA/BRASS (LP, also stereo CSD 1431) 15
62	Storyville SLP 28	JOHN COLTRANE & DAVE CHAMBERS (LP) 15
62	HMV CLP 1590	LIVE AT THE VILLAGE VANGUARD (LP, also stereo CSD 1456) 15
63	United Artists (S)ULP 1018	COLTRANE TIME (LP) 15
63	London HA-K/SH-K 8017	COLTRANE PLAYS THE BLUES (LP, as John Coltrane Group) 18

John COLTRANE

63	Esquire 32-179	STANDARD COLTRANE (LP)	18
63	HMV CLP 1629	COLTRANE (LP, also stereo CSD 1483)	15
63	HMV CLP 1647	BALLADS (LP, also stereo CSD 1496)	15
63	HMV CLP 1657	DUKE ELLINGTON & JOHN COLTRANE (LP, also stereo CSD 1502)	15
64	HMV CLP 1695	IMPRESSIONS (LP, also stereo CSD 1509)	15
64	HMV CLP 1700	JOHN COLTRANE WITH JOHNNY HARTMAN (LP)	15
64	Realm RM 157	ON WEST 42nd STREET (LP)	12
64	Realm RM 181	TRANE RIDE (LP)	12
64	HMV CLP 1741	LIVE AT BIRDLAND (LP, also stereo CSD 1544)	15
65	HMV CLP 1799	CRESCENT (LP, also stereo CSD 1567)	15
65	Stateside SL 10124	BLACK PEARLS (LP)	15
65	HMV CLP 1869	A LOVE SUPREME (LP, also stereo CSD 1605)	15
65	Atlantic ATL/SAL 5022	MY FAVOURITE THINGS (LP)	15
65	Realm RM 52226	TANGANYIKA STRUT (LP)	12
65	HMV CLP 1897	COLTRANE PLAYS (LP, also stereo CSD 1619)	15
66	Stateside SL 10162	BAHIA (LP)	15
66	HMV CLP/CSD 3543	ASCENSION (LP, as John Coltrane Orchestra)	15
66	HMV CLP/CSD 3551	NEW THING AT NEWPORT (LP, with Archie Shepp)	15
66	Atlantic 587/588 004	THE AVANT-GARDE (LP, with Don Cherry)	15
66	HMV CLP/CSD 3575	MEDITATIONS (LP)	15
67	Atlantic 587/588 039	COLTRANE'S SOUND (LP)	15
67	HMV CLP/CSD 3599	COLTRANE LIVE AT THE VILLAGE VANGUARD AGAIN! (LP)	15
67	Atlantic ATL 1311	GIANT STEPS (LP, reissue)	12
67	Atlantic ATL/SAL 1354	COLTRANE JAZZ (LP, reissue)	12
67	HMV CLP/CSD 3617	OM (LP, withdrawn)	25
67	HMV CLP/CSD 3617	KULU SE MAMA (LP)	15
68	Transatlantic PR 7280	DAKAR (LP)	15
68	Transatlantic PR 7378	LAST TRANE (LP)	15
68	Impulse MIPL/SIPL 502	EXPRESSION (LP)	15
69	Atlantic 588 139	THREE LITTLE WORDS (LP)	15
69	Atlantic 588 146	MY FAVOURITE THINGS (LP, reissue)	12
69	Impulse MIPL/SIPL 515	COSMIC MUSIC (LP, by Alice & John Coltrane)	15
69	Atlantic 588 168	GIANT STEPS (LP, reissue)	12
69	Realm 52157	ON WEST 42nd STREET (LP, reissue)	10
70	Impulse SIPL 522	SELFLESSNESS (LP)	15
71	Probe SPB 1025	AFRO BLUE (LP)	12
73	CBS PR 24003	JOHN COLTRANE (2-LP)	15
73	CBS PR 24014	MORE LASTING THAN BRONZE (2-LP)	15
74	Atlantic K 60052	THE ART OF JOHN COLTRANE: THE ATLANTIC YEARS (2-LP)	14
74	CBS PR 24037	BLACK PEARLS (2-LP)	14

(see also Miles Davis , Thelonious Monk)

COLTS

65	Pye 7N 15955	San Miguel/Where Has Our Love Gone?	5

COLUMBIA BOYS

68	Pye 7N 17513	Baby Come Back/Born To Lose	5
69	Pye 7N 17763	That's My Pa/She Thinks I Still Care	4

COLUMBUS

70	Deram DM 294	Ev'rybody Loves The U.S. Marshall/Tired	6

KEN COLYER('S JAZZMEN)

55	Decca F 10504	Early Hours/Cataract Rag	6
55	Decca F 10519	If I Ever Cease To Love/The Entertainer	6
55	Decca F 10565	It Looks Like A Big Time Tonight/Red Wing	6
56	Tempo A 117	Just A Closer Walk With Thee/Sheik Of Araby	6
56	Tempo A 120	If I Ever Cease To Love You/Isle Of Capri	6
56	Tempo A 126	My Bucket's Got A Hole In It/Wabash Blues	6
56	Tempo A 136	Maryland, My Maryland/The World Is Waiting For The Sunrise	6
56	Decca FJ 10755	All The Girls Go Crazy About The Way I Walk/Dippermouth Blues	6
61	Columbia DB 4676	The Happy Wanderer/Maryland, My Maryland	4
56	Melodisc EPM7 59	KEN COLYER JAZZMEN AND THE CRANE RIVER JAZZ BAND (EP)	10
60s	Melodisc EPM7 105	KEN COLYER (EP)	8
60s	K.C. KCS 11EP	GREEN CORN (EP)	8
60s	Storyville SEP 301	KEN COLYER JAZZMEN (EP)	7
60s	Storyville SEP 305	KEN COLYER'S JAZZMEN (EP)	8
60s	Storyville SEP 309	KEN COLYER'S JAZZMEN (EP)	8
60s	Storyville SEP 412	WILDCAT BLUES (EP)	7
55	Decca DFE 6268	AND BACK TO NEW ORLEANS VOL. 1 (EP)	7
55	Decca DFE 6299	AND BACK TO NEW ORLEANS VOL. 2 (EP)	7
58	Decca DFE 6435	KEN COLYER AND HIS OMEGA BRASS (EP)	7
58	Decca DFE 6466	THEY ALL PLAYED RAGTIME (EP)	7
56	Vogue EPV 1102	KEN COLYER IN NEW ORLEANS (EP)	7
55	Vogue EPV 1202	KEN COLYER IN NEW ORLEANS (EP)	7
55	Tempo EXA 26	KEN COLYER JAZZMEN (EP)	7
56	Tempo EXA 31	KEN COLYER JAZZMEN (EP)	7
57	Tempo EXA 53	KEN COLYER IN NEW ORLEANS (EP)	7
59	Esquire EP 233	RUM AND COCA COLA (EP, with Christie Brothers Stompers)	7
60	Decca DFE 6645	WALKING THE BLUES (EP, also stereo STO 143)	7/9
60	Columbia SEG 8038	THIS IS JAZZ (EP)	7
61	Storyville SEP 392	TRAD JAZZ SCENE IN EUROPE VOL. 2 (EP)	7
61	Columbia SEG 8104	THIS IS JAZZ VOL. 1 NO. 2 (EP)	7
61	Esquire EP 243	STOMPING (EP)	7
62	Columbia SEG 8145	THIS IS JAZZ VOL. 2 (EP)	7
62	Columbia SEG 8180	TOO BUSY (EP)	7
54	Decca LF 1152	NEW ORLEANS TO LONDON (10" LP)	25
54	Decca LF 1196	BACK TO THE DELTA (10" LP, as Ken Colyer's Jazzmen & Skiffle Group)	25
55	Vogue LDE 161	KEN COLYER IN NEW ORLEANS (10" LP)	25

MINT VALUE £

56	Tempo LAP 11	KEN COLYER'S JAZZMEN (10" LP) 20
57	Decca LK 4178	CLUB SESSION (LP) 12
58	Decca LF 1301	IN GLORY LAND (10" LP, as Ken Colyer & His Omega Brass Band) 20
59	Decca LF 1319	COLYER IN HAMBURG (10" LP) 15
59	Decca LK 4294	PLAYS STANDARDS (LP) 12
60	Columbia 33SX 1220	THIS IS JAZZ (LP) 10
61	Columbia 33SX 1297	THIS IS JAZZ VOL. 2 (LP, also stereo SCX 3360) 10/12

KEN COLYER'S SKIFFLE GROUP

55	Decca F 10631	Take This Hammer/Down By The Riverside 8
56	Decca FJ 10711	Streamline Train/Go Down Old Hannah 8
56	Decca FJ 10751	Down Bound Train/Mule Skinner 8
56	Decca FJ 10772	Old Riley/Stack O'Lee Blues 8
57	Decca FJ 10889	The Grey Goose/I Can't Sleep 7
57	Decca FJ 10926	Sporting Life/House Rent Stomp 7
57	Decca FJ 10972	Ella Speed/Go Down Sunshine 7
55	Decca DFE 6286	KEN COLYER'S SKIFFLE GROUP (EP) 10
58	Decca DFE 6444	KEN COLYER'S SKIFFLE GROUP NO. 2 (EP) 10
60	Decca DFE 6563	KEN COLYER'S SKIFFLE GROUP IN HAMBURG (EP) 12

COMBAT 84

83	Victory VIC 1	ORDERS OF THE DAY (EP) 12
83	Victory VIC 2	Rapist/The Right To Choose (p/s) 8

COME

79	Come Org. WDC 88001	Come Sunday/Shaved Slits 30
81	Come Org. WDC 880012	I'M JACK (LP, orange vinyl) 60
79	Come Org. WDC 88203	PRESENT RAMPTON (LP) 70

COMIC ROMANCE

78	Do It DUN 3	Cry Myself To Sleep/Cowboys And Indians (p/s) 5
79	WEA K 17418	Cry Myself To Sleep/Cowboys And Indians (reissue, p/s) 4

(see also M, Robin Scott)

COMMANCHES

64	Pye 7N 15609	Tomorrow/Missed Your Loving 5

(see also Bobby Allen)

COMMANDERS

55	Brunswick 05366	The Elephants' Tango/Commanders Overture 4
55	Brunswick 05433	The Cat From Coos Bay/Camptown Boogie 6
55	Brunswick 05467	The Monster/Cornball No. 1 6

(see also Louis Armstrong)

COMMITTEE

68	Liberty LBF 15154	Hard Way/Hey You 4

COMMITTEE

69	Pye 7N 17826	Sleep Tight Honey/Memories Of Melinda 4

COMMODORES

55	London HLD 8209	Riding On A Train/Uranium 175
55	London HLD 8209	Riding On A Train/Uranium (78) 35
56	London HLD 8251	Speedo/Whole Lotta Shakin' Goin' On 350
56	London HLD 8251	Speedo/Whole Lotta Shakin' Goin' On (78) 50

COMMODORES

69	Atlantic 584 273	Keep On Dancing/Rise Up 5
74	Tamla Motown TMG 924	The Zoo (The Human Zoo)/I'm Looking For A Love 4
75	Tamla Motown TMG 944	I Feel Sanctified/Determination 4
75	Tamla Motown TMG 952	Slippery When Wet/The Bump 4

(see also Lionel Richie)

COMMON ROUND

70s	Galliard GAL 4015	FOUR PENCE A DAY (LP) 15

COMMUNARDS

85	London LONT 77	You Are My World/Breadline Britain/Sentimental Journey/Heaven's Above (10", p/s) 5
85	London LONDP 77	You Are My World/Breadline Britain//Sentimental Journey/Heaven's Above (double pack, gatefold p/s) 6
86	London LONPD 89	Disenchanted (Total Dance Mix)/Disenchanted/Johnny Verso (12", picture disc) .7
86	London LONPD 103	Don't Leave Me This Way/Sanctified (picture disc) 4
86	London LONXP 103	Don't Leave Me This Way/Don't Leave Me This Way/Sanctified/Don't Leave Me This Way (logo-shaped picture disc) 5
86	London LONXR 103	Don't Leave Me This Way (Gotham City Mix)/Don't Leave Me This Way/ Sanctified/Don't Leave Me This Way (12", p/s) 7
86	London LONXRR 103	Don't Leave Me This Way (Son Of Gotham City Mix)/Sanctified (Son Of Gotham City Remix) (12", p/s) 8
86	London LONG 110	So Cold The Night/When The Walls Come Tumbling Down//Don't Leave Me This Way/Sanctified (double pack, gatefold p/s) 4
87	London LON 123	You Are My World '87/Judgement Day (p/s, with cassette "Reprise"/ "When The Walls Come Tumbling Down"/"Czardas" [LONFC 123]) 4
87	London LONB 143	Tomorrow/I Just Want To Let You Know (p/s, red vinyl, with postcards & stickers) 4
87	London LONR 143	Tomorrow (Remix)/I Just Want To Let You Know (p/s) 4
87	London LONT 143	Tomorrow (Remix)/I Just Want To Let You Know (10", p/s) 5

(see also Bronski Beat, Jimmy Somerville)

PERRY COMO

51	HMV B 10042	If/Zing Zing — Zoom Zoom (78) 5
53	HMV 7M 102	The Ruby And The Pearl/My Love And Devotion 10

MINT VALUE £

53	HMV 7M 110	Some Enchanted Evening/Bali Ha'i	12
53	HMV 7M 118	Don't Let The Stars Get In Your Eyes/To Know You (Is To Love You) (w/ Fontane Sisters)	20
53	HMV 7M 124	Wild Horses/Please Believe Me	12
53	HMV 7M 138	My Lady Loves To Dance/A Bushel And A Peck (B-side with Betty Hutton)	15
53	HMV 7M 149	My One And Only Heart/Say You're Mine Again	12
53	HMV 7M 155	Hello, Young Lovers/We Kiss In A Shadow	10
53	HMV 7M 163	Pa-Paya Mama/Why Did You Leave Me?	10
54	HMV 7M 175	You Alone/Surprising	12
54	HMV 7M 200	Idle Gossip/Look Out The Window	12
54	HMV 7M 215	Wanted/Give Me Your Hand	12
54	HMV 7M 241	Hit And Run Affair/If You Were Only Mine	12
54	HMV 7M 263	There Never Was A Night So Beautiful/Papa Loves Mambo	15
54	HMV 7M 278	Frosty The Snowman/The Twelve Days Of Christmas	10
55	HMV 7M 296	Ko Ko Mo (I Love You So)/You'll Always Be My Lifetime...	12
55	HMV 7M 305	Door Of Dreams/Nobody	10
55	HMV 7M 326	There's No Place Like Home For The Holidays/Tina Marie	12
56	HMV 7M 366	Fooled/The Rose Tattoo	10
56	HMV POP 191	Juke Box Baby/The Things I Didn't Do (78)	6
56	HMV 7M 404	Hot Diggity (Dog Ziggity Boom)/My Funny Valentine	12
56	HMV 7MC 39	Hot Diggity (Dog Ziggity Boom)/Juke Box Baby (export issue)	35
56	HMV POP 240	Glendora/More	12
56	HMV 7MC 49	Glendora/More (export issue)	15
56	HMV POP 271	Moonlight Love/Chincherinchee	8
57	HMV POP 304	Somebody Up There Likes Me/Dream Along With Me (I'm On My Way To A Star)	8
57	HMV 7MC 51	Somebody Up There Likes Me/Dream Along With Me (I'm On My Way To A Star) (export issue)	12
57	HMV POP 328	Round And Round/My House Is Your House	8
57	RCA RCA 1001	The Girl With The Golden Braids/My Little Baby	5
57	HMV POP 369	Silk Stockings/Childhood Is A Meadow	6
57	HMV POP 394	As Time Goes By/All At Once You Love Her	6
57	RCA RCA 1016	Marching Along To The Blues/Dancin'	4
57	RCA RCA 1027	Just Born (To Be Your Baby)/Ivy Rose	4
58	RCA RCA 1036	Magic Moments/Catch A Falling Star	5
58	RCA RCA 1055	Kewpie Doll/Dance Only With Me	5
58	RCA RCA 1055	Kewpie Doll/Dance Only With Me (78)	5
58	RCA RCA 1062	I May Never Pass This Way Again/Prayer For Peace	4
58	RCA RCA 1086	Love Makes The World Go Round/ Mandolins In The Moonlight (78)	5
59	RCA RCA 1111	Tomboy/Kiss Me And Kiss Me And Kiss Me (78)	5
60	RCA RCA 1170	Delaware/I Know What God Is (78)	15
54	HMV 7EG 8013	PERRY COMO (EP)	7
56	HMV 7EG 8171	SO SMOOTH (EP)	7
56	HMV 7EG 8192	COMO SWINGS (EP)	7
57	HMV 7EG 8244	WITH A SONG IN MY HEART (EP)	7
54	HMV DLP 1026	PERRY COMO SINGS (10" LP)	15
57	RCA RD 27035	WE GET LETTERS (LP)	10
57	RCA RD 27070	WE GET LETTERS VOL. 2 (LP)	12
57	RCA RD 27078/SF 5011	DEAR PERRY (LP, mono/stereo)	10/12
57	RCA RD 27082	SINGS MERRY CHRISTMAS MUSIC (LP)	10
58	RCA RD 27100	COMO'S GOLDEN RECORDS (LP)	10
58	RCA RD 27106/SF 5021	WHEN YOU COME TO THE END OF THE DAY (LP, mono/stereo)	10/12
58	RCA RD 27139/SF 5045	SINGS THE SONGS OF CHRISTMAS (LP, mono/stereo)	10/12
59	RCA RD 27154/SF 5053	COMO SWINGS (LP, mono/stereo)	10/12
60	RCA RD 27206/SF 5089	FOR THE YOUNG AT HEART (LP, mono/stereo)	10/12
61	RCA RD 27232	SING TO ME, MR. C (LP)	10
63	RCA Victor RD 7582	THE SONGS I LOVE (LP)	10
66	RCA Victor RD 7802	LIGHTLY LATIN (LP)	10
66	RCA Victor RD 7836	IN ITALY (LP)	10

(see also Fontane Sisters, Betty Hutton)

LES COMPAGNONS DE LA CHANSON

53	Columbia SCM 5005	The Three Bells (The Jimmy Brown Song)/Ave Maria	12
53	Columbia SCM 5056	The Galley Slave/Dreams Never Grow Old	10
59	Columbia DB 4358	The Three Bells (The Jimmy Brown Song)/Ave Maria (reissue)	5
60	Columbia DB 4454	Down By The Riverside/Margoton	4

COMPLEX

| 70 | CLPM 001 | COMPLEX (LP, private pressing, red vinyl) | 700 |
| 71 | Deroy | THE WAY WE FEEL (LP, private pressing) | 600 |

COMSAT ANGELS

79	Junta JUNTA 1	Red Planet/I Get Excited/Specimen No. 2 (p/s, reissued on red vinyl)	8/6
81	Polydor POSPX 242	Eye Of A Lens/At Sea/Another World Gone (12", double pack)	7
81	Polydor POSP 359	Do The Empty House/Now I Know/Red Planet Revisited (double pack)	5
84	Jive JIVE 54	Independence Day/Intelligence//After The Rain/Mister Memory/Total War (double pack)	4
83	Jive HIP 8	LAND (LP, picture disc)	10

BOBBY COMSTOCK (& COUNTS)

59	Top Rank JAR 223	The Tennessee Waltz/Sweet Talk	6
60	London HLE 9080	Jambalaya/Let's Talk It Over (as Bobby Comstock & Counts)	15
63	Stateside SS 163	Let's Stomp/I Want To Do It	10
63	Stateside SS 221	Susie Baby/Take A Walk	6
65	United Artists UP 1086	I'm A Man/I'll Make You Glad	15

COMUS

| 71 | Dawn DNX 2506 | Diana/In The Lost Queen's Eyes/Winter Is A Coloured Bird (p/s) | 10 |

| 71 | Dawn DNLS 3019 | FIRST UTTERANCE (LP, gatefold sleeve with lyric sheet) | 75 |
| 74 | Virgin V 2018 | TO KEEP FROM CRYING (LP) | 12 |

(see also Gong, Henry Cow, Esperanto)

CON-CHORDS
| 65 | Polydor BM 56059 | You Can't Take It Away/Let Me Walk With You | 10 |

CONCORDS
| 69 | Blue Cat BS 170 | Buttoo/I Need Your Loving | 6 |

CONCRETE
| 70s | Concrete Prod. CON 001 | GHOULISH PRACTICES (EP, poster p/s, stamped labels) | 5 |

(see also 400 Blows)

EDDIE CONDON & ALL-STARS
60	Philips JAZ 115	Heebies Jeebies/What-cha-call-'em Blues (as Eddie Condon & All-Stars)	4
62	Stateside SL 10005	JAM SESSIONS AT COMMODORE (LP, as Eddie Condon & Group)	10
62	Stateside SL 10010	CONDON A LA CARTE (LP)	10

HOWIE G. CONDOR
| 65 | Fontana TF 613 | Big Noise From Winnetka/The Fix | 8 |

CONEY ISLAND KIDS
| 55 | London HLJ 8207 | Baby, Baby You/Moonlight Beach | 18 |
| 55 | London HLJ 8207 | Baby, Baby You/Moonlight Beach (78) | 5 |

CONFLICT
81	Corp. Christi CHRIST IT'S 4	A Nation Of Animal Lovers/Liberate (poster p/s)	4
82	Crass 221984/1	THE HOUSE THAT MAN BUILT (EP, foldout poster p/s)	4
80s	Xntrix XN 2001	LIVE AT THE CENTRE IBERICO (EP)	4
85	Mortarhate MORT 15	The Battle Continues (both sides) (p/s, different colours, with insert)	4
88	FUND 1	FROM PROTEST TO RESISTANCE (LP, mail order, w/l, stickered plain sleeve)	10

ARTHUR CONLEY
67	Atlantic 584 083	Sweet Soul Music/Let's Go Steady	5
67	Atlantic 584 121	Shake, Rattle And Roll/You Don't Have To See Me	6
67	Atlantic 584 143	Whole Lotta Woman/Love Comes And Goes	6
68	Atlantic 584 175	Funky Street/Put Our Love Together	5
68	Atlantic 584 197	People Sure Act Funny/Burning Fire	5
68	Atlantic 584 224	Aunt Dora's Love Soul Shack/Is That You Love	4
69	Atco 226 004	Star Review/Love Sure Is A Powerful Thing	4
70	Atco 226 011	They Call The Wind Maria/Hurt	4
70	Atlantic 2091 025	All Day Singing/God Bless	4
71	Atlantic 2091 120	I'm Living Good/I'm So Glad You're Here	4
73	Capricorn K 17506	Rita/More Sweet Soul Music	4
67	Atlantic 587 069	SWEET SOUL MUSIC (LP)	12
68	Atlantic 587 084	SHAKE, RATTLE AND ROLL (LP)	10
68	Atlantic 587 128	SOUL DIRECTION (LP)	10
69	Atco 228 019	MORE SWEET SOUL (LP)	10

FRANK CONN COMPANY
| 60 | MGM MGM 1055 | My Bonnie/Swanee River | 5 |

BRIAN CONNELL & ROUND SOUND
66	Mercury MF 956	Just My Kind Of Loving/Something You've Got	8
66	Mercury MF 991	The Same Thing's Happened To Me/Mister Porter	8
68	Philips BF 1661	What Good Am I/Just Another Wedding Day	8
68	Philips BF 1718	I Know/Mister Travel Company	8

RAY CONNIFF & ROCKIN' RHYTHM BOYS
| 55 | Vogue Coral QW 5001 | Piggy Bank Boogie/Short Stuff | 12 |

BILLY CONNOLLY & CHRIS TUMMINGS & Singing Rebels Band
| 85 | Audiotrax ATX 10 | Freedom/JIMMY HELMS: Celebration (some with p/s) | 10/4 |

(see also Humblebums, George Harrison, Ringo Starr, Eric Clapton)

BRIAN CONNOLLY
| 82 | Carrere CAR 231 | Hypnotised/Fade Away (p/s) | 10 |

(see also Sweet)

KIEV CONNOLLY & MISSING PASSENGERS
| 89 | Sulan SUS 1080 | The Real Me/Haze On Mizan Head (p/s, export release for Ireland) | 6 |

CHRIS CONNOR
59	London HLE 8869	Hallelujah I Love Him So/I Won't Cry Anymore	7
59	London HLE 8869	Hallelujah I Love Him So/I Won't Cry Anymore (78)	6
60	London HLK 9124	I Only Want Some/That's My Desire	7
56	London EZ-N 19010	CHRIS CONNOR SINGS LULLABYS OF BIRDLAND (EP, with Ellis Larkin Trio)	10
57	London RE-N 1093	LONDON'S GIRL FRIENDS NO. 2 (EP)	10
57	London HB-N 1074	CHRIS (10" LP)	15
56	London HA-K 2030	PRESENTING CHRIS CONNOR (LP, also stereo SAH-K 6032)	15
57	London HA-K 2066	HE LOVES ME, HE LOVES ME NOT (LP)	12
60	London Jazz LTZK 15183	THE BALLAD OF THE SAD CAFÉ (LP)	12
60	London Jazz LTZK 15185	WITCHCRAFT (LP)	12
60	London Jazz LTZK 19195	CHRIS IN PERSON (LP, also stereo SAH-K 6088)	12

EDRIC CONNOR
| 57 | Oriole CB 1362 | Manchester United Calypso | 5 |

KENNETH CONNOR
| 59 | Top Rank JAR 138 | Rail Road Rock/Ramona | 5 |
| 59 | Top Rank JAR 138 | Rail Road Rock/Ramona (78) | 6 |

CAROL CONNORS
| 62 | London HLN 9619 | Big Big Love/Two Rivers | 4 |

NORMAN CONNORS & MICHAEL HENDERSON

| 76 | Buddah BDS 449 | You're My Starship/Bubbles | 4 |
| 78 | Buddah BDLP 4058 | THIS IS YOUR LIFE (LP) | 10 |

CONNY

| 62 | Columbia DB 4845 | Gino/Midi-Midinette | 12 |

CONQUERORS

67	Doctor Bird DB 1119	Won't You Come Home Now?/Oh That Day	10
67	Treasure Isle TI 7035	Lonely Street/I Fell In Love	10
68	Amalgamated AMG 832	Secret Weapon (actually by Ansell Collins)/Jumpy Jumpy Girl	5
69	High Note HS 016	If You Can't Beat Them/Anywhere You Want To Go	5
69	High Note HS 025	National Dish/Mr D.J.	5

JESS CONRAD

60	Decca F 11236	Cherry Pie/There's Gonna Be A Day	5
60	Decca F 11259	Unless You Meant It/Out Of Luck	4
61	Decca F 11315	Mystery Girl/The Big White House	4
61	Decca F 11348	This Pullover/Why Am I Living?	4
61	Decca F 11375	Oh You Beautiful Doll/I See You	4
61	Decca F 11394	Walkaway/Every Breath I Take	4
61	Decca F 11412	Twist My Wrist/Hey Little Girl (some in p/s)	8/4
62	Decca F 11511	Pretty Jenny/You Can Do It If You Try	4
64	Columbia DB 7223	Pussycat/Tempted	4
65	Columbia DB 7561	Things I'd Like To Say/Don't Turn Around	4
65	Pye 7N 15849	Hurt Me/It Can Happen To You	12
60	Decca DFE 6666	JESS CONRAD (EP)	10
62	Decca DFE 6702	TWIST MY WRIST (EP)	8
63	Decca DFE 8524	THE HUMAN JUNGLE (EP)	8
78	SRT	AN EVENING WITH JESS CONRAD (EP)	7
61	Decca LK 4390	JESS FOR YOU (LP)	25

(see also Guvners)

TONI CONRAD & FAUST

| 72 | Caroline C 1501 | OUTSIDE THE DREAM SYNDICATE (LP) | 12 |

(see also Faust)

CONROY RECORDED MUSIC LIBRARY

72	Conroy	LONDON UNDERGROUND VOL. 1 (LP)	60
70s	Conroy	LONDON UNDERGROUND VOL. 2 (LP)	40
70s	Conroy	BACKGROUND ACTION (LP)	75
70s	Conroy	WAY IN WAY OUT (LP)	15
70s	Conroy	INDIAN SUITE (LP)	15
70s	Conroy	PSYCHOSIS SUITE (LP)	15

(there are numerous other Conroy LPs but none appear to be of significant interest)

CONSORTIUM

68	Pye 7N 17635	All The Love In The World/Spending My Life Saying Goodbye	4
69	Pye 7N 17725	When The Day Breaks/Day The Train Never Came	4
69	Pye 7N 17797	Beggar Man/Cynthia Serenity	4
69	Pye 7N 17841	I Don't Want Her Anymore/The House Upon The Hill	4
70	Trend TNT 52	Melanie Cries Alone/Copper Coloured Years	4

CONSUMATES

| 68 | Coxsone CS 7054 | What Is It/ROLAND ALPHONSO: Musical Happiness | 12 |

CONTACT

| 79 | Object Music OM 11 | FUTURE/PAST (EP) | 4 |

(see also Passage)

CONTINENTALS

| 62 | Island WI 010 | Going Crazy/Give Me All Of Your Love | 10 |

CONTINUUM

| 70 | RCA Victor SF 8157 | CONTINUUM (LP) | 12 |
| 71 | RCA Victor SF 8196 | AUTUMN GRASS (LP, gatefold sleeve) | 20 |

CONTOURS

62	Oriole CB 1763	Do You Love Me/Move Mister Man	15
63	Oriole CB 1799	Shake Sherry/You Better Get In Line	30
63	Oriole CB 1831	Don't Let Him Be Your Baby/It Must Be Love	50
64	Stateside SS 299	Can You Do It/I'll Stand By You	25
65	Stateside SS 381	Can You Jerk Like Me/That Day She Needed Me	20
65	Tamla Motown TMG 531	First I Look At The Purse/Searching For A Girl	30
66	Tamla Motown TMG 564	Determination/Just A Little Misunderstanding	30
67	Tamla Motown TMG 605	It's So Hard Being A Loser/Your Love Grows More Precious Every Day	30
70	Tamla Motown TMG 723	Just A Little Misunderstanding/First I Look At The Purse	5
65	Tamla Motown TME 2002	THE CONTOURS (EP)	30
63	Oriole PS 40043	DO YOU LOVE ME (LP)	50
74	M. For Pleasure MFP 50054	BABY HIT AND RUN (LP)	10

CONTRASTS featuring BOB MORRISON

| 64 | Parlophone R 5190 | Call Me/Come On Let's Go | 4 |
| 68 | Monument MON 1018 | What A Day/Lonely Child | 6 |

CONTROLLED BLEEDING

| 86 | Sterile SR 11 | HEADCRACK (LP) | 25 |

CONVAIRS

| 66 | HMV POP 1549 | Tomorrow Is A Long Time/Midnight Mary | 8 |

BERT CONVY & THUNDERBIRDS

| 55 | London HLB 8190 | C'mon Back/Hoo Bop De Bow | 80 |

55	London HLB 8190	C'mon Back/Hoo Bop De Bow (78)	15
56	Capitol CL 14601	Heaven On Earth/CHEERS: Que Pasa Muchacha	15
56	Capitol CL 14601	Heaven On Earth/CHEERS: Que Pasa Muchacha (78)	5

(see also Cheers, Thunderbirds)

CONNIE CONWAY
60	London HA-W 2214	CONNIE CONWAY (LP)	10

MIKE CONWAY
68	Plexium PXM 1	Reign Of King Sadness/I'm Gonna Get Me A Women	4

RUSS CONWAY
57	Columbia DB 3920	Roll The Carpet Up/The Westminster Waltz	4
57	Columbia DB 3971	Soho Fair/The Spotlight Waltz	4
57	Columbia DB 3999	Late Set/Red Cat	4
61	Columbia DB 4564	Pepe/Matador From Trinidad (with John Barry Orchestra)	4

(see also John Barry, Billy Cotton, Ronnie Harris)

STEVE CONWAY
55	Columbia SEG 7573	MEMORIES OF STEVE CONWAY (EP)	7
56	Columbia SEG 7649	MORE MEMORIES OF STEVE CONWAY (EP)	7

JIMMY CONWELL
72	Jay Boy BOY 64	Cigarette Ashes/Second Hand Happiness	5
76	Contempo CS 9001	Cigarette Ashes/Second Hand Happiness (reissue)	4

COO-COO RACHAS
59	Capitol CL 15024	Chili Beans/Track Down	5

RY COODER
71	Reprise R 23497	How Can A Poor Man Stand Such Times And Live/Goin' To Brownsville	4
82	W.B. K 17952F/SAM 149	Gypsy Woman/Alimony//Teardrops Will Fall/It's All Over Now (double pack)	4
71	Reprise RSLP 6402	RY COODER (LP)	10

(see also Don Everly)

LITTLE JOE COOK (U.K.)
65	Sue WI 385	Stormy Monday Blues Pts 1 & 2	35

(see also Chris Farlowe, Beazers)

LITTLE JOE COOK (U.S.)
73	Sonet SON 2002	Don't You Have Feelings/Hold On To Your Money	10

PETER COOK
65	Pye 7N 15847	Georgia/There And Bach Again	12

(see also Peter London)

PETER COOK
65	Decca F 12182	The Ballad Of Spotty Muldoon/Lovely Lady Of The Roses	4
61	Parlophone PMC 1145	BEYOND THE FRINGE (LP, with other artists)	15
63	Parlophone PMC 1190	BRIDGE ON THE RIVER WYE (LP, with other artists)	12
63	Parlophone PMC 1198	PETER COOK PRESENTS THE ESTABLISHMENT (LP, with other artists)	12
65	Decca LK 4722	PETER COOK PRESENTS MISTY MR. WISTY (LP)	12
65	Transatlantic TRA 131	PRIVATE EYE'S BLUE RECORD (LP, with other artists)	15

PETER COOK & DUDLEY MOORE
62	Parlophone R 4969	Excerpts From "Beyond The Fringe": Sitting On The Bench/The End Of The World (with Alan Bennett & Jonathan Miller)	8
65	Decca F 12158	Goodbyeee (& Dudley Moore Trio)/DUDLEY MOORE TRIO: Not Only But Also	4
66	Decca F 12380	Isn't She A Sweetie/Bo Dudley	4
67	Decca F 12551	The L.S. Bumble Bee/The Bee Side	7
67	Decca F 12710	Bedazzled/Love Me	4
65	Parlophone GEP 8940	PETER COOK AND DUDLEY MOORE (EP)	8
65	Decca DFE 8644	BY APPOINTMENT (EP)	7
65	Decca LK 4703	NOT ONLY PETER COOK BUT ALSO DUDLEY MOORE (LP)	12
66	Decca LK 4785	ONCE MOORE WITH COOK (LP)	12
68	Decca LK/SKL 4923	BEDAZZLED (LP, Soundtrack)	15
71	Decca LK 5080	NOT ONLY BUT ALSO (LP)	10

(see also Dudley Moore Trio)

ROGER (JAMES) COOKE
69	Columbia DB 8510	Not That It Matters Anymore/Paper Chase	4
70	Columbia SCX 6388	STUDY (LP)	12
72	Regal Zono. SRZA 8508	MEANWHILE BACK AT THE WORLD (LP)	25
73	Regal Zono. SLRZ 1035	MINSTREL IN FLIGHT (LP)	30

(see also David & Jonathan)

SAM COOKE
57	London HLU 8506	You Send Me/Summertime	35
57	London HLU 8506	You Send Me/Summertime (78)	10
58	London HLU 8615	That's All I Need To Know/I Don't Want To Cry	25
58	London HLU 8615	That's All I Need To Know/I Don't Want To Cry (78)	10
58	HMV POP 568	Love You Most Of All/Win Your Love For Me	15
58	HMV POP 568	Love You Most Of All/Win Your Love For Me (78)	20
59	HMV POP 610	Everybody Likes To Cha Cha Cha/The Little Things You Do	15
59	HMV POP 610	Everybody Likes To Cha Cha Cha/The Little Things You Do (78)	20
59	HMV POP 642	Only Sixteen/Let's Go Steady Again	15
59	HMV POP 642	Only Sixteen/Let's Go Steady Again (78)	20
59	HMV POP 675	There, I've Said It Again/One Hour Ahead Of The Posse	12
60	London HLU 9046	Happy In Love/I Need You Now	15
60	RCA RCA 1184	Teenage Sonata/If You Were The Only Girl	7
60	HMV POP 754	Wonderful World/Along The Navajo Trail	8
60	RCA RCA 1202	Chain Gang/I Fall In Love Everyday	6
61	RCA RCA 1221	Sad Mood/Love Me	7

Sam COOKE

61	RCA RCA 1230	That's It, I Quit, I'm Movin' On/What Do You Say	6
61	RCA RCA 1242	Cupid/Farewell, My Darling	5
61	RCA RCA 1260	Feel It/It's Alright	6
62	RCA RCA 1277	Twisting The Night Away/One More Time	4
62	RCA RCA 1296	Bring It On Home To Me/Having A Party	6
62	RCA RCA 1310	Nothing Can Change This Love/Somebody Have Mercy	5
63	RCA RCA 1327	Send Me Some Loving/Baby Baby Baby	7
63	RCA RCA 1341	Another Saturday Night/Love Will Find A Way	5
63	RCA RCA 1361	Frankie And Johnny/Cool Train	5
63	RCA RCA 1367	Little Red Rooster/Shake Rattle And Roll	7
64	RCA RCA 1386	Good News/Basin Street Blues	4
64	RCA RCA 1405	Good Times/Tennessee Waltz	6
65	RCA RCA 1436	Shake/A Change Is Gonna Come	7
65	RCA RCA 1452	It's Got The Whole World Shakin'/Ease My Troublin' Mind	6
65	RCA RCA 1476	Sugar Dumpling/Bridge Of Tears	7
68	RCA RCA 1701	Another Saturday Night/DUANE EDDY: Dance With The Guitar Man (withdrawn)	12
69	RCA RCA 1817	Cupid/Farewell, My Darling (reissue)	4
63	RCA RCX 7117	HEART AND SOUL (EP)	15
64	RCA RCX 7128	SWING SWEETLY (EP)	15
58	HMV CLP 1261	SAM COOKE (LP, with Bumps Blackwell Orchestra)	55
59	HMV CLP 1273	ENCORE (LP)	50
61	RCA RD 27190	COOKE'S TOUR (LP, also stereo SF 5076)	25/30
61	RCA RD 27215	HITS OF THE FIFTIES (LP, also stereo SF 5098)	25/30
61	RCA RD 27222	SWING LOW (LP)	25
62	RCA RD 27245	MY KIND OF BLUES (LP, also stereo SF 5120)	22/25
62	RCA RD 27263	TWISTIN' THE NIGHT AWAY (LP, also stereo SF 5133)	18/20
63	RCA RD/SF 7539	MR. SOUL (LP, mono/stereo)	20/22
63	RCA RD/SF 7583	NIGHT BEAT (LP)	25/30
64	RCA RD/SF 7635	AIN'T THAT GOOD NEWS (LP, mono/stereo)	18/20
65	RCA RD/SF 7674	AT THE COPA (LP, mono/stereo)	16/18
65	London HA-U 8232	THE SOUL STIRRERS FEATURING SAM COOKE (LP)	25
66	RCA RD 7730	A CHANGE IS GONNA COME (LP)	18
66	RCA RD/SF 7764	TRY A LITTLE LOVE (LP)	18
66	Immediate IMLP 002	THE WONDERFUL WORLD OF SAM COOKE (LP)	20
74	BBC	SAM COOKE AND OTHERS (LP, white label test pressing)	80
70s	RCA Int'l INTS 1080	THE LATE AND GREAT SAM COOKE (LP)	10

(see also Paul Anka, Sam Cooke & Neil Sedaka)

COOKIES

62	London HLU 9634	Chains/Stranger In My Arms	10
63	London HLU 9704	Don't Say Nothin' Bad About My Baby/Softly In The Night	10
63	Colpix PX 11012	Willpower/I Want A Boy For My Birthday	7
64	Colpix PX 11020	Girls Grow Up Faster Than Boys/Only To Other People	7

JOE COOL & KILLERS

| 77 | Ariola ARO 165 | I Just Don't Care/My Way | 5 |

OLIVER COOL

| 60 | Columbia DB 4552 | Oliver Cool/I Like Girls | 4 |
| 61 | Columbia DB 4616 | Give Me The Summertime/I Said Yeah | 4 |

COOL BREEZE

70s	Pathway PAT 103	People Ask What Love Is/There'll Be No More Sad Tomorrows	15
72	Decca F 13324	Summertime Sunshine/Sing Out Your Love	4
75	Bus Stop BUS 1023	Do It Some More/Citizen Jones	4

COOL CATS

| 68 | Jolly JY 007 | What Kind Of Man/HELMSLEY MORRIS: Little Things | 8 |
| 68 | Jolly JY 009 | Hold Your Love/ALVA LEWIS: Hang My Head And Cry | 8 |

EDDIE COOLEY & DIMPLES

| 57 | Columbia DB 3873 | Priscilla/Got A Little Woman | 90 |
| 57 | Columbia DB 3873 | Priscilla/Got A Little Woman (78) | 25 |

SPADE COOLEY & HIS FIDDLIN' FRIENDS

| 51 | Brunswick 04812 | Horse Hair Boogie/Down Yonder (78) | 5 |

RITA COOLIDGE

| 83 | A&M AM 007 | All Time High/All Time High (Extended Instrumental) | 6 |
| 83 | Scanlite BOND 1 | All Time High/All Time High (Extended Instrumental) | 12 |

COOL MEN

| 58 | Parlophone GEP 8739 | COOL FOR CATS NO. 1 (EP) | 12 |
| 58 | Parlophone GEP 8752 | COOL FOR CATS NO. 2 (EP) | 12 |

COOL STICKY

| 68 | Amalgamated AMG 825 | Train To Soulsville/ERIC MONTY MORRIS: Cinderella (actually by Errol Dunkley) | 8 |

CHRIS COOMBES & others

| 65 | Holyground HG 110 | WHERE IT'S AT (EP, 99 only) | 30 |

ALICE COOPER

71	Straight W 7209	Eighteen/Body	10
71	Warner Bros K 16127	Under My Wheels/Desperado	7
72	Warner Bros K 16154	Be My Lover/You Drive Me Nervous	7
72	Warner Bros K 16188	School's Out/Gutter Cat (p/s)	8
72	Warner Bros K 16214	Elected/Luney Tune (p/s)	10
72	Warner Bros K 16248	Hello Hurray/Generation Landslide	4
73	Warner Bros/ Lyntone LYN 2585/6	Slick Black Limousine/Extracts From: Unfinished Sweet/Elected/No More Mr Nice Guy/Billion Dollar Babies/I Love The Dead (33rpm flexi free with 'NME')	7/4
73	Warner Bros K 16262	No More Mr. Nice Guy/Raped And Freezin'	4

Alice COOPER

74	Warner Bros K 16345	Teenage Lament '74/Hard Hearted Alice	4
74	Warner Bros K 16127	Under My Wheels/Desperado (reissue)	4
74	Warner Bros K 16409	School's Out/No More Mr. Nice Guy/Elected/Billion Dollar Babies (maxi-45)	6
75	Anchor ANC 1012	Department Of Youth/Cold Ethyl (p/s)	6
75	Anchor ANC 1018	Only Women Bleed/Devil's Food	4
75	Anchor ANC 1025	Welcome To My Nightmare/Black Widow	4
75	Anchor ANE 7001	Welcome To My Nightmare/Department Of Youth/Black Widow/ Only Women Bleed (EP, p/s)	5
76	Warner Bros K 16792	I Never Cry/Got To Hell (p/s)	5
77	Warner Bros K 16935	(No More) Love At Your Convenience/It's Hot Tonight (p/s, gothic type on label)	4
77	Anchor ANE 12001	Welcome To My Nightmare/Department Of Youth/Black Widow/ Only Women Bleed (12", p/s, reissue)	10
79	Warner Bros K 17287	School's Out/Elected (p/s, reissue)	5
80	Warner Bros K 17598	Clones (We're All)/Model Citizen (p/s)	7
82	Warner Bros K 17924	Seven And Seven Is (live)/Generation Landslide '81 (gatefold p/s)	5
82	Warner Bros K 17940M	For Britain Only/Under My Wheels (live) (picture disc, unreleased)	
82	Warner Bros K 17940T	Who Do You Think We Are? (live)/Model Citizen (live)/For Britain Only/ Under My Wheels (live) (12", p/s)	12
83	Warner Bros ALICE 1T	I Love America/Fresh Blood/Pass The Gun Around (12", p/s)	10
86	MCA MCA 1090	He's Back (The Man Behind The Mask)/Billion Dollar Babies (poster p/s)	4
87	MCA MCA 1113	Teenage Frankenstein/School's Out (live)	4
89	Epic 6550 652	Poison/Trash/Ballad Of Dwight Fry (live)/I Got A Line On You (CD, 'bottle' pack)	12
89	Epic ALICEG/R/B 3	Bed Of Nails/I'm Your Gun (p/s, green, red or blue vinyl)	5
89	Epic ALICE 3	Bed Of Nails/I'm Your Gun (p/s, with poster)	4
89	Epic ALICEP 3	Bed Of Nails/I'm Your Gun/Go To Hell (live) (12", picture disc)	7
89	Epic ALICER/Y 4	House Of Fire/This Maniac's In Love With You (p/s, red or yellow vinyl)	5
89	Epic ALICEX 4	House Of Fire/Poison (live) (p/s)	4
89	Epic ALICEP 4	House Of Fire/This Maniac's In Love With You (shaped picture disc)	6
89	Epic ALICEQ 4	House Of Fire/Poison (live)/Spark In The Dark (live)/Under My Wheels (live) (12", with tour poster)	7
91	Epic 6574389	Love's Like A Loaded Gun/Fire/Eighteen (live) (CD, gun-shaped p/s)	7
69	Straight STS 1051	PRETTIES FOR YOU (LP, purple label, gatefold sleeve)	25
69	Straight STS 1061	EASY ACTION (LP, purple label, gatefold sleeve)	25
71	Straight STS 1065	LOVE IT TO DEATH (LP, purple label, gatefold sleeve)	25
71	Warner Bros K 56005	KILLER (LP, green label, gatefold sleeve with calendar/poster)	15
72	Warner Bros K 56007	SCHOOL'S OUT (LP, green label, gatefold sleeve, with 'paper panties' inner)	15
73	Warner Bros K 56013	BILLION DOLLAR BABIES (LP, green label, gatefold sleeve with cards, $ billion bill & inner sleeve)	10
73	Warner Bros K 66021	SCHOOL DAYS (2-LP, gatefold sleeve, reissue of STS 1051 & 1061)	15
74	Warner Bros K 56018	MUSCLE OF LOVE (LP, 'palm tree' label, 'cardboard box' sleeve)	10
80	Warner Bros K 56805	FLUSH THE FASHION (LP)	10
82	Warner Bros K 56927	SPECIAL FORCES (LP)	10
83	Warner Bros 92-396-69-1	DADA (LP)	10

GARNELL COOPER & KINFOLKS
63	London HL 9757	Green Monkey/Long Distance	5

LES COOPER & SOUL ROCKERS
62	Stateside SS 142	Wiggle Wobble/Dig Yourself	8

MIKE COOPER
70	Dawn DNX 2501	Your Lovely Ways Pts 1 & 2/Watching You Fall Pts 1 & 2	4
71	Dawn DNX 2511	Too Late Now/Good Times	4
72	Dawn DNS 1022	Time In Hand/Schaabisch Hall	4
60s	Saydisc SD 137	UP THE COUNTRY BLUES (EP)	18
68	Matchbox SDM 159	THE INVERTED WORLD (LP, with Ian A. Anderson)	40
69	Pye NSPL 18281	OH REALLY!? (LP)	15
70	Dawn DNLS 3005	DO I KNOW YOU? (LP)	10
70	Dawn DNLS 3011	TROUT STEEL (LP, some with poster insert)	15/10
71	Dawn DNLS 3026	PLACES I KNOW (LP, with insert)	10
72	Dawn DNLS 3031	THE MACHINE GUN COMPANY (LP)	10

(see also Ian A. Anderson)

TOMMY COOPER
61	Palette PG 9019	Don't Jump Off The Roof Dad/How Come There's No Dog Day?	10

COOPERETTES
75	Brunswick BR 22	Shing-A-Ling/Don't Trust Him	4

COWBOY COPAS
51	Vogue V 9001	The Feudin' Boogie (with Grandpa Jones)/Strange Little Girl (78)	8
53	Parlophone R 3708	It's No Sin To Love You/I've Grown So Used To You (78)	5
53	Parlophone R 3756	Doll Of Clay/If Wishes Were Horses (78)	5
54	Parlophone MSP 6079	Tennessee Senorita/If You Will Let Me Be Your Love	18
54	Parlophone MSP 6109	A Heartbreak Ago/The Blue Waltz	18
55	Parlophone MSP 6164	I'll Waltz With You In My Dreams/Return To Sender	18
60	Melodisc M 1566	Alabam/I Can	8
55	Parlophone GEP 8527	FAVOURITE COWBOY SONGS (EP)	10
56	Parlophone GEP 8575	WESTERN STYLE (EP)	10
62	Top Rank JKP 3014	COUNTRY MUSIC (EP)	9
63	Stateside SE 1003	COUNTRY HITS (EP)	9
64	London R-ED 1418	THE UNFORGETTABLE COWBOY COPAS VOLUME 1 (EP)	8
64	London R-ED 1419	THE UNFORGETTABLE COWBOY COPAS VOLUME 2 (EP)	8
64	London R-ED 1420	THE UNFORGETTABLE COWBOY COPAS VOLUME 3 (EP)	8
61	Melodisc MLP 12-119	COWBOY COPAS (LP)	15
63	Stateside SL 10035	SONGS THAT MADE HIM FAMOUS (LP)	10
63	London HA-B 8088	COUNTRY ENTERTAINER NO. 1 (LP)	12
64	London HA-B 8180	STARS OF THE GRAND OLE OPRY — COWBOY COPAS (LP)	12

(see also Johnny Bond)

JULIAN COPE

83	Mercury COPE 1	Sunshine Playroom/Hey High Class Butcher (p/s)	4
83	Mercury COPE 1	Sunshine Playroom/Hey High Class Butcher/Wreck My Car/Eat The Poor (12", p/s)	7
83	Mercury MER 155	The Greatness And Perfection Of Love/24A Velocity Crescent (p/s)	4
84	Mercury MER 155	The Greatness And Perfection Of Love/24A Velocity Crescent/Pussyface (12", p/s)	7
85	Mercury MER 1822	Sunspots/I Went On A Chourney///Mik Mak Mok/Land Of Fear (double pack)	8
87	Island ISW 305	Trampolene/Disaster/Mock Turtle/Warwick The Kingmaker (numbered envelope p/s with poster)	4
89	Island 10ISP 406	China Doll/Desi/Crazy Farm Animal/Rail On (10" picture disc, printed PVC sleeve)	5
80s	Antar ANTAR 1	Christmas Mourning/(interview) (fan club box with card, bio., photos & stickers)	6
91	Island JC 1	Safesurfer/If You Love Me At All (33rpm, stickered white sleeve)	15
87	Island ILPS 9861	SAINT JULIAN (LP, with free 12" interview LP [JCCLP 1])	20
89	Copeco JULP 89	SKELLINGTON (LP)	15
89	Copeco JUCD 89	SKELLINGTON (CD)	20
90	Mofo MOFOCOLP 90	DROOLIAN (LP)	15
90	Mofo MOFOCOCD 90	DROOLIAN (CD)	20

(see also Teardrop Explodes, Rabbi Joseph Gordon)

SUZY COPE

61	HMV POP 941	Teenage Fool/Juvenile Delinquent	4
62	HMV POP 1047	Not Never Not Now/Kisses And Tears	4
63	HMV POP 1167	Biggity Big/Doing What You Know Is Wrong	4
65	CBS 201792	You Can't Say I Never Told You/And Now I Don't Want You	6

AL(L)AN COPELAND

57	Vogue Coral Q 72237	Feeling Happy/You Don't Know	10
57	Vogue Coral Q 72277	How Will I Know?/Will You Still Be Mine	6
59	Pye Intl. 7N 25007	Flip Flop/Lot's More Love (as Allan Copeland)	7

JOHNNY COPELAND

72	Atlantic K 10242	Sufferin' City/It's My Own Tears	10

KEN COPELAND

57	London HLP 8423	Pledge Of Love/MINTS: Night Air	175
57	London HLP 8423	Pledge Of Love/MINTS: Night Air (78)	35

COPPERFIELD

69	Instant IN 004	Any Old Time/I'm No Good For Her	10
70	Parlophone R 5818	I'll Hold Out My Hands/Far Away Love	5

COPS 'N ROBBERS

64	Decca F 12019	St. James Infirmary/There's Gotta Be A Reason	30
65	Pye 7N 15870	Just Keep Right On/I Could Have Danced All Night	18
65	Pye 7N 15928	It's All Over Now Baby Blue/I've Found Out	15

COPY CATS

69	Bullet BU 419	Copy Cat (with Derrick Morgan)/BUNNY LEE ALL STARRS: Hot Lead	4

CORBAN

78	Acorn	A BREAK IN THE CLOUDS (LP, with insert)	25

HARRY H. CORBETT

62	Pye 7N 15468	Junk Shop/The Isle Of Clerkenwell	4
63	Pye 7N 15552	Like The Big Guys Do/The Green Eye	4
63	Pye 7N 15584	The Table And The Chair/Things We Never Had	4
67	Decca F 12714	Flower Power Fred/(I'm) Saving All My Love (with Unidentified Flower Objects)	4

(see also Steptoe & Son)

HARRY H. CORBETT & WILFRED BRAMBELL

64	Pye NPL 18081	STEPTOE AND SON (LP)	12
65	Pye NPL 18135	LOVE AND HAROLD STEPTOE (LP)	15
66	Pye NPL 18153	GEMS FROM THE STEPTOE SCRAP HEAP (LP)	15
67	Golden Guinea GGL 0373	STEPTOE A LA CARTE (LP)	10

RONNIE CORBETT

68	Columbia DB 8512	Big Man/Fancy You Fancying Me	4

CORBY & CHAMPAGNE

66	Pye 7N 17203	Time Marches On/I'll Be Back	4

KEVIN CORCORAN (& JEROME COURTLAND)

58	Pye 7N 15145	Old Yeller (with Jerome Courtland)/How Much Is That Doggie In The Window	4

FRANK CORDELL & HIS ORCHESTRA

56	HMV 7M 397	Port-Au-Prince/"Double Cross" TV Theme	4
56	HMV 7M 419	Sadie's Shawl/Flamenco Love	5

CORDES

65	Cavern Sound IMSTL 1	Give Her Time/She's Leaving	25

LOUISE CORDET

62	Decca F 11476	I'm Just A Baby/In A Matter Of Moments	5
62	Decca F 11524	Sweet Enough/Someone Else's Fool	5
63	Decca F 11673	Around And Around/Which Way The Wind Blows	5
64	Decca F 11824	Don't Let The Sun Catch You Crying/Loving Baby	5
64	Decca F 11875	Don't Make Me Over/Two Lovers	6
62	Decca DFE 8515	THE SWEET BEAT OF LOUISE CORDET (EP)	20

(see also Caravelles)

CORDUROYS

66	Planet PLF 122	Tick Tock/Too Much Of A Woman	20

CHICK COREA & RETURN TO FOREVER

71	Blue Note BST 84353	SONG OF SINGING (LP)	10

MINT VALUE £

72	Polydor 2310 247	LIGHT AS A FEATHER (LP, with Flora Purim)	10
73	ECM ECM 1009	ARC (LP, with others)	10
74	Atlantic K 60081	INNER SPACE (2-LP)	14
74	People PLEO 9	SUNDANCE (LP)	10
74	Epic EPC 65558	ROUND TRIP (LP, with S. Watanabe)	10
74	ECM ECM 1014	PIANO IMPROVISATIONS VOL. 1 (LP)	10
74	ECM ECM 1018/9	PARIS CONCERT (2-LP, as Corea & Braxton & Holland)	14
75	ECM ECM 1020	PIANO IMPROVISATIONS VOL. 2 (LP)	10
75	ECM ECM 1022	RETURN TO FOREVER (LP)	10

(see also Return To Forever)

CHICK COREA & STAN GETZ
| 75 | Verve 2304 225 | CAPTAIN MARVEL (LP) | 10 |

(see also Stan Getz)

CORKSCREW
| 79 | Highway SHY 7005 | FOR OPENERS (LP) | 30 |

CORNBREAD & JERRY
| 61 | London HLG 9352 | L'il Ole Me/Loco Moto | 4 |

CORN DOLLIES
87	Farm FARM 001	Forever Steven/About To Believe (p/s)	6
88	Medium Cool MC 8	Being Small (12", p/s)	7
88	Medium Cool MC 009T	Forever Steven/Big Care Call/Sweetheart Rose Special/About To Believe (12", p/s)	7

DON CORNELL
54	Vogue Coral Q 2013	Hold My Hand/I'm Blessed	25
54	Vogue Coral Q 2037	S'Posin'/I Was Lucky	10
55	Vogue Coral Q 72058	No Man Is An Island/All At Once	8
55	Vogue Coral Q 72070	Give Me Your Love/When You Are In Love	8
55	Vogue Coral Q 72071	Athena/Size 12	8
55	Vogue Coral Q 72073	Stranger In Paradise/The Devil's In Your Eyes	12
55	Vogue Coral Q 72080	Unchained Melody/Most Of All	10
55	Vogue Coral Q 72104	Love Is A Many Splendored Thing/The Bible Tells Me So	12
56	Vogue Coral Q 72132	There Once Was A Beautiful/Make A Wish	8
56	Vogue Coral Q 72144	Teenage Meeting (Gonna Rock It Right)/I Still Have A Prayer	18
56	Vogue Coral Q 72144	Teenage Meeting (Gonna Rock It Right)/I Still Have A Prayer (78)	8
56	Vogue Coral Q 72152	Rock Island Line/Na-Ne Na-Na	12
56	Vogue Coral Q 72152	Rock Island Line/Na-Ne Na-Na (78)	5
56	Vogue Coral Q 72164	But Love Me (Love But Me)/Fort Knox	8
56	Vogue Coral Q 72203	All Of You/Heaven Only Knows	6
57	Vogue Coral Q 72218	See-Saw/From The Bottom Of My Heart	10
57	Vogue Coral Q 72234	Let's Be Friends/Afternoon In Madrid	6
57	Vogue Coral Q 72257	Sittin' In The Balcony/Let's Get Lost	12
57	Vogue Coral Q 72257	Sittin' In The Balcony/Let's Get Lost (78)	8
57	Vogue Coral Q 72276	Mama Guitar/A Face In The Crowd	15
57	Vogue Coral Q 72276	Mama Guitar/A Face In The Crowd (78)	15
57	Vogue Coral Q 72291	There's Only You/Non Dimenticar	7
58	Coral Q 72308	Before It's Time To Say Goodnight/Mailman, Bring Me No More Blues	12
58	Coral Q 72313	I've Got Bells On My Heart/Keep God In The Home	7
59	Pye International 7N 25041	Sempe Amore/Forever Couldn't Be Long Enough	6
59	London HLD 8937	This Earth Of Mine/The Gang That Sang "Heart Of My Heart"	6
59	London HLD 8937	This Earth Of Mine/The Gang That Sang "Heart Of My Heart" (78)	5
54	Vogue Coral LVC 10004	DON CORNELL FOR YOU (10" LP)	25
56	Coral LVA 9037	LET'S GET LOST (LP)	20

JERRY CORNELL
| 55 | London HL 8157 | Please Don't Talk About Me When I'm Gone/St. Louis Blues | 18 |

LYN CORNELL
60	Decca F 11227	Like Love/Demon Lover	4
60	Decca F 11260	Teaser/What A Feeling	4
60	Decca F 11277	Never On Sunday/Swain Kelly	4
60	Decca F 11301	The Angel And The Stranger/Xmas Stocking	4

CORNFLAKES
| 62 | Fontana 267 227TF | Oh, Listen To The Band/Moonstruck | 4 |

ARNOLD CORNS
71	B&C CB 149	Moonage Daydream/Hang Onto Yourself (as 'The Arnold Corns')	45
71	B&C CB 189	Hang Onto Yourself/Man In The Middle	25
74	Mooncrest MOON 25	Hang Onto Yourself/Man In The Middle (reissue)	10

(see also David Bowie)

HUGH CORNWELL & ROBERT WILLIAMS
| 79 | United Artists BP 320 | White Room/Losers In A Lost Land (Instrumental) (p/s) | 5 |
| 79 | United Artists UAG 30251 | NOSFERATU (LP) | 10 |

(see also Stranglers)

CORONADOS
| 64 | London HL 9895 | Love Me With All Your Heart/Querida | 5 |
| 67 | Stateside SS 2043 | Johnny B. Goode/Shook Me Down | 4 |

CORONETS
54	Columbia SCM 5117	Do, Do, Do, Do, Do, Do, Do It Again/I Ain't Gonna Do It No More	10
56	Columbia SCM 5235	Lizzie Borden/My Believing Heart	10
56	Columbia SCM 5261	There's No Song Like An Old Song/The Magic Touch	12
56	Columbia DB 3827	Someone To Love/The Rocking Horse Cowboy	6
56	Columbia SEG 7603	RHYTHM AND BLUES (EP, as Coronets with Eric Jupp Orchestra)	10
56	Columbia SEG 7621	THE PERFECT COMBINATION (EP, as Coronets with Eric Jupp Orchestra)	7

(see also Chris Sandford & Coronets, Tony Brent, Ronnie Harris, Benny Hill, Eric Jupp, Lee Lawrence)

CORPORATION
69	Capitol E-ST 175	CORPORATION (LP)	20

CORRIE FOLK TRIO
66	Waverley ZLP 2042	CORRIE FOLK TRIO WITH PADDIE BELL (LP, also stereo SZLP 2043)	20
69	Fontana STL 5337	THOSE WILD CORRIES (LP)	10

CORSAIRS (U.S.)
62	Pye International 7N 25142	I'll Take You Home/Sitting On Your Doorstep (with Jay 'Bird' Uzzel)	6

CORSAIRS (U.K.)
67	CBS 202624	Pay You Back With Interest/I'm Gonna Shut You Down	8

BOB CORT (SKIFFLE GROUP)
57	Decca FJ 10831	It Takes A Worried Man To Sing A Worried Blues/ Don't You Rock Me Daddy-O	12
57	Decca F 10892	Six-Five Special/Roll Jen Jenkins	12
57	Decca F 10899	Maggie May/Jessamine (with Liz Winters)	6
57	Decca F 10905	Schoolday (Ring! Ring! Goes The Bell)/Ain't It A Shame (To ...)	12
57	Decca F 10951	'Bob Cort Skiffle Party' Medley Pts 1 & 2	6
58	Decca F 10989	The Ark (Noah Found Grace In The Eyes Of God)/Yes! Suh!	6
59	Decca F 11109	Foggy Foggy Dew/On Top Of Old Smokey (solo)	5
59	Decca F 11145	Waterloo/Battle Of New Orleans (solo)	6
59	Decca F 11160	Kissin' Time/I'm Gonna Get Married (solo)	6
60	Decca F 11197	El Paso/A Handful Of Gold (solo)	6
60	Decca F 11256	Mule Skinner Blues/The Ballad Of Walter Williams (solo)	6
60	Decca F 11285	The Ballad Of The Alamo/Five Brothers (solo)	5
57	Decca LK 4222	AIN'T IT A SHAME (LP)	20
59	Decca LK 4301	ESKIMO NELL (LP)	18
65	Ace Of Clubs ACL 1197	YES! SUH! (LP, reissue of LK 4222 with different sleeve)	10

(see also Liz Winters & Bob Cort)

DAVE 'BABY' CORTEZ
59	London HLU 8852	The Happy Organ/Love Me As I Love You	12
59	London HLU 8852	The Happy Organ/Love Me As I Love You (78)	15
59	London HLU 8919	The Whistling Organ/I'm Happy	12
59	London HLU 8919	The Whistling Organ/I'm Happy (78)	12
60	Columbia DB 4404	Piano Shuffle/Dave's Special	8
60	London HLU 9126	Deep In The Heart Of Texas/You're Just Right	12
62	Pye International 7N 25159	Rinky Dink/Getting Right	10
66	Roulette RK 7001	Countdown/Summertime	6
60	London REU 1233	DAVE 'BABY' CORTEZ (EP)	25
64	London HA-U 8142	THE GOLDEN HITS OF DAVE 'BABY' CORTEZ (LP)	20

CORTINAS
68	Polydor 56255	Phoebe's Flower Shop/Too Much In Love	6

CORTINAS
77	Step Forward SF 1	Fascist Dictator/Television Families (p/s)	5
78	Step Forward SF 6	Defiant Pose/Independence (p/s)	5
78	Step Forward SF 6	Defiant Pose/Independence (12", pink die-cut sleeve)	8
78	CBS 6759	Heartache/Ask Mr Waverly (p/s)	4
78	CBS 82831	TRUE ROMANCES (LP)	10

LARRY CORYELL
69	Vanguard SVRL 19051	LADY CORYELL (LP)	15
69	Vanguard SVRL 19059	CORYELL (LP)	15
70	Philips 6359 005	SPACES (LP)	15
72	Philips 6369 407	BAREFOOT BOY (LP)	12
72	Philips 6369 411	FAIRYLAND (LP)	12
72	Vanguard VSD 6558	SPACES (LP, reissue)	10
72	Vanguard VSD 6573	AT THE VILLAGE GATE (LP)	10
73	Vanguard VSD 79319	OFFERING (LP)	10
73	Vanguard VSD 79329	THE REAL GREAT ESCAPE (LP)	10
74	Vanguard VSD 79342	INTRODUCING 11TH HOUSE (LP)	10
74	Vanguard VSD 79345	SPACES (LP, reissue)	10
75	Vanguard VSD 79353	THE RESTFUL MIND (LP)	10

BILL COSBY
67	Warner Bros WB 7072	Little Ole Man (Uptight Everything's Alright)/Don'cha Know (some in p/s)	12/6
65	Warner Bros W(S) 1567	I STARTED OUT AS A CHILD (LP)	10
66	Warner W(S) 1634	WONDERFULNESS (LP)	10
68	Warner W(S) 1770	IT'S TRUE, IT'S TRUE (LP)	10

COSEY FANNI TUTTI
82	Flowmotion	TIME TO TELL (C30 cassette, some with 24-page magazine)	15/10

COSMIC EYE
72	Regal Zono. SLRZ 1030	DREAM SEQUENCE (LP)	100

COSMO
63	Blue Beat BB 175	Gypsy Woman/Do Unto Others	8
64	Blue Beat BB 244	One God/BUSTER'S ALLSTARS: Prince Royal (actually "Reincarnation")	10
64	Blue Beat BB 269	Rice And Badgee/BUSTER'S ALLSTARS: The Tickler	8

(see also Cosmo & Dennis)

FRANK COSMO
63	Island WI 058	Revenge/Laughin' At You	8
63	Island WI 100	Merry Christmas/Greetings From Beverley's	8
63	R&B JB 119	I Love You/DON DRUMMOND: Close Of Play	12
64	Island WI 135	Better Get Right/Ameletia	8
64	Black Swan WI 446	Alone/Beautiful Book	8

COSMO & DENNIS (alias Denzil)

62	Blue Beat BB 145	Bed Of Roses/Tonight And Evermore	10
64	Blue Beat BB 296	Sweet Rosemarie/Lollipop I'm In Love	8
64	Blue Beat BB 312	Come On Come On/I Don't Want You	8

(see also Cosmo)

DON COSTA, HIS ORCHESTRA & CHORUS

55	London HLF 8186	Love Is A Many Splendoured Thing/Safe In The Harbour	18
55	London HLF 8186	Love Is A Many Splendoured Thing/Safe In The Harbour (78)	5
59	London HLT 8992	I Walk The Line/Cat Walk	6
59	London HLT 8992	I Walk The Line/Cat Walk (78)	18
60	London HLT 9137	Theme From "The Unforgiven"/Streets Of Paris	4
60	London HLT 7103	Theme From "The Unforgiven"/FERRANTE & TEICHER: Theme From "The Apartment"(exp.)	4
60	London HLT 9195	Never On Sunday/The Sound Of Love	4
61	London HLT 9320	The Misfits/Chi Chi	4

JACK COSTANZO

61	London HLG 9401	Theme From Route 66/Naked City Theme	4

JACK COSTANZO & TUBBY HAYES

62	Fontana TFL 5190/ STFL 598	CONSTANZO PLUS TUBBS — EQUATION IN RHYTHM (LP, mono/stereo)	40/45

(see also Tubby Hayes)

DANNY COSTELLO

57	Oriole CB 1393	Like A Brook Gets Lost In A River/That's Where I Shine	4

DAY COSTELLO

71	Spark SRL 1042	The Long And Winding Road/Free	8

(see also Ross McManus)

ELVIS COSTELLO (& ATTRACTIONS)

77	Stiff BUY 11	Less Than Zero/Radio Sweetheart (p/s, originally with "Street Music Co" on left side of label)	5/4
77	Stiff BUY 14	Alison/Welcome To The Working Week (p/s)	5
77	Stiff BUY 14	Alison/Welcome To The Working Week (p/s, A-side mispressed on white vinyl)	20
77	Stiff BUY 15	Red Shoes/Mystery Dance (art sleeve, press-out centre)	4
77	Stiff BUY 15	Red Shoes/Mystery Dance (p/s, mispress, plays "Dream Tobacco" by Max Wall)	6
77	Stiff BUY 20	Watching The Detectives/Blame It On Cain (live)/Mystery Dance (live) ('telephone directory' or other p/s)	5/4
78	Radar ADA 3	(I Don't Want To Go To) Chelsea/You Belong To Me (p/s)	4
78	Radar ADA 10	Pump It Up/Big Tears (p/s)	4
78	Radar ADA 24	Radio Radio/Tiny Steps (p/s)	4
78	Radar RG 1	Talking In The Dark/Wednesday Week (gig freebie)	10
79	Radar ADA 35	Accidents Will Happen/Talking In The Dark/Wednesday Week ('Fish Is Brain Food' p/s or various other designs)	5/4
80	2-Tone CHS TT 7	I Can't Stand Up For Falling Down/Girls Talk(unreleased, later a gig freebie, more common issue has XX1 in run-off groove, 13,000 only)	18/12
80	F-Beat XX 5	NEW AMSTERDAM (EP)	4
80	F-Beat XX 5P	NEW AMSTERDAM (EP, picture disc; a few with black rim)	12/7
80	Stiff GRAB 3	STIFF SINGLES FOUR PACK (BUY 11, 14, 15 & 20 in clear plastic wallet)	18
81	F-Beat XX 17	A Good Year For The Roses/Your Angel Steps Out Of Heaven (withdrawn p/s)	20
85	F-Beat ZB 40085	Green Shirt/Beyond Belief (green vinyl, PVC sleeve)	4
85	F-Beat ZB 40085/7	Green Shirt/Beyond Belief//Oliver's Army/A Good Year For The Roses (double pack)	4
85	F-Beat ZT 40086	Green Shirt/(Extended Mix)/Beyond Belief (12", green vinyl in PVC sleeve)	7
77	Stiff SEEZ 3	MY AIM IS TRUE (LP, with poster, various coloured rear sleeves)	10
78	Radar RAD 3	THIS YEAR'S MODEL (LP, with free single "Stranger In The House"/ "Neat Neat Neat (live)" [die-cut company sleeve, SAM 83], 50,000 only)	10
79	Radar RAD 15	ARMED FORCES (LP, foldout stickered sleeve with free EP "Live At Hollywood High" [p/s, SAM 90] & postcards)	10
80	F-Beat XXC 6	TEN BLOODY MARYS AND TEN HOW'S YOUR FATHERS? (gold cassette in gold case)	12
86	Demon X FIEND CASS 80	BLOOD AND CHOCOLATE (cassette in 'chocolate' packaging, withdrawn)	15

(see also Nick Lowe, George Jones, Coward Brothers)

BILLY COTTON (& HIS ORCHESTRA/BAND)

54	Decca F 10299	Friends And Neighbours/The Kid's Last Fight	7
54	Decca F 10377	This Ole House/Somebody Goofed	8
54	Decca F 10405	Do You Love Old Santa Claus?/When Santa Got Stuck Up The Chimney	5
54	Decca F 10421	When You're Home With The Ones You Love/He's A Real Tough Guy	5
55	Decca F 10459	The Naughty Lady Of Shady Lane/Hearts Of Stone	5
55	Decca F 10491	Ready, Willing And Able/Bambino	5
55	Decca F 10501	Someone Else I'd Like To Be/Where Did The Chickie Lay ...	4
55	Decca F 10524	Play Me Hearts And Flowers/A Present For Bob	4
55	Decca F 10546	Pals/Why Did The Chicken Cross The Road?	4
55	Decca F 10602	Yellow Rose Of Texas/Domani	4
55	Decca F 10630	The Dam Busters March/Bring Your Smile Along	5
55	Decca F 10642	Nuts In May/A-Hunting We Will Go	4
56	Decca F 10664	Ballad Of Davy Crockett/The One Finger Song	5
56	Decca F 10682	Robin Hood/Happy Trails	5
56	Decca F 10702	Lizzie Borden/Little Child	5
56	Decca F 10739	The March Hare/Get Neighbourly	4
56	Decca F 10754	Friends/The Family's Always Around	4
56	Decca F 10767	Reach For The Sky — March/Whatever Will Be, Will Be	4
56	Decca F 10805	Just Walking In The Rain/The Rocking Horse Cowboy	4
56	Decca F 10826	Giant/Yaller Yaller Gold	4
57	Decca F 10841	The Garden Of Eden/You Don't Owe Me A Thing	4

Billy COTTON

MINT VALUE £

57	Decca F 10854	Amore/Commando Patrol	4
57	Decca F 10881	The Amethyst March/Absent Friends	4
67	Philips BF 1551	Thunderbirds Theme/Zero X (as Billy Cotton Orchestra)	10
53	Decca LF 1124	SOLDIERS OF THE QUEEN (10" LP)	10
54	Decca LF 1185	WAKEY, WAKEY! (10" LP)	10
61	Columbia 33SX 1383	WAKEY, WAKEY! (LP, as Billy Cotton Bandshow with Alma Cogan & Russ Conway)	16

(see also Alma Cogan, Russ Conway)

JAMES COTTON (BLUES BAND)
| 78 | Buddah BDS 471 | Rock'n'Roll Music/Help Me | 4 |
| 68 | Vanguard SVRL 19035 | CUT YOU LOOSE! (LP, as James Cotton Blues Band) | 15 |

JIMMY COTTON
| 62 | Columbia SEG 8141 | CHRIS BARBER PRESENTS JIMMY COTTON (EP) | 7 |
| 62 | Columbia SEG 8189 | CHRIS BARBER PRESENTS JIMMY COTTON No. 2 (EP) | 7 |

(see also James Cotton Blues Band)

MIKE COTTON SOUND
63	Columbia DB 7029	Swing That Hammer/Heartaches (as Mike Cotton Jazzmen)	6
63	Columbia DB 7134	Midnite Flyer/One Mint Julep (as Mike Cotton Band)	7
64	Columbia DB 7267	I Don't Wanna Know/This Little Pig	25
64	Columbia DB 7382	Round And Round/Beau Dudley	40
65	Columbia DB 7623	Make Up Your Mind/I've Got My Eye On You	20
66	Polydor BM 56096	Harlem Shuffle/Like That	20
67	Pye 7N 17313	Step Out Of Line/Ain't Love Good, Ain't Love Proud	15
64	Columbia 33SX 1647	MIKE COTTON SOUND (LP)	250

(see also Lucas & Mike Cotton Sound)

JOHN COUGAR
(see under John Cougar Mellencamp)

COUGARS
63	Parlophone R 4989	Saturday Night At The Duckpond/See You In Dreamland	7
63	Parlophone R 5038	Red Square/Fly-By-Nite	7
64	Parlophone R 5115	Caviare And Chips/While The City Sleeps	8
63	Parlophone GEP 8886	SATURDAY NIGHT WITH THE COUGARS (EP)	25

CATHAL COUGHLAN
| 80s | Caff CAFF 1 | I'm, Long Me Measaim/EAST VILLAGE: Freeze Out (no p/s, flexi with fanzines) | 12/10 |

DENIS COULDRY & SMILE
| 68 | Decca F 12734 | James In The Basement/I Am Nearly There | 6 |
| 68 | Decca F 12786 | Penny For The Wind/Tea And Toast, Mr. Watson? | 6 |

COULSON, DEAN, McGUINNESS, FLINT
| 72 | DJM DJLPS 424 | LO AND BEHOLD (LP) | 10 |

(see also Manfred Mann, McGuinness Flint)

PHIL COULTER ORCHESTRA
| 68 | Pye 7N 17511 | Congratulations/Gold Rush | 4 |

(COUNT) BISHOPS
76	Chiswick SW 1	SPEEDBALL (EP)	5
76	Chiswick NS 5	Train Train/Taking It Easy (p/s)	4
77	Chiswick NS 12	Baby You're Wrong/Stay Free (p/s)	4
78	Chiswick NS 33	I Take What I Want/No Lies (p/s, as Bishops)	4
78	Chiswick NS 35	Mr Jones/Human Bean/Route 66/Too Much Too Soon (unissued, as Bishops)	
78	Chiswick NS 37	I Want Candy/See That Woman (p/s, as Bishops)	5
78	Chiswick NS 376	I Want Candy/See That Woman (6", p/s)	6
78	Chiswick NS 3710	I Want Candy/See That Woman (10", p/s)	7
78	Chiswick CHIS 101	I Want Candy/See That Woman (p/s, reissue, as Bishops)	4
78	Chiswick CHIS 1016	I Want Candy/See That Woman (6", p/s, reissue)	5
78	Chiswick CHIS 10110	I Want Candy/See That Woman (10", p/s, reissue)	6
79	Chiswick CHIS 111	Mr Jones/Human Bean/Route 66/Too Much Too Soon (p/s, as Bishops)	4
77	Chiswick WIK 1	THE COUNT BISHOPS (LP)	10
78	Chiswick CH 7	LIVE AT THE ROUNDHOUSE (10" mini-LP)	8

(see also Cannibals)

COUNT DOWNE & ZEROS
| 64 | Ember EMB S 189 | Hello My Angel/Don't Shed A Tear | 25 |

COUNT FIVE
| 66 | Pye Intl. 7N 25393 | Psychotic Reaction/They're Gonna Get You | 15 |

COUNTRY BOY
| 63 | Blue Beat BB 236 | I'm A Lonely Boy (act. by Shenley Duffas)/ EDWARD'S ALLSTARS: He's Gone Ska | 8 |

COUNTRY GAZETTE
| 72 | United Artists UAG 29404 | TRAITOR IN OUR MIDST (LP) | 10 |
| 73 | United Artists UAS 29491 | DON'T GIVE UP YOUR DAY JOB (LP) | 10 |

(see also Flying Burrito Brothers)

COUNTRY GENTLEMEN
| 63 | Decca F 11766 | Greensleeves/Baby Jean | 25 |

(see also High Society)

COUNTRY HAMS
| 74 | EMI EMI 2220 | Walking In The Park With Eloise/Bridge Over The River Suite (p/s, red & brown label) | 35 |
| 82 | EMI EMI 2220 | Walking In The Park With Eloise/Bridge Over The River Suite (p/s, reissue, beige label) | 8 |

(see also Paul McCartney/Wings, Chet Atkins, Floyd Cramer)

COUNTRY JOE & THE FISH

67	Fontana TF 882	Not So Sweet Martha Lorraine/Love	10
69	Vanguard VA 3	Here I Go Again/It's So Nice To Have Love	8
70	Vanguard 6076 250	I Feel Like I'm Fixin' To Die/Maria	8
67	Fontana TFL 6081	ELECTRIC MUSIC FOR THE MIND AND BODY (LP)	25
67	Fontana TFL 6086	I-FEEL-LIKE-I'M-FIXIN'-TO-DIE (LP)	25
68	Vanguard SVRL 19006	TOGETHER (LP)	15
68	Vanguard SVRL 19026	ELECTRIC MUSIC FOR THE MIND AND BODY (LP, reissue)	12
68	Vanguard SVRL 19029	I-FEEL-LIKE-I'M-FIXIN'-TO-DIE (LP, reissue)	12
69	Vanguard SVRL 19048	HERE WE ARE AGAIN (LP)	15
69	Vanguard SVRL 19058	THE BEST OF COUNTRY JOE AND THE FISH (LP)	12
70	Vanguard 6359 002	C.J. FISH (LP)	10
72	Vanguard VSD 79244	ELECTRIC MUSIC FOR THE MIND AND BODY (LP, 2nd reissue)	10
72	Vanguard VSD 79266	I-FEEL-LIKE-I'M-FIXIN'-TO-DIE (LP, 2nd reissue)	10
73	Vanguard VSD 27/28	THE LIFE AND TIMES OF (2-LP, gatefold sleeve, quadrophonic/stereo)	20/16

(see also Country Joe McDonald)

COUNTS

74	Janus 6146 603	(Why Not) Start All Over Again/Thinking Single	4

COUNT SUCKLE

50s	Q 2201	Please Don't Go/Chicken Scratch	6

COUNT VICTORS

62	Coral Q 72456	Peepin' 'N' Hidin'/Don't Laugh At Me ('Cos I'm A Fool)	6
63	Coral Q 72462	Road Runner/Lorie	8

WAYNE COUNTY/ELECTRIC CHAIRS

77	Sweet F.A. WC 1	Fuck Off/On The Crest (p/s)	6
77	Illegal IL 002	Stuck On You/Paranoia Paradise/The Last Time (p/s)	5
77	Illegal IL 005	Thunder When She Walks/What You Got (p/s)	5
77	Safari WC 2	BLATANTLY OFFENSIVE (EP, gold or silver vinyl)	5
78	Safari SAFE 6	I Had Too Much To Dream Last Night/Fuck Off (unissued)	
78	Safari SAFE 7	Eddie And Sheena/Rock And Roll Cleopatra (p/s, some with cartoon insert)	5/4
78	Safari SAFE 9	Trying To Get On The Radio/Evil Minded Momma (p/s)	4
78	Safari SAFE 13	Berlin/Waiting For The Marines (p/s)	4
78	Safari SAFELS 13	Berlin (Long Version)/Waiting For The Marines/Midnight Pal (12", p/s, pink vinyl)	7
79	Safari SAFE 18	So Many Ways/J'Attends Les Marines (p/s)	4
78	Safari LONG 1	ELECTRIC CHAIRS (LP)	10
78	Safari GOOD 1	STORM THE GATES OF HEAVEN (LP, multicoloured vinyl)	10

(see also Mystere Five's)

DIANA COUPLAND

59	HMV POP 690	Love Him/I Am Loved	4

COURIERS

66	Ember EMB S 218	Take Away/Done Me Wrong (some with p/s)	40/25

(see also William E. Kimber)

BILL COURTNEY

59	RCA RCA 1142	Judy Is/Without Her Love	4
59	RCA RCA 1142	Judy Is/Without Her Love (78)	5
60	Columbia DB 4512	Petticoats Fly/Blanket On The Beach	4

DEAN COURTNEY

75	RCA RCA 2534	I'll Always Need You/Tammy	5

COURTSHIPS

75	UK USA 6	Oops It Just Slipped Out/Love Ain't Love	4

COUSIN EMMY & HER KINFOLK

56	Brunswick OE 9258	KENTUCKY MOUNTAIN BALLADS VOL. 1 (EP)	10
56	Brunswick OE 9259	KENTUCKY MOUNTAIN BALLADS VOL. 2 (EP)	10

COUSINS (Belgium)

61	Palette PG 9011	Kili Watch/Feugo	4
61	Palette PG 9017	Bouddha/Kana Kapila	4
62	Palette PG 9035	Anda/Danseuse	4

COUSINS (U.K.)

64	Decca F 11924	Yes Sir That's My Baby/Two Lovely Black Eyes	4

DAVE COUSINS

72	A&M AMS 7032	Going Home/Ways And Means	4
72	A&M AMLS 68118	TWO WEEKS LAST SUMMER (LP)	25
79	Sly SLURP 1	OLD SCHOOL SONGS (LP, with Brian Willoughby)	15

(see also Strawbs)

DON COVAY (& GOODTIMERS)

61	Pye Intl. 7N 25075	Pony Time/Love Boat	8
61	Philips PB 1140	Shake Wid The Shake/Every Which Way	10
62	Cameo Parkway C 239	The Popeye Waddle/One Little Boy Had Money	20
64	Atlantic AT 4006	Mercy, Mercy/Can't Stay Away	7
65	Atlantic AT 4016	Take This Hurt Off Me/Please Don't Let Me Know	7
65	Atlantic AT 4056	See Saw/I Never Get Enough Of Your Love	6
66	Atlantic AT 4078	Sookie Sookie/Watching The Late Late Show	7
66	Atlantic 584 025	You Put Something In Me/Iron Out The Rough Spots	5
66	Atlantic 584 059	See Saw/Somebody's Got To Love You	5
67	Atlantic 584 082	Shingalin' '67/I Was There	6
67	Atlantic 584 094	Sookie Sookie/Mercy Mercy	5
67	Atlantic 584 114	40 Days — 40 Nights/The Usual Place	6
70	Atlantic 2091 018	Everything I Do Goin' Be Funky/Key To The Highway	4
65	Atlantic ATL 5025	MERCY! (LP, plum label)	50

Don COVAY

67	Atlantic 587 062	SEE-SAW (LP)	15
69	Atlantic K 50225	HOUSE OF BLUE LIGHT (LP)	12
73	Mercury 6338 211	SUPERDUDE (LP)	10
75	Mercury 9100 010	HOT BLOOD (LP)	10

DAVID COVERDALE
77	Purple PUR 133	Hole In The Sky/Blind Man (p/s)	6
78	Purple PUR 136	Breakdown/Only My Soul (p/s)	6
90	Epic 6562927	Last Note Of Freedom/HANS ZIMMER: Car Building (poster p/s)	4
77	Purple TPS 3509	DAVID COVERDALE'S WHITESNAKE (LP)	10
78	Purple TPS 3513	NORTHWINDS (LP, with inner sleeve)	10

(see also Whitesnake, Deep Purple, Wizard's Convention, Roger Glover)

JULIAN COVEY & MACHINE
67	Island WIP 6009	A Little Bit Hurt/Sweet Bacon	15

JULIE COVINGTON
70	Columbia DB 8649	The Magic Wasn't There/The Way Things Ought To Be	10
70	Columbia DB 8705	Tonight Your Love Is Over/If I Had My Time Again	10
72	RCA RCA 2181	Day By Day/With Me It Goes Deeper	4
71	Columbia SCX 6466	THE BEAUTIFUL CHANGES (LP)	100

NOEL COWARD
54	Philips PB 2001	Mad Dogs And Englishmen/A Room With A View (78)	5
54	Philips PB 2002	Poor Little Rich Girl/Uncle Harry (78)	5

COWARD BROTHERS
85	Imp IMP 006	The People's Limousine/They'll Never Take Her Love Away From Me (die-cut sl.)	4

(see also Elvis Costello)

COWBOY CHURCH SUNDAY SCHOOL
55	Brunswick 05371	Open Up Your Heart/The Lord Is Counting On You	4
55	Brunswick 05455	Go On By/The Little Black Sheep	4
56	Brunswick 05533	These Bad Bad Kids/A Handful Of Shame	4
56	Brunswick 05598	It Is No Secret/Don't Send Those Kids To Sunday School	4

COWBOY JUNKIES
89	Cooking Vinyl FRUX 011	Blue Moon Revisited (Song For Elvis)/You Will Be Loved Again/Shining Moon/Walking After Midnight (10", fold-out poster p/s)	7

COWBOYS INTERNATIONAL
79	Virgin VS 267	Nothing Doing/2 Millions (p/s with blank clear flexidisc "Many Times")	4

COWSILLS
67	MGM MGM 1353	The Rain, The Park And Other Things/River Blue	4
68	MGM MGM 1383	We Can Fly/A Time For Remembrance	4
68	MGM MGM 1400	In Need Of A Friend/Mr. Flynn	4
68	MGM MGM 1424	Indian Lake/Newspaper Blanket	4
69	MGM MGM 1469	Hair/What Is Happy	4
69	MGM MGM 1484	The Prophecy Of Daniel And John The Divine/Gotta Get Away From It All	4
69	MGM MGM 1490	Love American Style/Silver Threads And Golden Needles	4
71	London HLY 10329	On My Side/There Is A Child	4
67	MGM C(S) 8059	THE COWSILLS (LP)	10
68	MGM CS 8077	WE CAN FLY (LP)	10
68	MGM CS 8095	CAPTAIN SAD AND HIS SHIP OF FOOLS (LP)	10
68	Fontana SFL 13055	THE COWSILLS AND THE LINCOLN PARK ZOO (LP)	10
71	London SH-U 8421	ON MY SIDE (LP)	10

BILLY COX
71	Pye Intl. NSPL 25158	NITRO FUNCTION (LP)	30

(see also Jimi Hendrix)

IDA COX
44	Parlophone R 2832	Last Mile Blues/I Can't Quit That Man (78)	10
45	Parlophone R 2948	Hard Times Blues/ Take Him Off My Mind (78)	12
46	Parlophone R 2974	Four Day Creep/Death Letter Blues (78)	10
40s	Signature 907	Graveyard Dream/Weary Way Blues (78)	10
52	Jazz Collector L 22	Graveyard Dream Blues/Weary Way Blues (78)	5
50s	Jazz Collector	Mama Do Shee Blues/Worried Mama Blues (78)	5
59	Fontana TFE 17136	IDA COX (EP)	10
54	London AL 3517	SINGS THE BLUES (10" LP)	25
60s	Riverside RLP 374	BLUES FOR RAMPART STREET (LP)	20
74	Fountain FB 301	IDA COX VOLUME 1 (LP)	15
75	Fountain FB 304	VOLUME 2: 1923-1924 (LP)	15
75	Gannet GEN 5371-5376	PARAMOUNT RECORDINGS (6-LP set)	40

IDA COX/MA RAINEY
60	Jazz Collector JEL 12	THE FEMALE BLUES (EP)	8

(see also Ma Rainey)

IDA COX/ETHEL WATERS
50s	Poydras 104	IDA COX AND ETHEL WATERS (LP)	30

MICHAEL COX
59	Decca F 11166	Boy Meets Girl/Teenage Love	8
59	Decca F 11166	Boy Meets Girl/Teenage Love (78)	20
59	Decca F 11182	Too Hot To Handle/Serious	8
59	Decca F 11182	Too Hot To Handle/Serious (78)	30
60	Triumph RGM 1011	Angela Jones/Don't Want To Know	10
60	Ember EMB S 103	Angela Jones/Don't Want To Know (reissue)	15
60	HMV POP 789	Along Came Caroline/Lonely Road	10
61	HMV POP 830	Teenage Love/Linda	10
61	HMV POP 905	Sweet Little Sixteen/Cover Girl	10

62	HMV POP 972	Young Only Once/Honey Cause I Love You	10
62	HMV POP 1065	Stand Up/In April	10
63	HMV POP 1137	Don't You Break My Heart/Hark Is That A Cannon I Hear	10
63	HMV POP 1220	Gee What A Party/See That Again	10
64	HMV POP 1293	Rave On/Just Say Hello	12
65	HMV POP 1417	Gypsy/It Ain't Right	10
66	Parlophone R 5436	I Hate Getting Up In The Morning/Love 'Em And Leave 'Em	6
67	Parlophone R 5580	I'll Always Love You/You Never Can Tell (Till You Try)	5

MICK COX
| 73 | Capitol ST 11175 | MICK COX BAND (LP) | 10 |

WALLY COX
| 61 | Vogue V 9175 | I Can't Help It/The Heebie Jeebees | 15 |
| 74 | Pye Disco Demand DDS 105 | This Man/I've Had Enough | 4 |

LOL COXHILL
78	Chiltern Sound CS 100	MURDER IN THE AIR (12" EP)	8
71	Dandelion DSD 8008	EAR OF THE BEHOLDER (2-LP, gatefold sleeve, also listed as 69001)	40
72	Mushroom 150 MR 23	TOVERBAL SWEET (LP)	70
73	Caroline C 1503	COXHILL MILLER (LP, with Stephen Miller)	12
74	Caroline C 1507	THE STORY SO FAR ... OH REALLY? (LP, with Stephen Miller)	12
75	Caroline C 1514	LOL COXHILL & WELFARE STATE (LP)	12
75	Caroline C 1515	FLEAS IN THE CUSTARD (LP)	12
76	Ogun OG 510	DIVERSE (LP)	10
78	Ogun OG 525	THE JOY OF PARANOIA (LP)	10
78	Ictus 0008	MOOT (LP)	10
78	Ictus 0011	LID (LP)	10
79	Random Radar RRR 005	DIGWELL DUETS (LP)	10
80	Pipe PIPE 1	SLOW MUSIC (LP)	10

(see also Kevin Ayers & Whole World)

COXHILL-BEDFORD DUO
| 71 | Polydor 2001 253 | Pretty Little Girl Pts 1 & 2 | 5 |

(see also David Bedford, Lol Coxhill)

KEVIN COYNE
72	Polydor 2001 357	Cheat Me/Flowering Cherry	4
72	Dandelion 2310 228	CASE HISTORY (LP)	45
73	Virgin VD 2501	MARJORY RAZORBLADE (2-LP)	15
74	Virgin V 2012	BLAME IT ON THE NIGHT (LP)	12
75	Virgin V 2033	MATCHING HEAD AND FEET (LP)	12
76	Virgin V 2047	HEARTBURN (LP)	10
82	Butt BUTBOX 1	THE DANDELION YEARS (3-LP boxed set)	20

(see also Clague, Siren)

CRABBY APPLETON
| 70 | Elektra EKS 74067 | CRABBY APPLETON (LP) | 10 |
| 71 | Elektra EKS 74106 | ROTTEN TO THE CORE (LP) | 10 |

(see also Michael Fennelly)

CRACK
| 81 | Bridgehouse BHS 8 | Silly Fellow/Fairy Story (p/s) | 4 |

CRACK
| 82 | RCA RCA 214 | Don't You Ever Let Me Down/I Can't Take It (die-cut 'Battle of the Bands' sleeve) | 6 |
| 83 | RCA CRACK 1 | All Or Nothing/I Caught You Out (p/s) | 4 |

CRACKED MIRROR
| 83 | private pressing | CRACKED MIRROR (LP, 200 only) | 50 |

CRACKERS
| 69 | Fontana TF 995 | Honey Do/It Happens All The Time | 5 |

(see also Merseys)

(BILLY) 'CRASH' CRADDOCK
59	Philips PB 966	Boom Boom Baby/Don't Destroy Me (as 'Crash' Craddock)	15
59	Philips PB 966	Boom Boom Baby/Don't Destroy Me (78)	50
60	Philips PB 1006	Since She Turned Seventeen/I Want That (as 'Crash' Craddock)	20
60	Philips PB 1092	Good Time Billy (Is A Happiness Fool)/Heavenly Love	12
61	Mercury AMT 1146	How Lonely He Must Be/Truly True	10

CRAIG
| 65 | King KG 1022 | Ain't That A Shame/International Blues | 12 |

CRAIG
| 66 | Fontana TF 665 | A Little Bit Of Soap/Ready Steady Let's Go | 35 |
| 66 | Fontana TF 715 | I Must Be Mad/Suspense | 125 |

WENDY CRAIG
| 68 | Philips BF 1704 | Hushabye Mountain/Windows Of The World | 4 |

DON CRAINE'S NEW DOWNLINERS SECT
| 67 | Pye 7N 17261 | I Can't Get Away From You/Roses | 80 |

(see also Downliners Sect)

BEN CRAMER
| 73 | Philips 6000 097 | The Old Street Musicians/Sylvia Come Dance With Me | 4 |

FLOYD CRAMER
54	London HL 8012	Fancy Pants/Five Foot Two Eyes Of Blue	25
54	London HL 8012	Fancy Pants/Five Foot Two Eyes Of Blue (78)	5
54	London HL 8062	Jolly Cholly/Oh! Suzanna	25
54	London HL 8062	Jolly Cholly/Oh! Suzanna (78)	5
55	London HLU 8195	Rag-A-Tag/Aunt Dinah's Quiltin' Party	25

Floyd CRAMER

55	London HLU 8195	Rag-A-Tag/Aunt Dinah's Quiltin' Party (78)	6
58	RCA RCA 1050	Flip Flop And Bop/Sophisticated Swing	20
58	RCA RCA 1050	Flip Flop And Bop/Sophisticated Swing (78)	5
60	RCA RCA 1211	Last Date/Sweetie Baby	6
61	RCA RCA 1231	On The Rebound/Mood Indigo	5
61	RCA RCA 1241	San Antonio Rose/I Can Just Imagine	4
61	RCA RCA 1259	Hang On/Your Last Goodbye	5
62	RCA RCA 1275	Chattanooga Choo Choo/Let's Go	5
62	RCA RCA 1284	Lovesick Blues/First Hurt	5
62	RCA RCA 1301	Hot Pepper/For Those That Cry	4
62	RCA RCA 1311	Swing Low/Losers Weepers	4
55	London REP 1023	PIANO HAYRIDE (EP)	30
63	RCA RCX 7120	THAT HANDSOME PIANO (EP)	12
61	RCA RD 27221/SF 5103	ON THE REBOUND (LP, mono/stereo)	12/15
62	RCA RD 27250/SF 5124	AMERICA'S BIGGEST SELLING PIANIST (LP, mono/stereo)	10/12
62	RCA RD 27260/SF 5130	GETS ORGAN-IZED (LP)	10
62	RCA RD/SF 7518	I REMEMBER HANK WILLIAMS (LP)	10
63	RCA RD/SF 7540	SWING ALONG WITH FLOYD CRAMER (LP)	10
63	RCA RD/SF 7575	COMING ON (LP)	10
64	RCA RD/SF 7622	COUNTRY PIANO — CITY STRINGS (LP)	10
64	RCA RD/SF 7646	AT THE CONSOLE (LP)	12
65	RCA RD 7665	THE BEST OF FLOYD CRAMER (LP)	12
65	RCA RD/SF 7748	CLASS OF '65 (LP)	10

(see also Country Hams)

CRAMP

78	Rip Off RIP 7	She Doesn't Love Me/Suzy Lie Down (p/s)	4

CRAMPS

79	Illegal ILS 12013	GRAVEST HITS (12" EP, black vinyl, later on blue vinyl)	10/15
80	Illegal ILS 0017	Fever/Garbage Man (withdrawn 1st 'full band' p/s; re-pressed in different p/s with 4 separate shots)	15/10
80	Illegal ILS 021	Drug Train/Love Me/I Can't Hardly Stand It (p/s)	12
81	IRS PFS 1003	Goo Goo Muck/She Said (p/s, yellow vinyl)	10
81	IRS PFSX 1008	The Crusher/Save It/New Kind Of Kick (12", p/s)	15
85	Big Beat NS 110	Can Your Pussy Do The Dog?/Blue Moon Baby (p/s, orange see-through vinyl)	5
83	Illegal ILP 012	OFF THE BONE (LP, with 3-D sleeve & glasses)	10
83	Illegal ILP 012	OFF THE BONE (LP, picture disc with extra track)	10
84	Big Beat NED 6	THE SMELL OF FEMALE (LP, red see-through vinyl)	10
84	Big Beat BEDP 6	THE SMELL OF FEMALE (LP, picture disc)	12
86	Big Beat WIKA 46	A DATE WITH ELVIS (LP, blue vinyl)	10

TONY CRANE

67	Pye 7N 17337	Anonymous Mr Brown/In This World	4
68	Pye 7N 17517	Scratchin' Ma Head/Patterns In The Sky	4

(see also Merseybeats)

VINCENT CRANE & CHRIS FARLOWE

72	Dawn DNS 1034	Can't Find A Reason/Moods	6

(see also Atomic Rooster, Chris Farlowe)

CRANE RIVER JAZZ BAND

51	Delta D 5	Kentucky Home/Moose March (78)	7
51	Delta D 6	If I Ever Cease To Love/Gipsy Lament (78)	7
51	Esquire 12-013	Eh La Bas!/CHRIS BARBER'S JAZZ BAND: Oh, Didn't He Ramble (78)	7
51	Melodisc 1027	Eh, La-Bas/Just A Closer Walk With Thee (78)	7
51	Melodisc 1030	Dauphin St. Blues/Just A Little While To Stay Here (78)	7
51	Parlophone R 3427	I'm Travelling/(Saints Jazz Band track) (78)	7
51	Melodisc 1165	Down By The River/Blanche Touquatouz (78)	7
52	Melodisc 1202	Sheik Of Araby/Sobbin' Blues (78)	6
53	Parlophone MSP 6008	Lily Of The Valley/Till We Meet Again	4

CRANES

87	Biteback	FUSE (cassette LP)	25

CRANES SKIFFLE GROUP

57	Embassy WB 223	The Banana Boat Song/Don't You Rock Me Daddy-O (78)	5
57	Embassy WB 238	Freight Train/Cumberland Gap (78)	6

(see also Chas McDevitt Skiffle Group)

CRASH

86	Remorse LOST 2	Don't Look Now (Now!)/International Velvet/Don't Look Now (Acoustic) (12", p/s)	8
86	Remorse LOST 4	Almost/My Machine/On And On (Version) (12", p/s)	8
87	Remorse REMLP 2	I FEEL FINE (LP)	10

(see also Ultra Vivid Scene)

CRASHERS

69	Amalgamated AMG 834	Hurry Come Up/Off Track	6

CRASS

78	Small Wonder WEENY 2	THE FEEDING OF THE 5000 (12" EP, with 4-page insert & poster)	10
78	Crass 621984	THE FEEDING OF THE 5000 (12" EP, reissue in different sleeve)	7
79	Crass 521984/1	Reality Asylum/Shaved Women (brown cardboard gatefold p/s; later white newspaper fold-out sleeve)	6/4
80	Crass/Xntrix 421984/1	Bloody Revolutions/POISON GIRLS: Persons Unknown (foldout p/s)	4
80	Crass 421984/5	Nagasaki Nightmare/Big A Little A (foldout p/s, some with patch)	6/4
81	Crass 421984/6	Rival Tribal Rebel Revel/Bully Boys Go Out Fighting (flexidisc with 'Toxic Graffiti' fanzine)	6/4
81	Crass 421984/6	Rival Tribal Rebel Revel/Bully Boys Go Out Fighting (p/s)	25
82	Crass 121984/4	Who Dunnit? Parts 1 & 2 (p/s, brown vinyl; some on black vinyl)	4/5
82	Crass 221984/6	How Does It Feel (To Be The Mother Of 1000 Dead?)/The Immortal Death/Don't Tell Me You Care (foldout p/s)	4

83	Crass 121984/3	Sheep Farming In The Falklands/Gotcha! (live) (foldout p/s with lyric insert)	4
80s	no label listed	Gotcha! (clear flexidisc)	4

(see also Joy De Vivre, Eve Libertene, Poison Girls)

CRAVATS
78	The Cravats CH 004	Gordon/Situations (p/s)	6
79	Small Wonder SMALL 15	The End/Burning Bridges/I Hate The Universe (p/s)	4
80	Small Wonder SMALL 24	Precinct/Who's In Here With Me? (p/s, some with free flexidisc)	7/4
80	Small Wonder SMALL 25	You're Driving Me Mad/I Am The Dregs (p/s)	4
81	Small Wonder SMALL 26	Off The Beach/And The Sun Shone On (p/s)	4
85	Reflex 12 RE 10	THE LAND OF THE GIANTS (12" EP)	8
80	Small Wonder CRAVAT 1	THE CRAVATS IN TOYTOWN (LP)	12

(see also Very Things)

CAROLYN CRAWFORD
65	Stateside SS 384	When Someone's Good To You/My Heart	100

JIMMY CRAWFORD
60	Columbia DB 4525	Unkind/Long Stringy Baby	20
61	Columbia DB 4633	Love Or Money/Does My Heartache Show	5
61	Columbia DB 4717	I Love How You Love Me/Our Last Embrace	4
62	Columbia DB 4841	I Shoulda Listened To Mama/A Boy Without A Girl	4

JOHNNY CRAWFORD
62	Pye International 7N 25145	Cindy's Birthday/Patti Ann	4
62	London HL 9605	Your Nose Is Gonna Grow/Something Special	4
62	London HL 9638	Rumors/No One Really Loves A Clown	4
63	London HL 9669	Proud/Lonesome Town	4
64	London HL 9836	Judy Loves Me/Living In The Past	4
62	London RE 1343	JOHNNY CRAWFORD (EP)	15
64	London RE 1416	WHEN I FALL IN LOVE (EP)	12
63	London HA 8060	RUMORS (LP)	20
64	London HA 8197	JOHNNY CRAWFORD — HIS GREATEST HITS (LP)	18

ROSETTA CRAWFORD
24	Parlophone E 5234	Down On The Levee Blues/Lonesome Woman's Blues (78)	40
40s	Vocalion S 240	Stop It Joe/My Man Jumped Salty On Me (78)	20
44	Vocalion S 247	I'm Tired Of Fattenin' Frogs For Snakes/Double Crossin' Papa (78)	20
51	Vocalion V 1002	Stip It Joe/My Man Jumped Salty On Me (78)	10

CRAWFORD BROTHERS
57	Vogue V 9077	Midnight Mover Groover/Midnight Happenings	60
57	Vogue V 9077	Midnight Mover Groover/Midnight Happenings (78)	25
59	Vogue V 9140	It Feels Good/I Ain't Guilty	70
59	Vogue V 9140	It Feels Good/I Ain't Guilty (78)	35

CRAWLER
77	Epic EPC 82083	CRAWLER (LP)	10
78	Epic EPC 82965	SNAKE RATTLE AND ROLL (LP)	10

CRAWLING CHAOS
80	Factory FAC 17	Sex Machine/Berlin (p/s)	5

CRAYS
65	Polydor BM 56033	Nancy's Minuet/Don't Pity Me	4

PEE WEE CRAYTON
78	Vanguard VSD 6566	THINGS I USED TO DO (LP)	12

CRAZE
79	Cobra COB 3	Motions/Spartans (p/s)	6
80	Harvest HAR 5200	Motions/Spartans (reissue in different p/s)	5
80	Harvest HAR 5205	Lucy/Stop Living In The Past (p/s)	6

(see also Skunks, Hard Corps)

CRAZY ELEPHANT
69	Major Minor MM 609	Gimme Gimme Good Lovin'/Dark Part Of My Mind	4
70	Major Minor MM 672	Space Buggy/There's A Better Day Coming	4
69	Major Minor SMLP 62	CRAZY ELEPHANT (LP)	15

CRAZY FEELINGS
67	Polydor NH 56723	Please Lie/Time Is Running Out	4

CRAZYHEAD
87	Antar ANT 4504	Buy A Gun (live)/Buy A Gun (p/s, numbered gig freebie, 500 only)	6

CRAZY HORSE
71	Reprise RS 23503	Dance Dance Dance/Look At All The Things	4
72	Reprise K 14159	All Alone Now/One Thing I Love	4
73	Epic EPC 1121	We Ride/Outside Looking In	4
71	Reprise RSLP 8438	CRAZY HORSE (LP)	10
72	Reprise K 44171	LOOSE (LP)	10
73	Epic EPC 65223	AT CROOKED CREEK (LP)	10

(see also Neil Young, Nils Lofgren)

CRAZY ROCKERS
64	King KG 1001	Third Man Theme/Mama Papa	4

PAPA JOHN CREACH
71	Grunt FTR 1003	PAPA JOHN CREACH (LP)	10

(see also Jefferson Airplane)

CREAM
66	Reaction 591 007	Wrapping Paper/Cat's Squirrel	6

CREAM

66	Reaction 591 011	I Feel Free/N.S.U. 5
67	Reaction 591 015	Strange Brew/Tales Of Brave Ulysses 6
68	Polydor 56258	Anyone For Tennis/Pressed Rat And Warthog 6
68	Polydor 56288	Sunshine Of Your Love/SWLABR 5
68	Polydor 56300	White Room/Those Were The Days 5
69	Polydor 56315	Badge/What A Bringdown 4
71	Polydor 2058 120	Wrapping Paper/I Feel Free 4
72	Polydor 2058 285	Badge/What A Bringdown 4
66	Reaction 593/594 001	FRESH CREAM (LP, mono/stereo) 18/15
67	Reaction 593/594 003	DISRAELI GEARS (LP, mono/stereo) 18/15
67	Reaction 593/594 003	DISRAELI GEARS (LP, later pressing) 15/12

(sleeve originally laminated front & back, cat. no. rear top left; later laminated front only & cat. no. in white box rear top right)

68	Polydor 582/583 031/2	WHEELS OF FIRE (2-LP, gatefold sleeve, mono/stereo; set no. 2612 001) 20/15
68	Polydor 582/583 033	WHEELS OF FIRE — IN THE STUDIO (LP, mono/stereo) 12/10
68	Polydor 582/583 040	WHEELS OF FIRE — LIVE AT THE FILLMORE (LP, mono/stereo) 12/10
69	Polydor 583 053	GOODBYE (LP, gatefold sleeve) 10
71	Polydor 2855 002	CREAM ON TOP (LP, mail-order only) 20

(see also Eric Clapton, Jack Bruce, Ginger Baker, Blind Faith)

CREAMERS
| 89 | Fierce FRIGHT 045 | Sunday Head/Think I'm Gonna Be Sick (p/s) .... 10 |

CREATION
66	Planet PLF 116	Making Time/Try And Stop Me 15
66	Planet PLF 119	Painter Man/Biff Bang Pow 15
67	Polydor 56177	If I Stay Too Long/Nightmares 20
67	Polydor 56207	Through My Eyes/Life Is Just Beginning 25
68	Polydor 56230	How Does It Feel To Feel/Tom Tom 20
68	Polydor 56246	Midway Down/The Girls Are Naked 20
73	Charisma CB 213	Making Time/Painter Man 6
77	Raw RAW 4	Making Time/Painter Man (reissue, p/s) 5
84	Edsel E 5006	Making Time/Uncle Bert (p/s) 4
73	Charisma CS 8	CREATION '66-67 (LP) 30

(see also Mark Four, Kenny Pickett, Birds, Ashton Gardner & Dyke, Kennedy Express)

CREATION
| 72 | Stateside SS 2205 | I Got The Fever/Soul Control .... 6 |

(see also Prophets)

CREATIONS
| 67 | Rio R 133 | Meet Me At Eight/Searching .... 8 |
| 68 | Amalgamated AMG 818 | Holding Out/Get On Up .... 7 |

CREATIVE SOURCE
74	Sussex SXX 1	Who Is He And What Is He To You/Who Is He And What Is He To You (Version) ..4
76	Polydor 6006 680	Don't Be Afraid (Take My Love)/Pass The Feelings On 4
74	Sussex LPSX 6	CREATIVE SOURCE (LP) 12
74	Sussex LPSX 7	MIGRATION (LP) 10
76	Polydor 2391 196	PASS THE FEELIN' ON (LP) 10

CREATOR & NORMA
| 63 | Island WI 105 | We Will Be Lovers/Come On Pretty Baby .... 8 |

CREATURES
66	CBS 202048	Turn Out The Light/It Must Be Love 6
66	CBS 202350	String Along/Night Is Warm 6
67	CBS 2666	Looking At Tomorrow/Someone Needs You 6

(see also Horslips)

CREATURES
81	Polydor POSPG 354	WILD THINGS (double pack EP, gatefold p/s; picture labels) 8
81	Polydor POSPD 354	WILD THINGS (double pack EP, single p/s; picture or plastic labels) 8
83	Wonderland SHE 1	Miss The Girl/Hot Spring In The Snow (p/s) 4
83	Wonderland SHE 2	Right Now/Weathercade (gatefold or single p/s) 7/4
83	Wonderland SHEX 2	Right Now/Weathercade/Festival Of Colours/Dancing On Glass (12", p/s) 7

(see also Siouxsie & Banshees)

CREEDENCE CLEARWATER REVIVAL
69	Liberty LBF 15223	Proud Mary/I Put A Spell On You (withdrawn) 20
69	Liberty LBF 15223	Proud Mary/Born On The Bayou 4
69	Liberty LBF 15230	Bad Moon Rising/Lodi 4
69	Liberty LBF 15250	Green River/Commotion 4
70	Liberty LBF 15283	Down On The Corner/Fortunate Son 4
70	Liberty LBF 15310	Travellin' Band/Who'll Stop The Rain 4
70	Liberty LBF 15354	Up Around The Bend/Run Through The Jungle (initially in p/s) 8/4
70	Liberty LBF 15384	Long As I Can See The Light/Lookin' Out My Back Door (initially in p/s) 8/4
71	Liberty LBF 15440	Have You Ever Seen Rain/Hey Tonight 4
71	United Artists UP 35210	Hey Tonight/Have You Ever Seen The Rain 6
71	United Artists UP 35261	Sweet Hitch-Hiker/Door To Door 5
73	Fantasy FTC 101	Born On The Bayou/I Put A Spell On You 4
73	Fantasy FTC 104	It Came Out Of The Sky/Side O' The Road 4
78	Fantasy FTC 164	Who'll Stop The Rain/Proud Mary/Hey Tonight (p/s) 4
79	Fantasy FTC 178	I Heard It Through The Grapevine/Rockin' All Over The World (p/s) 4
79	Fantasy 12 FTC 178	I Heard It Through The Grapevine/Keep On Chooglin' (Full Length) (12") 7
69	Liberty LBS 83259	CREEDENCE CLEARWATER REVIVAL (LP) 12
69	Liberty LBS 83261	BAYOU COUNTRY (LP) 12
69	Liberty LBS 83273	GREEN RIVER (LP) 12
70	Liberty LBS 83338	WILLIE AND THE POORBOYS (LP) 10
70	Liberty LBS 83388	COSMO'S FACTORY (LP) 10
70	Liberty LBG 83400	PENDULUM (LP) 10

MINT VALUE £

72	Fantasy FAN 9404	MARDI GRAS (LP)	12
73	Fantasy FT 506	CREEDENCE CLEARWATER REVIVAL (LP)	10

(see also John Fogerty, Golliwogs, Blue Ridge Rangers)

CREEPERS
66	Blue Beat BB 366	Beat Of My Soul/LLOYD ADAMS: I Wish Your Picture Was You	8

CREEPY JOHN THOMAS
69	RCA RCA 1912	Ride A Rainbow/Moon And Eyes Song	8
69	RCA SF 8061	CREEPY JOHN THOMAS (LP)	55

(see also Paul Kossoff)

CREME CARAMEL
69	Pye International 7N 25495	My Idea/Excursion	4

CRESCENDOS
58	London HLU 8563	Oh Julie/My Little Girl	40
58	London HLU 8563	Oh Julie/My Little Girl (78)	15

CRESCENTS
58	Columbia DB 4093	Wrong/Baby, Baby, Baby	35
58	Columbia DB 4093	Wrong/Baby, Baby, Baby (78)	10

CRESCENTS
64	London HLN 9851	Pink Dominos/Breakout	8

CRESSIDA
70	Vertigo VO 7	CRESSIDA (LP, gatefold sleeve, spiral label)	50
71	Vertigo 6360 025	ASYLUM (LP, gatefold sleeve, spiral label)	85

CRESTAS
65	Fontana TF 551	To Be Loved/When I Fall In Love	15

CRESTERS
64	HMV POP 1249	I Just Don't Understand/I Want You	4
64	HMV POP 1296	Put Your Arms Around Me/Do It With Me	4

CRESTS
59	London HL 8794	16 Candles/Beside You	35
59	London HL 8794	16 Candles/Beside You (78)	20
59	Top Rank JAR 150	Flower Of Love/Molly Mae	10
59	Top Rank JAR 150	Flower Of Love/Molly Mae (78)	30
59	Top Rank JAR 168	Six Nights A Week/I Do	15
59	Top Rank JAR 168	Six Nights A Week/I Do (78)	30
59	London HL 8954	The Angels Listened In/I Thank The Moon	30
59	London HL 8954	The Angels Listened In/I Thank The Moon (78)	40
60	Top Rank JAR 302	A Year Ago Tonight/Paper Crown	15
60	Top Rank JAR 372	Step By Step/Gee (But I'd Give The World)	15
60	HMV POP 768	Always You/Trouble In Paradise	15
60	HMV POP 808	Isn't It Amazing/Molly Mae	10
61	HMV POP 848	Model Girl/We've Got To Tell Them	10
62	HMV POP 976	Little Miracles/Baby I Gotta Know	10
63	London HLU 9671	Guilty/Number One With Me	10

(see also Johnny Maestro)

CREW
69	Plexium PXM 12	Marty/Danger Signs	4

CREW-CUTS
53	Mercury MB 3135	Crazy 'Bout You Baby/Angela Mia (78)	5
54	Mercury MB 3140	Sh-Boom/I Spoke Too Soon (78)	5
54	Mercury MB 3159	Oop-Shoop/Do Me Good, Baby (78)	5
54	Mercury MB 3177	Barking Dog/All I Wanna Do (78)	5
55	Mercury MB 3202	Earth Angel/Ko Ko Mo (78)	5
55	Mercury MB 3222	Unchained Melody/Two Hearts, Two Kisses (78)	5
55	Mercury MB 3228	Don't Be Angry/Chop Chop Boom (78)	5
56	Mercury MT 100	Angels In The Sky/Seven Days (78)	5
56	Mercury 7MT 2	Angels In The Sky/Seven Days (export issue)	15
56	Mercury MT 108	A Story Untold/Honey Hair, Sugar Lips, Eyes Of Blue (78)	5
56	Mercury MT 127	Rebel In Town/Bei Mir Bist Du Shoen (78)	5
57	Mercury MT 140	Young Love/Little By Little (78)	5
57	Mercury MT 161	Susie-Q/Such A Shame (78)	10
57	Mercury MT 178	I Sit In My Window/Hey, You Face (78)	5
58	RCA RCA 1075	Hey, Stella! (Who Zat Down Your ...)/Forever, My Darling	30
58	RCA RCA 1075	Hey, Stella! (Who Zat Down Your ...)/Forever, My Darling (78)	20
56	Mercury MEP 9002	PRESENTING THE CREW-CUTS (EP)	35
56	Mercury MPT 7501	THE CREW-CUTS ON PARADE (LP)	50

BOB CREWE (GENERATION)
60	London HLI 9077	Water Boy/Voglio Cantare (solo)	4
64	Stateside SS 356	Maggie Maggie May/We Almost Made It	6
67	Stateside SS 582	Music To Watch Girls By/Girls On The Rocks	4
67	Stateside SS 2032	You Only Live Twice/A Lover's Concerto	4
68	Stateside S(S)L 10260	BARBARELLA (LP, soundtrack)	15

CREWSY FIXERS
80s	Big Mix ACE 22	CAST IRON ARM (EP, gatefold p/s)	4

BERNARD CRIBBINS
60	Parlophone R 4712	Folk Song/My Kind Of Someone (B-side with Joyce Blair)	4
62	Parlophone R 4869	The Hole In The Ground/Winkle Picker Shoes	4
62	Parlophone R 4923	Right Said Fred/Quietly Bonkers	4
62	Parlophone R 4961	Gossip Calypso/One Man Band	4

Bernard CRIBBINS

| 67 | Parlophone R 5603 | When I'm Sixty-Four/Oh My Word .... | 4 |
| 62 | Parlophone PMC 1186 | A COMBINATION OF CRIBBINS (LP) .... | 10 |

CRICKETS featuring Buddy Holly

57	Vogue Coral Q 72279	That'll Be The Day/I'm Lookin' For Someone To Love	15
57	Vogue Coral Q 72279	That'll Be The Day/I'm Lookin' For Someone To Love (78)	10
58	Coral Q 72279	That'll Be The Day/I'm Lookin' For Someone To Love (2nd issue)	12
58	Coral Q 72279	That'll Be The Day/I'm Lookin' For Someone To Love (78)	10
57	Coral Q 72298	Oh Boy!/Not Fade Away	12
57	Coral Q 72298	Oh Boy!/Not Fade Away (78)	10
58	Coral Q 72307	Maybe Baby/Tell Me How	12
58	Coral Q 72307	Maybe Baby/Tell Me How (78)	10
58	Coral Q 72329	Think It Over/Fool's Paradise	12
58	Coral Q 72329	Think It Over/Fool's Paradise (78)	15
58	Coral Q 72343	It's So Easy/Lonesome Tears	10
58	Coral Q 72343	It's So Easy/Lonesome Tears (78)	20

(all the above 45s originally came with triangular centres; round centre reissues are worth £6-£8)

68	MCA MU 1017	Oh, Boy/That'll Be The Day	4
68	Decca AD 1012	Oh, Boy/That'll Be The Day (export issue)	12
81	PBF 0005	That'll Be The Day (1-sided flexidisc, free from	
		7UP DJ Rock'n'Roll Show)	4
58	Coral FEP 2003	THE CRICKETS (EP)	25
59	Coral FEP 2014	IT'S SO EASY (EP)	25
60	Coral FEP 2060	FOUR MORE BY THE CRICKETS (EP)	25
60	Coral FEP 2062	THAT'LL BE THE DAY (EP)	25
58	Vogue Coral LVA 9081	THE CHIRPING CRICKETS (LP)	50
58	Coral LVA 9081	THE CHIRPING CRICKETS (LP, 2nd issue)	35

(see also Buddy Holly)

CRICKETS

59	Coral Q 72365	Love's Made A Fool Of You/Someone, Someone	8
59	Coral Q 72365	Love's Made A Fool Of You/Someone, Someone (78)	30
59	Coral Q 72382	When You Ask About Love/Deborah	8
59	Coral Q 72382	When You Ask About Love/Deborah (78)	35
60	Coral Q 72395	More Than I Can Say/Baby My Heart	7
60	Coral Q 72395	More Than I Can Say/Baby My Heart (78)	40
61	Coral Q 72417	Peggy Sue Got Married/Don'tcha Know	8
61	Coral Q 72440	I Fought The Law/A Sweet Love	8
61	London HLG 9486	He's Old Enough To Know Better/I'm Feeling Better	8
62	Liberty LIB 55441	Don't Ever Change/I Am Not A Bad Guy	4
62	Liberty LIB 55495	Little Hollywood Girl/Parisian Girl	8
63	Liberty LIB 10067	My Little Girl/Teardrops Fall Like Rain	5
63	Liberty LIB 10092	Don't Try To Change Me/Lost And Alone	6
63	Liberty LIB 10113	Right Or Wrong/You Can't Be In Between	5
64	Liberty LIB 10145	Lonely Avenue/Playboy	5
64	Liberty LIB 55696	(They Call Her) La Bamba/All Over You	6
64	Liberty LIB 10174	I Think I've Caught The Blues/We Gotta Get Together	6
65	Liberty LIB 10196	Now Hear This/Everybody's Got A Little Problem	5
66	Liberty LIB 55603	April Avenue/Don't Say You Love Me	6
68	Liberty LBF 15089	My Little Girl/Lonely Avenue	4
72	United Artists UP 35457	Don't Ever Change/Playboy	4
73	Philips 6006 269	My Rockin' Days/Lovesick Blues	4
73	Philips 6006 294	Wasn't It Nice In New York City/Hayride	5
74	Mercury 6008 006	Ooh Las Vegas/Rhyme And Time	5
60	Coral FEP 2053	THE CRICKETS (EP)	25
61	Coral FEP 2064	THE CRICKETS DON'T EVER CHANGE (EP)	15
63	Liberty (S)LEP 2094	STRAIGHT NO STRINGS (EP, mono/stereo)	15/20
64	Liberty LEP 2173	COME ON (EP)	14
61	Coral LVA 9142	IN STYLE WITH THE CRICKETS (LP)	30
62	Liberty (S)LBY 1120	SOMETHING OLD, SOMETHING NEW, SOMETHING BLUE,	
		SOMETHING ELSE! (LP, mono/stereo)	16/20
65	Liberty LBY 1258	THE CRICKETS — A COLLECTION (LP)	20
71	CBS 64301	ROCKIN' FIFTIES, ROCK 'N' ROLL (LP)	10
73	Philips 6308 149	BUBBLEGUM, POP, BALLADS & BOOGIES (LP)	10
74	Mercury 6310 007	A LONG WAY FROM LUBBOCK (LP)	12

(see also Buddy Holly & Crickets, Jerry Allison & Crickets, Ivan, Sonny Curtis)

CRICKETS & BOBBY VEE

63	Liberty LEP 2084	JUST FOR FUN (EP)	15
63	Liberty (S)LEP 2116	BOBBY VEE MEETS THE CRICKETS (EP, mono/stereo)	18/25
63	Liberty LEP 2149	BOBBY VEE MEETS THE CRICKETS VOL. 2 (EP)	18
63	Liberty (S)LBY 1086	BOBBY VEE MEETS THE CRICKETS (LP, mono/stereo)	15/18

(see also Bobby Vee)

CRIMINAL CLASS

| 82 | Inferno HELL 7 | Fight The System/Soldier (p/s) .... | 4 |

CRIMSON BRIDGE

| 72 | Myrrh MST 6503 | CRIMSON BRIDGE (LP) .... | 22 |

CRISIS

79	Peckham Action NOTH 1	No Town Hall (Southwark)/Holocaust/P.C. One Nine Eight Four (p/s)	12
79	Ardkor CRI 002	UK '79/White Youth (p/s)	8
80	Ardkor CRI 003	HYMNS OF FAITH (12" EP)	15
81	Ardkor CRI 004	Alienation/Brückwood/Hospital (p/s, with insert)	10
82	Crisis NOTH 1/CRI 002	HOLOCAUST UK (12" EP)	12

(see also Death In June, Current 93)

CRISIS

| 70s | private pressing | ANOTHER FINE MESS (LP) .... | 60 |

CRISPY AMBULANCE
79	Aural Assault AAR 001	From The Cradle To The Grave/4 Minutes From The Frontline (glossy or matt p/s) 10/8
81	Factory FAC 32	Unsightly And Serene: Not What I Expected/Deaf (10", p/s) 6
83	CBST 7	BLUE & YELLOW OF THE YACHT CLUB (cassette) 8
83	CBST 8	OPEN GATES OF FIRE (cassette) 8
89	Temps Moderne LTMV:X	FIN (LP) 12

(see also Ram Ram Kino)

GARY CRISS
| 62 | Stateside SS 104 | Our Favourite Melodies/Welcome Home To My Heart .....4 |

PETER CRISS
| 79 | Casablanca CAN 139 | You Matter To Me/Hooked On Rock And Roll (p/s, green vinyl with mask) .....20 |

(see also Kiss)

LINDA CRISTAL
| 59 | Coral Q 72350 | A Perfect Romance/It's Better In Spanish .....4 |

CRISTINA
| 80 | Island/Ze WIP 6560 | Is That All There Is/Jungle Love (withdrawn) .....6 |
| 80 | Island/Ze WIP 6560T | Is That All There Is/Jungle Love (12", withdrawn) .....10 |

BOBBY CRISTO & REBELS
| 64 | Decca F 11913 | The Other Side Of the Track/I've Got You Out Of My Mind .....20 |

MARY CRISTY
| 76 | Polydor 2056 513 | Thank You For Rushing Into My Life/We Can't Hide This Time .....10 |

CRITICS & NYAH SHUFFLE
| 70s | Joe JRS 1 | Behold/SEXY FRANKIE: Tea, Patty, Sex And Ganja .....6 |

CRITTERS
66	London HLR 10047	Younger Girl/Gone For Awhile 5
66	London HLR 10071	Mr. Dieingly Sad/It Just Won't Be That Way 5
66	London HLR 10101	Bad Misunderstanding/Forever Or No More 5
67	London HLR 10119	Marryin' Kind Of Love/New York Bound 4
67	London HLR 10149	Don't Let The Rain Fall Down On Me/Walk Like A Man Again 4
66	London HA-R 8302	THE CRITTERS (LP) 12

JIM CROCE
| 71 | Vertigo 6360 700 | YOU DON'T MESS AROUND WITH JIM (LP, gatefold sleeve, spiral label) .....12 |

CROCHETED DOUGHNUT RING
67	Polydor 56204	Two Little Ladies (Azalea And Rhododendron)/Nice 25
67	Deram DM 169	Havana Anna/Happy Castle 25
68	Deram DM 180	Maxine's Parlour/Get Out Your Rock And Roll Shoes 15

(see also Doughnut Ring)

CROCODILE RIDE
| 80s | Thunderball Surfacer 002 | Ex-Hipster/Satellite/14 ICED BEARS: Falling Backwards/World I Love (Speed Mix) (1,000 only, numbered & stickered mailer) .....8 |

TONY CROMBIE
54	Decca F 10424	Stop It All/All Of Me (& His Orchestra) 8
55	Decca F 10454	Perdido/Love You Madly (& His Orchestra) 12
55	Decca F 10547	Early One Morning/Flying Home (& His Orchestra) 8
55	Decca F 10592	Flying Hickory/String Of Pearls (& His Orchestra) 10
55	Decca F 10637	I Want You To Be My Baby (with Annie Ross)/Three Little Words 10
56	Columbia DB 3822	Teach You To Rock/Short'nin' Bread Rock (as Tony Crombie & Rockets) 25
56	Columbia DB 3822	Teach You To Rock/Short'nin' Bread Rock (78) 5
56	Columbia DB 3859	Sham Rock/Let's You And I Rock (as Tony Crombie & Rockets) 22
56	Columbia DB 3859	Sham Rock/Let's You And I Rock (78) 5
57	Columbia DB 3880	Rock, Rock, Rock/The Big Beat (78, as Tony Crombie & Rockets) 12
57	Columbia DB 3881	Lonesome Train (On A Lonesome Track)/We're Gonna Rock Tonight (78, as Tony Crombie & Rockets) 12
57	Columbia DB 3921	London Rock/Brighton Rock (as Tony Crombie & Rockets) 20
57	Columbia DB 3921	London Rock/Brighton Rock (78) 10
57	Columbia DB 4000	Sweet Beat/Sweet Georgia Brown (as Tony Crombie & His Sweet Beat) 10
57	Columbia DB 4000	Sweet Beat/Sweet Georgia Brown (78) 5
58	Columbia DB 4076	Dumplin's/Tw'on Special 8
58	Columbia DB 4145	Unguaua/Piakukaungcung (as Tony Crombie Men) 7
58	Columbia DB 4189	Rock-Cha-Cha/The Gigglin' Gurgleburp (as Tony Crombie Men) 6
59	Columbia DB 4253	Champagne Cha-Cha/Shepherd's Cha Cha (as Tony Crombie Men) 4
59	Top Rank JAR 182	"Man From Interpol" Theme/Interpol Cha Cha Cha & Chase 4
62	Ember JBS 706	Gutbucket/Just Like Old Times 6
56	Decca DFE 6247	PRESENTING TONY CROMBIE NO. 1 (EP) 7
56	Decca DFE 6281	PRESENTING TONY CROMBIE NO. 2 (EP) 7
57	Columbia SEG 7676	ROCK ROCK ROCK (EP) 30
57	Columbia SEG 7686	LET'S YOU AND I ROCK (EP) 30
61	Decca DFE 6670	FOUR FAVOURITE FILM THEMES (EP) 7
57	Columbia 33S 1108	ROCKIN' WITH TONY CROMBIE & ROCKETS (10" LP) 100
59	Top Rank 35/043	MAN FROM INTERPOL (LP, TV series music, by Tony Crombie & Band) 20
60	Top Rank BUY 027	DRUMS! DRUMS! DRUMS! (LP, as Tony Crombie & His Band) 18
61	Decca SKL 4114	SWEET WIDE AND BLUE (LP) 18
61	Decca LK 4385	TWELVE FAVOURITE FILM THEMES (LP, also stereo SKL 4127) 15

(see also Annie Ross, Ray Ellington)

BILL CROMPTON
| 58 | Fontana H 152 | A Hoot An' A Holler/The Popocatepetl Beetle .....6 |

Bill CROMPTON

59   Fontana H 178   Out Of Sight, Out Of Mind/My Lover 5

CROMWELL
75   WELL 1   AT THE GALLOP (LP, private pressing) 200
(see also Establishment)

LINK CROMWELL
66   London HLB 10040   Crazy Like A Fox/Shock Me 10
(see also Patti Smith Group)

CROOKED OAK
76   private pressing   FROM LITTLE ACORNS (LP) 40

CROOKS
79   Blue Print BLU 2002   Modern Boys/The Beat Goes On (p/s) 6
80   Blue Print BLU 2006   All The Time In The World/Bangin' My Head (p/s) 8
80   Blue Print BLUP 5002   JUST RELEASED (LP) 12

STEVE CROPPER
70   Stax STAX 147   Funky Broadway/Crop Dustin' 4
71   Stax SXATS 1008   WITH A LITTLE HELP FROM MY FRIENDS (LP) 10
71   Stax SXATS 1020   JAMMED TOGETHER (LP, with Albert King & Pop Staples) 10
(see also Booker T. & M.G.'s, Albert King)

BING CROSBY
54   Brunswick 03384   White Christmas/Let's Start The New Year Right 7
54   Brunswick 03929   Adeste Fideles/Silent Night, Holy Night 7
54   Brunswick 05224   What A Little Moonlight Can Do/Down By The Riverside (with Gary Crosby) 6
54   Brunswick 05244   Changing Partners/Y'All Come 7
54   Brunswick 05269   Secret Love/My Love, My Love 8
54   Brunswick 05277   Young At Heart/I Get So Lonely 6
54   Brunswick 05304   If There's Anybody Here (From Out Of Town)/Back In The Old Routine
(with Donald O'Connor) 5
54   Brunswick 05315   Cornbelt Symphony/The Call Of The South (with Gary Crosby) 5
54   Brunswick 05339   Count Your Blessings Instead Of Sheep/What Can You Do With A General 7
54   Brunswick 05354   White Christmas/Snow (with Danny Kaye, Peggy Lee & Trudy Stevens) 5
55   Brunswick 05377   The Song From "Desiree" (We Meet Again)/I Love Paris 4
55   Brunswick 05385   Tobermory Bay/The River (Sciummo) 4
55   Brunswick 05403   Dissertation On The State Of Bliss (with Patty Andrews)/It's Mine, It's Yours 5
55   Brunswick 05404   The Search Is Through/The Land Around Us 4
55   Brunswick 05410   Stranger In Paradise/Who Gave You The Roses 7
55   Brunswick 05419   Ohio/A Quiet Girl 4
55   Brunswick 05430   Jim, Johnny And Jonas/Nobody 4
55   Brunswick 05451   All She'd Say Was "Umh."/She Is The Sunshine Of Virginia 4
55   Brunswick 05486   Angel Bells/There's Music In You 4
55   Brunswick 05501   Let's Harmonize/Sleigh Bell Serenade 4
56   Brunswick 05511   Farewell/Early American 4
56   Brunswick 05543   In A Little Spanish Town/Ol' Man River 5
56   Brunswick 05558   No Other Love/Sleepy Time Gal 4
56   Brunswick 05585   Honeysuckle Rose/Swanee 4
56   Brunswick 05620   Christmas Is A-Comin'/Is Christmas Only A Tree 4
56   Capitol CL 14645   True Love (with Grace Kelly)/Well, Did You Evah? (with Frank Sinatra) 5
57   Brunswick 05674   Around The World/VICTOR YOUNG ORCHESTRA: Around The World 5
57   Capitol CL 14761   Man On Fire/Seven Nights A Week 4
57   London HLR 8504   Never Be Afraid/I Love You Whoever You Are 5
57   London HLR 8513   How Lovely Is Christmas/My Own Individual Star 4
57   Brunswick 05726   Chicago/Alabamy Bound 4
58   Philips PB 817   Straight Down The Middle/Tomorrow's My Lucky Day 5
58   Brunswick 05760   Love In A Home/In The Good Old Summer Time 4
58   Brunswick 05764   It's Beginning To Look Like Christmas/I Heard The Bells 4
59   Brunswick 05770   Gigi/The Next Time It Happens 4
59   Brunswick 05790   Rain/Church Bells 4
59   Philips PB 921   Say One For Me/I Couldn't Care Less 4
59   Gala GSP 801   My Own Individual Star/Never Be Afraid 4
60   Brunswick 05840   Happy Birthday & Auld Lang Syne/Home Sweet Home 4
60   MGM MGM 1098   The Second Time Around/Incurably Romantic 4
65   Brunswick 05928   Where The Blue Of The Night/Goodnight Sweetheart 4
68   MCA MU 1010   Around The World/VICTOR YOUNG ORCHESTRA: Around The World 4
51   Brunswick LA 8513   SINGS COLE PORTER SONGS (10" LP) 15
51   Brunswick LA 8514   STARDUST (10" LP) 15
51   Brunswick LA 8529   EL BINGO — A SELECTION OF LATIN AMERICAN FAVOURITES (10" LP) 15
52   Brunswick LA 8505   SINGS JEROME KERN SONGS (10" LP) 15
54   Columbia 33S 1036   CROSBY CLASSICS (10" LP) 15
56   Brunswick LAT 8106   SHILLELAGHS AND SHAMROCKS (LP) 12
52   Brunswick LA 8558   BING AND CONNIE (10" LP, with Connie Boswell) 12
53   Brunswick LA 8571   STEPHEN FOSTER SONGS (10" LP) 12
53   Brunswick LA 8579   BING CROSBY AND THE DIXIELAND BANDS (10" LP) 12
53   Brunswick LA 8584   THE QUIET MAN (10" LP) 12
53   Brunswick LA 8585   OLD LANG SYNE (10" LP) 12
53   Brunswick LA 8592   HOLIDAY INN (10" LP, with Fred Astaire) 12
53   Brunswick LA 8595   BLUE OF THE NIGHT (10" LP) 12
53   Brunswick LA 8600   BING CROSBY SINGS VICTOR HERBERT SONGS (10" LP) 12
53   Brunswick LA 8602   BLUE SKIES (10" LP, with Fred Astaire) 12
53   Brunswick LA 8606   WHEN IRISH EYES ARE SMILING (10" LP) 12
53   Brunswick LA 8620   DOWN MEMORY LANE (10" LP) 12
53   Brunswick LA 8624   DOWN MEMORY LANE VOL. 2 (10" LP) 12
54   Brunswick LA 8645   LE BING — SONGS HITS OF PARIS (10" LP) 12
54   Brunswick LA 8656   'WAY BACK HOME (10" LP) 12
54   Brunswick LA 8666   GEORGE GERSHWIN SONGS (10" LP) 12

Bing CROSBY

54	Brunswick LA 8673	SOME FINE OLD CHESTNUTS (10" LP)	12
54	Brunswick LA 8674	BING SINGS THE HITS (10" LP)	12
54	Brunswick LA 8675	SONG HITS FROM BROADWAY SHOWS (10" LP)	12
54	Brunswick LA 8684	YOURS IS MY HEART ALONE (10" LP)	12
54	Brunswick LA 8686	MERRY CHRISTMAS (10" LP)	12
54	Brunswick LA 8687	CROSBY COLLECTOR'S CLASSICS VOL. 1 (10" LP)	12
54	Brunswick LAT 8051-8055	BING — A MUSICAL AUTOBIOGRAPHY (5-LP box set)	30
55	Brunswick LA 8714	COUNTRY GIRL/LITLE BOY LOST (10" LP)	12
55	Brunswick LA 8723	CROSBY COLLECTOR'S CLASSICS VOL. 2 (10" LP)	12
55	Brunswick LA 8724	COUNTRY STYLE (10" LP)	12
55	Brunswick LA 8726	CROSBY COLLECTOR'S CLASSICS VOL. 3 (10" LP)	12
55	Brunswick LA 8727	CROSBY COLLECTOR'S CLASSICS VOL. 4 (10" LP)	12
55	Brunswick LA 8730	FAVOURITE HAWAIIAN SONGS (10" LP)	12
50s	Brunswick	FAVOURITE HAWAIIAN SONGS VOL. 2 (10" LP)	12
50s	Brunswick LA 8741	BING THE EARLY THIRTIES VOL. 2 (10" LP)	12
56	Brunswick LAT 8138	SONGS I WISH I'D SUNG (LP)	10
56	Brunswick LAT 8152	HOME ON THE RANGE (LP)	10
57	Brunswick LAT 8154	HIGH TOR (LP, with Julie Andrews)	10
57	Brunswick LAT 8216	A CHRISTMAS SINGS WITH BING (LP)	12
57	Brunswick LAT 8217	NEW TRICKS (LP)	10
58	Brunswick LAT 8228	BING AND THE DIXIELAND BANDS (LP)	10
58	Brunswick LAT 8253	TWILIGHT ON THE TRAIL (LP)	10
58	Fontana TFR 6000	DON'T BINGLE (10" LP)	15
59	Brunswick LAT 8278	WHEN IRISH EYES ARE SMILING (LP)	10
59	Brunswick LAT 8281	BING CROSBY SINGS (LP)	10
50s	HMV CLP 1088	BING SINGS WHILST BREGMAN SWINGS (LP)	10
50s	MGM C 844	BING AND SATCHMO (LP, with Louis Armstrong)	10
50s	Philips BBL 7335	SAY ONE FOR ME (LP, soundtrack, with Debbie Reynolds)	12
57	RCA RD 27032	BING WITH A BEAT (LP, with Bob Scobey's Frisco Jazz Band)	10
50s	Reprise R 6106	RETURN TO PARADISE ISLAND (LP)	10
62	Brunswick BING 1-15	BING'S HOLLYWOOD (15 LPs)	each 10

(see also Louis Armstrong, Bob Hope, Jane Wyman)

BOB CROSBY & HIS BOBCATS

59	London HLD 8828	Petite Fleur/Such A Long Night	7
60	London HLD 9228	The Dark At The Top Of The Stairs/Night Theme	6
60	London HA-D 2293	BOB CROSBY'S GREAT HITS (LP, also stereo SAH-D 6105)	10/12

(see also Modernaires)

DAVID CROSBY

71	Atlantic 2401 005	IF I COULD ONLY REMEMBER MY NAME (LP, gatefold sleeve)	10

(see also Byrds, Crosby [Stills] Nash [& Young])

GARY CROSBY

54	Brunswick 05340	Mambo In The Moonlight/Got My Eyes On You	8
54	Brunswick 05340	Mambo In The Moonlight/Got My Eyes On You (78)	5
55	Brunswick 05365	Palsy Walsy/Loop-De-Loop Mambo (with Cheer Leaders)	8
55	Brunswick 05365	Palsy Walsy/Loop-De-Loop Mambo (78)	5
55	Brunswick 05378	Ready, Willing And Able/There's A Small Hotel	12
55	Brunswick 05378	Ready, Willing And Able/There's A Small Hotel (78)	5
55	Brunswick 05400	Ko Ko Mo (I Love You So)/Struttin' With Some Barbecue (w/ Louis Armstrong)	12
55	Brunswick 05400	Ko Ko Mo (I Love You So)/Struttin' With Some Barbecue (78)	5
55	Brunswick 05446	Ayuh Ayuh/Mississippi Pecan Pie	8
55	Brunswick 05446	Ayuh Ayuh/Mississippi Pecan Pie (78)	5
55	Brunswick 05496	Truly/Give Me A Band And My Baby (B-side with Paris Sisters)	8
55	Brunswick 05496	Truly/Give Me A Band And My Baby (78)	5
56	Brunswick 05546	Yaller Yaller Gold/Get A Load O' Me	6
56	Brunswick 05546	Yaller Yaller Gold/Get A Load O' Me (78)	5
56	Brunswick 05574	Easy Street/Lazybones (with Louis Armstrong)	4
56	Brunswick 05633	Yaller Yaller Gold/Noah Found Grace In The Eyes Of God (with Dreamers)	5
58	HMV POP 550	Judy, Judy/Cheatin' On Me	15
58	HMV POP 550	Judy, Judy/Cheatin' On Me (78)	15
59	HMV POP 648	The Happy Bachelor/This Little Girl Of Mine	6
57	Vogue VA 160118	GARY CROSBY (LP)	15

(see also Bing Crosby)

CROSBY & NASH

71	Atlantic K 10192	Southbound Train/Whole Cloth	4
71	Atlantic K 50011	GRAHAM NASH & DAVID CROSBY (LP)	10

CROSBY, STILLS & NASH

69	Atlantic 584 283	Marrakesh Express/Helplessly Hoping	4
69	Atlantic 584 304	Suite: Judy Blue Eyes/Long Time Gone	4
69	Atlantic 588 189	CROSBY, STILLS & NASH (LP, with lyric sheet)	10

CROSBY, STILLS, NASH & YOUNG

70	Atlantic 2091 002	Teach Your Children/Country Girl	4
70	Atlantic 2091 010	Woodstock/Helpless	4
70	Atlantic 2091 023	Ohio/Find The Cost Of Freedom	5
70	Atlantic 2091 039	Our House/Deja Vu	4
87	Atlantic A 9003TX	American Dream/Compass/Soldiers Of Peace/Ohio (12", p/s)	7
70	Atlantic 2401 001	DEJA VU (LP, gatefold sleeve with thick cover & pasted-on photo)	10
71	Atlantic 2657 007	FOUR WAY STREET (2-LP, gatefold sleeve with lyric sheet)	15

(see also Stephen Stills [Manassas], Neil Young, Graham Nash, David Crosby)

CROSS

87	Virgin VS 1007	Cowboys And Indians (4.32)/Love Lies Bleeding (p/s)	5
87	Virgin VST 1007	Cowboys And Indians (5.53)/Love Lies Bleeding (12", p/s)	8
87	Virgin CDEP 10	Cowboys And Indians (4.32)/Love Lies Bleeding (CD)	12

CROSS

87	Virgin VSTC 1007	Cowboys And Indians (4.32)/Love Lies Bleeding/Cowboys And Indians (5.53) (cassette)	8
88	Virgin VS 1026	Shove It (3.28)/Rough Justice (p/s)	6
88	Virgin VS 1026-12	Shove It (3.28)/Shove It (Metropolix)/Rough Justice (12", p/s)	15
88	Virgin CDEP 20	Shove It (3.28)/Cowboys And Indians (4.32)/Rough Justice/Shove It (5.03) (CD)	12
88	Virgin VS 1062	Heaven For Everyone/Love On A Tightrope (Like An Animal) (p/s)	4
88	Virgin VST 1062	Heaven For Everyone/Love On A Tightrope (Like An Animal)/Contact (12", p/s)	8
90	EMI CDR 6251	Power To Love (5.22)/Passion For Trash/Power To Love (3.28) (CD)	7

(see also Roger Taylor, Queen)

JIMMIE CROSS

66	Red Bird RB 10042	Super Duper Man/Hey Little Girl	12

(Keith) CROSS & (Peter) ROSS

71	Decca F 13224	Can You Believe It?/Blind Willie Johnson	6
72	Decca F 13316	Peace In The End/Prophets Guiders	6
72	Decca SKL 5129	BORED CIVILIANS (LP)	60

(see also T2)

CROSSBEATS

70s	Pilgrim PSR 7001	If Only/He Wants To Know	4
70s	Pilgrim PSR 7002	I Know/He Waits	4
70s	Pilgrim PSR 7003	Step Aside/Forgive Me	4
70s	Pilgrim PSR 7004	Busy Man/Change (p/s)	4
70s	Pilgrim KLP 12	CRAZY MIXED UP GENERATION (LP)	40

CROW

70	Stateside SSL 10301	CROW MUSIC (LP)	12
70	Stateside SSL 10310	CROW BY CROW (LP)	12

CROW

75	Right On R 101	Your Autumn Of Tomorrow/Uncle Funk	4

CROW BAR

84	Skinhead SKIN 1	Hippie Punks/White Riot (p/s)	12

CROWD

79	SRT SRTS/79/CUS 377	Ronnie (Is A Headbanger)/A Little Of What I Fancy/Let's Fly Together (p/s)	4

CROWDED HOUSE

86	Capitol CL 416	World Where You Live/That's What I Call Love (p/s)	5
86	Capitol TCCL 416	World Where You Live (Extended)/Something So Strong/Don't Dream It's Over/That's What I Call Love (cassette)	7
86	Capitol 12 CL 416	World Where You Live (Extended)/Can't Carry On/That's What I Call Love (12", p/s)	10
86	Capitol CDCL 416	World Where You Live (Extended)/Something So Strong/Don't Dream It's Over/That's What I Call Love (CD)	25
87	Capitol CL 438	Don't Dream It's Over/That's What I Call Love (p/s)	4
87	Capitol TCCL 438	Don't Dream It's Over (Extended)/(7")/That's What I Call Love (cassette)	6
87	Capitol 12 CL 438	Don't Dream It's Over (Extended)/(7")/That's What I Call Love (12", p/s)	8
87	Capitol CL 456	Something So Strong/I Walk Away (p/s)	4
87	Capitol 12 CL 456	Something So Strong/Something So Strong (live)/I Walk Away/Don't Dream It's Over (live) (12", p/s)	7
88	Capitol CDCL 498	Better Be Home Soon/Don't Dream It's Over (live)/Kill Eye (CD)	10
88	Capitol CDCL 509	Sister Madly/Mansion In The Slums/Something So Strong (live) (CD)	10
91	Capitol CDP 7935592	WOODFACE (CD, foldout pack)	15

(see also Split Enz, Tim Finn)

CROWDY CROWN

73	private pressing	CROWDY CROWN (LP)	45

CROWN HEIGHTS AFFAIR

80	Mercury MERX 28	Far Out/You've Been Gone (12")	7
76	Polydor 2310 424	DREAMING A DREAM (LP)	10

CROWNS

68	Pama PM 725	I Know, It's Alright/I Surrender	5
68	Pama PM 736	Jerking The Dog/Keep Me Going	5
68	Pama PM 745	She Ain't Gonna Do Right/I Need Your Loving	5
68	Pama PM 759	Since You Been Gone/Call Me	5

CROWS

54	Columbia SCM 5119	Gee/I Love You So	300
54	Columbia DB 3478	Gee/I Love You So (78)	75

CRUCIFIXION

80	Miramar MIR 4	The Fox/Death Sentence	6
82	Neat NEAT 19	Take It Or Leave It/On The Run (p/s)	5
84	Neat NEAT 37	Green Eyes/Moon Rising/Jailbait (p/s)	5
84	Neat NEAT 3712	Green Eyes/Moon Rising/Jailbait (12", p/s, purple vinyl)	10

ARTHUR 'BIG BOY' CRUDUP

64	RCA RCA 1401	My Baby Left Me/I Don't Know It	15
64	RCA RCX 7161	RHYTHM AND BLUES VOL. 4 (EP)	15
69	Blue Horizon 7-63855	MEAN OLE FRISCO (LP)	40
70	Delmark DS 614	LOOK ON YONDERS WALL (LP)	12
71	Delmark DS 621	CRUDUP'S MOOD (LP)	12
71	RCA RD 8224	FATHER OF ROCK 'N' ROLL (LP)	12
74	United Artists UAS 29092	ROEBUCK MAN (LP)	10

CRUISERS

65	Decca F 12098	It Ain't Me Babe/Baby What You Want Me To Do	8

(see also Dave Berry)

CRUISERS

78	Badge/Feelgood FLG 113	Rebel Ed's Rebel Hop/Ranchero (p/s)	4
78	Feelgood FLG 114	WONDERFULL DREAM (EP)	5
80	Harbour HRB 11	Get A Job/I'll Never Let You Down (p/s, B-side by Cruiser Flying Saucers)	4

SIMON CRUM

58	Capitol CL 14965	Country Music Is Here To Stay/Stand Up, Sit Down, Shut Your Mouth	25
59	Capitol CL 15077	I Fell Out Of Love With Love/Morgan Poisoned The Water Hole	12
61	Capitol CL 15183	Enormity In Motion/Cuzz Yore So Sweet	12

(see also Ferlin Husky)

CRUSADERS

72	Blue Thumb WIP 6143	Put It Where You Want It/Mosadi Woman	5
75	ABC ABC 4051	Stomp And Buck Dance/Ballad For Joe (Louis)	4
75	ABC ABC 4088	Creole/I Felt The Love	4
75	ABC ABC 4122	Keep That Same Old Feeking/Till The Sun Shines	4
71	Rare Earth SRE 3001	OLD SOCKS NEW SHOES (LP)	15
72	Blue Thumb ILPS 9218	CRUSADERS (2-LP)	15
73	Mowest MWS 7004	HOLLYWOOD (LP)	20
75	ABC ABCD 607	SOUTHERN COMFORT (2-LP)	14
75	ABC ABCL 5144	CHAIN REACTION (LP, gatefold sleeve)	10
76	ABC ABCL 5164	THOSE SOUTHERN KNIGHTS (LP, gatefold sleeve)	10

BETTYE CRUTCHER

| 75 | Stax STX 1035 | LONG AS YOU LOVE ME (LP) | 10 |

CRUX/CRASH

| 82 | No Future OI 18 | KEEP ON RUNNING (EP) | 5 |

CRYAN' SHAMES (U.S.)

(see under Shames)

BARRY CRYER

58	Fontana H 139	The Purple People Eater/Hey! Eula	5
58	Fontana H 139	The Purple People Eater/Hey! Eula (78)	5
58	Fontana H 151	Nothin' Shakin'/Seven Daughters	6
58	Fontana H 151	Nothin' Shakin'/Seven Daughters (78)	5
59	Fontana H 177	Angelina/Kissin'	4
59	Fontana H 177	Angelina/Kissin' (78)	5

CRYIN' SHAMES (U.K.)

| 66 | Decca F 12340 | Please Stay/What's News Pussycat | 12 |
| 66 | Decca F 12425 | Nobody Waved Goodbye/You | 15 |

(see also Paul & Ritchie & Cryin' Shames, Gary Walker & Rain)

CRYING SHAMES

| 80 | Logo GO 385 | That's Rock'n'Roll/Too Late (p/s) | 4 |

CRYSTALITES

69	Big Shot BI 510	Biafra/Drop Pan	4
69	Nu Beat NB 036	Splash Down/Finders Keepers	4
70	Bullet BU 424	Fistful Of Dollars/BOBBY ELLIS: Crystal	4
70	Song Bird SB 1030	Sic Him Rover/Drop Pon	4
70	Song Bird SB 1035	Undertaker's Burial/Ghost Rider	4
71	Song Bird SB 1057	Earthly Sounds/Version	4

CRYSTAL MANSION

| 69 | Capitol CL 15577 | The Thought Of Loving You/Hallelujah | 4 |
| 70 | Polydor 2058 070 | Carolina On My Mind/If I Live | 4 |

CRYSTALS

62	Parlophone R 4867	There's No Other Like My Baby/Oh Yeah Maybe Baby	90
62	London HLU 9611	He's A Rebel/I Love You Eddie	12
63	London HLU 9661	He's Sure The Boy I Love/Walking Along (La-La-La)	15
63	London HLU 9732	Da Doo Ron Ron/Git It	6
63	London HLU 9773	Then He Kissed Me/Brother Julius	6
64	London HLU 9837	Little Boy/Uptown (withdrawn)	35
64	London HLU 9852	I Wonder/Little Boy	12
64	London HLU 9909	All Grown Up/PHIL SPECTOR GROUP: Irving (Jaggered Sixteenths)	12
65	United Artists UP 11110	My Place/You Can't Tie A Girl Down	25
69	London HLU 10239	Da Doo Ron Ron/He's A Rebel	4
74	Warners/Spector K 19010	Da Doo Ron Ron/Then Kissed Me (blue vinyl)	4
63	London RE-U 1381	DA DOO RON RON (EP)	40
63	London HA-U 8120	HE'S A REBEL (LP)	75

CUBAN HEELS

78	Housewive's Choice JY 1/2	Downtown/Do The Smoke Walk (p/s)	6
80	Greville GR 1	Little Girl/Fast Living Friend (p/s)	4
81	Cuba Libre DRINK 1	Walk On Water/Take A Look (p/s)	4
81	Virgin VS 440	Walk On Water/Hard Times (p/s, with free flexidisc)	4

CUBY & BLIZZARDS

68	Philips BF 1638	Distant Smile/Don't Know Which Way To Go	8
68	Philips BF 1719	Windows Of My Eyes/Checkin' Up On My Baby	6
69	Philips BF 1827	Appleknockers Flophouse/Go Down Sunshine	8
68	Philips SBL 7874	DESOLATION (LP)	20
69	Philips SBL 7918	APPLEKNOCKERS FLOPHOUSE (LP)	20

CUD

87	Reception REC 007/12	You're The Boss/Mind The Gap/Van Van Van/You're The Boss (Out To Lunch Mix) (12", p/s)	20
88	Ediesta CALC 049	Under My Hat/Punishment-Reward Relationship/Art! (12", p/s)	15
88	Dug/Nightime DUGNI 001T	Slack Time/I've Had It With Blondes/Make No Bones (12", p/s)	15

MINT VALUE £

89	Imaginary MIRAGE 007	Lola/The Day Crime Paid (some in mispressed blue p/s)	7/4
90	Imaginary MIRAGE 18T	Haywire (12", 1-sided, plain black sleeve; 800 only, 500 signed in silver)	12/8
90	Imaginary MIRAGE 21T	Robinson Crusoe/Nightmares On Wax (Club Remix)/(12" Version) (12", p/s)	7
91	Imaginary MIRAGE 027	Magic (Farsley Mix)/Magic (Stockport Mix) (plain die-cut sleeve)	4
92	Flexi/Sunflower (no cat. no.)	Backdoor Santa (flexidisc, 'Xmas' gig freebie)	4

'CUDDLY' DUDLEY (Heslop)

59	HMV POP 586	Lots More Love/Later	8
60	HMV POP 725	Too Pooped To Pop/Miss In-Between	8
61	Ember EMB S 136	Sitting On A Train/One Thing I Like	4
64	Oriole International ICB 9	Blarney Blues/Peace On Earth	8
64	Oriole International ICB 10	Way Of Life/When Will You Say You'll Be Mine	8

CUES

56	Capitol CL 14501	Burn That Candle/O My Darlin'	100
56	Capitol CL 14501	Burn That Candle/O My Darlin' (78)	15
56	Capitol CL 14651	Crackerjack/The Girl I Love (featuring Jimmy Breedlove)	100
56	Capitol CL 14651	Crackerjack/The Girl I Love (78)	15
57	Capitol CL 14682	Prince Or Pauper/Why	90
57	Capitol CL 14682	Prince Or Pauper/Why (78)	15
	(see also Jimmy Breedlove)		

CUFF LINKS

| 69 | MCA MU 1101 | Tracy/Where Do You Go? | 4 |
| 69 | MCA MUP(S) 398 | TRACY (LP) | 10 |

CUL DE SAC

| 92 | Shock SX 017 | Sakhalin/Cant (p/s, numbered, 1,000 only) | 4 |

CULPEPPERS ORCHARD

| 72 | Polydor 2480 123 | SECOND SIGHT (LP) | 60 |

CULT

84	Situation 2 SIT 33	Spiritwalker/A Flower In The Desert (p/s)	4
84	Situation 2 SIT 33T	Spiritwalker/A Flower In The Desert/Bone Bag (12", p/s)	7
84	Beggars Banquet BEG 115P	Go West/Sea And Sky (foldout poster p/s)	7
84	Beggars Banquet BEG 115T	Go West (Crazy Spinning Circles)/Sea And Sky/Brothers Grimm (live) (12", p/s)	7
85	B. Banquet BEGTP 135	She Sells Sanctuary (Howling Mix)/Assault On Sanctuary (12", p/s)	7
85	Beggars Banquet BEG 135C	She Sells Sanctuary/Howling Mix/The Snake/Assault On Sanctuary (cassette)	5
85	Beggars Banquet BEG 152D	Revolution (Remix)/All Souls Avenue//Judith/Sunrise (double pack)	4
85	Beggars Banquet BEG 152C	Revolution (Full Length Remix)/All Souls Avenue/Judith/Sunrise (cassette)	4
87	Beggars Banquet BEG 182P	Love Removal Machine/Wolf Child's Blues (picture disc)	5
87	Beggars Banquet BEG 182D	Love Removal Machine/Wolf Child's Blues//Conquistador/Groove Co. (double pack, gatefold p/s)	5
87	Beggars Banquet DBEG 182D	Love Removal Machine/Wolf Child's Blues//Conquistador/Groove Co. (double pack; mispress, credit on 2nd single to 'Rick Rubin')	6
87	Beggars Banquet BEG 188TD	Lil' Devil/Zap City/She Sells Sanctuary (live)/Phoenix (live)/Wild Thing/ Louie Louie (live) (12" double pack, gatefold p/s)	10
87	Beggars Banquet BEG 188CD	Lil' Devil/Zap City/She Sells Sanctuary (live)/Phoenix (live)/ Love Removal Machine (CD, gatefold card sleeve)	15
87	Beggars Banquet BEG 195D	Wild Flower/Love Trooper//Outlaw (live)/Horse Nation (double pack, gatefold p/s)	4
87	Beggars Banquet BEG 195P	Wild Flower/Love Trooper (picture disc, stickered PVC sleeve)	5
87	B. Banquet BEG 195TP	Wild Flower (Extended Rock Mix)/(Guitar Dub)/Love Trooper (12", picture disc)	7
87	RM Flexidisc 3	Wild Flower (Unavailable Mix)/Interview (gatefold p/s flexidisc free with 'Record Mirror' magazine)	6/4
89	Beggars Banquet BEG 230G	Edie (Ciao Baby)/Bleeding Heart Graffiti (numbered gatefold p/s)	4
89	Beggars Banquet BEG 235TH	Sun King (Full Length)/Edie (Ciao Baby) (Full Length)/She Sells Sanctuary (12", PVC hologram wallet sleeve)	7
84	Beggars Banquet BEGA 57	DREAMTIME (LP, with free LP, "Dreamtime Live At The Lyceum")	15
84	Beggars Banquet BEGA 57P	DREAMTIME (LP, picture disc)	15
87	B. Banquet BEGA 80G	ELECTRIC (LP, gold vinyl, 5,000 only)	12
89	Beggars Banquet BEGA 98	SONIC TEMPLE (LP, red vinyl)	12
	(see also Southern Death Cult, Death Cult, Lonesome No More)		

CULT FIGURES

79	Rather GEAR 4/RT 020	Zip Nolan (Highway Patrolman)/P.W.T. (Playing With Toys)/ Zip Dub (folded p/s)	6
81	Rather GEAR EIGHT	In Love: I Remember/Laura Kate/Almost A Love Song (p/s)	5
	(see also Swell Maps)		

CULT HERO

| 79 | Fiction FICS 006 | I'm A Cult Hero/I Did You (p/s, 2,000 only) | 45 |
| | *(see also Cure)* | | |

CULT MANIAX

82	Next Wave NXT 2/BAK 1	Frenzie/The Russians Are Coming/Black Horse/Death March (p/s)	6
80s	Anti-Hype DL 001	Frontier/I Always Lose My Temper/It'll Take Time (p/s)	4
84	Xcentric Noise EIGHTH 1	The Amazing Adventures Of Johnny The Duck And The Bath Time Blues/ Freedom/Maniax (p/s)	4
84	Xcentric Noise EIGHTH 1T	The Amazing Adventures Of Johnny The Duck And The Bath Time Blues/ Blue Baby/Village Ritual/Freedom/Maniax (12", p/s)	7

CULTURE CLUB

83	Virgin VSY 558	Time (Clock Of My Heart)/White Boys Can't Control It (picture disc)	5
84	Virgin VSY 657	It's A Miracle/Love Twist (picture disc)	6
84	Virgin VSY 694	War Song/La Cancion De Guerra (withdrawn picture disc)	40
86	Virgin VSX 845	Move Away/Sexuality (5" 33rpm picture disc with booklet & gatefold p/s)	4
86	Virgin VSY 861	God Thank You Woman/From Luxury To Heartache (picture disc)	10
86	Noise	I'll Tumble For You/BLUE RONDO: Change (blue 1-sided flexidisc with 'Noise' magazine)	5/4
83	Virgin VP 2285	COLOUR BY NUMBERS (LP, picture disc)	10

84	Virgin VP 2330	WAKING UP WITH THE HOUSE ON FIRE (LP, picture disc)	10

(see also Jesus Loves You)

CULVER STREET PLAYGROUND

68	President PT 145	Alley Pond Park/A Decent Sort Of Guy	8

CUMBERLAND THREE

60	Columbia DB 4460	Johnny Reb/Come Along Julie	5
64	Parlophone R 5113	The Cumberland Crew/Chilly Winds	4
61	Columbia 33SX 1302	FOLK SCENE, U.S.A. (LP, also stereo SCX 3364)	10
61	Columbia 33SX 1318	CIVIL WAR ALMANAC — YANKEES (LP)	10
61	Columbia 33SX 1325	CIVIL WAR ALMANAC — REBELS (LP)	10

(see also John Stewart)

BARBARA CUMMINGS

67	London HLU 10110	She's The Woman/There's Something Funny Going On	4

DAVID CUNNINGHAM

80	Piano PIANO 001	GREY SCALE (LP)	10

CUPIDS

58	Vogue V 9102	Now You Tell Me/Lillie Mae	250
58	Vogue V 9102	Now You Tell Me/Lillie Mae (78)	50

CUPID'S INSPIRATION

68	NEMS 56-3500	Yesterday Has Gone/Dream	4
68	NEMS 56-3702	My World/Everything Is Meant To Be	4
68	NEMS 63553	YESTERDAY HAS GONE (LP)	12

CUPOL

80	4AD BAD 9	Like This For Ages/Kluba Cupol (12", p/s, 45/33rpm)	10

(see also Wire)

CUPPA T

67	Deram DM 144	Miss Pinkerton/Brand New World	12
68	Deram DM 185	Streatham Hippodrome/One Man Band	12

CUPS

68	Polydor 56777	Good As Gold/Life And Times	10

MIKE CURB CONGREGATION

70	Polydor 2058 075	Burning Bridges/Sweet Gingerbread Man	4

CURE

78	Small Wonder SMALL 11	Killing An Arab/10.15 Saturday Night (p/s, 15,000 only)	18
79	Fiction FICS 001	Killing An Arab/10.15 Saturday Night (p/s, reissue)	12
79	Fiction FICS 002	Boys Don't Cry/Plastic Passion (p/s)	14
79	Fiction FICS 005	Jumping Someone Else's Train/I'm Cold (p/s)	18
80	Fiction FICS 010	A Forest/Another Journey By Train (p/s & blue plastic labels or 'radiophonic' die-cut sleeve with silver plastic labels)	12/8
80	Fiction FICSX 010	A Forest (Extended Version)/Another Journey By Train (12", p/s)	25
81	Fiction FICS 012	Primary/Descent (p/s)	10
81	Fiction FICSX 012	Primary (Extended)/Descent (12", p/s)	20
81	Fiction FICS 12	Primary (1-sided promo, no p/s)	20
81	Fiction FICS 014	Charlotte Sometimes/Splintered In Her Head (p/s)	8
81	Fiction FICSX 014	Charlotte Sometimes/Splintered In Her Head/Faith (live) (12", p/s)	15
82	Fiction FICS 015	The Hanging Garden/Killing An Arab (p/s)	10
82	Fiction FICG 015	The Hanging Garden/100 Years//A Forest/Killing An Arab (double pack, gatefold p/s, 5,000 only)	18
82	Lyntone LYN 12011	Lament (1-sided flexidisc with 'Flexipop' issue 22, some on red vinyl, most on green; without magazine, £12/£9)	15/12
82	Fiction CURE 1	One Hundred Years/The Hanging Garden (12", p/s, promo/gig freebie)	40
82	Fiction FICS 017	Let's Go To Bed/Just One Kiss (p/s)	6
82	Fiction FICSX 017	Let's Go To Bed (Extended)/Just One Kiss (Extended) (12", p/s)	10
83	Fiction FICS 018	The Walk/The Dream (poster p/s, paper labels)	12
83	Fiction FICS 018	The Walk/The Dream (re-pressing, silver plastic labels, standard p/s)	5
83	Fiction FICSP 018	The Walk/The Dream (picture disc)	30
83	Fiction FICSX 018	Upstairs Room/The Dream (The Walk, p/s)	10
83	Fiction FICSX 018	Upstairs Room/The Dream/The Walk/Lament/Let's Go To Bed (Extended)/Just One Kiss (Extended) (12" double pack, shrinkwrapped with sticker)	20
83	Fiction FICS 019	The Lovecats/Speak My Language (p/s, paper labels)	5
83	Fiction FICSP 019	The Lovecats/Speak My Language (picture disc, PVC sleeve)	30
83	Fiction FICSX 019	The Lovecats (Extended)/Speak My Language/Mr Pink Eyes (12", p/s)	8
84	Fiction FIXSP 020	The Caterpillar/Happy Man (picture disc, PVC sleeve)	25
84	Fiction FICSX 020	The Caterpillar/Happy Man/Throw Your Foot (12", p/s)	8
85	Fiction FICS 22	In Between Days/The Exploding Boy (p/s)	5
85	Fiction FICSX 22	In Between Days/The Exploding Boy/A Few Hours After This (12", p/s)	8
85	Fiction 080182-2	In Between Days/The Exploding Boy/A Few Hours After This/Six Different Ways (live)/Push (live) (CD video)	8
85	Fiction FICS 23	Close To Me (Remix)/A Man Inside My Mouth (p/s)	5
85	Fiction FICSG 23	Close To Me (Remix)/A Man Inside My Mouth (poster p/s; some copies with blue & white 'Head On The Door' sticker)	10/7
85	Fiction FICST 23	Half An Octopus: Close To Me (Remix)/A Man Inside My Mouth/New Day/Stop Dead (10", p/s)	15
85	Fiction FICSX 23	Close To You (Extended Remix)/A Man Inside My Mouth/Stop Dead (12", p/s)	7
85	Fiction 080180-2	Close To Me (12" Remix)/A Man Inside My Mouth/Stop Dead/New Day (CDV)	8
86	Fiction FICSX 24	Boys Don't Cry (New Voice Club Mix)/Pill Box Tales/Do The Hansa (12", p/s)	7
87	Fiction FICSG 25	Why Can't I Be You?/A Japanese Dream/Six Different Ways (live)/Push (live) (numbered double pack, gatefold p/s)	10
87	Fiction FICSX 25	Why Can't I Be You (12" Extended Remix)/A Japanese Dream (Remix) (12", p/s)	8

MINT VALUE £

90	Fiction 080184-2	Why Can't I Be You? (12" Remix)/A Japanese Dream (5.40 Remix)/ Hey You!!! (CD video) 8
87	Fiction FICS 26	Catch/Breathe (p/s, in carrier bag) 7
87	Fiction FICSP 26	Catch/Breathe (clear vinyl, printed PVC sleeve) 12
87	Fiction FICSC 26	Catch/Breathe/A Chain Of Flowers (cassette) 4
87	Fiction FICSE 26	Catch/Breath/Kyoto Song (live)/A Night Like This (live) (12" EP with booklet) 8
87	Fiction 080186-2	Catch/Breathe/A Chain Of Flowers/Icing Sugar (Remix) (CD video) 12
87	Fiction FICS 27	Just Like Heaven/Snow In Summer (p/s, numbered, white vinyl) 9
87	Fiction FICS 27	Just Like Heaven/Snow In Summer (p/s, mispress, A-side plays both sides) 6
87	Fiction FICSP 27	Just Like Heaven/Snow In Summer (picture disc in custom PVC sleeve) 12
87	Fiction FIXCD 27	Just Like Heaven (Remix)/Snow In Summer/Sugar Girl (CD) 10
88	Fiction FIXCD 28	Hot Hot Hot!!! (Extended Remix)/(7" Remix)/Hey You!!! (Extended Remix) (CD, with insert for '10 Imaginary Years' book) 8
89	Fiction FICSG 29	Lullaby (Remix)/Babble (gatefold p/s, numbered) 5
89	Fiction FICSP 29	Lullaby (Remix)/Babble (clear vinyl, no'd printed 'spider web' PVC sleeve) 10
89	Fiction FICVX 29	Lullaby (Remix)/Babble/Out Of Mind (12" pink vinyl, numbered with stickers) ...12
89	Fiction FICCD 29	Lullaby (Remix)/Babble/Out Of Mind/Lullaby (Extended Remix) (3" CD, gatefold p/s) 8
89	Fiction FICSG 30	Lovesong/2 Late ('The Love Box' set with linen print) 6
89	Fiction FICSX 30	Lovesong (Extended)/2 Late/Fear Of Ghosts (12" picture disc, unreleased, test pressings only) 50
89	Fiction 081398-2	Lovesong (Extended Mix)/2 Late/Fear Of Ghosts/Lovesong (12" Mix) (CDV) 12
90	Fiction FICPA 34	Pictures Of You (Remix)/Last Dance (live) (p/s, green vinyl with sticker) 6
90	Fiction FICPB 34	Pictures Of You (Remix)/Prayers For Rain (p/s, purple vinyl, no'd sticker) 8
90	Fiction FIXPA 34	Pictures Of You (Extended Remix)/Last Dance (live)/Fascination Street (live) (12", p/s, green vinyl) 8
90	Fiction FIXPB 34	Pictures Of You (Strange Mix)/Prayers For Rain (live)/Disintegration (live) (12", p/s, purple vinyl) 12
85	CURE 1	An Interview With Simon Gallup Of The Cure (picture disc, 2 designs) 5
89	CURE 7	Interview (coloured vinyl, picture labels) 4
89	CURE 7P	Interview (black & white picture disc) 4
90	CURE 90	An Interview With Robert Smith (picture disc) 4
79	Fiction FIX 1	THREE IMAGINARY BOYS (LP, with inner sleeve, some in gold-embossed 'limited edition price' cover, initial copies with postcard) 12/10
79	Fiction FIXC 1	THREE IMAGINARY BOYS (original, cassette, paper labels) 10
80	Fiction FIX 004	17 SECONDS (LP, with inner sleeve & textured cover) 10
80	Fiction FIXC 4	17 SECONDS (original cassette, paper labels) 10
80	Fiction FIXC 6	FAITH/CARNAGE VISORS (double-play cassette, b&w cover, paper labels) 12
82	Fiction FIX 7	PORNOGRAPHY (LP, with lyric sheet) 10
84	Fiction FIXS 9	THE TOP (LP, with badge & poster, green inner sleeve) 12
84	Fiction FIXS 9	THE TOP (LP, promo with plastic snake & top) 20
85	Fiction 825 354-2	17 SECONDS (CD, original non-picture disc issue) 15
85	Fiction 827 687-2	FAITH (CD, original non-picture disc issue) 15
86	Fiction 827 688-2	PORNOGRAPHY (CD, original non-picture disc issue) 15
86	Fiction 815 011-2	BOYS DON'T CRY (CD, original non-picture disc, with extra track "So What" & without "Object" & "World War") 15
87	Fiction 817 470-2	JAPANESE WHISPERS (CD, original non-picture disc issue) 15
87	Fiction FIXH 13/FIXHA 13	KISS ME, KISS ME, KISS ME (LP, with orange vinyl 6-track 12" [FIXHA 13], in custom PVC sleeve) 20
89	Fiction FIXHP 14	DISINTEGRATION (LP, picture disc, printed PVC sleeve) 10
89	Fiction S CIFCD 3 01	STRANGER THAN FICTION (6-track sampler CD, 200 only) 50
90	Fiction FIXC 17	ENTREAT (HMV promotion cassette) 12
90	Fiction FIXCD 17	ENTREAT (HMV promotion CD) 15
92	Fiction 513 600-0	LIMITED EDITION CD BOX (15-CD hinged box set, 2,500 only) 170

(see also Cult Hero, Siouxsie & Banshees, Glove, Fools Dance, Tim Pope, Lockjaw, Obtainers)

MARTIN CURE & PEEPS

67	Philips BF 1605	It's All Over Now/I Can Make The Rain Fall Up 20

(see also Peeps)

JOHNNY CURIOUS & STRANGERS

78	Illegal IL 009	In Tune/Road To Cheltenham/Pissheadsville/Jennifer (p/s) 7
79	Bugle BLAST 2	Someone Else's Home/Backwards In The Night (p/s) 12

CURIOSITY SHOPPE

68	Deram DM 220	Baby I Need You/So Sad 20

CURRANT KRAZE

70	Deram DM 292	Lady Pearl/Breaking The Heart Of A Good Man 8

CURRENT 93

87	Maldorer MAL 108	Crowleymass/Christmassacre/Crowleymass (Mix Mix Mix) (12", p/s) 10
88	Yangki 002	Faiths Favourites (with Nurse With Wound)/Ballad Of The Pale Girl 10
88	Maldorer MAL 088	Red Face Of God/The Breath And The Pain Of God (12", p/s) 8
80s	Harbinger 001	No Hiding From The Blackbird/NURSE WITH WOUND: Burial Of The Stoned Sardine (reissue) 5
80s	Shock SX 003	She Is Dead And All Fall Down/God Has Three Faces And Wood Has No Name (folded sleeve in bag, 974 only, 26 signed/lettered) 20/15
80s	Cerne 004	This Ain't The Summer Of Love (live) (with Sol Invictus, gig freebie, printed labels, no p/s, 93 copies with ticket) 15/10
86	Maldorer UDO 22M	IN MENSTRUAL NIGHT (LP, picture disc) 10
88	Maldorer MAL 666	CHRIST AND THE PALE QUEEN (LP, 93 only) 55
89	Durtro DURTRO 001	LIVE AT BAR MALDORER (LP, white label, 1,000 only) 30

(see also Nurse With Wound, 23 Skidoo, Psychic TV, Crisis)

CLIFFORD CURRY

69	Action ACT 4549	She Shot A Hole In My Soul/We're Gonna Hate Ourselves In The Morning 6
69	Pama PM 793	You Turn Out The Light/Good Humour Man 6

MINT VALUE £

69	Pama PM 797	I Can Get A Hold Of Myself/Ain't No Danger	8

ALLEN CURTIS
64	Hickory 45-1226	Fireball Mail/The Hole He Said He'd Dig For Me	4

CHRIS CURTIS
66	Pye 7N 17132	Aggravation/Have I Done Something Wrong	30

(see also Searchers)

DENNY CURTIS
68	Plexium PXM 2	Crying Over You/You Don't Love Me No More	4
69	Plexium PXM 6	Message/You Gotta Be Mine	4

JOHNNY CURTIS
66	Parlophone R 5529	Our Love's Disintegrating/Legend In Our Time	20

LEE CURTIS (& ALL STARS)
63	Decca F 11622	Little Girl/Just One More Dance (solo)	12
63	Decca F 11690	Let's Stomp/Poor Unlucky Me	15
64	Decca F 11830	What About Me/I've Got My Eyes On You	12
65	Philips BF 1385	Ecstasy/A Shot Of Rhythm And Blues	15

(see also Pete Best Four)

MAC CURTIS
57	Parlophone R 4279	The Low Road/You Ain't Treatin' Me Right	600
57	Parlophone R 4279	The Low Road/You Ain't Treatin' Me Right (78)	100
74	Polydor 2310 293	ROCKABILLY KINGS (LP, with Charlie Feathers)	15

SONNY CURTIS
60	Coral Q 72400	The Red Headed Stranger/Talk About My Baby	15
64	Colpix PX 11024	A Beatle I Want To Be/So Used To Loving You	5
64	Liberty LIB 55710	Bo Diddley Bach/I Pledged My Love To You	5

(see also Crickets)

DAVE CURTISS & TREMORS
63	Philips BF 1257	You Don't Love Me/Sweet Girl Of Mine	6
63	Philips BF 1285	What Kind Of Girl Are You?/Dreamer's Funfair	6
64	Philips BF 1330	Summertime Blues/I'm A Hog For You Baby	6

BOBBY CURTOLA (& MARTELLS)
61	Columbia DB 4672	Don't You Sweetheart Me/My Heart's Tongue-Tied (solo)	6
62	London HL 9577	Fortune Teller/Johnny Take Your Time (solo)	5
62	London HL 9639	Aladdin/I Don't Want To Go On Without You (solo)	4
63	Decca F 11670	Gypsy Heart/I'm Sorry	4
63	Decca F 11725	Three Rows Over/Indian Giver	4

CURVE
91	Anxious ANXP 27	Ten Little Girls/Blindfold (picture disc)	6

CURVED AIR
71	Warner Bros WB 8023	It Happened Today/Vivaldi/What Happens When You Blow Yourself Up	5
72	Warner Bros K 16164	Sarah's Concern/Phantasmagoria	5
75	Deram DM 426	Back Street Luv (live)/It Happened Today (live)	4
76	BTM SBT 103	Desiree/Kids To Blame	4
76	BTM SBT 106	Baby Please Don't Go/Broken Lady	4
84	Pearl Key PK 07350	Renegade/We're Only Human (p/s)	4
70	Warner Bros WSX 3012	AIR CONDITIONING (LP, picture disc with booklet)	25
70	Warner Bros K 56004	AIR CONDITIONING (LP)	12
71	Warner Bros K 46092	SECOND ALBUM (LP, fold-out sleeve)	12
72	Warner Bros K 46158	PHANTASMAGORIA (LP, with inner lyric card)	12
73	Warner Bros K 46224	AIR CUT (LP, gatefold sleeve)	12
75	Deram SML 1119	CURVED AIR LIVE (LP)	10

(see also Kirby, Sonja Kristina, Klark Kent)

ADGE CUTLER & WURZELS
67	Columbia SX 6126	ADGE CUTLER AND THE WURZELS (LP)	10
67	Columbia SX 6165	ADGE CUTLER'S FAMILY ALBUM (LP)	10
68	Columbia S(C)X 6263	CUTLER OF THE WEST (LP)	10
69	Columbia S(C)X 6367	CARRY ON CUTLER (LP)	10

IVOR CUTLER TRIO
67	Parlophone R 5624	I Had A Little Boat/A Great Grey Grasshopper	5
59	Fontana TFE 17144	OF Y'HUP (EP)	15
61	Decca DFE 6677	GET AWAY FROM THE WALL (EP)	12
61	Decca LK 4405	WHO TORE YOUR TROUSERS? (LP)	30
67	Parlophone PCS 7040	LUDO (LP)	30

T. TOMMY CUTRER (& GINNY WRIGHT)
54	London HL 8093	Mexico Gal/Wonderful World (B-side with Ginny Wright)	30

(see also Ginny Wright)

CUTTERS
59	Decca F 11110	I've Had It/Rockaroo	6

CYANIDE
78	Pye 7N 46048	I'm A Boy/Do It (p/s)	6
78	Pye 7N 46094	Mac The Flash/Hate The State (p/s)	5
79	Pinnacle PIN 23	Fireball/Your Old Man (p/s)	5
78	Pye NSPL 18554	CYANIDE (LP)	12

CYAN THREE
66	Decca F 12371	Since I Lost My Baby/Face Of A Loser	15

CYBERMEN
78	Rockaway AERE 101	THE CYBERMEN (EP)	8

MINT VALUE £

78   Rockaway LUV 002   You're To Blame/It's You I Want (with inserts) 6

CYCLONES
63   Oriole CB 1898   Nobody/Little Egypt 15

CYCLONES
71   Banana BA 338   My Sweet Lord/DENNIS BROWN: Silky
                           (B-side actually by Monty Alexander & Cyclones) 5

CYMANDE
73   Alaska ALA 4   The Message pts 1 & 2 5
73   Alaska ALA 10   Bras/Ras Tafarian Folk Song 5
74   Contempo CS 2019   Brothers On The Slide/Pon De Dugle 7
73   Alaska ALKA 100   CYMANDE (LP) 18
74   Contempo CLP 508   PROMISED HEIGHT (LP) 20

JOHNNY CYMBAL
60   MGM MGM 1106   It'll Be Me/Always, Always 10
63   London HLR 9682   Mr Bass Man/Sacred Lovers Vow 6
63   London HLR 9731   Teenage Heaven/Cinderella Baby 10
63   London HLR 9762   Dum Dum Dee Dum/Surfing At Tijuana 8
64   London HLR 9911   Mitsou/Robinson Crusoe On Mars 8
65   United Artists UP 1093   Go V.W. Go/Sorrow And Pain 15
63   London RER 1375   MISTER BASS MAN (EP) 25
64   London RER 1406   CYMBAL SMASHES (EP) 25
     (see also Derek)

CYMBALINE
65   Pye 7N 15916   Please Little Girl/Coming Home Baby 20
65   Mercury MF 918   Top Girl/Can You Hear Me? 6
66   Mercury MF 961   I Don't Want It/Where Did Love Go Wrong 6
66   Mercury MF 975   Peanuts And Chewy Macs/Found My Girl 4
67   Philips BF 1624   Matrimonial Fears/You Will Never Love Me 25
68   Philips BF 1681   Down By The Seaside/Fire 6
69   Philips BF 1749   Turn Around/Come Back Baby 6

CYMERONS
64   Decca F 11976   I'll Be There/Making Love To Another 5
66   Polydor 56098   Everyday (Will Change)/I Can See You 6

CYNTHIA & ARCHIE
64   R&B JB 168   Every Beat/DELROY WILSON: Sammy Dead 10

CYRKLE
66   CBS 202064   Red Rubber Ball/How Can I Leave Her 4
66   CBS 202246   Turn Down Day/Big Little Woman 4
67   CBS 202516   Bony Maronie/Please Don't Ever Leave Me 4
67   CBS 202577   I Wish You Could Be There/The Visit (She Was Here) 5
67   CBS 2790   We Had A Good Thing Goin'/Two Rooms 4
67   CBS 2917   Penny Arcade/Words 4
67   CBS 62977   NEON (LP) 15

CZAR
70   Philips 6006 071   Oh Lord I'm Getting Heavy/Why Don't We Be A Rock'n'Roll Band 25
70   Fontana 6309 009   CZAR (LP) 180

EDDIE COCHRAN

MINT VALUE £

KIM D
| 65 | Pye 7N 15953 | The Real Thing/Come On Baby | 8 |
(see also Kim Davis)

TONY D & SHAKEDOWNS
| 64 | Piccadilly 7N 35168 | Is It True/Never Let Her Go | 5 |

DA BAND
| 70s | Rip Off RIP 2 | I Like It/Pirate's Lullaby (p/s) | 4 |

DA BIZ
| 80 | Small Operations SO 002 | On The Beach/This Is No Audition (p/s) | 4 |

MIKE D'ABO
69	Immediate IM 075	(See The Little People) Gulliver's Travels/ Anthology Of Gulliver's Travels Pt 2	10
70	Uni UNS 525	Let It Roar/California Line	5
70	Uni UNLS 114	D'ABO (LP, gatefold sleeve)	12
(see also Manfred Mann, Band Of Angels)

PAULINO DA COSTA
| 82 | Pablo Jazz 231 2102 | HAPPY PEOPLE (LP) | 10 |

RITA DACOSTA
| 75 | Contempo CS 2061 | Don't Bring Me Down/No! No! No! | 6 |

TERRY DACTYL & DINOSAURS
| 72 | Sonet SNTF 630 | ALIAS TERRY DACTYL & DINOSAURS (LP, actually by Brett Martin & Thunderbolts) | 10 |
(see also Brett Martin &Thunderbolts)

DADA
| 70 | Atco 2400 030 | DADA (LP) | 12 |
(see also Robert Palmer, Elkie Brooks)

DADDY LONGLEGS
70	Warner Bros WB 8012	High Again/To The Rescue	4
70	Warner Bros 3004	DADDY LONGLEGS (LP)	10
71	Vertigo 6360 038	OAKDOWN FARM (LP, gatefold sleeve, spiral label)	20
72	Polydor 2371 261	THREE MUSICIANS (LP)	10
72	Polydor 2371 323	SHIFTING SANDS (LP)	12

DADDY-O'S
| 58 | Oriole CB 1454 | Got A Match?/Have A Cigar | 7 |
| 58 | Oriole CB 1454 | Got A Match?/Have A Cigar (78) | 5 |

DADDY'S ACT
| 67 | Columbia DB 8242 | Eight Days A Week/Gonna Get You | 10 |

D.A.F. (DEUTSCH AMERIKANISCHE FREUNDSCHAFT)
80	Mute MUTE 005	Kebabträume/Gewalt (p/s)	4
80	Mute MUTE 011	Der Rauber Und Der Prinz/Tanz Mit Mir (p/s, with insert)	4
81	Virgin VS 418	Der Mussolini/Der Räuber Und Der Prinz (no p/s, possibly promo only)	5
81	Virgin VS 418-12	Der Mussolini/Der Räuber Und Der Prinz (12", p/s, original issue)	7
81	Mute STUMM 1	DIE KLEINEN UND DIE BÖSEN (LP, with inner sleeve)	10

CALVIN DAFOS
| 65 | Blue Beat BB 347 | Brown Sugar/I'm Gone | 7 |
| 69 | Doctor Bird DB 1174 | Lash Them/C.D.s: Medicine Master | 6 |

DAGABAND
| 83 | MHM A-M 094 | Second Time Around/Reds Under The Beds/I Can See For Miles (p/s) | 7 |

DAGGERMEN
| 86 | Empire UPW 258J | INTRODUCING THE DAGGERMEN (EP) | 7 |
| 86 | Own Up DAG 001 | DAGGERS IN MY MIND (LP) | 10 |
(see also James Taylor Quartet)

JACK DAILEY
| 60 | Columbia DB 4487 | Please Understand/Little Charmer | 4 |

DAILY FLASH
| 84 | Psycho PSYCHO 32 | I FLASH DAILY (LP) | 10 |

TONY DAINES
| 63 | Fontana TF 433 | Chapel In The Moonlight/Echo Of Footsteps | 4 |
| 64 | Fontana TF 472 | Too Late/I Told You So | 4 |

DAINTEES
84	Kitchenware SK 3	Roll On Summertime/Involved With Love (p/s)	8
84	Kitchenware SK 13	Trouble Town/Better Plan (p/s, original with paper labels)	4
84	Kitchenware SKX 13	Trouble Town/Better Plan/Jealous Mind (12", p/s, original with paper labels)	7
86	Jamming!/London J 1	Watch The Running Water/REDSKINS: You Want It They've Got It (Red Soul & Fury Unleashed Mix)/THEN JERICO: The Big Sweep/COMMUNARDS: Breadline Britain (free with 'Jamming!' magazine)	8/6

DAISY CLAN
| 69 | MCA MU 1057 | Bonnie Bonnie Bonnie/Friends | 4 |

70	Major Minor MM 671	Mister Walkie Talkie Man/Lions In The Tree	4
70	Pye Intl. 7N 25532	Love Needs Love/Glory Be	4
71	Decca F 23168	San Francisco China Town/Ridin' A Rainbow	4

DAISY HILL PUPPY FARM
| 88 | Lakeland LKND 006 | Rocket Boy/Heartbreak Soup/Speedball/Heart Of Glam (p/s) | 4 |

DAISY PLANET
| 60s | Oak (no cat. no.) | DAISY PLANET (EP, no p/s) | 50 |

DAKOTA JIM
| 66 | Blue Beat BB 358 | Only Soul Can Tell (actually by Slim Smith)/DAKOTA'S ALLSTARS: Call Me Master (actually by Prince Buster Allstars) | 10 |

(see also Slim Smith)

DAKOTAS
63	Parlophone R 5044	The Cruel Sea/The Millionaire	5
63	Parlophone R 5064	Magic Carpet/Humdinger	7
64	Parlophone R 5203	Oyeh/My Girl Josephine	12
67	Page One POF 018	I'm 'N 'Ardworkin' Barrow Boy/Seven Pounds Of Potatoes	18
68	Philips BF 1645	I Can't Break The News To Myself/The Spider And The Fly	40
63	Parlophone GEP 8888	MEET THE DAKOTAS (EP)	30

(see also Billy J. Kramer & Dakotas)

MICHAEL D'ALBUQUERQUE
| 74 | RCA SF 8383 | WE MAY BE CATTLE BUT WE ALL HAVE NAMES (LP, with lyric sheet) | 10 |
| 76 | Warner Bros K 56276 | STALKING THE SLEEPER (LP) | 10 |

(see also E.L.O.)

DALE & GRACE
63	London HL 9807	I'm Leaving It Up To You/That's What I Like About You	10
64	London HL 9857	Stop And Think It Over/Bad Luck	8
69	London HL 10249	I'm Leaving It Up To You/Love Is Strange	6
64	London RE 1428	DALE AND GRACE NO. 1 (EP)	15
64	London RE 1429	DALE AND GRACE NO. 2 (EP)	15
64	London RE 1430	DALE AND GRACE NO. 3 (EP)	15

ALAN DALE
55	Vogue Coral Q 72072	Cherry Pink And Apple Blossom White/I'm Sincere	10
55	Vogue Coral Q 72089	Sweet And Gentle/You Still Mean The Same To Me	7
55	Vogue Coral Q 72105	Rockin' The Cha-Cha/Wham! (There I Go In Love Again)	8
55	Vogue Coral Q 72105	Rockin' The Cha-Cha/Wham! (There I Go In Love Again) (78)	8
56	Vogue Coral Q 72121	Robin Hood/Lisbon Antigua	20
56	Vogue Coral Q 72156	Dance On/Mr. Moon	5
56	Vogue Coral Q 72156	Dance On/Mr. Moon (78)	5
56	Vogue Coral Q 72166	The Birds And The Bees/I Promise	5
56	Vogue Coral Q 72191	Be My Guest/Pardners (with Buddy Hackett)	5
56	Vogue Coral Q 72194	The Test Of Time/I Cry More	7
57	Vogue Coral Q 72225	Don't Knock The Rock/Your Love Is My Love	12
57	Vogue Coral Q 72225	Don't Knock The Rock/Your Love Is My Love (78)	7
57	Vogue Coral Q 72231	The Girl Can't Help It/Lonesome Road	12
57	Vogue Coral Q 72231	The Girl Can't Help It/Lonesome Road (78)	10
58	MGM MGM 986	Volare/Weeping Willow In The Wind	5

(see also Johnny Desmond)

DICK DALE & HIS DELTONES
63	Capitol CL 15296	Surf Beat/Peppermint Man	10
63	Capitol CL 15320	The Scavenger/Wild Ideas	10
63	Capitol T 1886	SURFERS' CHOICE (LP)	20
63	Capitol T 1930	KING OF THE SURF GUITAR (LP)	20

GLEN DALE
| 66 | Decca F 12475 | Good Day Sunshine/Make Me Belong To You | 4 |

JIM DALE
57	Parlophone R 4329	Piccadilly Line/I Didn't Mean It	9
57	Parlophone R 4329	Piccadilly Line/I Didn't Mean It (78)	5
57	Parlophone R 4343	Be My Girl/You Shouldn't Do That	6
57	Parlophone R 4343	Be My Girl/You Shouldn't Do That (78)	5
57	Parlophone R 4356	All Shook Up/Wandering Eyes (with Vipers & King Brothers)	9
57	Parlophone R 4356	All Shook Up/Wandering Eyes (with Vipers & King Brothers) (78)	5
57	Parlophone R 4376	Just Born (To Be Your Baby)/Crazy Dream	6
57	Parlophone R 4376	Just Born (To Be Your Baby)/Crazy Dream (78)	5
58	Parlophone R 4402	Sugartime/Don't Let Go	6
58	Parlophone R 4402	Sugartime/Don't Let Go (78)	5
58	Parlophone R 4424	Jane Belinda/Tread Softly Stranger	5
58	Parlophone R 4424	Jane Belinda/Tread Softly Stranger (78)	5
59	Parlophone R 4522	Gotta Find A Girl/The Legend Of Nellie D.	5
59	Parlophone R 4522	Gotta Find A Girl/The Legend Of Nellie D. (78)	5
60s	Academy AD 001	Somewhere There's A Someone/If You Come Back	6
62	Piccadilly 7N 35039	One Boy, One Girl/My Resistance is Low	5
62	Piccadilly 7N 35100	Start All Over Again/It's For Them	5
57	Parlophone GEP 8656	JIM DALE (EP)	18
58	Parlophone PMD 1055	JIM (10" LP)	45

PAUL DALE BAND
| 82 | KA KA 6/PAUL 1 | Alright On The Night/Hold On (p/s, clear vinyl) | 4 |

(see also Marseille)

SYD DALE ORCHESTRA
| 65 | Decca F 22300 | C'mon In/Disc A Go Go | 4 |
| 66 | Decca F 22370 | It Started With Eve/Hell Raisers | 4 |

MINT VALUE £

DALEK I LOVE YOU
80   Backdoor CLOSE 1   Dalek I Love You/Eight Track (p/s, original version) 4

DALEKS
(see under Century 21)

DALE SISTERS
60   HMV POP 781   The Kiss/Billy Boy, Billy Boy 8
61   Ember EMB S 140   My Sunday Baby/All My Life 6
62   Ember EMB S 151   Secrets/Road To Love 6

BASIL DALEY
68   Studio One SO 2054   Hold Me Baby/HEPTONES: I Got A Feeling 12

JIMMY DALEY & DING-A-LINGS
57   Brunswick 05648   Rock, Pretty Baby/Can I Steal A Little Love 85
57   Brunswick 05648   Rock, Pretty Baby/Can I Steal A Little Love (78) 15

SALVADOR DALI
62   Decca SET 230   DALI IN VENICE (LP, gatefold sleeve with booklet) 15

DALI'S CAR
84   Paradox DOXY 1   The Judgement Is The Mirror/High Places (picture disc) .4
(see also Bauhaus, Peter Murphy, Japan, Mick Khan)

TONY DALLI
59   Columbia SEG 7897   SONGS FROM THE SHOWS (EP) 7

MIKI DALLON
66   Strike JH 306   Cheat And Lie/(I'm Gonna Find A) Cave 8
66   Strike JH 318   What Will Your Mama Say Now?/Two At A Time 5
65   RCA RCA 1438   Do You Still Call That Love?/Apple Pie 20
65   RCA RCA 1478   I Care About You/I'll Give You Love 25
(see also Neil Christian & Crusaders)

KATHY DALTON
73   Discreet K 59202   AMAZING (LP) 10

MIKE DALTON
61   Bi-Tapes RRE 1114   GOT WHAT IT TAKES (EP, reel-to-reel tape) 7
61   Bi-Tapes RRA 104   GOT WHAT IT TAKES (reel-to-reel tape) 10
61   Bi-Tapes RRB 107   LIVING NOW (reel-to-reel tape) 10

DALTONS
67   Fab FAB 30   Never Kiss You Again/RIGHTEOUS FLAMES: When A Girl Loves A Boy 8

ROGER DALTREY
72   Ode ODS 66302   I'm Free/Overture (p/s) 5
73   Track 2094 110   Giving It All Away/The Way Of The World 4
73   Track 2094 014   Thinking/There Is Love 4
73   Track 2094 016   It's A Hard Life/One Man Band 5
75   A&M AMS 7206   Orpheus Song/Love's Dream 4
75   Lyntone LYN 3176/7   Wagner's Dream/Love's Theme/RICK WAKEMAN: Count Your Blessings
                                 (flexidisc with '19' mag) 7/5
77   Polydor 2058 948   Say It Ain't So Joe/Satin And Lace (withdrawn, any pressed?) . . . . .10+
78   Polydor 2058 986   Say It Ain't So Joe/The Prisoner 4
80   Polydor POSP 181   Without Your Love/Say It Ain't So Joe (p/s, without extra track "Free Me") 4
86   10 TEND 81   Under A Raging Moon/Move Better In The Night//Behind Blue Eyes/5:15/
                                 Won't Get Fooled Again (double pack, gatefold p/s) 4
86   10 TENG 8112   Under A Raging Moon (6.43)/Move Better In The Night/Under A Raging
                                 Moon (4.30) (12", gatefold p/s) 7
86   10 TEND 103   The Pride You Hide/Don't Talk To Strangers//Pictures Of Lily/Break Out
                                 (double pack) 4
73   Track 2406 107   DALTREY (LP) 10
75   Polydor ACB 199   RIDE A ROCK HORSE (LP, Record Club edition) 10
80   Polydor POLD 5034   McVICAR (LP, soundtrack, clear vinyl) 10
(see also Who)

DALYS
65   Fontana TF 546   Me Japanese Boy/Never Kind Of Love 4
65   Fontana TF 637   She's My Girl/When Love Has Gone 4
66   Strike JH 317   Don't Go Breaking My Heart/Little Stranger 5
67   Fontana TF 809   Sweet Maria/Leaving Time 4
67   Fontana TF 841   A Fistful Of Dollars/Man With No Name 5
68   Fontana TF 907   Let Me Go Lover/A Place In The Sun 4
68   Fontana TF 988   Early Morning Rain/Chanson D'Amour 4

TADD DAMERON ORCHESTRA
54   Capitol CL 14201   Focus/John's Delight 5
50s Capitol EAP1 20388   TADD'S DELIGHT (EP) 7
(see also Clifford Brown)

DAMIAN
86   Sedition EDITL 3311   The Time Warp/Dancin' (12", p/s) 7

DAMITA JO
54   HMV JO 390   I'd Do It Again/Do I, Do I, Do I (B-side with Steve Gibson) (export issue) 8
60   Mercury AMT 1085   Widow Walk/Dearest Darling 4
60   Mercury AMT 1116   I'll Save The Last Dance For You/Forgive 4
60   Mercury AMT 1133   Keep Your Hands Off Him/Hush, Somebody's Calling My Name 4
61   Mercury AMT 1141   Do What You Want/Sweet Georgia Brown 4
61   Mercury AMT 1155   I'll Be There/Love Laid It's Hands On Me 4
61   Mercury ZEP 10118   I'LL SAVE THE LAST DANCE FOR YOU (EP) 8

DAMNED

74	Youngblood YB 1067	Morning Bird/Theta	4

DAMNED

76	Stiff BUY 6	New Rose/Help! (with original press-out centre & 'Delga' credit on p/s)	8
76	Stiff BUY 6	New Rose/Help! (p/s, later issues)	5-7
77	Stiff BUY 10	Neat Neat Neat/Stab Yor Back/Singalongascabies (p/s, originals have "The Damned" printed in ornate gothic type on label)	8
77	Stiff BUY 10	Neat Neat Neat/Stab Yor Back/Singalongascabies (p/s, 'Four Pack' issue without 'Delga' on sleeve & "The Damned" printed in plain type)	6
77	Stiff DAMNED 1	Stretcher Case Baby/Sick Of Being Sick ('NME' competition freebie)	35
77	Stiff BUY 18	Problem Child/You Take My Money (p/s, originally with press-out centre)	7/5
77	Stiff BUY 24	Don't Cry Wolf/One Way Love (20,000 on pink vinyl, no p/s)	8/5
77	Stiff BUY 24	Don't Cry Wolf/One Way Love (with Dave Vanian freebie p/s)	50+
78	Dodgy Demo Co. SGS 105	Love Song/Burglar (mail order issue/gig freebie, plain sleeve, stickered labels)	.25
79	Chiswick CHIS 112	Love Song/Noise Noise Noise/Suicide (red vinyl, 4 different sleeves)	6
79	Chiswick CHIS 112	Love Song/Noise Noise Noise/Suicide (4 different sleeves)	4
79	Chiswick CHIS 116	Smash It Up/Burglar (p/s)	5
79	Chiswick CHIS 120	I Just Can't Be Happy Today/Ballroom Blitz/The Turkey Song (p/s)	8
80	Chiswick CHIS 130	White Rabbit/Rabid (Over You)/Seagulls (Europe only, unreleased in U.K., 2 x 1-sided white-label test pressings exist, hand-written labels)	50
80	Chiswick CHIS 135	The History Of The World Part 1/I Believe The Impossible/ Sugar And Spite (p/s)	6
80	Chiswick CHIS 12 135	The History Of The World Part 1/I Believe The Impossible/ Sugar And Spite (12", p/s)	8
80	Chiswick CHIS 139	There Ain't No Sanity Clause/Hit Or Miss/Looking At You (live) (p/s)	6
81	NEMS TRY 1	FRIDAY THE 13TH (EP)	6
81	Stiff GRAB 2	FOUR PACK (BUY 6, 10, 18 & 24, in a plastic wallet)	25
82	Big Beat NS 75	Love Song/Noise Noise Noise/Suicide (3 different sleeves, some on blue vinyl)	5/4
82	Big Beat NS 76	Smash It Up/Burglar (p/s, initially on red vinyl)	6/4
82	Big Beat NS 77	Wait For The Blackout/CAPTAIN SENSIBLE & SOFTIES: Jet Boy, Jet Girl (p/s, some with red/black 'Damned' labels)	7/4
82	Big Beat NSP 77	Wait For The Blackout/CAPTAIN SENSIBLE & SOFTIES: Jet Boy, Jet Girl (picture disc)	8
82	Bronze BRO 149	Lovely Money/(Disco Mix)/I Think I'm Wonderful (p/s)	5
82	Bronze BROP 149	Lovely Money/(Disco Mix)/I Think I'm Wonderful (picture disc)	7
82	Bronze BRO 156	Dozen Girls/Take That/Mine's A Large One, Landlord/Torture Me (p/s)	6
82	Big Beat NS 80	Lively Arts/Teenage Dream (p/s, some on green vinyl)	8/4
82	Big Beat NST 80	Lively Arts/Teenage Dream/I'm So Bored (10", p/s)	10
82	Bronze BRO 159	Generals/Disguise/Citadel Zombies (p/s)	12
83	Big Beat NS 85	White Rabbit/Rabid (Over You)/Seagulls (p/s)	4
83	Big Beat NST 85	White Rabbit/Curtain Call (New Version) (12", p/s)	7
84	Plus One DAMNED 1P	Thanks For The Night/Nasty (picture disc)	5
84	Plus One DAMNED 1	Thanks For The Night/Nasty (p/s, 1,000 each on red, white & blue vinyl)	6
84	Plus One DAMNED 1T	Thanks For The Night/Nasty/Do The Blitz (12", p/s, 1,000 on marbled vinyl)	7
84	Plus One DAMNED 1T	Thanks For The Night/Nasty/Do The Blitz (12", no'd p/s, multi-coloured vinyl)	8
84	Plus One DAMNED 1T	Thanks For The Night/Nasty ('woman'-shaped picture disc with plinth, 1,000 only)	35
85	MCA GRIM 1	Grimly Fiendish/Edward The Bear (gatefold p/s)	5
85	MCA GRIM 1	Grimly Fiendish/Edward The Bear (1,000 in gatefold p/s, autographed)	8
85	MCA GRIMP 1	Grimly Fiendish/Edward The Bear (picture disc)	6
85	MCA GRIMT 1	Grimly Fiendish (Spic'n'Span Mix)/Edward The Bear (12", autographed p/s)	10
85	MCA GRIMX 1	Grimly Fiendish (Bad Trip Mix)/Grimly Fiendish/Edward The Bear (12", PVC sleeve, white vinyl, numbered)	10
85	MCA GRIMX 2	The Shadow Of Love (Ten Inches Of Hell Mix)/Nightshift/Would You (10", p/s)	8
85	MCA GRIM 2/GRIMY 2	Edition Premier: The Shadow Of Love/Nightshift/Let There Be Rats/ Wiped Out (double pack)	10
85	MCA GRIM 3	Is It A Dream (Wild West End Mix)/Street Of Dreams (live) (p/s, with 5 badges)	4
85	MCA GRIMT 3	Is It A Dream (Wild West Express Mix)/Street Of Dreams (live)/Curtain Call (live)/Pretty Vacant (live)/Wild Thing (live) (12", p/s, with 5 Damned badges)	7
85	TALK 1	An Interview With The Damned 1985 Part 1- Rat & Bryn (picture disc)	5
85	TALK 2	An Interview With The Damned 1985 Part 2 - Dave & Roman (picture disc)	5
86	MCA GRIMX 4	Eloise (No Sleep Until Wednesday Mix)/Temptation/Beat Girl (12", p/s, blue vinyl, 2,000 only)	7
86	MCA GRIMT 4	Eloise/Temptation/Beat Girl (12", p/s, 2,000 on blue vinyl)	7
86	Stiff BUYIT 6	New Rose/Neat Neat Neat/Help/Stretcher Case Baby/Sick Of Being Sick (12", p/s, white vinyl)	7
86	Stiff BUY 6/BUYDJ 6	New Rose/Help//I'm So Bored (1-sided) (double pack, stickered PVC sleeve with insert, 1st disc on white vinyl, 2nd disc actually plays "I Fall" [live])	5
86	Stiff BUY 6	New Rose/Help (reissue, red vinyl, PVC sleeve, with card insert)	5
86	MCA GRIM 5	Anything/The Year Of The Jackal (with alternate numbered p/s)	6
86	MCA GRIMX 5	Anything (Another Mix)/Anything (Instrumental)/Anything (And Yet Another Mix)/The Year Of The Jackal (10", p/s, blue or yellow vinyl)	6/7
87	MCA GRIM 6	Gigilo/The Portrait (p/s, blue, green, red or lime green vinyl with poster)	ea. 4
87	MCA GRIMT 6	Gigilo/The Portrait (12", p/s, clear vinyl)	7
87	MCA DGRIM 7	Alone Again Or/Eloise (Version)/In Dulce Decorum/Psychomania (CD, 7" p/s with 'go-pack' holder, cloth protector & insert)	8
77	Stiff SEEZ 1	DAMNED DAMNED DAMNED (LP, some shrinkwrapped & stickered)	30/10
77	Stiff SEEZ 1	DAMNED DAMNED DAMNED (LP, 2,000 misprinted on rear sleeve with Eddie & Hot Rods photograph; some shrinkwrapped & stickered)	40/25
80	Chiswick CWK 3015	THE BLACK ALBUM (2-LP, gatefold sleeve)	16
81	Ace DAM 1	THE BEST OF THE DAMNED (LP, red or blue vinyl)	10
82	Ace DAM 2	MACHINE GUN ETIQUETTE (LP reissue, blue or white/clear vinyl with inner)	10
82	Ace DAM 3	THE BLACK ALBUM (single LP reissue, 12,000 with lyrics & poster)	10
82	Big Beat NED 1	LIVE SHEPPERTON 1980 (LP, with 'Collectors Catalogue', 5,000 only)	10

MINT VALUE £

83	Stiff MAIL 2	DAMNED DAMNED DAMNED/MUSIC FOR PLEASURE (2-LP, reissue, gatefold sleeve, yellow vinyl, mail order only)	14
83	Damned DAMU 2	LIVE IN NEWCASTLE (LP, 5,000 by mail order only)	20
83	Damned PDAMU 2	LIVE IN NEWCASTLE (LP, picture disc, 5,000 only)	18
85	MCA MCF 3275	PHANTASMAGORIA (LP, white vinyl)	10
85	MCA MCFP 3275	PHANTASMAGORIA (LP, picture disc)	10
85	MCA MC9 3275	PHANTASMAGORIA (LP, with free blue vinyl 12" "Eloise")	10
86	Stiff GET 4	THE CAPTAIN'S BIRTHDAY PARTY — LIVE AT THE ROUNDHOUSE (mini-LP, 45rpm, blue vinyl, stickered plain white sleeve)	12
86	MCA MCG 6015	ANYTHING (LP, with autographed inner)	10

(see also Captain Sensible, Brian James, Edge, Magic Michael, Naz Nomad & Nightmares, Rat & Whale, Auntiepus)

KENNY DAMON
65	Mercury MF 907	While I Live/Fountain In Capri	4
68	Mercury MF 1014	Turn Her Away/Till Then My Love	4

(see also Kenny Roberts)

RUSS DAMON
64	Stateside SS 258	Hip Huggers/Heaven Sent	6

VIC DAMONE
57	MGM MGM 949	And This Is My Beloved (with Howard Keel)/Night Of My Nights	4
57	MGM MGM 950	Stranger In Paradise (with Ann Blyth)/ANN BLYTH: Baubles, Bangles And Pearls	4
58	Philips PB 819	On The Street Where You Live/Arrirverderci Roma	4
58	Philips PB 837	Only Man On The Island/When My Love Smiles	4
54	Mercury EP1 3121	WALKING MY BABY BACK HOME (EP)	10
57	Philips BBE 12099	VIC DAMONE (EP)	7
58	Philips BBE 12197	DAMONE FAVOURITES (EP)	7
58	Philips BBE 12222	VIC DAMONE (EP)	7
58	Mercury MEP 9534	THE VOICE OF VIC DAMONE (EP)	7
59	Mercury ZEP 10022	YOURS FOR A SONG (EP)	7
59	Philips BBE 12245	DO I LOVE YOU (EP)	7
61	Philips BBE 12502	ON THE SWINGERS SIDE (EP)	7
62	Capitol EAP1 1646	LINGER AWHILE (EP)	7
57	Mercury MPT 7514	ALL-TIME SONG HITS (10" LP)	20
57	Philips BBL 7144	THAT TOWERING FEELING! (LP)	15
58	Philips BBL 7259	CLOSER THAN A KISS (LP)	12
60	Philips BBL 7347	THIS GAME OF LOVE (LP)	10
62	Capitol (S)T 1646	LINGER AWHILE (LP)	10
62	Capitol (S)T 1691	STRANGE ENCHANTMENT (LP)	10
62	Capitol (S)T 1748	THE LIVELY ONES (LP)	10
63	Capitol (S)T 1811	MY BABY LOVES TO SWING (LP)	10
63	Capitol (S)T 1944	THE LIVELIEST (LP)	10
64	Capitol (S)T 2133	ON THE STREET WHERE YOU LIVE (LP)	10

(see also Howard Keel)

DANA
70	Decca F 13004	All Kinds Of Everything/Channel Breeze (export issue)	4

DANCE CHAPTER
80	4AD AD 18	Anonymity/New Dance (p/s, some with card insert)	8/6
81	4AD BAD 115	CHAPTER II (12" EP)	8
80s	Pleasantly Surprised PS 10	WHEN THE SPIRIT MOVES THEM (cassette, in bag with inserts)	12

DANCING DID
79	Fruit & Veg F&V 1	Dancing Did/Lorry Pirates (p/s)	8
80	Fruit & Veg F&V 2	The Haunted Tearooms/Squashed Things On The Road (p/s)	5

DANDO SHAFT
72	RCA RCA 2246	Sun Clog Dance/This Gift	8
70	Youngblood SSYB 6	AN EVENING WITH DANDO SHAFT (LP)	50
71	RCA Neon NE 5	DANDO SHAFT (LP, gatefold sleeve)	45
72	RCA SF 8256	LANTALOON (LP, initially with poster)	50/40
77	Rubber RUB 034	KINGDOM (LP)	30

(see also Hedgehog Pie)

DANDY (& SUPERBOYS)
64	Blue Beat BB 308	To Love You/I'm Looking For Love	7
64	Blue Beat BB 319	Hey Boy Hey Girl/So Long Baby (as Dandy & Del)	7
64	Blue Beat BB 327	My Baby/I'm Gonna Stop Loving You	7
64	Dice CC 21	Rudie Don't Go/It's Just Got To Be	7
65	Dice CC 24	You Got To Pray/I Got To Have You (as Dandy & Barbara)	7
65	Blue Beat BB 336	I Found Love/You've Got Something Nice	7
66	Dice CC 29	The Operation/A Little More Ska	7
66	Ska Beat JB 247	The Fight/Do You Know	5
67	Ska Beat JB 269	One Scotch One Bourbon One Beer/Maximum Pressure	5
67	Ska Beat JB 273	Rudie A Message To You/Til Death Do Us Part	7
67	Ska Beat JB 279	You're No Hustler/No No	7
67	Giant GN 3	My Time Now/East Of Suez (& Superboys)	5
67	Giant GN 5	Puppet On A String/Have Your Fun (& Superboys)	5
67	Giant GN 7	We Are Still Rude/Let's Do Rocksteady (& Superboys)	5
67	Giant GN 10	Somewhere My Love/My Kind Of Love (& Superboys)	5
67	Giant GN 15	There Is A Mountain/This Music Got Soul (& Superboys)	5
68	Giant GN 20	Charlie Brown/Groovin' At The Cue (as Dandy & Charlie Griffiths)	5
68	Giant GN 27	Sweet Ride/Up The Hill (& Superboys)	6
68	Giant GN 30	Tears On My Pillow/Mad Them (& Superboys)	5
68	Giant GN 33	I'm Back With A Bang Bang/Jungle Walk (& Superboys)	5
68	Trojan TR 618	The Toast/Kicks Out	6
68	Trojan TR 629	Sentence (as Dandy & Lee)/LEE PERRY: You Crummy	6

69	Columbia Blue Beat DB 112	Play It Cool/Rude With Me	6
69	Downtown DT 410	Reggae In Your Jeggae/Reggae Shuffle	4
67	Giant GNL 1000	ROCKSTEADY WITH DANDY (LP)	25
68	Trojan TRL 2	DANDY RETURNS (LP)	20
69	Trojan TTL 26	YOUR MUSICAL DOCTOR (LP)	10

(see also Bobby Thompson, Sugar & Dandy, Rub A Dubs)

DANDY & AUDREY
| 69 | Trojan TRL 17 | I NEED YOU (LP) | 10 |
| 70 | Trojan TBL 118 | MORNING SIDE OF THE MOUNTAIN (LP) | 10 |

CHRIS DANE
| 55 | London HLA 8165 | Cynthia's In Love/My Ideal | 15 |

JERRY DANE
60	Decca F 11234	You're My Only Girl/Nothing But The Truth	4
60	Decca F 11284	Let's/Awhile In Love	4
63	Windsor WPS 127	Everybody Go Wild/Watcha Want	4

PATRICK DANE (& MARK 7)
65	Columbia DB 7466	In My Baby's Eyes/Only You	4
65	Columbia DB 7749	Go Out And Get Somebody/Go On Your Way	4
68	MGM MGM 1403	When You Lose The One You Love/Home (as Patrick Dane & Mark 7)	4

SHELLEY DANE
| 60 | Pye Intl. 7N 25064 | Hannah Lee/This Is The Time In My Life | 6 |

MICHAEL D'ANGELO ORCHESTRA
| 61 | Columbia DB 4705 | Rocco's Theme/Spinaree | 4 |

CAL DANGER
| 62 | Fontana 267 225 TF | Restless/Teenage Girlie Blues | 20 |

A.P. DANGERFIELD
| 68 | Fontana TF 935 | Conversations (In A Station Light Refreshment Bar)/Further Conversations | 15 |

KEITH DANGERFIELD
| 68 | Plexium P 1237 | No Life Child/She's A Witch | 125 |

(see also Keith Field)

TONY DANGERFIELD & THRILLS
| 64 | Pye 7N 15695 | I've Seen Such Things/She's Too Way Out | 35 |

DANGEROUS GIRLS
| 78 | Happy Face MM 115 | Dangerous Girls/I Didn't Want To Eat (With The Family) (p/s) | 4 |

DANI
| 74 | Pye Intl. 7N 25667 | La Vie A 25 Ans/Pour Que Ca Dure (p/s). | 6 |
| 74 | Pye Intl. 7N 25667 | That Old Familiar Feeling/Pour Que Ca Dure | 12 |

BILLY DANIELS
56	Vogue V 2386	I Live For You/Medley: Easy To Love, etc.	5
56	Oriole CB 1087	I Get A Kick Out Of You/Too Marvelous For Words	5
56	Oriole CB 1095	That Old Black Magic/I Concentrate On You	5
60	Vogue V 9172	That Old Black Magic/My Yiddishe Mamma	10
56	Mercury MEP 9001	BILLY DANIELS (EP)	10
58	HMV 7EG 8485	BEST OF BILLY DANIELS (EP)	7
60	Mercury ZEP 10066	THAT OLD BLACK MAGIC (EP)	8
53	Oriole/Mercury MG 10003	TORCH HOUR (10" LP, Oriole label with stickered U.S. Mercury sleeve)	25
54	Mercury MG 25103	TORCH HOUR (10" LP, reissue)	20
54	Mercury MG 25163	SONGS AT MIDNIGHT (10" LP)	25
56	Mercury MPT 7006	TORCH HOUR (10" LP, 2nd reissue)	15
56	Mercury MPT 7505	SONGS AT MIDNIGHT (10" LP, reissue)	18
56	Vogue LAE 12021	AT THE CRESCENDO (LP)	15
58	HMV DLP 1174	YOU GO TO MY HEAD (10" LP)	12
58	HMV CLP 1200	THE MASCULINE TOUCH (LP)	10

JOE DANIELS' JAZZ GROUP
54	Parlophone MSP 6111	I Wish I Could Shimmy Like My Sister Kate/Susie	5
54	Parlophone MSP 6129	Little Brown Jug/Mountain Wine	5
54	Parlophone MSP 6143	Crazy Rhythm/The Champagne Touch	5
56	Parlophone R 4236	"Dixieland Party (No. 2)" Medley (both sides)	4
57	Parlophone R 4273	When The Saints Go Marching In/Spanish Shawl (solo)	4
57	Parlophone R 4324	Avalon/New Orleans Parade	4
57	Parlophone R 4330	Oi! Oi! Oi!/Bottle Beatin' Blues	4
57	Parlophone R 4378	"Juke Box Jazz" Medley (both sides)	4

JULIUS DANIELS
| 65 | RCA RCX 7175 | R.C.A. VICTOR RACE SERIES VOL. 4 (EP) | 15 |

MAXINE DANIELS
57	Oriole CB 1366	Coffee-Bar Calypso/Cha-Cha Calypso	4
58	Oriole CB 1402	I Never Realised/Moonlight Serenade	4
58	Oriole CB 1440	Somebody Else Is Taking My .../You Brought A New Kind Of ...	4
58	Oriole CB 1449	When It's Springtime In The Rockies/My Summer Heart	4
58	Oriole CB 1462	Passionate Summer/Lola's Heart	4

MIKE DANIELS & HIS BAND
| 57 | Parlophone R 4285 | Hiawatha/Don't You Think I Love You | 4 |

REV R.A. DANIELS
| 51 | Capitol CL 13530 | He's The Lily Of The Valley/I Shall Wear A Crown (78) | 40 |

ROLY "YO YO" DANIELS
| 60s | Stardisc SD 101 | Yo Yo Boy/The Teacher | 12 |
| 61 | Parlophone R 4759 | Late Last Evening/Bella Bella Marie | 4 |

MINT VALUE £

| 62 | Decca F 11501 | Yo Yo Boy/The Teacher (reissue) | 6 |

SAM DANIELS

| 63 | Sway SW 003 | Tell Me Baby/ERNIE FAULKENER: Beautiful Girl (both with Planets) | 8 |

JOHNNY DANKWORTH ORCHESTRA

53	Parlophone MSP 6026	Honeysuckle Rose (with Cleo Laine)/Swingin'	5
53	Parlophone MSP 6032	Moon Flowers/Two Ticks	5
53	Parlophone MSP 6037	I Get A Kick Out Of You (with Frank Holder)/Easy Living (with Cleo Laine)	5
54	Parlophone MSP 6067	S' Wonderful/Younger Every Day	5
54	Parlophone MSP 6077	The Slider/It's The Talk Of The Town	5
54	Parlophone MSP 6083	The Jerky Thing/My Buddy	5
54	Parlophone MSP 6092	Runnin' Wild/Oo-Be-Doop	6
54	Parlophone MSP 6113	Perdido/Four Of A Kind	5
54	Parlophone MSP 6139	Bugle Call Rag/You Go To My Head	5
55	Capitol CL 14285	Singin' In The Rain/Non-Stop London	5
56	Parlophone MSP 6255	Experiments With Mice/Applecake	7
57	Parlophone R 4274	All Clare/Melbourne Marathon	4
57	Parlophone R 4294	Duke's Joke/Coquette	4
57	Parlophone R 4321	Big Jazz Story/Firth Of Fourths	4
58	Parlophone R 4456	The Colonel's Tune/Jim And Andy's	4
59	Top Rank JAR 209	We Are The Lambeth Boys/Duet For 16	4
61	Columbia DB 4590	African Waltz/Moanin'	4
61	Columbia DB 4695	The Avengers/Chano	10
63	Fontana TF 422	The Avengers/Off The Cuff	10
66	Fontana TF 700	Modesty Blaise Theme/The Frost Report	5
61	Columbia SEG 8137	AFRICAN WALTZ (EP)	7
58	Parlophone GEP 8653	DANKWORTH WORKSHOP NO. 1 (EP)	7
58	Parlophone GEP 8697	DANKWORTH WORKSHOP NO. 2 - EXPERIMENTS WITH DANKWORTH (EP)	8
60	Columbia SEG 8037	THE CRIMINAL (EP, soundtrack; also stereo ESG 7825)	7/8
60	Top Rank 25/019	LONDON TO NEWPORT (LP)	10
61	Columbia 33SX 1280	JAZZ ROUTES (LP, also stereo SCX 3347)	10
64	Fontana TL/STL 5203	WHAT THE DICKENS! (LP)	12
65	Fontana TL 5229	THE ZODIAC VARIATIONS (LP)	12
68	Fontana TL 5445	THE $1,000,000 COLLECTION (LP)	10

(see also Cleo Laine, Philip Green, Tony Mansell, Kenny Wheeler & Johnny Dankworth)

DANLEERS

| 58 | Mercury AMT 1003 | One Summer Night/Wheelin' And A-Dealin' | 50 |
| 58 | Mercury AMT 1003 | One Summer Night/Wheelin' And A-Dealin' (78) | 50 |

DANNY & DRESSMAKERS

| 70s | Fuck Off FEP 002 | Cathy And Clair | 4 |
| 70s | Weird Noise WEIRD 003 | 39 GOLDEN GRATES (C90 cassette) | 10 |

DANNY & JUNIORS

58	HMV POP 436	At The Hop/Sometimes (When I'm All Alone)	20
58	HMV POP 436	At The Hop/Sometimes (When I'm All Alone) (78)	10
58	HMV POP 467	Rock And Roll Is Here To Stay/School Boy Romance	35
58	HMV POP 467	Rock And Roll Is Here To Stay/School Boy Romance (78)	15
58	HMV POP 504	Dottie/In The Meantime	20
58	HMV POP 504	Dottie/In The Meantime (78)	20
60	Top Rank JAR 510	Twistin' U.S.A./Thousand Miles Away	10
61	Top Rank JAR 552	Pony Express/Daydreamer	10
61	Top Rank JAR 587	Back At The Hop/The Charleston Fish	10
62	Top Rank JAR 604	Twistin' All Night Long/Twistin' England	8
63	London HL 9666	Oo-La-La-Limbo/Now And Then	7
68	Stateside SS 2117	At The Hop/LLOYD PRICE: (You've Got) Personality	4

DANSE SOCIETY

81	Society SOC 3-81	The Clock/Continent (brown, black & white foldout p/s)	12
81	Society SOC 3-81	The Clock/Continent (black & white foldout p/s)	8
81	Pax PAX 2	There Is No Shame In Death/Dolphins/These Frayed Edges (12", p/s, blue vinyl)	40
81	Pax PAX 2	There Is No Shame In Death/Dolphins/These Frayed Edges (12", p/s)	10
82	Pax SOC 5	Woman's Own/We're So Happy (p/s)	10
82	Pax PAX 5	Woman's Own/Continent/We're So Happy/Belief (12", with spined p/s)	12
83	Society SOC 2	The Clock/Continent (reissue) (p/s)	4
83	Arista SOCPD 6	Heaven Is Waiting/Lizard Man (picture disc, PVC sleeve)	5
84	Arista SOC 77DSF 1	2000 Light Years From Home/Seen The Light/The Sway/Endless (double pack)	5
84	Arista SOCV 127	2000 Light Years From Home/Seen The Light/Angel (Self Indulgent Dub Mix) (12", p/s, on marble blue vinyl with sticker)	12
85	Arista SOC 8/FSOC 8	Sensimilia/Treat Me Right (double pack)	4
86	Arista SOC 9	Hold On (To What You've Got)/Danse: Move (p/s, with cassette "Hold On (To What You've Got)" (12", Version)/"2000 Light Years From Home"/"Wake Up")	6

DANSETTE DAMAGE

| 78 | Shoestring LACE 001 | New Musical Express/The Only Sound (p/s) | 5 |
| 79 | Pinnacle PIN 30 | 2001¾ Approximately/Must Be Love (p/s) | 4 |

DANTALION'S CHARIOT

| 67 | Columbia DB 8260 | The Madman Running Through The Fields/The Sun Came Bursting Through My Cloud | 45 |

(see also Zoot Money's Big Roll Band)

DANTE

| 61 | Brunswick 05857 | Bye Bye Baby/That's Why | 5 |

DANTE & EVERGREENS

| 60 | Top Rank JAR 402 | Alley-Oop/The Right Time | 15 |

TROY DANTE (& INFERNOS)

| 63 | Decca F 11639 | Golden Earings/Milord | 4 |

63	Decca F 11746	It's Alright/Tell Me (& Infernos)	4
64	Fontana TF 445	Tell Me When/It Had To Be (& Infernos)	4
64	Fontana TF 477	This Little Girl/Loving Eyes (& Infernos)	8
64	Fontana TF 498	Baby/Tell Me Now	4
65	Fontana TF 541	I Wish I Knew/Sad Tears	4
66	Polydor NH 56110	I'll Never Know/Security	4
68	Columbia DB 8381	My Friend The Scarecrow/Emma May Kingston	4

TERENCE TRENT D'ARBY

87	CBS TRENT Q1	If You Let Me Stay/Loving Is Another Word For Lonely (poster p/s)	4
87	CBS TRENT T1	If You Let Me Stay (Hardline Mix)/Loving Is Another Word For Lonely (12", p/s, with free shrink-wrapped 12" "If You Let Me Stay" [XPR 1338])	7
87	CBS TRENT G2	Wishing Well/Elevators And Hearts (poster p/s)	4
87	CBS TRENT Q3	Dance Little Sister Pts 1 & 2 (poster p/s)	4
87	CBS 450911-0	INTRODUCING THE HARDLINE ACCORDING TO... (LP, picture disc)	10
87	CBS 450911-0	INTRODUCING THE HARDLINE ACCORDING TO... (LP, picture disc, alt.version)	20

JOE DARENSBOURG & HIS DIXIE FLYERS

| 58 | Vogue V 2409 | Yellow Dog Blues/Careless Love | 4 |
| 50s | Vogue LAE 12149 | JOE DARENSBOURG & HIS DIXIE FLYERS (LP) | 10 |

BOBBY DARIN

56	Brunswick 05561	Rock Island Line/Timber (as Bobby Darin & Jaybirds)	70
56	Brunswick 05561	Rock Island Line/Timber (as Bobby Darin & Jaybirds) (78)	30
58	London HLE 8666	Splish Splash/Judy Don't Be Moody	25
58	London HLE 8666	Splish Splash/Judy Don't Be Moody (78)	25
58	London HLE 8679	Early In The Morning/Now We're One (as Rinky-Dinks featuring Bobby Darin)	45
58	London HLE 8679	Early In The Morning/Now We're One (78)	25
58	London HLE 8737	Queen Of The Hop/Lost Love	25
58	London HLE 8737	Queen Of The Hop/Lost Love (78)	25
58	London HL 7060	Lost Love/Queen Of The Hop (export issue)	12
59	London HLE 8793	Mighty Mighty Man/You're Mine (as Bobby Darin with Rinky Dinks)	30
59	London HLE 8793	Mighty Mighty Man/You're Mine (as Bobby Darin with Rinky Dinks) (78)	25
59	London HLE 8815	Plain Jane/While I'm Gone	25
59	London HLE 8815	Plain Jane/While I'm Gone (78)	25
59	London HL 7078	Plain Jane/Dream Lover (export issue)	15
59	London HLE 8867	Dream Lover/Bullmoose	6
59	London HLE 8867	Dream Lover/Bullmoose (78)	25
59	London HLK 8939	Mack The Knife/Was There A Call For Me	5
59	London HLK 8939	Mack The Knife/Was There A Call For Me (78)	25
60	London HLK 9034	La Mer (Beyond The Sea)/That's The Way Love Is	5
60	London HLK 9034	La Mer (Beyond The Sea)/That's The Way Love Is (78)	20

(all the above 45s came with tri centres, later round centre pressings are worth around two thirds the value)

60	London HLK 9086	Clementine/Down With Love	5
60	London HLK 9086	Clementine/Down With Love (78)	20
60	London HLK 9142	Bill Bailey Won't You Please Come Home/Tall Story	5
60	London HLK 9142	Bill Bailey Won't You Please Come Home/Tall Story (78)	20
60	Brunswick 05831	Hear Them Bells/The Greatest Builder	10
60	London HLK 9197	Beachcomber/Autumn Blues (credited to 'Bobby Darin At The Piano')	5
60	Lonson HLK 9215	Somebody To Love/I'll Be There	5
61	London HLK 9303	Lazy River/Oo-Ee-Train	5
61	London HLK 9375	Nature Boy/Look For My True Love	5
61	London HLK 9407	Theme From "Come September"/Walk Bach To Me (with Orchestra)	6
61	London HLK 9429	You Must Have Been A Beautiful Baby/Sorrow Tomorrow	5
61	London HLK 9474	Multiplication (From "Come September")/Irresistible You	5
62	London HLK 9540	What'd I Say/Ain't That Love	5
62	London HLK 9575	Things/Jailer Bring Me Water	5
62	Capitol CL 15272	If A Man Answers/A True, True Love	5
62	London HLK 9624	Baby Face/You Know How	5
63	London HLK 9663	I've Found A New Baby/Keep A-Walkin'	7
63	Capitol CL 15286	You're The Reason I'm Living/Now You're Gone	5
63	Capitol CL 15306	Eighteen Yellow Roses/Not For Me	5
63	Capitol CL 15328	Be Mad Little Girl/Since You've Been Gone	7
64	Capitol CL 15338	I Wonder Who's Kissing Her Now/As Long As I'm Singing	5
64	Atlantic AT 4002	Milord/Golden Earrings	5
64	Capitol CL 15360	The Things In This House/Wait By The Water	5
65	Capitol CL 15401	When I Get Home/Lonely Road	5
65	Capitol CL 15414	Gyp The Cat/That Funny Feeling	5
65	Atlantic AT 4046	We Didn't Ask To Be Brought Here/Funny What Love Can Do	5
66	Atlantic 584 014	Mame/Walking In The Shadow Of Love	5
66	Atlantic 584 051	If I Were A Carpenter/Rainin'	4
67	Atlantic 584 063	The Girl That Stood Beside Me/Reason To Believe	5
67	Atlantic 584 079	Lovin' You/Amy	5
67	Atlantic 584 105	The Lady Came From Baltimore/I Am	5
67	Atlantic 584 147	At The Crossroads/She Knows	4
68	Bell BLL 1040	Change/Long Line Rider	4
69	Bell BLL 1090	Sugar Man/Jive	4
70	Major Minor MM 697	Maybe We Can Get It Together/RX-Pyro (Prescription: Fire)	4
72	Atlantic K 10238	Splish Splash/Clementine/Dream Lover/Mack The Knife (p/s)	4
74	Mowest MW 3014	Blue Monday/Moritat: Mack The Knife	5
59	London REE 1173	BOBBY DARIN (EP)	40
59	London REE 1225	BOBBY DARIN NO. 2 (EP)	30
60	London REK 1243	THAT'S ALL (EP)	20
61	London REK 1286	FOR TEENAGERS ONLY (EP)	25
61	London REK 1290	UP A LAZY RIVER (EP)	15
61	London REK 1310	TWO OF A KIND (EP, with Johnny Mercer)	15
61	London REK 1321	THE 25TH DAY OF DECEMBER (EP)	25
61	London REK 1334	LOVE SWINGS (EP)	15

Bobby DARIN

62	London REK 1338	TWIST WITH BOBBY DARIN (EP)	15
62	London REK 1342	THINGS! (EP)	15
65	Atlantic AET 6013	MILORD (EP)	12
58	London HA-E 2140	BOBBY DARIN (LP)	50
59	London HA-E 2172	THAT'S ALL (LP)	18
59	London HA-K 2235	THIS IS DARIN (LP, also stereo SAH-K 6067)	15/20
60	London HA-K 2291	DARIN AT THE COPA (LP, also stereo SAH-K 6103)	15/20
60	London HA-K 2311	FOR TEENAGERS ONLY (LP)	25
61	London HA-K 2363	TWO OF A KIND (LP with Johnny Mercer; also stereo SAH-K 6164)	18/25
61	London HA-K 2372	THE BOBBY DARIN STORY (LP)	22
61	London HA-K 2394	LOVE SWINGS (LP, also stereo SAH-K 6194)	16/22
62	London HA-K 2456	DARIN SINGS RAY CHARLES (LP, also stereo SAH-K 6243)	16/22
62	Capitol T 1791	OH! LOOK AT ME NOW (LP)	15
62	London HA-K 8030	THINGS AND OTHER THINGS (LP)	18
63	London HA-K/SH-K 8102	IT'S YOU OR NO-ONE (LP, mono/stereo)	16/22
63	Capitol T 1826	EARTHY (LP)	15
63	Capitol T 1866	YOU'RE THE REASON I'M LIVING (LP)	16
63	Capitol (S)T 1942	EIGHTEEN YELLOW ROSES & 11 OTHER HITS (LP, mono/stereo)	16/20
64	Capitol (S)T 2007	GOLDEN FOLK HITS (LP, mono/stereo)	18/25
65	Capitol T 2194	FROM HELLO DOLLY TO GOODBYE CHARLIE (LP)	12
65	Atlantic ATL 5014	BOBBY DARIN WINNERS (LP)	16
65	Capitol T 2322	I WANNA BE AROUND (LP)	16
66	Capitol T 2571	THE BEST OF BOBBY DARIN (LP)	15
66	Atlantic 587/588 014	SINGS THE SHADOW OF YOUR SMILE (LP)	16
66	Atlantic 587/588 020	IN A BROADWAY BAG (MAME) (LP)	14
66	Atlantic 587/588 051	IF I WERE A CARPENTER (LP)	12
67	Atlantic 587 065	THE BOBBY DARIN STORY (LP)	14
67	Atlantic 587 073	SOMETHING SPECIAL (LP)	30
67	Atlantic 587 076	INSIDE OUT (LP)	14
67	Atlantic 587 089	SINGS DR. DOOLITTLE (LP)	12
69	Bell MBLL/SBLL 112	BORN WALDEN ROBERT CASSOTTO (LP)	12
69	Bell SBLL 128	COMMITMENT (LP)	12

(see also Rinky Dinks)

DARK

71	SR 0102S	DARK ROUND THE EDGES (LP, private pressing, 12 with booklet)	1500/1200
90	private pressing	DARK ROUND THE EDGES (LP, reissue, U.K. pressing marketed in U.S.)	60
92	Kissing Spell KSCD 9204	DARK ROUND THE EDGES (CD, with 8-page booklet, 1,500 only)	25

DARK

81	Fresh FRESH 2	My Friends/John Wayne (p/s)	4
82	Fall Out FALL LIVE 005	THE LIVING END (mini-LP)	15

(see also Hanoi Rocks)

DARKSIDE

90	Situation 2 SITU 29P	ALL THAT NOISE (LP, picture disc)	10
91	Acid Ray DARK 2	PSYCHEDELIC SUBURBIA (LP, mail order only, with poster)	10

(see also Spacemen 3)

DARK STAR

81	Avatar AAA 105	Lady Of Mars/Rock 'N' Romancin' (no p/s)	6
81	Avatar AAA 105	Lady Of Mars/Rock 'N' Romancin' (12")	12
81	Avatar AALP 5003	DARK STAR (LP)	12

DARLETTES

73	President PT 317	Lost/Sweet Kind Of Loneliness	6

DARLING BUDS

87	Darling Buds DAR 1	If I Said/Just To Be Seen (p/s, some with insert)	20/15
88	Bonk On 001	Spin/BUBBLEGUM SPLASH track (flexidisc free with 'So Naive' fanzine)	8/6
88	Native NTV 33L	It's All Up To You/Think Of Me/Spin (gatefold p/s)	5
88	Epic BLONDB 1	Burst/Big Head (box set with 2 badges & poster)	4
88	Epic BLONDQ 1	Burst/Big Head/Shame On You (Slightlydelic Version) (p/s)	4
88	Epic BLONDQ 2	Hit The Ground/Pretty Girl (in cloth sleeve)	4
89	Flexi FLX 448	Valentine (live)/That's The Reason (live) (fan club flexidisc)	6
90	Native NTV 54	Shame On You/Valentine//It's All Up To You/Spin//Think Of Me/ That's The Reason (triple pack in envelope sleeve)	6

BILL DARNEL

55	London HLU 8204	My Little Mother/Bring Me A Bluebird (with Frank Weir & His Orchestra)	22
56	London HLU 8234	The Last Frontier/Rock A Boogie Baby	25
56	London HLU 8267	Guilty Lips/Ain't Misbehavin'	22
56	London HLU 8292	Tell Me More/Satin Doll	20

(see also Frank Weir & His Orchestra)

GUY DARRELL (& MIDNIGHTERS)

63	Oriole CB 1932	Go Home Girl/You Won't Come Home (as Guy Darrell & Midnighters)	7
64	Oriole CB 1964	Sorry/Sweet Dreams (as Guy Darrell & Midnighters)	7
65	CBS 201806	Stupidity/One Of These Days	5
66	CBS 202033	Somewhere They Can't Find Me/It Takes A Lot To Laugh	5
66	CBS 202082	I've Been Hurt/Blessed	12
66	CBS 202296	Big Louie/My Way Of Thinking	5
67	CBS 202510	Hard Lovin'/I've Never Had A Love Like That	5
67	CBS 202642	Crystal Ball/Didn't I	5
67	Piccadilly 7N 35406	Evil Woman/What You Do About That	20
67	Pye 7N 17435	Cupid/What's Happened To Our Love	4
68	Pye 7N 17586	Skyline Pigeon/Everything	4
69	Page One POF 120	Turn To Me/What's Her Name	4
69	Page One POF 141	Birds Of A Feather/Keep The Rain From My Door	4
69	Page One POF 155	How Are You/Turtle Turquoise And The Hare (as Guy Darrell Syndicate)	4

MINT VALUE £

60s	CBS 53364	GUY DARRELL (LP)	12

JOHNNY DARRELL
69	United Artists UP 35012	Why You Been Gone So Long?/You're Always The One	4

JAMES DARREN
59	Pye Intl. 7N 25019	Gidget/There's No Such Thing (as Jimmy Darren)	6
59	Pye Intl. N 25019	Gidget/There's No Such Thing (as Jimmy Darren) (78)	5
59	Pye Intl. 7N 25034	Angel Face/I Don't Wanna Lose You (as Jimmy Darren)	6
59	Pye Intl. N 25034	Angel Face/I Don't Wanna Lose You (as Jimmy Darren) (78)	10
60	Pye Intl. 7N 25059	Because They're Young/Let There Be Love	5
61	Pye Intl. 7N 25116	Goodbye Cruel World/Valerie	5
62	Pye Intl. 7N 25125	Her Royal Majesty/If I Could Only Tell You	4
62	Pye Intl. 7N 25138	Conscience/Dream Big	4
62	Pye Intl. 7N 25155	Mary's Little Lamb/The Life Of The Party	4
62	Pye Intl. 7N 25168	Too Young To Go Steady/Hail To The Conquering Hero	4
63	Pye Intl. 7N 25170	Pin A Medal On Joey/I'll Be Loving You	4
63	Colpix PX 708	Backstage/Gegetta	4
65	Warner Bros WB 5648	Because You're Mine/Millions Of Roses	4
66	Warner Bros WB 5689	Tom Hawk/I Want To Be Lonely	4
67	Warner Bros WB 5874	All/Misty Morning Eyes	4
59	Pye Intl. NEP 44004	P.S. I LOVE YOU (EP)	10
62	Pye Intl. NEP 44008	JAMES DARREN HIT PARADE (EP)	12
63	Pye Intl. NPL 28021	LOVE AMONG THE YOUNG (LP)	15

JEANNIE DARREN & SECOND CITY SOUND
69	Major Minor MM 611	River Deep Mountain High/Julie	4

MAXINE DARREN
65	Pye 7N 15796	How Can I Hide It From My Heart/Don't You Know	4

CHRIS DARROW
73	United Artists UAG 29453	CHRIS DARROW (LP)	10
74	United Artists UAG 29634	UNDER MY OWN DISGUISE (LP)	10
	(see also Kaleidoscope)		

DARTELLS
63	London HLD 9719	Dartell Stomp/Hot Pastrami	12

BARRY DARVELL
60	London HL 9191	Geronimo Stomp/How Will It End?	40

DARWIN'S THEORY
67	Major Minor MM 503	Daytime/Hosanna	25

DAS DAMEN
89	What Goes On 16	Neon Daylight/Give Me Everything (p/s)	4

DAS PSYCH-OH RANGERS
86	ZTT ZTAS 24	Homage To The Blessed/The Essential Art Of Communication/He He Radical/Medeq Terrorists (p/s)	4
86	ZTT 12 ZTAS 24	The Essential Art Of Communication (Extra Extra)/Homage To The Blessed/He He Radical (Episode 2)/Medeq Terrorists (Living) (12", p/s)	7

DATE WITH SOUL
67	Stateside SS 2062	Yes Sir That's My Baby/PRISCILLA: He Noticed Me	7

DAUGHTERS OF ALBION
68	Fontana STL 5486	DAUGHTERS OF THE ALBION (LP)	16

DAVE DAVANI & D MEN
63	Columbia DB 7125	Don't Fool Around/She's The Best For Me	8
64	Decca F 11896	Midnight Special/Sho' Know A Lot About Love	10

DAVE DAVANI (FOUR)
65	Parlophone R 5329	Top Of The Pops/Workin' Out	12
66	Parlophone R 5490	Tossin' And Turnin'/Jupe	12
66	Parlophone R 5525	One Track Mind/On The Cooler Side (solo)	15
71	Philips 6006 195	King Kong Blues/Come Back Baby (solo)	4
65	Parlophone PMC 1258	FUSED (LP)	25

DAVE & DIAMONDS
65	Columbia DB 7692	I Walk The Lonely Night/You Do Love	8

BOB DAVENPORT
60	Collector JEB 4	GEORDIE SONGS (EP)	7
65	Columbia SX 1786	BOB DAVENPORT AND THE RAKES (LP)	10

COW COW DAVENPORT
44	Brunswick 03509	Don't You Loudmouth Me/Tha'll Get It (78)	15
50s	Tempo R 14	Chimes Blues/Slow Drag (78)	8
50s	Jazz Collector L 34	Chimes Blues/Slow Drag (78)	6

ALAN DAVEY
87	Hawkfan HWFB 3/4	THE ELF (EP, double pack)	4
	(see also Hawkwind)		

DAVEY & MORRIS
73	York FYK 417	DAVEY AND MORRIS (LP, with insert)	100
	(see also Strawbs)		

DAVID
69	Philips BF 1776	Please Mister Postman/Light Of Your Mind	25

DAVID & GIANTS
77	Capitol CL 15915	Ten Miles High/Super Love	4

MINT VALUE £

DAVID & JONATHAN

65	Columbia DB 7717	Laughing Fit To Cry/Remember What You Said	4
66	Columbia DB 7800	Michelle/How Bitter The Taste Of Love	4
66	Columbia DB 7873	Speak Her Name/Take It While You Can	4
66	Columbia DB 7950	Lovers Of The World Unite/Oh My Word	4
66	Columbia DB 8035	Ten Storeys High/Looking For My Life	4
66	Columbia DB 8167	Gilly Gilly Ossenfeffer Katzenellenbogen By The Sea/Scarlet Ribbons For Her Hair	4
67	Columbia DB 8208	She's Leaving Home/One Born Every Minute	4
67	Columbia DB 8287	Softly Whispering I Love You/Such A Peaceful Day	4
68	Columbia DB 8428	You Ought To Meet My Baby/I've Got That Girl On My Mind	4
67	Columbia S(C)X 6031	DAVID AND JONATHAN (LP)	15

(see also Roger Cook)

DAVID & ROZAA

70	Philips 6006 040	Time Of Our Life/We Can Reach An Understanding	12
71	Philips 6006 094	The Spark That Lights The Flame/Two Can Share	12

(see also David Essex)

ALAN DAVID

65	Decca F 12130	Crazy 'Bout My Baby/A Thousand Years Too Late	4
67	Polydor BM 56201	Flower Power/Completely Free	4

ANNE MARIE DAVID

79	Chrysalis CHS 2327	Je Suis L'Enfant Soleil/Just Like Loving You (p/s)	5

FRANKIE DAVIDSON & HI MARKS

61	Starlite ST45 5037	You're Driving Me Crazy/I Care For You (B-side with Unicords)	15
61	London HL 9309	Detour/Just For Today	5
68	Decca F 22780	Hector The Trash Collector/Somebody Come And Take My Wife	4

TOMMY DAVIDSON

56	London HLU 8219	Half Past Kissing Time/I Don't Know Yet But I'm Learning	30

HUTCH DAVIE

58	London HLE 8667	At The Woodchopper's Ball/Honky Tonk Train Blues (& His Honky Tonkers)	12
58	London HLE 8667	At The Woodchopper's Ball/Honky Tonk Train Blues (78)	5
60	London HLE 9076	Sweet Georgia Brown/Heartaches	4
62	Pye Intl. 7N 25149	But I Do/Time Was (& Orchestra)	5
60	London HA-E 2216	MUCH HUTCH (LP)	10

ALUN DAVIES

65	Parlophone R 5384	Girls Were Made To Love And Kiss/Rose Marie	4
68	Mercury MF 1043	One Day Soon/Pretend You Don't See Her	4
72	CBS 65108	DAYDO (LP)	10

BOB DAVIES

63	London HLU 9767	Rock'N'Roll Show/With You Tonight	20

CYRIL DAVIES (R&B ALLSTARS)

63	Pye Intl. 7N 25194	Country Line Special/Chicago Calling	15
63	Pye Intl. 7N 25221	Preachin' The Blues/Sweet Mary	12
69	Pye 7N 17663	Country Line Special/Sweet Mary	10
64	Pye Intl. NEP 44025	THE SOUND OF CYRIL DAVIES (EP)	35
57	'77' LP 2	THE LEGENDARY CYRIL DAVIES (10" LP, 99 only)	150
70	Folklore F-LEAT 9	THE LEGENDARY CYRIL DAVIES (LP, reissue, with 4 extra tracks)	50

(see also Alexis Korner)

DAVE DAVIES

67	Pye 7N 17356	Death Of A Clown/Love Me Till The Sun Shines	5
67	Pye 7N 17429	Susannah's Still Alive/Funny Face	6
68	Pye 7N 17514	Lincoln County/There's No Life Without Love	10
69	Pye 7N 17678	Hold My Hand/Creeping Jean	10
68	Pye NEP 24289	DAVE DAVIES HITS (EP)	150

(see also Kinks)

IRVING DAVIES & METHOD MEN

62	Decca F 11456	The Method/ABC The Method	4

JACKIE DAVIES & HIS QUARTET

57	Pye N 15115	Land Of Make Believe/Over The Rainbow (78)	10

(see also Chico Arnez)

MIAR DAVIES

64	Decca F 11805	Ten Good Reasons/I Won't Remember You	4
64	Decca F 11894	I Hear You Knocking/Navy Blue	6

NICOLA DAVIES

68	SNB 55-3627	Infatuation/My Boy	4

RAY DAVIES

72	Pye QUAD 1004	WHY CAN'T WE ALL GET (LP, quadrophonic)	10
72	Pye QUAD 1009	THE REAL SOUND OF BUTTON DOWN (LP, quadrophonic)	10

(these albums are NOT by Ray Davies of the Kinks)

RON DAVIES

70	A&M AMLS 933	SILENT SONG THROUGH THE LAND (LP)	10

BETTY DAVIS

75	Island USA 2011	Shut Off The Light/He Was A Big Freak	4
75	Island WIP 6255	Shut Off The Light/He Was A Big Freak (reissue)	4
75	Island ILPS 9329	NASTY GIRL (LP)	15

BILLIE DAVIS

63	Decca F 11572	Tell Him/I'm Thankful	4
63	Decca F 11658	He's The One/V.I.P.	4
63	Columbia DB 7115	It's So Funny I Could Cry/You And I	4
64	Columbia DB 7195	That Boy John/Say Nothin' Don't Tell	4
64	Columbia DB 7246	School Is Over/Give Me Love	4
64	Columbia DB 7346	Whatcha Gonna Do/Everybody Knows (as Billie Davis & Le Roys)	5
65	Piccadilly 7N 35227	Last One To Be Loved/You Don't Know	4
65	Piccadilly 7N 35266	No Other Baby/Hands Off	5
66	Piccadilly 7N 35308	Heart And Soul/Don't Take All Night	7
66	Piccadilly 7N 35350	Just Walk In My Shoes/Ev'ry Day	12
67	Decca F 12620	Wasn't It You/Until It's Time For You To Go	6
67	Decca F 12696	Angel Of The Morning/Darling Be Home Soon	4
68	Decca F 12823	I Want You To Be My Baby/Suffer	4
69	Decca F 12923	Nobody's Home To Go Home To/I Can Remember	8
69	Decca F 12977	Nights In White Satin/It's Over	4

(see also Keith & Billie, Le Roys)

BLIND GARY DAVIS (REVEREND GARY DAVIS)

63	'77' LA 12-14	PURE RELIGION AND BAD COMPANY (LP)	20
60s	Fontana 688 303 ZL	HARLEM STREET SINGER (LP)	15
66	Xtra XTRA 5014	SAY NO TO THE DEVIL (LP)	20
60s	Xtra XTRA 5042	A LITTLE MORE FAITH (LP)	20
69	Fontana SFJL 914	BRING YOUR MONEY HONEY (LP)	15
71	Transatlantic TRA 244	RAGTIME GUITAR (LP)	12
71	Transatlantic TRA 249	CHILDREN OF ZION (LP)	12
74	Kicking Mule SNKD 1	LO I BE WITH YOU ALWAYS (2-LP)	15

BOBBY DAVIS (U.S.)

61	Starlite ST45 056	I Was Wrong/Hype You Into Selling Your Head	25

BOBBY DAVIS (Jamaica)

71	Banana BA 344	Return Your Love/RILEY'S ALLSTARS: Version	4

BONNIE DAVIS

55	Brunswick 05507	Pepper-Hot Baby/For Always, Darling	20

CLIFFORD DAVIS

69	Reprise RS 27003	Before The Beginning/Man Of The World	4
70	Reprise RS 25008	Come On Down And Follow Me	4

(see also Fleetwood Mac)

DANNY DAVIS (U.K.)

60	Parlophone R 4657	Love Me/You're My Only Girl	5
60	Parlophone R 4796	Talking In My Sleep/Lullaby Of Love	5
61	Pye 7N 15391	Tell All The World/Rumours	5
62	Pye 7N 15427	Rome Wasn't Built In A Day/Tell Me	7
62	Pye 7N 15470	Patches/September In The Rain	5

(see also Marauders)

DANNY DAVIS ORCHESTRA (U.S.)

58	London HL 8766	Trumpet Cha-Cha-Cha/Lonesome Trumpet	4
65	MGM MGM 1277	Main Theme From "The Saint"/Little Bandits Of Juarez	6

EDDIE ('LOCKJAW') DAVIS

56	Parlophone GEP 8587	EDDIE LOCKJAW DAVIS TRIO (EP)	7
57	Parlophone GEP 8678	LOCKJAW (EP)	7
58	Parlophone GEP 8685	EDDIE LOCKJAW DAVIS TRIO (EP)	7
59	Esquire EP 217	EDDIE LOCKJAW DAVIS (EP)	8
61	Esquire EP 237	EDDIE LOCKJAW DAVIS QUARTET (EP)	8
60	Esquire 32-104	THE EDDIE 'LOCKJAW' DAVIS COOK BOOK (LP)	15
60	Esquire 32-117	VERY SAXY (LP, with Coleman Hawkins, Arnett Cobb & Bobby Tate)	15
61	Esquire 32-128	JAWS IN ORBIT (LP)	15
64	Stateside SL 10102	THE FIRST SET — LIVE AT MINTONS (LP, with Johnny Griffin)	12

(see also Coleman Hawkins, Johnny Griffin)

EDWARD H. DAVIS

74	Sain	HEN FFORDD GYMREIG O FYW (LP)	60
76	Sain	SNEB YN BECSO DAM (LP)	40

JACKIE DAVIS

60s	Pye	The Land Of Make Believe	15

JESSE (ED) DAVIS

71	Atlantic 2091 076	Every Night Is Saturday Night/Washita Love Child (as Jesse Davis)	6
71	Atco 2400 106	JESSE ED DAVIS (LP)	10
72	Atlantic K 40329	ULULU (LP)	10
73	CBS 65649	KEEP ON COMING (LP)	10

KIM DAVIS

66	Decca F 12387	Don't Take Your Lovin' Away/Feelin' Blue	20
67	CBS 202568	Tell It Like It Is/Losing Kind	8

(see also Kim D)

LARRY DAVIS/FENTON ROBINSON

72	Python PLP 24	LARRY DAVIS AND FENTON ROBINSON (LP)	25

MAXWELL STREET JIMMY DAVIS

66	Bounty BY 6009	MAXWELL STREET JIMMY DAVIS (LP)	20

MELVIN DAVIS

69	Action ACT 4531	Save It/This Love Was Meant To Be	15

MILES DAVIS

60	Philips JAZ 100	Budo/Tadd's Delight	5
70	CBS 5104	Miles Runs The Voodoo Down/Spanish Key	4
54	Capitol EAP1 459	MILES DAVIS ORCHESTRA (EP)	8
54	Capitol EAP2 459	MILES DAVIS ORCHESTRA (EP)	8
55	Vogue EPV 1075	MILES DAVIS SEXTET (EP)	7
57	Vogue EPV 1191	MILES DAVIS (EP)	7
59	Philips BBE 12266	MILES DAVIS (EP)	7
59	Esquire EP 212	MILES DAVIS NEW QUARTET (EP)	7
59	Esquire EP 222	MILES THEME (EP)	7
59	Fontana TFE 17119	MILES DAVIS (EP)	8
59	Fontana TFE 17195	MORE MILES (EP)	7
59	Fontana TFE 17197	STRAIGHT NO CHASER (EP)	7
60	Fontana TFE 17223	MILES DAVIS NO. 2 (EP)	8
60	Fontana TFE 17225	MILES DAVIS NO. 3 (EP)	8
60	Fontana TFE 17247	PORGY AND BESS (EP)	7
60	Esquire EP 232	BLUE MILES (EP)	7
60	Philips BBE 12351	MILES DAVIS (EP)	7
61	Philips BBE 12418	DAVIS CUP (EP)	7
61	Esquire EP 242	BLUE CHANGES (EP, with Milt Jackson)	7
61	Fontana TFE 17359	MILES DAVIS QT. (EP, with Cannonball Adderley/John Coltrane Group)	7
50s	Esquire EP 12	MILES DAVIS QUARTET (EP)	8
50s	Esquire EP 132	MILES DAVIS QUARTET (EP)	8
50s	Esquire EP 152	MILES DAVIS (EP)	7
50s	Esquire EP 172	MILES DAVIS QUARTET (EP)	7
55	Esquire 20-041	MILES DAVIS QUINTET (10" LP)	25
53	Esquire 20-017	MILES DAVIS PLAYS (10" LP)	25
53	Esquire 20-021	MILES DAVIS ALL STARS (10" LP)	25
54	Vogue LDE 064	MILES DAVIS AND HIS ORCHESTRA (10" LP)	25
54	Capitol LC 6683	CLASSICS IN JAZZ (10" LP)	25
50s	Esquire 20-052	MILES DAVIS ALL STARS (A HIFI MODERN JAZZ JAM SESSION) (10" LP)	25
50s	Esquire 20-056	MILES DAVIS ALL STARS (A SECOND HIFI MODERN JAZZ JAM SESSION) (10" LP)	25
50s	Esquire 20-062	MILES DAVIS ALL STARS SEXTET (10" LP)	25
50s	Esquire 20-072	MILES DAVIS QUINTET (10" LP)	25
50s	Esquire 32-012	THE MUSINGS OF MILES (LP)	25
50s	Philips BBL 7140	'ROUND ABOUT MIDNIGHT (LP)	18
57	Fontana TFL 5007	MILES AHEAD (LP)	20
58	Fontana TFL 5035	MILESTONES (LP)	20
59	Fontana TFL 5056	PORGY AND BESS (LP)	20
60	Fontana TFL 5081	JAZZ TRACK — "L'ANSCENSEUR POUR L'ECHAFAUD" ("LIFT TO THE SCAFFOLD") (LP)	20
60	Fontana TFL 5089	THE "MOST" OF MILES (LP)	15
60	Fontana STFL 513	A KIND OF BLUE (LP)	18
60	Esquire 32-098	WALKIN' (LP)	20
60	Esquire 32-100	MILES DAVIS AND THE MODERN JAZZ GIANTS VOL. 2 (LP)	20
60	Esquire 32-108	WORKIN' WITH THE MILES DAVIS QUINTET (LP)	20
61	Font.TFL 5100/STFL 531	SKETCHES OF SPAIN (LP)	18
61	Esquire 32-118	EARLY MILES (LP)	20
61	Esquire 32-138	STEAMIN' WITH THE MILES DAVIS QUINTET (LP)	18
61	Blue Note (B)BLP 1501	MILES DAVIS VOL. 1 (LP; stereo LP released in 1964)	18
61	Fontana TFL 5163	FRIDAY NIGHT AT THE BLACKHAWK, SAN FRANCISCO (VOL. 1) (with Cannonball Adderley & John Coltrane; also stereo STFL 580)	18
61	Fontana TFL 5164	SATURDAY NIGHT AT THE BLACKHAWK, SAN FRANCISCO (VOL. 2) (with Cannonball Adderley & John Coltrane; also stereo STFL 581)	18
62	Fontana TFL 5172	SOMEDAY MY PRINCE WILL COME (LP, also stereo STFL 587)	18
62	CBS (S)BPG 62081	AT THE CARNEGIE HALL, MAY 19TH 1961 (LP)	15
64	CBS (S)BPG 62170	SEVEN STEPS TO HEAVEN (LP)	15
64	CBS (S)BPG 62327	SKETCHES OF SPAIN (LP, reissue)	12
64	Blue Note (B)BLP 1502	MILES DAVIS VOL. 2 (LP)	20
64	CBS (S)BPG 62213	QUIET NIGHTS (LP)	15
64	CBS (S)BPG 62306	FRIDAY NIGHT AT THE BLACKHAWK (LP, reissue)	12
64	CBS (S)BPG 62307	SATURDAY NIGHT AT THE BLACKHAWK (LP, reissue)	12
64	Vocalion LAEF 584	BLUE MOODS (LP)	15
64	CBS (S)BPG 62389	MILES AND MONK AT NEWPORT (LP, with Thelonious Monk)	15
64	CBS (S)BPG 62390	DAVIS IN EUROPE (LP)	15
65	Stateside SL 10111	MILES DAVIS AND JOHN COLTRANE PLAY RICHARD ROGERS (LP, with John Coltrane)	12
65	Pacific Jazz 688 204 ZL	DAVIS AND COLTRANE PLAY RICHARD RODGERS (LP, with John Coltrane)	15
65	CBS (S)BPG 62510	MY FUNNY VALENTINE (LP)	10
66	CBS (S)BPG 62066	A KIND OF BLUE (LP, reissue)	12
66	CBS (S)BPG 62104	SOMEDAY MY PRINCE WILL COME (LP, reissue)	10
66	CBS (S)BPG 62108	PORGY AND BESS (LP, reissue)	10
66	CBS (S)BPG 62577	E.S.P. (LP)	12
66	Stateside SL 10168	MILES DAVIS PLAYS FOR LOVERS (LP)	12
66	Capitol T 1974	THE BIRTH OF THE COOL (LP)	12
66	CBS (S)BPG 62655	"FOUR" AND MORE (LP)	12
66	CBS (S)BPG 62496	MILES AHEAD (LP, reissue)	10
67	CBS (S)BPG 62933	MILES SMILES (LP)	12
67	Transatlantic PR 7150	MODERN JAZZ GIANTS (LP)	12
67	CBS 62308	MILESTONES (LP, reissue)	10
68	CBS (S)BPG 63097	THE SORCEROR (LP)	12
68	Transatlantic PR 7322	DAVIS AND COLTRANE PLAY RICHARD RODGERS (LP, reissue)	10
68	CBS 63248	NEFERTITI (LP)	12
69	CBS 63352	MILES IN THE SKY (LP)	12
69	CBS 63551	FILLES DE KILIMANJARO (LP)	12

69	CBS 63620	GREATEST HITS (LP)	10
70	CBS 63630	IN A SILENT WAY (LP)	12
70	CBS 66236	BITCHES BREW (2-LP)	15
70s	CBS BPG 62323	'ROUND ABOUT MIDNIGHT (LP, reissue)	10
70s	CBS 62390	MILES AT ANTIBES (LP)	10
70s	CBS 62637	FACETS (LP)	10
70s	CBS 62976	MILES IN BERLIN (LP)	10
70s	CBS 63417	MILES AT NEWPORT (LP)	10
73	CBS PR 24001	MILES DAVIS (2-LP)	14
73	CBS PR 24012	TALLEST TREES (2-LP)	14
73	CBS CQ 30997/Q 66236	BITCHES BREW (2-LP, quadrophonic)	18
73	CBS GQ 30954/Q 67219	LIVE-EVIL (2-LP, quadrophonic)	16
70s	Xtra XTRA 5004	EZZ THETIC (LP)	10
70s	Session Disc	123 (LP)	15

(see also Thelonius Monk, Dizzy Gillespie, Milt Jackson, Cannonball Adderley)

MILES DAVIS & JOHN COLTRANE
(see under Miles Davis, John Coltrane)

SAMMY DAVIS (Jnr.)

54	Brunswick 05326	Because Of You Pts 1 & 2	6
55	Brunswick 05383	The Birth Of The Blues/Love (Your Magic Spell Is Everywhere)	7
55	Brunswick 05389	Six Bridges To Cross/Glad To Be Unhappy	6
55	Brunswick 05409	And This Is My Beloved/The Red Grapes	5
55	Brunswick 05428	Love Me Or Leave Me/Something's Gotta Give	12
55	Brunswick 05450	That Old Black Magic/Give A Fool A Chance	12
55	Brunswick 05469	Hey There/My Funny Valentine	12
55	Brunswick 05478	Backtrack/It's Bigger Than You And Me	5
56	Brunswick 05518	In A Persian Market/The Man With The Golden Arm	7
56	Capitol CL 14562	Azure/Dedicated To You	6
56	Brunswick 05583	Adelaide/I'll Know	5
56	Brunswick 05594	Earthbound/Five	5
56	Brunswick 05611	Frankie And Johnny/Circus	5
56	Brunswick 05617	You're Sensational/Don't Let Her Go	5
56	Brunswick 05629	All Of You/Just One Of Those Things	6
57	Brunswick 05637	The Golden Key/All About Love	4
57	Brunswick 05647	Dangerous/The World Is Mine Tonight	4
57	Brunswick 05668	Too Close For Comfort/Jacques D'Iraque	4
57	Brunswick 05694	Goodbye, So Long, I'm Gone/French Fried Potatoes And ...	4
57	Brunswick 05717	Mad Ball/The Nearness Of You	4
57	Brunswick 05724	Long Before I Knew You/Never Like This	4
58	Brunswick 05732	I'm Comin' Home/Hallelujah, I Love Her	4
58	Brunswick 05732	I'm Comin' Home/Hallelujah, I Love Her (78)	5
58	Brunswick 05747	No Fool Like An Old Fool/Unspoken	4
58	Brunswick 05763	Song And Dance Man/I Ain't Gonna Change (The Way I Am)	4
59	Brunswick 05778	That's Anna/I Never Got Out Of Paris	4
60	Brunswick 05830	Happy To Make Your Acquaintance/Baby, It's Cold Outside	5
60	HMV POP 777	Eee-o Eleven/Ain't That A Kick In The Head?	4
64	Reprise R 20227	The Shelter Of Your Arms/Falling In Love With...	6
64	Reprise R 20289	Not For Me/Bang Bang	10
69	MCA MK 5016	Rhythm Of Life/Pompeii Club/Rich Man's Frug	4
50	Brunswick OE 9445	BOY MEETS GIRL (EP, with Carmen McRae)	7
50s	Capitol EAP1 555	SAMMY DAVIS JNR. (EP)	7
56	Brunswick LAT 8088	JUST FOR LOVERS (LP)	12
56	Brunswick LAT 8153	STARRING SAMMY DAVIS (LP)	12
57	Brunswick LAT 8157	HE'S LOOKING AT YOU (LP)	10
57	Brunswick LAT 8215	SAMMY SWINGS (LP)	10
58	Brunswick LAT 8248	IT'S ALL OVER BUT THE SWINGIN' (LP)	10
59	Brunswick LAT 8296	SAMMY AT THE TOWN HALL, NEW YORK (LP, also stereo STA 3012)	10/12
59	Brunswick LAT 8308	PORGY AND BESS (LP, with Carmen McRae, also stereo STA 3017)	10/12
60	Brunswick LAT 8330	SAMMY AWARDS (LP)	10
60	Brunswick LAT 8352	I GOTTA RIGHT TO SWING (LP)	10
70	Tamla Motown STML 11160	SOMETHING FOR EVERYONE (LP)	10

SKEETER DAVIS

60	RCA Victor RCA 1201	No Never/(I Can't Help You) I'm Falling Too	7
61	RCA Victor RCA 1222	My Last Date With You/Someone I'd To Forget	6
63	RCA Victor RCA 1328	The End Of The World/Somebody Loves You	5
63	RCA Victor RCA 1345	I'm Saving My Love/Somebody Else On Your Mind	5
63	RCA Victor RCA 1363	I Can't Stay Mad With You/It Was Only My Heart	6
64	RCA Victor RCA 1384	He Says The Same Things To Me/How Much	5
64	RCA Victor RCA 1398	Now You're Gone/Gonna Get Along Without Your Love	5
65	RCA Victor RCA 1474	Sun Glasses/He Loved Me Too Little	4
64	RCA Victor RCX 7153	SILVER THREADS AND GOLDEN NEEDLES (EP)	10
63	RCA Victor RD/SF 7563	THE END OF THE WORLD (LP, mono/stereo)	14/16
63	RCA Victor RD/SF 7604	CLOUDY, WITH OCCASIONAL TEARS (LP, mono/stereo)	14/16
64	RCA Camden CDN 5119	I FORGOT MORE THAN YOU'LL EVER KNOW (LP)	10
64	RCA Victor RD 7676	LET ME GET CLOSE TO YOU (LP)	15
69	RCA Victor SF 8068	MARY FRANCES (LP)	12

SKEETER DAVIS & BOBBY BARE

| 65 | RCA RD 7711 | TUNES FOR TWO (LP) | 12 |

(see also Bobby Bare)

SPENCER DAVIS GROUP

64	Fontana TF 471	Dimples/Sittin' And Thinkin'	8
64	Fontana TF 499	I Can't Stand It/Midnight Train	7
65	Fontana TF 530	Every Little Bit Hurts/It Hurts Me So	8
65	Fontana TF 571	Strong Love/This Hammer	7

Spencer DAVIS GROUP

65	Fontana TF 632	Keep On Running/High Time Baby	4
66	Fontana TF 679	Somebody Help Me/Stevie's Blues	4
66	Fontana TF 739	When I Come Home/Trampoline	5
66	Fontana TF 762	Gimme Some Loving/Blues In F	5
67	Fontana TF 785	I'm A Man/I Can't Get Enough Of It	5
67	Fontana TF 854	Time Seller/Don't Want You No More	6
67	United Artists UP 1203	Mr. Second Class/Sanity Inspector	4
68	United Artists UP 2213	After Tea/Moonshine	5
68	United Artists UP 2226	Short Change/Picture Of Heaven	4
73	Vertigo 6059 076	Catch You On The Rebop/The Edge	4
73	Vertigo	Don't Let It Bring You Down/World (unreleased)	
73	Vertigo 6059 082	Mr Operator/Touching Cloth	4
73	Vertigo 6059 087	Living In A Back Street/Helping Hand	4
65	Fontana TE 17444	YOU PUT THE HURT ON ME (EP)	12
65	Fontana TE 17450	EVERY LITTLE BIT HURTS (EP)	12
66	Fontana TE 17463	SITTIN' AND THINKIN' (EP)	15
68	Philips MCF 5003	THE HITS OF THE SPENCER DAVIS GROUP (cassette EP)	10
65	Fontana TL 5242	THEIR FIRST LP (LP)	25
66	Fontana TL 5295	THE SECOND ALBUM (LP)	25
66	Fontana TL 5349	AUTUMN '66 (LP)	25
67	Fontana TL 5443	THE BEST OF THE SPENCER DAVIS GROUP (LP, unissued)	
67	United Artists SULP 1186	HERE WE GO ROUND THE MULBERRY BUSH (LP, soundtrack, with Traffic)	18
68	United Artists SULP 1192	WITH THEIR NEW FACE ON (LP)	15
68	Wing WL 1165	EVERY LITTLE BIT HURTS (LP, reissue of "Their First LP")	12
68	Island ILP 970/ILPS 9070	THE BEST OF THE SPENCER DAVIS GROUP (LP, pink label)	18
71	United Artists UAS 29177	IT'S BEEN SO LONG (LP, solo with Peter Jameson, 'envelope' cover)	10
73	Vertigo 6360 088	GLUGGO (LP, gatefold sleeve)	10

(see also Stevie Winwood, Traffic, Anglos, Blind Faith, Ray Fenwick, Pete York, Hardin & York)

STEVE DAVIS

68	Fontana TF 922	Takes Time To Know Her/She Said Yeah	35

TYRONE DAVIS

68	Stateside SS 2092	What If A Man/Bet You Win	10
69	Atlantic 584 253	Can I Change My Mind?/A Woman Needs To Be Loved	6
69	Atlantic 584 265	Is It Something You've Got?/Undying Love	8
69	Atlantic 584 288	All The Waiting Is Not In Vain/Need Your Lovin' Everyday	5
70	Atlantic 2091 003	Turn Back The Hands Of Time/I Keep Coming Back	6
71	Atlantic 2091 078	Could I Forget You/Just My Way Of Loving You	5
71	Atlantic 2091 131	One Way Ticket/We Got Love	5
73	Brunswick BR 4	Without You In My Life/How Could I Forget You	4
73	Brunswick BR 6	There It Is/You Wouldn't Believe	4
74	Brunswick BR 10	I Wish It Was Me/You Don't Have To Beg To Stay	4
76	Brunswick BR 31	Turning Point/Don't Let It Be Too Late	4
77	Brunswick BR 40	Ever Lovin' Girl/Forever	4
70	Atlantic 2465 021	TURN BACK THE HANDS OF TIME (LP)	12
73	Brunswick BRLS 3002	I HAD IT ALL THE TIME (LP)	10
73	Brunswick BRLS 3005	GREATEST HITS (LP)	10
74	Polydor 588 209	CAN I CHANGE MY MIND (LP)	10
80	Manhattan MAN 5034	CAN I CHANGE MY MIND (LP)	10

WALTER DAVIS

64	RCA RCX 7169	R.C.A. VICTOR RACE SERIES VOL. 3 (EP)	12
70	RCA Intl. INTS 1085	THINK YOU NEED A SHOT (LP)	12

WARREN DAVIS MONDAY BAND

67	Columbia DB 8190	Wait For Me/I Don't Wanna Hurt You	15
67	Columbia DB 8270	Love Is A Hurtin' Thing/Without Fear	8

DAVIS SISTERS

53	HMV B 10582	Rock-A-Bye Boogie/I Forgot More Than You'll Ever Know (78)	25

BRIAN DAVISON

70	Charisma CAS 1021	EVERY WHICH WAY (LP, pink label)	10

(see also Habits, Nice)

DAVISON BROTHERS

60	Philips PB 1053	Journey Of Love/Seven Days A Week	4

TIM DAWE

69	Straight ST 1058	PENROD (LP)	20

CARL DAWKINS

67	Rio R 136	All Of A Sudden/Running Shoes	8
67	Rio R 137	Baby I Love You/Hard Time	8
68	Blue Cat BS 114	I Love The Way You Are/DERMOTT LYNCH: I Can't Stand It	8
68	Duke DU 3	I'll Make It Up/J.J. ALLSTARS: One Dollar Of Music	6
69	Nu Beat NB 030	Rodney's History/DYNAMITES: Tribute To Drumbage	4

(see also Rass Dawkins)

HORRELL DAWKINS

66	Ska Beat JB 240	Cling To Me/Butterfly	8

JIMMY DAWKINS

72	Mojo 2027 011	The Things I Used To Do/Put It On The Hawg	6
78	Sonet SNTF 758	TRANSATLANTIC 770 (LP)	10

RASS DAWKINS & WAILERS

71	Upsetter US 368	Picture On The Wall/UPSETTERS: Version	12

(see also Bob Marley/Wailers, Carl Dawkins)

JULIE DAWN
53   Columbia SCM 5035   Wild Horses/A Whistling Kettle And A Dancing Cat 6
(see also Tony Brent & Julie Dawn, Cyril Stapleton)

DAWN & DEEJAYS
65   RCA RCA 1470   These Are The Things About You/I Will Think Of You 5

DAWNBREAKERS
65   Decca F 12110   Let's Live/Lovin' For You 5

DAWNWATCHER
82   DWS   Backlash 6

DAWNWIND
76   Amron ARN 5003   LOOKING BACK ON THE FUTURE (LP, private press) 120

LES DAWSON SYNDICATE
60s   Melodisc MEL 1586   Last Chicken In The Shop/Oh Yeah 8
(see also Johnny Stevens)

LESLEY DAWSON
67   Mercury MF 946   Just Say Goodbye/Just A Passing Phase 6
67   Mercury MF 965   Run For Shelter/I'll Climb On A Rainbow 12

DANIELLE DAX
85   Awesome AOR 3   Bad Miss 'M'/Yummer Yummer Man (p/s) 4
83   Initial IRC 009   POP-EYES (LP, with 'Meat Harvest' cover & lyric sheet) 35
(see also Lemon Kittens)

BING DAY
59   Mercury AMT 1047   I Can't Help It/Mama's Place 50

BOBBY DAY (& SATELLITES)
57   HMV POP 425   Little Bitty Pretty One/When The Swallows Come Back To Capistrano
              (as Bobby Day & Satellites) 75
57   HMV POP 425   Little Bitty Pretty One/When The Swallows Come Back To Capistrano (78) 30
58   London HL 8726   Rockin' Robin/Over And Over 25
58   London HL 8726   Rockin' Robin/Over And Over (78) 15
59   London HL 8800   The Bluebird, The Buzzard And The Oriole/Alone Too Long 30
59   London HL 8800   The Bluebird, The Buzzard And The Oriole/Alone Too Long (78) 30
59   London HL 8964   Love Is A One Time Affair/Ain't Gonna Cry No More 18
59   London HL 8964   Love Is A One Time Affair/Ain't Gonna Cry No More (78) 30
60   London HLY 9044   My Blue Heaven/I Don't Want To 18
61   Top Rank JAR 538   Over And Over/Gee Whiz 12
65   Sue WI 388   Rockin' Robin/Over And Over (reissue) 15

DORIS DAY
52   Columbia DB 3123   Sugarbush/How It Lies, How It Lies, How It Lies! (78) 5
52   Columbia DB 3157   My Love And Devotion/When I Fall In Love (78) 5
53   Columbia SCM 5038   April In Paris/Your Mother And Mine (with Four Lads) 10
53   Columbia SCM 5039   That's What Makes Paris Paree/I Know A Place 8
53   Columbia SCM 5044   A Bushel And A Peck/If I Were A Bell 14
53   Columbia SCM 5045   The Second Star To The Right (with Four Lads)/I'm Gonna Ring The Bell Tonight   8
53   Columbia SCM 5059   The Cherries/Papa, Won't You Dance With Me? 8
53   Columbia SCM 5062   Mister Tap-Toe/Why Should We Both Be Lonely? 8
53   Columbia SCM 5067   We Kiss In A Shadow/Something Wonderful 8
53   Columbia SCM 5075   That's The Way He Does It/Cuddle Up A Little Closer 10
54   Columbia SCM 5087   A Load Of Hay/It Had To Be You 10
55   Columbia SCM 5171   Just One Of Those Things/Sometimes I'm Happy 10
57   Philips JK 1020   Twelve O'Clock Tonight/Today Will Be Yesterday Tomorrow! (jukebox issue) 8
57   Philips JK 1031   The Party's Over/Rickety-Rackety Rendezvous (jukebox issue) 8
64   CBS AAG 183   Move Over Darling/Twinkle Lullaby 4
64   CBS AAG 219   Oowee Baby/The Rainbow's End 4
64   CBS AAG 231   Send Me No Flowers/Love Him 4
65   CBS 201808   Catch The Bouquet/Summer Has Gone 4
65   CBS 201898   Do Not Disturb/Au Revoir Is Goodbye With A Smile 4
66   CBS 202229   Glass Bottomed Boat/Soft As The Starlight 4
54   Columbia SEG 7507   CANADIAN CAPERS (EP) 8
54   Columbia SEG 7515   WE KISS IN A SHADOW (EP) 8
54   Columbia SEG 7531   NOBODY'S SWEETHEART (EP) 8
54   Columbia SEG 7546   SOMETIMES I'M HAPPY (EP) 8
55   Columbia SEG 7572   VOCAL GEMS FROM THE FILM "YOUNG MAN OF MUSIC" (EP) 8
55   Philips BBE 12007   DORIS DAY (EP) 12
55   Philips BBE 12011   I'LL NEVER STOP LOVING YOU (EP) 12
56   Philips BBE 12089   DORIS DAY NO. 2 (EP) 9
57   Philips BBE 12151   DAY DREAMS (EP) 9
58   Philips BBE 12167   DORIS (EP) 9
58   Philips BBE 12187   THE SONG IS YOU (EP) 8
58   Philips BBE 12213   DREAM A LITTLE DREAM OF ME (EP) 8
59   Philips BBE 12298   LET'S FLY AWAY (EP, also stereo SBBE 9006) 7/12
59   Philips BBE 12339   PILLOW TALK (EP) 8
60   Philips BBE 12388   YOU CAN'T HAVE EVERYTHING (EP, also stereo SBBE 9021) 7/12
61   Philips SBBE 9034   SHOW TIME NO. 1 (EP, stereo) 8
62   CBS AGG 20009   I HAVE DREAMED (EP) 7
62   CBS AGG 20018   DUET (EP, with Andre Previn Trio) 7
63   CBS AGG 20029   DUET NO. 2 (EP, with Andre Previn Trio) 7
64   CBS AGG 20048   MOVE OVER DARLING (EP) 7
54   Columbia 33S 1038   LULLABY OF BROADWAY (10" LP, 2 different sleeves) 25
54   Philips BBR 8026   THE VOICE OF YOUR CHOICE (10" LP) 20
55   Philips BBR 8040   YOUNG AT HEART (10" LP, with Frank Sinatra) 20
55   Philips BBL 7047   LOVE ME OR LEAVE ME (LP) 30

Doris DAY

56	Philips BBR 8094	DORIS DAY FAVOURITES (10" LP)	20
56	Philips BBR 8104	CALAMITY JANE (10" LP, with Howard Keel)	20
57	Philips BBL 7120	DAY DREAMS (LP)	20
57	Philips BBL 7137	DORIS AND FRANK (LP, 6 tracks each by Doris Day & Frank Sinatra)	15
57	Philips BBL 7142	DAY BY DAY (LP)	30
58	Philips BBL 7175	DAY IN HOLLYWOOD (LP)	18
58	Philips BBL 7197	THE PYJAMA GAME (LP with other artists, 5 tracks by Doris Day)	12
58	Philips BBL 7211	DAY BY NIGHT (LP)	30
58	Philips BBL 7247	HOORAY FOR HOLLYWOOD VOL. 1 (LP)	20
58	Philips BBL 7248	HOORAY FOR HOLLYWOOD VOL. 2 (LP)	20
59	Philips BBL 7296	CUTTIN' CAPERS (LP, also stereo SBBL 540)	15/18
59	Philips BBL 7297	SHOWCASE OF HITS (LP)	14
59	Philips SBBL 519	HOORAY FOR HOLLYWOOD (LP, stereo reissue)	16
59	Philips SBBL 548	DAY BY NIGHT (LP, stereo reissue)	16
60	Philips BBL 7377	WHAT EVERY GIRL SHOULD KNOW (LP, also stereo SBBL 563)	15/18
60	Philips SBBL 537	IN THE STILL OF THE NIGHT (LP)	20
60	Philips BBL 7392	SHOW TIME (LP, also stereo SBBL 577)	12/15
61	Philips BBL 7471	BRIGHT AND SHINY (LP, also stereo SBBL 619)	20/25
61	Philips BBL 7496	I HAVE DREAMED (LP, also stereo SBBL 643)	20/25
62	CBS (S)BPG 62053	BRIGHT AND SHINY (LP, reissue)	12
62	CBS (S)BPG 62057	I HAVE DREAMED (LP, reissue)	12
62	CBS (S)BPG 62010	DUET (LP, with André Previn Trio)	15
63	CBS (S)BPG 62101	YOU'LL NEVER WALK ALONE (LP)	30
63	CBS (S)BPG 62129	ANNIE GET YOUR GUN (LP, with Robert Goulet)	15
64	CBS (S)BPG 62226	LOVE HIM (LP)	30
65	CBS (S)BPG 62419	GREATEST HITS (LP)	10
65	CBS (S)BPG 62461	WITH A SMILE AND A SONG (LP)	25
65	CBS (S)BPG 62502	LATIN FOR LOVERS (LP)	15
66	CBS (S)BPG 62562	SENTIMENTAL JOURNEY (LP)	15
66	CBS BPG 62785	SINGS HER GREAT MOVIE HITS (LP)	15
66	CBS (S)BPG 62712	THE DORIS DAY CHRISTMAS ALBUM (LP)	15
66	CBS BPG 63032	SINGS SONGS FROM "CALAMITY JANE" & "THE PYJAMA GAME" (LP, with Howard Keel)	12

(see also Four Lads, Frank Sinatra, Howard Keel)

DORIS DAY & JOHNNIE RAY

53	Columbia SCM 5033	Mama Says, Pa Says/A Full Time Job	12

(see also Johnnie Ray)

JACKIE DAY

67	Sue WI 4040	Before It's Too Late/Without A Love	60

JILL DAY

55	Parlophone MSP 6169	Sincerely/Chee-Chee-Oo Chee (Sang The Little Bird)	10
55	Parlophone MSP 6177	Promises/Whistlin' Willie	8
56	HMV 7M 362	I Hear You Knocking/Far Away From Everybody	12
56	HMV 7M 391	A Tear Fell/Holiday Affair	8
56	HMV POP 254	Happiness Street (Corner Sunshine Square)/Somewhere In The Great Beyond	5
57	HMV POP 288	I Dreamed/Give Her My Love When You See Her	5
57	HMV POP 320	Mangos/Cinco Robles (Five Oaks)	6

KENNY DAY

60	Top Rank JAR 339	Teenage Sonata/My Love Doesn't Love Me At All (some with p/s)	8/4
61	Top Rank JAR 400	Why Don't We Do This More Often/The Sheik Of Morocco (some with p/s)	8/4

MURIEL DAY

69	CBS 4115	The Wages Of Love/Thinking Of You	8
69	Page One POF 151	Optimistic Fool/Nine Times Out Of Ten	20

TANYA DAY

64	Polydor NH 52331	His Lips Get In The Way/I Get So Lonely (with Nu-Notes)	6

TERRY DAY

62	CBS AAG 104	That's All I Want/I Waited Too Long	8

DAY BROTHERS

60	Oriole CB 1575	Angel/Just One More Kiss	4

JOHNNY DAYE

69	Stax STAX 111	Stay Baby Stay/I Love Love	5

DAYLIGHT

71	RCA RCA 2106	Lady Of St. Clare/Wednesday People	6
71	RCA SF 8194	DAYLIGHT (LP)	40

DAYLIGHTERS

64	Sue WI 343	Oh Mom (Teach Me How To Uncle Willie)/Hard Headed Girl	10

DAY OF THE PHOENIX

70	Greenwich GLSPR 1002	WIDE OPEN N-WAY (LP)	45
72	Chapter One CNSR 812	THE NEIGHBOUR'S SON (LP)	60

DAYSHIFT

79	WOT WOT 1	Living In The UK/Cedric Wazza, Superstar/Yeah Oh Yeah Oh! (die-cut stamped p/s)	5

DAYTON

83	Capitol 12 CL 318	The Sound Of Music/Eyes On You/Love You Anyway (12", p/s)	7

DAZE

84	Myriah SDM 001	Deep South/Made In America (p/s)	4

DAZZLING ALL NIGHT ROCK SHOW
73	Magnet MAG 4	20 Fantastic Bands/Version	4

dB's
81	Albion ALB 105	STANDS FOR DECIBELS (cassette in sealed can)	10
82	Albion ALB 109	REPERCUSSIONS (LP, with free cassette taped to front)	12

BOBBY DEACON
60	Pye 7N 15270	Fool Was I/Where's My Love	8

DEACON BLUE
87	CBS DEAC 1	Dignity/Riches (p/s)	4
87	CBS DEAC 1	Dignity/Riches (p/s, with cassette of "Raintown" LP excerpts [XPC 4011], shrink-wrapped)	7
87	CBS DEAC T1	Dignity/Riches/Ribbons And Bows (12", p/s)	7
87	CBS DEAC 2	Loaded/Long Distance From Just Across The Road (p/s)	4
87	CBS DEAC T2	Loaded (Full Length Version)/Long Distance From Just Across The Road/ Which Side Are You On/Kings Of The Western World (12", p/s)	7
87	CBS DEAC C2	Loaded/Long Distance From Just Across The Road/Which Side Are You On/ Kings Of The Western World (cassette)	5
87	CBS DEAC 3	When Will You (Make My Telephone Ring)/Church (p/s)	4
87	CBS DEAC T3	When Will You (Make My Telephone Ring)/Church/ Town To Be Blamed (live)/Angeliou (live) (12", p/s)	7
88	CBS DEAC 4	Dignity/Suffering (p/s)	4
88	CBS DEAC EP 4	Dignity/Suffering/Raintown (Piano Version)/Ronnie Spector (EP)	8
88	CBS DEAC T4	Dignity (Extended)/Suffering/Just Like Boys/ Ronnie Spector (12", p/s)	7
88	CBS DEAC Q4	Dignity/Suffering/Shifting Sand (10", numbered p/s, 3,000 only)	12
88	CBS CD DEAC 4	Dignity/Suffering/Just Like Boys/Shifting Sand (CD)	10
88	CBS DEAC 5	When Will You (Make My Telephone Ring)/That Brilliant Feeling No. 1 (glossy p/s)	4
88	CBS DEAC B5	When Will You (Make My Telephone Ring)/That Brilliant Feeling No. 1 (box set with 6 postcards & lyric sheet)	7
88	CBS DEAC T5	When Will You (Make My Telephone Ring)/Punch And Judy Man/ That Brilliant Feeling No. 3/Disney World (12", p/s)	7
88	CBS CD DEAC 5	When Will You (Make My Telephone Ring)/That Brilliant Feeling No. 2/ Punch And Judy Man/Disney World (CD)	10
88	CBS CP DEAC 5	When Will You (Make My Telephone Ring)/That Brilliant Feeling No. 2/ Punch And Judy Man/Disney World (CD, picture disc)	12
88	CBS DEAC 6	Chocolate Girl/S.H.A.R.O.N. (p/s)	4
88	CBS DEAC EP 6	Chocolate Girl/S.H.A.R.O.N./The Very Thing/Love's Great Fears (EP)	10
88	CBS DEAC T6	Chocolate Girl (Long Version)/Dignity (live)/Love's Great Fears/ S.H.A.R.O.N. (12", p/s)	8
88	CBS CD DEAC 6	Chocolate Girl/S.H.A.R.O.N./The Very Thing/Love's Great Fears (CD)	12
88	CBS DEAC EP 7	Real Gone Kid/Little Lincoln/Born Again/It's Not Funny Anymore (EP, with 4-page booklet)	8
88	CBS DEAC QT7	Real Gone Kid (7")/Real Gone Kid (12")/Little Lincoln (12", p/s, with poster)	10
88	CBS CD DEAC 7	Real Gone Kid/Little Lincoln/Born Again/It's Not Funny Anymore (CD)	15
89	CBS DEAC EP 8	Wages Day/Take Me To The Place/Take The Saints Away/Trampolene (EP, gatefold sleeve)	4
89	CBS DEAC Q8	Wages Day/Take Me To The Place (special pack)	7
89	CBS CD DEAC 8	Wages Day/Take Me To The Place/Take The Saints Away/Trampolene (CD, wallet sleeve)	7
89	CBS DEAC B9	Fergus Sings The Blues/Long Window To Love (box set with lyric sheet & 6 cards)	4
89	CBS DEAC QT9	Fergus Sings The Blues/Long Window To Love /London A To Z/ Back Here In Beano Land (10", p/s)	6
89	CBS DEACQT 10	Love And Regret/Spanish Moon/Down In The Flood/Dark End Of The Street/ When Will You (Make My Telephone Ring) (10", p/s)	6
89	CBS DEACC 10	Love And Regret/Spanish Moon/Down In The Flood/Dark End Of The Street/ When Will You (Make My Telephone Ring) (CD)	8
90	CBS DEACEP 11	Queen Of The New Year/My America/Sad Loved Girl (Full Version)/ Las Vegas (EP, gatefold sleeve)	4
88	CBS 450549 0	RAINTOWN (LP, with free LP "Riches" [XPR 1361] & sticker)	30
88	CBS 450549 8	RAINTOWN (cassette, with free cassette "Riches")	20
88	CBS XPR 1361	RICHES (LP, white embossed sleeve, sold separately through fan club)	20

DEADBEATS
80	Red Rhino RED 3	Choose You/Julie's New Boyfriend/Oh No (p/s)	6
82	Sheet BULL 5	Crazy Hound Dog/Crazy When I Hear The Beat (p/s)	6

DEAD BOYS
77	Sire SRE 1004	Sonic Reducer/Little Girl/Down In Flames (no p/s)	5
77	Sire 6078 609	Sonic Reducer/Little Girl/Down In Flames (12", p/s)	12
78	Sire SRE 1029	Tell Me/Not Anymore/Ain't Nothin' To Do (p/s)	7
77	Sire 9103 329	YOUNG, LOUD & SNOTTY (LP)	15
78	Sire SRK 6054	WE HAVE COME FOR YOUR CHILDREN (LP)	15

(see also Stiv Bators, Lords Of The New Church, Wanderers)

DEAD KENNEDYS
80	Fast Products FAST 12	California Uber Alles/Man With The Dogs(p/s, moulded or paper labels)	4
81	Cherry Red CHERRY 13	Holiday In Cambodia/Police Truck ('digger' p/s)	4
81	Cherry Red CHERRY 13	Holiday In Cambodia/Police Truck ('burning man' p/s, with lyric sheet)	4
81	Cherry CHERRY 16	Kill The Poor/In-Sight (p/s, with badge)	5
81	Cherry CHERRY 24	Too Drunk To Fuck/The Prey (p/s, with lyric sheet)	4

DEADLY TOYS
79	Bonnaud/Hunt DT 1	Nice Weather/Roll On Doomsday/I'm Logical/Deadly Mess Around (gatefold hand-coloured p/s)	4

DEAD MAN'S SHADOW

80	Hog HOG 1	Neighbours/Poxy Politics/War Ploys/Morons (p/s)	5
81	Subversive ANARCHO 1	HEATHROW TOUCHDOWN (EP, 1 side by Action Pact)	6

DEAD OR ALIVE

80	Inevitable INEV 005	I'm Falling/Flowers (foldout p/s)	12
81	Inevitable INEV 008	Number Eleven/Name Game (live) (p/s)	8
82	Black Eyes BE 1	It's Been Hours Now/Whirlpool/Nowhere To Nowhere/ It's Been Hours Now (Alternative Mix) (12", p/s)	15
82	Black Eyes BE 2	The Stranger/Some Of That (p/s)	10
83	Epic A 3399	Misty Circles/Misty Circles (Instrumental) (p/s)	8
83	Epic TA 3399	Misty Circles (Dance Mix)/Misty Circles (Dub Mix)/Selfish Side (12", p/s)	15
83	Epic A 3676	What I Want/The Stranger (Remix) (withdrawn white 'floppy hat' p/s)	30
83	Epic A 3676	What I Want/The Stranger (black p/s)	20
83	Epic TA 3676	What I Want (Dance Mix)/The Stranger (12", p/s, some with poster)	15/10
84	Epic A 4069	I'd Do Anything/Anything (Dub) (p/s)	7
84	Epic QA 4069	I'd Do Anything (Dub)/Give It To Me (10", p/s)	15
84	Epic TA 4069	I'd Do Anything/Misty Circles/What I Want (12", p/s)	10
84	Epic WA 4271	That's The Way (I Like It)/Keep That Body Strong (That's The Way) (picture disc)	7
84	Epic TA 4271	That's The Way (I Like It) (Extended Version)/Keep That Body Strong (That's The Way) (12", p/s)	7
84	Epic A 4510	What I Want (Remix)/The Stranger (Remix) (p/s)	4
84	Epic A 4510	What I Want (Remix)/The Stranger (Remix) (poster p/s)	10
84	Epic TA 4510	What I Want (Dance Mix)/The Stranger (Remix) (12", p/s, some with poster)	10/8
84	Epic DA 4861	You Spin Me Round (Like A Record)/Misty Circles//Mighty Mix Pt 1/ Pt 1 (Continued) (double pack)	7
84	Epic TX 4861	You Spin Me Round (Like A Record) (Murder Mix)/Misty Circles (Extended Version) (12", p/s)	7
84	Epic TX 4861/TA 4510	You Spin Me Round (Like A Record) (Murder Mix)/Misty Circles (Extended Mix)//What I Want (Dance Mix)/The Stranger (12", p/s, double pack, shrink-wrapped)	15
84	Epic QTX 4861	You Spin Me Round (Like A Record) (Performance Mix)/Wish You Were Here/What I Want/Do It/Misty Circles (Mighty Mix Pt 2) (12", p/s)	10
85	Epic A 6086	Lover Come Back To Me/Far Too Hard (withdrawn p/s)	30
85	Epic WA 6086	Lover Come Back To Me/Far Too Hard (fan-shaped picture disc with plinth)	8
85	Epic QTA 6086	Lover Come Back To Me (Extended Remix)/Far Too Hard (12", poster p/s)	15
85	Epic GA 6360	In Too Deep/I'd Do Anything (gatefold p/s)	4
85	Epic QTA 6360	In Too Deep (Off Yer Mong Mix)/I'd Do Anything (12" Version)/ I'd Do Anything (12" Version) (12", p/s, with poster)	10
85	Epic DA 6571	My Heart Goes Bang (Get Me To The Doctor)/Big Daddy Of The Rhythm (live)//Cake And Eat It (live)/In Too Deep (live) (double pack, gatefold p/s)	7
85	Epic QTA 6571	My Heart Goes Bang (American Wipe-Out Mix)/Big Daddy Of The Rhythm (live)/My Heart Goes Bang (Instrumental) (12", p/s)	10
86	Epic 6500 758	Brand New Lover/In Too Deep (live) (gatefold p/s)	4
86	Epic 6500 759	Brand New Lover/In Too Deep (live) (picture disc)	4
86	Epic 6500 750	Brand New Lover (Up Ducky Mix)/Cake And Eat It (live)/In Too Deep (live) (12", poster p/s)	7
87	Epic BURNSG 1	Something In My House/D.J. Hit That Button (gatefold pop-up p/s)	4
87	Epic BURNSD 1/6500 757	Something In My House/D.J. Hit That Button//Brand New Lover/In Too Deep (live) (double pack, shrink-wrapped)	5
87	Epic BURNSQ 1	Something In My House (US Wipe-Out Mix Pt 2)/Something In My House (House Instrumental)/DJ Hit That Button (12", p/s)	7
87	Epic BURNSQ 2	Hooked On Love (Remix)/You Spin Me Round (Like A Record) (live) (p/s)	4
87	Epic BURNSD 2	Hooked On Love (Remix)/You Spin Me Round (Like A Record) (live)// Something In My House/DJ Hit That Button (double pack)	6
87	Epic BURNSG 3	I'll Save You All My Kisses/Lover Come Back To Me (gatefold p/s, some with 'censored' sticker)	6/4
87	Epic BURNSQ 3	I'll Save You All My Kisses (The Long Wet Sloppy Kiss Mix)/ Lover Come Back To Me/Whirlpool/Nowhere To Nowhere (12", p/s)	10
88	Epic BURNSP 4	Turn Around And Count 2 Ten/Something In My House (Instru-Mental) (poster p/s)	5
88	Epic BURNST 4	Turn Around And Count 2 Ten (The Pearl And Dean 'I Love BPM' Mix)/ Something In My House (Instru-Mental 12" Mix) (12", p/s)	7
88	Epic BURNSQ 4	Turn Around And Count 2 Ten (I Had A Disco Dream Mix)/Something In My House (Instru-Mental)/Then There Was You/Come Inside (12", p/s)	15
88	Epic BURNSC 4	Turn Around And Count 2 Ten/Something In My House (Instru-Mental)/ Turn Around And Count 2 Ten (I Love BPM Mix)/(Instru-Mental) (CD, picture disc)	10
85	Epic EPC 26420	YOUTHQUAKE (CD, with 2 extra 12" mixes)	30

(see also Nightmares In Wax, Sisters Of Mercy, Pauline Murray & Invisible Girls)

DEAD SEA FRUIT

67	Camp 602 001	Kensington High Street/Put Another Record On	12
68	Camp 602 004	Love At The Hippiedrome/My Naughty Bluebell	12
67	Camp 603 001	DEAD SEA FRUIT (LP)	40

BILL DEAL & RHONDELLS

69	MGM MGM 1479	I've Been Hurt/I've Got My Needs	8
69	MGM MGM 1488	What Kind Of Fool Do You Think I Am/Are You Ready For This	5

DEALER

83	Windrush	Better Things To Do (p/s)	4

ALAN DEAN (& HIS PROBLEMS)

55	MGM SP 1116	The Song From "Desiree"/Tonight, My Love	4
55	MGM SP 1139	Remember Me, Wherever You Go/Love Is All That Matters	4
56	MGM SP 1173	Without You/Take A Bow	4

MINT VALUE £

57	Columbia DB 3932	Rock 'n' Roll Tarantella/Life Is But A Dream	12
57	Columbia DB 3932	Rock 'n' Roll Tarantella/Life Is But A Dream (78)	5
64	Decca F 11947	The Time It Takes/Dizzy Heights (as Alan Dean & His Problems)	12
65	Pye 7N 15749	Thunder And Rain/As Time Goes By (as Alan Dean & His Problems)	40

LITTLE BILLY DEAN
| 67 | Strike JH 325 | That's Always Like You/Tic Toc | 20 |

BOBBY DEAN
| 65 | Parlophone R 5254 | More And More/Saint James' Infirmiary | 4 |

ELTON DEAN
| 71 | CBS 64539 | ELTON DEAN (LP) | 20 |
| 77 | Ogun OG 610 | THE CHEQUE IS IN THE POST (LP) | 12 |

(see also Soft Machine, Bluesology)

EMIL DEAN
| 68 | Island WIP 6033 | This Is Our Anniversary/Lonely Boy | 4 |

HAZELL DEAN
75	Decca F 13613	Our Day Will Come/Our Day Will Come (Instrumental)	4
76	Decca F 13622	I Couldn't Live Without You/You Promised Me The Love	4
76	Decca F 13668	Got You Where I Want You/You Were There	4
77	Decca F 13683	Look What I've Found At The End/Where Are We Going	4
77	Decca F 13736	No One's Ever Gonna Love You/Just One More Time	4
78	Decca F 13751	Who Was That Lady/One Bad Mistake	4
84	Proto ENAP 114	Jealous Love/Evergreen (picture disc)	4
85	Proto ENAP 123	No Fool (For Love)/No Fool (For Love) (Instrumental) (picture disc)	4

JIMMY DEAN
59	Philips PB 940	Weekend Blues/Sing Along	7
59	Philips PB 940	Weekend Blues/Sing Along (78)	5
60	Philips PB 984	There's Still Time, Brother/Thanks For The Dream	5
61	Philips PB 1187	Big Bad John/I Won't Go Hunting With You Jake	4
61	Philips PB 1210	The Cajun Queen/To A Sleeping Beauty	5
62	Philips PB 1223	Smoke Smoke (Smoke) That Cigarette/Dear Ivan	6
62	CBS AAG 107	Steelman/Little Bitty Big John	5
62	CBS AAG 122	Little Black Book/Please Pass The Biscuits	4
61	Philips BBE 12501	JIMMY DEAN (EP)	8
66	CBS EP 6075	THE BEST OF JIMMY DEAN (EP)	7
	Philips	LPs	12-15
63	CBS	PORTRAIT OF JIMMY DEAN (LP)	12
65	Fontana FJL 303	GOLDEN FAVOURITES (LP)	10

NORA DEAN
| 69 | Upsetter US 322 | The Same Thing You Gave To Daddy/UPSETTER PILGRIMS: A Testimony | 5 |
| 70 | Trojan TR 7735 | Barbwire/BARONS: Calypso Mama | 4 |

PAUL DEAN (& SOUL SAVAGES)
64	Polydor NH 59102	She Can Build A Mountain/A Day Gone By (probably unreleased)	
65	Decca F 12136	You Don't Own Me/Hole In The Head (as Paul Dean & Thoughts)	12
66	Reaction 591 002	She Can Build A Mountain/A Day Gone By (as Paul Dean & Soul Savages)	8

(see also Thoughts)

ROGER DEAN'S LYSIS
| 77 | Mosaic GCM 762 | LYSIS LIVE (LP) | 10 |
| 77 | Mosaic GCM 774 | CYCLE (LP) | 10 |

TERRI DEAN
59	Top Rank JAR 141	I'm Confessin' (That I Love You)/I Blew Out The Flame	5
59	Top Rank JAR 141	I'm Confessin' (That I Love You)/I Blew Out The Flame (78)	5
59	Top Rank JAR 179	Adonis/You Treat Me Like A Boy	4
59	Top Rank JAR 179	Adonis/You Treat Me Like A Boy (78)	5

DEAN & JEAN
64	Stateside SS 249	Tra La La La Suzy/I Love The Summertime	8
64	Stateside SS 283	Hey Jean Hey Dean/Please Don't Tell Me How	8
64	Stateside SS 313	Thread Your Needle/I Wanna Be Loved	10

DEAN & MARK
64	Hickory 45 -1227	With Tears In My Eyes/Kissin' Games	5
64	Hickory 45 - 1249	When I Stop Dreaming/There Oughta Be A Law	5
65	Hickory 45 -1294	Just A Step Away/Fallen Star	5

(see also Newbeats)

JASON DEANE
| 66 | King KG 1049 | Make Believe/Don't Ever Want To See You No More | 20 |
| 67 | King KG 1060 | Down In The Street/Ain't Got No Love | 40 |

PETER DE ANGELIS ORCHESTRA & CHORUS
| 58 | London HL 8743 | The Happy Mandolin/Holiday In Naples | 4 |

DEANO
| 67 | Columbia DB 8233 | What's The Matter With The Matador?/Baby, Let Me Be Your Baby | 5 |

BLOSSOM DEARIE
| 66 | Fontana TF 719 | I'm Hip/Wallflower Lonely, Cornflower Blue | 4 |
| 67 | Fontana TF 788 | Sweet Georgie Fame/One Note Samba | 4 |

DEARLY BELOVED
| 66 | CBS 202398 | Peep Peep Pop Pop/It Is Better | 10 |

DEAR MR. TIME
| 70s | Square SQA 101 | GRANDFATHER (LP) | 50 |

MINT VALUE £

DEATH CULT

83	Situation 2 SIT 23	Brothers Grimm/Ghost Dance (p/s)	4
83	Situation 2 SIT 23T	Brothers Grimm/Ghost Dance/Horse Nation/Christians (12" p/s, with A3 insert)	7
83	Situation 2 SIT 29	Gods Zoo/Gods Zoo (These Times) (p/s)	4

(see also Southern Death Cult, Cult)

DEATH IN JUNE

84	New European SA 29634	Heaven Street/We Drive East (p/s)	25
84	New European SA 29634	Heaven Street/We Drive East/In The Night Time (12", brown/gold embossed/textured or blue/white sleeve)	40/25
84	New European SA 30634	State Laughter/Holy Water (p/s)	20
84	New European BADVC 6	She Said Destroy/The Calling (p/s)	15
84	New European 12BADVC 6	She Said Destroy/Doubt To Nothing/The Calling (12", p/s, with insert)	20
85	New European BADVC 69	Born Again/The Calling (Mk II)/Carousel (Bolt Mix) (12", p/s)	15
85	New European BADVC 73	...And Murder Love/A.M.L. (Instrumental) (p/s)	12
85	New European 12BADVC73	Come Before Christ And Murder Love/Torture By Roses (12", p/s)	15
87	New European BADVC 10	To Drown A Rose/Zimmerit/Europa/The Gates Of Heaven (10", p/s)	12
88	Cenaz CENAZ 09	Born Again/The Calling/Carousel (Remix) (12" picture disc, 1st pressing has silver print & rim, 2nd pressing has bronze)	12/10
85	New European BAD VC 13	NADA (LP, blue or brownish sleeve)	25/15
88	New European BAD VC 88	WALL OF SACRIFICE (LP, red sleeve or green/yellow sleeve)	50/35
90	New European BAD VC 3	THE GUILTY HAVE NO PRIDE (LP)	10
90s	Leprosy Discs UBAD VC 4	BURIAL (LP, textured sleeve, brown or white vinyl)	20/30
90s	New European BAD VC 9	THE WORLD THAT SUMMER (2-LP, gatefold textured)	15

(see also Crisis)

DEBONAIRES (U.K.)

| 66 | Pye 7N 17151 | A Love Of Our Own/The Night Meets The Dawn | 4 |
| 66 | Pye 7N 17204 | Crying Behind Your Smile/Forever More | 4 |

DEBONAIRES (U.S.)

| 70 | Track 604 035 | I'm In Love Again/Headache In My Heart | 15 |

DEBONAIRS

| 63 | Parlophone R 5054 | That's Right/When True Love Comes Your Way | 4 |

DEBS

| 65 | Mercury MF 888 | Sloopy's Gonna Hang On/Under A Street Light | 4 |

DEB-TONES

| 59 | RCA RCA 1137 | Knock, Knock — Who's There?/I'm In Love Again | 10 |
| 59 | RCA RCA 1137 | Knock, Knock — Who's There?/I'm In Love Again (78) | 10 |

CHRIS DE BURGH

75	A&M AMS 7148	Hold On/Sin City	6
75	A&M AMS 7185	Flying/Watching The World	6
76	A&M AMS 7196	Lonely Sky/The Song For You	5
76	A&M AMS 7224	Patricia The Stripper/Old Friend	4
76	A&M AMS 7267	A Spaceman Came Travelling/Just A Poor Boy (initially in p/s)	7/4
77	A&M AMS 7320	Broken Wings/I Will	6
78	A&M AMS 7336	Discovery/Round And Around	6
78	A&M AMS 7347	Spanish Train/Perfect Day (initially in p/s)	6/4
79	A&M AMS 7416	I Had The Love In My Eyes/Just In Time	4
79	A&M AMS 7430	The Devil's Eye/It's Such A Long Way Home	4
80	A&M AMS 7546	Shadows And Lights/Walls Of Silence (initially in p/s)	6/4
80	A&M AMS 7562	The Traveller/Eastern Wind (initially in p/s)	6/4
81	A&M AMS 8160	Waiting For The Hurricane/Broken Wings (p/s)	4
82	A&M AMS 8268	The Getaway/Living On The Island (p/s)	5
82	A&M AMS 8309	Ship To Shore/Crying And Laughing (p/s)	4
84	A&M AMX 202	I Love The Night/Moonlight And Vodka (12", p/s)	8
88	A&M CDEE 486	Tender Hands/A Night On The River (3" CD)	7
80s	A&M C DE B 1	Sailor/Lonely Sky (p/s, clear vinyl, numbered)	7

DEBUTANTES

| 80 | Rok ROK XVII/XVIII | Man In The Street/INNOCENT BYSTANDERS: Where Is Johnny (co. sleeve) | 5 |

DECAMERON

73	Vertigo 6360 097	SAY HELLO TO THE BAND (LP)	10
74	Mooncrest CREST 19	MAMMOTH SPECIAL (LP)	10
75	Transatlantic TRA 304	THIRD LIGHT (LP)	10
75	Mooncrest CREST 28	BEYOND THE LIGHT (LP)	10
76	Transatlantic TRA 325	TOMORROW'S PANTOMIME (LP)	10

YVONNE DE CARLO

| 55 | Capitol CL 14380 | Take It Or Leave It/Three Little Stars | 5 |

PAULO DE CARVALHO

| 74 | Pye Intl. 7N 25647 | (And Then) After Love/E Depois Do Adeus (p/s) | 10 |

DE CASTRO SISTERS

54	London HL 8104	Teach Me Tonight/It's Love	25
55	London HL 8137	Boom Boom Boomerang/Let Your Love Walk In	25
55	London HL 8158	I'm Bewildered/To Say You're Mine	25
55	London HLU 8189	If I Ever Fall In Love/Cuckoo In The Clock	20
55	London HLU 8212	Christmas Is A-Comin'/Snowbound For Christmas	20
56	London HLU 8228	Give Me Time/Too Late Now	20
56	London HLU 8296	No One To Blame But You/Cowboys Don't Cry	20
58	HMV POP 527	Who Are They To Say?/When You Look At Me	8
59	HMV POP 583	The Things I Tell My Pillow/Teach Me Tonight Cha Cha	8
61	Capitol CL 15199	Red Sails In The Sunset/Bells	6

DECISIONS
71	A&M AMS 844	If It's Love That Really Counts/I Can't Forget About You	6

DIANA DECKER
54	Columbia SCM 5083	Oh, My Papa/Crystal Ball	10
54	Columbia SCM 5096	The Happy Wanderer/Till We Two Are One	7
54	Columbia SCM 5120	Jilted/The Man With The Banjo	8
54	Columbia SCM 5123	Kitty In The Basket/Never Never Land	12
54	Columbia SCM 5130	Mama Mia/Percy The Penguin	8
54	Columbia SCM 5145	Sisters/Abracadabra	10
55	Columbia SCM 5166	Open The Window Of Your Heart/The Violin Song	7
55	Columbia SCM 5173	Apples, Peaches And Cherries/Paper Valentine	7
56	Columbia SCM 5246	Rock-A-Boogie Baby/Willie Can	18
56	Columbia DB 3739	Rock-A-Boogie Baby/Willie Can (78)	5

(see also Ray Burns, Ruby Murray)

DECORATORS
81	New Hormones/Red RS 9	Pendulum And Swing/Rendezvous/Strange One (p/s)	4
81	New Hormones ORG 5	Twilight View/Reflections (p/s)	4

DE DANAAN
82	Cara CARA 1	Hey Jude/St. Jude's Hornpipe/Trip To Taum Reel/Teetotaller	4
77	Decca SKL-R 5287	DE DANAAN — SELECTED JIGS AND REELS (LP)	20
80	Decca SKL 5318	BANKS OF THE NILE (LP)	10

DEDICATED MEN'S JUG BAND
65	Piccadilly 7N 35245	Boodle-Am-Shake/Come On Boys	5
66	Piccadilly 7N 35283	Don't Come Knocking/Out Time Blues	5

DEDRINGER
80	DinDisc DIN 10	Sunday Drivers/We Don't Mind (p/s)	4
80	DinDisc DIN 11	Innocent 'Till Proven Guilty/Maxine//Took A Long Time/ We Don't Mind (double pack)	4
81	DinDisc DIN 12	Direct Line/She's Not Ready (p/s)	4
82	Neat NEAT 18	Hot Lady/Hot Licks And Rock'N'Roll (p/s)	6
80	DinDisc	SUNDAY DRIVERS (LP)	10
81	DinDisc DID 7	DIRECT LINE (LP)	10
83	Neat NEAT 1009	SECOND RISING (LP)	10

DAVE DEE
70	Fontana TF 1074	My Woman's Man/Gotta Make You Part Of Me	4
70	Philips 6006 061	Everything About Her/If I Believed In Tomorrow	4
70	Philips 6006 100	Wedding Bells/Sweden	4
71	Philips 6006 154	Hold On/Mary Morning, Mary Evening	4
71	Philips 6006 180	Swingy/Don't You Ever Change Your Mind	4
74	Fontana 6007 021	Annabella/Kelly	4

(see also Dave Dee, Dozy, Beaky, Mick & Tich)

DAVE DEE, DOZY, BEAKY, MICK & TICH
65	Fontana TF 531	No Time/Is It Love	15
65	Fontana TF 586	All I Want/It Seems A Pity	10
65	Fontana TF 630	You Make It Move/I Can't Stop	6
66	Fontana TF 671	Hold Tight!/You Know What I Want	4
66	Fontana TF 711	Hideaway/Here's A Heart	4
67	Fontana TF 873	Zabadak!/The Sun Goes Down	4
68	Fontana TF 903	The Legend Of Xanadu/Please	4
60s	Fontana	other 45s	3
67	Fontana TE 17488	LOOS OF ENGLAND (EP)	7
67	Philips MCF 5005	THE HITS OF MANFRED MANN AND DDDBM&T (cassette EP)	10
66	Fontana TL 5350	DAVE DEE, DOZY, BEAKY, MICK & TICH (LP)	10
66	Fontana (S)TL 5388	IF MUSIC BE THE FOOD OF LOVE (LP)	10
67	Fontana (S)TL 5441	GOLDEN HITS OF DAVE DEE, DOZY, BEAKY, MICK & TICH (LP)	10
68	Fontana (S)TL 5471	IF NO-ONE SANG (LP)	12

(see also Dozy, Beaky, Mick & Tich; Dave Dee)

JAY DEE
74	Warner Bros K 16395	Strange Funky Games And Things/(Version)	4

JEANNIE DEE
69	Beacon BEA 115	Come Into My Arms/Sun Shine On Me	4
69	Beacon BEA 142	Don't Go Home My Little Darling/Come See About Me	8

JOEY DEE & STARLI(GH)TERS
61	Columbia DB 4758	Peppermint Twist Pts 1 & 2	4
62	Columbia DB 4803	Hey, Let's Twist/Roly Poly	5
62	Columbia DB 4842	Shout Pts 1 & 2	5
62	Columbia DB 4862	Ya Ya/Fanny Mae	4
62	Columbia DB 4905	What Kind Of Love Is This?/Wing Ding	4
63	Columbia DB 4955	I Lost My Baby/Keep Your Mind On What You're Doin'	5
63	Columbia DB 7055	Hot Pastrami With Mashed Potatoes Pts 1 & 2	4
63	Columbia DB 7102	Dance, Dance, Dance/Let's Have A Party	4
61	Columbia 33SX 1406	DOIN' THE TWIST LIVE AT THE PEPPERMINT LOUNGE (LP, green label)	20
62	Columbia 33SX 1502	ALL THE WORLD IS TWISTIN' (LP, blue/black label)	20

JOHNNIE DEE
65	Columbia DB 7612	Frankie's Angel/Everything's Upside Down	5

JOHNNY DEE
57	Oriole CB 1367	Sittin' In The Balcony/A-Plus Love	75
57	Oriole CB 1367	Sittin' In The Balcony/A-Plus Love (78)	20

(see also John D. Loudermilk)

MINT VALUE £

KIKI DEE

63	Fontana TF 394	Lucky High Heels/Early Night	7
63	Fontana TF 414	I Was Only Kidding/Don't Put Your Heart In His Hand	5
64	Fontana TF 443	That's Right, Walk On By/Miracles	5
64	Fontana TF 490	Baby I Don't Care/How Glad I Am	6
65	Fontana TF 596	Runnin' Out Of Fools/There He Goes	5
66	Fontana TF 669	Why Don't I Run Away From You?/Small Town	7
67	Fontana TF 792	I'm Going Out (The Same Way I Came In)/	
		We've Got Everything Going For Us	5
67	Fontana TF 833	I/Stop And Think	4
67	Fontana TF 870	Excuse Me/Patterns	5
68	Fontana TF 926	Can't Take My Eyes Off You/Hungry Heart	4
68	Fontana TF 983	Now The Flowers Cry/On A Magic Carpet Ride	50
70	Tamla Motown TMG 739	The Day Will Come Between Sunday And Monday/My Whole World Ended	
		(The Moment You Left Me)	5
65	Fontana TE 17443	KIKI DEE (EP)	10
66	Fontana TE 17470	KIKI DEE IN CLOVER (EP)	10
68	Fontana (S)TL 5455	I'M KIKI DEE (LP)	15
70	Tamla Motown STML 11158	GREAT EXPECTATIONS (LP)	25

LENNY DEE

55	Brunswick 05440	Plantation Boogie/Birth Of The Blues	6

RICKY DEE & EMBERS

62	Stateside SS 136	Workout/JOHN MOBLEY: Tunnel Of Love	8

SANDRA DEE

61	Brunswick 05858	Tammy Tell Me True/Let's Fall In Love	6

SIMON DEE

69	Chapter One CH 105	Julie/Whatever Happened To Us?	4

TOMMY DEE

59	Melodisc 1516	Three Stars/TEEN JONES (TONES): I'll Never Change	40
59	Melodisc 1516	Three Stars/TEEN JONES (TONES): I'll Never Change (78)	50

DEE & DYNAMITES

60	Philips PB 1081	Blaze Away/South Bound Gasser	5

DEEJAYS

65	Polydor BM 56034	Dimples/Coming On Strong	35
65	Polydor BM 56501	Blackeyed Woman/I Just Can't Go To Sleep	70

ANTHONY DEELEY

68	Pama PM 728	Anytime Man/Don't Change Your Mind About Me	6

CAROL DEENE

61	HMV POP 922	Sad Movies/Don't Forget	5
62	HMV POP 973	Norman/On The Outside Looking In	4
62	HMV POP 1027	Johnny Get Angry/Somebody's Smiling	4
62	HMV POP 1058	Some People/Kissin'	4
62	HMV POP 1086	James/It Happened Last Night	5
63	HMV POP 1123	Let Me Do It My Way/Growin' Up	5
63	HMV POP 1200	Oh Oh Oh Willie/I Want To Stay Here	5
64	HMV POP 1275	Who's Been Sleeping In My Bed?/Love Is Wonderful	5
65	HMV POP 1405	I Can't Forget Someone Like You/Most People Do	5
65	Columbia DB 7743	He Just Don't Know/Up In The Penthouse	4
66	Columbia DB 7890	Dancing In Your Eyes/Please Don't Be Unfaithful Again	4
67	Columbia DB 8107	Time/Love Have I	4
68	CBS 3206	When He Wants A Woman/I'm Not Crying	4
69	Conquest CXT 102	One More Chance/Invisible Tears	4

DEEP FEELING

70	Page One POF 165	Do You Love Me/Move On	6
70	Page One POF 177	Skyline Pigeon/We've Thrown It All Away	6
71	DJM DJS 10231	Do You Wanna Dance/The Day My Lady Cried	5
72	DJM DJS 10237	Sweat, Dust And Red Wine/Turn Around	5
72	DJM DJS 10257	Country Heir/We've Thrown It All Away	5
74	Santa Ponsa PNS 12	Let's Spend The Night Together/Avalon	4
71	DJM DJLPS 419	DEEP FEELING (LP)	35

DEEP FREEZE

70s	Guardian GRL 43	Keeping You In Furs/Don't Look Back	4

DEEP FREEZE MICE

80s	Cordelia ERICAT 002	These Floors Are Smooth (p/s)	10
80s	Cordelia ERICAT 004	Hang On Constance Let Me Hear The News (p/s)	8
80s	Cordelia ERICAT 013	Rain Is When The Earth Is Television (p/s)	7
80s	Cordelia ERICAT 016	NEURON MUSIC (12")	8
79	Mole Embalming MOLE 1	MY GERANIUMS ARE BULLETPROOF (LP, 200 only with paste-on	
		sleeve, 8-page booklet & various A4 inserts)	60/30
81	Mole Embalming MOLE 2	TEENAGE HEAD IN MY REFRIGERATOR (LP)	30
81	Mole Embalming MOLE C2	HEGEL'S BRAIN (cassette)	10
81	Inedible MOLE 3	GATES OF LUNCH (LP)	15
83	Mole Embalming MOLE 4	SAW A RANCH BURNING LAST NIGHT (LP)	15
80s	Cordelia ERICAT 001	I LOVE YOU LITTLE BO BO WITH YOUR DELICATE GOLDEN LIONS	
		(2-LP)	15

DEEP PURPLE

68	Parlophone R 5708	Hush!/One More Rainy Day	15
68	Parlophone R 5708	Hush!/One More Rainy Day (in promo p/s)	50
68	Parlophone R 5745	Kentucky Woman/Wring That Neck (withdrawn)	25

69	Parlophone R 5763	Emmaretta/Wring That Neck	15
69	Harvest HAR 5006	Hallelujah (I Am The Preacher)/April Part 1	7
69	Harvest HAR 5006	Hallelujah (I Am The Preacher)/April Part 1 (in promo p/s)	18
70	Harvest HAR 5020	Black Night/Speed King	4
71	Harvest HAR 5033	Strange Kind Of Woman/I'm Alone	4
71	Harvest HAR 5045	Fireball/Demon's Eye	4
72	Purple PUR 102	Never Before/When A Blind Man Cries	4
74	Purple PUR 117	Might Just Take Your Life/Coronarias Redig	4
76	Purple PUR 130	You Keep On Moving/Love Child	4
77	Purple PUR 132	Smoke On The Water/Child In Time/ Woman From Tokyo (10,000 with p/s)	5
77	Purple PUR 135	NEW LIVE AND RARE VOL. 1 (EP, 15,000 on purple vinyl)	5
78	Purple PUR 137	NEW LIVE AND RARE VOL. 2 (EP)	4
80	Harvest SHEP 101	NEW LIVE AND RARE VOL. 3 (EP)	4
85	Polydor POSPP 719	Perfect Strangers (edit)/Son Of Alerik (edit) (picture disc)	6
87	Polydor POSPP 843	Call Of The Wild/Strange Ways (12" picture disc)	7
68	Parlophone PMC/PCS 7055	SHADES OF DEEP PURPLE (LP, yellow/black label, mono/stereo)	50/30
68	Parlophone PMC/PCS 7055	SHADES OF DEEP PURPLE (LP, later white/black label pressing)	15/12
69	Harvest SHVL 751	THE BOOK OF TALIESYN (LP)	10
69	Harvest SHVL 759	DEEP PURPLE (LP)	10
74	Purple Q4TPSA 7504	MACHINE HEAD (LP, quadrophonic)	25
78	Harvest SHSM 2026	THE SINGLES A's AND B's (LP, purple vinyl)	10
79	Purple TPS 3514	THE MARK 2 PURPLE SINGLES (LP, purple vinyl)	12
84	Polydor POLHP 16	PERFECT STRANGERS (LP, picture disc)	10
85	EMI EJ 34 0344 0	FIREBALL (LP, picture disc with poster)	10
85	EMI EJ 26 0343 0	IN ROCK (LP, picture disc with poster)	10
85	EMI EG26 0345 0	MACHINE HEAD (LP, picture disc with poster)	10

(see also Ritchie Blackmore, Rainbow, [Ian] Gillan [Band], [David Coverdale's] Whitesnake, Tommy Bolin, [Sheila Carter &] Episode [Six], Jon Lord, Roger Glover, Green Bullfrog, Wizard's Convention, Elf, Maze, M.I. Five, Warhorse, Captain Beyond)

DEEP RIVER BOYS

51	HMV B 10012	I Still Love You/September Song (78)	12
52	HMV B 10346	Only Fascination/Don't Trade Your Love For Gold (78)	10
52	HMV B 10381	Trying/Tennessee Newsboy (78)	10
53	HMV B 10542	The Biggest Fool/Oo-Shoo-Be-Do-Be (78)	10
54	HMV 7M 174	Sweet Mama Tree Top Tall/A Kiss And Cuddle Polka	18
54	HMV B 10625	Sweet Mama Tree Top Tall/A Kiss And Cuddle Polka (78)	10
54	HMV 7M 280	Shake, Rattle And Roll/St. Louis Blues	20
54	HMV B 10790	Shake, Rattle And Roll/St. Louis Blues (78)	10
54	HMV B 10633	Lucky Black Cat/My Castle On The Nile (78)	10
55	HMV POP 113	Rock Around The Clock/Adam Never Had A Mommy (78)	5
56	HMV 7M 361	Rock-A-Beatin' Boogie/Just A Little Bit More!	20
56	HMV POP 157	Rock-A-Beatin' Boogie/Just A Little Bit More! (78)	5
56	HMV POP 263	That's Right/Honey Honey	20
56	HMV POP 263	That's Right/Honey Honey (78)	5
57	HMV POP 395	Whole Lotta Shakin' Goin' On/There's A Goldmine In The Sky	20
57	HMV POP 395	Whole Lotta Shakin' Goin' On/There's A Goldmine In The Sky (78)	5
58	HMV POP 449	Not Too Old To Rock And Roll/Slow Train To Nowhere	12
58	HMV POP 449	Not Too Old To Rock And Roll/Slow Train To Nowhere (78)	5
58	HMV POP 537	Itchy Twitchy Feeling/I Shall Not Be Moved	10
58	HMV POP 537	Itchy Twitchy Feeling/I Shall Not Be Moved (78)	5
59	Top Rank JAR 172	Nola/Kissin'	6
59	Top Rank JAR 174	Timbers Gotta Roll/I Don't Know Why (I Just Do) (with Harry Douglass)	6
60	Top Rank JAR 352	Go Galloway, Go/Dum Dum De Dum (with Harry Douglass)	4
62	HMV POP 1081	Settle Down/Ashes Of Roses	8
55	Nixa 45EP 113	GO ON BOARD LITTLE CHILDREN (EP)	7
55	Nixa 45EP 114	SWING LOW SWEET CHARIOT (EP)	7
55	Nixa 45EP 130	WALK TOGETHER CHILDREN (EP)	7
55	Nixa 45EP 131	EZEKIEL SAW THE WHEEL (EP)	7
55	HMV 7EG 8133	DEEP RIVER BOYS (EP)	7
57	HMV 7EG 8321	ROMANCE A LA MODE (EP)	7
57	HMV 7EG 8445	NEGRO SPIRITUALS (EP)	7
54	Nixa XLTY 135	SPIRITUALS SUNG BY THE DEEP RIVER BOYS (10" LP)	15
54	Nixa XLTY 138	SPIRITUALS SUNG BY THE DEEP RIVER BOYS (10" LP)	15
60	Top Rank 35/108	THE BLUE DEEPS (LP)	10

(see also Fats Waller)

DEEP SET

| 68 | Pye 7N 17594 | That's The Way Life Goes/Hello Amy | 5 |
| 69 | Major Minor MM 607 | I Started A Joke/Spicks And Specks | 7 |

DEEP SIX

| 66 | Liberty LIB 55882 | Counting/When Morning Breaks | 4 |

SAM DEES

69	Major Minor MM 655	It's All Wrong/Don't Keep Me Hanging On	5
75	Atlantic K 10676	Fragile, Handle With Care/Save The Love At Any Cost	10
75	Atlantic K 50142	THE SHOW MUST GO ON (LP)	20

SAM DEES & BETTYE SWANN

| 76 | Atlantic K 10719 | Storybook Children/Just As Sure | 8 |

(see also Bettye Swann)

DEE SET

| 68 | Blue Cat BS 146 | I Know A Place/ROY BENNETT: I Dangerous | 6 |

DEE-TONERS

| 59 | RCA RCA 1137 | Knock Knock Who's There (78) | 10 |

DEFECTS

81	Casualty CR 001	Dance Till You Drop/Guilty Conscience/Brutality (p/s) 5
82	WXYZ ABCD 3	Survival/Brutality (p/s) 4
83	Lyntone LYN 12647	Dance/ANTI NOWHERE LEAGUE: World War III/METEORS: Mutant Rock (Instrumental) (red vinyl flexidisc free with 'Flexipop' magazine issue 26) 6/5

DEFENDANTS

80s	Edible EAT 001	Headmaster/Such A Spiv (stickered insert cover & stickered labels) 5

DEFENDERS

68	Doctor Bird DB 1104	Set Them Free/Don't Blame The Children (actually by Lee Perry & Sensations) ..12

DEF LEPPARD

79	Bludgeon Riffola MSB 001/ SRT/CUS/232	THE DEF LEPPARD EP: Ride Into The Sun/Getcha Rocks Off/ The Overture (p/s, red label, some with lyric sheet) 125/100
79	Bludgeon Riffola MSB 001	Ride Into The Sun/Getcha Rocks Off/The Overture (red label, no p/s) 40
79	Bludgeon Riffola MSB 001	Ride Into The Sun/Getcha Rocks Off/The Overture (yellow label, no p/s) 18
79	Phonogram 6059 240	Getcha Rocks Off/Ride Into The Sun/The Overture (no p/s) 8
79	Phonogram 6059 240	Getcha Rocks Off/Ride Into The Sun/The Overture (mispressing, both sides play "The Overture") 20
79	Phonogram 6059 247	Wasted/Hello America (p/s) 10
80	Phonogram LEPP 1	Hello America/Good Morning Freedom (p/s) 10
81	Phonogram LEPP 2	Let It Go/Switch 625 (p/s, some shrinkwrapped with patch) 15/8
82	Phonogram LEPP 3	Bringin' On The Heartbreak/Me And My Wine (p/s) 15
82	Phonogram LEPP 312	Bringin' On The Heartbreak/Me And My Wine/You Got Me Runnin' (12", p/s) 18
83	Phonogram VER 5	Photograph/Bringin' On The Heartbreak (p/s) 10
83	Phonogram VERQ 5	Photograph/Bringin' On The Heartbreak (pop-up 3-D card 'camera' p/s) 25
83	Phonogram VERP 5	Photograph/Bringin' On The Heartbreak (pop-up 3-D card sleeve, folds out into camera shape, different photo of Marilyn Monroe inside) 40
83	Phonogram VERX 5	Photograph/Bringin' On The Heartbreak/Mirror, Mirror (12", p/s) 20
83	Phonogram VER 6	Rock Of Ages/Action! Not Words (p/s) 6
83	Phonogram VERP 6	Rock Of Ages/Action! Not Words (guitar-shaped picture disc) 12
83	Phonogram VERQ 6	Rock Of Ages/Action! Not Words (foldout 'rock box' cube sleeve) 20
83	Phonogram VERX 6	Rock Of Ages/Action! Not Words (12", p/s) 15
83	Phonogram VER 8	Too Late For Love/Foolin' (p/s) 10
83	Phonogram VER 8	Too Late For Love/Foolin' (p/s with rear photo of band in football kit) 35
83	Phonogram VERX 8	Too Late For Love/Foolin'/High And Dry (12", p/s) 15
84	Phonogram VER 9	Photograph/Bringin' On The Heartbreak (reissue, 'wallet' p/s) 8
84	Phonogram VERG 9	Photograph/Bringin' On The Heartbreak (gatefold printed 'wallet' p/s) 20
84	Phonogram VERX 9	Photograph/Bringin' On The Heartbreak/Mirror, Mirror (12", p/s) 20
87	Phonogram LEP 1	Animal/Tear It Down (p/s) 4
87	Phonogram LEPC 1	Animal/Animal (Extended Mix)/Tear It Down (12", p/s, red vinyl) 15
87	Phonogram LEPCD 1	Animal/Animal (Extended Mix)/Tear It Down/Women (CD, numbered) 12
87	Phonogram LEP 2	Pour Some Sugar On Me/I Wanna Be Your Hero (p/s) 4
87	Phonogram LEPS 2	Pour Some Sugar On Me/I Wanna Be Your Hero (tri-shaped picture disc in silver 12" foldout sleeve with tour dates) 12
87	Phonogram LEPMC 2	Pour Some Sugar On Me/I Wanna Be Your Hero (cassette) 4
87	Phonogram LEPX 2	Pour Some Sugar On Me (Extended Mix)/Pour Some Sugar On Me/ I Wanna Be Your Hero (12", p/s) 7
87	Phonogram LEPPX 2	Pour Some Sugar On Me (Extended Mix)/Pour Some Sugar On Me/ I Wanna Be Your Hero (12", picture disc, unreleased)
87	Phonogram LEPS 3	Hysteria/Ride Into The Sun (1987 Version) (p/s, with free patch) 4
87	Phonogram LEPX 313	Hysteria/Ride Into The Sun (1987 Version)/Love And Affection (live) (12", in envelope sleeve with poster & international discography) 10
87	Phonogram LEPCD 3	Hysteria/Ride Into The Sun (1987 Version)/Love And Affection (live)/ I Wanna Be Your Hero (CD, 5,000 only with titles in red, numbered) 7
88	Phonogram LEPP 4	Armageddon It (The Atomic Mix)/Ring Of Fire (poster p/s) 5
88	Phonogram LEPXB 4	Armageddon It/Armageddon It (The Atomic Mix)/Ring Of Fire (12", numbered box set with poster, enamel badge & 5 postcards) 12
88	Phonogram LEPCD 4	Armageddon It/Armageddon It (Atomic Mix)/Ring Of Fire/Animal/ Pour Some Sugar On Me (CD, picture disc) 10
88	Phonogram LEPG 5	Love Bites/Billy's Got A Gun (live) (no'd gatefold p/s with 8-page lyric insert) 4
88	Phonogram LEPXB 5	Love Bites/Billy's Got A Gun (live)/Excitable (Orgasmic Mix) (12", box set with 4 cardboard inserts) 12
89	Phonogram LEPC 6	Rocket/Release Me (foldout 'Brit' pack, envelope sleeve with 6 inserts) 6
89	Phonogram LEPXP 6	Rocket (Lunar Mix)/(Radio Edit)/Release Me (12", numbered picture disc) 10
89	Phonogram LEPXP 6	Rocket (Lunar Mix)/(Radio Edit)/Release Me (12", un-numbered picture disc) 20
92	Phonogram DEFPD 7	Let's Get Rocked/Only After Dark/Women (live) (12", picture disc) 10
92	Phonogram DEFCD 7	Let's Get Rocked/Only After Dark/Women (live) (CD, picture disc, in box) 12
87	Phonogram HYSPD 1	HYSTERIA (LP, picture disc) 15
89	Phonogram 8366062	THE FOUR ALBUMS (4-CD box set, with booklet) 50

ZION DE GALLIER

68	Parlophone R 5710	Dream Dream Dream/Geraldine 10
68	Parlophone R 5686	Winter Will Be Cold/Me 10

GLORIA DE HAVEN

55	Brunswick 05369	So This Is Paris/The Two Of Us 4
55	Brunswick 05457	Red Hot Pepper Pot/Won't You Save Me? 5
59	Oriole CB 1524	Dearly Beloved/Life 4

DE-HEMS

60s	President	Don't Cross That Line 8

DE JOHN SISTERS

56	Philips PB 524	Hotta Chocolotta/I'm Learnin' The Charleston (78) 5
57	Mercury MT 174	What Am I/Where Would I Be 4
60	London HLT 9127	Yes Indeed/Be Anything (But Be Mine) 5

DEK & JERRY
66	Philips BF 1494	What's The Matter With Me?/Don't Waste Your Time	4

DESMOND DEKKER (& ACES)
63	Island WI 054	Honour Your Mother And Father/Madgie (solo)	10
63	Island WI 111	Parents/Labour Of Learning (solo)	10
64	Island WI 158	Jeserine/King Of Ska (with His Cherry Pies)	10
64	Black Swan WI 445	Dracula (as Desmond Dekkar)/DON DRUMMOND: Spitfire	10
65	Island WI 181	Get Up Adine (as Desmond Dekkar, actually with Four Aces)/	
		Be Mine Forever (as Desmond Dekker & Patsy)	10
65	Island WI 202	This Woman (as Desmond Dekker & Four Aces)/	
		LEE PERRY & UPSETTERS: Si Senora	10
67	Pyramid PYR 6003	Wise Man/ROLAND ALPHONSO: Middle East	8
67	Pyramid PYR 6004	007 (Shanty Town)/ROLAND ALPHONSO: El Torro	5
67	Pyramid PYR 6008	Rudy Got Soul/ROLAND ALPHONSO: The Cat	8
68	Pyramid PYR 6011	Rude Boy Train/ROLAND ALPHONSO: Nothing For Nothing	8
68	Pyramid PYR 6012	Mother's Young Girl/SOUL BROTHERS: Confucious	8
68	Pyramid PYR 6017	Unity/Sweet Music	8
68	Pyramid PYR 6020	Sabotage/Pretty Africa	8
68	Pyramid PYR 6020	Sabotage/It Pays	8
69	Pyramid PYR 6026	It Pays/Young Generation	8
69	Pyramid PYR 6031	Beautiful And Dangerous/I've Got The Blues	8
69	Pyramid PYR 6035	Bongo Gal/Shing A Ling	8
69	Pyramid PYR 6037	To Sir, With Love/Fu Manchu	8
69	Pyramid PYR 6044	Mother Pepper/Don't Blame Me	8
69	Pyramid PYR 6047	Hey Grandma/Young Generation	8
69	Pyramid PYR 6051	Music Like Dirt (Intensified)/Coconut Water	8
69	Pyramid PYR 6054	It Mek/Writing On The Wall	8
69	Pyramid PYR 6058	Israelites/BEVERLEY'S ALLSTARS: The Man	4
69	JJ PYR 6058	Israelites/BEVERLEY'S ALLSTARS: The Man (mis-labelled copies)	4
69	Pyramid PYR 6059	Christmas Day/I've Got The Blues	7
69	Pyramid PYR 6068	It Mek/Problems	4
67	Doctor Bird DLM 5007	007 SHANTY TOWN (LP)	50
69	Doctor Bird DLM 5013	THE ISRAELITES (LP, solo)	30
69	Trojan TTL 4	THIS IS DESMOND DEKKAR (LP, as Desmond Dekkar)	12
70	Trojan TBL 146	YOU CAN GET IT IF YOU REALLY WANT (LP, as Desmond Dekker)	10
73	Trojan TRLD 401	DOUBLE DEKKER (2-LP, as Desmond Dekker)	14

DEL AMITRI
83	No Strings NOSP 1	Sense Sickness/The Difference Is (p/s)	15
85	Chrysalis CHS 2859	Sticks And Stones Girl/This King Is Poor (p/s)	4
85	Chrysalis CHS 12 2859	Sticks And Stones Girl/This King Is Poor/The Difference Is (12", p/s)	7
85	Chrysalis CHS 2925	Hammering Heart/Lines Running North (p/s)	4
85	Chrysalis CHS 12 2925	Hammering Heart/Lines Running North (12", p/s)	7
85	Chrysalis CHR 1499	DEL AMITRI (LP, original)	10

ERIC DELANEY BAND
56	Pye N 15069	Rockin' The Tymps/Ain't She Sweet (78)	5
56	Pye N 15079	Rock 'N' Roll King Cole/Time For Chimes (78)	6
57	Pye 7N 15113	Fanfare Jump/Jingle Bells	4
60	Parlophone R 4646	Bass Drum Boogie/Let's Get Organised	5
50s	Pye	HI-FI DELANEY (10" LP)	10

ERIC DELANEY'S BIG BEAT SIX
65	Pye 7N 15782	The Big Beat/Big Noise From Winnetka	4

DELANEY & BONNIE (& FRIENDS)
69	Elektra EKSN 45066	Get Ourselves Together/Soldiers Of The Cross (withdrawn)	6
69	Elektra EKSN 45078	Someday/Dirty Old Man	4
69	Atlantic 584 308	Comin' Home/Groupie (Superstar) (as Delaney And Bonnie Friends	
		Featuring Eric Clapton; most with large centre hole)	4
69	Apple SAPCOR 7	THE ORIGINAL DELANEY & BONNIE (LP, unreleased, no sleeve)	800
69	Elektra K 42024	ACCEPT NO SUBSTITUTE (LP)	12
70	Atlantic 2400 013	ON TOUR WITH ERIC CLAPTON (LP)	12
70	Atlantic 2400 029	TO BONNIE FROM DELANEY (LP)	10
71	London ZGL 113	GENESIS (LP)	10
74	Polydor/Stax 2362 001	HOME (LP)	10

(see also Eric Clapton, Delaney Bramlett, King Curtis with Delaney & Friends)

DELACARDOS
61	HMV POP 890	Hold Back The Tears/Mister Dillon	25

DEL-CAPRIS
79	Grapevine GRP 112	Hey Little Way Out Girl/EULA COOPER: Beggars Can't Be Choosey (p/s)	5

DELFONICS
68	Bell BLL 1005	La La Means I Love You/Can't Get Over Losing You	4
68	Bell BLL 1028	Break Your Promises/Alfie	4
68	Bell BLL 1042	Ready Or Not Here I Come/Somebody Loves Me	4
68	Bell SBLL 106	LA-LA MEANS I LOVE YOU (LP)	10
60	Bell SBLL 121	THE SOUND OF SEXY SOUL (LP)	10
71	Bell SBLL 137	THE DELFONICS (LP)	10
74	Bell BELLS 245	ALIVE AND KICKING (LP)	10

TERESA DEL FUEGO
81	Satril HH 155	Don't Hang Up/Wonder Wonder	8

(see also Swing Out Sister)

DELICATES
59	London HLT 8953	Ronnie Is My Lover/Black And White Thunderbird	75
59	London HLT 8953	Ronnie Is My Lover/Black And White Thunderbird (78)	45

MINT VALUE £

60	London HLT 9176	Too Young To Date/The Kiss	30

DELICATESSEN
67	Vocalion VN 9286	The Red Baron's Revenge/The Dog Fight	4

DELIGHT'S ORCHESTRA
69	Atco 226 005	Do Your Thing/King Of The Horse	4

DELITES
80	Grapevine GRP 127	Lover/Do The Zombie	4

JOHNNY DE LITTLE
61	Columbia DB 4578	Not Guilty/They	4
62	Columbia DB 4907	Lover/You Made Me Love You	4
63	Columbia DB 7023	Days Of Wine And Roses/Ride On	4
63	Columbia DB 7044	The Wind And The Rain/Unchained Melody	4
65	CBS 201790	The Knack/What To Do With Laurie	4

DENNIS D'ELL
67	CBS 202605	It Breaks My Heart In Two/Better Use Your Head (withdrawn; demos £80)	175
67	Decca F 12647	A Woman Called Sorrow/The Night Has A Thousand Eyes (as Denny D'Ell)	5
	(see also Honeycombs)		

JIMMY DELL
58	RCA RCA 1066	Teeny Weeny/BARRY DE VORZON: Barbara Jean	60
58	RCA RCA 1066	Teeny Weeny/BARRY DE VORZON: Barbara Jean (78)	35
	(see also Barry De Vorzon)		

PETE DELLO & FRIENDS
71	Nepentha 6437001	INTO YOUR EARS (LP, gatefold sleeve)	50
	(see also Honeybus, Lace, Red Herring, Leah)		

DELLS
63	Pye Intl. 7N 25178	The (Bossa Nova) Bird/Eternally	10
67	Chess CRS 8066	O-O I Love You/There Is	6
68	Chess CRS 8071	Wear It On Our Face/Please Don't Change Me Now	8
68	Chess CRS 8079	Stay In My Corner/Love Is So Simple	7
68	President PT 223	It's Not Unusual/Stay In My Corner	4
69	Chess CRS 8084	Always Together/I Want My Momma	4
69	President PT 270	Oh What A Night/Moving On	6
70	Chess CRS 8102	Oh What A Night/Believe Me	4
70	Chess CRS 8105	Dock Of The Bay/When I'm In Your Arms	5
73	Chess 6145 022	Give Your Baby A Standing Ovation/Run For Cover	4
72	Chess 6145 008	It's All Up To You/Oh My Dear	6
79	20th Century TC 2463	All About The Paper/I Touched A Dream (12")	8
68	Chess CRLS 4554	GREATEST HITS (LP)	12
69	Joy JOYS 186	OH WHAT A NIGHT (LP)	10
69	Chess CRLS 4555	LOVE IS BLUE — I CAN SING A RAINBOW (LP)	12
73	Chess 6467 303	THE BEST OF THE DELLS (LP)	10
75	Chess 9109 100	THE MIGHTY MIGHTY DELLS (LP)	12

DELMONAS
84	Big Beat SW 101	Comin' Home Baby/Woa Now/He Tells Me He Loves Me (p/s)	4
84	Big Beat SW 102	Hello We Love You/I'm The One For You/Peter Gunn Locomotion (p/s)	4

DELMONTES
81	Rational RATE 1	Tous Les Soirs/Ga Ga/Infectious Smile (with insert in bag or normal p/s)	5/6
81	Rational RATE 3	Don't Cry Your Tears/So It's Not To Be (g/fold p/s in bag, yellow or blue p/s)	5

DELMORE BROTHERS
58	Parlophone GEP 8728	COUNTRY AND WESTERN (EP)	18

AL DE LORY
65	London HLU 9999	Yesterday/Traffic Jam	15
70	Capitol CL 15644	Song From MASH/Feeling Of Love	4

DELTA CATS
69	Bamboo BAM 3	I Can't Re-Live (actually "I Can't Believe")/I've Been Hurt	6

DELTA KINGS
61	London RER 1318	AT SUNDOWN (EP)	7
61	London Jazz LTZR 15204	AT SUNDOWN (LP, also stereo SAHR 6118)	10

DELTA RHYTHM BOYS
51	London L 1145	Blow Out The Candle/All The Things You Are (78)	5
54	Brunswick 05353	Mood Indigo/Have A Hope, Have A Wish, Have A Prayer	7
52	Esquire 15-001	DELTA RHYTHM BOYS WITH THE METRONOME ALLSTARS (10" LP)	12

DELTAS
64	Blue Beat BB 265	Georgia/The Party	10
64	Blue Beat BB 275	The Visitor/SKATALITES: Hanging The Beam	10

DELTA SKIFFLE GROUP
57	Esquire 10-504	Skip To My Lou/John Brown's Body (78)	5
57	Esquire 10-507	Pick A Bale Of Cotton/K.C. Moan (78)	5
58	Esquire 10-517	Ain't You Glad?/Open Up Them Pearly Gates (78)	5
58	Esquire EP 162	DELTA SKIFFLE GROUP (EP)	15

DEL-TONES
59	Top Rank JAR 171	Rockin' Blues/Moonlight Party	40
59	Top Rank JAR 171	Rockin' Blues/Moonlight Party (78)	35
70	Columbia DB 8719	Gimme Some Lovin'/Have A Little Talk With Myself	4

MILTON DE LUGG ORCHESTRA
65	Columbia DB 7474	The Addams Family Theme/The Alfred Hitchcock Theme	8
66	Columbia DB 7762	The Munsters Theme/The Addams Family Theme	10

DELUSION
80s	Wizzo WIZZO 2	Pessimists Paradise/Desert Island (gatefold p/s) 8

DEL(L)-VIKINGS
57	London HLD 8405	Come Go With Me/How Can I Find A True Love (gold or silver label) 80/45
57	London HLD 8405	Come Go With Me/How Can I Find A True Love (78) 20
57	London HLD 8464	Whispering Bells/Little Billy Boy 30
57	London HLD 8464	Whispering Bells/Little Billy Boy (78) 15
57	Mercury MT 169	Cool Shake/Jitterbug Mary (78) 15
58	Mercury 7MT 199	The Voodoo Man/Can't Wait 45
58	Mercury 7MT 199	The Voodoo Man/Can't Wait (78) 15
59	Mercury AMT 1027	Flat Tyre/How Could You 40
59	Mercury AMT 1027	Flat Tyre/How Could You (78) 30
62	HMV POP 1072	Confession Of Love/Kilimanjaro 10
63	HMV POP 1145	An Angel Up In Heaven/The Fishing Chant 10
70s	Contour 2870 388	COME GO WITH ME (LP) 10

LEO DE LYON
54	MGM SP 1087	The Band Played On/Say It Isn't So 4
60	Oriole CB 1561	Rich In Love/The Blue Train 4

RALPH DE MARCO
59	London HLL 9010	Old Shep/More Than Riches 4

DEMENSIONS
60	Top Rank JAR 505	Over The Rainbow/Nursery Rhyme Rock 15
61	Coral Q 72437	Count Your Blessings Instead Of Sheep/Again 6

DEMICK & ARMSTRONG
70	Decca F 13056	We're On The Right Track/Dreaming 5
71	MAM MAM/AS 1001	LITTLE WILLY RAMBLE (LP) 10
72	A&M AMLH 68908	LOOKING THROUGH (LP) 10

(see also Wheels, James Brothers, Yellow Dog)

DEMOB
81	Round Ear ROUND 1	Anti Police/Teenage Adolescence (foldout p/s) 4
81	Round Ear EAR 3	No Room For You/Think Straight/New Breed (p/s) 5

DEMON
81	Clay CLAY 4	Liar/Wild Woman (p/s, red vinyl) 6
82	Carrere CAR 226	One Helluva Night/Into The Nightmare (picture disc) 4
83	Clay CLAY 25	The Plague/The Only Sane Man (p/s) 5
84	Clay CLAY 41	Wonderland/Blackheath (p/s) 4
84	Clay 12CLAY 41	Wonderland/Blackheath/Nowhere To Run (12", p/s) 7
88	Clay CLAY 48D	Tonight (The Hero Is Back)/Hurricane//Night Of The Demon/
		Don't Break The Circle (double pack) 4
83	Clay CLAYLP 6P	THE PLAGUE (LP, picture disc) 10

DEMON FUZZ
70	Dawn DNX 2504	I Put A Spell On You/Message To Mankind/Oriental Blues 4
71	Dawn DNLS 3013	AFREAKA! (LP) 15

DEMON PACT
81	Slime PACT 1	Eaten Alive/Raiders (p/s) 15
81	Slime PACT 2	Escape/Demon Pact (unreleased, white labels only) 20

DEMON PREACHER
78	Illegal SRTS/CUS/78110	Royal Northern (N7)/Laughing At Me/Steal Your Love/Dead End Kidz (no'd) 15
78	Small Wonder SMALL TEN	Little Miss Perfect/Perfect Dub (p/s) 8

(see also Demons)

DEMONS (U.K.)
80	Crypt Music DEM 1	Action By Example/I Wish I Was A Dog (p/s) 8

(see also Alien Sex Fiend, Demon Preacher)

DEMONS (Jamaica)
73	Big Shot BS 523	You Belong To My Heart/Bless You 4

TERRY DENE
57	Decca F 10895	A White Sport Coat/The Man In The Phone Booth 25
57	Decca F 10914	Start Movin'/Green Corn 18
57	Decca F 10938	Come And Get It/Teenage Dream 12
57	Decca F 10964	Lucky Lucky Bobby/Baby, She's Gone 15
58	Decca F 10977	The Golden Age/C'Min And Be Loved 12
58	Decca F 11016	Stairway Of Love/Lover, Lover! 8
58	Decca F 11037	Seven Steps To Love/Can I Walk You Home 10
58	Decca F 11076	Who Baby Who/Pretty Little Pearly 10
59	Decca F 11100	I've Got A Good Thing Going/Bimbombey 8
59	Decca F 11136	There's No Fool Like A Young Fool/I've Come Of Age 8
59	Decca F 11154	Thank You Pretty Baby/A Boy Without A Girl 10
60	Oriole CB 1562	Geraldine/Love Me Or Leave Me 10
61	Oriole CB 1594	Like A Baby/Next Stop Paradise 12
63	Aral PS 107	The Feminine Look/Fever (initially in p/s) 10/5
57	Decca DFE 6427	THE GOLDEN DISC (EP) 25
58	Decca DFE 6459	TERRY DENE NO. 1 (EP) 20
58	Decca DFE 6507	TERRY DENE NO. 2 (EP) 20
66	Herald ELR 107	TERRY DENE NOW (EP) 7
70s	Pilgrim JLPS 175	IF THAT ISN'T LOVE (LP) 10
70s	Pilgrim JLPS 188	CALL TO THE WIND (LP) 10

DENE BOYS
57	HMV POP 374	Bye Bye Love/Love Is The Thing 10
57	HMV POP 374	Bye Bye Love/Love Is The Thing (78) 5

MINT VALUE £

| 58 | HMV POP 455 | Skylark/I Walk Down The Street | 5 |
| 58 | HMV POP 455 | Skylark/I Walk Down The Street (78) | 5 |

DENE FOUR
| 59 | HMV POP 666 | Hush-a-bye/Something New | 8 |

(see also Dene Boys)

DENIMS
| 65 | CBS 201807 | I'm Your Man/Ya Ya | 30 |

ROGER DENISON
| 66 | Parlophone R 5545 | I'm On An Island/I'm Running Out Of Time | 10 |
| 67 | Parlophone R 5566 | She Wanders Through My Mind/This Just Doesn't Seem To Be My Day | 7 |

WADE DENNING & PORT WASHINGTONS
| 67 | MGM MGM 1339 | Tarzan's March/Batman | 4 |

CATHY DENNIS
89	Polydor CATH 1	Just Another Dream/Just Another Dream (Version) (p/s)	4
89	Polydor CATHX 1	Just Another Dream (Remix)/Just Another Dream (Version) (12", p/s)	7
89	Polydor CATHR 1	Just Another Dream (Remix)/Just Another Dream (Version) (12", stickered p/s)	12
92	Polydor CATHX 7	Irresistlble (12", withdrawn p/s)	25

(see also De- Mob)

D.D. (Denzil) DENNIS
| 74 | Pama Supreme PS 391 | Women And Money/UPSETTERS: Ten Cent Skank | 5 |

DENZIL DENNIS
63	Blue Beat BB 181	Seven Nights In Rome/Love Is For Fools	8
68	Trojan TR 614	Donkey Train/Down By The Riverside	5
68	Trojan TR 615	Me Nah Worry/Hush Don't You Cry	5
68	Jolly JY 011	Oh Carol/Where Has My Little Girl Gone	4

(See Cosmo & Dennis)

JACKIE DENNIS
58	Decca F 10992	La Dee Dah/You're The Greatest	10
58	Decca F 11011	Miss Valerie/My Dream	8
58	Decca F 11033	The Purple People Eater/You-Oo	10
58	Decca F 11060	More Than Ever (Coma Prima)/Linton Addie	6
58	Decca F 11090	Gingerbread/Lucky Ladybug	7
59	Top Rank JAR 129	Summer Snow/Night Bird	5
58	Decca DFE 6513	JACKIE DENNIS NO. 1 (EP)	15

DENNIS & LIZZY
| 70 | Camel CA 56 | Everybody Bawlin'/Mr Brown | 4 |

(see also Dennis Alcapone)

DENNISONS
63	Decca F 11691	(Come On) Be My Girl/Little Latin Lupe Lu	10
64	Decca F 11880	Walkin' The Dog/You Don't Know What Love Is	10
64	Decca F 11990	Lucy/Nobody Like My Babe	10

MARTIN DENNY (& HIS ORCHESTRA)
59	London HLU 8860	Quiet Village/Llama Serenade	5
59	London SLW 4004	Quiet Village/Llama Serenade (stereo export issue)	20
59	London HLU 8976	The Enchanted Sea/Martinique	5
60	London REU 1241	THE EXOTIC SOUNDS OF MARTIN DENNY (EP)	10
58	London HB-U 1079	EXOTICA (10" LP)	18
58	London SAH-U 6004	FORBIDDEN ISLAND (LP, stereo only)	15
59	London HA-U 2196	AFRODESIA (LP, also stereo SAH-U 6048)	12/15
60	London HA-U 2208	QUIET VILLAGE (LP, also stereo SAH-U 6055)	10/12
60	London HA-G 2253	EXOTICA — VOL. 2 (LP, also stereo SAH-G 6076)	10/12
60	London HA-W 2239	EXOTICA — VOL. 3 (LP, also stereo SAH-W 6069)	10/12
60	London HA-G 2281	THE ENCHANTED SEA (LP, also stereo SAH-G 6098)	10/12
61	London HA-G 2317	THE SILVER SCREEN (LP, also stereo SAH-G 6122)	10/12
61	London HA-G 2387	EXOTIC PERCUSSION (LP, also stereo SAH-G 6187)	10/12
62	London HA-G 2417	ROMANTICA (LP, also stereo SAH-G 6215)	10/12

SANDY DENNY
72	Island WIP 6141	Here In Silence/Man Of Iron (soundtrack from 'Pass Of Arms' film, p/s)	40/6
72	Island WIP 6142	Listen Listen/Tomorrow Is A Long Time	4
73	Island WIP 6176	Whispering Grass/Friends	6
76	Mooncrest MOON 54	Make Me A Pellet On Your Floor/This Train	4
67	Saga EROS 8041	SANDY AND JOHNNY (LP, with Johnny Silvo)	35
70	Saga EROS 8153	SANDY DENNY (LP)	35
71	Island ILPS 9165	THE NORTH STAR GRASSMAN AND THE RAVENS (LP, gatefold sleeve)	15
72	Island ILPS 9207	SANDY (LP, gatefold sleeve)	15
73	Island ILPS 9258	LIKE AN OLD FASHIONED WALTZ (LP, gatefold sleeve)	15
73	Hallmark SHM 813	ALL OUR OWN WORK (LP, with Strawbs)	15
78	Mooncrest CREST 28	THE ORIGINAL SANDY DENNY (LP)	25
85	Island SDSP 100	WHO KNOWS WHERE THE TIME GOES? (4-LP box set)	20

(see also Fairport Convention, Bunch, Strawbs, Fotheringay, Alex Campbell)

DENTISTS
85	Spruck SP 003	Strawberries Are Growing In My Garden (And It's Wintertime)/ Burning The Thoughts From My Skin/Doreen (p/s)	6
85	Spruck SP 004	YOU AND YOUR BLOODY ORANGES (12" EP, p/s)	8
86	Tambourine SP 006	DOWN AND OUT IN PARIS AND CHATHAM (12" EP, brown/white or group p/s)	8/7
87	Tambourine URINE 3	Writhing On The Shagpile/Just Like Oliver Reed/A Strange Way To Go About Things/Calm You Down/The Turquoise Castle (12", p/s)	7
85	Spruck SPR 001	SOME PEOPLE ARE ON THE PITCH THEY THINK IT'S ALL OVER IT IS NOW (LP)	10

MICKEY DENTON
61	London HLX 9398	The Steady Kind/Now You Can't Give Them Away	5

KARL DENVER
61	Decca F 11360	Marcheta/Joe Sweeney	4
61	Decca F 11395	Mexicali Rose/Bonny Scotland	4
62	Decca F 11420	Wimoweh/Gypsy Davy	4
62	Decca F 11431	Never Goodbye/Highland Fling	4
62	Decca F 11470	A Little Love, A Little Kiss/Lonely Sailor	4
62	Decca F 11505	Blue Weekend/My Mother's Eyes	4
62	Decca F 11553	Dry Tears/Pastures Of Plenty	4
63	Decca F 11608	Can You Forgive Me/Love From A Heart Of Gold	4
63	Decca F 11674	Indian Love Call/My Melancholy Baby	4
63	Decca F 11720	Still/My Canary Has Circles Under His Eyes	4
64	Decca F 11828	My World Of Blue/The Green Grass Grows All Round	4
64	Decca F 11905	Love Me With All Your Heart/Am I That Easy To Forget	4
64	Decca F 12025	Sally/Swanee River	4
65	Mercury MF 878	Cry A Little Sometimes/Today Will Be Yesterday Tomorrow	4
65	Mercury MF 904	Marta/I'll Never Forget To Remember	4
65	Mercury MF 926	The Tips Of My Fingers/I'm Alone Because I Love You	4
68	Page One POF 063	You've Still Got A Place In My Heart/I Still Miss Someone (as Karl Denver Trio)	4
62	Decca DFE 8501	BY A SLEEPY LAGOON (EP)	10
62	Decca DFE 8504	KARL DENVER HITS (EP)	10
61	Ace Of Clubs ACL 1098	WIMOWEH (LP)	12
62	Ace Of Clubs ACL 1131	KARL DENVER (LP)	12
63	Decca LK 4540	LIVE AT THE YEW TREE (LP)	12
64	Decca LK 4596	WITH LOVE (LP)	10

DEODATO
73	CTI CTS 4000	Also Sprach Zarathustra/Spirit Of Summer	5
73	CTI CTS 4003	Do It Again pts 1& 2	4
73	CTI CTL 10	PRELUDE (LP)	10
73	CTI CTL 17	DEODATO 2 (LP)	10
74	CTI CTL 21	IN CONCERT (LP, with Airto)	10
74	MCA MCG 3518	WHIRLWINDS (LP)	10
75	MCA MCF 2587	ARTISTRY (LP)	10
75	MCA MCF 2728	FIRST CUCKOO (LP)	10

(see also Airto)

WILBUR DE PARIS' NEW ORLEANS BAND
59	London HLE 8816	Petite Fleur/Over And Over Again	4
60	London Jazz LTZK 15192	THAT'S A-PLENTY (LP, also stereo SAHK 6079)	10
61	London Jazz LTZK 15201	THE WILD JAZZ AGE (LP, also stereo SAHK 6115)	10

DEPECHE MODE
81	Mute MUTE 013	Dreaming Of Me/Ice Machine (p/s)	4
81	Lyntone LYN 10209	Sometimes I Wish I Was Dead/FAD GADGET: King Of The Flies (red flexidisc free with 'Flexipop' magazine issue 11)	12/10
83	Mute L12 BONG 2	Get The Balance Right/My Secret Garden (live)/See You (live)/ Satellite (live) (12", numbered p/s)	8
83	Mute L12 BONG 3	Everything Counts/Boys Say Go (live)/New Life (live)/Nothing To Fear (live)/ The Meaning Of Love (live) (12", p/s, numbered)	8
83	Mute L12 BONG 4	Love In Itself (2)/Just Can't Get Enough (live)/Photograph Of You (live)/ Photographic (live)/Shout (live) (12", p/s)	8
84	Mute L12 BONG 5	People Are People (On-U-Sound Remix)/In Your Memory/ People Are People (12", numbered in die-cut p/s)	10
84	Mute L12 BONG 6	Master And Servant (On-U-Sound Science Fiction Dancehall Classic)/ Are People People?/(Set Me Free) Remotivate Me (12", numbered p/s)	12
84	Mute 7BONG 7E	Blasphemous Rumours/Told You So (live)/Somebody (Remix)/ Everything Counts (live) (EP)	6
85	Mute L12 BONG 8	Edit The Shake/Master And Servant (live)/Flexible (Pre-Deportation Mix)/ Something To Do (Metal Mix) (12", p/s)	8
85	Mute 7BONG 9	It's Called A Heart/Fly On The Windscreen (p/s, with poster)	5
85	Mute D12 BONG 9	It's Called A Heart (Extended)/Fly On The Windscreen (Extended)// It's Called A Heart (Slow Mix)/Fly On The Windscreen (Death Mix) (12", double pack)	8
86	Mute CBONG 11	A Question Of Lust (Flood Mix)/If You Want (live)/Shame (live)/ Blasphemous Rumours (live) (cassette in 7" pack with book & badge)	6
86	Mute L12 BONG 12	A Question Of Time (Newtown Mix)/A Question Of Time (live)/Black Celebration (Black Tulip Mix)/More Than A Party (live) (12", p/s)	8
87	Mute L12 BONG 13	Strangelove (Blind Mix)/Pimpf/Strangelove (Pain Mix)/Agent Orange (12", p/s)	10
87	Mute CD BONG 13	Strangelove (Maximix)/(Midimix)/(LP Mix)/Pimpf/Agent Orange (CD)	8
87	Mute L12 BONG 14	Never Let Me Down Again (Tsangarides Mix)/Pleasure Little Treasure (Join Mix)/To Have And To Hold (Spanish Taster) (12", p/s)	8
87	Mute CBONG 14	Never Let Me Down Again (Split Mix)/(Aggro Mix)/Pleasure Little Treasure (Glitter Mix) (cassette)	4
87	Mute CD BONG 14	Never Let Me Down Again (Split Mix)/Pleasure Little Treasure (Remix)/ To Have And To Hold (Spanish Taster) (CD in pouch)	10
88	Mute L12 BONG 15	Behind The Wheel (Beatmasters Remix)/Route 66 (Casuality Mix) (12", p/s)	10
89	Mute 10 BONG 16	Everything Counts (Absolute Mix)/(1983 12" Mix)/Nothing (US 7" Mix) (10", p/s, with 2 postcards & window sticker)	10
89	Mute L12 BONG 16	Everything Counts (Tim Simenon & M. Saunders Remix)/Nothing (Justin Strauss Remix)/Strangelove (Tim Simenon & M. Saunders Remix)(12", p/s)	7
89	Mute LCD BONG 16	Everything Counts (Tim Simenon & M. Saunders Remix)/Nothing (Justin Strauss Remix)/Strangelove (Tim Simenon & M. Saunders Remix) (3" CD, 'filofax' p/s)	15
89	Mute GBONG 17	Personal Jesus/(Acoustic)/Dangerous (Hazchemix) (gatefold p/s with photos)	6
90	Mute XL12 BONG 18	Enjoy The Silence (The Quad: Final Mix) (12", p/s)	8

DEPECHE MODE

90	Mute XLCD BONG 18	Enjoy The Silence (The Quad: Final Mix) (CD) 10
90	Mute LCD BONG 19	Policy Of Truth (Trancentral Mix)/(Pavlov's Dub)/Kaleid (Remix) (CD) 10
90	Mute LCD BONG 20	World In My Eyes (Mode To Joy)/Happiest Girl (The Pulsating Orbital Vocal Mix)/World In My Eyes (Dub In My Eyes) (CD) 12
91	Mute DMBX 1	DEPECHE MODE (6-CD single box set) 25
91	Mute DMBX 2	DEPECHE MODE (6-CD single box set) 25
91	Mute DMBX 3	DEPECHE MODE (6-CD single box set) 25
87	Mute STUMM 47	MUSIC FOR THE MASSES (LP, clear, grey or blue vinyl) 12
87	Mute STUMM 47	MUSIC FOR THE MASSES (LP, with free 12" "Strangelove (Maximix)"/ "Never Let Me Down Again (Aggro Mix)" [HMV 1]) 12
87	Mute CSTUMM 55	MUSIC FOR THE MASSES (cassette, with extra tracks) 10
87	Mute CSTUMM 55	MUSIC FOR THE MASSES/BLACK CELEBRATION (double-play cassette) 12
88	Mute CD STUMM 5	SPEAK AND SPELL (CD, reissue with different booklet & 5 extra tracks) 15
88	Mute CD STUMM 9	A BROKEN FRAME (CD, original issue) 15
88	Mute CD STUMM 13	CONSTRUCTION TIME AGAIN (CD, original issue) 15
	(see also Erasure)	

DEPRESSIONS

77	Barn 2014 112	Living On Dreams/Family Planning (p/s) 4
78	Barn 2014 119	Messing With Your Heart/Street Kid (p/s) 4
78	Barn 2014 122	Get Out Of This Town/Basement Daze (p/s) 4
78	Barn 2314 105	THE DEPRESSIONS (LP) 10
	(see also DP's)	

DEPUTIES

66	Strike JH 305	Given Half A Chance/Where Do People Go 5

DEREK

68	London HLZ 10230	Cinnamon/This Is My Story 5
	(see also Johnny Cymbal)	

DEREK & CYNDI

74	Philadelphia Intl. PIR 2662	You Bring Out The Best In Me/I'll Do For You The Impossible 4

DEREK & DOMINOES

70	Polydor 2058 057	Tell The Truth/Roll It Over (withdrawn) 20
71	Polydor 2058 130	Layla/Bell Bottom Blues (original, red paper label) 4
	(see also Eric Clapton)	

DEREK & FRESHMEN

65	Oriole CB 305	Gone Away/I Stand Alone 8

DEREK & RAY

65	RCA RCA 1463	The Adventures Of Moll Flanders/Do Re Mi 4
78	RCA PB 9136	Interplay/MIKE McDONALD: God Knows 4

FRANK DE ROSA & HIS ORCHESTRA

58	London HLD 8576	Big Guitar/Irish Rock 20
58	London HLD 8576	Big Guitar/Irish Rock (78) 5

DERRICK (Morgan) & JENNIFER

70	Crab CRAB 47	Need To Belong/Let's Have Some Fun 4

DERRICK (Morgan) & LLOYD (Clarke)

62	Blue Beat BB 135	Love And Leave Me/Merry Twist 10
	(see also Lloyd Clarke)	

DERRICK (Morgan) & NAOMI (Campbell)

65	Island WI 193	Two Of A Kind/I Want A Lover 10
65	Ska Beat JB 185	Heart Of Stone/DERRICK MORGAN: Let Me Go 8
65	Ska Beat JB 188	I Wish I Were An Apple/DERRICK MORGAN: Around The Corner 8

DERRICK (Morgan) & PATSY (Todd)

61	Blue Beat BB 57	Feel So Fine/ROLAND ALPHONSO & GROUP: Mean To Me 10
61	Blue Beat BB 65	Baby Please Don't Leave Me/Let The Good Times Roll 10
62	Blue Beat BB 97	Love Not To Brag/DRUMBAGO'S ALLSTARS: Duck Soup 10
62	Blue Beat BB 100	In My Heart/BELL'S GROUP: Kingston 13 10
62	Blue Beat BB 110	Are You Going To Marry Me?/Troubles 10
62	Blue Beat BB 121	Crying In The Chapel/Come Back My Love 10
62	Blue Beat BB 123	Oh My Love/Let's Go To The Party 10
62	Island WI 018	Housewives Choice/Gypsy Woman 10
63	Blue Beat BB 152	Little Brown Jug/Mow Sen Wa (with Lloyd Clarke) 8
63	Blue Beat BB 160	Baby Please Don't Leave Me/Hold Me 8
63	Blue Beat BB 171	Call My Name/Take My Heart 8
63	Island WI 055	Look Before You Leap/Sea Wave 10
64	Blue Beat BB 207	Lover Boy/The Moon 8
64	Blue Beat BB 224	Steal Away/Money 8
64	Blue Beat BB 239	Miss Lulu/She's So Young 8
64	Blue Beat BB 247	Troubles/Baby Face 8
65	Blue Beat BB 291	You I Love/Steal Away 8
65	Island WI 224	The National Dance/DESMOND DEKKAR & FOUR ACES: Mount Zion 10
66	Blue Beat BB 318	Eternity/Want My Baby 8
68	Nu Beat NB 008	Hey Boy, Hey Girl/Music Is The Food Of Life 5
	(see also Patsy Todd)	

DERRICK (Morgan) & PAULETT

69	Nu Beat NB 027	I'll Do It/Give You My Love 5

DERRICK (Morgan) & PAULINE (Morgan)

68	Pyramid PYR 6027	You Never Miss Your Water/DERRICK MORGAN: Got You On My Mind 8
68	Pyramid/J.J. PYR 6063	Don't Say/DERRICK MORGAN: Johnny Pram Pram 8
	(see also Derrick Morgan)	

DERRICK & SOUNDS

68	Pye 7N 17601	Power Of Love/I'll Take You Home	4
69	Pye 7N 17709	My Sly Sadie/I Can't Lose That Girl	4
69	Pye 7N 17801	Morning Papers And Margarine/Winter Of Your Love	4

DERRICK, PATSY & BASIL

62	Blue Beat BB 106	Oh Shirley/DERRICK & PATSY: Sam The Fisherman	8

(see also Derrick Morgan, Patsy Todd, Basil Gabbidon)

DERRINGERS

61	Capitol CL 15189	True Love, True Love/Sheree	4

GLEN DERRY ORCHESTRA

61	Oriole CB 1609	Blue Sax/Beatnik	5

HENRI DES

70	United Artists UP 35109	Return/Retour	15

DES & DAVE

66	Columbia DB 7957	That's Us/Gotta Little Gal	4

SUGAR PIE De SANTO

64	Pye Intl. 7N 25249	Soulful Dress/Use What You Got	15
64	Pye Intl. 7N 25267	I Don't Wanna Fuss/I Love You So Much	12
66	Chess CRS 8034	There's Gonna Be Trouble/In The Basement	
		(B-side with Etta James)	10
69	Chess CRS 8093	Soulful Dress/There's Gonna Be Trouble	8

(see also Etta James & Sugar Pie De Santo)

DESCENDANTS

67	CBS 202545	Garden Of Eden/Lela	30

DESERT WOLVES

87	Ugly Man UGLY 6T	Love Shattered Lives/Stopped In My Tracks/Desolation/	
		Sunday Morning (12", p/s)	7
88	Ugly Man UGLY 9	Speak To Me Rochelle/Besotted (p/s)	4
88	Ugly Man UGLY 9T	Speak To Me Rochelle/Mexico/Besotted/La Petite Rochelle (12", p/s)	7

JACKIE DE SHANNON

62	Liberty LIB 55497	You Won't Forget Me/I Don't Think So Much	5
63	Liberty LIB 55563	Needles And Pins/Did He Call Today Mama?	7
64	Liberty LIB 55645	When You Walk In The Room/Till You Say You'll Be Mine	7
64	Liberty LIB 10165	Dancing Silhouettes/Hold Your Head High	4
65	Liberty LIB 10192	She Don't Understand Him Like I Do/The Prince	4
65	Liberty LIB 10202	What The World Needs Now Is Love/It's Love Baby	4
65	Liberty LIB 12019	A Lifetime Of Loneliness/I Remember The Boy	4
66	Liberty LIB 66171	Come And Get Me/Splendour In The Grass	4
66	Liberty LIB 66202	I Can Make It With You/To Be Myself	4
66	Liberty LIB 66224	Come On Down/Find Me Love	15
68	Liberty LBF 15133	The Weight/Effervescent Blue	4
69	Liberty LBF 15238	Put A Little Love In Your Heart/Always Together	4
69	Liberty LBF 15281	Love Will Find A Way/I Let Go Completely	4
65	Liberty LEP 2233	JACKIE (EP)	10
64	Liberty LBY 1182	THIS IS JACKIE DE SHANNON (LP)	12
65	Liberty LBY 1245	DON'T TURN YOUR BACK ON ME (LP)	15
66	Liberty (S)BLY 3085	ARE YOU READY FOR THIS? (LP)	15
68	Liberty LBS 83117E	GREAT PERFORMANCES (LP)	10

DESIGN

70	Epic 64322	DESIGN (LP)	25
71	Epic 64653	TOMORROW IS SO FAR AWAY (LP)	25
73	Regal Zono. SLRZ 1037	DAY OF THE FOX (LP)	20

ANDY DESMOND

75	Konk KOS 2	So It Goes/She Can Move Mountains	4
75	Konk KOS 4	Beware/Only Child	4
75	Konk KONK 103	LIVING ON A SHOESTRING (LP)	12

(see also Gothic Horizon)

JOHNNY DESMOND

53	MGM SP 1042	A Bushel And A Peck/ART LUND: If I Were A Bell	6
54	Vogue Coral Q 2019	The High And The Mighty/Got No Time	5
55	Vogue Coral Q 72055	Don't/There's No Happiness For Me (with Alan Dale & Buddy Greco)	5
55	Vogue Coral Q 72076	Play Me Hearts And Flowers/I'm So Ashamed	4
55	Vogue Coral Q 72090	Togetherness/A Straw Hat And A Cane	4
55	Vogue Coral Q 72099	Yellow Rose Of Texas/You're In Love With Someone	6
55	Vogue Coral Q 72110	Land Of The Pharaohs/This Too Shall Pass	4
56	Vogue Coral Q 72115	Sixteen Tons/Ballo Italiano	6
56	Vogue Coral Q 72153	Without You/I'll Cry Tomorrow	4
56	Vogue Coral Q 72170	A Little Love Can Go A Long Way/Please Don't Forget Me	4
56	Vogue Coral Q 72190	"The Proud Ones" Theme/I Only Know I Love You	4
56	Vogue Coral Q 72207	A Girl Named Mary/"Run For The Sun" Theme	4
57	Vogue Coral Q 72235	Where The River Meets The Sea/18th Century Music Box	
		(B-side with Jimmy Saunders)	6
57	Vogue Coral Q 72246	That's Where I Shine/I Just Want You To Want Me	4
57	Vogue Coral Q 72261	A White Sports Coat (And A Pink Carnation)/Just Lookin'	6
57	Vogue Coral Q 72261	A White Sports Coat (And A Pink Carnation)/Just Lookin' (78)	7
57	Vogue Coral Q 72269	Shenandoah Rose/Consideration	4
58	MGM MGM 994	Hot Cha Cha/I'll Close My Eyes	4
59	Philips PB 890	Willingly/Apple (When Ya Gonna Fall From The Tree?)	4
60	Coral Q 72398	The Most Happy Fella/LANCERS: Joey, Joey, Joey	4
60	Philips PB 1044	Hawk/Playing The Field	4

LORRAE DESMOND (& REBELS)

54	Decca F 10375	Hold My Hand/On The Waterfront	10
54	Decca F 10398	Far Away (My Love Is Far Away)/No One But You	10
54	Decca F 10404	I Can't Tell A Waltz From A Tango/For Better, For Worse (with Johnston Brothers)	10
55	Decca F 10461	A Boy On Saturday Night/Why — Oh Why?	10
55	Decca F 10510	Don't/Where Will The Baby's Dimple Be?	10
55	Decca F 10533	Stowaway/Heartbroken (B-side with Johnston Brothers)	8
55	Decca F 10612	You Should Know/Wake The Town And Tell The People	10
56	Parlophone R 4239	Written On The Wind/A House With Love In It	7
57	Parlophone R 4287	You Won't Be Around/Play The Music (as Lorrae Desmond & Rebels)	6
57	Parlophone R 4320	Kansas City Special/Preacher, Preacher (as Lorrae Desmond & Rebels)	8
57	Parlophone R 4320	Kansas City Special/Preacher, Preacher (78)	5
57	Parlophone R 4361	Ding-Dong Rock-a-billy Weddin'/Cabin Boy (as Lorrae Desmond & Rebels)	15
57	Parlophone R 4361	Ding-Dong Rock-a-billy Weddin'/Cabin Boy (78)	5
58	Parlophone R 4400	Two Ships/Little David	6
58	Parlophone R 4430	The Secret Of Happiness/Down By The River	6
58	Parlophone R 4463	Soda Pop Hop/Blue, Blue Day	7
58	Parlophone R 4463	Soda Pop Hop/Blue, Blue Day (78)	5
59	Parlophone R 4534	Tall Paul/Wait For It	6
60	Parlophone R 4670	Tell Me Again/Get Your Daddie's Car Tonight	5

MICHAEL DESMOND

57	Columbia DB 3954	Young And In Love/Two Loves	4
57	Columbia DB 4018	Chances Are/If You're Not Completely Satisfied	4

PAUL DESMOND

61	Warner Bros WM 4020	PAUL DESMOND & FRIENDS (LP, also stereo WS 8020)	10
62	RCA Victor RD 7525	TWO OF A MIND (LP, with Gerry Mulligan)	10

(see also Gerry Mulligan, Dave Brubeck)

DESOLATION ANGELS

84	AM	Valhalla	10
85	Thameside TRR 111	DESOLATION ANGELS (LP)	10

DESPERATE BICYCLES

77	Refill RR 1	Smokescreen/Handlebars (p/s, same tracks both sides)	5
78	Refill RR 2	The Medium Was Tedium/Don't Back The Front (p/s, same tracks both sides)	5
78	Refill RR 3	NEW CROSS NEW CROSS (EP)	4
78	Refill RR 4	Occupied Territory/Skill (p/s)	4
78	Refill RR 7	Grief Is Very Private/Obstructive/Conundrum (p/s)	4
80	Refill RR 6	REMORSE CODE (LP)	12

DESTROY ALL MONSTERS

79	Cherry Red CHERRY 3	Bored/You're Gonna Die (p/s, red vinyl)	5
79	Cherry Red CHERRY 7	Meet The Creeper/November 22nd 1963 (p/s)	4
79	Cherry Red CHERRY 9	Nobody Knows/What Do I Get? (p/s)	4

(see also MC5)

DESTROYER

70s	Clean	Evil Place	10

DESTROYERS

69	Amalgamated AMG 856	Niney Special/Danger Zone	4

DESTRUCTORS

82	Carnage BOOK 2	Meaningless Names/AK47/Police State/Dachau/Death Squad (p/s)	4
82	Carnage Benelux KILL 2	Religion/Soldier Boy/Agent Orange/Corpse Gas (p/s)	4

(see also Blanks)

DETAILS

80	Energy NRG 2	Keep On Running/Run Ins (p/s)	4
80	Energy NRG 002	Keep On Running/Run Ins (12", promo only, no p/s)	7
82	Energy NRG 6	Keep On Running/Run Ins (reissue, different 'dog' p/s)	4

DETERGENTS

65	Columbia DB 7513	Leader Of The Laundromat/Ulcers	10
65	Columbia DB 7591	I Don't Know/The Blue Kangaroo	6

DETONATORS

78	Local LR 1	Need Love Tonight/Great Big Ghetto/Shoob Shooby Do/ Give Me A Helping Hand (p/s)	5
70s	Big Blast	THE DANCE (EP)	4

DETOURS

68	CBS 3213	Run To Me Baby/Hangin' On	20
68	CBS 3401	Whole Lotta Lovin'/Pieces Of You	35

DETROIT

71	Paramount SPFL 277	DETROIT (LP)	15

(see also Mitch Ryder)

DETROIT EMERALDS

71	Pye Intl. 7N 25544	Do Me Right/Just Now And Then	5
73	Westbound 6146 103	You Want It, You Got It/Whatcha Gonna Wear Tomorrow	4
74	Janus 6146 007	You Want It, You Got It/Till You Decide To Come Home	4
74	Janus 6146 020	Feel The Need In Me/And I Love Her	4
71	Janus 6310 204	DO ME RIGHT (LP)	12
72	Janus 6310 207	YOU WANT IT YOU GOT IT (LP)	12
73	Janus 6309 101	ABE JAMES AND IVORY (LP)	10

DETROIT SPINNERS

65	Tamla Motown TMG 514	Sweet Thing/How Can I (initial pressings credit 'Spinners')	80/40

65	Tamla Motown TMG 523	I'll Always Love You/Tomorrow May Never Come	25
67	Tamla Motown TMG 627	For All We Know/I'll Always Love You (1st press has tall, narrow print)	15/10
70	Tamla Motown TMG 755	It's A Shame/Sweet Thing (as Motown Spinners)	4
71	Tamla Motown TMG 766	Together We Can Make Such Sweet Music/Truly Yours (as Motown Spinners)	4
72	Atlantic K 10243	I'll Be Around/How Can I Let You Get Away	4
74	Atlantic K 10416	Mighty Love Pts 1 & 2	4
74	Atlantic K 10480	I'm Coming Home/He'll Never Love You Like I Do	4
68	T. Motown (S)TML 11060	THE DETROIT SPINNERS (LP)	30
71	T. Motown STML 11182	SECOND TIME AROUND (LP, as Motown Spinners)	10

(see also Spinners, G.C. Cameron)

DEUCE COUP
67	Mercury MF 1013	A Clown In Town/Angela	4

DEUCE OF HEARTS
66	CBS 202345	Closer Together/The Times They Are A Changin'	4

JIMMY DEUCHAR & HIS PALS
58	Tempo A 167	Bewitched/My Funny Valentine	4
58	Tempo TAP 20	PAL JIMMY (LP)	10

DEVASTATING AFFAIR
73	Mowest MW 3020	That's How It Was/It's So Sad	4

WILLIAM B. DE VAUGHN
74	Chelsea 2005 002	Be Thankful For What You Got/Be Thankful For What You Got (Version)	4
82	Excalibur EXC 527	Creme De Creme/Creme De Creme (Instrumental)	5
82	Excalibur EXCL 527	Creme De Creme/Creme De Creme (Instrumental) (12")	10
74	Chelsea 2306 002	BE THANKFUL FOR WHAT YOU GOT (LP)	10

DEVIANTS
68	Stable STA 5601	You Got To Hold On/Let's Loot The Supermarket	25
67	Underground Imp. IMP 1	PTOOFF! (LP, poster sleeve, private pressing via 'IT' magazine)	75
68	Stable SLE 7001	DISPOSABLE (LP)	60
69	Transatlantic TRA 204	THE DEVIANTS (LP, some with booklet)	45/35
69	Decca LK-R/SKL-R 4993	PTOOFF! (LP, reissue)	30
78	Logo MOGO 4001	THE DEVIANTS (LP, reissue)	10
83	Psycho PSYCHO 16	PTOOFF! (LP, reissue in original sleeve)	20
84	Psycho PSYCHO 25	HUMAN GARBAGE (LIVE AT DINGWALLS '84) (LP)	10

(see also Mick Farren, Pink Fairies)

DEVILS HOLE GANG
70s	Slow Burning Fuse SSSS 1	Free The People/Isn't It/Something To Look Forward To (p/s, with insert)	6

ELDRIDGE DEVLIN
71	Beacon BEA 124	A Little Love (That's All I Want From You)/You're My Girl	4

JOHNNY DEVLIN (& DETOURS)
64	Pye 7N 15598	Sometimes/If You Want Someone (as Johnny Devlin & Detours)	5
66	CBS 202085	Hung On You/Prove It	4
66	CBS 202339	My Strength; Heart Of Soul/I Can't Get You Off My Mind	4
67	CBS 202452	Tender Lovin' Care/Five O'Clock World	4
67	CBS 2751	Hurtin'/You Gotta Tell Me	4

DEVO
78	Stiff DEV 1	Joko Homo/Mongoloid (foldout p/s)	4
78	Stiff DEV 2/BOY 1	(I Can't Get No) Satisfaction/Sloppy (I Saw My Baby Getting) (p/s)	4
78	Stiff BOY 1	(I Can't Get No) Satisfaction/Sloppy (I Saw My Baby Getting) (12", p/s, with sticker)	7
78	Stiff BOY 2	Be Stiff/Social Fools (clear or lemon yellow vinyl, company sleeve)	4
78	Stiff BOY 2	Be Stiff/Social Fools (black vinyl, p/s)	4
78	Stiff ODD 1	BE STIFF (12" EP, white vinyl)	7
78	Virgin VS 223	Come Back Jonee/Social Fools (p/s, grey vinyl with sticker)	4
79	Elevator NICE 1	Mechanical Man/Blockhead/Blackout/Auto-Modern (official bootleg, no'd p/s)	6
81	Virgin VS 450	Through Being Cool/Race Of Doom (poster p/s)	4
85	Warner Bros W 9119F	Shout/C'mon//Jocko Homo/Mongoloid (double pack)	4
78	Virgin V 2106	Q: ARE WE NOT MEN? (LP, with 'Flimsy Wrap' 33rpm 1-sided flexidisc [VDJ 27/Lyntone LYN 6260])	10
78	Virgin VP 2106	Q: ARE WE NOT MEN? (LP, picture disc)	10

DEVON (Russell) & TARTANS
68	Nu Beat NB 021	Let's Have Some Fun/Making Love	6

(see also Tartans)

DEVON (Russell) & SEDRIC (Myton)
69	Blue Cat BS 158	What A Sin Thing/Short Up Dress	6

DEVONNES
75	UK USA 5	I'm Gonna Pick Up My Toys/Limits	6

BARRY DE VORZON
58	RCA RCA 1066	Barbara Jean/JIMMY DELL: Teeny Weeny	60
60	Philips PB 993	Betty Betty (Go Steady With Me)/Across The Street From	10

(see also Jimmy Dell)

DEVOTED
68	Page One POF 076	I Love George Best/United (initially in p/s)	8/4

DEVOTIONS
64	Columbia DB 7256	Rip Van Winkle/For Sentimental Reasons	20

DEWDROPS
65	Blue Beat BB 381	Somebody's Knocking/By And By	8

MINT VALUE £

DANNY DEXTER
| 63 | London HLU 9690 | Sweet Mama/Go On | 6 |

EDDIE DEXTER & HIS BAND
| 55 | Capitol CL 14371 | Moonlight/The Verse Of Stardust | 5 |

RAY DEXTER & LAYABOUTS
| 62 | Decca F 11538 | The Coalman's Lament/Lonely Weekend | 15 |

DEXY'S MIDNIGHT RUNNERS
79	Parlophone R 6028	Dance Stance/I'm Just Looking (p/s)	5
80	Parlophone R 6042	Keep It Part Two/One Way Love (p/s)	4
81	Mercury DEXYS 6	Show Me/Soon (p/s, with 'essay' insert)	4
82	Mercury DEXYS 10	Jackie Wilson Said/Let's Make This Precious (p/s, with withdrawn mispressed B-side label "Howard's Not Home")	4
85	Mercury DEXYD 13	An Extract From "This Is What She's Like"/"This Is What She's Like" Finale// Marguerita Time/Reminisce Part One (double pack)	4
85	Mercury DEXYS 1310	An Extract From "This Is What She's Like"/"This Is What She's Like" Finale/ Marguerita Time/Reminisce Part One (10", p/s)	5

(see also Killjoys)

TRACY DEY
| 64 | Stateside SS 287 | Go Away/Gonna Get Along Without You Now | 15 |

DEZRO ORCHESTRA
| 75 | Route RT 19 | Reflections (Summer '75)/Witch Hunt | 4 |

BARRY D'FANO
| 62 | Palette PG 9038 | Message Of Love/The Kiss That Broke My Heart | 4 |

DHARMA BLUES BAND
| 69 | Major Minor SMPC 5017 | DHARMA BLUES (LP) | 70 |

DIALS
| 70s | Wessex WEX 266 | Maxine/Hey Denise (p/s) | 4 |

BRIAN DIAMOND & CUTTERS
63	Decca F 11724	Jealousy Will Get You Nowhere/Brady Brady	7
64	Fontana TF 452	Shake, Shout And Go/Whatcha Gonna Do Now Pretty Baby	8
65	Pye 7N 15779	Big Bad Wolf/See If I Care	8
65	Pye 7N 15952	Bone Idol/Sands Of Time	8

(GREGG DIAMOND'S) BIONIC BOOGIE
79	Polydor PB 50	Chains/Hot Butterfly	4
79	Polydor POSPX 50	Chains/Hot Butterfly (12")	10
88	Urban URBX 16	Hot Butterfly/Mess Up The Boogie/When The Shit Hits The Fan (12", p/s)	8
79	Polydor 2391 322	BIONIC BOOGIE (LP)	10

JERRY DIAMOND
| 57 | London HLE 8496 | Sunburned Lips/Don't Trust Love | 20 |
| 57 | London HLE 8496 | Sunburned Lips/Don't Trust Love (78) | 8 |

LEE DIAMOND (& CHEROKEES)
| 61 | Fontana H 310 | I'll Step Down/Josephine (as Lee Diamond & Cherokees) | 7 |
| 61 | Fontana H 345 | Stop Your Crying/You'll Want Me | 7 |
(see also Cherokees)

NEIL DIAMOND
66	London HLZ 10049	Solitary Man/Do It	5
66	London HLZ 10072	Cherry, Cherry/I'll Come Running	5
66	London HLZ 10092	I Got The Feelin' (Oh No No)/The Boat That I Row	5
67	London HLZ 10111	You Got To Me/Someday Baby	5
67	London HLZ 10126	Girl, You'll Be A Woman Soon/You'll Forget	5
67	London HLZ 10151	Thank The Lord For The Night Time/The Long Way Home	5
67	London HLZ 10161	Kentucky Woman/The Time Is Now	5
68	London HLZ 10177	New Orleans/Hanky Panky	5
68	London HLZ 10187	Red Red Wine/Red Rubber Ball	5
68	Uni UN 503	Brooklyn Roads/Holiday Inn Blues	4
68	MCA MU 1033	Two-Bit Manchild/Broad Old Woman	4
69	MCA MU 1070	Brother Love's Travelling Salvation Show/A Modern Day Version Of Love	4
69	MCA MU 1087	Sweet Caroline (Good Times Never Seemed So Good)/Dig In	4
69	Uni UN 512	Holy Holy/Hurtin' You Don't Come Easy	4
70	Uni UN 522	Soolaimon (African Trilogy II)/And The Grass Won't Pay No Mind	4
71	President PT 335	Kentucky Woman/Cherry Cherry/I Thank The Lord For The Night Time (p/s)	4
87	CBS 651201 7	I Dreamed A Dream/Sweet Caroline (box set with calendar)	5
66	London HA-Z 8307	THE FEEL OF NEIL DIAMOND (LP)	12
68	MCA MUPS 365	VELVET GLOVES AND SPIT (LP)	12
69	MCA MUPS 382	BROTHER LOVE'S TRAVELLING SALVATION SHOW (LP)	12
69	Uni UNLS 106	VELVET GLOVES AND SPIT (LP, reissue)	10
69	Uni UNLS 107	BROTHER LOVE'S TRAVELLING SALVATION SHOW (LP, reissue)	10
69	Uni UNLS 110	TOUCHING ME, TOUCHING YOU (LP)	10
69	Uni UNLS 116	GOLD (LP)	10
70	Uni UNLS 117	TAP ROOT MANUSCRIPT (LP)	10
71	Uni UNLS 121	STONES (LP)	10
74	CBS Q 69067	SERENADE (LP, quadrophonic)	12
76	CBS Q 86004	BEAUTIFUL NOISE (LP, quadrophonic)	12
81	World Records ALBUM 91	THE BEST OF NEIL DIAMOND (4-LP box set, mail order only)	20

DIAMOND BOYS
| 63 | RCA RCA 1351 | Hey Little Girl/What'd I Say | 7 |
(see also Albert Ammond)

DIAMOND HEAD

80	Happy Face MMDH 120	Shoot Out The Lights/Helpless	10
80	Media SCREEN 1	Sweet And Innocent/Streets Of Gold (p/s)	8
81	DHM DHM 004	Play It Loud/Waited Too Long (p/s)	7
81	Windsong DHM 005	Diamond Lights/We Won't Be Back/I Don't Got/It's Electric (12", p/s)	12
82	MCA DHM 101	FOUR CUTS (EP, p/s)	5
82	MCA DHMT 101	FOUR CUTS (12" EP, with insert)	8
82	MCA DHM 102/MSAM 23	In The Heat Of The Night/Play It Loud (live)//Sweet And Innocent (live)/(Interview With Tommy Vance) (double pack, gatefold p/s)	5
82	MCA DHMT 102	In The Heat Of The Night (Full Length Version)/Play It Loud (live) (12", p/s)	7
83	MCA DHM 103	Making Music/(Andy Peebles Interview) (p/s)	5
83	MCA DHMT 103	Making Music/(Andy Peebles Interview) (12", p/s)	7
83	MCA DHM 104	Out Of Phase/The Kingmaker (p/s)	5
83	MCA DHMP 104	Out Of Phase/The Kingmaker (picture disc)	6
83	MCA DHMT 104	Out Of Phase/The Kingmaker/Sucking My Love (12", p/s)	10
91	Bronze	Wild In The Streets (12", p/s, 1 side etched)	7
80	Happy Face MMDHLP 105	LIGHTNING TO THE NATIONS (LP, printed white label, plain white sleeve, sold at gigs)	25
81	MCA DH 1001	LIVING ON BORROWED TIME (LP, gatefold sleeve with inner sleeve, some with poster & fan club insert)	15/10
83	MCA DH 1002	CANTERBURY (LP)	12
86	Metal Masters METALP 110	BEHOLD THE BEGINNING (LP, remix of "Lightning To The Nations")	10

DIAMONDS (U.S.)

55	Vogue Coral Q 72109	Black Denim Trousers And Motorcycle Boots/Nip Sip	35
55	Vogue Coral Q 72109	Black Denim Trousers And Motorcycle Boots/Nip Sip (78)	18
56	Mercury MT 121	Love, Love, Love/Ev'ry Night About This Time	12
57	Mercury MT 148	Little Darlin'/Faithful And True (78)	5
57	Mercury MT 167	Don't Say Goodbye/Words Of Love (78)	8
57	Mercury MT 179	Oh, How I Wish/Zip Zip (78)	12
58	Mercury 7MT 187	Silhouettes/Honey Bird	20
58	Mercury MT 187	Silhouettes/Honey Bird (78)	5
58	Mercury 7MT 195	The Stroll/Land Of Beauty	18
58	Mercury MT 195	The Stroll/Land Of Beauty (78)	5
58	Mercury 7MT 207	High Sign/Don't Let Me Down	20
58	Mercury MT 207	High Sign/Don't Let Me Down (78)	5
58	Mercury 7MT 208	Straight Skirts/Patsy	25
58	Mercury MT 208	Straight Skirts/Patsy (78)	5
58	Mercury 7MT 233	Kathy-O/Where Mary Go?	10
58	Mercury MT 233	Kathy-O/Where Mary Go? (78)	5
58	Mercury AMT 1004	Eternal Lovers/Walking Along	12
58	Mercury AMT 1004	Eternal Lovers/Walking Along (78)	5
59	Mercury AMT 1024	She Say (Oom Dooby Doom)/From The Bottom Of My Heart	12
59	Mercury AMT 1024	She Say (Oom Dooby Doom)/From The Bottom Of My Heart (78)	20
60	Mercury AMT 1086	Tell The Truth/Real True Love	15
61	Mercury AMT 1156	One Summer Night/It's A Doggone Shame	15
57	Mercury MEP 9515	PRESENTING THE DIAMONDS (EP)	22
57	Mercury MEP 9523	THE DIAMONDS VOL. 1 (EP)	20
58	Mercury MEP 9527	THE DIAMONDS VOL. 2 (EP)	20
58	Mercury MEP 9530	THE DIAMONDS VOL. 3 (EP)	20
59	Mercury ZEP 10003	DIG THE DIAMONDS (EP)	25
59	Mercury ZEP 10020	THE DIAMONDS MEET PETE RUGOLO (EP)	18
59	Mercury ZEP 10026	DIAMONDS ARE TRUMPS (EP)	25
60	Mercury ZEP 10053	STAR STUDDED DIAMONDS (EP)	20
61	Mercury ZEP 10097	PETE RUGOLO LEADS THE DIAMONDS (EP, also stereo SEZ 10912)	20/25
57	Mercury MPT 7526	THE DIAMONDS (10" LP)	80
50s	Mercury	THE DIAMONDS (LP)	40
50s	Mercury	THE DIAMONDS MEET PETE RUGOLO (LP)	25
60	Mercury MMC 14039	SONGS FROM THE OLD WEST (LP)	20
	(see also Pete Rugolo)		

DIAMONDS (U.K.)

63	Philips BF 1264	The Lost City/Chasey Chasey	6

DIAMOND TWINS

66	HMV POP 1508	Crying The Night Away/Start The World Spinning Again	4

DIANE & JAVELINS

66	Columbia DB 7819	Heart And Soul/Who's The Girl	20

(PAUL) DI'ANNO

84	FM VHF 1	Heart User/Road Rat (p/s)	5
84	FM WKFM LP1	DI'ANNO (LP, blue vinyl)	12
84	FM WKFM PD1	DI'ANNO (LP, picture disc)	15
	(see also Gogmagog, Iron Maiden)		

DIATONES

61	Starlite ST45 057	Ruby Has Gone/Oh Baby Come Dance With Me	10

DANNY DIAZ & CHECKMATES

69	Pye 7N 17690	Solomon Grundy/Goodbye Baby	4

MANU DIBANGO

73	London HL 10423	Soul Makossa/Lily	4
73	London SH 8451	O BOSO (LP)	12
75	Creole CRLP 503	MAKOSSA MUSIC (LP)	10
78	Decca SKL-R 5296	AFROVISION (LP)	10
79	Decca SKL-R 5303	MANU '76 (LP)	10

MINT VALUE £

DICE THE BOSS
69	Duke DU 51	Gun The Man Down/JOE MANSANO: Thief	5

DICK & DEE DEE
61	London HLG 9408	Mountains High/I Want Someone	10
62	London HLG 9483	Goodbye To Love/Swing Low	8
62	Liberty LIB 55412	Tell Me/Will You Always Love Me	5
63	Warner Bros WB 96	Young And In Love/Say To Me	5
63	Warner Bros WB 111	Where Did The Good Times Go/Guess Our Love Must Show	5
63	Warner Bros WB 119	Turn Around/Don't Leave Me	5
64	Warner Bros WB 126	All My Trails/Don't Twice, It's All Right	6
64	Warner Bros WB 138	Remember When/You Were Mine	6
64	Warner Bros WB 145	Thou Shalt Not Steal/Just 'Round The River Bend	5
65	Warner Bros WB 156	Be My Baby/Room 404	6
65	Warner Bros WB 5671	Use What You've Got/P.S. 1402	5
63	Warner Bros WM/WS 8132	YOUNG AND IN LOVE (LP, mono/stereo)	22/25
63	Warner Bros WM/WS 8150	TURN AROUND (LP, mono/stereo)	20/22

DOLES DICKEN'S BAND
58	London HLD 8639	Piakukaungcung (Pie-ah-coo-ka-ung-chung)/Our Melody	5

DICKENS
70s	Hawkmoon	STANDING ALONE (LP, private press)	25
(see also Ice)			

CHARLES DICKENS
65	Pye 7N 15887	That's The Way Love Goes/In The City	5
65	Pye 7N 15938	I Stand Alone/Hey Little Girl	5
66	Immediate IM 025	So Much In Love/Our Soul Brothers	10
(see also Habits)			

LITTLE JIMMY DICKENS
65	CBS 201969	May The Bird Of Paradise Fly Up Your Nose/My Eyes Are Jealous	4

DICKIES
78	A&M AMS 7368	Paranoid/I'm OK, You're OK (p/s, clear vinyl)	6
78	A&M AMS 7373	Eve Of Destruction/Doggie Do (p/s, pink or black vinyl)	5/4
78	A&M AMS 7391	Give It Back/You Drive Me Ape (p/s, white or black vinyl)	5/4
78	A&M AMS 7403	Silent Night/The Sounds Of Silence (p/s, white or black vinyl)	5/4
79	A&M AMS 7431	Banana Splits/Hideous/Got It At The Store (p/s, opaque or luminous yellow vinyl, also black vinyl)	each 4
79	A&M AMS 7469	Nights In White Satin/Waterslide (p/s, white or black vinyl)	5/4
79	A&M AMS 7491	Manny, Moe And Jack/She Loves Me Not (p/s)	5
80	A&M AMS 7504	Fan Mail/Tricia Toyota (I'm Stuck In A Pagoda With) (red vinyl, poster p/s)	6
80	A&M AMS 7544	Gigantor/Bowling With Bedrock Barney (p/s, yellow vinyl)	6
90	Overground OVER 017	Roadkill (flexidisc available on 'Just Say Yes' European Tour, no p/s)	4
79	A&M AMLE 64742	THE INCREDIBLE SHRINKING DICKIES (LP, black or yellow vinyl)	10/12
79	A&M AMLE 64742	THE INCREDIBLE SHRINKING DICKIES (LP, blur or orange vinyl)	each 15
79	A&M AMLH 68510	DAWN OF THE DICKIES (LP, black, blue or yellow vinyl)	10/12/15
(see also Chuck Wagon)			

BRUCE DICKINSON
90	EMI EMPD 138	Tattooed Millionaire/Ballad Of Mutt (shaped picture disc)	4
90	EMI EMPD 142	All The Young Dudes/Darkness Be My Friend (shaped picture disc)	4
90	EMI EMPD 151	Dive! Dive! Dive!/Riding With The Angels (live)/Sin City (live)/ Black Night (live) (12", picture disc)	7
(see also Iron Maiden, Samson)			

VIC DICKINSON & JOE THOMAS GROUPS
60	London Jazz LTZ-K 15182	MAINSTREAM (LP, also stereo SAH-K 6066)	10

BARBARA DICKSON
69	Trailer LER 3002	THE FATE O'CHARLIE (LP)	10
70	Decca SKL 5041	THRO' RECENT YEARS (LP, with A. Fisher)	30
70	Decca SKL 5058	DO RIGHT WOMAN (LP)	40
72	Decca SKL 5116	FROM THE BEGGAR'S MANTLE (LP)	30
74	RSO 2394 141	JOHN, PAUL, GEORGE, RINGO AND BERT (LP, with London Cast)	10

DICTATORS with TONY & HOWARD
63	Oriole CB 1934	So Long Little Girl/Say Little Girl	5

DICTATORS
77	WEA K 13091	Search And Destroy/Sleepin' With The TV On (p/s)	4
77	WEA K 13091T	Search And Destroy/Sleepin' With The TV On (12", p/s)	7

BO DIDDLEY
59	London HLM 8913	The Great Grandfather/Crackin' Up	40
59	London HLM 8913	The Great Grandfather/Crackin' Up (78)	35
59	London HLM 8975	Say Man/The Clock Strikes Twelve	35
59	London HLM 8975	Say Man/The Clock Strikes Twelve (78)	35
60	London HLM 9035	Say Man, Back Again/She's Alright	35
60	London HLM 9112	Road Runner/My Story	40
62	Pye Intl. 7N 25165	I Can Tell/You Can't Judge A Book By The Cover	12
63	Pye Intl. 7N 25193	Who Do You Love?/The Twister	10
63	Pye Intl. 7N 25210	Bo Diddley/Detour	10
63	Pye Intl. 7N 25216	You Can't Judge A Book By The Cover/I Can Tell (reissue)	8
63	Pye Intl. 7N 25217	Pretty Thing/Road Runner	10
63	Pye Intl. 7N 25227	Bo Diddley Is A Lover/Doin' The Jaguar	8
64	Pye Intl. 7N 25235	Memphis/Monkey Diddle	8
64	Pye Intl. 7N 25243	Mona/Gimme Gimme	10
64	Pye Intl. 7N 25258	Mama Keep Your Big Mouth Shut/Jo-Ann	8
65	Chess CRS 8000	Hey Good Lookin'/You Ain't Bad (As You Claim To Be)	7

MINT VALUE £

65	Chess CRS 8014	Somebody Beat Me/Mush Mouth Millie	7
65	Chess CRS 8021	Let The Kids Dance/Let Me Pass	7
66	Chess CRS 8026	500% More Man/Stop My Monkey	7
66	Chess CRS 8036	We're Gonna Get Married/Easy	7
67	Chess CRS 8053	Ooh Baby/Back To School	6
67	Chess CRS 8057	Wrecking My Love Life/Boo-Ga-Loo Before You Go	6
68	Chess CRS 8078	Another Sugar Daddy/I'm High Again	6
69	Chess CRS 8088	Bo Diddley 1969/Soul Train	6
56	London RE-U 1054	RHYTHM AND BLUES WITH BO DIDDLEY (EP)	80
63	Pye Intl. NEP 44014	HEY! BO DIDDLEY (EP)	10
64	Pye Intl. NEP 44019	THE STORY OF BO DIDDLEY (EP)	10
64	Pye Intl. NEP 44031	BO DIDDLEY IS A LUMBERJACK (EP)	15
64	Pye Intl. NEP 44036	DIDDLING (EP)	12
65	Chess CRE 6008	I'M A MAN (EP)	10
66	Chess CRE 6023	ROOSTER STEW (EP)	10
59	London HA-M 2230	GO BO DIDDLEY (LP)	125
63	Pye Jazz NJL 33	BO DIDDLEY IS A GUNSLINGER (LP)	30
63	Pye Intl. NPL 28025	HEY! BO DIDDLEY (LP)	18
63	Pye Intl. NPL 28026	BO DIDDLEY (LP)	18
63	Pye Intl. NPL 28029	BO DIDDLEY RIDES AGAIN (LP)	18
63	Pye Intl. NPL 28032	BO DIDDLEY'S BEACH PARTY (LP)	15
64	Pye Intl. NPL 28034	BO DIDDLEY IN THE SPOTLIGHT (LP)	20
64	Pye Intl. NPL 28049	16 ALL-TIME HITS (LP)	18
64	Chess CRL 4002	HEY GOOD LOOKIN' (LP)	15
65	Chess CRL 4507	LET ME PASS (LP)	15
66	Golden Guinea GG 0358	HEY! BO DIDDLEY (LP, reissue)	10
67	Chess CRL 4525	THE ORIGINATOR (LP)	15
68	Chess CRL 4529	SUPER BLUES (LP, with Muddy Waters & Little Walter)	15
68	Chess CRL 4537	THE SUPER SUPER BLUES BAND (LP, with Muddy Waters & Howlin' Wolf)	20
71	Chess 6310 107	ANOTHER DIMENSION (LP)	10
73	Checker 6467 304	GOT ANOTHER BAG OF TRICKS (LP)	10
73	Chess 6499 476	THE LONDON SESSIONS (LP)	12

(see also Chuck Berry & Bo Diddley)

DIDDY MEN
| 65 | Columbia DB 7782 | The Song Of The Diddy Men/Hello Doddy | 4 |

DIE DORAUS & DIE MARINAS
| 82 | Mute MUTE 019 | Fred From Jupiter/Even Home Is Not Nice Anymore (p/s) | 4 |

DIE ELECTRIC EELS
| 79 | Rough Trade RT 008 | Agitated/Cyclotron (p/s) | 5 |

MARLENE DIETRICH
57	London HLD 8492	Near You/Another Spring, Another Love	6
57	London HLD 8492	Near You/Another Spring, Another Love (78)	5
63	HMV POP 1196	Lili Marlene/Sag Mir Wo Die Blumen Sind?	4
65	HMV POP 1379	Where Have All The Flowers Gone?/Blowin' In The Wind	4
65	Pye 7N 15770	Go Away From My Window/Shir Hatan	4
57	HMV 7EG 8257	MARLENE DIETRICH (EP)	7
58	London RED 1146	MARLENE DIETRICH (EP)	8
64	HMV 7EG 8844	RETURNS TO GERMANY (EP)	7
53	Brunswick LA 8591	SOUVENIR ALBUM (10" LP)	15
54	Philips BBR 8006	AT THE CAFÉ DE PARIS (10" LP, introduced by Noel Coward)	15
59	Philips BBL 7322	LILI MARLENE (LP)	10
60	Philips BBL 7386	DIETRICH IN RIO (LP, also stereo SBBL 571)	10/12
60s	Philips	other LPs	10
63	HMV CLP 1659	RETURNS TO GERMANY (LP)	10

(see also Rosemary Clooney)

DIF JUZ
81	4AD BAD 109	HUREMICS (12" EP)	15
81	4AD BAD 116	VIBRATING AIR (12" EP)	12
80s	Pleasantly Surprised PS 9	TIME CLOCK TURNS BACK (cassette, with inserts)	15
83	Red Flame RFM 24	WHO SAYS SO (LP)	12

DIGA RHYTHM BAND
| 76 | United Artists UAG 29975 | DIGA RHYTHM BAND (LP) | 10 |

(see also Grateful Dead, Mickey Hart)

STEVE DIGGLE
| 81 | Liberty BP 389 | Fifty Years Of Comparative Wealth/Shut Out The Light/ Here Comes The Fire Brigade (p/s) | 4 |

(see also Buzzcocks, Flag Of Convenience)

DIGITAL DINOSAURS
| 81 | Yucca Y1/81 | Don't Call Us/Orders From The C.O. (p/s) | 4 |

MOSES & JOSHUA (DILLARD)
67	Stateside SS 2059	My Elusive Dreams/What's Better Than Love (as Moses & Joshua Dillard)	10
68	Bell BELL 1018	Get Out Of My Heart/They Don't Want Us Together (as Moses & Joshua)	7
72	Mojo 2092 054	My Elusive Dreams/Get Out Of My Heart	4

DILLARD & CLARK
69	A&M AMS 764	Radio Song/Why Not Your Baby	6
69	A&M AMLS 939	THE FANTASTIC EXPEDITION OF DILLARD & CLARK (LP)	12
69	A&M AMLS 966	THROUGH THE MORNING (LP)	12

(see also Gene Clark, Byrds, Dillards)

DILLARDS
| 65 | Capitol CL 15420 | Nobody Knows/Ebo Walker | 4 |
| 68 | Elektra EKSN 45048 | Reason To Believe/Nobody Knows | 5 |

MINT VALUE £

69	Elektra EKSN 45062	She Sang Hymns Out Of Tune/Single Saddle	4
70	Elektra EKSN 45081	Rain Maker/West Montana Hanna	5
68	Elektra EKS 74035	WHEATSHEAF SUITE (LP)	10
70	Elektra EKS 74054	COPPERFIELDS (LP)	10
72	United Artists UAS 29366	ROOTS AND BRANCHES (LP)	10
73	United Artists UAS 29516	TRIBUTE TO THE AMERICAN DUCK (LP)	10

(see also Dillard & Clark)

DILLINGER
| 73 | Duke DU 149 | Headquarters (as Dellenger)/CHENLEY DUFFAS: Black Girl In My Bed (B-side actually by Shenley Duffas) | 5 |
| 73 | Downtown DT 512 | Tighten Up Skank/Middle East Rock | 5 |

PHYLLIS DILLON
66	Doctor Bird DB 1061	Don't Stay Away (as Phillis Dillon)/TOMMY McCOOK & SUPERSONICS: What Now	10
67	Trojan TR 006	This Is A Lovely Way/Thing Of The Past (as Phyllis Dellon)	10
67	Treasure Isle TI 7003	This Is A Lovely Way/Thing Of The Past	10
67	Treasure Isle TI 7015	Perfidia/It's Rocking Time	10
68	Treasure Isle TI 7041	I Wear This Ring/Don't Touch Me Tomato	10
69	Trojan TR 651	Love Is All I Had/Boys And Girls Reggae (as Phillis Dylon)	7
69	Trojan TR 671	The Right Track/TOMMY McCOOK & SUPERSONICS: Moonshot	7
69	Trojan TR 686	Lipstick On Your Collar (as Phillis Dillon)/TOMMY McCOOK & SUPERSONICS: Tribute To Rameses	7
70	Duke Reid DR 2508	This Is Me/Skabuvie (actually by Dorothy Reid & songs actually "If Your Name Is Andy"/"Ska Vovi")	7
70	Treasure Isle TI 7058	One Life To Live One Love To Give/TOMMY McCOOK: My Best Dress	6
71	Treasure Isle TI 7070	Midnight Confession/TOMMY McCOOK & SOUL SYNDICATE: Version	6
72	Trojan TRL 41	ONE LIFE TO GIVE (LP)	20

DIMENSIONALS
| 53 | London L 1217 | Sleepy Time Gal/DON BAKER & DIMENSIONALS: Drinkin' Pop-Sodee Odee (78) | 20 |

DIMENSIONS
| 65 | Parlophone R 5294 | Tears On My Pillow/You Don't Have To Whisper | 10 |

DIMPLES
| 66 | Decca F 12537 | The Love Of A Lifetime/My Heart Is Tied To You | 20 |

DINAH ROD & DRAINS
| 83 | Secret SHH 146 | Somebody's In My Drain/Somebodies (p/s) | 4 |
| 83 | Secret SHH 146-12 | Somebody's In My Drain/Somebodies (Parts I, II, III) (12", p/s) | 7 |

DINGER
| 85 | Face Value FVRA 221 | Air Of Mystery/I Love To Love (no p/s) | 30 |

(see also Erasure)

MARK DINNING
60	MGM MGM 1053	Teen Angel/Bye Now Baby	6
60	MGM MGM 1069	You Win Again/A Star Is Born (A Love Is Dead)	5
60	MGM MGM 1101	The Lovin' Touch/Come Back To Me (My Love)	5
61	MGM MGM 1125	Top Forty, News, Weather And Sport/Suddenly	5
62	MGM MGM 1148	In A Matter Of Moments/What Will My Mary Say	4
62	MGM MGM 1155	All Of This For Sally/The Pickup	4
65	Hickory 45-1293	Dial Al 1-4883/I'm Glad We Fell In Love	4

DINNING SISTERS
| 55 | London HLF 8179 | Drifting And Dreaming/Truly | 25 |
| 56 | London HLF 8218 | Hold Me Tight/Uncle Joe | 25 |

(see also 'Tennessee' Ernie Ford)

KENNY DINO
| 61 | HMV POP 960 | Your Ma Said You Cried In Your Sleep Last Night/Dream A Girl | 6 |

DINO, DESI & BILLY
| 65 | Reprise R 20367 | I'm A Fool/So Many Ways | 4 |
| 66 | Reprise R 23047 | Not The Loving Kind/Chimes Of Freedom | 4 |

DINOSAUR
| 79 | Sire SRE 1034 | Kiss Me Again/Kiss Me Again (Version) (p/s) | 8 |
| 79 | Sire SRE 1034 | Kiss Me Again/Kiss Me Again (Version) (12", p/s) | 12 |

(see also David Byrne, Talking Heads)

DINOSAUR JR
| 89 | The Catalogue CAT 069/2 | Just Like Heaven/LUNACHICKS: Get Off The Road (33rpm square flexidisc free with 'The Catalogue' magazine) | 6/4 |

DIO
75	Purple PUR 128	Sitting In A Dream (as Ronnie Dio featuring Roger Glover & Guests)/JOHN LAWTON: Little Chalk Blue	4
84	Vertigo DIOP 4	Mystery/Eat Your Heart Out (picture disc)	5
85	Vertigo DIOP 6	Hungry For Heaven/King Of Rock And Roll (dragon-shaped picture disc)	5
85	Vertigo DIOFP 6	Hungry For Heaven/King Of Rock And Roll (p/s, with poster & sticker)	4
86	Vertigo DIOEP 7	Hiding (From) The Rainbow/Hungry For Heaven//Shame On The Night/Egypt (double pack)	4
86	Vertigo DIOP 710	Hiding (From) The Rainbow/Hungry For Heaven/Shame On The Night/Egypt (12", picture disc)	7

(see also Elf, Rainbow, Roger Glover, Black Sabbath)

DION (& BELMONTS)
58	London HL 8646	I Wonder Why/Teen Angel (as Dion & Belmonts)	40
58	London HL 8646	I Wonder Why/Teen Angel (as Dion & Belmonts) (78)	40
58	London HL 8718	I Can't Go On (Rosalie)/No One Knows (as Dion & Belmonts)	20
58	London HL 8718	I Can't Go On (Rosalie)/No One Knows (as Dion & Belmonts) (78)	40

59	London HL 8799	Don't Pity Me/Just You (as Dion & Belmonts)	20
59	London HL 8799	Don't Pity Me/Just You (as Dion & Belmonts) (78)	40
59	London HLU 8874	A Teenager In Love/I've Cried Before (as Dion & Belmonts)	20
59	London HLU 8874	A Teenager In Love/I've Cried Before (as Dion & Belmonts) (78)	40
59	Pye Intl. 7N 25038	A Lover's Prayer/Every Little Thing I Do (as Dion & Belmonts)	12
59	Pye Intl. 7N 25038	A Lover's Prayer/Every Little Thing I Do (as Dion & Belmonts) (78)	50
60	London HLU 9030	Where Or When/That's My Desire (as Dion & Belmonts)	12
60	London HLU 9030	Where Or When/That's My Desire (as Dion & Belmonts) (78)	50
60	Top Rank JAR 368	When You Wish Upon A Star/My Private Joy (as Dion & Belmonts)	8
60	Top Rank JAR 503	In The Still Of The Night/Swinging On A Star (as Dion & Belmonts)	8
60	Top Rank JAR 521	Lonely Teenager/Little Miss Blue	6
61	Top Rank JAR 545	Havin' Fun/North-East End Of The Corner	7
61	Top Rank JAR 586	Runaround Sue/Runaway Girl	5
62	HMV POP 971	The Wanderer/The Majestic	5
62	HMV POP 1020	(I Was) Born To Cry/Lovers Who Wander	7
62	Stateside SS 115	Little Diane/Lost For Sure	6
62	Stateside SS 139	Love Came To Me/Little Girl	6
63	CBS AAG 133	Ruby Baby/He'll Only Hurt You	5
63	Stateside SS 161	Sandy/Faith	6
63	CBS AAG 145	This Little Girl/The Loneliest Man In The World	5
63	Stateside SS 209	Come Go With Me/King Without A Queen	7
63	CBS AAG 161	Be Careful Of Stones That You Throw/I Can't Believe (That You Don't Love Me Anymore)	5
63	CBS AAG 169	Donna, The Prima Donna/You're Mine	5
63	CBS AAG 177	Drip Drop/No One's Waiting For Me	6
64	CBS AAG 188	I'm Your Hoochie Coochie Man/The Road I'm On (Gloria)	6
64	CBS AAG 224	Johnnie B. Goode/Chicago Blues	8
65	CBS 201728	Sweet, Sweet Baby/Unloved, Unwanted Me (as Dion Di Mucci)	6
65	CBS 201780	Spoonful/Kickin' Child	6
66	HMV POP 1565	Berimbau/My Girl The Month Of May (as Dion & Belmonts)	5
67	HMV POP 1586	Movin' Man/For Bobbie (as Dion & Belmonts)	7
68	London HLP 10229	Abraham, Martin And John/Daddy Rollin'	4
69	London HLP 10277	Both Sides Now/You Better Watch Yourself (Sonny Boy)	4
70	Warner Bros WB 7401	Your Own Back Yard/Sit Down, Old Friend	4
62	HMV 7EG 8749	SWINGALONG WITH DION (EP)	25
63	Stateside SE 1006	DION'S HITS (EP)	40
59	London HA-U 2194	PRESENTING DION AND THE BELMONTS (LP, as Dion & Belmonts)	150
60	Top Rank 25-027	THE TOPPERMOST — VOL. 1 (LP, as Dion & Belmonts, with others)	30
61	HMV CLP 1539	RUNAROUND SUE (LP)	50
63	Stateside SL 10034	LOVERS WHO WANDER (LP)	30
63	CBS (S) BPG 62137	RUBY BABY (LP, mono/stereo)	18/22
64	CBS (S) BPG 62203	DONNA THE PRIMA DONNA (LP, mono/stereo)	18/22
67	HMV CLP 3618	TOGETHER AGAIN (LP, as Dion & Belmonts, also stereo CSD 3618)	25
69	London HA-P 8390	DION (LP, also stereo SH-P 8390)	15
70	Warner Bros WS 1826	SIT DOWN OLD FRIEND (LP)	10
71	Warner Bros WS 1872	YOU'RE NOT ALONE (LP)	10
72	Warner Bros K 46122	SANCTUARY (LP)	10
72	Warner Bros K 46199	SUITE FOR LATE SUMMER (LP)	10
73	Warner Bros K 46208	REUNION - LIVE AT MADISON SQUARE GARDEN, 1972 (LP, as Dion & Belmonts)	12
75	Phil Spector Intl. 2307 002	BORN TO BE WITH YOU (LP)	10

(see also Belmonts)

DION (Cameron) & THREE TOPS
| 67 | Doctor Bird DB 1101 | Miserable Friday/This World Has A Feeling | 10 |

(see also Three Tops)

DIPLOMATS
| 68 | Direction 58-3899 | I Can Give You Love/I'm So Glad I Found You | 4 |

DIPLOMATS
| 82 | Exchange EX 1 | Memories Of You/I'll Keep Holding On (p/s) | 6 |

DIRECT HITS
82	Whaam! WHAAM 007	Modesty Blaise/Sunny Honey Girl (p/s)	10
85	Direct POP 001	Christopher Cooper/She Really Didn't Care (p/s)	7
84	Whaam! BIG 7	BLOW UP (LP)	35

DIRECTIONS
| 79 | Tortch TOR 004 | Three Bands Tonite/On The Train (p/s) | 40 |

(see also Big Sound Authority)

DIRE STRAITS
79	Vertigo 6059 206	Sultans Of Swing/Eastbound Train (live) (p/s)	6
79	Vertigo 6059 230	Lady Writer/Where Do You Think You're Going (p/s)	6
81	Vertigo MOVIE 1	Romeo And Juliet/Solid Rock (p/s)	4
81	Vertigo MOVIE 2	Skateaway/Expresso Love (p/s)	4
81	Vertigo MOVIE 3	Tunnel Of Love Pts 1 & 2 (p/s)	5
82	Vertigo DSTR 101	Private Investigations/Badges Posters Stickers T-Shirts (10", p/s)	7
84	Vertigo DSTR 610	Love Over Gold (live)/Solid Rock (live) (10", p/s)	7
85	Vertigo DSTR 910	So Far Away/Walk Of Life (10", p/s)	7
85	Vertigo DSTR 1010	Money For Nothing/Love Over Gold (live) (10", p/s)	7
85	Vertigo DSPIC 10	Money For Nothing/Love Over Gold (live) (shaped picture disc with plinth)	12
85	Vertigo DSTRD 11	Brothers In Arms/Going Home — Theme From 'Local Hero' (Live Version)// The Sultans Of Swing/Eastbound Train (live) (double pack, PVC sleeve)	6
85	Vertigo DSPIC 11	Brothers In Arms/Going Home — Theme From 'Local Hero' (Live Version) (oblong picture disc in stickered PVC sleeve)	12
85	Vertigo DSTR 1110	Brothers In Arms/Going Home — Theme From 'Local Hero' (Live Version) (10", p/s)	7

DIRE STRATS

85	Vertigo 884 2852	Brothers In Arms (short)/Going Home (live)/Brothers In Arms (long)/ Why Worry (CD, promo only)	40
86	Vertigo DSTRD 12	Walk Of Life/Two Young Lovers (live)/Sultans Of Swing/Eastbound Train (live) (double pack, gatefold p/s)	6
82	Vertigo HS 6359 034	MAKING MOVIES (LP, half-speed master recording)	10
82	Vertigo HS 9102 021	DIRE STRAITS (LP, half-speed master recording)	10

(see also Mark Knopfler, David Knopfler)

DIRK & STIG
78	Ring O' DIB 1	Ging Gang Goolie/Mr Sheene	5
79	EMI EMI 2852	Ging Gang Goolie/Mr Sheene (reissue, khaki vinyl)	4

(see also Rutles, Neil Innes)

DIRTY BLUES BAND
68	Stateside S(S)L 10234	DIRTY BLUES BAND (LP)	15
69	Stateside S(S)L 10268	STONE DIRT (LP)	12

(see also Baconfat)

DIRTY DOG
78	Lightning GIL 511	Let Go Of My Hand/Shouldn't Do It/Gonna Quit/Guitar In My Hand (p/s)	4

DIRTY STRANGERS
89	Thrill TH 3	Bathing Belles/Oh Yeah/Hands Up (p/s, featuring Keith Richards)	4

(see also Keith Richards)

DISCHARGE
80	Clay CLAY 1	Realities Of War/They Declare It/But After The Gig/Society's Victim (p/s)	6
80	Clay CLAY 3	Fight Back/War's No Fairy Tale/Always Restrictions/ You Take Part In Creating This System/Religion Instigates (p/s)	5
80	Clay CLAY 5	Decontrol/It's No TV Sketch/Tomorrow Belongs To Us (p/s)	5
81	Clay CLAY 6	Never Again/Death Dealers/Two Monstrous Nuclear Stock-Piles (p/s)	4

DISCIPLE
69	Parlophone R 5760	Cherie Alamayonaika/Caucasoid Junkie	4

DISCO BIPEDS
79	Bun	Disco Bipeds/Bathroom Technology (p/s)	5

DISCO BROTHERS
76	United Artists UP 36057	Let's Go To The Disco/Everybody Dance	4
76	United Artists	THE DISCO BROTHERS/THE TARTAN HORDE (EP, p/s)	7

(see also Nick Lowe, Tartan Horde, Roogalator, Damned)

DISCO STUDENTS
79	Yeah Yeah Yeah UHHUH 1	South Africa House/Kafkaesque (no p/s)	5
80	Yeah Yeah Yeah UHHUH 2	A Boy With A Penchant For Open-Necked Shirts (no p/s)	5

DISCO 2000
87	KLF D 2001	I Gotta CD (7" Edit) (white label)	8
87	KLF D 2000	I Gotta CD/I Love Disco 2000 (12", p/s)	10
88	KLF D 2002	One Love Nation (Radio Edit)/(Full Length)/(Instrumental) (12", p/s)	8
89	KLF D 2003	Uptight (Everything's Alright - Edit)/(Mr Hotty Loves You - Edit)	4
89	KLF D 2003	Uptight (Everything's Alright - Discorama Mix)/(Mr Hotty Loves You) (12", p/s)	7

(see also JAMs, KLF, Timelords, Bill Drummond)

DISCO ZOMBIES
79	South Circular SGS 106	Drums Over London/Heartbeats Love (hand-made gatefold p/s, pink or green)	12/15
79	Uptown/Wizzo WIZZO 1	THE INVISIBLE (EP)	10
81	Dining Out TUX 2	Here Come The Buts/Mary Millington (p/s)	8

(see also Steppes, Fifty Fantastics)

DISCS
65	Columbia DB 7477	Not Meant To Be/Come Back To Me	5

DISGUISE IN LOVE
82	Purple Snow FLAKE 1	Ross Was My Best Friend/Back Issue Of 'Janus' (p/s, purple vinyl)	8
82	Purple Snow FLAKE 2	You Won't Like It/It'll Never Be Like It Was (p/s, mauve vinyl)	6

DISKORD DATKORD
88	Soho Girl 12 SG 002	Identity (House Wife Mix)/Identity (Play List Mix)/D.D. & E.O.F.K. (12", p/s)	7

(see also Specimen)

DISLOCATION DANCE
81	New Hormones ORG 7	Birthday Outlook/Perfectly In Control/It's So Difficult/Familiar View (poster p/s)	4

DISORDER
80	D. B. Centre BOOK 1	Reality Crisis/1984 (p/s, on Durham Book Centre label)	5
81	Disorder ORDER 1	Complete Disorder/Insane Youth/Today's World/Violent Crime (p/s)	4
81	Disorder ORDER 2	Distortion To Deafness/More Than Fights/Daily Life/ You've Got To Be Someone (p/s)	4

DISRUPTORS
82	Radical RC 1	Young Offender/UK Soldier/No Place For You (p/s)	6
82	Radical RC 2	Shelters For The Rich/Animal Farm/Self Rule (p/s)	6
84	Radical RC 6	Bomb Heaven/Die With Mother/Poem (p/s)	5
85	Radical RC 8	Alive In The Electric Chair (p/s)	5
85	Radical RC 128	ALIVE IN THE ELECTRIC CHAIR (12" EP)	7

DISTRACTIONS
79	TJM TJM 2	YOU'RE NOT GOING OUT DRESSED LIKE THAT (12" EP)	7

DISTRIBUTORS
80	Tap TAP 1	TV Me/Wireless (foldover p/s)	6
81	Red Rhino RED 9	Hold/Get Rid Of These Things/Wages For Lovers (12", p/s)	7

DIVERSIONS

75	Gull GULS 18	Fattie Bum-Bum/Jamaica	4
76	Gull GULS 28	But Is It Funky/To Make Us Happy	4
76	Polydor 2058 794	Raincheck/Disco Limbo	4

(see also Lene Lovich)

DIVINE

85	Proto ENAP 125	Walk Like A Man/Man Talk (shaped picture disc)	6

DIVINE HORSEMEN

86	Shock SX 010	My Sin/Devil's River (p/s)	4

(see also Flesheaters)

DIXIE BELLES

63	London HLU 9797	Down At Poppa Joe's/Rock, Rock, Rock	6
64	London HLU 9842	Southtown, U.S.A./Why Don't You Set Me Free?	5
64	London REU 1434	THE DIXIE BELLES (EP)	10
64	London HA-U/SH-U 8152	DOWN AT PAPA JOE'S (LP)	16

DIXIE CUPS

64	Pye Intl. 7N 25245	Chapel Of Love/Ain't That Nice	8
64	Red Bird RB 10006	People Say/Girls Can Tell	8
64	Red Bird RB 10012	You Should Have Seen The Way He Looked At Me/No True Love	7
64	Red Bird RB 10017	Little Bell/Another Boy Like Mine	8
65	Red Bird RB 10024	Iko Iko/Gee Baby Gee	6
65	Red Bird RB 10032	Gee The Moon Is Shining Bright/I'm Gonna Get You Yet	15
65	HMV POP 1453	Two Way Poc A Way/That's Where It's At	7
66	HMV POP 1524	What Kind Of Fool/Danny Boy	6
66	HMV POP 1557	Love Ain't So Bad (After All)/Daddy Said No	6
73	Chess 6145 024	Iko Iko/BOBBY CHARLES: See You Later, Alligator	4
65	Red Bird RB 20100	CHAPEL OF LOVE (LP)	25
66	HMV CLP 1916	RIDING HIGH (LP)	20

DIXIE FOUR

60s	Rarities RA 3	THE DIXIE FOUR (EP)	20

DIXIE HUMMINGBIRDS

64	Vogue V 2422	Have A Talk With Jesus/In The Morning	8

DIXIE JAZZERS WASHBOARD BAND

28	Actuelle 11530	Memphis Shake/My Old Daddy's Got A Brand New Way To Love (78)	75
28	Actuelle 11538	Kansas City Shuffle/Black Cat Bone (78)	75

(see also Bobbie Leecan's Need-More Band)

DIXIELANDERS

63	Vocalion V 9209	Cyclone/Mardyke	6

DIXIELAND JUG BLOWERS

40s	HMV 5398	Skit Scat Skoodle Doo/BOBBIE LEECAN'S NEED-MORE BAND: Washboard Cut Out (78)	35
54	HMV 7M 223	Memphis Shake/Boodle-Am-Shake	8
54	HMV B 10707	Memphis Shake/Boodle-Am-Shake (78)	8
54	HMV 7M 233	Hen Party Blues/Carpet Alley Breakdown	8
54	HMV B 10727	Hen Party Blues/Carpet Alley Breakdown (78)	8

(see also Johnny Dodds)

ERROL DIXON

60	Blue Beat BB 27	Midnight Track/Anytime Anywhere	10
61	Blue Beat BB 46	Mama Shut Your Door/Too Much Whisky	10
61	Blue Beat BB 86	Bad Bad Woman/Early This Morning	8
62	Island WI 017	Morning Train/Lonely Heart	8
63	Island WI 069	I Love You/Tell Me More	8
63	Carnival CV 7001	Oo Wee Baby/Twisting And Shaking	12
63	Carnival CV 7004	Mean And Evil Woman/Tutti Frutti	10
64	Oriole CB 1945	Rocks In My Pillow/Give Me More Time (as Errol Dixon & Bluebeaters)	20
65	Blue Beat BB 337	Gloria/Heavy Shuffle	8
65	Blue Beat BB 344	You're No Good/Midnight Bus	8
66	Rainbow RAI 104	I Need Someone To Love/I Want (as Errol Dixon & Goodtime Band)	7
67	Ska Beat JB 271	Midnight Party/It Makes No Difference	7
67	Direct DS 5002	I Don't Want/The Hoop	8
67	Decca F 12613	Six Questions/Not Again	12
67	Decca F 12717	True Love Never Runs Smooth/What Ya Gonna Do (B-side with Judy Kay)	12
68	Decca F 12826	Back To The Chicken Shack (as Big City Blues Of Errol Dixon)/I Done Found Out	15
69	Doctor Bird DB 1197	Why Hurt Yourself/She Started To Scream	7
65	Decca DFE 8626	SINGS FATS (EP, with Honeydrippers)	25
68	Decca LK/SKL 4962	BLUES IN THE POT (LP, with Chicken Shack)	40
70	Transatlantic TRA	THAT'S HOW YOU GOT KILLED BEFORE (LP)	20

(see also Chicken Shack)

HUGH DIXON

64	London HA-U 8188	FRANTIC GUITARS (LP)	12

JEFF DIXON

67	Coxsone CS 7015	The Rock/HAMBOYS: Harder On The Rock	12
68	Studio One SO 2051	Tickle Me/ENFORCERS: Forgive Me	12

WILLIE DIXON & ALLSTARS

56	London HLU 8297	Walking The Blues/Crazy For My Baby	700
56	London HLU 8297	Walking The Blues/Crazy For My Baby (78)	70

MINT VALUE £

| 64 | Pye Intl. 7N 25270 | Crazy For My Baby/Walkin' The Blues (reissue) | 15 |
| 74 | London HA-O 8465 | CATALYST (LP, unreleased) | |

DIXON HOUSE BAND
| 79 | Infinity INS 2006 | FIGHTING ALONE (LP) | 10 |

DIXXY SISTERS
| 54 | Columbia SCM 5105 | Spin The Bottle Polka/The Game Of Broken Hearts | 6 |

D-MOB
| 89 | FX 117 | C'mon And Get My Love (Dance Hall Mix)/C'mon And Get My Love (Spaghetti Western Remix) (12", p/s) | 7 |
| 90 | FX 132 | That's The Way Of The World (Essential Beat Mix)/(Instrumental)/ (Acapella Mix)/(D Beats Mix) (12", p/s) | 7 |

(see also Cathy Dennis)

JED(RZEZ) DMOCHOWSKI
| 83 | Whaam! WHAAM 009 | Sha-La-La-La (Dance With Me)/Ruined City (p/s, with or without 'Jed' on sleeve) | 8/10 |
| 82 | Whaam! WHAAM 84 | STALLIONS OF MY HEART (LP) | 12 |

(see also V.I.P.'s)

DNV
| 79 | New Pleasures Z2 | Mafia/Death In Venice/Goodbye 70s (foldout p/s) | 30 |

(see also Another Pretty Face, Funhouse, Waterboys, TV21)

D.O.A.
81	Alt. Tentacles VIRUS 7	POSITIVELY D.O.A. (EP)	7
84	Alt. Tentacles VIRUS 24	WAR ON 45 (12" EP)	10
85	Alt. Tentacles VIRUS 42	DON'T TURN YOUR BACK (ON DESPERATE TIMES) (12" EP)	7
85	Alt. Tentacles VIRUS 44	LET'S WRECK THE PARTY (LP, with insert & small 'spy' logo)	10

CARL DOBKINS JNR.
59	Brunswick 05804	My Heart Is An Open Book/My Pledge To You	8
59	Brunswick 05804	My Heart Is An Open Book/My Pledge To You (78)	7
59	Brunswick 05811	If You Don't Want My Lovin'/Love Is Everything	18
59	Brunswick 05811	If You Don't Want My Lovin'/Love Is Everything (78)	12
60	Brunswick 05817	Lucky Devil/(There's A Little Song A-Singing) In My Heart	8
60	Brunswick 05832	Exclusively Yours/One Little Girl	6
60	Brunswick LAT 8329	CARL DOBKINS JNR. (LP)	12

BONNIE DOBSON
| 69 | RCA RCA 1901 | I'm Your Woman/I Got Stung | 4 |

DOBBY DOBSON (& DELTAS)
64	Blue Beat BB 246	Tell Me/I'm Going Home (with Chuck Josephs)	10
65	King KG 1008	Cry A Little Cry/Diamonds And Pearls (as Dobby Dobson & Deltas)	8
67	Trojan TR 011	Loving Pauper/TOMMY McCOOK & SUPERSONICS: Sir Don	12
68	Studio One SO 2068	Walking In The Footsteps/SOUL VENDORS: Studio Rock	12
68	Coxsone CS 7058	Seems To Me I'm Losing You/GAYLADS: Red Rose	12
69	Blue Cat BS 171	Strange/Your New Love	4
69	Pama SECO 33	STRANGE (LP)	15
70	Trojan TBL 145	THAT WONDERFUL SOUND (LP)	15

LYN DOBSON
| 74 | Fresh Air 6370 501 | JAM SANDWICH (LP) | 12 |

(see also Manfred Mann, Soft Machine)

ROY DOCKER
68	Domain D3	Mellow Moonlight/MUSIC THROUGH SIX: Riff Raff	5
68	Pama PM 750	When/Go	6
68	Pama PM 756	I'm An Outcast/Everyday Will Be A Holiday	6

DOCTOR & MEDICS
| 82 | Whaam! WHAAM 6 | The Druids Are Here/The Goats Are Trying To Kill Me (p/s) | 15 |
| 80s | white label | LIVE AT ALICE IN WONDERLAND (EP, sold at gigs) | 6 |

DOCTOR DARK
| 76 | Target TGT 102 | Red Hot Passion/Instrumental | 6 |

(see also Snivelling Shits)

DOCTOR FATHER
| 70 | Pye 7N 17977 | Umbopo/Roll On | 4 |

(see also 10cc)

DOCTORS OF MADNESS
| 76 | Polydor 2383 378 | LATE NIGHT MOVIES (LP) | 10 |
| 76 | Polydor 2383 403 | FIGMENTS OF EMANCIPATION (LP) | 10 |

PAT DODD
| 59 | Pye Intl. 7N 25030 | Stag Party/Odds'n'Dodds | 6 |

DODD'S ALLSTARS
| 69 | Coxsone CS 7096 | Mother Aitken (actually by Lord Power)/What A Love (actually by Denzil Laing) | 12 |

JOHNNY DODDS
51	HMV B 10082	Bucktown Stomp/Weary City Stomp (78)	8
53	London AL 3505	JOHNNY DODDS VOLUME 1 (10" LP)	15
54	London AL 3513	JOHNNY DODDS VOLUME 2 (10" LP)	15
55	Vogue Coral LRA 10025	JOHNNY DODDS VOL. 1 (10" LP)	15
55	HMV DLP 1073	JOHNNY DODDS WASHBOARD BAND (10" LP)	12
56	London AL 3555	JOHNNY DODDS VOLUME 3 (10" LP)	15
57	London AL 3560	JOHNNY DODDS VOLUME 4 (10" LP)	15

MALCOLM DODDS

59	Brunswick 05774	This Is Real (This Is Love)/I'll Always Be With You	4
59	Brunswick 05774	This Is Real (This Is Love)/I'll Always Be With You (78)	5
59	Brunswick 05796	Tremble/Deep Inside	4
59	Brunswick 05796	Tremble/Deep Inside (78)	5

NELLA DODDS

65	Pye 7N 25281	Come See About Me/You Don't Love Me Anymore	15
65	Pye 7N 25291	Finders Keepers, Losers Weepers/A Girl's Life	15

DODGERS

60	Downbeat CHA 2	Let's Make A Whole Lot Of Love/You Make Me Happy	15

DODO RESURRECTION

72	Elegiac SNT 7926	NOSTRADAMUS (LP, private pressing, with fold-out 'treatise' insert)	800

(see also Underwater Hairdressers)

DODO'S

67	Polydor BM 56153	I Made Up My Mind/Can't Make It Out	8

ERNIE K-DOE

(see under 'K')

DOG FACED HERMANS

87	Demon Radge RADGE 1	UNBEND (EP)	4
88	Calculus KIT 003	Miss O'Grady/Bella Ciao (p/s, with inserts)	4

DOGFEET

70	Reflection RS 7	Sad Story/On The Road	35
70	Reflection REFL 8	DOGFEET (LP)	350

TYMON DOGG

81	Ghost Dance GHO 1	Lose This Skin (featuring the Clash)/Indestructable (p/s)	6

(see also Timon, Clash)

DOGGEREL BANK

73	Charisma CAS 1079	SILVER FACES (LP)	10
75	Charisma CAS 1102	MISTER SKILLCORN DANCES (LP)	10

BILL DOGGETT

56	Parlophone R 4231	Honky Tonk Pts 1 & 2 (gold lettering on labels, later silver)	25/18
56	Parlophone R 4231	Honky Tonk Pts 1 & 2 (78)	12
57	Parlophone R 4265	Slow Walk/Peacock Alley	15
57	Parlophone R 4265	Slow Walk/Peacock Alley (78)	5
57	Parlophone R 4306	Ram-Bunk-Shush/Blue Largo	15
57	Parlophone R 4306	Ram-Bunk-Shush/Blue Largo (78)	5
57	Parlophone R 4379	Hot Ginger/Soft	15
57	Parlophone R 4379	Hot Ginger/Soft (78)	10
58	Parlophone R 4413	Leaps And Bounds Pts 1 & 2	10
58	Parlophone R 4413	Leaps And Bounds Pts 1 & 2 (78)	15
60	Parlophone R 4629	Smokie/Evening Dreams	8
61	Warner Bros WB 32	The Hully Gully Twist/Jackrabbit	5
61	Warner Bros WB 46	You Can't Sit Down Pts 1 & 2	7
57	Parlophone GEP 8644	HONKY TONK (EP)	10
57	Parlophone GEP 8674	PLAYS DUKE ELLINGTON (EP)	8
58	Parlophone GEP 8711	BILL DOGGETT (EP)	10
58	Parlophone GEP 8727	RAINBOW RIOT (EP)	8
59	Parlophone GEP 8771	A JOLLY CHRISTMAS (EP)	8
58	Parlophone PMD 1067	DAME DREAMING (10" LP)	20
59	Parlophone PMD 1073	DANCE AWHILE WITH DOGGETT (10" LP)	20
60	Parlophone PMC 1124	ON TOUR (LP)	15
60	Parlophone PMC 1118	DOGGETT'S BIG CITY DANCE PARTY (LP)	15
61	Warner Bros WM 402	3046 PEOPLE DANCED 'TIL 4 A.M. (LP, live, as Bill Doggett & His Combo)	12
62	Parlophone PMC 1165	BACK WITH MORE BILL DOGGETT (LP)	12
62	Warner Bros WM 4056	THE BAND WITH THE BEAT (LP, with His Combo, also stereo WS 8056)	10/12
65	HMV CLP 1884	WOW (LP)	15

(see also Ella Fitzgerald, Earl Bostic)

DOGS D'AMOUR

87	Supertrack DOGS 1	How Come It Never Rains/Sometimes/Last Bandit (p/s)	12
88	China CHINA 1	How Come It Never Rains/Sometimes/Last Bandit (p/s, reissue)	4
88	China CHINAX 1	How Come It Never Rains/Sometimes/Last Bandit (12", p/s)	7
88	China CHING 5	The Kid From Kensington/Everything I Want (poster p/s)	4
88	China CHINX 5	The Kid From Kensington (Extended Version)/Everything I Want/The State I'm In (12", p/s)	7
88	China CHIXP 5	The Kid From Kensington (Extended Version)/Everything I Want/The State I'm In (12", yellow vinyl, stickered p/s)	8
88	China CHING 10	I Don't Want To Go/Heroine (poster p/s)	4
88	China CHIXP 10	I Don't Want To Go/Heroine/Ugly (12", p/s, pink vinyl)	8
89	China CHING 13	How Come It Never Rains (Dynamite Remix)/Baby Glass (live) (gatefold p/s)	4
89	China CHINX 13	How Come It Never Rains (Dynamite Remix)/Baby Glass (live)/Kirsten Jet (live) (12", p/s)	7
89	China CHIXP 13	How Come It Never Rains (Dynamite Remix)/Baby Glass (live)/Kirsten Jet (live) (12" picture disc)	8
89	China CHIXP 17	Satellite Kid/She Thinks Too Much Of Me/Drunk Like Me/Things He'd Do (12", picture disc, gatefold p/s with cartoon story part 1)	7
89	China CHIXP 20	Trail Of Tears/Pourin' Out My Heart/As I See The Poppies Fall/In The Dynamite Jet Saloon/Swingin' The Bottle (12", picture disc with story part 2)	7
88	China WOL 7	THE (UN)AUTHORISED BOOTLEG (LP, 3,000 only, numbered)	30
89	China WOL 11	A GRAVEYARD OF EMPTY BOTTLES (10" mini-LP, 15,000 only, numbered)	8

MINT VALUE £

DOG SOLDIER
75	United Artists UAS 29769	DOG SOLDIER (LP)	10

(see also Keef Hartley, Miller Anderson, Artwoods)

DOG THAT BIT PEOPLE
71	Parlophone R 5880	Lovely Lady/Merry-Go-Round	20
71	Parlophone PCS 7125	THE DOG THAT BIT PEOPLE (LP)	220

DOGWATCH
79	Bridgehouse BHLP 002	PENFRIEND (LP, with insert)	50

NED DOHENY
81	CBS 9481	To Prove My Love/On The Swing Shift (p/s)	4
81	CBS 13-9481	To Prove My Love/On The Swing Shift (12", p/s)	7

DOKKEN
82	Carrere CAR 229	We're Illegal/Paris (p/s)	4
82	Carrere CAL 136	BREAKIN' THE CHAINS (LP)	10

THOMAS DOLBY
81	Armageddon AS 7	Urges/Leipzig (p/s)	10
82	Statik TAK 4	Urges/Leipzig (p/s, reissue)	7
82	Venice In Peril VIP 1001	THE GOLDEN AGE OF WIRELESS (LP, with inner sleeve)	10

(see also Low Noise)

DOLE
78	Ultimate ULT 402	New Wave Love/Hungry Men No Longer Steal Sheep But Are There Hanging Judges? (die-cut p/s)	5

MICKEY DOLENZ
67	London HLH 10117	Don't Do It/FINDERS KEEPERS: Lavender Blue	7
67	London HLH 10152	Huff Puff/OBVIOUS: Fate	8
73	MGM 2006 265	Daybreak/Lovely War	4
74	MGM 2006 392	Ooh She's Young/Love War	4

(see also Monkees)

DOLL
78	Beggars Banquet 2xBEG 11/SAM 93	Desire Me/T.V. Addict//Burning Up Like A Fire/Desire Me (Extended Version) (double pack, gatefold p/s)	4

ANDY DOLL
62	Starlite ST45 068	Wild Desire/Wyat	8
63	Starlite STLP II	ON STAGE (LP, by Andy Doll Band & Guests)	20

LINDA DOLL & SUNDOWNERS
64	Piccadilly 7N 35166	Bonie Maronie/He Don't Want Your Love Anymore	5

DOLLAR
79	Carrere CAR 110	Who Were You With In The Moonlight?/Star Control (picture disc)	4
79	Carrere CAR 122	Love's Gotta Hold On Me/Tokyo (p/s, coloured vinyl)	4
80	WEA K 18353	Takin' A Chance On You/No Man's Land (picture disc)	4
81	WEA K 18423	You Take My Breath Away/Don't Change Your Life (picture disc)	4

DOLL BY DOLL
79	Automatic K 17330	Palace Of Love/Fountain Is Red, Fountain Is White (p/s)	4
79	Automatic K 17496	Teenage Lightning/One Two Blues (p/s)	4
80	Automatic K 17559	Gypsy Blood/Love Myself (p/s)	4

DOLLY MIXTURE
80s	Cordelia ERICAT 017	THE FIRESIDE EP (12", p/s with inserts)	7
83	Dead Good Dolly Platters GOOD 1	DEMONSTRATION TAPES — A DOUBLE ALBUM (2-LP)	15

DOLPHIN
77	Private Stock PVLP 1055	GOODBYE (LP)	10
80	Gale LP 02	MOLECULES (LP)	20

ERIC DOLPHIN QUINTET
61	Esquire 32-123	THE ERIC DOLPHIN QUINTET (LP)	10

DOLPHINS
65	Stateside SS 375	Hey Da Da Dow/I Don't To Go On Without You	5

ERIC DOLPHY
69	Transatlantic PR 7311	OUTWARD BOUND (LP)	10

ERIC DOLPHY & BOOKER LITTLE
66	Stateside SL 10160	ERIC DOLPHY AND BOOKER LITTLE MEMORIAL ALBUM (LP)	10

BILLY DOLTON
61	Parlophone R 4733	Winkie Doll/Girls	5

DOME
80s	Dome DOME 3	Jasz (1-sided flexidisc)	5
80	4AD CAD 16	3R4 (mini-LP)	10
80	Dome DOME 1	DOME ONE (LP)	10
80	Dome DOME 2	DOME 2 (LP)	10
81	Dome DOME 3	DOME 3 (LP)	10

(see also Wire, Gilbert & Lewis, A.C. Marias A.C.)

FATS DOMINO
54	London HL 8007	Rose Mary/You Said You Love Me (78)	50
54	London HL 8063	Little School Girl/You Done Me Wrong (78)	50
54	London HL 8096	Don't Leave Me This Way/Something's Wrong (78)	40
55	London HL 8124	Love Me/Don't You Hear Me Calling You	150
55	London HL 8124	Love Me/Don't You Hear Me Calling You (78)	18

55	London HL 8133	Thinking Of You/I Know	125
55	London HL 8133	Thinking Of You/I Know (78)	18
55	London HLU 8173	Ain't That A Shame/La La	60
55	London HLU 8173	Ain't That A Shame/La La (78)	8
56	London HLU 8256	Bo Weevil/Don't Blame It On Me	80
56	London HLU 8256	Bo Weevil/Don't Blame It On Me (78)	18
56	London HLU 8280	I'm In Love Again/My Blue Heaven	60
56	London HLU 8280	I'm In Love Again/My Blue Heaven (78)	8
56	London HLU 8309	When My Dream Boat Comes Home/So Long	60
56	London HLU 8309	When My Dream Boat Comes Home/So Long (78)	8
56	London HLU 8330	Blueberry Hill/I Can't Go On (Rosalie)	60
56	London HLU 8330	Blueberry Hill/I Can't Go On (Rosalie) (78)	7
57	London HLU 8356	Honey Chile/Don't You Know	50
57	London HLU 8356	Honey Chile/Don't You Know (78)	7
57	London HLP 8377	Blue Monday/What's The Reason I'm Not Pleasing You	50
57	London HLP 8377	Blue Monday/What's The Reason I'm Not Pleasing You (78)	7

(all the above 45s came with tri centres & gold lettering labels; silver label re-pressings are worth around half these values)

57	London HLP 8407	I'm Walkin'/I'm In The Mood For Love	22
57	London HLP 8407	I'm Walkin'/I'm In The Mood For Love (78)	7
57	London HLP 8449	The Valley Of Tears/It's You I Love	20
57	London HLP 8449	The Valley Of Tears/It's You I Love (78)	7
57	London HLP 8471	What Will I Tell My Heart/When I See You	25
57	London HLP 8471	What Will I Tell My Heart/When I See You (78)	7
57	London HLP 8519	Wait And See/I Still Love You	20
57	London HLP 8519	Wait And See/I Still Love You (78)	8
58	London HLP 8575	The Big Beat (from the film)/I Want You To Know	15
58	London HLP 8575	The Big Beat (from the film)/I Want You To Know (78)	7
58	London HLP 8628	Sick And Tired/No, No	15
58	London HLP 8628	Sick And Tired/No, No (78)	8
58	London HLP 8663	Little Mary/The Prisoner's Song	20
58	London HLP 8663	Little Mary/The Prisoner's Song (78)	7
58	London HLP 8727	Young School Girl/It Must Be Love	20
58	London HLP 8727	Young School Girl/It Must Be Love (78)	10
58	London HLP 8759	Whole Lotta Loving/Coquette	20
58	London HLP 8759	Whole Lotta Loving/Coquette (78)	10
59	London HLP 8822	When The Saints Go Marching In/Telling Lies	15
59	London HLP 8822	When The Saints Go Marching In/Telling Lies (78)	15

(HLP 8407-8822 45s had tri-centres & silver lettering on black-top labels; re-pressings are worth around half these values)

59	London HLP 8865	Margie/I'm Ready (tri centre on silver-top label, later round centre)	15/8
59	London HLP 8865	Margie/I'm Ready (78)	20
59	London HLP 8942	I Want To Walk You Home/I'm Gonna Be A Wheel Some Day (tri or round)	15/8
59	London HLP 8942	I Want To Walk You Home/I'm Gonna Be A Wheel Some Day (78)	20
59	London HLP 9005	Be My Guest/I've Been Around (very few with tri centre, most round)	30/10
59	London HLP 9005	Be My Guest/I've Been Around (78)	25

(subsequent London 45s all had round centres & silver top labels)

60	London HLP 9073	Country Boy/If You Need Me	10
60	London HLP 9073	Country Boy/If You Need Me (78)	30
60	London HLP 9133	Tell Me That You Love Me/Before I Grow Too Old	15
60	London HLP 9163	Walking To New Orleans/Don't Come Knockin'	10
60	London HLP 9163	Walking To New Orleans/Don't Come Knockin' (78)	35
60	London HLP 9198	Three Nights A Week/Put Your Arms Around Me, Honey	10
60	London HLP 9244	My Girl Josephine/Natural Born Lover	8
61	London HLP 9301	What A Price/Ain't That Just Like A Woman	10
61	London HLP 9327	Fell In Love On Monday/Shu-Rah	12
61	London HLP 9374	It Keeps Rainin'/I Just Cry	20
61	London HLP 9415	Let The Four Winds Blow/Good Hearted Man	10
61	London HLP 9456	What A Party/Rockin' Bicycle	10
62	London HLP 9520	Jambalaya/You Win Again	8
62	London HLP 9557	My Real Name/My Heart Is Bleeding	12
62	London HLP 9590	Dance With Mr. Domino/Nothing New (Same Old Thing)	12
62	London HLP 9616	Did You Ever See A Dream Walking/Stop The Clock	12
63	London HLP 9738	You Always Hurt The One You Love/Trouble Blues	10
63	HMV POP 1164	There Goes My Heart Again/Can't Go On Without You	10
63	HMV POP 1197	When I'm Walkin'/I've Got A Right To Cry	8
63	HMV POP 1219	Red Sails In The Sunset/Song For Rosemary	6
63	HMV POP 1265	Just A Lonely Man/Who Cares	7
64	HMV POP 1281	I Don't Want To Set The World On Fire/Lazy Lady	6
64	HMV POP 1303	If You Don't Know What Love Is/Something You Got Baby	8
64	HMV POP 1324	Mary Oh Mary/Packin' Up	6
64	HMV POP 1370	Kansas City/Heartbreak Hill	7
65	HMV POP 1421	Why Don't You Do Right/Wigs	7
67	HMV POP 1582	I'm Livin' Right/I Don't Want To Set The World On Fire	7
67	Liberty LBF 12055	It Keeps Rainin'/Blue Monday	6
68	Liberty LBF 15098	Walking To New Orleans/Blueberry Hill	4
65	Mercury MF 869	(I Left My Heart) In San Francisco/I Done Got Over It	10
65	Mercury MF 873	What's That You Got?/It's Never Too Late	8
69	Mercury MF 1104	What's That You Got?/Jambalaya (On The Bayou)	8
68	Reprise RS 20696	Honest Mamas Love Their Papas Better/One For The Highway (withdrawn)	10
68	Reprise RS 20763	Lady Madonna/One For The Highway	6
69	Reprise RS 20810	Everybody's Got Something To Hide Except Me And My Monkey/ So Swell When You're Well	6
69	Liberty LBF 15274	I'm Ready/The Fat Man	10

(the below singles are all export issues)

57	London HL 7028	Wait And See/I Still Love You	10
58	London HL 7040	Sick And Tired/No, No	10
58	London HL 7054	The Big Beat (from the film)/Little Mary	10

Fats DOMINO

MINT VALUE £

55	London RE-U 1022	BLUES FOR LOVE (EP, 1st pressing with gold lettering label, later silver)	30/25
56	London RE-U 1062	BLUES FOR LOVE NO. 2 (EP, 1st pressing with gold label, later silver)	25/20
57	London RE-U 1073	FATS (EP, 1st pressing with gold lettering label, later silver)	60/50
57	London RE-U 1079	HERE COMES FATS PART 1 (EP)	20
58	London RE-U 1080	HERE COMES FATS PART 2 (EP)	20
58	London RE-U 1115	CARRY ON ROCKIN' PART 1 (EP)	20
58	London RE-U 1116	CARRY ON ROCKIN' PART 2 (EP)	20
58	London RE-U 1117	BLUES FOR LOVE VOL. 3 (EP)	20
58	London RE-U 1121	BLUES FOR LOVE VOL. 4 (EP)	20
58	London RE-U 1138	HERE COMES FATS PART 3 (EP)	20
59	London RE-U 1206	THE ROCKIN' MR. D VOL. 1 (EP)	20
59	London RE-U 1207	THE ROCKIN' MR. D VOL. 2 (EP)	20

(the above EPs originally had triangular centres; later round centre pressings are worth two-thirds these values)

60	London RE-U 1261	BE MY GUEST (EP)	15
60	London RE-U 1265	THE ROCKIN' MR. D VOL. 3 (EP)	20
62	London RE-U 1340	WHAT A PARTY (EP)	18
64	HMV 7EG 8862	RED SAILS IN THE SUNSET (EP)	12
65	Liberty LEP 4026	MY BLUE HEAVEN (EP)	12
66	Liberty LEP 4045	ROLLIN' (EP)	12
56	London HA-U 2028	FATS' ROCK AND ROLLIN' (LP)	40
56	London HA-P 2041	CARRY ON ROCKIN' (LP)	40
57	London HA-P 2052	HERE STANDS FATS DOMINO (LP)	40
56	London HA-P 2073	THIS IS FATS DOMINO (LP)	35
58	London HA-P 2087	THIS IS FATS (LP)	35
58	London HA-P 2135	THE FABULOUS "MR. D" (LP)	30
59	London HA-P 2223	LET'S PLAY FATS DOMINO (LP)	30
60	London HA-P 2312	A LOT OF DOMINOES (LP)	30
61	London HA-P 2364	I MISS YOU SO (LP)	35
61	London HA-P 2420	LET THE FOUR WINDS BLOW (LP)	35
61	London HA-P 2426	WHAT A PARTY (LP)	35
62	London HA-P 2447	TWISTIN' THE STOMP (LP)	40
63	London HA-P 8039	JUST DOMINO (LP)	40
63	London HA-P 8084	WALKING TO NEW ORLEANS (LP)	40
63	HMV CLP 1690	HERE COMES FATS DOMINO (LP, also stereo CSD 1520)	18/20
63	HMV CLP 1740	FATS ON FIRE (LP, also stereo CSD 1543)	18/20
65	Liberty LBY 3033	MILLION SELLERS BY FATS VOL. 1 (LP)	15
65	Liberty LBY 3046	MILLION SELLERS BY FATS VOL. 2 (LP)	12
65	HMV CLP 1821	GETAWAY WITH FATS DOMINO (LP, also stereo CSD 1580)	18/20
65	Mercury (S)MCL 20070	DOMINO '65 (LP, mono/stereo)	12/14
67	Liberty LBL 83023	MILLION SELLERS BY FATS VOL. 1 (LP, reissue)	10
67	Liberty LBL 83024	MILLION SELLERS BY FATS VOL. 2 (LP, reissue)	10
68	Liberty LBL 83101	MILLION SELLERS BY FATS VOL. 3 (LP)	12
68	Stateside (S)SL 10240	FANTASTIC FATS (LP)	10
68	Liberty LBL/LBS 83142E	FAT SOUND (LP)	10
70	Liberty LBL/LBS 83174E	RARE DOMINO'S (LP)	10
70	Liberty LBS 83331E	VERY BEST OF FATS DOMINO (LP)	10

DOMINOES (U.S.)

51	Vogue V 9102	Sixty Minute Man/I Can't Escape From You (78)	30
52	Vogue V 2135	Have Mercy, Baby/That's What You're Doing To Me (78)	20

DOMINOES/SWALLOWS

56	Vogue EPV 1113	RHYTHM AND BLUES (EP, 2 tracks each)	125

(see also Billy Ward & Dominoes)

DOMINOES (Jamaica)

68	Melody MRC 002	A Tribute (actually by Ann Reid)/Hooray (actually by Uniques)	8

DON & DEWEY

64	London HL 9897	Get Your Hat/Annie Lee	10
66	Cameo Parkway CP 750	Soul Motion/Stretchin' Out	15
67	Sue WI 4032	Soul Motion/Stretchin' Out (reissue)	12

(see also Don 'Sugarcane' Harris)

DON & GOODTIMES

67	Columbia DB 8199	I Could Be So Good To You/And It's So Good	4
67	Columbia DB 8266	Happy And Me/If You Love Her, Cherish Her And Such	4

DON & JUAN

62	London HLX 9529	What's Your Name?/Chicken Necks	20

DON & PETE

66	Columbia DB 7881	And I'm Crying Again/Time Will Tell	4

SAM DONAHUE & HIS ORCHESTRA

55	Capitol CL 14349	Saxaboogie/September In The Rain	12

BO DONALDSON & HEYWOODS

74	Probe PRO 614	Deeper And Deeper/Drive Me Crazy	4
75	Anchor ABC 4026	Heartbreak Kid/Girl Don't Make Me Wait	5

ERIC DONALDSON

71	Dynamic DYN 420	Cherry Oh Baby/LLOYD CHARMERS: Sir Charmers Special	4
72	Trojan TRL 42	ERIC DONALDSON (LP)	15

JAMES DONALDSON BAND

79	Look LKLP 7-6060	JUSTIFIED (LP)	10

LOU DONALDSON

70	Blue Note SBN 1956	Everything I Do Gonh Be Funky/Minor Bash	6

DONAYS

62	Oriole CB 1770	Devil In His Heart/Bad Boy	75

DON BRADSHAW LEATHER

70s	Distance	DISTANCE BETWEEN US (2-LP, private pressing)	50

(see also Robert John Godfrey, Enid)

DON, DICK & JIMMY

54	Columbia SCM 5110	Brand Me With Your Kisses/Angela Mia	15
55	London HL 8117	You Can't Have Your Cake And Eat It Too/That's What I Like	18
55	London HL 8144	Make Yourself Comfortable/(Whatever Happened To The) Piano Players (That Played Like This)	18
56	HMV POP 280	That's The Way I Feel/Two Voices In The Night	8
55	London RE-U 1043	DON, DICK AND JIMMY (EP)	20

DOROTHY DONEGAN

56	MGM MGM-EP 532	DOROTHY DONEGAN TRIO (EP)	7

LONNIE DONEGAN

55	Decca F 10647	Rock Island Line/John Henry (tri-centre, as Lonnie Donegan Skiffle Group)	12
56	Decca FJ 10695	Diggin' My Potatoes/Bury My Body (tricentre, as Lonnie Donegan Skiffle Group)	12
56	Oriole CB 1329	The Passing Stranger/TOMMY REILLY: The Intimate Stranger (78)	8
56	Columbia DB 3850	On A Christmas Day/Take My Hand, Precious Lord (as Lonnie Donegan with Chris Barber's Jazz Band)	12
56	Columbia DB 3850	On A Christmas Day/Take My Hand, Precious Lord (78)	5
57	Pye Nixa 7N 15116	Jack O' Diamonds/Ham 'N' Eggs	5
58	Pye Nixa 7N 15129	The Grand Coolie Dam/Nobody Loves Like An Irishman	4
58	Pye Jazz 7NJ 2006	Midnight Special/When The Sun Goes Down	8
58	Pye Nixa 7N 15148	Sally, Don't You Grieve/Betty, Betty, Betty	5
58	Pye Nixa 7N 15158	Lonesome Traveller/Times Are Getting Hard Boys	5
58	Pye 7N 15165	Lonnie's Skiffle Party Pts 1 & 2	5
58	Pye 7N 15172	Tom Dooley/Rock O' My Soul	4
59	Pye 7N 15181	Does Your Chewing Gum Lose Its Flavour/Aunt Rhody	4
59	Pye 7N 15198	Fort Worth Jail/Whoa Buck	4
59	Pye 7N 15206	Battle Of New Orleans/Darling Corey	4
59	Pye 7N 15219	Kevin Barry/My Laggan Love (Irish-only issue)	12
59	Pye 7N 15223	Sal's Got A Sugar Lip/Chesapeake Bay	4
59	Pye 7N 15237	San Miguel/Talking Guitar Blues	4
60	Pye 7N 15256	My Old Man's A Dustman/The Golden Vanity	4
60	Pye 7N 15267	I Wanna Go Home/Jimmy Brown The Newsboy	4
60	Pye 7N 15275	Lorelei/In All My Wildest Dreams	4
60	Pye 7N 15312	Lively/Black Cat (Cross My Path Today)	4
62	Pye 7N 15455	Pick A Bale Of Cotton/Steal Away (some in p/s)	12/4
62	Pye 7N 15493	The Market Song/Tit-bits (with Max Miller & Lonnie Donegan Group)	5
67	Pye 7N 17232	Aunt Maggie's Remedy/(Ah) My Sweet Marie	4
68	Columbia DB 8371	Toys/Relax Your Mind	4
69	Decca F 12984	My Lovely Juanita/Who Knows Where The Time Goes	4
56	Decca DFE 6345	THE LONNIE DONEGAN SKIFFLE GROUP (EP, tri centre)	12
56	Polygon Jazz JTE 107	BACKSTAIRS SESSION (EP)	20
56	Pye Nixa Jazz NJE 1014	BACKSTAIRS SESSION (EP, reissue)	10
56	Pye Nixa Jazz NJE 1017	SKIFFLE SESSION (EP)	7
57	Pye Nixa NEP 24031	HIT PARADE (EP)	8
57	Pye Nixa NEP 24040	HIT PARADE VOL. 2 (EP)	8
58	Pye Nixa NEP 24067	HIT PARADE VOL. 3 (EP)	8
58	Pye Nixa NEP 24075	DONEGAN ON STAGE (EP)	8
58	Pye Nixa NEP 24081	HIT PARADE VOL. 4 (EP)	7
59	Pye Nixa NEP 24104	HIT PARADE VOL. 5 (EP)	7
59	Pye Nixa NEP 24107	RELAX WITH LONNIE (EP)	7
59	Pye Nixa NEP 24114	HIT PARADE VOL. 6 (EP)	7
60	Pye Nixa NEP 24127	YANKEE DOODLE DONEGAN (EP)	7
61	Pye Nixa NEP 24134	HIT PARADE VOL. 7 (EP)	8
61	Pye Nixa NEP 24149	HIT PARADE VOL. 8 (EP)	8
56	Pye Nixa NPT 19012	LONNIE DONEGAN SHOWCASE (10" LP)	16
57	Pye Nixa NPT 19027	LONNIE (10" LP)	16
58	Pye NPL 18034	TOPS WITH LONNIE (LP)	12
59	Pye NPL 18043	LONNIE RIDES AGAIN (LP)	12
61	Pye NPL 18063	MORE TOPS WITH LONNIE (LP)	12
62	Pye NPL 18073	SING HALLELUJAH (LP)	14
62	Golden Guinea GGL 0135	GOLDEN AGE OF DONEGAN (LP)	10
63	Golden Guinea GGL 0170	GOLDEN AGE OF DONEGAN VOL. 2 (LP)	10
65	Pye NPL 18126	THE LONNIE DONEGAN FOLK ALBUM (LP)	18
67	Golden Guinea GGL 0382	THE LONNIE DONEGAN FOLK ALBUM (LP, reissue)	10

DONKEYS

80	Rhesus GO APE 102	What I Want/Four Letters (p/s)	4
80	Rhesus GO APE 3	No Way/You Jane (p/s)	4
80	Rhesus GO APE 105	Don't Go/Living Legends (p/s)	4

JIMMY DONLEY

57	Brunswick 05715	South Of The Border/The Trail Of The Lonesome Pine	10
57	Brunswick 05715	South Of The Border/The Trail Of The Lonesome Pine (78)	5
59	Brunswick 05807	The Shape You Left Me In/What Must I Do	75
59	Brunswick 05807	The Shape You Left Me In/What Must I Do (78)	30

DONNA & FREEDOM SINGERS

70	Bamboo BAM 53	Oh Me Oh My/JACKIE MITTOO: Gold Mine	5

RAL DONNER

61	Parlophone R 4820	You Don't Know What You've Got/So Close To Heaven	7
61	Parlophone R 4859	Please Don't Go/I Didn't Figure On Him	8
62	Parlophone R 4889	I Don't Need You/She's Everything (I Wanted You To Be)	10
62	Stateside SS 109	Bells Of Love/Loveless Life	12

Ral DONNER

63	Reprise R 20141	I Got Burned/A Tear In My Eye	16

DONNIE & DREAMERS
61	Top Rank JAR 571	Count Every Star/Dorothy	8

DONOVAN
65	Pye 7N 15801	Catch The Wind/Why Do You Treat Me Like You Do	6
65	Pye 7N 15866	Colours/To Sing For You	4
65	Pye 7N 15984	Turquoise/Hey Gyp (Dig The Slowness)	4
66	Pye 7N 17067	Josie/Little Tin Soldier	5
66	Pye 7N 17088	Remember The Alamo/The Ballad Of A Crystal Man (withdrawn)	12
66	Pye 7N 17241	Sunshine Superman/The Trip	4
67	Pye 7N 17267	Mellow Yellow/Preachin' Love	4
67	Pye 7N 17403	There Is A Mountain/Sand And Foam	4
68	Pye 7N 17457	Jennifer Juniper/Poor Cow	4
68	Pye 7N 17537	Hurdy Gurdy Man/Teen Angel	4
68	Pye 7N 17660	To Susan On The West Coast/Atlantis (withdrawn, any pressed?)	15+
68	Pye 7N 17660	Atlantis/I Love My Shirt	5
69	Pye 7N 17778	Goo Goo Barabajagal (Love Is Hot)/Bed With Me (with Jeff Beck Group)	8
69	Pye 7N 17778	Goo Goo Barabajagal (Love Is Hot)/Trudi (B-side actually "Bed With Me")	8
70	Dawn DNS 1006	Riki Tiki Tavi/Roots Of Oak (as Donovan with Open Road)	4
71	Dawn DNS 1007	Celia Of The Seals/Mr. Wind (as Donovan with Danny Thompson)	4
65	Pye NEP 24219	THE UNIVERSAL SOLDIER (EP)	8
65	Pye NEP 24299	COLOURS (EP)	8
66	Pye NEP 24239	DONOVAN VOLUME ONE (EP)	8
68	Pye NEP 24287	CATCH THE WIND (EP)	8
68	Pye NEP 24299	HURDY GURDY DONOVAN (EP)	10
65	Pye NPL 18117	WHAT'S BIN DID AND WHAT'S BIN HID (LP)	15
65	Pye NPL 18128	FAIRYTALE (LP)	15
66	World Records ST 951	DONOVAN (LP)	10
67	Pye NPL 18181	SUNSHINE SUPERMAN (LP)	15
68	Pye NPL 20000	A GIFT FROM A FLOWER TO A GARDEN (2-LP, box set, mono with 12-page insert)	30
68	Pye NSPL 20000	A GIFT FROM A FLOWER TO A GARDEN (2-LP, box set, stereo with 12-page insert)	25
68	Pye N(S)PL 18237	DONOVAN IN CONCERT (LP)	12
69	Pye N(S)PL 18283	DONOVAN'S GREATEST HITS (LP, with insert)	12
70	Dawn DNLS 3009	OPEN ROAD (LP)	12
71	Dawn DNLP 4001	H.M.S. DONOVAN (2-LP)	40
73	Epic EPC 65450	COSMIC WHEELS (LP, gatefold sleeve with poster insert)	10
73	Pye 11PP 102	H.M.S. DONOVAN/GREATEST HITS/OPEN ROAD (4-LP box set)	25
	(see also Jeff Beck)		

DONTELLS
65	Fontana TF 566	In Your Heart/Nothing But Nothing	30
74	President PT 373	In Your Heart/Nothing But Nothing (reissue)	5

DICKY DOO & DON'TS
58	London HLU 8589	Click Click/Did You Cry	35
58	London HLU 8589	Click Click/Did You Cry (78)	10
58	London HLU 8754	Leave Me Alone/Wild, Wild Party (with Orchestra)	35
58	London HLU 8754	Leave Me Alone/Wild, Wild Party (with Orchestra) (78)	18
60	Top Rank JAR 318	Wabash Cannonball/WEST TEXAS MARCHING BAND: The Drums Of Richard A Doo	6

DOOF
70s	Doof	EXIST (10" mini-LP, with booklet)	8
	(see also Exhibit A)		

TOM DOOLEY
69	London HLE 10236	My Groovy Baby/You'd Better Stop	4

DOOLEYS
75	Beeb BEEB 10	On The Move/Easy To Love You	4
83	R'N'R RNRPD 1	Casuality/I Don't Want You Hanging Around (picture disc)	4

DOOLEY SISTERS
55	London HL 8128	Ko Ko Mo (I Love You So)/Heart Throb	25
55	London HL 8128	Ko Ko Mo (I Love You So)/Heart Throb (78)	5

THE DOOR & THE WINDOW
79	NB NB 3	He Feels Like A Doris/I Like Sound/Innocent/Dig/Production Line (white label with stickers & insert p/s in poly bag)	4
80	NB NB 5	DETAILED TWANG (LP, blank labels)	12
	(see also Alternative TV)		

DOORS
67	Elektra EKSN 45009	Break On Through (To The Other Side)/End Of The Night	8
67	Elektra EKSN 45012	Alabama Song (Whisky Bar)/Take It As It Comes	6
67	Elektra EKSN 45014	Light My Fire/The Crystal Ship	8
67	Elektra EKSN 45017	People Are Strange/Unhappy Girl	8
67	Elektra EKSN 45022	Love Me Two Times/Moonlight Drive	7
68	Elektra EKSN 45030	We Could Be So Good Together/The Unknown Soldier	7
68	Elektra EKSN 45037	Hello, I Love You/Love Street	5
69	Elektra EKSN 45050	Touch Me/Wild Child	6
69	Elektra EKSN 45059	Wishful Sinful/Who Scared You?	6
69	Elektra EKSN 45065	Tell All The People/Easy Ride	7
70	Elektra 2101 004	You Make Me Real/The Spy	7
70	Elektra 2101 008	Roadhouse Blues/Blue Sunday	6
71	Elektra EK 45726	Love Her Madly/(You Need Meat) Don't Go No Further	4
71	Elektra K 12004	We Could Be So Good Together/The Unknown Soldier (reissue)	4

MINT VALUE £

71	Elektra K 12036	Tightrope Ride/Variety Is The Spice Of Life 4
72	Elektra K 12048	Ship with Sails/In The Eye Of The Sun 4
72	Elektra K 12059	Get Up And Dance/Tree Trunks 4
79	Elektra K 12215/SAM 94	Love Me Two Times/Hello, I Love You//Ghost Song/Roadhouse Blues (double pack) 5
67	Elektra EKL 4007	THE DOORS (LP, orange label, also stereo EKS 74007) 25
68	Elektra EKL 4014	STRANGE DAYS (LP, orange label, inner sleeve, also stereo EKS 74014) 25
68	Elektra EKL 4024	WAITING FOR THE SUN (LP, orange label, gatefold sleeve, also stereo EKS 74024) 20
69	Elektra EKS 75005	THE SOFT PARADE (LP, orange label, gatefold sleeve, with lyric sheet) 20
70	Elektra EKS 75007	MORRISON HOTEL (LP, gatefold sleeve) 12
70	Elektra 2665 002	ABSOLUTELY LIVE (2-LP, gatefold sleeve) 15
71	Elektra K 42062	13 (LP) 12
71	Elektra K 42090	L.A. WOMAN (LP, with clear plastic 'window' sleeve & yellow inner sleeve) 18
74	Elektra K2 42143	THE BEST OF THE DOORS (LP, quadrophonic) 12
78	Elektra K 52111	AN AMERICAN PRAYER (LP, with 8-page booklet, gatefold sleeve) 10

DORA
| 86 | CBS A 7208 | You're Hurting Me/This Will Be The Last Time (p/s) .... 5 |
| 87 | CBS 651572 7 | I'll Come Back/Voltarei (withdrawn, promo copies may exist) .... 6 |

DOREEN (Campbell) & ALL STARS
| 67 | Rainbow RAI 114 | Rude Girls/Please Stay .... 7 |

DOREEN (Shaeffer) & JACKIE (Opel)
| 65 | Ska Beat JB 208 | Welcome Home/You And I .... 10 |
| | *(see also Jackie & Doreen)* | |

HAROLD DORMAN
| 60 | Top Rank JAR 357 | Mountain Of Love/To Be With You .... 12 |
| 61 | London HLS 9386 | There They Go/I'll Stick By You .... 10 |

DORMANNU
| 83 | Illuminated ILL 24 | Powdered Lover/Until The Fear (p/s) .... 4 |
| 83 | Illuminated ILL 2412 | Powdered Lover/Until The Fear (12", p/s) .... 7 |

DOROTHY
| 80 | Industrial IR 0014 | I Confess/Softness (p/s) .... 10 |

RALPH DORPER
| 83 | Operation Twilight OPT 18 | THE ERASERHEAD EP (12") .... 10 |
| | *(see also Propaganda)* | |

DIANA DORS
53	HMV B 10613	I Feel So Mmm.../A Kiss And A Cuddle (And A Few ...) (78) 15
60	Pye 7N 15242	April Heart/Point Of No Return 5
64	Fontana TF 506	So Little Time/It's Too Late 4
66	Polydor BM 56111	Security/Gary 4
60	Pye NPL 18044	SWINGIN' DORS (LP, fold-out sleeve, red vinyl) 30

RAY DORSET
| 72 | Dawn DNLS 3033 | COLD BLUE EXCURSION (LP) .... 10 |
| | *(see also Mungo Jerry)* | |

DORSETS
| 65 | Sue WI 391 | Pork Chops/Cool It .... 10 |

GERRY DORSEY
59	Decca F 11108	Mister Music Man/Crazy Bells 5
59	Parlophone R 4595	I'll Never Fall In Love Again/Every Day Is A Wonderful Day 5
61	Parlophone R 4739	Big Wheel/The Sentimental Joker 4
64	Pye 7N 15622	Baby I Do/Take Your Time 4
65	Hickory 45-1337	Baby Turn Around/Things I Wanna Do 10
	(see also Engelbert Humperdinck)	

JACK DORSEY ORCHESTRA
| 68 | Pye 7N 17501 | Soul Coaxing/Elizabeth's Waltz .... 4 |
| 65 | Polydor 56020 | Dance Of The Daleks/Likely Lads .... 10 |

JIMMY DORSEY ORCHESTRA
57	HMV POP 324	So Rare/Sophisticated Swing 6
57	HMV POP 324	So Rare/Sophisticated Swing (78) 5
57	HMV POP 383	Jay-Dee's Boogie Woogie/June Night 12
57	HMV POP 383	Jay-Dee's Boogie Woogie/June Night (78) 5
54	Columbia 33S 1026	DIXIE BY DORSEY (10" LP) 10

LEE DORSEY
62	Top Rank JAR 606	Do-Re-Mi/People Gonna Talk 10
65	Sue WI 367	Do-Re-Mi/Ya Ya 10
65	Stateside SS 441	Ride Your Pony/The Kitty Cat Song 7
65	Stateside SS 465	Work Work Work/Can You Hear Me 7
66	Sue WI 399	Messed Around/When I Meet My Baby 10
66	Stateside SS 485	Get Out Of My Life, Woman/So Long 5
66	Stateside SS 506	Confusion/Neighbour's Daughter 6
66	Stateside SS 528	Working In A Coalmine/Mexico 5
66	Stateside SS 552	Holy Cow/Operation Heartache 4
67	Stateside SS 593	Rain Rain Go Away/Gotta Find A Job 6
67	Stateside SS 2017	My Old Car/Why Wait Until Tomorrow 5
67	Stateside SS 2055	Go-Go Girl/I Can Hear You Callin' 5
68	President PT 226	Ya Ya/Give Me You 4
68	Bell BLL 1006	Can You Hear Me/Cynthia 4
69	Bell BLL 1051	I'm Gonna Sit Right Down And Write Myself A Letter/Little Baby 5
69	Bell BLL 1060	Ride Your Pony/Get Out Of My Life Woman 4

Lee DORSEY

69	Bell BLL 1074	Everything I Do Gonh Be Funky/There Should Be A Book	4
72	Polydor 2066 063	Occapella/Yes We Can (Part 1)	4
74	Mojo 2093 009	Freedom For The Stallion/If She Won't (Find Someone Who Will)	4
66	Stateside SE 1038	RIDE YOUR PONY (EP)	12
66	Stateside SE 1043	YOU'RE BREAKING ME UP (EP)	12
65	Sue ILP 924	THE BEST OF LEE DORSEY (LP)	40
66	Stateside S(S)L 10177	LEE DORSEY — RIDE YOUR PONY (LP)	15
66	Stateside S(S)L 10192	THE NEW LEE DORSEY (LP)	12
70	Polydor 2489 006	YES WE CAN (LP)	10

LEE DORSEY & BETTY HARRIS

82	Buffalo BFS 1002	Love Lots Of Lovin'/Take Care Of Your Love	6

(see also Betty Harris)

TOMMY DORSEY

58	Brunswick 05757	Tea For Two Cha Cha/My Baby Just Cares For Me (with Warren Covington)	4
59	Top Rank TR 5010	Swing High/The Minor Goes Muggin'	4
54	HMV 7EG 8004	TOMMY DORSEY AND HIS ORCHESTRA (EP, 2 tracks with Frank Sinatra)	9
54	Brunswick OE 9012	TOMMY DORSEY AND HIS ORCHESTRA (EP)	7
58	RCA RCX 1002	TOMMY DORSEY No. 1 (EP)	8
53	Brunswick LA 8610	TOMMY DORSEY (10" LP)	12
54	Brunswick LA 8640	TENDERLY (10" LP)	12
54	Brunswick LA 8669	ECSTASY (10" LP)	12
58	RCA RD 27069	FRANKIE AND TOMMY (LP, with Frank Sinatra)	20

(see also Frank Sinatra, Jo Stafford)

DORSEY BROTHERS

58	Brunswick LAT 8256	DIXIELAND JAZZ 1934-5 (LP)	10

JOHNNY DOT & DASHERS

62	Salvo SLO 1805	I Love An Angel/Just For You	6

DOTTY & BONNIE

64	Rio R 43	I'm So Glad/DOUGLAS BROTHERS: Got You On My Mind	10
64	Island WI 143	Your Kisses/Why Worry	10
64	Island WI 148	Dearest/Tears Are Falling	10
64	Island WI 161	A Bunch Of Roses/DON DRUMMOND: Corner Stone	10
65	Ska Beat JB 183	Foul Play/ROLAND ALPHONSO & GROUP: Yard Broom	10
67	Ska Beat JB 274	I'll Know/Love Is Great	8

DOUBLE FEATURE

67	Deram DM 115	Baby Get Your Head Screwed On/Come On Baby	20
67	Deram DM 165	Handbags And Gladrags/Just Another Lonely Night	10

DOUBLES with GAY BLADES

59	HMV POP 613	Hey Girl!/Little Joe	50

DOUGHNUT RING

68	Deram DM 215	Dance Around Julie/The Bandit	18

(see also Crocheted Doughnut Ring)

CARL DOUGLAS & BIG STAMPEDE

67	United Artists UP 1206	Nobody Cries/Serving A Sentence Of Life (as Carl Douglas)	50
66	Go AJ 11401	Crazy Feeling/PETER PERRY SOUL BAND: Keep It To Myself	10
67	Go AJ 11408	Let The Birds Sing/Something For Nothing	10
68	United Artists UP 2227	Sell My Soul To The Devil/Good Hard Worker	8

CHIC DOUGLAS

58	Fontana H 121	I'm Not Afraid Anymore/Jo-Ann	5

CRAIG DOUGLAS

58	Decca F 11055	Nothin' Shakin'/Sitting In A Tree House	7
58	Decca F 11075	Go Chase A Moonbeam/Are You Really Mine	6
59	Top Rank JAR 110	Come Softly To Me/Golden Girl	6
59	Top Rank JAR 110	Come Softly To Me/Golden Girl (78)	5
59	Top Rank JAR 133	Teenager In Love/The 39 Steps	6
59	Top Rank JAR 133	Teenager In Love/The 39 Steps (78)	5
59	Top Rank JAR 159	Only Sixteen/My First Love Affair	6
59	Top Rank JAR 159	Only Sixteen/My First Love Affair (78)	5
59	Top Rank JAR 204	The Riddle Of Love/Wish It Were Me	4
59	Top Rank TR 5004	Battle Of New Orleans/Dream Lover/SHEILA BUXTON: Personality/ Where Were You On Our Wedding Day/BERT WEEDON: I Need Your Love Tonight ('King-Size' 7", special sleeve)	6
60	Top Rank JAR 268	Pretty Blue Eyes/Sandy	4
60	Top Rank JAR 340	Heart Of A Teenage Girl/New Boy	4
60	Top Rank JAR 406	Oh, What A Day/Why, Why, Why	4
60	Top Rank JAR 515	Where's The Girl (I Never Met)/My Hour Of Love	4
61	Top Rank JAR 543	The Girl Next Door/Hey Mister Conscience	4
61	Top Rank JAR 555	A Hundred Pounds Of Clay/Hello Spring	8
61	Top Rank JAR 556	A Hundred Pounds Of Clay (censored version)/Hello Spring (some in p/s)	12/5
61	Top Rank JAR 569	Time/After All	4
61	Top Rank JAR 589	No Greater Love/We'll Have A Lot To Tell	4
62	Top Rank JAR 603	A Change Of Heart/Another You	4
62	Top Rank JAR 610	When My Little Girl Is Smiling/Ring A Ding	4
62	Columbia DB 4854	Our Favourite Melodies/Rainbows	5
63	Decca F 11575	Town Crier/I'd Be Smiling Now	4
63	Decca F 11665	Teenage Mona Lisa/Danke Shoen	4
63	Decca F 11722	I'm So Glad I Found Her/Love Her While She's Young	4
63	Decca F 11763	Counting Up The Kisses/From Russia With Love	4
64	Fontana TF 458	Silly Boy/Love Leave Me Alone	5
64	Fontana TF 475	Come Closer/She's Smiling At Me (with Tridents)	5
65	Fontana TF 525	Across The Street/Party Girl	5

MINT VALUE £

65	Fontana TF 580	Around The Corner/Find The Girl	5
66	Fontana TF 690	I'm On The Outside Looking In/Knock On Any Door	5
69	Pye 7N 17746	How Do You Feel About That/Then	4
69	Pye 7N 17863	Raindrops Keep Falling On My Head/Don't Mind If I Cry	4
59	Top Rank JKR 8033	CRAIG SINGS FOR 'ROXY' (EP)	8
60	Decca DFE 6633	CRAIG (EP)	8
62	Decca DFE 8509	CUDDLE UP WITH CRAIG (EP)	7
63	Columbia SEG 8219	CRAIG MOVIE SONGS (EP)	10
60	Top Rank BUY 049	CRAIG DOUGLAS (LP)	25
61	Top Rank 35-103	BANDWAGON BALL (LP)	20
62	Columbia 33SX 1468	OUR FAVOURITE MELODIES (LP)	70

JOHNNY DOUGLAS & HIS ORCHESTRA

| 54 | Decca F 10276 | Ballet Of The Bells/Solfeggio | 4 |

KIRK DOUGLAS & MELLOMEN

| 55 | Brunswick 05408 | A Whale Of A Tale/And The Moon Grew Brighter And Brighter | 4 |

LEW DOUGLAS & HIS ORCHESTRA

| 54 | MGM SP 1093 | Caesar's Boogie/Turn Around Boy | 5 |

MARK DOUGLAS

| 62 | Ember EMB S 166 | It Matters Not/Upside Down | 30 |

NORMA DOUGLAS

| 57 | London HLZ 8475 | Be It Resolved/Joe He Gone | 8 |

ROBB & DEAN DOUGLAS

| 67 | Deram DM 132 | I Can Make It With You/Phone Me | 4 |
| 67 | Deram DM 148 | A Rose Growing In The Ruins/Gentle People | 4 |

DOUGLAS BROTHERS

| 66 | Rio R 57 | Valley Of Tears/CHARMERS: Where Do I Turn | 10 |
| 66 | Rio R 63 | Down And Out/RONALD WILSON: Lonely Man | 10 |

RONNIE DOVE

65	Stateside SS 412	One Kiss For Old Times' Sake/Bluebird	5
68	Stateside SS 2119	Mountain Of Love/Never Gonna Cry (The Way I'll Cry Tonight)	5
65	Stateside SL 10149	RONNIE DOVE (LP)	10

DOVELLS

61	Columbia DB 4718	The Bristol Stomp/Out In The Cold Again	8
62	Columbia DB 4810	Do The New Continental/Mopitty Mope Stomp	6
62	Columbia DB 4877	Bristol Twistin' Annie/The Actor	6
62	Cameo Parkway P 845	Hully Gully Baby/Your Last Chance	5
63	Cameo Parkway P 861	You Can't Run Away From Yourself/Save Me Baby	5
63	Cameo Parkway P 867	You Can't Sit Down/Stompin' Everywhere	6
63	Cameo Parkway P 882	Betty In Bermudas/Dance The Froog	6
63	Cameo Parkway P 901	Be My Girl/Dragster On The Prowl	8

JOE DOWELL

| 62 | Mercury AMT 1180 | The One I Left For You/Little Red Rented Rowboat | 5 |
| 60s | Wing | WOODEN HEART (LP) | 12 |

DOWLANDS

62	Oriole CB 1748	Julie/Little Sue	30
62	Oriole CB 1781	Big Big Fella/Don't Ever Change	100
63	Oriole CB 1815	Break Ups/A Love Like Ours	30
63	Oriole CB 1892	Lucky Johnny/Do You Have To Have Me Blue?	200
64	Oriole CB 1897	All My Loving/Hey Sally	15
64	Oriole CB 1926	I Walk The Line/Happy Endings	25
64	Oriole CB 1947	Wishing And Hoping/You Will Regret It	25
65	Columbia DB 7547	Don't Make Me Over/Someone Must Be Feeling Sad	15

DOWNBEATS

| 61 | Starlite ST45 051 | Thinkin' Of You/Midnight Love | 15 |

BOB DOWNES

70	Vertigo 6059 011	No Time Like The Present/Keep Off The Grass	4
70	Vertigo 6360 005	ELECTRIC CITY (LP, gatefold sleeve, spiral label)	15
70	M. For Pleasure MFP 1412	DEEP DOWN HEAVY (LP)	10
70	Philips SBL 7922	BOB DOWNES' OPEN MUSIC (LP)	80
73	Ophenian BDOM 001	DIVERSIONS (LP)	12
74	Ophenian BDOM 002	EPISODES AT 4AM (LP, with insert)	12
75	Ophenian BDOM 003	HELLS ANGELS (LP)	12

DEIRDRE DOWNES & BROADSIDERS

| 69 | Pye 7N 17781 | Lady Mary/Did He Mention My Name | 4 |

BIG AL DOWNING

| 64 | Sue WI 341 | Yes I'm Loving You/Please Come Home | 15 |

DON DOWNING

| 73 | People PEO 102 | Lonely Days And Lonely Nights/I'm So Proud Of You | 4 |
| 73 | People PEO 108 | Dream World/The Miracle | 5 |

DOWNLINERS SECT

64	Columbia DB 7300	Baby What's Wrong/Be A Sect Maniac	15
64	Columbia DB 7347	Little Egypt/Sect Appeal	10
64	Columbia DB 7415	Find Out What's Happening/Insecticide	15
65	Columbia DB 7509	Wreck Of The Old '97/Leader Of The Sect	15
65	Columbia DB 7597	I Got Mine/Waiting In Heaven Somewhere	15
65	Columbia DB 7712	Bad Storm Coming/Lonely And Blue	15
66	Columbia DB 7817	All Night Worker/He Was A Square	15
66	Columbia DB 7939	Glendora/I'll Find Out	25

MINT VALUE £

66	Columbia DB 8008	The Cost Of Living/Everything I've Got To Give	20
76	Charly CYS 1020	Little Egypt/Sect Appeal (p/s)	4
77	Raw RAW 10	Showbiz/Killing Me (p/s)	4
64	Contrast Sound RBCSP 1	NITE IN GREAT NEWPORT STREET (EP)	150
65	Columbia SEG 8438	THE SECT SING SICK SONGS (EP)	60
78	Charly CEP 119	DOWNLINERS SECT (EP, reissue of "The Sect Sing Sick Songs")	7
64	Columbia 33SX 1658	THE SECT (LP)	40
65	Columbia 33SX 1745	THE COUNTRY SECT (LP)	35
66	Columbia S(C)X 6028	THE ROCK SECT'S IN (LP, mono/stereo)	40/45

(see also Don Crane's Downliners Sect)

LAMONT DOZIER

74	Probe PRO 618	Trying To Hold On To My Woman/We Don't Want Nobody To Come	4
74	Anchor ABC 4003	Fish Ain't Bitin'/Breaking Out All Over	4
75	Anchor ABC 4056	All Cried Out/Rose	5
77	Warner Bros K 16942	Going Back To My Roots/Going Back To My Roots (Version)	4
81	CBS A 1235	To Cool Me Out/Starting Over	4
74	ABC ABCL 5042	OUT HERE ON MY OWN (LP)	10
75	ABC ABCL 5096	BLACK BACH (LP)	10
70s	Warner Bros	PEDDLIN' MUSIC ON THE SIDE (LP)	12

(see also Holland & Dozier)

DOZY, BEAKY, MICK & TICH

69	Fontana TF 1061	Tonight Today/Bad News	5
70	Philips 6006 066	Festival/Leader Of A Rock'N'Roll Band	4
70	Philips 6006 114	I Want To Be There/For The Use Of Your Son	4
72	Philips 6006 198	They Won't Sing My Song/Soukie	4
74	Fontana 6007 022	Mr. President/Frisco Annie	4
70	Philips 6308 029	FRESH EAR (LP)	10

(see also Dave Dee Dozy Beaky Mick & Tich)

DP's

78	Barn 2014 126	If You Know What I Mean (p/s)	4
78	Barn 2014 129	Television Romeo (p/s)	4
78	Barn 2314 107	IF YOU KNOW WHAT I MEAN (LP)	10

(see also Depressions)

DRAGON

76	Acorn	DRAGON (LP, gatefold sleeve)	50

DRAGONFLY

74	Retreat RTS 257	Gondola/Almost Abandoned	4
75	Retreat RTS 261	Driving Around The World/Since I Left My Home	4
74	Retreat RTL 6002	ALMOST ABANDONED (LP)	15

DRAGONSFIRE

82	Belltree	RISING PHOENIX (LP, with insert)	25

DRAG SET

66	Go AJ 11405	Get Out Of My Way/Day And Night	100

(see also Open Mind)

DRAGSTER

81	Heavy Metal HEAVY 4	Ambition/Won't Bring You Back (p/s)	5

CHARLIE DRAKE

58	Parlophone R 4461	Splish Splash/Hello, My Darlings	5
58	Parlophone R 4461	Splish Splash/Hello, My Darlings (78)	5
58	Parlophone R 4478	Volare/Itchy Twitchy Feeling	5
58	Parlophone R 4478	Volare/Itchy Twitchy Feeling (78)	5
58	Parlophone R 4496	Tom Thumb's Tune/Goggle Eye Ghee	5
59	Parlophone R 4552	Sea Cruise/Starkle, Starkle Little Twink	6
59	Parlophone R 4552	Sea Cruise/Starkle, Starkle Little Twink (78)	5
60	Parlophone R 4675	Naughty/Old Mr. Shadow	4
60	Parlophone R 4701	Mr. Custer/Glow Worm	4
75	Charisma CB 270	You'll Never Know/I'm Big Enough For Me (with Peter Gabriel)	4
58	Parlophone GEP 8720	HELLO MY DARLINGS (EP)	8
60	Parlophone GEP 8812	NAUGHTY CHARLIE DRAKE (EP)	7
64	Parlophone GEP 8903	HITS FROM THE MAN IN THE MOON (EP)	7

(see also Peter Gabriel)

NICK DRAKE

69	Island ILPS 9105	FIVE LEAVES LEFT (LP, gatefold sleeve, pink label, later 'palm tree' label)	20/12
70	Island ILPS 9134	BRYTER LATER (LP)	15
72	Island ILPS 9184	PINK MOON (LP)	18
79	Island NDSP 100	FRUIT TREE — THE COMPLETE RECORDED WORKS (3-LP box set)	25

DRAMATICS

72	Stax 2025 053	Whatcha See Is Whatcha Get/Thankful For Your Love	4
73	Stax 2025 101	In The Rain/Get Up And Get Down	4
73	Stax 2025 117	Toast To A Fool/Your Love Was Strange	4
76	ABC ABC 4101	You're Fooling You/I'll Make It So Good	4
72	Stax 2362 025	WHATCHA SEE IS WHATCHA GET (LP)	15
74	Stax STX 1021	A DRAMATIC EXPERIENCE (LP)	10
75	ABC ABCL 5121	DRAMATIC JACKPOT (LP, gatefold sleeve)	10
75	ABC ABCL 5150	DRAMA V (LP, gatefold sleeve)	10

DRAMATIS

82	Rocket XPRES 79-12	The Shame (Dance Party Mix 1)/Only Find Rewind (12", p/s, with poster)	7

(see also Gary Newman)

BARRY DRANSFIELD
72	Polydor 2383 160	BARRY DRANSFIELD (LP)	125

(see also Robin & Barry Dransfield, Dransfields)

ROBIN & BARRY DRANSFIELD
70	Trailer LER 2011	THE ROUT OF THE BLUES (LP)	15
71	Trailer LER 2026	LORD OF ALL I BEHOLD (LP)	15

(see also Barry Dransfield, Dransfields)

DRANSFIELDS
76	Transatlantic TRA 322	THE FIDDLER'S DREAM (LP)	20
77	Free Reed 018	POPULAR TO CONTRARY BELIEF (LP)	10
78	Transatlantic TRA 386	BOWIN' AND SCRAPIN' (LP)	10

(see also Robin & Barry Dransfield, Barry Dransfields)

RUSTY DRAPER
53	Oriole CB 1214	Gambler's Guitar/Free Home Demonstration (78)	5
53	Oriole CB 1220	I Love To Jump/Lighthouse (78)	5
54	Oriole CB 1277	The Train With The Rhumba Beat/Melancholy Baby (78)	5
56	Mercury MT 101	Are You Satisfied?/Wabash Cannonball (78)	5
56	Mercury MT 113	Rock And Roll Ruby/House Of Cards (78)	12
56	Mercury MT 128	In The Middle Of The House/Pink Cadillac (78)	8
57	Mercury MT 137	Giant/Tiger Lilly (with Jack Halloran Singers) (78)	5
57	Mercury MT 147	Let's Go Calypso/Should I Never Love Again (78)	5
57	Mercury MT 155	Freight Train/Seven Come Eleven (with Dick Noel Singers) (78)	5
58	Mercury MT 194	Buzz Buzz Buzz/I Get The Blues When It Rains (78)	8
58	Mercury 7MT 211	Gamblin' Gal/That's My Doll	10
58	Mercury 7MT 211	Gamblin' Gal/That's My Doll (78)	10
58	Mercury 7MT 229	Chicken-Pickin' Hawk/June, July And August	10
58	Mercury 7MT 229	Chicken-Pickin' Hawk/June, July And August (78)	5
59	Mercury AMT 1019	Shoppin' Around/With This Ring	15
59	Mercury AMT 1019	Shoppin' Around/With This Ring (78)	20
59	Mercury AMT 1034	The Sun Will Always Shine/Hey Li Lee Li Lee Li	7
60	Mercury AMT 1101	Mule Skinner Blues/Please Help Me, I'm Falling	8
60	Mercury AMT 1110	Luck Of The Irish/It's A Little More Like Heaven	5
61	Mercury AMT 1127	Jealous Heart/Ten Thousand Years Ago	4
63	London HLU 9786	Night Life/That's Why I Love You Like I Do	5
65	London HLU 9989	Folsom Prison Blues/You Can't Be True, Dear	7
56	Mercury MEP 9506	PRESENTING RUSY DRAPER (EP)	18
59	Mercury ZEP 10016	RUSTY DRAPER (EP)	10
60	Mercury ZEP 10059	RUSTY IN GAMBLING MOOD (EP)	10
60	Mercury ZEP 10095	MULE SKINNER BLUES (EP)	10
64	London RE-U 1431	RUSTY DRAPER NO. 1 (EP)	10
64	London RE-U 1432	RUSTY DRAPER NO. 2 (EP)	10
60	Mercury MMC 14040	HITS THAT SOLD A MILLION (LP)	15

DR. CALCULUS
84	10 TEN 32	Programme 7/Killed By Poetry (p/s)	4
84	10 TEN 3212	Programme 7/Killed By Poetry/Programme 7 (Extended Version) (12", p/s)	7
86	10 TEN 131	Perfume From Spain/Straight Stereo (p/s)	4
86	10 TENT 131	Perfume From Spain/Straight Stereo (12", p/s)	7
86	10 DIX 45	DESIGNER BEATNIK (LP)	10
86	10 DIXCD 45	DESIGNER BEATNIK (CD)	15

(see also Stephen 'Tin Tin' Duffy)

DREAM ACADEMY
85	Blanco Y Negro NEG 16/ SAM 252	The Love Parade/Girl In A Million (For Edie Sedgwick)//The Love Parade/ The Things We Said (double pack, gatefold sleeve)	4

DREAMERS
68	Columbia DB 8340	The Maybe Song/The Long Road	6

(see also Freddie & Dreamers)

DREAM KINGDOM
76	De Wolfe	DREAM KINGDOM (LP, library issue)	12

DREAMLETS
65	Ska Beat JB 182	Really Now/SKATALITES: Street Corner	10

DREAM LOVERS
61	Columbia DB 4711	When We Get Married/Just Because	60

DREAM MERCHANTS
67	Decca F 12617	Rattler/I'll Be With You In Apple Blossom Time	4

DREAM POLICE
70	Decca F 12998	Living Is Easy/I'll Be Home	8
70	Decca F 13078	Our Song/Much Too Much	5
70	Decca F 13105	I've Got No Choice/What's The Cure For Happiness	5

(see also Average White Band)

DREAMS
68	United Artists UP 2249	I Will See You There/A Boy Needs A Girl	4
69	CBS 4247	Baby I'm Your Man/Softly Softly	4
70	CBS 64203	DREAMS (LP)	10
71	CBS 64597	IMAGINE MY SURPRISE (LP)	10

DREAMTIMERS
61	London HLU 9368	The Dancin' Lady/An Invitation	6

DREAM WEAVERS
56	Brunswick 05515	It's Almost Tomorrow/You've Got Me Wondering	30
56	Brunswick 05515	It's Almost Tomorrow/You've Got Me Wondering (78)	5

56	Brunswick 05568	A Little Love Can Go A Long, Long Way/Into The Night (featuring Wade Buff)	25
56	Brunswick 05607	You're Mine/Is There Somebody Else? (featuring Wade Buff)	15

DREGS
79	Disturbing DRO 1	THE DREGS EP (p/s, numbered, 150 only)	8

JOHN DREVAR('S EXPRESSION)
67	MGM MGM 1367	The Closer She Gets/When I Come Home	50
68	Polydor BM 56290	What Greater Love/I've Decided (solo)	5

PATTI DREW
68	Capitol CL 15557	Workin' On A Groovy Thing/Without A Doubt	8

DR. FEELGOOD & INTERNS (U.S.)
62	Columbia DB 4838	Dr. Feelgood/Mister Moonlight	10
64	Columbia DB 7223	Blang Dong/The Doctor's Boogie	10
66	CBS 202099	Don't Tell Me No Dirty/Where Did You Go	12
68	Capitol CL 15569	Sugar Bee/You're So Used To It	15
64	Columbia SEG 8310	DR. FEELGOOD AND THE INTERNS (EP)	20

DR. FEELGOOD (U.K.)
75	United Artists UP 35857	Back In The Night/I'm A Man	4
77	United Artists UP 36632	Baby Jane/Looking Back	4
79	United Artists UP 36468	Milk And Alcohol/Every Kind Of Vice (p/s, brown or white vinyl)	4
79	United Artists X/Y/ZUP 36506	As Long As The Price Is Right/Down At The Doctors (p/s, purple vinyl, 3 different sleeves)	4
76	United Artists UAS 29990	STUPIDITY (LP & 7" "Riot In Cell Block No. 9"/"Johnny B. Goode" [FEEL 1])	10
79	United Artists UAK 30239	AS IT HAPPENS (LP, with free 7" "Riot In Cell Block No. 9"/"Blues Had A Baby Named Rock'N'Roll"/"Lights Out"/"Great Balls Of Fire" [FEEL 2])	10

(see also Wilko Johnson, Lew Lewis, Oil City Shieks)

DIXIE DRIFTER
65	Columbia DB 7710	Soul Heaven/Three Chairs Theme	12

DRIFTERS (U.S.)
56	London HLE 8344	Soldier Of Fortune/I Gotta Get Myself A Woman	225
56	London HLE 8344	Soldier Of Fortune/I Gotta Get Myself A Woman (78)	50
58	London HLE 8686	Moonlight Bay/Drip-Drop	85
58	London HLE 8686	Moonlight Bay/Drip-Drop (78)	30
59	London HLE 8892	There Goes My Baby/Oh, My Love	25
59	London HLE 8892	There Goes My Baby/Oh, My Love (78)	40
59	London HLE 8988	Dance With Me/True Love, True Love	15
59	London HLE 8988	Dance With Me/True Love, True Love (78)	40
60	London HLE 9081	This Magic Moment/Baltimore	15
60	London HLE 9081	This Magic Moment/Baltimore (78)	50
60	London HLK 9145	Lonely Winds/Hey Senorita	15
60	London HLK 9201	Save The Last Dance For Me/Nobody But Me	4
61	London HLK 7114	Save The Last Dance For Me/This Magic Moment (export issue)	7
61	London HLK 7115	I Count The Tears/Dance With Me (export issue)	7
61	London HLK 9287	I Count The Tears/Sadie My Lady	5
61	London HLK 9326	Some Kind Of Wonderful/Honey Bee	8
61	London HLK 9382	Please Stay/No Sweet Lovin'	7
61	London HLK 9427	Sweets For My Sweet/Loneliness Or Happiness	7
62	London HLK 9500	Room Full Of Tears/Somebody New Dancin' With You	7
62	London HLK 9522	When My Little Girl Is Smiling/Mexican Divorce	5
62	London HLK 9554	Stranger On The Shore/What To Do	6
62	London HLK 9626	Up On The Roof/Another Night With The Boys	6
63	London HLK 9699	On Broadway/Let The Music Play	7
63	London HLK 9750	Rat Race/If You Don't Come Back	7
63	London HLK 9785	I'll Take You Home/I Feel Good All Over	5
64	London HLK 9848	Vaya Con Dios/In The Land Of Make Believe	6
64	London HLK 9886	One Way Love/Didn't It	5
64	Atlantic AT 4001	Under The Boardwalk/I Don't Want To Go On Without You	6
64	Atlantic AT 4008	I've Got Sand In My Shoes/He's Just A Playboy	7
64	Atlantic AT 4012	Saturday Night At The Movies/Spanish Lace	5
65	Atlantic AT 4019	At The Club/Answer The Phone	6
65	Atlantic AT 4023	Come On Over To My Place/Chains Of Love	6
65	Atlantic AT 4034	Follow Me/The Outside World	12
65	Atlantic AT 4040	I'll Take You Where The Music's Playing/Far From The Maddening Crowd	6
66	Atlantic AT 4062	We Gotta Sing/Nylon Stockings	6
66	Atlantic AT 4084	Memories Are Made Of This/My Island In The Sun	4
66	Atlantic 584 020	Up In The Streets Of Harlem/You Can't Love 'Em All	4
67	Atlantic 584 065	Baby What I Mean/Aretha	7
68	Atlantic 584 152	I'll Take You Where The Music's Playing/On Broadway	4
68	Atlantic 584 195	Still Burning In My Heart/I Need You Now	4
76	Atlantic K 10700	You Gotta Pay Your Dues/Black Silk	4
61	London RE-K 1282	THE DRIFTERS' GREATEST HITS (EP)	15
63	London RE-K 1355	THE DRIFTERS (EP)	15
63	London RE-K 1385	DRIFTIN' (EP)	15
64	Atlantic AET 6003	DRIFTIN' VOL. 2 (EP)	12
65	Atlantic AET 6012	TONIGHT (EP)	12
60	London HA-K 2318	THE DRIFTERS' GREATEST HITS (LP)	30
62	London HA-K 2450	SAVE THE LAST DANCE FOR ME (LP)	25
65	Atlantic ATL 5015	OUR BIGGEST HITS (LP)	12
65	Atlantic ATL 5023	THE GOOD LIFE WITH THE DRIFTERS (LP)	12
66	Atlantic ATL/STL 5039	I'LL TAKE YOU WHERE THE MUSIC'S PLAYING (LP, mono/stereo)	12/15
67	Atlantic 587 038	BIGGEST HITS (LP)	10
67	Atlantic 587 061	I'LL TAKE YOU WHERE THE MUSIC'S PLAYING (LP, reissue)	10
67	Atlantic 590 010	SOUVENIRS (LP)	10

67	Atlantic 587 063	SAVE THE LAST DANCE FOR ME (LP, reissue)	12
68	Atlantic 587/588 103	THE DRIFTERS' GOLDEN HITS (LP)	10
68	Atlantic 587 123	ROCKIN' AND DRIFTIN' (LP)	15
68	Atlantic 587 144	GOOD GRAVY (LP, as Clyde McPhatter & Drifters)	20
69	Atlantic 587/588 160	UP ON THE ROOF (LP)	10

(see also Clyde McPhatter, Ben E. King)

DRIFTERS (U.K.)

59	Columbia DB 4263	Feelin' Fine/Don't Be A Fool (With Love)	50
59	Columbia DB 4263	Feelin' Fine/Don't Be A Fool (With Love) (78)	60
59	Columbia DB 4325	Driftin'/Jet Black	30

(see also Shadows, Cliff Richard)

DRIFTING SLIM

| 66 | Blue Horizon 45-1005 | Good Morning Baby/My Sweet Woman | 35 |

DRIFTWOOD

70	Decca F 13084	Shylock Bay/The Wind Cried Above You	4
71	Decca F 13139	Say The Right Things/Still I'll Stay With You	4
70	Decca SKL 5069	DRIFTWOOD (LP)	25

JIMMY DRIFTWOOD

60	RCA RCX 191	COUNTRY GUITAR VOL. 13 (EP)	7
60	RCA RCX 193	TALL TALES IN SONG VOL. 1 (EP)	7
60	RCA RCX 195	TALL TALES IN SONG VOL. 2 (EP)	7
60	RCA RCX 198	TALL TALES IN SONG VOL. 3 (EP)	7
61	RCA RD 27226	SONGS OF BILLY YANK AND JOHNNY REB (LP)	10

JULIE DRISCOLL

63	Columbia DB 7118	Take Me By The Hand/Stay Away From Me	12
65	Parlophone R 5296	Don't Do It No More/I Know You	15
66	Parlophone R 5444	I Didn't Want To Have To Do It/Don't Do It No More	8
67	Parlophone R 5588	I Know You Love Me Not/If You Should Ever Leave Me	8
67	Marmalade 598 005	Save Me Pts 1 & 2	6
71	Polydor 2480 074	JULIE DRISCOLL — 1969 (LP)	15
72	Polydor 2383 077	JULIE DRISCOLL — 1969 (LP, reissue)	10

JULIE DRISCOLL, BRIAN AUGER & TRINITY

68	Marmalade 598 006	This Wheel's On Fire/A Kind Of Love In	6
68	Marmalade 598 011	Road To Cairo/Shadows Of You	5
69	Marmalade 598 018	Take Me To The Water/Indian Rope Man	5
67	Marmalade 607/608 002	OPEN (LP)	15
68	M. For Pleasure MFP 1265	JOOLS/BRIAN (LP, tracks shared by Julie Driscoll & Brian Auger)	10
68	Marmalade 608 005/6	STREETNOISE (2-LP)	20
69	Marmalade 608 014	STREETNOISE PART 1 (LP)	10
69	Marmalade 608 015	STREETNOISE PART 2 (LP)	10

(see also Brian Auger & Trinity)

DRIVE

| 78 | NRG NE 46 | Jerkin'/Push'N'Shove (no p/s) | 6 |

DRIVE

| 90 | First Strike FST 007 | No Girls/Peephole (hand-made numbered gatefold p/s with insert) | 12 |
| 92 | First Strike FST 020L | This Ain't No Picnic/My World (p/s, white vinyl in bag, numbered, 120 only) | 6 |

DR. JOHN

70	Atlantic 2091 019	Wash Mama Wash/Mama Roux	5
72	Atlantic K 10158	Iko Iko/Huey Smith Medley	4
72	Atlantic K 10214	Wang Dang Doodle/Big Chief	4
73	Atlantic K 10291	Right Place, Wrong Time/I Been Hoodooed	4
73	Atlantic K 10329	Such A Night/Life	4
74	Atlantic K 10445	(Everybody Wanna Get Rich) Rite Away/Mos' Scocious	4
68	Atlantic 587 147	GRIS GRIS (LP)	15
69	Atlantic 228 018	BABYLON (LP)	12
70	Atlantic 2400 015	REMEDIES (LP)	12
71	Atlantic 2400 161	SUN, MOON AND HERBS (LP)	12
72	Atlantic K 40384	GUMBO (LP)	10
73	Atlantic K 50017	IN THE RIGHT PLACE (LP)	10

DR. K'S BLUES BAND

| 68 | Spark UK 101 | DR. K'S BLUES BAND (LP) | 50 |

DR. MARIGOLD'S PRESCRIPTION

68	Pye 7N 17493	My Old Man's A Groovy Old Man/People Get Ready	4
69	Pye 7N 17832	You've Got To Build Your Love/My Picture Of Love	4
69	Marble Arch MALS 1222	PICTURES OF LIFE (LP)	15
73	Pye/Santa Ponsa PNL 501	HELLO GIRL (LP)	10

DR. MIX & REMIX

79	Rough Trade RT 17	No Fun/No Fun (Version) (as Doctor Mix) (p/s)	4
79	Rough Trade RT 032	I Can't Control Myself/Version (no p/s)	4
79	Rough Trade ROUGH 6	WALL OF NOISE (mini-LP)	10

(see also Metal Urbain)

DRONES

77	Ohms GOOD MIX 1	TEMPTATIONS OF A WHITE COLLAR WORKER (EP, different coloured sleeves, some with writing on inner sleeve)	6
77	Valer VRSP 1	Be My Baby/Lift Off The Bans (12", white label, unreleased)	30
77	Valer VALER VRS 1	Bone Idle/I Just Wanna Be Myself (gatefold p/s, made in France or England)	12/6
80	Fabulous JC 4	Can't See/Fooled Today (p/s)	7
77	Valer VRLP 1	FURTHER TEMPTATIONS (LP)	25

MINT VALUE £

DROWNING CRAZE
81	Situation 2 SIT 3	Storage Case/Damp Bones (p/s)	5
81	Situation 2 SIT 13	Trance/I Love The Fjords (poster p/s)	4
82	Situation 2 SIT 16	Heat/Replays (p/s)	4

DR. STRANGELY STRANGE
69	Island ILPS 9196	KIP OF THE SERENES (LP)	70
70	Vertigo 6360 009	HEAVY PETTING (LP, gatefold sleeve, spiral label)	50

(see also Sweeney's Men)

DR. TECHNICAL & MACHINES
83	Hawkfan HWFB 1	Zones/Processed (1-sided with insert, mail order issue, no p/s)	10

(see also Dave Brock, Hawkwind)

DRUG ADDIX
78	Chiswick SW 39	MAKE A RECORD (EP)	5

DRUG SQUAD
80	Bathroom Floor BFR 001	Operation Julie/Switchcleaner (p/s)	5

DRUID
75	EMI EMC 3081	TOWARDS THE SUN (LP)	15
76	EMI EMC 3128	FLUID DRUID (LP)	15

DRUID CHASE
67	CBS 3053	Take Me In Your Garden/I Wanna Get My Hands On You	15

DRUIDS
63	Parlophone R 5097	Love So Blue/Long Tall Texan	6
64	Parlophone R 5134	See What You've Done/It's Just A Little Bit Too Late	10

DRUIDS
71	Argo ZFB 22	BURNT OFFERING (LP)	110
73	Argo ZFB 39	PASTIME WITH GOOD COMPANY (LP)	80

DRUMBAGO
63	Island WI 85	I Am Drunk/Sea Breeze	10
68	Blue Cat BS 145	Reggae Jeggae (with Blenders)/TYRONE TAYLOR: Delilah	7
68	Trojan TR 638	Dulcemania (with Dynamites)/CLANCY ECCLES: China Man	6

BILL DRUMMOND
87	Creation CRE 039T	King Of Joy/The Manager (12", p/s)	8

(see also Big In Japan, Lori & Chameleons, J.A.M.s, KLF, Disco 2000, Timelords)

DON DRUMMOND
62	Island WI 021	Schooling The Duke/BASIL GABBIDON: Bitter Rose	12
63	Black Swan WI 406	Scrap Iron/DRAGONAIRE: Prevention	10
63	Blue Beat BB 179	Reload/Far East	10
63	Island WI 094	Scandal/W. SPARKS: My Ideal	10
63	R&B JB 103	Royal Flush/MAYTALS: Matthew Mark	10
63	R&B JB 105	The Shock/TONETTES: Tell Me You're Mine	10
64	Ska Beat JB 178	Silver Dollar/TOMMY McCOOK: My Business	10
64	Island WI 149	Eastern Standard Time/DOTTY & BONNIE: Sun Rises	10
64	Island WI 153	Musical Storeroom/STRANGER COLE: He Who Feels	10
64	Island WI 162	Garden Of Love/STRANGER COLE: Cherry Mae	10
65	Island WI 192	Stampede/JUSTIN HINDS & DOMINOES: Come Bail Me	10
65	Island WI 204	Coolie Baby/LORD ANTICS: You May Stray	10
65	Island WI 208	Man In The Street/RITA & BUNNY: You Are My Only Love	10
65	Island WI 242	University Goes Ska/DERRICK & NAOMI: Pain In My Heart	10
69	Studio One SO 2078	Heavenless/GLEN BROWN & DAVE BARKER: Lady Lovelight	12
69	Trojan TR 678	Memory Of Don/JOHN HOLT: Darling I Love You	7
69	Studio One SO 9008	THE BEST OF DON DRUMMOND (LP)	70
69	Trojan TTL 23	MEMORIAL ALBUM (LP)	20

DON DRUMMOND JUNIOR
67	Caltone TONE 104	Sir Pratt Special/HEMSLEY MORRIS: Love Is Strange	8
68	Caltone TONE 124	Dirty Dozen/PHIL PRATT: Reach Out	8

(see Vincent Gordon)

DRUNKS WITH GUNS
90	Shock SX 005	Drunks Theme/Punched In The Head (p/s)	5

ROY DRUSKY
59	Brunswick 05785	Just About That Time/Wait And See	7
59	Brunswick 05785	Just About That Time/Wait And See (78)	5
61	Brunswick 05856	Three Hearts In A Tangle/I'd Rather Loan You Out	5

DR. WEST'S MEDICINE SHOW & JUNK BAND
67	CBS 202658	Gondoliers, Shakespeares, Overseers/Daddy I Know	4
67	CBS 202492	The Eggplant That Ate Chicago/You Can't Fight City Hall Blues	4
68	Page One POF 061	Bullets La Verne/Jigsaw	25
68	Page One POLS 017	THE EGGPLANT THAT ATE CHICAGO (LP)	35

DR. WHO
70s	Argo ZSW 564	DR. WHO AND THE PESCATONS (LP)	10
70s	BBC 364	GENESIS OF THE DALEKS (LP)	10

DRY ICE
70	B&C CB 115	Running To The Convent/Nowhere To Go	10

DRY RIB
79	Clockwork COR 001	THE DRY SEASON (EP, photocopied foldover p/s, screen-printed labels)	20

(see also Television Personalities)

DR. Z
74	Fontana 6007 023	Lady Ladybird/People In The Street	25
71	Vertigo 6360 048	3 PARTS TO MY SOUL (LP, gatefold sleeve, spiral label)	175

AMANCIO D'SILVA
69	Columbia S(C)X 6322	INTEGRATION (LP)	25
70	Columbia SCX 6465	REFLECTIONS (LP)	20

D-TRAIN
82	Prelude EPCA 12-2016	You're The One For Me/You're The One For Me (Version) (12", p/s)	7

DUALS
61	London HL 9450	Stick Shift/Cruising	18

DUBLINERS
68	Major Minor MM 552	Dirty Old Town/Peggy Gordon	4

DUBS
57	London HLU 8526	Could This Be Magic/Such Lovin'	150
57	London HLU 8526	Could This Be Magic/Such Lovin' (78)	40
58	London HL 8684	Gonna Make A Change/Beside My Love	225
58	London HL 8684	Gonna Make A Change/Beside My Love (78)	45

DUB SEX
87	Lyntone LYN 18236/DEB 5	Tripwire/TWO THIEVES & A LIAR: Shackles & Chains (flexidisc free with 'Debris' magazine issue 13)	8/6
87	Skysaw SKY 7	Then And Now/Tripwire/Green/Man On The Inside (12", p/s)	10
88	Cut Deep 001	The Underneath/Instead Of Flowers (p/s)	4
88	Cut Deep 12 001	The Underneath/Every Secret (That I Ever Made)/Caved In/Instead Of Flowers (12", p/s)	7
88	Ugly Man MAN 1	PUSH (LP, with insert & booklet)	10

DUCKS DELUXE
73	RCA RCA 2438	Coast To Coast/Bring Back That Packard Car	6
74	RCA LPBO 5019	Fireball/Saratoga Suzie	5
74	RCA RCA 2477	Love's Melody/Two Time Twister	5
75	RCA RCA 2531	I Fought The Law/Cherry Pie	5
74	RCA LPL1 5008	DUCKS DELUXE (LP)	10
74	RCA SF 8402	TAXI TO THE TERMINAL ZONE (LP)	10
82	Blue Moon BMLP 001	LAST NIGHT OF A PUB ROCK BAND (2-LP)	14

(see also Snakes, Motors)

DUDLEY
60	Vogue V 9171	Lone Prairie Rock/El Pizza	12

DAVE DUDLEY
63	United Artists UP 1029	Six Days On The Road/I Feel A Cry Coming On	5
67	Mercury MF 1003	Trucker's Prayer/Don't Come Cryin' To Me	4
68	Mercury MF 1037	There Ain't No Easy Run/Why Can't I Be With You (Is A Shame)	4
69	Mercury MF 1134	George (And The North Wind)/It's Not A Very Pleasant Day Today	4

ROBERTA DUDLEY
50s	Tempo R 22	Krooked Blues/When You're Alone (78)	15
50s	Poydras 3	Krooked Blues/When You're Alone (78)	8

SHENLEY DUFFAS
62	Island WI 036	Give To Get/What You Gonna Do (with Millie Small)	10
63	Island WI 063	Fret Man Fret/Doreen	10
63	Island WI 093	What A Disaster/I Am Rich	10
63	Island WI 115	Know The Lord/TOMMY McCOOK: Ska Ba	10
63	Island WI 125	Easy Squeal/Things Ain't Going Right	10
63	R&B JB 134	No More Wedding Bells/Let Them Fret	10
64	R&B JB 146	Big Mouth/FRANKIE ANDERSON: Peanut Vendor	10
64	R&B JB 152	Christopher Columbus/CARL BRYAN ORCHESTRA: Barber Chair	10
64	R&B JB 154	Mother-In-Law/DON DRUMMOND & GROUP: Festival	10
64	Black Swan WI 440	Digging A Ditch/He's Coming Down	10
64	Black Swan WI 443	Gather Them In/Crucifixion	10
64	Rio R 41	I Will Be Glad/Heariso	10
65	Island WI 184	You Are Mine/UPCOMING WILLOWS: Red China	10
65	Island WI 186	Khaki Pants/One Morning	10
72	Upsetter US 380	Bet You Don't Know/UPSETTERS: Ring Of Fire	5

DUFFY
73	Chapter One CH 184	The Joker/Running Away	12
70	Chapter One CHSR 814	SCRUFFY DUFFY (LP)	125

CHRIS DUFFY
68	SNB 55-3681	Mr Jones, Mr Brown, Mr Smith (& Not Forgetting Charlie Green)/Something For Now	4

STEPHEN 'TIN TIN' DUFFY
85	10 TIN 2	Kiss Me (1985)/In This Twilight (p/s with inner sleeve)	5
85	10 TINP 2	Kiss Me (1985)/In This Twilight (picture disc)	5
85	10 TING 2	Kiss Me (1985)/In This Twilight//Kiss Me (1983)/Holes In My Shoes (double pack, gatefold p/s)	5
85	10 TIN 2-12	Kiss Me (1985)/In This Twilight (12", gatefold p/s with 8-page portfolio)	7
85	10 TING 2-12	Kiss Me (1985)/In This Twilight//Kiss Me (1983)/Holes In My Shoes (12", double pack)	7
85	10 TIN 3	Icing On The Cake/Broken Home (gatefold p/s with poster)	4
85	10 TING 3	Icing On The Cake/Broken Home/Hold It/She Makes Me Quiver (double pack, gatefold p/s)	4
85	10 TIN 3-12	Icing On The Cake (7.10)/Icing On The Cake (3.50)/Broken Home (12", gatefold p/s with poster)	7

Stephen 'Tin Tin' DUFFY

85	10 TING 3-12	Icing On The Cake (7.10)/Icing On The Cake (3.50)/Broken Home//Hold It/ She Makes Me Quiver (12", double pack, gatefold p/s) 7	
85	10 TIND 4	Unkiss That Kiss/Done For//"Love's Duet"/Holes In My Shoes (Carry On Version) (double pack, gatefold p/s) 4	
86	10 TENP 91	I Love You (Aversion)/I Love You)/Love Is Driving Me Insane (gatefold p/s with poster) 4	
86	10 TIND 5-10	I Love You (Inversion)/Wednesday Jones (Dixie)//Icing On The Cake/ Kiss Me (10", double pack, gatefold p/s) 6	

(see also Hawks, Tin Tin, Dr. Calculus, Lilac Time)

DUFFY'S NUCLEUS
67	Decca F 22547	Hound Dog/Mary Open The Door 10	

BILLY DUKE
62	Ember EMB S 153	Walking Cane/Amen 4	
62	Ember EMB S 160	Ain't She Pretty/Timbuctu 4	
64	London HLU 9907	While The Bloom Is On The Rose 4	
65	London HLU 9960	Sugar'N'Spice/Prisoner Of Love 5	

DENVER DUKE & JEFFREY NULL BLUEGRASS BOYS
63	Starlite STEP 33	DENVER DUKE & JEFFREY NULL BLUEGRASS BOYS (EP) 12	

DORIS DUKE
71	Mojo 2092 017	If She's Your Wife Who Am I/It Sure Was Fun 4	
72	Mojo 2916 001	I'M A LOSER (LP) 15	
75	Contempo CRM 111	A LEGEND IN HER TIME (LP) 10	
75	Contempo CLP 519	WOMAN (LP) 15	

GEORGE DUKE
71	Sunset SLS 50232	LIVE IN LOS ANGELES (LP) 10	
74	BASF BAP 5064	THE AURA WILL PREVAIL (LP) 10	
75	BASF BAP 5071	I LOVE THE BLUES, SHE HEARD MY CRY (LP) 10	
80	Epic EPC 84311	A BRAZILIAN LOVE AFFAIR (LP) 10	

DUKE ALL STARS
68	Blue Cat BS 111	Letter To Mummy And Daddy Pts 1 & 2 8	

DUKE & DUCHESS
55	London HLU 8206	Borrowed Sunshine/Get Ready For Love (with Sir Hubert Pimm) 15	

(see also Sir Hubert Pimm)

DUKE'S NOBLEMEN
68	Philips BF 1691	City Of Windows/Thank You For Your Loving 5	

AGGIE DUKES
57	Vogue V 9090	John John/Well Of Loneliness 80	
57	Vogue V 9090	John John/Well Of Loneliness (78) 45	

DUKES OF IRON
54	Melodisc 1316	Last Train To San Fernando/Big Bamboo (78) 5	

DUKES OF STRATOSPHEAR
85	Virgin VS 763	The Mole From The Ministry/My Love Explodes (no p/s) 5	
87	Virgin VSY 982	You're A Good Man Albert Brown/Vanishing Girl (p/s, 5,000 on multi-coloured vinyl) 6	
87	Virgin VP 2440	PSONIC PSUNSPOT (LP, gatefold sleeve, 5,000 on multi-coloured vinyl) 10	

(see also XTC)

DULCIMER
71	Nepentha 6437 003	AND AS I TURNED AS A BOY (LP, gatefold sleeve) 45	
80	private pressing	A LAND FIT FOR HEROES (LP) 15	

DUM
74	RAK RAK 179	In The Mood/Watching The Clock 6	

(see also Mud)

DUMB ANGELS
88	Fierce FRIGHT 033	Love And Mercy/Love And Mercy (p/s, numbered) 10	

(see also Pooh Sticks)

DUMBELLS
80	Polydor POSP 209/EGO 3	Giddy Up/A Christmas Dream 6	

(see also Roxy Music)

JOHN DUMMER (BLUES BAND)
68	Mercury MF 1040	Travelling Man/40 Days (as John Dummer Blues Band) 8	
69	Mercury MF 1119	Try Me One More Time/Riding At Midnight (as John Dummer Blues Band) 8	
70	Fontana 6007 027	Happy/Nightingale (unissued in U.K.; France only)	
70	Philips 6006 111	Nine By Nine/Going In The Out (as Famous Music Band with John Dummer) 8	
71	Philips 6006 176	Medicine Weasel/The Endgame (with Nick Picket) 5	
72	Vertigo 6059 074	Oobleedooblee Jubilee/The Monkey Speaks His Mind (as John Dummer Oobleedooblee Band) 5	
69	Mercury SMCL 20136	CABAL (LP) 60	
69	Mercury SMCL 20167	JOHN DUMMER'S BLUES BAND (LP) 80	
70	Philips 6309 008	FAMOUS MUSIC BAND (LP) 45	
72	Philips 6382 039	THIS IS JOHN DUMMER (LP) 20	
73	Philips 6382 040	VOLUME II — TRY ME ONE MORE TIME (LP) 20	
72	Vertigo 6360 055	BLUE (LP, gatefold sleeve, spiral label) 80	
73	Vertigo 6360 083	OOBLEEDOOBLEE JUBILEE (LP, spiral label) 25	

(see also Nick Pickett)

DUMMIES
79	Cheapskate FWL 001	When The Lights Are Out/She's The Only Woman (no p/s) 5	
80	Pye 7P 163	When The Lights Are Out/She's The Only Woman (no p/s, reissue) 4	
80	Cheapskate CHEAP 003	Didn't You Used To Use To Be You?/Miles Out To Sea (p/s) 6	

81　Cheapskate CHEAP 014　Maybe Tonite/When I'm Dancin' I Ain't Fightin' (p/s) 12
(see also China Dolls, Slade)

DUMPY'S RUSTY NUTS
81　Cool King CNK 006　Just For Kicks/Ride With Me (p/s, reissued as Dumpy's Rusty Bolts) 10/6
82　Cool King CK 008　Boxhill Or Bust/It's Got To Be Blues (p/s, initially with free patch) 8/5

AYNSLEY DUNBAR (RETALIATION)
67　Blue Horizon 57-3109　Warning/Cobwebs (some in p/s) 35/15
68　Liberty LBF 15132　Watch 'N' Chain/Roamin' And Ramblin' 6
68　Liberty LBL/LBS 83154　AYNSLEY DUNBAR RETALIATION (LP) 25
68　Liberty LBS 83177　DR. DUNBAR'S PRESCRIPTION (LP) 30
69　Liberty LBS 83223　TO MUM FROM AYNSLEY AND THE BOYS (LP) 25
70　Liberty LBS 83316　REMAINS TO BE HEARD (LP) 20
70　Warner Bros K 46062　BLUE WHALE (LP) 12
(see also Bluesbreakers, Heavy Jelly)

SCOTT DUNBAR
71　Ahura Mazda AMS SDS 1　FROM LAKE MARY (LP) 25

JOHNNY DUNCAN (& BLUE GRASS BOYS)
57　Columbia DB 3925　Kaw-Liga/Ella Speed 10
57　Columbia DB 3959　Last Train To San Fernando/Rock-A-Billy Baby 12
57　Columbia DB 3959　Last Train To San Fernando/Rock-A-Billy Baby (78) 5
57　Columbia DB 3996　Blue, Blue Heartache/Jig Along Home 8
57　Columbia DB 4029　Footprints In The Snow/Get Along Home, Cindy 7
58　Columbia DB 4074　If You Love Me Baby/Goodnight Irene 12
58　Columbia DB 4118　Itching For My Baby/I Heard The Bluebirds Sing 9
58　Columbia DB 4167　All Of The Monkeys Ain't In The Zoo/More And More 7
58　Columbia DB 4179　My Lucky Love/Geisha Girl 6
59　Columbia DB 4282　Rosalie/This Train 6
59　Columbia DB 4311　Kansas City/That's All Right Darlin' 6
59　Columbia DB 4311　Kansas City/That's All Right Darlin' (78) 5
60　Columbia DB 4415　Any Time/Yellow, Yellow Moon (solo) 5
61　Pye 7N 15358　Tobacco Road/Sleepy-Eyed John (solo) 6
61　Pye 7N 15380　The Legend Of Gunga Din/Hannah (solo) 6
62　Pye 7N 15420　A Long Time Gone/Waitin' For The Sandman (solo) 6
63　Columbia DB 7164　The Ballad Of Jed Clampett/Will You Be Mine? (with Kingpins) 6
64　Columbia DB 7334　Dang Me/Which Way Did He Go? (solo) 5
66　Columbia DB 7833　My Little Baby/I Thank My Lucky Stars (solo) 4
57　Columbia SEG 7708　JOHNNY DUNCAN AND HIS BLUE GRASS BOYS (EP) 15
57　Columbia SEG 7773　JOHNNY DUNCAN AND HIS BLUE GRASS BOYS NO. 2 (EP) 15
58　Columbia SEG 7753　FOOTPRINTS IN THE SNOW (EP) 10
58　Columbia SEG 7850　TENNESSEE SING SONG (EP) 10
57　Columbia 33S 1122　TENNESSEE SONG BAG (10" LP) 30
58　Columbia 33S 1129　JOHNNY DUNCAN SALUTES HANK WILLIAMS (10" LP) 30
61　Columbia 33SX 1328　BEYOND THE SUNSET (LP) 15
68　M For Pleasure MFP 1032　BEYOND THE SUNSET (LP, reissue) 10
(see also Chris Barber's Skiffle Group)

LESLEY DUNCAN
63　Parlophone R 5034　I Want A Steady Guy/Movin' Away 4
64　Parlophone R 5106　Tell Him/You Kissed Me 4
64　Mercury MF 830　When My Baby Cries/Did It Hurt? 5
65　Mercury MF 847　Just For The Boy/See That Guy 7
65　Mercury MF 876　Run To Love/Only The Lonely And Me 4
65　Mercury MF 939　Hey Boy/I Go To Sleep 5
79　CBS 8061　Sing Children Sing/Rainbow Games (p/s, with Kate Bush) 20
71　CBS 64202　SING CHILDREN SING (LP) 12
72　CBS 64807　EARTH MOTHER (LP) 10
74　GM GML 1007　EVERYTHING CHANGES (LP) 10

TOMMY DUNCAN
66　Sue WI 4002　Dance Dance Dance/Let's Try It Over Again 12
(see also Bob Wills)

BARBARA DUNKLEY
71　Banana BA 342　We'll Cry Together/BOBBY DAVIS: Got To Get Away 4

ERROL(L) DUNKLEY
61　Blue Beat BB 37　Gypsy/Miss May (as Errol & His Group) 10
67　Rio R 109　Love Me Forever/VIETNAM ALLSTARS: The Toughest 10
67　Rio R 131　You're Gonna Need Me/Seek And You'll Find 10
68　Island WI 3150　Once More/I'm Not Your Man 10
68　Amalgamated AMG 800　Please Stop Your Lying/Feel So Fine (B-side actually by
　　　　　　　　　Tommy McCook & Band) 8
68　Amalgamated AMG 805　I'm Going Home/I'm Not Your Man 8
68　Amalgamated AMG 807　The Scorcher/Do It Right Tonight 8
68　Amalgamated AMG 820　Love Brother/I Spy 8
69　Fab FAB 117　I'll Take You In My Arms/KING CANNON: Daphney Reggae 5
70　Banana BA 302　Satisfaction/CECEIL LOCKE: Sing Out Loud 5

BLIND WILLY DUNN'S GIN BOTTLE FOUR with KING OLIVER
54　Columbia SCM 5100　Jet Black Blues/Blue Blood Blues 12
54　Columbia DB 3440　Jet Black Blues/Blue Blood Blues (78) 15
(see also Eddie Lang & Lonnie Johnson)

CATHAL DUNNE
79　Epic SEPC 7190　Happy Man/Sweet Woman Of Mine (p/s) 4

TONY DUNNING (& TREMELOS)
60　Palette PG 9006　Seventeen Tomorrow/Be My Girl 4

MINT VALUE £

| 61 | Palette PG 9018 | Pretend/Don't Bother To Call | 4 |
| 61 | Palette PG 9027 | Under Moscow Skies/Sixteen Candles | 4 |

SEAN DUNPHY
| 67 | Pye 7N 17291 | If I Could Choose/Yellow Bandana | 5 |

CHAMPION JACK DUPREE
51	Jazz Parade B 16	Fisherman's Blues/County Jail Special (78)	15
62	Storyville A 45051	Whiskey Head Woman/Shirley May	15
67	Decca F 12611	Barrelhouse Woman/Under Your Hood	12
67	Blue Horizon 45-1007	Get Your Head Happy/Easy Is The Way (with T.S. McPhee)	75
68	Blue Horizon 57-3140	I Haven't Done No-One No Harm/How Am I Doing It (with Stan Webb)	12
68	Blue Horizon 57-3152	Ba'la Fouche/Kansas City	12
69	Blue Horizon 57-3158	I Want To Be A Hippy/Goin' Back To Louisiana	12
61	Storyville SEP 381	BLUES ANTHOLOGY VOL. 1 (EP)	15
64	RCA RCX 7137	RHYTHM AND BLUES VOL. 1 (EP)	12
64	Decca DFE 8586	LONDON SPECIAL (EP, with Keith Smith Climax Band)	25
65	Ember EMB 4564	JACK DUPREE (EP)	15
60s	XX MIN 716	CHAMPION JACK DUPREE (EP)	8
59	London Jazz LTZ-K 15171	BLUES FROM THE GUTTER (LP)	35
61	London Jazz LTZ-K 15217	CHAMPION JACK'S NATURAL AND SOULFUL BLUES (LP, also stereo SAH-K 6151)	35
65	Storyville SLP 145	TROUBLE TROUBLE (LP)	12
65	XTRA 1028	CABBAGE GREENS (LP)	15
65	Storyville SLP 161	PORTRAITS IN BLUES (LP)	15
66	Decca LK/SKL 4747	FROM NEW ORLEANS TO CHICAGO (LP)	50
67	Storyville 670 194	CHAMPION JACK DUPREE (LP)	15
67	Decca SKL 4871	CHAMPION JACK DUPREE AND HIS BIG BLUES BAND (LP)	45
68	Blue Horizon 7-63206	WHEN YOU FEEL THE FEELING YOU WAS FEELING (LP)	55
69	Blue Horizon 7-63214	SCOOBYDOOBYDOO (LP)	60
70	Sonet SNTF 614	INCREDIBLE (LP)	10
72	Sonet SNTF 626	LEGACY OF THE BLUES (LP)	10
72	Atlantic K 40434	BLUES FROM MONTREUX (LP)	10
75	Atlantic K 40526	BLUES FROM THE GUTTER (LP)	10

(see also T.S. McPhee)

CHAMPION JACK DUPREE/JIMMY RUSHING
| 64 | Ember CJS 800 | TWO SHADES OF BLUE (LP) | 15 |

(see also Jimmy Rushing)

SIMON DUPREE & BIG SOUND
66	Parlophone R 5542	I See The Light/It Is Finished	8
67	Parlophone R 5574	Reservations/You Need A Man	7
67	Parlophone R 5594	Day Time, Night Time/I've Seen It All Before	7
67	Parlophone R 5646	Kites/Like The Sun Like The Fire	5
68	Parlophone R 5670	For Whom The Bell Tolls/Sleep	5
68	Parlophone R 5697	Part Of My Past/This Story Never Ends	7
68	Parlophone R 5727	Thinking About My Life/Velvet And Lace	6
69	Parlophone R 5757	Broken Hearted Pirates/She Gave Me The Sun	6
69	Parlophone R 5816	The Eagle Flies Tonight/Give It All Back	6
67	Parlophone PMC/PCS 7029	WITHOUT RESERVATIONS (LP, yellow & black label)	25
69	Parlophone PCS 7029	WITHOUT RESERVATIONS (LP, re-pressing, white & black label)	12

(see also Moles, Gentle Giant)

DUPREES
62	HMV POP 1073	You Belong To Me/Take Me As I Am	15
62	Stateside SS 143	My Own True Love/Ginny	6
63	London HLU 9678	I'd Rather Be Here In Your Arms/I Wish I Could Believe You	6
63	London HLU 9709	Gone With The Wind/Let's Make Love Again	5
63	London HLU 9774	Why Don't You Believe Me?/My Dearest One	5
63	London HLU 9813	Have You Heard?/Love Eyes	5
64	London HLU 9843	It's No Sin/The Sand And The Sea	5
65	CBS 201803	Around The Corner/They Said It Couldn't Be Done	4
66	CBS 202028	She Waits For Him/Norma Jean	4
68	MGM MGM 460	My Special Angel/Ring Of Love	4
70	Polydor 2058 077	Check Yourself/The Sky's The Limit	4

DURAN DURAN
81	EMI EMI 5137	Planet Earth/Late Bar (glossy p/s)	4
81	EMI 12EMI 5137	Planet Earth (Night Version)/Planet Earth/Late Bar (12", p/s)	8
81	EMI EMI 5168	Careless Memories/Khanada (p/s)	4
81	EMI 12EMI 5168	Careless Memories/Fame/Khanada (12", p/s)	10
81	EMI EMI 5206	Girls On Film/Faster Than Light (p/s)	4
81	EMI 12EMI 5206	Girls On Film (Night Version)/(7" Mix)/Faster Than Light (12", p/s)	8
81	EMI EMI 5254	My Own Way/Like An Angel (glossy p/s)	4
81	EMI 12EMI 5254	My Own Way (Night Version)/Like An Angel/My Own Way (Short Version) (12", p/s)	8
82	EMI 12EMI 5295	Hungry Like The Wolf (Night Version)/Careless Memories (live) (12", p/s)	7
82	EMI 12EMI 5327	Save A Prayer/Hold Back The Rain (Remix) (12", p/s)	8
82	EMI 12EMI 5346	Rio (Part 2)/Rio (Part 1)/My Own Way (12", p/s)	7
82	EMI 12EMI 5371	Is There Something I Should Know (Monster Mix)/Is There Something I Should Know (Short Mix)/Faith In This Colour (12", p/s)	7
84	EMI 12DURAN 1	New Moon On Monday/New Moon On Monday (Mix)/Tiger Tiger (12", p/s)	7
84	EMI DURANP 2	The Reflex/Make Me Smile (poster p/s)	6
84	EMI 12 DURAN 2	The Reflex (Dance Mix)/The Reflex/Make Me Smile (live) (12", p/s)	7
84	EMI 12 DURANP 2	The Reflex (Dance Mix)/Make Me Smile/The Reflex (12", picture disc)	8
84	EMI DURANC 3	The Wild Boys/Cracks In The Pavement (Simon Le Bon or John Taylor p/s)	6
84	EMI DURANC 3	The Wild Boys/Cracks In The Pavement (Andy Taylor, Roger Taylor or Nick Rhodes p/s)	4

84	EMI 12DURAN 3	The Wild Boys (Wilder Than The Wild Boys) (BXT Mix)/The Wild Boys/ (I'm Looking For) Cracks In The Pavement (1984) (12", p/s) 7
85	Parlophone DURANG 007	A View To A Kill/A View To A Kill (That Fatal Kiss) (white vinyl, gatefold p/s) 6
86	Parlophone 12 DDNX 45	Notorious (Latin Rascals Mix)/Winter Marches On/Notorious (12", p/s) 12
86	Parlophone TCDDNX 45	Notorious (Latin Rascals Mix)/Winter Marches On/Notorious (cassette) 7
87	Parlophone TRADEX 1	Skin Trade/We Need You (poster p/s) 6
87	Parlophone TRADE 1	Skin Trade/We Need You ('bum' p/s) 12
87	Parlophone 12TRADE 1	Skin Trade (Stretch Mix)/Skin Trade/We Need You (12", p/s) 7
87	Parlophone TC TRADE 1	Skin Trade (Stretch Mix)/We Need You/Skin Trade (cassette in 'video' case) 7
87	Parlophone TOUR G1	Meet El Presidente/Vertigo Do The Demolition (gatefold p/s) 4
87	Parlophone CDTOUR 1	The Presidential Suite: Meet El Presidente/Meet El Presidente (Meet El Beat)/Meet El Presidente/Vertigo (Do The Demolition) (CD) 7
88	Parlophone 12 YOURS 1	I Don't Want Your Love (Big Mix)/(LP Mix) (12", p/s, 1-side etched) 7
88	Parlophone DDP11	All She Wants Is (45 Mix)/I Believe (poster p/s) 4
88	Parlophone 12 DDX 11	All She Wants Is (US Master Mix)/All She Wants Is (45 Mix)/I Believe — All I Need To Know (Medley) (12", p/s) 8
88	Parlophone CD DD 11	All She Wants Is (45 Mix)/Skin Trade (Parisian Mix)/I Believe — All I Need To Know (Medley) (CD) 8
89	Parlophone DDA/B/C 12	Do You Believe In Shame?/The Krush Brothers LSD Edit//Do You Believe In Shame?/God (London)/This Is How A Road Gets Made/Palomino// Do You Believe In Shame?/Drug — It's Just A State Of Mind (triple-pack, foldout p/s with 3 postcards) 12
89	Parlophone 10 DD 12	Do You Believe In Shame?/The Krush Brothers LSD Edit/Notorious (live) (10", numbered p/s) 6
89	Parlophone CD DD 12	Do You Believe In Shame?/The Krush Brothers LSD Edit/Notorious (live)/ God (London)/This Is How A Road Gets Made (CD) 12
89	Parlophone CDDD 13	Burning The Ground/Decadence/Decadence (Extended Mix) (CD) 8
92	Parlophone CDDDS 16	Ordinary World/My Antarctica/The Reflex (live) (CD, part 1 of 2) 10

(see also Arcadia, Power Station)

JIMMY DURANTE

55	Brunswick 05395	Pupalina (My Little Doll)/Little People 7
55	Brunswick 05445	It's Bigger Than Both Of Us (with Patty Andrews)/ When The Circus Leaves Town 6
55	Brunswick 05495	Swingin' With Rhythm And Blues (with Peter Lawford)/ I Love You, I Do (with Eddie Jackson) 7
60	Brunswick 05829	Shine On Harvest Moon/The Best Things In Life Are Free 5
63	Warner Bros WB 112	September Song/Young At Heart 4
64	Warner Bros WB 149	Old Man Time/I Came Here To Swim 5
57	MGM MGM-EP 597	SCHNOZZLES (EP) 7
52	MGM MGM-D 102	IN PERSON (10" LP) 15
53	Brunswick LA 8582	JIMMY DURANTE SINGS (10" LP) 15
50s	Brunswick	12" LP 12

(see also Ethel Merman)

JUDITH DURHAM

67	Columbia DB 8207	The Non Performing Lion Qiuckstep/The Olive Tree 4
67	Columbia DB 8290	Again And Again/Memories 6
69	Columbia SCX 6374	FOR CHRISTMAS WITH LOVE (LP) 15
70	A&M AMLS 967	GIFT OF SONG (LP) 10
71	A&M AMLS 2011	CLIMB EV'RY MOUNTAIN (LP) 10

(see also Seekers)

TERRY DURHAM

69	Deram DML/SML 1042	CRYSTAL TELEPHONE (LP) 15

(see also Fleur De Lys)

DURUTTI COLUMN

82	Factory FAC 64	I Get Along Without You Very Well/Prayer (p/s) 4
80	Factory FACT 14	THE RETURN OF THE DURUTTI COLUMN (LP, with sandpaper sleeve, some with Martin Hannett's "Testcard" flexidisc [FACT 14C]) 16/12
83	Factory FACT 74	ANOTHER SETTING (LP, with perfumed cut-out insert) 10
83	VU VINI 1	LIVE AT THE VENUE LONDON (LP) 15
88	Factory FACT 244	VINI REILLY (LP, with free p/s 7" "I Know Very Well How I Got My Note Wrong" [FAC 244++] by Vincent Gerard & Stephen Patrick) 15
88	Factory FACD 244	VINI REILLY (CD, with 3" CD "I Know Very Well How I Got My Note Wrong" [FAC CD 244++] by Vincent Gerard & Stephen Patrick) 18

(see also Nosebleeds, Gammer & His Familiars, Morrissey)

IAN DURY (& BLOCKHEADS)

77	Stiff BUY 17	Sex And Drugs And Rock And Roll/Razzle In My Pocket (p/s) 4
77	Stiff BUY 17	Sex And Drugs And Rock And Roll/Razzle In My Pocket (p/s, orange vinyl) 5
77	Stiff BUY 23	Sweet Gene Vincent/You're More Than Fair (p/s) 4
78	Stiff FREEBIE 1	Sex And Drugs And Rock And Roll/England's Glory/Two Steep Hills (p/s, free at 'NME' party/competition) 7
78	Stiff BUY 2712	What A Waste/Wake Up (12", p/s) 8
85	EMI EMIP 5534	Profoundly In Love With Pandora/Eugenious (picture disc) 4
77	Stiff SEEZG 4	NEW BOOTS AND PANTIES (LP, gold vinyl, including "Sex And Drugs And Rock And Roll") 10
84	Polydor POLD 5112	4,000 WEEKS' HOLIDAY (LP, withdrawn) 10
86	Demon FIEND 63	NEW BOOTS AND PANTIES (LP, reissue, with free interview LP) 10

(see also Kilburn & High Roads, Greatest Show On Earth, Loving Awareness)

SLIM DUSTY

58	Columbia DB 4212	A Pub With No Beer/Once When I Was Mustering (with His Country Rockers) 5
59	Columbia DB 4294	The Answer To A Pub With No Beer/Winter Winds (with His Bushlanders) 4
60	Columbia SEG 8009	SLIM DUSTY AND HIS COUNTRY ROCKERS (EP) 12

DUTCH

68	Philips BF 1673	What Is Soul?/Down Here 4

DUTCH SWING COLLEGE BAND
60	Philips PB 1029	Milord/Marina	4

JOSE DUVAL
57	London HLR 8458	Message Of Love/That's What You Mean To Me	8

BOEING DUVEEN & BEAUTIFUL SOUP
68	Parlophone R 5696	Jabberwock/Which Dreamed It (some with p/s)	100/50

MARK DWAYNE
62	Oriole CB 1712	Remember Me Huh/Poorest Boy In Town	5
62	Oriole CB 1744	Today's Teardrops/Little Bitty Heart	5

DYAKS
78	Bonaparte BONE 2	Gutter Kids/It's A Game (p/s)	4

DYKE & BLAZERS
67	Pye Intl. 7N 25413	Funky Broadway Pts 1 & 2	15

BOB DYLAN
65	CBS 201751	The Times They Are A-Changin'/Honey, Just Allow Me One More Chance	6
65	CBS 201753	Subterranean Homesick Blues/She Belongs To Me	6
65	CBS 201781	Maggie's Farm/On The Road Again	7
65	CBS 201811	Like A Rolling Stone/Gates Of Eden	5
65	CBS 201824	Positively 4th Street/From A Buick 6	6
65	CBS 201900	Can You Please Crawl Out Your Window/Highway 61 Revisited	6
66	CBS 202053	One Of Us Must Know (Sooner Or Later)/Queen Jane Approximately	5
66	CBS 202307	Rainy Day Women Nos. 12 & 35/Pledging My Time	4
66	CBS 202258	I Want You/Just Like Tom Thumb's Blues (live)	7

(later copies may exist of a few of the above singles with four-figure catalogue numbers, worth around £4 each)
67	CBS 2700	Leopard-Skin Pill-Box Hat/Most Likely You Go Your Way And I'll Go Mine (p/s)	35
67	CBS 2700	Leopard-Skin Pill-Box Hat/Most Likely You Go Your Way And I'll Go Mine	5
69	CBS 4219	I Threw It All Away/The Drifter's Escape	4
69	CBS 4611	Tonight I'll Be Staying Here With You/Country Pie	4
70	CBS 5122	Wigwam/Copper Kettle (The Pale Moonlight)	4
71	CBS 7092	If Not For You/New Morning	4
71	CBS 7329	Watching The River Flow/Spanish Is The Loving Tongue	8
71	CBS 7688	George Jackson (Acoustic)/(Big Band Version)	8
74	CBS 2006	A Fool Such As I/Lily Of The West	5
74	Island WIP 6168	On A Night Like This/Forever Young	6
75	CBS 3160	Tangled Up In Blue/If You See Her, Say Hello	6
75	CBS 3665	Million Dollar Bash/Tears Of Rage	6
76	CBS 3878	Hurricane (Part 1)/(Full Version)	
		(some labels state 'Pt 1'/'Pt 2', initially in p/s)	8/4
77	CBS 4859	Rita May/Stuck Inside Of Mobile With The Memphis Blues Again (p/s)	8
85	CBS GA 5020	Highway 61 Revisited (live)/It Ain't Me Babe (live) (gatefold p/s)	5
65	CBS EP 6051	BOB DYLAN (EP)	15
66	CBS EP 6070	ONE TOO MANY MORNINGS (EP)	20
66	CBS EP 6078	MR TAMBOURINE MAN (EP)	15
62	CBS (S)BGP 62022	BOB DYLAN (LP, mono/stereo)	12/14
63	CBS (S)BGP 62193	THE FREEWHEELIN' BOB DYLAN (LP, mono/stereo)	12/14
63	CBS (S)BGP 62251	THE TIMES THEY ARE A-CHANGIN' (LP, mono/stereo)	12/14
64	CBS (S)BGP 62429	ANOTHER SIDE OF BOB DYLAN (LP, mono/stereo)	12/14
65	CBS (S)BGP 62515	BRINGING IT ALL BACK HOME (LP)	12
65	CBS (S)BGP 62572	HIGHWAY 61 REVISITED (LP, mono/stereo)	14/12
66	CBS (S)DDP 66012	BLONDE ON BLONDE (2-LP, gatefold sleeve, mono/stereo)	20/14
67	CBS (S)BGP 62847	BOB DYLAN'S GREATEST HITS (LP, mono/stereo)	10

(all the above LPs originally came with rough textured labels and flipback sleeves; later copies are worth two-thirds the value)
68	CBS (S)BGP 63252	JOHN WESLEY HARDING (LP, textured label, mono/stereo)	12/10
76	CBS Q 86003	DESIRE (LP, quadrophonic)	15
85	CBS 65509	BIOGRAPH (5-LP box set with 2 booklets)	30

DYLANS
92	Imaginary FREE 002	Who Loves The Sun/SWERVEDRIVER: Jesus (promo only)	5

DYNAMICS (U.S.)
63	London HLX 9809	Misery/I'm The Man	15
64	King KG 1007	So In Love With Me/Say You Will	12
69	Atlantic 584 270	Ice Cream Song/The Love That I Need	5

DYNAMICS (Jamaica)
68	Blue Cat BS 104	My Friends/NEVILLE IRONS: Soul Glide	10

DYNAMITES
69	Duke DU 30	John Public/CLANCY ECCLES: Fire Corner (B-side actually by King Stitt)	4
69	Clandisc CLA 200	Mr. Midnight (Skokiaan)/KING STITT: Who Yeah	4
69	Trojan/Clandisc TTL 21	FIRE CORNER (LP, with King Stitt)	15

(see also Clancy Eccles & Dynamites)

DYNATONES
59	Top Rank JAR 149	Steel Guitar Rag/The Girl I'm Searching For	8
66	Pye International 7N 25389	The Fife Piper/And I Always Will	40

ALAN DYSON
68	Pye NPL 18212	THE STILL SMALL VOICE OF ALAN DYSON (LP)	25

RONNIE DYSON
70	CBS 5285	I Don't Wanna Cry/She's Gone	6
74	CBS 1968	I Think I'll Tell Her/Girl Don't Come	4
74	CBS 2430	We Can Make It Last Forever/Just A Little Love From Me	8
75	CBS 1659	Point Of No Return/But Don't Want To Be Lonely	4

BOB DYLAN

MINT VALUE £

VINCE EAGER

58	Decca F 11023	Tread Softly Stranger & Yea Yea (as Vince Eager & Vagabonds; unreleased, 2 x 1-sided demos only) .... each 20
58	Parlophone R 4482	Five Days, Five Days/No More 15
58	Parlophone R 4482	Five Days, Five Days/No More (78) 15
59	Parlophone R 4531	When's Your Birthday, Baby?/The Railroad Song 10
59	Parlophone R 4531	When's Your Birthday, Baby?/The Railroad Song (78) 10
59	Parlophone R 4550	This Should Go On Forever/No Other Arms, No Other Lips 10
59	Top Rank JAR 191	Makin' Love/Primrose Lane 6
60	Top Rank JAR 275	Why/El Paso 6
60	Top Rank JAR 307	No Love Have I/Lonely Blue Boy 8
61	Top Rank JAR 539	(I Wanna) Love My Life Away/I Know What I Want 5
61	Top Rank JAR 593	The World's Loneliest Man/Created In A Dream 5
63	Piccadilly 7N 35110	Any Time Is The Right Time/Heavenly 4
63	Piccadilly 7N 35157	I Shall Not Be Moved/It's Only Make Believe 4
58	Decca DFE 6504	VINCE EAGER AND THE VAGABONDS NO. 1 (EP) 30
70s	Avenue AVE 093	VINCE EAGER PAYS TRIBUTE TO ELVIS PRESLEY (LP) 10

EAGLE

70	Pye Intl. 7N 25530	Kickin' It Back To You/Come In, It's All For Free 6
69	Pye Intl. NSPL 28138	COME UNDER NANCY'S TENT (LP) 10

EAGLES (U.K.)

62	Pye 7N 15451	Bristol Express/Johnny's Tune 6
62	Pye 7N 15473	Exodus: The Main Theme/March Of The Eagles 6
62	Pye 7N 15503	The Desperados/Special Agent 6
63	Pye 7N 15550	Come On Baby (To The Floral Dance)/Theme From Station Six Sahara . 6
63	Pye 7N 15571	Eagles Nest/Poinciana (unreleased)
64	Pye 7N 15613	Andorra/Moonstruck 6
64	Pye 7N 15650	Write Me A Letter/Wishin' And Hopin' 10
62	Pye NEP 24166	NEW SOUND T.V. THEMES (EP) 12
63	Pye NPL 18084	SMASH HITS (LP) 30

(see also Valerie Mountain)

EAGLES (Jamaica)

72	Duke Reid DR 2522	Your Enemies Can't Hurt You/Version 5
73	Techniques TE 927	Rub It Down/TOMMY McCOOK ALLSTARS: Rub It Down Version 4

EAGLES (U.S.)

75	Asylum K 53003	DESPERADO (LP, audiophile pressing, mail-order via 'Hi-Fi Today' mag) 10

SNOOKS EAGLIN

60s	Storyville A 45056	Country Boy/Alberta 12
60s	Storyville SEP 386	BLUES ANTHOLOGY VOL. 6 (EP) 10
61	Heritage HLP 1002	SNOOKS EAGLIN (LP) 30
60s	Storyville SLP 119	NEW ORLEANS STREET SINGER (LP) 12
60s	Storyville SLP 140	VOL. 2 — BLUES FROM NEW ORLEANS (LP) 12
70s	Storyville 670 146	PORTRAITS IN BLUES VOLUME 1 (LP) 15

JIM EANES

59	Melodisc 1530	Christmas Doll/It Won't Seem Like Christmas 6

ROBERT EARL

58	Philips PB 805	I May Never Pass This Way Again/Someone 4
58	Philips PB 867	More Than Ever (Come Prima)/No One But You (In My Heart) 4
59	Philips PB 891	The Wonderful Secret Of Love/The Boulevard Of Broken Dreams 4
58	Philips BBE 12032	ROBERT EARL (EP) 7
59	Philips BBE 12240	THE WONDERFUL SECRET OF LOVE (EP) 7
60	Philips BBL 7394	SHOWCASE (LP) 10

EARL & DEAN

66	Strike JH 323	Slowly Goin' Out Of My Head/Little Buddy 4

CHARLES EARLAND

76	Mercury 6167 360	Intergalactic Love Song/From My Heart To Yours 4
76	Mercury 6167 414	We All Live In The Jungle/Intergalactic Love Song 4
78	Mercury 6167 703	Let The Music Play/Broken Heart 4
78	Mercury 9199 831	Let The Music Play/Broken Heart (12") 7
70s	Prestige PR 10041	INTENSITY (LP) 10
76	Mercury SRM 11049	ODYSSEY (LP) 10

KENNETH EARLE

60	Decca F 11205	The New Frankie And Johnny/40-30-40 4
60	Decca F 11224	Standing On The Corner/Put Your Arms Around Me, Honey 4

STEVE EARLE

87	MCA MCA 1209	The Rain Came Down/I Love You Too Much//Guitar Town/No. 29 (double pack, gatefold p/s) 4
88	MCA WMCA 1301ADL	Johnny Come Lately/Nothing But A Girl (featuring Pogues) (promo envelope p/s) 7

EARLS

63	Stateside SS 153	Remember Then/Let's Waddle 20
63	London HL 9702	Never/I Keep-A Tellin' You 25
71	Atlantic 2091 129	Remember Then/I Believe 4

EARTH
69	CBS 4671	Resurrection City/Comical Man	25
69	Decca F 22908	Stranger Of Fortune/Everybody Sing The Song	10

EARTH & FIRE
74	Polydor 2121 235	Love Of Life/Tuffy The Cat	4
71	Nepentha 6437 004	EARTH AND FIRE (LP, gatefold sleeve)	150
73	Polydor 2925 013	ATLANTIS (LP)	10
75	Polydor 2925 033	TO THE WORLD A FUTURE (LP)	10

EARTH BOYS
59	Capitol CL 14979	Barbara Ann/Space Girl	8

EARTHLINGS
65	Parlophone R 5242	Landing Of The Daleks/March Of The Robots	15

EARTH OPERA
68	Elektra EKSN 45035	Close Your Eyes And Shut The Door/Dreamless	5
68	Elektra EKSN 45049	American Eagle Tragedy/When You Were Full Of Wonder	4
69	Elektra EKSN 45061	Alfie Finney/Home To You	4
68	Elektra EKS 74016	EARTH OPERA (LP, gatefold sleeve)	15
69	Elektra EKS 74038	GREAT AMERICAN EAGLE TRAGEDY (LP)	15
	(see also Rowan Brothers)		

EARTHQUAKE
74	Cloud One HIT 4	Friday On My Mind/Madness	4
75	United Artists UP 35787	Tall Order For A Short Guy/Mr Security	4
75	United Artists UAS 29853	LIVE (LP)	12

EARTHQUAKERS
67	Stateside SS 2050	Whistling In The Sunshine/Dreaming In The Moonlight	6

EARTH, WIND & FIRE
71	Warner Bros WB 6125	Help Somebody/Love Is Life	5
73	CBS 1792	Evil/Clover	4
74	CBS 2033	Keep Your Head To The Sky/Build Your Nest	4
74	CBS 2284	Mighty Mighty/Drum Song	4
74	CBS 2782	Kalimba Story/The Nine Chee Bit	4
73	CBS 65208	LAST DAYS AND TIME (LP)	15
73	CBS Q 65604	HEAD TO THE SKY (LP, quadrophonic)	12
73	CBS 65604	HEAD TO THE SKY (LP)	10
74	CBS 65844	OPEN OUR EYES (LP, with inner sleeve)	10
75	CBS 80575	THAT'S THE WAY OF THE WORLD (LP, gatefold sleeve with inner)	10
75	CBS 88160	GRATITUDE (2-LP, with inner sleeves)	14

TIM EASLEY
68	Bell BLL 1036	Susie Q Pts 1 & 2	4

EASTER & TOTEM
80s	Smoking Beagle LYN 11873/4	HIP REPLACEMENT (LP)	10

EASTERHOUSE
85	Easterhouse EIREX 1	IN OUR OWN HANDS (12" EP, some with stickered w/l & hand-stencilled p/s)	10/7
88	Easterhouse EAST 1	Come Out Fighting (4.26)/(4.25) (12" in gatefold folder with photos & inserts)	8
86	Rough Trade ROUGH 94	CONTENDERS (LP, with 7" "Get Back To Russia" [RDJ 94]	4

EAST MAIN ST. EXPLOSION
69	Fontana TF 1039	Hop, Skip And Jump/Little Jackie Horner	4

EAST OF EDEN
69	Atlantic 584198	King Of Siam/Ballad Of Harvey Kaye	12
69	Deram DM 242	Northern Hemisphere/Communion	12
70	Deram DM 297	Jig A Jig/Marcus Junior	4
71	Deram DM 338	Ramadhan/In The Snow For A Blow	5
72	Harvest HAR 5055	Boogie Woogie Flu/Last Dance Of The Clown (p/s)	5
72	United Artists UP 35567	Sin City Girls/All Our Yesterdays	4
69	Deram DML/SML 1038	MERCATOR PROJECTED (LP)	20
70	Deram SML 1050	SNAFU (LP)	15
71	Harvest SHVL 792	EAST OF EDEN (LP)	10
71	Harvest SHVL 796	NEW LEAF (LP)	12

SHEENA EASTON
89	MCA MCAT 1348	101/101 (Instrumental) (12", poster p/s)	7
	(see also Prince)		

BUGSY EASTWOOD
68	President PT 209	Blackbird Charlie/My Sun	4
	(see also Exception)		

EASY
91	Blast First BFFP 61	He Brings The Honey/# 25 (p/s)	4

EASYBEATS
66	United Artists UP 1144	Come And See Her/Make You Feel Alright (Women)	8
66	United Artists UP 1157	Friday On My Mind/Made My Bed, Gonna Lie In It	4
66	United Artists UP 1175	Who'll Be The One?/Saturday Night	6
67	United Artists UP 1183	Heaven And Hell/Pretty Girl	7
67	United Artists UP 1201	The Music Goes Round My Head/Come In, You'll Get Pneumonia	7
68	United Artists UP 2205	Hello, How Are You?/Falling Off The Edge Of The World	4
68	United Artists UP 2219	The Land Of Make-Believe/We All Live Happily	5
68	United Artists UP 2243	Good Times/Lay Me Down And Die	5
69	Polydor 56335	St. Louis/Can't Find Love	6
70	Polydor 2001 028	(Who Are My) Friends?/Rock'N'Roll Boogie	7

EASYBEATS

67	United Artists (S)ULP 1167	GOOD FRIDAY (LP)	70
68	United Artists (S)ULP 1193	VIGIL (LP)	30
70	Polydor Special 2482 010	FRIENDS (LP)	40

(see also Paintbox, Haffy's Whisky Sour)

EASY RIDERS

58	Philips PB 823	Salute To Windjammer/Kari Waits For Me	4
60	London HLR 9204	Young In Love/Saturday's Child	5
60	London HA-R 2323	REMEMBER THE ALAMO (LP, also stereo SAH-R 6126)	10/12

(see also Terry Gilkyson & Easy Riders, Vic Damone, Frankie Laine)

EAT

89	Fiction WAN 100	THE AUTOGIFT EP	4
89	Fiction WANTX 100	THE AUTOGIFT EP (12")	7
89	Fiction WANCD 100	THE AUTOGIFT EP (CD)	7
89	Fiction CIF 1	THE PLASTIC BAG EP	4
89	Fiction CIFX 1	THE PLASTIC BAG EP (12")	8
89	Fiction CIFCD 1	THE PLASTIC BAG EP (CD)	8
89	Fiction CIFX 2	Summer In The City/Two Nations/Gyrate (Extended Jib Mix) (12", p/s)	7
89	Fiction CIFCD 2	Summer In The City/Two Nations/Gyrate (Extended Jib Mix) (CD)	7

EATER

77	The Label TLR 001	Outside View/You (p/s)	5
77	The Label TLR 003	Thinkin' Of The USA/Space Dreamin'/Michael's Monetary System (p/s)	5
77	The Label TLR 004	Lock It Up/Jeepster (p/s)	5
77	The Label TLR 004/12	Lock It Up/Jeepster (12", p/s)	10
78	The Label TLR 007	GET YOUR YO-YO'S OUT (EP, white vinyl; blue, green or red p/s)	4-5
78	The Label TLR 007	GET YOUR YO-YO'S OUT (12" EP, white vinyl; blue, green or red p/s)	7-8
78	The Label TLR 009	What She Wants She Needs/Reaching For The Sky (p/s)	5
78	The Label TLRLP 001	THE ALBUM (LP, with inner sleeve)	22
85	De Lorean EAT 1	THE HISTORY OF EATER (LP, 1,000 each on red, white & blue vinyl, with free single [EAT FREEBIE 1, no p/s])	10

KOOKIE EATON

| 68 | Condor PS 1002 | Cream Machine/Joke B-Side | 5 |

EBONIES

| 68 | Philips BF 1648 | Never Gonna Break Your Heart Again/Shoeshine Boy | 6 |

EBONYS

| 71 | CBS 7384 | You're The Reason Why/Sexy Ways | 4 |

KATJA EBSTEIN

| 70 | Liberty LBF 15317 | No More Love For Me/Without Love | 12 |

ECCENTRICS

| 65 | Pye 7N 15850 | What You Got/Fe Fi Fo Fum | 20 |

CLANCY ECCLES (& DYNAMITES)

61	Blue Beat BB 34	River Jordan/I Live And I Love	10
61	Blue Beat BB 67	Freedom/More Proof	10
63	Island WI 044	Judgement/Baby Please	10
63	Island WI 098	Glory Hallelujah/Hot Rod (B-side actually by Roland Alphonso)	10
65	Ska Beat JB 194	Sammy No Dead/Roam Jerusalem	8
65	Ska Beat JB 198	Miss Ida/KING ROCKY: What Is Katty	8
67	Doctor Bird DB 1156	Feel The Rhythm/Easy Snapping (B-side actually by Theo Beckford)	8
67	Pama PM 701	What Will Your Mama Say/Darling Don't Do That	6
68	Pama PM 712	The Fight/Great	6
68	Nu Beat NB 006	Festival '68/I Really Love You	5
68	Trojan TR 639	Sweet Africa/Let Us Be Lovers	5
69	Trojan TR 647	Bangarang Crash/DYNAMITES: Rahthid	5
69	Trojan TR 648	Constantinople/Deacon Sun	5
69	Trojan TR 649	Demonstration/VAL BENNETT: My Girl	5
69	Trojan TR 658	Fattie Fattie/SILVERSTARS: Last Call	5
69	Duke DU 9	Auntie Lulu/SLICKERS: Bag A Boo	5
69	Clandisc CLA 201	The World Needs Loving/Dollar Train	4
69	Clandisc CLA 209	Open Up/HIGGS & WILSON: Agane (B-side actually called "Again")	4
70	Clandisc CLA 212	Black Beret (with Dynamites)/BARRY & AFFECTIONS: Love Me Tender	4
70	Clandisc CLA 213	Phantom/Skank Me (with Dynamites)	4
70	Clandisc CLA 214	Africa/Africa Part Two (with Dynamites)	4
69	Trojan TTL 72	FREEDOM (LP)	15

(see also Dynamites)

ECHO & BUNNYMEN

79	Zoo CAGE 004	The Pictures On My Wall/Read It In Books (p/s, various different label colours, with "The Revenge Of Voodoo Billy" scratched in B-side run-off)	10
80	Korova KOW 1	Rescue/Simple Stuff (2 different p/s designs)	6
80	Korova KOW 1T	Rescue/Simple Stuff/Pride (12", p/s)	10
80	Korova KOW 11	The Puppet/Do It Clean (p/s)	10
81	Korova ECHO 1	SHINE SO HARD (live 12" EP)	8
81	Korova ECHO 1M	SHINE SO HARD (live cassette EP)	7
81	Korova KOW 15	A Promise/Broke My Neck (p/s)	4
81	Korova KOW 15T	A Promise/Broke My Neck (Long Version) (12", p/s)	7
83	Korova KOW 26	The Cutter/Way Out And Up We Go/Zimbo (12", with Peel Session cassette [KOW 26C] & poster)	10
84	Korova KOW 34T	Silver (Tidal Wave)/Silver/Angels And Devils (12", p/s)	7
84	Korova KOW 35F/ SAM 202	Seven Seas/All You Need Is Love//The Killing Moon/Stars Are Stars/ Villiers Terrace (numbered double pack, gatefold p/s)	6
84	Korova KOW 35T	Seven Seas/All You Need Is Love (12", p/s)	8
88	Korova KOW 43P	Bring On The Dancing Horses/Over Your Shoulder ('cow'-shaped picture disc in stickered PVC sleeve)	8

87	WEA YZ 134	The Game/Lost And Found (unreleased alternate p/s, promo only) 5
87	WEA YZ 144B	Lips Like Sugar/Rollercoaster (box set) 4
91	Imaginary FREE 001	Foggy Notion/MOCK TURTLES: Pale Blue Eyes (promo only) 7
81	Korova KODE 1	CROCODILES (LP, with free 7", "Do It Clean"/"Read It In Books"
		[SAM 128] & inner sleeve) 10
83	Korova KODE 6	PORCUPINE (LP, with Peel Session cassette [KOW 26C]) 12
85	Korova KODE 13	SONGS TO LEARN AND SING (LP, with free 7", "The Pictures On My Wall"/
		"Read It In Books" [p/s, yellow/blue labels, CAGE 004], some signed) 14/10
85	Korova KODE 13P	SONGS TO LEARN AND SING (LP, picture disc) 10

ECHOES (U.S.)

| 60 | Top Rank JAR 399 | Born To Be With You/My Guiding Light ....10 |
| 61 | Top Rank JAR 553 | Baby Blue/Boomerang ....10 |

ECHOES (U.K.)

62	Fontana 267254 TF	Cloak And Dagger/Sounds Like Winter 6
62	Fontana TF 392	The Happy Whistler/Sticks And Stones 4
63	Fontana TF 415	The Jog/Marching Thru' 5
64	Fontana TF 439	My Little Girl/More 5
64	Philips BF 1370	Don't You Believe Them/I'll Get Over You 4
66	Philips BF 1480	Got To Run/Thanks A Lot 5
68	Philips BF 1687	Searchin' For You Baby/Listen To Me Baby 10

ECHOES (Jamaica)

| 61 | Blue Beat BB 89 | You Are Mine/I'll Love You Forever ....10 |

BILLY ECKSTINE

51	Vogue V 9005	I Stay In The Mood For You/I Want To Talk About You (78) 6
53	MGM SP 1011	Kiss Of Fire/I Apologise 8
53	MGM SP 1020	Come To The Mardi Gras/Be Fair 5
53	MGM SP 1040	Coquette/A Fool In Love 4
53	MGM SP 1055	I've Never Been In Love Before/I'll Know 4
53	MGM SP 1060	St. Louis Blues Pts 1 & 2 (as Billy Eckstine & Metronome All Stars) 4
54	MGM SP 1082	Tenderly/Fortune Telling Cards 4
54	MGM SP 1084	Rendezvous/Don't Get Around Much Anymore 4
54	MGM SP 1095	Seabreeze/Sophisticated Lady 4
54	MGM SP 1101	No One But You/I Let A Song Go Out Of My Heart 7
54	MGM SP 1107	Beloved/Olay Olay (The Bullfighter's Song) 4
55	MGM SP 1117	Mood Indigo/Do Nothin' Till You Hear From Me 4
55	MGM SP 1124	What More Is There To Say?/Prelude To A Kiss 4
55	MGM SP 1136	Love Me Or Leave Me/The Life Of The Party 6
55	MGM SP 1140	More Than You Know/La De Do De Do (Honey Bug Song) 4
56	MGM SP 1153	Farewell To Romance/Lost In Loveliness 4
56	MGM SP 1167	Good-bye/You've Got Me Crying Again 4
56	MGM SP 1170	The Show Must Go On/You'll Get Yours 4
56	MGM MGM 925	Solitude/I Got It Bad (And That Ain't Good) 4
57	MGM MGM 948	A Man Doesn't Know/My Fickle Heart 4
57	HMV POP 341	Pretty, Pretty/Blue Illusion 4
57	MGM MGM 970	Bring Back The Thrill/Over The Rainbow 4
58	Mercury 7MT 191	Boulevard Of Broken Dreams/If I Can Help Somebody 4
58	Mercury 7MT 224	Vertigo/In The Rain 4
58	Mercury AMT 1008	Prisoner Of Love/Funny 4
59	Mercury AMT 1018	Gigi/Trust In Me 4
59	Columbia DB 4334	I Want A Little Girl/Lonesome Lover Blues (with Count Basie Orchestra) ...4
60	Columbia DB 4407	Anything You Wanna Do (I Wanna Do With You)/Like Wow 4
62	Ember JBS 703	Good Jelly Blues/If That's The Way You Feel 4
65	Tamla Motown TMG 533	Had You Been Around/Down To Earth 35
69	Mercury MF 1103	I Apologise/My Foolish Heart (p/s) 4
69	Mercury MF 1106	Gigi/Coquette (p/s) 4
55	MGM MGM-EP 511	BILLY ECKSTINE (EP) 7
55	MGM MGM-EP 523	THE CASHMERE VOICE (EP) 7
57	MGM MGM-EP 598	FOUR GREAT STANDARDS (EP) 7
57	Parlophone GEP 8672	A DATE WITH RHYTHM (EP, with His All Star Band) 7
59	Mercury ZEP 10005	THE BEST OF MISTER B. NO. 1 (EP) 7
60	Emarcy JAZZYEP 9509	THE BEST OF MISTER B. NO. 2 (EP) 7
61	Columbia SEG 8042	BASIE — ECKSTINE INCORPORATED
		(EP, & Count Basie, also stereo ESG 7827) 7
54	MGM MGM-D 126	TENDERLY (10" LP) 15
56	MGM MGM-D 138	THAT OLD FEELING (10" LP) 15
58	MGM MGM-D 151	A WEAVER OF DREAMS (10" LP) 15
59	Mercury MMB 12002	BILLY ECKSTINE'S IMAGINATION (LP) 12
60	Mercury MMC 14043	BILLY'S BEST (LP) 12
60	London HAD 2241	GOLDEN SAXOPHONES (LP, also stereo SAHD 6070) 12
60	Columbia 33SX 1249	ONCE MORE WITH FEELING (LP, also stereo SCX 3322) 12
61	Columbia 33SX 1327	NO COVER, NO MINIMUM (LP, also stereo SCX 3381) 12
61	Columbia 33SX 1249	ONCE MORE WITH FEELING (LP, also stereo SCX 3322) 12
61	Columbia 33SX 1327	NO COVER, NO MINIMUM (LP) 12
62	Ember EMB 3338	MR. B (LP) 12
62	Mercury MMC 14100	AT BASIN STREET EAST (LP, also stereo CMS 18066) 12/14
64	Mercury 20012 MCL	NOW SINGING 12 GREAT MOVIES (LP) 10
66	T. Motown TML 11025	THE PRIME OF MY LIFE (LP) 40
67	T. Motown (S)TML 11046	MY WAY (LP) 30
68	Fontana SFL 13039	AT BASIN STREET EAST (LP, reissue) 10
69	T. Motown (S)TML 11101	GENTLE ON MY MIND (LP) 20

(see also Sarah Vaughan & Billy Eckstine)

ECLECTION

| 68 | Elektra EKSN 45033 | Nevertheless/Mark Time ....6 |
| 68 | Elektra EKSN 45040 | Another Time, Another Place/Betty Brown ....6 |

ECLECTION

68	Elektra EKSN 45042	Please/Saint George And The Dragon	6
68	Elektra EKSN 45046	Please (Mark II)/In The Early Days	5
68	Elektra EKS 74023	ECLECTION (LP)	35

(see also Fairport Convention, Fotheringay, Doris Henderson & J. Renbourn)

ECSTASY, PASSION & PAIN
74	Pye Intl. 7N 25669	Ask Me/I'll Take The Blame	4
74	Pye Intl. NSPL 28204	ECSTASY, PASSION & PAIN (LP)	10

JASON EDDIE & CENTREMEN
65	Parlophone R 5388	Whatcha Gonna Do Baby/Come On Baby (as Jason Eddie & Centremen)	60
66	Parlophone R 5473	Singing The Blues/True To You (as Jason Eddie & Centremen)	70
69	Tangerine DP 0010	Heart And Soul/Playing The Clown (solo)	6

EDDIE & CRAZY JETS
64	King KG 1000	Come On Let's Slop/Down By The Riverside	4

EDDIE & ERNIE
75	United Artists UP 35782	I Can't Do It/Lost Friends	4

EDDIE & HOT RODS
76	Island WIP 6270	Writing On The Wall/Cruisin' (In The Lincoln) (promos in generic title p/s)	15
76	Island WIP 6270	Writing On The Wall/Cruisin' (In The Lincoln) (some in black & white p/s)	15/4
76	Island WIP 6306	Wooly Bully/Horseplay (Weary Of The Schmaltz) (p/s)	4
77	Island WIP 6354	Do Anything You Wanna Do/Schoolgirl (p/s)	5
76	Island IEP 2	LIVE AT THE MARQUEE (EP)	4
77	Island IEP 5	AT THE SPEED OF SOUND (EP)	4
77	Island IEP 5	AT THE SPEED OF SOUND (12", plain sleeve)	7

(see also Rods, Rob Tyner & Hot Rods, Lew Lewis)

EDDIE'S CROWD
66	CBS 202078	Baby Don't Look Down/Take It Easy Baby	25

DUANE EDDY (& REBELS)
58	London HL 8669	Rebel-Rouser/Stalkin' (initially with triangular centre, later with round centre)	10/5
58	London HL 8669	Rebel-Rouser/Stalkin' (78)	12
58	London HL 8723	Ramrod/The Walker (as Duane Eddy & Rebels, tri-centre or round centre)	8/4
58	London HL 8723	Ramrod/The Walker (78)	15
58	London HL 8764	Cannonball/Mason-Dixon Lion (as Duane Eddy & Rebels, tri or round centre)	8/5
58	London HL 8764	Cannonball/Mason-Dixon Lion (78)	18
59	London HLW 8821	The Lonely One/Detour (triangular centre or round centre)	8/5
59	London HLW 8821	The Lonely One/Detour (78)	15
59	London HLW 8879	Peter Gunn/Yep!	6
59	London HLW 8879	Peter Gunn/Yep! (78)	20
59	London HLW 8929	Forty Miles Of Bad Road/The Quiet Three	6
59	London HLW 8929	Forty Miles Of Bad Road/The Quiet Three (78)	20
59	London HLW 9007	Some Kind-A Earthquake/First Love, First Tears	5
59	London HLW 9007	Some Kind-A Earthquake/First Love, First Tears (78)	25
60	London HLW 9050	Bonnie Come Back/Movin' 'N' Groovin'	6
60	London HLW 9050	Bonnie Come Back/Movin' 'N' Groovin' (78)	35
60	London HLW 9104	Shazam!/The Secret Seven	4
60	London HLW 9104	Shazam!/The Secret Seven (78)	40
60	London HLW 9162	Because They're Young/Rebel Walk	4
60	London HLW 9162	Because They're Young/Rebel Walk (78)	40
60	London HLW 9225	Kommotion/Theme For Moon Children	5
61	London HLW 9257	Pepe/Lost Friend	4
61	London HLW 9324	Theme From Dixie/The Battle	4
61	London HLW 9370	Ring Of Fire/Gidget Goes Hawaiian	5
61	London HLW 9406	Drivin' Home/My Blue Heaven	5
61	London HLW 9477	The Avenger/Londonderry Air	6
61	Parlophone R 4826	Caravan Pts 1 & 2 (actually by Al Casey)	6
62	RCA RCA 1288	Deep In The Heart Of Texas/Saints And Sinners	4
62	RCA RCA 1300	The Ballad Of Paladin/Wild Westerner	4
62	RCA RCA 1316	(Dance With The) Guitar Man/Stretchin' Out	4
63	RCA RCA 1329	Boss Guitar/Desert Rat	5
63	RCA RCA 1344	Joshin'/Lonely Boy, Lonely Guitar	5
63	RCA RCA 1357	You're Baby's Gone Surfin'/Shuckin'	5
63	RCA RCA 1369	My Baby Plays The Same Old Song On His Guitar All Night Long/Guitar'd And Feather'd	5
64	RCA RCA 1389	The Son Of Rebel Rouser/The Story Of Three Loves	5
64	RCA RCA 1425	Guitar Star/The Iguana	6
64	Colpix PX 779	Trash/South Phoenix	8
64	Colpix PX 788	The House Of The Rising Sun/Don't Think Twice, It's All Right	8
66	Reprise RS 20504	Daydream/This Guitar Was Made For Twangin'	8
67	Reprise RS 20557	Monsoon/Roarin'	8
68	Reprise RS 20690	Niki Hoeky/Velvet Nights (Theme From "Elvira Madigan")	8
68	RCA RCA 1701	Dance With The Guitar Man/SAM COOKE: Another Saturday Night (withdrawn)	12
68	London HLW 10191	Peter Gunn/Rebel-Rouser	4
69	CBS 3962	Break My Mind/Loving Bird	12
75	Target 101	Love Confusion/Love Is A Warm Emotion	8
87	Capitol CL 463	Rockestra Theme/Rockestra Theme (Version) (p/s)	4
87	Capitol 12 CL 463	Rockestra Theme/Rockestra Theme (Version)/Blue City (12", p/s)	7

(the below singles are all export issues)

58	London HL 7057	Ramrod/The Walker (as Duane Eddy & Rebels)	6
59	London HL 7072	The Lonely One/Detour	5
59	London HL 7076	Yep!/Three-30-Blues	20
59	London SLW 4001	Peter Gunn/Yep! (stereo)	50
59	London HL 7080	Forty Miles Of Bad Road/The Quiet Three	5

Rare Record Price Guide

MINT VALUE £

60	London HL 7090	Bonnie Come Back/Lost Island	20
60	London HL 7096	Because They're Young/Rebel Walk	5
58	London RE 1175	REBEL ROUSER (EP, as Duane Eddy)	12
59	London RE-W 1216	THE LONELY ONE (EP)	10
59	London RE-W 1217	YEP! (EP)	10
60	London RE-W 1252	BECAUSE THEY'RE YOUNG (EP)	10
60	London RE-W 1257	TWANGY (EP)	10
61	London RE-W 1287	PEPE (EP)	10
61	London RE-W 1303	DUANE EDDY PLAYS MOVIE THEMES (EP)	10
61	London RE-W 1341	TWANGY NO. 2 (EP)	10
63	RCA RCX 7115	A COUNTRY TWANG (EP)	14
63	RCA RCX 7129	MR. TWANG (EP)	15
64	RCA RCX 7146	TWANGIN' UP A SMALL STORM (EP)	18
65	Colpix PXE 304	COTTONMOUTH (EP)	25
58	London HA-W 2160	HAVE 'TWANGY' GUITAR, WILL TRAVEL (LP)	25
59	London HA-W 2191	ESPECIALLY FOR YOU (LP, also stereo SAH-W 6045)	15/20
60	London HA-W 2236	THE "TWANG'S" THE "THANG!" (LP, also stereo SAH-W 6068)	15/20
60	London HA-W 2285	SONGS OF OUR HERITAGE (LP, also stereo SAH-W 6119)	16/20
61	London HA-W 2325	A MILLION DOLLARS' WORTH OF TWANG (LP)	16
61	London HA-W 2373	GIRLS, GIRLS, GIRLS (LP, also stereo SAH-W 6173)	15/20
62	London HA-W 2435	A MILLION DOLLARS' WORTH OF TWANG VOL. 2 (LP)	16
62	RCA RD 27264/SF 5134	TWISTIN' AND TWANGIN' (LP, mono/stereo)	15/20
62	RCA RD/SF 7510	TWANGY GUITAR — SILKY STRINGS (LP, mono/stereo)	12/18
63	RCA RD/SF 7545	DANCE WITH THE GUITAR MAN (LP, mono/stereo)	15/20
63	RCA RD/SF 7560	TWANG A COUNTRY SONG (LP, mono/stereo)	15/20
63	RCA RD/SF 7568	TWANGIN' UP A STORM (LP, mono/stereo)	15/20
64	RCA RD/SF 7621	LONELY GUITAR (LP, mono/stereo)	18/22
64	RCA RD/SF 7656	WATER SKIING (LP, mono/stereo)	20/24
65	RCA RD/SF 7689	TWANGIN' THE GOLDEN HITS (LP, mono/stereo)	15/20
65	RCA RD/SF 7754	WELCOME TO TWANGSVILLE (LP, mono/stereo)	18/25
65	Colpix PXL 490	DUANE A-GO-GO (LP)	16
66	Colpix PXL 494	DUANE DOES BOB DYLAN (LP)	18
67	Reprise R(S)LP 6218	THE BIGGEST TWANG OF THEM ALL (LP, mono/stereo)	12/16
67	Reprise R(S)LP 6240	THE ROARIN' TWANGIES (LP)	25
67	G. Guinea GG(S)L 10337	DUANE DOES BOB DYLAN (LP, reissue, mono/stereo)	12/18
70	Valiant VS 108	THE BIGGEST TWANG OF THEM ALL (LP)	10
70	London ZGW 105	MOVIN' & GROOVIN' (LP)	10
84	private pressing	REBEL ROUSIN' (LP, Duane Eddy convention anniversary issue)	10

(see also Lee Hazlewood)

PEARL EDDY

54	HMV 7M 262	Devil Lips/That's What A Heart Is for	7

EDDY & TEDDY

61	London HLU 9367	Bye Bye Butterfly/Star Crossed Lovers	5

EDDYSONS

68	Olga OLE 010	Ups And Downs/Sweet Memories	4

DAVID EDE BAND

60	Pye 7N 15280	Easy Go/The Blue Bird (as David Ede & Rabin Rock)	4
61	Pye 7N 15329	Bootnik/Obsession	4
61	Pye 7N 15370	Last Night/Ding Dong John	4
61	Pye 7N 15394	Twelfth Street Rag/No Hats On Ilkley	4
62	Pye 7N 15417	Twistin' Those Meeces To Pieces/Twistin' The Trad	4

(see also Oscar Rabin)

TONI EDEN

60	Columbia DB 4409	Teen Street/No One Understands (My Johnny)	8
60	Columbia DB 4458	Grown Up Dreams/Whad'ya Gonna Do	6
60	Columbia DB 4527	Will I Ever/The Waitin' Game	5
61	Decca F 11342	Send Me/Interesting Facts	5

EDEN'S CHILDREN

68	Stateside (S)SL 10235	EDEN'S CHILDREN (LP)	20

EDGE

78	Albion ION 4	Macho Man/I'm Cold (p/s)	4
79	Hurricane FIRE 3	Downhill/American Express (p/s, white vinyl)	5

(see also Damned, Culture Club)

EDGE with SINEAD O'CONNOR

86	Virgin VS 897	Heroine (Theme From "Captive")/Heroine (Mix II) (p/s)	6
86	Virgin VS 897-12	Heroine (Theme From "Captive")/Heroine (Mix II) (12", p/s)	12

(see also U2, Sinéad O'Connor)

HARRY 'SWEETS' EDISON SEXTET

60	HMV POP 720	Hollering At The Watkins/K.M. Blues	4

EDISON LIGHTHOUSE

71	Bell BLL 1153	What's Happening/Take A Little Time	4
72	Bell BLL 1206	Find Mr Zebedee?/Reconsider My Belinda	4

LADA EDMUND JR

75	MCA MU 172	The Larue/Soul Au Go-Go	5

DAVE EDMUNDS (& ROCKPILE)

71	Regal Zonophone RZ 3032	I'm Coming Home/Country Roll	6
71	Regal Zonophone RZ 3037	Blue Monday/I'll Get Along	6
72	Regal Zonophone RZ 3059	Down Down Down/It Ain't Easy	5
73	Rockfield ROC 1	Baby I Love You/Maybe	4
73	Rockfield ROC 2	Born To Be With You/Pick Axe Rag (with Mickie Gee)	4

Dave EDMUNDS

74	Rockfield ROC 4	Need A Shot Of Rhythm And Blues/Let It Be Me	5
75	Rockfield ROC 6	I Ain't Never/Some Other Guy	5
76	Swan Song SSK 19408	Here Comes The Weekend/As Lovers Do	4
76	Swan Song SSK 19409	Where Or When/New York's A Lonely Town	4
77	Swan Song SSK 19410	Ju Ju Man/What Did I Do Last Night?	4
78	Swan Song SSK 19413	Deborah/What Looks Best On You	4
79	Swan Song SSK 19418	Girls Talk/Bad Is Bad (p/s, clear vinyl)	4
71	Regal Zono. SRZA 8503	ROCKPILE COLLECTION (LP, unreleased)	
71	Regal Zono. SLRZ 1026	ROCKPILE (LP)	30
75	Rockfield RRL 101	SUBTLE AS A FLYING MALLET (LP)	10
82	Arista SPART 1184	DE 7TH (LP, with free EP "Live At The Venue" [JUKE 1])	10

(see also Image, Human Beings, Love Sculpture, Rockpile)

EDOUARD
66	CBS 202200	My Name Is Edouard/N'aie Pas Peur Antoinette (p/s)	5

EDSEL AUCTIONEER
89	Decoy DYS 6	Our New Skin/Strung (p/s)	4
90	Decoy DYS 14	Stickleback/Colour Of Guilt (Demo) (p/s)	4

EDSELS
61	Pye Intl. 7N 25086	Rama Langa Ding Dong/Bells	40

IAN EDWARD & ZODIACS
(see under Ian & Zodiacs)

(KING) EDWARDS GROUP
63	Island WI 040	Dear Hearts/OSBOURNE GRAHAM: Oh Mary	10
63	Island WI 047	Russian Roulette (actually by King Edwards Allstars)/You're Mine (actually by Douglas Brothers)	10
63	Island WI 082	He Gave You To Me/Kings Priests And Prophets (both actually by Schoolboys)	10
63	Island WI 087	Hey Girl/Skies Are Grey (both actually by Osbourne Graham)	10

EDWARD'S HAND
71	RCA SF 8154	STRANDED (LP)	12
73	Regal Zono. SRZA 8513	RAINSHINE (LP)	60

BOBBY EDWARDS
61	Top Rank JAR 584	You're The Reason/I'm A Fool Loving You	7

BRENT EDWARDS
63	Pye Intl. 7N 25197	Pride/Over The Weekend	7

CHUCK EDWARDS
68	Soul City SC 104	Downtown Soulville/I Need You	10

GARY EDWARDS (COMBO)
62	Oriole CB 1700	Twist Or Bust/The Franz Liszt Twist (as Gary Edwards Combo)	6
62	Oriole CB 1717	The Method/Twistful Thinkin'	4
62	Oriole CB 1733	Africa/One Fifteen A.M.	6
62	Oriole CB 1759	Hopscotch/Theme For A Broken Dream	6

(WILFRED) JACKIE EDWARDS (Jamaica)
60	Starlite ST45 016	We're Gonna Love/Your Eyes Are Dreaming (as Wilfred Edwards & Caribs)	10
60	Starlite ST45 026	I Know/Tell Me Darling (as Wilfred Edwards)	10
61	Starlite ST45 046	Whenever There's Moonlight/Heaven Just Knows (as Wilfred Edwards)	8
61	Starlite ST45 062	More Than Words Can Say/I Love You No More (as Wilfred Edwards)	8
62	Starlite ST45 076	Little Bitty Girl/Never Go Away (as Wilfred Edwards)	10
62	Island WI 008	All My Days/Hear Me Cry (as Wilfred Jackie Edwards)	10
62	Island WI 019	One More Week/Tears Like Rain (as Wilfred Jackie Edwards)	10
62	Decca F 11547	Lonely Game/Suddenly	7
63	Black Swan WI 404	Why Make Believe/Do You Want Me (as Wilfred Jackie Edwards & Velvetts)	10
64	Black Swan WI 416	The Things You Do/Little Smile (as Wilfred Jackie Edwards)	10
64	Fontana TF 465	Sea Cruise/Little Princess	12
64	Sue WI 329	Stagger Lee/Pretty Girl	12
65	Aladdin WI 601	He'll Have To Go/Gotta Learn To Love Again	7
65	Aladdin WI 605	Hush/I Am In Love With You No More	10
65	Aladdin WI 611	The Same One/I Don't Know	8
65	Island WI 255	White Christmas/My Love And I	8
66	Island WI 270	Sometimes/Come On Home	7
66	Island WI 274	L-O-V-E/What's Your Name	7
66	Island WI 287	Think Twice/Oh Mary	7
66	Island WI 3006	I Feel So Bad/I Don't Want To Be Made A Fool Of	45
66	Island WI 3018	Royal Telephone/It's No Secret	7
67	Horse 001	I Must Go Back/Baby I Want To Be Near You	5
67	Island WI 3030	Only A Fool Breaks His Own Heart/The End	7
67	Island WIP 6008	Come Back Girl/Tell Him You Lied	5
68	Island WIP 6026	Julie On My Mind/If This Is Heaven	5
68	Island WI 3157	You're My Girl/Heaven Only Knows	6
69	Direction 58-4096	Why Must I Be Alone/I'm Gonna Make You Cry	4
69	Direction 58-4402	Too Experienced/Someone To Love	4
69	Direction 58-4630	Oh Manio/Here We Go Again	4
76	Island WIP 6285	Come On Home/I Feel So Bad	4
66	Island IEP 701	SACRED HYMNS VOL. 1 (EP, no p/s)	12
66	Island IEP 702	SACRED HYMNS VOL. 2 (EP, no p/s)	12
66	Island IEP 708	HUSH (EP)	25
64	Island ILP 906	THE MOST OF WILFRED JACKIE EDWARDS (LP)	50
64	Island ILP 912	STAND UP FOR JESUS (LP)	40
66	Island ILP 931	COME ON HOME (LP)	50
66	Island ILP 936	THE BEST OF JACKIE EDWARDS (LP)	45
66	Island ILP 940	BY DEMAND (LP)	45

67	Island ILP(S) 960	PREMATURE GOLDEN SANDS (LP)	30
69	Island IWP 4	PUT YOUR TEARS AWAY (LP)	30
69	Direction 8-63977	LET IT BE ME (LP)	10
70	Trojan TTL 40	THE MOST OF WILFRED JACKIE EDWARDS (LP, as Wilfred Jackie Edwards)	15
70	Trojan TTL 45	COME ON HOME (LP)	15
70	Trojan TTL 46	BY DEMAND (LP)	15
70	Trojan TTL 57	PREMATURE GOLDEN SANDS (LP, reissue)	15
70	Trojan TBL 156	PREMATURE GOLDEN SANDS (LP, 2nd reissue)	12

JACKIE EDWARDS & JIMMY CLIFF
68	Island WIP 6036	Set Me Free/Here I Come	4
68	Island WIP 6042	You're My Girl/Heaven Only Knows	4

(see also Jackie & Millie, Millie, Jimmy Cliff, Wilfred & Millie)

JIMMY EDWARDS (U.S.)
58	Mercury 7MT 193	Love Bug Crawl/Honey Lovin'	200
58	Mercury MT 193	Love Bug Crawl/Honey Lovin' (78)	45

JIMMY EDWARDS (U.K.)
60	Fontana H 260	I've Never Seen A Straight Banana/Rhymes	4

JIMMY EDWARDS (& PROFILE) (U.K.)
79	Warner Bros K 17415	Nora's Diary/Call Me A Fraud (as Jimmy Edwards & Profile) (p/s)	4
79	Warner Bros K 17464	Twentieth Century Time/Seven Hail Marys (as Jimmy Edwards & Profile) (p/s)	4
80	Polydor 2059 240	Toys/Hard Heart (as Jimmy Edwards & Profile) (p/s)	4
80	Polydor 2059 256	Cabaret/Drag It Back (p/s)	4
81	Polydor POSP 240	In The City/Five Minute Girl (p/s)	4

(see also Time U.K.)

JOHN EDWARDS
76	Cotillion K 10817	Baby Hold On/Key To My Life	4

JONATHAN & DARLENE EDWARDS
57	Philips BBE 12155	THE PIANO ARTISTRY OF JONATHAN EDWARDS (EP)	7
58	Philips BBE 12179	THE PIANO ARTISTRY OF JONATHAN EDWARDS NO. 2 (EP)	7
60	Philips BBL 7412	JONATHAN & DARLENE EDWARDS IN PARIS (LP, stereo SBBL 590)	10/12
64	RCA Victor RD/SF 7698	SING ALONG WITH JONATHAN AND DARLENE EDWARDS (LP)	10

(see also Gordon MacRae, Jo Stafford)

MILL EDWARDS
73	Action ACT 4617	I Found Myself/Don't Forget About Me	4

RUPERT/RUPIE EDWARDS
61	Blue Beat BB 90	Guilty Convict/Just Because	10
68	Doctor Bird DB 1163	I Can't Forget/I'm Writing Again	8
69	Crab CRAB 35	Long Lost Love/Uncertain Love	4

TOM EDWARDS
57	Vogue Coral Q 72236	What Is A Teen Age Girl?/What Is A Teen Age Boy?	5

TOMMY EDWARDS
52	MGM MGM 466	It's All In The Game/My Concerto (78)	5
53	MGM SP 1030	(Now And Then, There's) A Fool Such As I/Take These Chains From My Heart	8
53	MGM MGM 598	(Now And Then, There's) A Fool Such As I/Take These Chains From My Heart (78)	5
56	MGM SP 1168	Baby, Let Me Take You Dreaming/MARION SISTERS: Life Could Not Better Be	7
56	MGM MGM 894	Baby, Let Me Take You Dreaming/MARION SISTERS: Life Could Not Better Be (78)	5
58	MGM MGM 989	It's All In The Game/Please Love Me Forever	5
58	MGM MGM 989	It's All In The Game/Please Love Me Forever (78)	5
58	MGM MGM 995	Love Is All We Need/Mr. Music Man	4
59	MGM MGM 1006	Please, Mr. Sun/The Morning Side Of The Mountain	4
59	MGM MGM 1020	My Melancholy Baby/It's Only The Good Times	5
59	MGM MGM 1020	My Melancholy Baby/It's Only The Good Times (78)	5
59	MGM MGM 1032	I've Been There/I Looked At Heaven	4
59	MGM MGM 1045	(New In) The Ways Of Love/Honestly And Truly	4
60	MGM MGM 1065	Don't Fence Me In/I'm Building Castles Again	4
60	MGM MGM 1080	I Really Don't Want To Know/Unloved	4
60	MGM MGM 1097	Blue Heartaches/It's Not The End Of Everything	4
59	MGM MGM-EP 707	I'VE BEEN THERE (EP)	12
60	MGM MGM-EP 712	THE WAYS OF LOVE (EP)	12
59	MGM MGM-C 734	IT'S ALL IN THE GAME (LP)	15
59	MGM MGM-C 791	FOUR YOUNG LOVERS (LP)	15
60	MGM MGM-C 824	YOU STARTED ME DREAMING (LP)	15

VINCE EDWARDS
58	Capitol CL 14825	Widget/Lollipop	4
64	Colpix PX 771	No Not Much/See That Girl (p/s)	6
66	United Artists UP 1166	I Like It/Skip To Ma Loo	4
67	United Artists UP 1179	I Can't Turn Back Time/Lively One	8
68	United Artists UP 2230	County Durham Dream/It's The Same Old Song	6
68	United Artists UP 2236	Aquarius/Hair	4
60s	United Artists	BEN CASEY (EP)	10

WEBLEY EDWARDS' HAWAII CALLS ORCHESTRA
56	Capitol CL 14636	Lovely Hula Hands/Twilight In Hawaii	4

WILFRED EDWARDS
(see under Jackie Edwards)

EDWICK RUMBOLD
66	CBS 202393	Specially When/Come Back	40

MINT VALUE £

67	Parlophone R 5622	Shades Of Grey/Boggle Woggle	40

E.F. BAND
80	Aerco/EF Band EF 1	Night Angel/Another Day Gone (p/s)	10
80	Redball RR 026	Self Made Suicide/Sister Syne (p/s)	7
80	Redball RR 036	The Devil's Eye/Comprende (p/s)	6
80	Rok ROK XI/XII	Another Day Gone/SYNCHROMESH: October Friday (company sleeve)	6
83	Bullet CULP 2	DEEP CUT (LP)	10

WALTER EGAN
77	United Artists UP 36245	Only The Lucky/I'd Rather Have Fun	4

(see also Buckingham-Nicks)

WILLIE EGANS
60s	XX MIN 714	WILLIE EGANS (EP)	12
70s	Flyright LP 6000	ROCKS, BOOGIES AND ROLLS (LP)	12

JOSEPH EGER
69	Charisma CAS 1008	CLASSICAL HEADS (LP)	15

EGG
69	Deram DM 269	Seven Is A Jolly Good Time/You Are All Princes	8
70	Deram Nova SDN 14	EGG (LP)	18
70	Deram SML 1074	THE POLITE FORCE (LP)	18
74	Caroline C 1510	THE CIVIL SURFACE (LP)	12

(see also Hatfield & North, Arzachel)

EGGY
70	Spark SRL 1024	Hookey/You're Still Mine	15

8-EYED SPY
82	Fetish FE 19	Diddy Wah Diddy/Dead You Me B Side (p/s)	8
81	Fetish FR 2003	8-EYED SPY (LP)	12

(see also Lydia Lunch)

EIGHTH DAY
71	Invictus INV 514	She's Not Just Another Woman/I Can't Fool Myself	4
72	Invictus INV 521	Eeny Meeny Miny Mo/Rock In My Head	4

EIGHTH WONDER
85	CBS QTX 6594	Stay With Me/Loser In Love (12", poster p/s)	20
87	CBS 650264-6	Will You Remember/Having It All (12", poster p/s)	8
87	CBS PHONE P1	When The Phone Stops Ringing (Single Version)/Let Me In (picture disc)	6
88	CBS SCARE 1	I'm Not Scared/J'ai Pas Peur (Disco Mix) (p/s)	4
88	CBS SCARE T1	I'm Not Scared/I'm Not Scared (Disco Mix)/J'ai Pas Peur (12", p/s)	7
88	CBS SCARE Y1	I'm Not Scared/I'm Not Scared (Disco Mix)/J'ai Pas Peur (10", p/s)	12
88	CBS SCARE C1	I'm Not Scared/I'm Not Scared (Disco Mix)/J'ai Pas Peur (CD)	12
88	CBS BABEQT 1	Baby Baby (Balearic Beat Baby Remix)/Dusted (12", p/s)	18
88	CBS BABECD 1	Baby Baby (Balearic Beat Baby Remix)/Dusted (CD)	7
89	CBS 6515522	Cross My Heart/Let Me In/Cross My Heart (Dance Mix)/(House Mix) (CD)	8

(see also Pet Shop Boys)

EIGHTIES LADIES
86	Music Of Life MOLIF 6	Turned On To You/Turned On To You (Alternative Mix) (12", p/s)	15

808 STATE
88	Creed STATE 003	Let Yourself Go (303 Mix)/Let Yourself Go (D50 Mix)/Deepville (12", plain stickered sleeve)	12
89	ZTT ZANG 1TX	Pacific — 909 (Mellow Birds Mega Edit)/Bonus Bird Beats/Cobra Bora (12", plain stickered sleeve)	10
88	Creed STATE 002	NEWBUILD (LP)	20
89	Creed STATE 003	QUADRASTATE (LP)	10

(see also Hit Squad, Biting Tongues)

EINSTÜRZENDE NEUBAUTEN
85	Some Bizzare BART 12	Yü-Gung/Seelebrennt/Sand (12", p/s)	7
85	Some Bizzare BART 451	Das Shcaben/Das Schaben (LP freebie, no p/s)	8

EIRE APPARENT
67	Track 604 019	Follow Me/Here I Go Again	10
69	Buddah 2011 039	Rock'N'Roll Band/Yes I Need Someone	8
72	Buddah 2011 117	Rock'N'Roll Band/Yes I Need Someone (reissue)	5
69	Buddah 203 021	SUNRISE (LP)	25

EJECTED
82	Riot City RIOT 14	HAVE YOU GOT 10p (EP)	4
82	Riot City RIOT 19	NOISE FOR THE BOYS (EP)	4

BRITT EKLAND
79	Jet JET 161	Do It To Me/Private Party (gatefold p/s)	4
79	Jet JETP 161	Do It To Me/Private Party (picture disc)	4

EKSEPTION
69	Philips 6314 001	BEGGAR JULIAN'S TIME TRIP (LP)	15
70	Philips 6314 005	EKSEPTION (LP)	15
71	Philips 6423 005	EKSEPTION III (LP)	12
72	Philips 6423 019	00.04 (LP)	12
72	Philips 6423 042	V (LP)	12
74	Philips 6423 079	CLASSICS IN POP (LP)	10
75	Philips 6423 082	MIND MIRROR (LP)	10
75	Philips 6314 044	EKSEPTIONAL CLASSICS (LP)	10

ELASTIC BAND
68	Decca F 12763	Think Of You Baby/It's Been A Long Time Baby	20
68	Decca F 12815	Do Unto Others (From "Mr. Rose" T.V. Series)/8½ Hours Of Paradise	20

69	Decca Nova (S)DN 6	EXPANSIONS ON LIFE (LP, mono/stereo)	40/35

(see also Mayfields Mule, Sweet, Love Affair, Northwind)

ELASTICK BAND

67	Stateside SS 2056	Spazz/Papier Mache (unissued, demos only)	40

DONNIE ELBERT

58	Parlophone R 4403	Wild Child/Let's Do The Stroll	40
58	Parlophone R 4403	Wild Child/Let's Do The Stroll (78)	30
65	Sue WI 377	A Little Piece Of Leather/Do Watcha Wanna	15
65	Sue WI 396	You Can Push It (Or Pull It)/Lily Lou	15
67	CBS 2807	Get Ready/Along Came Pride	5
68	Polydor BM 56234	In Between The Heartaches/Too Far Gone	6
68	Polydor BM 56265	This Old Heart Of Mine (Is Weak For You)/Run Little Girl	6
69	Deram DM 235	Without You/Baby Please Come Home	4
70s	New Wave NW 1	Without You/Baby Please Come Home (reissue)	4
73	Ember	THE ROOTS OF DONNIE ELBERT (LP)	10

ELCORT

66	Parlophone R 5447	Tammy/Searchin'	10

ELDORADOS (U.K.)

63	Decca DFE 8543	THE ELDORADOS (EP)	18

ELDORADOS (U.S.)

72	Mojo 2092 050	Loose Booty Pts 1 & 2	4

ROY ELDRIDGE & CLAUDE BOLLING

56	Vogue V 2373	Wild Man Blues/Fireworks	4

ELECAMPANE

75	Dame Jane ODJ 1	WHEN GOD'S ON THE WATER (LP, private pressing with insert)	80
78	Dame Jane ODJ 2	FURTHER ADVENTURES OF MR PUNCH (LP, private pressing with booklet)	30
87	Dame Jane ODJ 3	SWINGS AND ROUNDABOUTS (private cassette)	10

ELECTRIC BANANA

67	De Wolfe DWSLP 3280	ELECTRIC BANANA (LP, with other artists)	15
68	De Wolfe DWSLP 3281	MORE ELECTRIC BANANA (LP)	15
60s	De Wolfe DWSLP 3282	EVEN MORE ELECTRIC BANANA (LP)	15
70s	De Wolfe DWSLP 3283	THE RETURN OF THE ELECTRIC BANANA (LP)	15
73	De Wolfe DWSLP 3284	HOT LICKS (LP)	15
79	Butt NOTT 001	THE SEVENTIES (LP, with other artists)	10
80	Butt NOTT 003	THE SIXTIES (LP, with other artists)	10

(see also Pretty Things)

ELECTRIC CHAIRS

(see under Wayne County/Electric Chairs)

ELECTRIC CRAYONS

89	Emergency MIV 3	Hip Shake Junkie/Happy To Be Hated (p/s)	12

(see also Charlatans)

ELECTRIC EELS (U.K.)

80	Slippery Discs XPRES 3410	Not In Love (With The Modern World)/Double Complications/Jellied Reggae (10", p/s)	7

ELECTRIC EELS (U.S.)

(see under Die Electric Eels)

ELECTRIC FLAG

68	CBS 3584	Groovin' Is Easy/Over-Lovin' You	7
69	CBS 4066	Sunny/Soul Searchin'	7
68	CBS 62394	A LONG TIME COMIN' (LP)	10
69	CBS 63462	ELECTRIC FLAG (LP)	10
74	Atlantic K 50090	THE BAND KEPT PLAYING (LP)	10

(see also Mike Bloomfield, Buddy Miles, Barry Goldberg)

ELECTRIC GUITARS

81	Fried Egg EGG 12	Health/The Continental Shelf (p/s, with insert)	4

ELECTRICIANS

67	Columbia DB 8228	Champion House Theme/DON HARPER & ELECTRICIANS: Shin Bone	4

(see also Don Harper)

ELECTRIC INDIAN

69	United Artists UP 35039	Keem O Sabe/Broad Street	4

ELECTRIC JOHNNY

61	London HLU 9384	Black-Eyes Rock/Johnny On His Strings	20

ELECTRIC LIGHT ORCHESTRA (E.L.O.)

73	Harvest HAR 5063	Roll Over Beethoven/Manhattan Rumble (with withdrawn B-side)	8
73	Harvest HAR 5077	Showdown/In Old England Town (Instrumental)	5
75	Warner Bros K 16510	Can't Get It Out Of My Head/Illusions In G Major	4
76	Jet SJET 769	Night Rider/Daybreaker	6
76	Jet UP 36184	Livin' Thing/Fire On High (blue vinyl)	8
77	Jet UP 36209	Rockaria!/Poker (p/s)	5
77	Harvest HAR 12-5121	Showdown/Roll Over Beethoven (12", p/s)	8
77	Jet UP 36313	Turn To Stone/Mr. Kingdom (p/s)	4
78	Jet UP 36342	Mr. Blue Sky/One Summer Dream (p/s, some on blue vinyl)	7/4
78	Jet SJET 100	Rockaria!/Poker (reissue, no p/s)	4
78	Jet SJET 101	Telephone Line/Call Boy (reissue, no p/s)	4
78	Jet SJET 103	Turn To Stone/Mr. Kingdom (reissue, no p/s)	4
78	Jet SJET 104	Mr. Blue Sky/One Summer Dream (reissue, no p/s)	4
78	Jet SJET 109	Wild West Hero/Eldorado (p/s)	4

ELECTRIC LIGHT ORCHESTRA

78	Jet SJET 12-109	Wild West Hero/Eldorado (12", yellow vinyl, die-cut company sleeve, most with picture labels, some with 'Jet' labels) 8/10
78	Jet SJET 121	Sweet Talkin' Woman/Bluebird Is Dead (p/s, mauve or black vinyl) 5/4
78	Jet SJET 12-121	Sweet Talkin' Woman/Bluebird Is Dead (12", p/s, mauve vinyl) 10
78	Jet ELO 1	THE ELO EP (p/s) 5
79	Jet SJET 144	Shine A Little Love/Jungle (p/s) 4
79	Jet SJET 12-144	Shine A Little Love/Jungle (12", white vinyl, company sleeve) 7
79	Jet SJET 150	The Diary Of Horace Wimp/Down Home Town (p/s) 5
79	Jet SJET 153	Don't Bring Me Down/Dreaming Of 4000 (p/s) 4
79	Jet SJET 12-153	Don't Bring Me Down/Dreaming Of 4000 (12", p/s) 7
79	Jet JET 166	Confusion/Last Train To London (p/s, some with sticker) 6/5
80	Jet SJET 179	I'm Alive/Drum Drums (p/s) 4
80	Jet JET 185	Xanadu/Fool Country (gatefold p/s, with Olivia Newton-John) 6
80	Jet JET 10-185	Xanadu/Fool Country (10" pink vinyl, die-cut p/s, with Olivia Newton-John) 10
80	Jet JET 195	All Over The World/Midnight Blue (p/s) 4
80	Jet JET 10-195	All Over The World/Midnight Blue (10", die-cut p/s, blue vinyl) 10
81	Jet JET 7011	Hold On Tight/When Time Stood Still (p/s) 6
81	Jet JET 7015	Twilight/Julie Don't Live Here (p/s) 4
81	Jet JET 7018	Ticket To The Moon/Here Is The News (p/s) 6
81	Jet JET 12-7018	Ticket To The Moon/Here Is The News (12", picture disc) 12
83	Jet A 3720	Secret Messages/Buildings Have Eyes (p/s) 4
83	Jet PA 3720	Secret Messages/Buildings Have Eyes (picture disc) 7
83	Jet A 3869	Four Little Diamonds/Letter From Spain (p/s) 4
83	Jet TA 3869	Four Little Diamonds/Letter From Spain/The Bouncer (12", p/s) 10
86	Epic EPC A 6844	Calling America/Caught In The Trap (p/s) 4
86	Epic QTA 6844	Calling America/Caught In The Trap/Destination Unknown (12", p/s) 8
86	Epic QTA A 7090	So Serious/Matter Of Fact (p/s) 4
86	Epic QTA 7090	So Serious/Matter Of Fact/Matter Of Fact (Alternate Lyrics) (12", p/s) 8
86	Epic EPC A 7317	Getting To The Point/Secret Lives (p/s) 4
86	Epic QTA 7317	Getting To The Point/Secret Lives/E.L.O. Megamix (12", p/s) 10
78	Jet JETBX 1	THREE LIGHT YEARS (3-LP, boxed set of "On The Third Day", "Eldorado" & "Face The Music", with booklet) 15
78	Jet JETLP 200	A NEW WORLD RECORD (LP, with inner sleeve, red vinyl) 15
78	Jet JETLP 201	FACE THE MUSIC (LP, with inner sleeve, green vinyl) 15
78	Jet JETLP 202	ON THE THIRD DAY (LP, with inner sleeve, clear vinyl) 12
78	Jet JETLP 203	ELDORADO (LP, with inner sleeve, yellow vinyl) 15
78	Jet JETDP 400	OUT OF THE BLUE (2-LP, with inner sleeves, clear or dark blue vinyl) 14
82	Jet JETBX 2	FOUR LIGHT YEARS (4-LP, boxed set of "A New World Record", "Out Of The Blue" & "Discovery", with booklet) 18

(see also Idle Race, Move, Violinski, Michael D'Alberquerque, Olivia Newton-John, Louis Clark, Wilson Gale & Co., Tandy-Morgan, Kelly Groucutt)

ELECTRIC PERSONALITIES
79	Barclay Towers BT 3	Cage At The Zoo/Hot Spot (p/s) 4

ELECTRIC PRUNES
66	Reprise RS 20532	I Had Too Much To Dream (Last Night)/Luvin' 10
67	Reprise RS 20564	Get Me To The World On Time/Are You Lovin' Me More 10
67	Reprise RS 20607	The Great Banana Hoax/Wind-Up Toys 10
67	Reprise RS 23212	A Long Day's Flight/The King Is In His Counting House 12
68	Reprise RS 20652	Everybody Knows You're Not In Love/You Never Had It Better 15
73	Elektra K 12102	I Had Too Much To Dream (Last Night)/KNICKERBOCKERS: Lies 5
79	Radar ADA 16	I Had Too Much To Dream (Last Night)/Luvin' (p/s, reissue) 4
67	Reprise R(S)LP 6248	THE ELECTRIC PRUNES (LP) 25
68	Reprise R(S)LP 6275	MASS IN F MINOR (LP) 18
68	Reprise RSLP 6316	RELEASE OF AN OATH (LP) 20

ELECTRIC TOILET
83	Psycho PSYCHO 8	IN THE HANDS OF KARMA (LP) 15

ELECTRIX
79	ELX 001	HOLLAND (EP) 5

ELECTRO TUNES
80	Cobra COS 5	If This Ain't Love/Bodywork (p/s) 4

ELEGANTS
58	HMV POP 520	Little Star/Getting Dizzy 20
58	HMV POP 520	Little Star/Getting Dizzy (78) 15
58	HMV POP 551	Please Believe Me/Goodnight 25
58	HMV POP 551	Please Believe Me/Goodnight (78) 20

ELEPHANT BAND
72	Mojo 2092 036	Stone Penguin/Groovin' At The Apollo 8

ELEPHANT ILLNESS
91	Trunk CALL 003	The Beatles Were Always My Favourites/Charlie Mingus-mungous (no p/s) 15

ELEPHANT'S MEMORY
69	Buddah 201055	Crossroads Of The Stepping Stones/Yoghurt Song 4
69	Buddah 201067	Old Man Willow/Jungle Gym At The Zoo 4
72	Apple APPLE 45	Power Boogie/Liberation Special 8
70	CBS 5207	Mongoose/I Couldn't Dream 4
69	Buddah BDLH 5033	ELEPHANT'S MEMORY (LP) 10
72	Apple SAPCOR 22	ELEPHANT'S MEMORY (LP, gatefold sleeve, with inner) 20

(see also John Lennon)

11.59
74	Dovetail DOVE 4	THIS IS OUR SACRIFICE OF PRAISE (LP, with insert) 65

ELEVENTH HOUR
74	Pye Intl. 7N 25653	So Good/My Bed 4

75	20th Century BTC 2215	Hollywood Hot/Hollywood Hotter	4

ELF
74	Purple PUR 118	L.A. '59/Ain't It All Amusing	5
74	Purple TPS 3506	CAROLINA COUNTRY BALL (LP)	25

(see also Roger Glover, Dio, Rainbow, Black Sabbath)

ELGINS
66	Tamla Motown TMG 551	Put Yourself In My Place/Darling Baby	30
66	Tamla Motown TMG 583	Heaven Must Have Sent You/Stay In My Lonely Arms	18
67	Tamla Motown TMG 615	It's Been A Long Long Time/I Understand My Man	20
68	Tamla Motown TMG 642	Put Yourself In My Place/Darling Baby (reissue)	8
71	Tamla Motown TMG 771	Heaven Must Have Sent You/Stay In My Lonely Arms (reissue)	4
68	T. Motown (S)TML 11081	DARLING BABY (LP)	25

ELIAS & HIS ZIG-ZAG JIVE FLUTES
58	Columbia DB 4109	Tom Hark/Ry-Ry	7
58	Columbia DB 4146	Zeph Boogie/Vucka' Magcwabeni (Back From The Dead)	5

ELIAS HULK
70	Youngblood SSYB 8	UNCHAINED (LP)	175

ELIGIBLES
59	Capitol CL 15067	Faker, Faker/24 Hours (Till My Date With You)	5
59	Capitol CL 15098	The Little Engine/My First Christmas With You	5
60	Capitol (S)T 1310	ALONG THE TRAIL (LP)	10
61	Capitol (S)T 1411	LOVE IS A GAMBLE (LP)	10

ELIMINATORS
66	Pye NPL 18160	GUITARS AND PERCUSSION (LP)	12

ELIXIR
86	Elixir	THE SON OF ODIN (LP)	10

ELIZABETH
73	Paramount PARA 3032	Stop Killing Me With Kindness/Oh Bird	4
68	Vanguard SVRL 19010	ELIZABETH (LP)	12

JIMMY ELLEDGE
62	RCA RCA 1274	Swanee River Rocket/Funny How Time Slips Away	10
65	Hickory 45-1363	Pink Dally Rue/Legend In My Time	6
64	RCA RCX 7132	FUNNY HOW TIME SLIPS AWAY (EP)	15

ELLI
67	Parlophone R 5575	Never Mind/I'll Be Looking Out For You	4

YVONNE ELLIMAN
71	MCA MK 5063	I Don't Know How To Love Him/Jesus Christ Superstar Overture	4

DUKE ELLINGTON & HIS (FAMOUS) ORCHESTRA
53	HMV 7M 156	Otto Make That Riff Staccato/Time's A-Wastin'	6
54	HMV JO 303	Flamingo/Jump For Joy (export issue)	5
54	HMV JO 268	In A Sentimental Mood/Let A Song Go Out Of My Heart (export issue)	5
54	HMV 7M 170	The Flaming Sword/BARNEY BIGARD ORCHESTRA: A Lull At Dawn	6
54	Capitol CL 14186	Smile/If I Give My Heart To You	6
55	Capitol CL 14229	Twelfth Street Rag (Mambo)/Chile Bowl	6
55	Capitol CL 14260	Tyrolean Tango/All Day Long	5
55	Columbia SCM 5182	Brown Betty/Ting-A-Ling	6
59	Philips PB 946	Anatomy Of A Murder/Flirtibird	4
59	Philips PB 243	Skin Deep Pts 1 & 2	5
60	Philips JAZ 101	Malletoba Skank/All Of Me	4
60	Philips JAZ 117	Duke's Place/Jones	4
54	Capitol EAP1 477	THE DUKE PLAYS ELLINGTON (EP)	7
54	Capitol EAP2 477	THE DUKE PLAYS ELLINGTON PT. 2 (EP)	7
54	HMV 7EG 8033	DUKE ELLINGTON AND HIS ORCHESTRA (EP)	7
55	HMV 7EG 8158	DUKE ELLINGTON AND AL HIBBLER (EP)	7
55	Capitol EAP1 521	ELLINGTON '55 (EP)	7
55	Capitol EAP2 521	ELLINGTON '55 (EP)	7
55	Capitol EAP3 521	ELLINGTON '55 (EP)	7
55	Vogue EPV 1051	DUKE ELLINGTON — BILLY STRAYHORN (EP)	7
55	Vogue EPV 1060	DUKE ELLINGTON AND THE CORONETS (EP)	7
55	Philips BBE 12002	DUKE ELLINGTON — BETTY ROCHE (EP)	7
56	Capitol EAP2 637	DANCE TO THE DUKE NO. 2 (EP)	7
56	Capitol EAP3 637	DANCE TO THE DUKE NO. 3 (EP)	7
56	HMV 7EG 8189	DUKE ELLINGTON AND JIMMY BLANTON (EP)	7
57	HMV 7EG 8209	DUKE ELLINGTON PRESENTS IVIE ANDERSON (EP)	7
57	Capitol EAP 1004	DANCE TO THE DUKE (EP)	7
57	Decca DFE 6376	THE DUKE IN LONDON (EP)	7
58	RCA RCX 1006	DUKE ELLINGTON (EP)	7
59	RCA RCX 1022	CARAVAN (EP)	7
59	Fontana TFE 17117	HARLEM TWIST (EP, with Lonnie Johnson Harlem Footwarmers & Chicago Footwarmers)	7
61	Capitol EAP1 20114	ULTRA DELUXE (EP)	7
53	HMV DLP 1007	ELLINGTON'S GREATEST (10" LP)	15
53	Vogue LDE 035	DUKE ELLINGTON AND THE CORONETS (10" LP)	15
53	Capitol LC 6616	PREMIERED BY ELLINGTON (10" LP)	15
54	Capitol LC 6670	THE DUKE PLAYS ELLINGTON (10" LP)	15
54	HMV DLP 1025	GREAT ELLINGTON SOLOISTS (10" LP)	12
54	HMV DLP 1034	ELLINGTON HIGHLIGHTS, 1940 (10" LP)	12
54	Columbia 33S 1044	JAZZ COCKTAIL (10" LP)	12
54	Capitol LCT 6008	ELLINGTON '55 (LP)	12
54	Philips BBL 7003	ELLINGTON UPTOWN (LP)	12

Duke ELLINGTON

55	HMV DLP 1070	PERFUME SUITE/BLACK BROWN AND BEIGE (10" LP)	12
55	HMV DLP 1094	SATURDAY NIGHT FUNCTION (10" LP)	12
55	Vogue Coral LRA 10027	DUKE ELLINGTON AND HIS ORCHESTRA VOL. 1 (10" LP)	12
55	Vogue Coral LRA 10028	DUKE ELLINGTON AND HIS ORCHESTRA VOL. 2 (10" LP)	12
55	Philips BBR 8044	MOOD ELLINGTON (10" LP)	15
56	London AL 3551	THE DUKE — 1926 (10" LP)	15
56	London Jazz LTZ-N 15029	HISTORICALLY SPEAKING — THE DUKE (LP)	12
56	Capitol T 679	ELLINGTON SHOWCASE (LP)	12
57	Philips BBL 7133	AT NEWPORT (LP)	12
58	HMV DLP 1172	A BLUES SERENADE (10" LP)	12
60	Philips SBBL 514	ANATOMY OF A MURDER (LP, soundtrack)	10
60	Philips SBBL 543	AT THE BALL MASQUE (LP)	10
60	Philips BBL 7355	FESTIVAL SESSION (LP, also stereo SBBL 556)	10
60	Philips BBL 7381	BLUES IN ORBIT (LP, also stereo SBBL 567)	10
61	Philips BBL 7418	THE NUTCRACKER SUITE (LP, also stereo SBBL 594)	10
61	Philips BBL 7443	ELLINGTON UPTOWN (LP)	10
61	HMV CLP 1374	SIDE BY SIDE (LP, with Johnny Hodges)	10
61	Parlophone PMC 1136	DUKE ELLINGTON PRESENTS . . . (LP)	10

MARC ELLINGTON

68	Philips BF 1665	I Shall Be Released/Mrs. Whittle	5
69	Philips BF 1742	DId You Give The World Some Love/Bless The Executioner	4
69	Philips BF 1779	Four In The Morning/Peggy Day	4
69	Philips SBL 7883	MARC ELLINGTON (LP)	15
71	B&C CAS 1033	RAINS, REINS AND CHANGES (LP)	15
72	Philips 6308 120	A QUESTION OF ROADS (LP)	18
72	Philips 6308 143	RESTORATION (LP)	15
72	Xtra XTRA 1154	MARC TIME (LP, with Fairport Convention)	15

RAY ELLINGTON QUARTET

53	Columbia SCM 5050	The Little Red Monkey/Kaw-Liga	6
54	Columbia SCM 5088	All's Going Well (My Lady Montmorency) (with Marion Ryan)/Ol' Man River	6
54	Columbia SCM 5104	Rub-A-Dub-Dub/The Owl Song	6
54	Columbia SCM 5147	A.B.C. Boogie/Christmas Cards	12
54	Columbia DB 3534	A.B.C. Boogie/Christmas Cards (78)	5
55	Columbia SCM 5177	Ko Ko Mo (I Love You So)/Woodpecker	12
55	Columbia DB 3601	Ko Ko Mo (I Love You So)/Woodpecker (78)	5
55	Columbia SCM 5187	Play It Boy, Play/The Irish Were Egyptians Long Ago	6
55	Columbia DB 3636	Play It Boy, Play/The Irish Were Egyptians Long Ago (78)	5
55	Columbia SCM 5199	Cloudburst/Pet	6
55	Columbia DB 3672	Cloudburst/Pet (78)	5
56	Columbia SCM 5250	Hold Him Tight/Who's Got The Money?	6
56	Columbia DB 3744	Hold Him Tight/Who's Got The Money? (78)	5
56	Columbia SCM 5274	Keep The Coffee Hot/Lucky 13	6
56	Columbia DB 3784	Keep The Coffee Hot/Lucky 13 (78)	5
56	Columbia DB 3821	Stranded In The Jungle/Left Hand Boogie	12
56	Columbia DB 3821	Stranded In The Jungle/Left Hand Boogie (78)	5
56	Columbia DB 3838	Giddy-Up-A Ding Dong/The Green Door	12
56	Columbia DB 3838	Giddy-Up-A Ding Dong/The Green Door (78)	5
57	Columbia DB 3905	Marianne/That Rock 'N' Rollin' Man	15
57	Columbia DB 3905	Marianne/That Rock 'N' Rollin' Man (78)	5
57	Columbia DB 4013	Don't Burn Me Up/Swaller-Tail Coat (solo)	5
57	Columbia DB 4013	Don't Burn Me Up/Swaller-Tail Coat (solo) (78)	5
58	Columbia DB 4057	Living Doll/Long Black Nylons (solo)	10
58	Columbia DB 4057	Living Doll/Long Black Nylons (solo) (78)	5
58	Pye 7N 15159	The Sultan Of Bezaaz/You Gotta Love Somebody	6
59	Pye 7N 15189	Charlie Brown/Chip Off The Old Block	6
59	Oriole CB 1512	Carina/I Was A Little Too Lonely	4
60	Ember EMB S 102	The Madison/Jump Over (with Tony Crombie Orchestra)	6
60	Ember EMB S 114	Tres Jolie/Dracula's Three Daughters	4

ELLINGTONS

79	Grapevine GRP 114	(I'm Not) Destined To Become A Loser/MILLIONAIRES: You've Got To Love Your Baby	4

MAMA CASS (ELLIOT)

68	RCA Victor RCA 1726	Dream A Little Dream Of Me/Midnight Voyage (as Mama Cass)	4
68	Stateside SS 8002	California Earthquake/Talkin' To Your Toothbrush	4
69	Stateside SS 8014	I Can Dream Can't I?/Move A Little Closer Baby	4
69	Stateside SS 8021	It's Getting Better/Who's To Blame (as Mama Cass)	4
69	Stateside SS 8031	Make Your Own Kind Of Music/Lady Love	4
70	Stateside SS 8039	New World Coming/Blow Me A Kiss	4
70	Stateside SS 8057	A Song That Never Comes/I Can Dream Can't I?	4
71	Probe PRO 519	Easy Come, Easy Go/Ain't Nobody Else Like You	4
68	Stateside S(S)L 5004	DREAM A LITTLE DREAM (LP)	10
69	Stateside S(S)L 5014	BUBBLEGUM, LEMONADE AND SOMETHING FOR MAMA (LP)	10

(see also Mamas & Papas, Big Three, Dave Mason & Cass Elliot, Mugwumps)

BERN ELLIOTT (& FENMEN)

63	Decca F 11770	Money/Nobody But Me	4
64	Decca F 11852	New Orleans/Everybody Needs A Little Love	5
64	Decca F 11970	Good Times/What Do You Want With My Baby (as Bern Elliot & Clan)	6
65	Decca F 12051	Guess Who/Make It Easy On Yourself (solo)	7
65	Decca F 12171	Lipstick Traces/Voodoo Woman (solo)	6
64	Decca DFE 8561	BERN ELLIOTT AND THE FENMEN (EP)	18

BILL ELLIOTT & ELASTIC OZ BAND

71	Apple APPLE 36	God Save Us/Do The Oz (initially with p/s)	20/6

(see also John Lennon/Yoko Ono, Splinter)

MARI ELLIOTT

76	GTO GT 58	Silly Billy/Half Past One	15

(see also Poly Styrene, X Ray Spex)

PETER ELLIOTT

57	Parlophone R 4355	To The Aisle/All At Once (You Love Her)	6
58	Parlophone R 4457	Devotion/No Fool Like An Old Fool	6
59	Parlophone R 4514	Call Me/Flamingo	4
59	Parlophone R 4529	The Young Have No Time/Over And Over	4
61	Top Rank JAR 390	Waiting For Robert E Lee/Toot Toot Tootsie	4
66	Strike JH 311	Thinking/Song Is Love	4
60s	Honey Hit TB 123	The Devil's Workshop/Three Little Peggies (p/s)	5

(RAMBLIN') JACK ELLIOTT

65	Fontana TF 575	More Pretty Girls/Roll On Buddy (as Ramblin' Jack Elliott)	4
65	Columbia DB 7593	Rusty Jigs And Sandy Sam/Rocky Mountain Belle (as Ramblin' Jack Elliott)	4
63	Collector JEA 5	RAMBLING JACK ELLIOTT (EP)	10
64	Collector JEA 6	BLUES AND COUNTRY (EP)	10
50s	Topic T 5	WOODY GUTHRIE'S BLUES (8" mini-LP)	25
50s	Topic 10T 15	JACK TAKES THE FLOOR (10" LP)	25
59	Encore ENC 194	IN LONDON (LP)	20
60	Columbia 33SX 1291	RAMBLIN' JACK ELLIOTT SINGS WOODY GUTHRIE AND JIMMIE RODGERS (LP)	20
65	Fontana TFL 6044	JACK ELLIOTT (LP)	12
65	Stateside SL 10143	JACK ELLIOTT COUNTRY STYLE (LP)	15
66	Stateside SL 10167	SINGS THE SONGS OF WOODY GUTHRIE (LP)	12

SHAWN ELLIOTT

62	Stateside SS 124	Goodbye My Lover/Ain't That A Shame	5
63	Stateside SS 174	Sincerely And Tenderly/Why Don't You Love Me Anymore	5
64	Columbia DB 7418	My Girl/Shame And Scandal In The Family	6

ELLIOTT'S SUNSHINE

68	Philips BF 1649	Is It Too Late/'Cause I'm Lonely	4

ALTON ELLIS (& FLAMES)

65	Island WI 239	Dance Crasher (with Flames)/BABBA BROOKS: Vitamin A	12
66	Doctor Bird DB 1044	Blessings Of Love/Nothing Sweeter (as Alton & Flames)	12
66	Doctor Bird DB 1049	The Preacher (as Alton & Flames)/LYNN TAITT & COMETS: Tender Loving Care	12
66	Doctor Bird DB 1055	Shake It (with Flames)/SILVERTONES: Whoo Baby	12
66	Doctor Bird DB 1059	Girl I've Got A Date (with Flames)/LYN TAITT & TOMMY McCOOK: The Yellow Basket	12
67	Island WI 3046	Cry Tough (with Flames)/TOMMY McCOOK & SUPERSONICS: Mr Solo	12
67	Treasure Isle TI 7004	Rocksteady (with Flames)/TOMMY McCOOK & SUPERSONICS: Wall Street Shuffle	10
67	Treasure Isle TI 7010	Duke Of Earl/All My Tears (with Flames)	10
67	Treasure Isle TI 7016	Ain't That Loving You (with Flames)/TOMMY McCOOK & SUPERSONICS: Tommy's Rocksteady	10
67	Treasure Isle TI 7030	Oowee Baby/How Can I (with Flames)	10
67	Treasure Isle TI 7044	Willow Tree/I Can't Stop Now	10
67	Trojan TR 004	Ain't That Loving You (with Flames)/TOMMY McCOOK & SUPERSONICS: Comet Rocksteady	12
67	Trojan TR 009	Wise Birds Follow Spring/TOMMY McCOOK & SUPERSONICS: Soul Rock	12
67	Studio One SO 2028	I Am Just A Guy/SOUL VENDORS: Just A Little Bit Of Soul	15
67	Studio One SO 2033	Only Sixteen/Baby (both actually by Heptones)	15
68	Studio One SO 2037	Live And Learn/HEPTONES: Cry Baby Cry	15
68	Nu Beat NB 010	I Can't Stand It/Tonight	6
68	Nu Beat NB 013	Bye Bye Love/MONTY MORRIS: My Lonely Days	6
68	Nu Beat NB 014	La La Means I Love You/Give Me Your Love	6
68	Trojan TR 630	I Can't Stand It/Trying To Reach My Goal	8
68	Trojan TR 642	Breaking Up/Party Time	8
68	Pama PM 707	The Message/Some Talk	6
68	Pama PM 717	My Time Is The Right Time/JOHNNY MOORE: Tribute To Sir Alex	6
69	Studio One SO 2084	Change Of Plans/CABLES: He'll Break Your Heart (B-side actually by Mad Lads)	15
69	Gas GAS 105	Diana/Some Talk	5
69	Duke DU 14	Diana/Personality	5
69	Bamboo BAM 2	Better Example/DUKE MORGAN: Lick Olt Back	6
70	Gas GAS 151	Suzie/Life Is Down In Denver (some copies credit Alton Ellis & Flames)	4
70	Gas GAS 161	Deliver Us/NEVILLE HINDS: Originator	4
70	Duke DU 72	Remember That Sunday/TOMMY McCOOK & SUPERSONICS: Last Lick	5
70	Duke Reid DR 2501	What Does It Take/TOMMY McCOOK & SUPERSONICS: Reggae Merengue	6
70	Duke Reid DR 2512	You Made Me So Very Happy/TOMMY McCOOK & SUPERSONICS: Continental	6
70	Bamboo BAM 29	Tumbling Tears/SOUND DIMENSION: Today Version	5
70	Banana BA 318	Sunday Coming/CARL BRYAN: Sunday Version	5
71	Banana BA 330	Bam Bye/Keep On Yearning	5
71	Banana BA 347	Hey World/Harder And Harder	5
71	Gas GAS 164	Back To Africa/NEVILLE HINDS: Originator	4
71	Fab FAB 165	Good Good Loving/Since I Fell For You	5
72	Spur SP 3	All That We Need Is Love/KEITH HUDSON: Better Love	6
72	Grape GR 3029	Big Bad Boy/HUDSON ALLSTARS: Version	5
72	Ackee ACK 145	Oppression/Oppression Version (both with Zoot Simms)	4
72	Ackee ACK 148	Let's Stay Together/Version	4
72	Ackee ACK 502	Too Late To Turn Back Now/IMPACT ALLSTARS: Version	4
72	Ackee ACK 511	Alton's Official Daughter/Aquarius Dub (both with Herman)	4
72	Jackpot JP 796	Play It Cool/AGGROVATORS: King Of The Zozas	4

Alton ELLIS

67	Coxsone CSL 8008	SINGS ROCK AND SOUL (LP) 70
71	Bamboo BDLPS 214	SUNDAY COMING (LP) 25
73	Count Shelly SSLO 02	ALTON ELLIS'S GREATEST HITS (LP) 20

(see also Alton & Eddy, Hortense & Alton)

BOBBY ELLIS
| 68 | Island WI 3136 | Dollar A Head/RUDY MILLS: I'm Trapped ....10 |

DON ELLIS (ORCHESTRA)
69	CBS 4518	Eli's Comin'/House In The Country 4
67	Fontana (S)TL 5426	'LIVE' AT MONTEREY (LP) 10
68	Liberty LBL/LBS 83060	THE DON ELLIS ORCHESTRA LIVE (LP) 10
68	CBS 63230	ELECTRIC BATH (LP) 10
69	CBS 63356	SHOCK TREATMENT (LP) 10
69	CBS 63503	AUTUMN (LP) 10
69	CBS 63680	THE NEW DON ELLIS BAND GOES UNDERGROUND (LP) 10
69	CBS 66261	LIVE AT THE FILLMORE (2-LP) 14

HERB ELLIS-JIMMY GIUFFRE ALL STARS
| 60 | HMV POP 721 | Goose Grease/My Old Flame ....4 |

HORTENSE ELLIS
63	R&B JB 101	I'll Come Softly/I'm In Love (with Alton Ellis) 10
64	Blue Beat BB 295	I've Been A Fool/Hold Me Tenderly 8
67	Fab FAB 20	Somebody Help Me (with Buster's All Stars)/PRINCE BUSTER & ALL STARS: Rock & Shake 5

(see also Hortense & Alton, Hortense & Delroy, Hortense & Jackie)

JO-JO ELLIS
| 70s | Fury FY 302 | The Fly/Perdona Mia ....10 |

JOHN ELLIS
| 80 | Rat Race RAT 6 | Hit Man/Hollow Graham (p/s) ....4 |

(see also Vibrators)

LARRY ELLIS
| 58 | Felsted AF 110 | Buzz Goes The Bee/Nothing You Can Do ....10 |

MATTHEW ELLIS
71	Regal Zono. RZ 3033	Avalon/You Are 4
71	Regal Zono. RZ 3039	Birthday Song/Salvation 4
72	Regal Zono. RZ 3045	Palace Of Plenty/Two By Two 4
71	Regal Zono. SRZA 8501	MATTHEW ELLIS (LP) 15
71	Regal Zono. SRZA 8505	AM I? (LP, with Chris Spedding) 25

(see also Procol Harum, Chris Spedding)

SHIRLEY ELLIS
63	London HLR 9824	The Nitty Gritty/Give Me A List 5
65	London HLR 9946	The Name Game/Whisper To Me Wind 5
65	London HLR 9961	The Clapping Song/This Is Beautiful 5
65	London HLR 9973	The Puzzle Song/I See It, I Like It, I Want It 5
66	London HLR 10021	Ever See A Diver Kiss His Wife While The Bubbles Bounce About Above The Water/Stardust 4
67	CBS 202606	Soul Time/Waitin' 12
67	CBS 2817	Sugar Let's Shing-A-Ling/How Lonely Is Lonely 10
71	CBS 7463	Soul Time/Waitin' (reissue) 5
77	CBS 4901	Soul Time/Waitin' (2nd reissue, coloured vinyl) 4
67	CBS (S)BPG 63044	SOUL TIME WITH SHIRLEY ELLIS (LP) 20

ANDY ELLISON
67	Track 604 018	It's Been A Long Time/JOHN'S CHILDREN: Arthur Green 30
68	CBS 3357	Fool From Upper Eden/Another Lucky Lie 40
68	S.N.B. 55-3308	You Can't Do That/Casbah 45

(see also John's Children, Jet, Radio Stars)

LORRAINE ELLISON
66	Warner Bros WB 5850	Stay With Me/I Got My Baby Back 8
68	Warner Bros WB 2094	Try (Just A Little Bit Harder)/In My Tomorrow 5
70	Warner Bros WB 7394	You've Really Got A Hold On Me/You Don't Know Anything About Love 5
71	Mercury 6052 073	Call Me Anytime You Need Some Lovin'/Please Don't Teach Me To Love You 8
70	Warner Bros WS 1821	STAY WITH ME (LP) 12

ELMER HOCKETT'S HURDY GURDY
| 68 | Parlophone R 5716 | Fantastic Fair/MOOD MOSAIC: The Yellow Spotted Capricorn ....4 |

(see also Mood Mosaic, Mark Wirtz)

ELOY
83	Heavy Metal HM INT 1	Fools/Heartbeat 4
82	Heavy Metal HMI PD1	PLANETS (LP, picture disc) 15
83	Heavy Metal HMI LP3	TIME TO TURN (LP, clear vinyl) 12
83	Heavy Metal HMIPD 12	PERFORMANCE (LP, picture disc) 10
84	Heavy Metal HMIPD 21	METROMANIA (LP, picture disc) 12
89	FM Revolver REV PD120	RA (LP, picture disc) 10

EL PASO
| 71 | Big Shot BI 572 | Out De Light Baby/Mosquito I ....5 |
| 71 | Punch PH 61 | Mosqutio One/Out De Light (reissue) ....4 |

(see also Dennis Alcapone)

JEFF ELROY & BLUE BOYS
| 66 | Philips BF 1533 | Honey Machine/Three Woman ....18 |

ELTI-FITS
| 70s | Worthing Street WSEF 1 | GOING STRAIGHT (EP, foldover p/s) ....4 |

ELVES
70	MCA MU 1114	Amber Velvet/West Virginia	6

LEE & JAY ELVIN
59	Fontana H 191	So The Story Goes/When You See Her	5
	(see also Jerry Lordan)		

EMANON
77	Clubland SJP 777	Raging Pain/Rip A Bough	8

EMBERS
63	Decca F 11625	Chelsea Boots/Samantha	8

EMERALDS (U.K.)
65	Decca F 12096	Don't Listen To Your Friends/Say You're Mine	4
65	Decca F 12304	King Lonely The Blue/Someone Else's Fool	30

EMERALDS (U.S.)
64	London HL 9839	Sittin' Bull/Donkey Kick Back	4

EMERGENCY
83	Riot City RIOT 21	POINTS OF VIEW (EP)	4

EMERSON
83	Neat NEAT 34	Something Special/Stars In Hollywood (p/s)	5

KEITH EMERSON
76	Manticore K 13513	Honky Tonk Train Blues/Barrell House Shake Down (p/s)	5
	(see also Emerson Lake & Palmer, Nice)		

EMERSON, LAKE & PALMER
73	Manticore K 13503	Jerusalem/When The Apple Blossoms Bloom, In The Windmills Of Your Mind, I'll Be Your Valentine	4
74	Lyntone/Manticore LYN 2762	Brain Salad Surgery/(excerpts from "Brain Salad Surgery" LP) (flexidisc in gatefold p/s free with 'NME')	6/4
77	Atlantic K 10946	Fanfare For The Common Man/Brain Salad Surgery (p/s)	4
77	Atlantic K 10946T	Fanfare For The Common Man (Album Version)/Brain Salad Surgery (12")	15
	(see also Nice, Keith Emerson, Greg Lake, Shame, Asia, King Crimson)		

DICK EMERY
68	Pye 7N 17644	If You Love Her/Day After Day	4

EMILY
80s	Sha La La 007	The Old Stone Bridge/REMEMBER FUN: Hey Hey Hate (flexidisc, p/s)	7
87	Big Fun BIG FUN 001	The Old Stone Bridge/What The Fool Said (flexidisc)	7

EMJAYS
59	Top Rank JAR 145	Al My Love All My Life/Cross My Heart	12
59	Top Rank JAR 145	Al My Love All My Life/Cross My Heart (78)	18

EMMET SPICELAND
68	Page One POF 089	Lowlands Low/Bunclody	4
69	Page One POF 143	So Long Marianne/Ballad Of Franklin	4
68	Page One POLS 011	THE FIRST (LP)	40

EMMETT
65	Columbia DB 7582	Baby Ain't No Lie/Hard Travelling	4
65	Columbia DB 7695	Nancy/Kilkenny Mountains	4

EMOTIONS (U.K.)
65	Polydor BM 56025	Lonely Man/Line Shooter	4

EMOTIONS (U.S.)
62	London HLR 9640	Come Dance Baby/Echo	12
63	London HLR 9701	L-O-V-E/A Million Reasons	12
63	Stateside SS 237	A Story Untold/One Life One Love One You	10
69	Stax STAX 123	So I Can Love You/Got To Be The Man	4
70	Deep Soul DS 9104	Somebody New/Brushfire	10
75	Stax STXS 2020	Baby I'm Through/I Wanna Come Back	4
77	CBS 81639	FLOWERS (LP)	10
77	CBS 82065	REJOICE (LP)	10

EMOTIONS (Jamaica)
66	Ska Beat JB 263	Rude Boy Confession/Heartbreaking Gypsy	8
67	Caltone TONE 100	A Rainbow/TONY & DOREEN: Just You And I	10
68	Caltone TONE 118	Soulful Music/No Use To Cry	8
68	Caltone TONE 129	Careless Hands/TOMMY McCOOK & SUPERSONICS: Caltone Special	8
69	High Note HS 018	The Storm/Easy Squeeze	5
	(see also Romeo & Emotions)		

EMPEROR
77	Private Stock	EMPEROR (LP)	10

EMPERORS
66	Stateside SS 565	Karate/I've Got To Have Her	10
69	Pama PM 786	Karate/I've Got To Have Her (reissue)	6

EMPIRE
80	White Line DE 001	EXPENSIVE SOUND (LP)	10
	(see also Generation X)		

EMPYRE
86	EMP	Worlds Apart/Sword Play (p/s)	5

ENCHANTED FOREST
68	Stateside SS 2080	You're Never Gonna Get My Lovin'/Suzanne	6

MINT VALUE £

ENCHANTERS
67	Warner Bros WB 2054	We Got Love/I've Lost All Communications	10

ENCHANTMENT
77	United Artists UP 36268	Sunshine/Sexy Lady	4
77	United Artists UAS 30089	ENCHANTMENT (LP)	10
78	United Artists UAS 30149	ONCE UPON A DREAM (LP)	10

END
65	Philips BF 1444	I Can't Get Any Joy/Hey Little Girl	10
68	Decca F 22750	Shades Of Orange/Loving, Sacred Loving	15
69	Decca LK-R/SKL-R 5015	INTROSPECTION (LP)	60

(see also Tucky Buzzard)

ENDEVERS
68	Decca F 12817	Remember When We Were Young/Taking Care Of Myself	4
68	Decca F 12859	She's My Girl/She's That Kind Of Girl	4
69	Decca F 12939	Sunny And Me/I Really Hope You Do	4

SERGIO ENDRIGO
68	Pye Intl. 7N 25502	Marianne/Il Dolce Paese	10

MELVIN ENDSLEY
57	RCA RCA 1004	I Like Your Kind Of Love/Is It True	25
57	RCA RCA 1004	I Like Your Kind Of Love/Is It True (78)	10
58	RCA RCA 1051	I Got A Feelin'/There's Bound To Be	20
58	RCA RCA 1051	I Got A Feelin'/There's Bound To Be (78)	12

ENERGY IQ
80	Optimistic OPT 008	THROUGH THE PLUGHOLE (EP)	4

ENERGY ORCHARD
90	MCA MCA 1402	Sailortown/Jesus Christ (gatefold, numbered p/s with lyric booklet)	4

SCOTT ENGEL
58	Vogue V 9125	Blue Bell/Paper Doll	70
58	Vogue V 9125	Blue Bell/Paper Doll (78)	20
59	Vogue V 9145	The Livin' End/Good For Nothin' (with Count Dracula & Boys)	100
59	Vogue V 9145	The Livin' End/Good For Nothin' (with Count Dracula & Boys) (78)	50
59	Vogue V 9150	Charlie Bop/All I Do Is Dream Of You	80
59	Vogue V 9150	Charlie Bop/All I Do Is Dream Of You (78)	20
66	Liberty LEP 2261	SCOTT ENGEL (EP)	15

(see also Scott Walker, Walker Brothers)

SCOTT ENGEL & JOHN STEWART
66	Capitol CL 15440	I Only Came To Dance With You/Greens	6

(see also Scott Walker, Walker Brothers)

ENGLAND
76	Deroy DER 1356	ENGLAND (LP, private press)	250

ENGLAND
77	Arista ARIST 88	Pariffinalea/Nanagram	6
77	Arista ARTY 153	GARDEN SHED (LP)	35

ENGLAND'S GLORY
73	private pressing	ENGLAND'S GLORY (LP, promo only)	150
87	Five Hours Back TOCK 4	ENGLAND'S GLORY (LP, stickered sleeve)	10

(see also Only Ones)

ENGLAND SISTERS
60	HMV POP 710	Heartbeat/Little Child	20

ENGLISH
81	Albion ION 1008	Hooray For The English/When You Fly (p/s)	4

BARBARA JEAN ENGLISH
74	Contempo CS 2031	Breaking Up A Happy Home/Guess Who	4
75	Contempo CS 2062	I'm Living In A Lie/Key In The Mailbox	4

MR JOE ENGLISH
69	Fontana TF 1034	Lay Lady Lay/Two Minute Silence	4

ENGLISH SUBTITLES
79	Small Wonder SMALL 22	Time Tunnel/Sweat/Reconstruction (p/s)	4
82	Glass 007/10 SEC 21	Tannoy/Cars On Fire (folded p/s in bag with insert)	4

ENID
76	Buk BUK 3002	The Lovers/In The Region Of The Summer Stars	15
77	EMI Intl. INT 534	Jubilee/Omega	6
77	EMI Intl. INT 540	Golden Earrings/Omega (p/s)	12
79	Pye 7P 106	Dambusters March - Land Of Hope And Glory/The Sloyeboat Song (p/s, coloured vinyl)	12
80	Pye 7P 187	Fool/Tito (p/s)	10
80	EMI EMI 5109	Golden Earrings/665 The Great Bean (p/s)	10
81	Bronze BRO 127	When You Wish Upon A Star/Jessica (p/s)	6
81	Bronze BRO 134	Heigh Ho/Twinkle Twinkle Little Star (p/s)	6
82	Rak RAK 349	And Then There Were None/Letter From America (p/s)	5
84	EMI EMI 5505	And Then There Were None/Letter From America/Raindown (12", p/s)	10
86	Sedition EDIT 3314	Itchycoo Park/Sheets Of Blue (p/s)	4
86	Sedition EDITL 3314	Itchycoo Park/Sheets Of Blue (12", p/s)	7
90	Enid ENID 7999	Salome/Salomee (p/s)	4
90	Enid ENID 6999	Salome/Salomee (12", p/s)	7
77	Buk BULP 2014	IN THE REGION OF THE SUMMER STARS (LP, 1st issue via Decca; 2nd issue via CBS with insert & band's name on front; 3rd issue via EMI Intl.)	15/12/10

77	Honeybee INS 3012	AERIE FAIRIE NONSENSE (LP)	12
77	Honeybee TC-INS 3012	AERIE FAIRIE NONSENSE (cassette, 1,000 only)	10
79	Pye NSPH 18593	TOUCH ME (LP)	12
79	Pye NH 116	SIX PIECES (LP, 2,000 only)	15
79	Pye ZCNH 116	SIX PIECES (cassette, 500 only)	10
84	The Enid ENID 1	LIVE AT HAMMERSMITH VOL. I (LP, 5,500 only)	20
84	The Enid ENID 1C	LIVE AT HAMMERSMITH VOL. I (cassette)	10
84	The Enid ENID 2	LIVE AT HAMMERSMITH VOL. II (LP, 2,000 only)	25
84	The Enid ENID 2C	LIVE AT HAMMERSMITH VOL. II (cassette)	10
84	The Enid ENID 3	SOMETHING WICKED THIS WAY COMES (LP)	12
84	The Enid ENID 4	SIX PIECES (LP, new version, 3,500 only)	15
84	The Enid ENID 5	TOUCH ME (LP, new version, 4,000 only)	15
84	The Enid ENID 6	AERIE FAERIE NONSENSE (LP, new version)	10
84	The Enid ENID 7	IN THE REGION OF THE SUMMER STARS (LP, new version)	12
84	The Enid ENID 8	THE SPELL (2-LP, 45rpm, gatefold sleeve)	15
85	The Enid ENID 9	FAND (LP, re-recorded version for fan club, 3,000 only)	15
86	The Enid ENID 10	SALOME (LP)	20
87	Dojo DOJOLP 24	LOVERS AND FOOLS (2-LP)	15
84	The Stand STAND 1	THE STAND 1984 (LP, fan club issue, 5,000 only)	25
85	The Stand STAND 2	THE STAND 1985 (LP, fan club issue, 2,000 only)	30
80s	The Stand LE 1	LIVERPOOL (LP, fan club, 800 only)	35
80s	Nuage MM 2	INNER PIECES (cassette)	10
80s	Nuage MM 3	INNER VISIONS (cassette)	10
80s	The Stand HAM 1	AT HAMMERSMITH 17TH OCTOBER 1986 (cassette, official bootleg)	10
80s	The Stand HAM 2	AT HAMMERSMITH 30TH OCTOBER 1987 (cassette, official bootleg)	10

(see also Robert John Godfrey, Godfrey & Stewart, William Arkle, Glen Baker)

ENJAYS

59	Top Rank JAR 145	All My Love, All My Life/Cross My Heart	8

RAY ENNIS & BLUE JEANS

68	Columbia DB 8431	What Have They Done To Hazel/Now That You've Got Me (You Don't Seem To Want Me)	15

(see also Swinging Blue Jeans, Blue Jeans)

BRIAN ENO

74	Island WIP 6178	Seven Deadly Finns/Later On	6
75	Island WIP 6233	The Lion Sleeps Tonight (Wimoweh)/I'll Come Running	5
78	Polydor 2001 762	The King's Lead Hat/R.A.F. (B-side with Snatch)	4
74	Island ILPS 9268	HERE COME THE WARM JETS (LP)	10
74	Island ILPS 9309	TAKING TIGER MOUNTAIN (BY STRATEGY) (LP)	10
75	Island ILPS 9351	ANOTHER GREEN WORLD (LP)	10
75	Island/HELP 22	EVENING STAR (LP, as Fripp & Eno)	10
75	Island/Obscure OBS 3	DISCREET MUSIC (LP)	10
76	Island ILPS 9444	801 LIVE (LP)	10
76	Editions EG EGM 1	MUSIC FOR FILMS (LP, private pressing)	200
77	Polydor 2302 071	BEFORE AND AFTER SCIENCE (LP, with 4 Peter Schmidt prints)	12
83	EG EGBS 002	WORKING BACKWARDS 1983-1973 (9-LP boxed set with "Music For Films, Vol. 2" LP & "Rarities" 12")	40

(see also Robert Fripp, Roxy Music, Lady June, Ayers Cale Nico & Eno, David Toop)

BRIAN ENO & DAVID BYRNE

81	EG EGO 1	The Jezebel Spirit/Regiment (p/s)	4

(see also David Byrne, Talking Heads)

ENORMOUS ROOM

86	Sharp CAL 5	100 Different Words/Sylvia's Children/Melanie And Martin/ You Wrote A Book (12", p/s)	7
86	Medium Cool MC 001	I Don't Need You/Melanie And Martin (flexidisc, p/s)	6

ENTICERS

71	Atlantic 2091 136	Calling For Your Love/Storyteller	8

JOHN ENTWISTLE('S OX)

71	Track 2094 008	I Believe In Everything/My Size	5
75	Decca FR 13567	Mad Dog/Cell No.7 (as John Entwistle's Ox)	4
81	WEA K 79249P	Too Late The Hero/I'm Coming Back (picture disc, some autographed)	8/4
71	Track 2406 005	SMASH YOUR HEAD AGAINST THE WALL (LP)	10
72	Track 2406 104	WHISTLE RYMES (LP)	10
75	Decca TXS 114	MAD DOG (LP, as John Entwistle's Ox)	10

(see also Who, Rigor Mortis)

ENYA

87	BBC RESL 201	I Want Tomorrow/The Celts Theme (p/s)	5
87	BBC CDRSL 201	I Want Tomorrow/The Celts Theme/To Go Beyond I/ To Go Beyond II (CD)	20
80s	WEA YZ 368 CDX	Storms In Africa/The Kelts/Aldebaran (3" CD)	7

EPICS

65	Pye 7N 15829	There's Just No Pleasing You/My Little Girl	5
66	Pye 7N 17053	Just How Wrong Can You Be/Blue Turns To Grey	6
68	CBS 3564	Travelling Circus/Henry Long	6

(see also Acid Gallery, T. Rex)

EPILEPTICS

80	Stortbeat/Mirror BEAT 8	1970'S EP (black & white p/s, stencilled white labels)	7
81	Spiderleg SDL 1	1970'S EP (re-recorded, printed labels, folded different printed b&w p/s)	7
81	Spiderleg SDL 2	LAST BUS TO DEBDEN (EP, hand-written labels & photocopied p/s)	6
81	Spiderleg SDL 2	LAST BUS TO DEBDEN (EP, with printed labels in printed card gatefold p/s)	5

EPISODE

68	MGM MGM 1409	Little One/Wide Smiles	25

EPISODE SIX

66	Pye 7N 17018	Put Yourself In My Place/That's All I Want	15
66	Pye 7N 17110	I Hear Trumpets Blow/True Love Is Funny That Way	15
66	Pye 7N 17147	Here, There And Everywhere/Mighty Morris Ten	15
67	Pye 7N 17244	Love, Hate, Revenge/Baby Baby Baby	20
67	Pye 7N 17330	Morning Dew/Sunshine Girl	15
67	Pye 7N 17376	I Can See Through You/When I Fall In Love	15
68	Chapter One CH 103	Lucky Sunday/Mr. Universe	15
69	Chapter One CH 104	Mozart Versus The Rest/Jak D'Or	15

(see also Episode, Sheila Carter & Episode Six, Jon Lord, Gillan, Deep Purple, Quatermass)

MINNIE EPPERSON

| 68 | Action ACT 4503 | Grab Your Clothes (And Get On Out)/No Love At All | 10 |

PRESTON EPPS

59	Top Rank JAR 140	Bongo Rock/Bongo Party	12
59	Top Rank JAR 140	Bongo Rock/Bongo Party (78)	20
59	Top Rank JAR 180	Doin' The Cha Cha Cha/Bongo In Pastel	5
59	Top Rank JAR 180	Doin' The Cha Cha Cha/Bongo In Pastel (78)	8
60	Top Rank JAR 345	Bongo Boogie/Flamenco Boogie	6
60	Top Rank JAR 413	Bongo Bongo Bongo/Hully Gully Bongo	6
60	Top Rank JAR 522	Bongola/Blue Bongo	5

EQUALS

68	President PT 117	I Won't Be There/Fire	4
68	President PT 135	Baby, Come Back/Hold Me Closer	4
68	President PT 200	Laurel And Hardy/The Guy Who Made Her A Star	4
69	President PT 260	Viva Bobby Joe/I Can't Let You Go	4
70	President PT 303	I Can See But You Don't Know/Gigolo Sam	12
76	Mercury 6007 106	Funky Like A Train/If You Didn't Miss Me	5
76	Mercury 6007 106	Funky Like A Train/If You Didn't Miss Me (12")	7
67	President PTL 1006	UNEQUALLED EQUALS (LP)	12
68	President PTL 1015	EQUALS EXPLOSION (LP)	10
68	President PTL(S)1020	SENSATIONAL EQUALS (LP)	10
68	President PTLS 1025	SUPREME (LP)	10
70	President PTS 1038	AT THE TOP (LP)	10
76	Mercury 9109 601	BORN YA! (LP)	10

(see also Little Grants & Eddie, Pyramids, Hickory)

EQUATIONS

| 69 | Fontana TF 1035 | Waiting On The Shores Of Nowhere/You Stood Beside Me | 4 |

EQUINOX

| 73 | Boulevard 4118 | HARD ROCK (LP) | 25 |

EQUIPPE 84

| 67 | Major Minor MM 517 | Auschwitz/Twenty Ninth Of September | 15 |

ERASURE

85	Mute L12 MUTE 40	Who Needs Love Like That (Mexican Mix)/Push Me Shove Me (Tacos Mix) (12", p/s)	30
85	Mute L12 MUTE 42	Heavenly Action (Yellow Brick Mix)/Don't Say No (Ruby Red Mix) (12", p/s)	75
85	Mute DMUTE 42	Heavenly Action (Yellow Brick Mix)/Don't Say No (Ruby Red Mix)// Who Needs Love Like That (Mexican Mix)/Push Me Shove Me (Tacos Mix) (12", double pack)	50
86	Mute MUTE 45	Oh L'Amour/March On Down The Line (withdrawn 'Thomas The Tank Engine' p/s)	8
86	Mute 12 MUTE 45	Oh L'Amour/March On Down The Line/Gimme! Gimme! Gimme! (12", withdrawn 'Thomas The Tank Engine' p/s)	20
86	Mute 12 MUTE 45	Oh L'Amour/March On Down The Line/Gimme! Gimme! Gimme! (12", die-cut sleeve)	7
86	Mute L12 MUTE 45	Oh L'Amour (Funky Sisters Mix)/March On Down The Line/ Gimme! Gimme! Gimme! (Remix) (12", p/s)	20
86	Mute CMUTE 51	Sometimes/Sexuality/Who Needs Love Like That/Heavenly Action/ Oh L'Amour (cassette)	5
86	Mute DMUTE 51	Sometimes/Sexuality//Who Needs Love Like That/Push Me Shove Me (double pack, shrinkwrapped with sticker)	5
86	Mute L12 MUTE 51	Sometimes (Shiver Mix)/Sexuality (Private Mix)/Senseless (CD Mix) (12", p/s)	10
87	Mute DMUTE 56	It Doesn't Have To Be/In The Hall Of The Mountain King//Sometimes/ Sexuality (double pack, shrinkwrapped with sticker)	4
87	Mute L12 MUTE 56	It Doesn't Have To Be (Cement Mix)/Heavenly Action/ In The Hall Of The Mountain King (12", p/s)	8
87	Mute CD MUTE 56	It Doesn't Have To Be/Sometimes/Oh L'Amour/Heavenly Action/ Who Needs Love Like That/Gimme Gimme Gimme/In The Hall Of The Mountain King (CD, 7"-sized 'tray' tray)	12
87	Mute L12 MUTE 61	Victim Of Love (Vixen Vitesse Mix)/The Soldier's Return (The Machinery Mix)/If I Could (Japanese Mix) (12", p/s)	8
88	Mute CD MUTE 74	Ship Of Fools (Shiver Me Timbers Mix)/When I Needed You (Melancholic Mix)/ River Deep Mountain High (Private Dance Mix) (3" CD)	7
88	Mute L12 MUTE 74	Ship Of Fools (RC Mix)/River Deep Mountain High (Private Dance Mix)/ When I Needed You (12", p/s)	8
88	Mute CD MUTE 83	Chains Of Love (Foghorn Mix)/The Good, The Bad & The Ugly (Dangerous Mix)/Don't Suppose (Country Joe Mix) (CD)	8
88	Mute L12 MUTE 83	Chains Of Love (Truly In Love With The Marks Brothers Mix)/The Good, The Bad & The Ugly (Dangerous Mix)/Don't Suppose (12", p/s)	8
88	Mute L12 MUTE 85	A Little Respect (Big Train Mix)/Like Zsa Zsa Zsa Gabor (Rico Conning Mix)/Love Is Colder Than Death (12", p/s)	10
88	Mute LCD MUTE 85	A Little Respect/(Extended Mix)/Like Zsa Zsa Zsa Gabor (Rico Conning Mix)/Love Is Colder Than Death ('picture' CD)	10

88	Mute L12 MUTE 93	Crackers International II: Stop! (Mark Saunders Remix)/Knocking On Your Door (Mark Saunders Remix)/God Rest Ye Merry Gentlemen (12", p/s)	8
88	Mute LCD MUTE 93	Crackers International II: Stop! (Mark Saunders Remix)/Knocking On Your Door (Mark Saunders Remix)/God Rest Ye Merry Gentlemen (3" CD, Xmas pack with card & gift label, 6" x 3" sleeve; later in 5" case or 3" pouch)	15/8
89	Mute L12 MUTE 99	You Surround Me (Remix)/Supernature (William Orbit Mix)/91 Steps (6 Pianos Mix) (12", p/s)	7
89	Mute LCD MUTE 99	You Surround Me (Remix)/Supernature (William Orbit Mix)/91 Steps (6 Pianos Mix) (CD)	10
90	Mute XL12 MUTE 99	Supernature (Mark Saunders Remix)/You Surround Me (Gareth Jones Remix)/ Supernature (Daniel Miller & Phil Legg Remix) (12", envelope p/s)	15
90	Mute L12 MUTE 109	Blue Savannah (Der Deutsche Mix II)/No G.D.M. (Unfinished Mix)/ Runaround On The Underground (12", embossed p/s, with sticker)	7
90	Mute LCD MUTE 109	Blue Savannah (Der Deutsche Mix II)/No G.D.M. (Unfinished Mix)/ Runaround On The Underground (CD)	7
90	Mute XL12 MUTE 109	Blue Savannah (Der Deutsche Mixes I & II) (12", numbered envelope p/s)	15
90	Mute L12 MUTE 111	Star (Interstellar Mix)/Star (Soul Mix)/Star (Dreamlike State 24 Hour Technicolour Mix) (12", p/s)	7
86	Mute STUMM 25	WONDERLAND (LP, with shrinkwrapped 12" "Oh L'Amour" [12 MUTE 45])	12
87	Mute LSTUMM 35	THE TWO RING CIRCUS (LP, as 2 x 12")	10
87	Mute CSTUMM 35D	THE CIRCUS/WONDERLAND (double-play cassette)	12
88	Mute CSTUMM 55D	THE INNOCENTS/THE TWO RING CIRCUS (double-play cassette)	10
89	Mute STUMM 75	WILD! (LP, with free 12" "Blue Savannah" [XL12 MUTE 109])	12
91	Mute STUMM 95	CHORUS (CD, box set with 8 prints)	15

(see also Depeche Mode, Dinger, Yazoo)

ERAZERHEAD
81	Test Pressing TP 4	Ape Man/Wipeout/Rock And Roll Zombie (p/s)	4
82	Flicknife FLS 210	Teenager In Love/All For Me (p/s)	4

ERIC (Sykes) & HATTIE (Jacques)
63	Decca LK 4507	ERIC, HATTIE AND THINGS (LP)	15

(see also Eric Sykes)

EREWHON
81	Harvest HAR 5213	Tiny Goddess/The Hero (p/s)	4

(see also Patrick Campbell-Lyons)

ERIC HYSTERIC & ESOTERICS
70s	Wasted Vinyl WASTE 1	Tropical Vision/Dance And Sing (p/s)	4

ROKY ERICKSON (& ALIENS)
77	Virgin VS 180	Bermuda/The Interpreter	4
80	CBS 8888	Creature With The Atom Brain/The Wind And More (no p/s, with Aliens)	4
80	CBS 9055	Mine Mine Mind/Bloody Hammer (Acoustic Version) (p/s, with Aliens)	4
87	Bucketfull Of Brains BOB 13	Don't Shake Me Lucifer (live) (flexidisc free with 'Bucketfull Of Brains' magazine)	5/4
87	Five Hours Back TOCK 7P	CASTING THE RUNES (LP, picture disc)	10

(see also 13th Floor Elevators)

ERNEST & FREDDIE
70	Crab CRAB 21	Moon Hop	4

ERROL & HIS GROUP
(see under Errol Dunkley)

ERSATZ
81	Raw RAW 35	Motorbody Love/One Good Reason/Gimme A Chance (poster p/s)	6
80s	Leisure Sounds SRS 32	Smile In Shadow/House Of Cards (p/s)	6

NORMAN ERSKINE
57	Capitol CL 14784	Till We Meet Again/What's To Become Of Me	4

BLUEGRASS ERWIN
59	Top Rank JAR 252	I Won't Cry Alone/I Can't Love You	6

ESCALATORS
83	Big Beat NS 86	Something's Missing/The Edge (p/s)	4
83	Big Beat NS 87	The Munsters Theme/Monday (p/s)	4
85	Rococco COCO 1	Beach Boys/Ford Escort (p/s, double pack)	4

ESCORTS (U.S.)
63	Coral Q 72458	Submarine Race Watching/Somewhere	5

ESCORTS (U.K.)
64	Fontana TF 453	Dizzy Miss Lizzy/All I Want Is You	8
64	Fontana TF 474	The One To Cry/Tell Me Baby	8
65	Fontana TF 516	I Don't Want To Go On Without You/Don't Forget To Write	8
65	Fontana TF 570	C'Mon Home Baby/You'll Get No Lovin' That Way	12
66	Fontana TF 651	Let It Be Me/Mad Mad World	10
66	Columbia DB 8061	From Head To Toe/Night Time	15

(see also Big Three, Paddy, Klaus & Gibson, Terry Sylvester)

ESCORTS & KAY JUSTICE
54	Columbia SCM 5132	If You Took Your Love From Me/Yes, Indeed	7

ESCOURTS
76	Alaska ALA 1014	Disrespect Can Wreck/Bam A Lam A Boogie	4

E.S.G.
81	Factory FAC 34	You're No Good/U.F.O./Moody (p/s)	4

ESPERANTO ROCK ORCHESTRA
73	A&M AMLH 68175	ESPERANTO ROCK ORCHESTRA (LP)	10

ESPERANTO ROCK ORCHESTRA

| 74 | A&M AMLH 63624 | DANSE MACABRE (LP, with Keith Christmas) ....10 |
| 75 | A&M AMLH 68294 | LAST TANGO (LP) ....10 |

(see also Keith Christmas)

ESPRIT DE CORPS
| 73 | Jam JAM 24 | If (Would It Turn Out Wrong)/Picture On The Wall ....15 |
| 73 | Jam JAM 32 | Lonely/Do You Remember Me ....10 |

(see also Mike Read, David Ballantyne, Just Plain Smith, Just Plain Jones, Trainspotters)

ESPRIT DE CORPS
| 80s | Come 0001 | Anxiety/The Tea Cup Song (hand-made silk-screened sleeve) ....4 |

ESQUERITA
| 58 | Capitol CL 14938 | Rockin' The Joint/Esquerita And The Voola ....75 |
| 60s | Ember SPE 6603 | WILDCAT SHAKEOUT (LP) ....15 |

ESQUIRES
67	Stateside SS 2048	Get On Up/Listen To Me 10
68	Stateside SS 2077	And Get Away/Everybody's Laughing 7
73	Action ACT 4618	My Sweet Baby/Henry Ralph 5
68	London HA-Q/SH-Q 8356	GET ON UP AND GET AWAY (LP) 10

ESSENTIAL BOP
| 80 | Monopause MOAN 1001 | ELOQUENT SOUNDS (EP) ....4 |
| 81 | Monopause MOAN 1002 | Croaked/Butler (In Running Shorts) (p/s) ....4 |

ESSENTIAL LOGIC
| 78 | Cells SELL 1 | Aerosol Burns/World Friction (p/s) ....4 |

(see also X-Ray Spex)

ESSEX
63	Columbia DB 7077	Easier Said Than Done/Are You Going My Way 6
63	Columbia DB 7122	A Walkin' Miracle/What I Don't Know Won't Hurt Me (with Anita Humes) 6
63	Columbia DB 7178	She's Got Everything/Out Of Sight, Out Of Mind 6
63	Columbia 33SX 1593	EASIER SAID THAN DONE (LP) 15
64	Columbia 33SX 1613	A WALKIN' MIRACLE (LP) 15

DAVID ESSEX
65	Fontana TF 559	And The Tears Came Tumbling Down/You Can't Stop Me Loving You 25
65	Fontana TF 620	Can't Nobody Love You/Baby I Don't Mind 25
66	Fontana TF 680	This Little Girl Of Mine/Brokenhearted 25
66	Fontana TF 733	Thigh High/De Boom Lay Boom 22
68	Uni UN 502	Love Story/High Than High 12
68	Pye 7N 17621	Just For Tonight/Goodbye 10
69	Decca F 12935	That Takes Me Back/Lost Without Linda 18
69	Decca F 12967	The Day The Earth Stood Still/Is It So Strange? 18
73	CBS 1686	Rock On/On And On (p/s) 5
74	CBS 1902	Lamplight/We All Insane (p/s) 5
74	CBS 2828	Stardust/Miss Sweetness (p/s) 5
79	United Artists UP 605	World/I Who Am I (p/s) 5
83	Mercury ESSEP 1	The Smile/Slave (picture disc) 4
83	Mercury ESSEX 22	You're In My Heart/Come On Little Darlin'//A Winter's Tale/Verity (double pack) ..4
79	Mercury 6359 017	IMPERIAL WIZARD (LP, blue vinyl) 10

(see also David & Rozaa)

NEVILLE ESSON
| 61 | Blue Beat BB 37 | Lover's Jive/Wicked And Dreadful ....10 |

ESTABLISHMENT
| 81 | Foetain | BAD CATHOLICS (LP) ....40 |

(see also Cromwell)

GLORIA ESTEFAN/MIAMI SOUND MACHINE
87	Epic 650805 7	Rhythm Is Gonna Get You/Give It Up ('red dress' p/s) 5
87	Epic 650805 8	Rhythm Is Gonna Get You/Rhythm Is Gonna Get You (Dub Mix)/Give It Up (12", 'red dress' p/s) 8
87	Epic 651125 7	Betcha Say That/Love Toy (p/s) 4
87	Epic 651125 8	Betcha Say That/Betcha Say That (Dub)/Love Toy (12", p/s) 7
87	Epic 651125 9	Betcha Say That/Love Toy/The Megamix (12", p/s) 7
88	Epic 650805 7	Rhythm Is Gonna Get You/Give It Up (reissue, 'Stakeout' p/s) 7
88	Epic 650805 8	Rhythm Is Gonna Get You/Rhythm Is Gonna Get You (Dub Mix)/Give It Up (reissue, 12", white or black 'Stakeout' p/s) 10/12
88	Epic 651444 0	Can't Stay Away From You/Let It Loose (poster p/s) 10
88	Epic 651444 7	Can't Stay Away From You/Let It Loose ('dreamy' p/s) 4
88	Epic 651444 8	Can't Stay Away From You/Let It Loose/Primitive Love (12", 'dreamy' p/s) 8
88	Epic 651444 9	Can't Stay Away From You/Let It Loose/Bad Boy (Remix) (12", 'dreamy' p/s) 10
88	Epic 651444 2	Can't Stay Away From You/Rhythm Is Gonna Get You/Surrender (Remix) (3" CD with adaptor in 5" p/s) 10
88	Epic 651444 2	Can't Stay Away From You/Rhythm Is Gonna Get You/Surrender (Remix) (5" CD) 7
88	Epic 651673 9	Anything For You (English)/Words Get In The Way/The Megamix (12", p/s) 10
88	Epic 652958 0	1-2-3/Surrender (poster p/s, record has cat. no. 652958 7) 7
88	Epic 652958 1	1-2-3 (Dancing By Numbers Mix)/Anything For You (English/Spanish Version)/Surrender (Remixed By Humberto Gatica) (12", p/s) 8
88	Epic 654534 7	Rhythm Is Gonna Get You/Give It Up (reissue, badge shrinkwrapped to p/s) 8
88	Epic 654514 0	Rhythm Is Gonna Get You/Give It Up (calendar gatefold p/s) 7
88	Epic 654514 9	Rhythm Is Gonna Get You/Give It Up (poster p/s) 8
88	Epic 654514 8	Rhythm Is Gonna Get You/Rhythm Is Gonna Get You (live)/Give It Up (12", p/s) ..8
87	Epic 450910 1	LET IT LOOSE (LP) 12
87	Epic 450910 4	LET IT LOOSE (cassette) 10
87	Epic EPC 450910 2	LET IT LOOSE (CD) 20

(see also Gloria Estefan, Miami Sound Machine)

GLORIA ESTEFAN

89	Epic 653195 0	Can't Stay Away From You/Let It Loose (reissue, poster p/s)	5
89	Epic 653195 7	Can't Stay Away From You/Let It Loose (shaped picture disc)	6
89	Epic 655054 9	Don't Wanna Lose You/Words Get In The Way (live) (foldout poster p/s)	6
89	Epic 655054 1	Don't Wanna Lose You/Anything For You/Can't Stay Away From You/ Words Get In The Way (12", 'The Ballads Twelve Inch', p/s)	7
89	Epic 655287 8	Oye Mi Canto (Def 12" Mix)/(Def Dub Mix)/(House Mix) (12", p/s)	7
89	Epic 655287 5	Oye Mi Canto (Edit)/Anything For You (Spanish)/Words Get In The Way (Spanish)/Si Voy A Perderte (Spanish) (CD, picture disc)	12
89	Epic 655450 0	Get On Your Feet/1-2-3 (Live) (p/s, with 4 postcards)	4
89	Epic 655450 5	Get On Your Feet (Pop Vocal)/(Special Mix)/1-2-3 (live) (12", calendar gatefold p/s)	7
89	Epic 655450 8	Get On Your Feet (House Vocal)/Get On Your Feet (House Techno Dub)/ Get On Your Feet (Deep Bass Vocal) (12", p/s)	8
90	Epic 655 728 7	Here We Are/Don't Let The Sun Go Down On Me (envelope pack with print)	5
90	Epic 655982 0	Cuts Both Ways/You Made A Fool Of Me (poster p/s)	4
91	Epic 656574 0	Coming Out Of The Dark/Desde La Oscuridad (frame pack with 2 prints)	4
91	Epic 656968 0	Remember Me With Love/Your Love Is Bad For Me (envelope pack with 4 photos & lyrics)	4

(see also Miami Sound Machine)

SLEEPY JOHN ESTES

44	Brunswick 03562	Married Woman Blues/Drop Down Mama (78)	25
66	Delmark DJB 3	SLEEPY JOHN'S GOT THE BLUES (EP)	10
63	Esquire 32-195	THE LEGEND OF SLEEPY JOHN ESTES (LP)	30
63	'77' LA 12-27	TENNESSEE JUG BUSTERS (LP)	20
65	Storyville SLP 172	PORTRAITS IN BLUES VOLUME 10 (LP)	15

JOHN ESTES/FURRY LEWIS/WILL SHADE

71	Revival RVS 1008	OLD ORIGINAL TENNESSEE BLUES (LP)	15

JACKIE ESTICK

61	Blue Beat BB 64	Boss Girl/COUNT OSSIE & GROUP: Cassavubu	10
63	Island WI 042	Since You've Been Gone/Daisy I Love You	10
66	Ska Beat JB 256	The Ska/Daisy I Love You	7

EDDIE ESWELL

68	Toast TT 504	Don't Say You're Gonna Leave Me/Don't Knock It	4

ETCETERAS

64	Oriole CB 1973	Little Lady/Now I Know	15

ETERNALS (U.S.)

59	London HL 8995	Rockin' In The Jungle/Rock 'N' Roll Cha-Cha (triangular or round centre)	50/30
59	London HL 8995	Rockin' In The Jungle/Rock 'N' Roll Cha-Cha (78)	30

ETERNALS (Jamaica)

60s	Moodisc MU 3507	Push Me In The Corner/MUDIE's ALL STARS: Mudie's Madness	4
60s	Moodisc MU 3508	Keep On Dancing/HAZEL WRIGHT: My Jealous Eyes	4
69	Coxsone CS 7091	Queen Of The Minstrels/Stars	10

ETERNAL SCREAM

82	Eternal ERO 1	Hypocrite/Action In My Life (p/s)	4

ETERNAL TRIANGLE

69	Decca F 12954	Windows/Turn To Me	5
69	Decca F 12979	I Guess The Lord Must Be In New York City/Perfumed Candle	5

ETERNITY'S CHILDREN

68	Capitol CL 15558	Mrs. Bluebird/Little Boy	4

ETHEL THE FROG

80	EMI EMI 5041	Eleanor Rigby/Fight Back (no p/s)	6
80	EMI EMC 3329	ETHEL THE FROG (LP, with Terry Hopkinson & Doug Sheppard)	20

ETHIOPIANS

66	Ska Beat JB 260	Live Good/SOUL BROTHERS: Soho	10
66	Island WI 3015	I Am Free/SOUL BROTHERS: Shanty Town	10
67	Rio R 110	Owe Me No Pay Me/SHARKS: I Wouldn't Baby	10
67	Rio R 114	I'm Gonna Take Over Now/JACKIE MITTOO: Home Made	10
67	Rio R 126	Dun Dead A'Ready/Stay In My Lonely Arms	10
67	Rio R 130	Train To Skaville/You Are The Girl (B-side actually by Gladiators)	8
67	Doctor Bird DB 1092	I Need You/Do It Sweet	10
67	Doctor Bird DB 1096	The Whip/Cool It, Amigo	10
67	Doctor Bird DB 1103	Stay Loose, Mama/The World Goes Ska	10
68	Doctor Bird DB 1141	Come On Now/Sh'Boom	10
68	Doctor Bird DB 1147	Engine 54/Give Me Your Love	10
68	Doctor Bird DB 1148	Train To Glory/You Got The Dough	10
68	Doctor Bird DB 1169	Everything Crash/I'm Not Losing You	8
68	Crab CRAB 2	Fire A Muss Tail/Blacker Black (B-side actually by Count Ossie)	6
68	Crab CRAB 4	Reggae Hit The Town/Ding Dong Bell	6
69	Crab CRAB 7	I Am A King/What A Big Surprise	6
69	Doctor Bird DB 1172	Not Me/Cut Down	8
69	Doctor Bird DB 1185	Hong Kong Flu/Clap Your Hands	8
69	Doctor Bird DB 1186	What A Fire/You	8
69	Doctor Bird DB 1199	Everyday Talking/Sharing You	8
69	Trojan TR 666	Woman Capture Man/One	5
69	Trojan TR 697	Well Red/J.J. ALLSTARS: R.F.K.	5
69	Randy's RAN 510	True Man/RANDY'S ALLSTARS: Version	5
69	Randy's RAN 512	Mr Tom/Sad News	5

ETHIOPIANS

69	Nu Beat NB 031	My Testimony/J.J. ALLSTARS: One Dollar Of Soul	5
69	Nu Beat NB 038	Buss Your Mouth/REGGAE BOYS: Rough Rough Way Ahead	5
70s	J.J. JJ 3302	Wreck It Up/Don't Go	6
70s	J.J. JJ 3303	Hong Kong Flu/Everything Crash	5
70	Duke Reid DR 2507	Mother's Tender Care/TOMMY McCOOK: Soldier Man	7
70	Bamboo BAM 26	Walkie Talkie/SOUND DIMENSION: Moan And Groan	6
70	Bamboo BAM 38	You'll Want To Come Back/JACKIE MITTOO: Baby Why Instrumental (B-side actually by Sound Dimension)	6
70	Songbird SB 1040	No Baptism/CRYSTALITES: Version	5
70	Songbird SB 1047	Good Ambition/CRYSTALITES: Version	5
70	Gas GAS 142	Satan Girl/MATADORS: The Pum	4
70	Duke DU 61	Make You Go On So/WINSTON WRIGHT: Neck Tie	4
70	Duke DU 102	Drop Him/J.J. ALLSTARS: Version	4
71	Randy's RAN 509	Me Want Girl/RANDY'S ALLSTARS: Version	5
71	Fab FAB 180	Monkey Money/Version	6
71	Treasure Isle TI 7067	Pirate/TOMMY McCOOK & SOUL SYNDICATE: Depth Charge	7
71	Songbird SB 1059	What A Pain/CRYSTALITES: Version	5
71	Songbird SB 1062	Lot Wife/DERRICK HARRIOTT: Slave	5
71	Songbird SB 1064	Best Of Five Pts 1 & 2	5
71	Big Shot BI 569	He's Not A Rebel/J.J. ALLSTARS: Version	4
71	Big Shot BI 574	The Selah/Don't Let It Go	4
71	Duke DU 108	Rim Bim Bam/RANDY'S ALLSTARS: Version	4
71	Explosion EX 2050	Starvation/TROJAN ALLSTARS: Version	4
71	G.G. GG 4519	Love Bug/Sound Of Our Forefathers	4
71	Supreme SUP 221	Love Bug/Sound Of Our Forefathers	4
71	Supreme SUP 226	Starvation/MAXIE & GLEN: Jordan River	4
72	Prince Buster PB 38	You Are For Me/Playboy	5
72	Techniques TE 919	Promises/TIVOLIS: Version	4
68	Doctor Bird DLM 5011	GO ROCK STEADY (LP)	100
69	Trojan TTL 10	REGGAE POWER (LP)	20
70	Trojan TBL 112	WOMAN CAPTURE MAN (LP)	25

ETTA (James) & HARVEY (Fuqua)

60	London HLM 9180	If I Can't Have You/My Heart Cries	15

(see also Etta James, Moonglows, Harvey & Moonglows)

JACK EUBANK'S ORCHESTRA

61	London HLU 9312	What'd I Say/Chiricahua	6
62	London HLU 9501	Searchin'/Take A Message To Mary	6

EUREKA BRASS BAND OF NEW ORLEANS

64	London HA-K/SH-K 8162	JAZZ AT PRESERVATION HALL VOL. 1 (LP)	10

EUREKA STOCKADE

70	Decca F 22996	Sing No Love Songs/Jump Down And Turn Around	5

EUROPE

87	Epic EUR 1	Rock The Night/Seven Doors Hotel (p/s, coloured vinyl)	4
87	Epic EURP 2	Carrie/Love Chaser (p/s, coloured vinyl)	4
87	Epic EURD 2	Carrie/Love Chaser (p/s, with free single)	4
88	Epic EURQ 3	Superstitious/Lights And Shadows (poster p/s)	4
88	Epic 462 449 1	OUT OF THIS WORLD (LP, red vinyl)	10

EUROPEANS

79	Heartbeat PULSE 2	Europeans/Voices (p/s)	5

EURYTHMICS

81	RCA RCA 68	I'm Never Gonna Cry Again/Le Sinistre (p/s)	8
81	RCA RCA 68	I'm Never Gonna Cry Again (Extended)/Le Sinistre (Extended) (12", p/s)	25
81	RCA RCA 115	Belinda/Heartbeat, Heartbeat (p/s)	22
82	RCA RCA 199	This Is The House/Home Is Where The Heart Is (p/s)	12
82	RCA RCAT 199	This Is The House/Your Time Will Come (live)/Never Gonna Cry Again/4/4 In Leather (live)/Take Me To Your Heart (live) (12", p/s)	30
82	RCA RCA 230	The Walk/Step On The Beast/The Walk (Part 2) (p/s)	12
82	RCA RCAT 230	The Walk/Invisible Hands/Dr Trash/The Walk (Part 2) (12", printed die-cut sleeve)	35
82	RCA DA 1	Love Is A Stranger/Monkey, Monkey (with gold lettering on p/s)	5
82	RCA DA 1	Love Is A Stranger/Monkey, Monkey (with reverse print on rear of p/s)	5
82	RCA DAP 1	Love Is A Stranger/Monkey, Monkey (picture disc)	6
82	RCA DAT 1	Love Is A Stranger/Let's Just Close Our Eyes/Monkey, Monkey (12", blue p/s)	7
83	RCA DAP 2	Sweet Dreams (Are Made Of This)/I Could Give You (A Mirror) (picture disc)	8
83	RCA DAP 3	Who's That Girl?/You Take Some Lentils ... And You Take Some Rice (picture disc)	7
83	RCA DA 4/EUC 001	Right By Your Side/(Party Mix) (p/s, with promo cassette: "Intro Speech"/"Step On The Beast"/"Invisible Hands"/"Angel (Dub)"/"Satellite Of Love" [EUC 001])	35
83	RCA DAP 4	Right By Your Side/Right By Your Side (Party Mix) (picture disc)	6
84	RCA DAP 5	Here Comes The Rain Again/Paint A Rumour (picture disc)	5
84	Virgin VSY 728-12	Sex Crime (1984) (Extended Mix)/Sex Crime (Single Version)/I Did It Just The Same (12", picture disc)	7
85	Virgin VSY 734	Julia/Ministry Of Love (picture disc in pop-up p/s)	7
85	Virgin VSY 734-12	Julia (Extended Version)/Ministry Of Love (12", picture disc, pop-up p/s)	10
85	RCA PB 40101	Would I Lie To You?/Here Comes That Sinking Feeling (p/s, red, blue, or yellow vinyl)	5
85	RCA PT 40102	Would I Lie To You? (E.T. Mix)/(Extended Remix)/Here Comes That Sinking Feeling (12", p/s, red, blue or yellow vinyl)	7
85	RCA PT 40248R	There Must Be An Angel (Playing With My Heart) (Special Dance Mix)/Grown Up Girls (12", p/s)	7

85	RCA PB 40339	Sisters Are Doin' It For Themselves (with Aretha Franklin)/I Love You Like	
		A Ball And Chain ('mob', 'racing driver', 'WRAF' or 'typist' p/s) . . . . each 4	
85	RCA PB 40375	It's Alright (Baby's Coming Back)/Conditioned Soul ('video still' p/s) 5	
85	RCA PB 40375/PB 40101	It's Alright (Baby's Coming Back)/Conditioned Soul//Would I Lie To You?/	
		Here Comes That Sinking Feeling (double pack, with free coloured vinyl 7") 7	
85	RCA PB 40376/PB 40102	It's Alright (Baby's Coming Back)/Conditioned Soul/Tous Les Garcons Et	
		Les Filles//Would I Lie To You? (E.T. Mix)/Would I Lie To You? (Extended Remix)/	
		Here Comes That Sinking Feeling (12", double pack, gatefold PVC sleeve,	
		2nd on coloured vinyl) 10	
86	RCA DA 8	Thorn In My Side/In This Town (p/s, with shrinkwrapped badge) 6	
86	RCA DAT 8	Thorn In My Side (Houston Remix)/Thorn In My Side/In This Town	
		(12", p/s, with sticker) 7	
86	RCA DA 9P	The Miracle Of Love/When Tomorrow Comes (live) (shaped picture disc) 6	
87	RCA DA 11P	Beethoven (I Love To Listen To)/Heaven (poster p/s) 10	
87	RCA DA 11CD	Beethoven (I Love To Listen To)/Heaven/Beethoven (Dance Mix) (CD) 7	
87	RCA DAT 14P	Shame (Dance Mix)/I've Got A Lover (Back In Japan)/Shame	
		(12", p/s with print) 7	
88	RCA DA 15R	I Need A Man (live)/I Need A Man/I Need You (numbered gatefold p/s) 4	
88	RCA DA 15X	I Need A Man/I Need You/There Must Be An Angel (Playing With My Heart)	
		(live)/Missionary Man (live) (10", p/s) 6	
88	RCA DA 15CD	I Need A Man (live)/Missionary Man (live)/I Need You/I Need A Man	
		(Macho Mix) (picture CD in numbered metal tin) 7	
88	RCA DA 16CD	You Have Placed A Chill In My Heart (Remix)/Do You Want To Break Up?	
		(Dance Mix)/Here Comes The Rain Again (live)/You Have Placed A Chill	
		In My Heart (Acoustic) (CD in numbered black metal tin) 10	
89	RCA DAT 18P	Revival (Extended E.T. Dance Mix)/Precious/Revival (12", gatefold p/s	
		with numbered print & paper strip) 7	
89	RCA DAT 20	Don't Ask Me Why/Rich Girl/When The Day Goes Down (Acoustic Version)/	
		Don't Ask Me Why (Acoustic Version) (12", numbered poster p/s) 7	
89	RCA DACD 20	Don't Ask Me Why/Rich Girl/When The Day Goes Down (Acoustic Version)/	
		Don't Ask Me Why (Acoustic Version) (CD, numbered black box with poster) 7	
90	RCA DAT 23	King And Queen Of America (Dance Remix)/King And Queen Of America	
		(Dub Mix)/See No Evil (12", stickered p/s with poster) 8	
90	RCA DACD 24	King And Queen Of America/There Must Be An Angel (live)/I Love You Like	
		A Ball And Chain (live)/See No Evil (CD in wood box) 8	
90	RCA DAT 25	Angel (Remix)/Sweet Dreams (Are Made Of This) (Nightmare Mix) (12", p/s) 10	
83	Lyntone LYN 13916	A CHRISTMAS MESSAGE (fan club flexidisc, no p/s) 5	
84	Lyntone LYN 15292	A YULETIDE MESSAGE TO ALL OUR PALS (fan club flexidisc, no p/s) 5	
87	Lyntone (no cat. no.)	DAVE AND ANNIE'S CHRISTMAS MESSAGE '87 (fan club flexidisc, no p/s) 5	
89	Flexi FLX 880	DAVE AND ANNIE'S CHISTMAS MESSAGE '89	
		(fan club flexidisc, foldout p/s) 4	
83	Flexi FLX 1000	DAVE AND ANNIE'S CHRISTMAS MESSAGE (fan club flexidisc, foldout p/s) 4	
83	RCA RCALP 6063	SWEET DREAMS (LP, picture disc) 15	
83	RCA PL 70109	TOUCH (LP, picture disc) 10	

(see also Catch, Tourists, Chris & Cosey)

BARBARA EVANS
50s	RCA RCA 1122	Souvenirs (78) 20	
61	Mercury AMT 1151	Charlie Wasn't There/Nothing You Can Do 4	

CHRISTINE EVANS
65	Philips BF 1406	Growing Pains/Someone In Love 4	
66	Philips BF 1496	Somewhere There's Love/Right Or Wrong 12	

DAVE EVANS
71	Village Thing VTS 6	THE WORDS IN BETWEEN (LP) 12	
72	Village Thing VTS 14	ELEPHANTASIA (LP) 10	
70s	Kicking Mule	SAD PIG DANCE (LP, with booklet) 10	

GIL EVANS ORCHESTRA
60	Vogue EPV 1266	GREAT JAZZ STANDARDS (EP) 7	
60	Vogue LAE 12234	GREAT JAZZ STANDARDS (LP) 10	

JIM EVANS
60s	Melodisc MEL 1530	Christmas Doll 12	

JOHN EVANS
62	Palette PG 9040	Melodie Pour Madame/Cry Me A River 4	

LARRY EVANS
56	London HLU 8269	Crazy 'Bout My Baby/Henpecked 120	
56	London HLU 8269	Crazy 'Bout My Baby/Henpecked (78) 45	

MAUREEN EVANS
58	Embassy WB 300	Carolina Moon/Stupid Cupid 4	
58	Embassy WB 303	Fever/Born Too Late 4	
58	Embassy WB 309	The Hula Hoop Song/Hoopa Hoola 4	
58	Embassy WB 313	I'll Get By/Someday (You'll Want Me To Want You) 4	
58	Embassy WB 316	You Always Hurt The One You Love/The Day The Rains Came 4	
58	Embassy WB 319	To Know Him Is To Love Him/Kiss Me, Honey Honey, Kiss Me 4	
59	Embassy WB 344	Goodbye Jimmy, Goodbye/May You Always 4	
59	Embassy WB 348	Lipstick On Your Collar/What A Diff'rence A Day Made 4	
59	Embassy WB 356	Broken-Hearted Melody/Plenty Good Lovin' 4	
59	Embassy WB 371	Among My Souvenirs/Happy Anniversary 4	
59	Oriole CB 1517	Don't Want The Moonlight/The Years Between 5	
60	Oriole CB 1533	The Big Hurt/I Can't Begin To Tell You 5	
60	Oriole CB 1540	Love, Kisses And Heartaches/We Just Couldn't Say Goodbye 5	
60	Oriole CB 1550	Paper Roses/Please Understand 5	
61	Oriole CB 1563	Mama Wouldn't Like It/My Little Corner Of The World 5	
61	Oriole CB 1578	As Long As He Needs Me/Where Is Love? 5	

Maureen EVANS

61	Oriole CB 1581	Till/Why Don't You Believe Me	5
61	Oriole CB 1613	My Foolish Heart/Oh Gypsy Oh Gypsy	5
62	Oriole CB 1743	Never In A Million Years/We Had Words	5
62	Oriole CB 1760	Like I Do/Starlight Starbright	4
63	Oriole CB 1804	Pick The Petals/Melancholy Me	4
63	Oriole CB 1806	Tomorrow Is Another Day/Acapulco Mexico	4
63	Oriole CB 1851	What A Difference A Day Made/Oh What A Guy	4
63	Oriole CB 1875	Like You Used To Do/As You Love Her	4
64	Oriole CB 1906	I Love How You Love Me/John John	4
64	Oriole CB 1939	He Knows I Love Him Too Much/Don't Believe Him	4
64	Oriole CB 1969	Get Away/I've Often Wondered	4
65	CBS 201733	All The Angels Sing/Speak Sugar Speak	4
65	CBS 201752	Never Let Him Go/Poco Sole	4
67	CBS 202621	Somewhere There's Love/It Takes A Little Time	7
68	CBS 3222	I Almost Called Your Name/Searching For Home	4
63	Oriole EP 7076	MELANCHOLY ME (EP)	20
63	Oriole PS 40046	LIKE I DO (LP)	35

PAUL EVANS (& CURLS)

59	London HLL 8968	Seven Little Girls Sitting In The Back Seat/Worshipping An Idol (with Curls)	6
59	London HLL 8968	Seven Little Girls Sitting In The Back Seat/Worshipping An Idol (78)	20
60	London HLL 9045	Midnite Special/Since I Met You, Baby	10
60	London HLL 9129	Happy-Go-Lucky Me/Fish In The Ocean	6
60	London HLL 9183	Brigade Of Broken Hearts/Twins	6
60	London HLL 9239	Hushabye Little Guitar/Blind Boy	6
62	London HLR 9636	The Bell That Couldn' Jingle/Gilding The Lily	4
63	London HLR 9770	Even Tan/Ten Thousand Years	4
62	London RE-R 1349	PAUL EVANS (EP)	25
60	London HA-L 2248	PAUL EVANS SINGS THE FABULOUS TEENS (LP)	50

RICHARD EVANS

79	A&M AMS 7438	Do-Re-Me-For-Soul/Burning Spear	4

RUSSELL EVANS & NITEHAWKS

66	Atlantic 584 010	Send Me Some Cornbread/The Bold	8

EVEN DOZEN JUG BAND

66	Bounty BY 6023	THE EVEN DOZEN JUG BAND (LP)	15

(see also Lovin' Spoonful, John Sebastian)

BETTY EVERETT

64	Stateside SS 259	You're No Good/Chained To Your Love	10
64	Stateside SS 280	It's In His Kiss (The Shoop Shoop Song)/Hands Off	6
64	Stateside SS 321	I Can't Hear You/Can I Get To Know You	8
64	Fontana TF 520	Getting Mighty Crowded/Chained To A Memory	5
64	King KG 1002	Happy I Long To Be/Your Loving Arms	7
65	Sue WI 352	I've Got A Claim On You/Your Love (Is Important To Me)	12
68	President PT 215	It's In His Kiss (The Shoop Shoop Song)/Getting Mighty Crowded	4
69	President PT 251	You're No Good/Hands Off	4
69	MCA Soul Bag BAG 3	I Can't Say No To You/Better Tomorrow Than Today	5
69	MCA MU 1055	There'll Come A Time/Take Me	4
70	Uni UN 517	Sugar/Hold On	4
70	Liberty LBF 15428	I Got To Tell Somebody/Why Are You Leaving	4
70s	President PT 372	Trouble Over The Weekend	4
65	Fontana TL 5236	IT'S IN HIS KISS (LP)	25
69	Uni UNLS 109	THERE'LL COME A TIME (LP)	10
70	Joy JOYS 106	IT'S IN HIS KISS (LP, reissue)	10

BETTY EVERETT & JERRY BUTLER

64	Stateside SS 339	Let It Be Me/Ain't That Lovin' You Baby	7
65	Fontana TF 528	Smile/Love Is Strange	7
68	President PT 214	Let It Be Me/Smile	5
69	President PT 252	Our Day Will Come/Just Be True	5
65	Fontana TL 5237	DELICICUS TOGETHER (LP)	15
71	Joy JOYS 123	DELICIOUS TOGETHER (LP, reissue)	10

(see also Jerry Butler)

KENNY EVERETT

68	MGM MGM 1421	It's Been So Long/Without Her	4
69	Deram DM 245	Nice Time/And Now For A Little Train Number	4

(see also Kenny & Cash)

VINCE EVERETT

65	Fontana TF 606	Bless You/'Til(I) I Lost You	5
67	Fontana TF 818	Endlessly/Who's That Girl?	4
68	Fontana TF 915	Every Now And Then/Barbarella	20

EVERGREEN BLUES

67	Mercury MF 1012	Midnight Confessions/(Yes) That's My Baby	6
68	Mercury MF 1025	Laura (Keep Hangin' On)/Yesterday's Coming	6
68	Mercury SMCL 20122	7 DO ELEVEN (LP)	12

EVERGREEN BLUESHOES

69	London HA-U/SH-U 8399	THE BALLAD OF THE EVERGREEN BLUESHOES (LP)	15

(see also Skip Battin, Byrds)

EVERLY BROTHERS

57	London HLA 8440	Bye Bye, Love/I Wonder If I Care As Much (triangular centre, later round)	18/7
57	London HLA 8440	Bye Bye, Love/I Wonder If I Care As Much (78)	10
57	London HLA 8498	Wake Up Little Susie/Maybe Tomorrow (triangular centre, later round)	12/6
57	London HLA 8498	Wake Up Little Susie/Maybe Tomorrow (78)	10
58	London HLA 8554	Should We Tell Him/This Little Girl Of Mine (triangular centre, later round)	20/8

58	London HLA 8554	Should We Tell Him/This Little Girl Of Mine (78) 15
58	London HLA 8618	All I Have To Do Is Dream/Claudette (triangular centre, later round) 10/5
58	London HLA 8618	All I Have To Do Is Dream/Claudette (78) 8
58	London HLA 8685	Bird Dog/Devoted To You (triangular centre, later round centre) 10/5
58	London HLA 8685	Bird Dog/Devoted To You (78) 10
58	London HLA 8781	Problems/Love Of My Life 10
58	London HLA 8781	Problems/Love Of My Life (78) 10
59	London HLA 8863	Poor Jenny/Take A Message To Mary 10
59	London HLA 8863	Poor Jenny/Take A Message To Mary (78) 12
59	London HLA 8934	('Til) I Kissed You/Oh, What A Feeling 10
59	London HLA 8934	('Til) I Kissed You/Oh, What A Feeling (78) 15
60	London HLA 9039	Let it Be Me/Since You Broke My Heart 8
60	London HLA 9039	Let it Be Me/Since You Broke My Heart (78) 35
60	Warner Bros WB 1	Cathy's Clown/Always It's You 4
60	Warner Bros WB 1	Cathy's Clown/Always It's You (78) 60
60	London HLA 9157	When Will I Be Loved/Be-Bop-A-Lula 8
60	London HLA 9157	When Will I Be Loved/Be-Bop-A-Lula (78) 50
60	Warner Bros WB 19	So Sad (To Watch Good Love Go Bad)/Lucille 4
60	Warner Bros WB 19	So Sad (To Watch Good Love Go Bad)/Lucille (78) 100
60	London HLA 9250	Like Strangers/Leave My Woman Alone 8
61	Warner Bros WB 33	Walk Right Back/Ebony Eyes 5
61	Warner Bros WB 42	Temptation/Stick With Me Baby 5
61	Warner Bros WB 50	Muskrat/Don't Blame Me 5
62	Warner Bros WB 56	Crying In The Rain/I'm Not Angry 5
62	Warner Bros WB 67	How Can I Meet Her?/That's Old Fashioned 6
62	Warner Bros WB 79	No One Can Make My Sunshine Smile/Don't Ask Me To Be Friends 6
63	Warner Bros WB 94	So It Will Always Be/Nancy's Minuet 6
63	Warner Bros WB 99	It's Been Nice/I'm Afraid 6
63	Warner Bros WB 109	The Girl Sang The Blues/Love Her 6
64	Warner Bros WB 129	Ain't That Lovin' You Baby/Hello Amy 6
64	Warner Bros WB 135	The Ferris Wheel/Don't Forget To Cry 5
64	Warner Bros WB 143	You're The One I Love/Ring Around My Rosie (withdrawn) 12
64	Warner Bros WB 146	Gone, Gone, Gone/Torture 6
65	Warner Bros WB 154	You're My Girl/Don't Let The Whole World Know 6
65	Warner Bros WB 158	That'll Be The Day/Give Me A Sweetheart 6
65	Warner Bros WB 161	The Price Of Love/It Only Costs A Dime 5
65	Warner Bros WB 5628	The Price Of Love/It Only Costs A Dime (reissue) 5
65	Warner Bros WB 5639	I'll Never Get Over You/Follow Me 5
65	Warner Bros WB 5649	Love Is Strange/Man With Money 5
66	Warner Bros WB 5682	It's All Over/I Used To Love You (unissued)
66	Warner Bros WB 5743	(You Got) The Power Of Love/Leave My Girl Alone 5
66	Warner Bros WB 5754	I've Been Wrong Before/Hard Hard Year 7
67	Warner Bros WB 7520	Bowling Green/I Don't Want To Love You 7
67	Warner Bros WB 7062	Mary Jane/Talking To The Flowers 7
67	Warner Bros WB 7088	Love Of The Common People/A Voice Within 7
68	Warner Bros WB 7192	It's My Time/Empty Boxes 7
68	Warner Bros WB 7226	Milk Train/Lord Of The Manor 8
69	Warner Bros WB 6056	Cathy's Clown/Walk Right Back 5
70	Warner Bros WB 6074	Oh Boy!/Good Golly, Miss Molly 6
70	Warner Bros WB 7425	Yves/Human Race 8
72	RCA Victor RCA 2232	Ridin' High/Stories We Could Tell 5
72	RCA Victor RCA 2286	Not Fade Away/Lay It Down 4
79	Old Gold OG 9018	Bird Dog/Devoted To You (picture disc) 4
80	Old Gold SET 1	THE EVERLY BROTHERS SINGLES SET (15 x p/s 7", box set with book) 25
58	London RE-A 1113	THE EVERLY BROTHERS (EP) 16
58	London RE-A 1148	THE EVERLY BROTHERS — NO. 2 (EP) 16
58	London RE-A 1149	THE EVERLY BROTHERS — NO. 3 (EP) 16
59	London RE-A 1174	THE EVERLY BROTHERS — NO. 4 (EP) 16
59	London RE-A 1195	SONGS OUR DADDY TAUGHT US PART 1 (EP) 18
59	London RE-A 1196	SONGS OUR DADDY TAUGHT US PART 2 (EP) 18
59	London RE-A 1197	SONGS OUR DADDY TAUGHT US PART 3 (EP) 18
60	London RE-A 1229	THE EVERLY BROTHERS — NO. 5 (EP) 20
61	London RE-A 1311	THE EVERLY BROTHERS — NO. 6 (EP) 20
61	Warners W(S)EP 6034	ESPECIALLY FOR YOU (EP, mono/stereo) 15/45
62	Warners W(S)EP 6049	FOREVERLY YOURS (EP, mono/stereo) 15/45
62	Warners W(S)EP 6056	IT'S EVERLY TIME (EP, mono/stereo) 15/45
63	Warners W(S)EP 6107	A DATE WITH THE EVERLY BROTHERS VOL. 1 (EP, mono/stereo) 16/45
63	Warners W(S)EP 6109	A DATE WITH THE EVERLY BROTHERS VOL. 2 (EP, mono/stereo) 16/45
63	Warners W(S)EP 6111	INSTANT PARTY VOL. 1 (EP, mono/stereo) 16/45
63	Warners W(S)EP 6113	INSTANT PARTY VOL. 2 (EP, mono/stereo) 16/45
63	Warners W(S)EP 6115	BOTH SIDES OF AN EVENING — FOR DANCING VOL. 1 (EP, mono/stereo) . .18/45
64	Warners W(S)EP 6117	BOTH SIDES OF AN EVENING — FOR DREAMING VOL. 2 (EP, mono/stereo) . .18/45
64	Warners WEP 6128	THE EVERLY BROTHERS SING GREAT COUNTRY HITS VOL. 1 (EP) 16
64	Warners WEP 6131	THE EVERLY BROTHERS SING GREAT COUNTRY HITS VOL. 2 (EP) 16
64	Warners WEP 6132	THE EVERLY BROTHERS SING GREAT COUNTRY HITS VOL. 3 (EP) 16
65	Warner Bros WEP 6138	BOTH SIDES OF AN EVENING — FOR FUN VOL. 3 (EP) 18
65	Warner Bros WEP 604	THE PRICE OF LOVE (EP) 15
65	Warner Bros WEP 608	ROCK'N'SOUL VOL. 1 (EP) 15
65	Warner Bros WEP 609	ROCK'N'SOUL VOL. 2 (EP) 15
66	Warner Bros WEP 610	LOVE IS STRANGE (EP) 15
66	Warner Bros WEP 612	PEOPLE GET READY (EP) 15
66	Warner Bros WEP 618	WHAT AM I LIVING FOR? (EP) 15
67	Warner Bros WEP 622	LEAVE MY GIRL ALONE (EP) 15
67	Warner Bros WEP 623	SOMEBODY HELP ME (EP) 16
74	Warner Bros K 16407	WAKE UP LITTLE SUSIE (EP) 8
58	London HA-A 2081	THE EVERLY BROTHERS (LP) 40

MINT VALUE £

58	London HA-A 2150	SONGS OUR DADDY TAUGHT US (LP)	40
60	Warner Bros WM 4012	IT'S EVERLY TIME (LP, also stereo WS 8012)	25/30
60	London HA-A 2266	THE FABULOUS STYLE OF THE EVERLY BROTHERS (LP)	30
60	Warner Bros WM 4028	A DATE WITH THE EVERLY BROTHERS (LP, also stereo WS 8028)	25/30
61	Warner Bros WM 4052	BOTH SIDES OF AN EVENING (LP, also stereo WS 8052)	25/30
62	Warner Bros WM 4061	INSTANT PARTY (LP, also stereo WS 8061)	20/25
62	Warner Bros WM/WS 8108	THE GOLDEN HITS OF THE EVERLY BROTHERS (LP, mono/stereo)	15/18
62	Warner Bros WM/WS 8116	CHRISTMAS WITH THE EVERLY BROTHERS AND THE BOYS TOWN CHOIR (LP, mono/stereo)	25/30
63	Warner Bros WM/WS 8138	SING GREAT COUNTRY HITS (LP, mono/stereo)	18/20
64	Warner Bros WM/WS 8163	THE VERY BEST OF THE EVERLY BROTHERS (LP, mono/stereo)	12/15
65	Warner Bros WM/WS 8169	GONE GONE GONE (LP, mono/stereo)	20/25
65	Warner Bros WM/WS 8171	ROCK 'N' SOUL (LP, mono/stereo)	22/25
65	Warner Bros W(S) 1471	THE GOLDEN HITS OF THE EVERLY BROTHERS (LP, reissue, m/s)	10/12
65	Warner Bros W(S) 1554	THE VERY BEST OF THE EVERLY BROTHERS (LP, reissue, m/s)	10/12
65	Warner Bros W(S) 1578	ROCK 'N' SOUL (LP, reissue)	18/22
65	Warner Bros W(S) 1605	BEAT 'N' SOUL (LP)	22
65	Warner Bros W(S) 1620	IN OUR IMAGE (LP, mono/stereo)	20/25
65	Warner Bros W(S) 1646	TWO YANKS IN ENGLAND (LP, mono/stereo)	20/25
67	Warner Bros W(S) 1676	THE HIT SOUND OF THE EVERLY BROTHERS (LP, mono/stereo)	20/25
67	Warner Bros W(S) 1708	THE EVERLY BROTHERS SING (LP, mono/stereo)	18/22
68	Warner Bros W(S) 1752	ROOTS (LP)	20
70	Valiant VS 109	THE EVERLY BROTHERS SHOW (2-LP)	18
70	Warner Bros WS 1858	GONE GONE GONE (LP, reissue)	12
70	CBS 66255	THE EVERLY BROTHERS' ORIGINAL GREATEST HITS (2-LP)	15
71	CBS 66259	END OF AN ERA (2-LP)	15
72	RCA Victor SF 8270	STORIES WE COULD TELL (LP)	12
73	RCA Victor SF 8332	PASS THE CHICKEN AND LISTEN (LP)	15

(see also Don Everly, Phil Everly)

DON EVERLY

74	Ode ODS 66046	Warmin' Up The Band/Evelyn Swing	5
76	DJM DJS 10692	Yesterday Just Passed Away Again/Never Like This	4
77	DJM DJS 10760	So Sad/Love At Last Sight (p/s)	5
77	DJM DJS 10842	Brother Juke Box/Oh What A Feeling	4
71	A&M AMLS 2007	DON EVERLY (LP, with Ry Cooder)	18
74	Ode 77023	SUNSET TOWERS (LP, with Heads, Hands & Feet)	18

PHIL EVERLY

73	RCA 2409	The Air That I Breathe/God Bless Older Ladies	5
74	Pye 7N 45398	Invisible Man/It's True	4
74	Pye 7N 45415	Sweet Music/Goodbye Line	4
75	Pye 7N 45544	Better Than Now/You And I Are A Song	4
73	RCA SF 8370	STAR SPANGLED SPRINGER (LP)	20
74	Pye NSPL 18448	THERE'S NOTHING TOO GOOD FOR MY BABY (LP)	15
75	Pye NSPL 18473	MYSTIC LINE (LP)	12

EVERREADY'S

80	Taaga TAG 3	Don't Do It Again/Matrian Girl (gatefold p/s)	4

LENNY EVERSONG

57	Vogue Coral Q 72255	Jezebel/Jealousy	5

EVERYBODY

70	Page One POF 163	Shape Of Things To Come/Do Like The Little Children Do	4

EVERY MOTHER'S SON

67	MGM MGM 1341	Come And Take A Ride In My Boat/I Believe In You	8
67	MGM MGM 1350	Put Your Mind At Ease/Proper Four Leaf Clover	8
67	MGM MGM 1372	Pony With The Golden Mane/Dolls In The Clock	8
67	MGM C(S) 8044	EVERY MOTHER'S SON (LP)	12
68	MGM C(S) 8061	EVERY MOTHER'S SON'S BACK (LP)	12

EVERYONE

71	B&C CAS 1028	EVERYONE (LP)	10

EVERYONE INVOLVED

72	Arcturus ARC 3	The Circus Keeps On Turning/Motor Car Madness	30
72	Arcturus ARC 4	EITHER OR (LP, private pressing, embossed plain white sleeve with inserts)	300

EVERYTHING BUT THE GIRL

83	Cherry Red CHERRY 37	Night And Day/Feeling Dizzy/On My Mind (yellow or white p/s)	5/4

(see also Ben Watt, Marine Girls)

EVERYTHING IS EVERYTHING

69	Vanguard VA 1	Oooh Baby/Witchi Tai To	5
68	Vanguard SVRL 19036	EVERYTHING IS EVERYTHING (LP)	10

EVERY WHICH WAY

69	Charisma BD 1	Go Placidly	4

(see also Griffin, Heavy Jelly, Skip Bifferty)

EWAN (McDermott) & DENVER

67	Giant GN 17	I Want You So Bad/ERIC McDERMOTT: I'm Gonna Love You	7

EWAN (McDermott) & JERRY

65	Blue Beat BB 385	Oh Babe/Dance With Me	10
67	Giant GN 5	The Right Track/We Got To Be One	8
67	Giant GN 10	Rock Steady Train/My Baby Is Gone	8
67	Giant GN 14	Tennessee Waltz/You've Got Something	8

EX

86	Ron Johnson ZRON 11	'1936' THE SPANISH REVOLUTION (double pack with book)	5

EX/ALERTA
84   CNT CNT 017   THE RED DANCE PACKAGE (12", split EP) 7

EXCALIBUR
88   Clay PLATE 1   HOT FOR LOVE (12" EP) 8
85   Conquest QUEST 5   THE BITTER END (mini-LP) 12

EXCEL
80   Polydor POSP 110   What Went Wrong?/Junita (p/s) 4

EXCELS
67   Atlantic 584 133   California On My Mind/The Arrival Of Mary 5

EXCELSIOR SPRING
68   Instant IN 002   Happy Miranda/It 12

EXCEPTION(S)
65   Decca F 12100   What More Do You Want?/Soldier Boy (as Exceptions) 7
67   CBS 202632   The Eagle Flies On Friday/Girl Trouble 15
67   CBS 2830   Gaberdine Saturday Night Street Walker/
         Sunday Night At The Prince Rupert 15
68   President PT 181   Rub It Down/It's Snowing In The Desert 4
68   President PT 205   Helicopter/Back Room 4
68   President PT 218   Tailor Made Babe/Turn Over The Soil 5
69   President PT 236   Jack Rabbit/Keep The Motor Running 5
69   President PT 271   Pendulum/Don't Torture Your Mind 4
69   President PTLS 1026   THE EXCEPTIONAL EXCEPTION (LP) 20
(see also Bugsy Eastwood)

EXCHECKERS
64   Decca F 11871   All The World Is Mine/It's All Over 8

EXCITERS
63   United Artists UP 1011   Tell Him/Hard Way To Go 7
64   United Artists UP 1014   Do Wah Diddy Diddy/If Love Came Your Way 12
64   United Artists UP 1017   He's Got The Power/Drama Of Love 7
64   United Artists UP 1026   Get Him/It's So Exciting 7
65   Columbia DB 7479   I Want You To Be My Boy/Tonight, Tonight 7
65   Columbia DB 7544   Just Not Ready/Are You Satisfied 8
65   Columbia DB 7606   Run Mascara/My Father 8
66   London HLZ 10018   A Little Bit Of Soap/I'm Gonna Get Him Someday 8
66   London HLZ 10038   You Better Come Home/Weddings Make Me Cry 12
69   United Artists UP 2274   Do Wah Diddy Diddy/Hard Way To Go 8
65   United Artists UEP 1005   DO WAH DIDDY DIDDY (EP) 40
64   United Artists ULP 1032   THE EXCITERS (LP) 60

EXECUTIVE(S)
64   Columbia DB 7323   March Of The Mods/Why, Why, Why 7
64   Columbia DB 7393   Strictly For The Beat/No Room For Squares 6
65   Columbia DB 7573   It's Been So Long/You're For Me 6
65   Columbia DB 7770   Return Of The Mods/How Sad 8
66   Columbia DB 7919   Lock Your Door/In My Arms 6
67   CBS 202652   Smokey Atmosphere/Sensation 7
67   CBS 3067   Ginza Strip/I'll Always Love You 7
68   CBS 3431   Tracy Took A Trip/Gardena Dreamer (as Executive) 10
68   CBS 3431   Tracy Took A Trip/Gardena Dreamer (as Executive, promo in p/s) 25
69   CBS 4013   I Ain't Got Nobody/To Kingdom Come (as Executive) 7

EXECUTIVES
80   Attrix RB 05   Shy Little Girl/Never Go Home/JOHNNIE & LUBES: I Got Rabies/
         Terror In The Parking Lot (p/s) 5

EXECUTIVE SLACKS
80s   Fundamental DEITY 9   Say It Isn't So/Rock & Roll (no p/s, promo only) 5

EXECUTIVE SUITE
75   Cloud One HIT 1   When The Fuel Runs Out/You Got It 5

EXHIBIT A
80   Irrelevant Wombat DAMP1   NO ELEPHANTS THIS SIDE OF THE WATFORD GAP (EP, with insert) 5
80   Irrelevant Wombat DAMP2   DISTANCE (EP) 4
(see also Doof)

EXILE
77   Boring BO 1   DON'T TAX ME (EP) 10
78   Charly CYS 1033   The Real People/Tomorrow Today/Disaster Movie 6

EXITS
78   Way Out WOO 1   YODELLING (EP, numbered, gatefold p/s, hand-stamped labels) 30

EXITS
78   Lightning GIL 519   The Fashion Plague/Cheam (p/s) 8
(see also Direct Hits)

EXOTICS
64   Decca F 11850   Cross My Heart/Ooh La La 4

EXOTICS
68   Columbia DB 8418   Don't Lead Me On/You Can Try 4

EXPELAIRES
79   Zoo CAGE 007   To See You/Frequency (p/s) 5
80   Rockburgh ROCS 222   Sympathy (Don't Be Taken In)/Kicks (p/s) 4
(see also Mission)

MINT VALUE £

EXPERIMENTS WITH ICE
81	United Dairies EX 001	EXPERIMENTS WITH ICE (LP) 20

EX PISTOLS
84	Virginia PISTOL 76P	Land Of Hope And Glory/The Flowers Of Romansk (picture disc) 4

EXPLICIT CORPSE
81	Gistol	That Day Before.../I Gotta Gistol (stickered white labels, plastic gatefold p/s) 5

EXPLODING SEAGULLS
81	Fried Egg EGG 8	Johnny Runs For Paregoric/Take Me To The Cinema (p/s) 5

(see also Blue Aeroplanes)

EXPLOITED
81	Exploited EXP 001	Army Life/Fuck The Mods/Crashed Out (p/s) 5
81	Exploited EXP 002	Exploited Barmy Army/I Believe In Anarchy/What You Gonna Do (p/s) 4
81	Exploited EXP 003	EXTRACTS FROM EDINBURGH NITE CLUB (EP) 5
81	Exploited EXP 1001	PUNK'S NOT DEAD (LP) 10
81	Exploited EXP 1002	ON STAGE (LP) 10

EXPLOSIVE
68	President PT 221	Crying All Night/I Close My Eyes 4
69	President PT 244	Cities Make The Country Colder/Step Out Of Line 8
69	President PT 262	Who Planted Thorns In Miss Alice's Garden/I Get My Kicks From Living 8

EXPORT
81	His Master's Vice VICE 2	Wheeler Dealer/You've Got To Rock (title sleeve) 7
80	His Master's Vice VICE 1	EXPORT (LP) 15

EX POST FACTO
80s	Ying Yang YY 001	Ex Post Facto/Money (p/s) 4

EXPOZER
83	Hard	Rock Japan/Exposed At Last (p/s) 7

EXPRESSOS
80	WEA K 18431	Tango In Mono/Thumbs On The Ground (p/s) 4
81	WEA K 18736	Kiss You All Over/The End (p/s) 4
81	WEA K 58303	PROMISES AND TIES (LP) 10

EXTREEM
66	Strike JH 236	On The Beach/Don't You Ignore Me 5

EXTREME
89	A&M AM 504	Kid Ego/Flesh 'N' Blood (unissued; Dutch only)
89	A&M AMY 504	Kid Ego/Flesh 'N' Blood (12", unissued; Dutch only)
91	A&M AMX 737	Get The Funk Out/Li'l Jack Horny/Little Girls (12", foldout poster p/s) 7
91	A&M AMP 737	Get The Funk Out/Li'l Jack Horny/Nice Place To Visit (12", picture disc) 8
91	A&M AMY 839	Hole Hearted/Get The Funk Out (12" Remix)/Suzi (Wants Her All Day What?)/
		Sex And Love (12", box set with poster) 8

EXUMA
71	Mercury 6052 080	Damn Fool/You Don't Know What's Going On 4
72	Mercury 6052 112	We Got To Go/Zandoo 4
70	Mercury 6338 018	EXUMA (LP) 12

EYE FULL TOWER
67	Polydor BM 56734	How About Me/Carol Cartoon 6

EYELESS IN GAZA
80	Ambivalent Scale ASR 2	Kodak Ghosts Run Amok/China Blue Vision/The Feeling's Mutual (p/s) 15
81	Cherry Red CHERRY 20	Invisibility/Three Kittens/Plague Of Years (p/s, with insert) 5
81	Cherry Red CHERRY 31	Others/Jane Dancing/Ever Present/Avenue With Trees (p/s) 5
82	Cherry Red CHERRY 47	Veil Like Calm/Taking Steps (p/s) 4
81	Cherry Red BRED 18	CAUGHT IN THE FLUX (LP, with free 12" EP [12 BRED 18]) 10

(see also Martyn Bates)

EYES
65	Mercury MF 881	When The Night Falls/I'm Rowed Out 50
66	Mercury MF 897	The Immediate Pleasure/My Degeneration 45
66	Mercury MF 910	Man With Money/You're Too Much 70
65	Mercury MF 934	Good Day Sunshine/Please Don't Cry 35
66	Mercury 10035 MCE	THE ARRIVAL OF THE EYES (EP) 150

(see also Pupils)

EYES OF BLUE
66	Deram DM 106	Heart Trouble/Up And Down 20
67	Deram DM 114	Supermarket Full Of Cans/Don't Ask Me To Mend Your Broken Heart 20
68	Mercury MF 1049	Largo/Yesterday 7
68	Mercury SMCL 20134	CROSSROADS OF TIME (LP) 35
69	Mercury SMCL 20164	IN FIELDS OF ARDATH (LP) 35

(see also Ancient Grease, Big Sleep, Man, Ritchie Francis, Gary Pickford-Hopkins & Friends)

EYNESBURY GIANT
78	private pressing	FROM THE CASK (LP) 20

WILL EZELL
50s	Signature 910	Heifer Dust/Barrelhouse Woman (78) 10
50s	Signature 911	Old Mill Blues/Mixed Up Rag (78) 10
50s	Tempo R 31	Old Mill Blues/Mixed Up Rag (78) 8
50s	Jazz Collector L 46	Just Can't Stay Here/Pitchin' Boogie (78) 5
50s	Jazz Collector L 63	Heifer Dust/Barrelhouse Woman (78) 5
50s	Jazz Collector L 84	Old Mill Blues/Mixed Up Rag (78) 5
50s	London AL 3539	GIN MILL JAZZ (10" LP) 25
73	Gannet 12-002	CHICAGO PIANO (LP) 15

JEFF LYNNE OF E.L.O.

ANDY BELL OF ERASURE

MINT VALUE £

SHELLEY FABARES
62	Pye Intl. 7N 25132	Johnny Angel/Where's It Gonna Get Me? (blue label, later yellow label)	8/6
62	Pye Intl. 7N 25133	She Can't Find Her Keys/Very Unlikely (with Paul Peterson)	5
62	Pye Intl. 7N 25151	Johnny Loves Me/I'm Growing Up	6
62	Pye Intl. 7N 25166	The Things We Did Last Summer/Breaking Up Is Hard To Do	5
63	Pye Intl. 7N 25184	Telephone (Won't You Ring)/Big Star	5
63	Pye Intl. 7N 25207	Ronnie, Call Me When You A Chance/I Left A Note To Say Goodbye	5
65	Fontana TF 592	My Prayer/Pretty Please	5

(see also Paul Peterson & Shelley Fabares)

FABIAN
59	HMV POP 587	I'm A Man/Hypnotized	25
59	HMV POP 587	I'm A Man/Hypnotized (78)	40
59	HMV POP 612	Turn Me Loose/Stop Thief!	20
59	HMV POP 643	Tiger/Mighty Cold (To A Warm, Warm Heart)	15
59	HMV POP 659	Got The Feeling/Come On And Get Me	12
60	HMV POP 695	Hound Dog Man/This Friendly World	12
60	HMV POP 724	String Along/About This Thing Called Love	6
60	HMV POP 778	I'm Gonna Sit Right Down And Write Myself A Letter/Strollin' In The Springtime	6
60	HMV POP 800	Tomorrow/King Of Love	6
60	HMV POP 810	Kissin' And Twistin'/Long Before	6
61	HMV POP 829	You Know You Belong To Somebody Else/Hold On	5
61	HMV POP 869	Grapevine/David And Goliath	5
61	HMV POP 934	You're Only Young Once/The Love That I'm Giving To You	5
59	HMV CLP 1301	HOLD THAT TIGER (LP)	40
60	HMV CLP 1345	THE FABULOUS FABIAN (LP)	35
61	HMV CLP 1433	YOUNG AND WONDERFUL (LP, also stereo CSD 1352)	30/35

FABLE
74	Magnet MAG 5002	FABLE (LP)	12

FABULOUS COUNTS
71	Mojo 2092 021	Get Down People/Lunar Funk	5

FABULOUS DIALS
63	Pye Intl. 7N 25200	Bossa Nova Stomp/Forget Me Not	15

FABULOUS FLAMES
69	Clandisc CLA 204	Holly Holy/LORD CREATOR: Kingston Town	4

FABULOUS POODLES
78	Pye 7N 46118	Mirror Star/B' Movies (pink vinyl)	4
78	Pye 7N PX 46188	Workshy/Toytown (picture disc)	4
80	Blueprint BLU 2015	Stompn' With The Cat/Anna Rexia/Don't You Lie To Me (p/s)	4

FABULOUS SWINGTONES
58	HMV POP 471	Geraldine/You Know Baby	100
58	HMV POP 471	Geraldine/You Know Baby (78)	35

FABULOUS TALBOT BROTHERS
50s	Melodisc M 1507	Bloodshot Eyes/She's Got Freckles	5
50s	Melodisc M 1507	Bloodshot Eyes/She's Got Freckles (78)	10

FACELLS
60s	Kalypso AB 116	So Fine/If You Love Me (I Won't Care)	4

FACES
70	Warner Bros WB 8005	Flying/Three-Button Hand-Me-Down	5
70	Warner Bros WB 8014	Wicked Messenger/Nobody Knows (unissued)	
70	Warner Bros WB 8018	Had Me A Real Good Time/Rear Wheel Skid	5
73	Warner Bros K 16281	Borstal Boys (withdrawn, any pressed?)	10+
73	Warner Bros/Sound For Industry SFI 139	Dishevelment Blues/Ooh La La (flexidisc free with 'NME' magazine)	7/4
70	Warner Bros K 46053	FIRST STEP (LP, green label)	10
71	Warner Bros K 46064	LONG PLAYER (LP, stitched die-cut sleeve, green label)	10
71	Warner Bros K 56006	A NOD IS AS GOOD AS A WINK (TO A BLIND HORSE) (LP, green label, some with poster)	15/10
73	Warner Bros K 56011	OOH LA LA (LP, 'Faces' sleeve with lyric poster)	10

(see also Small Faces, Birds, Rod Stewart, Rolling Stones, Ronnie Lane & Slim Chance)

FACTION
81	Inevitable INEV 006	Jamaica Day/Disney (12", p/s with insert in bag)	7
81	Inevitable INEV 007	Faction/Wrong Again (p/s)	4

(see also Wah! Heat)

FACTORY
68	MGM MGM 1444	Path Through The Forest/Gone	120
69	CBS 4540	Try A Little Sunshine/Red Chalk Hill	125

(see also Peter & Wolves, Norman Conquest)

FACTORY
70	Oak RGJ 718	Time Machine/Castle On The Hill	125

FACTOTUMS
65	Immediate IM 009	In My Lonely Room/Run In The Green And Tangerine Flaked Forest	12

MINT VALUE £

65	Immediate IM 022	You're So Good To Me/Can't Go Home Anymore My Love	12
66	Piccadilly 7N 35333	Here Today/In My Room	7
66	Piccadilly 7N 35355	I Can't Give You Anything But Love/Absolutely Sweet Marie	7
67	Pye 7N 17402	Cloudy/Easy Said, Easy Done	6
69	CBS 4140	Mr And Mrs Regards/Driftwood	6

FADERS
| 70s | Rip Off RIP 8 | Cheatin'/Library Book (p/s) | 4 |

FAD GADGET
| 79 | Mute MUTE 002 | Back To Nature/The Box (p/s) | 4 |
| 81 | Lyntone LYN 10209 | King Of The Flies/DEPECHE MODE: Sometimes I Wish I Was Dead (red vinyl flexidisc free with 'Flexipop' magazine, issue 11) | 12/10 |

FADING COLOURS
| 66 | Ember EMB S 229 | (Just Like) Romeo And Juliet/Billy Christian | 6 |

BRIAN FAHEY & HIS ORCHESTRA
60	Parlophone R 4686	At The Sign Of The Swingin' Cymbals/The Clanger	5
65	United Artists UP 1115	Twang/You Can't Catch Me	6
69	Studio 2 TWO 175	TIME FOR TV (LP)	10

JOHN FAHEY
67	Transatlantic TRA 173	THE TRANSFIGURATION OF BLIND JOE DEATH (LP, some with booklet)	20/15
68	Vanguard SVRL 19033	YELLOW PRINCESS (LP)	10
68	Vanguard SVRL 19055	REQUIA (LP)	10
67	Sonet SNTF 607	THE TRANSFIGURATION OF BLIND JOE DEATH (LP, reissue)	10
69	Sonet SNTF 608	VOLUME 2 (DEATH CHANTS & BREAKDOWNS) (LP)	10
72	Reprise K 44213	OF RIVERS AND RELIGION (LP)	10
73	Reprise K 44246	AFTER THE BALL (LP)	10

JAD FAIR
| 80 | Armageddon AEP 003 | THE ZOMBIES OF MORA-TAU (EP, die-cut p/s with insert) | 15 |
| | *(see also Half Japanese)* | | |

YVONNE FAIR
74	Tamla Motown TMG 913	Funky Music Sho Nuff Turns Me On/Let Your Hair Down	5
75	Tamla Motown TMG 1013	It Should Have Been Me/You Can't Judge A Book By It's Cover	4
75	Tamla Motown STML 12008	THE BITCH IS BLACK (LP)	15

WERLY FAIRBURN & DELTA BOYS
| 56 | London HLC 8349 | I'm A Fool About Your Love/All The Time | 350 |
| 56 | London HLC 8349 | I'm A Fool About Your Love/All The Time (78) | 80 |

JOHNNY FAIRE
| 58 | London HLU 8569 | Bertha Lou/Till The Law Says Stop | 150 |
| 58 | London HLU 8569 | Bertha Lou/Till The Law Says Stop (78) | 40 |

FAIRFIELD PARLOUR
70	Vertigo 6059 003	Bordeaux Rose/Chalk On The Wall	5
70	Vertigo 6059 008	Just Another Day/Caraminda/I Am All The Animals/Song For You	15
76	Prism PRI 1	Bordeaux Rose/Baby Stay For Tonight	8
70	Vertigo 6360 001	FROM HOME TO HOME (LP, gatefold sleeve, spiral label)	60
	(see also Kaleidoscope [U.K.], I Luv Wight)		

FAIRIES
64	Decca F 11943	Don't Think Twice, It's Alright/Anytime At All	60
65	HMV POP 1404	Get Yourself Home/I'll Dance	120
65	HMV POP 1445	Don't Mind/Baby Don't	60
	(see also Twink, Cops 'N Robbers)		

FAIRPORT CONVENTION
67	Track 604 020	If I Had A Ribbon Bow/If (Stomp)	15
68	Island WIP 6047	Meet On The Ledge/Throwaway Street Puzzle	10
69	Island WIP 6064	Si Tu Dois Partir/Genesis Hall	4
70	Island WIP 6089	Now Be Thankful/Sir B. McKenzie's Daughter's Lament	10
70	Polydor 2058 014	If (Stomp)/Chelsea Morning	10
71	Island WIP 6128	John Lee/The Time Is Near (some in p/s)	7/4
73	Island WIP 6155	Rosie/Knights Of The Road	4
75	Island WIP 6241	White Dress/Tears	5
79	Simons PMW 1	Rubber Band/The Bonny Black Hare	4
68	Polydor 583 035	FAIRPORT CONVENTION (LP, mono/stereo)	50/40
69	Island ILPS 9092	WHAT WE DID ON OUR HOLIDAYS (LP, pink label)	15
69	Island ILPS 9102	UNHALFBRICKING (LP, pink label)	15
69	Island ILPS 9115	LIEGE AND LIEF (LP, gatefold sleeve, pink label)	15
70	Island ILPS 9130	FULL HOUSE (LP, gatefold sleeve)	10
71	Island ILPS 9162	ANGEL DELIGHT (LP, with 'stuck-on' photos)	10
71	Island ILPS 9176	BABBACOME LEE (LP, with booklet & stickers)	10
72	Island ICD 4	THE HISTORY OF FAIRPORT CONVENTION (2-LP, with book & blue ribbons, later with book & green ribbons)	20/18
73	Island ILPS 9208	ROSIE (LP)	12
73	Island ILPS 9246	FAIRPORT NINE (LP, gatefold sleeve)	10
74	Island ILPS 9285	LIVE CONVENTION: A MOVEABLE FEAST (LP, with insert)	25
75	Island ILPS 9313	RISING FOR THE MOON (LP, with insert)	12
75	Island ISS 2	FAIRPORT TOUR SAMPLER (LP, free in 'NME' competition, 500 only)	80
76	Island ILPS 9389	GOTTLE O' GEER (LP)	10
76	Island HELP 28	LIVE AT THE L.A. TROUBADOR 1974 (LP)	20
77	Vertigo 9102 015	BONNY BUNCH OF ROSES (LP)	12
78	Vertigo 9102 022	TIPPLER'S TALES (LP)	12
79	Simons GAMA 1	FAREWELL FAREWELL (LP)	10
79	Woodworm BEAR 22	FAREWELL FAREWELL (LP)	15
82	Woodworm WR 001	MOAT ON THE LEDGE — LIVE 1981 (LP)	10

FAIRPORT CONVENTION

84	Woodworm WR 1	AT 2 (fan club cassette)	10
80s	Woodworm	AIRING CUPBOARD BLUES (fan club cassette)	10

(see also Richard Thompson, Ian Matthews, Dave Swarbrick, Sandy Denny, Fotheringay, Eclection, Vashti Bunyan, Uglys, Trader Horne, Ashley Hutchings, Thieves, Grease Band, Pyramid)

FAIRWAYS (featuring GARY STREET)
69	Mercury MF 1116	Yoko Ono/I Don't Care	8

FAIRWEATHER
71	RCA Neon NE 1000	Lay It On Me/Looking For The Red Label Pt 2	4
71	RCA Neon NE 1	BEGINNING FROM AN END (LP)	10

(see also Andy Fairweather-Low, Amen Corner)

AL FAIRWEATHER
60	Columbia 33SX 1221	AL'S PALS (LP)	10
61	Columbia 33SX 1306	DOCTOR McJAZZ (LP, also stereo SCX 3367)	10
63	Columbia 33SX 1509	THE INCREDIBLE McJAZZ (LP, with Sandy Brown's All Stars)	10

ANDY FAIRWEATHER-LOW
76	A&M AMLH 64602	BE BOP'N'HOLLA (LP, blue vinyl)	10

(see also Amen Corner, Fairweather, Gary Pickford-Hopkins)

FAIRY'S MOKE
75	Deroy private pressing	FAIRY'S MOKE (LP)	70

(see also Baby Sunshine)

FAIRYTALE
67	Decca F 12644	Guess I Was Dreaming/Run And Hide	50
67	Decca F 12665	Lovely People/Listen To Mary Cry	45

ADAM FAITH (& ROULETTES)
58	HMV POP 438	(Got A) Heartsick Feeling/Brother Heartache And Sister Tears	60
58	HMV POP 438	(Got A) Heartsick Feeling/Brother Heartache And Sister Tears (78)	25
58	HMV POP 557	Country Music Holiday/High School Confidential	40
58	HMV POP 557	Country Music Holiday/High School Confidential (78)	25
59	Top Rank JAR 126	Runk Bunk/Ah, Poor Little Baby!	15
59	Top Rank JAR 126	Runk Bunk/Ah, Poor Little Baby! (78)	30
59	Parlophone R 4591	What Do You Want?/From Now Until Forever (78)	20
60	Parlophone R 4623	Poor Me/The Reason (78)	20
60	Parlophone R 4665	When Johnny Comes Marching Home/Made You	5
62	Parlophone R 4864	Lonesome/Watch Your Step	4
63	Parlophone R 5091	We Are In Love/Made For Me	4
64	Parlophone R 5109	If He Tells You/Talk To Me	4
64	Parlophone R 5138	I Love Being In Love With You/It's Alright	4
64	Parlophone R 5174	I Just Don't Know/Only One Such As You	4
64	Parlophone R 5201	A Message To Martha/It Sounds Good To Me	4
65	Parlophone R 5235	Stop Feeling Sorry For Yourself/I've Gotta See My Baby	4
65	Parlophone R 5260	Hand Me Down Things/Talk About Love	4
65	Parlophone R 5289	Someone's Taken Maria Away/I Can't Think Of Anyone Else (with Roulettes)	4
65	Parlophone R 5349	I Don't Need That Kind Of Lovin'/I'm Used To Losing You	4
66	Parlophone R 5398	Idle Gossip/If You Ever Need Me	4
66	Parlophone R 5412	To Make A Big Man Cry/Here's Another Day	4
66	Parlophone R 5516	Cheryl's Goin' Home/Funny Kind Of Love	6
67	Parlophone R 5556	What More Can Anyone Do/You've Got A Way With Me	6
67	Parlophone R 5635	Cowman Milk Your Cow/Daddy, What'll Happen To Me	6
67	Parlophone R 5649	To Hell With Love/Close The Door ....ᵥ..................	6
68	Parlophone R 5673	You Make My Life Worth While/Hey Little Lovin' Girl	6
	Parlophone R series	other 45s (1959-1964)	3-4
60	Parlophone GEP 8811	ADAM'S HIT PARADE (EP)	8
60	Parlophone GEP 8824	ADAM NO. 1 (EP, also stereo SGE 2014)	8/12
60	Parlophone GEP 8826	ADAM NO. 2 (EP, also stereo SGE 2015)	8/12
60	Parlophone GEP 8831	ADAM NO. 3 (EP, also stereo SGE 2018)	8/12
61	Parlophone GEP 8841	ADAM'S HIT PARADE VOL. 2 (EP)	8
62	Parlophone GEP 8851	ADAM FAITH NO. 1 (EP)	8
62	Parlophone GEP 8852	ADAM FAITH NO. 2 (EP)	8
62	Parlophone GEP 8854	ADAM FAITH NO. 3 (EP, with John Barry)	8
62	Columbia SEG 8138	BEAT GIRL (EP, 2 Faith tracks, with John Barry Orchestra)	30
62	Parlophone GEP 8862	ADAM'S HIT PARADE VOL. 3 (EP)	10
63	Parlophone GEP 8877	ADAM'S LATEST HITS (EP)	10
64	Parlophone GEP 8893	TOP OF THE POPS (EP, with Roulettes)	12
64	Parlophone GEP 8904	FOR YOU — ADAM (EP)	10
65	Parlophone GEP 8929	A MESSAGE TO MARTHA — FROM ADAM (EP)	10
65	Parlophone GEP 8939	SONGS AND THINGS (EP)	12
60	Columbia 33SX 1225	BEAT GIRL (LP, soundtrack, with John Barry Orchestra)	30
60	Parlophone PMC 1128	ADAM (LP, also stereo PCS 3010)	14/20
61	Parlophone PMC 1162	ADAM FAITH (LP, also stereo PCS 3025)	14/20
62	Parlophone PMC 1192	FROM ADAM WITH LOVE (LP, also stereo PCS 3038)	15/20
63	Parlophone PMC 1213	FOR YOU — ADAM (LP, also stereo)	16/22
64	Parlophone PMC 1228	ON THE MOVE (LP)	25
65	Parlophone PMC 1249	FAITH ALIVE! (LP, with Roulettes)	40
60	EMI Regal (S)REG 1033	ADAM (LP, mono/stereo export issue in different sleeve) ....ₐ.....	12/14
65	EMI Regal	FAITH ALIVE! (LP, export issue in different sleeve)	10

(see also Roulettes, John Barry)

HORACE FAITH
69	B&C CB 104	Spinning Wheel/Like I Used To Do	4
69	Downtown DT 446	Daddy's Home/EMOTIONS: Give Me A Love	4

PERCY FAITH ORCHESTRA
60	Philips PB 989	Theme From 'A Summer Place'/Go-Go-Po-Go	4

FAITH BROTHERS
84	FBI FBI 1	The Trademan's Entrance/The Thrill Of The Kill (p/s)	6
85	Siren SIREN 2	The Country Of The Blind/Thrill Of The Kill//Eventide/Easter Parade (double pack)	4
85	Flexi FLX 404	Newtown/BIG SOUND AUTHORITY: Person I Want To Be (clear flexidisc free with 'Jamming!' magazine)	5/4

AUSTIN FAITHFUL
68	Blue Cat BS 140	Uncle Joe/Can't Understand	7
68	Pyramid PYR 6016	I'm In A Rocking Mood/ROLAND ALPHONSO: Stream Of Life	8
69	Pyramid PYR 6028	Eternal Love/ROLAND ALPHONSO: Goodnight My Love	8
69	Pyramid PYR 6042	Ain't That Peculiar/Miss Anti-Social	8

MARIANNE FAITHFULL
64	Decca F 11923	As Tears Go By/Greensleeves	4
64	Decca F 12007	Blowin' In The Wind/The House Of The Rising Sun	8
65	Decca F 12075	Come And Stay With Me/What Have I Done Wrong?	6
65	Decca F 12162	This Little Bird/Morning Sun	4
65	Decca F 12193	Summer Nights/The Sha La La Song	4
65	Decca F 12268	Yesterday/Oh Look Around You	4
66	Decca F 12408	Tomorrow's Calling/That's Right Baby	5
66	Decca F 12443	Counting/I'd Like To Dial Your Number	6
66	Decca F 22524	Is This What I Get For Loving You?/Tomorrow's Calling	6
69	Decca F 12889	Something Better/Sister Morphine (withdrawn)	25
75	NEMS NES 004	Dreamin' My Dreams/Lady Madalene	4
76	NEMS NES 013	All I Wanna Do In Life/Wrong Road Again	4
77	NEMS NES 014	Wrong Road Again/The Way You Want Me To Be	4
78	NEMS NES 117	The Way You Want Me To Be/That Was The Day (Nashville)	4
65	Decca DFE 8624	MARIANNE FAITHFULL (EP)	10
65	Decca LK 4688	COME MY WAY (LP)	20
65	Decca LK 4689	MARIANNE FAITHFULL (LP)	20
66	Decca LK 4778	NORTH COUNTRY MAID (LP)	25
67	Decca LK/SKL 4854	LOVE IN A MIST (LP)	30

FAITH, HOPE & CHARITY
70	Crewe CRW 3	So Much Love/Life Won't Be The Same Without You	5

FAITH NO MORE
88	Slash LASH 17	We Care A Lot/Spirit (p/s)	6
88	Slash LASHX 17	We Care A Lot/Spirit/Chinese Arithmetic (Radio Mix) (12", p/s)	12
88	Slash LASH 18	Anne's Song (Remix)/Greed (p/s)	6
88	Slash LASHP 18	Anne's Song (Remix)/Greed (picture disc)	12
88	Slash LASHX 18	Anne's Song (Remix)/Greed (12", p/s)	12
89	Kerrang! FIEND 3	Sweet Emotion/(Balaam & The Angel track) (flexidisc free with 'Kerrang!')	5/4
89	Slash LASH 19	From Out Of Nowhere/Cowboy Song (p/s)	4
89	Slash LASHX 19	From Out Of Nowhere/Cowboy Song/The Grave (12", p/s)	7
90	Slash LASHG 21	Epic/War Pigs (live)/Surprise You're Dead (live) (gatefold p/s)	4
90	Slash LASHG 21	Epic/War Pigs (live)/Surprise You're Dead (live)/Chinese Arithmetic (live) (12", p/s)	7
90	Slash LASPD 21	Epic/War Pigs (live) (shaped picture disc)	8
90	Slash LASHG 24	From Out Of Nowhere/Woodpecker From Mars (live)/Epic (live) (gatefold p/s)	4
90	Slash LASPX 24	From Out Of Nowhere/Woodpecker From Mars (live)/The Real Thing (live) (12", picture disc)	7
90	Slash LASPD 25	Falling To Pieces/We Care A Lot (live)/From Out Of Nowhere (live) (12", poster p/s)	7
90	Slash LASPD 26	Epic/Falling To Pieces (live) (shaped picture disc, 12" insert in PVC sleeve)	5
92	Slash LASPD 37	Midlife Crisis/ (12" picture disc)	7
92	Slash LASPD 39	A Small Victory/ (12" picture disc)	7
89	Slash 828 217 1	THE REAL THING (LP, picture disc)	10

FAKES
79	Deep Cuts DEEP TWO	Production/Look-Out (p/s)	4

TAV FALCO'S PANTHER BURNS
(see under Panther Burns)

EDDIE FALCON
60	Columbia DB 4420	The Young Have No Time To Lose/My Thanks To You	5
61	Columbia DB 4646	Lida Rose/If Ever I Should Fall In Love	4

FALCONS (U.S.)
59	London HLT 8876	You're So Fine/Goddess Of Angels	50
59	London HLT 8876	You're So Fine/Goddess Of Angels (78)	35
62	London HLK 9565	I Found A Love/Swim	30

(see also Wilson Pickett, Eddie Floyd)

FALCONS (U.K.)
64	Philips BF 1297	Stampede/Kazutzka	8

FALL
78	Step Forward SF 7	BINGO-MASTERS' BREAKOUT! (EP)	8
78	Step Forward SF 9	It's The New Thing/Various Times (p/s)	7
79	Step Forward SF 11	Rowche Rumble/In My Area (p/s)	7
80	Step Forward SF 13	Fiery Jack/Second Dark Age/Psykick Dancehall #2 (b&w or yellow p/s)	10/8
80	Rough Trade RT 048	How I Wrote 'Elastic Man'/City Hobgoblins (p/s)	6
80	Rough Trade RT 056	Totally Wired/Putta Block (p/s)	6
81	Rough Trade RT 071	SLATES (10" EP, 33rpm)	10
81	Kamera ERA 001	Lie, Dream Of A Casino Soul/Fantastic Life (p/s)	6
82	Kamera ERA 004	Look, Know/I'm Into C.B. (p/s)	6
82	Rough Trade RT 133	The Man Whose Head Expanded/Ludd Gang (p/s)	6
82	Kamera ERA 014	Marquis Cha Cha/Papal Visit (plays "Room To Live") (withdrawn) (p/s)	22
83	Rough Trade RT 143	Kicker Conspiracy/Wings//Container Drivers/New Puritan (g/fold double pack)	10

84	Beggars Banquet BEG 116T	C.R.E.E.P./(Extended Version)/Pat-Trip Dispenser (12" p/s, green vinyl) 7
84	B. Banquet BEG 116TP	C.R.E.E.P./(Extended Version)/Pat-Trip Dispenser (12", p/s, with art print) 8
84	Beggars Banquet BEG 120E	CALL FOR ESCAPE ROUTE (7"/12" double pack EP) 8
87	Beggars Banquet BEG 187H	There's A Ghost In My House/Haf Found Bormann (hologram p/s) 5
87	Beggars Banquet BEG 200P	Hit The North Pts 1 & 2 (picture disc, printed PVC sleeve) 4
87	Beggars Banquet BEG 206B	Victoria/Tuff Life Boogie (box set with inserts & badge) 5
88	Beggars Banquet FALL 2B	Jerusalem/Acid Priest 2088//Big New Prince/Wrong Place Right Time No. 2 (double pack box set, with postcard) 5
90	Cog Sinister SINR 5	Popcorn Double Feature/Zandra (p/s) 4
90	Cog Sinister SINDJ 6	White Lightning (stickered sleeve) 4
79	Step Forward SFLP 1	LIVE AT THE WITCH TRIALS (LP) 12
79	Step Forward SFLLP 4	DRAGNET (LP) 12
80	Rough Trade ROUGH 10	TOTALE'S TURNS (IT'S NOW OR NEVER) (LP) 15
80	Rough Trade ROUGH 18	GROTESQUE (AFTER THE GRAMME) (LP) 15
81	Step Forward SFLP 6	THE EARLY YEARS 1977-79 (LP) 10
82	Chaos LIVE 006	LIVE AT ACKLAM HALL (cassette) 10
	(see also Adult Net, Fall)	

FALLEN ANGELS (U.S.)

67	London HL 10166	I Don't Want To Fall/Most Children Do 4
68	London HA-Z/SH-Z 8359	THE FALLEN ANGELS (LP) 10

FALLEN ANGELS (U.K.)

84	Fallout FALL 022	Amphetamine Blues/He's A Rebel 6
84	Fallout FALL 12 027	INNER PLANET LOVE (mini-LP) 7
84	Fallout FALL LP 23	FALLEN ANGELS (LP) 10
84	Fallout FALL CLP 23	FALLEN ANGELS (cassette with extra track) 10
	(see also Knox, Hanoi Rocks, Troops Of Tomorrow)	

JOHNNY FALLIN

59	Capitol CL 15043	Party Kiss/The Creation Of Love 15
59	Capitol CL 15091	Wild Streak/If I Could Write A Love Song 20

FALLING LEAVES

65	Parlophone R 5233	She Loves To Be Loved/Not Guilty 35
66	Decca F 12420	Beggar's Parade/Tomorrow Night 15

FALLOUT

83	Mouth Too Small To Fight F2	SALAMI TACTICS (EP) 5
84	I FLP 2	BUTCHERY (LP) 25

FALSE IDOLS

78	Old Knew Wave BOG 005	Broken Judy/Marbled Hands/H-Brain (gatefold p/s) 4
78	Old Knew Wave BOG 007	Ego Wino/Good Night (p/s, pink vinyl) 4

AGNETHA FALTSKOG

83	Epic WA 3436	The Heat Is On/Man (picture disc) 5
83	Epic EPC A 3812	Can't Shake Loose/To Love (p/s) 4
83	Epic EPC A 3812	Can't Shake Loose/To Love (poster p/s) 7
83	Epic EPC WA 3812	Can't Shake Loose/To Love (picture disc) 5
85	Epic EPC A 6133	I Won't Let You Go/You're There (p/s) 4
85	Epic TA 6133	I Won't Let You Go (Extended)/You're There (12", p/s) 8
68	Embassy EMB 31094	AGNETHA (LP) 50
	(see also Abba)	

GEORGIE FAME (& BLUE FLAMES)

63	R&B JB 114	J.A. Blues/Orange Street (as Blue Flames) 20
63	R&B JB 126	Stop Right Here/Rik's Tune (as Blue Flames) 20
64	Columbia DB 7193	Do The Dog/Shop Around 8
64	Columbia DB 7255	Do-Re-Mi/Green Onions 6
64	Columbia DB 7328	Bend A Little/I'm In Love With You (solo) 5
64	Columbia DB 7428	Yeh Yeh/Preach And Teach (some copies list "Yeah, Yeah" on label) 4
65	Columbia DB 7494	In The Meantime/Telegram 5
65	Columbia DB 7633	Like We Used To Be/It Ain't Right 4
65	Columbia DB 7727	Something/Outrage 4
66	Columbia DB 7946	Getaway/El Bandido 4
	(all the above singles were credited to Georgie Fame & Blue Flames unless stated; all the below singles were solo)	
66	Columbia DB 8015	Sunny/Don't Make Promises 4
66	Columbia DB 8096	Sitting In The Park/Many Happy Returns 4
67	CBS 202587	Because I Love You//Bidin' My Time (p/s) 5
67	CBS 2945	Try My World/No Thanks (p/s) 5
67	CBS 3124	The Ballad Of Bonnie And Clyde/Beware Of The Dog (p/s) 6
68	CBS Special Prod. WB 73	By The Time I Get To Phoenix/SIMON & GARFUNKEL: Sound Of Silence (p/s) ...4
73	CBS 1151	The Ballad Of Bonnie And Clyde/Seventh Son (p/s) 6
64	Columbia SEG 8334	RHYTHM AND BLUEBEAT (EP) 15
64	Columbia SEG 8382	RHYTHM AND BLUES AT THE FLAMINGO (EP) 15
64	Columbia SEG 8393	FAME AT LAST (EP) 10
65	Columbia SEG 8406	FATS FOR FAME (EP) 12
65	Columbia SEG 8454	MOVE IT ON OVER (EP) 12
66	Columbia SEG 8518	GETAWAY (EP) 10
67	CBS EP 6363	KNOCK ON WOOD (EP) 7
64	Columbia 33SX 1599	RHYTHM AND BLUES AT THE FLAMINGO (LP) 30
64	Columbia 33SX 1638	FAME AT LAST (LP) 15
66	Columbia SX 6043	SWEET THINGS (LP) 15
66	Columbia SX 6076	SOUND VENTURE (LP) 12
67	Columbia SX 6120	HALL OF FAME (LP) 12
67	CBS 63018	TWO FACES OF FAME (LP) 10
68	CBS (S) 63293	THE THIRD FACE OF FAME (LP) 10
69	CBS (S) 63650	GEORGIE DOES HIS OWN THING WITH STRINGS (LP) 10

MINT VALUE £

69	CBS S 63786	SEVENTH SON (LP)	10

(see also Jimmy Nicol, Perry Ford & Sapphires)

FAMILY

67	Liberty LBF 15031	Scene Thru The Eye Of A Lens/Gypsy Woman	60
68	Reprise RS 23270	Me My Friend/Hey Mr. Policeman	6
68	Reprise RS 23315	Second Generation Woman/Home Town	6
69	Reprise RS 27001	No Mule's Fool/Good Friend Of Mine (initially in p/s)	10/4
70	Reprise RS 27005	Today/Song For Lots (initially in p/s)	10/4
71	Reprise RS 27009	The Weaver's Answer/Strange Band/Hung Up Down (initially in p/s)	7/4
71	Reprise K 14090	In My Own Time/Seasons (initially in p/s)	7/4
72	Reprise K 14196	Burlesque/The Rockin' R's	4
73	Reprise K 14218	My Friend The Sun/Glove	4
71	Reprise SAM 1	Larf And Sing/Children (promo only)	12
73	Raft RA 18501	Boom Bang/Stop This Car	4
73	Raft RA 18503	Sweet Desiree/Drink To You	4
68	Reprise R(S)LP 6312	MUSIC FROM A DOLL'S HOUSE (LP, with poster, mono/stereo)	20/18
69	Reprise R(S)LP 6340	FAMILY ENTERTAINMENT (LP, with poster, mono/stereo)	18/16

(both the above LPs originally came with 'steamboat' label designs, later pressings are worth £8)

70	Reprise RSLP 9001	A SONG FOR ME (LP, with lyric sheet)	10
70	Reprise RSX 9005	ANYWAY (LP)	10
71	Reprise RMP 9007	OLD SONGS NEW SONGS (LP)	10
71	Reprise K 54003	FEARLESS (LP)	10
72	Reprise K 54006	BANDSTAND (LP)	10
73	Raft RA 58501	IT'S ONLY A MOVIE (LP)	10

(see also Farinas, Stud, Rick Grech, Mogul Thrash, Hellions, Ashton Gardner & Dyke, Steve Harley & Cockney Rebel)

FAMILY AFFAIR

60s	Saga	FAMILY AFFAIR (LP)	10

FAMILY AFFAIR

76	Pye 7N 45609	Call Me/Love Hustle	4

(see also Jackie Trent)

FAMILY CAT

89	Bad Girl 12BGRLT 001	TOM VERLAINE (12", p/s)	8
89	Bad Girl BGRIFC 01	Tom Verlaine (Demo Version) (gig freebie flexidisc, hand-sprayed p/s & insert)	6
90	Bad Girl BGRLE 03	Remember What It is That You Love/Push Comes To Shove (numbered p/s)	4
91	Clawfist HUNKA 008	Jesus Christ/Chill Out Ye Merry Gentlemen/Jesus Karaoke Christ/Christ Jesus (p/s)	5
92	Dedicated FCUK 001	Steamroller (Pt 1)/Steamroller (Pt 2) (p/s)	4

FAMILY DOGG

67	MGM MGM 1360	Family Dogg/The Storm	7
68	Fontana TF 921	I Wear A Silly Grin/Couldn't Help It	4
68	Fontana TF 968	Brown-Eyed Girl/Let It Rain	5
69	Bell BLL 1055	A Way Of Life/Throw It Away	5
69	Bell BLL 1077	Arizona/The House In The Heather	4
70	Bell BLL 1100	When Tomorrow Comes Today/This Unhappy Heart Of Mine	4
71	Bell BLL 1139	Coat Of Many Colours/Jeses Loves You	4
69	Bell SBLL 122	A WAY OF LIFE (LP)	12
72	Polydor 2318 061	THE VIEW FROM ROWLAND'S HEAD (LP)	10

FAMILY PLANN

75	President PT 441	Sexy Summer/Can You Get Into The Music	5

FAMOUS ECCLES & MISS FREDA THING

56	Parlophone R 4251	My September Love/JIM MORIARTY: You Gotta Go Oww!	7

(see also Spike Milligan, Goons)

FAMOUS JUG BAND

69	Liberty LBF 15224	The Only Friend I Own/A Leaf Must Fall	6
69	Liberty LBS 83246	SUNSHINE POSSIBILITIES (LP)	30
70	Liberty LBS 83355	CHAMELEON (LP)	20

(see also Incredible String Band, C.O.B.)

FAMOUS MUSIC BAND

69	Philips 6006 111	Nine By Nine/Going In The Out (with John Dummer)	8

(see also John Dummer)

FAN-CLUB

78	M&S SJP 791B	Avenue/Night Caller (photocopied wraparound p/s)	12

(see also Transvision Vamp)

FANCY

73	Atlantic K 10383	Wild Thing/Fancy	4
76	Arista ARIST 32	Music Maker/Bluebird	4
75	Arista ARTY 102	SOMETHING TO REMEMBER (LP)	10

(see also Ray Fenwick)

FANNY

70	Reprise RSLP 6416	FANNY (LP)	10
71	Reprise K 44144	CHARITY BALL (LP)	10

FANS

80	Albion ION 1004	True/Death Wish//Cars And Explosions/Dangerous Goodbyes (double pack with 2 inserts, stickered PVC sleeve)	5

FANTASIA

67	Stateside SS 2031	Gotta Get Away/She Needs My Love	4

FANTASTIC BAGGYS

76	United Artists UP 36142	Summer Means Fun/JAN & DEAN: Surf City/Sidewalk Surfin'	8

(see also Jan & Dean)

FANTASTIC FOUR
| 68 | Tamla Motown TMG 678 | I Love You Madly/I Love You Madly (Instrumental) .... 10 |
| 69 | T. Motown (S)TML 11105 | THE FANTASTIC FOUR (LP) .... 18 |

FANTASTIC JOHNNY C
(see under C)

FANTASTICS
68	MGM MGM 1434	Baby Make Your Own Sweet Music/Who Could Be Loving You 6
69	Deram DM 264	Face To Face With Heartache/This Must Be Your Rainy Day 4
70	Deram DM 283	Waiting Round For Heartaches/Ask The Lonely 4
71	Deram DM 334	For Old Times Sake/Exodus Main Theme 4

FANTASY
| 73 | Polydor 2058 405 | Politely Insane/I Was Once Aware .... 20 |
| 73 | Polydor 2383 246 | PAINT A PICTURE (LP) .... 225 |

BARRY FANTONI
| 66 | Fontana TF 707 | Little Man In A Little Box/Fat Man .... 15 |
| 67 | Columbia DB 8238 | Nothing Today/The Spanish Lady Tango .... 5 |

FAPARDOKLY
| 83 | Psycho PSYCHO 5 | FAPARDOKLY (LP, 300 only) .... 15 |

FARAWAY FOLK
70s	Tabitha TAB 3	Shadow Of A Pie/Folsom Prison Blues/Rent A Man/Soulful Shade Of Blue 8
70s	RA EP 7001	INTRODUCING THE FARAWAY FOLK (EP) 20
70s	RA LP 6006ST	LIVE AT THE BOLTON (LP) 80
70s	RA LP 6012ST	TIME AND TIDE (LP) 80
70s	RA LP 6019	ON THE RADIO (LP) 40
70s	RA LP 6022	ONLY AUTHORISED EMPLOYEES TO BREAK BOTTLES
		(LP, with Harry H. Corbett) 30
75	RA LP 6029	SEASONAL MAN (LP) 100
80s	RA	BATTLE OF THE DRAGONS (cassette) 15

FAR CRY
| 69 | Vanguard SVRL 19041 | THE FAR CRY (LP) .... 20 |

DON FARDON
67	Pye Intl. 7N 25437	(The Lament Of The Cherokee) Indian Reservation/Dreamin' Room 6
68	Pye Intl. 7N 25475	(The Lament Of The Cherokee) Indian Reservation/Dreamin' Room (reissue) 4
70	Young Blood SSYB 13	RELEASED (LP) 10
	(see also Sorrows)	

FAR EAST FAMILY BAND
| 75 | Vertigo 6370 850 | NEPPORJIN (LP) .... 18 |

FAREWELL NANCY
| 64 | Topic 12T 110 | SEA SONGS AND SHANTIES (LP) .... 15 |

RICHARD & MIMI FARINA
65	Fontana STFL 6060	CELEBRATIONS FOR A GREY DAY (LP) 12
65	Fontana STFL 6075	REFLECTIONS IN A CRYSTAL WIND (LP) 12
73	Vanguard VSD 21/22	THE BEST OF RICHARD & MIMI FARINA (2-LP) 14

FARINAS
| 64 | Fontana TF 493 | You'd Better Stop/I Like It Like That .... 40 |
| | *(see also Family)* | |

TERRY FARLAN
| 71 | Hallmark HM 637 | SINGS BUDDY HOLLY'S GREATEST HITS (LP) .... 10 |

CHRIS FARLOWE (& THUNDERBIRDS)
62	Decca F 11536	Air Travel/Why Did You Break My Heart? 20
63	Columbia DB 7120	I Remember/Push Push (as Chris Farlowe & Thunderbirds) 10
64	Columbia DB 7237	Girl Trouble/Itty Bitty Pieces (as Chris Farlowe & Thunderbirds) 10
64	Columbia DB 7311	Just A Dream/What You Gonna Do? (as Chris Farlow & Thunderbirds) 10
64	Columbia DB 7379	Hey, Hey, Hey/Hound Dog (as Chris Farlow & Thunderbirds) 10
65	Columbia DB 7614	Buzz With The Fuzz/You're The One (withdrawn,
		as Chris Farlow & Thunderbirds) 70
65	Immediate IM 016	The Fool/Treat Her Good 8
66	Immediate IM 023	Think/Don't Just Look At Me 5
66	Immediate IM 035	Out Of Time/Baby Make It Soon 5
66	Columbia DB 7983	Just A Dream/Hey, Hey, Hey, Hey 10
66	Immediate IM 038	Ride On Baby/Headlines 5
67	Immediate IM 041	My Way Of Giving/You're So Good To Me 8
67	Immediate IM 049	Yesterday's Papers/Life Is But Nothing 5
67	Immediate IM 056	Moanin'/What Have I Been Doin'? 5
67	Immediate IM 065	Handbags And Gladrags/Everyone Makes A Mistake 5
68	Immediate IM 066	The Last Goodbye/Paperman Fly In The Sky (B-side with Thunderbirds) 8
68	Immediate IM 071	Paint It Black/I Just Need Your Lovin' 6
69	Immediate IM 074	Dawn/April Was The Month 7
69	Immediate IM 078	Out Of Time/Ride On Baby 4
71	Polydor 2066 017	Black Sheep/Fifty Years 5
71	Polydor 2066 046	Put Out The Light/Questions (as Chris Farlowe & Hill) 4
75	Polydor 2066 650	We Can Work It Out/Only Women Bleed 4
75	Virgin SV 102	Out Of Time/Handbags And Gladrags//Yesterday's Papers/Ride On Baby
		(double pack) 5
65	Decca DFE 8665	CHRIS FARLOWE (EP) 40
66	Island IEP 709	STORMY MONDAY (EP) 50
65	Immediate IMEP 001	FARLOWE IN THE MIDNIGHT HOUR (EP) 20
66	Immediate IMEP 004	CHRIS FARLOWE HITS (EP) 20
66	Columbia SX 6034	CHRIS FARLOWE AND THE THUNDERBIRDS (LP) 40

MINT VALUE £

66	Immediate IMLP 005	14 THINGS TO THINK ABOUT (LP)	30
66	Immediate IMLP 006	THE ART OF CHRIS FARLOWE (LP)	30
67	MFP MFP 1186	STORMY MONDAY (LP, reissue of SX 6034 in different sleeve)	10
68	Immediate IMLP 010	THE BEST OF CHRIS FARLOWE VOLUME ONE (LP)	15
69	Immediate IMLP 021	THE LAST GOODBYE (LP)	40
60s	Regal REG 2025	CHRIS FARLOWE (LP, export issue)	10
70	Polydor 2425 029	FROM HERE TO MAMA ROSA (LP, as Chris Farlowe & Hill)	10
75	Polydor 2469 259	THE CHRIS FARLOWE BAND LIVE (LP)	10

(see also Beazers, Little Joe Cook, Vincent Crane & Chris Farlowe, Atomic Rooster, Colosseum)

FARM

84	Skysaw END 1	Hearts And Minds/(Dub)/Information Man/Same Old Story (12", p/s)	10
85	Admiralty PRA 1	Steps Of Emotion/Memories (p/s)	5
85	Admiralty PRAT 1	Steps Of Emotion/Power Over Me/No Man's Land/Better/	
		Living For Tomorrow (12", p/s)	8
86	Fire BLAZE 13	Some People/The Moroccan (p/s)	4
86	Fire BLAZE 13T	Some People/The Moroccan/Sign Of The Cross/Stand Together (12", p/s)	7
89	Foresight FR 2301	Body And Soul/Colonels (no p/s)	4
89	Foresight FR 2301	Body And Soul/Colonels And Heroes/Stuck On You (12", p/s)	7
87	private pressing	EAST & WEST TOUR 87 (cassette)	10

ART FARMER

56	Vogue EPV 1045	ART FARMER (EP, as Art Farmer New Jazz All Stars)	7
54	Esquire 20-033	ART FARMER SEXTET — WORK OF ART (10" LP)	15
59	London SAH-T 6028	MODERN ART (LP)	12
60	London Jazz LTZ-T 15184	BRASS SHOUT (LP)	10
60	London Jazz LTZ-T 15198	THE AZTEC SUITE (LP)	10
61	Esquire 32-120	EARTHY (LP)	10
64	London HA-K/SH-K 8135	INTERACTION (LP, as Art Farmer Quartet featuring Jim Hall)	10

(see also Clifford Brown, Benny Golson)

JULES FARMER

| 59 | London HLP 8967 | Love Me Now/Part Of Me (Is Still With You) | 6 |

FARMER'S BOYS

82	Waap WAAP 3	I Think I Need Help/Squit (p/s)	5
82	Waap 12 WAAP 3	I Think I Need Help/Squit/More Squit/Squittest (12", p/s)	7
82	Backs NCH 001	Whatever Is He Like/I Lack Concentration (p/s)	4
82	Backs NCH 003	More Than A Dream/The Country Line (p/s)	4
82	Masterbag BAG 006	Muck It Out 5.02 (square 33rpm 1-sided flexidisc with 'Masterbag' magazine)	5/4
82	EMI EMI P5380	Muck It Out!/Funky Combine, John (pig-shaped picture disc)	4
84	EMI FAB 2	In The Country/Mama Never Told Me (picture disc)	4

FARMLIFE

| 82 | Dining Out TUX 19 | Susie's Party/Simple Men | 6 |
| 83 | Whaam WHAAM 13 | Big Country 1 & 2 (unreleased; Echantillan test pressings only) | 40 |

(see also Bomb Party)

GILES FARNABY'S DREAM BAND

| 73 | Argo ZDA 158 | GILES FARNABY'S DREAM BAND (LP) | 80 |

FARON'S FLAMINGOS

| 63 | Oriole CB 1834 | Do You Love Me/See If She Cares | 10 |
| 63 | Oriole CB 1867 | Shake Sherry/Give Me Time | 12 |

WAYNE FARO'S SCHMALTZ BAND

| 69 | Deram DM 222 | There's Still Time/Give It Time | 8 |

GARY FARR (& T-BONES)

65	Columbia DB 7608	Give All She's Got/Don't Stop And Stare (as Gary Farr & T-Bones)	25
68	Marmalade 598 007	Everyday/Green (with Kevin Westlake)	6
69	Marmalade 598 017	Hey Daddy/The Vicar And The Pope	8
71	CBS 5430	Revolution Of The Season/Old Man Boulder	5
65	Columbia SEG 8414	DEM BONES, DEM BONES, DEM T-BONES (EP)	70
69	Marmalade 608 013	TAKE SOMETHING WITH YOU (LP)	35
71	CBS 64138	STRANGE FRUIT (LP, with Richard Thompson & Mighty Baby)	25

(see also T-Bones, Richard Thompson, Mighty Baby, Meic Stevens)

TOMMY FARR

| 37 | Regal Zono. MR 2616 | Remember Me/Maybe I'll Find Someone Else (78) | 6 |

(see also George Formby)

MARY ANN FARRAR & SATIN SOUL

| 76 | Brunswick BR 38 | Stoned Out Of My Mind/Living In The Footsteps Of Another Girl | 4 |

BILLY FARRELL

55	Mercury MB 3206	It May Sound Silly/Rock Love (78)	5
58	Philips PB 828	Yeah Yeah/Someday (You'll Want Me To Want You)	4
58	Philips PB 828	Yeah Yeah/Someday (You'll Want Me To Want You) (78)	8

DO & DENA FARRELL

| 57 | HMV POP 427 | Young Magic/New Love Tonight | 8 |

MICK FARREN

78	Stiff LAST 4	ALL SCREWED UP (EP, as Mick Farren & Deviants)	5
78	Logo GO 321	Half Price Drinks/I Don't Want To Go This Way	4
79	Logo GO 345	Broken Statue/It's All In The Picture	4
70	Transatlantic TRA 212	MONA (THE CARNIVOROUS CIRCUS) (LP)	50
78	Logo LOGO 2010	VAMPIRES STOLE MY LUNCH MONEY (LP)	12
84	Psycho PSYCHO 20	MONA (THE CARNIVEROUS CIRCUS) (LP, reissue)	10

(see also Deviants, Twink)

MIA FARROW

| 68 | Dot DOT 116 | Lullaby From Rosemary's Baby Pts 1 & 2 | 4 |

FASCINATIONS
67	Stateside SS 594	Girls Are Out To Get You/You'll Be Sorry	40
68	Sue WI 4049	Girls Are Out To Get You/You'll Be Sorry (reissue)	20
71	Mojo 2092 004	Girls Are Out To Get You/You'll Be Sorry (2nd reissue)	6
71	Mojo 2092 018	I'm So Lucky He Loves Me/Say It Isn't So	4

FASCINATORS
58	Capitol CL 14942	Chapel Bells/I Wonder Who	45
59	Capitol CL 15062	Oh, Rose Marie/Fried Chicken And Macaroni	30

FASHION
79	Fashion Music FM 001	Steady Eddie Steady/Killing Time (initially in green p/s; later black & white)	6/4
79	Fashion Music FM 002	Cininite/Wastelife (p/s)	4
79	Fashion Music FM 003	Silver Blades/Silver Blades (A Deeper Cut) (p/s)	4
84	CBS DA 4502	You In The Night/Yamashta Theme//Hurricane/White Stuff (double pack)	4

FASHIONS
68	Stateside SS 2115	I.O.U. (A Lifetime Of Love)/When Love Slips Away	8
69	Evolution E 2444	I.O.U. (A Lifetime Of Love)/He Gives Me Love	6

FAST
76	CBS S CBS 6236	Boys Will Be Boys/Wow Pow Bash Crash	4

FASTBACKS
89	Subway Org. SUBWAY 24	In The Winter/Dream (p/s)	4

FAST BREEDER & RADIO ACTORS
78	Virgin NO NUKE 235	Nuclear Waste/Digital Love (some with insert)	20/10

(see also Radio Actors)

FAST CARS
79	Streets Ahead SA 3	The Kids Just Wanna Dance/You're So Funny (p/s)	4

FAST SET
80	Axis AXIS 1	Junction One/Children Of The Revolution (p/s)	15

FAT
70	RCA LPS 4368	FAT (LP)	20

FATAL CHARM
79	Company CR 005	Paris/Glitterbit/Out Of My Head	6
82	DD FATAL 1	Christine/Paris (p/s)	5

FATAL MICROBES
79	Small Wonder SMALL 20	Violence Grows/Beautiful Pictures/Cry Baby (p/s)	4

(see also Pete Fender, Honey Bane)

FATBACK BAND
75	Polydor 2066 494	Keep On Steppin'/Breakin' Up Is Hard To Do	5
75	Polydor 2066 524	Wicky Wacky/Can't Fight The Flame	5
75	Polydor 2066 590	Yum Yum (Gimme Some)/Trompin'	4
75	Polydor 2066 637	(Are You Ready) Do The Bus Stop/Got To Learn How To Dance	4
76	Polydor 2066 682	Par-r-rty Time/Put Your Love In My Tender Care	4
75	Polydor 2391 143	KEEP ON STEPPIN' (LP)	10
75	Polydor 2391 184	YUM, YUM (LP)	10

FAT CITY
69	Probe SPB 1008	REINCARNATION (LP)	12

FATHER'S ANGELS
68	MGM MGM 1459	Bok To Bach/Don't Knock It	75
75	Black Magic BM 103	Bok To Bach/Disco Trucking	5

FAT LADY SINGS
86	Good Vibrations FLS 1	Fear And Favour/Wishing Well (p/s)	12
88	Harbour Sound HSS 1	Be Still/King Of Freedom (p/s)	8
89	Fourth Base TFLS 3	Arclight/Behind Your Back (p/s)	5
89	Fourth Base 12 TFLS 3	Arclight/Behind Your Back/Fear And Favour (12", p/s)	8
90	Fourth Base TFLS 4	Dronning Maud Land/A Message (live) (p/s)	5
90	Fourth Base 12 TFLS 4	Dronning Maud Land/A Message (live)/Heavy Duty (12", p/s)	8

FAT MATTRESS
69	Polydor BM 56352	Naturally/Iredescent Butterfly	8
70	Polydor BM 56367	Magic Lanterns/Bright New Way	8
70	Polydor 2058 053	Highway/Black Sheep Of The Family	6
69	Polydor 583 056	FAT MATTRESS (LP, open-out sleeve)	15
70	Polydor 2383 025	FAT MATTRESS II (LP)	12

(see also Jimi Hendrix Experience)

FATS & CHESSMEN
62	Pye Intl. 7N 25122	Big Ben Twist/Old Macdonald Had A Twist	6
61	Golden Guinea GGL 0117	LET'S TWIST (LP)	10
62	Golden Guinea GGL 0125	LET'S TWIST TO THE OLDIES (LP)	10

ERIC FATTER
69	Camel CA 20	Since You've Been Gone (actually Eric Fratter)/WINSTON HINES: Cool Down	4

(see also Eric Fratter)

ERNIE FAULKNER
63	Sway SW 003	Beautiful Girl/SAM DANIELS: Tell Me Baby (both with Planets)	8

FAUST
80	Recommended RRI 15	EXTRACTS FROM FAUST PARTY 3 (EP)	5
71	Polydor 2310 142	FAUST (LP, initially on clear vinyl in printed PVC sleeve)	16/12
72	Polydor 2310 196	FAUST SO FAR (LP, with 10 prints in wallet)	15
73	Virgin V 2004	FAUST 4 (LP)	10

| 79 | Recommended RRA 1 | FAUST ONE (LP, reissue of "Faust") | 15 |
| 79 | Recommended R.R. TWO | FAUST SO FAR (LP, reissue, with 10 insert prints, 600 only, numbered) | 30 |

(see also Toni Conrad & Faust)

FAVOURITES
| 80 | 4 Play FOUR 002 | S.O.S./Favourite Shoes (p/s) | 6 |
| 80 | 4 Play FOUR 003 | Angelica/Cold (p/s) | 5 |

FAVOURITE SONS
| 65 | Mercury MF 911 | That Driving Beat/Walkin' Walkin' Walkin' | 50 |

FAWCETT'S DESIGN FOR LIVING
| 81 | Boys Own B.O. 2 | Is There Somebody There?/Overcoat (p/s) | 4 |

WALLY FAWKES & HIS TROGLODYTES
57	Decca FJ 10855	Petite Fleur/Baby Brown (with Sandy Brown Quintet)	4
57	Decca FJ 10936	Sent For You Yesterday And Here .../Why Can't You Behave	4
58	Decca F 11002	The Pilot Fish And The Whale/Pale Blues	4

BILL FAY
67	Deram DM 143	Some Good Advice/Screams In The Ears	40
70	Deram Nova SDN 12	BILL FAY (LP)	25
71	Deram SML 1079	TIME OF THE LAST PERSECUTION (LP)	60

FRANCIS FAYE
61	Vogue V 9186	I Wish I Could Shimmy Like My Sister Kate/Night And Day	10
61	HMV POP 898	Frenesi/Miserlou	6
65	Stateside SL 10129	YOU GOTTA GO! GO! GO! (LP)	10

LITTLE RITA FAYE
| 53 | MGM MGM 671 | Rock City Boogie/Wait A Little Longer (78) | 7 |
| 53 | MGM MGM 697 | I Fell Out Of The Christmas Tree/I'm A Problem Child (78) | 7 |

F.B.I. (FOLK BLUES INC.)
66	Eyemark EMS 1006	Don't Hide/When The Ship Comes In	7
73	A&M AMS 7050	I Wonder What She's Doing Tonight/Boogaloo Boo Boo	4
76	Good Earth GD 6	F.B.I./The Time Is Right To Leave The City	4
77	Good Earth GDS 802	F.B.I. (LP)	50

FEARIE SYMPHONY
| 77 | Decca F 13735 | Dance Of The Theena Shee/The Unseelie Court | 4 |

(see also Tom Newman)

FEARN'S BRASS FOUNDRY
| 68 | Decca F 12721 | Don't Change It/John White | 10 |
| 68 | Decca F 12835 | Now I Taste The Tears/Love, Sink And Drown | 8 |

FEAR OF FALLING
| 83 | Excellent XL 7 | Like A Lion/You My Prodigal Son (p/s) | 20 |

CHARLIE FEATHERS
| 74 | Polydor 2310 293 | ROCKABILLY KINGS (LP, with Mac Curtis) | 15 |

FEATURES
| 70s | Progress PR 01 | Drab City/Job Satisfaction | 4 |

FEDERALS (U.K.)
63	Parlophone R 4988	Brazil/In A Persian Market	6
63	Parlophone R 5013	Boot Hill/Keep On Dancing With Me	6
64	Parlophone R 5100	The Climb/Dance With A Dolly	6
64	Parlophone R 5139	Marlena/Please Believe Me	6
64	Parlophone R 5193	Twilight Time/Lost And Alone	6
65	Parlophone R 5320	Bucket Full Of Love/Leah	7

(see also Winston's Fumbs, Yes)

FEDERALS (Jamaica)
67	Island WI 3126	Penny For Your Song/I've Passed This Way Before	10
68	Island WI 3152	Shocking Love/By The River	10
69	High Note HS 024	Wailing Festival/Me And My Baby (B-side actually "By The River")	5
70	Camel CA 40	In This World/Shocking Love	4

FEDERATION
| 76 | 20th Century BTC 1023 | 25 Minutes To Love/Hooked On Love | 5 |

FEELIES
| 79 | Stiff (no cat. no.) | Face La/The Boy With Perpetual Nervousness/
Everybody's Got Something To Hide (Except Me And My Monkey)
(flexidisc, promo, with 'Be Stiff' fanzine issue 6, 5,000 only) | 7/5 |

FELDER'S ORIOLES
65	Piccadilly 7N 35247	Down Home Girl/Misty	15
65	Piccadilly 7N 35269	Sweet Tasting Wine/Turn On Your Lovelight	15
66	Piccadilly 7N 35311	I Know You Don't Love Me No More/Only Three Can Pay	15
66	Piccadilly 7N 35332	Back Street/Something You Got	12

(see also Timebox, V.I.P.s)

MARTY FELDMAN
68	Pye 7N 17643	Funny He Never Married/Travel Agency (with Tim Brooke-Taylor)	4
68	Decca F 12857	A Joyous Time Of Year/B Side	4
68	Pye NPL 18258	MARTY (LP)	10
69	Decca LK/SKL 4983	I FEEL A SONG GOING OFF (LP)	10

VICTOR FELDMAN BIG BAND/QUARTET
| 56 | Tempo A 142 | Big Top/Cabaletto | 4 |
| 57 | Tempo A 154 | Jackpot/You Are My Heart's Desire | 4 |

Victor FELDMAN

55	Tempo LAP 5	VICTOR FELDMAN'S SEXTET (10" LP)	12
56	Tempo LAP 6	VICTOR FELDMAN MODERN JAZZ QUARTET (10" LP)	12
57	Tempo TAP 8	VICTOR FELDMAN IN LONDON VOL. 1 (LP)	10
57	Tempo TAP 12	VICTOR FELDMAN IN LONDON VOL. 2 (LP)	10
58	Tempo TAP 19	TRANSATLANTIC ALLIANCE (LP)	10

VICTOR FELDMAN, TERRY GIBBS & LARRY BUNKER
60	Top Rank 30/007	VIBES TO THE POWER OF THREE (LP)	10

JOSE FELICIANO
68	RCA RCA 1715	(Baby Will You) Light My Fire/California Dreamin'	4
68	RCA RCA 1769	Hi Heel Sneakers/Hitchcock Railway	4
69	RCA RCA 1871	And The Sun Will Shine/Rain	4

FELIUS ANDROMEDA
67	Decca F 12694	Meditations/Cheadle Heath Delusions	35

JULIE FELIX
64	Decca LK 4626	JULIE FELIX (LP)	10
65	Decca LK 4683	SINGS DYLAN AND GUTHRIE (LP)	10
65	Decca LK 4724	SECOND ALBUM (LP)	10
66	Decca LK 4820	THIRD ALBUM (LP)	10
66	Fontana (S)TL 5368	CHANGES (LP)	10
67	Fontana (S)TL 5437	FLOWERS (LP)	10
68	Fontana (S)TL 5473	THIS WORLD GOES ROUND AND ROUND (LP)	10

MIKE FELIX
66	Pye 7N 17058	You Belong To Me/Booga Dee	4
67	Decca F 12701	Blueberry Hill/I Don't Think You Want Me Anymore	4

FELIX & HIS GUITAR
59	London HLU 8875	Chili Beans/Puerto Rican Riot	8
59	London HLU 8875	Chili Beans/Puerto Rican Riot (78)	5

RAY FELL
70	Columbia DB 8734	Today I Killed A Man I Didn't Know/Roots Of Our Past	4

FELT
79	Shanghai S79/CUS 321	Index/Break It (p/s, early copies have notes on rear sleeve)	50/40
81	Cherry Red CHERRY 26	Something Sends Me To Sleep/Red Indians/Something Sends Me To Sleep (Version)/Red Indians (p/s)	12
82	Cherry Red CHERRY 45	My Face Is On Fire/Trails Of Colour Dissolve (p/s)	8
83	Cherry Red CHERRY 59	Penelope Tree/A Preacher In New England (p/s)	6
83	Cherry Red 12CHERRY 59	Penelope Tree/A Preacher In New England/Now Summer's Spread Its Wings Again (12", p/s)	8
84	Cherry Red CHERRY 78	Mexican Bandits/The World Is As Soft As Lace (p/s)	5
84	Cherry Red CHERRY 81	Sunlight Bathed The Golden Glow/Fortune (p/s)	6
84	Cherry Red 12CHERRY 81	Sunlight Bathed The Golden Glow/Fortune/Sunlight Strings (12", p/s)	8
85	Cherry Red 12CHERRY 89	Primitive Painters/Cathedral (12", p/s, with Liz Frazer)	7
86	Creation CRE 027	Ballad Of The Band/I Didn't Mean To Hurt You (p/s)	4
86	Creation CRE 032	Rain Of Crystal Spires/I Will Die With My Head In Flames (p/s)	4
88	Cherry Red CDCHERRY 89	Primitive Painters/Cathedral (reissue, picture CD)	7
88	Creation CRE 060	Space Blues/Tuesday's Secret (company die-cut sleeve)	4
89	él GPO F44	Get Out Of My Mirror (flexidisc)	4
89	él GPO 44	Get Out Of My Mirror (hard vinyl test pressing, 200 only)	15

(see also Cocteau Twins, Versatile Newts)

FEMININE TOUCH featuring DUKE DURRELL
76	Paladin PAL 11	You Make Me Come Alive/You Make Me Come Alive (Instrumental)	5

JAYMES FENDA & VULCANS
64	Parlophone R 5210	Mistletoe Love/The Only Girl	8

JAN FENDER
71	Prince Buster PB 5	Sea Of Love/Heaven Help Us All	5
71	Fab FAB 164	Sweet P/CLIFF & ORGANIZERS: Mr Brown	5
71	Fab FAB 166	Holly Holy Version/Old Kentrone Version (as Jal Fender)	5

PETE FENDER
81	Xntrix	FOUR FORMULAS (EP, some in 8" silkscreened book p/s)	10/5

(see also Fatal Microbes)

FENDER BENDERS
82	Sticky SL 001	Big Green Thing/Hillman Hunter Paranoia (textured p/s, various colours)	5

FENDERMEN
60	Top Rank JAR 395	Mule Skinner Blues/Torture	8
60	Top Rank JAR 513	Don't You Just Know It/Beach Party	10

FENMEN
64	Decca F 11955	Be My Girl/Rag Doll	8
65	Decca F 12269	I've Got Everthing You Need Babe/Every Little Day Now	7
66	CBS 202075	California Dreamin'/Is This Your Way	7
66	CBS 202236	Rejected/Girl Don't Bring Me Down	20

(see also Bern Elliott & Fenmen)

MICHAEL FENNELLY
74	Epic EPC 80230	LANE CHANGER (LP)	10

PETER FENTON
66	Fontana TF 748	Marble Breaks, Iron Bends/Small Town	4

SHANE FENTON (& FENTONES)
61	Parlophone R 4827	I'm A Moody Guy/Five Foot Two, Eyes Of Blue	7
62	Parlophone R 4866	Walk Away/Fallen Leaves On The Ground	8

MINT VALUE £

62	Parlophone R 4883	Why Little Girl/It's All Over Now	8
62	Parlophone R 4921	It's Gonna Take Magic/Cindy's Birthday	7
62	Parlophone R 4951	Too Young For Sad Memories/You're Telling Me	7
63	Parlophone R 4982	I Ain't Got Nobody/Hey Miss Ruby	6
63	Parlophone R 5020	A Fool's Paradise/You Need Love (solo)	7
63	Parlophone R 5047	Don't Do That/I'll Know (solo)	7
64	Parlophone R 5131	Hey, Lulu/I Do, Do You?	7
72	Fury FY 305	Eastern Seaboard/Blind Fool	10
74	Contour 2870 409	GOOD ROCKIN' TONIGHT (LP)	10

(see also Alvin Stardust, Fentones)

FENTONES

| 62 | Parlophone R 4899 | The Mexican/Lover's Guitar | 8 |
| 62 | Parlophone R 4937 | The Breeze And I/Just For Jerry | 7 |

FENWAYS

| 65 | Liberty LIB 66082 | Walk/Whip And Jerk | 10 |

RAY FENWICK

| 78 | Mercury 6007 176 | Queen Of The Night/I Wanna Boogie | 4 |
| 71 | Decca SKL 5090 | KEEP AMERICA BEAUTIFUL (CUT YOUR HAIR) (LP) | 20 |

(see also Spencer Davis Group, After Tea, Ian Gillan Band, Fancy, Wizard's Convention)

FENZUX

| 81 | Ellie Jay EJSP 9655 | Soldiers/Angels Of Mercy (p/s) | 4 |

DOTTIE FERGUSON

| 57 | Mercury MT 182 | Happy Happy Birthday Baby/Darling, It's Wonderful (78) | 5 |

H-BOMB FERGUSON

| 54 | Esquire 10-372 | Feel Like I Do/My Love (78) | 25 |

HELENA FERGUSON

| 67 | London HLZ 10164 | Where Is The Party/My Terms | 20 |

JESSIE LEE FERGUSON & OUTER LIMITS

| 69 | Pye Intl. 7N 25492 | New Shoes/Puttin' It On, Puttin' It Off | 5 |

JOHNNY FERGUSON

| 60 | MGM MGM 1059 | Angela Jones/Blue Serge And White Lace | 6 |
| 61 | MGM MGM 1119 | No One Can Love You/The Valley Of Love | 4 |

MAYNARD FERGUSON ORCHESTRA

60	Mercury MMC 14050	THE BOY WITH LOTS OF BRASS (LP, also stereo CMS 18034)	10
60	Columbia 33SX 1270	JAZZ FOR DANCING (LP, also stereo SCX 3338)	10
61	Columbia 33SX 1301	NEWPORT SUITE (LP, also stereo SCX 3368)	10

FERKO STRING BAND

55	London HL 8140	Alabama Jubilee/Sing A Little Melody	18
55	London HLF 8183	Ma (She's Making Eyes At Me)/You Are My Sunshine	16
55	London HLF 8215	Happy Days Are Here Again/Deep In The Heart Of Texas	16
58	London HL 7052	Happy Days Are Here Again/Alabama Jubilee (export issue)	5
56	London REF 1041	PHILADELPHIA MUMMERS PARADE VOL. 1 (EP)	10
56	London REF 1052	PHILADELPHIA MUMMERS PARADE VOL. 2 (EP)	10
57	London HB-C 1064	THE FERKO STRING BAND VOL. 1 (10" LP)	12

PHIL FERNANDO

| 58 | Pye 7N 15142 | Blonde Bombshell/Make Ready for Love | 7 |
| 62 | Palette PG 9029 | Do The High Life/High Life Girl | 5 |

ANDY FERNBACH

| 69 | Liberty LBS 83233 | IF YOU MISS YOUR CONNEXION (LP) | 80 |

(see also Groundhogs)

MAJA FERNICK

| 72 | Philips 6006 196 | Give Me Your Love Again/Flowers In The City | 7 |

FERRANTE & TEICHER

60	London HLT 9164	Theme From "The Apartment"/Lonely Room	4
60	London HLT 7103	Theme From "The Apartment"/DON COSTA & HIS ORCHESTRA: Theme From "The Unforgiven" (export issue)	5
61	London HLT 9298	Theme From "Exodus"/Twilight	4
61	London HLT 7105	Theme From "Exodus"/Twilight (export issue)	4
61	HMV POP 881	Theme From "Exodus"/Twilight (reissue)	4
65	United Artists UP 1097	The Knack/Country Boy	6

DIANE FERRAZ & NICKY SCOTT

66	Columbia DB 7824	Me And You/Don't Pretend	5
66	Columbia DB 7897	You've Got To Learn/Like You As You Are	5
66	Columbia DB 7963	Sh-Boom, Sh-Boom/Allah Mobish	5

(see also Nicky Scott)

FERRE GRIGNARD

| 70 | Major Minor SMLP 72 | CAPTAIN DISASTER (LP) | 12 |

JOE FERRER & HIS DEVILS BOYS

| 61 | Oriole CB 1629 | Rockin' Crickets/Blue Guitar | 8 |

FERRETS

| 78 | Charisma CB 324 | Don't Fall In Love/Lies (p/s) | 4 |

EUGENE FERRIS

| 66 | Planet PLF 112 | There Was A Smile In Your Eyes/Soft Moonlight | 8 |

FERRIS WHEEL

| 67 | Pye 7N 17387 | I Can't Break The Habit/Number One Guy | 15 |
| 68 | Pye 7N 17538 | Let It Be Me/You Look At Me | 6 |

MINT VALUE £

68	Pye 7N 17631	The Na Na Song/Three Cool Cats	6
69	Polydor 56366	Can't Stop Now/I Know You Well	5
67	Pye NPL 18203	CAN'T BREAK THE HABIT (LP)	20
70	Polydor 583 086	FERRIS WHEEL (LP)	10

BRYAN FERRY

73	Island WIP 6170	A Hard Rain's Gonna Fall/2 HB	4
74	Island WIP 6196	The 'In' Crowd/Chance Meeting (initially in p/s)	6/4
74	Island WIP 6205	Smoke Gets In Your Eyes/Another Time, Another Place	4
75	Island WIP 6234	You Go To My Head/Re-Make, Re-Model	4
76	Island WIP 6307	Let's Stick Together/Sea Breezes	4
76	Island IEP 1	EXTENDED PLAY (EP, p/s)	5
78	Polydor PPSP 10	Hold On I'm Coming/Take Me To The River (12", unissued, promo only, numbered stamped p/s)	15
85	EG FEREP 3	Windswept/Crazy Love/Feel The Need/Broken Wings (p/s)	4
85	EG FERPX 2	Don't Stop The Dance (Special 12" Remix)/Slave To Love (Special 12" Remix)/Nocturne (12", picture disc, printed PVC sleeve)	10
76	Island ILPS 9367	LET'S STICK TOGETHER (LP, original issue)	12
78	Polydor POLD 5003	THE BRIDE STRIPPED BARE (LP, original with 2 different tracks, white label test pressings only, some in different proof sleeve)	300/150

(see also Roxy Music)

CATHERINE FERRY

76	Barclay BAR 42	One, Two, Three/1, 2, 3	12

FEVER TREE

68	MCA MU 1043	San Francisco Girls/Come With Me	7
68	Uni UNLS 102	FEVER TREE (LP)	20
68	MCA MUPS 347	ANOTHER TIME, ANOTHER PLACE (LP)	25

FIAT LUX

82	Cocteau COQ 9	Feels Like Winter Again/This Illness (p/s)	4

FICKLE FINGER

69	Page One POF 150	Fickle Lizzie Anne/Cellophane Mary Jane	4

FICKLE PICKLE

70	Explosion	SINFUL SKINFUL (LP)	60

(see also Motherlight, Smoke)

EDDIE FICTION

79	Absurd ABSURD 2	U.F.O. (Pt. 2)/U.F.O. (Pt. 1) (p/s)	4

FI-DELS

73	Jay Boy BOY 69	Try A Little Harder/You Never Do Right	7
70s	DJM DJS 10689	Try A Little Harder/KEYMAN STRINGS: Instrumental Version	4

KEITH FIELD

68	Polydor 56278	Day That War Broke Out/Stop Thief	10

(see also Keith Dangerfield)

ALAN FIELDING

58	Fontana H 124	Just Remember/Don't Say Goodbye	5
60	Decca F 11261	I'll Never Understand/I Love Suzie Brown	4
61	Decca F 11487	Scatter Brain/I've Got To Learn To Forget	5
62	Decca F 11404	How Many Nights, How Many Days/Building Castles In The Air	6
62	Decca F 11518	Too Late To Worry Too Blue To Cry/You Reap Just What You Sow	6

FENELLA FIELDING

66	Columbia DB 8056	Big Bad Mouse/Later	4

JERRY FIELDING & HIS ORCHESTRA

54	London HL 8017	When I Grow Too Old To Dream/Button Up Your Overcoat	18
55	London HL 7001	Faintly Reminiscent/Blues Serenade (export issue)	6
55	London HL 7002	Pea-nut Vendor/Can't Help Lovin' Dat Man (export issue)	6
55	London HL 7003	Tea For Two/Here In My Arms (export issue)	6
55	London HL 7004	I'm In Love/Blue Prelude (export issue)	6
55	Brunswick 05399	The Gypsy In My Soul/The Glory Of Love	6
55	London REP 1026	DANCE DATE VOL. 1 (EP)	10
54	London H-APB 1022	FAINTLY REMINISCENT (10" LP)	12
54	London H-APB 1027	PLAYS A DANCE CONCERT (10" LP)	12

FIELD MICE

88	Sarah SARAH 012	Emma's House/When You Sleep/Fabulous Friend/The Last Letter (p/s)	4
90	Caff CAFF 2	I Can See Myself (foldaround p/s in poly bag)	20

FIELDS

71	CBS 7555	Friends Of Mine/Three Minstrels	5
71	CBS 69009	FIELDS (LP, a few with poster)	30/15

(see also Rare Bird)

FIELDS

69	Uni UNLS 104	FIELDS (LP)	15

BILLY FIELDS

55	MGM SP 1126	Sincerely/Thrilled	4
59	Mercury AMT 1067	The Greatest Love In The World/No Other Love	4

ERNIE FIELDS & HIS ORCHESTRA

59	London HL 8985	In The Mood/Christopher Columbus	8
59	London HL 8985	In The Mood/Christopher Columbus (78)	20
60	London HL 9100	Chattanooga Choo Choo/Workin' Out	8
60	London HL 9227	Raunchy/My Prayer	7
60	London RE 1260	SAXY (EP)	25

| 60 | London HA 2263 | IN THE MOOD (LP) | 20 |

GRACIE FIELDS

55	Decca F 10614	Twenty/Summertime In Venice	4
56	Decca F 10824	A Letter To A Soldier/The Sweetest Prayer In All The ...	4
57	Columbia DB 3953	Around The World/Far Away	5
52	Decca LF 1080	NOW IS THE HOUR (10" LP)	10
53	Decca LF 1140	GRACIE FIELDS (10" LP)	10

IRVING FIELDS TRIO & ORHCESTRA

| 58 | Oriole CB 1436 | Ragtime Rock/Syncopated Sadie | 4 |

KANSAS FIELDS & MILTON SEALEY

| 56 | Ducretet DEP 95017 | KANSAS FIELDS & MILTON SEALEY (EP) | 7 |

FIELDS OF NEPHILIM

84	Tower N1	BURNING THE FIELDS (12" EP, red/black p/s)	80
85	Tower N1/Jung. JUNG 28T	BURNING THE FIELDS (12" EP, green p/s with insert & band photo label)	20
85	Tower N1/Jung. JUNG 28T	BURNING THE FIELDS (12" EP, green & other coloured vinyl export issue)	12
87	Situation 2 SIT 46	Preacher Man/Laura II (p/s, some with Beggars Banquet sticker)	20/18
87	Situation 2 SIT 48	Blue Water/In Every Dream Home A Heartache (p/s)	12
87	Situation 2 SIT 48T	Blue Water (Electrostatic)/In Every Dream Home A Heartache (live)/ Blue Water (Hot Wire) (12", p/s, some with poster)	15/8
87	House Of Dolls HOD 15	Dawnrazor (on free EP with 'House Of Dolls' magazine, issue 15)	8/6
88	Situation 2 SIT 52TR	Moonchild (Second Seal)/Shiva/Power/Vet For The Insane (12", p/s)	8
89	Situation 2 SIT 57	Psychonaut/Celebrate (Second Seal) (blue/green p/s)	5
90	Beggars Banquet BEG 250	Sumerland/Phobia (live) (no p/s)	5
88	Situation 2 SITU 22L	THE NEPHILIM (LP, as 2 x 45rpm 12", gatefold sleeve, numbered)	10

FIESTAS

| 59 | London HL 8870 | So Fine/Last Night I Dreamed | 18 |
| 59 | London HL 8870 | So Fine/Last Night I Dreamed (78) | 18 |

FIFTEENTH

| 86 | Tanz TANZ 3 | ANDELAIN (12" EP) | 10 |

FIFTH AVENUE

| 65 | Immediate IM 002 | The Bells Of Rhymney/Just Like Anyone Would Do | 20 |

FIFTH COLUMN

| 66 | Columbia DB 8068 | Benjamin Day/There's Nobody There | 10 |

FIFTH DIMENSION

67	Liberty LIB 12051	Go Where You Wanna Go/Too Poor To Die	15
67	Liberty LIB 12056	Another Day Another Heartache/Rosecrans Blvd.	4
67	Liberty LBF 15014	Up Up And Away/Pattern People	4
68	Liberty LBF 15052	Carpet Man/Magic Garden	4
68	Liberty LBF 15081	Ticket To Ride/Orange Air	4
69	Liberty LBF 15193	Aquarius/Let The Sun Shine In/Don'tcha Hear Me Callin' To Ya	4
69	Liberty LBF 15288	Wedding Bell Blues/Let It Be Me	4
70	Liberty LBF 15356	I'll Be Loving You Forever/Train Keep On Moving	10
76	ABC ABC 4118	Love Hangover/Will You Be There	4
68	Liberty LBL/LBS 83098E	THE MAGIC GARDEN (LP)	10
68	Liberty LBL/LBS 83155E	STONED SOUL PICNIC (LP)	10
	Liberty LBL/LBS series	other LPs	10

FIFTH ESTATE

67	Stateside SS 2034	Ding Dong The Witch Is Dead/Rub A Dub	4
67	Stateside SS 2068	Heigh Ho/It's Waiting There For You	4
68	Stateside SS 2105	Do Drop In/That's Love	4
69	Stateside SS 2125	Coney Island Sally/Tomorrow Is My Turn	4

FIFTY FANTASTICS

| 79 | South Circular SGS 108 | God's Got Religion/STEPPES: The Beat Drill (white label) | 10 |
| 80 | Dining Out TUX 5 | God's Got Religion/The Beat Drill (reissue, foldout p/s, handdone labels) | 8 |

(see also Steppes, Disco Zombies)

FIFTY FOOT HOSE

| 69 | Mercury | CAULDRON (LP) | 35 |

PAULINE FILBY

| 69 | Herald LLR 567 | SHOW ME A RAINBOW (LP) | 125 |

(see also Narnia, Accolade, Gordon Giltrap)

FILE UNDER POP

| 79 | Rough Trade RT 011 | Heathrow/Corrugate/Heathrow SLB (p/s) | 5 |

FINDERS KEEPERS (U.S.)

| 67 | London HLH 10117 | Lavender Blue/MICKEY DOLENZ: Don't Do It | 7 |

(see also Mickey Dolenz)

FINDERS KEEPERS (U.K.)

67	Fontana TF 892	On The Beach/Friday Kind Of Monday	20
68	Fontana TF 938	Sadie (The Cleaning Lady)/Without Her	10
66	CBS 202249	Light/Power Of Love (withdrawn, promos may exist)	50+
66	CBS 202249	Light/Come On Now	10

FINE YOUNG CANNIBALS

85	London LONP 68	Johnny Come Home/Good Times And Bad (picture disc)	4
85	London LONC 79	Blue/Wade In The Water (p/s, with calendar)	4
85	London LONDP 79	Blue/Wade In The Water//Blue/Love For Sale (double pack)	4
86	London LONP 82	Suspicious Minds/Prick Up Your Ears (picture disc)	4
86	London LONP 88	Funny How Love Is/Motherless Child (picture disc)	4
88	London LONT 199	She Drives Me Crazy/Pull The Sucker Off (in 7" tin)	4

FINE YOUNG CANNIBALS

| 89 | London LONB 218 | Good Thing/Social Security (in 7" tin, numbered) | 4 |

| 89 | London LONT 218 | Good Thing/Social Security (gatefold p/s) | 4 |

(see also Akrylykz, Beat)

FINGERPRINTZ
| 79 | Virgin VS 252 | Who's Your Friend/Secret/Nervz/Night Nurse (p/s, blue vinyl) | 4 |

FINGERS
| 66 | Columbia DB 8026 | I'll Take You Where The Music's Playing/My Way Of Thinking | 5 |
| 67 | Columbia DB 8112 | All Kinds Of People/Circus With A Female Clown | 15 |

FINI TRIBE 101
| 91 | Finiflex/One Little Indian | 101: Sonic Shuffle (Edit)/101: 303 (3D Bass Edit) | |
| | 54 TP 7 | (promo only, plain stickered sleeve) | 5 |

FINK BROTHERS
85	Zarjazz JAZZ 2	Mutants In Mega-City One/Mutant Blues	4
85	Zarjazz JAZZ S2	Mutants In Mega-City One/Mutant Blues (square picture disc)	6
85	Zarjazz JAZZ 2-12	Mutants In Mega-City One (Mutie Mix)/Mutant Blues (12")	7

(see also Madness)

LEE FINN & RHYTHM MEN
| 63 | Starlite ST45 103 | High Class Feelin'/Pour Me A Glass Of Wine | 150 |

MICKEY FINN & BLUE MEN
63	Blue Beat BB 203	Tom Hark Goes Bluebeat/Please Love Me	20
64	Oriole CB 1927	Pills/Hush Your Mouth (as Mickey Finn & Blue Men)	18
64	Oriole CB 1940	I Still Want You/Reelin' & Rockin' (as Mickey Finn & Blue Men)	30

(DON'T see also Mickey Finn under 'M')

SIMON FINN
| 70 | Mushroom 100 MR 2 | PASS THE DISTANCE (LP, with lyric insert) | 60 |

TIM FINN
83	Epic A 3932	Fraction Too Much Friction/Below The Belt (p/s)	6
86	Virgin VS 849	No Thunder No Fire No Car/Searching For The Streets (p/s)	4
86	Virgin VS 849-12	No Thunder No Fire No Car/Searching For The Streets (12", p/s)	7
86	Virgin VS 866	Carve You In Marble/Hole In My Heart (p/s)	4
86	Virgin VS 866-12	Carve You In Marble/Hole In My Heart (12", p/s)	7

(see also Split Enz, Crowded House)

LARRY FINNEGAN
62	HMV POP 1022	Dear One/Candy Lips	10
62	London HLU 9613	Pretty Suzy Sunshine/It's Walkin' Talkin' Time	8
65	Ember EMB S 207	The Other Ringo (A Tribute To Ringo Starr)/When My Love Passes By (p/s)	12/8

MIKE FINNIGAN
| 78 | CBS 6656 | Just One Minute More/Blood Is Thicker Than Water | 8 |

FINN MACCUILL
| 77 | private pressing | SINK YE SINK YE (LP) | 80 |

ELISA FIORILLO
| 88 | Chrysalis ELISAP 1 | How Can I Forget You?/How can I Forget You? (Version) (picture disc) | 5 |

FIRE
68	Decca F 12753	Father's Name Is Dad/Treacle Toffee World	80
68	Decca F 12856	Round The Gum Tree/Toothie Ruthie	20
70	Pye NSPL 18343	THE MAGIC SHOEMAKER (LP)	250

(see also Strawbs)

FIREBALLS
59	Top Rank JAR 218	Torquay/Cry Baby	7
60	Top Rank JAR 276	Bulldog/Nearly Sunrise	7
60	Top Rank JAR 354	Foot-Patter/Kissin'	6
60	Top Rank JAR 507	Vaquero (Cowboy)/Chief Whoopin'-Koff	6
61	Pye Intl. 7N 25092	Quite A Party/Gunshot	6
62	Stateside SS 106	Rik-A-Tik/Yacky Doo	5
63	Stateside SS 151	Carioca/Find Me A Golden Street	5
65	Stateside SS 417	Baby What's Wrong/Yummie Yama Papa	5
67	Stateside SS 2095	Bottle Of Wine/Ain't That Rain	4
68	Stateside SS 2106	Goin' Away/Groovy Motions	4
69	Stateside SS 2134	Come On, React!/Woman Help Me	4
69	London HLZ 10260	Long Green/Light In The Window	4
61	Top Rank 35/105	VAQUERO (LP)	40
68	Stateside S(S)L 10237	BOTTLE OF WINE (LP)	20
69	London HA/SH 8396	COME ON, REACT! (LP)	12

(see also Jimmy Gilmer, Buddy Holly)

FIREBALL XL5
(see under Century 21)

FIREBRAND
| 85 | What WR 71 | Never Felt This Way Before/I'm Leaving | 4 |

FIRECLOWN
| 83 | Fireclown | FIRECLOWN (3-track EP, no sleeve) | 80 |

FIRE ENGINES
80	Codex Comms. CDX 01	Get Up And Use Me/Everything's Roses (p/s)	6
81	Pop:Aural POP 010	Candy Skin/Meat Whiplash (foldout p/s)	6
81	Pop:Aural POP 013	Big Gold Dream/Sympathetic Anaesthetic (p/s)	4
81	Pop:Aural POP 01312	Big Gold Dream/Sympathetic Anaesthetic/New Thing In Cartons (12", non-gatefold p/s; gatefold p/s £5)	7

MINT VALUE £

81	Accessory ACC 001	LUBRICATE YOUR LIVING ROOM (LP, in plastic bag)	10

(see also Win)

FIRE EXIT
79	Time Bomb Explosion 1	Timewall/Talkin' About Myself (p/s, stamped labels)	5

FIREFLIES
59	Top Rank JAR 198	You Were Mine/Stella Got A Fella	12
59	Top Rank JAR 198	You Were Mine/Stella Got A Fella (78)	25
60	London HLU 9057	I Can't Say Goodbye/What Did I Do Wrong	12

FIREHOUSE FIVE PLUS TWO
56	Good Time Jazz GV 2192	Runnin' Wild/Lonesome Railroad Blues	4
50s	Good Time Jazz LDG 036	GOES SOUTH VOL. 1 (10" LP)	10
50s	Good Time Jazz LDG 079	GOES SOUTH VOL. 2 (10" LP)	10
50s	Good Time Jazz LDG 094	GOES SOUTH VOL. 3 (10" LP)	10
50s	Good Time Jazz LDG 169	GOES SOUTH VOL. 4 (10" LP)	10
50s	Good Time Jazz LDG 183	FIREHOUSE FIVE (10" LP)	10
50s	G. Time Jazz LAG 12079	THE FIREHOUSE FIVE PLUS TWO (LP)	10
50s	G. Time Jazz LAG 12089	THE FIREHOUSE FIVE PLUS TWO VOL. 2 (LP)	10

FIRESIGN THEATRE
68	CBS 65129	WAITING FOR THE ELECTRICIAN OR SOMEONE LIKE HIM (LP)	15
68	CBS 65130	HOW TO BE IN TWO PLACES AT ONCE WHEN YOU'RE NOT ANYWHERE AT ALL? (LP)	15

FIRESTONES
62	Decca F 11436	Party Twist (Medley) Pts 1 & 2	4

FIRING SQUAD
64	Parlophone R 5152	A Little Bit More/Bull Moose	18

FIRING SQUAD
80	Shattered SHAT 1	Nut Bush City Limits/Fragments (p/s)	4
80	Shattered SHAT 5	Night Manoeuvres/Big Red Car (p/s)	4

FIRM
85	Atlantic A 9586P	Radioactive/Together (shaped picture disc)	6
85	Atlantic 781 239-2	THE FIRM (CD)	15
86	Atlantic 781 628-2	THE FIRM MEAN BUSINESS (CD)	15

(see also Jimmy Page, Bad Company)

FIRST AID
77	Decca TXS 117	NOSTRADAMUS (LP)	25

FIRST CHOICE
73	Pye Intl. 7N 25613	This Is The House Where Love Died/One Step Away (demos may exist)	50+
74	Bell BLL 1376	The Player Pts 1 & 2	4

FIRST CHURCH OF NAPOLEON SOLO
84	Off Beaten Track Offbeat 2	Debbydid/Game Of Bagatelle (hand-painted, stickered p/s)	4

FIRST EDITION
68	Reprise RS 20655	Just Dropped In (To See What Condition My Condition Was In)/Shadow In The Corner Of Your Mind	5
68	Reprise RS 20693	Charlie The Fer'de Lance/Look Around I'll Be There	4
68	Reprise RS 20799	But You Know I Love You/Homemade Lies	5
68	Reprise RSLP 6276	THE FIRST EDITION (LP)	10

(see also Kenny Rogers)

FIRST GEAR
64	Pye 7N 15703	A Certain Girl/Leave My Kitten Alone	100
65	Pye 7N 15763	The In Crowd/Gotta Make Their Future Bright	20

FIRST IMPRESSION
67	Saga SOC 1045	BEAT CLUB (LP)	10

FIRST IMPRESSION/GOOD EARTH
68	Saga FID 2117	SWINGING LONDON (LP)	10

(see also Good Earth)

FIRST IMPRESSIONS
65	Pye 7N 15797	I'm Coming Home/Looking For Her	4

FIRST OFFENCE
88	Metalother OTH 11	FIRST OFFENCE (LP)	10

FIRST STEPS
80	English Rose ER 1	The Beat Is Back/She Ain't In Love/Let's Go Cuboids (p/s)	6
81	English Rose ER 3	Anywhere Else But Here (p/s)	8

WILD MAN FISCHER
70	Reprise RSLP 6332	AN EVENING WITH WILD MAN FISCHER (2-LP)	30

FISCHER Z
79	United Artists UP 36509	The Worker/Kitten Curry (picture disc)	4

FISH
89	EMI 12EMPD 109	State Of Mind/The Voyeur (I Like To Watch)/State Of Mind (Presidential Mix) (12", picture disc)	8
89	EMI EMPD 135	A Gentleman's Excuse Me/Whiplash (shaped picture disc)	5

(see also Marillion, Tony Banks)

CHIP FISHER
59	Parlophone R 4604	Poor Me/No One	5
59	RCA RCX 143	AT THE SUGAR BOWL (EP)	25

EDDIE FISHER

53	HMV 7M 101	I'm Yours/That's The Chance You Take	20
53	HMV 7M 115	Everything I Have Is Yours/You'll Never Know	15
53	HMV 7M 116	Trust In Me/Forgive Me	18
53	HMV 7M 117	Outside Of Heaven/Lady Of Spain	15
53	HMV 7M 125	Even Now/If It Were Up To Me	15
53	HMV 7M 126	Downhearted/Am I Wasting My Time On You	12
53	HMV 7M 133	I'm Walking Behind You (with Sally Sweetland)/Hold Me	12
53	HMV 7M 146	Just Another Polka/When I Was Young (Yes, Very Young)	15
53	HMV 7M 159	Wish You Were Here/A Fool Was I	12
53	HMV 7M 168	Many Times/With These Hands	12
54	HMV 7M 172	Oh My Papa/(I Never Missed You) Until You Said "Goodbye"	12
54	HMV 7M 185	How Deep Is The Ocean/That Old Feeling	12
54	HMV 7M 201	April Showers/Just To Be With You	12
54	HMV 7M 212	I'm In The Mood For Love/A Girl, A Girl	12
54	HMV 7M 235	May I Sing To You/My Friend	12
54	HMV 7M 242	How Do You Speak To An Angel?/My Arms, My Heart, My Love	10
54	HMV 7M 251	I Need You Now/Heaven Was Never Like This	10
54	HMV 7M 257	They Say It's Wonderful/Green Years	10
54	HMV 7M 266	Count Your Blessings Instead Of Sheep/White Christmas	10
55	HMV 7M 294	(I'm Always Hearing) Wedding Bells/A Man Chases A Girl	12
56	HMV 7M 353	Magic Fingers/My One And Only Love	10
56	HMV 7M 374	Dungaree Doll/If It Hadn't Been For You	15
56	HMV POP 171	Dungaree Doll/If It Hadn't Been For You (78)	5
56	HMV 7M 402	Without You/No Other One	10
56	HMV 7M 421	Sweet Heartaches/What Is This Thing Called Love?	10
56	HMV POP 273	Cindy, Oh Cindy/Fanny	20
57	HMV POP 296	Some Day Soon/All About Love	6
57	HMV POP 342	Tonight My Heart She Is Crying/Blues For Me	8
57	RCA RCA 1009	A Second Chance/Slow Burning Love	5
58	RCA RCA 1030	Sayonara/That's The Way It Goes	6
58	RCA RCA 1061	Kari Waits For Me/I Don't Hurt Anymore	6
59	RCA RCA 1147	The Last Mile Home/I'd Sail A Thousand Seas	5
61	London HL 9469	Tonight/Breezin' Along With The Breeze	5
54	HMV 7EG 8026	NIGHT AND DAY (EP)	8
54	HMV 7EG 8046	APRIL SHOWERS (EP)	7
55	HMV 7EG 8146	HOW DEEP IS THE OCEAN (EP)	7
55	HMV 7EG 8156	EDDIE FISHER SINGS NO. 3 — TAKE MY LOVE (EP)	7
56	HMV 7EG 8207	BUNDLE OF JOY (EP, with Debbie Reynolds)	7
54	HMV DLP 1040	TIME FOR ROMANCE (10" LP)	25
55	HMV DLP 1074	MY SERENADE IS YOU (10" LP)	25
56	HMV CLP 1095	SINGS ACADEMY AWARD WINNING SONGS (LP)	14
50s	HMV	other 12" LPs	12-14
59	RCA Camden CDN 123	HEART! (LP)	10

RAY FISHER

72	Trailer LER 2038	THE BONNY BIRDY (LP)	20

TONI FISHER

60	Top Rank JAR 261	The Big Hurt/Memphis Belle	6
60	Top Rank JAR 341	How Deep Is The Ocean/Blue, Blue, Blue	4
62	London HLX 9564	West Of The Wall/What Did I Do	5

FISHER BROTHERS

64	London HLN 9928	Big Round Wheel/By The Time You Read This Letter	4

FISHER FAMILY

60s	Topic TOP 67	FAR OVER THE FORTH (EP)	7
60s	Topic 12T 137	THE FISHER FAMILY (LP)	10

FISH TURNED HUMAN

79	Sequel PART 1	TURKEYS IN CHINA (EP)	5
81	Detour DEEP 2	Drinking Milk In Cars/ANIMAL TRANSPORT: Animal Magnetism (p/s)	5

FIST

80	Neat NEAT 04	Name Rank And Serial Number (p/s)	5
80	MCA MCA 615	Name Rank And Serial Number (p/s)	10
80	MCA MCA 640	Forever Amber/Brain Damage (p/s)	7
81	MCA MCA 663	Collision Course/Law Of The Jungle (p/s)	6
82	Neat NEAT 021	The Wanderer/Too Hot (p/s)	5
85	Neat NEAT 1003	BACK WITH A VENGEANCE (LP)	10

FITS

81	Lightbeat FIT 1	YOU SAID WE'D NEVER MAKE IT (EP)	5
82	Rondelet ROUND 13	Think For Yourself: Burial/Straps (p/s)	4
82	Rondelet ROUND 30	THE LAST LAUGH (EP)	4

FITZ & COOZERS

68	Nu Beat NB 003	Cover Me/Darling	5

ELLA FITZGERALD

50	Brunswick 04617	Ain't Nobody's Business If I Do/I'll Never Be Free (78, with Louis Jordan)	5
54	Brunswick 05324	Who's Afraid (Not I, Not I, Not I)/I Wished On The Moon (with Gordon Jenkins)	6
55	Brunswick 05392	Lullaby Of Birdland/Later	6
55	Brunswick 05427	Moanin' Low/Take A Chance On Love	6
55	Brunswick 05468	Lover, Come Back To Me/Old Devil Moon	6
55	Brunswick 05473	Pete Kelly's Blues/Hard Hearted Hannah	6
55	Brunswick 05477	Soldier Boy/Air Mail Special (with Bill Doggett)	6
56	Brunswick 05514	My One And Only Love/(Love Is) The Tender Trap	6
56	Brunswick 05539	Ella's Contribution To The Blues/Early Autumn	5

56	Brunswick 05584	You'll Never Know/But Not Like Mine	6
56	HMV POP 266	The Silent Treatment/The Sun Forgot To Shine This Morning	5
57	HMV POP 290	A Beautiful Friendship/Too Young For The Blues	5
57	HMV POP 316	Hotta Chocolatta/Stay There	5
57	HMV POP 348	Johnny One Note/To Keep My Love Alive	5
57	HMV POP 373	Ev'ry Time We Say Goodbye/Manhattan	5
57	HMV POP 380	Goody Goody/A Tisket, A Tasket	5
58	HMV POP 486	The Swingin' Shepherd Blues/Midnight Sun	5
58	HMV POP 499	Beale Street Blues/St. Louis Blues	4
58	HMV POP 518	Your Red Wagon/Trav'lin Light	4
59	Brunswick 05783	My Happiness/A Satisfied Mind	4
59	HMV POP 657	But Not For Me/You Make Me Feel So Young	5
59	HMV POP 686	The Christmas Song/You Make Me Feel So Young	4
60	HMV POP 701	Like Young/Beat Me Daddy Eight To The Bar	5
60	HMV POP 719	It's All Right With Me/Don'cha Go Way Mad (with Oscar Peterson)	4
60	HMV POP 736	Mack The Knife/Lorelei	5
60	HMV POP 782	How High The Moon Pts 1 & 2	5
60	HMV POP 809	Good Morning Blues/Jingle Blues	4
60	HMV POP 817	We Three Kings Of Orient Are/White Christmas	4
61	HMV POP 849	The Lady Is A Tramp/Misty	4
64	Verve VS 502	Desafinado/Stardust	4
65	Verve VS 519	Can't Buy Me Love/Sweetest Sound	4
65	Verve VS 524	Why Was I Born/All The Things You Are	4
66	Stateside SS 569	These Boots Were Made for Walkin'/Stardust	4
69	Reprise RS 20850	Get Ready/Open Your Window	7
69	Polydor 56767	Hey Jude/Sunshine Of Your Love	4
53	Brunswick LA 8581	SOUVENIR ALBUM (10" LP)	15
54	Brunswick LA 8648	ELLA SINGS GERSHWIN (10" LP)	15
55	Brunswick LAT 8056	ELLA — SONGS IN A MELLOW MOOD (LP)	12
56	Brunswick LAT 8091	SWEET AND HOT (LP)	12
56	Brunswick LAT 8115	LULLABIES OF BIRDLAND (LP)	12
56	HMV CLP 1083	THE COLE PORTER SONGBOOK VOLUME 1 (LP)	12
56	HMV CLP 1084	THE COLE PORTER SONGBOOK VOLUME 2 (LP)	12
57	Brunswick LAT 8223	ELLA AND HER FELLAS (LP)	12
57	HMV CLP 1116	THE RODGERS AND HART SONGBOOK VOLUME 1 (LP)	12
57	HMV CLP 1117	THE RODGERS AND HART SONGBOOK VOLUME 2 (LP)	12
58	HMV CLP 1166	LIKE SOMEONE IN LOVE (LP)	10
58	HMV CLP 1183	THE IRVING BERLIN SONGBOOK VOLUME ONE (LP)	10
58	HMV CLP 1184	THE IRVING BERLIN SONGBOOK VOLUME TWO (LP)	10
58	HMV CLP 1213/1214	THE DUKE ELLINGTON SONGBOOK NUMBER ONE (2-LP)	14
58	HMV CLP 1227/1228	THE DUKE ELLINGTON SONGBOOK NUMBER TWO (2-LP)	14
59	HMV CLP 1267	ELLA SWINGS LIGHTLY (LP)	10
59	HMV CLP 1338	SINGS GERSHWIN VOL. 1 (LP)	10
59	HMV CLP 1339	SINGS GERSHWIN VOL. 2 (LP)	10
60	HMV CLP 1347	SINGS GERSHWIN VOL. 3 (LP, also stereo CSD 1299)	10/12
60	HMV CLP 1348	SINGS GERSHWIN VOL. 4 (LP, also stereo CSD 1300)	10/12
60	HMV CLP 1353	SINGS GERSHWIN VOL. 5 (LP, also stereo CSD 1304)	10/12
60	HMV CSD 1287	SWEET SONGS FOR SWINGERS (LP)	10
60	HMV CLP 1391	ELLA IN BERLIN — MACK THE KNIFE (LP)	10
60	HMV CLP 1396	SONGS FROM THE FILM "LET NO MAN WRITE MY EPITAPH" (LP)	10
60	HMV CLP 1397	ELLA WISHES YOU A SWINGING CHRISTMAS (LP)	10
61	HMV CLP 1383	HELLO LOVE! (LP, also stereo CSD 1315)	10/12
63	Verve VLP 9020	RHYTHM IS MY BUSINESS (LP)	10
65	Verve VLP 9083	ELLA AT JUAN-LES PINS (LP)	10

(see also Oscar Peterson, Count Basie)

ELLA FITZGERALD & LOUIS ARMSTRONG

56	HMV CLP 1098	ELLA AND LOUIS (LP)	12
57	HMV CLP 1146	ELLA AND LOUIS AGAIN NO. 1 (LP)	10
57	HMV CLP 1147	ELLA AND LOUIS AGAIN NO. 2 (LP)	10
59	HMV CLP 1245	PORGY AND BESS (LP)	10
59	HMV CLP 1246	PORGY AND BESS (LP)	10

(see also Louis Armstrong)

ELLA FITZGERALD/BILLIE HOLIDAY

58	Columbia Clef 33CX 10100	AT NEWPORT (LP)	10

G.F. FITZGERALD

70	Uni UNLS 115	MOUSEPROOF (LP, with insert)	50

(see also Sam Gopal)

PATRICK FITZGERALD

77	Small Wonder SMALL 4	SAFETY PIN STUCK IN MY HEART (EP, with lyrics)	4
78	Small Wonder SMALL 6	Buy Me, Sell Me/The Little Dippers/Trendy/The Backstreet Boys (p/s)	4
78	Small Wonder WEENY ONE	THE PARANOID WARD/THE BEDROOM TAPES (EP, mono/stereo, 33rpm)	4
79	Polydor 2383 533	GRUBBY STORIES (LP)	10

SCOTT FITZGERALD

75	GTO GT 26	Never Too Young To Rock/Boogie Woogie Woman	4

FIVE AMERICANS

66	Pye Intl. 7N 25354	I See The Light/The Outcasts	12
66	Pye Intl. 7N 25373	Evol — Not Love/Don't Blame Me	20
67	Stateside SS 2012	Western Union/Now That It's All Over	5
67	Stateside SS 2036	Sound Of Love/Sympathy	5
68	Stateside SS 2097	7.30 Guided Tour/See-Saw Man	5

5 a.m. EVENT

66	Pye 7N 17154	Hungry/I Wash My Hands (In Muddy Water)	80

FIVE & A PENNY
68	Polydor 56282	You Don't Know Where Your Interest Lies/Mary Go Round	20

FIVE BLIND BOYS
64	Vocalion EPVP 1282	FIVE BLIND BOYS (EP)	12
64	Vocalion EPVP 1276	NEGRO SPIRITUALS (EP, with Spirits Of Memphis)	12

FIVE BLOBS
58	Philips PB 881	Saturday Night In Tijuana/The Blob	6
58	Philips PB 881	Saturday Night In Tijuana/The Blob (78)	8

FIVE BY FIVE
68	Pye Intl. 7N 25477	Fire/Hang Up	20

FIVE CARD STUD
67	Philips BF 1567	Beg Me/Once	5

FIVE CHESTERNUTS
58	Columbia DB 4165	Jean Dorothy/Teenage Love	80
58	Columbia DB 4165	Jean Dorothy/Teenage Love (78)	40
(see also Shadows, Pete Chester)			

FIVE COUNTS
62	Oriole CB 1769	Watermelon Walk/Spanish Nights	6

FIVE DALLAS BOYS
57	Columbia DB 4005	Shangri-La/By The Fireside	4
57	Columbia DB 4041	I Never Had The Blues/All The Way	5
58	Columbia DB 4102	26 Miles (Santa Catalina)/Sail Along, Silv'ry Moon	5
58	Columbia DB 4154	Big Man/Lonesome Traveller	6
58	Columbia DB 4231	Fatty Patty/Do You Wanna Jump Children	8
59	Columbia DB 4313	Morning Papers/I'm Aware	4
60	Columbia DB 4445	Boston Tea Party/Ramona	4
61	Columbia DB 4599	One Finger, One Thumb, Keep Movin'/Nice To Know You Care	5
60	Columbia SEG 8035	THE FIVE DALLAS BOYS (EP)	7

FIVE DAY RAIN
70	private pressing	FIVE DAY RAIN (LP, test pressing, 15 copies only; beware of re-pressings!) ..	1000

FIVE DAY WEEK STRAW PEOPLE
68	Saga FID 2123	FIVE DAY WEEK STRAW PEOPLE (LP)	60
(see also Attack, Andromeda)			

FIVE DE MARCO SISTERS
53	MGM SP 1043	Bouillabasse/I'm Never Satisfied	8
54	Brunswick 05349	Love Me/Just A Girl That Men Forget	10
54	Brunswick 05349	Love Me/Just A Girl That Men Forget (78)	5
55	Brunswick 05425	Dreamboat/Two Hearts, Two Kisses (Make One Love)	12
55	Brunswick 05474	The Hot Barcarolle/Sailor Boys Have Talk To Me In English	10
56	Brunswick 05526	Romance Me/This Love Of Mine	8

FIVE DU-TONES
63	Stateside SS 206	Shake A Tail Feather/Divorce Court	12
68	President PT 134	Shake A Tail Feather/Divorce Court (reissue)	6

FIVE EMPREES
65	Stateside SS 470	Little Miss Sad/Hey Lover	4

FIVE FLEETS
58	Felsted AF 103	Oh What A Feeling/I Been Cryin'	150
58	Felsted AF 103	Oh What A Feeling/I Been Cryin' (78)	45

FIVE GO DOWN TO THE SEA
83	Kabuki KAFIVE 5	KNOT A FISH (EP)	6
84	Abstract 12 ABS 027	THE GLEE CLUB (12" EP)	7
85	Creation CRE 021T	Singing In Braille/Aunt Nelly/Silk Brain Worm/Women (12", p/s) ...	8

FIVE GUYS NAMED MOE
89	No Moe MOE 001	Fairvan/Eyes Like Thunder/Beneath The Willow (12", p/s)	7

FIVE KEYS
54	Capitol CL 14184	Ling, Ting, Tong/I'm Alone (78)	30
55	Capitol CL 14313	The Verdict/Make Me Um Pow Pow (triangular centre)	350
55	Capitol CL 14313	The Verdict/Make Me Um Pow Pow (78)	35
55	Capitol CL 14325	Doggone It, You Did It/(Close Your Eyes) Take A Deep Breath (triangular centre)	275
55	Capitol CL 14325	Doggone It, You Did It/(Close Your Eyes) Take A Deep Breath (78)	30
56	Capitol CL 14545	Gee Whittakers!/'Cause You're My Lover	75
56	Capitol CL 14545	Gee Whittakers!/'Cause You're My Lover (78)	10
56	Capitol CL 14582	She's The Most/I Dreamt I Dwelt In Heaven	75
56	Capitol CL 14582	She's The Most/I Dreamt I Dwelt In Heaven (78)	15
56	Capitol CL 14639	That's Right/Out Of Sight, Out Of Mind	75
56	Capitol CL 14639	That's Right/Out Of Sight, Out Of Mind (78)	12
57	Capitol CL 14686	The Wisdom Of A Fool/Now Don't That Prove I Love You?	75
57	Capitol CL 14686	The Wisdom Of A Fool/Now Don't That Prove I Love You? (78)	12
57	Capitol CL 14736	Four Walls/Let There Be You	40
57	Capitol CL 14736	Four Walls/Let There Be You (78)	8
57	Capitol CL 14756	The Blues Don't Care/This I Promise You	45
57	Capitol CL 14756	The Blues Don't Care/This I Promise You (78)	15
58	Capitol CL 14829	From Me To You/Whippety Whirl	50
58	Capitol CL 14829	From Me To You/Whippety Whirl (78)	20
58	Capitol CL 14967	One Great Love/Really-O Truly-O	50
50s	Capitol	FIVE KEYS ON STAGE (LP)	125

FIVE MILES OUT
73	Action ACT 4614	Super Sweet Girl Of Mine/Set Your Mind Free	4

FIVE OF DIAMONDS
65	Oak RGJ 150 FD	FIVE OF DIAMONDS (EP)	250

FIVE OR SIX
81	Cherry Red CHERRY 19	Another Reason/The Trial (p/s)	4
81	Cherry Red 12CHERRY 23	POLAR EXPOSURE (12" EP)	7
82	Cherry Red 12CHERRY 43	FOUR FROM FIVE OR SIX (12" EP)	7
82	Cherry Red FRIZBEE 2	A THRIVING AND HAPPY LAND (LP)	10

FIVE ROYALES
60	Ember EMB S 124	Dedicated To The One I Love/Miracle Of Love	70

FIVE SATINS
57	London HL 8501	To The Aisle/Wish I Had My Baby	250
57	London HL 8501	To The Aisle/Wish I Had My Baby (78)	35
59	Top Rank JAR 199	Wonderful Girl/Weeping Willow	20
59	Top Rank JAR 239	Shadows/Toni My Love	15
60	MGM MGM 1087	Your Memory/I Didn't Know	35

FIVE'S COMPANY
66	Pye 7N 17118	Sunday For Seven Days/The Big Kill	8
66	Pye 7N 17162	Some Girls/Big Deal	5
66	Pye 7N 17199	Session Man/Dejection	15
69	Saga FID 2151	THE BALLAD OF FRED THE PIXIE (LP)	18

(see also Brunning Hall Sunflower Blues Band)

FIVE SMITH BROTHERS
54	Decca F 10403	A.B.C. Boogie/Veni-Vidi-Vici (with Dennis Wilson Quartet)	15
55	Decca F 10507	Paper Valentine/You're As Sweet Today (As Yesterday)	6
55	Decca F 10527	Don't Worry/I'm In Favour Of Friendship	10
56	Decca F 10698	You Took My Heart (My Only Heart)/The Grass Is Green	5

(see also Smith Brothers)

FIVE STAIRSTEPS (& CUBIE)
68	Pye Intl. 7N 25448	A Million To One/Something's Missing (with Cubie)	8
68	Buddah 201 026	Stay Close To Me/I Made A Mistake (with Cubie)	4
69	Buddah 201 070	We Must Be In Love/Little Young Lovers (with Cubie)	8
69	Buddah 201 083	Dear Prudence/O-o-h Child	4
70	Buddah 2011 036	O-o-h Child/Who Do You Belong To	4
70	Buddah 2011 053	Because I Love You/America Standing	4

(see also Stairsteps)

FIVE STAR
83	Tent TENT 4	Problematic/Big Funk (p/s)	10
83	Tent TENT T4	Problematic (Extended)/Problematic (Vocal) (12", p/s)	7
84	RCA RCA 399	Hide And Seek/I'm Gonna Make This A Night You'll Never Forget (p/s)	4
84	RCA RCAT 399	Hide And Seek (Extended Dance Mix)/Hide And Seek (Dub)/ I'm Gonna Make This A Night You'll Never Forget (12", p/s)	7
84	RCA RCA 451	Crazy/I Like The Way You Dance (p/s)	4
84	RCA RCAT 451	Crazy/Crazy (Crazy Mix)/I Like The Way You Dance (12", p/s)	7
85	RCA PT 40040R	All Fall Down (M&M Remix)/All Fall Down (Instrumental)/First Avenue (12", p/s)	7
85	RCA PT 40194R	Let Me Be The One (Philadelphia Remix)/Let Me Be The One (Long Hot Soulful Summer Mix)/All Fall Down (M&M Dub Mix) (12", p/s)	7
85	RCA PT 40194RR	Let Me Be The One (Philadelphia Remix)/Let Me Be The One (Hardrock Dance Mix)/All Fall Down (M&M Dub Mix)/Beat 47 (12", p/s)	7
85	RCA PB 40353	Love Takeover/Keep In Touch (picture disc)	4
85	RCA PT 40354R	Love Takeover (Limited Edition Mix)/Love Takeover (Dub Takeover)/ Keep In Touch/Let Me Be The One (Instrumental) (12", p/s)	7
85	RCA PB 40445	R.S.V.P./Say Goodbye (p/s, with cassette "Hide And Seek (12" Version)"/ "Crazy (12" Version)" [FSK 001])	5
85	RCA PB 40445	R.S.V.P./Say Goodbye (poster sleeve)	4
85	RCA PB 40515	System Addict/Pure Energy (with cassette "All Fall Down (Dub)"/ "Love Takeover (Dub)"/"System Addict (Dub)" [FSK 002])	4
86	RCA PB 40799	Find The Time/Sky (picture disc)	5
86	RCA PT 40800R	Find The Time (Shep Pettibone Remix Pts 1 & 2)/(Midnight Mix) (12", p/s)	7
86	RCA PB 40901PB	Rain Or Shine/Summer Groove (poster p/s)	4
86	RCA PB 40981P	If I Say Yes/Let Me Down Easy (logo-shaped picture disc)	5
86	Music Lab	CRUNCHIE LIVE TOUR (12" EP, picture disc)	5
87	RCA PB 41131	Stay Out Of My Life/(How Dare You) Stay Out Of My Life (p/s, with 5 badges)	4
87	RCA PT 41265B	The Slightest Touch/Stone Court (box set with free 7" & 5 colour photos)	4
87	RCA PT 41566R	Strong As Steel/The Man/The Five Star Hit Mix (12", p/s)	7
87	RCA PB 41661P	Somewhere Somebody/Have A Good Time (logo-shaped picture disc)	5
87	RCA PB 41661AC	Somewhere Somebody/Have A Good Time (p/s, with advent calendar)	4
87	RCA PB 42145W	Rock My World/Sweetest Innocence (foldout circular p/s)	4
88	Tent TENT 4	Problematic/Big Funk (picture disc, fan club edition)	8
88	Tent TENT T4	Problematic (Extended)/(Vocal)/Big Funk (12", fan club edition with stamped labels)	8

5:30/FIVE THIRTY
85	Other 12 OTH 2	Catcher In The Rye/Weight Of The World/Mood Suite/Suburban Town (12", p/s)	25
90	East West YZ 530	Abstain!/You (p/s)	4
90	East West YZ 530C	Abstain!/You (cassette)	4
90	East West YZ 530T	Abstain!/You/Catcher In The Rye/Coming Up For Air (12", p/s)	7
90	East West YZ 530CD	Abstain!/You/Catcher In The Rye/Coming Up For Air (CD)	7

FIVE TOWNS
67	Direction 58-3115	It Isn't What You've Got/Advice	4

FIXX
82	MCA FIXX 3	Red Skies/Is It By Instinct (picture disc)	4
83	MCA FIXX 5	One Thing Leads To Another/Opinions//Red Skies/Stand Or Fall (double pack)	4

FIZZBOMBS
87	Narodnik NRK 003	Sign On The Line/The Lines That (p/s)	8
87	Wild Rumpus SHEP 001	You Worry Me/JESSE GARON & DESPERADOS: Hank Williams Is Dead (p/s, flexidisc)	6
88	Calculus KIT 002	THE SURFIN' WINTER EP (p/s)	4
88	Calculus KIT 002T	THE SURFIN' WINTER EP (12", p/s)	7

FK 9
81	A Bigger Splash ABS 1	Our Condition/These Children/All That Fall (p/s)	4
81	A Bigger Splash ABS 2	Stranger At The Heart/Complete Surveillance (foldover p/s)	4

ROBERTA FLACK
69	Atlantic 584 294	Hey, That's No Way To Say Goodbye/Compared To What	4
73	Atlantic K 10282	Killing Me Softly With His Song/Just Like A Woman	4
69	Atlantic 588 204	FIRST TAKE (LP, with Donny Hathaway)	15
71	Atlantic K 40040	FIRST TAKE (LP, reissue)	10
71	Atlantic K 40097	CHAPTER TWO (LP)	12
71	Atlantic K 40297	QUIET FIRE (LP)	12
73	Atlantic K 50021	KILLING ME SOFTLY (LP)	10
75	Atlantic K 50049	FEEL LIKE MAKIN' LOVE (LP)	10

FLAG OF CONVENIENCE
82	Sire SIR 4057	Life On The Telephone/The Other Man's Sin (p/s)	4

(see also Steve Diggle, Buzzcocks)

FLAIRS
57	Oriole CB 1392	Swing Pretty Mama/I'd Climb The Hills And Mountains	200
57	Oriole CB 1392	Swing Pretty Mama/I'd Climb The Hills And Mountains (78)	60

FLAME
70	Stateside SS 2183	See The Light/Get Your Mind Made Up	4
71	Stateside SSL 10312	THE FLAME (LP)	10

FLAME'N'KING & BOLD ONES
79	Grapevine GRP 123	Ho Happy Day/Ain't Nobody Jivin'	4

FLAMES
64	Island WI 130	He's The Greatest/Someone Going To Call	10
64	Island WI 136	Little Flea/Good Idea	10
64	Island WI 138	When I Get Home/Neither Silver Nor Gold	10
64	Island WI 139	Broadway Jungle/Beat Lied	10

(see also Maytals, Vikings)

FLAMES
64	Blue Beat BB 205	Helena Darling/My Darling Heart (both actually by Plamers)	10

FLAMES
68	Nu Beat NB 020	Mini Really Fit Dem/Soul Train (both actually by Alton Ellis & Flames)	5

(see also Alton Ellis & Flames)

FLAMES
68	Page One FOR(S) 009	BURNING SOUL (LP)	12

FLAMING EMBER
71	Hot Wax HWX 101	Westbound No. 9/Why Don't You Stay	4
70	Hot Wax SHW 5001	WESTBOUND NO. 9 (LP)	10

FLAMING EMERALDS
78	Grapevine GRP 104	Have Some Everybody/Have Some Everybody (Instrumental)	4

JOHNNY FLAMINGO
57	Vogue V 9089	My Teen-Age Girl/When I Lost You	50
57	Vogue V 9089	My Teen-Age Girl/When I Lost You (78)	20
58	Vogue V 9100	So Long/Make Me A Present Of You	45
58	Vogue V 9100	So Long/Make Me A Present Of You (78)	20

FLAMINGOS
57	London HLN 8373	Would I Be Crying/Just For A Kick	300
57	London HLN 8373	Would I Be Crying/Just For A Kick (78)	50
57	Brunswick 05696	The Ladder Of Love/Let's Make Up	400
57	Brunswick 05696	The Ladder Of Love/Let's Make Up (78)	45
59	Top Rank JAR 213	Love Walked In/Yours	20
60	Top Rank JAR 263	I Only Have Eyes For You/I Was Such A Fool	75
60	Top Rank JAR 367	Nobody Loves Me Like You/You, Me And The Sea	20
60	Top Rank JAR 519	Mio Amore/At Night	20
66	Philips BF 1483	Boogaloo Party/Nearness Of You	12
69	Philips BF 1786	Boogaloo Party/Nearness Of You (reissue)	4

FLAMIN' GROOVIES
71	Kama Sutra 2013 031	Teenage Head/Evil Hearted Ada	7
72	Kama Sutra 2013 042	Gonna Rock Tonite/Keep A-Knockin'/SHA NA NA: Rock'n'Roll Is Here To Stay/At The Hop/Duke Of Earl	6
72	United Artists UP 35392	Slow Death/Talahassie Lassie	7
72	United Artists UP 35392	Slow Death/Talahassie Lassie (promo p/s)	12
72	United Artists UP 35464	Married Woman/Get A Shot Of Rhythm And Blues	8
76	Sire 6198 086	Don't You Lie To Me/She Said Yeah/Shake Some Action (p/s)	5
76	Sire 6078 602	Shake Some Action/Teenage Confidential (p/s, 2 versions of A-side)	4-6
76	Kama Sutra KSS 707	Teenage Head/Headin' For The Texas Border	6
78	Sire 6078 619	Feel A Whole Lot Better/Paint It Black/Shake Some Action (p/s)	7
78	Sire 6078 619	Feel A Whole Lot Better/Paint It Black/Shake Some Action (12", p/s)	8

78	Sire SIR 4002	Move It/When I Heard Your Name	6
79	Sire SIR 4018	Absolutely Sweet Marie/Werewolves Of London/Next One Crying (p/s)	6
76	United Artists REM 406	SLOW DEATH (EP)	8
71	Kama Sutra 2683 003	FLAMIN' GROOVIES (2-LP)	14
77	Sire 9103 251	SHAKE SOME ACTION (LP)	12
78	Sire 9103 333	THE FLAMIN' GROOVIES NOW! (LP)	10

FLAMING YOUTH

69	Fontana TF 1057	Guide Me Orion/From Now On (Immortal Invisible)	15
70	Fontana 6001 002	Every Man, Woman And Child/Drifting	15
70	Fontana 6001 003	From Now On/Space Child	15
69	Fontana STL 5533	ARK II (LP, with plastic window sleeve)	30

(see also Genesis, Phil Collins)

FLAMMA-SHERMAN

68	SNB 55-3488	No Need To Explain/Bassa Love	4
68	SNB 55-3769	Love Is In The Air/Super Day	4
69	SNB 55-4142	Move Me/Where Is He	20

BUD FLANAGAN

| 59 | Columbia DB 4265 | Strollin'/Home Is Where Your Heart Is | 4 |

FLANAGAN & ALLEN

| 53 | Columbia 33S 1010 | FLANAGAN AND ALLEN (10" LP) | 10 |
| 53 | Decca LF 1125 | FAVOURITES (10" LP) | 10 |

FLANAGAN BROTHERS

| 58 | Vogue Coral Q 72342 | Salton City/Early One Evening | 12 |

MICHAEL FLANDERS (& DONALD SWANN)

57	Parlophone R 4354	A Gnu/Misalliance	4
59	Parlophone R 4528	The Little Drummer Boy/DONALD SWANN: The Youth Of The Heart	4
57	Parlophone PMC 1033	AT THE DROP OF A HAT (LP, also stereo PCS 3001)	10
61	Parlophone PMC 1164	BESTIARY OF FLANDERS AND SWANN (LP)	10
64	Parlophone PMC 1216	AT THE DROP OF ANOTHER HAT (LP)	10

TOMMY FLANDERS

| 69 | Verve SVLP 6020 | MOONSTONE (LP) | 15 |

(see also Blues Project)

FLARES

| 61 | London HLU 9441 | Foot Stompin'/Hotcha Cha-Cha Brown | 15 |
| 63 | London HA-U 8034 | FOOT STOMPIN' HITS (LP) | 30 |

FLASH

72	Sovereign SVNA 7251	FLASH (LP)	12
72	Sovereign SVNA 7255	FLASH IN THE CAN (LP)	12
73	Sovereign SVNA 7260	OUT OF OUR HANDS (LP)	12

(see also Peter Banks)

FLASH & BOARD OF DIRECTORS

| 68 | Bell BLL 1007 | Busy Signal/Love Ain't Easy | 6 |

FLAT EARTH SOCIETY

| 68 | Psycho PSYCHO 17 | WALEECO (LP) | 15 |

FLATMATES

| 86 | Subway Organisation SUBWAY 6 | I Could Be In Heaven/Tell Me Why/So In Love With You (foldaround p/s with insert in poly bag) | 6 |
| 88 | Subway Org. SUBWAY 17T | Shimmer/On My Mind/If Not For You/Bad (12", p/s, with 'flat sharing guide') | 7 |

(Lester) FLATT & (Earl) SCRUGGS

65	CBS 201793	Ballad Of Jed Clampett/Gonna Give Myself A Ball	6
67	CBS 3038	Foggy Mountain Breakdown/California Uptight Band	4
67	Mercury MF 1007	Foggy Mountain Breakdown/My Cabin In Caroline	4
61	Mercury ZEP 10106	C & W TRAIL BLAZERS NO. 4 (EP)	7
64	Mercury 10010 MCE	COUNTRY AND WESTERN ACES (EP)	7
63	CBS BPG 62095	FOLK SONGS OF OUR LAND (LP)	10

JACKIE FLAVELL

| 70s | York FYK 408 | ADMISSION FREE (LP) | 10 |

FLAVOUR

| 68 | Direction 58-3597 | Sally Had A Party/Shop Around | 6 |

(FABULOUS) FLEE-REKKERS/FLEE-RAKKERS

60	Triumph RGM 1008	Green Jeans/You Are My Sunshine	25
60	Top Rank JAR 431	Green Jeans/You Are My Sunshine (reissue)	20
60	Pye 7N 15288	Sunday Date/Shiftless Sam	8
60	Pye 7N 15326	Blue Tango/Bitter Rice	8
61	Piccadilly 7N 35006	Lone Rider/Miller Like Wow	12
62	Piccadilly 7N 35048	Stage To Cimarron/Twistin' The Chestnuts	12
62	Piccadilly 7N 35081	Sunburst/Black Buffalo	10
63	Piccadilly 7N 35109	Fireball XL5/Fandango	10
61	Pye NEP 24141	THE FABULOUS FLEE-REKKERS (EP)	25

(see also Rick Wayne & Fabulous Flee-Rakkers)

(PETER GREEN'S) FLEETWOOD MAC

67	Blue Horizon 57-3051	I Believe My Time Ain't Long/Rambling Pony (as Peter Green's Fleetwood Mac, initially with p/s)	18/8
68	Blue Horizon 57-3138	Black Magic Woman/The Sun Is Shining	7
68	Blue Horizon 57-3139	Need Your Love So Bad/Stop Messin' Around	6
68	Blue Horizon 57-3145	Albatross/Jigsaw Puzzle Blues	4
69	Immediate IM 080	Man Of The World/EARL VINCE & VALIANTS: Somebody's Gonna Get Their Head Kicked In Tonight	6

69	Blue Horizon 57-3157	Need Your Love So Bad/Black Magic Woman (withdrawn, any pressed?)	
69	Blue Horizon 57-3157	Black Magic Woman/No Place To Go (withdrawn, any pressed?)	
69	Blue Horizon 57-3157	Need Your Love So Bad/No Place To Go	5
69	CBS 3051	I Believe My Time Ain't Long/Rambling Pony (reissue)	4
69	Reprise RS 27000	Oh Well Pts 1 & 2	6
70	Reprise RS 27007	The Green Manalishi (With The Two-Prong Crown)/World In Harmony (p/s)	10/5
71	Reprise RS 27010	Dragonfly/The Purple Dancer	5
72	Reprise K 14194	Sunny Side Of Heaven/Spare Me A Little Of Your Love	4
73	Reprise K 14280	Did You Ever Love Me/The Derelict	4
73	CBS 1722	Black Magic Woman/Stop Messin' Around	4
74	Reprise K 14315	For Your Love/Hypnotised	4
75	Reprise K 14388	Heroes Are Hard To Find/Born Enchanter	4
75	DJM DJS 10620	Man Of The World/DANNY KIRWAN: Second Chapter	4
75	Reprise K 14403	Warm Ways/Blue Letter	4
76	Reprise K 14413	Over My Head/I'm So Afraid	4
82	Warner Bros FLEET 1P	Oh Diane/Only Over You (picture disc)	6
87	Warner Bros W 8398	Big Love/You And I Part 1//The Chain/Go Your Own Way (double pack, gatefold p/s)	5
87	Warner Bros W 8398TP	Big Love (Extended)/You And I Part /The Chain/Go Your Own Way (12," picture disc)	7
87	Warner Bros W 8317TP	Seven Wonders (Extended Remix)/Seven Wonders (Dub)/Book Of Miracles (12", picture disc)	8
87	Warner Bros W 8291	Little Lies/Ricky (picture disc)	4
87	Warner Bros W 8291TP	Little Lies (Extended)/Little Lies (Dub)/Ricky (12", picture disc)	8
87	Warner Bros W 8114B	Family Man/Down Endless Street (box set, with 2 colour prints)	5
68	Blue Horizon 7-63200	PETER GREEN'S FLEETWOOD MAC (LP)	20
68	Blue Horizon 7-63205	MR. WONDERFUL (LP, gatefold sleeve)	20
69	Blue Horizon 7-63215	THE PIOUS BIRD OF GOOD OMEN (LP)	18
69	Reprise RSLP 9000	THEN PLAY ON (LP, gatefold sleeve)	15
70	Reprise RSLP 9004	KILN HOUSE (LP)	15
71	CBS Blue Horizon 63875	THE ORIGINAL FLEETWOOD MAC (LP)	15
75	Reprise K 54043	FLEETWOOD MAC (LP, white vinyl with lyric sheet)	12

(see also Peter Green, Stevie Nicks, Buckingham-Nicks, John Mayall, Otis Spann, Eddie Boyd, Duster Bennett, Chicken Shack, Jeremy Spencer, Christine Perfect, Shotgun Express, Bo Street Runners, Tramp, Clifford Davis)

FLEETWOODS

59	London HLU 8841	Come Softly To Me/I Care So Much	15
59	London HLU 8841	Come Softly To Me/I Care So Much (78)	10
59	London HLW 4004	Come Softly To Me/I Care So Much (stereo export issue)	30
59	London HLU 8895	Graduation's Here/Oh Lord Let It Be Me	12
59	London HLU 8895	Graduation's Here/Oh Lord Let It Be Me (78)	12
59	Top Rank JAR 202	Mr. Blue/You Mean Everything To Me	10
59	Top Rank JAR 202	Mr. Blue/You Mean Everything To Me (78)	25
60	Top Rank JAR 294	Outside My Window/Magic Star (some in p/s)	12/7
60	Top Rank JAR 383	Runaround/Truly Do	8
61	London HLG 9341	Tragedy/Little Miss Sad One	10
61	London HLG 9426	He's The Great Imposter/Poor Little Girl	10
65	Liberty LIB 10191	Almost There/Before And After (Losing You)	6
64	Liberty LIB 62	They Tell Me It's Summer/Lovers By Night Strangers By Day	6
64	Liberty LIB 75	Goodnight My Love Pleasant Dreams/Jimmy Beware	6
64	Liberty LIB 93	Ruby Red Baby Blue/Lonesome Town	6
60	Top Rank BUY 028	MR BLUE (LP, with 3 tracks by other artists)	25
61	London HA-G 2388	SOFTLY (LP, also stereo SAH-G 6188)	35/45
61	London HA-G 2419	DEEP IN A DREAM (LP)	25

HELEN FLEMING

| 65 | Blue Beat BB 341 | Eve's Ten Commandments/Don't Take Your Love Away | 8 |

JOY FLEMING

| 75 | Antic K 11518 | A Bridge Of Love/Divorcee | 4 |

WADE FLEMONS

59	Top Rank JAR 206	Slow Motion/Walkin' By The River	6
60	Top Rank JAR 327	What's Happening/Goodnight, It's Time To Go	6
60	Top Rank JAR 371	Easy Lovin'/Woops Now	6

FLESH

| 70s | Dancing Industries DI 001 | My Boy Lollipop/Flesh (p/s) | 5 |

FLESHEATERS

| 81 | Initial IRC 007 | A MINUTE TO PRAY, A SECOND TO DIE (LP) | 10 |

(see also Divine Horsemen)

FLESH FOR LULU

83	Polydor POSP 653	Roman Candle/Coming Down (p/s)	5
83	Polydor POSPX 653	Roman Candle/Coming Down/Lame Train/The Power Of Suggestion (12", p/s)	8
84	Polydor FFL 2	Restless/Cat Burglar (p/s)	4
84	Polydor FFLX 2	Restless/Cat Burglar (12", p/s)	7
84	Polydor FFL 2/POSP 653	Restless/Cat Burglar//Roman Candle/Coming Down (stickered shrinkwrapped double pack)	8
84	Polydor FFL 1	Subterraneans/Why Me? (p/s)	4
84	Polydor FFLD 1	Subterraneans/Why Me?//Endless Sleep/Ten Foot Tall (stickered shrinkwrapped double pack)	8
84	Polydor FFLX 1	Subterraneans/Why Me?/Gurl At The Bar (12", p/s)	7

FLESH PUPPETS

| 85 | Plague CAV 018 | Deadline/Pain (foldout p/s) | 4 |

FLESHTONES

| 81 | IRS PFP 1004 | Girl From Baltimore/Feel The Heat (p/s) | 4 |
| 81 | IRS PFP 1012 | Shadow Line/All Around The World (p/s) | 4 |

FLESHTONES

82	IRS PFP 1018	Right Side Of A Good Thing/Wheelman (p/s) 4
83	IRS PFP 1024	Screaming Skull/Burnin' Hell (p/s) 4

FLESH VOLCANO
88	Some Bizzare SLUT 1	Slut/The Universal Cesspool/Bruisin Chain (12", p/s) 8

(see also Marc Almond)

DARROW FLETCHER
66	London HLU 10024	The Pain Gets A Little Deeper/My Judgement Day 50

DON FLETCHER
66	Vocalion VP 9271	Two Wrongs Don't Make A Right/I'm So Glad 12

DUSTY FLETCHER
47	Parlophone R 3037	Open The Door Richard Pts 1 & 2 (78) 25

SAM FLETCHER
59	MGM MGM 1024	Time Has A Way/No Such Luck 4

FLEUR-DE-LYS
65	Immediate IM 020	Moondreams/Wait For Me 80
66	Immediate IM 032	Circles/So Come On 100
66	Polydor NH 56124	Mud In Your Eye/I've Been Trying 100
67	Polydor NH 56200	I Can See A Light/Prodigal Son 35
68	Polydor NH 56251	The Gong With The Luminous Nose/Hammer Head 40
68	Atlantic 584 193	Stop Crossing The Bridge/Brick By Brick (Stone By Stone) 25
69	Atlantic 584 243	You're Just A Liar/One Girl City 40

(see also John Bromley, Terry Durham, Tony & Tandy, Sharon Tandy, Ruperts People, Quotations, Bryn Haworth)

VIC FLICK SOUND
70s	Chapter One CH 136	Hang On/Wonderful World 8

FLIES
66	Decca F 12533	I'm Not Your Stepping Stone/Talk To Me 40
67	Decca F 12594	House Of Love/It Had To Be You 30
68	RCA RCA 1757	The Magic Train/Gently As You Feel 20

SHELBY FLINT
61	Warner Bros WB 30	Angel On My Shoulder/Somebody 6

FLINTLOCK
70s	Pinnacle PLP 8307	FLINTLOCK ON THE WAY (LP) 15

FLINTLOCKS
66	Decca F 12412	What Goes On?/I Walked Right Into A Heaven 4

FLINTSTONES
64	HMV POP 1266	Safari/Work Out 12

FLIP & DATELINERS
64	HMV POP 1359	My Johnny Doesn't Come Around Anymore/Please Listen To Me 35

FLIPS
62	London HLU 9490	Rockin' Twist/Oh, You Beautiful Doll — Twist 8

SHERRY FLIPS
80	Dining Out TUX 11	Schizo (p/s) 4

FLIRTATIONS
68	Deram DM 195	Someone Out There/How Can You Tell Me 4
68	Deram DM 216	Nothing But A Heartache/Christmas Time Is Here Again 4
69	Deram DM 252	What's Good About Goodbye My Love?/Once I Had A Love 4
70	Deram DM 281	Keep On Searchin'/Moma I'm Coming Home 4
70	Deram DM 295	Can't Stop Loving You/Everybody Needs Somebody 4
71	Deram DM 329	Give Me Love/This Must Be The End Of The Line 4
72	Deram DM 351	Need Your Lovin'/I Wanna Be There 5
71	Polydor 2058 167	Take Me In Your Arms And Love Me/Little Darlin' 5
72	Polydor 2058 249	Love A Little Longer/Hold On To Me Babe 4
74	Polydor 2058 295	Dirty Work/No Such Thing As A Miracle 4
69	Deram DML/SML 1046	SOUNDS LIKE THE FLIRTATIONS (LP) 10

FLO & EDDIE
72	Reprise K 44201	PHLORESCENT LEECH AND EDDIE (LP) 12
73	Reprise K 44234	FLO AND EDDIE (LP) 12

(see also Turtles, Mothers Of Invention)

FLOATING BRIDGE
69	Liberty LBS 83271	FLOATING BRIDGE (LP) 15

FLOCK
70	CBS 4932	Tired Of Waiting For You/Store Bought — Store Thought 4
69	CBS 63733	THE FLOCK (LP) 12
71	CBS 64055	DINOSAUR SWAMPS (LP) 10

FLOCK OF SEAGULLS
(see under A Flock Of Seagulls)

DICK FLOOD
59	Felsted AF 125	The Three Bells/Far Away 6

FLOWERED UP
90	Heavenly 10 HVN 3	It's On — Feel Pain (10", p/s, 1 side etched) 6
90	The Catalogue CAT 084	It's On (The Posh Facker Mix)/SAINT ETIENNE: Only Love Can Break Your Heart (remixed by Flowered Up) (square flexidisc with 'The Catalogue' mag) ...5/4

FLOWERPOT MEN
67	Deram DM 142	Let's Go To San Francisco Pts 1 & 2 (original pressing) 5
68	Page One POF 065	Mighty Quinn/Voices From The Sky 5

FLOWERPOT MEN

67	Deram DM 160	A Walk In The Sky/Am I Losing You	6
68	Deram DM 183	A Man Without A Woman/You Can Never Be Wrong	6
69	Deram DM 248	In A Moment Of Madness/Young Birds Fly	4

(see also Friends, Carter-Lewis & Southerners, Ivy League)

FLOWERPOT MEN
84	Compost 01	Jo's So Mean To Josephine/I. Rapids/UG (12", p/s)	7
85	Compost 703	Walk On Gilded Splinters/Melting Down On Motor Angel (p/s)	4

LLOYD FLOWERS
62	Blue Beat BB 88	I'm Going Home/Lover's Town	10

PHIL FLOWERS
69	A&M AMS 766	Like A Rolling Stone/Keep On Sockin' It Children	4

FLOWER TRAVELLING BAND
71	Atlantic 2091 128	Satori (Enlightment) Pts 1 & 2	4

BOBBY FLOYD
72	Pama PM 860	Sound Doctor/YOUNG DILLINGER: Doctor Skank	4

EDDIE FLOYD
66	Atlantic 584 041	Knock On Wood/Got To Make A Comeback	5
67	Stax 601 001	Raise Your Hand/I've Just Been Feeling Bad (dark blue label)	7
67	Stax 601 001	Raise Your Hand/I've Just Been Feeling Bad (light blue label)	4
67	London HL 10129	Set My Soul On Fire/Will I Be The One	7
67	Speciality SPE 1001	Never Get Enough Of Your Love/Bye Bye Baby	12
67	Stax 601 016	Things Get Better/Good Love, Bad Love	6
67	Stax 601 024	On A Saturday Night/Under My Nose	6
68	Stax 601 035	Big Bird/Holding On With Both Hands	6
68	Stax STAX 104	I've Never Found A Girl (To Love Me Like You Do)/I'm Just The Kind Of Fool	4
68	Stax STAX 108	Bring It On Home To Me/Sweet Things You Do	4
69	Stax STAX 116	I've Got To Have Your Love/Girl I Love You	4
69	Stax STAX 125	Don't Tell Your Mama/Consider Me	4
74	Stax STXS 2005	Soul Street/The Highway Man	4
67	Stax 589 006	KNOCK ON WOOD (LP)	15
67	Atco 228 014	KNOCK ON WOOD (LP, reissue)	12
68	Stax SXATS 1003	I'VE NEVER FOUND A GIRL (LP)	15
68	Ember EMBS 3398	LOOKING BACK WITH THE PRIMETTES AND EDDIE FLOYD (LP)	35
74	Stax STX 1002	SOUL STREET (LP)	10
74	Polydor 2363 010	YOU'VE GOT TO HAVE EDDIE (LP)	10

(see also Primettes, Falcons)

FLUKE
80s	Fluke FLUKE 001T	Thumper!/Cool Hand Flute (12", stamped white label with stickered sleeve)	7

FLUX OF PINK INDIANS
81	Crass 321984/2	NEU SMELL (EP, foldout poster sleeve)	5
85	Spiderleg SDL 16	TAKING A LIBERTY (EP, with booklet sleeve)	5
83	Spiderleg SDL 8	STRIVE TO SURVIVE CAUSING THE LEAST SUFFERING POSSIBLE (LP)	10

FLYER
70s	Redball RR 004	FLYER (EP)	4

FLYING BURRITO BROTHERS
69	A&M AMS 756	Train Song/Hot Burrito No. 1	6
70	A&M AMS 794	Older Guys/Down In The Churchyard	4
70	A&M AMS 816	Tried So Hard/Lazy Days	6
69	A&M AMLS 931	THE GILDED PALACE OF SIN (LP)	10
70	A&M AMLS 983	BURRITO DELUXE (LP)	10
71	A&M AMLS 64295	THE FLYING BURRITO BROTHERS (LP)	10
72	A&M AMLS 64343	LAST OF THE RED-HOT BURRITOS (LP)	10
73	Bumble GEXD 301	LIVE IN AMSTERDAM (2-LP)	15

(see also Byrds, Gram Parsons, Stephen Stills & Manassas, Rick Roberts)

FLYING CIRCUS
70	Harvest SHSP 4010	PREPARED IN PEACE (LP)	12

FLYING MACHINE
69	Pye 7N 17722	Smile A Little Smile For Me/Maybe We've Been Loving Too Long	6
69	Pye 7N 17722	Baby Make It Soon/Smile A Little Smile For Me	5
69	Pye 7N 17811	Send My Baby Home Again/Look At Me, Look At Me	5
70	Pye 7N 17914	Hanging On The Edge Of Sadness/Flying Machine	7
70	Pye 7N 45001	The Devil Has Possession Of Your Mind/Hey Little Girl	4
70	Pye 7N 45093	Yes I Understand/Pages Of Your Life	4
70	Pye NSPL 18328	DOWN TO EARTH WITH THE FLYING MACHINE (LP)	12

(see also Pinkertons, Pinkerton's Assorted Colours)

FLYING SAUCERS
78	Alaska 101	KEEP ON COMING (LP)	10

ERROL FLYNN
55	Philips PB 380	Lily Of Laguna/We'll Gather Lilacs (B-side with Patrice Wymore) (78)	5

STEVE FLYNN
67	Parlophone R 5625	Mister Rainbow/Let's Live For Tomorrow	15
68	Parlophone R 5689	Your Life, My Life/Come Tomorrow	6

FLY ON THE WALL
79	Next Wave NEXT 1	DEVON DUMB (EP, numbered)	5

FLYS
77	Zama ZA 10 EP	BUNCH OF FIVE (33rpm EP, die-cut p/s)	8
78	EMI EMI 2747	Love And A Molotov Cocktail/Can I Crash Here/Civilisation (p/s)	4
78	EMI EMIY 2867	Waikiki Beach Refugees/We Don't Mind The Rave (p/s, yellow vinyl)	4

FM
87	Portrait MERVP 1	Let Love Be The Leader/Let Love Be The Leader (Version) (picture disc)	4
87	Portrait MERVB 1	Let Love Be The Leader/Let Love Be The Leader (Version) (box set with signed photo & biography)	4

FOCAL POINT
68	Deram DM 186	Love You Forever/Sycamore Sid	25

FOCUS
71	Polydor 2001 134	House Of The King/Black Beauty	6
71	Blue Horizon 2094 006	Hocus Pocus/Janis	10
72	Blue Horizon 2096 008	Tommy/Focus II	10
76	Polydor 2001 640	House Of The King/O Avendrood	4
71	Polydor 2344 003	IN AND OUT OF FOCUS (LP, gatefold sleeve)	10
71	Blue Horizon 2096 002	MOVING WAVES (LP, with poster)	12
73	Polydor 2443 118	LIVE AT THE RAINBOW (LP, gatefold sleeve)	10

(see also Jan Akkerman, Thijs Van Leer, Brainbox, Robin Lent)

FOCUS THREE
67	Columbia DB 8279	10,000 Years Behind My Mind/The Sunkeeper	30

FOETUS ART TERRORISM
84	Self Immolation FAT 1122	Calamity Crush/Catastrophe (12", p/s)	8

FOETUS CORRUPTUS
80s	Rifle RIFLE 1	RIFE (2-LP, stickered black sleeve)	25

FOETUS UBER FRISCO
82	Self Immolation WOMB 125/SUSC 12	Custom Built For Capitalism/1.0.4.5./Birthday (12", p/s)	30
85	Self Imm. WOMB UNC 7.12	Finely Honed Machine/Sick Minutes (12", p/s)	7

FOETUS UNDER GLASS
85	Self Imm. WOMB S201	OKFM/Spite Your Face (p/s)	25

(see also You've Got Foetus On Your Breath, Philip & His Foetus Vibrations, Scraping Foetus Off The Wheel)

FOGCUTTERS
64	Liberty LIB 55793	Cry Cry Cry/You Say	8

JOHN FOGERTY
74	Fantasy FTC 111	Comin' Down The Road/Ricochet	4
75	Fantasy FTC 119	Rockin' All Over The World/The Wall	4
75	Fantasy FTC 120	Almost Saturday Night/Sea Cruise	4
76	Fantasy FTC 133	You Got The Magic/Evil Thing	5
75	Fantasy FT 526	JOHN FOGERTY (LP)	10

(see also Creedence Clearwater Revival, Blue Ridge Rangers)

TOM FOGERTY
71	United Artists UP 35264	Goodbye Media Man	4
72	Fantasy F 680	Cast The First Stone/Lady Of Fatima	4
73	Fantasy FTC 109	Joyful Resurrection/Heartbeat	4
72	Fantasy FAN 9407	TOM FOGERTY (LP)	10

(see also Creedence Clearwater Revival, Ruby)

FOGGY
72	York SYK 534	How Come The Sun/Take Your Name	5
73	York SYK 542	Kitty Starr/She's Far Away (p/s)	7
72	York FYK 411	SIMPLE GIFTS (LP, with Strawbs, with insert)	50
73	Canon	PATCHWORK (LP)	35

(see also Strawbs)

FOGGY DEW-O
68	Decca F 12776	Reflections/Grandfather's Clock	5
68	Decca LK/SKL 4940	THE FOGGY DEW-O (LP)	22
69	Decca SKL 5035	BORN TO TAKE THE HIGHWAY (LP)	20

FOGHAT
74	Bearsville K 15511	Long Way To Go/Ride Ride Ride	5
74	Bearsville K 15517	Step Outside (Edit)/Mabellene	5
76	Bearsville K 15522	Slow Ride (Edit)/Save Your Loving (For Me)	5
78	Bearsville K 15537	I Just Want To Make Love To You (Live Edit)/Fool For The City (Live Edit)	5
80	Bearsville WIP 6582	Third Time Lucky/Somebody's Been Sleeping In My Bed	4
72	Bearsville K 45503	FOGHAT (LP)	12
73	Bearsville K 45514	ROCK'N'ROLL (LP)	10

(see also Savoy Brown)

ELLEN FOLEY (& CLASH)
81	Epic EPC A 9522	The Shuttered Palace/Beautiful Waste Of Time (p/s)	6
81	Epic EPC A 1160	Torchlight/Game Of A Man (p/s)	5
81	Epic SEPC 84809	SPIRIT OF ST. LOUIS (LP, with inner sleeve)	10

(see also Clash)

RED FOLEY
51	Brunswick 04679	Hot Rod Race/The Chicken Song (B-side with Ernest Tubb) (78)	5
53	Brunswick 05076	Hot Toddy/ROBERTA LEE & HARDROCK GUNTER: Sixty Minute Man (78)	8
54	Brunswick 05307	Pin Ball Boogie/Jilted (78)	7
54	Brunswick 05321	Thank You For Calling/Skinnie Minnie (Fishtail)	10
55	Brunswick 05363	Hearts Of Stone/RED FOLEY & BETTY FOLEY: Never	15
60	Brunswick LAT 8343	SING ALONG WITH RED FOLEY (LP, also stereo STA 3034)	15

RED FOLEY & BETTY FOLEY
55	Brunswick 05508	Croce Di Oro (Cross Of Gold)/RED FOLEY: The Night Watch	12

MINT VALUE £

RED FOLEY & ERNEST TUBB

55	Brunswick OE 9148	COUNTRY DOUBLE DATE (EP, with Minnie Pearl)	12
57	Brunswick LAT 8206	RED AND ERNIE (LP)	20

(see also Ernest Tubb)

FOLKAL POINT

70s	Midas	FOLKAL POINT (LP)	40

CALVIN FOLKES

63	Rio R 5	Someone/Kentucky Home	7
63	Rio R 8	You'll Never Know/Is It Time	7
64	Port-O-Jam PJ 4117	My Bonnie/What A Day	7
64	Port-O-Jam PJ 4118	Hello Everybody/IRVING SIX: King's Boogie	7

FOLK(E)S BROTHERS

61	Blue Beat BB 30	Carolina/I Met A Man (original, blue label, as Folkes Brothers)	10
60s	Fab BB 30	Carolina (as Folks Brothers)/ERIC 'HUMPTY DUMPTY' MORRIS: Humpty Dumpty	5
70s	Blue Beat BB 30	Carolina/I Met A Man (reissue, white label)	5

FOLKLANDERS

60s	Urban PB 001	TWO LITTLE FISHES (EP)	7

FOLKWAYS

72	Folk Heritage	NO OTHER NAME (LP)	10

EDDIE FONTAINE

55	HMV 7M 304	Rock Love/All My Love Belongs To You (with Neil Hefti & Excels)	125
55	HMV B 10852	Rock Love/All My Love Belongs To You (with Neil Hefti & Excels) (78)	40
56	Brunswick 05624	Cool It, Baby/Into Each Life Some Rain Must Fall	75
56	Brunswick 05624	Cool It, Baby/Into Each Life Some Rain Must Fall (78)	20
58	London HLM 8711	Nothin' Shakin' (But The Leaves On The Trees)/Don't Ya Know	30
58	London HLM 8711	Nothin' Shakin' (But The Leaves On The Trees)/Don't Ya Know (78)	15
50s	Decca	export single	30

ARLENE FONTANA

59	Pye Intl. 7N 25010	I'm In Love/Easy	7
59	Pye Intl. N 25010	I'm In Love/Easy (78)	5

WAYNE FONTANA

65	Fontana TF 642	It Was Easier To Hurt Her/You Made Me What I Am Today	5
66	Fontana TF 684	Come On Home/My Eyes Break Out In Tears	4
66	Fontana TF 737	Goodbye Bluebird/The Sun's So Hot Today	4
66	Fontana TF 770	Pamela Pamela/Something Keeps Calling Me Back	6
67	Fontana TF 827	24 Sycamore/From A Boy To A Man	4
67	Fontana TF 866	The Impossible Years/In My World	4
67	Fontana TF 889	Gina/We All Love The Human Race	5
68	Fontana TF 911	Storybook Children/I Need To Love You	4
68	Fontana TF 933	The Words Of Bartholomew/Mind Excursion	4
68	Fontana TF 976	Never An Everyday Thing/Waiting For A Break In The Clouds	4
69	Fontana TF 1008	Dayton Ohio 1903/Say Goodbye To Yesterday	4
69	Fontana TF 1054	We're Building A Love/Charlie Cass	4
69	Fontana TF 1054	Charlie Cass/Linda	10
70	Philips 6006 035	Give Me Just A Little More Time/I'm In Love (withdrawn)	35
66	Fontana (S)TL 5351	WAYNE ONE (LP)	15
69	Fontana SFL 13144	WAYNE ONE (LP, reissue)	10

WAYNE FONTANA & MINDBENDERS

63	Fontana TF 404	Hello! Josephine/Road Runner	7
63	Fontana TF 418	For You, For You/Love Potion No.9	6
64	Fontana TF 436	Little Darlin'/Come Dance With Me	6
64	Fontana TF 451	Stop Look And Listen/Duke Of Earl	5
64	Fontana TF 497	Um, Um, Um, Um, Um/First Taste Of Love	4
65	Fontana TF 535	The Game Of Love/Since You've Been Gone	4
65	Fontana TF 579	It's Just A Little Bit Too Late/Long Time Comin'	6
65	Fontana TF 611	She Needs Love/Like I Did	4
64	Fontana TE 17421	ROAD RUNNER (EP)	25
64	Fontana TE 17435	UM, UM, UM, UM, UM (EP)	12
65	Fontana TE 17449	THE GAME OF LOVE (EP)	10
65	Fontana TE 17453	WALKING ON AIR (EP)	25
64	Fontana TL 5230	WAYNE FONTANA AND THE MINDBENDERS (LP)	30
65	Fontana TL 5257	ERIC, RICK, WAYNE, BOB — IT'S WAYNE FONTANA AND THE MINDBENDERS (LP)	30
67	Wing WL 1166	WAYNE FONTANA AND THE MINDBENDERS (LP, reissue)	18
69	Fontana SFL 13106	WAYNE FONTANA AND THE MINDBENDERS (LP, 2nd reissue)	12

(see also Mindbenders)

FONTANE SISTERS

54	London HL 8099	Happy Days And Lonely Nights/If I Didn't Have You	25
55	London HL 8113	Hearts Of Stone/Bless Your Heart	75
55	London HL 8113	Hearts Of Stone/Bless Your Heart (78)	8
55	London HL 8126	Rock Love/You're Mine	60
55	London HL 8126	Rock Love/You're Mine (78)	6
55	London HLD 8177	Seventeen/If I Could Be With You	60
55	London HLD 8177	Seventeen/If I Could Be With You (78)	6
55	London HLD 8211	Rolling Stone/Daddy-O	40
56	London HLD 8225	Adorable/Playmates	20
56	London HLD 8265	Eddie My Love/Yum Yum	30
56	London HLD 8265	Eddie My Love/Yum Yum (78)	6
56	London HL 7009	Eddie My Love/Yum Yum (export issue)	10
56	London HLD 8289	I'm In Love Again/You Always Hurt The One You Love	22
56	London HLD 8318	Voices (with narration by Pat Boone)/Willow Weep For Me	18

MINT VALUE £

56	London HLD 8343	Silver Bells/Nuttin' For Christmas	15
56	London HLD 8343	Silver Bells/Nuttin' For Christmas (78)	5
57	London HLD 8378	The Banana Boat Song/Lonesome Lover Blues	18
57	London HLD 8415	Please Don't Leave Me/Still	15
57	London HLD 8415	Please Don't Leave Me/Still (78)	5
57	London HLD 8488	Fool Around/Which Way To Your Heart	12
58	London HLD 8621	Chanson D'Amour (Song Of Love)/Cocoanut Grove	8
59	London HLD 8861	Billy Boy/Encore D'Amour	8
60	London HLD 9037	Listen To Your Heart/Please Be Kind	6
60	London HLD 9078	Theme From "A Summer Place"/Darling, It's Wonderful	5
55	London RE-D 1029	FONTANE SISTERS No. 1 (EP)	25
55	London RE-D 1037	FONTANE SISTERS No. 2 (EP)	25
57	London HA-D 2053	THE FONTANE'S SING (LP)	35

(see also Pat Boone, Perry Como)

SAM FONTEYN
| 66 | Parlophone R 5519 | Lost In Space/BERNARD SHARPE: Jorrocks | 4 |

BILLY FONTEYNE
| 63 | Oriole CB 1917 | Little Child/Look Before You Leap | 5 |

FOOL
| 69 | Mercury SMCL 20138 | THE FOOL (LP) | 25 |

FOOLS DANCE
87	L. T. T. Slaughter LTS 22	They'll Never Know/Empty Hours (p/s)	12
87	L. T. T. Slaughter LTS 22T	They'll Never Know/The Collector/Empty Hours/The Ring (12", p/s)	18
85	Top Hole Turn TURN 19	FOOLS DANCE (mini-LP)	20
86	Top Hat TH 22	FOOLS DANCE (mini-LP, reissue)	15
86	L. T. T. Slaughter LTS 18	FOOLS DANCE (mini-LP, 2nd reissue)	12

(see also Cure, Stranglers)

CHUCK FOOTE
| 62 | London HLU 9495 | You're Running Out Of Kisses/Come On Back | 6 |

FOOT IN COLD WATER
| 74 | Elektra K 52011 | FOOT IN COLD WATER (LP) | 10 |

FORBES
| 77 | Power Exchange PX 253 | The Beatles/Sweet Kiss Of Fire | 7 |

BILL FORBES
58	Columbia DB 4232	My Cherie/God's Little Acre	5
58	Columbia DB 4232	My Cherie/God's Little Acre (78)	5
59	Columbia DB 4269	Once More/Believe In Me	8
59	Columbia DB 4386	Too Young/It's Not The End Of The World	4
61	Columbia DB 4566	You're Sixteen, You're Beautiful/Backward Child	6
61	Columbia DB 4619	That's It, I Quit, I'm Moving On/Big City Boy	4
61	Columbia DB 4747	Goodbye Cruel World/Next Time	4
62	Columbia DB 4855	Laughter Or Tears/Like A Good Girl Should	4
62	Columbia DB 4945	Poker Face/Marianne	4

(see also Contrasts)

FORCE FIVE
64	United Artists UP 1051	Don't Make My Baby Blue/Shaking Postman	10
65	United Artists UP 1089	Yeah, I'm Waiting/I Don't Want To See You Again	15
65	United Artists UP 1102	Baby Don't Care/Come Down To Earth	25
65	United Artists UP 1118	I Want You Babe/Gee Too Tiger	20
66	United Artists UP 1141	Don't Know Which Way To Turn/Baby Let Your Hair Down	20

FORCE WEST
65	Decca F 12223	I Can't Give What I Haven't Got/Why Won't She Stay	8
66	Columbia DB 7908	Gotta Find Another Baby/Talkin' About Our Love	10
66	Columbia DB 7963	When The Sun Comes Out (Weatherman)/Gotta Tell Somebody	8
67	Columbia DB 8174	All The Children Sleep/Desolation	10
68	CBS 3632	I'll Walk In The Rain/What's It To Be	6
68	CBS 3798	I'll Be Moving On/Like The Tide Like The Ocean	6
69	CBS 4385	Sherry/Mister Blue	8

CLINTON FORD
58	Oriole CB 1425	Sweet Sixteen/Eleven More Months And Ten More Days	5
58	Oriole CB 1425	Sweet Sixteen/Eleven More Months And Ten More Days (78)	5
58	Oriole CB 1427	Jesus Remembered Me/In The Sweet Bye And Bye (78, with Hallelujah Skiffle Group)	5
59	Oriole CB 1483	I Cried A Tear/(You Were Only) Teasin'	5
59	Oriole CB 1483	I Cried A Tear/(You Were Only) Teasin' (78)	5
59	Oriole CB 1500	Old Shep/Nellie Dean Rock	6
59	Oriole CB 1500	Old Shep/Nellie Dean Rock (78)	5
59	Oriole CB 1516	Lovesick Blues/Give A Little, Take A Little	4
59	Oriole CB 1518	Silver Threads Among The Gold/Red Indian Christmas Carol	4
61	Oriole CB 1551	Mustapha/Two Brothers	4
61	Oriole CB 1612	Oh By Jingo/Get Out And Get Under	4
61	Oriole CB 1623	Too Many Beautiful Girls/Everybody's Doing It	4
62	Oriole CB 1706	Fanlight Fanny/Dreamy City Lullaby	4
62	Oriole CB 1747	Under The Bamboo Tree/Who's Next In Line	4
62	Oriole CB 1768	Opening Night In Loveland/Madam Moscovitch	4
63	Oriole CB 1798	Popsy Wopsy/You Can Tell Her Anything	4
63	Oriole CB 1884	Rainbow/On Mother Kelly's Doorstep	4
60s	Columbia	45s	3
66	Piccadilly 7N 35343	Dandy/Why Don't Women Like Me	4
60s	Piccadilly, Pye	other 45s	3
67	Piccadilly NEP 34057	DANDY (EP)	8

MINT VALUE £

63	Columbia 33SX 1560	THE MELODY MAN (LP, also stereo SCX 3496)	10/12
64	Realm RM 147	BY JINGO (LP)	10
67	Pye NPL 18210	CLINTON THE CLOWN (LP)	10
67	Piccadilly N(S)PL 38028	DANDY (LP)	10
67	Piccadilly N(S)PL 38034	BIG WILLY BROKE JAIL TONIGHT (LP)	10

(see also Hallelujah Skiffle Group)

DEAN FORD & GAYLORDS
64	Columbia DB 7264	Twenty Miles/What's The Matter With Me?	12
64	Columbia DB 7402	Mr Heartbreak's Here Instead/I Won't	12
65	Columbia DB 7610	The Name Game/That Lonely Feeling	12

(see also Gaylords, Marmalade)

DEE DEE FORD
| 60 | London HLU 8355 | Good-Morning Blues/I Just Can't Believe | 30 |
| 60 | London HLU 8355 | Good-Morning Blues/I Just Can't Believe (78) | 8 |

EDDIE FORD
| 73 | Duke Reid DR 2523 | Guess I This Riddle/Riddle Version | 5 |

EMILE FORD (& CHECKMATES)
59	Pye 7N 15225	What Do You Want To Make Those Eyes At Me For/Don't Tell Me Your Troubles	5
59	Pye N 15225	What Do You Want To Make Those Eyes At Me For/Don't Tell Me Your Troubles (78)	8
60	Pye 7N 15245	On A Slow Boat To China/That Lucky Old Sun	5
60	Pye N 15245	On A Slow Boat To China/That Lucky Old Sun (78)	8
60	Pye 7N 15268	You'll Never Know What You're Missin' 'Til You Try/Still	5
60	Pye 7N 15279	Red Sails In The Sunset/Afraid	5
60	Pye 7N 15282	Question/Them There Eyes (solo)	4
60	Pye 7N 15314	Counting Teardrops/White Christmas	4
61	Pye 7N 15331	A Kiss To Build A Dream On/What Am I Gonna Do	4
61	Piccadilly 7N 35003	Half Of My Heart/Gypsy Love (solo)	4
61	Piccadilly 7N 35007	Hush, Somebody's Calling My Name/After You've Gone	4
61	Piccadilly 7N 35019	The Alphabet Song/Keep A Lovin' Me (solo)	4
62	Piccadilly 7N 35033	I Wonder Who's Kissing Her Now/Doin' The Twist (solo)	4
62	Piccadilly 7N 35078	Your Nose Is Gonna Grow/Rains Come	4
63	Piccadilly 7N 35116	Doin' What You Do To Me/Hold Me Thrill Me Kiss Me	4
69	Decca F 12959	Set Me Free/Don't Remind Me (export issue)	10
59	Pye NEP 24119	EMILE (EP)	8
60	Pye NEP 24124	EMILE FORD HIT PARADE (EP)	10
60	Pye NEP 24133	EMILE FORD HIT PARADE VOL. 2 (EP)	10
59	Pye NPL 18049	NEW TRACKS WITH EMILE (LP)	15
61	Piccadilly NPL 38001	EMILE (LP)	20
60s	Golden Guinea	UNDER THE MIDNIGHT SUN (LP)	10

FRANKIE FORD
59	London HL 8850	Sea Cruise/Roberta (with Huey 'Piano' Smith & Clowns)	40
59	London HL 8850	Sea Cruise/Roberta (with Huey 'Piano' Smith & Clowns) (78)	25
59	Top Rank JAR 186	Alimony/Can't Tell My Heart (What To Do) (with Huey 'Piano' Smith & Clowns)	10
59	Top Rank JAR 186	Alimony/Can't Tell My Heart (What To Do) (with Huey 'Piano' Smith & Clowns) (78)	30
60	Top Rank JAR 282	Cheatin' Woman/HUEY 'PIANO' SMITH & CLOWNS: Don't You Just Know Kokomo	20
60	Top Rank JAR 299	Time After Time/I Want To Be Your Man	8
60	London HLP 9222	You Talk Too Much/If You've Got Troubles	20
65	Sue WI 366	Sea Cruise/Roberta (reissue)	10
65	Sue WI 369	What's Going On/Watchdog	20
78	Chiswick NS 38	Sea Cruise/Alimony (p/s)	4

(see also Huey 'Piano' Smith)

JON FORD
68	Philips BF 1690	Two's Company Three's A Crowd/Place In Your Heart	6
69	Philips BF 1791	I Know It's Love/Look Before You Leap	4
69	Philips BF 1817	Ice Cream Man/This Was The Time	4
70	Philips 6006 030	You've Got Me Where You Want Me/You're All Alone Tonight	50

PERRY FORD (& SAPPHIRES)
59	Parlophone R 4573	Bye, Baby, Goodbye/She Came As A Stranger	5
60	Parlophone R 4633	Crazy Over You/Garden Of Happiness	5
60	Parlophone R 4683	Don't Weep (Little Lady)/Little Grown-Up	4
62	Decca F 11497	Baby, Baby (Don't You Worry)/Prince Of Fools (with Sapphires & Blue Flames)	6

RICKY FORD (& TENNESSEANS)
| 63 | Parlophone R 5018 | Cheat Cheat/Sweet And Tender Romance | 4 |
| 64 | Parlophone R 5230 | You Are My Love/Long Way From Home (with Tennesseans) | 4 |

'TENNESSEE' ERNIE FORD
49	Capitol CL 13211	Smokey Mountain Boogie/Country Junction (78)	7
50	Capitol CL 13237	Mule Train/Milk 'Em In The Morning Blues (78)	5
50	Capitol CL 13271	The Cry Of The Wild Goose/Anticipation Blues (78)	5
51	Capitol CL 13447	The Shot Gun Boogie/My Hobby (78)	7
51	Capitol CL 13599	Leetle Juan Pedro (with Eddie Kirk)/Feed 'Em In The Mornin' Blues (78)	5
51	Capitol CL 13604	Kissin' Bug Boogie/Woman Is A Five Letter Word (78)	5
52	Capitol CL 13682	Rock City Boogie/Streamlined Cannon Ball (78, with Dinning Sisters)	5
52	Capitol CL 13797	Blackberry Boogie/Tennessee Local (78)	5
53	Capitol CL 14006	Catfish Boogie/Kiss Me Big (78)	5
54	Capitol CL 14006	Catfish Boogie/Kiss Me Big	25
54	Capitol CL 14005	Give Me Your Word/River Of No Return	15
55	Capitol CL 14261	His Hands/I Am A Pilgrim	10
55	Capitol CL 14273	Losing You/There Is Beauty In Everything	10
56	Capitol CL 14500	Sixteen Tons/You Don't Have To Be A Baby To Cry	12

MINT VALUE £

56	Capitol CL 14506	The Ballad Of Davy Crockett/Farewell	12
56	Capitol CL 14557	That's All/Bright Lights And Blonde-Haired Women	8
56	Capitol CL 14616	Who Will Shoe Your Pretty Little Foot/Gaily The Troubadour	6
56	Capitol CL 14657	First Born/Have You Seen Her?	5
57	Capitol CL 14691	The Watermelon Song/One Suit	5
57	Capitol CL 14734	The Lonely Man/False Hearted Girl	5
57	Capitol CL 14759	In The Middle Of An Island/Ivy League	6
58	Capitol CL 14846	Down Deep/Bless Your Pea Pickin' Heart	4
58	Capitol CL 14896	Love Makes The World Go 'Round/Sunday Barbecue	6
59	Capitol CL 14972	Glad Rags/Sleepin' At The Foot Of The Bed	4
59	Capitol CL 15010	Blackeyed Susie/Code Of The Mountains	6
59	Capitol CL 15100	Sunny Side Of Heaven/Love Is The Only Thing	4
60	Capitol CL 15148	Joshua Fit The Battle Of Jericho/O Mary, Don't You Weep	4
60	Capitol CL 15171	Little Klinker/Jingle-O-The-Brownie	4
61	Capitol CL 15190	Dark As A Dungeon/His Love	4
61	Capitol CL 15210	Little Red Rockin' Hood/I Gotta Have My Baby Back	10
65	Capitol CL 15403	Sixteen Tons/Hicktown	5
65	Capitol CL 15426	The Little Drummer Boy/Sing We Now Of Christmas	4
56	Capitol EAP 1014	SIXTEEN TONS (EP)	12
57	Capitol EAP 1-639	"TENNESSEE" ERNIE FORD (EP)	10
60	Capitol EAP1 1227	GATHER ROUND (EP)	12
61	Capitol EAP1 20067	ANTICIPATION BLUES (EP)	18
52	Capitol LC 6573	CAPITOL PRESENTS (10" LP)	35
56	Capitol LC 6825	THIS LUSTY LAND (10" LP)	20
58	Capitol T 888	OL' ROCKIN' ERN (LP)	30
60	Capitol T 1380	SIXTEEN TONS (LP)	25
61	Capitol (S)T 1473	COME TO THE FAIR (LP)	12

'TENNESSEE' ERNIE FORD & BETTY HUTTON
| 54 | Capitol CL 14133 | This Must Be The Place/The Honeymoon's Over | 12 |

EDDIE BUSTER FOREHAND
| 69 | Action ACT 4519 | Young Boy Blues/You Were Meant For Me | 10 |

FOREHEADS IN A FISH TANK
| 80s | Stuff FAB 4 | Happy Shopper/She Loves You Yeah (foldover p/s, withdrawn) | 6 |
| 80s | Stuff FAB 5 | I Want To Masturbate At Castle Donnington/Happy Shopper (foldover p/s with band) | 4 |

FOREIGNER
77	Atlantic K 10917	Feels Like The First Time/Woman On Woman	4
77	Atlantic K 10986	Cold As Ice/I Need You (p/s)	4
77	Atlantic K 10986	Cold As Ice/I Need You (clear vinyl, printed PVC sleeve)	5
78	Atlantic K 11167	Hot Blooded/Tramontaine (red vinyl, printed PVC sleeve)	4
79	Atlantic K 11236	Blue Morning, Blue Day (picture disc)	5
85	Atlantic A 9596	I Want To Know What Love Is/Street Thunder ('F'-shaped disc)	6
85	Atlantic A 9539/SAM 247	Cold As Ice/Reaction To Action//Head Games (live)/Hot Blooded (live) (double pack)	4
87	Atlantic A 9169B	Say You Will/Hot Blooded (live)/Night To Remember (sealed box set with patch poster & tour pass)	4

FORERUNNERS
| 64 | Solar SRP 100 | Bony Maronie/Pride | 5 |

FORERUNNERS
68	Key KL 001	THE FORERUNNERS (LP)	12
70	Key KL 004	RUNNING BACK (LP)	12
70	Key KL 008	GENUINE IMITATION LIFE (LP)	12

FOREST
69	Harvest HAR 5007	Searching For Shadows/Mirror Of Life	15
69	Harvest SHVL 760	FOREST (LP)	50
70	Harvest SHVL 784	FULL CIRCLE (LP)	75

FORRESTERS
65	Polydor BM 56038	Broken Hearted Clown/Lonely Boy	7
65	Polydor BM 56057	How Can I Tell Her/So Shy	7
66	Polydor BM 56104	Early Morning Hours/World Is Mine	7
66	Columbia DB 8040	Sometimes When You're Lonely/Today Or Tomorrow (as Forresters)	6
66	Columbia DB 8086	Mr Smith/Ship On The Sea	5
67	Columbia DB 8176	Comin' Home In The Evening/Sunshine's On Its Way	5

FOREST FIRE
| 76 | Target TGT 117 | I Will Return/Midnight Calling | 4 |

FOREVER AMBER
| 69 | Advance | THE LOVE CYCLE (LP, private pressing) | 1,000 |

FOREVER MORE
70	RCA SF 8016	YOURS FOREVER MORE (LP)	15
71	RCA LSP 3015	WORDS ON BLACK PLASTIC (LP)	15
	(see also Average White Band)		

FORK IN THE ROAD
| 70 | Ember EMB S 311 | I Can't Turn Around | 150 |

FORMAT
| 69 | CBS 4600 | Maxwell's Silver Hammer/Music Man | 5 |
| | (see also Fourmost) | | |

FORMATIONS
| 68 | MGM MGM 1399 | At The Top Of The Stairs/Magic Melody | 60 |
| 71 | Mojo 2027 001 | At The Top Of The Stairs/Magic Melody (reissue) | 5 |

George FORMBY

GEORGE FORMBY

MINT VALUE £

26	Edison Bell Winner 4409	John Wilie, Come On/I Was Always A Willing Young Lad (78)	15
26	Edison Bell Winner 4418	John Wilie's jazz Band/I Parted My Hair In The Middle (78)	15
26	Edison Bell Winner 4437	The Man Was A Stranger To Me/Rolling Around Piccadilly (78)	15
29	Dominion A 197	All Going Back/In The Congo (78)	15
32	Decca F 3259	John Willie At The Licence Office (Pts 1 & 2) (78)	6
33	Decca F 3615	With My Little Ukulele In My Hands/As The Hours And The Years Roll By (78, withdrawn, advance copies exist)	15
35	Regal Zonophone MR 1932	The Isle Of Man/Riding In The TT Races (78)	5
36	Regal Zonophone MR 2060	Galant Dick Turpin (Pts 1 & 2) (78)	10
36	Regal Zonophone MR 2162	Quick Fire Medley/Ring Your Little Bell (Ting Ting) (78)	5
41	Regal Zonophone MR 3482	Formby Favourites For The Forces (Pts 1& 2) (78)	6
41	Regal Zonophone MR 3550	The George Formby Crazy Record (Pts 1 & 2) (78)	6
42	Regal Zonophone MR 3599	Formby Film Favourites (Pts 1 & 2) (78)	5
43	Regal Zonophone MR 3694	Under The Blasted Oak/Oh, You Have No Idea (78, second pressing, matrix number; CAR 3686/4)	6
43	Regal Zono. MR 3705	British Isles Medley/American Medley (78)	6
45	Regal Zono. MR 3761	She's Got Two Of Everything/Up In The Air And Down In The Dumps (78)	5
60	Pye 7N 15269	Banjo Boy/Happy Go Lucky Me	4
55	Decca DFE 6144	GEORGE FORMBY AND HIS UKULELE GUITAR (EP)	7
56	Decca DFE 6328	GEORGE FORMBY AND HIS UKULELE GUITAR, No. 2 (EP)	7
56	Decca DFE 6355	GEORGE FORMBY AND HIS UKULELE GUITAR, No. 3 (EP)	7
61	Decca ACL 1062	GEORGE FORMBY SOUVENIR (LP)	10
63	Decca ACL 1145	TURNED OUT NICE AGAIN (LP)	10

(see also Jack Hylton, Tommy Farr)

FORMERLY FAT HARRY
71	Harvest SHSP 4016	FORMERLY FAT HARRY (LP)	15

FORMULA
65	HMV POP 1438	Close To Me/If Ever	5

FORMULA 1
65	Warner Bros WB 155	I Just Can't Go To Sleep/Sure Know A Lot About Love	15

ANDY FORRAY
68	Parlophone R 5715	Sarah Jane/Don't Care Anymore	6
68	Parlophone R 5729	The Proud One/Messin' Round With Me	6
68	Decca F 12733	Epitaph To You/Dream With Me	25
69	Fontana TF 999	Let The Sunshine In/Baby Is Coming	5

HELEN FORREST
56	Capitol CL 14594	Taking A Chance On Love/I Love You Much Too Much	4

JANE FORREST
56	Columbia SCM 5213	Sincerely Yours/A Girl Can't Say	4

THOMAS FORSTNER
89	Ariola 112 298	Song Of Love/Nur Ein Lied (p/s, withdrawn)	5
89	Ariola 662 298	Song Of Love (12" Version)/Nur Ein Lied/Song Of Love (7") (CD, withdrawn)	7

BRUCE FORSYTH
65	Pye 7N 15879	Hush Hush Sweet Charlotte/Don't Say Goodbye	4
68	Mercury MF 1047	Star/Do, Do, Do	4
69	Decca F 12940	When You Gotta Go/By The Fireside	4
68	Pye 7N 17460	I'm Backing Britain/There's Not Enough Love In The World	4
60	Parlophone GEP 8807	I'M IN CHARGE (EP)	7
60	Parlophone PMC 1132	MR ENTERTAINMENT (LP, also stereo PCS 3031)	10

FORTES MENTUM
68	Parlophone R 5684	Saga Of A Wrinkled Man/Mr. Partridge Passed Away Today	20
68	Parlophone R 5726	I Can't Go On Loving You/Humdiggle We Love You	8
69	Parlophone R 5768	Gotta Go/Marrakesh	8

FORTRAN 5
90	Mute MUTE 120R	Love Baby (Edit)/Midnight Trip (N29 Mix) (Edit) (no p/s)	4

LANCE FORTUNE
60	Pye 7N 15240	Be Mine/Action	7
60	Pye 7N 15260	This Love I Have For You/All On My Own	5
60	Pye 7N 15297	I Wonder/Will You Still Be My Girl?	4

FORTUNES
63	Decca F 11718	Summertime Summertime/I Love Her Still (as Fortunes & Cliftones) (some in p/s)	20/12
64	Decca F 11809	Caroline/If You Don't Want Me Now	15
64	Decca F 11912	I Like The Look Of You/Come On Girl	6
64	Decca F 11985	Look Homeward Angel/I'll Have My Tears To Remind Me	6
65	Decca F 12173	You've Got Your Troubles/I've Got To Go	4
65	Decca F 12243	Here It Comes Again/Things I Should Have Known	5
66	Decca F 12321	This Golden Ring/Someone To Care	5
66	Decca F 12429	You Gave Me Somebody To Love/Silent Street	5
66	Decca F 12485	Am I Losing My Touch/Is It Really Worth Your While?	5
67	Decca F 12612	Our Love Has Gone/Truly Yours	5
67	United Artists UP 1188	The Idol/His Smile Was A Lie	4
68	United Artists UP 2218	Loving Cup/Hour At The Movies	4
69	Decca F 12874	Here It Comes Again/Our Love Has Gone	4
70	United Artists UP 35054	Lifetime Of Love/Sad Sad Sad (withdrawn, any pressed?)	
70	United Artists UP 35054	Books And Films/Sad Sad Sad	4
65	Decca LK 4736	THE FORTUNES (LP)	16
72	Capitol ST 21891	THE FORTUNES (LP)	10

45's
79	Chopper CHEAP 5	Couldn't Believe A Word/Lonesome Lane (p/s)	7
79	Stiff BUY 52	Couldn't Believe A Word/Lonesome Lane (p/s, reissue)	4

48 CHAIRS
70	Absurd # 3	Snap It Around/Psycle Sluts (p/s)	4

49 AMERICANS
80	No Bad NB 4	THE HIT ALBUM (14-track EP)	6
80	Choo Choo Train CHUG 2	TOO YOUNG TO BE IDEAL (12" EP)	8
80	Choo Choo Train CHUG 1	EL PLURIBUS UNUM (LP)	12

FORUM
70	B&C CB 119	The River Is Wide/I Fall In Love Again	4

SHIRLEY FORWOOD
57	London HLD 8402	Two Hearts (With An Arrow Between)/Juke Box Lovers	12
57	London HLD 8402	Two Hearts (With An Arrow Between)/Juke Box Lovers (78)	5

JOHN FOSTER
66	Island ILP 939	JOHN FOSTER SINGS (LP)	25

VINCENT FOSTER
69	Escort ES 803	Shine Eye Gal/Who Nest (B-side actually "Who Next" by Carl Bryan)	4

FOTHERINGAY
70	Island WIP 6085	Peace In The End/Winter Winds	6
70	Island ILPS 9125	FOTHERINGAY (LP, pink label, gatefold sleeve)	15
	(see also Sandy Denny)		

MR FOUNDATION
(see under M)

FOUNDATIONS
67	Pye 7N 17366	Baby, Now That I've Found You/Come On Back To Me	4
68	Pye 7N 17417	Back On My Feet Again/I Can Take Or Leave Your Loving	4
68	Pye 7N 17503	Any Old Time (You're Lonely And Sad)/We Are Happy People	4
68	Pye 7N 17636	Build Me Up Buttercup/New Direction	4
69	Pye 7N 17702	In The Bad Bad Old Days/Give Me Love	4
69	Pye 7N 17809	Born To Live, Born To Die/Why Did You Cry	4
69	Pye 7N 17849	Baby I Couldn't See/Penny Sir	4
70	Pye 7N 17904	Take A Girl Like You/I'm Gonna Be A Rich Man	4
70	Pye 7N 17956	I'm Gonna Be A Rich Man/In The Beginning	4
71	MCA MCA 5075	Stoney Ground/I'll Give You Love	4
68	Pye NEP 24297	IT'S ALL RIGHT (EP)	7
67	Pye NPL 18206	FROM THE FOUNDATIONS (LP)	10
68	Pye NPL 18227	ROCKING THE FOUNDATIONS (LP)	10
69	Pye NPL 18290	DIGGING THE FOUNDATIONS (LP)	10

JAMES FOUNTAIN
76	Cream CRM 5002	Seven Day Lover/Malnutrition	6

PETE FOUNTAIN
60	Coral Q 72389	A Closer Walk/Do You Know What It Means To Miss New ...	4
60	Coral Q 72404	Columbus Stockade Blues/Sentimental Journey	4

FOUR
64	Decca F 11999	It's Alright/There's Nothing Like It	7

FOUR ACES (U.S.)
54	Brunswick 05256	The Gang That Sang "Heart Of My Heart"/Heaven Can Wait	7
54	Brunswick 05308	Three Coins In The Fountain/Wedding Bells (Are Breaking Up This Gang Of Mine)	15
54	Brunswick 05322	It Shall Come To Pass/Dream	6
54	Brunswick 05348	It's A Woman's World/The Cuckoo Bird In The Pickle Tree	8
54	Brunswick 05355	Mister Sandman/(I'll Be With You) In Apple Blossom Time	12
55	Brunswick 05379	Melody Of Love/There Is A Tavern In The Town	8
55	Brunswick 05401	There Goes My Heart/Take Me In Your Arms	6
55	Brunswick 05418	Stranger In Paradise/You'll Always Be The One	12
55	Brunswick 05429	Sluefoot/I'm In The Mood For Love	6
55	Brunswick 05480	Love Is A Many Splendored Thing/Shine On Harvest Moon	12
55	Brunswick 05504	Jingle Bells/The Christmas Song (Merry Christmas To You)	5
56	Brunswick 05562	To Love Again/Charlie Was A Boxer	6
56	Brunswick 05566	The Gal With The Yaller Shoes/Of This I'm Sure	6
56	Brunswick 05573	If You Can Dream/It's The Talk Of The Town	6
56	Brunswick 05589	A Woman In Love/I Only Know I Love You	8
56	Brunswick 05601	Dreamer/Let's Fall In Love	5
56	Brunswick 05613	You Can't Run Away From It/Written On The Wind	5
56	Brunswick 05623	Friendly Persuasion (Thee I Love)/Someone To Love	7
57	Brunswick 05651	Heart/What A Difference A Day Made	6
57	Brunswick 05663	Bahama Mama/You're Mine	6
57	Brunswick 05695	Three Sheets To The Wind/Yes, Sir, That's My Baby	5
57	Brunswick 05712	Half Of My Heart/When My Sugar Walks Down The Street	5
58	Brunswick 05743	Rock And Roll Rhapsody/I Wish I May, I Wish I Might	6
58	Brunswick 05743	Rock And Roll Rhapsody/I Wish I May, I Wish I Might (78)	5
58	Brunswick 05758	Hangin' Up A Horseshoe/Two Arms, Two Lips, One Heart!	6
58	Brunswick 05767	The World Outside/The Christmas Tree	
59	Brunswick 05773	The World Outside/The Inn Of The Sixth Happiness	5
59	Brunswick 05812	Waltzin' Matilda/Roses Of Rio	4
50s	Decca A 73010	I'm Yours/I Understand (export issue)	10
54	Brunswick OE 9090	PRESENTING THE FOUR ACES (EP)	10
55	Brunswick OE 9157	MOOD FOR LOVE VOL. 1 (EP)	7

FOUR ACES (U.S.)

55	Brunswick OE 9192	MOOD FOR LOVE VOL. 2 (EP)	7
57	Brunswick OE 9324	ACES SING FILM TITLES (EP)	8
59	Brunswick OE 9458	THE FOUR ACES (EP)	7
53	Brunswick LA 8614	JUST SQUEEZE ME (10" LP)	20
57	Brunswick LAT 8221	SHUFFLIN' ALONG (LP)	15
58	Brunswick LAT 8249	HITS FROM HOLLYWOOD (LP)	15
59	Brunswick STA 3014	THE SWINGIN' ACES (LP, stereo)	18

(see also Al Alberts)

FOUR ACES (Jamaica)

65	Island WI 178	Hoochy Koochy Kai Po/River Bank Cobberly Again	10
65	Island WI 179	Sweet Chariot/Peace And Love	10

(see also Desmond Dekker)

4 BE 2's

79	Island WIP 6530	One Of The Lads/Ummbaba (p/s)	4
79	Island 12 WIP 6530	One Of The Lads (Dub)/Ummbaba/One Of The Lads (Vocal) (12", p/s)	7
80	WEA K 18290	Frustration/I Can't Explain (p/s)	4

FOUR COINS

58	Fontana H 168	The World Outside/Be Still My Heart	7

FOUR DOLLS

57	Capitol CL 14778	Three On A Date/Proud Of You	4
58	Capitol CL 14845	Whoop-A-Lala/I'm Following You	4

FOUR ESCORTS

54	HMV 7M 277	Loop De Loop Mambo/Love Me	5
54	HMV B 10795	Loop De Loop Mambo/Love Me (78)	10

FOUR ESQUIRES

55	London HL 8152	The Sphinx Won't Tell/Three Things (A Man Must Do)	30
55	London HL 8152	The Sphinx Won't Tell/Three Things (A Man Must Do) (78)	5
56	London HLA 8224	Adorable/Thunderbolt	25
56	London HLA 8224	Adorable/Thunderbolt (78)	5
57	London HL 8376	Look Homeward Angel/Santo Domingo (unreleased)	
57	London HL 8376	Look Homeward Angel/Santo Domingo (unreleased) (78)	
58	London HLO 8533	Love Me Forever/I Ain't Been Right Since You Left	12
58	London HLO 8533	Love Me Forever/I Ain't Been Right Since You Left (78)	5
58	London HLO 8579	Always And Forever/I Walk Down The Street	8
58	London HLO 8579	Always And Forever/I Walk Down The Street (78)	5
58	London HL 8746	Hideaway/Repeat After Me	6
58	London HL 8746	Hideaway/Repeat After Me (78)	5
59	Pye Intl. 7N 25012	Non E Cosi/Land Of You And Me	5
59	Pye Intl. 7N 25027	Act Your Age/So Ends The Night	6
60	Pye Intl. 7N 25049	Wouldn't It Be Wonderful/Wonderful One	6

FOUR FRESHMEN

54	Capitol CL 14196	Love Turns Winter To Spring/Mood Indigo	5
55	Capitol CL 14338	Day By Day/How Can I Tell Her	5
56	Capitol CL 14580	Love Is Just Around The Corner/Angel Eyes	4
56	Capitol CL 14610	Graduation Day/Lonely Night In Paris	4
56	Capitol CL 14633	You're So Far Above Me/He Who Loves And Runs Away	4
54	Capitol LC 6685	VOICES IN MODERN (10" LP)	10

FOUR GEES

67	President PT 160	Ethiopia/Rough Rider	4

FOUR GIBSON GIRLS

58	Oriole CB 1447	No School Tomorrow/June, July And August	8
58	Oriole CB 1447	No School Tomorrow/June, July And August (78)	5
58	Oriole CB 1453	Safety Sue/Safety Sue (B-side by different artist)	6

FOUR GUYS

55	Vogue Coral Q 72054	Half Hearted Kisses/Mine	10

(see also Modernaires)

400 BLOWS

82	Concrete Prods. CPROD 2	Beat The Devil/The Beat Continues (foldout p/s with insert)	7

(see also Concrete)

FOUR INSTANTS

66	Society	DISCOTHEQUE (LP)	15

FOUR JACKS

58	Decca F 10984	Hey! Baby/The Prayer Of Love	7
58	Decca DFE 6460	HEY BABY (EP)	18

FOUR JACKS & A JILL

68	RCA Victor RCA 1669	Master Jack/I Looked Back	4

FOUR JONES BOYS

55	Decca F 10568	A Real Romance/When I Let You Go	5
55	Decca F 10671	Moments To Remember/Sing-ing-ing-ing	5
56	Decca F 10717	Tutti Frutti/Are You Satisfied?	10
56	Decca F 10789	Happiness Street (Corner Of Sunshine Square)/Someone To Love	5
56	Decca F 10829	Priscilla/It Isn't Right	5

(see also Jones Boys, Annette Klooger)

FOUR JUST MEN

64	Parlophone R 5186	That's My Baby/Things Will Never Be The Same	50

(see also Just Four Men, Wimple Winch)

FOUR KENTS

68	RCA RCA 1705	The Moving Finger Writes/Searchin'	7

FOUR KESTRELS
| 61 | Decca F 11333 | Sound Off/Can't Say I Do | 4 |

FOUR KINSMEN
| 67 | Decca F 22671 | It Looks Like The Daybreak/Forget About Him | 7 |

(see also Kinsmen)

FOUR KNIGHTS
54	Capitol CL 14076	I Get So Lonely/Till Then	15
54	Capitol CL 14154	Easy Street/In The Chapel In The Moonlight	12
54	Capitol CL 14204	I Don't Wanna See You Cryin'/Saw Your Eyes	10
55	Capitol CL 14244	Honey Bunch/Write Me, Baby	25
55	Capitol CL 14244	Honey Bunch/Write Me, Baby (78)	10
55	Capitol CL 14290	Inside Out/Foolishly Yours	8
56	Capitol CL 14516	Guilty/You	7
59	Coral Q 72355	Foolish Tears/O' Falling Star	7
55	Capitol EAP1 506	THE FOUR KNIGHTS (EP)	15
53	Capitol LC 6604	SPOTLIGHT SONGS (10" LP)	25

(see also Nat 'King' Cole)

FOUR LADS
57	Philips JK 1021	Golly/I Just Don't Know (jukebox issue)	8
58	Philips PB 839	Enchanted Island/Guess What The Neighbours'll Say	4
59	Philips PB 894	The Girl On Page 44/The Mocking Bird	4
60	Philips PB 1000	Standing On The Corner/Sunday	6
60	Philips PB 1020	Goona Goona/You're Nobody 'Til Somebody Loves You	4
55	Philips BBE 12044	MOMENTS TO REMEMBER (EP)	10
61	London RE-R 1289	FOUR LADS FOUR HITS (EP)	8
62	London HA-R 2413	DIXIELAND DOIN'S (LP, also stereo SAH-R 6213)	10/12

(see also Johnnie Ray, Frankie Laine, Doris Day)

FOUR LEAVED CLOVER
| 65 | Oak RGJ 207 | Alright Girl/Why | 175 |

FOUR MATADORS
| 66 | Columbia DB 7806 | A Man's Gotta Stand Tall/Fast Cars And Money | 40 |

FOURMOST
63	Parlophone R 5056	Hello Little Girl/Just In Case	4
63	Parlophone R 5078	I'm In Love/Respectable	4
64	Parlophone R 5128	A Little Loving/Waitin' For You	4
64	Parlophone R 5157	How Can I Tell Her/You Got That Way	5
64	Parlophone R 5194	Baby I Need Your Loving/That's Only What They Say	5
65	Parlophone R 5304	Everything In The Garden/He Could Never	6
65	Parlophone R 5379	Girls Girls Girls/Why Do Fools Fall In Love	5
66	Parlophone R 5491	Here, There And Everywhere/You've Changed	8
66	Parlophone R 5528	Auntie Maggie's Remedy/Turn The Lights Down	10
68	CBS 3814	Apples, Peaches, Pumpkin Pie/He Could Never	12
69	CBS 4041	Rosetta/Just Like Before	15
69	CBS 4461	Easy Squeezy/Do I Love You	12
64	Parlophone GEP 8892	THE SOUND OF THE FOURMOST (EP)	40
64	Parlophone GEP 8917	THE FOURMOST (EP)	40
65	Parlophone PMC 1259	FIRST AND FOURMOST (LP)	70

(see also Format)

FOURMYULA
| 69 | Columbia DB 8549 | Honey Chile/Come With Me | 6 |

FOUR PALMS
| 58 | Vogue V 9116 | Jeanie, Joanie, Shirley, Toni/Consideration | 150 |
| 58 | Vogue V 9116 | Jeanie, Joanie, Shirley, Toni/Consideration (78) | 35 |

FOUR PENNIES (U.S.)
| 63 | Stateside SS 198 | My Block/Dry Your Eyes | 12 |
| 63 | Stateside SS 244 | When The Boy's Happy (The Girl's Happy Too)/Hockaday Pt 1 | 10 |

(see also Chiffons)

FOUR PENNIES (U.K.)
63	Philips BF 1296	Do You Want Me To/Miss Bad Daddy	6
64	Philips BF 1322	Tell Me Girl/Juliet	4
64	Philips BF 1322	Juliet/Tell Me Girl (supposedly flipped after original release)	6
64	Philips BF 1349	I Found Out The Hard Way/Don't Tell Me You Love Me	4
64	Philips BF 1366	Black Girl/You Went Away	4
65	Philips BF 1398	The Way Of Love/A Place Where No-One Goes	5
65	Philips BF 1435	Until It's Time For You To Go/Till Another Day	4
66	Philips BF 1469	Trouble Is My Middle Name/Way Out Love	5
66	Philips BF 1491	Keep The Freeway Open/Square Peg	6
66	Philips BF 1519	No Sad Songs For Me/Cats	7
64	Philips BBE 12561	THE FOUR PENNIES (EP)	8
64	Philips BBE 12562	SPIN WITH THE PENNIES (EP)	10
64	Philips BBE 12570	THE SWINGING SIDE OF THE FOUR PENNIES (EP)	12
64	Philips BBE 12571	THE SMOOTH SIDE OF THE FOUR PENNIES (EP)	7
64	Philips BL 7642	TWO SIDES OF THE FOUR PENNIES (LP)	25
66	Philips BL 7734	MIXED BAG (LP)	80
67	Wing WL 1146	JULIET (LP)	18

FOUR PERFECTIONS
| 76 | Cream CRM 5006 | I'm Not Strong Enough/I'm Not Strong Enough (Instrumental) | 7 |
| 79 | Inferno HEAT 11 | I'm Not Strong Enough/I'm Not Strong Enough (Instrumental) (p/s, reissue) | 4 |

FOUR PLUGS
| 80s | Disposal THROWAWAY 1 | Wrong Treatment/Biking Girl | 4 |

FOUR + ONE

65	Parlophone R 5221	Time Is On My Side/Don't Lie To Me	40

(see also In Crowd, Tomorrow, Keith West)

FOUR PREPS

57	Capitol CL 14727	Falling Star/Where Wuz You	4
57	Capitol CL 14747	I Cried A Million Tears/Moonstruck In Madrid	4
57	Capitol CL 14768	Again 'n' Again 'n' Again/Promise Me Baby	4
57	Capitol CL 14783	Band Of Angels/How About That?	4
58	Capitol CL 14815	26 Miles (Santa Catalina)/Fools Will Be Fools	6
58	Capitol CL 14873	Big Man/Stop, Baby	5
58	Capitol CL 14914	Lazy Summer Night/Summertime Lies	4
59	Capitol CL 14992	The Riddle Of Love/She Was Five And He Was Ten	4
59	Capitol CL 15032	Cinderella/Gidget	4
59	Capitol CL 15044	The Big Surprise/Try My Arms	4
59	Capitol CL 15065	I Ain't Never/Memories, Memories	4
60	Capitol CL 15110	Listen Honey (I'll Be Home)/Down By The Station	5
60	Capitol CL 15128	Got A Girl/(Wait Till You) Hear It From Me	5
61	Capitol CL 15182	Calcutta/Gone Are The Days	5
61	Capitol CL 15217	More Money For You And Me (Medley) Pts 1 & 2	5
57	Capitol EAP1 862	DREAMY EYES (EP)	7
58	Capitol EAP1 1015	TWENTY SIX MILES (EP)	7
59	Capitol EAP1 1064	BIG MAN (EP)	7
59	Capitol EAP1 1139	LAZY SUMMER NIGHTS (EP)	7
61	Capitol EAP4 1647	CAMPUS ENCORES (EP)	7
59	Capitol T 1216	DANCING AND DREAMING (LP)	10
61	Capitol T 1291	DOWN BY THE STATION (LP)	10
61	Capitol T 1566	ON THE CAMPUS (LP)	10
61	Capitol (S)T 1647	CAMPUS ENCORE (LP)	10
62	Capitol (S)T 1814	CAMPUS CONFIDENTIAL (LP)	10
63	Capitol (S)T 1976	SONGS FOR A CAMPUS PARTY (LP)	10
64	Capitol (S)T 2169	HOW TO SUCCEED IN LOVE (LP)	10

4 SAXOPHONES IN 12 TONES

56	Vogue V 2355	Frantastic/Frankly Speaking	4

FOUR SEASONS

62	Stateside SS 122	Sherry/I've Cried Before	6
63	Stateside SS 145	Big Girls Don't Cry/Connie-O	5
63	Stateside SS 169	Walk Like A Man/Lucky Ladybug	5
63	Stateside SS 194	Ain't That A Shame/Soon (I'll Be Home Again)	5
63	Stateside SS 216	Candy Girl/Marlena	8
63	Stateside SS 241	Santa Claus Is Coming To Town/Christmas Tears	8
64	Stateside SS 262	Peanuts/Silhouettes	8
64	Philips BF 1317	Dawn (Go Away)/No Surfin' Today	5
64	Philips BF 1334	Ronnie/Born To Wander	5
64	Stateside SS 315	Alone/Long Lonely Nights	8
64	Philips BF 1347	Rag Doll/Silence Is Golden	5
64	Stateside SS 343	Since I Don't Have You/Sincerely	8
65	Philips BF 1364	Save It For Me/Funny Face	4
65	Philips BF 1372	Big Man In Town/Little Angel	4
65	Philips BF 1395	Bye Bye Baby (Baby Goodbye)/Searching Wind	4
65	Philips BF 1411	Toy Soldier/Betrayed	5
65	Philips BF 1420	Girl Come Running/Cry Myself To Sleep	4
65	Philips BF 1439	Let's Hang On!/On Broadway Tonight	4
66	Philips BF 1474	Working My Way Back To You/Too Many Memories	4
66	Philips BF 1493	Opus 17 (Don't Worry 'Bout Me)/Beggar's Parade	5
66	Philips BF 1511	I've Got You Under My Skin/Huggin' My Pillow	4
67	Philips BF 1538	Tell It To The Rain/Show Girl	5
67	Philips BF 1556	Beggin'/Dody	5
67	Philips BF 1584	C'mon Marianne/Let's Ride Again	5
67	Philips BF 1600	Around And Around/WONDER WHO: Lonesome Road	5
67	Philips BF 1621	Watch The Flowers Grow/Raven	6
68	Philips BF 1651	Will You Love Me Tomorrow?/Silhouettes	5
68	Philips BF 1685	Saturday's Father/Goodbye Girl	5
69	Philips BF 1743	Electric Stories/Pity	10
69	Philips BF 1763	Rag Doll/Working My Way Back To You (p/s)	5
71	Philips 6051 018	Rag Doll/Let's Hang On/I've Got You Under My Skin (maxi single)	4
71	Warner Bros K 16107	Whatever You Say/Sleeping Man (withdrawn, 300 only)	20
64	Stateside SE 1011	THE FOUR SEASONS SING (EP)	20
68	Philips MCP 1000	HITS OF THE FOUR SEASONS (cassette EP in plastic tray, cardboard sleeve)	10
63	Stateside SL 10033	SHERRY AND 11 OTHERS (LP)	20
63	Stateside SL 10042	AIN'T THAT A SHAME (LP)	20
63	Stateside SL 10051	THE FOUR SEASONS' GREETINGS (LP)	20
64	Philips BL 7611	BORN TO WANDER (LP)	14
64	Philips BL 7621	DAWN AND 11 OTHER GREAT SONGS (LP)	12
64	Philips BL 7643	RAG DOLL (LP)	12
65	Philips BL 7663	ENTERTAIN YOU (LP)	12
65	Philips (S)BL 7687	SING BIG HITS BY BACHARACH, DAVID AND DYLAN (LP)	12
65	Philips BL 7699	WORKING MY WAY BACK TO YOU (LP)	12
66	Philips (S)BL 7719	GOLD VAULT OF HITS (LP)	12
67	Philips (S)BL 7751	SECOND VAULT OF GOLDEN HITS (LP)	12
67	Philips (S)BL 7752	LOOKIN' BACK (LP)	15
67	Philips (S)BL 7753	CHRISTMAS ALBUM (LP)	15
69	Philips SBL 7880	GENUINE IMITATION LIFE GAZETTE (LP)	10
69	Philips (S)DBL 003	EDIZIONE D'ORO (GOLD EDITION) (2-LP)	14

(see also Frankie Valli, Wonder Who)

FOUR SENSATIONS
52	London L 1137	Heaven Knows Why/Believing In You (78)	6

FOUR SIGHTS
64	Columbia DB 7227	But I Can Tell/And I Cry	4

4 SKINS
81	Clockwork Fun CF 101	One Law For Them/Brave New World (p/s)	8
81	Secret SHH 125	Yesterday's Heroes/Justice/Get Out Of My Life (p/s)	6
82	Secret SHH 141	Low Life/Bread Or Blood (p/s)	6
82	Secret SEC 4	THE GOOD, THE BAD AND THE 4 SKINS (LP)	10
83	Syndicate SYN 1	A FISTFUL OF ... 4 SKINS (LP)	10
84	Syndicate SYN LP 5	FROM CHAOS TO 1984 (LP)	10

(see also Plastic Gangsters)

FOUR SPICES
57	MGM MGM 944	Armen's Theme (Yesterday And You)/Fire Engine Boogie	25

FOUR SQUARES
60s	Hollick & Taylor HT 1009	FOUR SQUARES (EP)	12

FOURTEEN (14)
68	Olga OLE 002	Through My Door/Meet Mr. Edgar	8
68	Olga OLE 006	Umbrella/Drizzle (Rain)	8
68	Olga S 051	Easy To Fool/Frosty Stars On A Window Pane	8

14 ICED BEARS
86	Frank COPPOLA 1	Inside/Bluesuit/Cut (paper hand-printed sleeve)	15
87	Frank CAPRA 202	Like A Dolphin/Balloon Song/Train Song/Lie To Choose (12", p/s)	10
87	Penetration	Balloon Song (flexidisc)	10
87	Penetration 001	Lie To Choose/SPLENDOUR IN THE GRASS: Twist Me (flexidisc)	6
88	Sarah SARAH 005	Come Get Me/Unhappy Days/Sure To See (poster p/s)	12
89	Thunderball 7TBL 2	Mother Sleep (7", unreleased, Mayking test pressings only)	25
80s	own label	FALLING BACKWARDS (EP, mail-order only)	7
90s	Thunderball Surfacer 002	Falling Backwards/World I Love/CROCODILE RIDE: Ex-Hipster/Satellite (Speed Mix) (1,000 only, numbered & stickered mailer)	8

FOUR TONES
58	Decca F 11074	Voom Ba Voom/Rickshaw Boy	7

FOUR TOPHATTERS
55	London HLA 8163	Leave-a My Gal Alone/Go Baby Go	125
55	London HLA 8163	Leave-a My Gal Alone/Go Baby Go (78)	20
55	London HLA 8198	Forty Five Men In A Telephone Booth/Wild Rosie	125
55	London HLA 8198	Forty Five Men In A Telephone Booth/Wild Rosie (78)	18

FOUR TOPS
64	Stateside SS 336	Baby I Need Your Lovin'/Call On Me	25
65	Stateside SS 371	Without The One You Love (Life's Not Worth While)/Love Has Gone	30
65	Tamla Motown TMG 507	Ask The Lonely/Where Did You Go?	30
65	Tamla Motown TMG 515	I Can't Help Myself (Sugar Pie, Honey Bunch)/Sad Souvenirs	12
65	Tamla Motown TMG 528	It's The Same Old Song/Your Love Is Amazing	12
65	Tamla Motown TMG 542	Something About You/Darling I Hum Our Song	15
66	Tamla Motown TMG 553	Shake Me, Wake Me (When It's Over)/Just As Long As You Need Me	20
66	Tamla Motown TMG 568	Loving You Is Sweeter Than Ever/I Like Everything About You	6
66	Tamla Motown TMG 579	Reach Out, I'll Be There/Until You Love Someone	4
67	Tamla Motown TMG 589	Standing In The Shadows Of Love/Since You've Been Gone	5
67	Tamla Motown TMG 601	Bernadette/I Got A Feeling	4
67	Tamla Motown TMG 612	Seven Rooms Of Gloom/I'll Turn To Stone	10
67	Tamla Motown TMG 623	You Keep Running Away/If You Don't Want My Love	5
67	Tamla Motown TMG 634	Walk Away Renee/Mame	4
68	Tamla Motown TMG 647	If I Were A Carpenter/Your Love Is Wonderful	4
68	Tamla Motown TMG 665	Yesterday's Dreams/For Once In My Life	4
68	Tamla Motown TMG 675	I'm In A Different World/Remember When	4
69	Tamla Motown TMG 698	What Is A Man?/Don't Bring Back Memories	4
69	Tamla Motown TMG 710	Do What You Gotta Do/Can't Seem To Get You Out Of My Mind	4
75	ABC ABC 4057	Seven Lonely Nights/I Can't Hold On Much Longer	4
66	Tamla Motown TME 2012	THE FOUR TOPS (EP)	10
67	Tamla Motown TME 2018	FOUR TOPS HITS (EP)	10
65	Tamla Motown TML 11010	THE FOUR TOPS (LP)	30
66	Tamla Motown TML 11021	SECOND ALBUM (LP)	30
66	T. Motown (S)TML 11037	FOUR TOPS ON TOP (LP, mono/stereo)	15/12
67	T. Motown (S)TML 11041	FOUR TOPS LIVE! (LP)	10
67	T. Motown (S)TML 11056	REACH OUT (LP, mono/stereo)	12/10
68	T. Motown (S)TML 11061	FOUR TOPS GREATEST HITS (LP)	10
68	T. Motown (S)TML 11087	YESTERDAY'S DREAMS (LP)	10
69	T. Motown (S)TML 11113	FOUR TOPS NOW (LP)	10
70	T. Motown (S)TML 11138	SOUL SPIN (LP)	10
72	Probe SPB 1064	KEEPER OF THE CASTLE (LP)	12
73	Probe SPB 1077	SHAFT IN AFRICA (LP, soundtrack, Johnny Pate)	15
73	Probe SPBA 6277	MAIN STREET PEOPLE (LP)	10
74	Probe SPBA 6283	MEETING OF THE MINDS (LP)	10
74	ABC ABCL 5035	SHAFT IN AFRICA (LP, soundtrack, reissue)	10
74	ABC ABCL 5062	LIVE AND IN CONCERT (LP)	10
75	ABC ABCL 5132	NIGHT LIGHTS HARMONY (LP)	10

(see also Supremes & Four Tops)

FOUR TUNES
54	London L 1231	I Gambled With Love/Marie (78)	30
54	London HL 8050	Do, Do, Do, Do, Do Do It Again/My Wild Irish Rose (78)	5
55	London HL 8151	I Sold My Heart To A Junkman/The Greatest Feeling In The World	60

MINT VALUE £

55	London HL 8151	I Sold My Heart To A Junkman/The Greatest Feeling In The World (78)	15
55	London HLJ 8164	Tired Of Waitin'/L'Amour Toujours L'Amour (Love Everlasting)	30
55	London HLJ 8164	Tired Of Waitin'/L'Amour Toujours L'Amour (Love Everlasting) (78)	10

FOUR VOICES

58	Philips PB 864	Tell Me You're Mine/Tight Spot	4

FOUR WINDS

58	London HLU 8556	Short Shorts/Five Minutes More	25
58	London HLU 8556	Short Shorts/Five Minutes More (78)	15

KIM FOWLEY

66	Parlophone R 5521	Lights/Something New And Different	15
66	CBS 202243	They're Coming To Take Me Away Ha-Haaa!!/You Get More For Your Money On The Flip Side Of This Record Talking Blues	8
66	CBS 202338	Lights (The Blind Can See)/Something New And Different (reissue)	10
66	Island WI 278	The Trip/Beautiful People	10
72	Action ACT 4606	Born To Make You Cry/Thunder Road	5
73	Capitol CL 15743	International Heroes/ESP Reader	4

(see also Freaks Of Nature, Hollywood Argyles, Napoleon XIII, B. Bumble & Stingers)

FOX

68	CBS 3381	Mister Carpenter/Seek And You Find	25

FOX

70	Fontana 6007 016	Second Hand Love/Butterfly	20
70	Fontana 6309 007	FOR FOX SAKE (LP)	60

FOX

77	GTO GTLP 020	BLUE HOTEL (LP)	10

DON FOX

57	Decca F 10927	Be My Girl/You'll Never Go To Heaven	6
57	Decca F 10955	The Majesty Of Love/Party Time	6
58	Decca F 10983	Pretend You Don't See Her/Wasteland	6
58	Decca F 11057	She Was Only Seventeen/When You're A Long, Long Way Away	7
60	Triumph RGM 1022	'Tain't What You Do/Out There	12
61	Oriole CB 1643	Don't Fool With Love/If You Go	4
60s	Honey Hit TB 125	Three Swinging Clicks/I Found The Girl I Love In My Home Town (p/s)	5

SAMANTHA FOX

84	Lamborghini LMG 10	Aim To Win/17 And Holding (p/s)	4
87	Jive FOXY 6	I Surrender/The Best Is Yet To Come (p/s, blue vinyl)	4

BRUCE FOXTON

83	Arista BFOX 1	Freak/Writing On The Wall (p/s, clear vinyl)	4
83	Arista BFPD 2	This Is The Way/Sign Of The Times (picture disc)	4

(see also Jam)

FOXX

71	MCA MUPS 419	REVOLT OF EMILY YOUNG (LP)	10

INEZ FOXX

71	Pye Intl. 7N 25546	You Shouldn't Have Set My Soul On Fire/Live For Today	5
73	Stax 2025 151	You Hurt Me For The Last Time/Watch The Dog (That Brings The Bone)	8

INEZ & CHARLIE FOXX

63	Sue WI 301	Mockingbird/He's The One You Love	15
64	Sue WI 304	Jaybirds/Brokenhearted Fool	18
64	Sue WI 307	Here We Go Round The Mulberry Bush/Competition	12
64	Sue WI 314	Ask Me/Hi Diddle Diddle	12
64	Sue WI 323	Hurt By Love/Confusion	12
64	Sue WI 356	La De Da I Love You/Yankee Doodle Dandy	12
65	London HLC 9971	My Momma Told Me/I Feel Alright	8
65	London HLC 10009	Hummingbird/If I Need Anyone (Let It Be You)	6
66	Stateside SS 556	No Stranger To Love/Come By Here	8
67	Stateside SS 586	Tightrope/My Special Prayer	15
67	Direction 58-2712	I Ain't Goin' For That/Undecided	5
67	Direction 58-3192	(1 2 3 4 5 6 7) Count The Days/A Stranger I Don't Know	5
68	Direction 58-3816	Come On In/Baby Drop Your Dime	6
69	Direction 58-4042	Baby Give It To Me/You Fixed My Heartache	5
69	United Artists UP 2269	Mockingbird/Hurt By Love	4
70	United Artist UP 35013	Le De Da I Love You/Don't Do It No More	5
71	Pye Intl. 7N 25561	Tightrope/Baby Take It All	5
64	Sue ILP 911	MOCKINGBIRD (LP)	40
65	London HA-C 8241	INEZ AND CHARLIE FOXX (LP)	15
68	Direction 8-63085	COME BY HERE (LP)	10
68	Direction 8-63281	GREATEST HITS (LP)	10

JOHN FOXX

80	Lyntone	My Face (yellow vinyl flexidisc free with 'Smash Hits')	6/4
80	Virgin VS 338	No-One Driving/Glimmer//This City/Mr. No (double pack, gatefold p/s)	5
80	Virgin VS 338	No-One Driving (2.53 DJ Version)/Glimmer//This City/Mr. No (double pack, stickered gatefold p/s, matrix no. VS 338 A5DJ)	15
80	Virgin VS 360	Burning Car/20th Century (picture disc)	5
82	Virgin VSY 513	Endlessly/Young Man (picture disc)	4
82	Virgin VS 513	Endlessly/Ghosts On Water//Dance With Me/A Kind Of Love (double pack)	5
84	Virgin VS 615	Your Dress/Woman On A Stairway//Lifting Sky/Annexe (double pack)	5
84	Virgin VSP 645	Like A Miracle/Wings And A Wind (shaped picture disc)	5
85	Virgin VS 771	The Stars On Fire/What Kind Of Girl (p/s, with free single)	4

(see also Ultravox)

FRABJOY & RUNCIBLE SPOON
69	Marmalade 598 019	I'm Beside Myself/Animal Song	10

(see also 10cc)

FRAME
66	RCA RCA 1556	My Feet Don't Fit In His Shoes/She	6
67	RCA RCA 1571	Doctor Doctor/I Can't Go On	40
70	Pye 7N 45213	Rockin' Machine/One More Time	4

FRAMES
79	Brain Booster BBC 2	False Accusations/69 (p/s)	4

PETER FRAMPTON
85	Virgin VSS 827	Crying/You Know So Well (shaped disc, no p/s)	5
72	A&M AMLS 68099	WIND OF CHANGE (LP)	10
73	A&M AMLH 68150	FRAMPTON'S CAMEL (LP, with poster)	10

(see also Herd, Humble Pie)

PETER FRANC
72	Dawn DNLS 3043	PROFILE (LP)	15
73	Dawn DNLS 3051	EN ROUTE (LP)	15

B. FRANCIS
65	Ska Beat JB 193	Judy Crowned/Who Crunch	7

BOBBY FRANCIS
67	Doctor Bird DB 1153	Chain Gang/Venus	7

(see also Winston Francis)

CONNIE FRANCIS
56	MGM MGM 902	My First Real Love (with Jaybirds)/Believe In Me (Credemi) (78)	20
56	MGM SP 1169	My First Real Love (with Jaybirds)/Believe In Me (Credemi)	80
56	MGM MGM 932	My Sailor Boy/Everyone Needs Someone	40
56	MGM MGM 932	My Sailor Boy/Everyone Needs Someone (78)	5
57	MGM MGM 945	Little Blue Wren/I Never Had A Sweetheart	35
57	MGM MGM 945	Little Blue Wren/I Never Had A Sweetheart (78)	20
57	MGM MGM 962	Faded Orchid/Eighteen	25
57	MGM MGM 962	Faded Orchid/Eighteen (78)	15
58	MGM MGM 975	Who's Sorry Now?/You Were Only Fooling (While I Was Falling In Love)	5
58	MGM MGM 975	Who's Sorry Now?/You Were Only Fooling (While I Was Falling In Love) (78)	5
58	MGM MGM 982	I'm Sorry I Made You Cry/Lock Up Your Heart	5
58	MGM MGM 982	I'm Sorry I Made You Cry/Lock Up Your Heart (78)	5
58	MGM MGM 985	Carolina Moon/Stupid Cupid	5
58	MGM MGM 985	Carolina Moon/Stupid Cupid (78)	5
58	MGM MGM 993	I'll Get By/Fallin'	6
58	MGM MGM 993	I'll Get By/Fallin' (78)	5
58	MGM MGM 998	You Always Hurt The One You Love/In The Valley Of Love	6
58	MGM MGM 998	You Always Hurt The One You Love/In The Valley Of Love (78)	5
59	MGM MGM 1001	My Happiness/Happy Days And Lonely Nights	5
59	MGM MGM 1001	My Happiness/Happy Days And Lonely Nights (78)	5
59	MGM MGM 1012	If I Didn't Care/Toward The End Of The Day	6
59	MGM MGM 1012	If I Didn't Care/Toward The End Of The Day (78)	5
59	MGM MGM 1018	Lipstick On Your Collar/Frankie	5
59	MGM MGM 1018	Lipstick On Your Collar/Frankie (78)	15
59	MGM MGM 1036	Plenty Good Lovin'/You're Gonna Miss Me	6
59	MGM MGM 1036	Plenty Good Lovin'/You're Gonna Miss Me (78)	20
59	MGM MGM 1046	Among My Souvenirs/Do You Love Me Like You Kiss Me?	5
59	MGM MGM 1046	Among My Souvenirs/Do You Love Me Like You Kiss Me? (78)	20
60	MGM MGM 1060	Valentino/It Would Be Worth It	6
60	MGM MGM 1070	Mama/Teddy (unreleased; demos more common, £30)	40
60	MGM MGM 1076	Mama/Robot Man	5
60	MGM MGM 1086	Everybody's Somebody's Fool/Jealous Of You	5
60	MGM MGM 1100	My Heart Has A Mind Of Its Own/Malaguena	4
60	MGM MGM 1111	Many Tears Ago/Senza Mama (With No-One)	5
61	MGM MGM 1121	Where The Boys Are/Baby Roo	5
61	MGM MGM 1136	Breakin' In A Brand New Broken Heart/Someone Else's Boy	5
61	MGM MGM 1138	Together/Too Many Rules	5
61	MGM MGM 1145	Baby's First Christmas/I'm Falling In Love With You Tonight	5
62	MGM MGM 1151	Don't Cry On My Shoulder/Mr. Twister	7
62	MGM MGM 1157	Don't Break The Heart That Loves You/Ain't That Better Baby?	6
62	MGM MGM 1165	Vacation/It's Gonna Take Me Some Time	6
62	MGM MGM 1171	Playin' Games/I Was Such A Fool	7
62	MGM MGM 1185	I'm Gonna Be Warm This Winter/Pretty Little Baby	6
62	MGM MGM 1193	Follow The Boys/Tonight's My Night	6
63	MGM MGM 1202	If My Pillow Could Talk/Lollipop Lips	6
63	MGM MGM 1207	Drownin' My Sorrows/Look At Him	6
63	MGM MGM 1212	Your Other Love/Whatever Happened To Rosemary	6
63	MGM MGM 1220	The Summer Of His Years/My Buddy	6
63	MGM MGM 1224	Blue Winter/Souvenirs	6
63	MGM MGM 1236	Be Anything (But Be Mine)/Tommy	6
64	MGM MGM 1253	Don't Ever Leave Me/Waiting For You	6
65	MGM MGM 1265	Forget Domani/(I Don't Want To Be) No Better Off	6
65	MGM MGM 1271	My Child/No One Ever Sends Me Roses	5
65	MGM MGM 1282	Roundabout/Love Is Me, Love Is You	7
66	MGM MGM 1293	Jealous Heart/Can I Rely On You?	6
66	MGM MGM 1295	The Phoenix Love Theme — Senza Fine/Bossa Nova Hand Dance	6
66	MGM MGM 1305	Love Is Me, Love Is You/I'd Let You Break My Heart All Over Again	6
66	MGM MGM 1320	Somewhere My Love (Lara's Theme)/Letter From A Soldier (Dear Mama)	6
66	MGM MGM 1327	Spanish Nights And You/Games That Lovers Play	6

Connie FRANCIS

MINT VALUE £

67	MGM MGM 1334	Another Page/Souvenir D'Italie	6
67	MGM MGM 1336	Time Alone Will Tell/Born Free	6
67	MGM MGM 1347	My Heart Cries For You/If My Friends Could See Me Now (Medley)	6
68	MGM MGM 1381	My World Is Slipping Away/Till We're Together	6
68	MGM MGM 1407	Why Say Goodbye?/Addio Mi Amore	6
68	MGM MGM 1446	Somebody Else Is Taking My Place/Brother Can You Spare A Dime?	6
69	MGM MGM 1471	The Wedding Cake/Overhill Underground	7
69	MGM MGM 1483	Who's Sorry Now?/Vacation	4
70	MGM MGM 1493	Mr Love/Zingara	7
73	MGM 2006 221	Lipstick On Your Collar/Who's Sorry Now?/Robot Man	4
73	MGM 2006 221	Lipstick On Your Collar/Frankie	4
73	GSF GSZ 10	The Answer/Paint The Rain	5
75	MGM 1110 004	Who's Sorry Now?/Mama	5
75	MGM 1110 005	Stupid Cupid/Carolina Moon	5
78	Polydor 2066 881	Burning Bridges/Let's Go Where The Good Times Go	5
78	United Artists UP 36430	Where The Boys Are/A-Ba-Ni-Bi	4
78	United Artists UP 26463	My Mother's Eyes/Lovin' Man	4
79	Polydor POSP 75	Three Good Reasons/What's Wrong With My World?	4
56	MGM MGM-EP 658	A GIRL IN LOVE (EP)	20
58	MGM MGM-EP 677	HEARTACHES (EP)	15
58	MGM MGM-EP 686	CONNIE FRANCIS (EP)	20
59	MGM MGM-EP 697	IF I DIDN'T CARE (EP)	18
60	MGM MGM-EP 711	YOU'RE MY EVERYTHING (EP)	20
60	MGM MGM-EP 717	ROCK AND ROLL MILLION SELLERS No. 1 (EP)	20
60	MGM MGM-EP 720	ROCK AND ROLL MILLION SELLERS No. 2 (EP)	20
60	MGM MGM-EP 731	ROCK AND ROLL MILLION SELLERS No. 3 (EP)	16
60	MGM MGM-EP 742	FIRST LADY OF RECORD (EP, laminated or matt rear sleeve)	16
61	MGM MGM-EP 756	WHERE THE BOYS ARE (EP)	20
61	MGM MGM-EP 759	CONNIE FRANCIS FAVOURITES (EP)	20
61	MGM MGM-EP 760	SINGS ITALIAN FAVOURITES (EP)	20
63	MGM MGM-EP 769	CONNIE'S AMERICAN HITS (EP)	18
63	MGM MGM-EP 773	HEY RING-A-DING (EP)	20
63	MGM MGM-EP 775	WHAT KIND OF FOOL AM I? (EP)	20
63	MGM MGM-EP 780	MALA FEMMENA (EP)	20
63	MGM MGM-EP 783	FROM ITALY ... WITH LOVE (EP)	20
65	MGM MGM-EP 789	SINGS FOR MAMA (EP)	20
66	MGM MGM-EP 792	JEALOUS HEART (EP)	20
58	MGM MGM-D 153	WHO'S SORRY NOW (10" LP)	55
59	MGM MGM-C 782	MY THANKS TO YOU (LP)	25
59	MGM MGM-C 786	THE EXCITING CONNIE FRANCIS (LP)	20
59	MGM MGM-C 797	CHRISTMAS WITH CONNIE (LP)	35
60	MGM MGM-C 804	ROCK AND ROLL MILLION SELLERS No. 1 (LP)	30
60	MGM MGM-C 812	COUNTRY AND WESTERN GOLDEN HITS (LP)	30
60	MGM MGM-C 819	FUN SONGS FOR CHILDREN (LP)	60
60	MGM MGM-C 821	SINGS ITALIAN FAVOURITES (LP, also stereo CS 6002)	18/22
60	MGM MGM-C 831	CONNIE'S GREATEST HITS (LP)	15
60	MGM MGM-C 836	SPANISH AND LATIN AMERICAN FAVOURITES (LP, also stereo CS 6012)	16/20
61	MGM MGM-C 845	SINGS JEWISH FAVOURITES (LP, also stereo CS 6021)	16/20
61	MGM MGM-C 854	MORE ITALIAN FAVOURITES (LP, also stereo CS 6029)	16/20
61	MGM MGM-C 861	AT THE COPA (LP, also stereo CS 6035)	16/20
61	MGM MGM-C 870	SONGS TO A SWINGIN' BAND (LP, also stereo CS 6044)	16/20
61	MGM MGM-C 875	SINGS NEVER ON SUNDAY AND OTHER TITLE SONGS FROM MOTION PICTURES (LP, also stereo CS 6047)	16/20
61	MGM MGM-C 879	DO THE TWIST (LP)	35
62	MGM MGM-C 883	SINGS FOLK SONG FAVOURITES (LP, also stereo CS 6054)	16/20
62	MGM MGM-C 898	SINGS IRISH FAVOURITES (LP, also stereo CS 6056)	25/30
62	MGM MGM-C 916	COUNTRY MUSIC CONNIE STYLE (LP, also stereo CS 6062)	20/25
63	MGM MGM-C 930	MORE ITALIAN HITS (LP, also stereo CS 6067)	16/20
63	MGM MGM-C 931	FOLLOW THE BOYS (LP, also stereo CS 6068)	16/20
63	MGM MGM-C 940	SINGS AWARD-WINNING MOTION PICTURE HITS (LP, stereo CS 6070)	16/20
64	MGM MGM-C 958	GREAT AMERICAN WALTZES (LP, also stereo CS 6075)	16/20
64	MGM MGM-C 970	16 OF CONNIE'S BIGGEST HITS (LP)	15
65	MGM MGM-C 983	LOOKING FOR LOVE (LP, also stereo CS 6079)	18
65	MGM MGM-C 998	A NEW KIND OF CONNIE ... (LP, also stereo CS 6080)	16
65	MGM MGM-C 1003	SINGS GREAT COUNTRY FAVOURITES (LP, with Hank Williams Jnr, also stereo CS 6081)	18/20
65	MGM MGM-C 1006	SINGS 'FOR MAMA' (LP, also stereo CS 6082)	18/20
65	MGM MGM-C 1012	SINGS THE ALL-TIME INTERNATIONAL HITS (LP, also stereo CS 6083)	16/18
66	MGM MGM-C(S) 8006	WHEN THE BOYS MEET THE GIRLS (LP, mono/stereo)	16/18
66	MGM MGM-C(S) 8009	JEALOUS HEART (LP)	18
66	MGM MGM-C(S) 8027	MOVIE GREATS OF THE SIXTIES (LP)	18
66	MGM MGM-C(S) 8036	LIVE AT THE SAHARA IN LAS VEGAS (LP)	18
66	World Record Club TP 618	MY THANKS TO YOU (LP)	12
67	MGM MGM-C 8041	THE BEST OF CONNIE FRANCIS (LP)	15
68	MGM MGM-C(S) 8050	LOVE ITALIAN STYLE (LP, mono/stereo)	15/17
68	MGM MGM-C(S) 8054	MY HEART CRIES FOR YOU (LP, mono/stereo)	16/18
68	MGM MGM-C(S) 8086	CONNIE AND CLYDE (LP)	18
69	MGM MGM-C(S) 8110	HAWAII CONNIE (LP)	35
70	MGM MGM-CS 8117	SINGS THE SONGS OF LES REED (LP)	18
73	MGM 2353 072	GREAT SONGS OF THE SIXTIES (LP)	10
74	MGM ACB 00143	SINGS GREAT COUNTRY HITS (LP, Audio Club Of Great Britain issue)	12
75	MGM ACB 00167	SINGS GREAT COUNTRY HITS VOL. 2 (LP, Audio Club Of G.B. issue)	15
76	MGM ACB 00195	THE SPECIAL MAGIC OF CONNIE FRANCIS (LP, Audio Club Of G.B. issue)	12
77	Polydor 2391 290	20 ALL TIME GREATS (LP, with original label)	10
78	United Artists ULP 30182	WHO'S HAPPY NOW? (LP, withdrawn sleeve with different lettering)	150
78	United Artists ULP 30182	WHO'S HAPPY NOW? (LP)	12

MINT VALUE £

| 79 | Polydor 2391 290 | 20 ALL TIME GREATS (LP, reissue) | 10 |
| 81 | Readers Digest GBCF-A-106 | THE BEST OF CONNIE FRANCIS (4-LP) | 30 |

CONNIE FRANCIS & MARVIN RAINWATER
| 58 | MGM MGM 969 | The Majesty Of Love/You My Darling You | 25 |

(see also Marvin Rainwater)

(KING) JOE FRANCIS
65	Blue Beat BB 323	Wicked Woman/King Joe's Ska (as King Joe Francis)	7
66	Ska Beat JB 262	Scarborough Ska/I Got A Scar (as Joe Francis & Ricky Logan & Snowballs)	7
66	Rio R 90	Have My Body (song actually "Have Mercy Baby")/Everybody's Got To Know (as King Joe Francis & Hijackers)	7
67	Rainbow RAI 114	My Granny/Pull It Out (as J. Francis & Rico's Boys)	6

JOHNNIE FRANCIS
| 55 | Decca F 10440 | Funny Thing/Give Me The Right | 4 |

LITTLE WILLIE FRANCIS
| 63 | Blue Beat BB 151 | Settle Down/I'm Ashamed | 8 |

(see also Wilbert Francis & Vibrators)

NAT FRANCIS
| 66 | Blue Beat BB 346 | Mama Kiss Him Goodnight (as Nat Francis & Sunsets)/BUSTER JUNIOR: Tra La La | 8 |
| 66 | Blue Beat BB 361 | Just To Keep You/BUSTER JUNIOR: You Only Want My Money | 8 |

RITCHIE FRANCIS
| 71 | Pegasus PEG 11 | SONGBIRD (LP) | 20 |

(see also Eyes Of Blue, Big Sleep)

STEVE FRANCIS
| 64 | King KG 1012 | Watch Your Step/Lovey Dovey | 4 |

WILBERT FRANCIS & VIBRATORS
| 66 | Ska Beat JB 267 | Memories Of You/CHUCK JACQUES: Now That You're Gone | 8 |

(see also Little Willie Francis)

WINSTON FRANCIS
69	Coxsone CS 7089	Reggae And Cry/FREEDOM SINGERS: Easy Come Easy Go (B-side actually by Righteous Flames)	10
69	Studio One SO 2086	The Games People Play/ALBERT GRIFFITHS: The Kicks	10
69	Punch PH 5	Too Experienced/JACKIE MITTOO: Mule Jerk	5
69	Bamboo BAM 10	The Same Old Song/SOUND DIMENSION: Rattle On	5
70	Bamboo BAM 46	Turn Back The Hands Of Time/Soul Bowl	5
70	Bamboo BAM 48	California Dreaming/JACKIE MITTOO & SOUND DIMENSION: Soul Stew	5
70	Bamboo BDLP 207	MR FIX IT (LP)	30
71	Bamboo BDLPS 216	CALIFORNIA DREAMING (LP)	25

(see also Bobby Francis)

JACKSON C. FRANK
| 65 | Columbia DB 7795 | Blues Run The Game/Can't Get Away From My Love | 7 |
| 65 | Columbia 33SX 1788 | JACKSON C. FRANK (LP) | 70 |

FRANKIE & CLASSICALS
| 67 | Philips BF 1586 | I Only Have Eyes For You/What Shall I Do | 90 |
| 74 | Pye Intl. DDS 101 | What Shall I Do/Goodbye Love, Hello Sadness | 4 |

FRANKIE & JOHNNY
| 66 | Decca F 22376 | Never Gonna Leave You/I'll Hold You | 80 |
| 66 | Parlophone R 5518 | Climb Ev'ry Mountain/I Wanna Make You Understand | 8 |

FRANKIE & KNOCKOUTS
| 81 | RCA RCALP 5026 | FRANKIE & THE KNOCKOUTS (LP) | 10 |

FRANKIE & LARRY
| 60 | Capitol CL 15153 | Not Yet/A Fool For You | 5 |

FRANKIE GOES TO HOLLYWOOD
83	ZTT P ZTAS 1	Relax (Move)/One September Monday (picture disc)	8
83	ZTT 12 ZTAS 1 (1A 1U)	Relax (16.00 Mix)/Ferry Across The Mersey/Relax Bonus (Again) (12", p/s, 33rpm)	25
83	ZZT 12 ZTAS 1 (1A 2U)	Relax (Sex Mix [8.20 "New York Mix"])/Ferry Across The Mersey/Relax Bonus (Again) (12", p/s)	20
83	ZTT 12P ZTAS 1	Relax (Sex Mix)/Ferry Across The Mersey/Relax Bonus (Again) (12", picture disc)	8
83	ZZT 12 ZTAS 1 (1A 5)	Relax (Sex Mix/16.00 Mix)/Ferry Across The Mersey/Relax Bonus (Again) (12", p/s, 45rpm)	18
83	ZZT CTIS 102	RELAX'S GREATEST BITS (cassette)	10
84	ZTT P ZTAS 3	Two Tribes (We Don't Want To Die)/One February Friday (picture disc)	8
84	ZTT 12 ZTAS 3	Two Tribes (Annihilation)/War (Hide Yourself)/Two Tribes (Surrender) (12", p/s, with poster: 3 different poster designs)	each 8
84	ZTT X ZTAS 3	Two Tribes (Carnage)/War (Hide Yourself)/Two Tribes (Surrender) (12", p/s)	7
84	ZTT X ZIP 1	Two Tribes (Hibakushu)/War (Hide Yourself)/Two Tribes (Surrender) (12", company sleeve)	20
84	ZTT CTIS 103	TWO TRIBES (KEEP THE PEACE) (cassette)	10
84	ZTT WARTZ 3	War (Hidden)/Two Tribes (Carnage)/One February Friday (12", picture disc)	8
84	ZTT P ZTAS 5	The Power Of Love/The World Is My Oyster (picture disc)	5
84	ZTT 12P ZTAS 5	The Power Of Love (Extended Version)/Trapped And Scrapped/Holier Than Thou (12", picture disc)	7
84	ZTT 12X ZTAS 5	The Power Of Love/The World Is My Oyster/Pleasurefix/Starfix (12", gatefold p/s with 5 photos)	10
84	ZTT CTIS 105	The Power Of Love (Extended Version)/Trapped And Scrapped/Holier Than Thou (cassette, picture 'envelope' box)	5

MINT VALUE £

85	ZTT ZTAS 7 (7A 7U)	Welcome To The Pleasure Dome (Altered Reel [plays "Video Mix 5.05"])/ Happy Hi Get It On (p/s, blue label) 12
85	ZTT ZTAS 7 (7A 7U)	Welcome To The Pleasure Dome (Altered Reel)/Happy Hi Get It On (p/s, standard label, also with matrix: ZTAS 7 [7A 8U]) 6
85	ZTT P ZTAS 7	Welcome To The Pleasure Dome (Alternative Reel ["Fruitiness Mix"])/ Happy Hi/Get It On (apple-shaped picture disc) 6
85	ZTT X ZTAS 7	Welcome To The Pleasure Dome (The Alternative Mix)/Happy Hi/Get It On/ Born To Run (live) (12", p/s) 8
85	ZTT CTIS 107	Welcome To The Pleasure Dome (Soundtrack From Bernard Rose Video)/ Happy Hi (All In The Mind)/Get It On/(How To Remake The World) (cassette) 6
86	ZTT ZTAX 22	Rage Hard (Stamped)/(Don't Lose What's Left) Of Your Little Mind (p/s) 6
86	ZTT ZTD 22	Rage Hard/(Don't Lose What's Left) Of Your Little Mind (pop-up fists p/s) 4
86	ZTT 12 ZTAQ 22	Rage Hard/(Don't Lose What's Left) Of Your Little Mind (Extended)/ Sufferin' In The City (12", p/s, with poster) 7
86	ZTT 12 ZTAX 22	Rage Hard (++ Mix)/(Don't Lose What's Left) Of Your Little Mind (Extended)/ Roadhouse Blues (12", p/s) 7
86	ZTT 12 ZTAX B 22	Rage Hard (++ Mix)/(Don't Lose What's Left) Of Your Little Mind (Extended)/ Roadhouse Blues (12", in 'action series 22' box) 7
86	ZTT ZCID 22	RAGE HARD (HIGHLIGHTS) (CD) 14
86	ZTT 12 ZTAX 25	Warriors (The Turn Of The Knife Mix)/Warriors (Return)/ Warriors (End) (12", p/s) 7
86	ZTT ZCID 25	WARRIORS OF THE WASTELAND (Compacted) (CD) 10
86	ZTT CTIS 25	WARRIORS OF THE WASTELAND (Cassetted) (cassette) 5
87	ZTT 12 ZTAX 26	Watching The Wildlife (Movement 2)/Wildlife Bit 3/Wildlife Bit 4/ The Waves (12", p/s) 7
87	ZTT ZTE 26	Watching The Wildlife (Die Letzen Tag Der Menscheit Mix)/Watching The Wildlife/The Waves (12", p/s) 10
87	ZTT CTIS 26	WATCHING THE WILDLIFE (Cassetted) (cassette, includes "Condom Mix" & "Orchestral Wildlife") 6
84	ZTT NEAT 1	WELCOME TO THE PLEASURE DOME (2-LP, picture discs, printed gatefold PVC sleeve) 14
84	ZTT CID 101	WELCOME TO THE PLEASURE DOME (CD, with "San José", omits "Happy Hi") 35
86	ZTT ZCIQ 8	LIPERPOOL (cassette, with "Wildlife" special mix, pink inlay) 10

(see also Holly, Spitfire Boys, Paul Rutherford)

ARETHA FRANKLIN

61	Fontana H 271	Love Is The Only Thing/Today I Sing The Blues (with Ray Bryant Combo) 12
61	Fontana H 343	Operation Heartbreak/Rock-A-Bye Your Baby With A Dixie Melody 8
65	CBS 201732	Can't You Just See Me/You Little Miss Raggedy Anne 6
67	CBS 202468	Cry Like A Baby/Swanee 5
67	CBS 3059	Take A Look/Lee Cross 5
67	Atlantic 584 084	I Never Loved A Man (The Way I Love You)/Do Right Woman – Do Right Man ...4
67	Atlantic 584 115	Respect/Save Me 5
67	Atlantic 584 127	Baby I Love You/Going Down Slow 4
67	Atlantic 584 141	(You Make Me Feel Like A) Natural Woman/Never Let Me Go 5
67	Atlantic 584 157	(I Can't Get No) Satisfaction/Night Life (withdrawn B-side) 7
67	Atlantic 584 157	(I Can't Get No) Satisfaction/Chain Of Fools 4
68	Atlantic 584 172	Since You've Been Gone/Ain't No Way 4
68	Atlantic 584 186	Think/You Send Me 5
68	Atlantic 584 206	I Say A Little Prayer/See-Saw 4
69	Atlantic 584 239	Don't Let Me Lose This Dream/The House That Jack Built 4
69	Atlantic 584 252	The Weight/The Tracks Of My Tears 4
69	Atlantic 584 285	Share Your Love With Me/Pledging My Love/The Clock 4
69	Atlantic 584 306	Eleanor Rigby/It Ain't Fair 4
70	Atlantic 584 322	Call Me/Son Of A Preacher Man 4
70	Atlantic 2091 027	Don't Play That Song/The Thrill Is Gone 4
70	Atlantic 2091 042	Border Song/You And Me (unissued)
70	Atlantic 2091 044	Oh No Not My Baby/You And Me 4
71	Atlantic 2091 063	You're All I Need To Get By/Border Song 4
71	Atlantic 2091 168	Rock Steady/Oh My, Oh My 4
74	Atlantic K 10399	Until You Come Back To Me/If You Don't Think 4
86	Arista ARIDP 624	Freeway Of Love/Until You Say You Love Me//Jump To It/Zoomin' To The Freeway (double pack) 4
86	Arista ARIST 22624	Freeway Of Love (Pink Cadillac Mix)/Until You Say You Love Me (p/s, pink vinyl) 8
86	Arista ARIST 22678	Jumpin' Jack Flash/Who's Zoomin' Who//Sweet Bitter Love/ Integrity (double pack) 4
62	Fontana TE 467217	TODAY I SING THE BLUES (EP) 12
61	Fontana TFL 5173	ARETHA (LP) 18
65	CBS (S)BPG 62566	YEAH!!! — IN PERSON (LP) 15
67	CBS (S)BPG 62744	SOUL SISTER (LP) 15
67	Atlantic 587/588 066	I NEVER LOVED A MAN (LP) 16
67	CBS (S)BPG 62969	TAKE IT LIKE YOU GIVE IT (LP) 15
67	CBS 63160	LEE CROSS (LP) 15
67	Atlantic 587/588 085	ARETHA ARRIVES (LP) 16
67	Chess (S)CRL 54550	SONGS OF FAITH (LP) 12
67	CBS 64536	GREATEST HITS (LP) 10
68	Atlantic 587/588 099	LADY SOUL (LP) 15
68	CBS 63269	TAKE A LOOK AT ARETHA FRANKLIN (LP) 12
68	Atlantic 587/588 114	ARETHA NOW (LP) 15
68	CBS 63064	GREATEST HITS VOL. 2 (LP) 10
68	Atlantic 587/588 149	LIVE AT THE OLYMPIA, PARIS (LP) 18
69	Atlantic 588 169	SOUL '69 (LP) 15
69	Atlantic 588 182	ARETHA'S GOLD (LP) 12
69	Atlantic 2400 004	THIS GIRL'S IN LOVE WITH YOU (LP) 12
70	Atlantic 2464 007	I SAY A LITTLE PRAYER (LP) 10
70	Atlantic 2400 021	DON'T PLAY THAT SONG (LP) 15

MINT VALUE £

71	Atlantic 2400 136	LIVE AT THE FILLMORE WEST (LP, gatefold sleeve)	15
72	Atlantic K 40095	SPIRIT IN THE DARK (LP)	10
72	Atlantic K 40323	YOUNG, GIFTED AND BLACK (LP)	12
72	Atlantic K 60023	AMAZING GRACE (2-LP)	18
73	Atlantic K 40504	HEY NOW HEY (THE OTHER SIDE OF THE SKY) (LP)	10
74	Atlantic K 50031	LET ME IN YOUR LIFE (LP)	10
75	Atlantic K 50093	WITH EVERYTHING I FEEL (LP)	10
75	Atlantic K 50159	YOU (LP)	10
76	Atlantic K 56248	SPARKLE (LP, soundtrack)	10

CAROLYN FRANKLIN

69	RCA RCA 1851	The Boxer/I Don't Want To Lose You	5

ERMA FRANKLIN

67	London HLZ 10172	Piece Of My Heart/Big Boss Man	10
68	London HLZ 10201	Open Up Your Soul/I Just Ain't Ready For Love	8
68	London HLZ 10220	The Right To Cry/Don't Catch The Dog's Bone	8
69	Soul City SC 118	Time After Time/Don't Wait Too Long	7
69	MCA MU 1073	Gotta Find Me A Lover (24 Hours A Day)/Change My Thoughts From You	6
71	Jay Boy BOY 36	I Just Ain't Ready For Love/The Right To Cry	4
71	Jay Boy BOY 41	Piece Of My Heart/Big Boss Man (reissue)	4
75	London HLZ 10501	Piece Of My Heart/Big Boss Man (2nd reissue)	4
70	MCA MUP MUPS 394	SOUL SISTER (LP)	20

MARIE FRANKLIN

68	MGM MGM 1455	You Ain't Changed/Don'tcha Bet No Money	4

JOHNNY FRANKS

55	Melodisc P 230	Tweedle Dee/Shake, Rattle And Roll (78)	15
56	Melodisc 1355	Rock Candy Baby/Sing-ing-ing (78)	6
58	Melodisc 1459	Good Old Country Music/Cheatin' On Me	6
58	Melodisc 1459	Good Old Country Music/Cheatin' On Me (78)	15

FRANTIC ELEVATORS

79	TJM TJM 5	Voice In The Dark/Passion/Every Day I Die (p/s)	15
80	TJM TJM 6	Hunchback Of Notre Dame/See Nothing And Everything/Don't Judge Me (unreleased; demos only)	50
80	Eric's ERIC'S 6	You Know What You Told Me/Production Prevention (p/s)	15
81	Crackin' Up CRAK 1	Searching For The Only One/Hunchback Of Notre Dame (p/s)	12
82	No Waiting WAIT 1	Holding Back The Years/Pistols In My Brain (p/s)	20
87	TJM TJM 101	THE EARLY YEARS (mini-LP)	20

(see also Simply Red)

ANDY FRASER BAND

75	CBS 80731	THE ANDY FRASER BAND (LP)	10
75	CBS 81027	IN YOUR EYES (LP)	10

(see also Free, Sharks)

JOHN FRASER

58	Pye 7N 15118	Trolley Stop/Don't Take Your Love From Me	4
59	Pye 7N 15212	Bye, Bye Baby, Goodbye/Golden Age	4
58	Pye NEP 24068	PRESENTING JOHN FRASER (EP)	8

FRATERNITY BROTHERS

59	HMV POP 582	Passion Flower/A Nobody Like Me (B-side with Gil Fields)	4

FRATERNITY OF MAN

70	Stateside SS 2166	Don't Bogart Me/Wispy Paisley Skies	4

ERIC FRATTER

69	Trojan TR 655	Since You've Been Gone/AFROTONES: Things I Love	5

(see also Eric Fatter)

FRAYS

65	Decca F 12153	Keep Me Covered/Walk On	80
65	Decca F 12229	My Girl Sloopy/For Your Precious Love	25

NORMA FRAZER

65	Ska Beat JB 223	Heartaches/Everybody Loves A Lover	8
67	Coxsone CS 7017	The First Cut Is The Deepest/BUMPS OAKLEY: Rag Doll	15
67	Studio One SO 2024	Come By Here/BOB MARLEY & WAILERS: I Stand Predominate	30
68	Coxsone CS 7060	Respect/Time	15

DALLAS FRAZIER

66	Capitol CL 15445	Elvira/That Ain't No Stuff	4
66	Capitol CL 15457	Just A Little Bit Of You/Walkin' Wonder	4
59	Capitol EAP 1035	DALLAS FRAZIER (EP)	7

JOE FRAZIER

74	Contempo CS 2022	Try It Again/Knock On Wood	4

FRAZIER CHORUS

87	4AD AD 708	Sloppy Heart/Typical (promo-only)	10
87	4AD BAD 708	Sloppy Heart/Typical (12", p/s)	8

FREAKS OF NATURE

66	Island WI 3017	People! Let's Freak Out/The Shadow Chasers	30

(see also Kim Fowley)

STAN FREBERG

51	Capitol CL 13465	John And Marsha/Ragtime Dan (78)	5
52	Capitol CL 13747	Try/Maggie (78)	5
52	Capitol CL 13846	The Boogie-Woogie Banjo Man From .../The World Is Waiting ... (78)	5
53	Capitol CL 14025	St. George And The Dragonet (with Daws Butler & June Foray)/Little Red Riding Hood (78)	7

STAN FREBERG

54	Capitol CL 14019	Christmas Dragnet (both sides) (78)	5
54	Capitol CL 14187	Sh-Boom (Life Could Be A Dream)/C'est Ci Bon (as Stan Freberg & Toads)	20
55	Capitol CL 14316	The Lone Psychiatrist/The Honey-Earthers (with Daws Butler)	14
56	Capitol CL 14509	The Yellow Rose Of Texas/Rock Around Stephen Foster	12
56	Capitol CL 14571	The Great Pretender/The Quest For Bridey Hammerschlaugen (B-side with June Foray)	12
56	Capitol CL 14608	Heartbreak Hotel/Rock Island Line	15
57	Capitol CL 14712	Banana Boat (Day-O)/Tele-vee-shun	8
58	Capitol CL 14966	Green Chritma (with Daws Butler)/The Meaning Of Christmas (with Jud Conlon Chorale)	8
60	Capitol CL 15122	The Old Payola Roll Blues (with Jesse White)/Sh-Boom (Life Could Be A Dream)	12
55	Capitol EAP1 496	ANY REQUESTS (EP)	8
56	Capitol EAP1 628	THE REAL SAINT GEORGE (EP)	10
61	Capitol EAP1 1101	OMAHA (EP)	7
61	Capitol EAP1 20050	THE GREAT PRETENDER (EP)	10
61	Capitol EAP1 20115	FREBERG AGAIN (EP, with Daws Butler)	8
57	Capitol T 777	A CHILD'S GARDEN OF FREBERG (LP)	16
64	Capitol T 2020	THE BEST OF STAN FREBERG (LP)	12

JOHN FRED & HIS PLAYBOY BAND

67	Pye Intl. 7N 25442	Judy In Disguise (With Glasses)/When The Lights Go Out	4
68	Pye Intl. 7N 25453	Hey Hey Bunny/No Letter Today	5
68	Pye Intl. 7N 25462	We Played Games/Lonely Are The Lonely	4
68	Pye Intl. 7N 25470	Little Dum Dum/Tissue Paper	4
68	CBS 3475	Shirley/High Heel Sneakers	8
67	Pye Intl. NPL 28111	AGNES ENGLISH (LP)	12

FRED BANANA COMBO

| 78 | Warm AWMR 2004 | No Destination Blues/Jerk Off All Nite Long (p/s) | 5 |

FREDDIE & DREAMERS

63	Columbia DB 7032	If You Gotta Make A Fool Of Somebody/Feel So Blue	4
63	Columbia DB 7086	I'm Telling You Now/What Have I Done To You?	4
63	Columbia DB 7147	You Were Made For Me/Send A Letter To Me	4
64	Columbia DB 7214	Over You/Come Back When You're Ready	4
64	Columbia DB 7286	I Love You Baby/Don't Make Me Cry	4
64	Columbia DB 7322	Just For You/Don't Do That To Me	4
64	Columbia DB 7381	I Understand/I Will	4
65	Columbia DB 7526	A Little You/Things I'd Like To Say	4
65	Columbia DB 7720	Thou Shalt Not Steal/I Don't Know	4
66	Columbia DB 7857	If You've Gotta Minute Baby/When I'm Home With You	4
66	Columbia DB 7929	Playboy/Some Day	4
66	Columbia DB 8033	Turn Around/Funny Over You	4
67	Columbia DB 8137	Hello, Hello/All I Ever Want Is You	4
67	Columbia DB 8200	Brown And Porter's (Meat Exporters) Lorry/Little Brown Eyes	4
68	Columbia DB 8496	Little Big Time/FREDDIE GARRITY: You Belong To Me	4
68	Columbia DB 8517	It's Great/Gaberdine Mac	4
69	Columbia DB 8606	Get Around Downtown Girl/What To Do	4
63	Columbia SEG 8275	IF YOU GOTTA MAKE A FOOL OF SOMEBODY (EP)	8
63	Columbia SEG 8287	SONGS FROM THE FILM "WHAT A CRAZY WORLD" (EP)	10
64	Columbia SEG 8302	YOU WERE MADE FOR ME (EP)	8
64	Columbia SEG 8323	OVER YOU (EP)	8
64	Columbia SEG 8349	FREDDIE SINGS JUST FOR YOU (EP)	8
65	Columbia SEG 8403	READY, FREDDIE, GO! (EP)	12
65	Columbia SEG 8457	FREDDIE AND THE DREAMERS (EP)	12
63	Columbia 33SX 1577	FREDDIE AND THE DREAMERS (LP)	16
64	Columbia 33SX 1663	YOU WERE MADE FOR ME (LP)	16
65	Columbia SX 1785	SING ALONG PARTY (LP)	12
66	Columbia S(C)X 6069	IN DISNEYLAND (LP, mono/stereo)	15/17
67	Columbia SX 6177	KING FREDDIE AND THE DREAMING KNIGHTS (LP)	15
67	M. For Pleasure MFP 1168	HITS WITH FREDDIE AND THE DREAMERS (LP, repackage of 33SX 1663)	10

(see also Freddie Garrity, Dreamers)

FREDDIE & DREAMERS/PETER & GORDON

| 64 | Columbia SEG 8337 | JUST FOR YOU (EP, 2 tracks each) | 8 |

DOTTY FREDERICK

| 59 | Top Rank JAR 106 | Ricky/Just Wait | 8 |
| 59 | Top Rank JAR 106 | Ricky/Just Wait (78) | 10 |

TOMMY FREDERICK & HI-NOTES

| 58 | London HLU 8555 | Prince Of Players/I'm Not Pretending | 45 |
| 58 | London HLU 8555 | Prince Of Players/I'm Not Pretending (78) | 15 |

BILL FREDERICKS

| 78 | Polydor 2059 035 | Almost/Wind Of Change | 10 |

DOLORES FREDERICKS

| 56 | Brunswick 05540 | Cha Cha Joe/Whole Lotta Shakin' Goin' On | 20 |
| 56 | Brunswick 05540 | Cha Cha Joe/Whole Lotta Shakin' Goin' On (78) | 6 |

MARC FREDERICKS

| 56 | London HLD 8281 | Mystic Midnight/Symphony To Anne | 12 |

FREE (Holland)

| 68 | Philips BF 1738 | Soul Party/Down To The Bone | 5 |
| 69 | Philips BF 1754 | Keep in Touch/Taking It Away | 25 |

FREE (U.K.)

| 69 | Island WIP 6054 | Broad Daylight/The Worm | 25 |
| 69 | Island WIP 6062 | I'll Be Creepin'/Sugar For Mr Morrison (initially in p/s) | 35/20 |

FREE (U.K.)

70	Island WIP 6082	All Right Now/Mouthful Of Grass (pink label)	6
70	Island WIP 6093	The Stealer/Lying In The Sunshine	6
71	Island WIP 6100	My Brother Jake/Only My Soul	4
72	Island WIP 6129	Little Bit Of Love/Sail On	4
72	Island WIP 6146	Wishing Well/Let Me Show You	4
73	Island WIP 6160	Travellin' In Style/Easy On My Soul	7
73	Island WIP 6223	Travellin' In Style/Easy On My Soul (reissue)	4
76	Island WIP 6351	The Hunter/Worry	4
78	Island IEP 6	THE FREE EP (p/s)	4
82	Island PIEP 6	THE FREE EP (12", picture disc)	7
69	Island ILPS 9089	TONS OF SOBS (LP, gatefold sleeve, pink label)	25
69	Island ILPS 9104	FREE (LP, pink label)	25
70	Island ILPS 9120	FIRE AND WATER (LP, pink label)	20
70	Island ILPS 9138	HIGHWAY (LP)	12
71	Island ILPS 9160	LIVE (LP, in envelope sleeve)	15
72	Island ILPS 9192	FREE AT LAST (LP)	10
73	Island ILPS 9217	HEARTBREAKER (LP)	10
74	Island ISLD 4	THE FREE STORY (2-LP, with 4-page booklet, numbered)	18

(see also Paul Kossoff, Bad Company, Rabbit, Kossoff Kirke Tetsu & Rabbit, Sharks)

FREE AGENTS
80	Groovy STP 1	FREE AGENTS (LP, hand-made p/s)	20

(see also Pete Shelley, Eric Random)

ALAN FREED & HIS ROCK'N'ROLL BAND
57	Vogue Coral Q 72219	Teen Rock/Right Now, Right Now (with Alan Freed's Rock'n'Rollers)	60
57	Vogue Coral Q 72219	Teen Rock/Right Now, Right Now (78)	25
57	Vogue Coral Q 72230	Rock'n'Roll Boogie/Teener's Canteen (with Alan Freed's Rock'n'Rollers)	60
57	Vogue Coral Q 72230	Rock'n'Roll Boogie/Teener's Canteen (78)	25
56	Vogue Coral LVA 9033	ROCK'N'ROLL DANCE PARTY VOL. 1 (LP, featuring Modernaires)	45
57	Vogue Coral LVA 9066	ROCK'N'ROLL DANCE PARTY VOL. 2 (LP, with Jimmy Cavello)	60

(see also Jimmy Cavello)

FREEDOM
68	Mercury MF 1033	Where Will You Be Tonight/Trying To Get A Glimpse Of You	10
68	Plexium PXM 3	Escape While You Can/Kandy Kay	8
70	Probe SPBA 6252	FREEDOM (LP)	20
71	Vertigo 6360 049	THROUGH THE YEARS (LP, gatefold sleeve, spiral label)	35
72	Vertigo 6360 072	FREEDOM IS MORE THAN A WORD (LP, gatefold sleeve, spiral label)	70

FREEDOM SINGERS
67	Studio One SO 2010	Have Faith/Work Crazy	12
70	Bamboo BAM 21	Give Peace A Chance/SOUND DIMENSION: In Cold Blood	5

FREE FERRY
69	CBS 4456	Mary, What Have You Become/Friend	8
70	CBS 4647	Haverjack Drive/Flying	4

ART FREEMAN
66	Atlantic 584 053	Slippin' Around/Can't Get You Out Of My Mind	45

BOBBY FREEMAN
58	London HLJ 8644	Do You Want To Dance/Big Fat Woman	20
58	London HLJ 8644	Do You Want To Dance/Big Fat Woman (78)	15
58	London HLJ 8721	Betty Lou Got A New Pair Of Shoes/Starlight	30
58	London HLJ 8721	Betty Lou Got A New Pair Of Shoes/Starlight (78)	18
59	London HLJ 8782	Need Your Love/Shame On You Miss Johnson	25
59	London HLJ 8782	Need Your Love/Shame On You Miss Johnson (78)	20
59	London HLJ 8898	Mary Ann Thomas/Love Me	18
59	London HLJ 8898	Mary Ann Thomas/Love Me (78)	25
60	London HLJ 9031	Sinbad/Ebb Tide (The Sea)	8
60	Parlophone R 4684	(I Do The) Shimmy Shimmy/You Don't Understand Me	8
64	Pye Intl. 7N 25260	C'mon And Swim Pts 1 & 2	12
64	Pye Intl. 7N 25280	S-W-I-M/That Little Old Heartbreaker Me	15
66	Pye Intl. 7N 25347	The Duck/Cross My Heart (some copies have "The Devil" as B-side)	each 10

BUD FREEMAN
58	Fontana TFE 17082	CHICAGO STYLE (EP, as Bud Freeman & Orchestra)	7
59	Parlophone GEP 8783	THE JAZZ SCENE (EP, as Bud Freeman & Trio)	7
59	Top Rank JKR 8021	JAZZ FOR SALE VOL. 1 (EP, as Bud Freeman & Quartet)	7
54	Columbia 33S 1016	COMES JAZZ (10" LP)	10
55	Capitol LC 6706	CLASSICS IN JAZZ (10" LP)	10

CAROL FREEMAN
67	CBS 202579	The Rolling Sea/Leaving You Now	10

ERNIE FREEMAN
57	London HLP 8523	Raunchy/Puddin'	12
57	London HLP 8523	Raunchy/Puddin' (78)	5
57	London HL 7029	Dumplin's/Beautiful Weekend (export issue)	6
58	London HLP 8558	Dumplin's/Beautiful Weekend	10
58	London HLP 8558	Dumplin's/Beautiful Weekend (78)	10
58	London HLP 8660	Indian Love Call/Summer Serenade	7
58	London HLP 8660	Indian Love Call/Summer Serenade (78)	5
60	London HLP 9041	Big River/Night Sounds	6
65	London HLP 9944	Raunchy '65/Jivin' Around	8
56	London REU 1059	ERNIE FREEMAN AND HIS RHYTHM GUITAR (EP)	25
59	London REP 1210	ERNIE FREEMAN VOL. 2 (EP)	20

EVELYN FREEMAN EXCITING VOICES
69	London HLU 10287	I Heard The Voice/I Dreamed Last Night	4

Rare Record Price Guide 371

MINT VALUE £

MARGARET FREEMAN
61 Starlite ST45 040   Forbidden Fruit/Mister Ting A Ling 8

R.B. FREEMAN
75 Avco/Embassy 6105 040   I'm Shaft/I'm Shaft You Ain't Shaft 4

RUSS FREEMAN & CHET BAKER QUARTET
60 Vogue EPV 1255   RUSS FREEMAN & CHET BAKER QUARTET (EP) 7
(see also Chet Baker)

FREE MOVEMENT
72 CBS 7768   The Harder I Try/Comin' Home 4

FREEWHEELERS
65 HMV POP 1406   Why Do You Treat Me Like A Fool/Ad Lib Blues 8

FREEZE
80 A1 A.1.1.S.1   Celebration/Cross-Over (EP) 6

FREEZE FRAME
85 Crackin' Up CRAK 2   Touch/Personal Touch (p/s) 4

ACE FREHLEY
78 Casablanca CAN 135   New York Groove/Snow Blind (p/s, blue vinyl with mask) 30
(see also Kiss)

FREIGHT TRAIN
86 Bam Caruso NRIC 031   Man's Laughter/Head On A Plate (foldout p/s) 4

DON FRENCH
59 London HLW 8884   Lonely Saturday Night/Goldilocks 80
59 London HLW 8884   Lonely Saturday Night/Goldilocks (78) 35
59 London HLW 8989   Little Blonde Girl/I Look Into My Heart 70
59 London HLW 8989   Little Blonde Girl/I Look Into My Heart (78) 30

RAY FRENCH
66 Pye 7N 17215   Since I Lost My Baby/Gun Me Down 8

FRENCH IMPRESSIONISTS
82 Operation Twilight OPT 20 Santa Baby/Jingle Bell Rock (p/s) 7
(see also Aztec Camera)

FRENCH REVOLUTION
69 Decca F 22898   Nine Till Five/Why 40

FRENZY
81 Frenzy FRENZY 1   This Is The Last Time/Gypsy Dancer (no p/s) 8
84 Nervous NEP 002   Robot Riot/All Alone (p/s) 6
84 Nervous 12 NEP 002   Robot Riot/All Alone/Cry Or Die/Torment (12", p/s) 8

FRESH
70 RCA RCA 2003   Stoned In Saigon/Just A Note 4
70 RCA SF 8122   FRESH OUT OF BORSTAL (LP) 10

FRESH AIR
69 Pye 7N 17736   Running Wild/Stop Look Listen 70
71 Philips 6006 187   It Takes Too Long/Here Comes Summer 5
72 Columbia DB 8872   Bye Bye Jane/It's All Over 5

FRESHIES
78 Razz RAZZXEP 1   BAISER (EP, with Chris Sievey solo tracks, 33rpm, no'd, handwritten labels) ...15
79 Razz RAZZXEP 2   STRAIGHT IN AT NO. 2 (EP, handwritten labels with inserts, 1,000 only, numbered, green or orange p/s) 10
79 Razz RAZZ 3   THE MEN FROM BANANA ISLAND WHOSE STUPID IDEAS NEVER CAUGHT ON IN THE WESTERN WORLD AS WE KNOW IT (EP) 7
79 Razz RAZZ 5   We're Like You/CHRIS SIEVEY: Hey (p/s) 5
80 Razz RAZZ 6   Yellow Spot/If It's News (p/s) 5
80 Razz RAZZ 7   No Money/Oh Girl (p/s) 4
80 Razz RAZZ 8   RED INDIAN MUSIC (EP, with Chris Sievey) 5
80 Razz RAZZ 11   I'm In Love With The Girl On The Manchester Checkout Desk/Singalong Version (p/s, some with free lyric book) 5/4
80 Razz RAZZ 12   I'm In Love With The Girl On The Manchester Checkout Desk (Radio Version)/Singalong Version ('bleeped') (white label radio issue, 200 only) 10
80 Razz RAZZ 13   One To One/House Beautiful (unreleased)
81 MCA MCAS 693   Wrap Up The Rockets And Its Gonna Get Better/Tell Her I'm Ill (cassette) 4
81 CV CVS 1   If You Really Love ... Buy Me A Shirt/I Am A Walrus (p/s) 4
81 HANNA 1   Virgin Megastore/Rap Up The Rockets/Buy Me A Shirt/Tell Her I'm Ill/Frank Talks To Chris (Conversation) (12", white label, stickered sleeve) 7
78 Razz RAZZC 1   ALL SLEEPS SECRETS (12-track cassette) 10
79 Razz RAZZCS-2   MANCHESTER PLAYS (6-track radio session cassette with interview, 1,000 only) 10
79 Razz RAZZCS-3   SING THE GIRLS FROM BANANA ISLAND (16-track cassette, 1,000 only) 10
80 Razz CS-4   ROUGH AND READY (12-track cassette, 1,000 only) 10
81 Razz CS-5   LONDON PLAYS (cassette, live & radio sessions, 1,000 only) 10
85 ETS 1   JOHNNY RADAR STORY (20-track cassette, some with free Frank Sidebottom 8-track: "Firm Favourites") 15/10
85 ETS 1   JOHNNY RADAR STORY (vinyl test pressing) 40
85 ETS 3   EARLY RAZZ (cassette) 10
85 ETS 4   STUDIO OUT-TAKES (cassette) 10
(see also Chris Sievey, Frank Sidebottom)

FRESH MAGGOTS
71 RCA SF 8205   FRESH MAGGOTS (LP) 150

FRESHMEN
67 Pye 7N 17432   Papa Oom Mow Mow/Let's Dance 6

MINT VALUE £

68	Pye 7N 17592	Go Granny Go/Look At The Sunshine	6
69	Pye 7N 17689	Just To See You Smile/Indian Lake	6
69	Pye 7N 17757	She Sang Hymns Out Of Tune/Mr. Beverly's Heavy Days	6
70	CBS 4842	Halfway To Where/Time Hasn't Changed Her	4
70	CBS 5168	Banquet For The World/Time Hasn't Changed Her	4
72	CBS 7694	Swanee River/Take The Time It Takes	4
68	Pye	MOVIN' ON (LP)	50
70	CBS 64099	PEACE ON EARTH (LP)	35

FRESH WINDOWS
| 67 | Fontana TF 839 | Fashion Conscious/Summer Sun Shines | 40 |

FREUR
| 83 | CBS WA 3141 | Doot Doot/Hold Me Mother (picture disc, stickered PVC sleeve) | 4 |
| 83 | CBS A13 3141 | Doot Doot (Extended Version)/Hold Me Mother (Extended) (12", textured p/s) | 7 |

FRIDA
82	Epic EPCA 2863	To Turn To Stone/I Got Something (p/s)	4
84	Epic EPCA 4886	Heart Of The Country/Slowly (p/s)	5
84	Epic TA 4886	Heart Of The Country/Slowly/I Know There's Something Going On (Extended) (12", p/s)	8

(see also Abba)

BOY FRIDAY
70	Downtown DT 470	Version Girl/Grumble Man	5
70	Downtown DT 471	Music So Good/Right Track (both with Groovers)	4
70	Downtown DT 472	Sounds I Remember/JOAN LONG: Reconsider Our Love	4
70	Downtown DT 473	Take A Message Ruby/Second Note	4
71	Downtown DT 476	There'll Always Be Sunshine/Sunshine Track	4
71	Downtown DT 477	Hot Pants Girl/Raunchy	4

CAROL FRIDAY
65	Parlophone R 5297	Gone Tomorrow/Show Me The Way	4
65	Parlophone R 5369	Everybody I Know/Wasted Days	20
67	Parlophone R 5567	Big Sister/I Look Around Me	4

GAVIN FRIDAY
| 87 | Baby BABY 9 | You Can't Always Get What You Want/Blessings (p/s, coloured vinyl) | 4 |

(see also Virgin Prunes)

FRIDAY KNIGHTS
| 60 | Oriole CB 1579 | Poor Man's Roses/Don't Open That Door | 4 |

FRIDGES
| 80 | Ink-Ink II 01 | Lynn Freeze/Shower Of B's/That's Why I Took Up The Harmonica/No Room! (p/s, with insert) | 4 |

KINKY FRIEDMAN
74	Vanguard VSD 79333	SOLD AMERICAN (LP)	10
75	ABC ABCL 5134	KINKY FRIEDMAN (LP)	10
76	Epic EPC 81640	LASSO FROM EL PASO (LP)	10

BRIAN JOSEPH FRIEL
| 74 | Dawn DNLS 3054 | BRIAN JOSEPH FRIEL (LP) | 10 |
| 75 | Dawn DNLS 3064 | ARRIVERDERCI ARDROSSAN (LP) | 10 |

TERRY FRIEND & FRIENDS
| 77 | Tramp | COME THE DAY (LP, private pressing, 100 only) | 20 |

(see also Stonefield Tramp)

FRIEND & LOVER
| 68 | Verve VS 1515 | Reach Out Of The Darkness/Time Is On Your Side | 4 |

FRIENDLY HOPEFULS
| 81 | Abstract ABS 004 | Tribute To The Punks Of '76/Tribute To The Punks Of '76 (Disco Dub Mix) (p/s, coloured vinyl) | 4 |

FRIENDLY PERSUASION
| 74 | Rare Earth RES 120 | Remember (Sha La La)/I'll Always Do The Best I Can | 4 |

FRIENDS
| 68 | Deram DM 198 | Piccolo Man/Mythological Sunday | 20 |

(see also Flowerpot Men)

FRIENDS AGAIN
| 83 | Moonboot MOON 1 | Honey At The Core/Lucky Star (p/s) | 4 |
| 84 | Mercury FAEP 1 | Lullaby No. 2 Love On Board/Wand You Wave/Thank You For Being An Angel//Sunkissed (New Version)/State Of Art (Remix) ('The Friends Again EP' double pack, stickered gatefold p/s) | 4 |

FRIJID PINK
70	Deram DM 288	The House Of The Rising Sun/Drivin' Blues	5
70	Deram DM 309	Sing A Song Of Freedom/End Of The Line	4
70	Deram DM 321	Heartbreak Hotel/Bye Bye Blues	5
71	Deram DM 332	Music For The People/Sloony	5
71	Deram DM 347	Lost Son/I Love Her	5
70	Deram SML 1062	FRIJID PINK (LP)	20
70	Deram SML 1077	DEFROSTED (LP)	20

(Robert) FRIPP & (Brian) ENO
| 73 | Island HELP 16 | NO PUSSYFOOTIN' (LP) | 10 |
| 75 | Island HELP 22 | EVENING STAR (LP) | 10 |

(see also Giles Giles & Fripp, King Crimson, Brian Eno, Roxy Music)

JACKIE FRISCO
| 63 | Decca F 11566 | Sugar Baby/You Can't Catch Me | 5 |

Jackie FRISCO

MINT VALUE £

| 63 | Decca F 11692 | When You Ask About Love/He's So Near | 5 |

VONNIE FRITCHIE
| 55 | London HLU 8178 | Sugar Booger Avenue/There I Stood (To Throw Old Shoes And Rice) | 30 |

FRED FRITH
| 74 | Caroline C 1508 | GUITAR SOLOS (LP) | 10 |
| 76 | Caroline C 1518 | GUITAR SOLOS 2 (LP) | 10 |

(see also Henry Cow)

FRITZ, MIKE & MO
| 65 | Philips BF 1427 | Somebody Stole The Sun/Let Me Hear Your Voice | 4 |
| 65 | Philips BF 1441 | What Colour Is A Man/So Now You're Gone | 4 |

WYNDER K. FROG
66	Island WI 280	Turn On Your Lovelight/Zooming	8
66	Island WI 3011	Sunshine Superman/Blues For A Frog	6
67	Island WIP 6006	Green Door/Dancing Frog	10
67	Island WIP 6014	I Am A Man/Shook Shimmy & Shake	8
68	Island WIP 6044	Jumping Jack Flash/Baldy	8
67	Island ILP 944/ILPS 9044	SUNSHINE SUPERFROG (LP, white label)	25
68	Island ILP 982/ILPS 9082	OUT OF THE FRYING PAN (LP, pink label)	20

RAYMOND FROGGATT
68	Polydor 56249	Callow-La-Vita/Lost Autumn	4
68	Polydor 56274	Just A Little Bit Of Love/ABC Gold Fish	4
68	Polydor 56284	The Red Balloon/Lost Autumn	4
68	Polydor 56294	Time Goes By/Rolly	4
69	Polydor 56314	Ring Ting A Ling/Anything You Want To	4
69	Polydor 56334	Movin' Down South/It's Only Me	4
69	Polydor 56358	Lazy Jack/Hasn't The Lord Blessed You	4
69	Polydor 583 044	THE VOICE AND WRITING OF RAYMOND FROGGATT (LP)	20
72	Bell BELLS 207	BLEACH (LP)	18
74	Reprise K 44257	ROGUES AND THIEVES (LP)	12

FROGMEN
| 61 | Oriole CB 1617 | Underwater/Mad Rush | 12 |

FROGMORTON
| 76 | Philips 6006 506 | White Swans/Uncivilised Man | 4 |
| 76 | Philips 6308 261 | AT LAST (LP) | 20 |

JANE FROMAN
54	Capitol CL 14208	The Song From "Desiree" (We Meet Again)/Mine	8
54	Capitol CL 14209	The Finger Of Suspicion Points At You/My Shining Hour	12
55	Capitol CL 14254	I Wonder/I'll Never Be The Same	12
56	Capitol CL 14340	Summertime In Venice/A Sound Foundation	6
56	Capitol CL 14658	You'll Never Walk Alone/One Little Candle	4
56	Capitol EAP1 600	JANE FROMAN (EP)	8
56	Capitol EAP1 889	SONGS AT SUNSET (EP)	7
56	Capitol EAP2 889	SONGS AT SUNSET (EP)	7
56	Capitol EAP3 889	SONGS AT SUNSET (EP)	7
50s	Capitol	LP	10

FRONT
| 77 | The Label TLR 005 | System/Queen's Mafia (p/s) | 4 |

DOM FRONTIERE & HIS ORCHESTRA
| 57 | London HLU 8385 | Jet Rink Ballad/Uno Mas | 18 |

FRONT LINE
| 65 | Atlantic AT 4057 | Got Love/I Don't Care | 30 |

DAVID FROST (& others)
66	Parlophone R 5441	Zookeeper/Deck Of Cards	4
66	Parlophone PMC 7005	THE FROST REPORT ON BRITAIN (LP)	12
67	Pye NPL 18199	THE FROST REPORT ON EVERYTHING (LP)	12

MAX FROST & TROOPERS
| 68 | Capitol CL 15565 | Shape Of Things To Come/Free Lovin' | 15 |

FROST LANE
| 71 | Cutty Wren | FROST LANE (LP) | 60 |

FRUGAL SOUND
66	Pye 7N 17062	Norwegian Wood/Cruel To Be Kind	5
66	Pye 7N 17129	Just Outside The Door/I'm On Your Side	4
67	RCA Victor RCA 1556	Backstreet Girl/Reason To Believe	5
67	RCA Victor RCA 1595	Abilene/Love Is A New Face	4
68	RCA Victor RCA 1659	All Strung Out/Miss Mary	4

FRUIT MACHINE
| 69 | Spark SRL 1003 | Follow Me/Cuddly Toy | 25 |
| 70 | Spark SRL 1027 | I'm Alone Today/Sunshine Of Your Love | 70 |

FRUMPY
| 71 | Vertigo 6305 067 | ALL WILL BE CHANGED (LP) | 12 |
| 72 | Vertigo 6305 098 | FRUMP 2 (LP, black & blue vinyl) | 16 |

FRUUP
74	Dawn DNS 1087	Prince Of Heaven/Jaunting Car	7
73	Dawn DNLS 3053	FUTURE LEGENDS (LP)	25
74	Dawn DNLS 3058	SEVEN SECRETS (LP, with lyric insert)	25
74	Dawn DNLH 2	THE PRINCE OF HEAVEN'S EYES (LP, some with book)	25/20
75	Dawn DNLS 3070	MODERN MASQUERADES (LP)	25

374 Rare Record Price Guide

FUCHSIA
| 71 | Pegasus PEG 8 | FUCHSIA (LP) | 60 |

FUGI
| 71 | Blue Horizon 2096 005 | Red Moon Pts 1 & 2 | 10 |

FUGITIVES (U.S.)
| 61 | Vogue V 9176 | Freeway/Fugitive | 15 |

FUGITIVES (Jamaica)
| 67 | Doctor Bird DB 1082 | Musical Pressure/LESLIE BUTLER & FUGITIES: Winchester Rocksteady | 10 |

(see also Jo Jo Bennett & Fugitives)

FUGS
68	Big T BIG 115	Crystal Liaison/When The Mode Of The Music Changes	7
68	Transatlantic TRA 180	TENDERNESS JUNCTION (LP, some with poster)	25/15
68	Transatlantic TRA 181	IT CRAWLED INTO MY HAND, HONEST (LP)	12
69	Fontana (S)TL 5501	VIRGIN FUGS (LP)	15
69	Fontana (S)TL 5513	THE FUGS ... FIRST ALBUM (LP)	15
69	Fontana (S)TL 5524	FUGS II (LP)	15
69	Reprise RSLP 6359	THE BELLE OF AVENUE A (LP)	10
75	ESP-Disk ESP 2018	ROUNDERS SCORE (LP)	10

HIROSHI FUKUMURA
| 80 | Champagne | HUNT UP THE WIND (LP) | 10 |

FULHAM FURIES
| 78 | GM GMS 9050 | These Boots Are Made For Walking/Under Pressure | 12 |

BLIND BOY FULLER
57	Philips BBL 7510	BLIND BOY FULLER 1935-40 (LP)	40
68	Matchbox SDR 143	BLIND BOY FULLER ON DOWN VOLUME 1 (LP)	15
69	Matchbox SDR 168	BLIND BOY FULLER ON DOWN VOLUME 2 (LP)	15
60s	Flyright LP 105	CAROLINA BLUES (LP)	12

GIL FULLER & DIZZY GILLESPIE
| 66 | Fontana 688 147 ZL | MAN FROM MONTEREY (LP) | 10 |

(see also Dizzy Gillespie)

JERRY FULLER
59	London HLH 8982	The Tennessee Waltz/Charlene	8
59	London HLH 8982	The Tennessee Waltz/Charlene (78)	35
61	London HLN 9439	Guilty Of Loving You/First Love Never Dies	6
62	Salvo SLO 1802	Lipstick And Rouge/Mother Goose At The Bandstand	8

JESSE FULLER
65	Good Time Jazz GV 2426	San Francisco Bay Blues/New Midnight Special	6
67	Good Time Jazz GV 2427	Runnin' Wild/The Monkey And The Engineer	6
67	Fontana TF 821	Going Back To My Old Used To Be/Bye And Bye	12
58	Good Time Jazz LAG 12159	JESSE FULLER (LP)	15
60	Good Time Jazz LAG 12279	LONE CAT (LP)	15
60	Topic 10T 59	JESSE FULLER (10" LP)	25
63	Good Time Jazz LAG 574	SAN FRANCISCO BAY BLUES (LP)	10
65	Stateside SL 10154	JESSE FULLER'S FAVOURITES (LP)	10
66	Fontana TL 5313	SESSION WITH JESSE FULLER (LP)	15
66	Topic 12T 134	MOVE ON DOWN THE LINE (LP)	25
66	Stateside SL 10166	SAN FRANCISCAN BAY BLUES (LP, reissue)	10
60s	Vocalion VRLP 574	SAN FRANCISCO BAY BLUES (LP)	15

JOHNNY FULLER
| 73 | Speciality SON 5017 | Haunted House/Swinging At The Creek | 6 |

RANDY FULLER
| 67 | President PT 111 | It's Love, Come What May/The Things You Do | 8 |

(see also Bobby Fuller Four)

BOBBY FULLER FOUR
66	London HLU 10030	I Fought The Law/Little Annie Lou	15
66	London HLU 10041	Love's Made A Fool Of You/Don't You Ever Let Me Know	10
67	President PTL 1003	MEMORIAL ALBUM (LP)	12

(see also Randy Fuller)

FULL TIME MEN
| 80s | Shigaku SHIG 1T | I Got Wheels/One More Time/Way Down South (12", p/s) | 8 |

(see also R.E.M.)

LOWELL FULSON/FULSOM
53	London L 1199	I Love My Baby/The Blues Came Rollin' In (78)	35
65	Sue WI 375	Too Many Drivers/Key To My Heart	15
66	Sue WI 4023	Talking Woman/Blues Around Midnight	25
66	Outasite 45-502	Stop And Think/Baby (with Leon Blue)	35
67	Fontana TF 795	Tramp/Pico	20
70	Polydor 56 515	Black Nights/Little Angel	12
76	Jet JET 770	Do You Love/Monday Morning	6
69	Fontana SFJL 920	SAN FRANCISCO BLUES (LP)	20
69	Polydor 2384 038	IN A HEAVY BAG (LP, as Lowell Fulsom)	10

FUMBLE
| 72 | Sovereign SVNA 7254 | FUMBLE (LP, gatefold sleeve) | 18 |

FUNBOY FIVE
| 80s | Cool Cat Daddy-O PHUN 1 | Life After Death/Compulsive Eater (foldover p/s) | 4 |

FUN BOY THREE
| 82 | Chrysalis CHSP 2609 | The Telephone Always Rings/The Alibi (2 different picture discs) | each 4 |

FUN BOY THREE

82	Chrysalis CHSP 2629	Summertime/Summer Of '82 (picture disc)	4
83	Chrysalis CHSP 2678	Tunnel Of Love/The Lunacy Legacy (picture disc)	4
83	Chrysalis FUNXP 1/	Our Lips Are Sealed/Our Lips Are Sealed (Version)//We're All Having Fun/	
	FBFRE 1	Going Home (double pack)	4

(see also Specials, Colour Field)

FUN FOUR
80	NMC NMC 010	Singing In The Showers/By Products/Elevator Crush (p/s)	8

(see also Orange Juice)

FUNHOUSE
82	Ensign ENY 222	Out Of Control/This Could Be Hell (p/s)	20
82	Ensign ENYT 222	Out Of Control (Full Version)/This Could Be Hell (12", p/s)	25

(see also Another Pretty Face, DNV, Waterboys)

FUNKADELIC
70	Pye Intl. 7N 25519	I Got A Thing, You Got A Thing, Everybody's Got A Thing/	
		Fish, Chips & Sweat	10
71	Pye Intl. 7N 25548	You & Your Folks, Me & Mine/Funky Dollar Bill	10
72	Janus 6146 001	Can You Get To That/Back In Our Minds	6
78	Warner Bros K 17246	One Nation Under A Groove Pts 1 & 2	4
78	Warner Bros K 17246T	One Nation Under A Groove Pts 1 & 2 (12")	7
78	Warner Bros SP 17246	One Nation Under A Groove Pts 1 & 2 (12")	10
79	Warner Bros K 17321	Cholly (Funk Getting Ready To Roll)/Into You	4
79	Warner Bros K 17494	(Not Just) Knee Deep Pts 1 & 2	4
81	Warner Bros K 17786	The Electric Spanking Of War Babies/(Instrumental Mix) (p/s)	4
81	Warner Bros K 17786T	The Electric Spanking Of War Babies/(Instrumental Mix) (12")	7
70	Pye Intl. NSPL 28137	FUNKADELIC (LP)	35
71	Pye Intl. NSPL 28144	FREE YOUR MIND AND YOUR ASS WILL FOLLOW (LP)	35
71	Westbound 6310 200	MAGGOT BRAIN (LP)	35
75	20th Century W 215	LET'S TAKE IT TO THE STAGE (LP)	15
78	Warner Bros K 56299	HARDCORE JOLLIES (LP)	18
78	Warner Bros K 56359	ONE NATION UNDER A GROOVE (LP)	10
79	Warner Bros K 56712	UNCLE JAM WANTS YOU (LP, gatefold sleeve)	18
81	Warner Bros K 56299	THE ELECTRIC SPANKING OF WAR BABIES (LP)	15

(see also Parliament, Parlet, Brides Of Funkenstein, Bootsy's Rubber Band)

FUNKAPOLITAN
82	London LON 1	As Time Goes By/As Time Goes By (Version) (box set)	4

FUNKEES
75	Contempo CD 2058	Tu Lay/Cool It Down	4
76	Black Magic BM 114	Abraka/Ole	4

FUNKY BOTTOM CONGREGATION
71	Beacon BEA 122	Hara-Krishna/Things About Yourself	4

FUNKY JUNCTION
73	St. Gold Award MER 373	PLAY TRIBUTE TO DEEP PURPLE (LP)	10

(members of Thin Lizzy are rumoured to perform on this record)

FUR BIBLE
85	New Rose NEW 61	Plunder The Tombs/Headbolt/Fumblefist (12", p/s)	7

FINBAR & EDDIE FUREY
68	Transatlantic	FINBAR AND EDDIE FUREY (LP)	25
72	Dawn DNLS 3037	THE DAWNING OF THE DAY (LP, with insert)	22

FURIOUS APPLES
83	Sonar SON 2	Engineering/Bella Donna (p/s)	4

FURNITURE
80	Guy From Paraguay PARA 1	Shaking Story/Take A Walk Down Town (no p/s)	10
84	Survival SUR 023	Dancing The Hard Bargain/Robert Nightman's Story (p/s)	4
85	Premonition PREM 3	I Can't Crack/Switch Off/Pause/I Can't Crack (Broken Mix) (12", p/s)	7
86	Survival SUR 53	Brilliant Mind/On A Bus With Peter Nero (promo, mail order only)	5
86	Stiff SEEZ 64	THE WRONG PEOPLE (LP, with inner sleeve)	10

TOMMY FURTADO
57	London HLA 8418	Sun Tan Sam/Isabella	12
57	London HLA 8418	Sun Tan Sam/Isabella (78)	5

BILLY FURY
59	Decca F 11102	Maybe Tomorrow/Gonna Type A Letter (triangular centre, later round)	15/20
59	Decca F 11102	Maybe Tomorrow/Gonna Type A Letter (78)	20
59	Decca F 11128	Margo, Don't Go/Don't Knock Upon My Door (triangular centre, later round)	15/10
59	Decca F 11128	Margo, Don't Go/Don't Knock Upon My Door (78)	25
59	Decca F 11158	Angel Face/The Time Has Come (triangular centre, later round)	30/25
59	Decca F 11158	Angel Face/The Time Has Come (78)	30
59	Decca F 11189	My Christmas Prayer/Last Kiss (triangular centre, later round)	45/35
59	Decca F 11189	My Christmas Prayer/Last Kiss (78)	40
60	Decca F 11200	Colette/Baby How I Cried (triangular centre, later round)	25/15
60	Decca F 11237	That's Love/You Don't Know (as Billy Fury & Four Jays)	10
60	Decca F 11267	Wondrous Place/Alright, Goodbye	10
60	Decca F 11311	A Thousand Stars/Push Push	10
61	Decca F 11334	Don't Worry/Talkin' In My Sleep (with Four Kestrels)	8
61	Decca F 11349	Halfway To Paradise/Cross My Heart	5
61	Decca F 11384	Jealousy/Open Your Arms	4
61	Decca F 11409	I'd Never Find Another You/Sleepless Nights	4
62	Decca F 11437	Letter Full Of Tears/Magic Eyes	6
62	Decca F 11458	Last Night Was Made For Love/A King For Tonight	4
62	Decca F 11485	Once Upon A Dream/If I Lose You	4

MINT VALUE £

62	Decca F 11508	Because Of Love/Running Around 4
63	Decca F 11582	Like I've Never Been Gone/What Do You Think You're Doing 4
63	Decca F 11655	When Will You Say I Love You/All I Wanna Do Is Cry 4
63	Decca F 11701	In Summer/I'll Never Fall In Love Again 4
63	Decca F 11744	Somebody Else's Girl/Go Ahead And Ask Her 5
63	Decca F 11792	Do You Really Love Me Too/What Am I Gonna Do 4
64	Decca F 11888	I Will/Ain't Nothin' Shakin' But The Leaves 7
64	Decca F 11939	It's Only Make Believe/Baby What Do You Want Me To Do 4
64	Decca F 40719	Hippy Hippy Shake/Glad All Over (export only, some with p/s) 50/25
65	Decca F 12048	I'm Lost Without You/You Better Believe It, Baby 4
65	Decca F 12178	In Thoughts Of You/Away From You 4
65	Decca F 12230	Run To My Lovin' Arms/Where Do You Run? 5
66	Decca F 12325	I'll Never Quite Get Over You/I Belong To The Wind 5
66	Decca F 12409	Don't Let A Little Pride Stand In Your Way/Didn't See The Real Thing
		Come Along 6
66	Decca F 12459	Give Me Your Word/She's So Far Out She's In 7
67	Parlophone R 5560	Hurtin' Is Loving/Things Are Changing 15
67	Parlophone R 5605	Loving You/I'll Go Along With It Now 10
67	Parlophone R 5634	Suzanne In The Mirror/It Just Don't Matter Now 12
67	Parlophone R 5658	Beyond The Shadow Of A Doubt/Baby Do You Love Me? 10
68	Parlophone R 5681	Silly Boy Blue/One Minute Woman 25
68	Parlophone R 5723	Phone Box/Any Morning Now 20
68	Parlophone R 5747	Lady/Certain Things 15
69	Parlophone R 5788	I Call For My Rose/Bye Bye 15
69	Parlophone R 5819	All The Way To The U.S.A./Do My Best For You 18
70	Parlophone R 5845	Why Are You Leaving?/Old Sweet Roll (Hi-De-Ho) 20
70	Parlophone R 5874	Paradise Alley/Well ... All Right 25
72	Fury FY 301	Will The Real Man Please Stand Up/At This Stage 12
74	Warner Bros WB 16402	I'll Be Your Sweetheart/Fascinating Candle Flame 4
76	NEMS NES 018	Halfway To Paradise/Turn My Back On You 6
81	Polydor POSP 355	Be Mine Tonight/No Trespassers (p/s) 4
82	Polydor POSP 488	Love Or Money/Love Sweet Love (p/s) 4
82	Polydor POSP 528	Devil Or Angel/Don't Tell Me Lies (p/s, with original 'orchestra' mix) 4
83	Polydor POSP 558	Forget Him/Your Words (p/s) 4
83	Polydor POSP 558	Forget Him/Your Words (mispress, plays "Let Me Go Lover") 12
83	Lyntone LYN 13078/BF 1	Devil Or Angel/Lost Without You (flexidisc) 5
83	Polydor	BILLY FURY IN INTERVIEW WITH STUART COLEMAN (10", 200 only) 20
59	Decca DFE 6597	MAYBE TOMORROW (EP, yellow or red sleeve; triangular centre,
		later round) 50/35
61	Decca DFE 6694	BILLY FURY (EP) 30
62	Decca DFE 6699	BILLY FURY NO. 2 (EP) 30
62	Decca DFE 6708	PLAY IT COOL (EP) 14
62	Decca DFE 8505	BILLY FURY HITS (EP) 15
63	Decca DFE 8525	BILLY FURY AND THE TORNADOS (EP) 25
63	Decca DFE 8558	AM I BLUE (EP) 25
65	Decca DFE 8641	BILLY FURY AND THE GAMBLERS (EP) 50
73	Ronco MR EP 001	LONG LIVE ROCK (EP, with others, no p/s) 15
83	Decca DFE 8686	MY CHRISTMAS PRAYER (EP) 7
60	Decca LF 1329	THE SOUND OF FURY (10" LP) 50
60	Ace Of Clubs ACL 1047	BILLY FURY (LP) 25
61	Ace Of Clubs ACL 1083	HALFWAY TO PARADISE (LP) 25
63	Decca LK 4533	BILLY (LP) 30
63	Decca LK 4548/SKL 4538	WE WANT BILLY! (live LP, with Tornados, mono/stereo) 30/40
65	Decca LK 4677	I'VE GOTTA HORSE (LP, soundtrack) 40
67	Ace Of Clubs ACL 1229	THE BEST OF BILLY FURY (LP) 20
81	Decca LFT 1329	THE SOUND OF FURY (10" LP, reissue) 10

(see also Tornados, Gamblers)

FURYS

63	Stateside SS 182	Never More/Zing! Went The Strings Of My Heart 5
72	Jay Boy BOY 61	What Is Soul/I Lost My Baby 4
73	Jay Boy BOY 68	I'm Satisfied With You/Just A Little Mixed Up 6

FURY'S TORNADOES

74	Warner Bros K 16442	Telstar '74/I Would Give You Anything 5

(see also Billy Fury, Tornados)

FUSION

79	Plastic F..... PFUL 1104	Cold Outside (12") 7
80	Telephone TEL 101	TILL I HEAR FROM YOU (LP, blue vinyl) 20

(see also Nik Kershaw)

FUSION ORCHESTRA

73	EMI 2056	When My Mama's Not At Home/Nuthouse Rock 6
73	EMI EMA 758	A SKELETON IN ARMOUR (LP) 60

FUT

69	Beacon BEA 160	Have You Heard The Word/Futting Around 20

(see also Bee Gees, Marbles, Maurice Gibb; this record has NO Beatles involvement)

FUTURA 2000 WITH THE CLASH

83	Celluloid CYZ 104	The Escapades Of Futura 2000/Instrumental (p/s) 4
83	Celluloid CYZ 104	The Escapades Of Futura 2000/Instrumental (12", p/s) 7

(see also Clash)

FUTURE HEROES

82	Eagle BSB 020	Antmania/Hold On (p/s) 5

FUTURE PRIMITIVES

81	Illuminated ILL 5	Running Away/The Last Sunset (p/s) 4

FUTURES
75	Buddah BDS 430	You Better Be Certain/No One Could Compare	10
75	Buddah BDLP 4031	CASTLES IN THE SKY (LP)	10

FUTURYTHM
85	Exoteric EX 1	Anti Matter/It Never Rains In Outer Space (p/s)	4
	(see also Martin O'Cuthbert)		

FUZZ FACE
68	Page One POF 065	Mighty Quinn/Voices From The Sky	5

FUZZY DUCK
71	MAM 37	Double Time Woman/Just Look Around You	15
71	MAM 51	Big Brass Band/One More Hour	15
71	MAM 1005	FUZZY DUCK (LP)	150
90	Reflection MM 05	FUZZY DUCK (LP, reissue with booklet & single "Double Time Woman"/"One More Hour" [MMS 01])	18

FYNN McCOOL
70	RCA 1956	U.S. Thumbstyle/Diamond Lil	7
70	RCA SF 8112	FYNN McCOOL (LP)	45

FRANKIE GOES TO HOLLYWOOD

JOHNNY G.
80   Beggars Banquet SAM 123   G BEAT (12" sampler, stickered white label, hand-made sleeve) 7

TOMMY G. & CHARMS
67   London HLB 10107   I Know What I Want/Want You So Bad 6

WINSTON G. (& WICKED)
65	Parlophone R 5266	Please Do.'t Say/Like A Baby 12
66	Parlophone R 5330	Until You Were Gone/That Way Too (as Winston G. & Wicked) 8
66	Decca F 12444	Cloud Nine/I'll Make You Cry Tomorrow 10
67	Decca F 12559	Mother Ferguson's Love Dust/Judge And Jury 12
67	Decca F 12623	Riding With The Milkman/Bye Bye Baby 12

BASIL GABBIDON
61	Blue Beat BB 38	No More Wedding (as Basil Gabbidon & Mellow Larks)/Light Of My Life 10
61	Blue Beat BB 69	Warpaint Baby/I Was Wrong 10
62	Blue Beat BB 106	Oh Shirley (with Patsy Todd)/ROLAND ALPHONSO: Sam The Fisherman 10
62	Blue Beat BB 111	Iverene/Lover Man 10
62	Blue Beat BB 124	Independence Blues/For You My Love 10
62	Blue Beat BB 129	Our Melody/Going Back To Ja 10
62	Island WI 033	I Found My Baby/No Fault Of Mine 10
63	Island WI 076	I Bet You Don't Know/Three Times Seven 10
63	Island WI 089	St. Louis Woman/Get On The Ball 10
63	Blue Beat BB 155	Ena Meena/Since You're Gone 10
63	Blue Beat BB 161	I'll Find Love/MELLOW LARKS: What You Gonna Do 10
65	Blue Beat BB 288	Tick Tock (actually by Theo Beckford)/The Streets Of Glory (actually by Theo Beckford & Yvonne Harrison) 8

(see also Derrick Patsy & Basil)

PETER GABRIEL
77	Charisma CB 301	Solsbury Hill/Moribund The Bürgermeister (p/s) 10
77	Charisma CB 302	Modern Love/Slow Burn (no p/s, 'nude' picture label) 40
77	Charisma CB 302	Modern Love/Slow Burn (no p/s, silver label) 5
78	Charisma CB 311	D.I.Y./Prospective (p/s) 8
78	Charisma CB 319	D.I.Y. (Remix)/Mother Of Violence/Me And My Teddy Bear (unissued) .... 25+
78	Sound For Ind'y SFI 381	Solsbury Hill (live) (1-sided flexidisc, concert freebie) 7
80	Charisma CB 354	Games Without Frontiers/The Start/I Don't Remember (Mix) (p/s) 5
80	Charisma CB 360	No Self Control/Lead A Normal Life (p/s) 4
80	Charisma CB 370	Biko/Shosholoza/Jetzt Kommt Die Flut (p/s) 8
80	Charisma CB 370-12	Biko/Shosholoza/Jetzt Kommt Die Flut (12", p/s) 8
82	Charisma SHOCK 1	Shock The Monkey/Soft Dog (p/s) 4
82	Charisma SHOCK 1	Shock The Monkey/Shock The Monkey (Instrumental) (p/s) 10
82	Charisma SHOCK 122	Shock The Monkey/Soft Dog (picture disc, PVC sleeve) 8
82	Charisma SHOCK 12	Shock The Monkey/Soft Dog (12", p/s) 7
82	Charisma SHOCK 343	Shock The Monkey (Vocal)/(Instrumental) (12", p/s) 8
82	Charisma CB 405	I Have The Touch/Across The River (p/s) 5
83	Virgin GAB 1	I Don't Remember (live remix)/Solsbury Hill (live) (p/s) 4
83	Virgin GAB 12/GAB 122	I Don't Remember (live remix)/Solsbury Hill (live)/Kiss Of Life (live)/Games Without Frontiers (live)/Schnappschuss (Ein Familien-Foto) (12", double pack) 10
84	Virgin VS 689	Walk Through The Fire/The Race (p/s) 4
84	Virgin VS 689-12	Walk Through The Fire/The Race/I Have The Touch (Remix) (12", p/s) 7
86	Virgin PGS 113	Sledgehammer (Dance Mix)/Don't Break This Rhythm/Biko (Original 12" Mix)/I Have The Touch ('85 Remix) (12", p/s) 7
86	Virgin PGT 112	Sledgehammer (Dance Mix)/Don't Break This Rhythm/Sledgehammer (Album Version)/Biko (Original 12" Mix) (cassette, gold card box) 7
87	Virgin PGT 312	Big Time (Extended)/Curtains/No Self Control/Across The River (cassette, silver card box) 7
87	Virgin GAIL 312	Big Time (Extended)/Curtains/No Self Control/Across The River/ Big Time (7" Mix) (CD) 8
87	Virgin PGSC 412	Red Rain/Ga Ga (I Go Swimming Instrumental) (cassette) 5
87	Virgin CDPGS 612	Biko (live)/No More Apartheid/I Have The Touch ('85 Remix) (CD) 7
87	Virgin PGSC 612	Biko (live)/No More Apartheid (cassette) 5

(see also Genesis, Charlie Drake)

PETER GABRIEL & KATE BUSH
| 86 | Virgin PGSP 2 | Don't Give Up/In Your Eyes (foldout poster p/s) ....6 |
| 86 | Virgin PGS 212 | Don't Give Up/In Your Eyes/This Is The Picture (12", p/s) ....7 |

(see also Kate Bush)

GABRIEL & ANGELS
63   Stateside SS 150   That's Life That's Tough/Don't Wanna Twist No More 6

GABRIELLI BRASS
65	Polydor 56031	Angel Cake/Cat Walk 4
65	Polydor 56047	Ride Your Pony/Anyone Who Had A Heart 8
68	Polydor 56252	'Canterbury Tales' Theme/Working My Way Back To You 8

GADGETS
| 83 | Glass GLASS 026 | We Had No Way Of Knowing/Acid Bath (unissued) |
| 83 | Glass GLASS 12026 | We Had No Way Of Knowing/Acid Bath (12", unissued) |

GADGETS

79	Final Solution FSLP 001	GADGETREE (LP, with insert, blue or beige picture on sleeve)	20
80	Final Solution FSLP 002	LOVE, CURIOSITY, FRECKLES & DOUBT (LP)	20
83	Glass GLALP 006	THE BLUE ALBUM (LP, with inner sleeve)	12
83	Glass GLAMC 006	THE BLUE ALBUM (cassette)	12

(see also The The, Matt Johnson, Colin Lloyd Tucker, Plain Characters)

MEL GADSON
60	London HLX 9105	Comin' Down With Love/I'm Gettin' Sentimental Over You	6

GAGALACTYCA
90	Holyground	GAGALACTYCA (LP, with booklet, actually by Lightyears Away	
	HG 1135/MM 3	& Thundermother, 425 only)	18

(see also Astral Navigations)

GAGS
79	Look LKLP 6312	DEATH IN BUZZARD'S GULCH (LP)	100

SLIM GAILLARD (QUARTET/TRIO)
47	Parlophone R 3035	Yep Roc Heresi/Novachord Boogie (78)	10
40s	MGM 10017	Arabian Boogie/Trip Light (78)	6
50	Parlophone R 3291	Jam Man/JOHNNY OTIS & MARCIE LEE: Harlem Nocturne (78)	8
51	Vogue V 2029	Voot Boogie/Queen's Boogie (78)	8
51	Vogue V 2044	Central Avenue Boogie/Sighing Boogie (78)	8
56	Parlophone GEP 8595	SLIM GAILLARD NO. 1 (EP)	20
56	Columbia Clef SEB 10046	MUSICAL AGGREGATIONS (EP)	25
60	London RED 1251	SLIM GAILLARD RIDES AGAIN (EP)	25

GAINORS
58	London HLU 8734	The Secret/Gonna Rock Tonite	150
58	London HLU 8734	The Secret/Gonna Rock Tonite (78)	20

GALACTIC FEDERATION
66	Polydor BM 56093	The March Of The Sky People/Moon Shot	18

GALACTIC SYMPOSIUM
80	Vague VOG 2	Money/In The Navy (gatefold p/s)	5

DIAMANDA GALAS
82	Y Y 18	LITANIES DU SATAN (LP)	12

GALAXIE 500
88	Caff CAFF 9	Rain/Don't Let Your Youth Go To Waste (p/s, with insert in bag)	25
90	Rough Trade G5SFI	Blue Thunder/Victory Garden/STRAITJACKET FITS: Hail (promo-only, stickered sleeve)	8

GALAXIES
60	Capitol CL 15158	The Big Triangle/Until The Next Time	4

DAVID GALBRAITH
57	Columbia DB 3947	Heartbreak Is New To Me/Miracle In Milan	4

SANDRA GALE
63	Ember EMB S 162	Hello Heartbreak/If She's Right For You	4

SUNNY GALE
53	HMV 7M 147	Teardrops On My Pillow/Send My Baby Back To Me	10
54	HMV 7M 243	Goodnight, Well It's Time To Go/Close To Me	10
55	HMV 7M 344	C'est La Vie/Looking Glass	8
57	Brunswick 05659	Two Hearts (With An Arrow Between)/Maybe You'll Be There	6
57	Brunswick 05661	Come Go With Me/Please Go	7
57	Brunswick 05661	Come Go With Me/Please Go (78)	5
58	Brunswick 05753	A Certain Smile/Just Friends	7
61	London HLU 9322	Please Love Me Forever/Sunny	5

GALE BROTHERS
66	Parlophone R 5535	Every Day Of My Life/All Strung Out	4

GALENS
63	London HLH 9804	Baby I Do Love You/Love Bells	5

FRANCE GALL
65	Philips BF 1408	Poupee De Cire, Poupee De Son/Le Coeur Qui Jazze	4

RORY GALLAGHER
79	Chrysalis CHS 2364	Philby/Hellcat/Country Mile (p/s, coloured vinyl)	4
80	Chrysalis CHS 2453	Wayward Child/Keychain (p/s, coloured vinyl)	4

GALLAGHER-LYLE
67	Polydor BM 56170	Trees/In The Crowd	8

(see also James Galt, McGuinness Flint)

GALLAHADS
55	Capitol CL 14282	Ooh-Ah/Careless	6

GALLANTS
64	Capitol CL 15366	Happy Beat/Rhino	4
65	Capitol CL 15408	"Man From U.N.C.L.E." Theme/Vagabond	10

GALLIARD
70	Deram DM 306	I Wrapped Her In Ribbons/The Hermit And The Knight	6
69	Deram Nova SDN 4	STRANGE PLEASURES (LP)	30
70	Deram SML 1075	NEW DAWN (LP)	80

BOB GALLION
59	MGM MGM 1028	Out Of A Honky Tonk/You Take The Table And I'll Take ...	6
60	MGM MGM 1057	Hey! Joe/Froggy Went A Courtin'	8
65	Hickory 45-1300	I Don't Have The Right (To Disagree)/Thank For The Devil For Hideaways	4

FRANK GALLUP
| 58 | HMV POP 509 | Got A Match?/I Beg Your Pardon | 4 |

JAMES GALT
| 65 | Pye 7N 15936 | Comes The Dawn/My Own Way | 8 |
| 65 | Pye 7N 17021 | With My Baby/Most Unusual Feeling | 30 |

(see also Gallagher & Lyle)

GALWAD AR HOLL FILWYR BYFFALO
| 70s | Anhrefn 006 | CYMRU (EP) | 5 |

ARMANDO GAMA
| 83 | WEA K 9801 | Esta Balada Que Te Dou/When Love Has Gone (unissued with this number; promos may exist) | 10 |
| 83 | WEA 24-9801-7 | Esta Balada Que Te Dou/When Love Has Gone (p/s) | 7 |

GAMBLERS
63	Decca F 11780	You've Really Got A Hold On Me/Can I See You Tonight	8
64	Decca F 11872	Nobody But Me/It's So Nice	10
65	Decca F 12060	Now I'm All Alone/Find Out What's Happening	8
66	Decca F 12399	Doctor Goldfoot/It Seems So Long	12
67	Parlophone R 5557	Cry Me A River/Who Will Buy	15

(see also Billy Fury)

GAME
65	Pye 7N 15889	But I Do/Gotta Keep On Moving Baby	40
66	Decca F 12469	Gotta Wait/Gonna Get Me Someone	50
67	Parlophone R 5553	The Addicted Man/Help Me Mummy's Gone (withdrawn)	150
67	Parlophone R 5569	It's Shocking What They Call Me/Help Me Mummy's Gone	125

GAMMER & HIS FAMILIARS
84	Gammer GAMMER 5	Will The New Baby/All Above (12", p/s)	10
81	Gammer EJ 9699	WON'T LOOK OUT (LP)	15
81	Gammer 4/EJ 9851	ROCKET TICKET (LP)	15

(see also Durutti Column)

GANDALF THE GREY
| | Heyoka | THE GREY WIZARD AM I (LP, reissue) | 12 |

RON WARREN GANDERTON
70s	Sound Ceremony RWG 2	RON WARREN GANDERTON (LP, private pressing)	20
73	Sound Ceremony RWG 3	GUITAR STAR (LP, private pressing)	20
70s	Sound Ceremony	PRECIOUS AS ENGLAND (LP, private pressing)	20

LITTLE JIMMY GANDY
| 69 | Roulette RO 510 | Cool Thirteen/I'm Not Like The Others | 4 |

GANGBUSTERS
| 63 | Fontana TF 419 | The Memory Of Your Face/When We Met | 4 |

GANG OF FOUR
| 80 | Fast Product FAST 5 | DAMAGED GOODS (EP, original with b&w labels, some with insert) | 6/5 |

GANGSTERS
79	Stortbeat A45/B45	Harlow Town/Record Company (p/s)	4
79	Stortbeat BEAT 3	Best Friend/Best Friend Dub (p/s)	4
79	Stortbeat BEAT 2	GANGSTERS (LP)	12

GANIM'S ASIA MINORS
| 58 | London HLE 8637 | Daddy Lolo/Halvah | 6 |

CECIL GANT
74	Flyright LP 4710	ROCK LITTLE BABY (LP)	15
75	Flyright LP 4714	CECIL'S BOOGIE (LP)	12
79	Magpie 1816	KILLER DILLER BOOGIE (LP)	10

CLENTT GANT
| 60 | Starlite ST45 023 | I Need You So/I'm Just A Lucky So-And-So | 5 |

DON GANT
| 65 | Hickory 45-1297 | Early In The Morning/Don't Ya Even Cry | 10 |

ELMER GANTRY'S (VELVET) OPERA
67	Direction 58-3083	Flames/Salisbury Plain	8
68	Direction 58-3481	Mary Jane/Dreamy	6
69	Direction 58-3924	Volcano/A Quick B	6
68	Direction 8-63300	ELMER GANTRY'S VELVET OPERA (LP)	40

(see also Velvet Opera, Stretch)

GANTS
| 65 | Liberty LIB 55829 | Road Runner/My Baby Don't Care | 15 |
| 67 | Liberty LIB 55940 | Greener Days/I Wonder | 6 |

GAP BAND
| 77 | Tattoo FBO 884 | Out Of The Blue/Little Bit Of Love | 4 |

DIGNO GARCIA Y SUS CARIOS
| 61 | Palette PG 9024 | Brigitte Bardot/Morena | 4 |

JERRY GARCIA
72	CBS 69013	HOOTEROLL (LP, with Howard Wales)	12
72	Warner Bros K 46139	GARCIA (LP)	12
74	Round RX 59301	GARCIA (LP)	10
73	Fantasy F 79002	LIVE AT THE KEYSTONE (LP)	10
76	United Artists UAG 29921	REFLECTIONS (LP)	10

(see also Grateful Dead)

GARDEN ODYSSEY ENTERPRISE
69	Deram DM 267	Sad And Lonely/Sky Pilot 10

PAUL GARDINER
81	Beggars Banquet BEG 61	Stormtrooper In Drag/Night Talk (p/s) 4
81	Beggars Banquet BEG 61T	Stormtrooper In Drag/Night Talk (12", unreleased, white label promos only) ...250

(see also Tubeway Army, Gary Numan)

AVA GARDNER
53	MGM SP 1005	Can't Help Lovin' Dat Man/Bill 5

BORIS GARDNER
68	Treasure Isle TI 7056	Hooked On A Feeling/Turn Around Twice (The Message) 5
69	Doctor Bird DB 1205	Elizabethan Reggae/Hooked On A Feeling 5
68	High Note HS 010	Lucky Is The Boy/Bobby Sox To Stockings 5
69	Duke DU 21	Never My Love/The Bold One 4
70	Trojan TBL 121	REGGAE HAPPENING (LP) 10

DAVE GARDNER
58	Brunswick 05740	Hop Along Rock/All By Myself (B-side with Anita Kerr Singers) 25
58	Brunswick 05740	Hop Along Rock/All By Myself (B-side with Anita Kerr Singers) (78) 7

DON GARDNER & DEE DEE FORD
62	Stateside SS 114	I Need Your Loving/Tell Me 8
62	Stateside SS 130	Don't You Worry/I'm Coming Home To Stay 10
68	Soul City SC 101	Don't You Worry/I'm Coming Home To Stay (reissue) 8

GARFIELD
70s	Polydor	REASON TO BE (LP) 10

JOHNNY GARFIELD
65	Pye 7N 15758	Stranger In Paradise/Anyone Can Lose A Heart 15

(Art) GARFUNKEL
74	CBS CQ 31474/Q 69021	ANGEL CLARE (LP, quadrophonic) 10

(see also Simon & Garfunkel, Tom & Jerry)

FRANK GARI
60	London HLU 9277	I Ain't Got A Girl/Utopia 4

JUDY GARLAND
53	MGM SP 1001	A Couple Of Swells/Medley: I Love A Piano/Snooky Ookums/When The Midnight Choo Choo Leaves (with Fred Astaire) 6
56	MGM MGM SP 1157	Look For The Silver Lining/Who? 6
57	Capitol CL 14789	Rock-a-bye Your Baby With A Dixie Melody/After You've Gone 4
57	Capitol CL 14790	I Feel A Song Coming On/Just Imagine 4
57	Capitol CL 14791	By Myself/It's Lovely To Be Back In London 4
55	Philips BBE 12012	BORN IN A TRUNK — SELECTIONS FROM A STAR IS BORN (EP) 8
56	MGM MGM-EP 568	IF YOU FEEL LIKE SINGING (EP) 7
56	MGM MGM-EP 641	EASTER PARADE — EXCERPTS (EP, with Fred Astaire & Peter Lawford) 7
56	MGM MGM-EP 672	WORDS AND MUSIC — SOUNDTRACK EXCERPTS (EP, 1 track with June Allyson & Mickey Rooney) 7
59	Capitol EAP1 1036	JUDY IN LOVE (EP) 8
59	Capitol EAP2 1036	JUDY IN LOVE (EP) 8
59	Capitol EAP3 1036	JUDY IN LOVE (EP) 8
59	Capitol EAP7 1569	JUDY AT CARNEGIE HALL (EP) 7
59	Capitol EAP8 1569	JUDY AT CARNEGIE HALL (EP) 7
60	Capitol EAP1 20051	A GARLAND FOR JUDY (EP) 8
55	Brunswick LA 8725	JUDY AT THE PALACE (10" LP) 20
55	MGM-D 134	BORN TO SING (10" LP) 15
55	Philips BBL 7007	A STAR IS BORN (LP, soundtrack) 15
56	Capitol LCT 6103	MISS SHOW BUSINESS (LP) 12
57	Capitol LCT 6121	JUDY (LP) 12
57	Capitol LCT 6136	ALONE (LP) 12
59	Capitol (S)T 1036	JUDY IN LOVE (LP, mono/stereo) 10/12
59	Capitol (S)T 1118	AT THE GROVE (LP, mono/stereo) 10/12
59	Capitol (S)T 1188	THE LETTER (LP, mono/stereo) 10/12
61	Capitol (S)T 1467	JUDY! THAT'S ENTERTAINMENT (LP) 10
63	Capitol T 1999	THE HITS OF JUDY GARLAND (LP) 10
63	Ace Of Hearts AH 11	GREATEST PERFORMANCES (LP) 10

(see Fred Astaire)

ERROL GARNER
60	Philips JAZ 103	Cheek To Cheek/The Way You Look Tonight 4
60	Philips JAZ 105	Lullaby Of Birdland/Easy To Love (some in p/s) 6/4
56	London RE-U 1066	THE PIANO WIZARDRY OF ERROL GARNER (EP) 10
60s	Realm REP 4006	UNDECIDED (EP) 7
53	Vogue LDE 034	ERROL GARNER TRIO VOLUME ONE (10" LP) 12
54	Felsted EDL 87002	MARGIE (10" LP) 12
54	Philips BBR 8002	PLAYS FOR DANCING (10" LP) 12
55	Philips BBR 8045	SOLO FLIGHT (10" LP) 12
55	Philips BBL 7034	GONE GARNER GONEST (LP) 10
55	Columbia 33S 1050	PIANO MOODS (10" LP) 12
55	Columbia 33S 1059	PIANO GEMS (10" LP) 12
55	Oriole MG 26042	GONE WITH GARNER (10" LP) 12
55	Felsted EDL 87015	PASSPORT TO FAME (10" LP) 12
56	Philips BBL 7078	AT THE PIANO (LP) 10
56	Mercury MPL 6501	MAMBO MOVES GARNER (LP) 10
57	Philips BBL 7106	CONCERT BY THE SEA (LP) 10
57	Mercury MPL 6507	AT THE PIANO (LP) 10
58	Mercury MPL 6539	AFTERNOON OF AN ELF (LP) 10

MINT VALUE £

| 59 | Mercury MMB 12010 | ERROL (LP) .... 10 |
| 60 | Vogue LAE 12209 | THE ERROL GARNER TRIO (LP) .... 10 |

BLIND LEROY GARNET

| 50s | Jazz Collector L 74 | Chain 'Em Down/Louisiana Glide (78) .... 8 |

COL GARNET

| 66 | Page One POF 002 | With A Girl Like You/Monday Monday .... 8 |

ALF GARNETT & FAMILY

| 68 | Pye NPL 18192 | SEX AND OTHER THOUGHTS (LP) .... 12 |

GALE GARNETT

| 64 | RCA RCA 1418 | We'll Sing In The Sunshine/Prism Song .... 4 |
| 65 | RCA RCA 1451 | I'll Cry Alone/Where Do You Go To Go Away .... 6 |

JESSE GARON & DESPERADOS

(see under J)

VERNON GARRETT

67	Stateside SS 2006	If I Could Turn Back The Hands Of Time/You And Me Together 15
67	Stateside SS 2026	Shine It On/Things Are Lookin' Better 10
68	Action ACT 4508	Shine It On/Things Are Lookin' Better (reissue) 6

DAVID GARRICK

66	Piccadilly 7N 35317	Lady Jane/Let's Go Somewhere 6
66	Piccadilly 7N 35335	Dear Mrs Applebee/You're What I'm Living For 4
68	Pye 7N 17509	Rainbow/I'll Be Home 4
68	Pye 7N 17610	A Little Bit Of This/Flutter By Butterfly 4
67	Piccadilly NEP 34056	DAVID (EP) 40
67	Piccadilly NPL 38024	A BOY CALLED DAVID (LP) 12
68	Piccadilly N(S)PL 38035	DON'T GO OUT INTO THE RAIN SUGAR (LP) 12

MICHAEL GARRICK

65	Argo EAF/ZFA 92	ANTHEM — MICHAEL GARRICK QUINTET (EP, mono/stereo) 20
66	Argo EAF 115	BEFORE NIGHT/DAY (EP) 20
63	Airborne	CASE OF JAZZ (LP) 40
64	Airborne	MOONSCAPE (LP) 40
64	Argo ZDA 26/27	POETRY AND JAZZ IN CONCERT (2-LP, with Norma Winstone) 60
65	Argo (Z)DA 33	OCTOBER WOMAN (LP, as Michael Garrick Quintet, with Joe Harriott) .. 55
65	Argo (Z)DA 36	PROMISES (LP, as Michael Garrick Sextet, with Ian Carr) 50
68	Argo (Z)DA 88	BLACK MARIGOLDS (LP, as Michael Garrick Septet) 45
68	Airborne NBP 0021	JAZZ PRAISES AT ST. PAULS (LP) 35
69	Argo ZPR 264/5	POETRY AND JAZZ IN CONCERT 250 (2-LP, as Michael Garrick Quintet) 40
70	Argo ZDA 135	HEART IS A LOTUS (LP, as Michael Garrick Sextet with Norma Winstone) 35
72	Argo ZDA 153	COLD MOUNTAIN (LP, as Michael Garrick Trio) 35
72	Argo ZDA 154	HOME STRETCH BLUES (LP) 35
74	Argo ZDA 163	TROPPO (LP) 30
70s	Impulse AS 49	ILLUMINATION (LP, as Michael Garrick Sextet) 25

(see also Ian Carr, Norma Winstone, Joe Harriott, Garrick's Fairground)

GARRICK'S FAIRGROUND

| 71 | Argo AFW 105 | Epiphany/Blessed Are The Peacemakers .... 6 |
| 71 | Argo ZAGF 1 | MR SMITH'S APOCALYPSE (LP) .... 35 |

(see also Michael Garrick)

FREDDIE GARRITY

68	Columbia DB 8348	Little Red Donkey/So Many Different Ways 4
68	Columbia DB 8496	You Belong To Me/Little Big Time 4
70	Starline SRS 5019	OLIVER IN THE OVERWORLD (LP, soundtrack) 15

(see also Freddie & Dreamers)

NICK GARVEY

| 82 | Virgin VS 504 | Take A Look Over My Shoulder/The Lion And Me (p/s) .... 4 |

(see also Ducks Deluxe, Motors)

REX GARVIN & MIGHTY CRAVERS

| 66 | Atlantic 584 028 | Sock It To 'Em J.B. Pts 1 & 2 .... 8 |
| 67 | Atlantic 584 097 | I Gotta Go Now (Up On The Floor)/Believe It Or Not .... 10 |

JOHN GARY

| 59 | Top Rank JAR 177 | Let Them Talk/Tell My Love .... 4 |
| 60 | Top Rank JAR 392 | Little Things Mean A Lot/Ever Since I Met Lucy .... 4 |

GARY & ARIELS

| 64 | Fontana TF 476 | Say You Love Me/Town Girl .... 8 |

GARY & STU

| 71 | Carnaby 6302 012 | HARLAN FARE (LP) .... 50 |

GAS

| 70s | Polydor | unreleased single (white labels only) .... 6 |

GASKIN

81	Rondelet ROUND 7	I'm No Fool/Sweet Dream Maker (p/s) 10
82	Rondelet ROUND 21	Mony Mony/Queen Of Hams (p/s) 10
81	Rondelet ABOUT 4	THE END OF THE WORLD (LP, gatefold sleeve) 20
82	Rondelet ABOUT 8	NO WAY OUT (LP) 12

GASLIGHT

| 70s | private pressing | GASLIGHT (LP) .... 125 |

GASOLINE BAND

| 72 | Cube HIFLY 9 | GASOLINE BAND (LP) .... 10 |

MINT VALUE £

GASS
65	Parlophone R 5344	One Of These Days/I Don't Know Why	10
66	Parlophone R 5456	The New Breed/In The City	20
67	CBS 202647	Dream Baby (How Long Must I Dream)/Jitterbug Sid	5
71	Polydor 2058 147	Something's Got To Change Your Ways/Mr Banana	4
70	Polydor 2383 022	JUJU (LP, featuring Peter Green)	20

GASS COMPANY
68	President PT 170	Everybody Needs Love/Nightmare	15

GAS WORKS
73	Regal Zono. SRLZ 1036	GAS WORKS (LP)	15

DAVID GATES
60	Top Rank JAR 504	The Happiest Man Alive/The Road That Leads To Love	12

(see also Bread)

REV J.M. GATES
40s	Square M 3	Need Of Prayer/Death's Black Train Is Coming (78)	50

GATES OF EDEN
66	Pye 7N 17195	Too Much On My Mind/I'm Warning You	12
67	Pye 7N 17252	In Your Love/Snoopy Versus The Red Baron	8
67	Pye 7N 17278	1 To 7/Hey Now	15

GATEWAY SINGERS
57	Brunswick LAT 8176	PUTTIN' ON THE STYLE (LP)	10

GATHERERS
73	Duke DU 153	Words Of My Mouth/UPSETTERS: Version	4

GATOR CREEK
71	Mercury 6052 058	Danny's Song/Take A Look	4
70	Mercury 6338 035	GATOR CREEK (LP)	12

GATURS
73	Atlantic K 10279	Cold Bear/The Boogie Man	4

JIMMY GAVIN
57	London HLU 8478	I Sit In My Window/Lonely Chair	50
57	London HLU 8478	I Sit In My Window/Lonely Chair (78)	10

JOHNNY GAVOTTE
60	Parlophone R 4631	It's Not Too Late/Can't Forget	4

ELAINE GAY
54	Parlophone MSP 6140	Love/Instantly	4
55	Parlophone R 3997	Rock Love/Ebony Eyes (78)	5

MAC GAYDEN
73	EMI EMA 760	McGAVOCK GAYDEN (LP)	30

(see also Area Code 615)

BILLY GAYE & GAYTONES
73	Waverley SLP 501	Oh Honey Love Me/I'll Never Say Never Again	4

MARVIN GAYE
63	Oriole CBA 1803	Stubborn Kind Of Fellow/It Hurt Me Too	50
63	Oriole CBA 1846	Pride And Joy/One Of These Days	50
63	Stateside SS 243	Can I Get A Witness/I'm Crazy 'Bout My Baby	30
64	Stateside SS 284	You're A Wonderful One/When I'm Alone I Cry	20
64	Stateside SS 326	Try It Baby/If My Heart Could Sing	15
64	Stateside SS 360	How Sweet It Is (To Be Loved By You)/Forever	20
65	Tamla Motown TMG 510	I'll Be Doggone/You've Been A Long Time Coming	40
65	Tamla Motown TMG 524	Pretty Little Baby/Now That You've Won Me	15
65	Tamla Motown TMG 539	Ain't That Peculiar/She's Got To Be Real	12
66	Tamla Motown TMG 552	One More Heartache/When I Had Your Love	15
66	Tamla Motown TMG 563	Take This Heart Of Mine/Need Your Lovin' (I Want You Back)	15
66	Tamla Motown TMG 574	Little Darlin' (I Need You)/Hey Diddle Diddle	12
67	Tamla Motown TMG 618	Your Unchanging Love/I'll Take Care Of You	10
68	Tamla Motown TMG 640	You/Change What You Can	6
68	Tamla Motown TMG 676	Chained/At Last (I Found A Love)	12
69	Tamla Motown TMG 686	I Heard It Through The Grapevine/Need Somebody	5
69	Tamla Motown TMG 705	Too Busy Thinking 'Bout My Baby/Wherever I Lay My Hat	5
69	Tamla Motown TMG 718	That's The Way Love Is/Gonna Keep On Tryin' Till I Win Your Love	5
70	Tamla Motown TMG 734	Abraham, Martin And John/How Can I Forget?	4
71	Tamla Motown TMG 775	What's Going On?/God Is Love	4
72	Tamla Motown TMG 817	Inner City Blues/Wholly Holy	4
73	Tamla Motown TMG 846	Trouble Man/Don't Mess With Mister 'T'	4
85	CBS DA 4894	Sanctified Lady/Sanctified Lady (Instrumental)//Sexual Healing/ Rockin' After Midnight (double pack)	4
66	Tamla Motown TME 2016	MARVIN GAYE (EP)	25
67	Tamla Motown TME 2019	ORIGINALS FROM MARVIN GAYE (EP)	25
64	Stateside SL 10100	MARVIN GAYE (LP)	40
65	Tamla Motown TML 11004	HOW SWEET IT IS TO BE LOVED BY YOU (LP)	30
65	Tamla Motown TML 11015	HELLO BROADWAY (LP)	60
66	T. Motown (S)TML 11022	A TRIBUTE TO THE GREAT NAT KING COLE (LP, mono/stereo)	40/60
66	T. Motown (S)TML 11033	MOODS OF MARVIN GAYE (LP)	20
68	T. Motown (S)TML 11065	MARVIN GAYE'S GREATEST HITS (LP)	10
69	T. Motown (S)TML 11091	IN THE GROOVE (LP)	20
69	T. Motown (S)TML 11119	M.P.G. (LP)	15
69	T. Motown (S)TML 11123	MARVIN GAYE AND HIS GIRLS (LP, with T. Terrell, M. Wells & K. Weston)	15
70	T. Motown (S)TML 11136	THAT'S THE WAY LOVE IS (LP)	15

71	T. Motown STML 11190	WHAT'S GOING ON (LP, original issue)	10
73	T. Motown STML 11225	TROUBLE MAN (LP, soundtrack)	12
76	T. Motown STML 12025	I WANT YOU (LP)	10
85	CBS 26239	DREAM OF A LIFETIME (LP, picture disc)	10

MARVIN GAYE & TAMMI TERRELL

67	Tamla Motown TMG 611	Ain't No Mountain High Enough/Give A Little Love	5
67	Tamla Motown TMG 625	Your Precious Love/Hold Me Oh My Darling	7
67	Tamla Motown TMG 635	If I Could Build My Whole World Around You/If This World Were Mine	6
68	Tamla Motown TMG 655	Ain't Nothin' Like The Real Thing/Little Ole Boy, Little Ole Girl	6
68	Tamla Motown TMG 668	You're All I Need To Get By/Two Can Have A Party	6
69	Tamla Motown TMG 681	You Ain't Living' Till You're Lovin'/Oh How I'd Miss You	6
69	Tamla Motown TMG 697	Good Lovin' Ain't Easy To Come By/Satisfied Feelin'	5
69	Tamla Motown TMG 715	The Onion Song/I Can't Believe You Love Me	5
68	T. Motown (S)TML 11062	UNITED (LP)	20
68	T. Motown (S)TML 11084	YOU'RE ALL I NEED (LP)	15
70	T. Motown (S)TML 11132	EASY (LP)	12
70	T. Motown (S)TML 11153	GREATEST HITS (LP)	10

MARVIN GAYE & MARY WELLS

| 64 | Stateside SS 316 | Once Upon A Time/What's The Matter With You, Baby | 18 |
| 64 | Stateside SL 10097 | TOGETHER (LP) | 35 |

MARVIN GAYE & KIM WESTON

64	Stateside SS 363	What Good Am I Without You/I Want You Around	20
67	Tamla Motown TMG 590	It Takes Two/It's Got To Be A Miracle (This Thing Called Love)	
		(1st pressing has tall, narrow print; later issues have fatter print)	8/5
67	T. Motown (S)TML 11049	TAKE TWO (LP)	20

(see also Tammi Terrell, Mary Wells, Kim Weston)

GAYE BYKERS ON ACID

86	In Tape IT 040	Everything's Groovy/T.V. Cabbage (p/s)	4
86	In Tape ITTI 040	Everything's Groovy/T.V. Cabbage (12", p/s)	7
87	Virgin VSX 1027	All Hung Up (Rough Rider Mix)/Afternoon Tea With Dave Greenfield/All Hung Up (Reprisal) (12", picture disc with poster & sticker, g/fold orange PVC sleeve)	7

GAYLADS

64	R&B JB 159	There'll Come A Day/BILLY COOKE: Iron Bar	10
64	R&B JB 165	What Is Wrong With Me/Whap Whap	10
66	Island WI 281	Goodbye Daddy/Your Eyes	10
66	Island WI 291	You'll Never Leave Him/Message To My Girl	10
66	Island WI 3002	Stop Making Love/They Call Her Dawn	10
66	Doctor Bird DB 1014	Lady With The Red Dress/Dinner For Two	8
66	Doctor Bird DB 1031	You Should Never Do That/WINSTON STEWART: I Don't Know Why I Love You	8
67	Island WI 3022	Don't Say No/SONNY BURKE: You Rule My Heart	10
67	Island WI 3025	Yes Girl/You No Good Girl	10
67	Studio One SO 2002	Tears From My Eyes/Never Let Your Country Down	15
67	Studio One SO 2013	I Am Going To Cool It (actually Little Roy)/MELODIANS: Let's Join Together	15
67	Studio One SO 2017	Love Me With All Your Heart/I Don't Care	12
67	Rio R 125	Put On Your Style/SOUL BROTHERS: Soul Serenade	8
68	Blue Cat BS 110	Go Away/SOUL VENDORS: Julie On My Mind	10
68	Doctor Bird DB 1124	It's Hard To Confess/I Need Your Loving	10
68	Doctor Bird DB 1145	She Want It/Joy In The Morning	10
68	Fab FAB 62	Looking For A Girl/Aren't You The Guy	7
68	High Note HS 001	A.B.C. Rocksteady/COUNT OSSIE & LESLIE BUTLER: Soul Drums	7
69	Trojan TR 688	You Had Your Chance/Wha' She Do Now	5
69	Upsetter US 323	The Same Things/I Wear My Slanders	5
70	Trojan TR 7738	That's What Love Will Do/This Time I Won't Hurt You	4
70	Trojan TR 7743	Young, Gifted And Black/BEVERLEY'S ALLSTARS: Moonglow	4
70	Trojan TR 7763	Tell The Children The Truth/Something Is Wrong Somewhere	4
70	Trojan TR 7771	Soul Sister/BEVERLEY'S ALLSTARS: Version	4
70	Trojan TR 7782	It's All In The Game/BEVERLEY'S ALLSTARS: Version	4
70	Trojan TR 7799	Fire And Rain/Cold And Lonely Night	4
71	Ackee AC 141	Accept My Apologies (actually by B.B. Seaton & Ken Boothe)/My Version (actually by Conscious Minds)	4
71	Big BG 319	Can't Hide The Feeling/RUPIE EDWARDS ALLSTARS: Version	4
71	Camel CA 79	Seven In One Medley Pts 1 & 2	4
71	Summit SUM 8514	My Jamaican Girl/BEVERLEY'S ALLSTARS: Version	4
67	Coxsone CSL 8005	ROCKSTEADY (LP)	70
67	Coxsone CSL 8006	SUNSHINE IS GOLDEN (LP)	45

(see also Gaylords, Rockstones, Delano Stewart)

GAYLET(T)S

68	Island WI 3129	Silent River Runs Deep/You're My Kind Of Man	10
68	Island WI 3141	I Like Your World/Lonely Feeling	8
68	Big Shot BI 502	If You Can't Be Good/Something About My Man	6
69	Big Shot BI 516	Son Of A Preacher Man/That's How Strong My Love Is	6
70	London HLJ 10302	Son Of A Preacher Man/I Like Your World	4

GAYLORDS (U.S.)

55	Mercury MB 3226	Mambo Rock/Plantation Boogie (78)	7
58	Mercury AMT 1006	Flamingo L'Amore/I'm Longin' For Love	4
59	Mercury AMT 1023	Again/How About Me	4
59	Mercury AMT 1049	Sweet Than You/Homin' Pigeon	4
60	Mercury MMC 14032	THAT'S AMORE (LP)	10

GAYLORDS (Jamaica)

| 66 | Island WI 269 | Chipmunk Ska/What Is Wrong (both actually by Gaylads) | 10 |

(see also Gaylads)

MINT VALUE £

GAYLORDS (U.K.)
66	Columbia DB 7805	He's A Good Face But He's Down And Out/You Know It Too 12

(see also Dean Ford & Gaylords, Marmalade)

WILTON 'BOGEY' GAYNAIR
60	Tempo EXA 103	BLUE BOGEY VOLUME ONE (EP) 7
59	Tempo TAP 25	BLUE BOGEY (LP) 12

GAYNOR (Junior English) & ERROL (Dunkley)
65	Blue Beat BB 286	My Queen/ROLAND ALPHONSO: Roland Plays Prince (B-side actually "Hanging The Beam" by Skatalites) 8

(see also Errol Dunkley)

MEL GAYNOR
55	Decca F 10497	Just A Man/How Important Can It Be? 4
55	Decca F 10542	With You Beside Me/Oh, My Love 4
55	Decca F 10618	Bella Notte/Sweet Kentucky Rose 4

(see also Oscar Rabin)

MITZI GAYNOR
59	Top Rank JAR 258	Happy Anniversary/Play For Keeps 4
60	Top Rank JAR 289	I Don't Regret A Thing/The Touch Of Time 4

ROSEMARY GAYNOR
55	Columbia SCM 5196	Ain't That A Shame/A Happy Song 7

PAUL GAYTEN
57	London HL 8503	Yo, Yo, Walk/TUNE WEAVERS: Happy Happy Birthday Baby 75
57	London HL 8503	Yo, Yo, Walk/TUNE WEAVERS: Happy Happy Birthday Baby (78) 20
59	London HLM 8998	The Hunch/Hot Cross Buns 100
59	London HLM 8998	The Hunch/Hot Cross Buns (78) 60

GAYTONES
73	Action ACT 4610	Soul Makossa/Soul Makossa (Version) 4

GBH
82	Clay CLAY 8	No Survivors/Self Destruct/Big Women (p/s) 4
82	Clay CLAY 11	Sick Boy/Slit Your Own Throat/Am I Dead Yet? (p/s) 4
82	Clay CLAY 16	Give Me Fire/Mantrap (p/s) 4
82	Clay CLAY 16P	Give Me Fire/Mantrap (picture disc) 5

G-CLEFS
56	Columbia DB 3851	Ka-Ding Dong/Darla, My Darlin' 150
56	Columbia DB 3851	Ka-Ding Dong/Darla, My Darlin' (78) 20
61	London HLU 9433	I Understand/Little Girl I Love You 8
62	London HLU 9530	A Girl Has To Know/(There Never Was A Dog Like) Dad 12
62	London HLU 9563	Make Up Your Mind/Call Me Away 12

GEDDES AXE
81	ACS ACS 1	Return Of The Gods/Wildfire + 1 (p/s, with insert) 12
82	Steel City AXE 1	Sharpen Your Wits/Rock 'N' Roll (p/s) 7
83	Bullet BOLT 4	Escape From New York/Six Six Six (12", p/s) 7

RON GEESIN
65	private pressing	MR. MAYOR, STOMP YOUR FOOT (EP, p/s) 50
67	Transatlantic (S)TRA 161	A RAISE OF EYEBROWS (LP) 25
72	KPM 1102	ELECTROSOUND (LP, library issue) 12
73	Ron Geesin RON 28	AS HE STANDS (LP, library issue) 12
75	Ron Geesin RON 31	PATRUNS (LP, library issue) 12
79	Ron Geesin RON 323	RIGHT THROUGH (LP, library issue) 15

RON GEESIN & ROGER WATERS
70	Harvest SHSP 4008	MUSIC FROM THE BODY (LP) 12

(see also Roger Waters, Pink Floyd)

J. GEILS BAND
82	EMI EAP 134	Freeze-Frame/Rage In The Cage (picture disc) 4
82	EMI EAP 141	Love Stinks/Till The Walls Come Tumblin' Down (picture disc) 4
71	Atlantic K 40108	THE J. GEILS BAND (LP) 10

GEMINI (U.K.)
65	Columbia DB 7638	Space Walk/Goodbye Joe 20

GEMINI (Portugal)
78	Philips 6031 070	Dal-Li-Dou (Falling In Love)/Dal-Li-Dou 12

GENE & DEBBE
67	London HLE 10165	Go With Me/Torch I Carry 6
68	London HLE 10179	Playboy/I'll Come Running 8
68	London HLE 10203	Lovin' Season/Love Will Give Us Wings 6

GENE & EUNICE
56	Vogue V 9062	I Gotta Go Home/Have You Changed Your Mind? 60
56	Vogue V 9062	I Gotta Go Home/Have You Changed Your Mind? (78) 20
57	Vogue V 9066	Move It Over, Baby/This Is My Story 70
57	Vogue V 9066	Move It Over, Baby/This Is My Story (78) 20
57	Vogue V 9071	Let's Get Together/I'm So In Love With You 40
57	Vogue V 9071	Let's Get Together/I'm So In Love With You (78) 20
57	Vogue V 9083	Doodle Doodle Doo/Don't Treat Me This Way 40
57	Vogue V 9083	Doodle Doodle Doo/Don't Treat Me This Way (78) 20
58	Vogue V 9106	I Mean Love/The Angels Gave You To Me 40
58	Vogue V 9106	I Mean Love/The Angels Gave You To Me (78) 20
58	Vogue V 9126	Strange World/The Vow 20
58	Vogue V 9126	Strange World/The Vow (78) 25

59	Vogue V 9136	Bom Bom Lulu/Hi Diddle Diddle 30
59	Vogue V 9136	Bom Bom Lulu/Hi Diddle Diddle (78) 25
59	London HL 8956	Poco-Loco/Go-On Kokomo 25
59	London HL 8956	Poco-Loco/Go-On Kokomo (78) 30

GENE & GENTS
| 68 | Pye 7N 17532 | C'mon Everybody/Hound Dog ....4 |

GENE & JERRY
| 71 | Mercury 6052 050 | You Just Can't Win/Sho' Is Grooving ....4 |

GENE LOVES JEZEBEL
82	Situation 2 SIT 18T	Shavin' My Neck/Sun & Insanity/Machismo/Glad To Be Alive (12", p/s) 30
82	Situation 2 SIT 20	Screaming (For Emmalene)/So Young (Heave Hard Heave Ho) (p/s) 7
82	Situation 2 SIT 20T	Screaming (For Emmalene)/So Young (Heave Hard Heave Ho) (12", p/s) 12
83	Situation 2 SIT 24	Bruises/Punch Drunk (p/s) 7
83	Situation 2 SIT 24T	Bruises/Punch Drunk/Brando Bruises (12", p/s) 12
84	Situation 2 SIT 31	Influenza (Relapse)/Walking In The Park (p/s) 4
84	Situation 2 SIT 31T	Influenza (Relapse)/Walking In The Park/Stephen (12", p/s) 7
84	Situation 2 SIT 35	Shame (Whole Heart Howl)/Thin Things (p/s) 4
84	Situation 2 SIT 35T	Shame (Whole Heart Howl)/Thin Things/Gorgeous (12", p/s) 7
85	Situation 2 SIT 36	Cow/One Someone (p/s) 4
85	Situation 2 SIT 36T	Cow (Extended)/Weep For Her (Cow) (12", p/s, label states "You Weaken Her (Cow)", initial copies with poster) 10/7
85	Situation 2 SIT 41	Desire/Flame (Steve Harley Mix) (p/s) 4
85	Situation 2 SIT 41T	Desire (Extended)/Flame (Steve Harley Mix)/The Immigrant (1st Mix) (12", p/s) ...7
86	Beggars Banquet BEG 156	Sweetest Thing/Psycho II (p/s, 1st 1,000 with free cassette [BEG 156]) 8/4
86	Beggars Banquet BEG 156T	Sweetest Thing/Psycho II/Sweetest Jezebel (12", p/s, 1st 1,000 with poster) 8
86	B. Banquet BEG 161TP	Heartache/Part 2/Beyond Doubt/Delibabies (12", p/s, 1st 5,000 with poster) 7
86	Beggars Banquet BEG 161C	Heartache/Vagabond/Lipstime/Down To The Water/Heartache Pt 2 (cassette) ...6
86	Beggars Banquet BEG 173TP	Desire (Come And Get It)/Version/Sapphire Scavenger/A New Horizon/ Message (12", p/s, 1st 5,000 with double-sided poster) 7
86	B. Banquet BEG 173TC	Desire (US Club Mix)/Heartache (UK Club Mix) (12", p/s, 5,000 only) 8
87	Beggars Banquet BEG 192D	Motion Of Love/Fresh Slice/Buggs Bruises/Vagabond (double pack) 4
87	Beggars Banquet BEG 202S	Gorgeous/Someone (On 6th Floor Of The Jezebel Palace) (p/s, 10,000 in numbered gatefold p/s with 2 postcards) 4
83	Situation 2 SITU 7	PROMISE (LP, 1st pressing with matrix number SITU 7B) 10
86	Beggars Banquet BEG 73	DISCOVER (LP, with free live LP "Glad To Be Alive") 15

GENERAL ACCIDENT
| 80s | Quicksilver QUIK 3 | Computer Dating/Person To Person (stamped p/s) ....4 |

GENERAL PUBLIC
| 84 | Virgin VSY 659 | General Public/Dishwasher (picture disc, stickered PVC sleeve) ....4 |

(see also Beat)

GENERAL STRIKE
| 79 | Canal CANAL 01 | Part 1: My Body/Part 2: (Parts Of) My Body (p/s) ....5 |
| 84 | Touch | GNERAL STRIKE (cassette in PVC wallet with inserts) ....6 |

GENERATION GAP
| 69 | Pye 7N 17845 | She's Coming Home/Reach The Top ....5 |
| 70 | Pye 7N 17979 | Any Old Time You're Lonely And Sad/Rainbows'N'Sorrow ....5 |

GENERATION X
77	Chrysalis CHS 2165	Your Generation/Day By Day (p/s) 5
77	Chrysalis CHS 2189	Wild Youth/Wild Dub (Version) (p/s) 5
77	Chrysalis CHS 2189	Wild Youth/No No No (p/s, mispressed, B-side with matrix: CHS 2189 B/1) ...20
78	Chrysalis CHS 2207	Ready Steady Go/No No No (p/s) 5
79	Chrysalis CHS 2261	King Rocker/Gimme Some Truth (p/s) 4
79	Chrysalis CHS (A/B/C/D) 2261	King Rocker/Gimme Some Truth (4 coloured vinyls in 4 sleeves; pink, red, yellow, orange; each p/s with different band member) 4-6
79	Chrysalis CHS 2310	Valley Of The Dolls/Shakin' All Over (p/s, streaked brown or black vinyl) 4/5
79	Chrysalis CHS 2330	Friday's Angels/Trying For Kicks/This Heat (p/s, pink vinyl) 5
78	Chrysalis CHR 1169	GENERATION X (LP, with 'T-shirt offer' wraparound) 10

(see also Billy Idol, Sigue Sigue Sputnik, Gen X, Empire)

GEN X
| 81 | Chrysalis CHS 2488 | Dancing With Myself/Untouchables/King Rocker/Rock On (p/s, clear vinyl) .....5 |

(see also Generation X)

GENESIS
68	Decca F 12735	The Silent Sun/That's Me 90
68	Decca F 12775	A Winter's Tale/One-Eyed Hound 100
69	Decca F 12949	Where The Sour Turns To Sweet/In Hiding 100
70	Charisma GS 1	Looking For Someone/Visions Of Angels (promo only) 250
71	Charisma CB 152	The Knife Part 1/The Knife Part 2 (some in p/s) 200/40
72	Charisma CB 181	Happy The Man/Seven Stones (some in p/s) 180/50
73	Charisma (no cat. no.)	Twilight Alehouse (1-sided flexidisc free with 'Zig Zag' & later via fan club, with/without magazine) 25/20
74	Charisma CB 224	I Know What I Like (In Your Wardrobe)/Twilight Alehouse 12
74	Charisma CB 238	Counting Out Time/Riding The Scree 15
75	Charisma CB 251	The Carpet Crawlers/Evil Jam (The Waiting Room live) 18
76	Charisma CB 277	A Trick Of The Tail/Ripples 4
77	Charisma CB 300	Your Own Special Way/It's Yourself 4
77	Charisma GEN 001	SPOT THE PIGEON EP (EP) 6
78	Charisma CB 309	Follow You, Follow Me/Ballad Of Big (p/s) 4
78	Charisma CB 315	Many Too Many/The Day The Light Went Out/Vancouver (p/s) 5
80	Charisma CB 356	Turn It On Again/Behind The Lines Part II (p/s) 4
80	Charisma CB 363	Duchess/Open Door (p/s) 5
80	Charisma CB 369	Misunderstanding/Evidence Of Autumn (p/s) 5

MINT VALUE £

81	Charisma CB 388	Abacab/Another Record (p/s, with picture labels) 4
81	Charisma CB 391	Keep It Dark/Naminanu (p/s) 4
81	Charisma CB 391-12	Keep It Dark/Naminanu/Abacab (Long Version) (12", p/s) 7
82	Charisma CB 393	Man On The Corner/Submarine (p/s, blue labels) 10
82	Charisma GEN 1	3 X 3 (EP, picture disc) 7
82	Lyntone LYN 11806	The Lady Lies (live) (green flexidisc free with 'Flexipop' mag, issue 21) 6/5
83	Genesis Information GI 01	Firth Of Forth (live edit) (flexidisc with numbered gatefold p/s,
		free with 'Genesis' mag; with/without magazine) 12/8
83	Charisma/Virgin TATA Y1	That's All/Taking It All Too Hard (shaped picture disc) 8
84	Charisma/Virgin ALS 1	Illegal Alien/Turn It On Again (live) (shaped picture disc) 8
86	Charisma/Virgin GENS 1	Invisible Touch/The Last Domino (clear vinyl, foldout p/s) 4
86	Virgin SNEG 3-12	Land Of Confusion (7")/Land Of Confusion (John Potoker Mix)/Land Of
		Confusion (Extended)/Feeding The Fire/Do The Neurotic (CD) 8
87	Virgin CD EP 1	Tonight Tonight Tonight/The Glow Of The Night/Invisible Touch (Extended
		Remix)/Tonight Tonight Tonight (John Potoker Remix) (CD) 40
87	Virgin DRAW 4-12	Tonight Tonight Tonight/The Glow Of The Night/Paper-Late/
		Tonight Tonight Tonight (John Potoker Remix) (CD) 7
69	Decca LK/SKL 4990	FROM GENESIS TO REVELATION (LP, with lyric sheet, mono/stereo) 80/30
70	Charisma CAS 1020	TRESPASS (LP, original dark pink label & gatefold sleeve with lyric sheet) ... 18
71	Charisma CAS 1052	NURSEY CRYME (LP, original dark pink label with insert & gatefold sleeve) ... 15
74	Decca SKL 4990	IN THE BEGINNING (LP) 25
75	Charisma CGS 102	GENESIS COLLECTION VOLUME ONE (2-LP, boxed set of "Trespass"
		& "Nursery Cryme", with poster) 60
75	Charisma CGS 103	GENESIS COLLECTION VOLUME TWO (2-LP, boxed set of "Foxtrot"
		& "Selling England By The Pound", with poster) 60
86	Metal Masters MACHMP 4	WHEN THE SOUR TURNS TO SWEET (LP, picture disc) 12

(see also Flaming Youth, Phil Collins, Tony Banks, Mike Rutherford, Peter Gabriel, Steve Hackett, Anthony Phillips)

GENEVEVE
66	CBS 202061	Once/Just A Whisper 4

GENGHIS KHAN (Germany)
79	Ariola ARO 163	Genghis Khan/Desert Land (unissued; promos may exist) 6
79	CBS 12-7317	Genghis Khan/Desert Land (12", clear vinyl with p/s insert) 8

GENGHIS KHAN (U.K.)
83	Wabbit WAB 61/63	Love You/Lady Lady//Mongol Nation/Gone For A Drive (double pack) 10

GENOCIDE
79	Safari SAP 2	GENOCIDE (EP) 4

GENOCIDES
82	Action TAKE 1	Is That All Right? (p/s) 4

GENTILES (U.K.)
68	Pye 7N 17530	Goodbye Baby/Marlena 8

GENTILES (Jamaica)
70	High Note HS 046	Your Destiny/Lock Love Away (actually by Melodians) 4

(see also Melodians)

JOHNNY GENTLE
59	Philips PB 908	Wendy/Boys And Girls (Were Meant For Each Other) 5
59	Philips PB 908	Wendy/Boys And Girls (Were Meant For Each Other) (78) 8
59	Philips PB 945	Milk From The Coconut/I Like The Way 5
59	Philips PB 945	Milk From The Coconut/I Like The Way (78) 8
60	Philips PB 988	This Friendly World/Darlin' Won't You Wait 5
60	Philips PB 1069	After My Laughter Came Tears/Sonja 5
59	Philips BBE 12345	THE GENTLE TOUCH (EP) 20

(see also Darren Young)

TIM GENTLE & HIS GENTLEMEN
65	Oriole CB 1988	Without You/Someone's In The Kitchen With Dinah 12

GENTLE GIANT
74	WWA WWP 1001	In A Glass House/An Intimate's Lullaby 4
74	WWA WWP 017	The Power And The Glory/Playing The Game 6
70	Vertigo 6360 020	GENTLE GIANT (LP, gatefold sleeve, spiral label, later 'spaceship' label) 20/10
71	Vertigo 6360 041	ACQUIRING THE TASTE (LP, gatefold sleeve,
		spiral or 'spaceship' label) 20/10
72	Vertigo 6360 070	THREE FRIENDS (LP, gatefold sleeve, spiral label, later 'spaceship' label) ... 18/10
72	Vertigo 6360 080	OCTOPUS (LP, gatefold sleeve, spiral label) 12
73	WWA WWA 002	IN A GLASS HOUSE (LP, silk-screen cover, with photo insert & lyric inner) 30
74	WWA WWA 010	THE POWER AND THE GLORY (LP, with insert) 15

(see also Simon Dupree & Big Sound)

GENTLE INFLUENCE
69	Pye 7N 17666	Never Trust In Tomorrow/Easy To Know 8
69	Pye 7N 17743	Always Be A Part Of My Living 8

GENTLE PEOPLE
67	Columbia DB 8276	It's Too Late/Sea Of Heartbreak 8

GENTLE PERSUASION
73	People PEO 103	Dynamite Explodes/Bring It On Home 4

GENTLEMEN & THEIR LADY
76	Pye Intl. 7N 25731	Like Her/Like Her (Long Version) 4

BOBBIE GENTRY
67	Capitol CL 15511	Ode To Billie Joe/Mississipi Delta 4
67	Capitol (S)T 2830	ODE TO BILLIE JOE (LP) 10
68	Capitol (S)T 2842	THE DELTA SWEETE (LP) 10

BO GENTRY & RITCHIE CORDELL
69	CBS 4299	Stone Go-Getter/Hung Up	4

GENTRYS
65	MGM MGM 1284	Keep On Dancing/Make Up Your Mind	7
66	MGM MGM 1296	Brown Paper Sack/Spread It On Thick	15
66	MGM MGM 1312	Everyday I Have To Cry/Don't Let It Be	6

GENTS
80	Posh POSH 001	The Faker/The Pink Panther (p/s)	7
82	Kosmic KOS 6886	Schooldays/True Stories (p/s)	6
83	Posh POSH 007	Revenge/Girl (p/s)	4
80s	Posh MEGA 1	Revenge/Over Me/The Gent (p/s)	4

GEOFFREY
78	Music Bank BECK 694	ABH (Who Wants To Listen To Punk Rock)/Colt 45 Rock (p/s)	5

GEORDIE
72	Regal Zonophone RZ 3067	Don't Do That/Keep On Rocking	4
73	EMI EMI 2008	All Because Of You/Ain't It Just Like A Woman	4
73	EMI EMI 2031	Can You Do It/Red Eyed Lady	4
73	EMI EMI 2048	Electric Lady/Geordie Stomp	4
74	EMI EMI 2226	Ride On Baby/Got To Know	4
73	EMI EMC 3001	HOPE YOU LIKE IT (LP)	12
74	EMI EMA 764	DON'T BE FOOLED BY THE NAME (LP)	15
76	EMI EMC 3134	SAVE THE WORLD (LP)	18
	(see also AC/DC)		

BARBARA GEORGE
62	London HL 9513	I Know/Love	10
64	Sue WI 316	Send For Me/Bless You	15

LLOYD GEORGE
62	London HLP 9562	Lucy Lee/Sing Real Loud	25

GEORGETTES
58	London HL 8548	Love Like A Fool/Oh Tonight	25
58	London HL 8548	Love Like A Fool/Oh Tonight (78)	8
60	Pye Intl. 7N 25058	Down By The River/A Pair Of Eyes	8

GEORGIA TOM
60s	Riverside RLP 8803	GEORGIA TOM AND FRIENDS (LP)	20

GEORGIE'S VARSITY 5
61	Vogue Pop V 9189	When My Sugar Walks Down The Street/Five Foot Two, Eyes Of Blue	5

GERALDINE
75	EMI EMI 2275	You/It's All For You	6

GERALDO & HIS (DANCE) ORCHESTRA
56	Oriole CB 1323	Rockin' Through Dixie/Stranger Than Fiction (78)	5
57	Polydor BM 6070	Laughing Rock'n'Roll/Thunderstorm (78)	5

WESLEY GERMS
72	Upsetter US 390	Whiplash/UPSETTERS: Version	5

GERONIMO BLACK
74	MCA MCF 2683	GERONIMO BLACK (LP)	15
	(see also Mothers Of Invention)		

DENNY GERRARD
70	Deram Nova SDN 10	SINISTER MORNING (LP, with High Tide)	35
	(see also Warm Sounds, High Tide, Open Road)		

GERRY & HOLOGRAMS
79	Absurd A-4	Gerry And The Holograms/Increased Resistance (p/s)	4
79	Absurd A-5	The Emperor's New Music (unplayable record, glued into p/s)	10

GERRY & PACEMAKERS
63	Columbia DB 4987	How Do You Do It?/Away From You	4
63	Columbia DB 7041	I Like It/It's Happened To Me	4
63	Columbia DB 7126	You'll Never Walk Alone/It's Alright	4
64	Columbia DB 7189	I'm The One/You've Got What I Like	4
64	Columbia DB 7268	Don't Let The Sun Catch You Crying/Show Me That You Care	4
64	Columbia DB 7353	It's Gonna Be Alright/It's Just Because	4
64	Columbia DB 7437	Ferry Cross The Mersey/You You You	4
65	Columbia DB 7504	I'll Be There/Baby, You're So Good To Me	4
65	Columbia DB 7738	Walk Hand In Hand/Dreams	4
66	Columbia DB 7835	La La La/Without You	4
66	Columbia DB 8044	Girl On A Swing/A Fool To Myself	6
74	DJM DJS 298	Remember (The Days Of Rock And Roll)/There's Still Time	4
78	EMI EMI 2814	Ferry Cross The Mersey/Don't Let The Sun Catch You Crying (promo p/s)	5
63	Columbia SEG 8257	HOW DO YOU DO IT? (EP)	12
63	Columbia SEG 8295	YOU'LL NEVER WALK ALONE (EP)	14
64	Columbia SEG 8311	I'M THE ONE (EP)	12
64	Columbia SEG 8346	DON'T LET THE SUN CATCH YOU CRYING (EP)	12
64	Columbia SEG 8367	IT'S GONNA BE ALRIGHT (EP)	15
65	Columbia SEG 8388	GERRY IN CALIFORNIA (EP)	16
65	Columbia SEG 8397	HITS FROM 'FERRY CROSS THE MERSEY' (EP)	16
65	Columbia SEG 8426	RIP IT UP (EP)	18
63	Columbia 33SX 1546	HOW DO YOU LIKE IT (LP, also stereo SCX 3492)	20/30
65	Columbia 33SX 1693	FERRY CROSS THE MERSEY (LP, soundtrack, also stereo SCX 3544)	20/25
67	M. For Pleasure MFP 1153	YOU'LL NEVER WALK ALONE (LP, reissue of "How Do You Like It")	10

GERRY & PACEMAKERS

60s EMI Regal   YOU'LL NEVER WALK ALONE (LP, export issue) 20
(see also Gerry Marsden)

GEORGE GERSHWIN
60 Ember EMB 3315   GEORGE GERSHWIN (LP) 10

GERVASE
68 Decca F 12822   Pepper Grinder/Visions 10

GESTURES
65 Stateside SS 379   Run Run Run/It Seems To Me 15

GETTING THE FEAR
84 RCA RCA 432   Last Salute/We Struggle (p/s) 5
84 RCA RCAT 432   Last Salute/We Struggle (12", p/s) 7
(see also Southern Death Cult, Into A Circle)

STAN GETZ (QUARTET)
60 HMV POP 735   I Hadn't Anyone Till You/With The Wind And The Rain In 4
53 Esquire 20-007   STAN GETZ PLAYS (10" LP) 15
54 Vogue LDE 089   AT STORYVILLE (10" LP) 15
55 Vogue LDE 147   STAN GETZ QUARTET (10" LP) 15
55 Columbia Clef 33CX 10000   AT THE SHRINE NO. 1 (LP, as Stan Getz Quintet) 12
55 Columbia Clef 33CX 10001   AT THE SHRINE NO. 2 (LP, as Stan Getz Quintet) 12
66 Stateside SL 10161   GREATEST HITS (LP) 10
(see also Dizzy Gillespie, Chick Corea & Stan Getz)

GEZA X
82 Alt. Tentacles VIRUS 20   WE NEED MORE POWER (EP) 4

G-FORCE
80 Jet JET 183   Hot Gossip/Because Of Your Love (p/s) 6
80 Jet JET 194   You/Trust You Lovin' (p/s) 6
80 Jet JET 7005   White Knuckles/Rockin' And Rollin'/I Look At You (p/s) 6
80 Jet JETPD 229   G-FORCE (LP, picture disc) 12
(see also Gary Moore)

G.G. RHYTHM SECTION
69 Blue Cat BS 165   T.N.T./MAYTONES: Botheration 5

WESS & DORI GHEZZI
75 Bradleys BRAD 7515   Fallin'/Era 8

GHOST
69 Gemini GMS 007   When You're Dead/Indian Maid 18
70 Gemini GMS 014   I've Got To Get To Know You/For One Second 15
70 Gemini GME 1004   WHEN YOU'RE DEAD — ONE SECOND (LP) 100
(see also Velvett Fogg, Shirley Kent, Virginia Tree)

GHOST DANCE
86 Karbon KAR 602T   River Of No Return/Yesterday Again/Both Ends Burning (12", p/s) 10
86 Karbon KAR 606   Heart Full Of Soul/Radar Love (promo-only) 10
86 Karbon KAR 606T   Heart Full Of Soul/Radar Love (12", p/s) 8
86 Karbon KAR 604   The Grip Of Love/Where Spirits Fly (p/s) 8
86 Karbon KAR 604T   The Grip Of Love/Last Train/A Deeper Blue/The Grip Of Love
                                 (Version) (12", p/s) 10
87 Karbon KAR 608T   A WORD TO THE WISE (12" EP) 7
86 Karbon KARXL 303   GATHERING DUST (LP) 12
(see also Skeletal Family, All About Eve)

BILL GIANT
61 MGM MGM 1135   Better Let Her Go/When I Grow Too Old To Dream 5

GIANT CRAB
68 Uni UN 509   Hot Line Conversation/E.S.P. 4

GIANT SUNFLOWER
67 CBS 2805   Big Apple/February Sunshine 8
67 CBS 3033   Mark Twain/What's So Good About Goodbye 7

BARRY GIBB
70 Polydor 2058 030   I'll Kiss Your Memory/This Time 4
84 Polydor POSPP 695   Shine Shine/She Says ('mirror' picture disc) 4
(see also Bee Gees)

MAURICE GIBB
70 Polydor 2058 013   Railroad/I've Come Back 4
(see also Bee Gees, Fut)

ROBIN GIBB
69 Polydor BM 56337   Saved By The Bell/Mother And Jack 4
69 Polydor BM 56337   Saved By The Bell/Alexandria Good Time (withdrawn) 15
69 Polydor BM 56368   One Million Years/Weekend 4
70 Polydor BM 56371   August October/Give Me A Smile 4
84 Polydor POSPG 668   Another Long Night In New York/I Believe In Miracles (with free single) . 4
69 Polydor 583 085   ROBIN'S REIGN (LP) 12
(see also Bee Gees)

STEVE GIBBONS (BAND)
82 RCA RCA 174   Loving Me, Loving You/That Makes A Touch (picture disc) 4
71 Wizzard SWZA 5501   SHORT STORIES (LP) 35
(see also Uglys)

CALY GIBBS
70 Amalgamated AMG 870   Seeing Is Believing/JOE GIBBS ALLSTARS: Ghost Capturer 5
(see also Carlton Gibbs)

CARLTON GIBBS
70	Amalgamated AMG 872	Ghost Walk/Joy Stick	4

GEORGIA GIBBS
54	Mercury MB 3172	Love Me/Mambo Baby (78)	5
55	Mercury MB 3196	Tweedle Dee/You're Wrong, All Wrong (78)	8
55	Mercury MB 3223	Dance With Me Henry/Ballin' The Jack (78)	6
55	Vogue Coral Q 72088	Ballin' The Jack/I Still Feel The Same About You	15
56	Mercury MT 110	Kiss Me Another/Rock Right (78)	6
56	Vogue Coral Q 72182	If I Were A Bell/I'll Know	10
57	Mercury MT 133	Tra La La/Morning, Noon And Night (78)	5
57	RCA RCA 1011	Sugar Candy/I'm Walking The Floor Over You	6
58	RCA RCA 1029	Great Balls Of Fire/I Miss You	15
58	RCA RCA 1029	Great Balls Of Fire/I Miss You (78)	12
58	Mercury 7MT 210	Arriverderci Roma/24 Hours A Day	8
58	Columbia DB 4201	The Hula Hoop Song/Keep In Touch	6
59	Columbia DB 4259	The Hucklebuck/Better Loved You'll Never Be	8
60	London HLP 9098	The Stroll That Stole My Heart/Seven Lonely Days	6
65	Stateside SS 423	Let Me Cry On Your Shoulder/Venice Blues	4
55	Mercury EP-1-3265	THE MAN THAT GOT AWAY (EP)	7
56	Mercury MEP 9505	SWEET GEORGIA GIBBS (EP)	7
57	Mercury MEP 9516	SWEET GEORGIA GIBBS VOL. 2 (EP)	12
56	Mercury MPT 7500	SINGS THE OLDIES (10" LP)	30
57	Mercury MPT 7511	HER NIBBS MISS GIBBS (10" LP)	30
57	Mercury MPL 6508	SWINGING WITH HER NIBS (LP)	18

JOE GIBBS & DESTROYERS
70	Amalgamated AMG 858	Franco Nero (actually by Count Machuki & Destroyers)/Version Two	4
70	Amalgamated AMG 859	Rock The Clock/Version Two	4
70	Amalgamated AMG 867	Movements/Caesar	4
70	Pressure Beat PB 5504	News Flash/Version Two	4

MICHAEL GIBBS
70	Deram SML 1063	MICHAEL GIBBS (LP)	30
71	Deram SML 1087	TANGLEWOOD '63 (LP)	25
73	Polydor 2683 011	JUST AHEAD (2-LP)	25
74	Polydor 2383 252	IN THE PUBLIC INTEREST (LP, with Gary Burton)	10

(see also Neil Ardley)

SIR GIBBS
68	Amalgamated AMG 822	People Grudgeful/Pan Ya Machet (both sides actually by Pioneers)	8

DEBBIE GIBSON
87	WEA A 9322	Only In My Dreams/Only In My Dreams (Version) (original red p/s)	6
87	WEA A 9322T	Only In My Dreams/Only In My Dreams (Version) (12", original blue p/s)	40
87	WEA A 9322TP	Only In My Dreams/Only In My Dreams (Version) (12", picture disc)	20
87	WEA A 9187T	Shake Your Love (Vocal Club Mix)/Shake Your Love (Bonus Beats)/Shake Your Love (Shake The House Version)/Wake Up To Love (12", with poster)	10
87	WEA A 9187TP	Shake Your Love (Vocal Club Mix)/Shake Your Love (Bonus Beats)/Shake Your Love (Shake The House Version)/Wake Up To Love (12", picture disc)	12
88	WEA A 9091T	Out Of The Blue/Fallen Angel (12", with poster exclusive to Woolworths)	18
88	WEA A 9059TP	Foolish Beat (Vocal Extended Mix)/Between The Tines/Shake Your Love (12" picture disc)	10
88	WEA A 9322W	Only In My Dreams (Vocal Mix)/Only In My Dreams (Dreamix) (poster p/s)	7
88	WEA A 9322P	Only In My Dreams (Vocal Mix)/Only In My Dreams (Dreamix) (picture disc)	6
89	WEA A 8970V	Lost In Your Eyes/Silence Speaks (A Thousand Words) (Acoustic Mix) (foldout 'mirror pack')	5
89	WEA A 8970TP	Lost In Your Eyes/Silence Speaks (A Thousand Words) (Acoustic Mix)/Lost In Your Eyes (Piano And Vocal Mix) (12", picture disc)	10
89	WEA A 8919	Electric Youth/We Could Be Together (Campfire Mix) (poster p/s)	5
89	WEA A 8919TP	Electric Youth (House Version)/We Could Be Together (Campfire Mix)/Electric Youth (12", picture disc)	8
89	WEA A 8919CDP	Electric Youth/We Could Be Together (Campfire Mix)/Electric Youth (Home Version) (CD, picture disc)	7
89	WEA A 8896P	We Could Be Together (Edit)/Over The Wall (Dub Version) (picture disc)	7
89	WEA A 8896P	We Could Be Together (Edit)/Over The Wall (Dub Version) (box set with 2 postcards & 2 badges)	6
91	East West A 7735P	Anything Is Possible (Remix Edit)/So Close To Forever (picture disc)	5
88	WEA WX 231Y	ELECTRIC YOUTH (LP, yellow vinyl, with poster, exclusive to Woolworths)	20

DON GIBSON
56	MGM SP 1177	Sweet Dreams/The Road Of Life Alone	100
56	MGM MGM 909	Sweet Dreams/The Road Of Life Alone (78)	10
58	RCA RCA 1056	Oh Lonesome Me/I Can't Stop Lovin' You	7
58	RCA RCA 1056	Oh Lonesome Me/I Can't Stop Lovin' You (78)	7
58	RCA RCA 1073	Blue Blue Day/Too Soon	7
58	RCA RCA 1073	Blue Blue Day/Too Soon (78)	7
58	RCA RCA 1098	Give Myself A Party/Look Who's Blue	6
58	RCA RCA 1098	Give Myself A Party/Look Who's Blue (78)	7
59	RCA RCA 1110	A Stranger To Me/Who Cares	5
59	RCA RCA 1110	A Stranger To Me/Who Cares (78)	7
59	RCA RCA 1150	Don't Tell Me Your Troubles/Heartbreak Avenue	6
59	RCA RCA 1150	Don't Tell Me Your Troubles/Heartbreak Avenue (78)	10
59	RCA RCA 1158	Big Hearted Me/I'm Movin' On	6
59	RCA RCA 1158	Big Hearted Me/I'm Movin' On (78)	10

(all the above RCA 45s originally came with triangular centres, later round centre copies are worth half the value)

60	RCA RCA 1183	Just One Time/I May Never Get To Heaven	5
60	RCA RCA 1200	Far Far Away/A Legend In My Time	4
60	RCA RCA 1217	Sweet Dreams/The Same Street	4

Don GIBSON

61	RCA RCA 1243	Sea Of Heartbreak/I Think It's Best (To Forget Me)	5
62	RCA RCA 1272	Lonesome Number One/The Same Old Trouble	4
62	RCA RCA 1297	I Can Mend Your Broken Heart/I Let Her Get Lonely	4
63	RCA RCA 1335	Head Over Heels In Love With You/It Was Worth It	4
65	RCA RCA 1456	Again/You're Going Away	4
66	RCA RCA 1524	(Yes) I'm Hurting/My Whole World Is Hurt	4
67	RCA RCA 1626	All My Love/No Doubt About It (as Don Gibson & Jordanaires)	4
68	RCA RCA 1680	Ashes Of Love/Good Morning Dear	4
60	RCA RCX 1050	BLUE AND LONESOME (EP)	10
62	RCA RCX 213	LOOK WHO'S BLUE (EP)	10
62	RCA RCX 214	THAT GIBSON BOY (EP)	10
63	RCA RCX 7122	MAY YOU NEVER BE ALONE (EP)	10
60	RCA RD 27158	THE GIBSON BOY (LP)	15
62	RCA Victor RD/SF 7506	SOME FAVOURITES OF MINE (LP)	15
63	RCA Victor RD/SF 7576	I WROTE A SONG (LP)	15
64	RCA Victor RD 7641	GOD WALKS THESE HILLS (LP)	15

GINNY GIBSON

| 55 | MGM SP 1121 | Like Ma-a-d/Once There Was A Little Girl | 5 |
| 58 | MGM MGM 953 | Whatever Lola Wants (Lola Gets)/If Anything Should Happen | 4 |

JODY GIBSON & MULESKINNERS

| 59 | Parlophone R 4579 | Kissin' Time/Man On My Trail | 6 |
| 60 | Parlophone R 4645 | If You Don't Know/So You Think You've Got Troubles | 6 |

STEVE GIBSON & RED CAPS

| 57 | HMV POP 417 | Silhouettes/Flamingo | 50 |
| 57 | HMV POP 417 | Silhouettes/Flamingo (78) | 8 |

WAYNE GIBSON (& DYNAMIC SOUNDS)

63	Decca F 11713	Linda Lu/Beachcomber	10
64	Decca F 11800	Come On Let's Go/Pop The Whip	10
64	Pye 7N 15680	See You Later Alligator/Kelly	6
65	Pye 7N 15798	Portland Town/Please Baby Please	6
65	Parlophone R 5357	Ding Dong The Witch Is Dead/In The Night	20
65	Columbia DB 7683	One Little Smile/Baby, Baby, Baby Pity Me	25
66	Columbia DB 7911	Under My Thumb/It Always Happens (Icey) (solo)	15
66	Columbia DB 7998	For No One/He's Got The Whole World In his Hands (solo)	6
75	Pye 7N 45455	Yesterday's Papers/Don't Waste Time Following Me (solo)	4

GIBSONS

65	CBS 202015	Any Time That You're Lonely/Born To Be Free	4
66	CBS 202063	Come Summertime/Summer Affair	4
66	Deram DM 103	Two Kinds Of Lovers/Hey Girl	4
67	Deram DM 119	The Magic Book/You Know I Need Your Lovin'	5

GIDIAN (& UNIVERSALS)

66	Columbia DB 7826	Try Me Out/There Isn't Anything	20
66	Columbia DB 7916	Fight For Your Love/See If She Cares	6
66	Columbia DB 8041	Feeling/Don't Be Sentimental (as Gidian & Universals)	7

(see also Universals, Chris Lamb & Universals)

GIFTED CHILDREN

| 81 | Whaam! WHAAM 001 | Painting By Numbers/Lichtenstein Girl (p/s) | 25 |

(see also Television Personalities)

GILBERT (O'Sullivan)

67	CBS 3089	Disappear/You	12
68	CBS 3399	What Can I Do/You	12
69	Major Minor MM 613	Mister Moody's Garden/I Wish I Could Cry	15

HERSCHEL BURKE GILBERT

| 63 | London HLD 9655 | Dick Powell Theme/Nervous Teaser Theme | 4 |

GILBERT & LEWIS

| 81 | 4AD AD 106 | Ends With The Sea/Hung Up To Dry Whilst Building An Arch (p/s) | 7 |
| 82 | Cherry Red BRED 27 | MZUI (LP, PVC cover, insert sleeve) | 12 |

(see also A.C. Marias A.C., Wire, Dome, Cupol)

ASTRUD GILBERTO

| 64 | Verve VS 520 | Girl From Ipanema (with Stan Getz)/STAN GETZ & JOAO GILBERTO: Blowin' In the Wind | 4 |
| 66 | Verve VEP 5019 | AND ROSES AND ROSES (EP, with Antonio Carlos Jobim) | 7 |

GILDED CAGE

| 69 | Tepee TPR 1003 | Long Long Road (For The Broken Heart)/Baby Grumpling | 4 |

GILES, GILES & FRIPP

68	Deram DM 188	One In A Million/Newly-Weds	35
68	Deram DM 210	Thursday Morning/Elephant Song	30
68	Deram DML/SML 1022	THE CHEERFUL INSANITY OF GILES, GILES AND FRIPP (LP, mono/stereo)	35/30
70	Deram SPA 423	THE CHEERFUL INSANITY OF GILES, GILES AND FRIPP (LP, stereo reissue)	25

(see also Brain, Trendsetters Ltd, League Of Gentlemen, King Crimson, Robert Fripp)

GILGAMESH

| 75 | Caroline CA 2007 | GILGAMESH (LP) | 12 |

(see also Hugh Hopper)

TERRY GILKYSON & EASY RIDERS

58	Philips JK 1007	Marianne/Goodbye Chaquita (jukebox issue)	12
60	Fontana TFE 17326	STROLLING BLUES (EP)	7
60	Fontana TFE 17327	LONESOME RIDER (EP)	7

Rare Record Price Guide

MINT VALUE £

61	London RER 1333	ROLLIN' (EP) 10
53	Brunswick LA 8618	GOLDEN MINUTES OF FOLK MUSIC (10" LP) 18
61	London HA-R 2301	ROLLIN' (LP, also stereo SAH-R 6111) 12/14
61	London HA-R 2323	REMEMBER THE ALAMO (LP, as Easyriders including Terry Gilkyson) 12

(see also Easy Riders)

(IAN) GILLAN (BAND)

78	Island WIP 6423	Mad Elaine/Mercury High (as Ian Gillan Band, Island sleeve) 7
79	Acrobat BAT 2	Vengeance/Smoke On The Water (p/s) 5
80	Virgin VS 355	Sleeping On The Job/Higher And Higher (p/s, with free patch) 4
80	Virgin VS 362	No Easy Way/Handles On Her Hips/I Might As Well Go Home (p/s) 5
80	Virgin VS 377	Trouble/Your Sister's On My List (poster p/s) 4
80	Virgin VS 377	Trouble/Your Sister's On My List//Mr Universe (live)/Vengeance (live)/
		Smoke On The Water (live) (double pack) 5
81	Virgin VSK 103	Mutually Assured Destruction/The Maelstrom (p/s, with booklet) 5
81	Sounds FREEBIE No. 2	I'll Rip Out Your Spine (extract)/PROFESSIONALS: Little Boys In Blue (extract)
		(33rpm 1-sided flexidisc, printed die-cut sleeve, free with 'Sounds') 5/4
81	Lyntone LYN 10599	Higher And Higher/Spanish Guitar
		(1-sided blue flexidisc with 'Flexipop' issue 13) 5/4
82	Virgin VS 465	Restless/On The Rocks (live) (foldout poster p/s) 4
82	Virgin VSY 465	Restless/On The Rocks (live) (picture disc) 5
82	Virgin VSY 519	Living For The City/Purple Sky (picture disc) 8
82	Virgin VSY 519	Living For The City/Purple Sky (mispress picture disc, plays "Breaking Chains") .5
82	Virgin VS 537	Long Gone/Fiji (foldout p/s) 5
82	Kerrang!	Purple Sky/GARY MOORE: Wishing Well/TELEPHONE: Squeeze
		(flexidisc free with/without 'Kerrang!' magazine) 5/4
76	Polydor/Oyster 2490 136	CHILD IN TIME (LP, gatefold sleeve, as Ian Gillan Band) 12
76	Polydor ACBR 261	CHILD IN TIME (LP, mail-order record club version) 15
77	Island ILPS 9500	CLEAR AIR TURBULENCE (LP, gatefold sleeve, as Ian Gillan Band) 10
78	Island ILPS 9545	LIVE AT THE BUDO-KAN (withdrawn LP)
80	Virgin V 2171	GLORY ROAD (LP, with free LP "For Gillan Fans Only" [VDJ 32],
		stickered, embossed sleeve & inner sleeve) 12
82	Virgin VP 2238	MAGIC (LP, picture disc in die-cut sleeve with insert) 10

(see also [Shelia Carter &] Episode [Six], Deep Purple, Ray Fenwick, Split Knee Loons, John McCoy, Johnny Gustafson, Black Sabbath)

DANA GILLESPIE

65	Pye 7N 15872	Donna Donna/It's No Use Saying If 8
65	Pye 7N 15962	Thank You Boy/You're A Heartbreak Man 6
67	Pye 7N 17280	Pay You Back With Interest/Adam Can You Beat That 6
68	Decca F 12847	You Just Gotta Know My Mind/He Loves Me, He Loves Me Not 5
74	RCA RCA 2466	Andy Warhol/Dizzy Heights 8
69	Decca SKL 5012	BOX OF SURPRISES (LP) 30
73	RCA APL1 0354	WEREN'T BORN A MAN (LP) 10
74	RCA APL1 0682	AIN'T GONNA PLAY NO SECOND FIDDLE (LP) 10

DIZZY GILLESPIE

56	Vogue V 2116	The Champ (Pts 1 & 2) 5
60	HMV POP 705	Doddlin'/Dizzy's Blues 4
50s	Esquire EP 193	DIZZY WITH STRINGS (EP, with Operatic Strings) 7
55	Vogue EPV 1022	DIZZY GILLESPIE (EP) 8
55	Vogue EPV 1049	DIZZY GILLESPIE WITH STRINGS (EP) 8
56	Vogue EPV 1078	DIZZY GILLESPIE (EP) 8
56	Vogue EPV 1094	THE CHAMP — DIZZY GILLESPIE (EP) 8
56	Vogue EPV 1157	DIZZY GILLESPIE AND HIS ORCHESTRA (EP) 8
56	Vogue EPV 1158	DIZZY GILLESPIE AND HIS ORCHESTRA (EP) 8
57	Columbia Clef SEB 10075	PILE DRIVER (EP) 7
57	Columbia Clef SEB 10096	BIRKS WORKS (EP) 7
60	HMV 7EG 8577	MELLOW SOUNDS (EP, as Dizzy Gillespie Quintet) 7
61	HMV 7EG 8646	MORE MELLOW SOUNDS (EP, as Dizzy Gillespie Quintet) 7
63	Philips 430 793BE	NEW SOUND IN JAZZ (EP) 7
64	Philips BE 12552	BE BOP (EP) 7
65	Philips BE 12583	FILM THEMES (EP) 7
66	Verve VRE 5022	ALWAYS (EP) 7
52	Esquire 20-003	OPERATIC STRINGS (10" LP) 15
53	Vogue LDE 017	DIZZY GILLESPIE PLAYS (10" LP) 15
53	Vogue LDE 033	DIZZY GILLESPIE PLAYS — JOHNNY RICHARDS CONDUCTS (10" LP) ..15
54	Vogue LDE 039	PARIS CONCERT (10" LP) 15
54	Vogue LDE 076	DIZZY GILLESPIE AND HIS ORCHESTRA (10" LP) 15
54	HMV DLP 1047	DIZZY GILLESPIE AND HIS ORCHESTRA (10" LP) 15
54	Felsted EDL 87006	DIZZY GILLESPIE'S OPERATIC STRINGS — JEALOUSY (10" LP) 15
55	Vogue LDE 135	DIZZY GILLESPIE AND HIS ORCHESTRA (10" LP) 15
55	Columbia Clef 33CX 10002	DIZZY GILLESPIE AND HIS ORCHESTRA (LP) 12
59	HMV CLP 1318	HAVE TRUMPET, WILL TRAVEL (LP) 10
60	HMV CLP 1381	THE GREATEST TRUMPET OF THEM ALL (LP) 10
61	HMV CLP 1431	PORTRAIT OF DUKE ELLINGTON (LP) 10
62	HMV CLP 1484	GILLESPIANA (LP, also stereo CSD 1392) 10/12
67	Fontana TL 5343	OPERATIC STRINGS (LP, reissue) 10
71	Pye PKL 4403	SOULED OUT (LP) 10
73	Mainstream MSL 1010	DIZZY GILLESPIE & MITCHELL RUFF DUO (LP) 10
70s	Pablo 231 0794	FREE RIDE (LP) 10

DIZZY GILLESPIE & STAN GETZ

| 60 | HMV 7EG 8596 | DIZZY GILLESPIE/STAN GETZ SEXTET (EP) ....7 |
| 55 | Columbia Clef 33C 9009 | DIZZY GILLESPIE — STAN GETZ SEXTET (LP) ....12 |

(see also Stan Getz)

DIZZY GILLESPIE & CHARLIE PARKER

| 57 | Columbia ClefSEB 10087 | ONE MORE TIME: WITH BIRD AND DIZ (EP) ....7 |

Dizzy GILLESPIE & Charlie PARKER

61	Vogue LAE 12252	DIZ 'N BIRD IN CONCERT (LP) 10

(see also Charlie Parker)

DIZZY GILLESPIE & ORCHESTRA/DON BYAS QUARTET
57	MGM MGM-EP 579	DIZZ AND DON (EP, 2 tracks each) 8

DIZZY GILLESPIE/KAI WINDING'S BIRDLANDERS
58	MGM MGM-EP 681	TWO BY TWO (EP, 2 tracks each) 7

JAZZ GILLUM
66	RCA Victor RD 7816	JAZZ GILLUM 1938-1947 (LP) 15
70	RCA Intl. INTS 1177	YOU GOT TO REAP WHAT YOU SOW (LP) 12

JIMMY GILMER & FIREBALLS
62	London HLD 9632	I'm Gonna Go Walkin'/Born To Be With You (as Chimmy Gilmer) 7
63	London HLD 9789	Sugar Shack/My Heart Is Free 6
64	London HLD 9827	Daisy Petal Pickin'/When My Tears Have Dried 6
64	London HLD 9872	Ain't Gonna Tell Nobody/Young Am I 6
64	London HLD 9898	Look At Me/I'll Send For You 6
65	Dot DS 16666	Thunder 'N' Lightnin'/Cry Baby (unissued)
65	Stateside SS 418	Thunder 'N' Lightnin'/What Do You Do 8
65	Stateside SS 472	She Belongs To Me/Rambler's Blues 6
68	London HL 10232	Three Squares/Baby 4
64	London HA-D/SH-D 8150	SUGAR SHACK (LP) 30
65	Dot DLP 3577	BUDDY'S BUDDY — BUDDY HOLLY SONGS BY JIMMY GILMER (LP) 25

(see also Fireballs, Jim & Monica)

DAVE GILMOUR
78	Harvest HAR 5167	There's No Way Out Of Here/Deafinitely 5
84	Harvest HAR 5226	Blue Light (LP Version)/Cruise (p/s) 4
84	Harvest 12HAR 5226	Blue Light (LP Version)/Cruise (12", p/s) 10
84	Harvest HAR 5229	Love On The Air/Let's Get Metaphysical (p/s) 4
84	Harvest HARP 5229	Love On The Air/Let's Get Metaphysical (shaped picture disc) 7

(see also Pink Floyd, Jokers Wild)

PETER GILMORE
60	HMV POP 740	Follow That Girl/Come Away 4

GORDON GILTRAP (BAND)
69	Transatlantic TRA 202	PORTRAIT (LP) 25
71	MCA MKPS 2020	TESTAMENT OF TIME (LP) 20
73	Philips 6308 175	GILTRAP (LP) 15
81	Themes International	THEMES (LP, by Gordon Giltrap Band, library issue) 12

(see also Accolade, Pauline Filby)

GINA X
80	Plastic Poison MRC 5014	Do It Yourself/Be A Boy (p/s) 4

GINGER JUG BAND
70s	GJB 001	GINGER JUG BAND (LP, private pressing) 30

GINGER SNAPS
65	RCA RCA 1483	The Sh Down Down Song/I've Got Faith In Him 5

HERMIONE GINGOLD & GILBERT HARDING
53	Philips PB 104	Oh, Grandma/Takes Two To Tango (78) 5

GINHOUSE
71	B&C CAS 1031	GINHOUSE (LP) 40

GINO & GINA
58	Mercury 7MT 230	Pretty Baby/Love's A Carousel 30

GINSBERGS
67	Saga	AT THE ICA (LP) 15

GIORGIO & MARCO'S MEN
66	Polydor 56101	Girl Without A Heart/Run Run 4
60s	Electratone EP 1003	Baby I Need You/Maureen 15

GIRL
79	Jet JET 159	My Number/My Number (Version) (clear vinyl, PVC sleeve with 2 stickers) 6
79	Jet JET 159	My Number/My Number (Version) (black vinyl, promo only) 4
80	Jet JET 169	Do You Love Me/Strawberries (p/s) 4
80	Jet JET 176	Hollywood Tease (Remix)/You Really Got Me (p/s) 4
80	Jet JET 176	Hollywood Tease (Remix)/You Really Got Me (poster p/s) 5
80	Jet JET 191	Love Is A Game/Little Miss Ann (white vinyl, patch & sticker in PVC sleeve) 4
80	Jet JET 10 191	Love Is A Game/Little Miss Ann/Sweet Kids
		(10", white vinyl with sticker in PVC sleeve) 6
81	Jet JET 7014	Thru The Twilite/McKitty's Back (p/s) 4
81	Jet JETP 7014	Thru The Twilite/McKitty's Back (picture disc) 6
82	Jet JET 7019	Old Dogs/Passing Clouds (p/s) 5
80	Jet JETLP 224	SHEER GREED (LP, stickered cover with inner sleeve) 10
82	Jet JETLP 238	WASTED YOUTH (LP, with inner sleeve) 10

GIRLFRIENDS
63	Colpix PX 712	Jimmy Boy/For My Sake 10

GIRLIE
67	Treasure Isle TI 7053	Boss Cocky/LOVE SHOCKS: Musical True 6
69	Bullet BU 400	Madame Straggae/LAUREL AITKEN: Stupid Married Man 4
69	Duke DU 42	African Meeting (as Girlie & Junior)/JOSH: Higher And Higher 4
70	Joe JRS 7	Small Change/Mind Your Business (with Joe Mansano) 5
71	Ackee ACK 124	Decimilization (with Paul)/Version 4

(see also Laurel Aitken & Girlie)

GIRLS AT OUR BEST
80	Records RR 001	Getting Nowhere Fast/Warm Girls (p/s)	6
81	Rough Trade RT 055	Politics/It's Fashion (p/s)	5
81	Happy Birthday UR 4	Go For Gold/I'm Beautiful Now (p/s)	4
81	Happy Birthday UR 6	Fast Boyfriends/This Train (p/s)	4
81	Happy Birthday RULP 1	PLEASURE (LP, 1st 15,000 with free 'pleasure bag')	12/10

GIRLSCHOOL
79	City NIK 6	Take It All Away/It Could Be Better (p/s, some on red vinyl)	6/4
80	Bronze BRO 110	Yeah Right/The Hunter (p/s)	4
81	Bronze BRO 118	Hit And Run/Tonight (p/s)	4
81	Bronze BROX 118	Hit And Run/Tonight (12", p/s)	7
81	Bronze BRO 126	C'mon Let's Go/Tonight (live) (p/s)	4
81	Bronze BROX 126	C'mon Let's Go/Tonight (live)/Demolition (live) (10", p/s)	6
82	Bronze BRO 144	Don't Call It Love/Wildlife (red vinyl, p/s)	4
83	Bronze BRO 169	1-2-3-4 Rock And Roll/Tush (p/s)	4
83	Bronze BROX 169	1-2-3-4 Rock And Roll/Tush + 2 (12", p/s)	7
83	Bronze BRO 171	20th Century Boy/Breaking All The Rules (p/s)	4
83	Bronze BROX 171	20th Century Boy/Breaking All The Rules/Like It Like That (12", p/s)	7
84	Bronze BRO 176	Burning In The Heat/Surrender (p/s)	4
84	Bronze BROX 176	Burning In The Heat/Surrender (12", p/s)	7
81	Bronze BRON 534	HIT AND RUN (LP, red vinyl)	10

(see also Motorhead)

JIMMY GIUFFRE
| 55 | Capitol LC 6699 | JIMMY GIUFFRE (10" LP) | 12 |

GIZMO
75	President PT 443	Just Like Velvet/Jesus Help Me Sleep (no p/s)	6
70s	MCM 4	Psychedelic Rock And Roll/Martyr For The Kingdom (p/s)	10
79	Ace ACE 001	JUST LIKE MASTER BATES (LP, private pressing, white vinyl, plastic sleeve)	40
70s	Sleep 'N' Eat	VICTIMS (LP, private pressing)	35
80s	own label	JUST LIKE MASTER BATES/VICTIMS (2-LP reissue, autographed, stickered 'victim' sleeve)	70

GLADDY (Anderson) & FOLLOWERS
| 69 | Blue Cat BS 172 | Judas/The World Come To An End | 5 |

(see also Stranger & Glady)

GLADIATORS (U.K.)
| 63 | HMV POP 1134 | Tovaritch/Bleak House | 15 |

(see also Nero & Gladiators)

GLADIATORS (U.S.)
68	Direction 58-3854	Girl Don't Make Me Wait/Can't Get Away From Heartbreak	6
69	Direction 58-4308	Waiting On The Shores Of Nowhere/I'll Always Love You	6
69	Direction 58-4507	As Long As I Live/Everything	4
69	Direction 58-4660	Twelfth Of Never/Lovin' My Baby Back Home	4

GLADIATORS (Jamaica)
69	Doctor Bird DB 1114	The Train Is Coming/So Fine	10
69	Studio One SO 2072	Hello Carol/RICHARD ACE: More Reggae	10
72	Ackee ACK 149	Sonia/SOUND DIMENSION: Solas	5

GLADIATORS (Jamaica)
| 70s | Rock Steady Rev. REVR 12 | Unusual Reggae/Andue | 4 |

GLADIOLAS
| 57 | London HLO 8435 | Little Darlin'/Sweetheart, Please Don't Go | 125 |
| 57 | London HLO 8435 | Little Darlin'/Sweetheart, Please Don't Go (78) | 25 |

GLADSTONE
| 72 | Probe SPBA 6264 | GLADSTONE (LP) | 10 |

GLASER BROTHERS
| 69 | MGM CS 8115 | NOW COUNTRY (LP) | 10 |

GLASGOW
84	Clydebank	GLASGOW'S MILES BETTER (12" EP)	7
84	Neat NEAT 40	Stranded/Heat Of The Night (p/s)	4
88	Zero 41 041 7	Secrets In The Dark/Meet Me Halfway (p/s)	4

GLASS
82	Glass GLASS 1	New Colours/Sweet Entropy (p/s)	5
80s	Glass GLASS 002	SIXTEEN GIGS (LP)	10
80s	Glass GLASS 002	SIXTEEN GIGS (cassette in freezer bag)	10

PHILIP GLASS
70s	Chatham Square LP 1001/2	MUSIC WITH CHANGING PARTS (2-LP)	25
70s	Chatham Square LP 1003	MUSIC IN FIFTHS/MUSIC IN A SIMILAR MOTION (LP)	15
70s	Folkways FTS 33902	TWO PAGES (LP)	10
76	Cardine LA 2010	MUSIC IN 12 PARTS 1 & 2 (LP)	10
78	Shandar SHAN 83515	SOLO MUSIC (LP)	10

GLASS HARP
72	MCA MUPS 431	GLASS HARP (LP)	10
72	MCA MUPS 449	SYNERGY (LP)	10
73	MCA MUPS 470	IT MAKES ME GLAD (LP)	10

GLASS MENAGERIE
68	Pye 7N 17518	She's A Rainbow/But That's When I Start To Love Her	8
68	Pye 7N 17568	You Didn't Have To Be So Nice/Let's All Run To The Sun	6
68	Pye 7N 17615	Frederick Jordan/I Said Goodbye To Me	25

MINT VALUE £

69	Polydor 56318	Have You Forgotten Who You Are/Do You Ever Think?	6
69	Polydor 56341	Do My Thing Myself/Watching The World Pass By	6

(see also Paladin, Toe Fat)

GLASS OPENING

68	Plexium P 1236	Silver Bells And Cockle Shells/Does It Really Matter	80

JACKIE GLEASON (& ORCHESTRA)

55	Capitol CL 14289	Rain/I'll Never Be The Same (with Orchestra)	6
55	Capitol CL 14363	Autumn Leaves/Oo! What You Do To Me (with Orchestra)	5
56	Capitol CL 14549	Capri In May/You're My Greatest Love (with Orchestra)	4
60	Brunswick 04775	What Is A Boy?/What Is A Girl?	8
70	MCA MU 1108	What Is A Boy?/What Is A Girl? (reissue)	4

CAPTAIN GLEASON'S GARDEN BAND

55	Capitol CL 14323	In The Good Old Summertime/The Band Played On	5

(see also Jackie Gleason)

GLEN (Brown) & CRYSTALITES

72	Songbird SB 1081	Smokey Eyes/CRYSTALITES: Smokey Eyes Version	4

GLEN (Brown) & LLOYD (Robinson)

66	Ska Beat JB 250	Live And Let Others Die/Too Late	8
67	Doctor Bird DB 1099	Feel Good Now/What You've Got (credited as Lloyd Glen)	10

GLENCOE

72	Epic EPC 65207	GLENCOE (LP)	12
73	Epic EPC 65717	SPIRIT OF GLENCOE (LP)	12

GARY GLITTER

75	Bell BELL 1451	Papa Oom Mow Mow/She Cat, Alley Cat	4
76	Bell REBEL 1	GARY GLITTER (EP)	5
81	Eagle ERS 009	When I'm On I'm On/Wild Horses (p/s)	8
84	Arista ARISD 570	Dance Me Up/Too Young To Dance (picture disc)	4
84	Arista ARISD 592	Another Rock'n'Roll Christmas (shaped picture disc with plinth)	5
84	Arista ARICV 586	Shout! Shout! Shout!/Hair Of The Dog ('mirror' picture disc)	4
85	Arista ARISD 615	Love Comes/Boys Will Be Boys (picture disc)	4

(see also Paul Raven, Paul Monday, Rubber Bucket)

GLITTERHOUSE

68	Stateside SS 2129	Barbarella/BOB CREWE: An Angel Is Love	6
68	Stateside SS 2129	Barbarella/Love Drags Me Down	6

GLOBAL VILLAGE TRUCKING COMPANY

76	Caroline C 1516	GLOBAL VILLAGE TRUCKING COMPANY (LP)	12

GLOBE SHOW

69	Page One POF 128	Yes Or No/Gettin' On Back	4

GLOOMYS

68	Columbia DB 8391	Daybreak/Queen And King	8

GLORIA MUNDI

78	RCA PB 5068	Fight Back/Do It (p/s)	4
78	RCA PL2 5157	I INDIVIDUAL (LP, with inner sleeve)	10
79	RCA PL2 5244	THE WORD IS OUT (LP)	10

GLORIES

67	CBS 2786	I Stand Accused (Of Loving You)/Wish They Could Write A Song	15
67	Direction 58-3084	Give Me My Freedom/Security	8
68	Direction 58-3300	Sing Me A Love Song/Oh Baby That's Love	4
68	Direction 58-3646	My Sweet Sweet Baby/Stand By (I'm Comin' Home)	4

GLOVE

83	Wonderland SHE 3	Like An Animal/Mouth To Mouth (p/s, some die-cut)	10/8
83	Wonderland SHEX 3	Like An Animal (Club, What Club? Mix)/Like Animal/Mouth To Mouth (12", p/s, some sleeves with centre hole)	16
83	Wonderland SHE 5	Punish Me With Kisses/The Tightrope (p/s)	14
83	Wonderland SHELP 2	BLUE SUNSHINE (LP, some with inner sleeve)	12/10
83	Wonderland SHEMC 2	BLUE SUNSHINE (cassette, blue paper labels)	10

(see also Cure, Siouxsie & Banshees)

ROGER GLOVER & GUESTS

74	Purple PUR 125	Love Is All/Old Blind Mole/Magician Moth	4
84	Safari SAF EP 1	Love Is All/Old Blind Mole/Magician Moth (p/s, reissue)	4
74	Purple TPSA 7514	THE BUTTERFLY BALL (AND THE GRASSHOPPER'S FEAST) (LP, gatefold sleeve)	10
78	Polydor 2391 306	ELEMENTS (LP, solo)	10

(see also Deep Purple, Elf, Eddie Hardin, Whitesnake, Rainbow, Glenn Hughes, John Lawton, Wizard's Convention)

GMT

91	Mausoleum BONE 12-83102	One By One (12", p/s)	10

GNIDROLOG

71	RCA SF 8261	IN SPITE OF HARRY'S TOENAIL (LP)	30
72	RCA SF 8322	LADY LAKE (LP)	75

GNOMES OF ZURICH

66	Planet PLF 121	Please Mr Sun/I'm Coming Down With The Blues	20
67	RCA RCA 1606	Second Fiddle/Publicity Girl	18
67	CBS 202556	Hang On Baby/Blues For My Baby	15
67	CBS 2694	High Hopes/Pretender	15

G-NOTES

58	Oriole CB 1456	Ronnie/I Would	8
58	Oriole CB 1456	Ronnie/I Would (78)	5

GOAT
82	Real Kavoom ARK 1	REAL KAVOOM (12" EP)	7

GOBBLEDEGOOKS
64	Decca F 12023	Now And Again/Where Have You Been	8

GOBBLINZ
70s	Bacon BECK 878/BAC 1	Love Me Too/All Of This And More/Communique (p/s)	4

GO-BETWEENS
80	Postcard 80-4	I Need Two Heads/Stop Before You Say It (brown label & brown company sleeve)	8
80	Postcard 80-4	I Need Two Heads/Stop Before You Say It (yellow label & cream company sleeve)	10
82	Rough Trade RT 108	Hammer The Hammer/By Chance (p/s)	4
83	Rough Trade RT 124	Cattle And Cane/Heaven Says (p/s)	4
83	Rough Trade RT 114	Man O'Sand To Girl O'See/This Girl Black Girl (p/s)	4
87	Beggars Banquet BEG 183D	Right Here/When People Are Dead/A Little Romance//Don't Call Me Gone/ A Little Romance (live) (double pack)	4
88	B. Banquet BEG 218B	Streets Of Your Town/Wait Until June (box set)	4

GOBLIN
79	EMI EMC 3222	SUSPIRIA (LP soundtrack)	30

KEITH & DONNA GODCHAUX
75	Round RX 104	KEITH & DONNA GODCHAUX (LP)	10

(see also Grateful Dead)

GEOFF GODDARD
61	HMV POP 938	Girl Bride/For Eternity	15
62	HMV POP 1068	My Little Girl's Come Home/Try Once More	18
63	HMV POP 1160	Saturday Dance/Come Back To Me	18
63	HMV POP 1213	Sky Men/Walk With Me My Angel	40

GODFATHERS
85	Corp. Image 7GFTR 010	Lonely Man/I Want You (p/s)	7
85	Corp. Image GFTR 010	Lonely Man/I Want You/Sticks And Stones (12", p/s)	10
86	Corp. Image GRFT 020	This Damnation/Can't Leave Her Alone/John Barry (12", p/s)	8
86	Corp. Image GFTR 030	Sunarise/I Want Everything (p/s)	5
86	Corp. Image GFTR 030T	Sunarise/I Want Everything/Unsatisfied (12", p/s)	7
87	Corp. Image GFTR 040	Love Is Dead/Angela (2,500 in gatefold autographed p/s)	5
88	Epic GFTB 1	Birth, School, Work, Death (Resurrection Mix)/S.T.B. (box set with 3 postcards & 4 badges)	4
88	Epic GFTP 1	Birth, School, Work, Death (Resurrection Mix)/S.T.B. (picture disc)	4
88	Epic GFTQ 1	Birth, School, Work, Death (12", plain black sleeve)	8
88	Epic GFTP 2	Cause I Said So/When Am I Coming Down (shrink wrapped with tour pass)	4
88	Epic GFTP 3	Love Is Dead (New Version)/Those Days Are Over (live) (picture disc)	4
89	Epic GFTB 4	She Gives Me Love/Walking Talking Johnny Cash Blues (box set)	4
89	Epic GFTP 4	She Gives Me Love/Walking Talking Johnny Cash Blues (picture disc)	4
90	Epic GFTQT 5	I'm Lost And Then I'm Found (live)/Walking Talking Johnny Cash Blues (live)/ How Low Is Low? (live) (10", p/s)	6

(see also Sid Presley Experience)

HUGH GODFREY
67	Coxsone CS 7001	A Dey Pon Dem/SOUL BROTHERS: Take Ten	12
67	Studio One SO 2015	Go Tell Him/MARCIA GRIFFITHS: After Laughter	15

RAY GODFREY
78	Grapevine GRP 111	Come And Get These Memories/I'm The Other Half Of You	4

ROBERT JOHN GODFREY
74	Charisma CAS 1084	FALL OF HYPERION (LP)	25
80s	Nuage MM 1	REVERBERATIONS (cassette)	10

(see also Enid, Godfrey & Stewart, William Arkle)

GODFREY & STEWART
80s	The Enid ENID 11	THE SEED AND THE SOWER (LP)	15
80s	The Stand HEARTLP	JOINED BY THE HEART (LP, fan club issue, 2,000 only)	25
80s	The Stand HEARTC	JOINED BY THE HEART (cassette, fan club issue)	10

(see also Robert John Godfrey, Enid)

GODIEGO
78	Satril SATL 4009	THE WATER MARGIN (LP)	10

GODLEY & CREME
79	Mercury SAMP 017	5 O'Clock/The Flood//Lost Weekend/Honolulu (promo double pack sampler)	6
81	Polydor POSP 322	Under Your Thumb (short vsn)/Power Behind The Throne (2,000 only with p/s)	5
85	Polydor POSP 372	Cry/Love Bombs (picture disc)	4
77	Mercury CONS 017	CONSEQUENCES (3-LP, box set with booklet)	20
81	Polydor POLD 543	ISMISM (LP, white sleeve with die-cut holes)	10

(see also Mockingbirds, Hotlegs, 10cc, Dave Berry, Frabjoy & Runcible Spoon)

GODS
68	Columbia DB 8486	Baby's Rich/Somewhere In The Street	10
69	Columbia DB 8544	Hey! Bulldog/Real Love Guaranteed	12
69	Columbia DB 8572	Maria/Long Time, Sad Time, Bad Time	10
68	Columbia S(C)X 6286	GENESIS (LP)	85
70	Columbia SCX 6372	TO SAMUEL A SON (LP)	70
76	Harvest SHSM 2011	GODS (LP)	10

(see also Uriah Heep, Shame, Toe Fat)

GODS (Thor, Hermes, Olympus, Mars)
67	Polydor 56168	Come On Down To My Boat Baby/Garage Man	50

(see also Rolling Stones)

MINT VALUE £

GOD'S GIFT
79	Newmarket	THESE DAYS (EP)	10
81	New Hormones ORG 14	Soldiers/Anthony Perkins/No God/The Hunger Of Millions (12", p/s)	8
80s	Pleasantly Surprised PS 7	FOLIE A QUATRE (cassette, in bag with inserts)	12

GOD'S TOYS
80	Badge BAD 4	All The Born Losers/I Love The Sound (Of My Own Voice) (no p/s)	4
80	Badge BA 7	Everybody's Got A Mother/Package Tours To Heaven (p/s)	4

GODZ
67	Fontana STL 5500	CONTACT WITH THE GODZ (LP)	20
69	Fontana STL 5512	GODZ II (LP)	20

GOGMAGOG
85	F. For Thought YUMT 109	I Will Be There/Living In A Timewarp/It's Illegal But It's Fun (12", p/s)	15

(see also Iron Maiden, Def Leppard, Whitesnake, Gillan, Di'Anno)

GO-GO's
65	Oriole CB 1982	Big Boss Man/I'm Gonna Spend Christmas	30

GO-GO's
80	Stiff BUY 78	We Got The Beat/How Much More (p/s)	8
81	IRS PFP 1007	Our Lips Are Sealed/Surfing And Spying (p/s, pink vinyl)	12
81	IRS PFP 1010	We Got The Beat/Skidmarks On My Heart (p/s)	4
81	IRS GON 101	Automatic/Tonite (p/s)	4
81	IRS GONP 101	Automatic/Tonite (picture disc)	7

(see also Belinda Carlisle, Jane Wiedlin)

HERBIE GOINS & NIGHT-TIMERS
66	Parlophone R 5478	No. 1 In Your Heart/Cruisin' (as Herbie Goins & Night-Timers)	40
66	Parlophone R 5533	Comin' Home To You/The Incredible Miss Brown	15
67	Parlophone PMC 7026	NUMBER ONE IN YOUR HEART (LP)	50

(see also Night-Timers, Herbie & Royalists)

HARRY GOLD with NORRIE PARAMOR ORCHESTRA
54	Columbia SCM 5144	Be Good To Me/Frou Frou	4

BARRY GOLDBERG (REUNION)
68	Pye Intl. 7N 25465	Another Day/Capricorn Blues (as Barry Goldberg Reunion)	6
68	Pye NSPL 28116	BARRY GOLDBERG REUNION (LP)	12
69	Buddah 203 020	TWO JEWS BLUES (LP, with Mike Bloomfield)	10
71	Buddah 2318 038	BLASTS FROM MY PAST (LP)	10

(see also Electric Flag, Mike Bloomfield)

GOLDEN APPLES OF THE SUN
65	Decca F 12194	Monkey Time/Chocolate Rolls, Tea And Monopoly (unissued)	
65	Immediate IM 010	Monkey Time/Chocolate Rolls, Tea And Monopoly	25

GOLDEN CRUSADERS
64	Columbia DB 7232	I'm In Love With You/Always On My Mind	12
64	Columbia DB 7357	Hey Good Lookin'/Come On, Come On	12
65	Columbia DB 7485	I Don't Care/That Broken Heart Is Mine	12

GOLDEN DAWN
88	Sarah SARAH 009	My Secret World/Spring-Heeled Jack/The Railway Track (p/s, with 14"x10" poster)	7

GOLDEN EARRING
69	Major Minor MM 601	Just A Little Peace In My Heart/Remember My Friend	7
69	Major Minor MM 633	It's Alright But It Could Be Better/Where Will I Be	7
70	Major Minor MM 679	Another Forty-Five Miles/I Can't Get Hold Of Her	7
70	Polydor BM 56514	That Day/Words I Need	12
70	Polydor 2001 073	Back Home/This Is The Time Of Year	7
73	Track 2094 116	Radar Love/Just Like Vince Taylor	4
74	Track 2094 121	Instant Poetry/From Heaven, From Hell	5
74	Track 2094 126	Candy's Going Bad/She Flies On Strange Wings	5
75	Track 2094 130	Ce Soir/Lucky Number	5
76	Polydor 2001 626	Sleepwalking/Babylon (no p/s)	5
77	Polydor 2121 312	Bombay/Faded Jeans (no p/s)	5
77	Polydor 2121 335	Radar Love (live)/Just Like Vince (live) (12", p/s)	7
83	Mercury MER 122	Twilight Zone/King Dark (p/s)	4
83	Mercury MERX 122	Twilight Zone/King Dark (12", blue or yellow p/s)	7
84	Carrere CAR 321	When The Lady Smiles/Orwell's Year (p/s)	4
84	Carrere CART 321	When The Lady Smiles/Orwell's Year (12", p/s)	7
69	Major Minor SMLP 65	EIGHT MILES HIGH (LP)	25
71	Polydor 2310 135	SEVEN TEARS (LP)	12
72	Polydor 2310 210	TOGETHER (LP)	12
73	Track 2406 109	HEARING EARRING (LP)	10
73	Track 2406 112	MOONTAN (LP)	10
75	Track 2406 117	SWITCH (LP)	10
76	Polydor 2430 330	TO THE HILT (LP, gatefold sleeve with insert)	10
77	Polydor 2344 059	CONTRABAND (LP, with insert)	10
77	Polydor 2625 034	LIVE (2-LP, gatefold sleeve)	14

GOLDEN EARRINGS
68	Capitol CL 15552	I've Just Lost Somebody/The Truth About Arthur	4
68	Capitol CL 15567	Dong Dong Di Ki Di Gi Dong/Wake Up — Breakfast	4

GOLDEN FLEECE
67	Decca F 12669	Athens 6 a.m./Girl From Syracuse	4

GOLDEN GATE QUARTET
51	COlumbia DB 3035	Do Unto Others/JEFF ALEXANDER CHOIR: Little Bitty Baby (78)	8
53	Columbia SCM 5054	Moses Smote The Waters/Bones, Bones, Bones	5

MINT VALUE £

53	Columbia DB 3310	Moses Smote The Waters/Bones, Bones, Bones (78)	10
58	Fontana TFR 6009	THAT GOLDEN CHARIOT (10" LP)	12
59	Columbia 33SX 1172	SHOUT FOR JOY! (LP)	10
61	Columbia 33SX 1370	GET ON BOARD (LP)	10

GOLDEN GATE STRINGS
65	Columbia DB 7634	Mr. Tambourine Man/With God On Our Side	6

GOLDEN HORDE
85	Hot Wire WAY OUT 1	DIG THAT CRAZY GRAVE (EP)	5
80s	Hot Wire HWS 855	Young And Happy/Little UFO/Fiona (p/s)	5
86	Media Burn MB 6	IN REALITY (mini-LP)	8
85	Hot Wire/I.D. NOSE 7	THE CHOCOLATE BISCUIT CONSPIRACY (LP)	10

GOLDIE (& GINGERBREADS)
65	Decca F 12070	Can't You Hear My Heartbeat/Little Boy	5
65	Decca F 12126	That's Why I Love You/Skip	6
65	Decca F 12199	Sailor Boy/Please Please	5
69	Decca F 12931	Can't You Hear My Heartbeat/That's Why I Love You	4
66	Immediate IM 026	Goin' Back/Headlines (solo)	20
66	Fontana TF 693	I Do/Think About The Good Times (solo)	10

(see also Ten Wheel Drive)

VIVIEN GOLDMAN
81	Window WIN 1	Launderette/Private Armies (gatefold p/s)	5

BOBBY GOLDSBORO
63	Stateside SS 193	The Runaround/The Letter	10
65	United Artists UP 1079	Little Things/I Just Can't Go On Pretending	8
65	United Artists UP 1091	Voodoo Woman/It Breaks My Heart	5
65	United Artists UP 1104	If You Wait For Love/If You've Got A Heart	4
66	United Artists UP 1120	Broomstick Cowboy/Ain't Got Time For Happy	4
66	United Artists UP 1128	It's Too Late/I'm Goin' Home	8
66	United Artists UP 1135	I Know You Better Than That/When Your Love Has Gone	4
66	United Artists UP 1146	Take Your Love/Longer Than Forever	10
67	United Artists UP 1156	It Hurts Me/Pity The Fool	5
67	United Artists UP 1166	No Fun At The Fair/Hold On	5
67	United Artists UP 1177	Too Many People/Goodbye To All You Women	25
68	United Artists UP 2215	H-O-N-E-Y/Danny	4
68	United Artists UP 2223	Autumn Of My Life/She Chased Me	5
68	United Artists UP 2264	Love Arrester/Dissatisfied Man	5
65	United Artists UEP 1006	LITTLE THINGS (EP)	15
66	United Artists UEP 1016	THE TALENTED BOBBY GOLDSBORO (EP)	15
66	United Artists (S)ULP 1135	IT'S TOO LATE (LP)	15
67	United Artists (S)ULP 1163	SOLID GOLDSBORO — GREATEST HITS (LP)	15
68	United Artists (S)ULP 1195	HONEY (LP)	14

GOLDSMITH
83	Bedlam BLM 001	Life Is Killing Me (p/s)	15

GOLIATH
71	CBS 5312	Port And Lemon Lady	6
70	CBS 64229	GOLIATH (LP)	40

GOLLIWOGS
66	Vocalion VF 9226	Brown-Eyed Girl/You Better Be Careful	25
67	Vocalion VF 9283	Fragile Child/Fight Fire	25
72	Fantasy FAN 5996	GOLLIWOGS (LP, pressed in U.S. for U.K. distribution)	10

(see also Creedence Clearwater Revival)

GOLLYWOGS
60	Parlophone R 4647	Parade Of The Jelly Babies/The Teddy Bears' Picnic	4

BENNY GOLSON
81	CBS A 1223	The New Killer Joe/Walkin' And Stalkin'	4
81	CBS 12A 1223	The New Killer Joe/Walkin' And Stalkin' (12")	7
60	Esquire 32-105	GROOVIN' WITH GOLSON (LP)	12

BENNY GOLSON & ART FARMER
62	Pye Intl. 7N 25120	Blues March/Serenata	5
65	Stateside SL 10150	STOCKHOLM SOJOURN (LP)	10

(see also Art Farmer)

GONADS
82	Secret SHH 131	PURE PUNK FOR NOW PEOPLE (EP)	4
82	Secret SHH 134	PEACE ARTISTS (EP)	4
83	Razor RZS 103	THE PUNK (EP)	4

GONDOLIERS
58	Starlite ST45 001	Fly, Seagull, Fly/God's Green Acres	7

NAT GONELLA & HIS GEORGIA JAZZ BAND
60	Columbia DB 4465	Show Me The Way To Go Home/My Gal Sal	4

GONG
71	Philips 6332 033	CONTINENTAL CIRCUS (LP, soundtrack)	20
73	Virgin V 2002	RADIO GNOME INVISIBLE PART 1 — THE FLYING TEAPOT (LP)	12
73	Virgin V 2007	RADIO GNOME INVISIBLE PART 2 — ANGEL'S EGG (LP, gatefold sleeve; some with book)	30/12
74	Caroline VC 502	CAMEMBERT ELECTRIQUE (LP)	12
74	Virgin V 2019	YOU (LP, with insert)	10
76	Virgin V 2046	SHAMAL (LP)	10

(see also Daevid Allen, Steve Hillage, Clearlight, Radio Actors, Sphynx, Tim Blake)

MINT VALUE £

GONG/CAMEL/HENRY COW/GLOBAL TRUCKING CO.
73   Greasy Truckers GT 4997   GREASY TRUCKERS (2-LP, 1 side each; with insert) 18
(see also Camel)

GONKS
64   Decca F 11984   The Gonk Song/That's All Right, Mama 10

PAUL GONSALVES
70   Deram SML 1064   HUMMINGBIRD (LP) 25
(see also Tubby Hayes & Paul Gonsalves)

GONZALES
74   EMI EMI 2706   I Haven't Stopped Dancing Yet/Carnival 4
74   EMI EMC 3046   GONZALES (LP) 30

BELLE GONZALEZ
72   Columbia SCX 6484   BELLE (LP) 80

DOUGLAS GOOD & GINNY PLENTY
68   Stateside SS 2104   Sunny And Me/Living In A World Of Make Believe 4

JACK GOOD'S FAT NOISE
60   Decca F 11984   The Fat Washerwoman/The Fat Noise 8

GOODBYE MR MACKENZIE
86   Precious JEWEL 2   The Rattler/Candlestick Park (p/s) 8
86   Precious JEWEL 2T   The Rattler/Candlestick Park/The End (12", p/s) 12
86   Claude MACK 001   Face To Face/Good Deeds/Secrets (12", p/s) 12
88   Capitol CLG 501   Goodbye Mr Mackenzie/Green Turn Red/Stars And Bars (12", gatefold p/s) 7
88   Capitol CLG 513   Open Your Arms/Secrets (gatefold p/s) 4
88   Capitol 12CLP 513   Open Your Arms/Secrets/Amsterdam (12", picture disc) 7
89   Capitol CLX 538   Goodwill City/I'm Sick Of You (box set with badge & postcards) 4
89   Capitol ESTX 2089   GOOD DEEDS AND DIRTY RAGS (LP, with 12" [stickered p/s] & inner sleeve) . . .10

GOOD EARTH
68   Saga FID 2112   IT'S HARD ROCK AND ALL THAT (LP) 15
(see also Mungo Jerry, First Impression/Good Earth)

GOODEES
69   Stax STAX 113   Condition Red/Didn't Know Love Was So Good 12

PHILIP GOODHAND-TAIT (& STORMSVILLE SHAKERS)
66   Parlophone R 5448   I'm Gonna Put Some Hurt On You/It's A Lie (with Stormsville Shakers) 10
66   Parlophone R 5498   No Problem/What More Do You Want (with Stormsville Shakers) 8
66   Parlophone R 5547   J.C. Greaseburger/You Can't Take Love (with Stormsville Shakers) 10
69   Decca F 12868   Love Has Got Hold Of Me/Too Pleased To Help 6
71   DJM DJLPS 411   REHEARSAL (LP) 12
71   DJM DJLPS 416   I THINK I'LL WRITE A SONG (LP) 12
72   DJM DJLPS 425   SONGFALL (LP, gatefold sleeve) 12
73   DJM DJLPS 432   PHILIP GOODHAND-TAIT (LP) 10
75   DJM DJLPS 453   JINGLE JANGLE MAN (LP) 10
(see also Circus, Larry Williams)

CUBA GOODING
83   London LONX 41   Happiness Is Just Around The Bend/(Version) (12") 7

JOHNNY GOODISON
70   Deram DM 319   A Little Understanding/One Mistake 6

GOODLETTSVILLE FIVE
64   London HLW 9854   EEF/Baby's Gone Eefing 4

BENNY GOODMAN
53   Columbia SCM 5053   Temptation Rag/Bugle Call Rag 6
55   Capitol CL 14258   Jumpin' At The Woodside/Let's Dance 6
56   Columbia SCM 5239   King Porter Stomp/Memories Of You 6
56   HMV 7M 380   Don't Be That Way/Down South Camp Meeting 6
56   Capitol CL 14531   Goody Goody/Sometimes I'm Happy 4
56   Capitol CL 14570   Don't Be That Way/And The Angels Sing 4
60   Philips JAZ 107   Liza/Slipped Disc 4
58   Philips BBE 12172   PEGGY WITH BENNY (EP, with Peggy Lee) 8
52   Capitol LC 6557   EASY DOES IT (10" LP) 12
52   Capitol LC 6565   AFTER HOURS (10" LP) 12
53   Capitol LC 6601   DIZZY FINGERS (10" LP) 12
53   Capitol LC 6620   THE GOODMAN TOUCH (10" LP) 12
54   Columbia 33S 1048   SESSION FOR SEXTET (10" LP) 12
54   Capitol LC 6680   CLASSICS IN JAZZ (10" LP) 12
54   Philips BBL 7000   CARNEGIE HALL JAZZ CONCERT (LP, auto-coupling) 10
54   Philips BBL 7001   CARNEGIE HALL JAZZ CONCERT (LP, auto-coupling) 10
55   Philips BBR 8064   LET'S HEAR THE MELODY (10" LP) 12
55   Philips BBL 7009   1937-1938 JAZZ CONCERT NO. 2 (LP, auto-coupling) 10
55   Philips BBL 7010   1937-1938 JAZZ CONCERT NO. 2 (LP, auto-coupling) 10
55   Philips BBL 7043   PRESENTS EDDIE SAUTER ARRANGEMENTS (LP) 10
56   Philips BBL 7073   MAKES HISTORY (LP) 10
56   Brunswick LAT 8102   THE BENNY GOODMAN STORY VOLUME ONE (LP) 10
56   Brunswick LAT 8103   THE BENNY GOODMAN STORY VOLUME TWO (LP) 10

DAVE GOODMAN & FRIENDS
78   The Label TLR 008   Justifiable Homicide/Take Down Your Fences (p/s, 15,000 on red vinyl;
also black vinyl, some with 'Steve Jones & Paul Cook' typed credit) 4/5/50
(see also Sex Pistols)

GOOD MISSIONARIES
80   Kif Kif's 1   Good Missionary Pts 1 & 2 (p/s) 4

80	Unnormality NORM 001	VIBING UP THE SENILE WORLD (EP)	5
80	Unnormality NORM 002	DERANGED IN HASTINGS (EP, with insert, PVC sleeve)	4
79	Deptford Fun City DLP 04	FIRE FROM HEAVEN (LP)	10

(see also Mark Perry, Alternative TV, Henry Badowski)

GOOD RATS
| 69 | London HLR 10237 | Hobo/Truth Is Gone | 5 |

GOOD SHIP LOLLIPOP
| 70 | Ember EMB S 276 | Maxwell's Silver Hammer/How Does It Feel | 6 |

GOOD THUNDER
| 72 | Elektra K 42123 | GOOD THUNDER (LP) | 10 |

GOOD TIME LOSERS
| 67 | Fontana TF 791 | Trafalgar Square/Where Did My Heart Go | 5 |

GOODTIMERS
| 62 | Fontana H 360 | It's Twistin' Time/Twisting Train | 5 |

RON GOODWIN CONCERT ORCHESTRA
53	Parlophone MSP 6020	Jet Journey/When I Fall In Love	4
53	Parlophone MSP 6035	Limelight/The Song From Moulin Rouge	7
53	Parlophone MSP 6044	The Melba Waltz (Dream Time)/Shane (Call Of The Far-Away Hills)	4
53	Parlophone MSP 6055	Tropical Mirage/The "Man Between" Theme	4
54	Parlophone MSP 6064	Grand Waltz Of The Flowers And The Dragonflies/ The Lobster Quadrille	4
54	Parlophone MSP 6085	Solfeggio (The Do-Re-Mi Song)/It May Be You	4
54	Parlophone MSP 6103	Guadalcanal March/The Song Of The High Seas	4
54	Parlophone MSP 6115	Three Coins In The Fountain/Cara Mia	4
54	Parlophone MSP 6116	The Messenger Boy/Theme From "Modern Times" (Smile)	4
54	Parlophone MSP 6136	On The Waterfront/Midnight Blue	4
55	Parlophone MSP 6154	You, My Love/When You're In Love	4
55	Parlophone MSP 6159	Under The Linden Tree/Last Love	4
56	Parlophone MSP 6221	Concetta/Handyman	4
56	Parlophone R 4250	Rock Around The Clock/Giddy-Up-A Ding Dong (78)	5
54	Parlophone PMD 1014	FILM FAVOURITES (10" LP)	10
56	Parlophone PMD 1038	MUSIC TO SET YOU DREAMING (10" LP)	10

GOOFERS
55	Vogue Coral Q 72051	Hearts Of Stone/You're The One	45
55	Vogue Coral Q 72051	Hearts Of Stone/You're The One (78)	15
55	Vogue Coral Q 72074	Flip, Flop And Fly/My Babe	45
55	Vogue Coral Q 72074	Flip, Flop And Fly/My Babe (78)	18
55	Vogue Coral Q 72094	Goofy Drybones/Nare	20
55	Vogue Coral Q 72094	Goofy Drybones/Nare (78)	12
56	Vogue Coral Q 72124	Sick! Sick! Sick!/Twenty One	20
56	Vogue Coral Q 72124	Sick! Sick! Sick!/Twenty One (78)	22
56	Vogue Coral Q 72171	Tear Drop Motel/Tennessee Rock And Roll	30
56	Vogue Coral Q 72171	Tear Drop Motel/Tennessee Rock And Roll (78)	22
57	Vogue Coral Q 72267	Wow!/Push, Push, Push Cart	18
57	Vogue Coral Q 72267	Wow!/Push, Push, Push Cart (78)	18
57	Vogue Coral Q 72289	The Dipsy Doodle/Take This Heart	20
57	Vogue Coral Q 72289	The Dipsy Doodle/Take This Heart (78)	5

GOONS
56	Decca F 10756	I'm Walking Backwards For Christmas/Bluebottle Blues	8
56	Decca F 10780	The Ying Tong Song/Bloodnok's Rock 'N' Roll Call	8
56	Parlophone R 4251	My September Love (with Eric Sykes)/You Gotta Go Oww!	8
57	Decca F 10885	Eeh! Ah! Oh! Ooh!/I Love You	6
57	Decca F 10945	A Russian Love Song/Whistle Your Cares Away	6
56	Decca DFE 6396	THE GOONS (EP)	8
64	Decca LF 1332	UNCHAINED MELODIES (10" LP)	18
59	Parlophone PMC 1108	BEST OF THE GOON SHOWS (LP)	12
60	Parlophone PMC 1129	BEST OF THE GOON SHOWS (NO. 2) (LP)	12

(see also Peter Sellers, Spike Milligan, Famous Eccles, Michael Bentine, Eric Sykes)

PETER GORDENO
65	Decca F 12088	Have You Looked Into Your Heart/Don't Come To Me	5
69	Decca F 12947	Everybody Knows/Man And Wife Time	5
68	MCA MU 1009	Shout It From The Hilltop/Born To Be Wanted	4
69	MCA MU 1058	My Girl Maria/I Appreciate	4

GORDON
(see under Gordon Waller)

ANITA GORDON
| 55 | Brunswick 05456 | Lonesome Like Nobody Knows/His Hands | 4 |

BARRY GORDON
| 56 | MGM MGM 928 | I Can't Whistle/The Milkman's Polka | 4 |
| 56 | MGM MGM 935 | Rock Around Mother Goose/Nuttin' For Christmas | 5 |

CURTIS GORDON
| 57 | Mercury MT 163 | Sixteen/Cry, Cry (78) | 10 |

FLESH GORDON & NUDE HOLLYWOOD
| 74 | Paramount PARA 3049 | Superstreaker/Naked | 4 |

JOE GORDON (FOLK FOUR)
59	HMV POP 600	Gotta Travel On/Ho Ro My Nutbrown Maid	5
59	HMV POP 634	Dream Lover/Dance To Your Daddy	5
60	HMV POP 737	Football Crazy/By The Bright Shining Light Of The Moon	4

RABBI JOSEPH GORDON

85	Bam Caruso Int. NRICO 30	Competition/Belief In Him (large centre hole, plain beige sleeve)	15

(see also Julian Cope)

PHIL GORDON

55	Brunswick 05481	Get A Load Of That Crazy Walk/Strip Polka	5
56	Brunswick 05545	Down The Road Apiece/I'm Gonna Move To The Outskirts Of Town	8

RONNIE GORDON

63	R&B JB 127	Shake Some Time/Comin' Home	15

ROSCO(E) GORDON

60	Top Rank JAR 332	Just A Little Bit/Goin' Home (as Rosco Gordon)	25
63	Stateside SS 204	Just A Little Bit/What I Wouldn't Do	20
65	Vocalion V-P 9245	Keep On Doggin'/Bad Dream	20
65	Island WI 256	Surely I Love You/What You Do To Me	15
66	Island WI 272	No More Doggin'/Goin' Home	20

VINCENT GORDON

69	Coxsone CS 7085	Soul Trombone/LARRY & ALVIN: Your Cheating Heart	10
69	Duke DU 37	Everybody Bawlin'/SILVERTONES: Come Look Here	5

LESLEY GORE

63	Mercury AMT 1205	It's My Party/Danny	5
63	Mercury AMT 1210	Judy's Turn To Cry/Just Let Me Cry	5
63	Mercury AMT 1213	She's A Fool/The Old Crowd	4
64	Mercury MF 803	You Don't Own Me/Run Bobby Run	4
64	Mercury MF 810	That's The Way Boys Are/That's The Way The Ball Bounces	4
64	Mercury MF 821	I Don't Wanna Be A Loser/It's Gotta Be You	4
64	Mercury MF 829	Maybe I Know/Wonder Boy	4
64	Mercury MF 837	Sometimes I Wish I Were A Boy/Hey Now	4
65	Mercury MF 846	The Look Of Love/Little Girl Go Home	4
65	Mercury MF 862	Sunshine Lollipops And Rainbows/You've Come Back	5
65	Mercury MF 872	My Town, My Guy And Me/Girl In Love	10
65	Mercury MF 889	I Won't Love You Anymore (Sorry)/No Matter What You Do	7
66	Mercury MF 902	Young Love/I Just Don't Know If I Can	4
66	Mercury MF 963	California Nights/I'm Going Out (The Same Way I Came In)	5
66	Mercury MF 984	I'm Fallin' Down/Summer And Sandy	8
68	Mercury MF 1017	Magic Colours/It's A Happening World	5
64	Mercury 10017 MCE	LESLEY GORE (EP)	10
63	Mercury MMC 14127	I'LL CRY IF I WANT TO (LP)	15
63	Mercury 20001 MCL	SINGS OF MIXED-UP HEARTS (LP)	14
64	Mercury 20020 MCL	BOYS BOYS BOYS (LP)	14
64	Mercury 20033 MCL	GIRL TALK (LP)	14
65	Mercury 20076 MCL	ALL ABOUT LOVE (LP)	12
67	Wing WL 1183	GIRL TALK (LP, reissue)	10

JOHN GORMAN

77	DJM DJF 20491	GO MAN GORMAN (LP)	10

(see also Scaffold, Grimms)

EYDIE GORME

54	Vogue Coral Q 2014	Frenesi/Climb Up The Wall	8
54	Vogue Coral Q 2027	Tea For Two/Sure	6
55	Vogue Coral Q 72067	Give A Fool A Chance/A Girl Can't Say (unissued)	
55	Vogue Coral Q 72092	Give A Fool A Chance/A Girl Can't Say	6
55	Vogue Coral Q 72103	Soldier Boy/What Is The Secret Of Your Success?	6
56	London HL 8227	Sincerely Yours/Come Home	12
57	HMV POP 400	Kiss In Your Eyes/Your Kisses Kill Me	6
58	HMV POP 432	Love Me Forever/Until They Sail	8
58	HMV POP 493	You Need Hands/The Gentleman Is A Dope	4
58	HMV POP 513	Gotta Have Rain/To You, From Me	4
58	HMV POP 529	Dormi, Dormi, Dormi/Be Careful, It's My Heart	4
59	HMV POP 577	Separate Tables/The Voice Of My Heart	4
59	HMV POP 616	I'm Yours/Don't Take Your Love From Me	5
60	HMV POP 767	The Dance Is Over/Too Young To Know	4
62	CBS AAG 105	Yes, My Darling Daughter/Sonny Boy	4
63	CBS AAG 131	Blame It On The Bossa Nova/Guess I Should Have Loved Him More	4
63	CBS AAG 170	Everybody Go Home/The Message	6
67	CBS 202470	Everybody Go Home/The Message (reissue)	5
59	HMV GES 5789	LOVE IS A SEASON (EP, stereo)	7
59	HMV GES 5795	I'LL REMEMBER APRIL (EP, stereo)	7
58	Coral LVA 9086	EYDIE GORME'S DELIGHT (LP)	12
58	HMV CLP 1156	EYDIE GORME (LP)	12
58	HMV CLP 1170	EYDIE SWINGS THE BLUES (LP)	12
58	HMV CLP 1201	VAMPS THE ROARING 20'S (LP)	12
59	HMV CLP 1250	EYDIE IN LOVE (LP)	12
59	HMV CLP 1257	GORME SINGS SHOWSTOPPERS (LP)	10
59	HMV CLP 1290	LOVE IS A SEASON (LP)	12
60	HMV CLP 1323	ON STAGE (LP)	10
60	HMV CLP 1392/CSD 1322	EYDIE IN DIXIE-LAND (LP, mono/stereo)	10/12

EYDIE GORME & STEVE LAWRENCE

55	Vogue Coral Q 72044	Make Yourself Comfortable/EYDIE GORME: Chain Reaction	6
55	Vogue Coral Q 72085	Besame Mucho/Take A Deep Breath	6
63	CBS AAG 163	I Want To Stay Here/Ain't Love	5
59	Vogue Coral FEP 2017	STEVE LAWRENCE AND EYDIE GORME (EP)	7
63	CBS AGG 20035	STEVE AND EYDIE (EP)	7
60	HMV CLP 1372/CSD 1310	STEVE AND EYDIE — WE GOT US (LP)	12
61	HMV CLP 1404/CSD 1329	THE GOLDEN HITS (LP)	10

MINT VALUE £

62	HMV CLP 1463	COZY (LP)	12

(see also Steve Lawrence)

FRANK GORSHIN
66	Pye Intl. 7N 25402	The Riddler/Never Let Her Go (some in p/s)	15/8

GO! SERVICE
85	Dreamworld DREAM 3	It Makes Me Realise/Real Life/I Just Don't Know (12", p/s)	8

G.O.S.H. (GREAT ORMOND STREET HOSPITAL CHARITY)
87	G.O.S.H. GOSHR 1	The Wishing Well (Remix)/Wishing Well Message (p/s)	4

(see also Andy Scott)

GOSPEL CLASSICS
68	Chess CRS 8080	More Love, That's What We Need/You Need Faith	25

GOSPEL GARDEN
68	Camp 602 006	Finders Keepers/Just A Tear	8

GOSPEL OAK
70	Uni UNS 527	Brown Haired Girl/Recollections Of Jessica	4
70	Uni UNLS 113	GOSPEL OAK (LP)	15

GOTHIC HORIZON
73	Argo AFW 107	If You Can Smile/Thoughts	10
70	Argo ZFB 26	JASON LODGE POETRY BOOK (LP)	60
72	Argo ZDA 150	TOMORROW IS ANOTHER DAY (LP)	100

(see also Andy Desmond)

GOTHIQUE
84	GEEC C 004	KRISTIANA (cassette)	10

DALE GOULDER & LIZ DYER
70	Argo ZFB 10	JANUARY MAN (LP)	20
71	Argo ZFB 30	RAVEN & CROW (LP)	20

GRAHAM GOULDMAN
66	Decca F 12334	Stop! Stop! Stop!/Better To Have Loved And Lost	25
68	RCA RCA 1667	Upstairs Downstairs/Chestnut	15
69	Spark SRL 1026	Windmills Of Your Mind/Harvey's Theme (as Graham Gouldman Orchestra)	10
72	CBS 7739	Nowhere To Go/Growing Older	5

(see also Whirlwinds, Mockingbirds, High Society, Manchester Mob, 10cc)

GOVE
69	London HLE 10295	Death Letter Blues/Sunday Morning Early	8

GO WEST
85	Chrysalis CHS 2850	We Close Our Eyes/Missing Persons (picture disc)	4
85	Chrysalis GOW 3	Don't Look Down/The Sequel (2 different picture discs)	4

GRAB GRAB THE HADDOCK
84	Cherry Red 12CHERRY 83	THREE SONGS BY GRAB GRAB THE HADDOCK (12" EP)	7
85	Cherry Red CHERRY 86	TWO MORE SONGS BY GRAB GRAB THE HADDOCK (EP)	4

(see also Marine Girls)

MICK GRABHAM
72	United Artists UAS 29341	MICK THE LAD (LP)	15

(see also Cochise)

CHARLIE GRACIE
57	Parlophone R 4290	Butterfly/Ninety-Nine Ways (initially gold lettering label, later silver)	40/18
57	Parlophone R 4290	Butterfly/Ninety-Nine Ways (78)	5
57	Parlophone R 4313	Fabulous/Just Lookin' (initially gold lettering label, later silver)	35/15
57	Parlophone R 4313	Fabulous/Just Lookin' (78)	5
57	London HL 8467	Wandering Eyes/I Love You So Much It Hurts	25
57	London HL 8467	Wandering Eyes/I Love You So Much It Hurts (78)	5
57	London HLU 8521	Cool Baby/You Got A Heart Like A Rock	25
57	London HLU 8521	Cool Baby/You Got A Heart Like A Rock (78)	10
58	London HLU 8596	Crazy Girl/Dressin' Up	30
58	London HLU 8596	Crazy Girl/Dressin' Up (78)	10
59	Coral Q 72362	Doodlebug/Hurry Up, Buttercup	15
59	Coral Q 72362	Doodlebug/Hurry Up, Buttercup (78)	10
59	Coral Q 72373	Angel Of Love/I'm A Fool, That's Why	12
59	Coral Q 72373	Angel Of Love/I'm A Fool, That's Why (78)	15
59	Coral Q 72381	Oh-Well-A/Because I Love You So	12
59	Coral Q 72381	Oh-Well-A/Because I Love You So (78)	20
60	Columbia DB 4477	The Race/I Looked For You	15
62	London HLU 9603	Pretty Baby/Night And Day, U.S.A.	15
65	Stateside SS 402	He'll Never Love You Like I Do/Keep My Love Next To Your Heart	35
57	Parlophone GEP 8630	THE FABULOUS CHARLIE GRACIE (EP)	35
79	London HA-U 8513	CAMEO PARKWAY SESSIONS (LP)	10

GRACIOUS!
68	Polydor 56333	Beautiful/What A Lovely Rain	20
70	Vertigo 6360 002	GRACIOUS! (LP, gatefold sleeve, spiral label)	40
72	Philips 6382 004	THIS IS GRACIOUS! (LP, gatefold sleeve, spiral label)	60

GRADUATE
80	Precision PAR 100	Elvis Should Play Ska/Julie Julie (p/s)	6
80	Precision PAR 104	Ever Met A Day/Shut Up (p/s)	8
80	Precision PAR 111	Ambition/Bad Dreams (p/s)	8
81	Precision PAR 117	Shut Up/Ever Met A Day (reissue, no p/s)	6
80s	Blue Hat 5 BHR	Mad One/Somebody Put Out The Fire (p/s)	12
80	Precision PART 001	ACTING MY AGE (LP)	10

(see also Tears For Fears)

MINT VALUE £

GRADUATES
79	Graduate GRAD 1	If You Want It/Hey Young Girl (p/s)	4

BILLY GRAHAM & ESCALATORS
67	Atlantic 584 073	Ooh Poo Pah Doo/East 24th Avenue	4

BOBBY GRAHAM
65	Fontana TF 521	Skin Deep/Zoom Widge And Wag (features Jimmy Page)	15
66	Fontana TF 667	Teensville/Grotty Drums	15

(see also Outlaws, Jimmy Page)

CHICK GRAHAM & COASTERS
64	Decca F 11859	Education/I Know	7
64	Decca F 11932	Dance Baby Dance/A Little You	7

DAVY GRAHAM
68	Decca F 12841	Both Sides Now/Tristano	6
62	Golden Guinea GGL 0224	GUITAR PLAYER (LP)	20
64	Decca LK 4649	FOLK, BLUES AND BEYOND (LP)	40
64	Decca LK 4652	FOLK ROOTS, NEW ROUTES (LP, with Shirley Collins)	80
66	Decca LK 4780	MIDNIGHT MAN (LP)	50
68	Decca SKL 4969	LARGE AS LIFE AND TWICE AS NATURAL (LP)	45
69	Decca SKL 5011	HAT (LP)	50
70	Decca SKL 5056	HOLLY KALEIDOSCOPE (LP)	50
70	President PTLS 1039	GODINGTON BOUNDARY (LP)	20
76	Eron ERON 007	ALL THAT MOODY (LP, private pressing)	150
78	Kicking Mule SNKF 138	COMPLETE GUITARIST (LP)	10
79	Kicking Mule SNKF 158	DANCE FOR TWO PEOPLE (LP)	10

DAVY GRAHAM & ALEXIS KORNER
62	Topic TOP 70	3/4 A.D. (EP, 1st pressing credits 'Alexis Korner & Davy Graham')	40

(see also Alexis Korner)

DAVY GRAHAM/THAMESIDERS
63	Decca DFE 8538	FROM A LONDON HOOTENANNY (EP, 2 tracks each)	12

ERNIE GRAHAM
78	Stiff OFF 2	Romeo And The Lonely Girl/Only Time Will Tell	4
71	Liberty LBS 83485	ERNIE GRAHAM (LP)	25

(see also Brinsley Schwartz, Help Yourself, Nick Lowe)

KENNY GRAHAM'S AFRO-CUBISTS
60	Starlite ST45 013	Bongo Chant/Beguine	5

LEO GRAHAM
73	Upsetter US 399	News Flash/UPSETTERS: Flashing Echo	5
73	Summit SUM 8539	Three Blind Mice/UPSETTERS: Mice Skank	4

LOU GRAHAM
58	Coral Q 72322	Wee Willie Brown/You Were Mean Baby	150
58	Coral Q 72322	Wee Willie Brown/You Were Mean Baby (78)	50

OSBOURNE GRAHAM
63	Island WI 087	Hey Girl/Skies Are Grey (Stormy Weather)	10

GRAHAM CENTRAL STATION
74	Warner Bros K 46206	GRAHAM CENTRAL STATION (LP)	10

RON GRAINER ORCHESTRA
60	Warner Bros WB 24	The Maigret Theme/Along The Boulevards (as Ron Grainer & His Music)	6
63	Decca F 11597	That Was The Week That Was/Petit Louis	6
67	Pye 7N 17383	A Man In A Suitcase/Andorra	8
67	RCA Victor RCA 1635	The Prisoner/Happening Sunday	40
68	RCA RCA 1698	Love Theme/Detective	4
69	RCA RCA 1898	The Paul Temple Theme/The Jazz Age	5
78	Casino Classics CC 5/6-12	A Touch Of Velvet — A Sting Of Brass/Theme From 'Joe 90'/ALLNIGHT BAND: The Wigan Joker/Six By Six (12", p/s, crimson vinyl, 'Disco DJ Version')	7
87	Six Of One LYN 18284	The Age Of Elegance/Arrival: The Awakening (Six Of One Fan Club flexidisc)	8
60	Warner Bros WEP 6012	THEME MUSIC FROM "INSPECTOR MAIGRET" (EP)	10
79	Six Of One 6 OF 1	THE PRISONER ARRIVAL (fan club EP)	15
69	RCA	TV THEMES (LP)	12

BILLY GRAMMER
58	London HLU 8752	Gotta Travel On/Chasing A Dream	10
59	Felsted AF 121	Bonaparte's Retreat/The Kissing Tree	10
59	Felsted AF 121	Bonaparte's Retreat/The Kissing Tree (78)	5
59	Felsted AF 128	Willy, Quit Your Playing/It Takes You	10
59	Felsted AF 128	Willy, Quit Your Playing/It Takes You (78)	8
61	Brunswick 05851	Rainbow Round My Shoulder/Columbus Stockade Blues	8
59	Felsted GEP 1005	BILLY GRAMMER HITS (EP)	40

GERRY GRANAHAN
58	London HL 8668	No Chemise, Please/Girl Of My Dreams	22
58	London HL 8668	No Chemise, Please/Girl Of My Dreams (78)	10
60	Top Rank JAR 262	It Hurts/RICHIE ROBIN: Strange Dream	12

ROCCO GRANATA
60	Oriole CB 1525	Marina/Manuela	5
61	Oriole CB 1564	Julia/Rocco Cha Cha	4

GRAND FUNK RAILROAD
70	Capitol CL 15632	Heartbreaker/Please Don't Worry	4
70	Capitol CL 15661	Closer To Home/Aimless Lady	4
69	Capitol EST 307	ON TIME (LP)	12

MINT VALUE £

70	Capitol EST 406	GRAND FUNK (LP) 12
70	Capitol EST 471	CLOSER TO HOME (LP) 12
70	Capitol ESTDW 1/2	LIVE (2-LP, gatefold sleeve) 14
71	Capitol ESW 764	SURVIVAL (LP) 12
72	Capitol EAS 853	E PLURIBUS FUNK (LP) 12
72	Capitol ESTSP 10	MARK, JOHN & MEL 1969/71 (2-LP) 15
73	Capitol EAST 11099	PHOENIX (LP, gatefold sleeve) 10
73	Capitol EAST 11027	WE'RE JUST AN AMERICAN BAND (LP) 10
74	Capitol SWAE 11278	SHININ' ON (2-LP) 14
75	Capitol E-ST 11356	ALL THE GIRLS IN THE WORLD BEWARE (LP) 10
75	Capitol ESTSP 15	CAUGHT IN THE ACT (2-LP, original with custom label) 14
76	Capitol E-ST 11482	BORN TO DIE (LP) 10
76	EMI EMC 1503	GOOD SINGING, GOOD PLAYING (LP) 10

GRANDISONS
63	RCA RCA 1339	All Right/True Romance 6

GRAND PRIX
80	RCA RCA 7	Thinking Of You/Feels Good (p/s) 4
81	RCA RCA 18	Which Way Did The Wind Blow/Feels Good (p/s) 6
81	RCA RCA 162	Give Me What's Mine/Life On The Line (p/s) 4
83	Chrysalis PRIX 1	Give Me What's Mine/One Five Jive (p/s) 4
83	Chrysalis PRIX 2	Shout/Keep On Believing (p/s) 4
83	Chrysalis PRIXP 2	Shout/Keep On Believing (picture disc) 5
83	Chrysalis PRIXX 2	Shout/Keep On Believing (12", p/s) 7
80	RCA PL 25321	GRAND PRIX — THE FIRST ALBUM (LP) 12

GERRI GRANGER
63	London HLX 9759	Just Tell Him Jane Said Hello/What's Wrong With Me 6

GRANNIE
71	SRT 71138	GRANNIE (LP, private pressing) 800

GRANNY'S INTENTIONS
67	Deram DM 158	The Story Of David/Sandy's On The Phone Again 8
68	Deram DM 184	Julie Don't Love Me Anymore/One Time Lovers 8
68	Deram DM 214	Never An Everyday Thing/Hilda The Bilda 8
70	Deram DM 293	Take Me Back/Maybe 8
70	Deram SML 1060	HONEST INJUN (LP) 45

EARL GRANT
58	Brunswick 05762	The End/Hunky Dunky Doo 7
58	Brunswick 05762	The End/Hunky Dunky Doo (78) 5
59	Brunswick 05779	Evening Rain/Kathy-O 5
59	Brunswick 05792	Last Night (I Went Out Of My Mind)/Imitation Of Life 4
60	Brunswick 05824	House Of Bamboo/Two Loves Have I 15
60	Brunswick 05841	Not One Minute More/Building Castles 4
62	Brunswick 05865	Tender Is The Night/Honey 4
62	Brunswick 05870	Swingin' Gently/Evening Rain 4
62	Brunswick 05877	Sweet Sixteen Bars/Learnin' The Blues 5
65	Brunswick 05945	Stand By Me/After Hours 6
60	Brunswick OE 9460	EARL GRANT (EP) 10
63	Brunswick OE 9493	SWINGING GENTLY (EP) 7
59	Brunswick LAT 8297	THE END (LP) 12
60	Brunswick LAT 8332	NOTHIN' BUT THE BLUES (LP) 12
60	Brunswick LAT 8351	THE MAGIC OF EARL GRANT (LP) 10
61	Brunswick LAT 8389	EBB TIDE (LP, also stereo STA 3051) 10
62	Brunswick LAT 8502	EARL AFTER DARK (LP) 10

ERKEY GRANT & EARWIGS
63	Pye 7N 15521	I'm A Hog For You/I Can't Get Enough Of You 20

GOGI GRANT
55	London HLB 8192	Suddenly There's A Valley/Love Is 18
56	London HLB 8257	Who Are We/We Believe In Love 15
56	London HLB 8282	Wayward Wind/No More Than Forever 15
57	London HLB 8364	You're In Love/When The Tide Is High 12
58	London HLB 8550	The Golden Ladder/All Of Me 10
58	RCA RCA 1038	It's A Wonderful Thing To Be Loved/What A Beautiful Combination ...5
58	RCA RCA 1047	Bonjour Tristesse/Johnny's Dream 4
59	RCA RCA 1101	Say A Prayer For Me Tonight/TONY MARTIN: She Is Not Thinking Of Me ...4
59	RCA RCA 1105	Kiss Me Honey Honey Kiss Me/Two Dreams 6
59	RCA RCA 1105	Kiss Me Honey Honey Kiss Me/Two Dreams (78) 5
60	London HLG 9185	Goin' Home/I'm Going To Live The Life 6
57	London HA-B 2032	SUDDENLY THERE'S GOGI GRANT (LP) 16
58	RCA RD 27054	BOTH ENDS OF THE CANDLE (LP, soundtrack) 12
59	RCA RD 27097	GIGI (LP, with Tony Martin) 12
60	London HA-G 2242	IF YOU WANT TO GET TO HEAVEN — SHOUT! (LP, also stereo SAH-G 6072) ...14

(see also Tony Martin)

JANIE GRANT
61	Pye Intl. 7N 25093	Triangle/She's Going Steady With You 5
62	Pye Intl. 7N 25148	That Greasy Kid Stuff/Trying To Forget You 4

JULIE GRANT
62	Pye 7N 15447	So Many Ways/Unimportant Things 5
62	Pye 7N 15483	Up On The Roof/When You Ask About Love 4
63	Pye 7N 15508	Count On Me/Then, Only Then 4
64	Pye 7N 15604	Come To Me/Can't Get You Out Of My Mind 4
64	Pye 7N 15615	Every Day I Have To Cry/Watch What You Do With My Baby 4
64	Pye 7N 15652	You Are Nobody 'Til Somebody Loves You/I Only Care About You 4

Julie GRANT

65	Pye 7N 15756	Baby Baby (I Still Love You)/My World Is Empty Without You	4
65	Pye 7N 15812	Giving Up/Cause I Believe In You	4
65	Pye 7N 15937	When The Lovin' Ends/Stop	4
62	Pye NEP 24171	THIS IS JULIE GRANT (EP)	8

LEE GRANT & CAPITOLS
| 66 | Parlophone R 5531 | Breaking Point/Don't Cry Baby | 15 |

NEVILLE GRANT
| 73 | Downtown DT 509 | Sick And Tired/PRINCE DJANGO: Hot Tip | 5 |

NORMAN GRANT ORCHESTRA
| 61 | Starlite ST45 060 | Jive Medley/Speak Low | 6 |

TOP GRANT
62	Island WI 034	Searching/David & Goliath	7
62	Island WI 052	Suzie/Jenny	7
63	Island WI 072	Riverbank Cobberley/Nancy	7
63	Island WI 074	Money Money Money/Have Mercy On Me	7
63	Island WI 077	War In Africa/The Birds	7

GRANT & WILSON
| 40 | Vocalion S 244 | Uncle Joe/Blue Monday On Sugar Hill (78) | 20 |

GRAPEFRUIT
68	RCA Victor RCA 1656	Dear Delilah/The Dead Boot	5
68	RCA Victor RCA 1677	Elevator/Yes	6
68	RCA RCA 1716	C'mon Marianne/Ain't It Good	5
68	Stateside SS 8005	Someday Soon/Theme For Twiggy	6
69	Stateside SS 8011	Round Going Round/This Little Man	6
69	RCA RCA 1855	Deep Water/Come Down To The Station	6
70	RCA RCA 1907	Lady Godiva/Thunder And Lightning	5
71	Deram DM 343	Universal Party/Sha Sha	4
69	Stateside S(S)L 5008	AROUND GRAPEFRUIT (LP)	18
69	RCA Victor SF 8030	DEEP WATER (LP)	22

(see also Tony Rivers & Castaways)

GRAPEVINE
| 68 | Liberty LBF 15063 | Things Ain't What They Used To Be Anymore/Ace In The Hole | 4 |

GRASS ROOTS
66	RCA Victor RCA 1532	Where Were You When I Needed You/These Are Bad Times	5
67	Pye Intl. 7N 25422	Let's Live For Today/Depressed Feeling	10
67	Pye Intl. 7N 25431	Things I Should Have Said/Tip Of My Tongue	6
68	RCA Victor RCA 1682	Melody For You/Hey Friend	4
68	RCA Victor RCA 1737	Midnight Confessions/Who Will You Be Tomorrow	7
69	Stateside SS 8006	Bella Linda/Hot Bright Lights	4
69	Stateside SS 8012	All Good Things Come To An End/Melody For You	4
69	Stateside SS 8018	The River Is Wide/(You Gotta) Live For Love	4
69	Stateside SS 8023	Who Will You Be Tomorrow/Midnight Confessions	4
69	Stateside SS 8029	I'd Wait A Million Years/Fly Me To Havana	4
69	Stateside SS 8033	Heaven Knows/Don't Remind Me	4
69	Stateside S(S)L 5005	GOLDEN GRASS (LP)	12
70	Stateside SSL 5012	LEAVING IT ALL BEHIND (LP)	12

(see also P.F. Sloan)

GRATEFUL DEAD
67	Warner Bros WB 7186	Born Cross-Eyed/Dark Star	12
70	Warner Bros WB 7410	Uncle John's Band/New Speedway Boogie	8
72	Warner Bros K 16167	One More Saturday Night (as Grateful Dead with Bobby Ace)/BOB WEIR: Bertha	5
73	Atlantic K 19301	Let Me Sing Your Blues Away/Here Comes Sunshine	4
74	United Artists UP 36030	U.S. Blues/Loose Lucy	4
77	Warner Bros SAM 79	Dark Star/Born Cross-Eyed (mail order issue with 'Dark Star' magazine)	10/8
67	Warner Bros W(S) 1689	THE GRATEFUL DEAD (LP)	18
68	Warner Bros WS 1749	ANTHEM OF THE SUN (LP)	15
69	Warner Bros WS 1790	AOXOMOXOA (LP)	15
70	Warner Bros WS 1830	LIVE/DEAD (2-LP)	18
70	Warner Bros WS 1869	WORKINGMAN'S DEAD (LP)	12
71	Warner Bros WS 1893	AMERICAN BEAUTY (LP)	12
71	Warner Bros K 66009	GRATEFUL DEAD LIVE (SKULL AND ROSES) (2-LP)	18
72	Polydor 2310 171	HISTORIC DEAD (LP)	18
72	Polydor 2310 172	VINTAGE DEAD (LP)	18
72	Warner Bros K 66019	EUROPE '72 (3-LP)	20
73	Warner Bros K 46246	HISTORY OF GRATEFUL DEAD (BEAR'S CHOICE) (LP)	10
76	United Artists	STEAL YOUR FACE (2-LP, with sampler LP
	UAD 60131/2	"For Dead Heads Only" [FREE 2])	20

(see also Jerry Garcia, Mickey Hart, Kingfish, Robert Hunter, Bob Weir, Keith & Donna Godchaux, New Riders Of Purple Sage)

NICK GRAVENITES
| 69 | CBS 63818 | MY LABORS (LP) | 15 |

(see also Big Brother & Holding Company)

CARL GRAVES
75	A&M AM 7151	Baby Hang Up The Phone/Walk Softly	6
75	A&M AM 7180	The Next Best Thing/Something Teling Me	4
76	A&M AM 7235	My Whole World Ended/Baby Don't Knock	5

GRAVY TRAIN
73	Dawn DNS 1036	Strength Of A Dream/Tolpuddle Episode	6
74	Dawn DNS 1058	Starbright Starlight/Good Time Thing	6
75	Dawn DNS 1115	Climb Aboard The Gravy Train/Sanctuary	5

70	Vertigo 6360 023	GRAVY TRAIN (LP, gatefold sleeve, spiral label)	40
71	Vertigo 6360 051	BALLAD OF A PEACEFUL MAN (LP, gatefold sleeve, spiral label)	150
73	Dawn DNLS 3046	SECOND BIRTH (LP)	30
74	Dawn DNLH 1	STAIRCASE TO THE DAY (LP)	35

BARRY GRAY (ORCHESTRA)

62	Lyntone LYN 249/250	Sabotage/Supercar Song/Supercar Twist (flexi, p/s may exist)	35+/18
64	Melodisc MEL 1591	Fireball/Zero G (by Barry Gray & His Spacemakers; some in p/s)	25/10
65	Pye 7N 17016	Thunderbirds/Parker — Well Done (some in p/s)	25/12
67	Pye 7N 17391	Captain Scarlet/The Mysterons Theme	15
68	Pye 7N 17625	Joe 90 — Title Theme/Joe 90 — Hijacked (LP, soundtrack, mono/stereo)	25/15
80s	Fanderson MAF 2	THE MUSIC OF BARRY GRAY VOL. 2 (33rpm EP)	7
62	Golden Guinea GGL 0106	SUPERCAR — FLIGHT OF FANCY (LP, with Edwin Astley)	40
67	United Artists (S)ULP 1159	THUNDERBIRDS ARE GO (LP, soundtrack, mono/stereo)	75/85

(see also Century 21, Mary Jane with Barry Gray)

CLAUDE GRAY

64	Mercury 10012 MCE	COUNTRY AND WESTERN ACES (EP)	12

DOBIE GRAY

65	London HL 9953	The In Crowd/Be A Man	8
65	Pye Intl. 7N 25307	(See You At The) Go Go/Walk With Love	15
69	London HL 10268	The In Crowd/Be A Man (reissue)	4
75	Black Magic BM 107	Out On The Floor/Be A Man	5
73	MCA MUPS 489	DRIFT AWAY (LP)	10
74	MCA MCF 2528	LOVING ARMS (LP)	10
74	MCA MCF 2576	HEY DIXIE (LP)	10

DOLORES GRAY

53	Brunswick 05111	Big Mamou/Say You're Mine (78)	5
55	Brunswick 05382	Heat Wave/After You Get What You Want, You Don't Want It	6
55	Brunswick 05407	Rock Love/One	15
55	Brunswick 05407	Rock Love/One (78)	5
57	Capitol CL 14732	There'll Be Some Changes Made/Fool's Errand	6
57	Capitol CL 14770	I'm Innocent/My Mama Likes You	4

DORIAN GRAY

67	Parlophone R 5612	Behind The Tear/Walking Down A Back Street	4
68	Parlophone R 5667	I've Got You On My Mind/Move On	4
68	Parlophone R 5705	Love Is All That It Should Be/Let Me Go Home	4
68	Parlophone R 5732	Jingle Down A Hill/Get Goin' Baby	4

HERBIE GRAY

68	Giant GN 38	We're Staying Here/Life Ska	5

JERRY GRAY & HIS ORCHESTRA

54	Brunswick 05351	The Ooh And Ah Mambo/Kettle Drum Hop	4

JOHNNIE 'THE GASH' GRAY

58	Fontana H 123	Big Guitar/Tequila	12
58	Fontana H 123	Big Guitar/Tequila (78)	5
58	Fontana H 134	Apache/Zach's Tune	12
58	Fontana H 134	Apache/Zach's Tune (78)	5

OWEN GRAY

60	Starlite ST45 015	Far Love/Please Let Me Go	12
60	Starlite ST45 019	Jenny Lee/The Plea	12
61	Starlite ST45 032	Mash It Pts 1 & 2	12
61	Blue Beat BB 8	Cutest Little Woman/Running Around (with Ken Richards Band)	10
61	Blue Beat BB 43	Sinners Weep/Get Drunk	10
62	Starlite ST45 078	I Feel Good/Someone To Help Me	12
62	Starlite ST45 088	Let Me Go Free/In My Dreams	12
62	Blue Beat BB 103	Lonely Days/No Good Woman	10
62	Blue Beat BB 108	Keep It In Mind/Do You Want To Jump	10
62	Blue Beat BB 113	Best Twist/Grandma Grandpa	10
62	Blue Beat BB 127	Pretty Girl/Twist So Fine	8
62	Blue Beat BB 136	They Got To Move/I Love Her	8
62	Blue Beat BB 139	Tree In The Meadow/Lizebella	8
62	Blue Beat BB 147	Big Mabel/Don't Come Knocking	8
62	Island WI 002	Twist Baby/Patricia	10
62	Island WI 020	Audrey/Dolly Baby (with Ernest Ranglin Orchestra)	10
62	Island WI 030	Midnight Trail/Time Will Tell	10
62	Island WI 048	I'm Still Waiting/Last Night	10
62	Chek TD 101	My One Desire/Come On Baby	8
62	Dice CC 3	On The Beach/Young Lover	8
63	Blue Beat BB 149	She's Gone To Napoli (with Laurel Aitken)/Have Mercy Mr Percy	8
63	Blue Beat BB 188	Call Me My Pet/Give Me Your Love	8
63	Blue Beat BB 201	Snow Falling/Oowee Baby	8
63	Blue Beat BB 217	Draw Me Nearer/Daddy's Girl	8
65	Blue Beat BB 290	Daddy's Gone/BUSTER'S ALLSTARS: Johnny Dark	8
65	Aladdin WI 607	Can I Get A Witness/Linda Lu	7
65	Island WI 252	Shook Shimmy And Shake/I'm Going Back	8
65	Island WI 258	You Don't Know Like I Do/Take Me Serious (with Sound System)	8
66	Island WI 267	Paradise/Bye Bye Love	8
67	Island WIP 6000	Help Me/Incense	8
67	Collins Downbeat CR 003	Collins Greetings/Rock It Down (with Sir Collins & Band)	8
67	Collins Downbeat CR 004	I'm So Lonely (with Sir Collins & Band)/EL RECO, SIR COLLINS & J. SATCH: Shock Steady	8
68	Collins Downbeat CR 007	Am Satisfy (with Sir Collins & Band)/BOB STACKIE & SIR COLLINS & BAND: Sweet Music	8
68	Collins Downbeat CR 010	I'm Gonna Take You Back (with Bob Stackie)/GLEN ADAMS: King Sized	8

Owen GRAY

68	Coxsone CS 7047	Give Me A Little Sign/Ain't Nobody Home	15
68	Coxsone CS 7053	Give It To Me/Isn't It So	15
68	Blue Cat BS 123	These Foolish Things/This I Promise	8
69	Blue Cat BS 156	I Can't Stop Loving You/Tell Me Darling	8
68	Trojan TR 632	Lovey Dovey/Grooving	5
69	Fab FAB 90	Three Coins In The Fountain/Tenneesee Waltz	6
69	Fab FAB 96	Ay Ay Ay/Let It Be Me (with Rudies)	6
69	Fab FAB 120	Understand My Love/Apollo 12	5
69	Fab FAB 126	Swing Low/Release Me	5
69	Trojan TR 650	I Can't Stop Loving You/Tell Me Darling	5
69	Trojan TR 670	Experienced/I Really Loved You Baby	5
69	Duke DU 12	Reggae Dance/I Know	5
69	Duke DU 33	Seven Lonely Days/He Don't Love You Like I Do	4
69	Downtown DT 423	Groovin'/HERBIE GRAY & RUDIES: These Memories	4
69	Downtown DT 428	Lovey Dovey (with Dandy)/HERBIE GRAY & RUDIES: Kitty Wait	4
69	Camel CA 25	Girl What You Doing To Me/Woman A Grumble	4
69	Camel CA 34	Don't Take Your Love Away/Two Lovers	4
69	Camel CA 37	Every Beat Of My Heart/Don't Cry	4
70	Camel CA 50	Don't Sign The Paper/Packing Up Loneliness	4
70	Camel CA 51	Bring Back Your Love/Got To Come Back	4
70	Bamboo BAM 47	I Can Feel It/I Don't Want (To Lose Your Love)	4
70	Pama PM 810	Sugar Dumpling/I Don't Know Why	4
70	Pama Supreme PS 299	I Am In Love Again/RANDY WILLIAMS: Version	4
70	Pama Supreme PS 302	Candida/When Will I Find My Way	4
70	Pama Supreme PS 310	You Gonna Miss Me/I Hear You Knocking	4
70	Supreme SUP 206	Surfin'/All The Love	4
70	Ackee ACK 102	No More/Don't Leave Me (both as Owen Gray & Omen)	4
71	Ackee ACK 123	Whispering Bells/CLANCY'S ALLSTARS: Whiplash (B-side actually "Jacket" by Dave Barker)	4
71	Camel CA 60	Groove Me/No Other One	4
71	Camel CA 73	Nothing Can Separate Us/Girl I Want You To Understand	4
71	Punch PH 87	Sincerely/Hold On I'm Coming	4
71	Pama Supreme PS 325	Summer Sand/Something To Remind Me	4
71	Pama Supreme PS 332	Greatest Hits Pts 1 & 2	4
72	Pama Supreme PS 351	Time/GRAHAM: Harlesden High Street	4
72	Pama Supreme PS 358	Hail The Man/I'll Follow You	4
72	Pama Supreme PS 360	Amazing Grace (with Graham Hawk)/SKETTO RICH: Don't Stay Out Late	4
70s	Rock Steady Rev. REV 004	Groovy Kind Of Love (with Elki & Rim Ram Band)/RIM RAM BAND: The Whistler	4
61	Starlite STLP 5	OWEN GRAY SINGS (LP)	100
69	Trojan TTL 24	REGGAE WITH SOUL (LP)	10
60s	Melodisc MLP 12153	CUPID (LP)	12

WARDELL GRAY

65	Stateside SL 10144	WARDELL GRAY MEMORIAL ALBUM (VOL. 1) (LP)	10
65	Stateside SL 10145	WARDELL GRAY MEMORIAL ALBUM (VOL. 2) (LP)	10

GRAY BROTHERS

68	Blue Cat BS 124	Always/Big Man	6
	(see also Owen Gray)		

KATHRYN GRAYSON

53	MGM SP 1002	(All Of A Sudden) My Heart Sings/Jealousy	4
53	MGM SP 1014	Smoke Gets In Your Eyes/The Touch Of Your Hand (B-side with Howard Keel)	4
54	MGM SP 1078	I Hate Men/ANN MILLER & TOMMY RALL: Always True To You In My Way	4

KATHRYN GRAYSON & HOWARD KEEL

53	MGM SP 1003	Why Do I Love You/Make Believe	4
54	MGM SP 1076	So In Love/ANN MILLER: Too Darn Hot	4
54	MGM SP 1077	We Open In Venice (with Ann Miller & Tommy Rall)/Wunderbar/HOWARD KEEL: Were Thine That Special Face	4
54	MGM SP 1079	So Kiss Me Kate/(by Ann Miller, Keenan Wynn & others)	4
	(see also Howard Keel)		

MILTON GRAYSON

60	London HLU 9068	Forget You/The Puppet	5

RUDY GRAYZELL

54	London HL 8094	Looking At The Moon And Wishing On A Star/The Heart That Once Was Mine	60
54	London HL 8094	Looking At The Moon And Wishing On A Star/The Heart That Once Was Mine (78)	10

GRAZINA

62	HMV POP 1094	Lover Please Believe Me/So What	8
63	HMV POP 1149	Don't Be Shy/Another Like You	7
63	HMV POP 1212	Be My Baby/I Ain't Gonna Knock On Your Door	7

GREASE BAND

72	Harvest HAR 5052	Laughed At The Judge/All I Want To Do/Jesse James	4
75	Goodear EAR 602	New Morning/Pont Ardawe Hop	4
71	Harvest SHVL 790	THE GREASE BAND (LP)	10
75	Goodear EAR 2902	AMAZING GREASE (LP)	10
	(see also Joe Cocker)		

JOHNNY B. GREAT (& GOODMEN)

63	Decca F 11740	School Is In/She's A Much Better Lover Than You (with Goodmen)	6
64	Decca F 11804	Acapulco 1922/You'll Never Leave Him (solo)	6
	(see also Quotations)		

GREAT AWAKENING

69	London HLU 10284	Amazing Grace/Silver Waterfall	7

GREAT BEAR
71 Wand WNS 8   GREAT BEAR (LP) 10

GREAT DIVIDE
82 Wimp WIMP 004   Who Broke The Love Bank/Bless My Soul (p/s) 4
(see also Bible)

GREATEST LITTLE SOUL BAND IN THE LAND
(see under J.J. Jackson)

GREATEST SHOW ON EARTH
70 Harvest HAR 5012   Real Cool World/Again And Again 5
70 Harvest HAR 5026   Tell The Story/Mountain Song 4
70 Harvest SHVL 769   HORIZONS (LP) 35
70 Harvest SHVL 783   THE GOING'S EASY (LP) 35
75 Harvest SHSM 2004   THE GREATEST SHOW ON EARTH (LP) 12
(see also Living Daylights, Ian Dury & Blockheads)

GREAT LEAP FORWARD
87 Ron Johnson ZRON 20   CONTROLLING THE EDGES OF TONE (EP) 7
(see also Big Flame)

GREAT SATURDAY NIGHT SWINDLE
77 CBS   GREAT SATURDAY NIGHT SWINDLE (LP, Irish-only issue) 60

GREAT SOCIETY
68 CBS 63476   CONSPICUOUS ONLY IN ITS ABSENCE (LP) 18
(see also Jefferson Airplane)

GREAT WHITE
84 EMI America EA 167   Substitute/No Better Than Hell (p/s) 4
84 EMI America 12EA 167   Substitute/No Better Than Hell/Bad Boys (live) (12", p/s) 7
89 Capitol ESTX 2096   TWICE SHY (LP, with free 'Official Bootleg' LP) 10

R.B. GREAVES
70 Atco 2091 013   Fire And Rain/Ballad Of Leroy 4
75 20th Century BTC 2191   Come On And Get Yourself Some/BMF (Beautiful) 4
70 Atco 228 034   R.B. GREAVES (LP) 10

JOE GRECH
71 Electro ES 152   Marija L-Maltija/In-Nassab (export release) 6

BUDDY GRECO
56 Vogue Coral Q 72192   They Didn't Believe Me/Here I Am In Love Again 5
57 Vogue Coral Q 72268   Paris Loves Lovers/Ain't No In Between 5
57 London HLR 8452   With All My Heart/Game Of Love (with B-G Skiffle Band) 15
57 London HLR 8452   With All My Heart/Game Of Love (with B-G Skiffle Band) (78) 8
58 London HLR 8613   I've Grown Accustomed To Her Face/On The Street Where You Live
                              (as Buddy Greco & His Quartet) 6
60 Fontana H 255   The Lady Is A Tramp/Like Young 4
62 Fontana H 374   Twistin' The Blues/I Ain't Got Nobody 4
56 Vogue Coral LVA 9021   AT MISTER KELLY'S (LP) 15
60 Fontana TFL 5098   MY BUDDY (LP) 12
61 Fontana TFL 5125   SONGS FOR SWINGING LOSERS (LP, also stereo STFL 552) 12/14
62 Columbia 33SX 1441   I LIKE IT SWINGING (LP, also stereo SCX 3445) 10/12
63 Columbia 33SX 1463   LET'S LOVE (LP, also stereo SCX 3457) 10/12
63 Columbia 33SX 1478   BUDDY AND SOUL (LP, also stereo SCX 3464) 10/12
63 Columbia 33SX 1519   BUDDY'S BACK IN TOWN (LP, also stereo SCX 3482) 10/12
63 Columbia 33SX 1544   SOFT AND GENTLE (LP, also stereo SCX 3491) 10/12
64 Columbia 33SX 1590   ONE MORE TIME (LP) 10
64 Columbia 33SX 1620   SINGS FOR INTIMATE MOMENTS (LP) 10
64 Columbia 33SX 1667   ON STAGE (LP) 10
65 Columbia 33SX 1701   MODERN SOUNDS OF HANK WILLIAMS (LP) 10
65 Columbia 33SX 1766   I LOVE A PIANO (LP) 10
(see also Johnny Desmond)

JULIETTE GRECO
54 Philips BBR 8023   JULIETTE GRECO SINGS (10" LP) 10

GREEDIES
80 Vertigo GREED 1   A Merry Jingle/A Merry Jangle (p/s) 4
(see also Professionals, Thin Lizzy)

AL GREEN(E)
68 Stateside SS 2079   Back Up Train/Don't Leave Me (by Al Greene & Soul Mates) 12
69 Action ACT 4540   Don't Hurt Me No More/Get Yourself Together (by Al Greene) 6
70 London HLU 10300   You Say It/Gotta Find A New World 4
71 London HLU 10324   I Can't Get Next To You/Ride Sally Ride 4
71 Bell BLL 1188   Back Up Train/Don't Leave Me (reissue, as Al Green & Soul Mates) .6
73 London HLU 10419   Love And Happiness/So You're Leaving 4
69 Action ACLP 6008   BACK UP TRAIN (LP) 20
71 London SHU 8424   GETS NEXT TO YOU (LP) 10
72 London SHU 8430   LET'S STAY TOGETHER (LP) 10
72 London SHU 8443   I'M STILL IN LOVE WITH YOU (LP) 10
73 London SHU 8457   CALL ME (LP) 10
74 London SHU 8464   LIVIN' FOR YOU (LP) 10
74 London SHU 8479   EXPLORES YOUR MIND (LP) 10

GARLAND GREEN
69 MCA Soul Bag BAG 9   Jealous Kinda Fella/I Can't Believe You Quit Me 4

GRANT GREEN
62 Blue Note (B)BLP 84071   GREEN STREET (LP) 15

Grant GREEN

63	Blue Note (B)BLP 4111	THE LATIN BIT (LP)	15
65	Blue Note (B)BLP 4139	AM I BLUE (LP)	15
66	Blue Note (B)BLP 4202	I WANT TO HOLD YOUR HAND (LP)	15
68	Blue Note BLP 4253	STREET OF DREAMS (LP, also stereo BST 84253)	12
69	Blue Note BST 84310	GOING WEST (LP)	10

HUGHIE GREEN
66	Columbia DB 8085	Cuddle Up Baby/Clap Your Hands (B-side with Monica Rose)	4

IAN GREEN (REVELATION)
67	Polydor 56194	Last Pink Rose/Green Blues (solo)	7
69	CBS 3997	When You Love A Man/Santa Maria	4
69	CBS 4623	Revelation/Groover's Grave	4
70	CBS 63840	REVELATION (LP)	12

KATHE GREEN
69	Deram DM 279	If I Thought You'd Ever Change Your Mind/Primrose Hill	6
69	Deram SML 1039	RUN THE LENGTH OF YOUR WILDNESS (LP)	40

PETER GREEN
71	Reprise RS 27012	Heavy Heart/No Way Out	5
72	Reprise K 14141	Beast Of Burden/Uganda Woman (with Nigel Watson)	5
78	PVK PV 16	Apostle/Tribal Dance (withdrawn)	4
79	PVK PV 24	In The Skies/Proud Pinto (p/s)	6
80	PVK PV 36	Walking In The Road/Woman Don't	4
80	PVK PV 41	Loser Two Times/Momma Doncha Cry	4
81	PVK PV 103	Give Me Back My Freedom/Lost My Love	4
81	PVK PV 112	Promised Land/Bizzy Lizzy	4
70	Reprise RSLP 9006	THE END OF THE GAME (LP, with Nigel Watson)	12
79	PVK PVLS 101	IN THE SKIES (LP, green vinyl)	10

(see also Fleetwood Mac, John Mayall & Blues Breakers, Gass)

PHILIP GREEN & PINEWOOD STUDIO ORCHESTRA
59	Top Rank JAR 112	Sapphire (with Johnny Dankworth)/Tiger Bay	4
60	Top Rank JAR 355	"League Of Gentlemen" March/"Golden Fleece" Theme	4

GREEN ANGELS
65	Parlophone R 5390	Let It Happen/Rockin' Red Wing	6
66	Parlophone R 5512	An Exile's Dream/Hanningan's Hooley	5

NORMAN GREENBAUM
70	Reprise RS 20846	Jubilee/Skyline	4
70	Reprise RS 20885	Spirit In The Sky/Milk Cow (reissue, mustard label)	4

GREEN BEAN
69	Regal Zono. RZ 3017	The Garden's Lovely/Sittin' In The Sunshine	5

GREENBEATS
65	Pye 7N 15843	So Sad/I'm On Fire	4
67	Spin SP 2007	Pretty Woman/Thing	6

GREEN BULLFROG
72	MCA MKPS 2021	GREEN BULLFROG (LP)	25

(see also Deep Purple)

CLAUDE 'FATS' GREENE & ORCHESTRA
66	Island WI 290	Fats Shake 'Em Up Pts 1 & 2	7

JACK GREENE
68	Decca AD 1005	What Locks The Door/My Elusive Dreams (export issue)	5

JEANIE GREENE
68	Atlantic 584 226	Sure As Sin/I've Been A Long Time Loving You	4

LAURA GREENE
79	Grapevine GRP 135	Can't Help Loving Dat Man/It's A Good Day For A Parade	4

LORNE GREENE
64	RCA RCA 1428	Ringo/Bonanza	4

GREENFIELD LEISURE
81	Strange Orch. CAMP 1	L'Orange/Sally (orange cut p/s)	4
81	Illuminated ILL 912	CANDIES (12" EP)	7

LEE GREENLEE
59	Top Rank JAR 226	Cherry, I'm In Love With You/Starlight	4

GREEN ON RED
89	China 841 013-0	LIVE AT THE TOWN AND COUNTRY CLUB (10" LP, numbered with insert)	10
89	China 841 013-4	LIVE AT THE TOWN AND COUNTRY CLUB (cassette)	10

(DAVE) GREENSLADE
73	Warner Bros K 16264	Temple Song/An English Western	4
75	Warner Bros K 16584	Catalan/Animal Farm	4
76	Warner Bros K 16828	Gangsters/Rubber Face, Lonely Eyes (as Dave Greenslade's Gangsters)	4
78	Beeb BEEB 022	Gangsters (vocal)/Sarah Gant Theme (as Dave Greenslade's Gangsters)	4
80	EMI EMI 5034	The Pentateuch Overture/Mischief And War (p/s, as Dave Greenslade)	5
73	Warner Bros K 46207	GREENSLADE (LP)	12
73	Warner Bros K 46259	BEDSIDE MANNERS ARE EXTRA (LP)	12
73	Warner Bros K 56055	SPYGLASS GUEST (LP, gatefold sleeve)	12
75	Warner Bros K 56126	TIME AND TIDE (LP, gatefold sleeve)	12
76	Warner Bros K 56306	CACTUS CHOIR (LP, as Dave Greenslade)	10
80	EMI EMSP 332	THE PENTATEUCH OF THE COSMOGONY (2-LP, with 47-page book, as Dave Greenslade)	25

(see also Colosseum)

ARTHUR GREENSLADE (& GEE MEN)
61	Decca F 11363	Rockin' Susannah/Eclipse (with Gee Men)	6
66	Columbia DB 7865	Watermelon Man/Serenade To A Broken Jaw	4

GREEN TELESCOPE
86	Imaginary MIRAGE 001	Two By Two/Make Me Stay/Thinkin' About Toady (p/s, various colours)	6
86	Wump BIF 4811	Face In The Crowd/Thoughts Of A Madman (p/s)	4

ELLIE GREENWICH
67	United Artists UP 1180	I Want You To Be My Baby/Goodnight Goodnight	7
68	United Artists UP 2214	Sunshine After The Rain/A Long Time Comin'	7
70	Bell BLL 1105	I Don't Wanna Be Left Outside/Ain't That Peculiar	4

MICK GREENWOOD
71	MCA MDKS 8003	THE LIVING GAME (LP, gatefold sleeve)	10
72	MCA MKPS 2026	TO FRIENDS (LP)	10

NICHOLAS GREENWOOD
72	Kingdom KVLP 9002	COLD CUTS (LP)	300

(see also Crazy World Of Arthur Brown, Khan)

STOCKER GREENWOOD & FRIENDS
79	Changes	BILLY AND NINE (LP)	50

BIG JOHN GREER
51	HMV J 0360	Woman Is A Five Letter Word/Got You On My Mind (78)	25

GINNY GREER
57	Brunswick 05673	Five Oranges, Four Apples/Kiss Me Hello (But Never Goodbye)	4

BOBBY GREGG & FRIENDS
62	Columbia DB 4825	The Jam Pts 1 & 2	8

BRIAN GREGORY
65	HMV POP 1412	Give Me Your Word/The Ballad Of Dick Turpin	4

GLENN GREGORY & CLAUDIA BRÜCKEN
85	ZTT ZTAS 15	When Your Heart Runs Out Of Time/(Drumless) (p/s)	4
85	ZTT P ZTAS 15	When Your Heart Runs Out Of Time/(Drumless) (book-shaped picture disc)	6
85	ZTT 12 ZTAS 15	When Your Heart Runs Out Of Time/(Voices Of)/(6.20)/(Drumless)/ STANLEY MYLES: Forever (What The Hell) (12", p/s)	7

(see also Heaven 17, Propaganda, Act)

IA(I)N GREGORY
60	Pye 7N 15295	Time Will Tell/The Night You Told A Lie (as Ian Gregory)	12
61	Pye 7N 15397	Can't You Hear The Beat Of A Broken Heart/Because	15
62	Pye 7N 15435	Mr. Lovebug/Pocketful Of Dreams	12
63	Columbia DB 7085	How Many Times/Yellow Teddy Boy	8

JOHNNY GREGORY & HIS ORCHESTRA
60	Fontana H 251	Honky Tonk Train Blues/"Sons And Lovers" Theme (with Cascading Strings)	4
60	Fontana H 286	Bonanza/Maverick	8
61	Fontana H 288	Wagon Train/Bronco	8
61	Fontana H 337	Sucu Sucu/Echo For Two	4
61	Fontana H 341	Route 66/M Squad	8
61	Fontana TFE 17325	MAVERICK! (EP)	10
61	Fontana TFE 17331	BONANZA (EP)	10
62	Fontana TFE 17389	T.V. THRILLERS (EP)	10
61	Fontana TFL 5110	T.V. WESTERN THEMES (LP, also stereo STFL 538)	10/12

(see also Chaquito)

TONY GREGORY
66	Doctor Bird DB 1007	Baby Come On Home/Marie Elena	8
66	Doctor Bird DB 1016	Give Me One More Chance/I've Lost My Love	8
67	Island WI 3029	Get Out Of My Life/SOUL BROTHERS: Sugar Cane	8
67	Coxsone CS 7013	Only A Fool (Breaks His Own Heart)/Pure Soul	12
67	Coxsone CSL 8011	TONY GREGORY SINGS (LP)	30

GREMLINS
66	Mercury MF 981	The Coming Generation/That's What I Want	12
67	Mercury MF 1004	You Gotta Believe It/I Can't Say	12

JOYCE GRENFELL
54	Philips BBL 7004	REQUESTS THE PLEASURE (LP)	10

JOEL GREY
57	Capitol CL 14779	Everytime I Ask My Heart/Moonlight Swim	4
58	Capitol CL 14832	Shoppin' Around/Be My Next	4

RONNIE GREY & JETS
55	Capitol CL 14329	Run, Manny, Run/Sweet Baby	25

GREYHOUND
71	Trojan TRLS 27	BLACK AND WHITE (LP)	12

GRID
(see also Dave Ball)

ROOSEVELT GRIER
68	Action ACT 4515	People Make The World/Hard To Forget	7
69	Pama PM 774	Who's Got The Ball	6
69	Pama PM 784	C'mon Cupid/High Society Woman	7

ZAINE GRIFF
82	Polydor POSP 506	Flowers/Mental Pictures (p/s)	4

MINT VALUE £

GRIFFIN
69	Bell BLL 1075	I Am The Noise In Your Head/Don't You Know	25
72	MGM 2006 088	In The Darkness/Calling You	8

(see also Heavy Jelly, Skip Bifferty, Every Which Way)

JOHNNY GRIFFIN BIG SOUL BAND
60s	Riverside REP 3203	BIG SOUL BAND (EP)	7

MERV GRIFFIN
61	London HLL 9339	The Charanga/Along Came Joe	5

VIRGIL GRIFFIN
71	Jay Boy BOY 43	La Da Da Da Da/Climbing	4

GRIFFIN BROTHERS' ORCHESTRA
52	Vogue V 2139	Weepin' And Cryin' (with Tommy Brown)/The Teaser Boogie (78)	10

ANDY GRIFFITH
55	Capitol CL 14263	Ko Ko Mo (I Love You So)/Make Yourself Comfortable	10
56	Capitol CL 14619	Make Yourself Comfortable/No Time For Sergeants	7
57	Capitol CL 14766	Mama Guitar/A Face In The Crowd	8
58	Capitol CL 14936	Midnight Special/She's Bad, Bad Business (with Dixie Seven)	7
59	Capitol CL 15003	Hamlet Pts 1 & 2	4
56	Capitol EAP1 630	ANDY GRIFFITHS (EP)	8
60	Capitol ST 1105	SHOUTS THE BLUES AND OLD TIMEY SONGS (LP, stereo)	10

MARCIA GRIFFITHS
66	Island WI 285	Funny/KING SPARROW: Beggars Have No Choice	8
67	Studio One SO 2008	Hound Dog (actually by Norma Fraser)/HUGH GODFREY: My Time	12
68	Coxsone CS 7035	Mojo Girl (actually Nora Dean)/HAMLINS: Tell Me That You Love Me	15
68	Coxsone CS 7055	Feel Like Jumping/HORACE TAYLOR: Thundering Vibrations	12
68	Coxsone CS 7062	Hold Me Tight/BASIES: Home Sweet Home (B-side actually by Basses)	12
68	Studio One SO 2047	Words (as Marcia Griffiths & Jeff Dixon)/SHARKS: How Could I Live	12
68	Studio One SO 2059	Truly/SIMMS & ROBINSON: Drought	12
69	Gas GAS 111	Tell Me Now/STAN HOPE: The Weight	6
69	High Note HS 029	Talk Pts 1 & 2 (correct title is actually "Toil")	5
69	Escort ES 808	Don't Let Me Down/REGGAEITES: Romper Room (B-side act. by Peter Tosh)	5
69	Trojan TR 693	Put A Little Love In Your Heart/J BOYS: Jay Fever	4

(see also Bob & Marcia)

CAROL GRIMES (& DELIVERY)
70	B&C CB 129	Harry Lucky/Homemade Ruin (with Delivery)	5
74	Virgin VS 109.	You're The Only One/Southern Boogie	4
74	Good Ear EAR 105	Give It Everything You've Got/Let's Do It Again (with London Boogie Band)	4
75	Good Ear EAR 605	Dynamite/I Betcha Didn't Know That	4
70	B&C CAS 1023	FOOLS MEETING (LP, with Delivery)	40
74	Caroline CA 2001	WARM BLOOD (LP)	12
76	Decca SKL-R 5258	CAROL GRIMES (LP)	10

(see also Uncle Dog)

TINY GRIMES & HIS R&B QUINTET
54	Esquire 10-349	Annie Laurie/Hot In Harlem (78)	8

GRIMMS
73	Island HELP 11	GRIMMS (LP)	12
73	Island ILPS 9248	ROCKIN' DUCK (LP)	12
76	DJM DJLPS 470	SLEEPERS (LP)	10

(see also Neil Innes, Liverpool Scene, Scaffold, Mike McGear, McGough & McGear, Zoot Money, Viv Stanshall)

GRIN
70	CBS 5239	We All Sung Together/See What Love Can Do	4
71	CBS 7405	Everybody's Missin' The Sun/18 Faced Lover	4
73	Epic EPC 1463	Ain't Love Nice/Love Or Else	4
71	Epic EPC 64272	GRIN (LP)	12
72	Epic EPC 64652	1 + 1 (LP)	12
72	Epic EPC 65166	ALL OUT (LP)	10

(see also Nils Lofgren)

GRINGO
71	MCA MK 5067	I'm Another Man/Soft Mud	4
71	MCA MKPS 2107	GRINGO (LP)	15

(see also Caravan)

JOE GRINNE
69	Coxsone CS 7098	Mr Editor/How I Feel (both sides actually by Melodians)	12

GRISBY DYKE
69	Deram DM 232	The Adventures Of Miss Rosemary La Page/Mary Anne She	6

DEWEY GROOM
62	Starlite ST 45 085	Butane Blues/That's All I Want Out Of Life	12
63	Starlite ST 45 095	You're Tearing My Heart Out Of Me/Walking Papers	10
63	Starlite ST 45 105	Heartaches For Sale/Sometimes If I'm Lucky	8

GROOP
68	CBS 3204	Woman You're Breaking Me/Mad Over You	4
68	CBS 3351	Lovin' Tree/Night Life	7

GROOVE
69	Parlophone R 5783	The Wind/Play The Song	8

GROOVE FARM
87	Raving Pop Blast RPBGF 1	SORE HEADS AND HAPPY HEARTS (EP, with insert & handwritten labels)	10

89	Raving Pop Blast RPBGF 2	ONLY THE MOST IGNORANT GUTLESS SHEEP-BRAINED POLTROON CAN DENY THEM NOW (EP) 8
80s	Raving Pop Blast RAVE 20	BAGISM (EP, hand-painted gatefold no'd p/s with insert, home-made labels) 5
87	Subway Org. SUBWAY 15T	GOING BANANAS WITH THE GROOVE FARM (12" EP) 8
88	Subway Organisation SUBWAY 19T	The Big Plastic Explosion! (It's Alright, It's Alright) (Dance Mix)/ Nancy Sinatra/Baby Blue Marine/Riot On Sunset Strip/Red Dress (p/s) 7
88	Subway Organisation SUBWAY 22N	Driving In Your New Car (Mini Mix)/Expanding Reindeer/ I Can't Dance With You/Epistle To Duppy (10", p/s) 6
88	Subway Organisation SUBWAY 22N	Driving In Your New Car (Mini Mix)/Expanding Reindeer/I Can't Dance With You/Epistle To Duppy (12", white label promos only, with press release) 20
88	Kvatch 001/LYN 18632	Baby Blue Marine/SEA URCHINS: Clingfilm (flexidisc, some with p/s) 20/12
80s	Woosh WOOSH 6	Heaven Is Blue/ESMERELDA'S KITE: Vampire Girl (flexidisc w/'Woosh' fanzine) 5/4

GROOVERS
67	Island WI 3080	You've Got To Cry/ALVA LEWIS: I'm Indebted 10

(see also Lloyd & Groovers)

WINSTON GROOV(E)Y
69	Attack ATT 8019	You Can't Turn Your Back On Me/PAMA DICE: The Worm 4
69	Jackpot JP 708	Funky Chicken/CIMARRONS: Part 2 (actually unknown instrumental) 4
69	Jackpot JP 709	Funny/CIMARRONS: Version 4
69	Nu Beat NB 041	Island In The Sun/Work It Up 4
69	Nu Beat NB 042	Josephine/Champagne & Wine 4
70	Nu Beat NB 053	Standing AT The Corner/You Send Me 4
70	Nu Beat NB 055	Yellow Bird/For Your Love 4
70	Nu Beat NB 058	Here Is My Heart/Birds & Flowers 4
69	Pama PMP 2011	FREE THE PEOPLE (LP) 10

WALTER GROSS
54	MGM SP 1070	Blue Moon/Tenderly 4
54	MGM SP 1071	You Won't Forget Me (with India Adams)/Follow Me 4

G.G. GROSSETT
69	Crab CRAB 10	Run Girl Run/DENNIS WALKS: The Drifter 5
69	Crab CRAB 33	Greater Sounds/Live The Life I Love 4

STEFAN GROSSMAN
68	Fontana (S)TL 5463	AUNT MOLLY'S MURRAY FARM (LP) 10
70	Transatlantic TRA 217	YAZOO BASIN BOOGIE (LP) 10
70	Transatlantic TRA 223	RAGTIME COWBOY JEW (LP) 10
71	Transatlantic TRA 246	THOSE PLEASANT DAYS (LP) 10
72	Transatlantic TRA 257	HOT DOGS (LP) 10
73	Transatlantic TRA 264	LIVE (2-LP) 14
73	Transatlantic TRA 274	MEMPHIS JELLYROLL (LP) 10

(see also Jon Renbourn & Stefan Grossman)

LUTHER GROSVENOR
71	Island WIP 6109	Here Comes The Queen/Heavy Day 4
72	Island WIP 6124	All The People/Waiting 4
71	Island ILPS 9168	UNDER OPEN SKIES (LP) 12

(see also Hellions, Revolution, Spooky Tooth, Mott The Hoople, Widowmaker)

CARL GROSZMANN
70	Decca F 13065	Thunderbird/Missouri Woman 4
75	Ring O' 2017 103	I've Had It/C'mon And Roll 4
77	Ring O' 2017 107	Face Of A Permanent Stranger/Your Own Affair 4

KELLY GROUCUTT
82	RCA RCA 182	Am I A Dreamer/Anything Goes With Me (p/s) 4
82	RCA RCA 245	Little Darling/I Can't Stand The Morning (p/s) 4
82	RCA RCALP 3063	KELLY (LP, with inner sleeve) 10

(see also E.L.O.)

GROUNDHOGS
68	Liberty LBF 15174	You Don't Love Me/Still A Fool 10
69	Liberty LBF 15263	B.D.D./TONY McPHEE: Gasoline 10
70	Liberty LBF 15346	Eccentric Man/Status People 10
73	W. Wide Artists WWS 006	Sad Go Round/Over Blue 5
74	W. Wide Artists WWS 012	Plea Sing, Plea Sing/TONY McPHEE: Dog Me Bitch 5
76	United Artists UP 36095	Live A Little Lady/Boogie Withus 4
76	United Artists UP 36177	Pastoral Future/Live Right 4
68	Liberty LBL/LBS 83199E	SCRATCHING THE SURFACE (LP) 40
69	Liberty LBS 83253	BLUES OBITUARY (LP) 30
70	Liberty LBS 83295	THANK CHRIST FOR THE BOMB (LP, gatefold sleeve) 15
71	Liberty LBS 83401	SPLIT (LP, gatefold sleeve) 12
72	United Artists UAG 29347	WHO WILL SAVE THE WORLD... (LP, gatefold sleeve) 12
72	United Artists UAG 29419	HOGWASH (LP) 12
74	United Artists UDF 31	GROUNDHOGS' BEST 1969-1972 (2-LP) 15
74	W. Wide Artists WWA 004	SOLID (LP) 12
76	United Artists UAG 29917	CROSSCUT SAW (LP) 10
76	United Artists UAG 29994	BLACK DIAMOND (LP) 10
84	Psycho PSYCHO 24	HOGGIN' THE STAGE (2-LP, with EP) 25

(see also John Lee's Groundhogs, Tony McPhee, Herbal Mixture)

GROUP B
67	Vocalion VF 9284	I Know Your Name Girl/I Never Really Know 4

GROUP 1850
69	Philips SBL 7884	AGEMO'S TRIP TO MOTHER EARTH (LP, 3-D gatefold sleeve) 100

GROUP ONE
58	HMV POP 463	She's Neat/Made For Each Other 12

GROUP ONE

58	HMV POP 463	She's Neat/Made For Each Other (78)	5
58	HMV POP 492	Chanson D'Amour/Londonderry Air	6

GROUP IMAGE
69	Stable SLE 8005	A MOUTH IN THE CLOUDS (LP)	20

GROUP SIX
59	Oriole CB 1488	Rock-A-Boogie/Rockin' The Blues	15
59	Oriole CB 1488	Rock-A-Boogie/Rockin' The Blues (78)	10

GROUP THERAPY
69	Philips BF 1744	River Deep Mountain High/Remember What You Said	4
69	Philips BF 1792	Can't Stop Lovin' You Baby/I Must Go	4
69	Philips SBL 7883	YOU'RE IN NEED OF GROUP THERAPY (LP)	10

GROUP TWO
68	Columbia DB 8374	It's Raining Outside/Western Man, Eastern Lady	4

GROUP X
63	Fontana 267 274 TF	There Are 8 Million Cossack Melodies — And This Is One Of Them/Teneriffe (some in p/s)	12/6
63	Fontana TF 417	Rohi Calliope/Cross Beat	7

GROW UP
80	Object Music OBJ 005	THE BEST THING (LP)	10
81	Rough Trade GROW 1	WITHOUT WINDS (LP)	10

GRUNT FUTTOCK
72	Regal Zono. RZ 3042	Rock 'N' Roll Christian/Free Sole	20

GRY
83	CBS A 3349	We're Like Starlight/For One More Night (promos only)	5

GRYPHON
73	Transatlantic TRA 262	GRYPHON (LP, gatefold sleeve)	15
74	Transatlantic TRA 282	MIDNIGHT MUSHROOMS (LP)	15
74	Transatlantic TRA 287	RED QUEEN TO GRYPHON THREE (LP)	12
75	Transatlantic TRA 302	RAINDANCE (LP)	12

(see also Richard Harvey)

G.T.O.'s
67	Polydor 56721	She Rides With Me/Rudy Vadoo	8

G.T.O.'s (Girls Together Outrageously)
69	Straight STS 1059	PERMANENT DAMAGE (LP)	45

G.T.R.
86	Arista GTRSD 1	When The Heart Rules The Mind/Reach Out (picture disc)	5

(see also Genesis)

GUARDIANS OF THE RAINBOW
68	President PT 186	What Do You Do When You've Lost Your Love/Cry Alone	4

JOSE GUARDIOLA & ROSE MARY
63	HMV POP 1147	Algo Prodigioso/Di Papa	20

LENIS GUESS
75	Route RT 11	Just Ask Me/Workin' For My Baby	4

GUESS WHO
65	Pye Intl. 7N 25305	Shakin' All Over/Till We Kissed	12
66	King KG 1044	His Girl/It's My Pride	15
67	Fontana TF 831	This Time Long Ago/There's No Getting Away From You	10
67	Fontana TF 861	Miss Felicity Grey/Flying On The Ground Is Wrong	8
69	RCA RCA 1832	These Eyes/Lightfoot	4
69	RCA RCA 1870	Laughing/Undun	4
70	RCA RCA 1943	American Woman/No Sugar Tonight	4
69	RCA SF 8037	WHEATFIELD SOUL (LP)	10
70	RCA SF 8107	AMERICAN WOMAN (LP)	10
70	RCA SF 8153	SHARE THE LAND (LP)	10
71	RCA SF 8216	SO LONG BANNATYNE (LP)	10
71	RCA SF 8269	ROCKIN' (LP)	10
72	RCA SF 8329	LIVE AT THE PARAMOUNT, SEATTLE (LP)	10
73	RCA SF 8349	ARTIFICIAL PARADISE (LP)	10

EARL GUEST
62	Columbia DB 4707	Winkle Picker Stomp/Honky Tonk Train Blues	6
62	Columbia DB 4926	Twistin' John/The Girl From The Fair Isle	5
64	Columbia DB 7212	Foxy/Begin The Beguine	8

REG GUEST SYNDICATE
65	Mercury MF 927	Underworld/Guys, Guns, Dolls And Danger	70
66	Mercury 20089MCL	UNDERWORLD (LP)	18

GUGGENHEIM
70s	Indigo GOLP 7001	GUGGENHEIM (LP)	75

ISAAC GUILLORY
74	Atlantic K 40521	ISAAC GUILLORY (LP)	15

GUILLOTEENS
65	Pye Intl. 7N 25324	I Don't Believe/Hey You	30

BONNIE GUITAR
58	London HLD 8591	A Very Precious Love/Johnny Vagabond	8
59	Top Rank JAR 260	Candy Red Apple/Come To Me, I Love You	4
58	London HA-D 2122	MOONLIGHT AND SHADOWS (LP)	15

GUITAR CRUSHER with JIMMY SPRUILL
69	Blue Horizon 57-3149	Since My Baby Hit The Numbers/Hambone Blues	20

GUITAR RED
63	Pye Intl. 7N 25219	Just You And I/(Give Me That) Old Fashioned Love	10

GUITAR SHORTY
72	Flyright LP 500	CAROLINA SLIDE GUITAR (LP)	15

GULLIVER
69	Elektra 2410 006	GULLIVER (LP)	12

(see also Daryl Hall & John Oates)

GULLIVER'S PEOPLE
66	Parlophone R 5435	Splendour In The Grass/Took This Land	5
66	Parlophone R 5464	Fi Fo Fum/Over The Hills	4
68	Parlophone R 5709	On A Day Like This/My Life	4
69	Columbia DB 8588	Somehow, Somewhere/I Found Love	4

GULLIVER'S TRAVELS
68	Instant INLP 003	GULLIVER'S TRAVELS (LP)	40

(see also Mike D'Abo, Andrew Oldham)

GUN (U.K.)
68	CBS 3764	Race With The Devil/Sunshine	5
68	CBS 3764	Race With The Devil/3-4 In The Middle	5
69	CBS 4052	Drives You Mad/Rupert's Travels	5
69	CBS 4443	Hobo/Don't Look Back	5
69	CBS 4443	Hobo/Long Hair Wild Man	8
70	CBS 4952	Runnin' Wild/Drown Yourself In The River	5
68	CBS 63552	GUN (LP)	20
69	CBS 62683	GUNSIGHT (LP)	25

(see also Ruperts People, Adrian Gurvitz, Three Man Army, Knack)

GUN (U.S.)
89	A&M CDEE 505	Better Days/When You Love Somebody/Come On Home (CD)	7
89	A&M AMP 531	Inside Out/Back To Where We Started (picture disc)	4
89	A&M CDEE 531	Inside Out/Back To Where We Started/Where Do We Go? (CD, picture disc)	7

GUN CLUB
82	Beggars Banquet BEG 80	Ghost On The Highway/Sex Beat (p/s)	6
82	Animal CH 2635	Fire Of Love/Walking With The Beast (p/s)	5
83	Animal GUN 1	The House On Highland Ave/The Lie/Death Party (p/s)	5
83	Animal GUN 12-1	The House On Highland Ave/The Lie/Light Of The World/Death Party/ Come Back Jim (12", p/s)	7

JON GUNN
67	Deram DM 133	I Just Made Up My Mind/Now It's My Turn	8
67	Deram DM 166	If You Wish It/I Don't Want To Get Hung Up On You Babe	5

JIM GUNNER
60	Decca F 11276	Hoolee Jump/Footloose (as Jim Gunner & Echoes)	8
61	Fontana H 313	Desperado/Baghdad (as Jim Gunner & His Sidekicks)	10

TONY GUNNER
62	London HLU 9492	Rough Road/You Gotta Get Home	5

GUNS FOR HIRE
80	Korova KOW 6	My Girlfriend's Boyfriend/I'm Famous Now (p/s)	4

(see also Main T. Possee)

GUNS N' ROSES
87	Geffen GEF 22	It's So Easy/Mr Brownstone (p/s)	12
87	Geffen GEF 22T	It's So Easy/Mr Brownstone/Shadow Of Your Love/Move To The City (12", p/s)	20
87	Geffen GEF 22TP	It's So Easy/Mr Brownstone/Shadow Of Your Love/Move To The City (12", picture disc with stickered PVC sleeve)	35
87	Geffen GEF 30	Welcome To The Jungle/Whole Lotta Rosie (live) (red p/s)	10
87	Geffen GEF 30T	Welcome To The Jungle/Whole Lotta Rosie (live)/It's So Easy (live)/Knockin' On Heaven's Door (live) (12", red p/s)	30
87	Geffen GEF 30TW	Welcome To The Jungle/Whole Lotta Rosie (live)/It's So Easy (live)/Knockin' On Heaven's Door (live) (12", poster sleeve)	20
87	Geffen GEF 30P	Welcome To The Jungle/Whole Lotta Rosie (live)/It's So Easy (live)/Knockin' On Heaven's Door (live) (12", picture disc)	35
88	Geffen GEF 43	Sweet Child O' Mine/Out Ta Get Me (p/s, with wraparound sticker)	6
88	Geffen GEF 43TE	Sweet Child O' Mine/Out Ta Get Me/Rocket Queen (10", revolving sleeve)	25
88	Geffen GEF 43TV	Sweet Child O' Mine/Out Ta Get Me (12", metallic sleeve)	15
88	Geffen GEF 47	Welcome To The Jungle/Nightrain (p/s)	5
88	Geffen GEF 47TW	Welcome To The Jungle/Nightrain/You're Crazy (12", poster sleeve)	10
88	Geffen GEF 47TV	Welcome To The Jungle/Nightrain/You're Crazy (12", p/s, with patch)	15
88	Geffen GEF 47TP	Welcome To The Jungle/Nightrain/You're Crazy (12", picture disc)	15
88	Geffen GEF 47CD	Welcome To The Jungle/Nightrain/You're Crazy (3" CD)	12
89	Geffen GEF 50P	Paradise City/I Used To Love Her (gun-shaped clear or white picture disc)	10/15
89	Geffen GEF 50X	Paradise City/I Used To Love Her (p/s, slotted in holster sleeve)	10
89	Geffen GEF 50T	Paradise City/I Used To Love Her/Anything Goes (12", p/s)	7
89	Geffen GEF 50CD	Paradise City/I Used To Love Her/Anything Goes/Sweet Child O' Mine (CD)	12
89	Geffen GEF 55W	Sweet Child O' Mine (Remix)/Out Ta Get Me (stickered p/s, with tattoo)	5
89	Geffen GEF 55P	Sweet Child O' Mine/Out Ta Get Me/Rocket Queen (cross-shaped picture disc & sticker)	10
89	Geffen GEF 55T	Sweet Child O' Mine (Remix)/Move To The City/Whole Lotta Rosie (live)/ It's So Easy (live) (12", p/s)	7
89	Geffen GEF 55CD	Sweet Child O' Mine (Remix)/Move To The City/Whole Lotta Rosie (live)/ It's So Easy (live) (3" CD)	10

89	Geffen GEF 56T	Patience/Rocket Queen/W. Axl Rose Interview (12", p/s)	7
89	Geffen GEF 56CD	Patience/Rocket Queen/W. Axl Rose Interview (3" CD)	12
89	Geffen GEF 60	Nightrain/Reckless Life (live) (p/s, with patch)	4
89	Geffen GEF 60P	Nightrain/Reckless Life (live) (case-shaped picture disc, stickered PVC sleeve)	8
89	Geffen GEF 60T	Nightrain/Reckless Life (live)/Knockin' On Heaven's Door (live) (12", p/s)	7
91	Geffen GFSTP 6	You Could Be Mine/Civil War (12", clear vinyl with insert in PVC sleeve)	8
91	Geffen GFSTD 6	You Could Be Mine/Civil War (CD, card p/s)	6
91	Geffen GFST 9	Don't Cry/Don't Cry (Alternate Lyrics)/Don't Cry (Demo) (12", hologram p/s)	8
91	Geffen GFSTD 9	Don't Cry/Don't Cry (Alternate Lyrics)/(Demo) (CD, cardboard gatefold p/s)	7
91	Geffen GFSX 17	Live And Let Die (LP Version)/(live) (12", yellow/orange vinyl, die-cut p/s)	8
91	Geffen GFSTD 17	Live And Let Die (LP Version)/Live And Let Die (live)/Shadow Of Your Love (live) (CD, stencil p/s)	7
92	Geffen GFST 18	November Rain/Sweet Child O' Mine (live)/Patience (live) (12", p/s, 1-side etched)	7
92	Geffen GFSTD 18	November Rain/Sweet Child O' Mine (live)/Patience (live) (CD)	8

ARTHUR GUNTER

| 71 | Blue Horizon 2431 012 | BLUES AFTER HOURS (LP) | 45 |
| 70s | Contempo COLP 119 | BLACK AND BLUES (LP) | 10 |

HARDROCK GUNTER

| 52 | Brunswick 04907 | Silver And Gold/The Senator From Tennessee (78) | 10 |
| 55 | Brunswick OE 9167 | MOUNTAIN MUSIC (EP) | 15 |

(see also Red Foley, Roberta Lee)

GURU GURU

| 73 | Atlantic K 50022 | DON'T CALL US WE'LL CALL YOU (LP) | 10 |
| 74 | Atlantic K 50044 | DANCE OF THE FLAMES (LP) | 10 |

GURUS

| 66 | United Artists UP 1160 | Blue Snow Night/Come Girl | 15 |

ADRIAN GURVITZ

| 79 | Jet JET 12-140 | The Way I Feel/Drifting Star (12", clear vinyl picture disc, stickered PVC sleeve with insert) | 7 |

(see also Knack, Ruperts People, Gun, Three Man Army)

JOHNNY GUSTAFSON

| 65 | Polydor BM 56022 | Just To Be With You/Sweet Day | 10 |
| 65 | Polydor BM 56043 | Take Me For A Little While/Make Me Your Number One | 15 |

(see also Big Three, Quotations, Hard Stuff, Gillan, Johnny & John)

CARL GUSTAV & 84's

| 81 | Convulsive CN 001 | I Want To Kill Russians/Through Birds, Through Fire, But Not Through Glass (p/s) | 5 |

ARLO GUTHRIE

67	Reprise RS 20644	Motorcycle Song/Now And Then	8
70	Reprise RS 20877	Alice's Rock'N'Roll Restaurant/Coming In To Los Angeles	5
70	Reprise RS 20951	Valley Of Pray/Gabriel's Mother's Hiway Ballad No. 16 Blues (demos only)	7
70	Reprise RS 20994	The Ballad Of Tricky Fred/Shackles And Chains	4
67	Reprise RLP 6267	ALICE'S RESTAURANT (LP)	10
68	Reprise RSLP 6269	ARLO (LP)	12
69	Reprise RSLP 6346	RUNNING DOWN THE ROAD (LP)	10
70	Reprise RSLP 6411	WASHINGTON COUNTY (LP)	10

GWEN GUTHRIE

| 86 | 4th + Broadway BRW 1252 | Seventh Heaven/It Should Have Been You/Getting Hot (12", p/s) | 7 |

WOODY GUTHRIE

51	Melodisc 1141	Ramblin' Blues/Talkin' Columbia Blues (78)	5
55	Melodisc EPM7 84	HARD AIN'T IT HARD (EP)	8
55	Melodisc EPM7 85	WORRIED MAN BLUES (EP)	8
55	Melodisc EPM7 91	HEY LOLLY LOLLY (EP)	8
55	Melodisc MLP 12-106	MORE SONGS BY GUTHRIE (LP)	30
56	Topic 12T 31	GUTHRIE'S STORY (LP)	30
64	RCA RD 7642	DUST BOWL BALLADS (LP)	25
65	Xtra XTRA 1012	WOODY GUTHRIE (LP)	12
66	Xtra XTRA 1064	WOODY GUTHRIE (LP)	12
66	Xtra XTRA 1065	POOR BOY (LP)	12
66	Xtra XTRA 1067	SONGS TO GROW ON VOL. 1 (LP)	12
68	Ember CW 129	WOODY GUTHRIE (LP)	10
69	Ember CW 136	BLIND SONNY TERRY & WOODY GUTHRIE (LP)	10

GUV'NERS

| 63 | Piccadilly 7N 35117 | Kissing Had To Stop/Let's Make A Habit | 5 |

(see also Jess Conrad, Dickie Pride, Nelson Keene)

BUDDY GUY

65	Chess CRS 8004	Let Me Love You Baby/Ten Years Ago	10
68	Fontana TF 951	Mary Had A Little Lamb/Sweet Little Angel	10
72	Atlantic K 10195	Honey Dripper/Man Of Many Words	4
65	Chess CRE 6004	CRAZY MUSIC (EP)	15
68	Chess CRLS 4546	I LEFT MY BLUES IN SAN FRANCISCO (LP)	15
68	Vanguard SVRL 19001	COMING AT YOU (LP)	15
68	Vanguard SVRL 19002	MAN AND HIS BLUES (LP)	15
68	Vanguard SVRL 19004	BLUES TODAY (LP)	15
69	Vanguard SVRL 19008	THIS IS BUDDY GUY (LP)	15
69	Vanguard SVRL 79290	HOT AND COOL (LP)	10
69	Python KM 2	FIRST TIME I MET THE BLUES (LP)	25
70	Harvest SHSP 4006	BUDDY AND THE JUNIORS (LP, with Junior Mance & Junior Wells)	20
72	Vanguard VSD 79323	HOLD THAT PLANE (LP)	10
72	Atlantic K 40240	PLAY THE BLUES (LP, with Junior Wells)	15

(see also Junior Wells)

MARVIN GAYE

MINT VALUE £

JENNE HAAN
78   EMI EMI 2949   We Drove Them All Mad/Forgotten Dreams (p/s) 4
HABIBIYYA
72   Island HELP 7   IF MAN BUT KNEW (LP, with inner sleeve) 18
(see also Mighty Baby)
HABITS
66   Decca F 12348   Need You/Elbow Baby 15
(see also Charles Dickens, Nice)
HACKENSACK
72   Island WIP 6149   Moving On/River Boat 12
74   Polydor 2383 263   UP THE HARD WAY (LP, with inner sleeve) 70
STEVE HACKETT
78   Charisma CB 312   How Can I/Kim 6
78   Charisma CB 318   Narnia/Please Don't Touch 5
79   Charisma CB 334   Every Day/Lost Time In Cordoba 5
79   Charisma CB 341   Clocks – The Angel Of Mons/Acoustic Set (p/s) 6
79   Charisma CB 341-12   Clocks – The Angel Of Mons/Acoustic Set/Tigermoth (12", p/s) 10
80   Charisma CB 357   The Show/Hercules Unchained (p/s) 5
80   Charisma CB 368   Sentimental Institution/The Toast (p/s) 4
81   Charisma CB 385   Hope I Don't Wake/Tales Of The Riverbank (p/s) 4
81   Charisma CB 390   Picture Postcard/Theme From Second Chance (p/s) 4
83   Charisma CELL 1   Cell 151/Time Lapse At Milton Keynes (p/s) 4
83   Charisma CELL 12/   Cell 151/Air Conditioned Nightmare/Time Lapse At Milton Keynes//Clocks –
     CELL 13   The Angel Of Mons/Acoustic Set/Tigermoth (12", p/s, 2,000 with 12"
    white label promo) 15
83   Charisma CELL 12   Cell 151/Air Conditioned Nightmare/Time Lapse At Milton Keynes (12", p/s) 7
(see also Quiet World, Genesis, Peter Banks)
HAFFY'S WHISKY SOUR
71   Deram DM 345   Shot In The Head/Bye Bye Bluebird 5
(see also Easybeats, Paintbox)
HAFLER TRIO
84   Doublevision DVR 4   BANG! — AN OPEN LETTER (LP, with insert) 12
86   Charrm 3   THREE WAYS OF SAYING TWO — THE NETHERLANDS LECTURES
    (LP, stickered sleeve with booklet) 15
(see also Cabaret Voltaire)
SAMMY HAGAR
76   Capitol CL 15872   Flamingoes Fly/Urban Guerilla 5
77   Capitol CL 15913   Catch The Wind/Rock'n'Roll Weekend 5
79   Capitol CL 16083   (Sittin' On) The Dock Of The Bay/I've Done Everything For You 5
82   Geffen GEF A11 1884   Piece Of My Heart/Baby's On Fire (picture disc) 4
77   Capitol E-ST 11599   SAMMY HAGAR (LP, red vinyl) 15
80   Capitol E-ST 25330   LOUD AND CLEAR (LP, red vinyl) 10
(see also Van Halen)
NINA HAGEN
79   CBS 7804   TV-Glotzer (White Punks On Dope)/Naturtrane 4
JOAN HAGER
57   Brunswick 05650   Happy Is A Girl Named Me/Run Darlin', Don't Walk 10
MERLE HAGGARD & STRANGERS
68   Capitol CL 15540   The Legend Of Bonnie And Clyde/I Started Loving You Again 4
67   Capitol (S)T 2702   I'M A LONESOME FUGITIVE (LP) 12
68   Capitol (S)T 2912   THE LEGEND OF BONNIE & CLYDE (LP) 12
68   Capitol (S)T 2972   MAMA TRIED (LP) 12
70   Capitol E-ST 11599   FIGHTIN' SIDE OF ME (LP) 10
71   Capitol ST 21377   A TRIBUTE TO JIMMIE RODGERS (LP) 10
76   Capitol E-ST 11544   MY LOVE AFFAIR WITH TRAINS (LP) 10
77   MCA MCF 2818   MY FAREWELL TO ELVIS (LP) 10
JOYCE HAHN
57   London HLA 8453   Gonna Find Me A Bluebird/I Saw You, I Saw You 7
PAUL HAIG
81   Rational   DRAMA (cassette) 15
82   Operation Twilight OPT 03   Running Away/Time (p/s) 4
84   Island ISX 198   The Only Truth (U.S. Remix)/Instrumental/Ghost Rider (12", p/s) ...7
80s Masterbag   square flexidisc (blue vinyl) 4
84   Island ILPS 9742   RHYTHM OF LIFE (LP) 10
85   Operation Afterglow OPA 3   THE WARP OF PURE FUN (LP, inner sleeve) 10
(see also Josef K, Rhythm Of Life, Juggernauts)
NORMAN HAINES (BAND)
70   Parlophone R 5871   Daffodil/Autumn Mobile (as Norman Haynes Band) 20
72   Parlophone R 5960   Give It To You Girl/Elaine (as Norman Haines) 20
71   Parlophone PCS 7130   DEN OF INIQUITY (LP) 400
(see also Brumbeats, Locomotive)

PERRY HAINES
81	Fetish FE 14	What's Funk?/What's What! (p/s)	4
81	Fetish FE 14T	What's Funk?/What's What! (12", p/s)	7

HAIR
70	Columbia SCX 6452	HAIRPIECE (LP)	120

HAIRBAND
69	Bell BLL 1076	Big Louis/Travelling Song	10
69	Bell SBLL 69	BAND ON THE WAGON (LP)	30

(see also Alex Harvey)

HAIRCUT 100
82	Arista CLIPD 3	Fantastic Day (live)/Ski Club Of Great Britain (picture disc)	5
83	Arista CLIP 5	Whistle Down The Wind (withdrawn, any pressed?)	7+
83	Polydor HC 1	Prime Time/So Tired (coloured vinyl, PVC sleeve)	4
81	Lyntone LYN 11175	Nobody's Fool (demo version) (green flexidisc free with "Flexipop", issue 17)	5/4
82	Arista HCC 101	BLUE HAT FOR A BLUE DAY (LP, withdrawn, test pressings only)	15

(see also Nick Heyward)

HAIRPOWER
70	CBS 4961	Royal International Love-in/Be There, Be Hair	4

DENNIS HALE
55	Parlophone MSP 6153	The Butterscotch Mop/S'posin'	4

(see also Jack Parnell)

WILLIE BEAVER HALE
80	TK TKR 7587	Groove On/Party Times	4
80	TK TKR 12-7587	Groove On/Party Times (12")	8

BILL HALEY (& HIS COMETS)
53	London L 1190	Crazy Man, Crazy/Whatcha Gonna Do (as Bill Haley with Haley's Comets) (78)	25
53	London L 1216	Pat-A-Cake/Fractured (78, as Bill Haley with Haley's Comets)	25
54	Brunswick 05317	(We're Gonna) Rock Around The Clock/Thirteen Women	60/25
54	Brunswick 05317	(We're Gonna) Rock Around The Clock/Thirteen Women (78)	8
54	Brunswick 05338	Shake, Rattle And Roll/A.B.C. Boogie	50/25
54	Brunswick 05338	Shake, Rattle And Roll/A.B.C. Boogie (78)	8
55	Brunswick 05373	Happy Baby/Dim, Dim The Lights (I Want Some Atmosphere)	45/20
55	Brunswick 05373	Happy Baby/Dim, Dim The Lights (I Want Some Atmosphere) (78)	8
55	Brunswick 05405	Birth Of The Boogie/Mambo Rock	50/20
55	Brunswick 05405	Birth Of The Boogie/Mambo Rock (78)	8
55	London HL 8142	Green Tree Boogie/Sundown Boogie	120/70
55	London HL 8142	Green Tree Boogie/Sundown Boogie (78)	8
55	Brunswick 05453	Two Hound Dogs/Razzle Dazzle	40/20
55	Brunswick 05453	Two Hound Dogs/Razzle Dazzle (78)	8
55	London HLF 8161	Farewell, So Long, Goodbye/I'll Be True	120/70
55	London HLF 8161	Farewell, So Long, Goodbye/I'll Be True (78)	8
55	London HLF 8194	Ten Little Indians/Rocking Chair On The Moon	120/70
55	London HLF 8194	Ten Little Indians/Rocking Chair On The Moon (78)	8
55	Brunswick 05509	Rock-A-Beatin' Boogie/Burn That Candle	40/20
55	Brunswick 05509	Rock-A-Beatin' Boogie/Burn That Candle (78)	6
56	Brunswick 05530	See You Later, Alligator/The Paper Boy (On Main Street, USA)	35/18
56	Brunswick 05530	See You Later, Alligator/The Paper Boy (On Main Street, USA) (78)	5

(when two prices are given for the above 45s, the first refers to original gold-lettering labels & the second to silver label reissues)

56	Brunswick 05565	The Saints Rock 'N' Roll/R-O-C-K	20
56	Brunswick 05565	The Saints Rock 'N' Roll/R-O-C-K (78)	5
56	Brunswick 05582	Rockin' Through The Rye/Hot Dog Buddy Buddy	20
56	Brunswick 05582	Rockin' Through The Rye/Hot Dog Buddy Buddy (78)	5
56	Brunswick 05615	Rip It Up/Teenager's Mother	20
56	Brunswick 05615	Rip It Up/Teenager's Mother (78)	5
56	Brunswick 05616	Rudy's Rock/Blue Comet Blues	20
56	Brunswick 05616	Rudy's Rock/Blue Comet Blues (78)	5
57	Brunswick 05640	Don't Knock The Rock/Calling All Comets	22
57	Brunswick 05640	Don't Knock The Rock/Calling All Comets (78)	5
57	Brunswick 05641	Hook, Line And Sinker/Goofin' Around	18
57	Brunswick 05641	Hook, Line And Sinker/Goofin' Around (78)	5
57	London HLF 8371	Rock The Joint/Yes Indeed! (gold or silver label)	120/60
57	London HLF 8371	Rock The Joint/Yes Indeed! (78)	10
57	Brunswick 05658	Forty Cups Of Coffee/Choo Choo Ch'Boogie	20
57	Brunswick 05658	Forty Cups Of Coffee/Choo Choo Ch'Boogie (78)	5
57	Brunswick 05688	(You Hit The Wrong Note) Billy Goat/Rockin' Rollin' Rover	15
57	Brunswick 05688	(You Hit The Wrong Note) Billy Goat/Rockin' Rollin' Rover (78)	6
57	Brunswick 05719	Miss You/The Dipsy Doodle	18
57	Brunswick 05719	Miss You/The Dipsy Doodle (78)	7
58	Brunswick 05735	Mary, Mary Lou/It's A Sin	18
58	Brunswick 05735	Mary, Mary Lou/It's A Sin (78)	8
58	Brunswick 05742	Skinny Minnie/How Many	18
58	Brunswick 05742	Skinny Minnie/How Many (78)	8
58	Brunswick 05752	Lean Jean/Don't Nobody Move	15
58	Brunswick 05752	Lean Jean/Don't Nobody Move (78)	8
58	Brunswick 05766	Whoa Mabel!/Chiquita Linda	18
58	Brunswick 05766	Whoa Mabel!/Chiquita Linda (78)	8
59	Brunswick 05788	I Got A Woman/Charmaine	15
59	Brunswick 05788	I Got A Woman/Charmaine (78)	12
59	Brunswick 05805	Shaky/Caldonia	18
59	Brunswick 05805	Shaky/Caldonia (78)	15

(all the above 45s came with tri centres; later round centres are worth half the value for earlier 45s to two-thirds for later 45s)

Bill HALEY (& HIS COMETS)

59	Brunswick 05810	Joey's Song/Ooh! Look-A There, Ain't She Pretty	12
59	Brunswick 05810	Joey's Song/Ooh! Look-A There, Ain't She Pretty (78)	20
60	Brunswick 05818	Puerto Rican Peddler/Skokiaan	10
60	Warner Bros WB 6	Candy Kisses/Tamiami	8
61	London HLU 9471	Spanish Twist/My Kind Of Woman	12
63	Stateside SS 196	Tenor Man/Up Goes My Love	7
64	Warner Bros WB 133	Rock Around The Clock/Love Letters In The Sand	10
64	Brunswick 05910	Happy Baby/Birth Of The Boogie	12
64	Brunswick 05917	The Green Door/Yeah! She's Evil	12
68	Decca AD 1010	(We're Gonna) Rock Around The Clock/Shake, Rattle And Roll (export issue)	7
68	MCA MU 1013	(We're Gonna) Rock Around The Clock/Shake, Rattle And Roll	4
68	Pye Intl. 7N 25455	Crazy Man, Crazy/Dance With A Dolly (With A Hole In Her Stocking)	15
74	Sonet SON 2016	Me And Bobby McGee/I Wouldn't Have Missed It For The World	5
74	Sonet SON 2043	Crazy Man, Crazy/Lawdy Miss Clawdy	5
74	MCA MCA 128	Rock Around The Clock/Shake, Rattle And Roll	4
74	MCA MCA 142	See You Later Alligator/Rudy's Rock	4
76	MCA MCA 263	Shake, Rattle And Roll/Razzle Dazzle/Rock-A-Beatin' Boogie	4
80	Rollercoaster RRC 2004	Rock The Joint/Fractured (reissue)	4
80	Sonet SON 2202	God Bless Rock And Roll/So Right Tonight	5
81	Thumbs Up TU 103	Rocket 88/Tearstains On My Pillow	4
55	Brunswick OE 9129	DIM, DIM THE LIGHTS (EP, gold label with 'stage' sleeve, various colours)	25
55	Brunswick OE 9129	DIM, DIM THE LIGHTS (EP, silver label with 'stage' or 'cameo' sleeve)	20
55	London REF 1031	ROCK AND ROLL (EP)	45
56	London REF 1049	LIVE IT UP Part 1 (EP)	30
56	London REF 1050	LIVE IT UP Part 2 (EP)	30
56	Brunswick OE 9214	ROCK AND ROLL WITH BILL HALEY (EP)	18
56	Brunswick OE 9250	ROCK AROUND THE CLOCK (EP)	15
56	Brunswick OE 9250	ROCK AROUND THE CLOCK (EP, round centre, different sleeve, same design as "Bill Haley" [OE 9459])	25
56	London REF 1058	LIVE IT UP Part 3 (EP)	30
56	Brunswick OE 9278	ROCK'N'ROLL STAGE SHOW PART 1 (EP)	18
56	Brunswick OE 9279	ROCK'N'ROLL STAGE SHOW PART 2 (EP)	18
56	Brunswick OE 9280	ROCK'N'ROLL STAGE SHOW PART 3 (EP)	18
58	Brunswick OE 9349	ROCKIN' THE OLDIES PART 1 (EP)	25
58	Brunswick OE 9350	ROCKIN' THE OLDIES PART 2 (EP)	25
58	Brunswick OE 9351	ROCKIN' THE OLDIES PART 3 (EP)	25
59	Brunswick OE 9446	ROCKIN' AROUND THE WORLD (EP)	40
59	Brunswick OE 9459	BILL HALEY (EP, tri or round centre)	35/25

(all the above EPs originally came with triangular centres, later round centres are worth two-thirds the value or more)

60	Warners WEP 6001	BILL HALEY AND HIS COMETS (EP)	15
61	Warners WEP 6025	BILL HALEY'S JUKE BOX (EP, also stereo WSEP 2025)	15/25
64	Warners WEP 6133	BILL HALEY VOLUME 1 (EP)	20
64	Warners WEP 6136	BILL HALEY VOLUME 2 (EP)	20
55	London H-APB 1042	LIVE IT UP (10" LP, gold or silver label)	100/60
56	Brunswick LAT 8117	ROCK AROUND THE CLOCK (LP)	30
56	Brunswick LAT 8139	ROCK AND ROLL STAGE SHOW (LP)	30
57	London HA-F 2037	ROCK THE JOINT (LP)	60
57	Brunswick LAT 8219	ROCKIN' THE OLDIES (LP)	40
57	Brunswick LAT 8268	ROCKIN' THE JOINT (LP)	40
59	Brunswick LAT 8295	BILL HALEY'S CHICKS (LP, also stereo STA 3011)	40/50
60	Brunswick LAT 8326	STRICTLY INSTRUMENTAL (LP)	40
61	Ace Of Hearts AH 13	ROCK AROUND THE CLOCK (LP, 2 slightly different sleeves)	18/15
62	Columbia 33SX 1460	TWISTIN' KNIGHTS AT THE ROUNDTABLE (LIVE!) (LP)	25
62	Ace Of Hearts AH 35	ROCKIN' THE OLDIES (LP)	15
64	Ace Of Hearts AH 66	BILL HALEY'S CHICKS (LP)	15
64	Golden Guinea GGL 0282	ROCK THE JOINT (LP)	15
65	Transatlantic XTRA 1027	BILL HALEY & THE COMETS (LP)	20
65	Warner Bros W 1391	BILL HALEY'S JUKE BOX (LP)	30
67	Marble Arch MAL 817	ROCK THE JOINT (LP)	10
67	Ember EMB 3386	REAL LIVE ROCK'N'ROLL (LP)	12
68	MCA MUP 318	RIP IT UP! (LP)	12
68	Ember EMB 3396	KING OF ROCK (LP)	12
69	Ember EMB 3401	MISTER ROCK'N'ROLL (LP)	12
70	Valiant VS 103	BILL HALEY & THE COMETS (LP)	15
71	Coral CP 55	ROCK AROUND THE CLOCK (LP)	10
71	Sonet SNTF 623	ROCK AROUND THE COUNTRY (LP)	10
73	Sonet SNTF 645	JUST ROCK AND ROLL MUSIC (LP)	10

(see also Kingsmen, Jodimars)

HALF JAPANESE

81	Armageddon AS 009	Spy/I Know How It Feels ... Bad/My Knowledge Was Wrong (p/s)	4
81	Armageddon ABOX 1	1/2 GENTLEMEN NOT BEASTS (3-LP box set with poster, booklet & lyric insert)	18
81	Armageddon ARM 7	LOUD (LP)	10

(see also Jad Fair)

HALF MAN HALF BISCUIT

86	Probe Plus TRUM 1-7	The Trumpton Riots/All I Want For Christmas Is A Dukla Prague Away Kit (p/s)	4

(see also Attempted Moustache)

HAL HOPPERS

54	London HL 8107	More Love/Do Nothin' Blues	25
55	London HL 8129	Mother Of Pearl/Baby I've Had It	22

BARBARA HALL

75	EMI INT 514	You Brought It On Yourself/Drop My Heart Off At The Door	4

BOB HALL & ALEXIS KORNER
| 78 | Logo GO 331 | Pinetop's Boogie Woogie/All I Got Is You .... 4 |

(see also Brunning Hall Sunflower Blues Band, Alexis Korner)

(DARYL) HALL & (JOHN) OATES
75	RCA RCA 2614	Camelia/Ennui On The Mountain 4
76	RCA RCA 2684	Gino/Soldiering 4
81	RCA RCALP 6001	PRIVATE EYES (LP, with free cassette) 10

DEREK HALL & MIKE COOPER
| 60s | Kennet KRS 766 | OUT OF THE SHADES (EP) .... 10 |

DICKSON HALL
57	MGM MGM EP626	OUTLAWS OF THE OLD WEST (EP) 12
58	London RER 1158	FABULOUS COUNTRY HITS NO. 1 (EP) 10
58	London RER 1159	FABULOUS COUNTRY HITS NO. 2 (EP) 10
58	London RER 1160	FABULOUS COUNTRY HITS NO. 3 (EP) 10
60	Fontana Z 4011	ALL-TIME COUNTRY AND WESTERN HITS (LP) 10

DOLORES HALL
| 73 | Jay Boy BOY 77 | Good Lovin' Man/W-O-M-E-N .... 4 |

(see also Jackie Lee & Dolores Hall)

GERRI HALL
| 66 | Sue WI 4026 | Who Can I Run To/I Lost A Key (unreleased?) .... 60+ |

JIMMY GRAY HALL
| 74 | Epic EPC 2312 | Be That Way/Possessed By The Moon .... 12 |

JUANITA HALL
| 62 | Storyville SEP 382 | STORYVILLE BLUES ANTHOLOGY VOL. 2 (EP) .... 7 |

LARRY HALL
| 60 | Parlophone R 4625 | Sandy/Lovin' Tree .... 4 |
| 62 | Salvo SLO 1811 | Ladder Of Love/The One You Left Behind .... 7 |

RENE HALL'S ORCHESTRA
| 58 | London HLU 8581 | Twitchy/Flippin' .... 25 |
| 58 | London HLU 8581 | Twitchy/Flippin' (78) .... 8 |

ROBIN HALL (& JIMMY MacGREGOR)
60	Collector JDS 3	Football Crazy/Rosin The Beau 4
60	Decca F 11266	Football Crazy/Rosin The Beau (reissue, p/s) 4
60	Collector JES 6	THE BONNIE LASS O'FYVIE (EP, solo) 7
60	Collector JES 7	MACPHERSON'S RANT (EP, solo) 7
61	Collector JES 9	GLASGOW STREET SONGS VOL. 3 (EP) 7

RONNIE HALL
61	Piccadilly 7N 35001	The Code Of Love/Who Cares 4
62	Piccadilly 7N 35040	My Very First Love/The Day After Forever 4
65	Fontana TF 569	I'll Stand Aside/I'm Getting Nowhere 12

ROY HALL
56	Brunswick 05531	See You Later, Alligator/Don't Stop Now 450
56	Brunswick 05531	See You Later, Alligator/Don't Stop Now (78) 60
56	Brunswick 05555	Blue Suede Shoes/Luscious 250
56	Brunswick 05555	Blue Suede Shoes/Luscious (78) 40
56	Brunswick 05627	Diggin' The Boogie/Three Alley Cats 275
56	Brunswick 05627	Diggin' The Boogie/Three Alley Cats (78) 40

CHANCE HALLADAY
| 62 | Vogue V 9203 | John Henry/Thirteen Women .... 7 |

HALLELUJAH SKIFFLE GROUP
| 58 | Oriole CB 1429 | I Saw The Light/A Closer Walk With Thee (with Clinton Ford) .... 6 |

(see also Clinton Ford)

DICK HALLMAN
| 56 | Brunswick 05608 | Two Different Worlds/Love Me As Though There Were No Tomorrow .... 4 |
| 60 | Vogue V 9162 | Born To Be Loved/Just Squeeze Me But Don't Teeze Me .... 4 |

JOHNNY HALLYDAY
62	Philips BF 1238	Shake The Hand Of A Fool/Hold Back The Sun 8
63	Philips 373 012BF	Hey Little Girl/Caravan Of Lonely Men 8
65	Philips BF 1449	Pour Moi Tu Es La Seule/They Call Him A Man 10
62	Philips 432 813BE	ROCKING (EP) 80
66	Vogue VRE 5013	JOHNNY HALLYDAY (EP) 60
61	Philips BBL 7556	SINGS AMERICA'S ROCKIN' HITS (LP) 80

HALOS
| 61 | London HLU 9424 | Nag/Copycat .... 20 |

STUART HAMBLEN
54	HMV 7MC 20	This Ole House/When My Lord Picks Up The 'Phone (export issue) 15
55	HMV 7MC 30	Go On By/Just A Man (export issue) 10
56	HMV 7M 394	Hell Train/A Few Things To Remember 8

BILLY HAMBRIC
| 79 | Grapevine GRP 139 | She Said Goodbye/I Found True Love .... 5 |

CLAIRE HAMILL
75	Konk KOS 1	Geronimo's Cadillac/Luck Of The Draw 4
81	WEA K 18440	First Night In New York/Ultraviolet Light (B-side with Gary Numan) (p/s) 6
71	Island ILPS 9182	ONE HOUSE LEFT STANDING (LP) 10
73	Island ILPS 9225	OCTOBER (LP) 10
74	Konk KONK 101	STAGE DOOR JOHNNIES (LP) 12

Claire HAMILL

75 Konk KONK 104   ABRACADABRA (LP, featuring Cafe Society) 12
(see also Transporter, Cafe Society)

BILLY HAMILTON & STRANDSMEN
67 Philips BF 1622   Try To Remember/Don't You Believe It 4

CHICO HAMILTON QUINTET
57 Vogue V 2407   The Sage/The Morning After 4

EDWARD HAMILTON & ARABIANS
79 Grapevine GRP 134   Baby Don't You Weep/I'm Gonna Love You 5

GARY HAMILTON
67 Decca F 12697   Let The Music Play/Don't Ask 4
69 CBS 4674   Easy Rider/Hare Krishna 4
(see also Hamilton & [Hamilton] Movement)

GAVIN HAMILTON
67 King KG 1067   It Won't Be The Same/Turn The Key Softly 20

GEORGE HAMILTON IV
57 London HL 8361   A Rose And A Candy Bar/If You Don't Know (gold or silver label print) 100/60
57 London HL 8361   A Rose And A Candy Bar/If You Don't Know (78) 20
57 HMV POP 429   Why Don't They Understand/Even Tho' 10
58 HMV POP 474   Now And For Always/One Heart 8
58 HMV POP 505   I Know Where I'm Goin'/Who's Taking You To The Prom? 6
58 HMV POP 534   Your Cheatin' Heart/When Will I Know? 7
60 HMV POP 813   Before This Day Ends/Loneliness Is All Around Us 6
63 RCA RCA 1353   Abilene/Oh So Many Years 4
58 HMV CLP 1202   ON CAMPUS (LP) 15
59 HMV CLP 1263   SING ME A SAD SONG — A TRIBUTE TO HANK WILLIAMS (LP) 15

GUY HAMILTON
65 HMV POP 1418   A Lifetime Of Loneliness/Give The Game Away 8
(see also Neil Christian)

M. HAMILTON
67 Ska Beat JB 265   Something Gotta Ring/DENNIS LYNWARD & HIS GROUP: Jazz Session 7

ROY HAMILTON
55 Philips PB 368   You'll Never Walk Alone/If I Loved You (78) 6
55 Philips PB 448   Unchained Melody/From Here To Eternity (78) 6
55 Philips PB 515   Forgive This Fool/You Wanted To Change Me (78) 6
56 Philips PB 551   Without A Song/Cuban Love Song (78) 6
56 Philips PB 583   Walk Along With Kings/There Goes My Heart (78) 6
58 Fontana H 113   Don't Let Go/The Right To Love 18
58 Fontana H 113   Don't Let Go/The Right To Love (78) 5
58 Fontana H 143   Crazy Feelin'/In A Dream 12
58 Fontana H 143   Crazy Feelin'/In A Dream (78) 5
59 Fontana H 180   Pledging My Love/My One And Only Love 12
59 Fontana H 180   Pledging My Love/My One And Only Love (78) 5
59 Fontana H 193   I Need Your Loving/Somewhere Along The Way 10
59 Fontana H 193   I Need Your Loving/Somewhere Along The Way (78) 10
61 Fontana H 298   You Can Have Her/Abide With Me 10
61 Fontana H 320   You're Gonna Need Magic/To The One I Love 10
63 MGM MGM 1210   Theme From "The VIPs"/The Sinner 6
64 MGM MGM 1251   There She Is/Panic Is On 75
65 MGM MGM 1268   A Thousand Tears Ago/Sweet Violet 8
66 RCA RCA 1500   And I Love Her/Tore Up Over You 4
70 Deep Soul DS 9106   Dark End Of The Street/100 Years Ago 12
59 Fontana TFE 17160   WHY FIGHT THE FEELING (EP) 12
60 Fontana TFE 17163   THE MOOD MOVES (EP) 10
61 Fontana TFE 17170   COME OUT SWINGING (EP) 12

RUSS HAMILTON
57 Oriole CB 1359   We Will Make Love/Rainbow 5
57 Oriole CB 1388   Wedding Ring/I Still Belong To You 5
58 Oriole CB 1404   Little One/I Had A Dream 4
58 Oriole CB 1406   I Don't Know Why/My Mother's Eyes 4
58 Oriole CB 1451   Drifting And Dreaming/Tip-toe Through The Tulips 4
58 Oriole CB 1459   I Wonder Who's Kissing Her Now/September In The Rain 5
59 Oriole CB 1465   Things I Didn't Say/Strange Are The Ways Of Love 5
59 Oriole CB 1492   The Reprieve Of Tom Dooley/Dreaming Of You 5
59 Oriole CB 1506   My Unbreakable Heart/I Found You 6
59 Oriole CB 1508   Smile, Smile, Smile (And Sing, Sing, Sing)/Shadow 6
60 Oriole CB 1527   Things No Money Can Buy/Mama 6
60 Oriole CB 1531   It's A Sin To Tell A Lie/Folks Get Married In The Spring 6
60 MGM MGM 1096   Gonna Find Me A Bluebird/Choir Girl 4
58 Oriole EP 7005   RUSS HAMILTON (EP) 12
58 Oriole MG 20031   WE WILL MAKE LOVE (LP) 35

SCOTT HAMILTON
66 Parlophone R 5492   Good Day Sunshine/For No One 4

HAMILTON & MOVEMENT
65 Polydor BM 56026   Really Saying Something/I Won't See You Tonight 25
67 CBS 202573   I'm Not The Marrying Kind/My Love Belongs To You 20
(see also Gary Hamilton, Paul Stewart Movement)

HAMLINS
67 Coxsone CS 7021   Trying To Keep A Good Man Down/BOB MARLEY: Oh My Darling 25
67 Coxsone CS 7022   Soul And Inspiration/ETHOPIANS: Let's Get Together 15
68 Coxsone CS 7048   Sentimental Reasons/SOUL VENDORS: Last Waltz 12

68	Blue Cat BS 115	Sugar And Spice/SOUL VENDORS: Mercy Mercy Mercy	10

JACK HAMMER
61	Oriole CB 1634	Young Only Once/Juliette	6
62	Oriole CB 1645	Kissin' Twist/Melancholy Boy	6
62	Oriole CB 1728	Crazy Twist/Twist Talk	6
62	Oriole CB 1753	Don't Let Baby Know/Number 2539	6
66	Polydor BM 56091	Thanks/Love Ladder	7
69	United Artists UP 35029	What Greater Love/The Mason Dixon Line	20

HAMMERS
69	President PT 247	Baby And Me/Little Butterfly	5
69	President PT 276	Sugar Baby/Power Of Love	5

HAMMERSMITH GORILLAS
74	Penny Farthing PEN 849	You Really Got Me/Leavin' 'Ome	10
77	Raw RAW 2	You Really Got Me/Leavin' 'Ome	4
	(see also Clique)		

PETER HAMMILL
75	Charisma CB 245	Birthday Special/Shingle Song	6
78	Charisma CB 339	The Polaroid (credited to Ricky Nadir)/The Old School Tie	10
81	Virgin VS 424	My Experience/Glue (p/s)	4
82	Naive NAV 3	Paradox Drive/Now More Than Ever (p/s)	6
83	Naive NAV 8	Film Noir/Seven Sonders	6
71	Charisma CAS 1037	FOOL'S MATE (LP, gatefold sleeve)	18
73	Charisma CAS 1067	CHAMELEON IN THE SHADOW OF THE NIGHT (LP)	12
74	Charisma CAS 1083	THE SILENT CORNER AND THE EMPTY STAGE (LP)	12
74	Charisma CAS 1089	IN CAMERA (LP, with inner sleeve)	12
75	Charisma CAS 1099	NADIR'S BIG CHANCE (LP)	12
77	Charisma CAS 1125	OVER (LP, some with inner lyric sleeve)	15/12
78	Charisma CAS 1137	FUTURE NOW (LP)	12
79	Charisma CAS 1146	pH 7 (LP)	12
	(see also Van Der Graaf Generator)		

ALBERT HAMMOND
73	MUM MUMS 65320	IT NEVER RAINS IN SOUTHERN CALIFORNIA (LP)	10
73	MUM MUMS 65554	FREE ELECTRIC BAND (LP)	10
74	MUM MUMS 80026	ALBERT HAMMOND (LP)	10

CLAY HAMMOND
73	Jay Boy BOY 78	Dance Little Girl/Twin Brother	5

JOHN HAMMOND
65	Fontana TF 560	Baby Won't You Tell Me/I Live The Life I Love	12
68	Atlantic 584 190	Brown Eyed Handsome Man/Crosscut Saw	8
64	Fontana TFL 6046	BIG CITY BLUES (LP)	25
65	Fontana TFL 6059	SO MANY ROADS (LP)	25
71	CBS 64365	SOURCE POINT (LP)	20
72	CBS 65051	I'M SATISFIED (LP)	20
74	Vanguard VSD 11/12	THE BEST OF JOHN HAMMOND — SOUTHERN FRIED (2-LP)	14

JOHNNY HAMMOND
71	Kudu KUL 3	HIGHER SOUND (LP)	10
70s	Kudu	WILD HORSES ROCK STEADY (LP)	10

STEVE HAMMOND
67	Pye 7N 17275	I Think We're Alone Now/Just Call My Name	5

CURLEY HAMNER
59	Felsted SD 80061	Twistin' And Turnin'/King And Queen	6

SUSAN HAMPSHIRE
65	Decca F 12185	When Love Is True/When The World Was Our Own	4

LIONEL HAMPTON (& HIS HAMP-TONES)
52	MGM MGM 468	Samson's Boogie/Helpless (78, & His Hamp-Tones, B-side with Sonny Parker)	8
57	Vogue V 2405	Flying Home/Perdido (with Just Jazz All Stars)	14
57	Vogue V 2406	Hamp's Boogie Woogie/The Blues (with Just Jazz All Stars)	16
56	MGM MGM-EP 552	LIONEL HAMPTON & HIS ORCHESTRA (EP)	7
57	Vogue EPV 1161	GENE NORMAN PRESENTS JUST JAZZ — LIONEL HAMPTON AT THE PASADENA AUDITORIUM (EP)	7
59	Columbia Clef SEB 10108	HAMPS BOOGIE WOOGIE (EP)	7
62	Oriole EP 7046	LIONEL HAMPTON ORCHESTRA (EP)	7
51	Brunswick LA 8527	HAMP'S BOOGIE WOOGIE (10" LP)	15
52	Brunswick LA 8551	MOONGLOW (10" LP)	15
53	Vogue LDE 043	LIONEL HAMPTON'S "JAZZ TIME PARIS" VOLUME 1 (10" LP)	15
54	Vogue LDE 051	NEW SOUNDS FROM EUROPE VOLUME 2 — FRANCE (10" LP)	15
54	Vogue LDE 063	LIONEL HAMPTON VOLUME 3 (10" LP)	15
54	Felsted EDL 87007	THE HAMP IN PARIS IN PARIS VOLUME 1 (10" LP)	15
54	Felsted EDL 87008	THE HAMP IN PARIS IN PARIS VOLUME 2 (10" LP)	15
55	Felsted PDL 85002	LIONEL HAMPTON AND HIS NEW FRENCH SOUND VOLUME 1 (10" LP) ..	15
55	HMV CLP 1023	HOT MALLETS (LP)	15
55	Columbia Clef 33C 9011	LIONEL HAMPTON QUARTET (10" LP)	15
55	Philips BBL 7015	APOLLO HALL CONCERT 1954 (LP)	15
56	Philips BBL 7119	HAMPTON AND THE OLD WORLD (LP)	12
56	Oriole MG 20012	HAMP 1956 (LP)	12
56	Brunswick LAT 8086	ALL AMERICAN AWARD CONCERT (LP)	12
57	RCA RD 27006	JAZZ FLAMENCO (LP)	10
59	RCA Camden CDN 129	JIVIN' THE VIBES (LP)	10
60	RCA Camden CDN 138	OPEN HOUSE (LP)	10

Lionel HAMPTON

61	Fontana Fortune Z 4053	THE ONE AND ONLY LIONEL HAMPTON (LP)	10

SLIDE HAMPTON & HIS BAND

62	London HA-K/SH-K 8008	JAZZ WITH A TWIST (LP)	10

HERBIE HANCOCK

63	Blue Note 45-1887	Blind Man, Blind Man Pts 1 & 2	6
70	Warner Bros WB 7358	Fat Mama/Wiggle-Waggle	7
74	CBS 2329	Chameleon/Vein Melter	4
75	CBS 3059	Palm Grease/Butterfly	4
64	Blue Note (B)BLP 4109	TAKIN' OFF (LP)	15
64	Blue Note (B)BLP 4126	MY POINT OF VIEW (LP)	15
64	Blue Note (B)BLP 4147	INVENTIONS AND DIMENSIONS (LP)	15
65	Blue Note (B)BLP 4175	EMPYREAN ISLES (LP)	15
66	Blue Note BLP 4195	MAIDEN VOYAGE (LP, also stereo BST 84195)	15
60s	Blue Note BST 84279	SPEAK LIKE A CHILD (LP)	10
60s	Blue Note BST 84321	THE PRISONER (LP)	10
60s	Blue Note BST 89907	THE BEST OF HERBIE HANCOCK (LP)	10
71	Warner Bros WS 1834	FAT ALBERT ROTUNDA (LP)	20
71	Warner Bros K 46077	MWANDISHI (LP)	10
72	Warner Bros K 46164	CROSSINGS (LP)	10
74	Warner Bros K 46039	FAT ALBERT ROTUNDA (LP, reissue)	15
74	CBS 80193	THRUST (LP)	10
74	CBS 65582	SEXTANT (LP)	10
74	CBS 65928	HEADHUNTERS (LP)	10
75	CBS 69185	MAN CHILD (LP)	10

SHEILA HANCOCK & MALCOLM TAYLOR

60s	Eyemark EMS 1007	I Got You/I'm Reformed	4

TONY HANCOCK

63	Pye 7N 15575	Wing Commander Hancock — Test Pilot/The Threatening Letters (with Kenneth Williams)	5
61	Pye NEP 24146	LITTLE PIECES OF HANCOCK (EP)	7
62	Pye NEP 24161	LITTLE PIECES OF HANCOCK VOL. 2 (EP)	7
62	Pye NEP 24170	HANCOCK'S HALF HOUR (EP)	7
63	Pye NEP 24175	THE BLOOD DONOR (EP)	7
60	Pye NPL 18045	THIS IS HANCOCK (LP)	12
60	Pye NPL 18054	PIECES OF HANCOCK (LP)	15
61	Pye NPL 18068	THE BLOOD DONOR AND THE RADIO HAM (LP)	12
65	Decca LK 4740	IT'S HANCOCK (LP)	12

OWEN HAND

60s	Transatlantic	SOMETHING NEW (LP)	65

JOHNNY HANDLE

63	Topic TOP 78	STOTTIN' DOON THE WAAL (EP)	7

GUTHRIE HANDLEY & WAYNE HUSSEY

87	L. T. T. Slaughter LTS 21	Where Was?/Ha Ha World (p/s)	4
87	L. T. T. Slaughter LTS 21T	Where Was?/Ha Ha World/Four Boats Still Negative (12", p/s)	7
	(see also Mission)		

HANDSOME BEASTS

81	Heavy Metal HEAVY 1	All Riot Now/Mark Of The Beast (p/s)	7
81	Heavy Metal HEAVY 2	Breaker/One In A Crowd/Crazy (wraparound p/s)	7
82	Heavy Metal HEAVY 11	Sweeties/You're One Your Own (p/s, with card sheet)	7
82	Heavy Metal	BESTIALITY (LP)	10

JOHN HANDY

76	Impulse IMP 7001	Hard Work/Young Enough To Dream	5
76	Impulse IMP 7001	Hard Work/Young Enough To Dream (12")	8
80	MCA MCA 626	Hard Work/Young Enough To Dream (reissue)	4

WAYNE HANDY

58	London HL 8547	Say Yeah/Could It Be (B-side with King Sisters)	200
58	London HL 8547	Say Yeah/Could It Be (B-side with King Sisters) (78)	45

PAUL HANFORD

60	Parlophone R 4680	Itsy Bitsy Teenie Weenie Little Polka Dot Bikini/Why Have You Changed Your Mind	5
60	Parlophone R 4694	If You Ain't Got Love/Ev'ry Little Girl	5
61	Parlophone R 4813	Memphis Address/Flutter Flutter	4
63	Oriole CB 1866	The Minute You're Gone/High School Dance	7

HANGMAN'S BEAUTIFUL DAUGHTERS

87	Dreamworld DREAM 11	Love Is Blue/Popular Trend (p/s)	7
87	Dreamworld DREAM 11T	Love Is Blue/Popular Trend/Jonathan/Don't Ask My Name (12", p/s)	8
80s	Yo Jo Jo 1	Darkside/Pushing Me Too Far (flexidisc, p/s)	8
88	Dreamworld BIG 5	TRASH MANTRA (mini-LP)	10

HANK & MELLOWMEN

60s	Lyntone LYN 153/154	Santa Anno/Mosology/(other artists) (Bangor University Rag flexidisc)	6
60s	Lyntone LYN 201	So In Love With You/Michael (Bangor University Rag flexidisc)	6
	(see also Rog Whittaker)		

BOBBY HANNA

67	Decca F 12604	Thanks To You/Here I Stand	4
67	Decca F 12695	Blame It On Me/Goin' Where The Lovin' Is	8
68	Decca F 12738	Too Much Love/What Do I Want For Tomorrow	4
68	Decca F 12783	Written On The Wind/Everybody Needs Love	8
68	Decca F 12833	To Wait For Love (Is To Waste Your Life Away)/Is It Wrong	4
69	Decca F 22917	Winter Love/Time	4

JOSH HANNA
65	Parlophone R 5385	When I Love You/Love Me, Love Me	4
66	Decca F 12532	Shut Your Mouth/Sweet To My Soul	12

HANNA BARBERA (cartoon soundtracks)
66	Hanna Barbera HBE 3	FLINTSTONES — GOLDILOCKS, BEAROSAURUS (EP)	7
66	Hanna Barbera HBE 5	YOGI BEAR AND BOO BOO TELL JACK AND THE BEANSTALK (EP)	7

HANNIBAL
74	B&C HB 1	Winds Of Change/Winter	6
70	B&C CAS 1022	HANNIBAL (LP)	25

LANCE HANNIBAL
68	Blue Cat BS 148	Read The News/RECO & RHYTHM ACES: Return Of The Bullet	5

(see also Tito Simon)

HANN'S EMPERORS OF SONG
26	Edison 52082	What Band Is This?/My Lord's Gonna Move This Wicked Race (78)	40

HANOI ROCKS
83	Lick LIX 1	Malibu Beach/Rebel On The Run (p/s)	6
83	Lick LIXT 1	Malibu Beach/Taxi Driver/Rebel On The Run/Beer And A Cigarette (12", p/s)	8
83	Lick LIXPD 1	Malibu Beach/Rebel On The Run (picture disc)	15
83	Lick LIX 2	Until I Get You/Tragedy (p/s)	5
83	Lick LIXT 2	Until I Get You/Tragedy/Oriental Beat (12", p/s)	8
84	CBS A 4513	Up Around The Bend/Until I Get You (p/s, some with free transfer)	6/4
84	CBS DA 4513	Up Around The Bend/Until I Get You//Under My Wheels/I Feel Alright/Train Kept A Rollin' (double pack)	15
84	CBS TA 4513	Up Around The Bend/Back To The Mystery City/Until I Get You/Mental 84 Beat (12", p/s, some with free transfer)	10/8
84	CBS A 4732	Underwater World/Shakes (p/s)	5
84	CBS TA 4732	Underwater World/Shakes/Magic Carpet Ride (12", p/s)	10
84	CBS WA 4732	Underwater World/Shakes/Magic Carpet Ride (12", picture disc)	15
84	CBS A 4685	Don't You Ever Leave Me/Shakes (p/s)	5
84	CBS TA 4685	Don't You Ever Leave Me/Oil And Gasoline/Malibu Beach (Calypso) (12", p/s)	14
84	CBS WA 4685	Don't You Ever Leave Me/Oil And Gasoline/Malibu Beach (Calypso) (12", 3-D picture disc)	15
83	Lick LICLP 1	BACK TO THE MYSTERY CITY (LP, some on white vinyl)	12/10
83	Lick LICLP 2	BANGKOK SHOCKS, SAIGON SHAKES, HANOI ROCKS (LP)	10
83	Lick LICLP 3	ORIENTAL BEAT (LP)	10
83	Lick LICLP 4	SELF DESTRUCTION BLUES (LP)	10
86	Lick LICLP PD4	SELF DESTRUCTION BLUES (LP, picture disc)	12
86	Lick BOOTLIC 7	ROCK'N'ROLL DIVORCE (LP)	10
88	Lick LICCD 8	THE BEST OF HANOI ROCKS (CD, with 16-page booklet)	15

(see also Fallen Angels, Dark, Idle Flowers, Urban Dogs)

HAPPENINGS
66	Fontana TF 735	See You In September/He Thinks He's A Hero	6
66	Fontana TF 766	Go Away Little Girl/Tea Time	6
67	Pye Intl. 7N 25501	My Mammy/I Believe In Nothing	5
67	Stateside SS 587	Goodnight My Love/Lillies By Monet	4
67	Stateside SS 2013	I Got Rhythm/You're In A Bad Way	5
67	BT Puppy BTS 45532	Why Do Fools Fall In Love/When The Summer Is Through	4
68	BT Puppy BTS 45538	Music Music Music/When I Lock My Door	4
68	BT Puppy BTS 45540	Randy/Love Song From Mummy & Dad	4
68	BT Puppy BTS 45543	Breaking Up Is Hard To Do/Anyway	4
67	Fontana TL 5383	BYE BYE, SO LONG, FAREWELL ... SEE YOU IN SEPTEMBER (LP)	12
67	BT Puppy BTLP 1003	PSYCLE (LP)	10
68	BT Puppy BTLPS 1004	GOLDEN HITS (LP)	10

HAPPY CATS
78	Grapevine GRP 110	These Boots Are Made For Walkin'/Destroy That Boy	4

HAPPY CONFUSION
70	Penny Farthing PEN 706	Yes Sir/Hereditary Impediment	4

HAPPY FAMILY
86	4AD AD 204	Puritans/Innermost Thoughts/The Mistake (p/s)	8
80s	4AD	LP	10

(see also Josef K, Momus)

HAPPY MAGAZINE
68	Polydor 56233	Satisfied Street/Do Right Woman Do Right Man	8
69	Polydor 56307	Who Belongs To You (Ooby Dooby Doo)/Beautiful Land	5

HAPPY MONDAYS
89	Factory FAC 242/7	Madchester Rave On EP (EP, gatefold p/s, 5,000 only, numbered)	4
87	Factory FACT 170	SQUIRREL & G-MAN TWENTY FOUR HOUR PARTY PEOPLE PLASTIC FACE CARNT SMILE (WHITE OUT) (LP, with "Desmond", 5,000 in plastic sleeve)	15/10

HAPSHASH & COLOURED COAT
69	Liberty LBF 15188	Colinda/The Wall	15
67	Liberty/Minit MLS 40001E	FEATURING THE HUMAN HOST AND THE HEAVY METAL KIDS (LP, initially red vinyl with insert; later copies on black vinyl)	40/25
69	Liberty LBL/LBS 83212R	THE WESTERN FLYER (LP)	15

(see also Tony McPhee, Warm Sounds, Marc Bolan/T. Rex)

HARBOUR LIGHT
70s	private pressing	HARBOUR LIGHT (LP)	10

HARBOUR LITES
65	HMV POP 1426	Come Back Silly Girl/Revenge	5

| 65 | HMV POP 1465 | I Would Give All/They Call The Wind Maria ....7 |
| 66 | Fontana TF 682 | Run For Your Life/Lonely Journey ....8 |

HARD CORPS

84	Hard Corps 1	Dirty/To Breathe (private 12", hand-written white labels, numbered) 35
84	Survival SUR 026	Dirty/Respirer (To Breathe) (white or printed labels, stickered plain black sleeve) 12
84	Survival SUR 12 026	Dirty/Respirer (To Breathe) (12", with sticker in plain black sleeve) 12
85	Immaculate 12 IMMAC 2	Je Suis Passée (Extended French Version)/(Extended Club Dub Mix) (12", p/s) 14
85	Polydor HARD 1	Je Suis Passée/Je Suis Passée (Instrumental Mix) (p/s) 6
85	Polydor HARDX 1	Je Suis Passée (Extended)/(Instrumental Mix) (12", p/s) 10
85	Polydor HARDA 1	Je Suis Passée (Hard Mix)/(French Mix)/(Dub Mix) (12", gatefold PVC sleeve, various colours, with poster) 30
85	Polydor HARD 2	To Breathe/Metal And Flesh (unreleased) 35
85	Polydor HARDX 2	To Breathe/Metal And Flesh/To Breathe (Instrumental) (12", unreleased) 40
87	Rhythm King TYPE 3	Lucky Charm/Porte-Bonheur (p/s) 5
87	Rhythm King TYPE 3T	Lucky Charm/Porte-Bonheur/Lucky Charm (The Music) (12", p/s) 8

(see also Craze, Skunks)

(Eddie) HARDIN & (Pete) YORK

69	Bell BLL 1064	Tomorrow Today/Candlelight 4
69	Bell SBLL 125	TOMORROW TODAY (LP) 12
70	Bell SBLL 136	HARDIN & YORK (THE WORLD'S SMALLEST BIG BAND) (LP) 12
71	Decca SKL 5095	FOR THE WORLD (LP) 10

(see also Pete York, Spencer Davis Group)

TIM HARDIN

66	Verve VS 1504	Hang On To A Dream/A Reason To Believe 5
67	Verve VS 1511	The Lady Came From Baltimore/Black Sheep Boy 5
68	Verve VS 1516	Don't Make Promises/Smugglin' Man 5
69	CBS 4441	A Simple Song Of Freedom/Question Of Birth 4
71	Verve 2009 006	If I Were A Carpenter/Hang On To A Dream 4
73	CBS 1016	Do The Do/Sweet Lady 4
66	Verve (S)VLP 5018	TIM HARDIN 1 (LP) 15
67	Verve (S)VLP 6002	TIM HARDIN 2 (LP) 15
67	Atlantic 587/588 082	THIS IS TIM HARDIN (LP) 18
68	Verve (S)VLP 6010	LIVE IN CONCERT (LP) 15
69	Verve (S)VLP 6016	TIM HARDIN 4 (LP) 15
70	CBS 63571	SUITE FOR SUSAN MOORE AND DAMIAN (LP, mono/stereo) 12
70	CBS 64335	BIRD ON A WIRE (LP) 12
73	CBS 65209	PAINTED HEAD (LP) 10
74	GM GML 1004	NINE (LP) 10
74	Verve 2683 048	TIM HARDIN 1/2 (2-LP reissue) 15

RICHARD HARDING

| 61 | HMV POP 887 | Jezebel/Temptation ....6 |

ROSEMARY HARDMAN (& BOB AXFORD)

69	Folk Heritage	QUEEN OF HEARTS (LP) 80
60s	Alida Star Cottage	JERSEY BURGER (LP) 70
70s	Trailer LER 2075	FIREBIRD (LP) 20
70s	Trailer LER 3018	SECOND SEASON CAME (LP, by Rosemary Hardman & Bob Axford) 18
78	Plant Life PLR 014	EAGLE OVER BLUE MOUNTAIN (LP, with insert) 12

HARD MEAT

69	Island WIP 6066	Rain/Burning Up Years 10
70	Warner Bros WB 8010	Ballad Of Marmalade, Emma & Ted/Yesterday, Today, Tomorrow 5
70	Warner Bros WS 1852	HARD MEAT (LP) 12
70	Warner Bros WS 1879	THROUGH A WINDOW (LP) 12

HARD ROAD

| 79 | Goodstuff LP 1002 | NO PROBLEM (LP, private press) ....25 |

HARD STUFF

72	Purple PUR 103	The Orchestrator/Jay Time 5
73	Purple PUR 116	Inside Your Life/How Do You Do It 5
72	Purple TPSA 7505	BULLETPROOF (LP, gatefold sleeve) 25
73	Purple TPSA 7507	BOLEX DEMENTIA (LP) 25

(see also Andromeda, Atomic Rooster, Johnny Gustafson)

HARD TRAVELLIN'

| 71 | Flams Ltd PR 1065 | HARD TRAVELLIN' (LP, private press) ....150 |

HARDWARE

| 79 | Narc NARC 001 | Speed Unit/Wall To Wall/Walking/Fire (folded p/s) ....6 |
| 79 | Narc NARC 002 | Rubberface/Face The Flag/The Seven Minutes ....5 |

FRANCOISE HARDY

64	Pye 7N 15612	Catch A Falling Star/Only Friends 5
64	Pye 7N 15653	Tous Les Garcons Et Les Filles/L'Amour S'en Va 5
64	Pye 7N 15696	Pourtant Tu M'Aimes/Jaloux 5
64	Pye 7N 15740	Et Meme/Le Temps De L'Amour 5
65	Pye 7N 15802	All Over The World/Another Place 5
66	Vogue VRS 7001	Just Call And I'll Be There/You Just Have To Say The Word 4
66	Vogue VRS 7004	So Many Friends/However Much 4
66	Vogue VRS 7010	This Little Heart/The Rose 4
66	Vogue VRS 7011	La Maison Ou J'ai Grandi/Je Ne Suis La Pour Personne 4
66	Vogue VRS 7014	Autumn Rendezvous/It's My Heart 4
66	Vogue VRS 7020	Si C'est Ca/Je Serai La Pour Toi 4
66	Vogue VRS 7025	Voila/Qui Peut Dire 4
67	Vogue VRS 7026	On Se Quitte Toujours/Les Petits Garcons 4

68	United Artists UP 1208	Fuddy Duddy, Now You Want To Be Loved/Tell Him You're Mine	4
68	United Artists UP 2253	Will You Love Me Tomorrow/Loving You	4
69	United Artists UP 35011	Comment Te Dire Adieu/La Mer Les Etoiles Et Le Vent	4
69	United Artists UP 35070	All Because Of You/Time Passing By	4
70	United Artists UP 35105	Soon Is Slipping Away/The Bells Of Avignon	4
64	Pye NEP 24188	C'EST FAB (EP)	7
64	Pye NEP 24192	FRANCOISE SINGS IN ENGLISH (EP)	7
64	Pye NEP 24193	C'EST FRANCOISE (EP)	7
64	Pye NPL 18094	FRANCOISE HARDY (LP)	15
64	Pye NPL 18099	IN VOGUE (LP)	12
65	Vogue VRL 3000	FRANCOISE HARDY (LP)	15
66	Vogue VRL 3021	FRANCOISE HARDY (LP)	12
66	Vogue VRL 3023	LE MEILLEUR DE FRANCOISE HARDY (LP)	12
66	Vogue VRL 3025	SINGS IN ENGLISH (LP)	12
67	Vogue VRL 3028	FRANCOISE (LP)	12
67	Vogue VRL 3031	VOILA! FRANCOISE HARDY (LP)	10

LAVELL HARDY
| 68 | Direction 58-3261 | Don't Lose Your Groove/Women Of The World | 5 |

HARDY BOYS
| 70s | Spectacle SP 1 | Tantalize/Dancing In The Depression | 4 |

COLIN HARE
72	Warner Bros K 16203	Didn't I Tell You/Seek Not In The Wide World	6
71	Penny Farthing PELS 516	MARCH HARE (LP)	30
	(see also Honeybus)		

RON HARGRAVE
| 58 | MGM MGM 956 | Latch On/Only A Daydream | 800 |
| 58 | MGM MGM 956 | Latch On/Only A Daydream (78) | 125 |

HARLAN COUNTY
| 70 | Nashville 6336 002 | HARLAN COUNTY (LP) | 10 |

HARLEM HAMFATS
45	Brunswick 03556	Hello Little Devil/The Barefoot Boy (78)	15
51	Vocalion V 1005	Weed Smoker's Dream (Why Don't You Do Now)/	
		ROSETTA HOWARD: Let Your Linen Hang Low (78)	12
60s	Ace Of Hearts AH 27	HARLEM HAMFATS (LP)	15

HARLEQUIN
| 85 | Epic EPC 26263 | HARLEQUIN (LP) | 10 |

STEVE HARLEY (& COCKNEY REBEL)
73	EMI EMI 2051	Sebastian/Rock And Roll Parade	5
74	EMI EMI 2128	Judy Teen/Spaced Out	4
74	EMI EMI 2191	Psychomodo/Such A Dream (unreleased)	
74	EMI EMI 2191	Mr Soft/Such A Dream	4
74	EMI EMI 2191	Mr Soft/Such A Dream (with 'Orchestrated by Alan Powell' credit)	6
75	EMI EMI 2263	Make Me Smile (Come Up & See Me)/Another Journey	5
75	EMI EMI 2299	Mr Raffles (Man It Was Mean)/Sebastian (live)	4
75	EMI EMI 2369	Black Or White/Mad Mad Moonlight (live)	4
76	EMI EMI 2409	White White Dove/Throw Your Soul Down Here	4
76	EMI EMI 2539	(I Believe) Love's A Prima Donna/Sidetrack One	6
77	EMI EMI 2673	The Best Years Of Our Lives (live)/Tumbling Down (live) (p/s)	10
77	EMI 12EMI 2673	The Best Years Of Our Lives (live)/Tumbling Down (live) (12", p/s)	7
82	Chrysalis CHS 2594	I Can't Even Touch You/I Can Be Anyone (p/s)	4

STEVE HARLEY
74	EMI EMI 2233	Big Big Deal/Bed In The Corner	15
78	EMI EMI 2830	Roll The Dice/Waiting (p/s)	6
83	Stiletto STIL 14	Ballerina (Prima Donna)/Face To Face (p/s)	4
83	Stiletto STLT 14	Ballerina (Prima Donna) (Ext)/Sebastian (New Version) (12", p/s)	7
78	EMI EMC 3524	HOBO WITH A GRIN (LP)	10
79	EMI EMC 3311	THE CANDIDATE (LP, with inner sleeve)	10
	(see also Anderson, Harley & Batt)		

LEE HARMER'S POPCORN
| 68 | Page One POF 053 | Love Is Coming/Hello Sunshine | 4 |

HARMONIANS
| 70 | Ackee ACK 107 | Music Street/Group Of Girls | 4 |

HARMONICA FATS
| 63 | Stateside SS 184 | Tore Up/I Get So Tired | 15 |
| 68 | Action ACT 4507 | Tore Up/I Get So Tired (reissue) | 12 |

HARMONISERS
| 69 | Duke DU 32 | Mother Hen/WINSTON SINCLAIR: Chastise Them | 5 |

HARMONY GRASS
68	RCA RCA 1772	Move In A Little Bit Closer Baby/Happiness Is Toy Shaped	4
69	RCA RCA 1828	First Time Loving/What A Groovy Day	4
69	RCA RCA 1885	I Remember/Summer Dreaming	4
70	RCA RCA 1932	Cecilia/Mrs. Richie	4
68	RCA SF 8034	THIS IS US (LP)	12
	(see also Tony Rivers & Castaways)		

BILLY HARNER
71	Kama Sutra 2013 029	What About The Music/Please Spare The Time	7
71	Kama Sutra 2013 029	What About The Music/Please Spare The Time/What About The Music	
		(Instrumental) (demos only, a few with extra track)	300+
72	Blue Horizon 2431 013	TRIGGER FINGER (LP)	15

PRINCE HAROLD
66 Mercury MF 952   Forget About Me/Baby You've Got Me 10

BUD HARPER
65 Vocalion VP 9252   Mr. Soul/Let Me Love You 20

CHARLIE HARPER
80 Gem GEMS 35   Barmy London Army/Talk Is Cheap (p/s, green vinyl) 4
(see also U.K. Subs)

DON HARPER SEXTET
58 Pye Jazz 7NJ 2024   Hi-Diddle-Fiddle/It's The Bluest Kind Of Blues 4

DON HARPER ORCHESTRA
68 Columbia DB 8519   "World Of Sport" March/England 88 4
73 Columbia DB 9023   World Of Sport/"Dr. Who" Theme (as Don Harper's Homo Electronicus) 5
(see also Electricians)

JANICE HARPER
57 HMV POP 376   Bon Voyage/Tell Me That You Love Me Tonight 4
58 Capitol CL 14899   Devotion/In Time 4
59 Capitol CL 14977   I Was Hoping You'd Ask Me/I'm Making Love To You 4
59 Capitol CL 15026   Let Me Call You Sweetheart/Just Whistle 4

JESSIE HARPER
92 acetate   GUITAR ABSOLUTION IN THE SHADE OF A MIDNIGHT SUN
     (LP, unissued, no sleeve, possibly 1 copy only!) 2000
92 Kissing Spell KSLP 9203   GUITAR ABSOLUTION IN THE SHADE OF A MIDNIGHT SUN
     (LP, reissue, 500 only) 20

JOE 'HARMONICA' HARPER
58 MGM MGM 983   Lazy Train/Her Lips Were Like Velvet 6

LEE HARPER'S POPCORN
68 Page One POF 053   Love Is Coming/Sunshine 5

MIKE HARPER
70s Concord CON 026   You've Got Too Much Going For You 15
76 RCA RCA 2719   Rip Off/I'm Crying 4

ROY HARPER
66 Strike JH 304   Take Me In Your Eyes/Pretty Baby (some in p/s) 25/10
67 CBS 203001   Midspring Dithering/Zengem 18
68 CBS 3371   Life Goes By/Nobody's Got Any Money In The Summer 15
72 Harvest HAR 5059   Bank Of The Dead/Little Lady 6
74 Harvest HAR 5080   (Don't You Think We're) Forever/Male Chauvinist Pig Blues 4
74 Harvest HAR 5089   Home (live)/Home (studio) 4
75 Harvest HAR 5096   When An Old Cricketer Leaves The Crease/Hallucinating Light (live) (p/s) 5
75 Harvest HAR 5102   Grown-Ups Are Just Silly Children/Referendum Legend 4
77 Harvest HAR 5120   One Of Those Days In England/Watford Gap (p/s) 4
77 Harvest HAR 5140   Sail Away/Cherishing The Lonesome (as Roy Harper's Black Sheep,
     withdrawn) 7
78 Harvest HAR 5160   When An Old Cricketer Leaves The Crease/Home (studio) (p/s) 5
80 Harvest HAR 5203   Playing Games/First Thing In The Morning (p/s) 4
80 Harvest HAR 5207   Short And Sweet/Water Sports/Unknown Soldier (p/s) 4
67 Strike JLH 105   THE SOPHISTICATED BEGGAR (LP) 50
67 CBS (S)BPG 63184   COME OUT FIGHTING, GHENGIS SMITH (LP) 18
69 Liberty LBS 83231   FOLKJOKEOPUS (LP) 15
70 Harvest SHVL 766   FLAT BAROQUE AND BERSERK (LP, gatefold sleeve) 12
70 Young Blood SYB 7   THE RETURN OF THE SOPHISTICATED BEGGAR (LP, reissue) 20
71 Harvest SHVL 789   STORMCOCK (LP, gatefold sleeve) 12
72 Birth RAB 3   THE RETURN OF THE SOPHISTICATED BEGGAR (LP, reissue) 18
73 Harvest SHVL 808   LIFEMASK (LP, split sleeve) 12
74 Harvest SHSP 4027   VALENTINE (LP, some with booklet) 20/12
74 Harvest SHDW 405   FLASHES FROM THE ARCHIVES OF OBLIVION (2-LP) 22
75 Harvest SHSP 4046   H.Q. (LP) 10
77 Harvest SHSP 4060   BULLINAMINGVASE (LP, with "Watford Gap"; some with 7": "Referendum"/
     "Another Day" (live)/"Tom Tiddler's Ground (live)" [PSR 407]) 20/15
77 Harvest SHSP 4077   COMMERCIAL BREAK (LP, test pressing with proof sleeve) 250
80s Public TC PUBLP 5001   WORK OF HEART (cassette on 'real time' high quality tape) 12
80s Hardup PUB 5002   BORN IN CAPTIVITY (LP, 880 only) 15
88 Awareness AWL 1002   WORK OF HEART (LP, reissue, 1st 1,000 with 2 x 7", later with 1 x 7") 12/10
88 Awareness AWL 1002   WORK OF HEART (cassette, 250 only on 'real time' high quality tape) 10

HARPER'S BIZARRE
67 Warner Bros WB 5890   59th Street Bridge Song (Feelin' Groovy)/Lost My Love Today 6
67 Warner Bros WB 7063   Anything Goes/Malibu U 4
67 Warner Bros WB 7090   Chattanooga Choo Choo/Hey You In The Crowd 4
68 Warner Bros WB 7172   Cotton Candy Sandman (Sandman's Coming)/Virginia City 4
68 Warner Bros WB 7223   Battle Of New Orleans/Green Apple Tree 4
69 Warner Bros WB 7238   I Love You, Alice B. Toklas!/Look To The Rainbow 4
67 Warner Bros WB 7528   Come To The Sunshine/The Debutante's Ball 4
67 Warner Bros W 1693   FEELIN' GROOVY (LP) 12
67 Warner Bros W 1716   ANYTHING GOES (LP) 10
68 Warner Bros W(S) 1739   THE SECRET LIFE OF HARPER'S BIZARRE (LP) 12

SLIM HARPO
61 Pye International 7N 25098   Rainin' In My Heart/Don't Start Cryin' Now 10
63 Pye International 7N 25220   Don't Start Cryin' Now/Rainin' In My Heart 12
66 Stateside SS 491   Baby Scratch My Back/I'm Gonna Miss You (Like The Devil) 12
66 Stateside SS 527   Shake Your Hips/Midnight Blues 20
66 Stateside SS 557   I'm A King Bee/I Got Love If You Want It 18

67	Stateside SS 581	I'm Your Breadmaker Baby/Loving You (The Way I Do)	15
67	President PT 164	I'm Gonna Keep What I've Got/I've Got To Be With You Tonight	6
68	Liberty LBF 15176	Something Inside Me/PAPPA LIGHTFOOT: Wine Whisky And Women	12
68	President PT 187	Tip On In Pts 1 & 2	6
70	Blue Horizon 57-3175	Folsom Prison Blues/Mutual Friend	15
65	Stateside SL 10135	A LONG DRINK OF THE BLUES (LP, with Lightnin' Slim)	35
68	President PTL 1017	TIP ON IN (LP)	10
70	Blue Horizon 7-63854	HE KNEW THE BLUES (LP)	45
71	Blue Horizon 2431 013	TRIGGER FINGER (LP)	45
76	Flyright LP 520	BLUES HANGOVER (LP)	10
78	Sonet SNTF 769	HE KNEW THE BLUES (LP)	12
80	Flyright FLY 558	GOT LOVE IF YOU WANT IT (LP)	10

(see also Lightnin' Slim)

GEORGE HARRASSMENT & HOMOSEXUALS

| 80s | Black Noise 12 NO 6 | MASAI SLEEP WALKING (LP) | 10 |

(see also Homosexuals)

DERRICK HARRIOTT (& CRYSTALITES)

62	Blue Beat BB 131	I Care/Have Faith In Me (as Derrick Harriott & Vagabonds)	8
63	Blue Beat BB 178	Be True/I Won't Cry	8
64	Island WI 157	What Can I Do/Leona	8
65	Island WI 170	I Am Only Human/ROY PANTON: Good Man	8
65	Island WI 237	My Three Loves/The Jerk	8
65	Island WI 245	Together/Mama Didn't Lie	8
65	Ska Beat JB 199	Monkey Ska/Derrick!	10
66	Doctor Bird DB 1002	Jon Tom/AUDREY WILLIAMS: Solas Market	8
67	Island WI 3063	The Loser/Bless You	10
67	Island WI 3064	Happy Times/You're My Everything	10
67	Island WI 3077	Walk The Streets/BOBBY ELLIS: Step Softly	10
67	Island WI 3089	Solomon/BOBBY ELLIS: The Emperor	10
68	Island WI 3135	Do I Worry?/BOBBY ELLIS & CRYSTALITES: Shuntin'	10
68	Island WI 3147	Born To Love You/IKE & CRYSTALITES: Alfred Hitchcock	10
68	Island WI 3153	Tang! Tang! Festival Song/CRYSTALITES: James Ray	10
68	Big Shot BI 505	Standing In/Bumble Bee	6
69	Big Shot BI 511	Another Lonely Night/Been So Long	6
69	Songbird SB 1013	Riding For A Fall/I'm Not Begging	4
69	Songbird SB 1014	Sitting On Top/You Were meant For Me	4
65	Island ILP 928	THE BEST OF DERRICK HARRIOTT (LP)	50
67	Island ILP 955	ROCKSTEADY PARTY (LP)	80
68	Island ILP 983	THE BEST OF VOLUME TWO (LP, as Derrick Harriott & Crystalites)	60
69	Pama SECO 13	SINGS JAMAICA REGGAE (LP)	30
70	Trojan TTL 43	THE BEST OF (LP)	15
70	Trojan TTL 54	ROCKSTEADY PARTY (LP)	25
70	Trojan TBL 114	THE UNDERTAKER (LP, as Derrick Harriott & Crystalites)	15
70	Trojan TBL 141	PSYCHEDELIC TRAIN (LP, as Derrick Harriott & Crystalites)	12

JOE HARRIOTT

50s	Polygon JTE 106	JOE HARRIOTT (EP)	10
50s	Pye Jazz NJE7 1003	NO STRINGS (EP)	10
50s	Melodisc EPM7 117	COOL JAZZ WITH JOE (EP)	10
50s	Columbia SEG 7665	JOE HARRIOTT QUARTET (EP)	7
59	Columbia SEG 7939	BLUE HARRIOTT (EP)	7
61	Columbia SEG 8070	A GUY CALLED JOE (EP)	7
60	Jazzland JLP 49	FREE FORM (LP)	40
67	Melodisc SLP 12150	SWINGS HIGH (LP)	40
62	Columbia 33SX 1477	ABSTRACT (LP)	50
63	Columbia 33SX 1627	MOVEMENT (LP)	50
64	Columbia 33SX 1692	HIGH SPIRITS (LP)	50
66	Columbia S(C)X 6025	DOUBLE QUINTET (LP, with John Mayer)	25
68	Columbia S(C)X 6215	INDO-JAZZ FUSIONS II (LP)	25
68	Columbia S(C)X 6249	PERSONAL PORTRAIT (LP)	35
69	Columbia SCX 6354	HUM-DONO (LP)	50
73	One Up OU 2011	MEMORIAL 1973 (LP)	50

(see also Tony Kinsey Trio & Joe Harriott, John Mayer, Michael Garrick)

JOE HARRIOTT/DON RENDELL QUARTET

| 50s | MGM MGM-EP 615 | JAZZ BRITANNIA (EP, 2 tracks each) | 10 |

(see also Don Rendell)

ANITA HARRIS

61	Parlophone R 4830	I Haven't Got You/Mr One And Only	4
64	Vogue V 9223	Lies/Don't Think About Love	4
65	Decca F 12082	Willingly/At Last Love	6
65	Pye 7N 15868	Trains And Boats And Planes/Upside Down	4
65	Pye 7N 15894	I Don't Know Anymore/When I Look At You	4
65	Pye 7N 15971	London Life/I Run To Hide	4
66	Pye 7N 17069	Something Must Be Done/Funny Kind Of Feeling	6
67	CBS 2991	The Playground/B.A.D. For Me	5
68	CBS 3211	Anniversary Waltz/Old Queenie Cole	4

ARTIE HARRIS & HIS BOYS

| 50s | Oriole CB 1816 | Go Go Gaudeamus/Mexicana | 5 |

BETTY HARRIS

63	London HL 9796	Cry To Me/I'll Be A Liar	10
65	Stateside SS 475	What A Sad Feeling/I'm Evil Tonight	12
67	Stateside SS 2045	Nearer To You/Twelve Red Roses	15
69	Action ACT 4535	Ride Your Pony/Trouble With My Lover	10
69	Action ACLP 6007	SOUL PERFECTION (LP)	15

MINT VALUE £

BRENDA JO HARRIS
68	Roulette RO 503	I Can Remember/Play With Fire	6

DON 'SUGARCANE' HARRIS
70	BASF MPS 68027	KEEP ON DRIVING (LP)	10
70	BASF MPS 68028	FIDDLER ON THE ROCK (LP)	10
72	BASF MPS 68029	GOT THE BLUES (LP)	10
73	BASF MPS 68030	CUPFUL OF DREAMS (LP)	10

(see also Don & Dewey)

EDDIE HARRIS
69	Atlantic 584 218	Listen Here/Theme — In Search Of A Movie	5
69	Atlantic 584 232	It's Crazy/Live Right Now (unissued)	
74	Atlantic K 10513	Is It In?/Funkarama	5
75	Atlantic K 10561	I Need Some Money/Don't Want Nobody	4
76	Atlantic K 10741	Get On Up And Dance/Why Must We Part	4
62	Stateside SL 10009	BREAKFAST AT TIFFANY'S (LP)	12
63	Stateside SL 10018	MIGHTY LIKE A ROSE (LP)	12
63	Stateside SL 10049	GOES TO THE MOVIES (LP)	12
69	Atlantic 588 177	SILVER CYCLES (LP)	12
74	Atlantic K 50084	IS IT IN? (LP)	10
75	Atlantic K 50127	I NEED SOME MONEY (LP)	10
76	Atlantic K 40220	THE ELECTRIFYING EDDIE HARRIS (LP)	12

EMMYLOU HARRIS
79	Pye Special PKL 5577	THE LEGENDARY GLIDING BIRD ALBUM (LP)	10

(see also Gram Parsons)

JET HARRIS
62	Decca F 11466	Besame Mucho/Chills And Fever	6
62	Decca F 11488	Main Title Theme (From "Man With The Golden Arm")/Some People	5
64	Decca F 11841	Bag Bad Bass/Rifka	8
67	Fontana TF 849	My Lady/You Don't Live Twice	12
75	SRT SRT 75355	Theme For A Fallen Idol/This Sportin' Life	7
75	SRT SRT 77389	Guitar Man/Theme	5
62	Decca DFE 8502	JET HARRIS (EP)	12
80	Ellie	INSIDE JET HARRIS — THE LAST CONCERT (live LP, 2,500 only)	10

(see also Shadows, Jet Harris & Tony Meehan)

JET HARRIS & TONY MEEHAN
63	Decca F 11563	Diamonds/Footstomp	4
63	Decca F 11644	Scarlett O'Hara/(Doing The) Hully Gully	4
63	Decca F 11710	Applejack/The Tall Texan	5
63	Decca DFE 7099	DIAMONDS (EP, export issue)	15
63	Decca DFE 8528	JET AND TONY (EP)	10

(see also Shadows, Jet Harris, Tony Meehan, Vipers Skiffle Group)

JOHNNY HARRIS
74	Warner Bros WB 8000	Footprints On The Moon/Lulu's Theme	4
72	Warner Bros K 46054	MOVEMENTS (LP)	25
73	Warner Bros K 46187	ALL TO BRING YOU MORNING (LP)	10

JUNE HARRIS
65	CBS 201774	Over And Over Again/Stand Back	10

MAJOR HARRIS
75	Atlantic K 50117	MY WAY (LP)	10
76	Atlantic K 50219	JEALOUSY (LP)	10

PAT HARRIS & BLACKJACKS
63	Pye 7N 15567	The Hippy Hippy Shake/You Gotta See Your Mama Ev'ry Night	8

(see also Blackjacks)

PHIL HARRIS
51	HMV B 10067	Southern Fried Boogie/Oh, What A Face (78)	5
54	HMV 7M 199	I Know An Old Lady/Take Your Girlie To The Movies	6
54	HMV 7M 231	I Guess I'll Have To Change My Plan/The Persian Kitten	6
55	HMV 7M 289	I Wouldn't Touch You With A Ten-Foot Pole/There's A Lot More	6
59	RCA Camden CDN 124	THAT'S WHAT I LIKE ABOUT THE SOUTH (LP)	10

RICHARD HARRIS
68	RCA RCA 1699	MacArthur Park/Paper Chase	4
68	Stateside SS 8001	The Yard Went On Forever/Lucky Me	4
68	RCA Victor RD/SF 7947	A TRAMP SHINING (LP)	12
68	Stateside (S)SL 5001	THE YARD WENT ON FOREVER (LP)	12
70	Stateside SSL 5019	A TRAMP SHINING (LP, reissue)	10

ROLF HARRIS
60	Columbia DB 4483	Tie Me Kangaroo Down Sport/Nick Teen And Al K. Hall	4
60	Columbia DB 4556	Tame Eagle/Uncomfortable Yogi	4
62	Columbia DB 4888	Sun Arise/Someone's Pinched My Winkles	4
64	Columbia DB 7349	Ringo For President/Head Hunter	4

RONNIE HARRIS (& CORONETS)
54	Columbia SCM 5138	Hold My Hand/No One Can Change Destiny	6
54	Columbia SCM 5139	I Love Paris/I Still Believe	6
55	Columbia SCM 5159	Don't Go To Strangers/Surprisingly (as Ronnie Harris & Coronets)	6
55	Columbia SCM 5176	Stranger In Paradise/I Wonder	8
55	Columbia SCM 5178	Hello, Mrs. Jones (Is Mary There?)/I Know You Love Me	6
55	Columbia SCM 5189	On The Way To Your Heart/Maria, Maria, Maria	6
55	Columbia SCM 5206	Cabaret/United	6
56	Columbia SCM 5242	I've Changed My Mind A Thousand Times/Come To Me (with Coronets)	6

56	Columbia SCM 5266	What Is the Reason?/Aurora	6
56	Columbia DB 3814	Cry Upon My Shoulder/Tell Me Why	6
56	Columbia DB 3836	That's Right/A House With Love In It	8
57	Columbia DB 3877	Armen's Theme (Yesterday And You)/Dancing Chandelier	4
57	Columbia DB 3934	Dear To Me/It's Not For Me To Say (B-side with Russ Conway)	4
57	Columbia DB 4007	Let Me Be Loved/Day By Day	4

(see also Coronets, Ruby Murray, Ray Burns, Russ Conway)

ROY HARRIS
| 60s | Topic 12T 256 | THE BITTER AND THE SWEET (LP) | 15 |

SHAKEY JAKE HARRIS
| 69 | Liberty LBS 83217 | FURTHER ON UP THE ROAD (LP) | 20 |
| 72 | Polydor 2391 015 | THE DEVIL'S HARMONICA (LP) | 20 |

THURSTON HARRIS (& SHARPS)
57	Vogue V 9092	Little Bitty Pretty One/I Hope You Won't Hold It Against Me (with Sharps)	50
57	Vogue V 9092	Little Bitty Pretty One/I Hope You Won't Hold It Against Me (with Sharps) (78)	20
58	Vogue V 9098	Do What You Did/I'm Asking Forgiveness (as Thurston Harris & Sharps)	125
58	Vogue V 9098	Do What You Did/I'm Asking Forgiveness (78)	30
58	Vogue V 9108	Be Baba Leba/I'm Out To Getcha	125
58	Vogue V 9108	Be Baba Leba/I'm Out To Getcha (78)	45
58	Vogue V 9122	Smokey Joe's/Only One Love Is Blessed	75
58	Vogue V 9122	Smokey Joe's/Only One Love Is Blessed (78)	45
58	Vogue V 9127	Tears From My Heart/Over Somebody Else's Shoulder	50
58	Vogue V 9127	Tears From My Heart/Over Somebody Else's Shoulder (78)	30
59	Vogue V 9139	Purple Stew (as Thurston Harris & Masters)/I Hear A Rhapsody	60
59	Vogue V 9139	Purple Stew (as Thurston Harris & Masters)/I Hear A Rhapsody (78)	50
59	Vogue V 9144	You Don't Know How Much I Love You/In The Bottom Of My Heart	50
59	Vogue V 9144	You Don't Know How Much I Love You/In The Bottom Of My Heart (78)	30
59	Vogue V 9146	Hey Little Girl/My Love Will Last	75
59	Vogue V 9146	Hey Little Girl/My Love Will Last (78)	40
59	Vogue V 9149	Runk Bunk/Bless Your Heart	80
59	Vogue V 9149	Runk Bunk/Bless Your Heart (78)	50
59	Vogue V 9151	Slip-Slop/Paradise Hill	75
59	Vogue V 9151	Slip-Slop/Paradise Hill (78)	50
66	Sue WI 4016	Little Bitty Pretty One/I Hope You Won't Hold It Against Me (reissue)	15

(see also Sharps)

WEE WILLIE HARRIS
57	Decca F 10970	Rockin' At The Two I's/Back To School Again	30
58	Decca F 10980	Love Bug Crawl/Rosie Lee	35
58	Decca F 11044	Got A Match/No Chemise, Please!	25
60	Decca F 11217	Wild One/Little Bitty Girl	12
63	HMV POP 1198	You Must Be Joking/Better To Have Loved	7
66	Parlophone R 5504	Someone's In The Kitchen With Diana/Walk With Peter And Paul (some A-sides list 'Dina')	6
66	Polydor 56140	Listen To The River Roll Along/Try Moving Baby (writing in black or white)	6
74	Decca F 13516	Together/Rock'n'Roll Jamboree	5
58	Decca DFE 6465	ROCKING WITH WEE WILLIE (EP)	65

WYNONIE 'MR BLUES' HARRIS
46	Brunswick 03561	Hurry Hurry/I Can't See For Looking (with Lucky Millinder Orchestra) (78)	12
51	Vogue V 2006	All She Wants To Do Is Rock/Drinkin' Wine Spo-Dee-O-Dee (78)	20
52	Vogue V 2111	Luscious Woman/Lovin' Machine (78)	20
52	Vogue V 2127	Bloodshot Eyes/Lollipop Mama (78)	20
52	Vogue V 2128	Just Like Two Drops Of Water/Good Mornin' Judge (78)	20
52	Vogue V 2133	Night Train/Do It Again Please (78)	20
52	Vogue V 2134	Rock, Mr. Blues/Put It Back (78)	20
52	Vogue V 2144	Teardrops From My Eyes/Keep On Churnin' (Till The Butter Comes) (78)	20
52	Vogue V 2166	I Like My Baby's Pudding/Adam Come And Get Your Rib (78)	20
56	Vogue V 2127	Bloodshot Eyes/Lollipop Mama (triangular or round centre)	80/50
56	Vogue V 2127	Bloodshot Eyes/Lollipop Mama (78)	20
61	Blue Beat BBEP 301	BATTLE OF THE BLUES (EP)	40
56	Vogue EPV 1103	WYNONIE 'MISTER BLUES' HARRIS (EP)	125

WYNONIE HARRIS/EDDIE 'CLEANHEAD' VINSON
| 72 | Polydor 2343 048 | JUMP BLUES (LP) | 12 |

WYNONIE HARRIS/TINY BRADSHAW
| 60s | Polydor 623 273 | KINGS OF RHYTHM AND BLUES (LP, 1 side each) | 15 |

HARRIS SISTERS
| 55 | Capitol CL 14232 | Kissin' Bug/We've Been Walkin' All Night | 12 |

DANNY HARRISON
62	Starlite ST45 77	No One To Love Me/All The World is Lonely	4
62	Starlite ST45 91	Broken Love Affair/Have I Wasted My Life	4
63	Starlite ST45 108	Have You Ever Been Lonely/Mary Ann I'm Lonesome	4
65	Coral Q 72479	Speak Of The Devil/I'm A Rollin' Stone	10
62	Starlite STEP 23	INTRODUCING DANNY HARRISON (EP)	7

EARL HARRISON
| 67 | London HL 10121 | Humphrey Stomp/Can You Forgive Me | 35 |

GEORGE HARRISON
71	Apple R 5884	My Sweet Lord/What Is Life (colour 'head' p/s)	12
71	Apple R 5912	Bangla Desh/Deep Blue (some in promo p/s; beware of counterfeits!)	50/5
73	Apple R 5988	Give Me Love (Give Me Peace On Earth)/Miss O'Dell (company sleeve)	4
74	Apple R 6002	Ding Dong Ding Dong/I Don't Care Anymore	5
75	Apple R 6001	Dark Horse/I Don't Care Anymore (withdrawn)	
75	Apple R 6001	Dark Horse/Hari's On Tour (Express) (p/s)	10/4

George HARRISON

75	Apple R 6007	You/World Of Stone (p/s) 10/4
76	Apple R 6012	This Guitar (Can't Keep From Crying)/Maya Love 8
76	Apple R 5884	My Sweet Lord/What Is Life (reissue, black & white 'gnome' p/s) 10
76	Dark Horse K 16856	This Song/Learning How To Love You (p/s) 6
77	Dark Horse K 16896	True Love/Pure Smokey 4
77	Dark Horse K 16967	It's What You Value/Woman Don't You Cry For Me 4
79	Dark Horse K 17327	Blow Away/Soft Touch (p/s) 4
79	Dark Horse K 17284	Love Comes To Everyone/Soft-Hearted Hana 4
79	Dark Horse K 17423	Faster/Your Love Is Forever 10
79	Dark Horse K 17423	Faster/Your Love Is Forever (picture disc, stickered PVC sleeve with insert) ..18
81	Dark Horse K 17807M	All Those Years Ago/Writing's On The Wall (cassette, cigarette-pack style box) ..8
81	Dark Horse K 17837	Teardrops/Save The World (p/s) 4
83	Dark Horse K 929846-7	Wake Up My Love/Greece 5
87	Dark Horse W 8178	Got My Mind Set On You/Lay His Head (p/s, with 1 or 3 'Dark Horse' logos on label) 4
87	Dark Horse W 8178	Got My Mind Set On You/Lay His Head (p/s, red label) 7
87	Dark Horse W 8178	Got My Mind Set On You/Lay His Head (p/s, green label) 15
87	Dark Horse W 8178B	Got My Mind Set On You/Lay His Head (box set with 2 postcards) 8
87	Dark Horse W 8178T	Got My Mind Set On You (Extended Version)/Got My Mind Set On You (Single Version)/Lay His Head (12", with poster) 18
87	Dark Horse W 8178TP	Got My Mind Set On You (Extended Version)/Got My Mind Set On You (Single Version)/Lay His Head (12", picture disc) 12
88	Dark Horse W 8131B	When We Was Fab/Zig Zag (box set with full-colour poster & cut-out) 6
88	Dark Horse W 8131TP	When We Was Fab (Unextended Version)/Zig Zag/That's The Way It Goes (Remix)/When We Was Fab (Reverse End) (12", picture disc) 8
88	Dark Horse W 7913CD	This Is Love/Breath Away From Heaven/All Those Years Ago (3" CD, 5" case) ...7
68	Apple (S)APCOR 1	WONDERWALL MUSIC (LP, with insert, mono/stereo) 60/30
69	Zapple ZAPPLE 02	ELECTRONIC SOUND (LP, with inner sleeve) 60
71	Apple STCH 639	ALL THINGS MUST PASS (3-LP set with poster & lyric inner sleeves; initial batch in U.K. box, later in U.S. box) 18/15
72	Apple STCX 3385	THE CONCERT FOR BANGLA DESH (3-LP boxed set, with booklet) 22
73	Apple PAS 10006	LIVING IN THE MATERIAL WORLD (LP, g/fold with booklet & brown inner) ...10
74	Apple PAS 10008	DARK HORSE (LP, gatefold sleeve with inner) 10
88	Genesis SGH 777	SONGS BY GEORGE HARRISON (Limited Edition) (4-track EP, 33rpm, issued with limited edition book "Songs By George Harrison") 250
88	Genesis SGHCD 777	SONGS BY GEORGE HARRISON (4-track CD, issued with ltd edition book) 250
92	Apple SAPCOR 1	WONDERWALL MUSIC (LP, reissue, gatefold sleeve, mispress, Side A plays Mary Hopkin's "Earth Song — Ocean Song") 15

(see also Beatles, Traveling Wilburys, Billy Connolly & Chris Tummings)

KATHLEEN HARRISON
66	Columbia DB 7871	Mrs. Thursday/Call Round Any Old Time 4

MIKE HARRISON
71	Island ILPS 9170	MIKE HARRISON (LP) 10
72	Island ILPS 9209	SMOKESTACK LIGHTNING (LP) 10

NOEL HARRISON
65	Decca F 12001	Trees/To Ramona 5
66	Decca F 12314	A Young Girl Of Sixteen/Tomorrow Is My Turn 4
66	Decca F 12345	It's All Over Now Baby Blue/Much As I Love You 4
69	Reprise RS 20758	Windmills Of Your Mind/Leitch On The Beach 4
65	Decca DFE 8639	TO RAMONA (EP) 8
57	HMV 7EG 8383	NOEL HARRISON (EP) 8
60	Philips BBL 7399	AT THE BLUE ANGEL (LP) 10
69	Reprise RSLP 6321	THE GREAT ELECTRIC EXPERIMENT IS OVER (LP) 12

WILBERT HARRISON
59	Top Rank JAR 132	Kansas City/Listen My Darling 12
59	Top Rank JAR 132	Kansas City/Listen My Darling (78) 35
62	Island WI 031	I'm Broke/Off To School 12
65	Sue WI 363	Let's Stick Together/Kansas City Twist 12
73	Action ACT 4613	Get It While You Can/Amen 5
70	London HL 10307	Let's Work Together/Stagger Lee 8
69	London HA/SH 8415	LET'S WORK TOGETHER (LP) 15

WILBERT HARRISON & BABY WASHINGTON
71	Joy JOYS 191	BATTLE OF THE GIANTS (LP) 10

(see also Baby Washington)

YVONNE HARRISON
67	Caltone TONE 102	The Chase/Take My Hand 8

DEBBIE HARRY
81	Chrysalis CHS 12 2554	Jam Was Moving/Inner City Spillover/Chrome (12", p/s) 7
86	Chrysalis CHS 12 3066B	French Kissin'/French Kissin' (Dub)/Rockbird (12", picture disc) 7
87	Chrysalis CHS 3093	Free To Fall/Feel The Spin (foldout p/s) 4
87	Chrysalis CHS 12 3093B	Free To Fall/Feel The Spin/Secret Life (12", picture disc) 7
89	Chrysalis CHS PB 3452	Brite Side (foldout p/s) 4

(see also Blondie, New York Blondes)

HARSH REALITY
68	Philips PB 1710	Tobacco Ash Sunday/How Do You Feel 8
69	Philips PB 1769	Heaven And Hell/Praying For Reprieve 10
69	Philips SBL 7891	HEAVEN AND HELL (LP, gatefold sleeve) 85

CAJUN HART
69	Warner Bros WB 7258	Got To Find A Way/Lover's Prayer 150

DERRY HART & HARTBEATS
59	Decca F 11138	Come On Baby/Nowhere In This World 12

MICKEY HART
72   Atlantic K 46182   ROLLING THUNDER (LP) 15
(see also Grateful Dead, Diga Rhythm Band)

MIKE HART
70   Dandelion 4781   Yawney Morning Song/Almost Liverpool 8 5
74   Deram DM 409   Son Son/Bad News Man 4
70   Dandelion 63756   MIKE HART BLEEDS (LP) 20
72   Dandelion 2310 211   BASHER, CHALKY, PONGO AND ME (LP, as Mike Hart & Comrades) 22
(see also Liverpool Scene)

TIM HART & MADDY PRIOR
71   B&C CAS 1035   SUMMER SOLSTICE (LP) 12
72   Ad-Rhythm ARPS 3   FOLK SONGS OF OLDE ENGLAND VOL. 1 (LP) 30
72   Ad-Rhythm ARPS 4   FOLK SONGS OF OLDE ENGLAND VOL. 2 (LP) 25
74   Mooncrest CREST 23   FOLK SONGS OF OLDE ENGLAND (LP, reissue) 10
(see also Steeleye Span)

CIARAN HARTE
81   Glass GLASS 003   Love Is Strange/Shimahero (p/s) 4

KEEF HARTLEY (BAND)
69   Deram DM 250   Just To Cry/Leave It 'Til Morning 6
69   Deram DM 273   Waiting Around/Not Foolish, Not Wise 6
70   Deram DM 316   Roundabout Pts 1 & 2 5
73   Deram DM 380   Dance To The Music/You And Me 5
69   Deram SML 1037   HALFBREED (LP) 20
70   Deram SML 1054   THE BATTLE OF N.W.6 (LP) 15
70   Deram SML 1071   THE TIME IS NEAR (LP, with booklet) 15
71   Deram SDL 2   OVERDOG (LP) 15
71   Deram SDL 4   LITTLE BIG BAND (LP) 15
72   Deram SDL 9   SEVENTY SECOND BRAVE (LP) 15
73   Deram SDL 13   LANCASHIRE HUSTLER (LP) 15
(see also Rory Storm & Hurricanes, Artwoods, John Mayall, Miller Anderson, Dog Soldier, Henry Lowther)

HARVESTERS
80   private pressing   A COLLECTOR'S ITEM (LP) 15

HARVEY (Fuqua) & MOONGLOWS
58   London HLM 8730   Ten Commandments Of Love/Mean Old Blues 125
58   London HLM 8730   Ten Commandments Of Love/Mean Old Blues (78) 30
(see also Moonglows, Etta & Harvey)

HARVEY BOYS
57   London HLA 8397   Nothing Is Too Good For You/Marina Girl 20

(SENSATIONAL) ALEX HARVEY (BAND)
64   Polydor NH 52264   I Just Wanna Make Love To You/Let The Good Times Roll 20
64   Polydor NH 52907   Got My Mojo Working/I Ain't Worried Baby
                           (as Alex Harvey & His Soul Band) 30
65   Polydor BM 56017   Ain't That Just Too Bad/My Kind Of Love
                            (as Alex Harvey & His Soul Band) 30
65   Fontana TF 610   Agent 00 Soul/Go Away Baby 25
66   Fontana TF 764   Work Song/I Can Do Without Your Love 20
67   Decca F 12640   The Sunday Song/Horizon's 20
67   Decca F 12660   Maybe Some Day/Curtains For My Baby 25
69   Fontana TF 1063   Midnight Moses/Roman Wall Blues 20
74   Vertigo 6059 098   The Faith Healer (Edit)/St. Anthony 4
75   Vertigo ALEX 002   Gamblin' Bar Room Blues/Shake That Thing (p/s) 6
77   Mountain TOP 32   Mrs. Blackhouse/Engine Room Boogie (p/s) 5
64   Polydor LPHM 46424   ALEX HARVEY AND HIS SOUL BAND (LP) 70
64   Polydor LPHM 46441   THE BLUES (LP) 70
69   Fontana (S)TL 5534   ROMAN WALL BLUES (LP) 80
72   Vertigo 6360 081   FRAMED (LP, gatefold sleeve, spiral label, later spaceship label) 60/10
74   Vertigo 6360 103   NEXT (LP, spaceship label, silver sleeve) 15
77   K-Tel NE 984   ALEX HARVEY PRESENTS THE LOCH NESS MONSTER (LP, withdrawn,
                            gatefold stickered sleeve, with 16-page 'descriptive diary') ....30+
(see also Tear Gas, Hairband, Rock Workshop, Nazareth, Michael Schenker Group)

JANCIS HARVEY
73   Pilgrim King KLPS 47   DISTANCE OF DOORS (LP) 30
76   Westwood   A PORTRAIT OF JANCIS HARVEY (LP) 25

JANE HARVEY
60   Pye International 7N 25046   I'm Gonna Go Fishin'/Hundred Dreams From Now 4

LANCE HARVEY & KINGPINS
64   Lyntone LYN 509   Since You Walked Out On Me/ESCORTS: I Can Tell (Keele Rag flexidisc) ...15

PETER HARVEY
62   Columbia DB 4873   Rainin' In My Heart/Please Don't Tell Joe 6
64   Columbia DB 7192   Heart Of Ice/Trace Of A Heartache 5

P.J. HARVEY
92   Too Pure PURED 10   DRY (LP, with free demos LP) 15
92   Too Pure PURECDD 010   DRY (CD, with free demos CD) 20
(see also Automatic Dlamini)

RICHARD HARVEY
75   Transatlantic TRA 292   DIVISIONS ON A GROUND (LP) 50
79   ICL 001   A NEW WAY OF SEEING (private press LP) 30
80s   KPM   FOLK SONGS (LP) 10
(see also Gryphon)

MINT VALUE £

CHRISTINE HARWOOD
70   Birth RAB 1   NICE TO MEET MISS CHRISTINE (LP) 30

GORDON HASKELL
69   CBS 63741   SAILIN' MY BOAT (LP) 120
72   Atlantic K 40311   IT IS AND IT ISN'T (LP) 15
(see also King Crimson)

JACK HASKELL
57   London HL 8426   Around The World/Away Out West 15
58   Oriole CB 1442   The Night Of The Senior Prom/Hungry For Love (with Honey-Dreamers) 4

MICHAEL HASLAM
65   Parlophone R 5267   There Goes The Forgotten Man/My Heart Won't Say Goodbye 8

HASSLES
67   United Artists UP 1199   You Got Me Hummin'/I'm Thinkin' 8
(see also Billy Joel)

HAT & TIE
66   President PT 105   Chance For Romance/California Jazz CLub U.S.A. 10
67   President PT 122   Bread To Spend/Finding It Rough 25
(see also Patrick Campbell-Lyons, Nirvana)

TONY HATCH ORCHESTRA
62   Pye 7N 15434   Ben Casey Theme/Perry Mason Theme 4
62   Pye 7N 15460   Out Of This World Theme/Cyril's Tune (p/s) 6
65   Pye 7N 15754   Crossroads Theme/The Marie Celeste (some with p/s) 8/4
66   Pye 7N 17169   Crossroads Theme/Round Every Corner (p/s) 6

TONY HATCH & CHERRY CHILDREN
70   Pye 7N 17912   Yoko/Bahama Sound 4

GEORGE HATCHER BAND
70s United Artists EXP 100   HAVE BAND WILL TRAVEL (10" LP) 10

HATE
70   Famous/Teargas   HATE KILLS (LP) 50

HATFIELD & NORTH
79   Virgin VR 5   AFTERS (LP, withdrawn) 20
(see also Matching Mole, Egg, Camel, National Health)

BOBBY HATFIELD
68   Verve VS 570   Hang-Ups/Soul Cafe 5
68   Verve VS 576   Only You/The Wonder Of You 5
72   Warner Bros K 16163 Oowee Baby, I Love You/Rock'n'Roll Woman 6
(see also Righteous Brothers)

DONNY HATHAWAY
70   Atco 226 010   The Ghetto Pts 1 & 2/Little Ghetto Boy 6
72   Atlantic K 10193   The Ghetto Pts 1 & 2/Little Ghetto Boy (reissue) 4
73   Atlantic K 10354   Love Love Love/Someday We'll Be Free 4
71   Atlantic K 40063   EVERYTHING IS EVERYTHING (LP) 15
71   Atlantic K 40241   DONNY HATHAWAY (LP) 10
72   Atlantic K 40369   LIVE (LP) 15
73   Atlantic K 40487   EXTENSION OF A MAN (LP) 12
(see also Roberta Flack)

HATS
70s Deadly Boring HAT 001   No Time Is A Good Time/Living On The Roof (p/s, with lyric insert) 4

ALAN HAVEN
64   United Artists UP 1057   Theme From "A Jolly Bad Fellow"/Jee B'ees 5
65   Fontana TF 542   Image/Romance On The North Sea 6
67   Fontana TF 835   Image/Romance Of The North Sea (reissue) 5

RICHIE HAVENS
68   Verve VS 1512   Three Day Eternity/No Opportunity Necessary No Experience Needed 4
69   Verve VS 1519   Lady Madonna/Indian Rope Man 6
69   Verve VS 1521   Rocky Raccoon/Stop Pulling And Pushing Me 4
69   Verve VS 1523   There's A Hole In The Future/Minstrel From Gault 4
69   Verve VS 1524   Handsome Johnny/Sandie 4
69   Big T BIG 119   Oxford Town/My Own Way 4
68   Verve (S)VLP 6005   SOMETHIN' ELSE AGAIN (LP) 12
68   Verve (S)VLP 6008   MIXED BAG (LP) 12
68   Verve (S)VLP 6021   STONEHENGE (LP) 12
69   Transatlantic TRA 187   ELECTRIC HAVENS (LP) 12
69   Transatlantic TRA 199   THE RICHIE HAVENS RECORD (LP) 12

PAT HAWES with DAVE CAREY's RHYTHM
56   Tempo A 141   Snowy Morning Blues/Sheik Of Araby 4

TOMMY HAWKE
60   Top Rank JAR 348   Good Gravy (I'm In Love Again)/Umpteen Years (And A Million Tears) 8

CHIP HAWKES
77   RCA PL 25044   NASHVILLE ALBUM (LP) 10
(see Tremeloes)

HAWKEYES
57   Capitol CL 14764   Someone Someday/Who Is He? 4

BUDDY BOY HAWKINS/WILLIAM MOORE
50s Heritage RE 102   BUDDY BOY HAWKINS/WILLIAM MOORE (EP) 15
(see also Blind Lemon Jefferson)

COLEMAN HAWKINS

55	Brunswick 05459	Lucky Duck/Bye 'N' Bye	10
55	Brunswick OE 9166	THE HAWK TALKS (EP)	7
58	London Jazz EZ-C 19020	THE HAWK RETURNS PART 1 (EP)	10
50s	Esquire EP 192	BEAN AND THE BOYS (EP)	7
61	Esquire EP 235	COLEMAN HAWKINS SEXTET (EP)	7
50s	Mercury EP1 6029	COLEMAN HAWKINS GROUP (EP)	7
55	Vogue EPV 1021	COLEMAN HAWKINS (EP)	7
53	Capitol LC 6580	CLASSICS IN JAZZ (10" LP)	15
53	Capitol LC 6650	CAPITOL PRESENTS COLEMAN HAWKINS AND SONNY GREER (10" LP)	15
54	HMV DLP 1055	TEN COLEMAN HAWKINS' SPECIALS (10" LP)	15
59	HMC CLP 1293	GENIUS OF COLEMAN HAWKINS (LP)	12
59	Felsted FJA 7005	THE HIGH AND MIGHTY HAWK (LP, also stereo SJA 2005)	12
61	Esquire 32-095	SOUL (LP)	12
61	Esquire 32-102	HAWK EYES (LP)	12
61	Moodsville MV 7	COLEMAN HAWKINS (LP)	12
62	Swingsville SV 2001	COLEMAN HAWKINS WITH THE RED GARLAND TRIO (LP)	12
62	Swingsville SV 2005	THE COLEMAN HAWKINS ALL STARS (LP)	12
62	Swingsville SVLP 2013	STASCH (LP)	10
63	HMV CLP 1630	DESAFINADO (LP, also stereo CSD 1484)	10
64	Verve VLP 9044	ALIVE! AT THE VILLAGE GATE (LP)	10
64	HMV CLP 1689	TODAY AND NOW (LP)	10
64	CBS BPG 62157	BACK IN BEAN'S BAG (LP, with Clark Terry)	10
65	Fontana TL 5273	MEDITATION (LP)	10
66	Fontana SJL 131	CATTIN' (LP)	10

(see also Hines & Eldridge, Milt Jackson & Coleman Hawkins, Eddie 'Lockjaw' Davis)

COLEMAN HAWKINS & LESTER YOUNG

65	Stateside SL 10117	CLASSIC TENORS (LP)	10

DALE HAWKINS

57	London HL 8482	Susie-Q/Don't Treat Me That Way	250
57	London HL 8482	Susie-Q/Don't Treat Me That Way (78)	60
58	London HLM 8728	La-Do-Dada/Cross Ties	30
58	London HLM 8728	La-Do-Dada/Cross Ties (78)	20
59	London HLM 8842	Yea-Yea/Lonely Nights	30
59	London HLM 8842	Yea-Yea/Lonely Nights (78)	20
59	London HLM 9016	Liza Jane/Back To School Blues	25
59	London HLM 9016	Liza Jane/Back To School Blues (78)	30
60	London HLM 9060	Hot Dog/Our Turn	25
70	Bell SBLL 127	L.A. MEMPHIS AND TYLER, TEXAS (LP)	10
73	Checker 6467 301	OH! SUSIE Q (LP)	12

HAWKSHAW HAWKINS

51	Vogue V 9003	Doghouse Boogie/Yesterday's Kisses (78)	8
51	Vogue V 9027	Slow Coach/Two Roads (78)	7
54	Parlophone CMSP 1	Betty Lorraine/Mexican Joe (export issue)	15
63	London HL 9737	Lonesome 7-7203/Everything Has Changed	8
58	Parlophone GEP 8742	COUNTRY AND WESTERN (EP)	15
58	Vogue VE 170117	HAWKSHAW HAWKINS — COUNTRY AND WESTERN (EP)	20
64	London HA 8181	THE ALL NEW HAWKSHAW HAWKINS (LP)	15

RONNIE HAWKINS (& HAWKS)

59	Columbia DB 4319	Forty Days (To Come Back Home)/One Of These Days	40
59	Columbia DB 4345	Mary Lou/Need Your Lovin' (Oh So Bad)	25
60	Columbia DB 4412	Southern Love (Whatcha-Gonna' Do)/Love Me Like You Can	15
60	Columbia DB 4442	Clara/Lonely Hours	20
63	Columbia DB 7036	Bo Diddley/Who Do You Love	18
69	Roulette RO 512	Who Do You Love/Bo Diddley	4
70	Atlantic 584 320	Down In The Alley/Matchbox	4
70	Atlantic 2091 007	Bitter Green/Forty Days	4
72	Monument MNT 8292	Cora Mae/Ain't That A Shame	4
60	Columbia SEG 7983	Rockin' With Ronnie (EP, also stereo ESG 7792)	50/75
60	Columbia SEG 7988	Rockin' With Ronnie (EP, also stereo ESG 7795)	50/75
60	Columbia 33SX 1238	MR. DYNAMO (LP, also stereo SCX 3315)	50/80
60	Columbia 33SX 1295	THE FOLK BALLADS OF RONNIE HAWKINS (LP, also stereo SCX 3358)	30/50
70	Roulette RCP 1003	ARKANSAS ROCK PILE (LP, with The Band)	12
70	Atlantic 2400 009	RONNIE HAWKINS (LP)	10
72	Monument MNT 65122	ROCK AND ROLL RESURRECTION (LP)	10

(see also Band)

SCREAMIN' JAY HAWKINS

58	Fontana H 107	I Put A Spell On You/Little Demon (78)	100
65	Columbia DB 7460	The Whammy/Strange	15
65	Sue WI 379	I Hear Voices/Just Don't Care	18
66	Sue WI 4008	I Put A Spell On You/Little Demon (unissued)	
69	Direction 58-4097	I Put A Spell On You/Little Demon	8
80	Polydor POSP 183	I Put A Spell On You/Armpit #6 (with Keith Richards)	5
66	Planet PLL 1001	THE NIGHT AND DAY OF SCREAMIN' JAY HAWKINS (LP)	25
69	Direction 8-63481	I PUT A SPELL ON YOU (LP)	20
69	Mercury SMCL 20178	WHAT THAT IS (LP)	12

HAWKLORDS

78	Charisma HL 1	PSI Power/Death Trap (no p/s, promo only)	10
78	Charisma CB 323	PSI Power/Death Trap (no p/s)	5
79	Charisma CB 332	25 Years/(Only) The Dead Dreams Of A Cold War Kid (no p/s)	4
79	Charisma CB 332 12	25 Years/(Only) The Dead Dreams Of A Cold War Kid/PXR 5 (12", grey vinyl)	7
79	Charisma CB 332 12	25 Years/(Only) The Dead Dreams Of A Cold War Kid/PXR 5 (12", mispressed on black vinyl)	8

HAWKLORDS

82 Flicknife FLS 209   Who's Gonna Win The War/Time Of (p/s) 4
(see also Hawkwind)

HAWKS
68 Stateside SS 2147   Grissle/SHEEP: Hide And Seek 8

HAWKS
80s Five Believers FB 001   Words Of Hope/Sense Of Ending (p/s) 10
(see also Lilac Time, Tin Tin)

(Johnny) HAWKSWORTH — (Ronnie) VERRLL JAZZ GROUP
56 Decca FJ 10726   Ring Dem Bells/Always 4

JOHNNY HAWKSWORTH (ORCHESTRA)
65 Pye 7N 15969   Lunar Walk/It's Murder (as Johnny Hawksworth Orchestra) 8
66 Columbia DB 8059   Goal/"Goal — World Cup 1966" Theme (as Sounds Of Johnny Hawksworth) 4
67 Columbia DB 8129   Wack Wack/On The Tiles 5
(see also Johnny's Jazz)

HAWKWIND
70 Liberty LBF 15382   Hurry On Sundown/Mirror Of Illusion (no p/s) 60
72 United Artists UP 35381   Silver Machine/Seven By Seven ('machine' art p/s) 10
73 United Artists (WD 3637) Sonic Attack (1-sided promo in cloth sleeve) 100
73 United Artists UP 35566   Urban Guerilla/Brainbox Pollution (no p/s) 10
74 United Artists UP 35715   The Psychedelic Warlords (Disappear In Smoke)/It's So Easy (no p/s) .. 6
75 United Artists UP 35808   Kings Of Speed/Motorhead (some in p/s) 30/5
76 Charisma CB 289   Kerb Crawler/Honky Dorky (no p/s) 5
77 Charisma CB 299   Back On The Streets/The Dream Of Isis (p/s) 6
77 Charisma CB 305   Quark, Strangeness & Charm/Forge Of Vulcan (no p/s) 5
78 United Artists UP 35381   Silver Machine/Seven By Seven (reissue, black-on-white p/s) 5
78 United Artists 12UP 35381 Silver Machine/Seven By Seven (12", silver p/s) 10
80 Bronze BRO 98   Shot Down In The Night/Urban Guerilla (p/s) 4
80 Bronze BRO 109   Who's Gonna Win The War/Nuclear Toy (p/s, cream or green labels) ... 10/4
81 RCA RCA 137   Angels Of Death/Trans-Dimensional Man (p/s) 4
82 RCA Active RCA 267   Silver Machine/Silver Machine (Full Version)/Psychedelic Warlords .. 5
82 RCA Active RCAP 267   Silver Machine/(Full Version)/Psychedelic Warlords (picture disc) . 10
83 United Artists UP 35381   Silver Machine/Seven By Seven (reissue, white-on-black p/s) 4
83 Liberty UPP 35381   Silver Machine/Seven By Seven (picture disc) 8
83 Liberty UPP 35381   Silver Machine/Seven By Seven (mispressed picture disc, plays Beatles'
                              "Ask Me Why") 15
83 Flicknife FLS 214   Hawkwind And Co: Your Last Chance (sampler with Hawkwind,
                              Robert Calvert & Michael Moorcock) 4
84 Flicknife FLEP 104   THE EARTH RITUAL PREVIEW (12" EP) 8
86 Samurai HW 001   Silver Machine/Magnu (motorcycle-shaped picture disc) 8
86 Flicknife FLS 034-A   Motorhead/Hurry On Sundown (p/s) 4
73 United Artists USEP 1   HURRY ON HAWKWIND (EP) 50
70 Liberty LBS 83348   HAWKWIND (LP, gatefold sleeve; blue or black labels) 22/18
71 United Artists UAG 29202 IN SEARCH OF SPACE (LP in foldout sleeve, some with 'log book') .. 16/10
72 United Artists UAG 29364 DOREMI-FASOL-LATIDO (LP, with inner sleeve, some with poster) .. 15/10
73 Utd Artists UAD 60037/8   SPACE RITUAL ALIVE (2-LP, foldout sleeve with inners) 20
74 United Artists UAG 29672 HALL OF THE MOUNTAIN GRILL (LP, with inner sleeve) 12
75 United Artists UAG 29766 WARRIOR ON THE EDGE OF TIME (LP, foldout sleeve with inner) 15
76 United Artists UAK 29919 ROADHAWKS (LP, gatefold sleeve with poster & sticker) 12
78 Charisma CDS 4014   25 YEARS ON (LP, very few with booklet) 12
79 Charisma CDS 4016   P.X.R.5 (LP, with family tree poster) 12
80 Bronze BRON 530   LEVITATION (LP, blue vinyl) 12
81 RCA Active RCALP 6004   SONIC ATTACK (LP with insert) 15
82 RCA Active RCALP 9004   CHURCH OF HAWKWIND (LP, with lyric booklet) 22
82 RCA Active RCALP 6055   CHOOSE YOUR MASQUES (LP) 15
85 Flicknife SHARP 033   CHRONICLE OF THE BLACK SWORD (LP with inner sleeve) 10
85 Flicknife SHARP 033CD   CHRONICLE OF THE BLACK SWORD (CD with 3 extra tracks) 15
86 Hawkfan HWFB 2   HAWKFAN 12 (LP with poster, sticker insert & carrier bag) 20
86 Samurai SMR 046   APPROVED HISTORY OF HAWKWIND (3-LP, picture discs with booklet) .. 25
87 Flicknife HWBOX 01   OFFICIAL PICTURE LOG BOOK (4-LP box set [3 picture discs & interview
                              disc] with badge & insert) 25
(see also Hawklords, Robert Calvert, Michael Moorcock, Nik Turner/Inner City Unit, Sphynx, Dave Brock, Steve Swindells,
Tim Blake, Huw Lloyd Langton Group, Alan Davey, Motorhead)

DEANE HAWLEY
60s Liberty LIB 55359   Pocketful Of Rainbows/That Dream Could Never Be 5

BRYN HAWORTH
74 Island ILPS 9287   LET THE DAYS GO BY (LP, with inner sleeve) 10
75 Island ILPS 9332   SUNNY SIDE OF THE STREET (LP, with inner sleeve) 10
(see also Fleur De Lys)

HAYDOCK'S ROCKHOUSE
66 Columbia DB 8050   Cupid/She Thinks 18
67 Columbia DB 8135   Lovin' You/Mix A Fix 18
(see also Hollies)

BILL HAYES
53 MGM SP 1036   The Donkey Song/My Ever-Lovin' 20
55 London HL 8149   The Berry Tree/Blue Black Hair 25
56 London HLA 8220   Ballad Of Davy Crockett/Farewell 20
56 London HLA 8239   Kwela Kwela/The White Buffalo 20
56 London HLA 8300   Das Ist Musik/I Know An Old Lady 15
56 London HLA 8325   The Legend Of Wyatt Earp/That Do Make It Nice 15
57 London HL 8430   Wringle Wrangle/Westward Ho The Wagons 12
59 London HLR 8833   Wimoweh/Goin' Down The Road Feelin' Bad (with Buckle Busters) 8
56 London RE-A 1051   GREAT PIONEERS OF THE WEST (EP) 20

ISAAC HAYES

69	Stax STAX 133	Walk On By/By The Time I Get To Phoenix	4
72	Stax 2025 069	Theme From "Shaft"/Cafe Regio's	4
76	ABC ABC 4100	Disco Connection/St. Thomas Square	4
76	ABC ABE 12007	Disco Connection/Chocolate Chip (12")	7
69	Stax SXATS 1028	HOT BUTTERED SOUL (LP)	12
70	Stax SXATS 1032	THE ISAAC HAYES MOVEMENT (LP)	12
70	Stax 2465 016	BLUE HAYES (LP)	12
71	Stax 2325 026	TO BE CONTINUED (LP)	12
71	Stax 2325 014	THE ISAAC HAYES MOVEMENT (LP, reissue)	10
71	Stax 2325 011	HOT BUTTERED SOUL (LP, reissue)	10
71	Stax 2659 007	SHAFT — ORIGINAL SOUNDTRACK (2-LP, soundtrack, gatefold sleeve)	14
72	Stax 2628 004	BLACK MOSES (2-LP)	14
74	Stax 2659 026	LIVE AT THE SAHARA TAHOE (2-LP)	14
74	Stax 2325 111	JOY (LP)	10
74	Stax STXD 4001/2	TRUCK TURNER (2-LP)	14
74	Stax STXH 5001	TOUGH GUYS (LP)	10
75	Stax STX 1043	USE ME (LP)	10
75	ABC ABCL 5129	CHOCOLATE CHIP (LP, gatefold sleeve)	12
75	ABC ABCL 5155	GROOVE-A-THON (LP, gatefold sleeve)	10

LINDA HAYES

55	Parlophone MSP 6174	Please Have Mercy (with Platters)/Oochi Pachi (with Tony Williams)	200
55	Parlophone MSP 6174	Please Have Mercy (with Platters)/Oochi Pachi (with Tony Williams) (78)	45

(see also Platters)

TUBBY HAYES

57	Tempo A 148	Ode To Ernie/No, I Woodyn't	8
62	Fontana H 397	Sally/I Believe In You (as Tubby Hayes Quintet)	6
50s	Tempo EXA 14	TUBBY HAYES AND HIS ORCHESTRA (EP)	20
50s	Tempo EXA 17	TUBBY HAYES AND HIS ORCHESTRA (EP)	20
50s	Tempo EXA 27	TUBBY HAYES QUARTET (EP)	20
50s	Tempo EXA 28	TUBBY HAYES QUARTET (EP)	20
50s	Tempo EXA 36	MODERN JAZZ SCENE (EP, as Tubby Hayes & His Orchestra)	20
50s	Tempo EXA 55	TUBBY HAYES QUINTET (EP)	20
50s	Tempo EXA 82	THE EIGHTH WONDER (EP, solo)	20
50s	Tempo TAP 6	TUBBY HAYES QUINTET (LP)	50
50s	Tempo TAP 15	JAZZ COURIERS (LP)	50
50s	Tempo TAP 17	SPEAK LOW (LP)	50
61	Tempo TAP 29	TUBBY'S GROOVE (LP)	45
61	Fontana TFL 5142	TUBBS (LP, also stereo STFL 562)	30
61	Ember EMB 3337	AN EVENING WITH MR. PERCUSSION (LP, with Tony Kinsey)	25
61	Fontana TFL 5183	TUBBS IN NEW YORK (LP, also stereo STFL 595)	100
63	Fontana 680 998 TL	DOWN IN THE VILLAGE (LP, also stereo 886 163TY)	200
64	Fontana (S)TL 5195	RETURN VISIT! (LP)	40
64	Fontana TL 5200	LATE SPOT AT SCOTT'S (LP)	50
66	Fontana (S)TL 5221	TUBBY TOURS (LP, with Orchestra)	25
66	Fontana (S)TL 5410	100% PROOF (LP)	30
67	Wing WL 1162	TUBBS IN NEW YORK (LP, reissue)	15
69	Fontana SFJL 911	MEXICAN GREEN (LP)	40
70	Fontana 6309 002	THE TUBBY HAYES ORCHESTRA (LP)	20
70	Philips 6382 041	THIS IS JAZZ (LP)	10

(see also Jack Constanzo & Tubby Hayes, Jazz Couriers)

TUBBY HAYES & CLEO LAINE

60s	Fontana (S)TFL 570	PALLADIUM JAZZ DATE (LP)	15
60s	Wing WL 1088	PALLADIUM JAZZ DATE (LP, reissue)	10

(see also Cleo Laine)

TUBBY HAYES & PAUL GONSALVES ALLSTARS

60s	Columbia SX 6003	JUST FRIENDS (LP)	20
60s	World Record Club T 631	CHANGE OF SETTING (LP)	15

(see also Paul Gonsalves)

RICHARD HAYMAN ORCHESTRA

50s	Mercury ZEP 10001	IT'S CHA CHA TIME (EP)	8

DICK HAYMES

56	Capitol CL 14618	You'll Never Know/Love Walked In	4
56	Capitol CL 14659	Two Different Worlds/Love Is A Great Big Nothin'	4
57	Capitol CL 14674	Never leave Me/New York's My Home	4
57	Capitol CL 14720	C'est La Vie/Now At Last	4
51	Brunswick LA 8516	IRVING BERLIN SONGS (10" LP)	12
51	Brunswick LA 8530	SOUVENIR ALBUM (10" LP)	12
50s	Capitol LC 6823	RAIN OR SHINE (10" LP)	12

GOLDIA HAYNES

52	Capitol CL 13550	Truth In The Gospel/Oh Lord How Long (78)	15

ROY HAYNES, PHINEAS NEWBORN, PAUL CHAMBERS TRIO

61	Esquire 32-103	WE THREE (LP)	10

JOE HAYWARD

65	Island WI 218	Warm And Tender Love/I Would If I Could	7

JUSTIN HAYWARD

65	Pye 7N 17041	London Is Behind Me/Day Must Come	50
66	Parlophone R 5496	I Can't Face The World Without You/I'll Be Here Tomorrow	50
80	CBS 11-7731	The Eve Of The War/Horsell (12" picture disc)	7
77	Deram SDL 15	SONGWRITER (LP)	10

(see also Moody Blues, Wilde Three)

MINT VALUE £

RICK HAYWARD
71 Blue Horizon 2431 006 RICK HAYWARD (LP) .... .50
(see also Accent, Christine Perfect)

SUSAN HAYWARD
56 MGM MGM EP 555 I'LL CRY TOMORROW — SOUNDTRACK SELECTION (EP) 7

LEON HAYWOOD
66 Vocalion VP 9280 Ain't No Use/Hey, Hey, Hey, One Of These Days 8
67 Vocalion VP 9288 Ever Since You Were Sweet Sixteen/Skate Awhile .... .15
69 MCA Soul Bag BAG 5 Mellow Moonlight/Tennessee Waltz 5
70 Capitol CL 15634 I Wanna Thank You/I Was Sent To You 4
73 Pye Intl. 7N 25611 La La Song/There Ain't Enough Hate Around To
Make Me Turn Around 4
75 20th Century BTC 2191 Come On And Get Yourself Some/BMF (Beautiful) 4
75 20th Century BTC 2228 I Wan'ta Do Something Freaky To You/I Know What Love Is 5
76 CBS 4735 The Streets Will Love You To Death Pts 1 & 2 4
67 Vocalion VAL 8064 SOUL CARGO (LP) .... .20
69 MCA MUPS 369 IT'S GOT TO BE MELLOW (LP) .... .12
73 Pye NSPL 28177 BACK TO STAY (LP) .... .10
75 20th Century BT 476 COME AND GET YOURSELF SOME (LP) .... .10

HAZE
86 Gabadon GABS 5 Tunnel Vision/Shadows (p/s) 5
84 Gabadon GABL 001 C'EST LA VIE (LP) .... .25
85 Gabadon GABC 2 CELLAR REPLAY (cassette) .... .10
85 Gabadon GABS 003 THE EMBER (4-track 12" EP) 7
87 Gabadon GABL 6 STOAT AND BOTTLE (LP) .... .10

HAZEL & JOLLY BOYS
67 Doctor Bird DB 1063 Stop Them/Deep Down .... .10

LEE HAZLEWOOD
60 London HLW 9223 Words Mean Nothing/The Girl On Death Row (with Duane Eddy) ... .12
66 MGM MGM 1310 Sand/My Autumn's Done Come 6
67 MGM MGM 1348 My Baby Cried All Night Long/These Boots Are
Made For Walkin' 8
67 Reprise RS 20613 Ode To Billie Joe/Charlie Bill Nelson 4
68 Reprise RS 20667 Rainbow Woman/I Am, You Are 7
68 Reprise RSLP 6297 LOVE AND OTHER CRIMES (LP) .... .18
70 London HA-N/SH-N 8398 TROUBLE IS A LONESOME TOWN (LP) .... .15
74 Stateside SSL 10315 POET, FOOL OR BUM (LP) .... .15
(see also Nancy Sinatra & Lee Hazlewood, Duane Eddy)

TONY HAZZARD
66 Columbia DB 7927 You'll Never Put Shackles On Me/Calling You Home 5
68 CBS 3452 Sound Of The Candyman's Trumpet/Everything's Gone Wrong .. .5
69 CBS 63608 DEMONSTRATION (LP) .... .12
71 Bronze ILPS 9174 LOUDWATER HOUSE (LP) .... .10
73 Bronze ILPS 9222 WAS THAT ALRIGHT THEN (LP) .... .10

MURRAY HEAD
65 Columbia DB 7635 Alberta/He Was A Friend Of Mine 4
65 Columbia DB 7771 The Bells Of Rhymney/Don't Sing No Sad Songs For Me 5
67 Columbia DB 8102 Someday Soon/You Bore Me 4
67 Immediate IM 053 She Was Perfection/Secondhand Monday .... .20
69 MCA MK 5019 Superstar/John Nineteen Forty One (p/s) 6
73 CBS 65503 NIGEL LIVED (LP) .... .15
75 Island ILPS 9347 SAY IT AIN'T SO (LP) .... .10

ROY HEAD (& TRAITS)
65 Pye Intl. 7N 25340 Just A Little Bit/Treat Me Right .... .10
65 Vocalion VP 9248 Treat Her Right/So Long, My Love 5
66 Vocalion VP 9254 Apple Of My Eye/I Pass The Day 5
66 Vocalion VP 9269 My Babe/Pain 5
66 Vocalion VP 9274 Wigglin' And Gigglin'/Driving Wheel 5
66 London HLZ 10097 To Make A Big Man Cry/Don't Cry No More 7
70 Stateside SS 8050 Mama Mama/I'm Not A Fool Anymore 4
75 London HLD 10487 The Most Wanted Woman In Town/Gingers Breademan 8
66 Pye Intl. NEP 44053 JUST A LITTLE BIT OF ROY HEAD (EP) .... .15
70 Stateside SSL 5033 SAME PEOPLE (LP) .... .10

HEADACHE
77 Lout 001 Can't Stand Still/No Reason For Your Call (p/s) 4

HEADHUNTERS (U.S.)
76 Arista ARTY 116 SURVIVAL OF THE FITTEST (LP) .... .25
77 Arista SPART 1046 STRAIGHT FROM THE GATE (LP) .... .15

HEADHUNTERS (U.K.)
83 Shout XS 005 Impossible/Straitjacket (p/s) 4

HEADLINERS
59 Parlophone R 4593 The Bubble Car Song/Andy's Theme 4

HEAD MACHINE
70 Major Minor SMLP 79 ORGASM (LP) .... .120
(see also Uriah Heep)

HEAD OF DAVID
86 Blast First BFFP 5 DOGBREATH (12" EP, stickered plain sleeve) 8
89 Blast First WANT 001 WHITE ELEPHANT (LP, mail-order only) .... .12

TOPPER HEADON
85	Mercury MERD 201	Leave It To Luck/Casablanca//Du Cane Road/Got To Get Out Of This Heat/ S.O.S. (double pack)	4

(see also Clash)

HEADS, HANDS & FEET
71	Island ILPS 9149	HEADS, HANDS AND FEET (LP)	15
72	Island ILPS 9185	ON THE TRACKS (LP)	12
73	Atlantic K 40465	OLD SOLDIERS NEVER DIE (LP)	10

(see also Don Everly)

HEALEY SISTERS
64	HMV POP 1313	Give Me Back My Heart/After The Party	4

JOE HEANEY
60	Collector JEI 5	MORRISSEY AND THE RUSSIAN SOLDIER (EP)	7

HEART
76	Arista ARISTA 71	Magic Man/How Deep It Goes (no p/s)	4
77	Arista ARISTA 86	Crazy On You/Soul Of The Sea (no p/s)	4
77	Arista ARISTA 104	Dreamboat Annie/Sing Child (no p/s)	4
77	Arista ARISTA 140	Heartless/Here Song (withdrawn)	10
86	Capitol CLD 394	These Dreams/If Looks Could Kill (live)//What About Love/ Heart Of Darkness (double pack)	5
86	Capitol CLP 406	Nothin' At All (Extended Remix)/The Wolf (heart-shaped picture disc)	5
87	Capitol CLP 457	Who Will You Run To?/Nobody Home (picture disc)	5
88	Capitol CLG 482	Never/These Dreams (poster p/s)	4
88	Capitol CLP 482	Never/These Dreams (picture disc with insert)	5
88	Capitol 12 CLE 482	These Dreams (Remix)/(Extended Remix)/(Instrumental)/Never (Extended Remix) (12", 1-side etched)	8
88	Capitol CLP 487	What About Love/Shell Shock (picture disc)	4
77	Arista SPART 1024	MAGAZINE (LP, withdrawn)	20
90	Capitol HGIFT 1	HEART BOX SET (3-LP: "Heart", "Bad Animals" & "Brigade" + 24pp booklet)	25

HEART BEATS
80	Red Shadow REDS 2	Talk To Me/Don't Want Romance	5
81	Nothing Shaking SHAD 1	Go/One Of The People (blue vinyl)	4

HEARTBREAKERS
77	Track 2094 135	Chinese Rocks/Born To Lose	6
77	Track 2094 135T	Chinese Rocks/Born To Lose (12")	8
77	Track 2094 137	One Track Mind/Can't Keep My Eyes On You (live)/Do You Love Me	7
77	Track 2094 142	It's Not Enough/Let Go (withdrawn)	60
79	Beggars Banquet BEG 21	Get Off The Phone (live)/I Wanna Be Loved (live) (p/s)	4
77	Track 2409 218	L.A.M.F. (LP)	10
81	Jungle FREUD 1	D.T.K. — LIVE AT THE SPEAKEASY (LP, white or pink vinyl)	10
84	Jungle FREUDP 4	L.A.M.F. REVISITED (LP, picture disc)	10
88	Jungle FREUDP 1	D.T.K. — LIVE AT THE SPEAKEASY (LP, reissue, picture disc)	10

(see also New York Dolls, Johnny Thunders)

HEARTHROBS
80	Detour Entertain. DET 1	READY TO SERVE (EP, foldover p/s)	4

HEARTS (U.S.)
64	Stateside SS 268	Dear Abby/Dear Abby (Instrumental)	7

HEARTS (U.K.)
64	Parlophone R 5147	Young Woman/Black Eyes	25

HEARTS & FLOWERS
67	Capitol CL 15492	Rock'N'Roll Gypsies/Road To Nowhere	8
68	Capitol CL 15549	She Sang Hymns Out Of Tune/Tin Angel	7

HEARTS OF SOUL
70	Columbia DB 8670	Waterman/Fat Jack	12

HEART THROBS
87	In Tape IT 043	Toy/Make My Day (p/s)	6
87	In Tape ITTI 043	Toy/Make My Day/I, The Jury (12", p/s)	8
87	Rough Trade RTT 211	Bang/Sick At Heart/Naked Bang (12", p/s)	7
88	Rough Trade RTT 221	Too Many Shadows/I See Danger/Things That Linger (12", p/s, blue vinyl)	7

HEATERS
70	Upsetter US 329	Melting Pot/UPSETTERS: Kinky Mood	5

TED HEATH ORCHESTRA
54	Decca F 10200	Seven Eleven/Lullaby Of Birdland	6
54	Decca F 10222	Creep/Slim Jim — Creep	6
54	Decca F 10246	Walking Shoes/Skin Deep	8
54	Decca F 10272	Viva Verrell/Holiday For Strings	6
54	Decca F 10273	Lush Slide/Fascinating Rhythm	6
55	Decca F 10425	Dig Deep/Asia Minor	6
55	Decca F 10447	Peg O' My Heart (Mambo)/In The Mood (For Mambo)	6
55	Decca F 10477	Haitian Ritual/Late Night Final	6
55	Decca F 10540	Bell Bell Boogie/Amethyst	6
55	Decca F 10590	Barber Shop Jump/Look For The Silver Lining	4
55	Decca F 10624	Malaguena/Cloudburst	4
56	Decca F 10683	The Man With The Golden Arm/Paris By Night	5
56	Decca F 10746	The Faithful Hussar/Siboney	4
58	Decca F 11000	Swingin' Shepherd Blues/Raunchy	4
58	Decca F 11003	Tequila/Little Serenade	4
58	Decca F 11025	Tom Hark/Cha Cha Baby	4
65	Decca F 12133	Sidewinder/Hit And Miss	4

Ted HEATH ORCHESTRA

55	Decca DFE 6025	TED HEATH AND HIS MUSIC (EP)	12
55	Decca DFE 6027	TED HEATH AND HIS MUSIC NO. 2 (EP)	12
55	Decca DFE 6120	LONDON PALLADIUM HIGHLIGHTS (EP)	8
55	Decca DFE 6159	FATS WALLER ALBUM NO. 2 (EP)	12
55	Decca DFE 6160	SELECTIONS FROM FATS WALLER ALBUM NO. 2 (EP)	8
55	Decca DFE 6189	HUNDREDTH LONDON PALLADIUM SUNDAY CONCERT VOL. 1 (EP)	8
55	Decca DFE 6190	HUNDREDTH LONDON PALLADIUM SUNDAY CONCERT VOL. 2 (EP)	8
55	Decca DFE 6191	HUNDREDTH LONDON PALLADIUM SUNDAY CONCERT VOL. 3 (EP)	8
56	Decca DFE 6290	GERSHWIN FOR MODERNS NO. 1 (EP)	8
56	Decca DFE 6300	AUSTRALIAN SUITE (EP)	12
56	Decca DFE 6304	KERN FOR MODERNS NO. 1 (EP)	8
56	Decca DFE 6305	KERN FOR MODERNS NO. 2 (EP)	8
56	Decca DFE 6306	KERN FOR MODERNS NO. 3 (EP)	8
56	Decca DFE 6317	LONDON PALLADIUM HIGHLIGHTS (EP)	8
56	Decca DFE 6323	FOUR CLASSICS (EP)	8
56	Decca DFE 6346	LONDON PALLADIUM HIGHLIGHTS NO. 3 (EP)	8
56	Decca DFE 6354	GERSHWIN FOR MODERNS NO. 2 (EP)	8
56	Decca DFE 6373	LONDON PALLADIUM HIGHLIGHTS NO. 4 (EP)	8
57	Decca DFE 6403	TED HEATH AND HIS MUSIC NO. 3 (EP)	8
57	Decca DFE 6432	TED HEATH AND HIS MUSIC NO. 4 (EP)	8
57	Decca DFE 6451	TED HEATH RECALLS THE FABULOUS DORSEYS NO. 1 (EP)	7
58	Decca DFE 6487	TED HEATH AND HIS MUSIC NO. 5 (EP)	7
58	Decca DFE 6500	OUR KIND OF JAZZ (EP)	7
58	Decca DFE 6509	HITS I MISSED NO. 1 (EP, also stereo STO 103)	7/8
58	Decca DFE 6510	TED HEATH PLAYS AL JOLSON CLASSICS NO. 1 (EP)	7
58	Decca DFE 6511	OLD ENGLISH NO. 1 (EP)	8
59	Decca STO 109	TED HEATH SWING SESSION (stereo EP)	12
59	Decca STO 113	TED HEATH SWINGS IN HI STEREO (stereo EP)	8
59	Decca DFE 6579	FOUR HITS FROM THE ALL TIME TOP TWELVE (EP, also stereo STO 122)	7/10
60	Decca DFE 6625	BEAULIEU FESTIVAL SUITE (EP, also stereo STO 135)	8/12
60	Decca DFE 6642	MY VERY GOOD FRIENDS THE BANDLEADERS (EP)	8
61	Decca STO 155	GREAT FILM HITS (stereo EP)	7
63	Decca STO 8532	MOMENTS AT MONTREUX (stereo EP)	7
51	Decca LF 1037	TEMPO FOR DANCERS (10" LP)	18
52	Decca LF 1060	LISTEN TO MY MUSIC (10" LP)	15
52	Decca LF 1064	SELECTION (10" LP)	15
53	Decca LK 4062	AT THE LONDON PALLADIUM (LP)	15
53	Decca LK 4064	STRIKE UP THE BAND (LP)	15
54	Decca LK 4074	TED HEATH'S FATS WALLER ALBUM (LP)	15
54	Decca LK 4075	TED HEATH'S 100TH LONDON PALLADIUM SUNDAY CONCERT (LP)	15
54	Decca LK 4098	GERSHWIN FOR MODERNS (LP)	12
56	Decca LK 4121	KERN FOR MODERNS (LP)	12
56	Decca LK 4134	AT THE LONDON PALLADIUM VOLUME 4 (LP)	12
56	Decca LK 4148	RODGERS FOR MODERNS (LP)	12
57	Decca LK 4165	AT CARNEGIE HALL (LP)	12
57	Decca LK 4167	FIRST AMERICAN TOUR (LP)	12
58	Decca LK 4275	HITS I MISSED (LP, also stereo SKL 4003)	12/14
58	Decca LK 4280	OLDE ENGLYSHE (LP)	12
58	Decca SKL 4023	SWINGS IN HI-STEREO (LP, stereo only)	12
59	Decca SKL 4030	SWING SESSION (LP, stereo only)	12
59	Decca LK 4307	PLAYS THE GREAT FILM HITS (LP)	10
60	Decca LK 4344	MY VERY GOOD FRIENDS THE BAND LEADERS (LP, stereo SKL 4090)	10
62	Decca PFM 24004	BIG BAND PERCUSSION (LP, also stereo PFS 34004)	10

(see also Max Bygraves & Ted Heath, Joan Regan, Bobbie Britton, Johnston Brothers, Annette Klooger)

HEATWAVE
77	GTO GTLP 027	CENTRAL HEATING (LP)	10

HEAVEN 17
81	Wool City Rocker LYN9296	Something's Wrong (flexidisc free with fanzine)	8/6
82	Virgin VS 483	Height Of The Fighting (He-La-Hu)/Honeymoon In New York (unissued, no p/s)	15
83	Virgin VSP 570	Temptation/We Live So Fast (picture disc)	4
83	Virgin VS 607	Come Live With Me/Let's All Make A Bomb (picture disc)	4
85	Virgin VSD 740	And That's No Lie/The Fuse (double pack)	4
86	Virgin VSD 881-12	Contenders/Diary Of A Contender//Penthouse And Pavement/Megamix (12", double pack)	7
87	Virgin VSD 920-12	Trouble/Move Out/Trouble//Contenders (U.S. Club Mix)/Trouble (U.S. Club Mix) (12", p/s double pack)	7
84	Virgin/fan club	HOW MEN ARE (cassette, studio demo via fan club)	10
86	Virgin TCV 2383	ENDLESS (cassette, double-play in presentation box with booklet)	10

(see also B.E.F., Human League)

HEAVY DUTY BREAKS
85	Illuminated ILL 5512	Heavy Duty Breaks (Radio Version)/Bonus Beats (12", p/s)	8
85	Illuminated JAMS 49	HEAVY DUTY BREAKS (LP, remixes of other artists)	12

(see also Youth, Killing Joke)

HEAVY JELLY
68	Island WIP 6049	I Keep Singing The Same Old Song/Blue	10

(see also Stevie Winwood, Spooky Tooth)

HEAVY JELLY
69	Head HDS 4001	Time Out Chewn In/The Long Wait	12
69	Island HELP	HEAVY JELLY (LP, promo-only)	100
84	Psycho PSYCHO 30	TAKE ME DOWN TO THE WATER (LP, reissue of promo-only LP)	10

(see also Jackie Lomax, Skip Bifferty, Griffin, Graham Bell, Aynsley Dunbar Retaliation)

HEAVY METAL KIDS
74	Atlantic K 50047	HEAVY METAL KIDS (LP)	10

(see also Gary Holton)

HEAVY PETTIN'
82	Neat NEAT 17	Roll The Dice/Love X Love (p/s)	5

HEAVY PUKE
80s	PUK 1	Spunk Bunny/Ozymandias (foldover p/s)	6

BOBBY HEBB
66	Philips BF 1503	Sunny/Bread	4
66	Philips BF 1522	A Satisfied Mind/Love Love Love	7
67	Philips BF 1541	Love Me/Babe I'm Crazy	8
67	Philips BF 1570	I Love Everything About You/Some Kinda Magic	6
67	Philips BF 1610	Everything Is Coming Up Roses/Bound By Love	4
68	Philips BF 1702	You Want To Change Me/Dreamy	20

DICK HECKSTALL-SMITH (QUINTET)
57	Pye Jazz NJE 1037	VERY SPECIAL OLD JAZZ (EP, as Dick Heckstall-Smith Quintet)	15
72	Bronze ILPS 9196	DUST IN THE AIR SUSPENDED MARKS THE PLACE ... WHERE A STORY ENDED (LP, gatefold sleeve with lyric inner sleeve)	15

(see also Graham Bond Organisation, Colosseum, John Mayall & Blues Breakers)

HEDGEHOG PIE
70s	Rubber TUB 12	WONDERFUL WORLD OF LAMBTON (EP)	8
72	Rubber RUB 002	HIS ROUND (LP, with Tony Capstick)	15
70s	Rubber RUB 009	HEDGEHOG PIE (LP)	20
70s	Rubber RUB 014	GREEN LADY (LP)	20
70s	Rubber RUB 024	JUST ACT NORMAL (LP)	20

(see also Dando Shaft)

HEDGEHOPPERS ANONYMOUS
65	Decca F 12241	It's Good News Week/Afraid Of Love	4
65	Decca F 12298	Don't Push Me/Please Don't Hurt Your Heart For Me	4
66	Decca F 12400	Baby (You're My Everything)/Remember	4
66	Decca F 12479	Daytime/That's The Time	4
66	Decca F 12530	Stop Press/Little Memories	5

NEIL HEFTI & ORCHESTRA
66	RCA RCA 1521	The Batman Theme/Batman Chase	12

LUCILLE HEGAMIN
73	VJM VLP 50	BLUE FLAME (LP)	12

DONALD HEIGHT
66	London HLZ 10062	Talk Of The Grapevine/There'll Be No Tomorrow	30
67	London HLZ 10116	Three Hundred & Sixty Five Days/I'm Willing To Wait	20
70	Jay Boy BOY 32	Talk Of The Grapevine/There'll Be No Tomorrow (reissue)	5
71	Avco/Embassy 6105 004	Rags To Riches To Rags/Dancin' To The Music Of Love	10
72	Jay Boy BOY 51	Three Hundred & Sixty Five Days/I'm Willing To Wait (reissue)	4
72	Jay Boy BOY 60	We Gotta Make Up/I Can't Get Enough	4

RONNIE HEIGHT
60	London HLN 9144	The One Finger Symphony/Mem'ries & Habits	4

HEINZ (& WILD BOYS)
63	Decca F 11652	Dreams Do Come True/Been Invited To A Party	12
63	Decca F 11693	Just Like Eddie/Don't You Knock At My Door	4
63	Decca F 11768	Country Boy/Long Tall Jack	6
64	Decca F 11831	You Were There/No Matter What They Say	8
64	Decca F 11920	Please Little Girl/For Loving Me This Way	10
64	Columbia DB 7374	Questions I Can't Answer/The Beating Of My Heart	10
65	Columbia DB 7482	Diggin' My Potatoes/She Ain't Comin' Back (with Wild Boys)	12
65	Columbia DB 7559	Don't Think Twice, It's All Right/Big Fat Spider	10
65	Columbia DB 7656	End Of The World/You Make Me Feel So Good	15
65	Columbia DB 7779	Heart Full Of Sorrow/Don't Worry Baby	15
66	Columbia DB 7942	Movin' In/I'm Not A Bad Guy	15
63	Decca DFE 8545	HEINZ (EP)	25
63	Decca DFE 8559	LIVE IT UP (EP)	25
64	Decca LK 4599	TRIBUTE TO EDDIE (LP)	40

(see also Tornados, Saints)

HEIR
69	Capitol E-T/E-ST 205	POLLUTION (LP)	10

HELDEN
83	Zica ZICA 01	Holding On/Once Upon A Time (p/s)	8
83	Zica 12 ZICA 01	Holding On/Once Upon A Time (12", p/s)	15
83	In The City ITC 1	Holding On/HOI POLLOI: When It's History (free with 'In The City' mag)	8/6

(see also Ultravox)

RICHARD HELL (& VOIDOIDS)
76	Stiff BUY 7	I Could Live With You In Another World/I Belong To The Blank Generation/ You Gotta Lose (numbered, 5,000 only)	8
77	Sire 6078 608	Blank Generation/Love Comes In Spurts	10
77	Sire 6078 608	Blank Generation/Liars Beware/Who Says? (12")	8
79	Radar ADA 30	The Kid With The Replaceable Head/I'm Your Man	6
77	Sire 9103 327	BLANK GENERATION (LP, some with inner sleeve)	15/10

DAVE HELLING
65	Stateside SS 409	It Ain't Me Babe/If You're Gonna Leave Me	6
66	Planet PLF 101	Christine/The Bells	12

HELLIONS
65	Piccadilly 7N 35213	Daydreaming Of You/Shades Of Blue	15
65	Piccadilly 7N 35232	Tomorrow Never Comes/Dream Child	15

HELLIONS

65	Piccadilly 7N 35265	A Little Lovin'/Think It Over	15

(see also Revolution, Traffic, Roaring Sixties, Jim Capaldi, Dave Mason, Luther Grosvenor)

HELLO

72	Bell BLL 1238	You Move Me/Ask Your Mama	15
73	Bell BLL 1333	Another School Day/C'mon Get Together (p/s)	15

HELL PREACHERS INC.

69	Marble Arch MALS 1169	SUPREME PSYCHEDELIC UNDERGROUND (LP)	30

(Deep Purple members are rumoured to be involved in this record)

BOBBY HELMS

57	Brunswick 05711	Fraulein/(Got A) Heartsick Feeling	6
57	Brunswick 05711	Fraulein/(Got A) Heartsick Feeling (78)	5
57	Brunswick 05721	My Special Angel/Standing At The End of My World	10
57	Brunswick 05721	My Special Angel/Standing At The End of My World (78)	5
58	Brunswick 05730	No Other Baby/The Magic Song	8
58	Brunswick 05730	No Other Baby/The Magic Song (78)	5
58	Brunswick 05741	Love My Lady/Just A Little Lonesome	7
58	Brunswick 05741	Love My Lady/Just A Little Lonesome (78)	5
58	Brunswick 05748	Jacqueline/Living In The Shadow Of The Past	7
58	Brunswick 05748	Jacqueline/Living In The Shadow Of The Past (78)	5
58	Brunswick 05754	Schoolboy Crush/Borrowed Dreams	10
58	Brunswick 05754	Schoolboy Crush/Borrowed Dreams (78)	6
58	Brunswick 05765	Jingle Bell Rock/Captain Santa Claus	12
58	Brunswick 05765	Jingle Bell Rock/Captain Santa Claus (78)	8
59	Brunswick 05786	Miss Memory/New River Train	6
59	Brunswick 05786	Miss Memory/New River Train (78)	5
59	Brunswick 05801	Soon It Can Be Told/I Guess I'll Miss The Prom	5
59	Brunswick 05801	Soon It Can Be Told/I Guess I'll Miss The Prom (78)	5
59	Brunswick 05813	My Lucky Day/Hurry Baby	5
59	Brunswick 05813	My Lucky Day/Hurry Baby (78)	8
61	Brunswick 05852	Sad Eyed Baby/You're The One	5
60	Brunswick OE 9461	BOBBY HELMS (EP)	25
57	Brunswick LAT 8250	SINGS TO MY SPECIAL ANGEL (LP)	40

JIMMY HELMS

63	Pye 7N 45440	Ragtime Girl/Romeo & Juliet	4
69	London HL 10255	If You Let Me/I Don't Care Who Knows It	5
73	Capitol CL 15762	My Little Devil/Magnificent Sanctuary Band	5

HELPLESS HUW

78	US US 001	Still Love You (In My Heart)	5
80	US US 002	Sid Vicious Was Innocent/Going Through The Motions/Baby We're Not In Love/When You're Weary (p/s in bag)	4

HELP YOURSELF

71	Liberty LBF 15459	Running Down Deep/Paper Leaves	6
72	United Artists UP 35355	Heaven Row/Brown Lady	4
72	United Artists UP 35466	Mommy Won't Be Home For Christmas/Johnny B. Goode	4
71	Liberty LBS 83484	HELP YOURSELF (LP)	35
72	United Artists UAS 29287	STRANGE AFFAIR (LP)	12
72	United Artists UAS 29413	BEWARE OF THE SHADOW (LP)	12
73	United Artists UDG 4001	THE RETURN OF KEN WHALEY/HAPPY DAYS (2-LP, box set [UAS 29487/FREE 1])	25

(see also Man, Deke Leonard, Shades Of Morley Brown)

HEMLOCK

73	Deram DM 379	Mr Horizontal/Beggar Man	6
73	Deram SML 1102	HEMLOCK (LP)	35

(see also Miller Anderson)

BERTHA HENDERSON/ROSA HENDERSON

60s	Jazz Collector JEL 14	THE FEMALE BLUES VOL. 2 (EP)	8

BILL HENDERSON

60	Top Rank JAR 412	Sweet Pumpkin/Joey, Joey, Joey	12
63	Stateside SL 10019	BILL HENDERSON (LP)	12

DORRIS HENDERSON

65	Columbia DB 7567	The Hangman/Leaves That Are Green	10
67	Fontana TF 811	Message To Pretty/Watch The Stars	10
65	Columbia SX 6001	THERE YOU GO (LP, with John Renbourn)	125
67	Fontana (S)TL 5385	WATCH THE STARS (LP, with John Renbourn)	60

(see also Eclection, John Renbourn)

EDDIE HENDERSON

77	Capitol CL 15937	Say You Will/The Funk Surgeon	4

EDMONIA HENDERSON

50s	Oriole 1005	Nobody Else Will Do (78)	20
50s	Tempo R 43	Mama Don't Want Sweet Man Any More/Hateful Blues (78)	8
50s	Jazz Collector L 21	Jelly Roll Blues/Lazy Daddy Blues (78)	5

FLETCHER HENDERSON

50s	Jazz Collector JE 111	FLETCHER HENDERSON JAZZ GROUP (EP)	7
50s	Jazz Collector JE 115	BIG BAND STORY VOL. 1 (EP)	7
55	London AL 3547	BIRTH OF BIG BAND JAZZ (10" LP)	15
55	HMV DLP 1066	AT CONNIE'S INN (10" LP)	12
50s	Audubon AAF-AAK	FLETCHER HENDERSON (10" 6-LP set)	60

JOE 'MR. PIANO' HENDERSON

57	Pye N 15099	Coffee Bar Jive/Forgotten Dreams (78)	5

| 63 | London REU 1376 | JOE HENDERSON (EP) .... 10 |

LORNA HENDERSON

| 60 | Oriole CB 1549 | Lollipops To Lipstick/Steady Eddie .... 5 |
| 60 | Oriole CB 1590 | A Thousand Stars/Murray, What's Your Hurry? .... 4 |

ROSA HENDERSON

25	Edison 51476	Undertaker's Blues/JOSIE MILES: Sweet Man Joe (78) 50
25	Edison 51478	Don't Advertise Your Man/VIOLA McCOY: Memphis Bound (78) 50
30s	Oriole 1001	Daddy Come Back/I've Got Somebody Now (78) 20
30s	Oriole 1006	Here Comes Baby (78) 15

WILLIE HENDERSON (& SOUL EXPLOSIONS)

70	MCA MU 1127	Funky Chicken/Oowee Baby I Love You (with Soul Explosions) 6
73	Contempo C 18	The Dance Master Pts 1 & 2 5
74	Contempo CS 9005	The Dance Master Pts 1 & 2 (reissue) 4
74	Pye Intl. 7N 25668	Gangster Boogie Bump/Let's Merengue 4

BOBBY HENDRICKS

58	London HL 8714	Itchy Twitchy Feeling/A Thousand Dreams 40
58	London HL 8714	Itchy Twitchy Feeling/A Thousand Dreams (78) 25
59	Top Rank JAR 193	Little John Green/Sincerely, Your Lover 8
61	Mercury AMT 1163	I'm Coming Home/Every Other Night 7
64	Sue WI 315	Itchy Twitchy Feeling/A Thousand Dreams (reissue) 10

JON HENDRICKS

56	Brunswick 05521	Four Brothers/Cloudburst (with Dave Lambert Singers) 5
68	Verve VS 572	No More/Rainbow's End 4
70	Philips 6006 088	I Got Soul/Slow Train 4
61	Vogue EPV 1268	A GOOT GIT-TOGETHER (EP) 7
60	Vogue LAE 12231	A GOOD GIT-TOGETHER (LP) 12
72	Philips 6438 019	LIVE (LP) 10
	(see also Dave Lambert)	

JIMI HENDRIX

66	Polydor 56139	Hey Joe/Stone Free 8
67	Track 604 001	Purple Haze/51st Anniversary (white or black label) 10/6
67	Track 604 004	The Wind Cries Mary/Highway Chile 6
67	Track 604 007	Burning Of The Midnight Lamp/The Stars That Play With Laughing Sam's Dice 6
67	Decca F 22652	How Would You Feel/You Don't Want Me (with Curtis Knight, unreleased)
67	Track 604 009	How Would You Feel/You Don't Want Me (with Curtis Knight) 8
67	London HL 10160	Hush Now/Flashing (with Curtis Knight) 8
68	Track 604 025	All Along The Watchtower/Long Hot Summer Night 6
69	Track 604 029	Crosstown Traffic/Gypsy Eyes 8
69	Track 604 033	Let Me Light Your Fire/The Burning Of The Midnight Lamp 8
70	London HL 10321	The Ballad Of Jimi/Gloomy Monday (with Curtis Knight) 6
70	London HL 7126	The Ballad Of Jimi/Gloomy Monday (with Curtis Knight, export issue) 15
70	Track 2095 001	Voodoo Chile/Hey Joe/All Along The Watchtower (initially in p/s) 8/4
70	RCA RCA 2033	No Such Animal Pts 1 & 2 (initially in p/s, with Curtis Knight) 12/5
71	Track 2094 007	Angel/Night Bird Flying 5
71	Track 2094 010	Gypsy Eyes/Remember/Purple Haze/Stone Free (initially in p/s) 10/4
72	Polydor 2001 277	Johnny B Goode/Little Wing 6
73	Reprise K 14286	Hear My Train A'Coming/Rock Me Baby 6
70s	Polydor/Sound F. Industry	Red House/Spanish Castle Magic (1-sided flexidisc with 'Rolling Stone') 10/6
80	Polydor 2608 001	6 SINGLES PACK (6 plain sleeve singles [2141 275-280], open-out card p/s) 15
81	Polydor POSPX 401	All Along The Watchtower/Foxy Lady/Purple Haze/Manic Depression (p/s) 5
82	CBS CBS A 2749	Fire/Are You Experienced (p/s) 4
67	Track 612 001/613 001	ARE YOU EXPERIENCED? (LP, mono/stereo) 25/18
67	Track 612 003	AXIS: BOLD AS LOVE (mono LP, gatefold sleeve, some with poster) 40/20
67	Track 613 003	AXIS: BOLD AS LOVE (stereo LP, gatefold sleeve, some with poster) 35/15
68	London HA/SH 8349	GET THAT FEELING (LP, with Curtis Knight) 15
68	Track 612 004/613 004	SMASH HITS (LP) 15
68	Track 613 008/009	ELECTRIC LADYLAND (2-LP, gatefold sleeve, mono/stereo) 25/20
68	London HA/SH 8369	STRANGE THINGS (LP, with Curtis Knight) 15
69	Track 613 010	ELECTRIC LADYLAND part 1 (LP) 15
69	Track 613 017	ELECTRIC LADYLAND part 2 (LP) 15
69	Track 2856 002	ELECTRIC JIMI HENDRIX (LP, mail order Record Club release) 500
70	Track Super 2406 002	BAND OF GYPSYS (LP, original doll cover) 20
70	Track Super 2406 002	BAND OF GYPSYS (LP, gatefold 'Isle Of Wight' sleeve) 15
70	Track Super 2406 002	BAND OF GYPSYS (LP, single sleeve) 15
70	Track 2407 010	ARE YOU EXPERIENCED? (LP, Backtrack 10 budget reissue) 10
70	Track 2407 011	AXIS: BOLD AS LOVE (LP, Backtrack 11 budget reissue) 10
71	Track 2408 101	THE CRY OF LOVE (LP, gatefold sleeve) 12
71	Track 2408 101	THE CRY OF LOVE (LP, red vinyl factory custom pressing) 600
71	Ember NR 5057	EXPERIENCE (LP, gatefold sleeve) 12
71	Polydor 2302 016	AT THE ISLE OF WIGHT (LP) 10
71	Reprise K 44159	RAINBOW BRIDGE (LP, gatefold sleeve) 10
72	Polydor 2302 018	HENDRIX IN THE WEST (LP, gatefold sleeve) 10
72	Ember NR 5061	MORE EXPERIENCE (LP) 10
72	Polydor 2302 020	WAR HEROES (LP) 10
73	Polydor 2302 023	BAND OF GYPSYS (reissue LP, different gatefold sleeve) 10
73	Reprise K 64017	SOUNDTRACK RECORDINGS FROM THE FILM JIMI HENDRIX (2-LP) 15
74	Polydor 2310 301	LOOSE ENDS (LP) 10
74	Ember EMB 3428	LOOKING BACK WITH JIMI HENDRIX (LP) 10
78	Polydor 2612 034	THE ESSENTIAL JIMI HENDRIX (2-LP with free 1-sided 33rpm 7" "Gloria" [JIMI 1] in special bag) 14
78	St. Michael	JIMI HENDRIX (LP) 35

Jimi HENDRIX

80	Polydor 262 5040	JIMI HENDRIX (13-LP box set)	60
80	Red Lightnin' RLP 0048	WOKE UP THIS MORNING AND FOUND MYSELF DEAD (LP, pic disc)	10
87	Polydor 833 004-1	LIVE AT WINTERLAND (2-LP with poster)	15
89	Castle Comms. HBLP 100	LIVE AND UNRELEASED — THE RADIO SHOW (5-LP)	30
89	Castle Comms. HBCD 100	LIVE AND UNRELEASED — THE RADIO SHOW (3-CD)	30
88	Polydor/HMV C88 LP 1-16	ARE YOU EXPERIENCED? (LP, box set sold via HMV stores, 1500 only)	10
88	Polydor/HMV C88 LP1-11	ARE YOU EXPERIENCED? (CD, box set, 1,500 only)	15

(see also Fat Mattress, Riot Squad, Loving Kind, Jayne Mansfield, McGough & McGear)

MARGIE HENDRIX

66	Mercury MF 976	I Call You Lover But You Ain't Nothin' But A Tramp/The Question	7
67	Mercury MF 1001	Restless/On The Right Track	12

LARRY HENLEY

64	Hickory 45 1272	My Reasons For Living/Stickin' Up For My Baby	20

(see also Newbeats, Dean & Larry)

ADRIAN HENRI

60s	Charivari	ADRIAN HENRI (LP)	10
60s	Argo PLP 1194	ADRIAN HENRI AND HUGO WILLIAMS (LP)	10

(see also Liverpool Scene, McGough & McGear)

ANN HENRY

60	Top Rank JAR 292	Like Young/Sugar Blues	4

BOB HENRY

65	Philips BF 1450	I Need Someone/Built Like A Man	10

(see also Robert Henry)

CLARENCE ('FROGMAN') HENRY

57	London HLN 8389	Ain't Got No Home/Troubles Troubles (as Clarence Henry)	150
57	London HLN 8389	Ain't Got No Home/Troubles Troubles (as Clarence Henry) (78)	30
61	Pye Intl. 7N 25078	(I Don't Know Why) But I Do/Just My Baby And Me	5
61	Pye Intl. 7N 25089	You Always Hurt The One You Love/Little Suzy	5
61	Pye Intl. 7N 25108	Lonely Street/Why Can't You	5
61	Pye Intl. 7N 25115	On Bended Knees/Standing In The Need Of Love	6
62	Pye Intl. 7N 25123	A Little Too Much/I Wish I Could Say The Same	6
62	Pye Intl. 7N 25141	Dream Myself A Sweetheart/Lost Without You	6
62	Pye Intl. 7N 25169	The Jealous Kind/Come On And Dance	6
64	London HLU 9936	Little Green Frog/Have You Ever Been Lonely	6
66	London HLU 10025	Ain't Got No Home/Baby, Ain't That Love	6
61	Pye Intl. NEP 44007	CLARENCE HENRY HIT PARADE (EP)	30
61	Pye Intl. NPL 28017	YOU ALWAYS HURT THE ONE YOU LOVE (LP)	40

RICHARD HENRY

68	Regal Zonophone RZ 3014	Oh Girl/Lay Your Head Upon My Shoulder	4

ROBERT HENRY

66	Philips BF 1476	Walk Away Like A Winner/That's All I Want	30

(see also Bob Henry)

HENRY COW

73	Virgin V 2005	THE LEGEND (LP)	10
74	Virgin V 2011	UNREST (LP)	10
75	Virgin V 2027	IN PRAISE OF LEARNING (LP)	10
76	Caroline CAD 3002	CONCERTS (LP)	10
79	Broadcast BC 1	WESTERN CULTURE (LP)	10

(see also Slapp Happy, Art Bears, Fred Frith)

HENRY'S FINAL DREAM

80s	Eskimo Vinyl ESK 1	In The Market Place/Autumn/Indian Summer (gatefold p/s)	4
80s	Eskimo Vinyl ESK 3	I Couldn't Jump/If I Knew (What Love Was)/Locked Inside Your Wardrobe (gatefold p/s with insert)	4

HENRY III

67	Island WI 3078	Thank You Girl/Take Me Back	8
67	Island WI 3081	I'll Reach The End/DON TONY LEE: Lee's Special	8
67	RCA RCA 1568	So Much Love/Sitting In The Park	10

JUDY HENSKE

65	Reprise RS 6203	DEATH DEFYING (LP)	15

JUDY HENSKE & JERRY YESTER

66	Reprise RS 20485	Road To Nowhere/Sing A Rainbow	5
69	Straight STS 1052	FAREWELL ALDEBARAN (LP)	20

ROBERT HENRY HENSLEY

68	Polydor 56295	You're Gonna See Me Cry/Montage	8

NICKY HENSON

63	Parlophone R 4976	Till I See You Cry/What Does It Mean	6

DAVID HENTSCHEL

75	Ring O' 2017 101	Oh My My/Devil Woman (die-cut custom sleeve)	4
75	Ring O' 2320 101	STA*RTLING MUSIC (LP)	10

NAT HEPBURN

60s	Jump Up JU 516	River/Political Girl	4

HEP STARS

66	Decca F 22446	Sunny Girl/No Response	25
67	Olga OLE 001	Wedding/Consolation	15
68	Olga OLE 013	Let It Be Me/Groovy Summertime (withdrawn)	45
68	Olga OLE 014	Malaika/It's Nice To Be Back (some in p/s)	25/15

| 68 | Olga S 064 | Let It Be Me/Groovy Summertime | 25 |

(see also Abba)

HEPTONES
66	Rio R 104	Gunmen Coming To Town/TOMMY McCOOK & SUPERSONICS: Riverton City	8
67	Ska Beat JB 266	We've Got Love/I Am Lonely	8
67	Caltone TONE 105	Schoolgirls/Ain't That Bad	10
67	Studio One SO 2005	A Change Is Gonna Come/Nobody Knows	15
67	Studio One SO 2014	Fat Girl/DELROY WILSON: Mother Word	15
67	Studio One SO 2021	If I Knew/Festival Day	15
67	Studio One SO 2026	Why Did You Leave/GAYLADS: Don't Try To Reach Me	15
67	Studio One SO 2027	Why Must I/SLIM SMITH: Try Again	15
67	Studio One SO 2033	Only Sixteen/Baby	12
68	Studio One SO 2049	Cry, Baby, Cry/Mama	15
68	Studio One SO 2052	Dock Of The Bay/KING ROCKY (ELLIS): The Ruler	15
68	Studio One SO 2055	Party Time/Oil In Your Lamp	15
69	Studio One SO 2083	I Shall Be Released/Love Me Always	15
68	Coxsone CS 7052	Love Won't Come Easy/Gee Wee	15
68	Coxsone CS 7068	Equal Rights/Ting-A-Ling	15
68	Coxsone CS 7082	Soul Power/Love Me Always	15
69	Bamboo BAM 11	I Shall Be Released/Love Me Always (Power)	6
70	Bamboo BAM 28	Young, Gifted and Black/SOUND DIMENSION: Joyland	5
70	Bamboo BAM 39	Young Generation/You Turned Away	5
70	Bamboo BAM 43	Message From A Blackman/SOUND DIMENSION: Jamaica Underground	5
70	Upsetter US 339	Hurry Up/Thanks We Get	6
70	Banana BA 311	Be A Man/U ROY: Shock Attack	5
71	Banana BA 325	Suspicious Minds/Haven't You Any Fight Left?	5
71	Banana BA 349	Freedom Line/SOUND DIMENSION: Version	5
72	Green Door GD 4020	Hypocrite/JOHNNY LOVER: Straight To The Head	5
72	Prince Buster PB 37	Our Day Will Come/PRINCE BUSTER: Protection	5
72	Ashanti ASH 411	I'm In The Mood For Love/TOMMY McCOOK & NOW GENERATION: Eight Years After	4
72	Duke DU 143	Save The Last Dance For Me/Be The One	4
72	Pama PM 843	You've Lost That Lovin' Feelin'/RUPIE EDWARDS ALLSTARS: Version	4
72	Pama Supreme PS 367	Save The Last Dance For Me/Save The Last Dance Version	4
72	Ackee ACK 407	I Miss You Pts 1 & 2	4
73	Grape GR 3053	Old Time/G.G. ALLSTARS: Dub	4
67	Studio One SOL 9002	THE HEPTONES (LP)	70
68	Studio One SOL 9010	ON TOP (LP)	70
72	Trojan TBL 183	THE HEPTONES AND THEIR FRIENDS MEET THE NOW GENERATION (LP)	20

HERB & KAY
| 54 | Parlophone MSP 6127 | This Ole House/Angels In The Sky | 15 |

HERBAL MIXTURE
| 66 | Columbia DB 8021 | A Love That's Died/Tailor Made | 60 |
| 66 | Columbia DB 8083 | Machines/Please Leave My MInd | 60 |

(see also Tony McPhee, Groundhogs)

HERBIE & ROYALISTS
| 68 | Saga FID 2121 | SOUL OF THE MATTER (LP) | 20 |

(see also Herbie Goins & Night-Timers)

HERBIE'S PEOPLE
65	CBS 202005	Sweet And Tender Romance/You Thrill Me To Pieces	20
66	CBS 202058	One Little Smile/You Never Know	7
67	CBS 202584	Residential Area/Humming Bird	8

HERD
65	Parlophone R 5284	Goodbye Baby, Goodbye/Here Comes The Fool	15
65	Parlophone R 5353	She Was Really Saying Something/It's Been A Long Time Baby	20
66	Parlophone R 5413	So Much In Love/This Boy's Always Been True	25
67	Fontana TF 819	I Can Fly/Diary Of A Narcissist	7
67	Fontana TF 856	From The Underworld/Sweet William	5
67	Fontana TF 887	Paradise Lost/Come On — Believe Me	4
68	Fontana TF 925	I Don't Want Our Loving To Die/Our Fairy Tale	4
68	Fontana TF 975	Sunshine Cottage/Miss Jones	6
69	Fontana TF 1011	The Game/Beauty Queen	6
73	Bumble GE 120	I Don't Want Our Loving To Die/The Game	4
73	Bumble GEX 1	From The Underworld/Paradise Lost/On My Way Home (maxi-single)	4
68	Fontana (S)TL 5458	PARADISE LOST (LP)	20
73	Bumble GEMP 5001	NOSTALGIA (LP)	15

(see also Peter Frampton, Humble Pie, Judas Jump)

HERE & NOW
78	Charly CYS 1055	End Of The Beginning/Choke A Koala (p/s)	5
79	Charly CEP 122	A Dog In Hell/Floating Anarchy Radio (p/s)	5
80	Charly NOW 1	Give And Take	4
78	Deptford Fun City DLP 02	WHAT YOU SEE ... IS WHAT YOU ARE (LP, 1 side by Alternative TV)	12

HERITAGE
| 81 | Rondelet ROUND 8 | Strange Place To Be/Misunderstood (p/s) | 10 |
| 82 | Rondelet | REMORSE CODE (LP, with insert) | 15 |

HERMAN (Chin-Loy)
71	Ackee ACK 133	Dunce Cap/AQUARIANS: Version Cap	4
71	Ackee ACK 140	Youth Man/AQUARIANS: Version	4
71	Big Shot BI 577	Tar Baby/TOMMY McCOOK: Archie	4
71	Big Shot BI 578	New Love/AUGUSTUS PABLO: The Mood	6
71	Explosion EX 2049	Love Brother/Uganda	4

MINT VALUE £

WOODY HERMAN (& HIS ORCHESTRA)

54	London HL 8013	Wooftie/Moten Stomp (as Woody Herman & New Third Herd)	20
54	London HL 8031	Fancy Woman/Eight Babies To Mind (as Woody Herman's Woodchoppers)	20
54	Capitol CL 14183	Muskrat Ramble/Woodchopper's Mambo (Woody Herman & His Orchestra)	10
55	London HL 8122	Sorry 'Bout The Whole Darned Thing/Love's A Dog (with New Third Herd)	18
55	Capitol CL 14231	Mexican Hat Trick/Sleepy Serenade (as Woody Herman & His Orchestra)	7
55	Capitol CL 14278	My Sin Is You/Have it Your Way (with Allen Sisters)	6
55	Capitol CL 14299	Kiss The Baby/Long, Long Night (as Woody Herman & New Third Herd)	6
55	Capitol CL 14333	The Girl Upstairs/You're Here, My Love (as Woody Herman & His Orchestra)	7
55	Capitol CL 14366	Love Is A Many Splendoured Thing/House Of Bamboo (as Woody Herman & His Orchestra & Singers)	6
56	Capitol CL 14522	Skinned/Skinned Again (as Woody Herman & His Orchestra)	5
56	Capitol CL 14578	To Love Again/For All We Know (as Woody Herman & His Orchestra)	5
57	HMV POP 371	Comes Love/Makin' Whoopee	5
60	Top Rank TR 5012	Blowin' Up A Storm/It's Coolin' Time (as Woody Herman Orchestra)	4
60	Philips JAZ 113	The Third Herd/Keen And Peachy	4
69	Chess CRS 8095	Hush/Light My Fire	7
54	London REP 1001	HERD FROM MARS VOL. 1 (EP, as Woody Herman & New Third Herd)	8
55	London REP 1002	HERD FROM MARS VOL. 2 (EP, as Woody Herman & New Third Herd)	8
52	Capitol LC 6560	CLASSICS IN JAZZ (10" LP)	15
52	MGM D 108	AT CARNEGIE HALL VOLUME 1 (10" LP)	15
53	MGM D 110	AT CARNEGIE HALL VOLUME 2 (10" LP)	15
53	London H-APB 1014	STOMPING AT THE SAVOY (10" LP, as Woody Herman & New Third Herd)	12
54	London H-APB 1018	MEN FROM MARS (10" LP, as Woody Herman & New Third Herd)	12
55	Columbia 33S 1060	HERE'S HERMAN (10" LP)	12
55	Columbia 33S 1068	SEQUENCE IN JAZZ (10" LP)	12
56	Brunswick LAT 8092	WOODCHOPPER'S BALL (LP)	12
58	Fontana TFR 6015	SUMMER SEQUENCE (10" LP)	12
59	Top Rank 35/038	THE HERD RIDES AGAIN (LP)	10
60	Top Rank BUY 009	MOODY WOODY (LP, as Woody Herman Orchestra featuring Charlie Byrd)	10
61	London Jazz LTZ-K 15200	AT THE MONTEREY JAZZ FESTIVAL (LP, also stereo SAH-K 6100)	10

(see also David Rose Orchestra)

HERMAN'S HERMITS

64	Columbia DB 7338	I'm Into Something Good/Your Hand In Mine	4
64	Columbia DB 7408	Show Me Girl/I Know Why	4
65	Columbia DB 7475	Silhouettes/Can't You Hear My Heartbeat	4
65	Columbia DB 7546	Wonderful Thing/Dream On	4
65	Columbia DB 7670	Just A Little Bit Better/Take Love, Give Love	4
65	Columbia DB 7791	A Must To Avoid/The Man With The Cigar	5
66	Columbia DB 7861	You Won't Be Leaving/Listen People	4
66	Columbia DB 7947	This Door Swings Both Ways/For Love	4
66	Columbia DB 8012	No Milk Today/My Reservation's Been Confirmed	4
66	Columbia DB 8076	East-West/What Is Wrong, What Is Right?	4
67	Columbia DB 8123	There's A Kind Of Hush (All Over The World)/Gaslite Street	4
67	Columbia DB 8235	Museum/Moonshine Man	4
68	Columbia DB 8237	I Can Take Or Leave Your Loving/Marcel's	4
68	Columbia DB 8404	Sleepy Joe/Just One Girl	4
68	Columbia DB 8446	Sunshine Girl/Nobody Needs To Know	4
68	Columbia DB 8504	Something's Happening/The Most Beautiful Thing In My Life	4
69	Columbia DB 8563	My Sentimental Friend/My Lady	4
69	Columbia DB 8626	Here Comes The Star/It's Alright Now	4
70	Columbia DB 8656	Years May Come, Years May Go/Smile Please	4
71	RCA RCA 2135	She's A Lady/Gold Mandela	4
72	RCA RCA 2265	The Man/Effen Curly	4
74	Buddah BDS 700	Train/Ride On The Water (withdrawn)	25
65	Columbia SEG 8380	HERMANIA (EP)	12
65	Columbia SEG 8440	MRS BROWN YOU'VE GOT A LOVELY DAUGHTER (EP)	10
65	Columbia SEG 8442	HERMAN'S HERMITS HITS (EP)	10
66	Columbia SEG 8477	A MUST TO AVOID (EP)	10
66	Columbia SEG 8503	MUSIC FROM THE SOUNDTRACK "HOLD ON" (EP)	12
67	Columbia SEG 8520	DANDY (EP)	12
65	Columbia 33SX 1727	HERMAN'S HERMITS (LP)	15
66	Columbia SX 6084	BOTH SIDES OF HERMAN'S HERMITS (LP)	15
67	Columbia S(C)X 6174	THERE'S A KIND OF HUSH ALL OVER THE WORLD (LP)	12
65	Columbia SCX 6303	MRS BROWN YOU'VE GOT A LOVELY DAUGHTER (LP, soundtrack)	10
60s	Regal SREG 1117	HERMAN'S HERMITS (LP, export issue)	12
60s	Columbia SCXC 27	THE BEST OF HERMAN'S HERMITS (LP, export issue)	20
60s	Columbia SCXC 32	THE BEST OF HERMAN'S HERMITS VOL. 2 (LP, export issue)	20
60s	Columbia SCXC 34	THERE'S A KIND OF HUSH ALL OVER THE WORLD (LP, export issue)	25
60s	Columbia SCXC 35	BLAZE (LP, export issue)	25

(see also Peter Noone)

CORRINE HERMES

83	Polydor POSPE 597	Words Of Love/Si La Vie Est Cadeau (p/s)	6

HEROES

75	United Artists UP 36016	Grown Up/Losing You	5

(see also Motors, Bram Tchaikovsky)

HERON

70	Dawn DNS 1015	Take Me Back Home/Minstrel And A King	7
71	Dawn DNX 2059	Bye And Bye/Through Time/Only A Hobo/I'm Ready To Leave (p/s)	8
70	Dawn DNLS 3010	HERON (LP, with insert)	35
72	Dawn DNLS 3025	TWICE AS NICE AT HALF THE PRICE (2-LP, with postcard)	40/35

MIKE HERON('S REPUTATION)

71	Island WIP 6101	Call Me Diamond/Lady Wonder	4

75	Neighbourhood NBH 3109	Evie/Down On My Knees After Memphis (as Mike Heron's Reputation)	4
78	Zoom ZUM 5	Sold On Your Love/Portland Rose (p/s)	4
71	Island ILPS 9146	SMILING MEN WITH BAD REPUTATIONS (LP)	12
75	Neighbourhood NBH80637	MIKE HERON'S REPUTATION (LP)	12

(see also Incredible String Band)

PAT HERVEY & TIARAS & ART SNIDER
| 67 | President PT 110 | Can't Get You Out Of My Mind/Givin' In | 8 |

HESITATIONS
69	London HLR 10180	Born Free/Push A Little Bit Harder	10
68	London HLR 10198	Impossible Dream/Nobody Knows You When You're Down & Out	8
68	London HA-R/SH-R 8360	THE NEW BORN FREE (LP)	12

CAROLYN HESTER
65	Dot DS 16750	Ain't That Rain/Ten Thousand Candles	4
65	Dot DS 16751	Playboys And Playgirls/High Flyin' Bird	4
65	Dot DS 26750	Come On Back/Three Young Men	4
65	Dot DS 26751	What Does It Get You/Now He's Gone	4
66	CBS 202409	A Reason To Believe/Early Morning Rain	5
65	Dot DLP 3604	THAT'S MY SONG (LP)	10
66	Dot DLP 3638	AT TOWN HALL (LP)	10
66	CBS (S)BPG 62033	CAROLYN HESTER (LP)	10
67	Realm RM 2338	THIS LIFE I'M LIVING (LP)	10
69	Pye Intl. NSPL 28121	THE CAROLYN HESTER COALITION (LP)	10

HEWETT SISTERS
| 59 | HMV POP 567 | Baby-O/Jerri-Lee (I Love Him So) | 12 |

BEN HEWITT
59	Mercury AMT 1041	You Break Me Up/I Ain't Givin' Up Nothin'	35
59	Mercury AMT 1055	For Quite A While/Patricia June	15
59	Mercury AMT 1084	I Want A New Girl Now/My Search	25
60	Mercury ZEP 10035	BREAK IT UP WITH BEN HEWITT (EP)	60

NICK HEYWARD
83	Arista HEYPD 3	Blue Hat For A Blue Day/Love At The Door (picture disc)	4
83	Arista HEY 4	On A Sunday/Stolen Tears//When It Started To Begin/ Love Sublime On Sunday (double pack, gatefold p/s)	4
83	Arista HEYPD 4	On A Sunday/Stolen Tears (picture disc)	4
84	Arista HEYPD 6	Warning Sign/Warning Sign (Instrumental Mix) (picture disc)	4
84	Arista HEYSPD 6	Warning Sign/Warning Sign (Instrumental Mix) (shaped picture disc)	5
85	Arista HEYSPD 8	Laura/Over The Weekend (shaped picture disc)	4

(see also Haircut 100)

ANNE HEYWOOD
| 59 | Top Rank JAR 130 | I'd Rather Have Roses (Than Riches)/Love Is | 6 |

EDDIE HEYWOOD
| 58 | Mercury 7MT 131 | Heywood's Bounce/Soft Summer Breeze | 7 |
| 64 | Stateside SS 264 | Theme From Film "The Prize"/Li'l Darlin' | 4 |

LENNIE HIBBERT & COUNT OSSIE BAND
| 69 | Doctor Bird DB 1113 | Pure Sole/PATSY: A Man Is Two Faced | 8 |

AL HIBBLER
55	Brunswick 05420	Unchained Melody/Daybreak	15
55	Brunswick 05420	Unchained Melody/Daybreak (78)	5
55	Brunswick 05454	They Say You're Laughing At Me/I Can't Put My Arms Around A Memory	12
55	London HL 8184	Now I Lay Me Down To Dream/Danny Boy	18
55	Brunswick 05492	He/Breeze (Blow My Baby Back To Me)	7
56	Brunswick 05523	The Eleventh Hour Melody/Let's Try Again	7
56	Brunswick 05552	After The Lights Go Down Low/Stella By Starlight	6
56	Brunswick 05590	Never Turn Back/Away All Boats	5
56	Brunswick 05619	Nightfall/I'm Free	5
57	Brunswick 05653	The Town Crier/Trees	5
57	Brunswick 05703	Around The Corner From The Blues/I Complain	5
58	Brunswick 05739	When Will I Forget You/My Heart Tells Me	5
58	Brunswick 05749	Honeysuckle Rose/Ain't Nothing Wrong With That Baby	5
58	Brunswick 05768	Love Land/Love Me Long, Hold Me Close, Kiss Me Warm And Tender	5
59	London HL 7086	Danny Boy/Now I Lay Me Down To Dream (export issue)	6
50s	Brunswick OE 9331	HERE'S HIBBLER PT. 1 (EP)	7
50s	Brunswick OE 9332	HERE'S HIBBLER PT. 2 (EP)	7
50s	Brunswick OE 9333	HERE'S HIBBLER PT. 3 (EP)	7
50s	HMV 7EG 8158	DUKE ELLINGTON AND AL HIBBLER (EP)	8
50s	HMV 7EG 8326	AL HIBBLER SINGS LOVE SONGS (EP)	7
56	Brunswick LAT 8140	STARRING AL HIBBLER (LP)	10

EDDIE HICKEY
59	Decca F 11153	Lady May/Cap And Gown	5
60	Decca F 11204	Who Could Be Bluer/Plain Jane	5
60	Decca F 11241	Another Sleepless Night/Barbara	6

ERSEL HICKEY
| 59 | Fontana H 198 | Don't Be Afraid of Love/You Threw A Dart | 30 |

DWAYNE HICKMAN
| 60 | Capitol CL 15164 | I'm A Lover, Not A Fighter/I Pass Your House | 8 |

HICKORY
| 69 | CBS 3963 | Green Light/Key | 25 |

(see also Equals)

COLIN HICKS (& CABIN BOYS)
57	Pye 7N 15114	Wild Eyes And Tender Lips/Empty Arms Blues (with Cabin Boys)	15
58	Pye 7N 15125	La Dee Dah/Wasteland	8
58	Pye 7N 15163	Little Boy Blue/Jambalaya	10

DAN HICKS & HIS HOT LICKS
72	Blue Thumb ILPS 9204	STRIKING IT RICH (LP)	10

EDNA HICKS
23	HMV B 1703	I'm Going Away (Just To Wear You Off My Mind)/ LIZZIE MILES: You're Always Messin' Around With My Man (78)	50
25	Guardsman 7003	You've Got Everything A Sweet Man Needs/ DAISY CLIFF: West Indies Blues (78)	75
30s	Poydras 79	Tin Roof Blues/Oh Daddy Blues (78)	20

(see also Lila Vivian (Edna Hicks), Viola McCoy (Daisy Cliff))

HIDDEN STRENGTH
76	United Artists UAS 29949	HIDDEN STRENGTH (LP)	12

HIDEAWAYS
69	Action ACT 4544	Hide Out/Jolly Joe	5
72	Jay Boy BOY 29	Hide Out/Jolly Joe (reissue)	4

HI-FI FOUR
56	Parlophone MSP 6210	Band Of Gold/Davy, You Upset My Life	60
56	Parlophone R 4130	Band Of Gold/Davy, You Upset My Life (78)	20

HI FI'S
63	Piccadilly 7N 35130	Take Me Or Leave Me/I'm Struck	6
64	Pye 7N 15635	Will Yer Won't Yer/She's The One	6
64	Pye 7N 15710	I Keep Forgettin'/Why Can't I Stop Loving You	20
65	Pye 7N 15788	Baby's In Black/Kiss And Run	10
66	Alp 595 010	It's Gonna Be Morning/I Wanna Hear You Say Yeah	30

(Joe) HIGGS & (Roy) WILSON
60	Blue Beat BB 3	Manny Oh/When You Tell Me Baby	12
61	Starlite ST45 035	Pretty Baby/I Long For The Day	15
61	Starlite ST45 036	Lover's Song/It Is A Day	15
61	Starlite ST45 042	Come On Home/The Robe	15
61	Starlite ST45 053	Sha Ba Ba/Change Of Mind	15
62	Blue Beat BB 95	How Can I Be Sure/Mighty Man	10
63	R&B JB 109	Let Me Know/Bye And Bye	8
63	Blue Beat BB 190	If You Want A Pardon/BABA BROOKS BAND: Musical Communion	8
63	Island WI 081	Lazy Saturday Night/BUSTER'S ALLSTARS: Going West	8
64	Rio R 29	Love Is Not For Me/Gone Is Yesterday	8

(see also Roy Wilson)

JOE HIGGS
67	Coxsone CS 7004	Neighbour Neighbour/MELODIANS: I Should Have Made It Up	12
67	Island WI 3026	I Am The Song/Worry No More	10
68	Island WI 3131	You Hurt My Soul/LYNN TAITT: Why Am I Treated So Bad	8

HIGH
69	CBS 4164	Long Live The High/Beggar Man Dan	8

HIGH & MIGHTY
66	HMV POP 1548	Tryin' To Stop Cryin'/Escape From Cuba	25

HIGH BROOM
70	Island WI 6088	Dancing In The Moonlight/Percy's On The Run	6

HIGH KEYS
63	London HLK 9768	Que Sera Sera/Daddy, Ooh Long Legs	10

HIGH NUMBERS
64	Fontana TF 480	I'm The Face/Zoot Suit	200
64	Fontana TF 480	Zoot Suit/I'm The Face (re-pressing with reversed sides)	225
80	Back Door DOOR 4	I'm The Face/Zoot Suit (reissue, p/s)	10

(see also Who)

HIGH SOCIETY
66	Fontana TF 771	People Passing By/Star Of Eastern Street	12

(see also Friday Browne, Graham Gouldman, Country Gentlemen, Manchester Mob)

HIGH SOCIETY
70s	AFC	Three Hippies In A Gas Chamber	10

HIGH TIDE
69	Liberty LBS 83264	SEA SHANTIES (LP)	40
70	Liberty LBS 83294	HIGH TIDE (LP)	40
84	Psycho PSYCHO 26	SEA SHANTIES (LP, reissue)	12
84	Psycho PSYCHO 27	HIGH TIDE (LP, reissue)	12

(see also Misunderstood, Denny Gerrard)

HIGH TIDE
81	Sunday Morning	Baby Dancing/Letter From A Coward (no p/s, mail order only)	10
82	WEA K 18930	Dancing In My Mind/Electric Blue (p/s)	5

DEAN HIGHTOWER
60	HMV CLP 1360	TWANGY — WITH A BEAT (LP)	20

DONNA HIGHTOWER
59	Capitol CL 15048	Lover, Come Back To Me/Because Of You	4
59	Capitol CL 15049	Ain't That Love/Forgive Them	4
60	Capitol ST 1273	GEE BABY (LP)	12

ROSETTA HIGHTOWER
68	Toast TT 506	Pretty Red Balloons/How Can You Mistreat (The One You Love)	5
68	Toast TT 509	I Can't Give Back The Love I Feel For You/Big Bird	5
69	CBS 4584	One Heart For Sale/What Do I Do	4
71	CBS 7668	Go Pray for Tomorrow/Give Me Just A Little More Time	6
73	Philips 6006 291	The Walls Fell Down/Captain's Army	4

HIGHWAY
74	EMI EMA 3019	HIGHWAY (LP)	12
75	EMI EMA 770	SMOKING AT THE EDGE (LP)	12

HIGHWAYMEN
62	United Artists UP 1001	Birdman (with narration from Burt Lancaster)/Cindy Oh Cindy	5
	United Artists	LPs	10

HIGH WINDOWS
68	CBS 3208	Maybe Someday/Your Eyes	4

HIGSONS
81	Romans In Britain HIG 2	I Don't Want To Live With Monkeys/Insect Love (p/s)	4
81	Waap WAAP 1	Got To Let This Heat Out/It Goes Waap (p/s)	4
81	Waap 12 WAAP 1	Got To Let This Heat Out/It Goes Waap (12", p/s)	7

HILARY HILARY
80	Modern STP 2	How Come You're So Dumb/Rich Kid Blues (p/s)	30
	(see also Roger Taylor, Queen)		

DIANE HILDEBRANDE
69	Elektra EKSN 45055	Jan's Blues/Early Morning Blues And Greens	4

HI LITES
65	London HL 9967	Hey Baby/Groovey	4

HI-LITERS
59	Mercury AMT 1011	Cha Cha Rock/Dance Me To Death	50

ALEX HILL
53	Vocalion V-1027	Stompin' 'Em Down/Track Head Blues (78)	15

BENNY HILL
55	Decca F 10442	I Can't Tell A Waltz From A Tango/Teach Me Tonight	8
56	Columbia SCM 5238	Memories Are Made Of This/Who Done It (as Benny Hill & Coronets)	6
61	Pye 7N 15327	Gather In The Mushrooms/Pepys' Diary	4
65	Pye 7N 15974	What A World/I'll Never Know	4
66	Pye 7N 17026	My Garden Of Love/The Andalucian Gypsies	4
66	Pye NPL 18133	SINGS? (LP)	10
	(see also Coronets)		

BUNKER HILL & RAYMEN
62	Stateside SS 135	Hide & Seek Pts 1 & 2	10

CHIPPIE HILL/HOCIEL THOMAS
72	Collectors Edition 1001	CHIPPIE HILL AND HOCIEL THOMAS (LP)	12

DAVID HILL
57	Vogue V 9076	All Shook Up/Melody For Lovers (with Ray Ellis Orchestra)	100
58	RCA RCA 1041	That's Love/Keep Me In Mind (with Joe Reisman's Orchestra & Chorus)	150

HONEY HILL
30s	Vocalion S 223	Boogie Woogie/Set 'Em (78)	25

JESSIE HILL
60	London HLU 9117	Ooh Poo Pah Doo Pts 1 & 2	15

VINCE HILL
62	Piccadilly 7N 35043	The Rivers Run Dry/Not Any More	4
62	Piccadilly 7N 35068	There You Go/Just As Long As (You Belong To Me)	4
63	Piccadilly 7N 35108	Day At The Seaside/Tricks Of The Trade	4
63	Piccadilly 7N 35148	Blue Velvet/Like Anything	4
64	Piccadilly 7N 35161	If You Knew/Fools & Lovers	4
64	Piccadilly 7N 35192	It's Only Make Believe/Let The Wind Blow	4
66	Columbia SEG 8509	FOUR SIDES OF VINCE HILL (EP)	7
66	Columbia S(C)X 6018	HAVE YOU MET? (LP)	10
66	Columbia S(C)X 6046	HEARTACHES (LP)	10
67	Columbia S(C)X 6096	AT THE CLUB (LP)	10
67	Columbia S(C)X 6141	EDELWEISS (LP)	10
68	Columbia S(C)X 6185	ALWAYS YOU AND ME (LP)	10
69	Columbia S(C)X 6304	YOU FORGOT TO REMEMBER (LP)	10
	(see also [Jackie] Raindrops)		

Z.Z. HILL
65	R&B MRB 5005	Have Mercy Someone/Someone To Love Me	20
69	Action ACT 4532	Make Me Yours/What Am I Living For	15
72	Mojo 2092 019	Faithful And True/I Think I'd Do It	4
75	United Artists UP 35727	I Keep On Loving You/Whoever's Thrilling You	8
77	CBS 5553	Love Is So Good When You're Stealin' It/Need You By My Side	4
66	Sue IEP 711	GIMME GIMME (EP, with Intentions)	35
69	Action ACLP 6004	WHOLE LOT OF SOUL (LP)	18
72	Mojo 2916 013	THE BRAND NEW Z.Z. HILL (LP)	12
75	Contempo CLP 515	THE BRAND NEW Z.Z. HILL (LP, reissue)	10

STEVE HILLAGE
76	Virgin VS 161	It's All Too Much/Shimmer	4
77	Virgin VS 171	Hurdy Gurdy Man/Om Nama Shivaya	4
77	Virgin VS 197	Not Fade Away/Saucer Surfing	4

Steve HILLAGE

78	Virgin VS 212	Getting Better/Palm Trees (Love Guitar) (p/s) 4
78	Virgin V 2098	GREEN (LP, green vinyl) 10
79	Virgin VR 1	RAINBOW DOME MUSICK (LP, clear vinyl) 10

(see also Gong, Khan, Arzachel, Clearlight, Radio Actors, System 7)

HILLER BROTHERS

| 70s | Honey Hit TB 124 | Little Darlin'/Changin' My Mind (p/s) ....5 |

JANE HILLERY

| 66 | Columbia DB 7918 | You've Got That Hold On Me/Take Me Away ....15 |

(see also Magistrates)

MABLE HILLERY

| 69 | Xtra XTRA 1063 | IT'S SO HARD TO BE A NIGGER (LP) ....15 |

HILLTOPPERS

52	Vogue V 9045	Trying/You Made Up My Mind (78) 6
53	London L 1204	P.S. I Love You/I'd Rather Die Young (78) 5
54	London HL 8003	Love Walked In/To Be Alone (78) 8
54	London HL 8026	From The Vine Came The Grape/Time Will Tell 30
54	London HL 8070	Poor Butterfly/Wrapped Up In A Dream 25
54	London HL 8081	Will You Remember/The Old Cabaret 25
54	London HL 8092	If I Didn't Care/Bettina 25
55	London HL 8116	Time Waits For No One/You Try Somebody Else 20
55	London HLD 8168	The Kentuckian Song/I Must Be Dreaming 20
55	London HLD 8208	Searching/All I Need Is You 20
56	London HLD 8221	Only You (And You Alone)/(It Will Have To Do) Until The Real Thing Comes Along 20
56	London HLD 8255	My Treasure/Last Word In Love 20
56	London HLD 8278	Do The Bop/When You're Alone 45
56	London HLD 8298	Tryin'/D-A-R-L-I-N' 18
56	London HLD 8333	So Tired/Faded Rose 18
57	London HLD 8381	Marianne/You're Wasting Your Time 18
57	London HLD 8441	I'm Serious/I Love My Girl 15
57	London HLD 8455	A Fallen Star/Footsteps 15
57	London HLD 8528	The Joker/Chicken, Chicken 18
58	London HLD 8603	You Sure Look Good To Me/Starry Eyes 10
60	London HLD 9038	Alone/The Prisoner's Song 6
55	London REP 1012	PRESENTING THE HILLTOPPERS (EP) 20
55	London RED 1030	THE HILLTOPPERS VOL. 2 (EP) 20
57	London RED 1099	THE HILLTOPPERS VOL. 3 (EP) 20
57	London HA-D 2029	THE TOWERING HILLTOPPERS (LP) 25
57	London HA-D 2071	TOPS IN POPS (LP) 22

(see also Sacca, Billy Vaughn)

HI-LO'S

62	Reprise RS 20095	A Taste Of Honey/My Baby Just Cares For Me 4
57	London REU 1077	UNDER GLASS (EP) 9
58	London RER 1110	THE HI-LOS (EP) 9
57	London HA-U 2026	UNDER GLASS (LP) 15
50s	Philips BBL 7154	SUDDENLY IT'S THE HI-LO'S (LP) 15
60	Philips BBL 7411	ALL OVER THE PLACE (LP, also stereo SBBL 589) 10/12
60s	Omega XSD 11	IN STEREO (LP) 12
60s	Reprise R 6034	HAPPEN TO FOLK SONGS (LP) 10

RONNIE HILTON

55	HMV 7M 285	Prize Of Gold/A Blossom Fell 12
55	HMV 7M 303	Just Say You Love Her/My Loving Hands 10
56	HMV 7M 336	Bella Notte/He 10
56	HMV 7M 358	Young And Foolish/Moments To Remember 12
56	HMV 7M 382	The Last Frontier/Here Comes My Love 8
56	HMV 7M 390	No Other Love/It's All Been Done Before (B-side with Alma Cogan) 25
56	HMV 7M 413	Who Are We/Give Me My Ranch 12
56	HMV POP 248	A Woman In Love/I Just Found Out About Love 12
56	HMV POP 274	Two Different Worlds/Constant And True 12
57	HMV POP 291	The Wisdom Of A Fool/Amore 7
57	HMV POP 307	For Your Love/Once 5
57	HMV POP 318	Heart/Penny Serenade 5
57	HMV POP 338	Around The World/I'd Give You The World 6
57	HMV POP 364	The Miracle Of Love/Wonderful! Wonderful! 6
57	HMV POP 393	Marching Along To The Blues/She 4
57	HMV POP 422	That's Why I Was Born/The Moonraker's Song 4
58	HMV POP 437	I'll Buy You A Star/You Should Belong To Me 4
58	HMV POP 446	Magic Moments/One Blade Of Grass (In A Meadow) 5
58	HMV POP 468	I May Never Pass This Way Again/Love Walked In 5
58	HMV POP 479	On The Street Where You Live/I've Grown Accustomed To Her Face 4
58	HMV POP 497	Her hair Was Yellow/Let Me Stay With You 4
58	HMV POP 556	The Day The Rains Came/Do I Love You (Because You're Beautiful) 4
58	HMV POP 559	The World Outside/As I Love You 4
59	HMV POP 560	Gigi (Gaston's Soliloquy)/Keep Your Kisses 4
59	HMV POP 638	The Wonder Of You/A Hundred Miles From Everywhere 4
67	HMV POP 1600	If I Were A Rich Man/Laughing Gnome 4
68	Columbia DB 8506	Glory Glory Leeds United/We Shall Not Be Moved (with Leeds United AFC) 4
50s	HMV 7EG 8121	THE STAR OF SONG (EP) 7
50s	HMV 7EG 8149	HEY THERE (EP) 7
57	HMV 7EG 8198	FOR THOSE IN LOVE (EP) 7
57	HMV 7EG 8202	FOR THOSE IN LOVE NO. 2 (EP) 7
58	HMV 7EG 8352	THE HITS FROM 'MY FAIR LADY' (EP, 1 side by Alma Cogan) 8
55	HMV DLP 1109	BY THE FIRESIDE (10" LP) 20

| 59 | HMV CLP 1295 | I'M BEGINNING TO SEE THE LIGHT (LP) | 12 |

(see also Alma Cogan)

HILTONAIRES
| 67 | Coxsone CSL 8004 | THE BEST OF THE HILTONAIRES (LP) | 70 |

HIM & OTHERS
| 66 | Parlophone R 5510 | I Mean It/She's Got Eyes That Tell Lies | 175 |

JUSTIN HINDS & DOMINOES
64	Ska Beat JB 176	King Samuel/River Jordan	8
65	Ska Beat JB 187	Mother Banner/DON DRUMMOND & HIS GROUP: Apanga	8
65	Island WI 171	Botheration/Satan	7
65	Island WI 174	Jump Out Of The Frying Pan/Early One Morning	10
65	Island WI 194	Love Up, Push Up/The Ark	10
65	Island WI 236	Love And Peace/SKATALITES: Ska-La-Rama	10
66	Doctor Bird DB 1048	The Higher The Monkey Climbs/Fight For Your Right	10
67	Island WI 3048	On A Saturday Night/Save A Bread	10
67	Treasure Isle TI 7002	Here I Stand/No Good Rudie	10
67	Treasure Isle TI 7005	Carry Go Bring Come/Fight Too Much	10
67	Treasure Isle TI 7014	On A Saturday Night/Save A Bread	10
67	Treasure Isle TI 7017	Once A Man/TOMMY McCOOK & SUPERSONICS: Persian Cat	10
68	Treasure Isle TI 7063	Botheration/VINCENT HINDS: Mouth Trombone	7
68	Treasure Isle TI 7068	Mighty Redeemer Pts 1 & 2	7
69	Trojan TR 652	You Should've Known Better/TOMMY McCOOK & SUPERSONICS: Third Figure	7
70	Duke Reid DR 2511	Say Me Say/I Want It	7
70	Duke DU 67	Drink Milk/Everywhere I Go	6

NEVILLE HINDS
| 70 | Duke Reid DR 2503 | Sunday Gravy/JOHN HOLT: Write Her A Letter | 7 |
| 72 | Upsetter US 384 | Blackman's Time/UPSETTERS: Version | 6 |

(see also Neville Irons)

GRAHAM HINE
| 69 | Liberty LBS 83252 | GASOLINE (LP) | 10 |

RUPERT HINE
72	Purple PUR 105	Hamburgers/Varlet Lad T'was Samuel Green	4
76	Electric WOT 8	Snakes Don't Dance Fast/Hopi Smile	4
71	Purple TPSA 7502	PICK UP A BONE (LP)	10

BABE HINES
| 30s | Vocalion S 245 | I've Lost My Head Over You/This Is The End (78) | 20 |

EARL 'FATHA' HINES
50s	HMV 7EG 8114	EARL HINES AND HIS ORCHESTRA (EP, 1 track with Billy Eckstine)	7
50s	MGM MGM-EP 573	MIDNIGHT IN NEW ORLEANS (EP, as Earl Hines All Stars)	7
54	Mercury MG 25018	EARL HINES AND HIS ALL STARS (10" LP)	12
55	Vogue Coral LRA 10031	FATS WALLER SONGS (10" LP)	12
55	Columbia 33S 1063	PIANO MOODS (10" LP)	12
60	MGM C 833	EARL'S PEARLS (LP,as Earl 'Fatha' Hines Quartet)	10
65	Stateside SL 10116	SPONTANEOUS EXPLORATIONS (LP)	10
67	Fontana SFJL 902	BLUES IN THIRDS (LP)	10
67	Fontana TL 5378	JAZZ MEANS HINES! (LP)	10

(see also Louis Armstrong)

FRAZER HINES
| 68 | Major Minor MM 579 | Who's Dr. Who/Punch And Judy Man | 4 |

HINES & ELDRIDGE
| 69 | Mercury SMWL 21041 | HINES AND ELDRIDGE WITH COLEMAN HAWKINS VOLUME 2 (LP) | 10 |

(see also Coleman Hawkins)

HINES, HINES & DAD
| 68 | CBS 3667 | Something Extra/Hambone | 5 |

HINGE
| 68 | RCA RCA 1721 | Village Postman/You'd Better Go Home | 18 |

JOE HINTON
| 64 | Vocalion VP 9224 | Funny How Time Slips Away/You Gotta Have Love | 15 |
| 66 | Vocalion VP 9258 | Just A Kid Named Joe/Pledging My Love | 8 |

HI-NUMBERS
| 65 | Decca F 12233 | Heart Of Stone/Dancing In The Street | 30 |

HIPPY BOYS
69	Trojan TR 668	Love/The Whole World	4
69	Trojan TR 669	Michael Row The Boat Ashore/Guess Who's Coming To Dinner	4
69	Bullet BU 412	Hog In A Me Minte/Lorna Run	4
69	Bullet BU 413	What's Your Excuse/Tell me Tell	4
69	Camel CA 29	Cat Nip/Cooyah (both as Hippie Boys)	4
69	High Note HS 021	Doctor No Go/Sailing (B-side actually "Faberge" by Baba Brooks & Band)	5
69	High Note HS 030	Chicken Lickin'/BABA BROOKS: Old Man Flint	6
69	High Note HS 035	Reggae Pressure/It Hurts	4
70	High Note HS 038	Nigeria Hop/Nigeria	4
69	Big Shot BSLP 5005	REGGAE WITH THE HIPPY BOYS (LP, actually on High Note label)	25

HIPSTER IMAGE
| 65 | Decca F 12137 | Can't Let Her Go/Make Her Mine | 30 |

HIPSWAY
| 85 | Mercury MER 195 | Ask The Lord/Pain Machine//The Broken Years/Forbidden (shrink-wrapped double pack with sticker) | 4 |

85	Mercury MER(X) 195	Ask The Lord/Pain Machine (stickered poster p/s) 4
85	Mercury MER 1952	Ask The Lord/Pain Machine (film pack with video stills, gatefold p/s) 4
85	Mercury MERX 1952	Ask The Lord (12")/Ask The Lord (7")//Pain Machine/The Broken Years
		(12", double folder pack) 8
86	Mercury LORDF 112	Ask The Lord (Extended)/Ask The Lord (New Extended Version)/
		Are You Ready To Listen//Main Theme From Film "Ask The Lord"/
		End Titles (12"/7" double folder pack) 8
86	Mercury MERDP 212	Honey Thief/Wild Sorrow//The Broken Years/Forbidden
		(double pack, envelope sleeve) 4
86	Mercury MERXD 212	Honey Thief (Extended)/Honey Thief (7" Version)/Wild Sorrow/Honey Thief
		(Marketing Mix)/Broken Years (12" Mix) (12" double pack in folder) 7

(see also Jazzateers)

AL HIRT
60	HMV POP 749	Tin Roof Blues/The Original Dixieland One Step (as Al Hirt's Jazz Band) 4
67	RCA RCA 1590	Theme From "The Monkees"/Tarzan March 5
68	RCA RCA 1662	Keep The Ball Rolling/Manhattan Safari 4
68	RCA RCA 1685	The Glory Of Love/Calypsoul 4

HIS NAME IS ALIVE
| 80s | 4AD HNIA 1 | How Ghosts Affect Relationships/If July (freebie, no p/s) ....8 |

HI-SPOTS
58	Melodisc 1457	Lend Me Your Comb/I Don't Hurt Anymore 15
58	Melodisc 1457	Lend Me Your Comb/I Don't Hurt Anymore (78) 5
58	Melodisc 1473	Secretly/I Got 10
58	Melodisc 1473	Secretly/I Got (78) 5

ROBYN HITCHCOCK (& THE EGYPTIANS)
81	Armageddon AS 008	The Man Who Invented Himself/Dancing On God's Thumb (p/s, some with
		flexi "It's A Mystic Trip"/"Grooving On An Inner Plane" [4 SPURT 1]) 12/7
82	Albion ION 103	America/It Was The Night/How Do You Work This Thing (p/s) 6
82	Midnight Music DING 2	Eaten By Her Own Dinner/Listening To The Higsons/Dr. Sticky (p/s) 6
83	Albion 12 ION 1036	Nightride To Trinidad (Long Version)/Kingdom Of Love/Midnight Fish (12", p/s) ..7
86	Glass Fish OOZE 1	If You Were A Priest/The Crawling (p/s) 6
84	Bucketfull Of Brains BOB 8	Happy The Golden Prince (flexidisc with 'Bucketfull Of Brains' mag) 8/6
84	Bucketfull Of Brains BOB 8	Happy The Golden Prince (hard vinyl white label test pressing, 20 only) 30
86	Midnight Music BM 80	EXPLODING IN SILENCE (LP, picture disc) 10

(see also Soft Boys, Knox)

HI-TENSION
77	Island IPR 2007	Hi-Tension/Girl I Bet Cha (12") 10
79	Island WIP 6493	There's A Reason/If It Moves You 5
79	Island 12 WIP 6493	There's A Reason/If It Moves You (12") 12
78	Island ILPS 9564	HI-TENSION (LP, with poster) 10

HI-TONES
| 63 | Island WI 086 | Ten Virgins/Too Young To Love ....10 |
| 63 | R&B JB 123 | You Hold The Key/DON DRUMMOND: Rock Away ....10 |

HIT PACK
| 65 | Tamla Motown TMG 513 | Never Say No To Your Baby/Let's Dance ....45 |

HIT PARADE
84	JSH JSH 1	Forever/Stop (die-cut p/s) 8
84	JSH JSH 2	My Favourite Girl/It Rained On Monday Morning (die-cut p/s) 7
85	JSH JSH 3	The Sun Shines In Gerrards Cross/You Hurt Me Too (die-cut p/s) 6
85	JSH JSH 4	You Don't Love Me Then/Huevo's Mexicana (die-cut p/s with card) 6
86	JSH JSH 5	See You In Havana/Wipe Away The Tears (die-cut p/s) 5
87	JSH JSH 6	I Get So Sentimental/Sue (die-cut p/s) 4

HIT SQUAD
| 88 | Eastern Bloc EASTERN 01 | Wax On The Melt/SPM MC Tunes/Shure.4 (12", white label promo, |
| | | plain stickered sleeve) ....60 |

(see also 808 State)

HITTERS
| 73 | United Artists UP 35530 | Hypocrite/The Version ....5 |

(see also Brinsley Schwarz)

HOAX
80	Hologram HOAX 1	ONLY THE BLIND CAN SEE IN THE DARK (EP) 5
81	Hologram HOAX 3	SO WHAT (12" EP, p/s) 7
82	Hologram HOAX 4	Quiet In The Sixpenny (p/s) 4

HOBBIES OF TODAY
| 78 | Waxworks H.O.T. WAX 01 | Metal Boys/Tight Rope Walker (p/s) ....5 |

HOBBIT
| 70s | Deroy private pressing | FIRST AND LAST (LP) ....75 |

HOBBITS
68	Decca AD 1004	Daffodil Days (The Affection Song)/Sunny Day Girl (export issue) 8
68	MCA MU 1002	Daffodil Days (The Affection Song)/Sunny Day Girl 4
67	MCA MUP 301	DOWN TO MIDDLE EARTH (LP) 15

HOBBS
| 78 | Big SOLD 4 | Bop Around The Shop/(You've Got Me In A) Whirl Girl (gatefold p/s) ....4 |

HOBBY SHOP
| 68 | Columbia DB 8395 | Why Must It Be This Way/Talk To Me ....5 |

HOBOKEN
| 73 | Oak | HOBOKEN (LP, 6 copies only!) ....500 |

EDMUND HOCKRIDGE

53	Parlophone MSP 6027	Luck Be A Lady/I'll Know	4
53	Parlophone MSP 6028	I've Never Been In Love Before/My Time Of Day	4
56	Pye NEP 24019	EDMUND HOCKRIDGE (EP)	7
57	Pye NEP 24026	BY THE FOUNTAINS OF ROME (EP)	7

CHRIS HODGE

72	Apple APPLE 43	We're On Our Way/Supersoul (initially in p/s)	20/5
74	RCA LPBO 5007	Beautiful Love/Sweet Lady From The Sky	4
74	DJM DJS 10337	I Love You/Old James Dean	4

MARVA HODGE

70	Polydor BM 56792	The Ghetto/Sometimes	5

CHARLES HODGES

69	Major Minor MM 654	Try A Little Love/Someone To Love	15

(see also Cliff Bennett & Rebel Rousers, Outlaws)

EDDIE HODGES

61	London HLA 9369	I'm Gonna Knock On Your Door/Ain't Gonna Wash For A Week	7
62	London HLA 9505	Bandit Of My Dreams/Mugmates	10
62	London HLA 9576	(Girls, Girls, Girls) Made To Love/I Make Believe It's You	5
63	MGM MGM 1232	Just A Kid In Love/Avalanche	4
65	Stateside SS 442	New Orleans/Hard Times For Young Lovers	4
65	Stateside SS 469	Love Minus Zero — No Limit/The Water Is Over My Head	4
62	London REA 1353	EDDIE HODGES (EP)	35

JOHNNY HODGES & HIS ORCHESTRA

61	HMV CLP 1430	BLUES-A-PLENTY (LP)	10

HOFFMANN & HOFFMANN

83	CBS A 3396	Love Gives/I Need You Now	4

ANNE HOGAN

85	Doublevision DVR 9	PLAYS KICKABYE (12" EP)	10

(see also Marc Almond)

SILAS HOGAN

71	Blue Horizon 2431 008	TROUBLE AT HOME (LP)	50
70s	Flyright FLY 595	I'M A FREE-HEARTED MAN (LP)	10

HOGARTH

68	Liberty LBF 15156	Suzie's Getting Married/I've Been Dreaming	5

SMOKEY HOGG

64	Realm RM 197	I'M SO LONELY (LP)	20
71	Ember EMB 3405	SINGS THE BLUES (LP)	15

(see also John Lee Hooker/Lightnin' Hopkins/Smokey Hogg)

HOGS

69	Jay Boy BOY 5	It's All Coming To Me Now/Motor Cycle Rider	4

HOHOKAM

84	Numa NU 3	King/The American Way (p/s)	4
84	Numa NUM 3	King/The American Way (12", p/s)	7

(see also Gary Numan)

SUZI JANE HOKUM

66	MGM 1323	Need All The Help I Can Get/Home	4

HOKUS POKE

72	Vertigo 6360 064	EARTH HARMONY (LP)	60

RON HOLDEN

60	London HLU 9116	Love You So/My Babe	30

FRANK HOLDER

57	Decca F 10880	The Caterpillar Bush/Red Beans And Rice	4
57	Decca F 10908	Battle Of The Century/Chinese Cricket Match	4
57	Decca F 10919	Champion Calypso/Sweetie Charlie	4
56	Nixa NPT 19007	CALYPSO TIME WITH FRANK HOLDER (10" LP)	10

(see also Johnny Dankworth)

RAM JOHN HOLDER

67	Columbia DB 8157	I Need Somebody/She's Alright	5
67	Columbia DB 8262	My Friend Jones/It Won't Be Long Before I Love You	5
71	Beacon 3-108	I Just Came To Get My Baby/Yes I Do	4
74	Beacon BEAS 2	BLACK LONDON BLUES (LP)	30
74	Beacon BEAS 17	BOOTLEG BLUES (LP)	20

RAM HOLDER BROTHERS

66	Parlophone R 5471	Just Across The River/Ram Blues	12

(see also Ram John Holder)

BILLIE HOLIDAY

56	Vogue V 2048	Detour Ahead/Blue, Turning Grey Over You	6
59	MGM MGM 1033	Don't Worry About Me/Just One More Chance	6
55	Brunswick OE 9172	LADY DAY VOL. 1 (EP)	8
56	Brunswick OE 9199	LADY DAY VOL. 2 (EP)	8
56	Brunswick OE 9251	LADY DAY VOL. 3 (EP)	8
55	Columbia Clef SEB 10009	BILLIE HOLIDAY (EP)	8
56	Columbia Clef SEB 10035	AN EVENING WITH BILLIE HOLIDAY (EP)	8
56	Columbia Clef SEB 10048	BILLIE HOLIDAY SINGS (EP)	8
59	Fontana TFE 17010	LADY DAY (EP)	8
60	Fontana TFE 17026	BLUE (EP)	8

MINT VALUE £

50s	Melodisc EPM7 125	EMBRACEABLE YOU (EP)	10
50s	Vogue EPV 1128	BILLIE HOLIDAY (EP)	10
54	Columbia 33S 1034	BILLIE HOLIDAY (10" LP)	15
54	Brunswick LA 8676	LOVER MAN (10" LP)	15
55	Philips BBR 8032	FAVOURITES (10" LP)	15
56	Columbia Clef 33C 9023	AT JAZZ AT THE PHILHARMONIC (10" LP)	15
56	Columbia Clef 33CX 10019	MUSIC FOR TORCHING (LP)	15
57	Columbia Clef 33CX 10064	VELVET MOOD (LP)	15
57	Columbia Clef 33CX 10076	SOLITUDE (LP)	15
57	Columbia Clef 33CX 10092	LADY SINGS THE BLUES (LP)	15
59	Columbia Clef 33CX 10145	SONGS FOR DISTINGUÉ LOVERS (LP)	12
59	MGM C 792	BILLIE HOLIDAY (LP)	12
59	Fontana TFL 5032	LADY IN SATIN (LP)	12
60	Fontana TFL 5106	A BILLIE HOLIDAY MEMORIAL (LP)	12
61	HMV CLP 1414	THE UNFORGETTABLE LADY DAY (LP)	12
62	Stateside SL 10007	BILLIE HOLIDAY (LP)	12
65	Fontana TL 5262	ONCE UPON A TIME (LP, with Teddy Wilson)	10
66	Fontana TL 5287	BILLIE HOLIDAY (LP)	10
66	Island ILP 929	LAST LIVE RECORDING (LP)	15
60s	Ace Of Hearts AH 64	THE LADY SINGS VOL. 3 (LP)	10

CHICO HOLIDAY

59	RCA RCA 1117	Young Ideas/Cuckoo Girl	8
59	RCA RCA 1117	Young Ideas/Cuckoo Girl (78)	5
61	Coral Q 72443	God, Country And My Baby/Fools	6
59	RCA RCX 171	CHICO HOLIDAY (EP)	25

JIMMY HOLIDAY

63	Vocalion VP 9206	How Can I Forget/Janet	20
64	London HLY 9868	I Lied/Alison	7
66	Liberty LIB 12040	Baby I Love You/You Won't Get Away	12
67	Liberty LIB 12048	Give Me Your Love/The Turning Point	12
67	Liberty LIB 12053	Everybody Needs Help/I'm Gonna Move To The City	8
68	Minit MLF 11008	Give Me Your Love/The Beauty Of A Girl In Love	10

JIMMY HOLIDAY & CLYDIE KING

67	Liberty LIB 12058	Ready, Willing And Able/We Got A Good Thing Goin'	20
67	Polydor BM 56166	One Man In My Life/Wand'rin Boy (unissued)	
67	Polydor BM 56187	Come And Love/May God Help You And Protect You (unissued)	
72	United Artists UP 35371	Ready, Willing And Able/JIMMY HOLIDAY: Give Me Your Love	4
	(see also Clydie King)		

HOLIDAYS

66	Polydor BM 56720	I'll Love You Forever/Makin' Up Time	70

HOLLAND

84	Ebony EBON 17	EARLY WARNING (LP)	10

BRIAN HOLLAND

74	Invictus INV 2553	I'm So Glad/I'm So Glad (Version)	4

EDDIE HOLLAND

62	Fontana H 387	Jamie/Take A Chance On Me	200
63	Oriole CBA 1808	If It's Love (It's All Right)/It's Not Too Late	300

JOOLS HOLLAND (& MILLIONAIRES)

77	Deptford Fun City DFC 03	BOOGIE WOOGIE 78 (EP)	4
81	A&M AMS 8111	Bumble Boogie/That Don't Matter To Me (p/s, coloured vinyl, with Millionaires)	4
	(see also Squeeze)		

TONY HOLLAND

63	HMV POP 1135	Sidewalk/Time Goes By	15

HOLLAND & DOZIER

72	Invictus INV 525	Why Can't We Be Lovers/Don't Leave Me	8
73	Invictus INV 528	Don't Leave Me Starving For Your Love/(Version)	4
	(see also Lamont Dozier)		

MICHAEL HOLLIDAY

56	Columbia SCM 5221	Sixteen Tons/The Rose Tattoo	15
56	Columbia SCM 5252	Nothin' To Do/Perfume, Candy And Flowers	12
56	Columbia SCM 5273	Hot Diggity (Dog Ziggity)/The Gal With The Yaller Shoes	12
56	Columbia DB 3813	Ten Thousand Miles/The Runaway Train	15
57	Columbia DB 3871	Yaller Yaller Gold/I Saw Esau	8
57	Columbia DB 3919	Love Is Strange/My House Is Your House	8
57	Columbia DB 3948	Four Walls/Wringle Wrangle	8
57	Columbia DB 3973	All Of You/It's The Good Things We Remember	10
57	Columbia DB 3992	Old Cape Cod/Love You Darlin'	7
58	Columbia DB 4058	The Story Of My Life/Keep Your Heart	5
58	Columbia DB 4087	In Love/Rooney	5
58	Columbia DB 4121	Stairway Of Love/May I?	5
58	Columbia DB 4155	I'll Always Be In Love With You/I'll Be Lovin' You, Too	5
58	Columbia DB 4188	She Was Only Seventeen/The Gay Vagabond	4
58	Columbia DB 4216	My Heart Is An Open Book/Careless Hands	4
59	Columbia DB 4255	Palace Of Love/The Girls From The County Armagh	4
59	Columbia DB 4307	Moments Of Love/Dearest	4
59	Columbia DB 4336	For You, For You/Life Is A Circus	4
59	Columbia DB 4378	Starry-Eyed/The Steady Game	4
60	Columbia DB 4437	Skylark/Dream Talk	4
60	Columbia DB 4475	Little Boy Lost/The One-Finger Symphony	4
60	Columbia DB 4578	Stay In Love/Catch Me A Kiss	4
62	Columbia DB 4890	Have I Told You Lately That I Love You/It Only Takes A Minute	4

MINT VALUE £

56	Columbia SEG 7638	MY GUITAR AND ME (EP)	8
57	Columbia SEG 7683	MUSIC WITH MIKE (EP)	10
58	Columbia SEG 7752	RELAX WITH MIKE (EP)	8
58	Columbia SEG 7761	ALL TIME FAVOURITES (EP)	8
58	Columbia SEG 7818	MELODY MIKE (EP)	10
59	Columbia SEG 7836	SENTIMENTAL JOURNEY (EP, with Edna Savage)	8
59	Columbia SEG 7892	MIKE AND THE OTHER FELLA (EP)	8
59	Columbia SEG 7972	MIKE NO. 1 (EP, also stereo ESG 7784)	8/10
60	Columbia SEG 7986	FOUR FEATHER FALLS (EP, also stereo ESG 7793)	18/22
60	Columbia SEG 7996	MIKE NO. 2 (EP, also stereo ESG 7803)	8/10
61	Columbia SEG 8074	MIKE NO. 3 (EP, also stereo ESG 7842)	8/10
61	Columbia SEG 8101	MIKE SINGS RAGTIME (EP, also stereo ESG 7856)	8/10
61	Columbia SEG 8115	MIKE IN A SENTIMENTAL MOOD (EP, also stereo ESG 7864)	8/10
62	Columbia SEG 8161	HAPPY HOLLIDAY (EP)	7
62	Columbia SEG 8186	MORE HAPPY HOLLIDAY (EP)	7
61	Columbia SEG 8242	MIKE SINGS COUNTRY AND WESTERN STYLE (EP)	7
64	Columbia SEG 8373	MEMORIES OF MIKE (EP)	7
58	Columbia 33S 1114	HI! (10" LP)	25
59	Columbia 33SX 1170	MIKE (LP)	16
60	Columbia 33SX 1262	HOLLIDAY MIXTURE (LP, also stereo SCX 3331)	14/16
61	Columbia 33SX 1354	HAPPY HOLLIDAY (LP)	15
62	Columbia 33SX 1426	TO BING FROM MIKE (LP, also stereo SCX 3441)	14/16
64	Columbia 33SX 1586	THE BEST OF MICHAEL HOLLIDAY (LP)	12
60s	World Record Club T 792	TO BING FROM MIKE (LP)	10

SUSAN HOLLIDAY

64	Columbia DB 7363	Street Of The Dark Despair/The Other Side	4
64	Columbia DB 7403	Any Day Now/Don't Come Knocking At My Door	8
65	Columbia DB 7616	Sometimes/Long Haired Boy	10
65	Columbia DB 7709	Nevertheless (I'm In Love With You)/Moonglow	4
66	Columbia SX 6067	I WANNA SAY HELLO (LP, as Su Holliday)	50

(see also Susan Singer)

TIM HOLLIER

68	United Artists (S)ULP 1211	MESSAGE TO A HARLEQUIN (LP)	18
71	Philips 6308 044	SKY SAIL (LP)	15

(see also Ian Matthews)

HOLLIES

63	Parlophone R 5030	(Ain't That) Just Like Me/Hey, What's Wrong With Me	8
63	Parlophone R 5052	Searchin'/Whole World Over	6
63	Parlophone R 5077	Stay/Now's The Time	5
64	Parlophone R 5104	Just One Look/Keep Off That Friend Of Mine	4
64	Parlophone R 5137	Here I Go Again/Baby That's All	4
64	Parlophone R 5178	We're Through/Come On Back	4
65	Parlophone R 5232	(I'll Be True To You) Yes I Will/Nobody	4
65	Parlophone R 5287	I'm Alive/You Know He Did	4
65	Parlophone R 5322	Look Through Any Window/So Lonely	4
65	Parlophone R 5392	If I Needed Someone/I've Got A Way Of My Own	5
66	Parlophone R 5409	I Can't Let Go/Running Through The Night	4
66	Parlophone R 5469	Bus Stop/Don't Run And Hide	4
66	United Artists UP 1152	After The Fox (with Peter Sellers)/BURT BACHARACH: The Fox-Trot	25
66	Parlophone R 5508	Stop! Stop! Stop!/It's You	4
67	Parlophone R 5562	On A Carousel/All The World Is Love	4
67	Parlophone R 5602	Carrie Anne/Signs That Will Never Change	4
67	Parlophone R 5637	King Midas In Reverse/Everything Is Sunshine	5
68	Parlophone R 5680	Jennifer Eccles/Open Up Your Eyes	4
68	Parlophone R 5733	Listen To Me/Do The Best You Can	4
69	Parlophone R 5806	He Ain't Heavy, He's My Brother/'Cos You Like To Love Me	4
70	Parlophone R 5837	I Can't Tell The Bottom From The Top/Mad Professor Blyth	4
70	Parlophone R 5862	Gasoline Alley Bred/Dandelion Wine	4
71	Parlophone R 5905	Hey Willy/Row The Boat Together	4
72	Polydor 2058 199	The Baby/Oh Granny	4
72	Parlophone R 5939	Long Cool Woman (In A Black Dress)/Cable Car	4
72	Polydor 2058 289	Magic Woman Touch/Indian Girl	4
73	Polydor 2058 403	The Day That Curly Billy Shot Down Crazy Sam McGhee/Born A Man	4
74	Polydor 2058 435	The Air That I Breathe/No More Riders	4
74	Polydor 2058 476	Son Of A Rotten Gambler/Layin' To The Music	4
74	Polydor 2058 533	I'm Down/Hello Lady Goodbye	4
75	Polydor 2058 595	(Fourth Of July, Asbury Park) Sandy/Second-Hand Hangups	4
75	EMI EMI 2353	Long Cool Woman In A Black Dress/Carrie Anne	4
76	Polydor 2058 694	Boulder To Birmingham/Crocodile Woman (She Bites)	4
76	Polydor 2058 719	Star/Love Is The Thing	4
81	Polydor POSP 379	Take My Love And Run/Driver (p/s)	4
64	Parlophone GEP 8909	THE HOLLIES (EP)	25
64	Parlophone GEP 8911	JUST ONE LOOK (EP)	25
64	Parlophone GEP 8915	HERE I GO AGAIN (EP)	25
64	Parlophone GEP 8927	WE'RE THROUGH (EP)	30
65	Parlophone GEP 8934	IN THE HOLLIES STYLE (EP)	30
65	Parlophone GEP 8942	I'M ALIVE (EP)	30
66	Parlophone GEP 8951	I CAN'T LET GO (EP)	30
64	Parlophone PMC 1220	STAY WITH THE HOLLIES (LP, y&b label, also stereo PCS 3054)	30/45
65	Parlophone PMC 1235	IN THE HOLLIES STYLE (LP, yellow & black label)	45
65	Parlophone PMC 1261	THE HOLLIES (LP, yellow & black label)	25
66	Parl. PMC/PCS 7008	WOULD YOU BELIEVE? (LP, yellow & black label, mono/stereo)	25/35
66	Parl. PMC/PCS 7011	FOR CERTAIN BECAUSE (LP, g/fold sleeve, y&b label; mono/stereo)	22/25
67	Parl. PMC/PCS 7022	EVOLUTION (LP, yellow & black label, mono/stereo)	16/20
67	Parl. PMC/PCS 7039	BUTTERFLY (LP, yellow & black label, mono/stereo)	18/20

MINT VALUE £

67	Regal SREG 2024	THE HOLLIES (LP, export compilation)	30
67	World Records ST 979	THE VINTAGE HOLLIES (LP)	30
68	World Records ST 1035	STAY WITH THE HOLLIES (LP, record club reissue)	30
68	World Records	IN THE HOLLIES STYLE (LP, record club reissue)	35
68	Parl. PMC/PCS 7057	THE HOLLIES' GREATEST (LP, yellow & black label)	12
69	Parlophone PMC 7057	THE HOLLIES' GREATEST (LP, mono, black & white label reissue)	10
69	Parl. PMC/PCS 7078	THE HOLLIES SING DYLAN (LP, yellow & black label; later silver/black)	18/12
69	Parlophone PCS 7092	HOLLIES SING HOLLIES (LP)	12
69	Regal Starline SRS 5008	REFLECTION (LP, reissue of "The Hollies")	10
70	Parlophone PCS 7116	CONFESSIONS OF THE MIND (LP)	15
71	Parlophone PAS 10005	DISTANT LIGHT (LP)	12
71	Regal Starline SRS 5013	STOP! STOP! STOP! (LP, reissue of "For Certain Because")	10
72	Parlophone PCS 7148	THE HOLLIES' GREATEST HITS VOL. 2 (LP)	10
72	Polydor 2383 144	ROMANY (LP)	12
74	Polydor 2383 262	HOLLIES (LP)	10

(see also Allan Clarke, Graham Nash, Terry Sylvester, Haydock's Rockhouse)

BRENDA HOLLOWAY

64	Stateside SS 307	Every Little Bit Hurts/Land Of A Thousand Boys	40
65	Tamla Motown TMG 508	When I'm Gone/I've Been Good To You	80
65	Tamla Motown TMG 519	Operator/I'll Be Available	50
66	Tamla Motown TMG 556	Together Till The End Of Time/Sad Song	45
66	Tamla Motown TMG 581	Hurt A Little Everyday/Where Were You	35
67	Tamla Motown TMG 608	Just Look What You've Done/Starting The Hurt All Over Again	20
67	Tamla Motown TMG 622	You've Made Me So Very Happy/I've Got To Find It	20
69	Tamla Motown TMG 700	Just Look What You've Done/You've Made Me So Very Happy	8
68	T. Motown (S)TML 11083	THE ARTISTRY OF BRENDA HOLLOWAY (LP)	80

PATRICE HOLLOWAY

| 66 | Capitol CL 15484 | Love And Desire/Ecstacy | 50 |

STANLEY HOLLOWAY

59	Decca F 11140	Dark Girl Dressed In Blue/Growing Old	4
60	Columbia DB 4517	Petticoat Lane/Sing A Song Of London	4
60	Pye 7N 15302	Lily Of Laguna/A Bachelor Gay	4
50s	Columbia SEG 8034	ADVENTURES WITH ALBERT (EP)	7
50s	Columbia SEG 8118	BRAHN BOOTS AND OTHER FAVOURITES (EP)	7
50s	Philips BBE 12326	MY WORD YOU DO LOOK QUEER (EP)	7
50s	Pye NEP 24097	NO TREES IN THE STREET (EP)	7
56	Columbia 33S 1093	FAMOUS ADVENTURES WITH OLD SAM & THE RAMSBOTTOMS (10" LP)	15
58	Philips BBL 7237	'ERE'S 'OLLOWAY (LP)	12
60	Pye NPL 18056	JOIN IN THE CHORUS (LP)	10

HOLLOW GROUND

| 80 | private pressing | WAR LORD (EP) | 10 |

HOLLOW MEN

| 81 | Big League H 001 | The Future/Microscope (p/s) | 4 |

HOLLOW MEN

85	Evensong EVE 107	Late Flowering Lust/Ocean Lies/Raindrop Children (p/s)	12
87	Evensong EVE 212	Gold And Ivory/Filth City Fever/Pandemonium Carousel/Autumn Avenue (12", p/s, some with postcard)	10/8
87	Evensong EVE 212	Gold And Ivory/Filth City Fever/Pandemonium Carousel/Autumn Avenue (12" white label, unreleased proof sleeve)	50
88	Gigantic GI 101	White Train/The Man Who Would Be King (promo-only, die-cut p/s)	10
89	Blind Eye BE 007	The Drowning Man/Whisper To Me/Ivory Blues (12", p/s, some signed, others with promo booklet)	10/12/7
86	Dead Man's Curve DMC 15	TALES OF THE RIVERBANK (LP)	12
88	Dead Man's Curve DMC 25	THE MAN WHO WOULD BE KING (LP)	10
88	D.M.C. VIVID ONE	THE MAN WHO WOULD BE KING (CD)	15

HOLLY (Johnson)

| 79 | Eric's ERIC'S 003 | Yankee Rose/Treasure Island/Desperate Dan (p/s) | 10 |
| 79 | Eric's ERIC'S 007 | Hobo Joe/Stars Of The Bars (p/s) | 12 |

(see also Frankie Goes To Hollywood, Holly Johnson, Big In Japan)

BUDDY HOLLY

56	Brunswick 05581	Blue Days — Black Nights/Love Me	300
56	Brunswick 05581	Blue Days — Black Nights/Love Me (78)	60
57	Vogue Coral Q 72293	Peggy Sue/Everyday	18
57	Vogue Coral Q 72293	Peggy Sue/Everyday (78)	10
58	Coral Q 72293	Peggy Sue/Everyday	12
58	Coral Q 72288	Listen To Me/I'm Gonna Love You Too	15
58	Coral Q 72288	Listen To Me/I'm Gonna Love You Too (78)	15
58	Coral Q 72325	Rave On/Take Your Time	12
58	Coral Q 72325	Rave On/Take Your Time (78)	15
58	Coral Q 72333	Early In The Morning/Now We're One	12
58	Coral Q 72333	Early In The Morning/Now We're One (78)	15
58	Coral Q 72346	Heartbeat/Well ... All Right	12
58	Coral Q 72346	Heartbeat/Well ... All Right (78)	25
59	Coral Q 72360	It Doesn't Matter Anymore/Raining In My Heart	7
59	Coral Q 72360	It Doesn't Matter Anymore/Raining In My Heart (78)	25
59	Brunswick 05800	Rock Around With Ollie Vee/Midnight Shift	30
59	Brunswick 05800	Rock Around With Ollie Vee/Midnight Shift (78)	40
59	Coral Q 72376	Peggy Sue Got Married/Crying, Waiting, Hoping	10
59	Coral Q 72376	Peggy Sue Got Married/Crying, Waiting, Hoping (78)	60

(all the above 45s came with triangular centres; reissues with round centres are worth around two-thirds the value)

| 60 | Coral Q 72392 | Heartbeat/Everyday | 7 |
| 60 | Coral Q 72392 | Heartbeat/Everyday (78) | 30 |

60	Coral Q 72397	True Love Ways/Moondreams	7
60	Coral Q 72397	True Love Ways/Moondreams (78)	60
60	Coral Q 72411	Learning The Game/That Makes It Tough	8
60	Coral Q 72411	Learning The Game/That Makes It Tough (78)	100
61	Coral Q 72419	What To Do/That's What They Say	7
61	Coral Q 72432	(You're So Square) Baby I Don't Care/Valley Of Tears	7
61	Coral Q 72445	Look At Me/Mailman, Bring Me No More Blues	7
62	Coral Q 72449	Listen To Me/Words Of Love	7
62	Coral Q 72455	Reminiscing/Wait Till The Sun Shines, Nellie	6
63	Coral Q 72459	Brown-Eyed Handsome Man/Slippin' And Slidin'	5
63	Coral Q 72463	Bo Diddley/It's Not My Failt	5
63	Coral Q 72466	Wishing/Because I Love You	6
63	Coral Q 72469	What To Do/Umm Oh Yeah (Dearest)	7
64	Coral Q 72472	You've Got Love/An Empty Cup (as Buddy Holly & Crickets)	7
64	Coral Q 72475	Love's Made A Fool Of You/You're The One	8
66	Coral Q 72483	Maybe Baby/That's My Desire	15
68	Decca AD 1009	Rave On/Peggy Sue (export reissue)	12
68	MCA MU 1012	Rave On/Peggy Sue (reissue)	5
69	MCA MU 1059	Love Is Strange/You're The One	4
69	MCA MU 1081	It Doesn't Matter Anymore/Maybe Baby (reissue)	4
70	MCA MU 1116	Rave On/Umm Oh Yeah (Dearest)	4
82	MCA HR 001	That'll Be The Day/True Love Ways (flexidisc, free with 'The History Of Rock' magazine issue 1)	5/4
85	MCA BHB 1	THAT'LL BE THE DAY (10 x 7" box set)	20
58	Coral FEP 2002	BUDDY HOLLY (EP, brown cover, p/s shows Holly without glasses)	200
58	Coral FEP 2002	BUDDY HOLLY (EP, various shades of green/brown, Holly with glasses)	30
58	Coral FEP 2005	RAVE ON (EP)	25
59	Coral FEP 2014	IT'S SO EASY (EP)	25
59	Coral FEP 2015	HEARTBEAT (EP)	25
59	Coral FEP 2032	THE BUDDY HOLLY STORY (EP)	25

(the above EPs all had triangular centres; reissues with round centres are worth around two-thirds the value)

59	Brunswick OE 9456	BUDDY HOLLY NO. 1 (EP, tri centre)	40
59	Brunswick OE 9457	BUDDY HOLLY NO. 2 (EP, tri centre)	40
60	Coral FEP 2044	THE LATE GREAT BUDDY HOLLY (EP)	20
64	Coral FEP 2065	BUDDY — BY REQUEST (EP)	25
64	Coral FEP 2066	THAT TEX-MEX SOUND (EP)	50
64	Coral FEP 2067	WISHING (EP)	30
64	Coral FEP 2068	SHOWCASE VOL. 1 (EP)	50
64	Coral FEP 2069	SHOWCASE VOL. 2 (EP)	50
65	Coral FEP 2070	BUDDY HOLLY SINGS (EP)	40
58	Vogue Coral LVA 9085	BUDDY HOLLY (LP)	35
58	Coral LVA 9085	BUDDY HOLLY (LP, 2nd pressing)	25
59	Coral LVA 9105	THE BUDDY HOLLY STORY (LP)	16
60	Coral LVA 9127	THE BUDDY HOLLY STORY VOL. 2 (LP)	14
61	Ace Of Hearts AH 3	THAT'LL BE THE DAY (LP)	15
63	Coral LVA 9212	REMINISCING (LP)	14
64	Coral LVA 9222	SHOWCASE (LP)	22
65	Coral LVA 9227	HOLLY IN THE HILLS (withdrawn LP, plays "Reminiscing")	40
65	Coral LVA 9227	HOLLY IN THE HILLS (LP, with Bob Montgomery, plays "Wishing")	30
67	Ace Of Hearts AH 148	BUDDY HOLLY'S GREATEST HITS (LP)	12
68	MCA MUP(S) 312	LISTEN TO ME (LP, initially yellow label)	12/10
68	MCA MUP(S) 313	RAVE ON (LP, initially yellow label)	12/10
68	MCA MUP(S) 314	BROWN-EYED HANDSOME MAN (LP, initially yellow label)	12/10
68	MCA MUP(S) 315	HE'S THE ONE (LP, initially yellow label)	12/10
68	MCA MUP(S) 319	TRUE LOVE WAYS (LP, initially yellow label)	12/10
68	MCA MUP(S) 320	WISHING (LP, initially yellow label)	12/10
69	MCA MUPS 371	GIANT (LP, initially yellow label)	12/10
70	Coral CPS 47	BUDDY HOLLY'S GREATEST HITS VOL. 2 (LP, stereo)	10
71	Coral CP 71	REMEMBER (LP)	10
75	World Records SM 301/5	THE BUDDY HOLLY STORY (5-LP boxed set)	30
75	Coral CDLM 8038	THE NASHVILLE SESSIONS (LP)	10
78	Marks & Spencers IMP 114	HEARTBEAT (LP)	40
79	MCA Coral CDSP 807	THE COMPLETE BUDDY HOLLY (6-LP boxed set with book)	35

(see also Crickets, Fireballs)

STEVE HOLLY

66	Planet PLF 107	A Strange World/Little Man	10

HOLLY & ITALIANS

82	Oval OVAL 1016	Tell That Girl To Shut Up/Chapel Of Love (p/s)	4

HOLLY & JOEY

82	Virgin VS 478	I Got You Babe/HOLLY & ITALIANS: One More Dance (p/s)	6

(see also Holly & Italians, Ramones)

KENNY HOLLYWOOD

62	Decca F 11546	Magic Star/The Wonderful Story Of Love	20

HOLLYWOOD ARGYLES

60	London HLU 9146	Alley Oop/Sho' Knew A Lot About Love	12
60	London HLU 9146	Alley Oop/Sho' Knew A Lot About Love (78)	45
60	Top Rank JAR 530	Gun Totin' Critter Called Jack/GARY PAXTON: Bug-Eye	8

(see also Kim Fowley, Skip & Flip)

HOLLYWOOD BRATS

79	Cherry Red CHERRY 6	Then He Kissed Me/Sick On You (p/s)	4
80	Cherry Red ARED 6	THE HOLLYWOOD BRATS (LP)	10

(see also Boys)

HOLLYWOOD FLAMES

HOLLYWOOD FLAMES
57	London HL 7030	Buzz Buzz Buzz/Crazy (export issue)	20
58	London HL 8545	Buzz Buzz Buzz/Crazy	35
58	London HL 8545	Buzz Buzz Buzz/Crazy (78)	15
59	London HLW 8955	Much Too Much/In The Dark	20
59	London HLW 8955	Much Too Much/In The Dark (78)	30
60	London HLE 9071	If I Thought You Needed Me/Every Day Every Way	15

HOLLYWOOD HURRICANES
64	Prima PR 1009	Beavershot/Have Love Will Travel	4

HOLLYWOOD VINES
61	Capitol CL 15191	When Johnny Comes Slidin' Home/Cruisin'	8

MIKE HOLM
69	Major Minor MM 659	Mendocino/Cutey Girl	5

BILL HOLMAN OCTET
54	Capitol KC 65000	Cousin Jack/Plain Folks	5

EDDIE HOLMAN
65	Cameo Parkway P 960	This Can't Be True/A Free Country	30
69	Action ACT 4547	I Surrender/I Love You	30
70	Stateside SS 2159	(Hey There) Lonely Girl/It's All In The Game	15
70	Stateside SS 2170	Since I Don't Have You/Don't Stop Now	12
72	GSF GSZ 1	My Mind Keeps Telling Me/Stranded In A Dream	5

IVAN HOLMES
67	Columbia DB 8119	The Light, The Love And The Life/Cocaine	4

JAKE HOLMES
69	Ember EMB S 269	Saturday Night	4
69	Polydor 583 579	JAKE HOLMES (LP)	12
70	Polydor 2425 036	SO CLOSE SO VERY FAR TO GO (LP)	10
72	CBS 64905	HOW MUCH TIME (LP)	10

LEROY HOLMES & ORCHESTRA
50	MGM MGM 356	Oh Babe/STARLINGS: Lying In The Hay (78)	5
68	United Artists UP 2222	The Good, The Bad And The Ugly/Live For Life	4

RICHARD 'GROOVES' HOLMES
68	Transatlantic PR 7493	RICHARD 'GROOVES HOLMES' (LP)	10

HOLOCAUST
80	Phoenix PSP 1	Heavy Metal Mania/Love's Power (p/s)	6
80	Phoenix 12 PSP 1	Heavy Metal Mania/Love's Power (12", p/s)	12
80	Phoenix 12 PSP 2	Smokin' Valves (p/s)	6
80	Phoenix 12 PSP 2	Smokin' Valves (12", p/s)	12
81	Phoenix PSP 3P	Lovin' Feelin' Danger (p/s)	10
82	Phoenix 12 PSP 4	Comin' Through/Don't Wanna Be A Loser (12", p/s)	10
81	Phoenix PSLP 1	NIGHTCOMERS (LP)	15
83	Phoenix PSPLP 4	LIVE (HOT CURRY AND WINE) (LP)	10
84	Phoenix PSPLP 5	NO MAN'S LAND (LP)	10

HOLOGRAM
83	Phoenix	STEAL THE STARS (LP)	10

(see also Holocaust)

JOHN HOLT
63	Island WI 041	I Cried A Tear/I'll Stay	10
68	Trojan TR 643	Tonight/Oh How It Hurts (B-side actually by Paragons)	8
69	Trojan TR 661	Ali Baba/I'm Your Man	7
69	Trojan TR 674	What You Gonna Do Now/Have You Ever Been To Heaven	7
69	Trojan TR 694	Have Sympathy/HARRY J ALLSTARS: Spyrone	7
69	Trojan TR 7702	Wooden Heart/All My Life	7
70	Duke Reid DR 2506	Come Out Of My Bed/WINSTON WRIGHT: Hide And Seek	6
70	Bamboo BAM 44	A Love I Can Feel/JOHNNY LAST: Long Liver Man (B-side actually by Hugh Black)	5
70	Bamboo BAM 55	A Stranger In Love/WAILERS: Jailhouse (Good Rudy)	15
70	Bamboo BAM 62	Holly Holy/Do You Love Me?	5
70	Banana BA 314	Why Can't I Touch You/SOUND DIMENSION: Touching Version	5
71	Banana BA 340	O.K. Fred/Fancy Make-Up	5
71	Banana BA 345	Build Our Dreams/LEROY SIBBLES: Love In Our Nation	5
71	Treasure Isle TI 7061	Let's Build Our Dreams/TOMMY McCOOK & SUPERSONICS: Testify Version	6
71	Treasure Isle TI 7065	Sister Big Stuff/TOMMY McCOOK & SUPERSONICS: Black River	6
71	Treasure Isle TI 7066	Paragons Medley/TOMMY McCOOK & SUPERSONICS: Medley Version	6
72	Blue Beat BB 424	O.K. Fred/BIG YOUTH: Chi Chi Run	5
72	Prince Buster PB 40	Close To Me/Version	4
72	Prince Buster PB 41	Get Ready/Version	4
72	Prince Buster PB 42	Rain From The Skies/Version	4
72	Prince Buster PB 43	The First Time/Version	4
72	Prince Buster PB 49	For Your Love/Version	4
72	Fab FAB 188	A Little Happiness/DELROY WILSON: Diamond Rings	4
73	Fab FAB 224	Let's Go Dancing/Version	4
73	Fab FAB 244	Let's Go Dancing/Version (reissue)	4
70	Bamboo BDLP 210	A LOVE I CAN FEEL (LP)	25
70s	Melodisc MLP 12170	GREATEST HITS (LP)	15
70s	Melodisc MLP 12180	OK FRED (LP)	15
70s	Melodisc MLP 12191	JOHN HOLT & FRIENDS (LP)	15
71	Trojan TRL(S) 37	STILL IN CHAINS (LP)	12
72	Trojan TRL(S) 43	HOLT (LP)	12

72	Trojan TBL 184	PLEDGING MY LOVE (LP)	10
73	Trojan TRLS 55	THE FURTHER YOU LOOK (LP)	10
74	Trojan TRLS 75	A THOUSAND VOLTS OF HOLT (LP)	10
73	Attack ATLP 1001	A LOVE I CAN FEEL (LP)	10
70s	Cactus CTLP 109	TIME IS THE MASTER (LP)	10

(see also Jay & Joya)

GARY HOLTON

84	Magnet GARY 2	Catch A Falling Star/Angel (star-shaped picture disc)	5
84	10 TEN 19	Shapes Of Things/Blinder (p/s)	4
84	10 TEN 19-12	Shapes Of Things/Blinder/The Alan Freeman Interview (12", p/s)	7

(see also Heavy Metal Kids, Slade)

ROOSEVELT HOLTS

| 68 | Blue Horizon 7-63201 | PRESENTING THE COUNTRY BLUES (LP) | 40 |

HOLY MACKEREL

| 72 | CBS 65297 | HOLY MACKEREL (LP) | 18 |

(see also Jason Crest)

HOLY MODAL ROUNDERS

68	Elektra EKL 4026	MORAY EELS EAT THE HOLY MODALS (LP)	15
70	Transatlantic TRA 7451	HOLY MODAL ROUNDERS (LP)	25
70	Transatlantic TRA	HOLY MODAL ROUNDERS 2 (LP)	25

HOMBRES

| 67 | Verve VS 1510 | Let It Out (Let It All Hang Out)/Go Girl Go | 12 |

HOME

71	CBS 64365	PAUSE FOR A HOARSE HORSE (LP)	25
72	CBS 64752	HOME (LP)	15
73	CBS 65550	THE ALCHEMIST (LP)	12
70s	CBS	(LP, unreleased, test pressings only)	150

HOMER & JETHRO

52	HMV B 10258	Cold Cold Heart No. 2/Alabama Jubilee (78)	5
53	HMV B 10581	How Much Is That Hound Dog/Rudolph The Flat-Nosed Reindeer (78)	5
54	HMV B 10687	Swappin' Partners/Crazy Mix-Up Song (78)	5
54	HMV 7M 211	Swappin' Partners/Crazy Mix-Up Song	7
59	RCA RCA 1148	Waterloo/The Battle Of Kookamonga	4
59	RCA RCA 1148	Waterloo/The Battle Of Kookamonga (78)	5

HOMESICK JAMES

| 64 | Sue WI 319 | Crossroads/My Baby's Sweet | 12 |
| 65 | Sue WI 330 | Set A Date/Can't Afford To Do It | 15 |

HOMESICK JAMES/SNOOKY PRYOR

| 74 | Caroline C 1502 | HOMESICK JAMES AND SNOOKY PRYOR (LP) | 12 |

HOMOSEXUALS

79	Black Noise F12 No. 2	Divorce Proceedings/Mecho Madness	4
79	L'Orelei PF 151	Hearts In Exile/South South Africans (p/s, with insert)	4
81	Black Noise BN 1	BIGGER THAN THE NUMBER YET MISSING THE DOT (EP, clear vinyl)	6
80s	Recommended RR # 18	THE HOMOSEXUALS RECORD (LP, with inserts)	12

(see also George Harrassment & Homosexuals, Ice La Bas, Amos & Sara)

MINAKO HONDA

| 87 | Columbia DB 9153 | Golden Days/Crazy Nights (features Brian May) (p/s) | 4 |

HONDELLS

64	Mercury MF 834	Little Honda/Hot Rod High	8
65	Mercury MF 925	Younger Girl/All American Girl	6
66	Mercury MF 967	Cheryl's Goin' Home/Show Me Girl	10

HONEST MEN

| 69 | Tamla Motown TMG 706 | Cherie/Baby | 6 |

HONEYBUS

67	Deram DM 131	Delighted To See You/The Breaking Up Scene	6
67	Deram DM 152	Do I Figure In Your Life/Throw My Love Away	8
68	Deram DM 182	I Can't Let Maggie Go/Tender Are The Ashes	4
68	Deram DM 207	Girl Of Independent Means/How Long	6
69	Deram DM 254	She Sold Blackpool Rock/Would You Believe	8
70	Deram DM 289	Story/The Night To Choose	5
72	Bell BLL 1205	She Is The Female To My Soul/For Where Have You Been	4
70	Deram SML 1056	STORY (LP)	40
73	Warner Bros K 46248	RECITAL (LP, withdrawn)	200

(see also Pete Dello, Colin Hare, Lace, Magic Valley, Red Herring)

HONEYCOMBS

64	Pye 7N 15664	Have I The Right/Please Don't Pretend Again	4
64	Pye 7N 15705	Is It Because/I'll Cry Tomorrow	4
64	Pye 7N 15736	Eyes/If You've Got To Pick A Baby	5
65	Pye 7N 15781	Don't Love You No More/I'll See You Tomorrow (withdrawn)	25
65	Pye 7N 15827	Something Better Beginning/I'll See You Tomorrow	6
65	Pye 7N 15890	That's The Way/Can't Get Through To You	4
65	Pye 7N 15979	This Year, Next Year/Not Sleeping Too Well Lately	5
66	Pye 7N 17089	Who Is Sylvia?/Wow Will I Know	8
66	Pye 7N 17138	It's So Hard/I Fell In Love	7
66	Pye 7N 17173	That Loving Feeling/Should A Man Cry	10
69	Pye 7N 17741	Have I The Right/Please Don't Pretend Again	4
65	Pye NEP 24230	THAT'S THE WAY (EP)	20
64	Pye NPL 18097	THE HONEYCOMBS (LP)	35
65	Pye NPL 18132	ALL SYSTEMS GO! (LP)	75

HONEYCOMBS

66   Golden Guinea GGL 0350   THE HONEYCOMBS (LP, reissue) 15
(see also Lemmings, Dennis D'Ell)

HONEYEND
72   Spark SRL 1072   Heartbreaker/Beautiful Downtown 5

HONEYS
63   Capitol CL 15299   Surfin' Down The Swanee River/Shoot The Curl 30
(see also Brian Wilson)

HONEYTONES
58   London HLX 8671   Don't Look Now, But.../I Know, I Know 30
58   London HLX 8671   Don't Look Now, But.../I Know, I Know (78) 15

ROBBIN HOOD
56   MGM SP 1178   The Rock-A-Bye Blues/Beautiful, Beautiful Love 4

HOOK
68   Uni UN 507   In The Beginning/Show You the Way 8

EARL HOOKER
69   Blue Horizon 57-3166   Boogie Don't Blot/Funky Blues 15
70   Blue Horizon 7-63850   SWEET BLACK ANGEL (LP) 45
70   Stateside SSL 10298   DON'T HAVE TO WORRY (LP) 20

JOHN LEE HOOKER
52   Vogue V 2102   Hoogie Boogie/Whistlin' And Moanin' Blues (78) 30
54   London HL 8037   Need Somebody/Too Much Boogie (78) 40
63   Stateside SS 203   Boom Boom/Frisco Blues 10
64   Stateside SS 297   Dimples/I'm Leaving 7
64   Stateside SS 341   I Love You Honey/Send Me Your Pillow 8
64   Pye Intl. 7N 25255   High Priced Woman/Sugar Mama 7
64   Polydor NH 52 930   Shake It Baby/Let's Make It Baby 10
65   Sue WI 361   I'm In The Mood/Boogie Chillun 15
66   Chess CRS 8039   Let's Go Out Tonight/In The Mood 10
66   Planet PLF 114   Mai Lee/Don't Be Messing With My Bread 15
60   Riverside REP 3202   WEDNESDAY EVENING (EP) 8
60   Riverside REP 3207   DEMOCRAT MAN (EP) 8
64   Stateside SE 1019   THE BLUES OF JOHN HOOKER (EP) 12
64   Stateside SE 1023   I'M JOHN LEE HOOKER (EP) 12
64   Ember EP 4561   THINKING BLUES (EP) 15
65   Pye Intl. NEP 44034   LOVE BLUES (EP) 18
65   Chess CRE 6000   DOWN AT THE LANDING (EP) 15
65   Atlantic AET 6010   JOHN LEE HOOKER (EP) 12
66   Chess CRE 6007   WALKING THE BOOGIE (EP) 15
66   Chess CRE 6014   THE JOURNEY (EP) 15
66   Chess CRE 6021   REAL FOLK BLUES VOL. 3 (EP) 15
73   Impulse 9103   SERVES YOU RIGHT TO SUFFER (EP) 10
62   Riverside RLP 12-838   THE FOLK BLUES OF JOHN LEE HOOKER (LP) 20
62   Stateside SL 10014   THE FOLK LORE OF JOHN LEE HOOKER (LP) 20
63   London HA-K 8097   DON'T TURN ME FROM YOUR DOOR (LP) 25
64   Stateside SL 10053   THE BIG SOUL OF JOHN LEE HOOKER (LP) 20
64   Stateside SL 10074   I WANT TO SHOUT THE BLUES (LP) 18
64   Pye Intl. NPL 28042   HOUSE OF THE BLUES (LP) 25
64   Fontana 688 700 ZL   THE FOLK-BLUES OF HOOKER (LP) 20
65   Fontana FJL 119   BLUE! (LP) 20
65   Ember EMB 3356   SINGS THE BLUES (LP) 15
65   Riverside RLP 008   BURNING HELL (LP) 20
65   Chess CRL 4500   JOHN LEE HOOKER PLAYS AND SINGS THE BLUES (LP) 15
66   HMV CLP 5032/CSD 3542   IT SERVES YOU RIGHT TO SUFFER (LP, mono/stereo) 20/25
66   Ember (ST)EMB 3371   DRIFTIN' THROUGH THE BLUES (LP) 15
67   Chess CRL 4527   THE REAL FOLK BLUES (LP) 15
67   Marble Arch MAL 663   HOUSE OF THE BLUES (LP, reissue) 10
67   HMV CLP/CSD 3612   LIVE AT THE CAFE A GO GO (LP) 18
67   Atlantic Special 590 003   DRIFTIN' BLUES (LP) 12
68   Joy JOY(S) 101   I'M JOHN LEE HOOKER (LP) 12
68   Joy JOY(S) 124   BURNIN' (LP) 12
68   Stateside (S)SL 10246   URBAN BLUES (LP) 12
69   Joy JOYS 129   TRAVELIN' (LP) 10
69   Joy JOYS 133   THE FOLKLORE OF JOHN LEE HOOKER (LP) 12
69   Stateside (S)SL 10280   SIMPLY THE TRUTH (LP) 12
69   Joy JOYS 142   CONCERT AT NEWPORT (LP) 12
69   Joy JOYS 147   THE BIG SOUL OF JOHN LEE HOOKER (LP) 12
69   Storyville 673 005   YOU'RE LEAVIN' ME BABY (LP) 12
69   Joy JOYS 152   IN PERSON (LP) 12
70   Storyville 673 020   TUPELO BLUES (LP) 12
70   Joy JOYS 156   THE BEST OF JOHN LEE HOOKER (LP) 12
70   Stax SXATS 1025   THAT'S WHERE IT'S AT (LP) 10
71   Probe SPB 1016   IF YOU MISS 'IM . . . I GOT 'IM (LP, with Earl Hooker) ...12
71   Probe SPB 1034   ENDLESS BOOGIE (LP) 10
71   Polydor 2362 017   THAT'S WHERE IT'S AT! (LP) 12
71   Xtra XTRA 1114   JOHN LEE HOOKER (LP) 15
71   United Artists UAS 29235   COAST TO COAST BLUES BAND (LP) 15
72   Speciality SNTF 5005   ALONE (LP) 10
72   Probe SPB 1057   NEVER GET OUT OF THE BLUES ALIVE (LP) 10
73   Green Bottle GN 4002   JOHNNY LEE (LP) 15
73   Checker 6467 305   MAD MAN BLUES (LP) 12
73   Polydor 2310 256   SLIM'S STOMP (LP) 10
74   ABC ABCL 5059   FREE BEER AND CHICKEN (LP) 10
75   New World NW 6003   JOHN LEE HOOKER (LP, reissue of above with 1 extra track) 12

| 75 | Atlantic K 40405 | DETROIT SPECIAL (LP) .... | 10 |
| 77 | DJM DJD 28026 | DIMPLES (2-LP) .... | 14 |

(see also Canned Heat)

JOHN LEE HOOKER/LIGHTNIN' HOPKINS/SMOKEY HOGG
| 73 | Sonet SNTF 5013 | HOOKER HOPKINS HOGG (LP) .... | 12 |

(see also Lightnin' Hopkins, Smokey Hogg)

STEVE HOOKER & HEAT
| 70s | Takeaway TAKE 1 | If You Don't Do The Business/Rock & Roll Doctor/I'm Hooked/ Marionette (stamped sleeve with insert, also listed as EJR 577) .... | 5 |

HOOKFOOT
69	Page One POF 144	Way Of The Musician/Hookfoot	5
71	DJM DJLPS 413	HOOKFOOT (LP)	15
72	DJM DJSLP 422	GOOD TIMES A COMIN' (LP)	10
73	DJM DJSLP 428	COMMUNICATIONS (LP)	10

(see also Loot, Caleb, Soul Agents)

MARSHALL HOOKS & CO.
| 71 | Blue Horizon 2096 002 | I Want The Same Thing Tomorrow/Hookin' It .... | 8 |
| 71 | Blue Horizon 2431 003 | MARSHALL HOOKS & CO. (LP) .... | 40 |

HOOTENANNY SINGERS
| 65 | United Artists UP 1082 | Gabriella/Darling .... | 20 |

(see also Abba, Northern Lights)

BOB HOPE
| 63 | Brunswick LAT 8539 | IN RUSSIA AND ONE OTHER PLACE (LP) .... | 10 |

BOB HOPE & ROSEMARY CLOONEY
| 59 | RCA RCA 1139 | Ain't A-Hankerin'/Protection .... | 4 |

(see also Rosemary Clooney)

BOB HOPE & BING CROSBY
| 58 | London HLU 8593 | Paris Holiday/Nothing In Common .... | 7 |

(see also Bing Crosby)

LYN(N) HOPE
57	Vogue V 9081	Blue Moon/Blues For Anna Bacca	20
57	Vogue V 9081	Blue Moon/Blues For Anna Bacca (78)	5
57	Vogue V 9082	Eleven Till Two/Blues For Mary	20
57	Vogue V 9082	Eleven Till Two/Blues For Mary (78)	5
58	Vogue V 9115	Temptation/The Scrunch	15
58	Vogue V 9115	Temptation/The Scrunch (78)	10
61	Blue Beat BB 21	Shocking/Blue And Sentimental	10
57	Vogue VE 170103	LYNN HOPE AND HIS TENOR SAX (EP)	40
60	Vogue VE 170146	LYNN HOPE AND HIS TENOR SAX (EP)	40

PETER HOPE & RICHARD H. KIRK
| 85 | Doublevision DVR 15 | Leather Hands (Master Mix)/(Radio Mix)/(Crash Mix) (12", p/s) ... | 8 |

(see also Cabaret Voltaire, Richard H. Kirk)

HOPETOWN (Lewis) & GLENMORE (Brown)
| 68 | Fab FAB 43 | Skinny Leg Girl/Live Like A King .... | 8 |

(see also Glenmore & Hopeton)

MARY HOPKIN
68	Apple APPLE 2	Those Were The Days/Turn Turn Turn (company sleeve)	4
69	Apple APPLE 7	Lontana Dagli Occhi/Game (Europe only, unreleased in U.K.)	
69	Apple APPLE 9	Prince En Avignon/The Game (France only, unreleased in U.K.)	
69	Apple APPLE 10	Goodbye/Sparrow (company sleeve)	4
69	Apple APPLE 16	Que Sera Sera/Fields Of St. Etienne	
70	Apple APPLE 22	Temma Harbour/Lontano Dagli Occhi (black or green lettering on p/s) ..	5
70	Apple APPLE 26	Knock, Knock Who's There?/I'm Going To Fall In Love Again (p/s)	5
70	Apple APPLE 27	Que Sera Sera/Fields Of St. Etienne (Europe only, unreleased in UK)	
70	Apple APPLE 30	Think About Your Children/Heritage (p/s)	8
71	Apple APPLE 34	Let My Name Be Sorrow/Kew Gardens (p/s)	15/4
71	Apple APPLE 39	Water, Paper And Clay/Jefferson (p/s)	20/4
74	Cambrian CSP 703	Aderynllwyd/Y Blodyn Gwyn	5
74	Cambrian CSP 712	Pleserau Serch/Tyrd Yn Ol (p/s)	7
68	Cambrian CEP 414	LLAIS SWYNOL MARY HOPKIN (EP)	8
69	Cambrian CEP 420	MARY AC EDWARD (EP, with Edward Morris Jones)	8
69	Apple (S)APCOR 5	POST CARD (LP, mono/stereo)	15/10
71	Apple SAPCOR 21	EARTH SONG — OCEAN SONG (LP, gatefold sleeve)	18
72	Apple SAPCOR 23	THOSE WERE THE DAYS (LP)	60

JOEL & LIGHTNIN' HOPKINS
| 60 | Heritage H 1000 | BLUES FROM EAST TEXAS (LP) .... | 40 |

(see also Lightnin' Hopkins)

LIGHTNIN' HOPKINS
61	Bluesville BV 1019	LIGHTNIN' HOPKINS (LP)	25
62	'77' LA 12/1	SAM LIGHTNIN' HOPKINS — THE ROOSTER CROWED IN ENGLAND (LP) ...	25
63	Stateside SL 10031	LIGHTNIN' STRIKES (LP)	15
63	Realm RM 128	LIGHTNIN' HOPKINS SINGS THE BLUES (LP)	15
63	Realm RM 171	DIRTY HOUSE BLUES (LP)	15
64	Stateside SL 10076	BLUES HOOT (LP, some tracks by Sonny Terry & Brownie McGhee) ...	15
65	Stateside SL 10110	HOOTIN' THE BLUES (LP)	15
65	Stateside SL 10155	DOWN HOME BLUES (LP)	15
65	Fontana TL 5264	THE BLUES (LP)	15
65	Fontana 688 301 ZL	LAST NIGHT BLUES (LP)	15
65	Fontana 688 801 ZL	BURNIN' IN L.A. (LP)	15

MINT VALUE £

66	Fontana 688 803 ZL	BLUE BIRD BLUES (LP)	15
66	Fontana 688 807 ZL	LIGHTNIN' HOPKINS (LP)	12
66	Verve (S)VLP 5003	ROOTS OF HOPKINS (LP)	15
66	Verve (S)VLP 5014	LIGHTNIN' STRIKES (LP, reissue)	12
67	Ember EMB 3389	A TIME FOR BLUES (LP)	15
67	Xtra XTRA 5036	BLUES IN MY BOTTLE (LP)	15
68	Xtra XTRA 5044	GOT TO MOVE YOUR BABY (LP, reissue of Fontana 688 301 ZL)	12
68	Minit MLL/MLS 40006	EARTH BLUES (LP)	18
69	Liberty LBL 83254	KING OF DOWLING STREET (LP)	20
69	Joy JOY(S) 115	LIGHTNIN' STRIKES (LP, 2nd reissue)	10
70	Ace Of Hearts (Z)AHT 183	THE BLUES (LP)	12
70	Poppy PYS 11000	LIGHTNIN'! VOLUME 1 (LP)	10
70	Poppy PYS 11002	LIGHTNIN'! VOLUME 2 (LP)	10
70	Liberty LBS 83293	THE CALIFORNIA MUDSLIDE AND EARTHQUAKE (LP)	15
71	Mayfair AMLB 4000 1/2	LIGHTNIN' STRIKES (2-LP)	15
71	Blue Horizon 2431 005	LET'S PLAY AWHILE (LP)	50
71	Xtra XTRA 1127	THE ROOTS OF LIGHTNIN' HOPKINS (LP)	15
72	Polydor 2941 005	LONESOME LIGHTNIN' (LP)	15
73	Mainstream MSL 1001	DIRTY BLUES (LP)	12
75	Mainstream MSL 1031	LOW DOWN DIRTY BLUES (LP)	12

(see also Sonny Terry & Brownie McGhee, Joel & Lightnin' Hopkins)

LIGHTNIN' HOPKINS & JOHN LEE HOOKER
| 72 | Storyville SLP 174 | LIGHTNIN' HOPKINS AND JOHN LEE HOOKER (LP) | 20 |

(see also John Lee Hooker)

LINDA HOPKINS
| 61 | Coral Q 72423 | I Diddle Dum Dum/All In My Mind | 20 |
| 62 | Coral Q 72448 | Mama's Doin' The Twist/My Mother's Eyes | 15 |

LINDA HOPKINS & JACKIE WILSON
| 65 | Coral Q 72480 | Yes Indeed/When The Saints Go Marching In | 12 |

(see also Jackie Wilson)

NICKY HOPKINS
66	CBS 202055	Mr Big/Jenni	10
67	Polydor BM 56175	Mister Pleasant/Nothing As Yet	12
68	Fontana TF 906	High On A Hill/Trumpet Serenade (actually by Nigel Hopkins)	6
73	CBS 1328	Speed On/Sundown In Mexico	4
66	CBS 62679	THE REVOLUTIONARY PIANO OF NICKY HOPKINS (LP)	25
73	CBS 65416	THE TIN MAN WAS A DREAMER (LP, featuring Mick Taylor)	12

(see also Neil Christian & Crusaders, Quicksilver Messenger Service, Aquarian Age)

WASH HOPKINS SINGERS
| 69 | Action ACT 4546 | He's Got Blessing/Rock In A Weary Land | 4 |

HUGH HOPPER
73	CBS 65466	1984 (LP)	12
76	Compendium FIDARDO 4	CRUEL BUT FAIR (LP)	15
77	Compendium FIDARDO 7	HOPPERTUNITY BOX (LP)	15
78	Ogun OG 527	ROGUE ELEMENT (LP, as Hopper, Dean, Gowen, Sheen — 'Soft Head')	10

(see also Soft Machine)

HOPSCOTCH
| 69 | United Artists UP 2231 | Look At The Lights Go Up/Same Old Fat Man | 10 |
| 69 | United Artists UP 35022 | Long Black Veil/Easy To Find | 4 |

(see also Scots Of St. James)

HORACE & IMPERIALS
| 68 | Nu Beat NB 012 | Young Love/Days Like These | 6 |

HORIZON
| 81 | SRT SRTS 81432 | Stage Struck/Remember The Bad Boys | 10 |

PAUL HORN
| 68 | Liberty LBL 83084E | COSMIC CONSCIOUSNESS (LP) | 10 |

LENA HORNE
55	HMV 7M 309	Love Me Or Leave Me/I Love To Love	6
55	HMV 7M 319	It's All Right With Me/It's Love	6
56	HMV 7M 423	If You Can Dream/What's Right For You (Is Right For Me)	5
56	MGM MGM 917	Can't Help Lovin' Dat Man/The Man I Love	4
59	RCA RCA 1120	A New Fangled Tango/Honeysuckle Rose	5
59	RCA RCA 1120	A New Fangled Tango/Honeysuckle Rose (78)	5
57	RCA RD 27021/SF 5007	AT THE WALDORF ASTORIA (LP, mono/stereo)	10/12
58	RCA RD 27063	STORMY WEATHER (LP)	10
59	RCA RD 27098/SF 5019	GIVE THE LADY WHAT SHE WANTS (LP, mono/stereo)	10/12
59	RCA RD 27141	A FRIEND OF YOURS (LP)	10
61	RCA RD 27255	LENA AT THE SANDS (LP, also stereo SF 5217)	10
63	RCA RD/SF 7530	LENA LOVELY AND ALIVE (LP)	10
64	Stateside S(S)L 10081	HERE'S LENA (LP)	10

(see also Harry Belafonte)

HANK HORNSBY
57	MGM MGM 955	Pots And Pans/Cotton	4
58	MGM MGM 972	The Legend Of The Birds And Bees/Girls Girls Girls	4
58	MGM MGM 972	The Legend Of The Birds And Bees/Girls Girls Girls (78)	5

HORNSEY AT WAR
| 70s | War WAR 001 | DEAD BEAT REVIVAL (EP, numbered p/s) | 8 |

HORRORCOMIC
| 77 | Lightning/B&C BVZ 0007 | I'm All Hung Up On Pierrepoint/The Exorcist/Sex In The Afternoon (p/s) | 5 |

78	Lightning GIL 512	I Don't Mind/England 77 (p/s)	5
79	B&C BCS 18	Jesus Christ/Cut Your Throat (p/s)	10

HORSE
70	RCA SF 8109	HORSE (LP)	125

(see also Saturnalia)

HORSLIPS
79	DJM DJT 15001	Loneliness/Homesick (leaf-shaped green vinyl)	4
72	Oats MOO 3	HAPPY TO MEET ... SORRY TO PART (LP, booklet octagonal sleeve)	18
73	Oats MOO 5	THE TAIN (LP)	12
76	Oats MOO 9	DRIVE THE COLD WINTER AWAY (LP)	10

(see also Creatures)

HORTENSE (Ellis) & ALTON (Ellis)
65	Island WI 230	Don't Gamble With Love/Something You Got (B-side actually Alton Ellis & Flames)	10

(see also Hortense Ellis, Alton Ellis)

HORTENSE (Ellis) & DELROY (Wilson)
66	Rio R 119	We're Gonna Make It/SOUL BROTHERS: Ska Shuffle	8

(see also Hortense Ellis, Delroy Wilson)

HORTENSE (Ellis) & JACKIE (Opel)
64	R&B JB 138	Stand By Me/JACKIE OPEL: Solid Rock	8

(see also Hortense Ellis, Jackie Opel)

JOHNNY HORTON
59	Philips PB 932	The Battle Of New Orleans/All For The Love Of A Girl	6
59	Philips PB 932	The Battle Of New Orleans/All For The Love Of A Girl (78)	15
59	Philips PB 951	Johnny Reb/Sal's Got A Sugar Lip	8
59	Philips PB 951	Johnny Reb/Sal's Got A Sugar Lip (78)	25
59	Philips PB 976	Take Me Like I Am/I'm Ready If You're Willing	6
59	Philips PB 976	Take Me Like I Am/I'm Ready If You're Willing (78)	25
60	Philips PB 995	Sink The Bismarck!/The Same Old Tale The Crow Told Me	8
60	Philips PB 1062	North To Alaska/The Mansion You Stole	6
61	Philips PB 1130	Mr. Moonlight/When It's Springtime In Alaska	6
61	Philips PB 1132	Sleepy Eyed John/They'll Never Take Her Love From Me	6
61	Philips PB 1170	Ole Slew Foot/Miss Nancy	6
62	Philips PB 1226	Honky Tonk Man/Words	7
63	CBS AAG 132	All Grown Up/I'm A One Woman Man	5
60	Mercury ZEP 10074	THE FANTASTIC JOHNNY HORTON (EP)	20
64	Mercury 10008 MCE	COUNTRY AND WESTERN ACES (EP)	20
60	Philips BBL 7464	THE SPECTACULAR JOHNNY HORTON (LP)	20
61	Philips BBL 7536	HONKY TONK MAN (LP)	25
63	London HA-U 8096	DONE ROVIN' (LP)	40
65	Fontana FJL 306	VOICE OF JOHNNY HORTON (LP)	12
60s	Hallmark SHM 634	THE UNFORGETTABLE JOHNNY HORTON (LP)	10

WALTER 'SHAKEY' HORTON
74	Xtra XTRA 1135	WALTER 'SHAKEY' HORTON WITH HOT COTTAGE (LP)	12

HOT CHOCOLATE (BAND)
69	Apple APPLE 18	Give Peace A Chance/Living Without Tomorrow (as Hot Chocolate Band)	25
72	Rak RAK 127	Marie Anne/Ruth	4
75	Rak RAK 199	Blue Night/You Sexy Thing	4

HOT CLUB QUINTET
53	Decca LF 1139	QUINTET OF THE HOT CLUB OF FRANCE (10" LP)	15

(see also Django Reinhardt)

HOTEL
79	MCA MCF 3036	HOTEL (LP)	10

HOT EYES
85	Columbia DB 9108	Catch Me If You Can/Sku Du Spørg Fra No'En	4

HOTHOUSE FLOWERS
87	Mother MUM 7	Love Don't Work This Way (DJ Edit)/Freedom (p/s, die-cut on front)	4
87	Mother 12MUM 7	Love Don't Work This Way (Ext.)/Freedom/Seeline Woman (live) (12", p/s)	7
88	London LONF 174	Don't Go/Saved (star-shaped foldout p/s, numbered)	5

HOTLEGS
70	Fontana 6007 019	Neanderthal Man/You Didn't Like It Because You Didn't Think Of It	4
71	Philips 6006 140	Lady Sadie/Loser	4
71	Philips 6308 047	THINKS: SCHOOL STINKS (LP)	12
71	Philips 6308 080	SONGS (LP)	15

(see also 10cc, Mindbenders, Godley & Creme, Tristar Airbus)

HOT POTATO
73	PMTB 1	HOT POTATO (LP, private press)	125

HOT ROD ALLSTARS
69	Duke DU 59	Lick A Pop/Treasure	5
70	Duke DU 66	Return Of The Bad Man/Caysoe Reggae	5
70	Trojan TR 7732	Strong Man/Sentimental	4
70s	Hot Rod HR 108	Beautiful World/Shocks Of A Drugs Man	5
70s	Torpedo TOR 1	Pussy Got Nine Life/BOSS SOUNDS: Lick It Back	4
70s	Torpedo TOR 5	Skinheads Don't Fear/Ten Commandments From The Devil	5
70s	Torpedo TOR 10	Moonhop In London/Skinhead Moondust	5

HOTRODS
65	Columbia DB 7693	I Don't Love You No More/Ain't Coming Back No More	30

HOT SNAX
80s	Munch MR 2	Pressure Drop/Treat Me Right, Tonight (12") 8

HOT SPRINGS
66	Columbia DB 7821	It's All Right/All I Know About Love 8

HOT-TODDYS
59	Pye Intl. 7N 25020	Shakin' And Stompin'/Rockin' Crickets 15
59	Pye Intl. 7N 25020	Shakin' And Stompin'/Rockin' Crickets (78) 25

HOT TUNA
72	Grunt 65-0502	Keep On Truckin'/Water Song 5
76	Grunt RCG 1002	It's So Easy/I Can't Be Satisfied 4
70	RCA SF 8125	HOT TUNA (LP) 10
71	RCA LSP 4550	ELECTRIC LIVE (FIRST PULL UP, THEN PULL DOWN) (LP) 10
72	Grunt FTR 1004	BURGERS (LP, with purple inner bag) 10
(see also Jefferson Airplane)		

HOT WATER
78	Duff	Different Morning/Premium Bondage (p/s) 6
79	Duff DWR 101	Get Lost!/Bird's Eye View (p/s) 5

HOUNDHEAD HENRY/FRANKIE JAXON
60s	Jazz Collector JEL 10	THE MALE BLUES VOLUME 6 (EP) 8

HOUR GLASS
68	Liberty LBL/LBS 83219E	THE HOUR GLASS (LP) 15
73	United Artists USD 303/4	THE HOUR GLASS (2-LP) 14
(see also Allman Brothers)		

SON HOUSE
(see under S)

HOUSEHOLD
67	United Artists UP 1190	Guess I'll Learn How To Fly/Nothing You Can Do But Cry 6
68	United Artists UP 2210	Twenty First Summer/Winter's Coming On 6

HOUSEMARTINS
85	Go! Discs GOD 7	Flag Day/Stand At Ease (p/s) 4
85	Go! Discs GODX 7	Flag Day/Stand At Ease/Coal Train To Hatfield Main (12", p/s) 7
85	Go! Discs GOD 7	Flag Day/Stand At Ease//Sheep/Drop Down Dead (shrinkwrapped double pack) 6
86	Go! Discs GODP 9	Sheep/I'll Be Your Shelter/Drop Down Dead (picture disc) 6
86	Go! Discs GODP 11	Happy Hour/The Mighty Ship (shaped picture disc) 5
86	Go! Discs GODP 13	Think For A Minute/Who Needs The Limelight (shaped picture disc) ...5
86	Go! Discs GODP 16	Caravan Of Love/When I First Met Jesus (rectangular picture disc) 5
86	Go! Discs GODB 16	THE HOUSEMARTINS' CHRISTMAS BOX SET (4 singles in foldout sleeve) 10
80s	private pressing	THEMES FROM THE WELL-DRESSED MAN (cassette) 15
80s	private pressing	THE HOUSEMARTINS FROM OUTER SPACE (cassette) 12

HOUSE OF LORDS
69	B&C CB 112	In The Land Of Dreams/Ain't Gonna Wait Forever 10

HOUSE OF LOVE
87	Creation CRE 043T	Shine On/Love/Flow (12", p/s, 3,000 only) 25
87	Creation CREFRE 5	Shine On (Fuck Version) (1-sided flexidisc, gig freebie) 10
88	Creation CRE 053	Christine/Loneliness Is A Gun (custom p/s) 10
88	Creation CRE 053T	Christine/The Hill/Loneliness Is A Gun (12", p/s) 18
89	Fontana HOLG 2	I Don't Know Why I Love You/Love II (gatefold, numbered p/s) 4
89	Fontana HOLG 3	Shine On/Allergy (gatefold, numbered p/s) 4
90	Fontana HOLG 4	Beatles And The Stones/Love IV (gatefold pack with poster, numbered) 4
88	Creation CRELP 034	HOUSE OF LOVE (LP, 1st 3,000 copies with free 7": "Christine [Demo Version]"/"Shine On [Demo Version]" [CREFRE 01], stickered cover) ...15
(see also Kingdoms, Colenso Parade)		

BOBBI HOUSTON
74	Action ACT 4622	I Want To Make It With You Pts 1 & 2 4

CISCO HOUSTON
60	Top Rank 30/028	THE CISCO SPECIAL (LP) 60
68	Fontana FJL 412	I AIN'T GOT NO HOME (LP) 10

CISCO HOUSTON & WOODY GUTHRIE
60s	Ember CW 135	CISCO HOUSTON AND WOODY GUTHRIE (LP) 10
(see also Woody Guthrie)		

CISSY HOUSTON
70	Major Minor MM 700	He/I Believe/I'll Be There 4
70	Major Minor MM 716	The Long And Winding Road/Be My Baby 4
70	Pye Intl. 7N 25537	I Just Don't Know What To Do With Myself/This Empty Place 15
70	Major Minor SMLP 80	PRESENTING CISSY HOUSTON (LP) 12
78	Private Stock PVLP 1044	THINK IT OVER (LP) 10

DAVID HOUSTON
55	London HL 8147	Blue Prelude/I'm Sorry I Made You Cry 18
63	Columbia DB 7159	Mountain Of Love/Poor Little Angeline 4

SAM HOUSTON
65	Island WI 172	My Mother's Eyes/Danny Boy 8

THELMA HOUSTON
69	Stateside SS 8026	Jumpin' Jack Flash/Sunshower 4
70	Stateside SS 8036	Save The Country/I Just Can't Stay Away 4
70	Stateside SS 8044	I Just Wanna Be Me/Crying In The Sunshine 4
72	Tamla Motown TMG 799	I Want To Go Back There Again/Pick Of The Week 4

72	Mowest MW 3001	No One's Gonna Be A Fool Forever/What If	4
73	Mowest MW 3004	Black California/I'm Letting Go (withdrawn)	10
69	Stateside SSL 5010	SUNSHOWER (LP)	10

WHITNEY HOUSTON

85	ARISTA ARIST 614	Someone For Me/The Greatest Love Of All (p/s)	4
85	Arista ARIST 12614	Someone For Me/The Greatest Love Of All (12", p/s)	8
85	Arista ARIST 625	You Give Good Love/How Will I Know (p/s)	4
85	Arista ARIST 12625	You Give Good Love (Extended)/How Will I Know/You Give Good Love (Remix)/Someone For Me (12", p/s)	8
86	Arista ARIST 12658	The Greatest Love Of All/Thinking About You/Shock Me (with Jermaine Jackson) (12", p/s)	7
87	Arista RISCD 1	I Wanna Dance With Somebody (Who Loves Me) (12" Remix)/Moment Of Truth/I Wanna Dance With Somebody (Who Loves Me) (Dub Mix) (CD)	10
87	Arista RISCD 31	Didn't We Almost Have It All/I Wanna Dance With Somebody (Who Loves Me) (Acappella Mix)/Shock Me (CD, with stickered p/s)	10
87	Arista RISCD 43	So Emotional (Extended Remix)/Didn't We Almost Have It All (live)/For The Love Of You (CD)	8
88	Arista 111 516P	Love Will Save The Day/Hold Me (picture disc)	6
88	Arista 111 516W	Love Will Save The Day/Hold Me (tour packs, Wembley or Birmingham p/s)	4
88	Arista 661 516	Love Will Save The Day (Extended Club Mix)/Love Will Save The Day (Single Version)/Hold Me (CD picture disc, with gatefold sleeve)	12
88	Arista 661 613	One Moment In Time/Olympic Joy/Rise To The Occasion/One Moment In Time (Instrumental) (CD)	8
89	Arista 662 545	It Isn't, It Wasn't, It Ain't Never Gonna Be (Remix)/(Extended Remix)/(Hip Hop Remix)/ARETHA FRANKLIN: Think (CD)	8
90	Arista 613 817	I'M YOUR BABY TONIGHT: THE REMIXES (12" EP)	7
90	Arista 613 817	I'm Your Baby Tonight (Club Mix)/(Whit-A-Pella)/(Dub Mix) (12", p/s)	7
80s	Arista	Wogan promo	15
86	Arista WHIT 1	WHITNEY HOUSTON (LP, box set with 10 postcards, songbook & calendar)	12

(see also JAMs)

LARRY HOVIS

| 58 | Capitol CL 14843 | Do I Love You/We Could Have Lots Of Fun | 4 |
| 59 | Columbia DB 15083 | My Heart Belongs To Only You/I Want To Fall In Love | 4 |

BRIAN HOWARD & SILHOUETTES

62	Columbia DB 4914	Somebody Help Me/Young And Evil	15
63	Columbia DB 7067	The Worryin' Kind/Come To Me	12
64	Fontana TF 464	Back In The U.S.A./Hooked	12

DAVE HOWARD SINGERS

| 87 | Hallelujah HAL 04 | Yon Yonson (1-sided, promo-only) | 5 |

JAN HOWARD

| 60 | London HL 7088 | The One You Slip Around With/I Wish I Could Fall In Love Again (export issue) | 10 |

JOHNNY HOWARD BAND

60	Decca F 11298	Up The Wall/Orbit	4
62	Decca F 11423	Mind Reader/Spanish Gipsy Dance	4
64	Decca F 11925	Rinky Dink/Java	4
65	Decca F 12065	El Pussy Cat/A Tune Called Harry	4
67	Deram DML/SML 1001	THE VELVET TOUCH OF JOHNNY HOWARD (LP)	10

KID HOWARD

| 50s | Mono RBM 464 | KID HOWARD'S BAND (LP) | 12 |

LES HOWARD

| 53 | HMV 7M 127 | Love Evermore/I Lived When I Met You | 4 |
| 53 | HMV 7M 171 | Rags To Riches/From Here To Eternity | 4 |

ROLAND S. HOWARD & LYDIA LUNCH

| 86 | 4AD BAD 210 | Some Velvet Morning/I Fell In Love With A Ghost (12", p/s, with postcard) | 8 |

(see also Lydia Lunch, Birthday Party)

ROSETTA HOWARD

30s	Vocalion S 202	Rosetta Blues/If You're A Viper	25
44	Brunswick 03467	Rosetta Blues/If You're A Viper (78)	12
51	Vocalion V 1005	Let Your Linen Hang Low/HARLEM HAMFATS: Weed Smoker's Dream (Why Don't You Do Now) (78)	12

CATHERINE HOWE

| 71 | Reflection | WHAT A BEAUTIFUL PLACE (LP) | 40 |

STEVE HOWE

| 75 | Atlantic K 50151 | BEGINNINGS (LP, gatefold sleeve, some with embossed 'Yes' logo) | 12/10 |
| 79 | Atlantic K 50621 | THE STEVE HOWE ALBUM (LP, gatefold sleeve) | 10 |

(see also In Crowd, Syndicats, Tomorrow, Bodast, Yes, Asia, Anderson Bruford Wakeman & Howe)

EDDIE HOWELL

| 76 | Warner Bros K 16701 | Man From Manhattan/Waiting In The Wings | 15 |

(see also Queen)

REUBEN HOWELL

| 74 | Mowest MW 3019 | Rings/I Believe When I Fall In Love It Will Be Forever | 4 |

FRANKIE HOWERD

54	Decca F 10420	(Don't Let The) Kiddy Geddin/Abracadabra	10
58	Columbia DB 4230	It's All Right With Me/Song And Dance Man	7
64	Decca F 12028	Last Word On The Election/Last Word On The Election (Version)	5
70	Pye 7N 45061	Up Je T'Aime/All Through The Night	4
71	Columbia DB 8757	Up Pompeii/Salute!	4
63	Decca LK 4556	AT THE ESTABLISHMENT (LP)	15

MINT VALUE £

60s Pye NPL .... SOMETHING FUNNY HAPPENED ON THE WAY TO THE FORUM (LP) 12

CHRIS HOWLAND
| 58 | Columbia DB 4114 | Mama (Ma, He's Making Eyes At Me)/Fraulein | 6 |
| 69 | Columbia DB 4194 | Susie Darlin'/The Rain Falls On Ev'rybody | 6 |

HOWLIN' WOLF
61	Pye Intl. 7N 25101	Little Baby/Down In The Bottom	12
63	Pye Intl. 7N 25192	Just Like I Treat You/I Ain't Superstitious	10
64	Pye Intl. 7N 25244	Smokestack Lightnin'/Going Down Slow ('Slow' or 'South' on B-side label)	15/8
64	Pye Intl. 7N 25269	Little Girl/Tail Dragger	10
64	Pye Intl. 7N 25283	Love Me Darling/My Country Sugar Mama	10
65	Chess CRS 8010	Killing Floor/Louise	10
65	Chess CRS 8016	Ooh Baby/Tell Me What I've Done	10
69	Chess CRS 8097	Evil/Tail Dragger	8
66	Chess CRE 6017	REAL FOLK BLUES (EP)	15
56	London REU 1072	RHYTHM AND BLUES WITH HOWLIN' WOLF (EP)	50
63	Pye Intl. NEP 44015	SMOKESTACK LIGHTNIN' (EP)	15
64	Pye Intl. NEP 44032	TELL ME (EP)	15
64	Chess CRL 4006	MOANIN' IN THE MOONLIGHT (LP)	20
65	Chess CRL 4508	POOR BOY (LP)	18
66	Ember EMB 3370	BIG CITY BLUES (LP)	15
67	Marble Arch MAL 665	MOANIN' IN THE MOONLIGHT (LP, reissue)	10
69	Chess CRLS 4543	THE HOWLIN' WOLF ALBUM (LP)	12
71	Chess 6310 108	MESSAGE TO THE YOUNG (LP)	12
71	Rolling Stones COC 49101	THE LONDON SESSIONS (LP)	10
71	Python PLP 13	HOWLIN' WOLF (LP)	25

(see also Hubert Sumlin)

HOWLIN' WOLF, MUDDY WATERS & BO DIDDLEY
| 68 | Chess CRL 4537 | THE SUPER SUPER BLUES BAND (LP) | 25 |

(see also Muddy Waters, Bo Diddley)

HOWLIN' WOLF/JUNIOR PARKER/BOBBY BLAND
| 74 | Polydor 2383 257 | BLUES FOR MR. CRUMP (LP) | 15 |

LINDA HOYLE
| 71 | Vertigo 6360 060 | PIECES OF ME (LP, gatefold sleeve, spiral label) | 120 |

(see also Affinity, Nucleus)

H.P. LOVECRAFT
67	Philips BF 1620	Wayfarin' Stranger/Tin Machine	7
68	Philips BF 1639	The White Ship Pts 1 & 2 (withdrawn)	
68	Philips BF 1639	The White Ship/I've Been Wrong Before	7
67	Philips (S)BL 7830	H.P. LOVECRAFT (LP)	30
68	Philips SBL 7872	H.P. LOVECRAFT II (LP, most with water-mark at start of each record)	30/15

H₂O
81	Spock PARA 2	Hollywood Dream/Children (with lyric insert)	6
83	RCA RCA 330	Dream To Sleep/Burn To Win (picture disc)	4
83	RCA RCA 349	Just Outside Of Heaven/Stranger To Stranger (picture disc)	4

FREDDIE HUBBARD
72	CTI CTL 5	STRAIGHT LIFE (LP)	10
73	CTI CTL 11	SKY DIVE (LP)	10
75	CTI CTI 6056	POLAR AC (LP)	10
75	Atlantic K 60053	ART OF FREDDIE HUBBARD ATLANTIC YEARS (2-LP)	14
75	Blue Note BST 84056	GOIN' UP (LP)	10
75	Blue Note BST 84085	READY FOR FREDDIE (LP)	10
75	Blue Note BST 84115	HUB TONES (LP)	10
75	Blue Note BST 84172	BREAKING POINT (LP)	10
75	Blue Note BST 84196	BLUE SPIRITS (LP)	10
75	Blue Note BST 84207	THE NIGHT OF THE COOKERS VOL. 1 (LP)	10
75	Blue Note BST 84208	THE NIGHT OF THE COOKERS VOL. 2 (LP)	10
75	CBS 80478	HIGH ENERGY (LP)	10

WENDY HUBER
| 65 | Philips BF 1446 | Come Away Melinda/I Belong To The Wind | 4 |

R.B. HUDMAN
| 76 | Atlantic K 10742 | How Can I Be A Witness/If You Don't Cheat On Me | 4 |

COLIN HUDSON
| 65 | Pye 7N 15907 | Girl You Don't Know Me/Little Boy Blue | 4 |

JOHNNY HUDSON & TEEN BEATS
| 63 | Decca F 11679 | Makin' Up Is Hard To Do/Charms | 6 |

KEITH HUDSON (& CHUCKLES)
69	Big Shot BI 528	Tambourine Man/Old Fashioned Way (both actually by Ken Boothe)	6
70	Smash SMA 2311	Don't Get Me Confused/DENNIS SMITH: Ball of Confusion (B-side actually by Dennis Alcapone)	5
71	Smash SMA 2526	Light Of Day/I Thought You Knew	5
71	Summit SUM 8514	Melody Maker/Uncover Me	5
72	Downtown DT 492	True True To My Heart/BIG YOUTH: Ace 90 Skank	5
72	Spur SP 1	Darkest Night On A Wet Looking Road/Version	5
72	Duke DU 145	Satan Side (with Chuckles)/DON T. JUNIOR: Evil Spirit	5

KEITH HUDSON & I ROY
| 73 | Randy's RAN 534 | Silver Platter/Jean You Change Everything | 5 |

(see also I Roy)

ROCK HUDSON
| 59 | Brunswick 05816 | Pillow Talk/Roly Poly | 4 |

HUDSON PEOPLE

79	Ensign ENY 27	Trip To Your Mind Pts 1 & 2	4
79	Ensign ENY 2712	Trip To Your Mind Pts 1 & 2 (12")	7
70s	Hithouse HIT 1	Trip To Your Mind Pts 1 & 2 (12")	25

HUE & CRY

86	Stampede STAMP 2	Here Comes Everybody/From First To Last/The Successes Of Monetarism (12", p/s)	18
87	Circa YR 2	I Refuse/Joe And Josephine//I Refuse (Extended)/Tempted/Shipbuilding/Dangerous Wreck (p/s, with free "Shuggy And Shout" cassette)	6
87	Circa YRTX 4	Labour Of Love (Version Super Bad)/Wide Screen/I Refuse (Bitter Suite) (10", p/s)	5
87	Circa YRC 4	Labour Of Love (Version Super Bad)/Wide Screen/Goodbye To Me (BBC Recording)/I Refuse (BBC Recording) (cassette)	5
87	Circa YRB 4	Strength To Strength/Dangerous Wreck (box set)	4
88	Circa YRC 8	I Refuse (Route '88)/Indifference/Just One Word (live)/Mad To Nuts (live) (cassette)	4
88	Circa YRCD 8	I Refuse (Route '88)/Indifference/Labour Of Love (Super Bad)/History City (live) (CD)	7
88	Circa YRTX 18	Ordinary Angel (Hoedown Mix)/I Am John's Heart/He Won't Smile/Remote (10", p/s)	5
88	Circa YRCD 18	Ordinary Angel (Hoedown Mix)/I Am John's Heart/Hymn To Hands/Spending You (CD)	7

HUES CORPORATION

74	RCA RCA 2444	Freedom Of The Stallion/Get Off My Cloud	4
74	RCA APL1 0323	FREEDOM OF THE STALLION (LP)	10
74	RCA APL1 0775	ROCKIN' SOUL (LP)	10

HUEYS

69	London HLU 10264	Coo Coo Over You/You Ain't No Hippie	8

HUG

75	Polydor 2383 330	NEON DREAM (LP)	10

MIKE HUGG

72	Polydor 2058 265	Blue Suede Shoes Again/Fool No More	4
72	Polydor 2383 140	SOMEWHERE (LP)	10
73	Polydor 2383 213	STRESS AND STRAIN (LP)	10

(see also Manfred Mann, Hug)

HUGGY BEAR

93	white label	Feburary 14th/Into The Mission (1-sided gig freebie, plain black sleeve)	4

CAROL HUGHES

58	Columbia DB 4094	Lend Me Your Comb/First Date	4
58	Columbia DB 4094	Lend Me Your Comb/First Date (78)	5

DANNY HUGHES

69	Pye 7N 17750	Hi Ho Silver Lining/I Washed My Hands In Muddy Waters	8

DAVID HUGHES

60	Top Rank JAR 316	Looking High, High, High/Mi Amor	4

FRED HUGHES

65	Fontana TF 583	Oo Wee Baby I Love You/Love Me Baby	20
76	Brunswick BR 37	Baby Boy/JOHNNY JONES & KING CASUALS: Purple Haze	4
76	DJM DJS 10717	Oo Wee Baby I Love You/My Cries Oh	4

'FRIDAY' HUGHES

51	MGM MGM 422	Lazy Morning/The Devil Ain't Lazy (78)	7

GLENN HUGHES

77	Safari LONG 2	PLAY ME OUT (LP, original with inner sleeve)	10

(see also Deep Purple, Roger Glover, Hughes-Thrall)

JIMMY HUGHES

63	London HL 9680	My Loving Time/I'm Qualified	15
64	Pye Intl. 7N 25254	Steal Away/Lollipops, Lace And Lipstick	8
66	Sue WI 4006	Goodbye My Love/It Was Nice	15
66	Atlantic 584 017	Neighbour, Neighbour/It's A Good Thing	8
67	Atlantic 584 135	Hi-Heel Sneakers/Time Will Bring You Back	8
69	Stax STAX 117	Sweet Things You Do/Let 'Em Down Baby	5
69	Stax STAX 126	Chains Of Love/I'm Not Ashamed To Beg Or Plead	6
69	Stax SXATS 1010	SOMETHING SPECIAL (LP)	10

HUGHES-THRALL

83	Epic EPC 25052	HUGHES-THRALL (LP)	10

(see also Glenn Hughes)

HUGO & LUIGI

57	Columbia DB 3978	Rockabilly Party/Shenandoah Rose	10
57	Columbia DB 3978	Rockabilly Party/Shenandoah Rose (78)	5
58	Columbia DB 4156	Twilight In Tennessee/Cha-Hua-Hua	7
58	Columbia DB 4156	Twilight In Tennessee/Cha-Hua-Hua (78)	5
59	RCA RCA 1127	La Plume De Ma Tante/Honolulu Lu	5
59	RCA RCA 1127	La Plume De Ma Tante/Honolulu Lu (78)	5
60	RCA RCA 1169	Just Come Home/Lonesome Stranger	4

HULA

85	Red Rhino RED 18	BLACK POP WORKOUT (12" EP)	7
85	Red Rhino RED 56	Get The Habit/Bad Blood (white label, screen-printed p/s)	6

ALAN HULL

70	Transatlantic BIG 129	We Can Swing Together/Obidiah's Grave	10

73	Charisma CAS 1069	PIPEDREAM (LP)	10

(see also Lindisfarne)

HULLABALLOOS
64	Columbia DB 7392	I'm Gonna Love You Too/Why Do Fools Fall In Love	5
65	Columbia DB 7558	I'll Show You How To Love/Did You Ever	5
65	Columbia DB 7626	Don't Stop/I Won't Turn Away Now	5

GEORGE HULTGREEN
70	Warner Bros WB 8017	Say Hello/Before You Say Goodbye	4

HUMAN BEANS
67	Columbia DB 8230	Morning Dew (Take Me For A Walk)/It's A Wonder	50

(see also Love Sculpture, Dave Edmunds)

HUMAN BEAST
70	Decca SKL 5053	HUMAN BEAST VOLUME 1 (LP)	140

HUMAN BEINZ
68	Capitol CL 15529	Nobody But Me/Sueno	20
68	Capitol CL 15542	Turn On Your Lovelight/It's Fun To Be Clean	15

HUMAN CABBAGES
81	Boys & Girls BAG TWO	The Witch/Air-Raid Shelter (Pill Mix)/One More Fool (p/s)	4

HUMAN INSTINCT
65	Mercury MF 951	Can't Stop Loving You/I Want To Be Loved By You My Friend	25
66	Mercury MF 927	Rich Man/Illusions	30
67	Mercury MF 990	Go-Go/I Can't Live Without You	20
68	Deram DM 167	A Day In My Mind's Mind/Death Of The Seaside	30
68	Deram DM 177	Renaissance Fair/Pink Dawn	25

HUMAN LEAGUE
78	Fast Product FAST 4	Being Boiled/Circus Of Death (p/s, original issue with b&w picture labels)	6
79	Fast Product FAST 10	THE DIGNITY OF LABOUR (12" EP with flexidisc)	7
79	Virgin VS 294	Empire State Human/Introducing (p/s)	4
80	Virgin SV 105	HOLIDAY '80 (EP, double pack, purple & blue labels)	10
80	Virgin SV 105	HOLIDAY '80 (12" EP, withdrawn)	15
80	Virgin VS 351	Empire State Human/Introducing//Only After Dark/Toyota City (Long Version) (p/s, shrinkwrapped with free single)	8
80	Virgin VS 351	Empire State Human/Introducing (p/s, reissue)	4
80	Virgin VS 351-12	Empire State Human/Introducing (12", p/s)	8
81	Virgin VS 395	Boys And Girls/Tom Baker (gatefold p/s)	4
81	Virgin VS 416-12	Love Action/Hard Times/Love Action/Hard Times (Instrumental) (as Human League Red, 12", p/s, with free flexidisc)	7
81	Virgin VS 453	Open Your Heart/Non Stop (p/s, coloured vinyl)	4
81	Virgin VS 466	Don't You Want Me?/Seconds (p/s, with poster)	4
81	Virgin SV 105	HOLIDAY '80 (EP, reissue double pack, green/red labels, gatefold p/s)	7
81	Virgin SV 105	HOLIDAY '80 (reissue 3-track EP, green/red or blue/pink labels)	4
82	Virgin VSY 522	Mirror Man/Gold (picture disc)	5
84	Virgin VSY 723	Louise/The Sign (Remix) (picture disc)	5
81	Virgin VP 2192	DARE (LP, white or black vinyl picture disc with black sleeve)	10
88	Virgin CDHLP 1	GREATEST HITS (CD, picture disc)	14

(see also Heaven 17, Men, Philip Oakey & Georgio Moroder, Jo Callis)

HUMBLEBUMS
69	Big T BIG 122	Saturday Roundabout Sunday/Bed Of Mossy Green	4
69	Transatlantic TRA 186	FIRST COLLECTION OF MELODIES (LP)	10
69	Transatlantic TRA 201	THE NEW HUMBLEBUMS (LP)	10
70	Transatlantic TRA 218	OPEN UP THE DOOR (LP)	10
74	Transatlantic TRA 288	THE COMPLETE (LP)	10

(see also Gerry Rafferty, Billy Connolly)

HUMBLE PIE
69	Immediate IM 082	Natural Born Boogie/Wrist Job	4
69	Immediate IMSP 025	AS SAFE AS YESTERDAY IS (LP)	12
69	Immediate IMSP 027	TOWN AND COUNTRY (LP)	12
70	A&M AMLS 986	HUMBLE PIE (LP)	10
71	A&M AMLS 2013	ROCK ON (LP)	10

(see also Steve Marriott, Small Faces, Peter Frampton, Herd)

HELEN HUMES
44	Brunswick 03409	Unlucky Woman/Mound Boyou (78)	12
52	Brunswick 05193	I Cried For You/Mean Way Of Loving (78)	12
56	Vogue V 2048	Million Dollar Secret/If I Could Be With You One Hour Of The Day	6
56	Vogue V 2048	Million Dollar Secret/If I Could Be With You One Hour Of The Day (78)	12
59	Contemporary CV 2415	When The Saints Come Marching In/Bill Bailey, Won't You Please Come Home (with Benny Carter's All-Stars)	6
61	Contemporary LAC 12245	HELEN HUMES AND THE BENNY CARTER ALL STARS (LP)	10

(see also Benny Carter)

ENGELBERT HUMPERDINCK
66	Decca F 12427	Stay/Come Over Here	4
66	Decca F 12496	Dommage Dommage/When I Say Goodnight	4
60s	Decca	other 45s	2-3
60s	Decca	LPs	7-8

(see also Gerry Dorsey)

BOBBI HUMPHREY
76	Blue Note UAG 20003	FANCY DANCER (LP)	10

DELLA HUMPHREY
69	Action ACT 4525	Don't Make The Good Girls Go Bad/Your Love Is All I Need	7

PAUL HUMPHREY
    75   Anchor ABC 4046   Cochise/What's That Noise P.K.? 5
LES HUMPHRIES SINGERS
    76   Antic K 11526   Sing Sang Song/Just Sit Down At The Old Piano 5
HUMPY BONG
    70   Parlophone R 5859   Don't You Be Too Long/We're Alright Till Then 4
    (see also Bee Gees)
HUNGER
    84   Psycho PSYCHO 14   STRICTLY FROM HUNGER (LP, reissue) 15
HUNGRY WOLF
    70   Philips 6308 009   HUNGRY WOLF (LP) 75
    (see also Czar)
GLORIA HUNNIFORD
    70s Tangerine DP 0012   Are You Ready For Love/Sound Of Love 4
GERALDINE HUNT
    69   Roulette RO 515   Never Never Never Leave Me/Push Sweep 8
MARSHA HUNT
    69   Track 604 030   Walk On Gilded Splinters/Hot Rod Poppa 5
    69   Track 604 034   Desdemona/Hippy Gumbo 10
    70   Track 604 037   Keep The Customer Satisfied/Lonesome Holy Roller 4
    71   Track 2410 101   WOMAN CHILD (LP) 25
MICHAEL HUNT & JOE LEATHERLAND
    67   Decca   WATER OF TYNE (LP) 10
PEE WEE HUNT & HIS ORCHESTRA
    55   Capitol CL 14225   It's Never Too Late To Fall In Love/A Room In Bloomsbury 5
    55   Capitol CL 14286   Save Your Love For Me/My Extraordinary Gal 5
TOMMY HUNT
    62   Top Rank JAR 605   The Door Is Open/I'm Wondering 10
    68   Direction 58-3216   I Need A Woman Of My Own/Searchin' For My Baby Looking
                                  Everywhere 5
    74   Pye 7N 45325   Sleep Tight Honey/Time Alone Will Tell 4
    75   Spark SRL 1132   Crackin' Up/Get Out 4
    (see also Ivorys)
WILLIE AMOS HUNT
    67   Camp 602 003   Would You Believe/My Baby Wants To Dance 30
HUNT & TURNER
    72   Village Thing VTS 11   MAGIC LANDSCAPE (LP) 20
ALBERTA HUNTER
    27   Parlophone R 3255   If You Can't Hold The Man You Love (Don't Cry When He's Gone)/
                                  BUTTERBEANS & SUSIE: Mama Stayed Out The Whole Night Long (78) ... 40
    30s Poydras 7   Come On Home/Aggravatin' Papa (78) 10
    30s Poydras 64   Down South Blues/Michigan Water Blues (78) 10
    50s Jazz Collector L 94   Everybody Loves My Baby/Texas Moaner Blues (78) 5
DANNY HUNTER (& GIANTS)
    60   HMV POP 722   Make It Up/Little Girl (as Danny Hunter & Giants) 10
    60   HMV POP 775   Who's Gonna Walk Ya Home?/Lonely And Blue 8
    61   Fontana H 300   Lost Weekend/Age For Love 6
DAVE HUNTER
    68   RCA RCA 1766   She's A Heartbreaker/Love Me A Lifetime 10
    69   RCA RCA 1841   Don't Throw Your Love To The Wind/Hitchcock Railway 5
GREG HUNTER
    66   Parlophone R 5483   Five O'Clock World/Away From Happiness 7
IAN HUNTER
    75   CBS 3194   Once Bitten Twice Shy/3,000 Miles From Here (p/s) 5
    76   CBS 4268   You Nearly Did Me In/Rape 6
    79   Chrysalis CHS 2324   When The Daylight Comes/Life After Death (p/s, white vinyl with mask) 4
    80   Chrysalis CHS 2434   We Gotta Get Out/Live Medley/Sons And Daughters//All The Young Dudes/
                                  (Live Medley) (double pack) 4
    (see also Mott The Hoople, At Last The 1958 Rock & Roll Show, Apex Rhythm & Blues All Stars)
IVORY JOE HUNTER
    50   MGM MGM 271   I Almost Lost My Mind/S.P. Blues (78, with Orchestra) 18
    56   London HLE 8261   A Tear Fell/I Need You By My Side 150
    56   London HLE 8261   A Tear Fell/I Need You By My Side (78) 30
    57   Columbia DB 3872   Since I Met You, Baby/You Can't Stop This Rockin' And Rollin' 110
    57   Columbia DB 3872   Since I Met You, Baby/You Can't Stop This Rockin' And Rollin' (78) ... 25
    57   London HLE 8486   Love's A Hurting Game/Empty Arms 90
    57   London HLE 8486   Love's A Hurting Game/Empty Arms (78) 20
    61   Capitol CL 15220   I'm Hooked/Because I Love You 10
    61   Capitol CL 15226   You Better Believe It, Baby/May The Man Win 10
ROBERT HUNTER
    74   Round RX 101   TALES OF THE GREAT RUM RUNNERS (LP) 10
    75   Round RX 105   TIGER ROSE (LP) 10
    (see also Grateful Dead)
SUSAN HUNTER
    55   Brunswick 05458   Not Yet/Was That The Right Thing To Do? 4

MINT VALUE £

TAB HUNTER

57	London HLD 8380	Young Love/Red Sails In The Sunset (gold label)	25
57	London HLD 8380	Young Love/Red Sails In The Sunset (78)	5
57	London HLD 8410	Ninety-Nine Ways/I Don't Get Around Much Anymore	12
57	London HLD 8410	Ninety-Nine Ways/I Don't Get Around Much Anymore (78)	5
58	London HLD 8535	Don't Let It Get Around/I'm Alone Because I Love You	15
60	Warner Bros WB 8	(What Can I Give) My Only Love/	
		(I'll Be With You) In Apple Blossom Time	6
60	Warner Bros WB 20	Waitin' For The Fall/Our Love	6
61	London HLD 9381	The Wild Side Of Life/My Devotion	10
62	London HLD 9559	Born To Lose/I Can't Stop Lovin' You	8
58	London RED 1134	YOUNG LOVE (EP)	20
61	Warner Bros WEP 6023	TAB HUNTER (EP, also stereo WSEP 2023)	15/18
60	Warner Bros WM 4008	TAB HUNTER (LP, also stereo WS 8008)	25/30
61	London HA-D 2401	YOUNG LOVE (LP, also stereo SAH-G 6201)	30/35

HUNTER MUSKETT

73	Bradleys BRAD 303	John Blair/Silver Coin (p/s)	6
70	Decca Nova SDN 20	EVERY TIME YOU MOVE (LP)	125
69	Bradleys BRADL 1003	HUNTER MUSKETT (LP)	25

HUNTERS (U.K.)

60	Fontana H 276	Teen Scene/Santa Monica Flyer	8
61	Fontana H 303	Golden Ear-rings/Tally Ho	6
61	Fontana H 323	The Storm/How's M'Chicks?	6
64	Fontana TF 514	Teen Scene/Someone Else's Baby	5
61	Fontana TFL 5140	TEEN SCENE — THE HUNTERS PLAY THE BIG HITS	
		(LP, also stereo STFL 561)	35/40
62	Fontana TFL 5175	HITS FROM THE HUNTERS (LP, also stereo STFL 572)	35/40

(see also Dave Sampson & Hunters)

HUNTERS (Holland)

| 66 | RCA RCA 1541 | Russian Spy And I/Spring | 12 |

(see also Jan Akkerman, Brainbox)

HUNTERS CLUB

| 87 | Trashcan THC 7002 | Give Me Your Soul/Angel (numbered plain sleeve) | 4 |

HURDY GURDY

| 71 | CBS | HURDY GURDY (LP) | 140 |

RED VINCENT HURLEY

| 76 | Pye 7N 45583 | When/Just A Little Love (p/s) | 7 |

HURRAH!

84	Kitchenware SK 2	The Sun Shines Here/I'll Be Your Surprise (p/s)	6
84	Kitchenware SK 6	Hip-Hip/Flowers (p/s)	5
86	Kitchenware SK 28G	Sweet Sanity/Hearts And Hands//Who'd Have Thought/	
		Who'd Have Thought (Slight Return) (double pack)	4
86	Kitchenware SK(X) 28	Sweet Sanity/Hearts And Hands (p/s, with cassette)	4
86	Kitchenware SK28	Sweet Sanity/Hearts And Hands (p/s, with poster booklet)	4
87	Esurient Comms PACE 2	WAY AHEAD (LP)	10

HURRICANES

| 71 | Upsetter US 363 | Got To Be Mine/UPSETTERS: Version | 5 |

HURRICANE STRINGS

| 63 | Columbia DB 7027 | Venus/In The Carrick | 4 |

MIKE HURST (& METHOD)

63	Philips BF 1295	The Banjo Song/Any Chance For Me	4
64	Philips BF 1319	Carol Anne/Anytime That You Want Me	4
64	Philips BF 1353	Half Heaven Half Heartache/Look In Your Eyes	4
65	Philips BF 1389	Last Time You'll Walk Out On Me/Something Told Me	4
65	Philips BF 1424	Show Me Around/I'm Running Away	4

(see also Remo Four, Ashton, Gardner & Dyke)

MISSISSIPPI JOHN HURT

67	Fontana TFL 6079	MISSISSIPPI JOHN HURT (LP)	18
71	Spookane SPL 1001	THE ORIGINAL 1928 RECORDINGS (LP)	40
71	Vanguard VSD 19/20	THE BEST OF MISSISSIPPI JOHN HURT (2-LP)	15
73	Vanguard VSD 79327	LAST SESSIONS (LP)	12
70s	Vanguard SVRL 19005	THE IMMORTAL MISSISSIPPI JOHN HURT (LP)	12

HUSH

| 68 | Fontana TF 944 | Elephant Rider/Grey | 80 |

HÜSKER DÜ

84	SST SST 025	Eight Miles High/Masochism World (live) (p/s)	5
86	Warner Bros W 8746	Don't Want To Know If You're Lonely/All Work And No Play (p/s)	5
86	Warner Bros W 8746T	Don't Want To Know If You're Lonely/All Work And No Play/	
		Helter Skelter (live) (12", p/s)	10
86	Warner Bros W 8612	Sorry Somehow/All This I've Done For You (p/s)	5
86	Warner Bros W 8612	Sorry Somehow/All This I've Done For You//Celebrated Summer (Acoustic)/	
		Flexible Flyer (double pack, gatefold sleeve)	10
86	Warner Bros W 8612T	Sorry Somehow/All This I've Done For You/Celebrated Summer (Acoustic)/	
		Flexible Flyer/Fattie (12", p/s)	10
87	Warner Bros W 8456	Could You Be The One/Everytime (p/s)	5
87	Warner Bros W 8456T	Could You Be The One/Everytime/Charity, Chastity, Prudence,	
		Hope (12", p/s)	10
87	Warner Bros W 8276	Ice Cold Ice/Gotta Lotta (p/s)	5
87	Warner Bros W 8276T	Ice Cold Ice/Gotta Lotta/Medley (12", p/s)	10

FERLIN HUSKY (& HIS HUSH PUPPIES)

57	Capitol CL 14702	Gone/Missing Persons (as Ferlin Husky & His Hush Puppies)	12
57	Capitol CL 14702	Gone/Missing Persons (as Ferlin Husky & His Hush Puppies) (78)	5
57	Capitol CL 14753	A Fallen Star/Prize Possession	18
57	Capitol CL 14785	This Moment Of Love/Make Me Live Again	7
58	Capitol CL 14824	Wang Dang Doo/What'cha Doin' After School	12
58	Capitol CL 14883	Slow Down Brother/The Drunken Driver (& His Hush Puppies)	12
58	Capitol CL 14916	I Feel That Old Heartache Again/I Saw God	8
58	Capitol CL 14922	The Kingdom Of Love/Terrific Together	7
58	Capitol CL 14954	I Will/All Of The Time	5
59	Capitol CL 14995	My Reason For Living/Wrong	5
59	Capitol CL 15027	Draggin' The River/Sea Sand	4
59	Capitol CL 15094	Black Sheep/I'll Always Return	4
60	Capitol CL 15160	The Wings Of A Dove/Next To Jimmy	4
57	Capitol EAP1 718	SONGS OF THE HOME AND HEART (EP)	10
57	Capitol EAP1 837	FERLIN HUSKY HITS (EP)	10
57	Capitol EAP1 921	COUNTRY MUSIC HOLIDAY (EP)	10
59	Parlophone GEP 8795	COUNTRY ROUND UP (EP)	20
60	Capitol EAP1 1280	FERLIN'S FAVOURITES (EP)	10
60	Capitol EAP2 1280	FERLIN'S FAVOURITES (EP)	10
60	Capitol EAP3 1280	FERLIN'S FAVOURITES (EP)	10
58	Capitol T 880	BOULEVARD OF BROKEN DREAMS (LP)	15
59	Capitol T 976	SITTIN' ON A RAINBOW (LP)	15
65	Fontana FJL 304	OLE OPRY FAVOURITES (LP)	10

JACQUES HUSTIN
74	EMI EMI 2143	Fleur De Liberté/Freedom For The Man	15

HUSTLER
74	A&M AMLS 68276	HIGH STREET (LP)	15
75	A&M AMLH 33001	PLAY LOUD (LP)	15

HUSTLERS
63	Philips BF 1275	Gimme What I Want/Not Much	6
64	Mercury MF 807	You Can't Sit Down/Be True To You	6
64	Mercury MF 817	Sick Of Giving/Easy To Find	15

WILLIE HUTCH
73	Tamla Motown STMA 8003	THE MACK (LP, soundtrack)	10
74	T. Motown STML 11269	FOXY BROWN (LP, soundtrack)	10
75	T. Motown STML 12015	ODE TO MY LADY (LP)	10

ASHLEY HUTCHINGS
(see under Morris On; see also Fairport Convention, Steeleye Span)

HUTCH HUTCHINS
70s	Goodwood GM 12324	FEELS LIKE RAIN (LP)	50

SAM HUTCHINS
69	Bell BLL 1044	Dang Me/I'm Tired Of Pretending	6

LEROY HUTSON
75	Warner Bros K 16536	All Because Of You Pts 1 & 2	8
74	Buddah BDLP 4013	THE MAN (LP)	15
75	Warner Bros K 56139	LEROY HUTSON (LP)	50

J.B. HUTTO & HIS HAWKS
73	Delmark DS 617	HAWK SQUAT (LP)	12

BETTY HUTTON
53	HMV 7M 103	Somebody Loves Me/Jealous (B-side with Pat Morgan)	7
56	Capitol CL 14568	Sleepy Head/Hit The Road To Dreamland	4
54	Capitol LC 6639	CAPITOL PRESENTS BETTY HUTTON (10" LP)	12
(see also Hutton Sisters, Perry Como, 'Tennessee' Ernie Ford)

DANNY HUTTON
66	MGM MGM 1314	Funny How Love Can Be/Dreamin' Isn't Good For You	4
65	Pye Intl. 7N 25325	Roses And Rainbows/Monster Shindig	4

HUTTON SISTERS (Betty & Marion)
55	Capitol CL 14250	Ko Ko Mo (I Love You So)/Heart Throb	15
(see also Betty Hutton)

CHARLIE HYATT
65	Island IEP 706	RASS! (EP, as Bam & Charlie Hyatt)	7
66	Island ILP 932	KISS ME NECK (LP)	25

HYDRA
74	Capricorn 2089 008	Glitter Queen/It's So Hard	4
74	Capricorn 2429 120	HYDRA (LP)	10

HYGRADES
65	Columbia DB 7734	She Cared/We're Through	6

BRIAN HYLAND
60	London HLR 9113	Rosemary/Library Love Affair	10
60	London HLR 9161	Itsy Bitsy Teeny Weeny Little Polka Dot Bikini/Don't Dilly Dally, Sally	6
60	London HLR 9161	Itsy Bitsy Teeny Weeny Little Polka Dot Bikini/Don't Dilly Dally, Sally (78)	50
60	London HLR 9203	Four Little Heels/That's How Much	5
61	London HLR 9262	I Gotta Go ('Cause I Love You)/Lop Sided, Over Loaded	5

Brian HYLAND

61	HMV POP 915	Let Me Belong To You/Let It Die	4
61	HMV POP 955	The Night I Cried/I'll Never Stop Wanting You	4
62	HMV POP 1013	Ginny Come Lately/I Should Be Gettin' Better	4
62	HMV POP 1051	Sealed With A Kiss/Summer Job	4
62	HMV POP 1079	Warmed Over Kisses/Walk A Lonely Mile	4
63	HMV POP 1113	I May Not Live To See Tomorrow/It Ain't That Way At All	4
63	HMV POP 1188	I'm Afraid To Go Home/Save Your Heart For Me	4
63	HMV POP 1143	If Mary's There/Remember Me	4
63	HMV POP 1169	Somewhere In The Night/I Wish Today Was Yesterday	4
63	HMV POP 1237	Let Us Make Our Own Mistakes/Nothing Matters But You	4
65	Philips BF 1429	Stay Away From Her/I Can't Keep A Secret	4
65	Philips BF 1486	Three Thousand Miles/Sometimes They Do	4
66	Philips BF 1508	The Joker Went Wild/I Can Hear The Rain	7
66	Philips BF 1528	Run, Run, Look And See/Why Did You Do It	4
67	Philips BF 1555	Hung Up In Your Eyes/Why Mine	4
67	Philips BF 1601	Get The Message/Kinda Groovy	4
62	HMV 7EG 8780	SEALED WITH A KISS (EP)	20
61	London HA-R 2289	THE BASHFUL BLONDE (LP)	50
62	HMV CLP 1553	LET ME BELONG TO YOU (LP)	50
63	HMV CLP 1759	COUNTRY MEETS FOLK (LP)	30
66	Philips BL 7762	THE JOKER WENT WILD (LP)	20

JACK HYLTON

32	Decca F 3222	The Baked Potato Man/The Old Kitchen Kettle (78)	7

(see also George Formby)

C. HYMAN

65	Ska Beat JB 200	The Ska Rhythm/The Ska Is Moving On	7

DICK HYMAN TRIO

56	MGM SP 1164	Theme From "The Threepenny Opera"/Baubles, Bangles And Beads	7
58	MGM MGM-EP 646	DICK HYMAN SWINGS (EP)	7

PHYLLIS HYMAN

79	Arista ARIST 323	You Know How To Love Me/Give A Little More (p/s)	4
79	Arista ARIST 12323	You Know How To Love Me/Give A Little More (12")	8
80	Arista SPART 1114	YOU KNOW HOW TO LOVE ME (LP)	10

HYPNOTICS

88	Hipsville HIP 1	Love In A Different Vein/All Night Long (p/s)	4

DEBBIE HARRY

JANIS IAN

67	Verve Forecast VS 1503	Society's Child (Baby I've Been Thinking)/Letter To Jon	7
67	Verve Forecast VS 1506	Society's Child (Baby I've Been Thinking)/Letter To Jon (reissue)	5
68	Verve Forecast VS 1513	Sunflakes Fall, Snowrays Call/Insanity Comes Quietly To The Structured Mind	8
67	Verve (S)VLP 6001	JANIS IAN (LP)	12

IAN & SYLVIA

63	Fontana TF 426	Four Strong Winds/Long Lonesome Road	4
65	Fontana TF 6053	EARLY MORNING RAIN (LP)	10
68	Vanguard SVRL 19004	THE BEST OF IAN & SYLVIA (LP)	10

IAN (EDWARD) & ZODIACS

63	Oriole CB 1849	Beechwood 4-5789/You Can Think Again	25
65	Fontana TF 548	Just The Little Things/This Won't Happen To Me (as Ian Edward with Zodiacs)	15
66	Fontana TF 708	No Money, No Honey/Where Were You?	15
66	Fontana TF 753	Wade In The Water/Come On Along, Girl	30
65	Wing WL 1074	GEAR AGAIN — 12 HITS (LP)	35

(see also Koppykats, Wellington Wade)

ICARUS

| 69 | Spark SRL 1012 | The Devil Rides Out/You're In Life | 12 |
| 72 | Pye NSPL 28161 | THE MARVEL WORLD OF ICARUS (LP) | 120 |

ICE

| 67 | Decca F 12680 | Anniversary (Of Love)/So Many Times | 40 |
| 68 | Decca F 12749 | Ice Man/Whisper Her Name (Maria Laine) | 40 |

ICE

| 79 | Storm SR 3307 | SAGA OF THE ICE KING (LP, private press with booklet) | 120 |

(see also Dickens)

ICEHOUSE

83	Chrysalis COOL 1	Street Cafe/Walls (picture disc)	4
83	Chrysalis COOL 2	Uniform/Great Southern Land//Can't Help Myself/ We Can Get Together (live) (double pack)	4
83	Chrysalis CHSP 2670	Hey Little Girl/Mysterious Thing (picture disc)	4
83	Chrysalis CHS 2670	Hey Little Girl/Mysterious Thing (p/s, coloured vinyl)	4

ICE LA BAS

| 80s | Black Noise 12 NO 4 | ICE LA BAS (12" EP, with booklet) | 8 |

(see also Homosexuals)

ICICLE WORKS

83	Troll Kitchen WORKS 1	Nirvana/Lovehunt/Scirocco (p/s)	12
83	Situation 2 SIT 22	Birds Fly (Whisper To A Scream)/Reverie Girl (p/s)	5
83	Situation 2 SIT 22T	Birds Fly (Whisper To A Scream)/Reverie Girl/Gun Boys (12", p/s)	7
83	B. Banquet BEG 99P	Love Is A Wonderful Colour/Waterline (picture disc)	8
83	Beggars Banquet BEG 99/ ICE 1	Love Is A Wonderful Colour/Waterline//In The Dance The Shaman Led/ The Devil On Horseback (double pack, gatefold p/s)	7
83	Beggars Banquet BEG 99PT	Love Is A Wonderful Colour/Waterline/In The Dance The Shaman Led (12", picture disc)	8
84	Beggars Banquet BEG 119	Hollow Horse/The Atheist (poster p/s)	4
85	Beggars Banquet BEG 133	All The Daughters (Of Her Father's House)/Pocket Full Of Nothing (p/s)	4
85	B. Banquet BEG 142D	Seven Horses/Slingshot/Beggars Legacy/Going Back (double pack)	6
85	Beggars Banquet BEG 154	Rapids (promo-only white label, stickered sleeve)	5
86	Beggars Banquet BEG 160	Understanding Jane/I Never Saw My Hometown Till I Went Around The World (p/s, with free live single)	5
86	Beggars Banquet BEG 172	What Do You Want For Your Love?/Understanding Jane (live) (p/s, with cassette & entry form)	4
87	B. Banquet BEG 203S	High Time/Broken Hearted Fool (tour souvenir pack)	4
88	Beggars Banquet BEG 220T	Here Comes Trouble/Starry Blue Eyed Wonder (live)/For What It's Worth (live)/Rock 'n' Roll (live) (12", tour souvenir box set)	8
88	B. Banquet BEG 215CD	Little Girl Lost/Tin Can (CD, picture disc)	15
90	Epic WORKSQ 101	Melanie Still Hurts/When The Crying's Done/Midnight Blue/ I Dreamt I Was A Beautiful Woman (33rpm, gatefold p/s)	5
80s	Private Cassette	ASCENDING (private 6-track cassette)	20+

(see also Melting Beer)

ICON A.D.

| 83 | Radical Change RC 3 | DON'T FEED US SHIT (EP, foldout p/s) | 4 |

IDEALS

| 61 | Pye Intl. 7N 25103 | Knee Socks/Mary's Lamb | 15 |

IDES OF MARCH

66	London HLU 10058	You Wouldn't Listen/I'll Keep Searching	6
68	London HLU 10183	Hole In My Soul/Girls Don't Grow On Trees	6
70	Warner Bros WB 7378	Vehicle/Lead Me Home Gently	4
70	Warner Bros WB 7403	Superman/Home	4

IDLE FLOWERS

| 84 | Miles Ahead AHEAD 1 | All I Want Is You/Fizz Music (p/s) | 15 |

(see also Hanoi Rocks)

IDLE RACE

67	Liberty LBF 15026	The Imposters Of Life's Magazine/Sitting In My Tree	20
68	Liberty LBF 15054	The Skeleton And The Roundabout/Knocking Nails Into My House	8
68	Liberty LBF 15101	The End Of The Road/The Morning Sunshine	8
68	Liberty LBF 15129	I Like My Toys/The Birthday (unissued)	
69	Liberty LBF 15218	Days Of Broken Arrows/Warm Red Carpet (B-side act. "Worn Red Carpet")	12
69	Liberty LBF 15242	Come With Me/Reminds Me Of You	8
71	Regal Zonophone RZ 3036	Dancing Flower/Bitter Green	8
76	United Artists UP 36060	The Skeleton And The Roundabout/Morning Sunshine	4
68	Liberty LBS 83132	THE BIRTHDAY PARTY (LP)	25
69	Liberty LBS 83221	THE IDLE RACE (LP)	35
71	Regal Zono. SLRZ 1017	TIME IS (LP)	70
73	Sunset SLS 50354	ON WITH THE SHOW (LP)	10
76	Sunset SLS 50381	THE BIRTHDAY PARTY (LP, reissue)	10

(see also Mike Sheridan & Nightriders, Nightriders, Mike Sheridan's Lot, Lemon Tree, Jeff Lynne, Move, ELO)

BILLY IDOL

81	Chrysalis CHS 2543	Mony Mony/Baby Talk (p/s)	4
81	Chrysalis CHS 12 2543	Mony Mony/Baby Talk/Untouchables/Dancing With Myself (Long Version) (12", 'Don't Stop' EP, p/s)	7
82	Chrysalis CHSP 2625	Hot In The City/Dead On Arrival (p/s)	4
82	Chrysalis CHSP 2625	Hot In The City/Dead On Arrival (picture disc)	6
82	Chrysalis CHS 12 2625	Hot In The City (Extended)/Dead On Arrival (12", p/s)	7
82	Chrysalis CHS 2656	White Wedding/Hole In The Wall (p/s)	4
82	Chrysalis CHS 12 2656	White Wedding (Long Version)/Hole In The Wall (12", p/s)	7
82	Chrysalis IDOL 1	Dancing With Myself/White Wedding (p/s, some on clear vinyl)	5/4
82	Chrysalis IDOLX 1	Dancing With Myself/Love Calling (Dub)/White Wedding (Extended)/Hot In The City (12", p/s)	7
84	Chrysalis IDOL 2	Rebel Yell/Crank Call//White Wedding/Hot In The City (double pack, g/f p/s)	5
84	Chrysalis IDOLP 2	Rebel Yell/Crank Call (square picture disc)	6
84	Chrysalis IDOLD 3/ CHS 2656	Eyes Without A Face/The Dead Next Door//Dancing With Myself/ Rebel Yell (double pack)	5
84	Chrysalis IDOLP 3	Eyes Without A Face/The Dead Next Door/Dancing With Myself/ Rebel Yell (12", picture disc)	8
84	Chrysalis IDOLP 124	Flesh For Fantasy (Ext.)/Blue Highway/Flesh For Fantasy (12", picture disc)	8
85	Chrysalis IDOL 5	White Wedding/Flesh For Fantasy (p/s, white vinyl)	4
85	Chrysalis IDOL 5	White Wedding (Shotgun Mix Pts 1 & 2)/Mega-Idol-Mix (clear vinyl, PVC sl.)	4
85	Chrysalis IDOLX 5	White Wedding (Shotgun Mix Pts 1 & 2)/Mega-Idol-Mix (12", p/s, white vinyl)	8
85	Chrysalis IDOLP 5	White Wedding (Shotgun Mix Pts 1 & 2)/Mega-Idol-Mix (12", picture disc)	7
85	Chrysalis IDOLP 6	Rebel Yell/Stand In The Shadows (live) (picture disc)	4
86	Chrysalis IDOL 8	To Be A Lover/All Summer Single (p/s, coloured vinyl)	4
86	Chrysalis IDOLP 8	To Be A Lover (Mercy Mix)/To Be A Lover/All Summer Single (12", picture disc)	7
86	Chrysalis IDOLD 8	To Be A Lover (Mercy Mix)/To Be A Lover/All Summer Single//Mega-Idol-Mix (12" double pack)	8
87	Chrysalis IDOL 9	Don't Need A Gun/Fatal Charm (p/s, coloured vinyl)	4
87	Chrysalis IDOLP 9	Don't Need A Gun/Don't Need A Gun/Fatal Charm (12", picture disc)	7
87	Chrysalis IDOLD 9	Don't Need A Gun/Fatal Charm (p/s, with free single)	4
87	Chrysalis IDOLP 10	Sweet 16/Beyond Belief/Rebel Yell (12", picture disc)	7

(see also Gen[eration] X)

IDOL DEATH

80s	I.D. DISPY 1234	New Lesson/Sticky Death (foldout p/s)	4

IDOLS

65	Mercury MF 840	Don't Walk Away/You Don't Care	4

(see also Mike Sax & Idols)

IDOLS

79	Ork NYC 2	You/Girl That I Love	5

(see also New York Dolls)

IF

70	Island WIP 6083	Raise The Level Of Your Conscious Mind/I'm Reaching Out On All Sides	5
71	United Artists UP 35263	Far Beyond/Forgotten Roads	4
72	United Artists UP 35356	You In Your Small Corner/Waterfall	4
70	Island ILPS 9129	IF (LP, pink label)	15
70	Island ILPS 9137	IF² (LP)	10
71	United Artists UAG 29158	IF³ (LP)	10
72	United Artists UAG 29315	IF IV (LP, gatefold sleeve with inner)	15

KRIS IFE

67	MGM MGM 1369	Hush/The Spectator	4
68	MGM MGM 1390	This Woman's Love/I Gotta Feeling	4
68	Music Factory CUB 3	Give And Take/Sands Of Time	5
68	Parlophone R 5741	Imagination/I'm Coming 'Round	4
69	Parlophone R 5770	Haven't We Had A Good Time/Will I Ever Fall In Love Again	4

FRANK IFIELD

60	Columbia DB 4399	Lucky Devil/Nobody Else But You	4
60	Columbia DB 4464	Happy-Go-Lucky Me/Unchained Melody	4
60	Columbia DB 4496	Gotta Get A Date/No Love Tonight	4
61	Columbia DB 4568	That's The Way It Goes/Phoebe Snow	5
61	Columbia DB 4658	Life's A Holiday/Tobacco Road	4
61	Columbia DB 4741	Your Time Will Come/That's The Way It Is	4
62	Columbia DB 4786	Alone Too Long/Bigger Than You Or Me	4
62	Columbia DB 4856	I Remember You/I Listen To My Heart	4
62	Columbia DB 4913	Lovesick Blues/She Taught Me How To Yodel	4
63	Columbia DB 4960	The Wayward Wind/I'm Smiling Now	4
63	Columbia DB 7007	Nobody's Darlin' But Mine/You Don't Have To Be A Baby To Cry	4

Frank IFIELD

MINT VALUE £

63	Columbia DB 7062	I'm Confessing (That I Love You)/Waltzing Matilda	4
63	Columbia DB 7131	Mule Train/One Man's Love	4
65	Columbia DB 7520	I'm So Lonesome I Could Cry	4
60s	Columbia	other 45s	3
60s	Columbia	EPs	5-6
62	Columbia SCX 3460	I'LL REMEMBER YOU (LP, stereo)	10
63	Columbia 33SX 1588	BLUE SKIES (LP, mono/stereo)	10/12
65	Columbia 33SX 1723	PORTRAIT IN SONG (LP, also stereo SCX 3551)	10
65	Columbia 33SX 1751	UP JUMPED A SWAGMAN (LP)	10
66	Columbia S(C)X 6009	BABES IN THE WOOD (LP, mono/stereo)	12/15
60s	Columbia/Decca	other LPs	8-12

'IGGINBOTTOM
| 69 | Deram SML 1051 | 'IGGINBOTTOM'S WRENCH (LP) | 75 |

JULIO IGLESIAS
| 70 | Decca F 23005 | Gwendolyne/Bla, Bla, Bla | 12 |

IGNERANTS
| 79 | Rundown ACE 008 | Radio Inteference/Wrong Place Wrong Time (p/s) | 6 |

IGUANA
| 72 | Polydor 2383 108 | IGUANA (LP) | 15 |

IGUANAS
| 65 | RCA RCA 1484 | This Is What I Was Made For/Don't Come Runnin' To Me | 8 |

I-JOG & TRACKSUITS
| 78 | Tyger TYG 1 | Red Box/Worrying Man (p/s) | 6 |

IKE & CRYSTALITES
| 68 | Island WI 3134 | Illya Kurayakin/BOBBY ELLIS & CRYSTALLITES: Anne Marie | 8 |
| 68 | Island WI 3151 | Try A Little Merriness/Patricia | 7 |

IKETTES
62	London HLU 9508	I'm Blue/Find My Baby	10
65	Stateside SS 407	Peaches'N'Cream/The Biggest Players	12
65	Stateside SS 434	(He's Gonna Be) Fine Fine Fine/How Come	10
65	Sue WI 389	Prisoner Of Love/Those Words	18
66	London HLU 10081	What'cha Gonna Do/Down, Down	10
70	Polydor BM 56506	I'm So Thankful/Don't Feel Sorry For Me	8
70	Polydor BM 56516	(Never More) Lonely For You/Sally Go Round The Roses	6
70	Polydor BM 56533	I'm So Thankful/Don't Feel Sorry For Me (reissue)	5
65	Stateside SE 1033	FINE FINE FINE (EP)	30

(see also Ike & Tina Turner)

ILANIT
| 77 | Pye Intl. 7N 25739 | I'm No One (If You Leave Me)/I Can't Say I Love You (p/s) | 10 |

I LIFE
| 64 | R&B JB 140 | Kiss You Gave Me/No More | 10 |

ILLUSION
69	Dot DOT 122	Did You See Her Eyes/Falling In Love	7
70	Dot DOT 133	Together/Don't Push It	4
70	Paramount PARA 3007	Let's Make Each Other Happy/Beside You	4
69	Dot (S)LPD 531	ILLUSION (LP)	15
70	Dot SLPD 537	TOGETHER (AS A WAY OF LIFE) (LP)	12
70	Paramount SPFL 264	IF IT'S SO (LP, planned for Dot SLPD 539)	15

ILLUSIVE DREAM
| 69 | RCA RCA 1791 | Electric Garden/Back Again | 10 |

SOLOMON ILORY
| 63 | Blue Note 45-1899 | Yabe E (Farewell) Pts 1 & 2 | 4 |

I, LUDICROUS
88	Kaleid. Sound KS 707	Quite Extraordinary/At The End Of The Day	4
88	Kaleid. Sound KS 107	Quite Extraordinary/At The End Of The Day/Kick Down The Stumps/Mistakes (12")	7
80s	Lyntone	flexidisc	4
87	Kaleid. Sound KSLP 4	IT'S LIKE EVERYTHING ELSE (LP)	10

I LUV WIGHT
| 70 | Philips 6006 043 | Let The World Wash In/Mediaeval Masquerade (some in p/s) | 75/20 |

(see also Kaleidoscope, Fairfield Parlour)

IM (Cedric Brooks) & DAVID
| 70 | Bamboo BAM 57 | Candid Eye/SOUND DIMENSION: Federated Backdrop | 5 |

IMAGE
65	Parlophone R 5281	Come To The Party/Never Let Me Go	25
65	Parlophone R 5352	Home Is Anywhere/I Hear Your Voice Again	30
66	Parlophone R 5442	I Can't Stop Myself/Let's Make the Scene	20

IMAGES
| 65 | Polydor BM 56011 | I Only Have Myself To Blame/Head Over Heels | 15 |

IMMACULATE FOOLS
| 85 | A&M AM 289 | Save It (Re-Recorded)/Counting On You (gatefold p/s) | 4 |
| 87 | A&M AMA 5151 | DUMB POET (LP, box set with 9 prints & poster) | 10 |

IMMORTALS
| 69 | Amalgamated AMG 851 | Bongo Jah/ANSELL COLLINS: My Last Waltz | 4 |

IMMORTALS
| 86 | MCA MCA 1057 | No Turning Back/No Turning Back (Chocs Away Mix) (p/s) | 18 |

MINT VALUE £

86	MCA MCAT 1057	No Turning Back (Joy Stick Mix)/(Chocs Away Mix)/ No Turning Back (7" Mix) (12", p/s)	30

(see also Queen)

IMPAC
| 66 | CBS 202402 | Too Far Out/Rat Tat Ta Tat ..... | 40 |

IMPALAS
59	MGM MGM 1015	Sorry (I Ran All The Way Home)/Fool, Fool, Fool	15
59	MGM MGM 1015	Sorry (I Ran All The Way Home)/Fool, Fool, Fool (78)	40
59	MGM MGM 1031	Oh, What A Fool/Sandy Went Away	12
60	MGM MGM 1068	Peggy Darling/'Bye Everybody	8
59	MGM MGM-EP 696	SORRY (I RAN ALL THE WAY HOME) (EP)	60

IMPERIALS
| 68 | Nu Beat NB 012 | Young Love/Days Like These ..... | 4 |

IMPERIALS
| 74 | Key KL 025 | FOLLOW THE MAN WITH THE MUSIC (LP) ..... | 12 |

IMPERSONATORS
| 69 | Big Shot BI 524 | Make It Easy On Yourself/I've Tried Before ..... | 4 |

IMPLIED CONSENT
| 84 | In Tape IT 003 | Nobody In Particular/A View Of The World From A Brown Paper Bag
(numbered p/s) ..... | 5 |

IMPOSSIBLE DREAMERS
80	Merciful Release MR 1	Books Books Books/Not A Love Song/Waiting For The Girl/What Can You Do When You See Someone As Beautiful As You?	12
82	One Hundred Things MR 5	Life On Earth/Spin (12", die-cut sleeve)	10
80s	One Hundred Things	READY FOR RHYTHM SECTION (LP)	10

IMPOSSIBLE YEARS
| 85 | Dreamworld DREAM 1 | SCENES WE'D LIKE TO SEE (12" EP) ..... | 10 |

IMPOSTERS
| 69 | Mercury MF 1080 | Apache '69/Q Three ..... | 12 |

IMPRESSIONS
61	HMV POP 961	Gypsy Woman/As Long As You Love Me	20
63	HMV POP 1129	I'm The One Who Loves You/I Need Your Love	8
63	HMV POP 1226	It's Alright/You'll Want Me Back	10
64	HMV POP 1262	Talkin' About My Baby/Never Too Much Love	8
64	HMV POP 1295	I'm So Proud/I Made A Mistake	8
64	HMV POP 1317	Keep On Pushing/I Love You (Yeah)	8
64	HMV POP 1343	You Must Believe Me/See The Real Me	8
65	HMV POP 1408	People Get Ready/I've Been Trying	7
65	HMV POP 1429	Woman's Got Soul/Get Up And Move	10
65	HMV POP 1446	A Meeting Over Yonder/I Found That I've Lost	8
65	HMV POP 1472	I Need You/Never Could You Be	7
65	HMV POP 1492	Amen/Long Long Winter	6
66	HMV POP 1498	You've Been Cheatin'/Just One Kiss From You	10
66	HMV POP 1516	Since I Lost The One I Love/Falling In Love With You	7
66	HMV POP 1526	Too Slow/No One Else	8
66	HMV POP 1545	Can't Satisfy/This Must End	12
67	HMV POP 1581	You Always Hurt Me/Little Girl	7
68	Stateside SS 2083	We're A Winner/You've Got Me Runnin'	6
68	Buddah 201 021	Fool For You/I'm Loving Nothing	4
69	Stateside SS 2139	Can't Satisfy/You've Been Cheatin'	6
69	Buddah 201 062	Choice Of Colors/Mighty Mighty Spade And Whitey	4
70	Buddah 2011 030	Check Out Your Mind/Can't You See?	4
70	Buddah 2011 045	(Baby) Turn On To Me/Soulful Love	4
71	Buddah 2011 068	Ain't Got Time/I'm So Proud	4
71	Buddah 2011 087	Love Me/Do You Want To Win	4
71	Buddah 2011 099	Inner City Blues/Amen/Keep On Pushin'	4
72	Buddah 2011 124	Our Love Goes On And On/This Love's For Real	4
65	HMV 7EG 8896	IT'S ALL RIGHT (EP)	20
66	HMV 7EG 8954	SOULFULLY (EP)	20
64	HMV CLP 1743	THE NEVER ENDING IMPRESSIONS (LP)	25
65	HMV CLP 1935	BIG SIXTEEN (LP, also stereo CSD 1642)	25
66	HMV CLP/CSD 3548	RIDIN' HIGH (LP)	22
67	HMV CLP/CSD 3631	THE FABULOUS IMPRESSIONS (LP)	20
68	Stateside (S)SL 10239	WE'RE A WINNER (LP)	15
68	Joy JOYS 104	FOR YOUR PRECIOUS LOVE (LP, with Jerry Butler)	10
69	Buddah 203 012	THIS IS MY COUNTRY (LP)	12
69	Stateside (S)SL 10279	BIG SIXTEEN (VOL. 2) (LP)	12
70	Buddah 2359 003	THE YOUNG MOD'S FORGOTTEN STORY (LP)	15
70	Buddah 2359 009	AMEN (LP)	12
71	Buddah 2318 017	CHECK OUT YOUR MIND (LP)	12
72	Buddah 2318 059	TIMES HAVE CHANGED (LP)	10
75	ABC ABCL 5104	BIG SIXTEEN (LP, reissue)	10

(see also Curtis Mayfield, Jerry Butler & Impressions)

IMPACT
| 76 | Atlantic K 10780 | Happy Man Pts 1 & 2 ..... | 4 |

IMPS
| 58 | Parlophone R 4398 | Let Me Lie/Dim Dumb Blonde ..... | 10 |

I'M SO HOLLOW
| 81 | Hologram ISH 001 | Dreams To Fill The Vacuum/Distraction
(clear vinyl, PVC sleeve) ..... | 6 |

INADEQUATES
59 Capitol CL 15051   Pretty Face/Audie 6

IN-BE-TWEENS
66 Columbia DB 8080   You Better Run/Evil Witchman 150
(see also Slade)

IN CAMERA
80 4AD AD 8   Die Laughing/Final Achievement (p/s) 7
80 4AD BAD 19   IV SONGS (12" EP) 10
82 4AD BAD 205   FIN (12" EP) 12

INCAS
66 Parlophone R 5551   One Night Stand/I'll Keep Holding On 25
60s Lyntone LYN 765/6   KEELE RAG RECORD (EP, flexidisc, with 3 other bands) 40

INCOGNITO
80 Ensign ENY 44   Parisienne Girl/Summer's Ended (p/s) 4
80 Ensign ENY 4412   Parisienne Girl/Summer's Ended (12", p/s) 10
81 Ensign ENYT 211   Incognito/Tracey (12", p/s) 8
81 Ensign ENYT 221   North London Boy (12", p/s) 7
81 Ensign ENVY 504   JAZZ FUNK (LP) 10

INCREDIBLE BONGO BAND
73 MGM 2006 161   Bongo Rock/Bongolia 4
76 DJM DJS 20452   BONGO ROCK (LP) 15

INCREDIBLE HOG
73 Dart 65372   VOLUME 1 (LP) 120

INCREDIBLE KIDDA BAND
78 Psycho P 2608   Everybody Knows/No Nerve (no p/s) 10

INCREDIBLES
67 Stateside SS 2053   There's Nothing Else To Say/Heart And Soul 70
74 Contempo CS 9008   There's Nothing Else To Say/Another Dirty Deal 4
74 Contempo CLP 512   HEART AND SOUL (LP) 12

INCREDIBLE STRING BAND
68 Elektra EKSN 45028   Painting Box/No Sleep Blues 6
69 Elektra EKSN 45074   Big Ted/All Writ Down 2
70 Elektra 2101 003   This Moment/Black Jack Davy 5
72 Island WIP 6145   Black Jack David/Moon Hang Low 4
73 Island WIP 6158   At The Lighthouse Dance/Jigs 4
66 Elektra EUK 254   THE INCREDIBLE STRING BAND (LP, white or red label) 60/40
67 Elektra EUK 257/EUKS 7257   THE 5000 SPIRITS OR THE LAYERS OF THE ONION
    (LP, red label) 18
67 Elektra EUK 258/EUKS 7258   THE HANGMAN'S BEAUTIFUL DAUGHTER (LP, red label) 18
67 Elektra EKL 254   THE INCREDIBLE STRING BAND (LP, reissue, red label) 15
68 Elektra EKL 4036/7   WEE TAM/THE BIG HUGE (2-LP & insert; red label, also
    stereo EKS 74036/7) 25
68 Elektra EKL 4036   WEE TAM (LP, reissue, red label; also stereo EKS 74036) 12
68 Elektra EKL 4037   THE BIG HUGE (LP, reissue, red label; also stereo EKS 74037) 12
69 Elektra EKS 74057   CHANGING HORSES (LP, red label) 15
70 Elektra EKS 74061   I LOOKED UP (LP, red label) 15
70 Elektra 2665 001   U (2-LP, red label) 20
70 Island ILPS 9140   BE GLAD FOR THE SONG HAS NO ENDING (LP) 10
71 Elektra EKS 74065   RELICS OF THE INCREDIBLE STRING BAND (LP) 10
71 Island ILPS 9172   LIQUID ACROBAT AS REGARDS THE AIR (LP) 10
72 Island ILPS 9211   EARTHSPAN (LP) 10
73 Island ILPS 9229   NO RUINOUS FEUD (LP) 10
74 Island ILPS 9270   HARD ROPE AND SILKEN TWINE (LP) 10
(see also Robin Williamson, Mike Heron, C.O.B.)

IN CROWD
65 Parlophone R 5276   That's How Strong My Love Is/Things She Says 70
65 Parlophone R 5328   Stop! Wait A Minute/You're On Your Own 35
65 Parlophone R 5364   Why Must They Criticize/I Don't Mind 30
(see also Tomorrow, Keith West, Steve Howe)

IN CROWD
69 Deram DM 272   Where In The World/I Can Make Love To You 12

INCUBUS
84 Guardian GRC 2165   TO THE DEVIL A DAUGHTER (LP) 10

INDIANS IN MOSCOW
84 Kennick KNK 1002   Miranda/Naughty Miranda (p/s) 4
84 Kennick KNK 1004   Jack Pelter And His Sex-Change Chickens/Salt (p/s, white vinyl) 4

INDIAN SUMMER
71 RCA Neon NE 3   INDIAN SUMMER (LP) 30
(see also Ross, Dodgers, Gary Pickford-Hopkins)

INDO JAZZMEN
60s Saga FID 2145   RAGAS AND REFLECTIONS (LP) 10

INDUSTRIAL CHIPMUNKS/AGA ZARO PÖLOTOK
80s Mauled By Iguana No. 1   INDUSTRIAL CHIPMUNKS/AGA ZARO PÖLOTOK (split EP, gatefold p/s) 4

INERTIA
80s Inertial ERT 1   The Screen/4 Submarine (p/s) 5

INFANTES JUBILATE
68 Music Factory CUB 5   Exploding Galaxy/Take It Now 30

INFA RIOT
81	Secret SHH 117	Kids Of The Eighties/Still Out Of Order (p/s)	4
82	Secret SHH 133	The Winner/School's Out (p/s)	4
84	Panache PAN 101	Sound And Fury/Triff Spiff Ya O.K. (as Infas)	4

INFLUENCE
69	Orange OAS 201	I Want To Live/Driving Me Wild	4

(see also John Miles)

INFORMATION
68	Beacon BEA 3-121	Orphan/Oh Strange Man	6
70	Evolution E 24615	Face To The Sun/Lovely To See You	8

RED INGLE
51	Capitol CL 13485	Chew Tobacco Rag/Let Me In (78)	7
59	Capitol EAP 20052	CIGAREETS, WHUSKY AND WILD WILD WOMEN (EP)	15

JORGEN INGMANN
61	Fontana H 311	Cherokee/Anna	5
61	Fontana H 333	Milord/Oceans Of Love	5
61	Fontana H 353	Pinetops Boogie Woogie/Violetta	5
62	Fontana 267237 TF	Africa/Johnny's Tune	5
63	Columbia DB 7013	I Loved You (Dansevise)/Little Boy (by Grethe & Jorgen Ingmann)	5
64	Columbia SEG 8340	DRINA (EP)	10

BRIMSTONE INGRAM
79	Grapevine RED 1	What Happened To The Songs/What Happened To The Songs (Instrumental)	4

LUTHER INGRAM
70	Stax STAX 142	My Honey And Me/Puttin' Game Down	6
70	Stax STAX 148	Home Don't Seem Like A Home/Ain't That Loving You	6

INITIALS
64	London HLR 9860	School Days/Song Is Number One	10

INK SPOTS
54	Parlophone MSP 6063	Here In My Lonely Room/Flowers, Mister Florist, Please	15
54	Parlophone MSP 6074	Ebb Tide/If You Should Say Goodbye	15
54	Parlophone MSP 6126	Planting Rice/Yesterdays	15
55	Parlophone MSP 6152	Melody Of Love/Am I Too Late?	12
55	Brunswick OE 9158	SWING HIGH SWING LOW VOL. 1 (EP)	8
56	Brunswick OE 9426	THEY SOLD A MILLION NO. 10 (EP)	7
56	Brunswick OE 9427	THEY SOLD A MILLION NO. 11 (EP)	12
57	HMV 7EG 8410	CHARLIE FUQUA'S INKSPOTS (EP)	8
57	Parlophone GEP 8673	YESTERDAYS (EP)	8
50s	Britone LP 1003	THE INK SPOTS (10" LP)	20
53	Brunswick LA 8590	SOUVENIR ALBUM VOLUME ONE (10" LP)	18
55	Brunswick LA 8710	STREET OF DREAMS (10" LP)	18

AUTREY INMAN
50s	Decca DFE 8571	AMERICAN COUNTRY JUBILEE NO. 1 (EP)	10

INMATES
79	Soho SH 7	Dirty Water/Danger Zone (p/s)	4

INNER CITY UNIT
79	Riddle RID 001/ICU 45	Solitary Ashtrays/Solitary Ashtrays (Version) (plain sleeve with colour insert)	4
79	Riddle RID 003	Paradise Beach/Amyl Nitrate (company die-cut sleeve)	4
79	Riddle RID 002	PASS OUT (THE 360° PSYCHO DELERIA SOUND) (LP)	10
80	Pompadour POMP 001	ERSATZ (LP, with Robert Calvert)	20

(see also Hawkwind, Sphynx, Radio Actors, Robert Calvert)

INNERVISION
75	Private Stock PVT 17	Honey Baby/We're Innervision	4

NEIL INNES
74	United Artists UP 35639	Momma B/Immortal Invisible	4
74	United Artists UP 35676	Recycled Vinyl Blues/Fluff On The Needle	4
75	United Artists UP 35745	Lie Down And Be Counted/Bandwagon	4
75	United Artists UP 35772	What Noise Annoys An Oyster/Oo-Chuck-A-Mao-Mao	4
73	United Artists UAG 29492	HOW SWEET TO BE AN IDIOT (LP)	12

(see also Grimms, Bonzo Dog Doo Dah Band, Rutles, World, Dirk & Stig)

INN KEEPERS
71	Banana BA 328	Duppy Serenade/Sunshine Version (actually by Dennis Alcapone)	7

INNOCENCE
66	Kama Sutra KAS 203	There's Got To Be A Word/I Don't Wanna Be Around You	4
66	Kama Sutra KAS 206	Lifetime Of Lovin' You/Mairzy Doats And Dozy Doats	4

INNOCENT BYSTANDERS
80	Rok ROK XVII/XVIII	Where Is Johnny?/DEBUTANTES: The Man In The Street (company sleeve)	5

INNOCENTS (U.S.)
60	Top Rank JAR 508	Honest I Do/My Baby Hully Gullys	10
61	Top Rank JAR 541	Gee Whiz/Please Mr Sun	8

(see also Kathy Young)

INNOCENTS (U.K.)
63	Columbia DB 7098	Stepping Stones/Grazina	7
63	Columbia DB 7173	A Fine, Fine Bird/Spanish Holiday	6
64	Columbia DB 7314	Stick With Me Baby/Not More Than Everything	6

(see also Mike Berry, Mike Sarne, Innocents & Leroys)

INNOCENTS & LEROYS
64	Regal Zonophone RZ 502	Don't Throw Your Love Away; My Girl Lollipop; I Love You Because; Not Fade Away (medley, across both sides)	4

(see also Innocents [Columbia], Le-Roys)

INNOCENTS (U.K.)
80	Kingdom KV 8010	One Way Love/Every Wednesday Night At Eight (p/s)	10

(see also Woodentops, Advertising, Secret Affair)

INQUISITIVE PEOPLE
67	Decca F 12699	Big White Chief/Rhapsody Of Spring	4

INSANE
82	Riot City RIOT 3	Politics/Dead And Gone/Last Day (p/s)	4

INSECT TRUST
68	Capitol E-ST 109	THE INSECT TRUST (LP)	25

INSPIRAL CARPETS
80s	demo cassette	SONGS OF SHALLOW INTENSITY (p/s, cassette)	20
80s	demo cassette	WAITING FOR OURS (p/s, cassette)	20
80s	demo cassette	COW (p/s, cassette)	20
87	Debris DEB 06	Garage Full Of Flowers/METRO INFINITY: Stupid Friends (flexidisc, most with 'Debris' fanzine)	12/8
88	Playtime AMUSE 2	Keep The Circle Around/Theme From Cow (p/s)	30
88	Playtime AMUSE 2T	PLANE CRASH (12" EP, later 'reissued' without p/s)	35/15
88	Playtime AMUSE 4	Butterfly/You Can't Take The Truth (unreleased, white label promos only)	8
88	Playtime AMUSE 4T	TRAIN SURFING (12" EP, unreleased, white label test pressings only)	30
89	Cow MOO 1	PLANE CRASH (12" EP, unreleased reissue, white labels only)	15
89	Cow MOO 2	TRAIN SURFING (12" EP, some with rear sticker & scratched-out matrix)	12/10
89	Cow MOO 3	Joe EP: Joe/Commercial Mix/Directing Traffic/Commercial Rain (12", p/s)	7
89	Cow DUNG 4	Keep The Circle Around/Seeds Of Doubt/Joe/Causeway/Butterfly/26/ Garage Full Of Flowers/96 Tears (p/s, demo cassette)	15
89	Cow DUNG 5L	Find Out Why/So Far (plain black sleeve with sticker)	4
89	Cow DUNG 5T	Find Out Why/So Far/Plane Crash (live) (12", p/s, signed with newsletter)	15
89	Cow DUNG 6X	Move/Out Of Time (stickered p/s, shrink-wrapped with badge)	7

(see also Too Much Texas)

INSPIRATIONS
67	Polydor 56730	Touch Me, Kiss Me, Hold Me/What Am I Gonna Do With You	85

INSPIRATIONS
70	Amalgamated AMG 857	Take Back Your Duck/Nothing For Nothing	5
70	Amalgamated AMG 861	La La/Reggae Fever	4
70	Amalgamated AMG 862	The Train Is Coming/Man Oh Man	4
70	Trojan TTL 27	REGGAE FEVER (LP)	15

(see also Untouchables)

INSTANT AGONY
82	H. Man H. Biscuit DUNK 1	THINK OF ENGLAND (EP)	4
82	H. Man H. Biscuit DUNK 2	FASHION PARADE (EP)	4

INSTANT AUTOMATONS
80	Deleted DEP 001	PETER PAINTS HIS FENCE (EP, gatefold p/s with inserts, numbered)	5

INSTANT SUNSHINE
68	Page One POF 085	Here We Go Again/Methylated	6
68	Page One POL 007	LIVE AT TIDDY DOLS (LP)	60

INTERNATIONAL RESCUE
90	Groovy Tunes GTE 1	So Way Down/I'm Doin' Fine	5
90	Davy Lamp DL 12	Yeah/Never Touch The Ground	4

INTERNS (U.K.)
64	Philips BF 1320	Don't You Dare/Here There Everywhere	8
64	Philips BF 1345	Cry To Me/There's Love For You	10
66	Parlophone R 5479	Is It Really What You Want/Just Like Me	25
67	Parlophone R 5586	Ray Of Sunshine/Please Say Something Nice	6

(see also John Rostill, Shadows)

INTERNS (Jamaica)
70	Jackpot JP 730	Mr Chatterbox/DOREEN SHAEFFER: Walk Through This World	25

(see also Bob Marley/Wailers)

INTESTINES
81	Altern. Capitalists ACS 1	Life In A Cardboard Box/New Recruit/Anyway (p/s)	6

IN THE NURSERY
84	Paragon VIRTUE 5	Witness To A Scream/1984	20
85	New European BADVC 55	SONORITY — A STRENGTH (12" EP)	12
85	Sweatbox SOX 008	Temper/Breach Birth/Joaquin/Arm Me Audacity (12", p/s)	9
87	Sweatbox SOX 019	Trinity: Elegy/Trinity: Elegy (Reprise)/Blind Me (12", p/s, with inner sleeve)	8
87	Sweatbox SOX 027	Compulsion/Libertaire (12", p/s)	7
83	Paragon VIRTUE 2	WHEN CHERISHED DREAMS COME TRUE (mini-LP, silk-screened gatefold p/s)	20

INTO A CIRCLE
86	Arcadia ARC 001	Rise/And In Flames/Gabriel (12", as In Two A Circle)	12
86	Abstract 12 ABS 042	Inside Out/Reward/Flow/Field Of Sleep (12")	7
87	Abstract ABS 044	Forever/O Siren	4
88	Abstract ABS 050	Evergreen/Beirut	4

(see also Getting The Fear, Southern Death Cult)

INTO PARADISE
80s	Setanta SET 002	BLUE LIGHT (EP)	7

MINT VALUE £

| 89 | Setanta CAO 001 | Under The Water (1-sided freebie) | 5 |

INTRA VEIN
| 79 | Bum FP 001 | Speed Of The City/Sick (initially in printed PVC sleeve) | 10/8 |

INTRIGUES
| 69 | London HL 10293 | In A Moment/Scotchman Rock | 10 |
| 74 | Janus 6146 008 | To Make A World/Mojo Hanna | 4 |

INTRUDERS
| 59 | Top Rank JAR 158 | Frankfurters And Sauercraut/Creepin' | 5 |

INTRUDERS
66	London HL 10069	Up And Down The Ladder/United	25
69	Ember EMB S 254	Cowboys To Girls/Turn Back The Hands Of Time	4
69	Action ACT 4523	Slow Drag/So Glad I'm Yours	12
72	Ember EMB S 325	Cowboys To Girls/GOOD VIBRATIONS: Shake A Hand	8

IN TUA NUA
| 86 | Mother MOTHER 1 | Comin' Thru/Laughing At The Moon | 5 |

INVADERS (Jamaica)
67	Columbia Bluebeat DB 105	Limbo Girl/Soul Of The Jungle	6
68	Columbia Bluebeat DB 109	Stop Teasing/Invaders At The Carnival	6
68	Studio One SO 2044	Soulful Music/SOUL VENDORS: Happy Organ	10

INVADERS (U.K.)
| 70s | Jovian ZIT 2 | Launderama/Plastic Nose | 4 |

INVICTAS
| 64 | United Artists UP 1013 | Green Bow Tie/Touch Of Orchid | 5 |

INVITATIONS
65	Stateside SS 453	Hallelujah/Written On The Wall	10
65	Stateside SS 478	What's Wrong With Me Baby?/Why Did My Baby Turn Bad	45
70	Jay Boy BOY 24	How'd We Ever Get This Way/Picking Up	4
72	Mojo 2092 055	What's Wrong With My Baby? (sic)/Why Did My Baby Turn Bad (reissue)	4

INXS
81	RCA RCA 89	Just Keep Walking/Scratch (p/s)	35
81	RCA RCA 89	Just Keep Walking/Scratch (no p/s)	18
83	Mercury INXS 1	Don't Change/You Never Used To Cry (p/s)	10
83	Mercury INXS 121	Don't Change/You Never Used To Cry/Golden Playpen (12", p/s)	20
83	Mercury INXS 2	The One Thing/The Sax Thing (p/s)	8
83	Mercury INXS 212	The One Thing/Black And White (12", p/s)	18
83	Mercury INXS 222	The One Thing/Black And White/Here Comes II (12", p/s)	15
84	Mercury INXS 3	Original Sin/Jans Song (live)/To Look At You (live) (p/s)	12
84	Mercury INXS 312	Original Sin/Original Sin (Extended Version)/Jan's Song (live)/To Look At You (live) (12", p/s)	20
84	Mercury PH 2	I Send A Message/Mechanical (p/s)	4
84	Mercury PH 2	I Send A Message/Mechanical (p/s, with postcard & biography)	6
84	Mercury PH 212	I Send A Message (Long Distance)/Mechanical/I Send A Message (Local Call) (12", p/s)	8
86	Mercury INXS 4	This Time/Original Sin (Extended Version) (p/s)	4
86	Mercury INXSD 4	This Time/Original Sin (Extended Version)/Burn For You (Extended Mix)/Dancing On The Jetty (double pack)	8
86	Mercury INXS 412	This Time/Original Sin (Extended Version)/Burn For You/Dancing On The Jetty (12", p/s)	7
86	Mercury INXSC 5	What You Need/Sweet As Sin (p/s, with cassette)	6
86	Mercury INXS 512	What You Need (Remix)/Sweet As Sin/What You Need (Live) (12", p/s)	7
86	Mercury INXSD 512	What You Need (Remix)/Sweet As Sin/What You Need (Live)//The One Thing (live)/Don't Change/Johnsons Aeroplane (12", double pack)	12
86	Mercury INXSD 6	Listen Like Thieves/Begotten//One X One/XS Verbiage (double pack)	6
86	Mercury INXSP 6	Listen Like Thieves/Begotten (flag-shaped picture disc)	8
86	Mercury INXS 612	Listen Like Thieves (Extended Remix)/Listen Like Thieves (Instrumental Remix)/Listen Like Thieves (live)/Begotten (12", p/s, with poster)	10
86	Mercury INXSD 7	Kiss The Dirt/6 Knots/The One Thing (live)/This Time/Original Sin (double pack)	6
86	Mercury INXS 712	Kiss The Dirt/6 Knots/The One Thing (live)/The Spy Of Love (12", p/s)	7
87	Mercury INXS 8	Need You Tonight/I'm Coming Home ('magic' pack)	6
87	Mercury INXS 812	Need You Tonight/Mediate/I'm Coming Home (12", p/s)	10
87	Mercury INXSP 9	New Sensation/Do Wot You Do (picture disc)	4
88	Mercury INXSP 912	New Sensation/Do Wot You Do/Love Is (What I Say)/Same Direction (12", poster sleeve)	7
88	Mercury INXS 1010	Devil Inside/On The Rocks/Dancing On The Jetty/Shine Like It Does (10", p/s)	6
88	Mercury INXSP 11	Never Tear Us Apart/Guns In The Sky (Kickass Remix) (poster pack)	4
88	Mercury INXS 1100	Never Tear Us Apart/Guns In The Sky (Kickass Remix) (picture disc)	5
88	Mercury INXS 1110	Never Tear Us Apart/Need You Tonight/Listen Like Thieves/Guns In The Sky (10", p/s, white vinyl, picture centre)	7
88	PMV 080 396 2	Never Tear Us Apart (CDV, 3-track)	7
88	Mercury INXSG 12	Need You Tonight/Move On ('magic puzzle' p/s with 2 photocards)	5
88	Mercury INXS 1222	Need You Tonight (Ben Liebrand Mix)/New Sensation (Remix) (12", p/s)	8
88	PMV 080 394 2	Need You Tonight (CDV, 5-track)	7
89	Mercury INXS 1322	Mystify/Biting Bullets/Shine Like It Does (live)/Never Tear Us Apart (live) (12", 'Global Tour' pack, with poster)	7
89	PMV 080 876 2	Mystify (CDV, 4-track)	7
91	Mercury INXSM 16	By My Side/The Other Side ('Magic Pack') (p/s)	4
86	Mercury MERH 82	LISTEN LIKE THIEVES (LP, with free LP "The Swing" [MERL 39], gatefold sleeve)	12
87	Mercury MERHP 114	KICK (LP, picture disc)	10

IONA
| 78 | Silver Scales | CUCKOO (LP) | 40 |

IONA

70s	Celtic Music CM 001	IONA (LP)	40

IPSISSIMUS

69	Parlophone R 5774	Hold On/Lazy Woman	25

IQ

82	Red Stripe LYN 12028/9	Beef In A Box/RE-FLEX: Praying To The Beat/ASTRAKHAN: And She Smiled/ JENNY JAY: Jane (flexi, sampler for "Melody Maker Playback Vol. 1" LP)	10
84	Jim White/IQ PROMO 101	Awake And Nervous/Through The Corridors (12", 500 only)	40
84	Sahara IQ 1002	Barbell Is In/Just Changing Hands (p/s)	10
84	Sahara IQ 12 1002	Barbell Is In (Liard Mix)/Dans Le Parc Du Chateau Noir (12", p/s)	15
84	IQFREEB 1	Hollow Afternoon (1-sided, Marquee gig freebie)	40
85	Sahara IQ 1003	Corners (Remix)/Thousand Days (p/s)	10
85	Sahara IQ 12 1003	Corners/Thousand Days/The Wake (12", p/s)	15
86	STAL Other Boxer 1	Nomzamo (Demo) (1-sided fan club 7")	20
86	Sahara IQSD 1	It All Stops Here/Intelligence Quotient (shaped picture disc)	20
87	Squawk VER 30	Passing Strangers/Nomzamo (p/s)	5
87	Squawk VERX 30	Passing Strangers/Colourflow/No Love Lost (12", p/s)	8
87	RLOG Another Boxer 1	Fascination/The Bold Grenadier Pt. 1 (fan club single)	20
87	Squawk VER 34	Promises/Human Nature (p/s)	5
87	Squawk VERX 34	Promises (Extended Remix)/Human Nature (12", p/s)	15
88	RLOG One More Boxer 1	A Different Magic Roundabout (Honest!)/The Big Balls Of Bert Christ (fan club single)	15
89	Squawk VER 42	Sold On You/Through My Fingers (p/s)	5
89	Squawk VERX 42	Sold On You/Through My Fingers/Wurensh (12", p/s)	8
89	Squawk VERCD 42	Sold On You/Through My Fingers/Promises/Colourflow (CD)	10
82	private pressing	SEVEN STORIES INTO EIGHT (cassette, different coloured sleeves)	10
83	private pressing	SEVEN STORIES INTO EIGHT (cassette reissue, with different intro to "Intelligence Quotient")	10
83	MJL MAJ 1001	TALES FROM THE LUSH ATTIC (LP, 1,000 copies in pale or dark blue numbered sleeve)	20
84	COSL MAJ 1001	TALES FROM THE LUST ATTIC (LP, reissue in brown sleeve)	15
84	private pressing	SEVEN STORIES INTO EIGHT (cassette, 2nd reissue, with studio version of "For Christ's Sake")	10
85	Sahara SAH 136	THE WAKE (LP)	15
85	STAL BOXER 1	NINE IN A POND IS HERE (2-LP, 1,000 copies only)	40
86	Samurai SAMRCD 136	THE WAKE (CD)	14
86	Sahara SAMRCD 1001	TALES FROM THE LUSH ATTIC (CD)	15
86	Samurai SAM 045	LIVING PROOF (LP)	15
86	Samurai SAMRCD 045	LIVING PROOF (CD)	15
87	Squawk VERH 43	NOMZAMO (LP)	10
89	Squawk 836 429-1	ARE YOU SITTING COMFORTABLY? (LP)	10

DONNIE IRIS

80	MCA MCA 3272	BACK ON THE STREETS (LP)	10

IRISH ROVERS

67	Brunswick STA 8679	FIRST OF THE IRISH ROVERS (LP)	10
68	MCA MUPS 310	THE UNICORN (LP)	10
69	MCA MUPS 353	LIVERPOOL LOU (LP)	10
69	MCA MUPS 389	TALES TO WARM YOUR MIND (LP)	10
70	MCA MUPS 406	LIFE OF THE ROVER (LP)	12

IRON BUTTERFLY

68	Atlantic 584 188	Possession/Unconscious Power	5
69	Atlantic 584 254	Soul Experience/In The Crowds	5
70	Atlantic 2091 024	In-A-Gadda-Da-Vida/Termination	4
67	Atco 2465 015	HEAVY (LP)	15
68	Atlantic 588 166	IN-A-GADDA-DA-VIDA (LP)	12
69	Atlantic 228 011	BALL (LP)	12
70	Atlantic 2400 014	LIVE (LP)	12
	(see also Ramatam)		

IRON MAIDEN

71	Gemini GMS 006	Falling/Ned Kelly	10

IRON MAIDEN

79	Rock Hard ROK 1	THE SOUNDHOUSE TAPES (EP)	60
80	EMI EMI 5032	Running Free/Burning Ambition (p/s)	25
80	EMI EMI 5065	Sanctuary/Drifter (live)/I've Got The Fire (live) (uncensored p/s)	25
80	EMI EMI 5065	Sanctuary/Drifter (live)/I've Got The Fire (live) (censored p/s)	15
80	EMI EMI 5105	Women In Uniform/Invasion (p/s)	12
80	EMI 12EMI 5105	Women In Uniform/Phantom Of The Opera (live)/Invasion (12", p/s)	12
81	EMI EMI 5145	Twilight Zone/Wrathchild (p/s, red or clear vinyl)	25
81	EMI EMI 5145	Twilight Zone/Wrathchild (p/s, brown vinyl mispress)	100
81	EMI EMI 5145	Twilight Zone/Wrathchild (p/s)	12
81	EMI EMIC 5145	Twilight Zone/Wrathchild (cassette)	10
81	EMI EMI 5184	Purgatory/Genghis Khan (p/s)	25
81	EMI 12EMI 5219	MAIDEN JAPAN EP (12" EP)	12
82	EMI EMI 5263	Run To The Hills/Total Eclipse (p/s)	8
82	EMI EMIP 5263	Run To The Hills/Total Eclipse (picture disc)	16
82	EMI EMI 5287	The Number Of The Beast/Remember Tomorrow (live) (p/s)	6
82	EMI EMI 5287	The Number Of The Beast/Remember Tomorrow (live) (p/s, red vinyl)	12
83	EMI EMI 5378	Flight Of Icarus/I've Got The Fire (p/s)	6
83	EMI 12EMIP 5378	Flight Of Icarus/I've Got The Fire (12", picture disc)	20
83	EMI TC IM4	Flight Of Icarus/I've Got The Fire (cassette)	10
83	EMI EMI 5397	The Trooper/Cross-Eyed Mary (p/s)	6
83	EMI EMIP 5397	The Trooper/Cross-Eyed Mary (soldier-shaped picture disc)	20

MINT VALUE £

84	EMI EMI 5489	2 Minutes To Midnight/Rainbow's Gold (p/s) 5
84	EMI 12EMI 5489	2 Minutes To Midnight/Rainbow's Gold/Mission From 'Arry (12", picture disc) ..15
84	EMI EMI 5502	Aces High/King Of Twilight (p/s) 5
84	EMI 12EMI 5502	Aces High/King Of Twilight/The Number Of The Beast (live) (12", picture disc) ..20
85	EMI EMI 5532	Running Free (live)/Sanctuary (live) (some in poster p/s) 8/4
85	EMI 12EMI 5532	Running Free (live)/Sanctuary (live)/Murders In The Rue Morgue (live) (12", p/s) ..7
85	EMI 12EMI 5532	Running Free (live)/Sanctuary (live)/Murders In The Rue Morgue (live) (12", picture disc) 15
85	EMI EMI 5542	Run To The Hills (live)/Phantom Of The Opera (live) (some with Xmas card) 8/4
85	EMI 12EMI 5542	Run To The Hills (live)/Phantom Of The Opera (live)/Losfer Words (The Big 'Orra) (live) (12", p/s) 7
85	EMI 12EMIP 5542	Run To The Hills (live)/Phantom Of The Opera (live)/Losfer Words (The Big 'Orra) (live) (12", picture disc) 15
86	EMI EMI 5583	Wasted Years/Reach Out (p/s) 4
86	EMI EMIP 5583	Wasted Years/Reach Out (computer-shaped picture disc) 15
86	EMI EMI 5589	Stranger In A Strange Land/That Girl (some with foldout poster p/s) 8/4
86	EMI 12EMIP 5589	Stranger In A Strange Land/That Girl/Juanita (12", picture disc) 15
88	EMI EMS 49	Can I Play With Madness/Black Bart Blues (p/s, with sticker & transfer) 5
88	EMI EMP 49	Can I Play With Madness/Black Bart Blues (shaped picture disc) 10
88	EMI CDEM 49	Can I Play With Madness/Black Bart Blues/Massacre (CD) 7
88	EMI EMP 64	The Evil That Men Do/Prowler '88 (shaped picture disc) 8
88	EMI 12EMS 64	The Evil That Men Do/Prowler '88/Charlotte The Harlot '88 (12", poster p/s) 8
88	EMI EMS 79	The Clairvoyant (live)/The Prisoner (live) (clear vinyl, poster p/s) 6
88	EMI EMP 79	The Clairvoyant (live)/The Prisoner (live) (shaped picture disc) 8
88	EMI 12EMP 79	The Clairvoyant (live)/The Prisoner (live)/Heaven Can Wait (live) (12", pic disc) ...7
88	Spiral Scratch 3/Iron 1	An Interview With (free with 'Spiral Scratch' magazine issue 3, 10,000 only) 4
89	EMI EMPD 117	Infinite Dreams (live)/Killers (live) (shaped picture disc) 5
90	EMI EMPD 171	Bring Your Daughter ... To The Slaughter/I'm A Mover (picture disc 'brain' pack) .6
92	EMI EMPD 263	Fear Of The Dark (live)/Hooks In You (live) (shaped picture disc, mispress, B-side plays "Tailgunner" [live]) 10
80	EMI EMC 3330	IRON MAIDEN (LP, with poster) 10
82	EMI EMCP 3400	THE NUMBER OF THE BEAST (LP, picture disc) 35
84	EMI POWERP 1	POWERSLAVE (LP, picture disc) 30
88	EMI EMDP 1006	SEVENTH SON OF A SEVENTH SON (LP, picture disc, with banner) 15
90	EMI (no cat. no.)	THE FIRST TEN YEARS — UP THE IRONS (10 x 12" double packs, box available by mail order with tokens from records) 50

(see also Bruce Dickinson, A.S.A.P., Di'Anno, Gogmagog, Samson, Urchin, Xero)

NEVILLE IRONS
68	Blue Cat BS 104	Soul Glide/LEADERS: My Friends 10

(see also Neville Hinds)

I ROY
74	Trojan TRLS 63	PRESENTING I ROY (LP) 10

(see also Keith Hudson & I Roy)

LONNIE IRVING
60	Melodisc MEL 1546	Pin-ball Machine/I Got Blues On My Mind 15

(BIG) DEE IRWIN
64	Stateside SS 261	Donkey Walk/Someday You'll Understand Why 8
64	Colpix PX 11040	Heigh Oh/It's My Birthday 5
64	Colpix PX 11050	Personality/It's Only A Paper Moon 5
65	Stateside SS 450	You Satisfy My Needs/I Wanna Stay Right Here With You 30
68	Minit MLF 11013	I Can't Stand The Pain/My Hope To Die Girl (as Dee Irwin) 6

BIG DEE IRWIN & LITTLE EVA
63	Colpix PX 11010	Swinging On A Star/Another Night With The Boys (Little Eva is uncredited) 5
64	Colpix PX 11021	I Wish You A Merry Christmas/Christmas Song 5
63	Colpix PXE 301	SWINGING ON A STAR (EP) 18
65	Gold Guinea GSGL 10497	SWINGING ON A STAR (LP) 10

(see also Little Eva, Suzi & Big Dee Irwin)

DAVID ISAACS
66	Island WI 261	I'd Rather Be Lonely/See That Man 8
68	Trojan TR 616	A Place In The Sun/UPSETTERS: Handy Cap 7
69	Upsetter US 302	Good Father/SLIM SMITH: What A Situation 4
69	Upsetter US 305	I've Got Memories/I'm Leaving 5
69	Upsetter US 311	He'll Have To Go/Since You're Gone 5
69	Upsetter US 319	Who To Tell/BUSTY BROWN: I Can't See Myself Cry 5
69	Punch PH 6	I Can't Take It Anymore/LLOYD DOUGLAS: Anyway 4
71	Punch PH 84	You'll Be Sorry/Knock Three Times 4
71	Bullet BU 459	Just Enough/ROY PATIN: Standing (B-side actually by Roy Panton) 4
73	Upsetter US 400	Stranger On The Shore/DILLINGER: John Devour 5
73	Bread BR 1118	Just Enough/We Are Neighbours 4

DAVID ISHERWOOD
67	Decca SKL 5051	A LAUGHING CRY (LP) 10

ISLANDERS
59	Top Rank JAR 215	The Enchanted Sea/Pollyanna 4
60	Top Rank JAR 305	Blue Train/Tornado 4

ISLANDERS
65	Fontana TF 577	It Ain't Me Babe/Four Strong Winds 4
65	Fontana TF 605	Walkin' Away/Roberta 4

JIMMY ISLE
59	London HLS 8832	Diamond Ring/I've Been Waiting 40
59	London HLS 8832	Diamond Ring/I've Been Waiting (78) 18
60	Top Rank JAR 274	Billy Boy/Oh Judy 8

ISLEY BROTHERS

59	RCA RCA 1149	Shout Pts 1 & 2	15
59	RCA RCA 1149	Shout Pts 1 & 2 (78)	60
60	RCA RCA 1172	Respectable/I'm Gonna Knock On Your Door	15
60	RCA RCA 1190	How Deep Is The Ocean/He's Got The Whole World In His Hands	12
60	RCA RCA 1213	Tell Me Who/Say You Love Me Too	12
62	Stateside SS 112	Twist And Shout/Spanish Twist	10
62	Stateside SS 132	Twistin' With Linda/You Better Come Home	8
63	Stateside SS 218	Nobody But Me/I'm Laughing To Keep From Crying	10
63	United Artists UP 1034	Tango/She's Gone	8
64	United Artists UP 1050	Shake It With Me Baby/Stagger Lee	8
64	Atlantic AT 4010	The Last Girl/Looking For A Love	12
66	Tamla Motown TMG 555	This Old Heart Of Mine (Is Weak For You)/There's No Love Left	
		(1st press has narrow print on label, reissued 1968 with wider print)	12/6
66	Tamla Motown TMG 566	Take Some Time Out For Love/Who Could Ever Doubt My Love	10
66	Tamla Motown TMG 572	I Guess I'll Always Love You/I Hear A Symphony	
		(1st press with narrow print on label)	15/8
67	Tamla Motown TMG 606	Got To Have You Back/Just Ain't Enough Love	10
68	Tamla Motown TMG 652	Take Me In Your Arms (Rock Me A Little While)/	
		Why When Love Is Gone	12
69	Tamla Motown TMG 683	I Guess I'll Always Love You/It's Out Of The Question	4
69	Tamla Motown TMG 693	Behind A Painted Smile/One Too Many Heartaches	4
69	Major Minor MM 621	It's Your Thing/Don't Give It Away	6
69	Tamla Motown TMG 708	Put Yourself In My Place/Little Miss Sweetness	4
69	Major Minor MM 631	I Turned You On/I Know Who You Been Socking It To	4
69	Tamla Motown TMG 719	Take Some Time Out For Love/Who Could Ever Doubt My Love (reissue)	4
70	Stateside SS 2162	Was It Good To You?/I Got To Get Myself Together	4
71	Stateside SS 2188	Warpath/I Got To Find Me One	6
71	Stateside SS 2193	Love The One You're With/He's Got Your Love	4
73	Tamla Motown TMG 877	Tell Me It's Just A Rumour, Baby/Save Me From This Misery	4
73	Epic EPC 1980	The Highways Of My Life/Don't Let Me Be Lonely Tonight	4
74	Epic EPC 2803	Need A Little Taste Of Love/If You Were There	4
76	DJM DJS 640	Twist And Shout/Time After Time (reissue)	4
79	RCA PC 9411	Shout/Respectable/Tell Me Who (12", p/s)	8
64	RCA RCX 7149	THE ISLEY BROTHERS (EP)	30
60	RCA RD 27165/SF 7055	SHOUT (LP, mono/stereo)	35/40
64	United Artists ULP 1064	THE FAMOUS ISLEY BROTHERS — TWISTING AND SHOUTING (LP)	20
66	Tamla Motown TML 11034	THIS OLD HEART OF MINE (IS WEAK FOR YOU) (LP)	15
68	T. Motown (S)TML 11066	SOUL ON THE ROCKS (LP)	20
69	Major Minor SMLP 59	IT'S OUR THING (LP)	10
69	T. Motown (S)TML 11112	BEHIND A PAINTED SMILE (LP)	18
70	Stateside SSL 10300	THE BROTHERS: ISLEY (LP)	10
70	RCA Intl. INTS 1098	SHOUT (LP)	10
73	Epic EPC 65740	3 + 3 (LP, gatefold sleeve)	10
74	Epic EPC 80317	LIVE IT UP (LP)	10
75	Epic EPC 69139	THE HEAT IS ON (LP)	10
76	Epic EPC 81268	HARVEST FOR THE WORLD (LP)	10
77	Epic EPC 86027	GO FOR YOUR GUNS (LP)	10
77	Epic EPC 86037	SHOWDOWN (LP)	10

ISOLATION

70s	private pressing	ISOLATION (LP)	800

ISRAELITES

69	Downtown DT 413	Moma Moma/Melody For Two	4
69	Downtown DT 433	Seven Books/Chaka Beat	4

ITALS

67	Giant GN 8	New Loving/SOUL BROTHERS: I Told You Little Girl	6
67	Giant GN 12	Don't Throw It Away/CARRIBEATS: Make Up Your Mind	6

IT BITES

86	Virgin VS 839	All In Red/Heartbreaker (p/s)	7
86	Virgin VS 839-12	All In Red (Full Version)/All In Red (7")/Heartbreaker (12", p/s)	8
86	Virgin VSD 872	Calling All The Heroes/Strange But True//All In Red/Heartbreaker	
		(double pack)	10
86	Virgin VSP 872	Calling All The Heroes/Strange But True (picture disc)	10
86	Virgin VSD 896	Whole New World/Black December//Calling All The Heroes (live)/	
		Screaming On The Beaches (live) (double pack)	10
87	Virgin MIKE 941-12	Old Man And The Angel (Full Version)/Castles (Full Version)/Old Man And	
		The Angel (7")/Calling All The Heroes (Full Version) (CD, gatefold p/s)	7
88	Virgin VSP 983-12	Kiss Like Judas (Extended Mix)/Staring At The Whitewash/	
		Kiss Like Judas (7") (12", giant poster pack)	7
88	Virgin CDEP 21	Kiss Like Judas (Extended Mix)/Staring At The Whitewash/	
		Kiss Like Judas (7") (CD)	7
88	Virgin VSS 1065	Midnight/You'll Never Go To Heaven (live) (square picture disc)	12
88	Virgin VSCD 1065	Midnight (7")/You'll Never Go To Heaven (live)/Midnight (Extended) (CD)	8
89	Virgin VSS 1184	Still Too Young To Remember/Vampires (shaped picture disc)	4
89	Virgin VSA 1215	Underneath Your Pillow (7")/Still Too Young To Remember (live)/Underneath	
		Your Pillow (live) (10" picture disc, last track not actually included!)	6
89	Virgin VSCD 1215	Underneath Your Pillow (Full Version)/Still Too Young To Remember	
		(live)/Underneath Your Pillow (live) (3" CD)	8
89	Virgin CDVX 2591	EAT ME IN ST. LOUIS (CD, with free 3" CD ["Having A Good Day"/"Reprise"/	
		"Bullet In The Barrel"])	12
91	Virgin VGD 3516	THANKYOU AND GOODNIGHT (LP, sealed picture disc in die-cut sleeve)	10

ITHACA

70s	Merlin	FRIENDS (LP, white label test pressing, 1 copy only!)	1500

MINT VALUE £

72   Merlin HF 6   A GAME FOR ALL WHO KNOW (LP, with insert) 600
(see also Alice Through The Looking Glass, Agincourt, Tomorrow Come Someday)

IT'S A BEAUTIFUL DAY
69   CBS 4457   White Bird/Wasted Union Blues 8
70   CBS 4933   Soapstone Mountain/Do You Remember The Sun 5
73   CBS 1625   Ain't That Lovin' You Baby/Time 4
69   CBS 63722   IT'S A BEAUTIFUL DAY (LP, gatefold sleeve) 15
70   CBS 64065   MARRYING MAIDEN (LP) 12
72   CBS 64314   CHOICE QUALITY STUFF (LP) 12
73   CBS 64929   LIVE AT CARNEGIE HALL (LP) 10
73   CBS 65483   TODAY (LP) 10

IT'S IMMATERIAL
80   The Hit Machine HIT 001   Young Man (Seeks Interesting Job)/Doosha (A Success Story) (p/s) 6
81   Inevitable INEV 009   A Gigantic Raft In The Philippines/No Place For A Prompter (p/s) 5
81   IHM IHM 002   Imitate The Worm/The Worm Turns (p/s) 5
84   Wonderful World Of WW 4   A Gigantic Raft In The Philippines/No Place For A Prompter
                               (p/s, reissue) 4
84   Eternal JF 4   A Gigantic Raft In The Philippines/No Place For A Prompter
                               (2nd reissue) 4
85   Siren SIREN 8   Ed's Funky Diner/Washing The Air (p/s, with free single) 4
86   Siren SIREN 24   We'll Turn Things Upside Down/Driving Away From Home//
                               Ed's Funky Diner/Only The Lonely (double pack) 4

IVAN
58   Coral Q 72341   Real Wild Child/Oh, You Beautiful Doll 300
58   Coral Q 72341   Real Wild Child/Oh, You Beautiful Doll (78) 65
(see also Jerry Allison, Crickets)

JOHN IVAN
67   United Artists UP 1155   Trouble Mountain/Games Men Play 4

IVANS MEADS
65   Parlophone R 5342   The Sins Of A Family/A Little Sympathy 15
66   Parlophone R 5503   We'll Talk About It Tomorrow/The Bottle 15

BURL IVES
56   Brunswick 05510   Ballad Of Davy Crockett/Goober Peas 8
56   Brunswick 05551   Dying Stockman/Click Go The Shears 6
56   Brunswick 05604   The Bus Stop Song/That's My Heartstrings 4
62   Brunswick 05863   Al Little Bitty Tear/Shanghied 4
53   Brunswick LA 8552   BALLADS AND FOLK SONGS VOL. 2 (10" LP) 12
53   Brunswick LA 8583   BALLADS AND FOLK SONGS VOL. 1 (10" LP) 12
54   Brunswick LA 8633   FOLK SONGS — DRAMATIC AND HUMOROUS (10" LP) 12
54   Brunswick LA 8641   WOMEN (10" LP) 12
55   Brunswick LAT 8048   CORONATION CONCERT (LP) 10
56   Brunswick LA 8739   AUSTRALIAN FOLK SONGS (10" LP) 12
56   Brunswick LAT 8142   DOWN TO THE SEA IN SHIPS (LP) 10
59   Philips BBL 7225   THE WAYFARING STRANGER (LP) 10
60   Fontana Z 4018   LITTLE WHITE DUCK (LP) 10
60   Brunswick LAT 8321   CHEERS (LP) 10
60   Brunswick LAT 8344   SONGS OF IRELAND (LP) 10
61   Brunswick LAT 8381   THE VERSATILE BURL IVES (LP) 10
62   Brunswick LAT 8395   SONGS OF THE WEST (LP) 10
62   Brunswick LAT 8404   FUNNY WAY OF LAUGHIN' (LP, also stereo STA 3063) 10/12
63   Brunswick LAT 8517   SUNSHINE IN MY SOUL (LP) 10
63   Brunswick LAT/STA 8554   SINGIN' EASY (LP) 10
64   Brunswick LAT 8591   PEARLY SHELLS (LP) 10
66   Brunswick LAT 8665   SOMETHING SPECIAL (LP) 10

IVEYS
68   Apple APPLE 5   Maybe Tomorrow/And Her Daddy's A Millionaire (company sleeve) 20
69   Apple APPLE 14   Dear Angie/No Escaping Your Love (unreleased; Europe & Japan only)
68   Apple SAPCOR 8   MAYBE TOMORROW (unissued LP; Europe & Japan only)
(see also Badfinger)

JACKIE IVORY
66   Atlantic AT 4075   Hi-Heel Sneakers/Do It To Death 10

IVORYS
85   Kent TOWN 103   Please Stay/TOMMY HUNT: The Work Song 4
(see also Tommy Hunt)

IVY LEAGUE
64   Piccadilly 7N 35200   What More Do You Want/Wait A Minute 6
65   Piccadilly 7N 35222   Funny How Love Can Be/Lonely Room 4
65   Piccadilly 7N 35228   That's Why I'm Crying/A Girl Like You 4
65   Piccadilly 7N 35251   Tossing And Turning/Graduation Day 4
65   Piccadilly 7N 35267   Our Love Is Slipping Away/I Could Make You Fall In Love 4
66   Piccadilly 7N 35294   Running Round In Circles/Rain Rain Go Away 5
66   Piccadilly 7N 35326   Willow Tree/One Day 5
66   Piccadilly 7N 35348   My World Fell Down/When You're Young 5
67   Piccadilly 7N 35365   Four And Twenty Hours/Arrivederci Baby 5
67   Piccadilly 7N 35397   Suddenly Things/Tomorrow Is Another Day 5
67   Pye 7N 17386   Thank You For Loving Me/In The Not Too Distant Future 4
65   Piccadilly NEP 34038 FUNNY HOW LOVE CAN BE (EP) 12
65   Piccadilly NEP 34042 TOSSING AND TURNING (EP) 12
65   Piccadilly NEP 34046 THE HOLLY AND THE IVY LEAGUE (EP) 15
66   Piccadilly NEP 34048 OUR LOVE IS SLIPPING AWAY (EP) 15
65   Piccadilly NPL 38015 THIS IS THE IVY LEAGUE (LP) 25

67	Marble Arch MAL 741	SOUNDS OF THE IVY LEAGUE (LP)	12
69	Marble Arch MALS 821	TOMORROW IS ANOTHER DAY (LP)	10

(see also Carter-Lewis, White Plains, Edison Lighthouse, Flowerpot Men, Kestrels, One & One, Johnny Shadow)

IVY THREE

60	London HLW 9178	Yogi/Was Judy There	7

THE ISLEY BROTHERS

Clue J.

CLUE J. & HIS BLUES BLASTERS
61   Blue Beat BB 60   Little Willie/Pine Juice 10

DAVID J. (& J. WALKERS)
81   4AD AD 112   Nothing/Armour (as David Jay & René Halkett) (p/s, some with lyric sheet) ...10/8
83   Situation 2 SIT 26   Joe Orton's Wedding/The Gospel According To Fear (p/s) 5
83   Situation 2 SIT 26T   Joe Orton's Wedding/Requiem For Joe/The Gospel According To Fear/
        Point Of Departure (12", p/s) 8
83   Glass GLASS 031   The Promised Land/Saint Jackie (as David J. & J. Walkers) 4
83   Glass GLASS 12031   The Promised Land/Saint Jackie/A Seducer, A Doctor, A Card You
        Cannot Trust (12", p/s, as David J. & J. Walkers) 7
84   Glass GLASS 12032   This Vicious Cabaret/(AV.T.V. Broadcast)/V's Theme (Intro)/Incidental/V's
        Theme (Outro) (12", p/s, as V For Vendetta [David J. & Alan Moore]) 12
84   Glass GLASS 039   I Can't Shake This Shadow Of Fear/War Game (p/s) 4
84   Glass GLASS 12039   I Can't Shake This Shadow Of Fear/War Game (12", p/s) 7
(see also Bauhaus)

HARRY J. ALL STARS
69   Harry J. TR 675   Liquidator/GLEN & DAVE: La La Always Stay (green or white label) 4
70   Trojan TBL 104   LIQUIDATOR (LP) 12

BILLY JACK
69   Grape GR 3018   Let's Work Together/CORPORATION: Jam Monkey 4

BOBBY JACK
59   Top Rank JAR 190   Tempting Me/Early Mornin' 4

JACK (Bernard) & BEANSTALKS
69   Supreme SUP 203   Work It Up/Chatty Chatty 4
(see also Kinstonians)

JACKAL
86   Crim. Damage CRI 12-134   Underneath The Arches/Thunder Machine (12", p/s) 10
(see also Renegade Soundwave)

JACKIE & BRIDIE
68   Major Minor MM 562   Come Me Little Son/We Only Needed Time 4
70   Concord   FOLK WORLD OF JACKIE AND BRIDIE (LP) 30

JACKIE & DOREEN
65   Ska Beat JB 209   Adorable You/The New Vow 6

JACKIE (Edwards) & MILLIE (Small)
65   Island WI 253   This Is My Story/SOUND SYSTEM: Never Again 10
66   Island WI 265   My Desire/MILLIE: That's How Strong My Love Is 10
67   Island WIP 6012   In A Dream/Ooh Ooh 8
67   Island ILP 941   PLEDGING MY LOVE (LP, as Jackie Edwards & Millie Small) 50
68   Island ILP 963   THE BEST OF JACKIE AND MILLIE VOLUME TWO (LP) 60
70   Trojan TTL 52   THE BEST OF JACKIE AND MILLIE VOLUME TWO (LP, reissue) 15
70   Trojan TBL 155   JACKIE & MILLIE (LP) 15
(see also Jackie Edwards, Millie, Wilfred & Millie)

JACKIE & RAINDROPS
(see under Jackie Lee & Raindrops)

JACKIE & ROY
58   Vogue V 9101   You Smell So Good/Let's Take A Walk Around The Block 40
58   Vogue V 9101   You Smell So Good/Let's Take A Walk Around The Block (78) 6

JACKPOTS
73   Sonet SON 2006   Jack In The Box/Henbane's Sacrifice 4

ALEXANDER JACKSON & TURNKEYS
65   Sue WI 386   The Whip/Tell It Like It Is 25

BO WEAVIL JACKSON
50s   Jazz Collector JDL 81   Some Scream High Yellow/Why Do You Moan? 10
59   Jazz Collector JDL 127   Some Scream High Yellow/Why Do You Moan? (reissue) 5

BULL MOOSE JACKSON & HIS ORCHESTRA
53   Vogue V 2129   Nosey Joe/I Know Who Threw The Whisky In The Well (78) 20

CHRIS JACKSON
69   Soul City SC 112   I'll Never Forget You/Forever I'll Stay With You 15
70   Soul City SC 120   Since There's No Doubt/We Will Be Together (unissued, maybe demos?) ....200+

CHUBBY JACKSON'S BIG BAND
60   Top Rank TR 5015   A Ballad For Jai/Hail, Hail, The Herd's All Here 4

CHUCK JACKSON
61   Top Rank JAR 564   I Don't Want To Cry/Just Once 20
62   Top Rank JAR 607   The Breaking Point/My Willow Tree 15
62   Stateside SS 102   Any Day Now/The Prophet '. 10
62   Stateside SS 127   I Keep Forgettin'/Who's Gonna Pick Up The Pieces 10
63   Stateside SS 171   Tell Him I'm Not Home/Getting Ready For The Heartbreak 10
64   Pye Intl. 7N 25247   Beg Me/For All Time 8
64   Pye Intl. 7N 25276   Any Day Now/The Prophet 8

65	Pye Intl. 7N 25287	Since I Don't Have You/Hand It Over	30
65	Pye Intl. 7N 25301	I Need You/Chuck's Soul Brothers Twist	6
65	Pye Intl. 7N 25321	If I Didn't Love You/Just A Little Bit Of Your Soul	8
66	Pye Intl. 7N 25384	Chains Of Love/I Keep Forgettin'	30
67	Pye Intl. 7N 25439	Shame On Me/Candy	7
68	Tamla Motown TMG 651	Girls, Girls, Girls/(You Can't Let The Boy Overpower) The Man In You	8
70	Tamla Motown TMG 729	Honey Come Back/What Am I Gonna Do Without You	10
75	All Platinum 614310	I've Got The Need/Beautiful Woman	6
75	Disco Demand DDS 116	These Chains Of Love/Any Day Now	4
85	Kent TOWN 104	Hand It Over/CANDY & KISSES: Mr Creator (withdrawn)	15
66	Pye Intl. NPL 28082	TRIBUTE TO RHYTHM AND BLUES (LP)	20
68	T. Motown (S)TML 11071	CHUCK JACKSON ARRIVES! (LP)	25
69	T. Motown (S)TML 11117	GOIN' BACK TO CHUCK JACKSON (LP)	15
72	Probe SPB 1084	THROUGH ALL TIMES (LP)	15
74	Anchor ABCL 5040	THROUGH ALL TIMES (LP, reissue)	10

CHUCK JACKSON & MAXINE BROWN

| 65 | Pye Intl. 7N 25308 | Something You Got/Baby Take Me | 8 |
| 65 | Pye Intl. NPL 28091 | SAYING SOMETHING (LP) | 15 |

(see also Maxine Brown)

DEON JACKSON

66	Atlantic AT 4070	Love Makes The World Go Round/You Said You Loved Me	15
66	Atlantic 584 012	Love Takes A Long Time Growing/Hush Little Baby	12
68	Atlantic 584 159	Ooh Baby/All On A Sunny Day	10
76	Contempo CS 9031	Love Makes The World Go Round/I Can't Go On (possibly unissued)	5+

EARL JACKSON

| 76 | ABC ABC 4110 | Soul Self Satisfaction/Looking Thru' The Eyes Of Love | 5 |

GEORGE JACKSON

69	Capitol CL 15605	Find 'Em, Fool 'Em And Forget 'Em/My Desires Are Getting The Best Of Me	8
72	London HLU 10373	Aretha, Sing One For Me/I'm Gonna Wait	4
73	London HLU 10413	Let 'Em Know You Care/Patricia	10

GORDON JACKSON

69	Marmalade 598 010	Me And My Zoo/A Day At The Cottage	5
69	Marmalade 598 021	Song For Freedom/Sing To Me Woman	5
69	Marmalade 608 012	THINKING BACK (LP)	25

HAROLD JACKSON & TORNADOES

| 58 | Vogue V 9105 | Move It On Down The Line Pts 1 & 2 | 40 |
| 58 | Vogue V 9105 | Move It On Down The Line Pts 1 & 2 (78) | 40 |

JACKIE JACKSON

| 74 | T. Motown STML 11249 | JACKIE JACKSON (LP) | 10 |

(see also Jacksons, Jackson 5)

JANET JACKSON

83	A&M AMS 8303	Come Give Your Love To Me/The Magic Is Working (p/s)	5
83	A&M AMSX 8303	Come Give Your Love To Me/The Magic Is Working (12", p/s)	8
83	A&M AM 112	Don't Mess Up This Good Thing/Young Love (p/s)	4
83	A&M AMX 112	Don't Mess Up This Good Thing/Young Love (12", p/s)	7
86	A&M AMS 337	When I Think Of You/Come Give Your Love To Me//What Have You Done To Me Lately/Young Love (clear vinyl/picture disc double pack)	6
86	A&M AMS 359	Control/Pretty Boy/Nasty (p/s, with extra track & free cassette ["Nasty (Cool Summer Mix)"])	6
87	Breakout USAD 601	Let's Wait A While/Nasty (Cool Summer Mix Pt. 1)//Nasty (Original Mix)/Control/Let's Wait A While (Remix) (picture disc/clear vinyl double pack)	7
87	Breakout USAP 601	Let's Wait A While/Nasty (Cool Summer Mix Pt 1) (picture disc)	4
87	Breakout USAS 613	Funny How Time Flies (When You're Having Fun)/When I Think Of You (poster p/s)	4
89	Breakout USAS 663	Miss You Much/You Need Me (poster p/s)	4
89	Breakout USAS 673	Rhythm Nation/Rhythm Nation (Version) (poster p/s)	4
89	Breakout USATP 673	Rhythm Nation/Rhythm Nation (Version) (12", picture disc)	7
90	Breakout USAB 681	Come Back To Me/Alright (box set with metal badge & foldout poster)	6
90	Breakout USAT 681	Come Back To Me/Alright (12", p/s with calendar poster)	7
90	Breakout USAP 693	Alright/Alright (Spanish Remix) (shaped picture disc with stand)	5
90	A&M AMY 587	Black Cat/Black Cat (3 Snaps Up Mix)/1814 Megamix (Long Version) (12", with 4 postcards, leather boot badge & competition form)	7
90	Breakout USAP 684	Escapade (We've Got It Made)/(Version) (picture disc)	4
90	A&M AMAP 3920	RHYTHM NATION 1814 (LP, picture disc)	10

JANET JACKSON & CLIFF RICHARD

| 84 | A&M AM 210 | Two To The Power Of Love/JANET JACKSON: Rock'n'Roll (p/s) | 7 |
| 84 | A&M AMX 210 | Two To The Power Of Love/JANET JACKSON: Rock'n'Roll/Don't Mess Up This Good Thing (12", p/s) | 10 |

(see also Cliff Richard)

JERMAINE JACKSON

73	Tamla Motown TMG 838	That's How Love Goes/I Lost My Love In The Big City	4
73	Tamla Motown TMG 851	Daddy's Home/Take Me In Your Arms	4
73	Tamla Motown TMG 874	The Bigger You Love (The Harder You Fall)/I'm In A Different World	4
84	Arista JJKPD 1	Sweetest Sweetest/Come To Me (picture disc)	4

(see also Jacksons, Jackson 5)

JERMAINE JACKSON & PIA ZADORA

| 84 | Arista ARISD 584 | When The Rain Begins To Fall/Substitute (picture disc) | 4 |

JERRY JACKSON

| 62 | Cameo Parkway P 100 | It's Rough Out There/I'm Gonna Paint A Picture | 80 |
| 63 | London HLR 9689 | Gypsy Eyes/Turn Back | 15 |

MINT VALUE £

JIM JACKSON
66	RCA RCX 7182	R.C.A. VICTOR RACE SERIES VOL. 7 (EP)	12

JIMMY JACKSON('S ROCK 'N' ROLL SKIFFLE)
57	Columbia DB 3898	California Zephyr/I Shall Not Be Moved	15
57	Columbia DB 3898	California Zephyr/I Shall Not Be Moved (78)	5
57	Columbia DB 3937	Sittin' In The Balcony/Good Morning Blues	22
57	Columbia DB 3937	Sittin' In The Balcony/Good Morning Blues (78)	10
57	Columbia DB 3957	River Line/Lonely Road	12
57	Columbia DB 3957	River Line/Lonely Road (78)	5
57	Columbia DB 3988	White Silver Sands/Build Your Love (On A Strong ...) (solo)	8
57	Columbia DB 3988	White Silver Sands/Build Your Love (On A Strong ...) (solo) (78)	5
58	Columbia DB 4085	Love-A Love-A Love A/Photographs (solo)	8
58	Columbia DB 4085	Love-A Love-A Love A/Photographs (solo) (78)	5
58	Columbia DB 4153	Swing Down, Sweet Chariot/This Little Light Of Mine (solo)	8
58	Columbia SEG 7750	ROCK 'N' SKIFFLE (EP)	25
58	Columbia SEG 7768	COUNTRY AND BLUES (EP)	25

J.J. JACKSON (& Greatest Little Soul Band In The Land)
67	Polydor 56718	But It's Alright/Do The Boogaloo	8
67	Strike JH 329	Come See Me/Try Me	8
67	Warner Bros WB 2082	Sho Nuff (Got A Good Thing Going)/Here We Go Again	6
68	Warner Bros WB 2090	Down, But Not Out/Why Does It Take So Long	4
68	Warner Bros WB 6029	Courage Ain't Strength/You Do It 'Cause You Wanna	4
69	Warner Bros WB 7276	Ain't Too Proud To Beg/But It's Alright	4
69	MCA Soul Bag BAG 4	Tenement Halls/Flat Black And Together	4
69	MCA Soul Bag BAG 6	Something For My People/Win Lose Or Draw	4
71	Mojo 2092 014	But It's Alright/Do The Boogaloo	4
67	Strike JLH 104	J.J. JACKSON WITH THE GREATEST LITTLE SOUL BAND (LP)	15
69	MCA SKA 100	GREATEST LITTLE SOUL BAND (LP)	12
71	RCA SF 8093	J.J. JACKSON'S DILEMMA (LP)	12

JOE JACKSON
78	A&M AMS 7392	Is She Really Going Out With Him?/Do The Instant Mash (p/s)	4
79	A&M AMSP 7433	One More Time/Don't Ask Me (10", p/s, white vinyl with free badge)	6
82	A&M AMS 8231	Real Men/Chinatown (picture disc)	4
84	A&M AM 200	Be My Number Two/Is She Really Going Out With Him? (p/s)	4
79	A&M AMLH 64743	LOOK SHARP! (LP, white vinyl)	10

(see also Arms & Legs)

LEVI JACKSON
71	Columbia DB 8807	This Beautiful Day/Don't You Be A Sinner	40

(see also Solomon King)

MAHALIA JACKSON
58	Philips PB 869	For My Good Fortune/Have You Any Rivers	4
59	Philips PB 933	Trouble Of The World/Tell The World About This	4
60	Philips PB 1040	Onward Christian Soldiers/The Lord's Prayer	4
60	Vogue V 2418	The Lord's Prayer/Bless This House	5
52	Vogue LDE 005	MAHALIA JACKSON (10" LP)	15
59	Philips BBL 7289	NEWPORT 1958 (LP, also stereo SBBL 547)	10/12
60	Top Rank 30/006	JUST AS I AM (LP)	10
60	Philips BBL 7362	GREAT GETTIN' UP MORNING (LP)	10
60	Philips BBL 7391	THE POWER AND THE GLORY (LP, also stereo SBBL 576)	10/12
61	Philips BBL 7456	I BELIEVE (LP, also stereo SBBL 610)	10/12

MICHAEL JACKSON
73	Tamla Motown TMG 863	Morning Glow/My Girl	4
74	Tamla Motown TMG 900	Music And Me/Johnny Raven	5
75	Tamla Motown TMG 1006	Just A Little Bit Of You/Dear Michael	4
79	Epic S EPC 12-7135	You Can't Win Pts 1 & 2 (picture disc)	8
82	Epic EPCA 2729	The Girl Is Mine (with Paul McCartney)/Can't Get Outta The Rain (p/s)	4
82	Epic EPCA 11-2729	The Girl Is Mine (with Paul McCartney)/Can't Get Outta The Rain (picture disc)	15
82	Epic EPCA 40 2906	GREATEST ORIGINAL HITS (cassette EP)	6
83	Motown TMGP 986	Happy/We're Almost There (picture disc, PVC sleeve)	10
83	Motown CTME 2035	FLIPHITS (cassette EP)	6
83	Epic MJ 1-9	NINE SINGLES PACK (9 x 7", p/s, red vinyl, in PVC foldout wallet)	25
87	Epic 6502020	I Just Can't Stop Loving You/Baby Be Mine (poster p/s)	10
87	Epic 6502026	I Just Can't Stop Loving You/Baby Be Mine (12", p/s, with poster)	12
87	Epic 6511556	Bad (Dance Extended Mix)/(7" Single Mix)/(The Bad Dance Remix Radio Edit)/(The Dub Version)/(A Cappella) (12", p/s, red vinyl)	15
87	Epic 6512753	The Way You Make Me Feel/(Instrumental) (p/s, double-groove)	8
87	Epic 6512757	The Way You Make Me Feel/(Instrumental) (p/s, with competition leaflet)	15
87	Epic 6512759	The Way You Make Me Feel (Dance Extended Mix)/The Way You Make Me Feel (Instrumental)/The Way You Make Me Feel (Dub Version) (CD)	7
87	Epic 6530260	Smooth Criminal/(Instrumental) (box set with postcards)	10
87	Epic 6530261	Smooth Criminal/Smooth Criminal (Dance Mix)/Smooth Criminal (Instrumental) (12", with advent calendar)	15
87	Epic 6530263	Smooth Criminal/Smooth Criminal (Instrumental) (CD)	10
88	Epic 6513889	Man In The Mirror (square-shaped picture disc)	8
88	Epic MJ 5	BAD (5 x 7" pack, square picture discs in foldout PVC wallet)	12
88	Epic 6528646	Dirty Diana/Dirty Diana (Instrumental) (12", poster p/s)	12
88	Epic 6528449	Another Part Of Me/(Instrumental) (p/s, with backstage pass)	6
88	Epic 6528440	Another Part Of Me/Another Part Of Me (Instrumental) (poster p/s)	10
89	Epic 6549479	Liberian Girl/Girlfriend (star mobile pack)	10
89	Epic 6549472	Liberian Girl/Girlfriend/You Can't Win + 1 (CD)	7
89	Epic 6546722	Leave Me Alone/Don't Stop 'Til You Get Enough/Human Nature/Wanna Be Startin' Something (Extended) (CD)	10
92	Pepsi/Epic 01-982789-35	Someone Put Your Hand Out/"Dangerous Medley" (freebie cassette)	6

80	Epic EPC 83458	OFF THE WALL (LP, gatefold sleeve, with free 7" picture disc "You Can't Win Pts 1 & 2" [S EPC 12-7135])	25
82	Epic EPC 11-85930	THRILLER (LP, picture disc in PVC sleeve)	15
87	Epic 4502900	BAD (LP, picture disc)	10
87	Epic 450290	BAD GIFT PACK (cassette pack, with note pad, highlighter pen & calender)	20
92	Epic 4658029	DANGEROUS (CD, 10" x 10" pop-up 'play set')	18

(see also Jackson 5, Paul McCartney)

MILLIE JACKSON

72	Mojo 2093 011	A Child Of God Pts 1 & 2	5
72	Mojo 2093 022	My Man, A Sweet Man/I Gotta Get Away (From My Own Self)	5
73	Polydor 2066 317	Breakaway/Strange Things	4
75	Polydor 2066 536	If Loving You Is Wrong/The Rap	5
75	Polydor 2006 612	Loving Arms/Left Over	6
76	Spring 2066 713	A House For Sale/There You Are	4
72	Mojo 2918 005	MILLIE JACKSON (LP)	15
75	Polydor 2391 147	CAUGHT UP (LP)	10
75	Polydor 2391 183	STILL CAUGHT UP (LP)	10

(see also Elton John)

MILT JACKSON

50s	London EZ-C 19004	THE MILT JACKSON SEPTET (EP)	12
62	London RE-K 1315	THE BALLAD ARTISTRY OF MILT JACKSON (EP)	8
53	Vogue LDE 044	MILT JACKSON AND HIS NEW GROUP (10" LP)	15
55	Esquire 20-042	MILT JACKSON QUINTET (10" LP)	15
55	London Jazz LZ-C 14006	MILT JACKSON QUARTET (10" LP)	15
57	London Jazz LTZ-K 15064	BALLADS AND BLUES (LP)	12
57	London Jazz LTZ-K 15074	THE JAZZ SKYLINE (LP)	12
57	London Jazz LTZ-K 15091	JACKSON'SVILL (LP)	12
57	Vogue LAE 12046	WIZARD OF THE VIBES (LP)	12
59	London Jazz LTZ-K 15141	PLENTY, PLENTY SOUL (LP)	12
59	London Jazz LTZ-T 15172	BAGS' OPUS (LP, also stereo SAH-T 6049)	12
60	London Jazz LTZ-T 15177	BAGS AND FLUTES (LP)	12
60	London Jazz LTZ-K 15196	BEAN BAGS (LP, also stereo SAH-K 6095; with Coleman Hawkins)	12
61	London Jazz LTZ-K 15220	THE ARTISTRY OF MILT JACKSON (LP)	12
61	London Jazz LTZ-K 15232	BAGS AND TRANE (LP, with John Coltrane; also stereo SAH-K 6192)	12
61	Philips BBL 7459	MILT JACKSON (LP)	12
62	Esquire 32-134	MILT JACKSON MODERN JAZZ QUARTET/QUINTET (LP)	12
62	Blue Note BLP 1509	MILT JACKSON (LP)	15
62	Riverside RLP (9)407	BAGS MEETS WES (LP, with Wes Montgomery)	12
63	Realm RM 119	THE MILT JACKSON QUARTET (LP)	12
63	HMV CLP 1589	STATEMENTS (LP, also stereo CSD 1455)	12
63	Realm RM 156	ROLL 'EM BAGS (LP)	12
64	Atlantic ATL/SAL 5012	VIBRATIONS (LP)	12
65	Mercury LML/SML 4008	IN A NEW SETTING (LP)	12
65	Mercury LML/SML 4016	AT THE MUSEUM OF MODERN ART (LP)	12
66	Mercury LML/SML 4028	BORN FREE (LP)	12
73	CTI CTL 8	CHERRY (LP, with Stanley Turrentine)	10
73	CTI CTL 15	SUNFLOWER (LP)	10
74	CTI CTH 1002	GOODBYE (LP, with Hubert Laws)	10
75	CTI CTH 1004	OLINGA (LP)	10
75	Atlantic K 60100	ART OF MILT JACKSON — THE ATLANTIC YEARS (LP)	10
75	Pablo/Polydor 2310 753	MILT JACKSON, OSCAR PETERSON, ETC (LP)	10

(see also Ray Charles, Modern Jazz Quartet, Stanley Turrentine)

PAPA CHARLIE JACKSON

50	Tempo R 30	Long Gone Lost John/ I'm Looking For A Woman Who Knows How To Treat Me Right (78)	10
60	Heritage R 100	PAPA CHARLIE JACKSON (EP)	20
60	Heritage HLP 1011	PAPA CHARLIE JACKSON (LP)	50

RALPH SOUL JACKSON

| 69 | Atlantic 584 258 | 'Cause I Love You/Sunshine Of Your Love | 4 |

ROOT & JENNY JACKSON

| 69 | Beacon BEA 136 | Let's Go Somewhere/If I Didn't Love You | 4 |

SHAWNE JACKSON

| 74 | Pye Intl. 7N 25656 | Just As Bad As You/He May Be Your Man | 4 |

SHIRLEY JACKSON

| 63 | Decca F 11788 | Broken Home/No Greater Love Than Mine | 8 |

SHOVELVILLE K. JACKSON

| 50s | Melodisc MEL 1683 | Be Careful Of Stones That You Throw/Kentucky Blues | 10 |

SIMONE JACKSON

62	Piccadilly 7N 35087	Pop Pop Popeye/He Ain't Got No Time For Love	4
63	Piccadilly 7N 35124	Ain't Gonna Kiss Ya/Slow Motion	4
63	Piccadilly 7N 35149	Tell Me What To Do/Done What You Know Is Wrong	4

STONEWALL JACKSON

59	Philips PB 941	Waterloo/Smoke Along The Track	8
59	Philips PB 941	Waterloo/Smoke Along The Track (78)	5
60	Philips PB 1073	I'm Gonna Find You/A Little Guy Called Joe	6
65	CBS BPG 62587	GREATEST HITS (LP)	15

TONY JACKSON (& VIBRATIONS)

64	Pye 7N 15685	Bye Bye Baby/Watch Your Step	10
64	Pye 7N 15745	This Little Girl Of Mine/You Beat Me To The Punch	12
65	Pye 7N 15766	Love Potion No. 9/Fortune Teller	25
65	Pye 7N 15876	Stage Door/That's What I Want	12

Tony JACKSON

66	CBS 202039	You're My Number One/Let Me Know (as Tony Jackson Group)	25
66	CBS 202069	Never Leave Your Baby's Side/I'm The One She Really Thinks A Lot Of (as Tony Jackson)	25
66	CBS 202297	Follow Me/Walk That Walk (as Tony Jackson)	30
66	CBS 202408	Anything Else You Want/Come On And Stop (as Tony Jackson)	25

(see also Searchers)

WALTER JACKSON

65	Columbia DB 7620	Welcome Home/Blowin' In The Wind	10
66	Columbia DB 7949	It's An Uphill Climb To The Bottom/Tear For Tear	15
66	Columbia DB 8054	A Corner In The Sun/Not You	10
67	Columbia DB 8154	Speak Her Name/They Don't Give Medals (To Yesterday's Heroes)	10
70	Atlantic 584 311	Any Way That You Want Me/Life Has Its Ups And Downs	4
73	Brunswick BR 5	Easy Evil/I Never Had It So Good	5

WANDA JACKSON

59	Capitol CL 15033	You're The One For Me/A Date With Jerry	12
59	Capitol CL 15090	Reaching/I'd Rather Have You	12
60	Capitol CL 15147	Let's Have A Party/Cool Love	15
61	Capitol CL 15176	Mean Mean Mean/Honey Bop	15
61	Capitol CL 15223	Right Or Wrong/Funnel Of Love	8
62	Capitol CL 15234	In The Middle Of A Heartache/I'd Be Ashamed	10
62	Capitol CL 15249	If I Cried Every Time You Hurt Me/Let My Love Walk In	10
58	Capitol EAP1 1041	WANDA JACKSON (EP)	30
62	Capitol EAP1 20353	A LITTLE BITTY TEAR (EP)	20
60	Capitol T 1384	ROCKIN' WITH WANDA (LP)	50
61	Capitol T 1511	THERE'S A PARTY GOIN' ON (LP)	35
61	Capitol T 1596	RIGHT OR WRONG (LP)	25
62	Capitol T 1776	WONDERFUL WANDA (LP)	18
64	Capitol T 2030	TWO SIDES OF WANDA (LP)	18
64	Capitol (S)T 2306	BLUES IN MY HEART (LP)	12
66	Capitol (S)T 2438	SINGS COUNTRY SONGS (LP, yellow label)	10
67	Capitol (S)T 2606	SALUTES THE COUNTRY MUSIC HALL OF FAME (LP, yellow label)	10
67	Capitol (S)T 2812	YOU'LL ALWAYS HAVE MY LOVE (LP, yellow label)	10
69	Capitol (S)T 2976	CREAM OF THE CROP (LP, with Party Timers, yellow label)	10

JACKSON & SMITH

| 65 | Polydor BM 56051 | Ain't That Loving You Baby/Every Day I Have The Blues | 10 |
| 66 | Polydor BM 56086 | Party '66/And That's It | 8 |

JACKSON BROTHERS

| 59 | London HLX 8845 | Tell Him No/Love Me | 20 |
| 59 | London HLX 8845 | Tell Him No/Love Me (78) | 8 |

JACKSON 5

70	Tamla Motown TMG 724	I Want You Back/Who's Loving You	4
70	Tamla Motown TMG 738	ABC/The Young Folks	4
70	Tamla Motown TMG 738	ABC/The Young Folks (demo in p/s)	75
70	Tamla Motown TMG 746	The Love You Save/I Found That Girl	4
70	Tamla Motown TMG 758	I'll Be There/One More Chance	4
71	Tamla Motown TMG 769	Mama's Pearl/Darling Dear	4
71	Tamla Motown TMG 778	Never Can Say Goodbye/She's Good	4
72	Tamla Motown TMG 809	Sugar Daddy/I'm So Happy	4
72	Tamla Motown TMG 825	Little Bitty Pretty One/Maybe Tomorrow	4
72	Tamla Motown TMG 833	Lookin' Through The Windows/Love Song	4
72	Tamla Motown TMG 833	Lookin' Through The Windows/Love Song (demo in p/s)	15
72	Tamla Motown TMG 837	Santa Claus Is Coming To Town/Someday At Christmas/Christmas Won't Be The Same This Year	4
73	Tamla Motown TMG 842	Doctor My Eyes/My Little Baby	4
73	Tamla Motown TMG 865	Skywriter/Ain't Nothin' Like The Real Thing	4
73	Tamla Motown TMG 865	Skywriter/Ain't Nothin' Like The Real Thing (demo in p/s)	10
73	Tamla Motown TMG 878	Get It Together/Touch	4
74	Tamla Motown TMG 895	The Boogie Man/Don't Let Your Baby Catch You	4
74	Tamla Motown TMG 904	Dancing Machine/It's Too Late To Change The Time	4
74	Tamla Motown TMG 927	The Life Of The Party/Whatever You Got I Want	4
75	Tamla Motown TMG 942	I Am Love Pts 1 & 2	4
75	Tamla Motown TMG 1001	Forever Came Today/I Can't Quit Your Love	4
74	Lyntone LYN 2639	Talk And Sing Personally To Valentine Readers (33rpm flexidisc free with 'Valentine' magazine)	10/8
75	Rice Krispies (no cat. no.'s)	Rice Krispies cut-out card discs (3 different tracks)	each 30
70	T. Motown (S)TML 11142	DIANA ROSS PRESENTS THE JACKSON 5 (LP, flipback sleeve)	10
70	T. Motown (S)TML 11156	ABC (LP, flipback sleeve)	10
70	T. Motown STML 11168	CHRISTMAS ALBUM (LP, flipback sleeve)	10
71	T. Motown STML 11174	THIRD ALBUM (LP, flipback sleeve)	12
71	T. Motown STML 11188	MAYBE TOMORROW (LP)	10
73	T. Motown STML 11231	SKYWRITER (LP)	10
73	T. Motown STML 11243	GET IT TOGETHER (LP)	10
74	T. Motown STML 11275	DANCING MACHINE (LP)	10
75	T. Motown STML 11290	MOVING VIOLATIONS (LP)	20
77	T. Motown TMSP 6004	ANTHOLOGY (2-LP, original issue)	14

(see also Michael Jackson, Jermaine Jackson, Jacksons)

JACKSON HEIGHTS

70	Charisma JH 1	Doubting Thomas/Insomnia	4
70	Charisma CAS 1018	KINGS PROGRESS (LP, pink label)	10
72	Vertigo 6360 067	5TH AVENUE BUS (LP, gatefold sleeve, spiral label)	25
73	Vertigo 6360 077	RAGAMUFFIN'S FOOL (LP, gatefold sleeve, spiral label, some with poster)	25/18
73	Vertigo 6360 092	BUMP AND GRIND (LP, 'spaceship label')	15

JACKSONS

76	Epic EPC 4708	Enjoy Yourself/Style Of Life	4
81	Epic EPC A 11-1294	Walk Right Now/Your Ways (picture disc)	6
84	Epic WA 4431	State Of Shock/Your Ways (picture disc, with Mick Jagger)	6
84	Epic QTA 4675	Torture (New Mix)/Torture (Instrumental)	
		(p/s, with wraparound tour poster)	6
84	Epic EPC 86303	VICTORY (LP, with 'Special Sports' competition)	10

(see also Jackson 5, Michael Jackson, Jermaine Jackson)

JACKSON SISTERS

73	Mums MUM 18257	I Believe In Miracles/Day In The Blue	20
73	Mums MUM 1591	(Why Can't We Be) More Than Just Friends/Rockin' On My Porch	4
75	Mums MUM 2896	Boy You're Dynamite/Shake Her Loose	6
75	CBS 2896	Boy You're Dynamite/Shake Her Loose (reissue)	4

JACK THE LAD

73	B&C CB 128	Why Can't I Be Satisfied/Make Me Happy	4

JACKY

68	Philips BF 1647	White Horses/Too Many Chiefs (Not Enough Indians)	4
68	Philips SBL 7851	WHITE HORSES (LP)	10

(see also Jackie & Raindrops, Raindrops)

JACOBITES

69	Pye 7N 17852	Like Now	4

DICK JACOBS (& HIS ORCHESTRA)

56	Vogue Coral Q 72147	Saxophone/Never Come Sunday	5
56	Vogue Coral Q 72154	"The Man With The Golden Arm" Theme/Butternut	5
56	Vogue Coral Q 72178	Golden Baton/Te Amo	4
56	Vogue Coral Q 72187	Proud Ones/Catered Affair	4
56	Vogue Coral Q 72204	Petticoats Of Portugal/East Of Eden	4
57	Vogue Coral Q 72245	The Big Beat/The Tower Trot	10
57	Vogue Coral Q 72245	The Big Beat/The Tower Trot (78)	5
57	Vogue Coral Q 72260	Rock-a-billy Gal/The Golden Strings	6
57	Vogue Coral Q 72260	Rock-a-billy Gal/The Golden Strings (78)	5
57	Vogue Coral Q 72280	Fascination/Summertime In Venice	4
57	Vogue Coral LVA 9076	THE SKIFFLE SOUND (LP, as Dick Jacobs & His Skiffle Group)	25
50s	Vogue Coral	HORROR MOVIE THEMES (LP)	10

HANK JACOBS

64	Sue WI 313	So Far Away/Monkey Hips And Rice	20

JIMMY JACOBS & NITESPOTS

60s	Gargoyle (no cat. no.)	SWINGIN' SOHO — JIMMY SINGS THE NITESPOTS SWING (LP)	15

BRIAN JACQUES & BRIGANTINE

74	Sweet Folk & C. SFAO 11	A GIG WID BRIG (LP)	15

(see also Liverpool Fishermen)

CHUCK JACQUES & LYNN TAITT & COMETS

67	Ska Beat JB 264	Dial 609/VIBRATORS & TOMMY McCOOK & COMETS: Wait For Me	10

ILLINOIS JACQUET & HIS ORCHESTRA

56	Vogue V 2387	Blow Illinois Blow/Destination Moon	6
53	Vogue LDE 026	ILLINOIS JACQUET (10" LP)	12
56	Columbia Clef 33C 9018	ILLINOIS JACQUET (10" LP)	12
57	Columbia Clef 33CX 10085	GROOVIN' WITH JACQUET (LP)	10

JADE

70s	DJM	FLY ON STRANGE WINGS (LP)	30

JADE WARRIOR

72	Vertigo 6059 069	The Demon Trucker/Snake	8
78	Island JAD 1	Way Of The Sun/Sun Ra	4
71	Vertigo 6360 033	JADE WARRIOR (LP, gatefold sleeve, spiral label)	30
71	Vertigo 6360 062	RELEASED (LP, gatefold sleeve, spiral label)	50
72	Vertigo 6360 079	LAST AUTUMN'S DREAM (LP, gatefold sleeve, spiral label)	30
74	Island ILPS 9290	FLOATING WORLD (LP)	10
75	Island ILPS 9318	WAVES (LP)	10
76	Island ILPS 9393	KITES (LP)	10
78	Island ILPS 9552	WAY OF THE SUN (LP)	10
79	Butt BUTT 001	REFLECTIONS (LP)	10

(see also July)

MAX JAFFA (& HIS ORCHESTRA)

55	Decca F 10426	Camille/The Song Of The Barefoot Contessa (My Gipsy Heart)	
		(as Max Jaffa & His Violin)	4
56	Columbia SCM 5226	China Boogie/Slap Happy	4
59	Columbia SCD 2122	The Great Waltz Selection/The Vagabond Prince Selection	
		(as Max Jaffa & Palm Court Orchestra)	4
59	Columbia SCD 2127	Black Eyes/Czardas (as Max Jaffa Trio & Orchestra)	4
59	Columbia DB 4280	Gypsy Cha Cha/Cha Cha Boogie	4
60	Columbia DB 4474	Love Is Like A Violin/Romantica (with Norrie Paramor Orchestra)	4

CHRIS JAGGER

73	GM GMS 3	Something New/Joy Of The Ride	4
73	GM GML 1003	CHRIS JAGGER (LP)	10

MICK JAGGER

70	Decca F 13067	Memo From Turner/Natural Magic	6
70	Decca F 13067	Memo From Turner/Natural Magic (export p/s)	30
87	CBS 651028-0	Let's Work/Catch As Catch Can (poster p/s)	4

| 87 | CBS THROWP 1 | Throwaway/Peace For The Wicked (picture disc) | 4 |

(see also Rolling Stones, Original Soundtracks, Jacksons)

JAGS
| 61 | Decca F 11397 | Cry Wolf/The Hunch | 8 |

JAGUAR
81	Heavy Metal HEAVY 10	Back Street Woman/Chasing The Dragon (p/s)	8
82	Neat NEAT 16	Axe Crazy/War Machine (p/s)	12
83	Neat NEAT 1007	POWER GAMES (LP)	10
84	Roadrunner RR 9851	THIS TIME (LP)	10

JAH SCOUSE
| 85 | Better Things BETS 1 | Merge/Vegan Mix (p/s) | 4 |

JAKE & FAMILY JEWELS
| 70 | Polydor 2425 027 | JAKE AND THE FAMILY JEWELS (LP) | 12 |

JAKLIN
| 69 | Stable SLE 8003 | JAKLIN (LP) | 175 |

JAM
77	Polydor 2058 866	In The City/Takin' My Love (p/s)	7
77	Polydor 2058 903	All Around The World/Carnaby Street (p/s)	6
77	Polydor 2058 945	The Modern World/Sweet Soul Music/Back In My Arms Again/(Bricks And Mortar) (p/s)	6
78	Polydor 2058 995	News Of The World/Aunties And Uncles/Innocent Man (p/s)	5
78	Polydor 2058 995	News Of The World/Aunties And Uncles/Innocent Man (p/s, mispressing, B-side both sides)	25
78	Polydor 2059 054	David Watts/A-Bomb In Wardour Street (p/s)	4
78	Polydor POSP 8	Down In The Tube Station At Midnight/So Sad About Us/The Night (p/s)	4
79	Polydor POSP 34	Strange Town/Butterfly Collector (p/s)	4
79	Polydor POSP 69	When You're Young/Smithers-Jones (p/s)	4
79	Polydor POSP 69	When You're Young/Smithers Jones (p/s, mispressing, B-side both sides)	25
79	Polydor POSP 83	Eton Rifles/See-Saw (laminated p/s)	4

(all the above singles were reissued in their picture sleeves; early originals have curved edges on sleeve openings whereas the reissues are straight. Lettering on the reissue labels tends to be fatter. Reissues are worth £2-£3)

80	Polydor POSJ 113/ 2816 024	Going Underground/Dreams Of Children/The Modern World/Away From The Numbers/Down In The Tube Station At Midnight (p/s, double pack)	8
80	Polydor 2059 266	Start/Liza Radley (p/s)	4
80	Polydor 2059 266	Start/Liza Radley (p/s, mispressing, plays Village People's "Can't Stop The Music")	6
81	Polydor POSP 350	Absolute Beginners/Tales From The Riverbank (p/s, with lyric sheet)	4
82	Polydor POSPJ 540/JAM 1	Beat Surrender/Shopping//Move On Up/Stoned Out Of My Mind/War (double pack, gatefold p/s)	6
82	Polydor POSP 540X	Beat Surrender/Shopping/Move On Up/Stoned Out Of My Mind/War (12", p/s, mispress, B-side plays French LP)	30
80s	PJAM 1	Interview With Paul Weller And Bruce Foxton (no'd pic disc with insert)	15
80	Lyntone LYN 9048	Pop Art Poem/Boy About Town (Version) (blue or yellow 1-sided flexidisc free with 'Flexipop' magazine issue 2)	5/4
81	Lyntone	When You're Young (live) (1-sided fan club flexidisc)	20
82	Fan Club	Tales From The Riverbank (Version) (33rpm fan club 1-sided flexidisc)	20
82	Fan Club	Funeral Pyre (Version) (fan club flexidisc)	20
82	Polydor PAULO 100	Move On Up (live) (flexidisc free with 'Melody Maker')	6/5
90	Polydor SNAP 1	SNAP! (2-LP, with 4-track EP 'Live At Wembley' [SNAP 45])	15

(see also Style Council, Bruce Foxton)

JAMAICA FATS
| 65 | Blue Beat BB 368 | Jacqueline/Please Come Home (actually by Al T. Joe & Celestials) | 8 |

(see also Al T. Joe)

JAMAICA'S GREATEST
| 64 | Blue Beat BB 313 | Everybody Yeah Yeah/BUSTER'S ALLSTARS: Gun The Man Down | 10 |

JAMAICAN ACTIONS
| 68 | Coxsone CS 7070 | Catch The Quinella/JACKIE MITTOO: Songbird | 12 |

JAMAICAN COUSINS
| 67 | President PT 168 | Just A Little Love/Were You There | 4 |

JAMAICAN FOUNDATIONS
| 68 | Coxsone CS 7036 | Take It Cool/VICEROYS: Try Hard To Leave | 15 |

JAMAICANS
66	Doctor Bird DB 1109	Cool Night/Ma And Pa	12
67	Trojan TR 007	Dedicated To You/The Things I Said To You	12
67	Treasure Isle TI 7007	Things You Say You Love/I've Got A Pain	10
67	Treasure Isle TI 7012	Bab Boom (Festival Song 1967)/TOMMY McCOOK & SUPERSONICS: Real Cool	10
67	Treasure Isle TI 7037	Peace And Love/Woman Gone Home	10
69	Escort ES 806	Early In The Morning/Mr. Lonely	5
70	Harry J. HJ 6604	Fire Pts 1 & 2	4
71	Dynamc DYN 410	Love Uprising/My Love For You	4

(see also Norris Weir & Jamaicans)

JAMAICAN SHADOWS
| 67 | Coxsone CS 7005 | Have Mercy/Blending Love | 15 |
| 69 | Upsetter US 320 | Dirty Dozen (actually by Upsetters)/Crying Too Long | 6 |

AHMED JAMAL
59	London Jazz LTZ-M 15162	BUT NOT FOR ME (LP)	15
59	London Jazz LTZ-M 15170	AHMED JAMAL (LP)	15
62	Pye Jazz NJL 38	ALHAMBRA (LP)	12

63	Pye Jazz NJL 50	MACANUDO (LP)	12
68	Chess CRL 4530	STANDARD-EYES (LP)	12
68	Chess CRL 4532	CRY YOUNG (LP)	12

JAMES

84	Factory FAC 78	Jimone: What's The World/Fire So Close/Folklore (p/s)	12
85	Factory FAC 119	James II: Hymn From A Village/If Things Were Perfect (p/s)	10
86	Sire JIM 3	Chain Mail/Hup Springs (p/s)	8
86	Sire JIM 3T	SIT DOWN (12" EP)	15
86	Sire JIM 4	So Many Ways/Withdrawn (p/s)	8
86	Sire JIM 4T	So Many Ways/Just Hipper/Withdrawn (12", p/s)	15
88	Blanco Y Negro NEG 26	Yaho/Mosquito (p/s)	6
88	Blanco Y Negro NEG 26T	Yaho/Mosquito/Left Out Of Her Will/New Nature (12", p/s)	12
88	Blanco Y Negro NEG 31	What For/Island Swing (p/s)	6
88	Blanco Y Negro NEG 31T	What For (Climax Mix)/Island Swing/Not There (12", p/s)	12
88	Blanco Y Negro NEG 31C	What For (Climax Mix)/Island Swing/Not There (cassette)	8
89	Rough Trade RT 225	Sit Down/Sky Is Falling (p/s)	7
89	Rough Trade RTT 225	Sit Down/Goin' Away/Sound Investment/Sky Is Falling (12", p/s)	12
89	Rough Trade RTT 225 CD	Sit Down/Goin' Away/Sound Investment/Sky Is Falling (3" CD)	12
89	Rough Trade RT 245	Come Home/Promised Land (p/s)	6
89	Rough Trade RTT 245	Come Home (Long Version)/Come Home (7" Version)/Promised Land/Slow Right Down (Demo Version) (12", p/s)	7
89	Rough Trade RTT 245 CD	Come Home (Long Version)/Come Home (7" Version)/Promised Land/Slow Right Down (Demo Version) (5" CD)	10
90	Fontana JIMM 512	How Was It For You!/(Different Mix)/Lazy/Undertaker (12", p/s, with stencil)	7
90s	Lyntone	Weather Change (Demo Version) (flexidisc, with tour programme)	10/5

BOB JAMES

| 75 | CTI CTI 6043 | BOB JAMES ONE (LP) | 10 |
| 75 | CTI CTI 6057 | BOB JAMES TWO (LP) | 10 |

BRIAN JAMES

| 68 | Olga OLE 005 | Come Back Silly Girl/It Just Happened That Way | 4 |

BRIAN JAMES

79	BJ BJ 1	Ain't That A Shame/Living In Sin/I Can Make You Cry (p/s)	4
79	BJ BJLP 1	Ain't That A Shame/Living In Sin/I Can Make You Cry (12", p/s)	7
82	Illegal ILS 0026	Why? Why? Why?/Where Did I Find A Girl Like You (p/s, green vinyl)	5

(see also Damned, Tanz Der Youth, Lords Of The New Church)

CALVIN JAMES

| 65 | Columbia DB 7516 | Some Things You Never Get Used To/Remember | 10 |

(pseudonym for George Underwood; see also Davie Jones & King Bees, Manish Boys)

COL JAMES

| 62 | Oriole CB 1736 | Doesn't Anybody Make Short Moves/Oooh Looka There Ain't She Pretty | 4 |

DICK JAMES

53	Parlophone MSP 6039	Mother Nature And Father Time/Don't You Care	8
53	Parlophone MSP 6047	The Joker/Guessing	8
55	Parlophone MSP 6170	Unchained Melody/Come Back (Come Back To Me)	10
55	Parlophone MSP 6190	He/So Must I Love You	8
56	Parlophone MSP 6199	Robin Hood/The Ballad Of Davy Crockett	15
56	Parlophone MSP 6230	"Summer Sing-Song" Medley	5
56	Parlophone R 4220	I Only Know I Love You/Mirabelle	6
56	Parlophone R 4241	"Sing Song Time (No. 3)" Medley	5
57	Parlophone R 4255	The Garden Of Eden/I Accuse	10
57	Parlophone R 4314	Westward Ho! The Wagons!/The Gay Cavalier	6
57	Parlophone R 4375	"Skiffling Sing Song" Medley	6
58	Parlophone R 4498	Daddy's Little Girl/When You're Young	4
59	Parlophone R 4606	There But For Your Love Go I/Minus One Heart	4
64	Parlophone R 5212	"Sing A Song Of Beatles With Dick James" Medley Pts 1 & 2	4

ELMORE JAMES

64	Sue WI 335	Dust My Blues/Happy Home (as Elmore James & Broom Dusters)	15
65	Sue WI 383	It Hurts Me Too/Bleeding Heart	15
65	Sue WI 392	Calling The Blues/Knocking At Your Door (actually by Junior Wells & Earl Hooker)	40
66	Sue WIP 4007	I Need You/Mean Mistreating Mama	15
65	Sue ILP 918	THE BEST OF ELMORE JAMES (LP)	30
65	Sue ILP 927	THE ELMORE JAMES MEMORIAL ALBUM (LP)	30
68	Bell MBLL/SBLL 104	SOMETHING INSIDE OF ME (LP)	25
68	Ember EMB 3397	THE LATE FANTASTICALLY GREAT ELMORE JAMES (LP)	15
70	United Artists UAS 29109	THE LEGEND OF ELMORE JAMES (LP)	18
70	Blue Horizon 7-66230	TO KNOW A MAN (2-LP)	55
70	Blue Horizon 7-63204	TOUGH (LP, with 4 tracks by John Brim)	40
73	Polydor 2383 200	COTTON PATCH HOTFOOTS (LP, shared with Walter Horton)	12
75	DJM DJLMD 8008	ALL THEM BLUES (2-LP)	15
83	Ace CH 68	KING OF THE SLIDE GUITAR (LP, yellow vinyl)	12

ETTA JAMES

60	London HLM 9139	All I Could Do Was Cry/Tough Mary	20
60	London HLM 9234	My Dearest Darling/Girl Of My Dreams	15
61	Pye Intl. 7N 25079	At Last/I Just Want To Make Love To You	10
61	Pye Intl. 7N 25080	Trust In Me/Anything To Say You're Mine	10
61	Pye Intl. 7N 25113	Dream/Fool That I Am	10
62	Pye Intl. 7N 25131	Something's Got A Hold On Me/Waiting For Charlie To Come Home	10
62	Pye Intl. 7N 25162	Stop The Wedding/Street Of Tears	10
63	Pye Intl. 7N 25205	Pushover/I Can't Hold It In Any More	10
65	Sue WI 359	Roll With Me Henry/Good Rockin' Daddy	18
67	Chess CRS 8052	I Prefer You/I'm So Glad (I Found Love In You)	10

Etta JAMES

67	Chess CRS 8063	Tell Mama/I'd Rather Go Blind	10
67	Chess CRS 8069	Security/I'm Gonna Take What He's Got	8
68	Chess CRS 8076	I Got You Babe/I Worship The Ground You Walk On	5
68	Chess CRS 8082	You Got It/Fire	6
74	Chess 6145 033	Out On The Streets Again/Come A Little Closer	5
65	Chess CRL 4502	ETTA JAMES ROCKS THE HOUSE (LP)	15
67	Chess CRL 4524	AT LAST (LP)	15
68	Ember EMB 3390	THE SOUL OF ETTA JAMES (LP)	12
69	Chess CRL 4536	TELL MAMA (LP)	15
72	Chess 6310 126	GOLDEN DECADE (LP)	10

ETTA JAMES & SUGAR PIE DeSANTO

65	Chess CRS 8025	Do I Make Myself Clear/Somewhere Down The Line	10

(see also Sugar Pie DeSanto)

HARRY JAMES & HIS ORCHESTRA

65	Dot DS 16729	Love Theme From In Harm's Way/Green Onions	4
55	Columbia SEG 7552	ROSEMARY CLOONEY AND HARRY JAMES (EP)	10
54	Philips BBR 8010	SOFT LIGHTS, SWEET TRUMPET (10" LP)	10
54	Columbia 33S 1014	ALLTIME FAVOURITES (10" LP)	10
54	Columbia 33S 1031	RHYTHM SESSION WITH HARRY JAMES (10" LP)	10
55	Columbia 33S 1052	TRUMPET TIME (10" LP)	10
56	Capitol LC 6800	IN HI-FI (10" LP)	10

JASON JAMES

67	CBS 2705	Miss Pilkington's Maid/Count Me Out	15

JERRY JAMES & BANDITS

64	Solar SRP 101	Sweet Little Sixteen/Three Steps To Heaven	5

JESSE JAMES

54	Vocalion V 1037	Southern Casey Jones/Lonesome Day Blues (78)	15

JIMMY JAMES (& VAGABONDS)

62	Dice CC 4	Bewildered And Blue/I Don't Want To Cry (solo)	8
63	R&B JB 112	Jump Children/Tell Me (solo)	8
64	Black Swan WI 437	Thinking Of You/Shirley (solo)	8
65	Columbia DB 7653	Shoo Be Doo You're Mine/We'll Never Stop Loving You	10
66	Ska Beat JB 242	Your Love/Someday (solo)	7
66	Piccadilly 7N 35298	I Feel Alright/I Wanna Be Your Everything	8
66	Piccadilly 7N 35320	Hi Diddley Dee Dum Dum (It's A Good Good Feelin')/Come To Me Softly	8
66	Piccadilly 7N 35331	This Heart Of Mine/I Don't Wanna Cry	10
66	Piccadilly 7N 35349	Ain't Love Good, Ain't Love Proud/Don't Know What I'm Gonna Do	10
67	Piccadilly 7N 35360	I Can't Get Back Home To My Baby/Hungry For Love (solo)	10
67	Piccadilly 7N 35374	No Good To Cry/You Showed Me The Way	8
68	Pye 7N 17579	Red Red Wine/Who Could Be Loving You	5
69	Pye 7N 17719	Close The Door/Why	5
70	Pye 7N 17886	Better By Far/Give Us A Light	4
70	Trojan TR 7806	Help Yourself/Why	12
71	Stateside SS 2209	A Man Like Me/Survival	6
74	People PEO 117	Help Yourself/Why (reissue)	4
75	Pye 7N 45524	Whatever Happened To The Love We Knew/Let's Have Fun	5
66	Piccadilly NEP 34053	JIMMY JAMES AND THE VAGABONDS (EP)	15
66	Piccadilly NPL 38027	NEW RELIGION (LP)	15
68	Pye N(S)PL 18231	OPEN UP YOUR SOUL (LP)	15
68	Marble Arch MAL 823	THIS IS JIMMY JAMES (LP)	10
70	Marble Arch MAL 1244	NEW RELIGION (LP, reissue)	10
75	Pye NSPL 18457	YOU DON'T STAND A CHANCE IF YOU CAN'T DANCE (LP)	15

JIMMY JAMES & VAGABONDS/ALAN BOWN SET

67	Pye N(S)PL 18156	LONDON SWINGS — LIVE AT THE MARQUEE CLUB (LP, 1 side each)	20

JOHN JAMES

70	Transatlantic TRA 219	MORNING BRINGS THE LIGHT (LP)	10
71	Transatlantic TRA 242	JOHN JAMES (LP)	10
72	Transatlantic TRA 250	SKY IN MY PIE (LP)	10

JONI JAMES

53	MGM SP 1013	Why Don't You Believe Me?/Wishing Ring	12
53	MGM SP 1025	Have You Heard/Purple Shades	10
53	MGM SP 1026	Your Cheatin' Heart/I'll Be Waiting For You	12
53	MGM SP 1041	Almost Always/Is It Any Wonder?	12
53	MGM SP 1064	I'll Never Stand In Your Way/Why Can't I	12
54	MGM SP 1081	I Need You Now/You're Nearer	8
54	MGM SP 1089	I'll Be Seeing You/Am I In Love	10
54	MGM SP 1094	You're My Everything/Maybe Next Time	8
54	MGM SP 1100	In A Garden Of Roses/Every Day	8
54	MGM SP 1105	Pa Pa Pa/Mama, Don't Cry At My Wedding	8
55	MGM SP 1125	This Is My Confession/How Important Can It Be?	8
55	MGM SP 1135	When You Wish Upon A Star/Is This The End Of The Line?	8
56	MGM SP 1149	You Are My Love/My Believing Heart	8
57	MGM MGM 918	Give Us This Day/How Lucky You Are	7
57	MGM MGM 954	Only Trust Your Heart/I Need You So	6
58	MGM MGM 973	My Funny Valentine/My Darling, My Darling	5
58	MGM MGM 978	Never 'Till Now/Love Works Miracles	5
58	MGM MGM 991	There Goes My Heart/Funny	5
59	MGM MGM 1002	There Must Be A Way/I'm Sorry For You, My Friend	6
59	MGM MGM 1002	There Must Be A Way/I'm Sorry For You, My Friend (78)	5
59	MGM MGM 1022	Perhaps/I Still Get A Thrill (Thinking Of You)	5
59	MGM MGM 1034	I Still Get Jealous/Prayer Of Love	5
59	MGM MGM 1041	Are You Sorry?/What I Don't Know Won't Hurt Me	5

59	MGM MGM 1050	Little Things Mean A Lot/I Laughed At Love	4
60	MGM MGM 1064	You Belong To Me/I Need You Now	4
60	MGM MGM 1089	We Know/They Really Don't Know You	4
60	MGM MGM 1105	Be My Love/Tall As A Tree	4
54	MGM EP 504	JONI JAMES (EP)	10
55	MGM EP 518	SINGS TO YOU (EP)	10
56	MGM EP 530	LITTLE GIRL BLUE (EP)	10
60	MGM EP 728	THE SONGS OF HANK WILLIAMS (EP, also stereo MGM ES 3501)	8/12
54	MGM D 127	LET THERE BE LOVE (10" LP)	25
59	MGM C 777	ONE HUNDRED SONGS AND JONIE (LP)	15
59	MGM C 785	JONIE SINGS SONGS OF HANK WILLIAMS (LP)	15
60	MGM C 809	TI VOGLIO BENE (I LOVE YOU SO) (LP)	15
60	MGM C 823/CS 6005	SINGS IRISH FAVOURITES (LP, mono/stereo)	14/16
60	MGM C 825	SWINGS SWEET (LP)	15
61	MGM C 839/CS 6015	100 STRINGS AND JONI IN HOLLYWOOD (LP, mono/stereo)	14/16
63	MGM C 933	AFTER HOURS (LP)	15

NICKY JAMES

| 63 | Pye 7N 15560 | My Colour Is Black/Take Me Back | 4 |

NICKY JAMES (MOVEMENT)

65	Columbia DB 7747	Stagger Lee/I'm Hurtin' Inside (as Nicky James Movement)	15
67	Philips BF 1566	I Need To Be Needed/So Glad We Made It	4
68	Philips BF 1635	Would You Believe/Silver Butterfly	8
68	Philips BF 1694	Lookin' Through Windows/Nobody But Me	4
69	Philips BF 1755	Time/Little Bit Of Paper	4
69	Philips BF 1804	Reaching For The Sun/No Life At All	4
71	Philips 6308 069	NICKY JAMES (LP)	10
73	Threshold THS 10	EVERY HOME SHOULD HAVE ONE (LP)	12
76	Threshold THS 19	THUNDERTHROAT (LP)	10
	(see also Move)		

PHILIP JAMES

| 65 | Island WI 219 | Wide Awake In A Dream/MAYTALS: Tell Me The Reason | 10 |
| | (see also Blues Busters) | | |

RICK JAMES

| 82 | Motown TMG 1266 | Dance With Me/Dance With Me (Version) (picture disc) | 4 |

RICKY JAMES

57	HMV POP 306	Knee Deep in The Blues/Bluer Than Blue	15
57	HMV POP 306	Knee Deep in The Blues/Bluer Than Blue (78)	5
57	HMV POP 334	Party Doll/Ninety-Nine Ways	18
57	HMV POP 334	Party Doll/Ninety-Nine Ways (78)	5

ROGER JAMES FOUR

65	Columbia DB 7556	Letter From Kathy/Leave Me Alone	4
66	Columbia DB 7813	Better Than Here/You're Gonna Come Home Cryin' (withdrawn)	8
66	Columbia DB 7829	Better Than Here/You're Gonna Come Home Cryin'	4

RUBY JAMES

| 69 | Fontana TF 1051 | Gettin' Mighty Crowded/Don't Play That Song | 8 |

SIDNEY JAMES & DEAN ROGERS

| 61 | HMV POP 886 | Kids/One Last Kiss | 5 |

SKIP JAMES

65	Vanguard VSD 79219	SKIP JAMES TODAY (LP)	15
68	Vanguard VSD 79273	DEVIL GOT MY WOMAN (LP)	15
70	Spokane SPL 1003	THE ORIGINAL 1930/31 RECORDINGS (LP)	40
78	Vanguard VDP 20001	I'M SO GLAD (LP)	12
70s	Storyville 670 185	THE GREATEST OF THE DELTA BLUES SINGERS (LP)	15
83	Matchbox MSE 207	1931 COMPLETE RECORDINGS (LP)	10

SONNY JAMES

56	Capitol CL 14635	The Cat Came Back/Hello Old Broken Heart	15
56	Capitol CL 14664	Twenty Feet Of Muddy Water/For Rent (One Empty Heart)	12
57	Capitol CL 14683	Young Love/You're The Reason I'm In Love	12
57	Capitol CL 14708	First Date, First Kiss/Speak To Me	10
57	Capitol CL 14742	Dear Love/Lovesick Blues	8
57	Capitol CL 14788	Love Conquered (Love Came, Love Saw)/A Mighty Lovable Man	15
57	Capitol CL 14814	Uh-Huh-Mm/Why Can't They Remember?	15
58	Capitol CL 14848	Kathaleen/Walk To The Dance	8
58	Capitol CL 14879	Are You Mine/Let's Play Love	6
58	Capitol CL 14915	You Got That Touch/I Can See It In Your Eyes	6
58	Capitol CL 14952	I Can't Stay Away From You/Let Me Be The One To Love You	5
59	Capitol CL 14991	Yo-Yo/Dream Big	10
59	Capitol CL 15022	Talk Of The School/The Table	5
59	Capitol CL 15046	Pure Love/This Love Of Mine	4
59	Capitol CL 15079	Red Mud/Who's Next In Line	4
60	London HL 9132	Jenny Lou/Passin' Through	8
65	Capitol CL 15377	You're The Only World I Know/Tying The Pieces Together	4
67	Capitol CL 15494	Take Good Care Of Her/On The Fingers Of One Hand	4
69	Capitol CL 15580	Only The Lonely (Know The Way I Feel)/The Journey	4
57	Capitol EAP1 827	YOUNG LOVE (EP)	20
64	Capitol EAP1 20654	YOU'RE THE ONLY WORLD I KNOW (EP)	12
57	Capitol T 779	SOUTHERN GENTLEMAN (LP)	30
57	Capitol T 867	SONNY (LP)	30
58	Capitol T 988	HONEY (LP)	25
63	London HA-D 8049	YOUNG LOVE (LP)	50

Stu(art) JAMES

STU(ART) JAMES (& MOJOS)
65	Decca F 12231	Wait A Minute/Wonder If She Knows (as Stu James & Mojos)	15
74	Bradleys BRAD 7406	I Only Wish I Had The Time/Back To Basingstoke (Part 1)	4
76	Bradleys BRAD 7614	I'm In The Mood/Firefly (as Stuart James)	4

(see also Mojos)

SULLIVAN JAMES BAND
| 66 | Parlophone R 5465 | Goodbye Mr. Heartache/We're Gonna Make It | 5 |

TOMMY JAMES & SHONDELLS
66	Roulette RK 7000	Hanky Panky/SHONDELLS: Thunderbolt	8
66	Pye Intl. 7N 25398	It's Only Love/Ya! Ya!	5
67	Major Minor MM 511	I Think We're Alone Now/Gone Gone Gone	5
67	Major Minor MM 548	Out Of The Blue/Love's Closing In On Me	4
68	Major Minor MM 558	Wish It Were You/Get Out Now	6
68	Major Minor MM 567	Mony Mony/One, Two, Three And I Fell	4
68	Roulette RO 500	Do Something To Me/Somebody Cares	4
68	Roulette RO 502	Crimson And Clover/Some Kind Of Love	4
69	Roulette RO 506	Sweet Cherry Wine/Breakaway	4
69	Roulette RO 507	Crystal Blue Persuasion/I'm Alive	4
69	Roulette RO 511	Ball Of Fire/Makin' Good Time	4
70	Roulette RO 513	She/Loved One	4
70	Roulette RO 516	Come To Me/Talkin' And Signifyin'	4
70	Roulette RO 518	Ball And Chain/Candy Makers	4
68	Major Minor MMLP/SMLP 27	SOMETHING SPECIAL (LP)	14
68	Roulette RRLP/SRLP 1	MONY MONY (LP)	12
68	Roulette RRLP/SRLP 2	CRIMSON AND CLOVER (LP)	12
69	Roulette RRLP/SRLP 3	CELLOPHANE SYMPHONY (LP)	12

TONY JAMES
| 68 | Jolly JY 002 | Treat Me Right/Me Donkey's Dead | 4 |

JAMES BOYS
| 68 | Direction 58-3721 | The Mule (Instrumental)/The Horse (Vocal) | 7 |

JAMES BROTHERS
| 68 | Page One POF 077 | I Forgot To Give You Love/The Truth About It | 6 |
| 68 | Page One POF 088 | Does It Have To Be Me/You Don't Really Love Me | 6 |

(see also Wheels)

JAMES GANG
70	Stateside SS 2158	Funk No. 48/Collage	5
70	Stateside SS 2173	Stop/Take A Look Around (withdrawn)	8
70	Stateside SSL 10295	YER' ALBUM (LP)	12
70	Probe SPB 6253	RIDES AGAIN (LP)	10
71	Probe SPB 1038	THIRDS (LP)	10
71	Probe SPB 1045	LIVE IN CONCERT (LP)	10
72	Probe SPB 1056	STRAIGHT SHOOTER (LP)	10
73	Probe SPB 1065	PASSIN' THRU (LP)	10

(see also Joe Walsh)

BOBBY JAMESON
| 64 | London HL 9921 | I Wanna Love You/I'm Lonely | 8 |

BOBBY JAMESON
| 64 | Decca F 12032 | All I Want Is My Baby/Each And Every Day | 18 |
| 65 | Brit WI 1001 | Rum-Pum/I Want To Know Why | 10 |

STEPHEN JAMESON
| 70 | Pye 7N 45189 | Margie Make It March/Happiness Road | 4 |
| 73 | Dawn DNLS 3044 | STEPHEN JAMESON (LP) | 15 |

JAMESON RAID
| 79 | GBH GRC 1 | Seven Days Of Splendour/It's A Crime/Catcher In The Rye (p/s, with lyric sheet) | 12 |
| 80 | Blackbird BRAID 001 | The Hypnotist/The Raid/Getting Hotter/Straight From The Butchers (p/s) | 10 |

JAMIES
58	Fontana H 153	Summertime Summertime/Searching For You	20
58	Fontana H 153	Summertime Summertime/Searching For You (78)	12
62	Columbia DB 4885	Summertime Summertime/Searching For You (reissue)	12

JAMIE'S AGENT ORANGE
90	Emma EC 002	Losing My Way/Tumbling Down (no p/s)	8
91	Emma JWD 001	The Hamster Song ('Lovely Gary' Mix)/Don't Cry Chief (At Least You're Not Stuart) (fold-out p/s with free compass)	6
91	Emma JWD 002	Ooh Lovely Gary (The Mick & Dave Rave)/Star Trek Song (p/s)	4

JAMIE WEDNESDAY
85	Pink 7 PINKY 6	Vote For Love/White Horses (no p/s)	7
85	Pink PINKY 6	Vote For Love/The Wall/White Horses/Buttons And Bows (12", p/s)	10
86	Pink 7 PINKY 10	We Three Kings Of Orient Aren't/Last Night I Had The Strangest Dream (no p/s)	7
86	Pink PINKY 10	We Three Kings Of Orient Aren't/Last Night I Had The Strangest Dream/I Think I'll Throw A Party For Myself (12", p/s)	10

(see also Carter The Unstoppable Sex Machine)

JOE JAMMER
| 73 | Regal Zono. SRZA 8514 | BAD NEWS (LP) | 20 |

J.A.M.s
(see under Justified Ancients Of Mu Mu)

JAM TODAY
| 80s | Stroppy Cow SC-JT 1 | STEREOTYPING (EP) | 4 |

Rare Record Price Guide

JAN & ARNIE

58	London HL 8653	Jennie Lee/Gotta Getta Date	35
58	London HL 8653	Jennie Lee/Gotta Getta Date (78)	30

(see also Jan & Dean)

JAN & DEAN

59	London HLN 8936	Baby Talk/Jeanette, Get Your Hair Done	18
59	London HLN 8936	Baby Talk/Jeanette, Get Your Hair Done (78)	45
59	London HLU 8990	There's A Girl/My Heart Sings	15
59	London HLU 8990	There's A Girl/My Heart Sings (78)	50
60	London HLU 9063	Clementine/You're On My Mind	12
61	London HLH 9395	Heart And Soul/Midsummer Night's Dream	12
62	Liberty LIB 55397	A Sunday Kind Of Love/Poor Little Puppet	6
63	Liberty LIB 55531	Linda/When I Learn How To Cry	5
63	Liberty LIB 55580	Surf City/She's My Summer Girl	4
63	Liberty LIB 55613	Honolulu Lulu/Someday You'll Go Walkin' By	4
64	Liberty LIB 55641	Drag City/Schlock Rod Pt 1	5
64	Liberty LIB 55672	Dead Man's Curve/The New Girl In School	5
64	Liberty LIB 55704	The Little Old Lady From Pasadena/My Mighty GTO	5
64	Liberty LIB 55724	Ride The Wild Surf/The Anaheim, Azusa And Cucamonga Sewing Circle, Book Review And Timing Association	6
65	Liberty LIB 55727	Sidewalk Surfin'/When It's Over	6
65	Liberty LIB 55766	(Here They Come) From All Over The World/Freeway Flyer	8
65	Liberty LIB 55792	You Really Know How To Hurt A Guy/It's As Easy As 1, 2, 3	8
65	Liberty LIB 55833	I Found A Girl/It's A Shame To Say Goodbye	6
66	Liberty LIB 10225	Norwegian Wood/A Beginning From An End	8
66	Liberty LIB 55860	Batman/Bucket 'T'	8
66	Liberty LIB 10244	Popsicle/The Joker Is Wild	8
66	Liberty LIB 55923	The New Girl In School/School Day (Ring Ring Goes The Bell)	7
66	Liberty LIB 10252	Tennessee/Horace The Swinging School Bus Driver	12
67	CBS 202630	Yellow Balloon/A Taste Of Rain	10
65	Liberty LEP 2213	SURF 'N' DRAG HITS (EP)	15
66	Liberty LEP 2258	THE TITANIC TWOSOME (EP)	15
63	Liberty LBY 1163	SURF CITY AND OTHER SWINGING CITIES (LP)	18
64	Liberty LBY 1220	DEAD MAN'S CURVE/NEW GIRL IN SCHOOL (LP)	15
64	Liberty LBY 1229	RIDE THE WILD SURF (LP)	18
65	Liberty LBY 1279	GOLDEN HITS (LP)	20
65	Liberty LBY 1304	FOLK 'N' ROLL (LP)	15
66	Liberty LBY 1309	MEET BATMAN (LP)	20
66	Liberty LBY 1339	FILET OF SOUL (A LIVE ONE) (LP)	15
67	Liberty LBL/LBS 83016	GOLDEN HITS (LP)	12

(see also Fantastic Baggys)

JAN & KELLY

62	Philips 326 567 BF	Oo He Didn't	4
62	Philips BF 1253	I Could Have Died/Make Me A Doormat	4
63	Philips BF 1265	Ooh! I Can't/Write Me A Letter	4
64	Philips BF 1323	And Then He Kicked Me/My Country	4
64	Philips BF 1377	There Was A Girl/There Was A Boy/And Then There Was Nothing	4
63	Philips BE 12536	TIME FOR A LAUGH (EP)	7

JAN & KJELD

59	Pye Intl. 7N 25013	Buona Sera/Tiger Rag	4
60	Ember EMB S 101	Banjo Boy/Don't Raise A Storm (some in p/s)	8/4
60	Ember EMB 3312	THE KIDS FROM COPENHAGEN (LP, label states "The Boys From ...")	10

BRUCE JANAWAY

70s	Deep Range SRT/CUS/216	PURITANICAL ODES (LP, with insert)	45

JAN DUKES DE GREY

70	Decca Nova SDN 8	SORCERERS (LP)	30
71	Transatlantic TRA 234	MICE AND RATS IN THE LOFT (LP)	45

JANE

83	Cherry Red CHERRY 65	It's A Fine Day/Of All Leaves Here Falling (p/s)	5

(see also Jane & Barton)

JANE & BARTON

83	Cherry Red MRED 53	JANE AND BARTON (mini-LP)	10

JANE FROM OCCUPIED EUROPE

80s	Seven Per Cent JANE 001	Ocean Run Dry/Annabel Lee/Kingdom By The Sea	5

JANE'S ADDICTION

88	WEA W 7520	Mountain Song/Jane Says (p/s)	5
88	WEA W 7520T	Mountain Song/Jane Says/Had A Dad (live) (12", p/s)	8
91	WEA W 0031TP	Classic Girl/No One's Leaving (live)/Ain't No Right (live) (12", picture disc, die-cut sleeve)	7

PETER JANES

68	CBS 3299	Do You Believe/For The Sake Of Time	8

JANET & JOHNS

85	Vindaloo UGH 3	I Was A Young Man/Let Bygones Be Bygone (gatefold p/s)	4

JANGLETTIES

81	Eskimo Vinyl ESK 4	Happy All The Time/Backseat (folded, stapled p/s)	4

JANIE

61	Capitol CL 15180	You Better Not Do That/Only Girls Can Tell	7

(see also Jeanne Black)

Johnny JANIS

MINT VALUE £

JOHNNY JANIS

58	London HLU 8650	The Better To Love You/Can This Be Love	10
60	Philips PB 1090	Gina/If The Good Lord's Willin'	4
66	London HA-U 8270	ONCE IN A BLUE MOON (LP)	10

HORST JANKOWSKI

65	Mercury MF 861	Walk In The Black Forest/Nola	4
65	Mercury MF 884	Heidi/Simpel Gimpel	4
65	Mercury MF 892	Play A Simple Melody/Cruising Down The Reine	4
66	Mercury MF 966	The Spy With A Cold Nose/Black Forest Holiday	4
68	Mercury MF 1019	The Glory Of Love/Lazy	4
68	Mercury MF 1029	Un Homme Et Une Femme/Moon River	4
68	Mercury MF 1041	Zabadak/Touch Of Heidelberg	4

BERT JANSCH

67	Big T BIG 102	Life Depends On Love/Little Sweet Sunshine	8
66	Transatlantic EP 145	BERT JANSCH (EP)	10
65	Transatlantic TRA 125	BERT JANSCH (LP)	15
65	Transatlantic TRA 132	IT DON'T BOTHER ME (LP)	15
66	Transatlantic TRA 143	JACK ORION (LP)	20
67	Transatlantic TRA 157	NICOLA (LP)	20
68	Transatlantic TRA 179	BIRTHDAY BLUES (LP)	12
69	Vanguard VSD 79292	STEPPING STONES (LP)	10
69	Transatlantic TRASAM 10	THE BERT JANSCH SAMPLER (LP)	12
71	Transatlantic TRA 235	ROSEMARY LANE (LP)	10
75	Charisma CAS 1107	SANTA BARBARA HONEYMOON (LP)	10

BERT JANSCH & JOHN RENBOURN

66	Transatlantic TRA 144	BERT AND JOHN (LP)	15

(see also Pentangle, John Renbourn)

JAPAN

78	Ariola Hansa AHA 510	Don't Rain On My Parade/Stateline (solid or press-out centre, no p/s)	15
78	Ariola Hansa AHA 525	The Unconventional/Adolescent Sex (some with p/s)	20/6
78	Ariola Hansa AHA 529	Sometimes I Feel So Low/Love Is Infectious (p/s, initially on blue vinyl)	12/8
79	Ariola Hansa AHA 540	Life In Tokyo (Short Version)/Life In Tokyo Pt 2 (p/s, red vinyl)	6
79	Ariola Hansa AHAD 540	Life In Tokyo (Long Version)/Life In Tokyo (Short Version) (12", p/s, red vinyl)	10
80	Ariola Hansa AHA 559	I Second That Emotion/Quiet Life (dull red vinyl, card or paper p/s)	8/6
80	Ariola Hansa AHA 559	I Second That Emotion/Quiet Life (p/s, black vinyl)	4
80	Virgin VS 379	Gentlemen Take Polaroids/The Experience of Swimming (autographed p/s)	20
80	Virgin VS 379	Gentlemen Take Polaroids/The Experience of Swimming//The Width Of A Room/Burning Bridges (double pack, gatefold p/s)	6
82	Virgin VSY 472	Ghosts/The Art Of Parties (Version) (picture disc, stickered PVC cover)	7
82	Virgin VS 502	Cantonese Boy/Burning Bridges//Gentlemen Take Polaroids/ The Experience Of Swimming (double pack, gatefold p/s)	5
80	Ariola Hansa AHAL 8011	QUIET LIFE (LP, gatefold sleeve)	10
80	Virgin V 2180	GENTLEMEN TAKE POLAROIDS (LP, with misprinted sleeve with sticker, "Some Kind Of Fool" listed instead of "Burning Bridges")	10
81	Ariola Hansa ZCHAN 001	ASSEMBLAGE (cassette with unreleased live & remixed material)	10

(see also David Sylvian, Mick Khan, Dali's Car)

JOHNNY JAPES & HiS JESTICLES

87	VIZ 1	Bags Of Fun With Buster/Scrotal Scratch Mix (p/s)	4

(see also XTC, John Otway)

JARMELS

61	Top Rank JAR 560	She Loves To Dance/Little Lonely One	12
61	Top Rank JAR 580	A Little Bit Of Soap/The Way You Look Tonight	20

COOK E. JARR

69	RCA RCA 1820	Pledging My Love/If I Were A Carpenter	5

JEAN-MICHEL JARRE

77	Polydor 2001 721	Oxygene 4/Oygene 6 (p/s)	4
78	Polydor POSP 20	Equinoxe 5/Equinoxe 1 (p/s, with etched autographed on run-off)	8
79	Polydor 2001 896	Equinoxe 4 (Remix)/Equinoxe 3 (p/s)	5
80	Polydor 2001 968	JARRE AT THE CONCORDE: Equinoxe 7 (live)/Equinoxe 8 (live) (p/s)	12
81	Polydor POSP 292	Magnetic Fields 2 (Remix)/Magnetic Fields 1 (Excerpt) (p/s)	5
81	Polydor POSP 363	Magnetic Fields 4 (Remix)/Magnetic Fields 1 (Excerpt) (p/s)	10
82	Polydor POSP 430	Orient Express/Fishing Junks At Sunset (p/s)	10
84	Polydor POSP 718	Zoolook/Wooloomooloo (p/s)	5
84	Polydor POSPX 718	Zoolook (Remix)/Wooloomooloo/Zoolook (Ext.)/Zoolook (Effects) (12", p/s)	20
85	Polydor POSP 740	Zoolookologie (Remix)/Ethnicolor 2 (p/s)	5
85	Polydor POSPG 740	Zoolookologie (Remix)/Ethnicolor 4/Oxygene 4/Oxygene 4 (double pack)	15
85	Polydor POSPX 740	Zoolookologie (Extended Remix)/(Remix)/Ethnicolor 2 (12", p/s)	20
86	Polydor POSPX 788	Rendezvous 4 (Special Remix)/Rendezvous 4/Moon Machine (12", 'face' or 'city skyline' p/s)	20
88	Polydor PZCD 25	Revolutions (Extended)/Revolutions (LP Mix)/Industrial Revolution 2 (CD, jewel case or card sleeve)	15
88	Polydor PZCD 32	London Kid (Full Version)/Industrial Revolution 3/Revolutions (Remix) (CD in pouch)	10
89	Polydor PZCD 55	Oxygene 4 (Remix)/Industrial Revolution Overture/Oxygene 4 (live)/ September (CD in pouch)	10
90	Polydor PZCD 84	Calypso (CD)	12
81	Polydor Super POLS 1033	MAGNETIC FIELDS (LP, original pressing with inner sleeve)	10
83	Polydor PROLP 3	THE ESSENTIAL (LP, original pressing, b&w labels)	10
87	Polydor 833 737-2	THE JEAN MICHEL JARRE 10TH ANNIVERSARY CD BOX SET (5,000 only)	50
88	Polydor C88 1-3	OXYGENE (LP, HMV-only box set with booklet, 3,300 only)	16
88	Polydor C88-1-3	OXYGENE (CD, HMV-only box set with booklet, 5,000 only)	20

AL JARREAU
87	WEA U 8407	'Moonlighting' Theme/'Moonlighting' Theme (Version) (p/s)	4

MARIAN JARVIS
75	Chelsea 2005 038	A Penny For Your Thoughts/A Good Man To Wake Up To	6

JASMINE MINKS
84	Creation CRE 004	Think!/Work For Nothing (foldaround sleeve in poly bag)	15
84	Creation CRE 008	Where The Traffic Goes/Mr Magic (foldaround sleeve in poly bag)	12
85	Creation CRE 018	What's Happening/Black And Blue (foldaround sleeve in poly bag)	8
87	Esurient Comms. PACE 1	PURE (live EP)	5
84	Creation CRELP 003	1, 2, 3, 4, 5, 6, 7, ALL GOOD PREACHERS GO TO HEAVEN (mini-LP, red/black or yellow/black sleeve)	10

JASON CREST
68	Philips BF 1633	Turquoise Tandem Cycle/Good Life	25
68	Philips BF 1650	Juliano The Bull/Two By The Sea	15
68	Philips BF 1687	(Here We Go Round) The Lemon Tree/Patricia's Dream	20
69	Philips BF 1752	Waterloo Road/Education	15
69	Philips BF 1809	Black Mass/Place In The Sun	70
(see also Holy Mackerel)			

JASON'S GENERATIONS
66	Polydor BM 56042	It's Up To You/Insurance Co.'s Are Very Unfair	40

JASPER
69	Spark SRLP 103	LIBERATION (LP)	250

JASPER
70s	SRT	FRONT AND BACK (LP)	100

JAWBONE
70	Carnaby CNS 4007	How's Ya Pa/Mister Custer	10
71	Carnaby CNS 4020	Way Way Down/Bulldog Goes West	10
72	B&C CB 190	Gotta Go/Automobile Blues	6
70	Carnaby CNLS 6004	JAWBONE (LP)	80

BOB JAXON (& HI-TONES)
55	London HL 8156	Ali Baba/Why Does A Woman Cry (as Bob Jaxon & Hi-Tones)	25
55	London HL 8156	Ali Baba/Why Does A Woman Cry (as Bob Jaxon & Hi-Tones) (78)	8
57	RCA RCA 1019	Beach Party/(Gotta Have Something In The) Bank Frank	75
57	RCA RCA 1019	Beach Party/(Gotta Have Something In The) Bank Frank (78)	20

FRANKIE JAXON
50s	Collector JE 110	MALE BLUES VOL. 6 (EP)	12

FRANKIE 'HALF PINT' JAXON & HOTSHOTS
34	Brunswick 01719	Mama Don't Allow/Fifteen Cents (78)	25

JAY
64	Coral Q 72471	I Rise, I Fall/How Sweet It Is	15
(see also Jay & Americans)			

ABNER JAY
63	London HLN 9791	Cleo/Thresher	5

DAVID JAY
(see under David J.)			

ERIC JAY
59	London HL 9004	The Little Drummer Boy/Blue Champagne Cha Cha	4

LAURIE JAY COMBO
62	Ember JBS 710	Shades Of Red/Nevada Sunsets	4
63	HMV POP 1234	Teenage Idol/Think Of Me	5
64	HMV POP 1300	Love In My Heart/'Til You're Mine	4
64	HMV POP 1335	Maybe/Be Good To Me	4
65	Decca F 12083	A Song Called Soul/Just A Little Bit	20
(see also Nero & Gladiators)			

LONNIE JAY & JAYNES
63	Stateside SS 197	Around And Around We Go/Somewhere	4

PETER JAY (& BLUE MEN)
60	Triumph RGM 1000	Just Too Late/Friendship (as Peter Jay & Blue Men)	15
60	Pye 7N 15290	Paradise Garden/Who's The Girl?	15
(see also Blue Men)			

PETER JAY & JAYWALKERS
62	Decca F 11531	Can Can '62/Redskins	5
63	Decca F 11593	Totem Pole/Jaywalker	6
63	Decca F 11659	Poet And Peasant/Oo La La	6
63	Decca F 11757	Kansas City/The Parade Of Tin Soldiers	7
64	Decca F 11840	You Girl/If You Love Me	7
64	Piccadilly 7N 35199	Where Did Our Love Go/Caroline	8
64	Piccadilly 7N 35212	Tonight You're Gonna Fall In Love/Red Cabbage	6
65	Piccadilly 7N 35220	Parchman Farm/What's Easy For Two Is So Hard For One	12
65	Piccadilly 7N 35259	Before The Beginning/Solitaire	10
(see also Terry Reid)			

JAY & AMERICANS
62	HMV POP 1009	She Cried/Dawning	10
63	United Artists UP 1002	This Is It/It's My Turn To Cry	6
63	United Artists UP 1018	What's The Use/Strangers Tomorrow	6
64	United Artists UP 1039	Come Dance With Me/Look Into My Eyes Maria	6

JAY & AMERICANS

64	United Artists UP 1069	Come A Little Bit Closer/Goodbye Boys Goodbye	6
65	United Artists UP 1075	Let's Lock The Door (And Throw Away The Key)/I'll Remember You	7
65	United Artists UP 1088	Think Of The Good Times/If You Were Mine Girl	5
65	United Artists UP 1094	Cara Mia/When It's All Over	6
65	United Artists UP 1108	Some Enchanted Evening/Girl	7
66	United Artists UP 1119	Sunday And Me/Through This Doorway	7
66	United Artists UP 1129	Why Can't You Bring Me Home/Baby Stop Your Crying	5
66	United Artists UP 1132	Crying/I Don't Need A Friend	6
66	United Artists UP 1142	Livin' Above Your Head/She's The Girl (That's Messing Up My Mind)	15
66	United Artists UP 1162	(He's) Raining In My Sunshine/Reason For Living	5
67	United Artists UP 1178	You Ain't As Hip As All That Baby/Nature Boy	6
67	United Artists UP 1191	(We'll Meet In The) Yellow Forest/Got Hung Up Along The Way	25
68	United Artists UP 2211	French Provincial/Shanghai Noodle Factory	5
69	United Artists UP 2268	This Magic Moment/Since I Don't Have You	5
69	United Artists UP 35008	When You Dance/So Much In Love	4
69	United Artists UP 35026	Hushabye/No I Don't Know Her	4
69	United Artists UP 35074	Walkin' In The Rain/For The Love Of A Lady	4
65	United Artists UEP 1003	COME A LITTLE BIT CLOSER (EP)	15
66	United Artists UEP 1017	LIVING WITH JAY AND THE AMERICANS (EP)	15
66	United Artists ULP 1117	JAY AND THE AMERICANS (LP)	16

(see also Jay)

JAY (John Holt) & JOYA (Landis)
68	Trojan TR 633	I'll Be Lonely/SUPERSONICS: Second Fiddle	7

(see also John Holt, Joya Landis)

JAY & TECHNIQUES
67	Philips PB 1597	Apples, Peaches, Pumpkin Pie/Stronger Than Dirt	8
67	Philips PB 1618	Keep The Ball Rollin'/Here We Go Again	6
68	Philips PB 1644	Strawberry Shortcake/Still (In Love With You)	6
68	Mercury MF 1034	Baby Make Your Own Sweet Music/Help Yourself To All My Lovin'	8
75	Polydor 2066 473	I Feel Love Comin' On/This World Of Mine	6
67	Philips (S)BL 7834	APPLES, PEACHES, PUMPKIN PIE (LP)	12

JAYBIRDS
64	Embassy WB 635	Juliet/Here I Go Again	8
64	Embassy WB 663	All Day And All Of The Night/Google Eye	12

(see also Ten Years After)

JAYBIRDS
66	Sue WI 4013	Somebody Help Me/The Right Kind	15

JAY BOYS
69	Trojan TR 665	Splendour Splash/TREVOR SHIELD: Please	5

JERRY JAYE
67	London HLU 10128	My Girl Josephine/Five Miles From Home	15

JAYE SISTERS
59	London HLT 9011	Sure Fire Love/G-3	25

JAYHAWKS
56	Parlophone R 4228	Stranded In The Jungle/My Only Darling	150
56	Parlophone R 4228	Stranded In The Jungle/My Only Darling (78)	60

JAYNETTS
63	Stateside SS 227	Sally Go Round The Roses/Sally Go Round The Roses (Instrumental)	5

JAYS
63	Parlophone R 4764	Shock A Boom/Across The Sea	6

JAYWALKERS
76	Cream CRM 5003	Can't Live Without You/Heartbroken Memories	6

JAZZATEERS
83	Rough Trade RT 138	Sixteen Reasons/Show Me The Door (p/s)	5
85	Stampede STAMP 1	Pressing On/Spiral (12", p/s)	7
84	Rough Trade ROUGH 46	JAZZATEERS (LP, with insert)	12

(see also Hipsway)

JAZZ BUTCHER
83	Glass GLASS 027	Southern Mark Smith/Jazz Butcher Meets Count Dracula (p/s)	5
85	Glass GLASS 12041	Real Men/The Jazz Butcher V The Prime Minister/Southern Mark Smith (Original) (12", p/s)	7
80s	Glass	Christmas freebie (given away at gigs)	10

JAZZ COURIERS
50s	Tempo EXA 75	JAZZ COURIERS (EP)	8
50s	Tempo EXA 87	JAZZ COURIERS (EP)	8
58	Tempo TAP 22	IN CONCERT (LP)	25
59	Tempo TAP 26	THE LAST WORD (LP)	25
60	London Jazz LTZ-L 15188	THE COURIERS OF JAZZ! (LP)	25
60s	M. For Pleasure MFP 1072	IN CONCERT (LP)	10

(see also Tubby Hayes, Ronnie Scott)

JAZZ CRUSADERS
66	Fontana 688 149 ZL	THE THING (LP)	12

(see also Crusaders)

JAZZ HIP TRIO
69	Major Minor MMLP 8	JAZZ IN RELIEF (LP)	10

JAZZ MAKERS
6-	Ember FA 2023	SWINGIN' SOUNDS (LP)	10

JAZZ MODES
60	London Jazz LTZ-K 15191	THE MOST HAPPY FELLA (LP)	10
61	London Jazz LTZ-K 15203	THE JAZZ MODES (LP, also stereo SAH-K 6117)	10

JAZZ ROCK EXPERIENCE
70	Deram Nova SDN 19	JAZZ ROCK EXPERIENCE (LP)	20

J.B.
66	Polydor 56095	Wow Wow Wow/There She Goes	5

J.B.'s
71	Mojo 2001 115	These Are The JBs Pts 1 & 2	7
71	Mojo 2027 002	The Grunt Pts 1 & 2	8
74	Mojo 2093 007	Gimme Some More/The Rabbit Got The Gun	7
74	Mojo 2093 016	Hot Pants Road/Pass The Peas	7
74	Mojo 2093 021	Givin' Up Food For Funk Pts 1 & 2	7
72	Mojo 2918 004	PASS THE PEAS (LP)	40
72	Polydor 2391 034	FOOD FOR THOUGHT (LP)	40
74	Polydor 2391 087	DOING IT TO DEATH (LP)	45
75	Polydor 2391 194	HUSTLE WITH SPEED (LP)	35
76	Polydor 2391 204	GIVIN' UP FOOD FOR FUNK — THE BEST OF THE JB's (LP)	40

(see also Fred Wesley & JB's, James Brown)

J. BOYS & TREVOR SHIELD
69	Trojan TR 665	Splender Splash/TREVOR SHIELD & BELTONES: Please	4

J.C.'s MAIN MEN
81	Fresh FRESH 28	Casual Trousers/Ear Bending (p/s)	4

BOBBI JEAN
65	Mercury MF 921	Dry Your Tears/Pity The Man	4

CATHY JEAN & ROOMATES
61	Parlophone R 4764	Please Love Me Forever/Canadian Sunset	20

EARL-JEAN
64	Colpix PX 729	I'm Into Somethin' Good/We Love And Learn	18
64	Colpix PX 748	Randy/They're Jealous Of Me	12

LANA JEAN
63	Pye Intl. 7N 25214	It Hurts To Be Sixteen/Bad Boy	12

JEAN & STATESIDES
64	Columbia DB 7287	Putty In Your Hands/One Fine Day	8
64	Columbia DB 7439	You Won't Forget Me/Cold, Cold Winter	7
65	Columbia DB 7651	Mama Didn't Lie/Just Let Me Cry	8

(see also Jeannie [& Big Guys], Cindy Cole)

JEAN-ETTES
59	Pye 7N 15185	May You Always/I Saw A Light	4

JEAN JACQUES
69	Pye Intl. 7N 25489	Maman/Les Beaux Dimanches	5

JEANNE & JANIE
60	Capitol CL 15146	Journey Of Love/JEANNE BLACK: Lisa	4
60	Capitol CL 15165	Sleep Walkin'/JEANNE BLACK: You'll Find Out	4

(see also Jeanne Black)

JEANNIE (& BIG GUYS)
63	Piccadilly 7N 35147	Don't Lie To Me/Boys (as Jeannie & Big Guys)	6
64	Piccadilly 7N 35164	I Want You/Sticks And Stones (as Jeannie & Big Guys)	6
65	Parlophone R 5343	I Love Him/With Any Other Girl	4

(see also Cindy Cole, Jean & Statesides)

JEANNIE & HER REDHEADS
64	Decca F 11829	Animal Duds/ANDREW OLDHAM GROUP: Funky And Fleopatra	20

(see also Andrew Oldham Orchestra)

AUDREY JEANS
56	Decca F 10768	Ticky Ticky Tick (I'm Gonna Tell On ...)/Will You, Willyum	8
56	Decca F 10788	It's Better In The Dark/The Bus Stop Song	4
58	Decca F 11035	Send A Letter To Jeanette — Yet!/Bad Pianna Rag	4
61	HMV POP 876	How Lovely To Be A Woman/What Did I See In Him	4

JEEPS
66	Strike JH 308	He Saw Eesaw/The Music Goes Round	5
66	Strike JH 315	Ain't It A Great Big Laugh/I Put On My Shoes	5

BLIND LEMON JEFFERSON
50	Tempo R 38	Weary Dog Blues/Change My Luck Blues (78)	8
50	Tempo R 39	Lock Step Blues/Hangman's Blues (78)	8
51	Tempo R 46	Shuckin' Sugar Blues/Rabbit Foot Blues (78)	8
52	Tempo R 54	Gone Dead On You Blues/One Dime Blues (78)	8
53	Jazz Collector L 91	Shuckin' Sugar Blues/Rabbit Foot Blues (78)	5
53	Jazz Collector L 103	Jack O'Diamons Blues/Clock House Blues (78)	5
54	Jazz Collector L 126	Gone Dead On You Blues/One Dime Blues (78)	5
50s	Poydras 99	BLIND LEMON JEFFERSON (10" EP)	20
53	London Jazz AL 3508	FOLK BLUES OF BLIND LEMON JEFFERSON (10" LP)	30
55	London Jazz AL 3546	PENITENTIARY BLUES (10" LP)	30
57	London Jazz AL 3564	SINGS THE BLUES (10" LP)	30
70s	Roots Matchbox RL 301	BLIND LEMON JEFFERSON VOLUME 1 (LP)	12
70s	Roots Matchbox RL 306	BLIND LEMON JEFFERSON VOLUME 2 (LP)	12
70s	Roots Matchbox RL 331	BLIND LEMON JEFFERSON VOLUME 3 (LP)	12
75	Milestone M 47022	BLIND LEMON JEFFERSON (2-LP)	15

Blind Lemon JEFFERSON

BLIND LEMON JEFFERSON/ED BELL
50s Jazz Collector JEL 8   THE MALE BLUES VOLUME 7 (EP) 8

BLIND LEMON JEFFERSON/BUDDY BOY HAWKINS
50s Jazz Collector JEL   THE MALE BLUES VOLUME 5 (EP) 8

BLIND LEMON JEFFERSON/LEADBELLY
50s Jazz Collector JEL 24   THE MALE BLUES VOLUME 8 (EP) 10

BLIND LEMON JEFFERSON & RAMBLING THOMAS
50s Heritage HLP 1007   BLIND LEMON JEFFERSON AND RAMBLING THOMAS (LP) 50

EDDIE JEFFERSON
67   Stateside SS 591   Some Other Time/When You Look In The Mirror 5

GEORGE PAUL JEFFERSON
68   Fontana TF 923   Looking For My Mind/Out Of Place 12

JEFFERSON AIRPLANE
67   RCA Victor RCA 1594   Somebody To Love/She Has Funny Cars 6
67   RCA Victor RCA 1631   White Rabbit/Plastic Fantastic Lover 8
67   RCA Victor RCA 1647   Ballad Of You And Me and Pooneil/Two Heads 7
68   RCA Victor RCA 1711   Greasy Heart/Share A Little Joke (With The World) 8
68   RCA Victor RCA 1736   If You Feel Like China Breaking/Triad 7
70   RCA RCA 1933   Volunteers/We Can Be Together 5
70   RCA RCA 1964   Somebody To Love/White Rabbit 4
70   RCA RCA 1989   Mexico/Have You Seen The Saucers? 5
71   Grunt 65-0500   Pretty As You Feel/Wild Turkey 6
72   Grunt 65-0506   Long John Silver/Milk Train 5
67   RCA Victor RD/SF 7889   SURREALISTIC PILLOW (LP, black label, later orange label) 18/10
67   RCA Victor RD/SF 7926   AFTER BATHING AT BAXTERS (LP, black label, later orange label) 18/10
68   RCA Victor RD/SF 7976   CROWN OF CREATION (LP, black label, later orange label) 18/10
69   RCA RD/SF 8019   BLESS ITS POINTED LITTLE HEAD (LP) 15
69   RCA SF 8076   VOLUNTEERS (LP, gatefold sleeve) 12
71   RCA SF 8164   THE WORST OF JEFFERSON AIRPLANE (LP, matt sleeve) 10
71   Grunt FTR 1001   BARK (LP, bag cover, lyric sheet, brown inner sleeve) 12
71   RCA SF 8195   JEFFERSON AIRPLANE TAKES OFF (LP) 10
72   Grunt FTR 1007   LONG JOHN SILVER (LP, open-out box cover, inner lyric sleeve) 12
73   Grunt FTR 0147   30 SECONDS OVER WINTERLAND (LP with inner sleeve) 10
(see also Great Society, Jefferson Starship, Paul Kantner, Grace Slick, Papa John Creach, Hot Tuna)

JEFFERSON STARSHIP
75   Grunt FB 10367   Miracles/Al Garimasu 4
78   Grunt FL 13247   GOLD (LP, gatefold sleeve; with free 7" "Light The Sky On Fire"/
                                   "Hyperdrive" [FB 1426]) 10

JOE JEFFREY GROUP
69   Pye Intl. 7N 25494   My Pledge Of Love/Margie 4

FRAN JEFFRIES
67   Monument MON 1006   My Lonely Corner/Life Goes On 4

JELLY BEANS
64   Pye Intl. 7N 25252   I Wanna Love Him So Bad/So Long 10
64   Red Bird RB 10011   Baby Be Mine/Kind Of Boy You Can't Forget 10
75   Right On R 102   You Don't Mean Me No Good/I'm Hip To You 10

JELLYBREAD
69   Blue Horizon 57-3162   Chairman Mao's Boogaloo/No One Else 6
70   Blue Horizon 57-3169   Comment/Funky Wasp 6
70   Blue Horizon 57-3174   Rockin' Pneumonia And The Boogie-Woogie Flu/
                                   Readin' The Meters 6
70   Blue Horizon 57-3180   Old Man Hank/Faded Grace 6
71   Blue Horizon 2096 001   Creepin' And Crawlin'/The Loser/The Clergyman's Daughter 6
71   Blue Horizon 2096 006   Down Along The Cove/Sister Lucy 7
60s Liphook 1   JELLYBREAD (mini-LP) ....100+
69   Blue Horizon 7-63853   FIRST SLICE (LP) 30
70   Blue Horizon 2431 002   65 PARKWAY (LP) 30
72   Blue Horizon 2931 004   BACK TO THE BEGINNING AGAIN (LP) 70

JELLYROLL
71   MCA MUPS 420   JELLYROLL (LP) 10

JOHNNY JENENE
59   Pye 7N 15210   No Matter Where/Shame, Shame, Johnny, Shame 4

DIANE JENKINS
76   Crystal CR 7025   Two A Way Zone/Anniversary 4

GORDON JENKINS ORCHESTRA
60   London HLR 9089   The Clock Song/Romantica 4
(see also Ella Fitzgerald)

JOHNNY JENKINS
69   Atco 226 009   The Voodoo In You/Backside Blues 4
70   Atco 2400 033   TON TON MACOUTE (LP) 12
72   Atlantic K 40105   TON TON MACOUTE (LP, reissue) 10

JENNIFER
69   London HLU 10278   Let The Sun Shine In/Easy To Be Hard 4
70   London HLU 10312   Cajun Train/Old Folks 4

BILL JENNINGS
55   Parlophone MSP 6146   Stuffy/Solitude (as Bill Jennings-Leo Parker Quintet) 4
55   Parlophone MSP 6156   Soft Winds/What's New? (as Bill Jennings Quartet) 4

WAYLON JENNINGS
68	RCA SF 8003	ONLY THE GREATEST (LP)	10

JENNORS
67	Coxsone CS 7024	Pressure And Slide (actually by Tennors)/SOUL BROTHERS: One Stop	15

(see also Tennors)

DICK JENSEN
73	Epic EPC 1521	I Don't Want To Cry/Tamika	4

KRIS JENSEN
62	Fontana 267241TF	Torture/Let's Sit Down	8
63	Fontana 267267TF	Claudette/Don't Take Her From Me	10
64	Hickory 45-1224	Donna Donna/Big As I Can Dream	8
64	Hickory 45-1243	Lookin' For Love/In Time	6
64	Hickory 45-1256	Come Back To Me/You've Only Got Me To Lose	6
65	Hickory 45-1285	Somebody's Smiling While I'm Crying/Wind-Up Doll	8
65	Hickory 45-1311	What Should I Do/That's A Whole Lotta Love	8

KRIS JENSEN/SUE THOMPSON
65	Hickory LPE 1507	INTRODUCING KRIS JENSEN AND SUE THOMPSON (EP, 2 tracks each)	12

(see also Sue Thompson)

PAUL JENSEN & CARTHYS
78	Albatross	single	6

JENSENS
68	Philips BF 1686	Deep Thinking/Marguerite	10

(see also Tempus Fugit)

BILL JENTIES
70	Smash SMA 2307	Stop Them (actually by Bill Gentles)/MAXINE: I Don't Care	4

JERICHO (JONES)
72	A&M AMS 7037	Mama's Gonna Take You Home/So Come On	15
71	A&M AMLH 68050	JUNKIES, MONKEYS & DONKEYS (LP, as Jericho Jones)	100
72	A&M AMLS 68079	JERICHO (LP, beware of counterfeits with slightly thicker sleeves!)	60

JERIDALE THREE
63	Fontana TF 410	Keep Your Hands In Your Pockets/In A Little Spanish Town	4

JERKS
78	Lightning GIL 549	Cool/Jerkin' (p/s)	5
78	Underground URA 1	Get Your Woofing Dog Off Me/Hold My Hand (p/s, with lyric sheet)	5
80	Laser LAS 25	Come Back Bogart (I Wish You Would)/Are You Strong Enough?/The Strangest Man Of All (p/s)	6

JERMZ
85	One Way EFP 1	Power Cut/Me And My Baby (p/s)	8

JERRY JEROME
55	MGM SP 1118	Honey/In A Little Spanish Town	4

JERRY & FREEDOM SINGERS
70	Banana BA 308	It's All In The Game/IM: The Way To My Heart	5

JERRY O
67	London HLZ 10162	Karate Boogaloo/The Pearl	5

JERRY THE FERRET
78	Own Label	1st single (no p/s)	5
82	Dead Horse	THE MUSIC GOES ON AND ON (EP)	4

JERUSALEM
72	Deram DM 358	Kamakazi Moth/Frustration	8
72	Deram SDL 6	JERUSALEM (LP, gatefold sleeve)	50

(see also Pussy, Ian Gillan)

JESS & JAMES
68	MGM MGM 1389	Move/What Was I Born For	5
68	MGM MGM 1420	Something For Nothing/I Let The Day Go By (with J.J. Band)	7
68	MGM MGM 1454	Thank You Show Biz/Motherless Child	4

JESSE GARON & DESPERADOES
80s	Wild Rumpus SHEP 001	Hank Williams Is Dead/FIZZBOMBS: You Worry Me (flexidisc, p/s)	5
86	Narodnik NRK 001	Splashing Along/Presence Dear (p/s)	7
87	Narodnik NRK 002	The Rain Fell Down/I'm Up Here (p/s)	5
87	Narodnik NRK 005	BILLY THE WHIZZ (12" EP)	8
88	Velocity SPEED 002	You'll Never Be That Young Again/And If The Sky Should Fall (p/s)	4

JESTERS
60s	R&L RL 15/16	Casa Pedro/Little Girl	8

JESUS & MARY CHAIN
84	Creation CRE 012	Upside Down/Vegetable Man (black, red & white wraparound sleeve in poly bag with address on rear)	15
84	Creation CRE 012	Upside Down/Vegetable Man (pink, blue or yellow wraparound sleeves in poly bag; some with small T-shirt offer insert)	10-12
84	Creation CRE 012	Upside Down/Vegetable Man (reissue, different printed p/s)	7
84	Creation CRE 012T	Upside Down/Vegetable Man/Upside Down (demo) (12" white label, no sleeve)	60
85	Fierce FRIGHT 004	RIOT (EP with 'LSD bar' & badge; 2 different sleeves)	25
85	Blanco Y Negro NEG 008	Never Understand/Suck (p/s)	8
85	Blanco Y Negro NEGT 008	Never Understand/Suck/Ambition (12", p/s)	12
85	Blanco Y Negro NEG 13	You Trip Me Up/Just Out Of Reach (p/s)	6
85	Blanco Y Negro NEGT 13	You Trip Me Up/Just Out Of Reach/Boyfriend's Dead (12", p/s)	10
85	Blanco Y Negro NEG 17	Just Like Honey/Head (p/s)	5

JESUS & MARY CHAIN

85	Blanco Y Negro NEGT 17	Just Like Honey/Head/Cracked/Just Like Honey (Demo Oct 84) (12", p/s)	7
85	Blanco Y Negro NEG 17F	Just Like Honey/Head//Inside Me/Just Like Honey (Demo Oct 84) (double pack)	10
85	The Hit HOT 001	Just Like Cindy/STYLE COUNCIL: Walls Come Tumbling Down (live)/ SIMPLY RED: Every Bit Of Me/REDSKINS: Kick Over The Statues (The Ramsey McKinnock Mix) (p/s, freebie EP with 'The Hit' mag, issue 1)	6/4
86	Blanco Y Negro NEG 19	Some Candy Talking/Psycho Candy/Hit (p/s)	4
86	Blanco Y Negro NEG 19F	Some Candy Talking/Psycho Candy/Hit//Cut Dead/You Trip Me Up/ Some Candy Talking/Psycho Candy (double pack, 2nd 7" all acoustic)	7
86	Blanco Y Negro NEGT 19	Some Candy Talking/Taste Of Cindy/Hit/Psycho Candy (12", p/s, some with poster)	10/7
87	Blanco Y Negro NEGF 24	April Skies/Kill Surf City//Mushroom (Live In Nuremburg 86)/ Bo Diddley Is Jesus (double pack, stickered gatefold p/s)	6
87	Blanco Y Negro NEGT 024	April Skies (Extended)/Kill Surf City/Who Do You Love (12", p/s)	7
87	Blanco Y Negro NEGB 25	Happy When It Rains/Everything Is Alright When You're Down (box set with postcards)	8
87	Blanco Y Negro NEGTE 25	Happy When It Rains (Extended)/Shake/Everything Is Alright When You're Down/Happy When It Rains (Demo) (10", p/s)	7
87	Blanco Y Negro NEG 29	Darklands/Rider/Here It Comes Again/On The Wall (Portastudio Demo) (gatefold sleeve)	4
87	Blanco Y Negro NEGTE 29	Darklands/Rider/Here It Comes Again/On The Wall (Portastudio Demo) (10", p/s)	7
87	Blanco Y Negro NEGCD 29	Darklands/Rider/Here It Comes Again/On The Wall (Portastudio Demo) (CD)	7
89	Blanco Y Negro NEG 41TE	Blues From A Gun/Shimmer/Penetration/Break Me Down (10", gatefold p/s)	20
89	Blanco Y Negro NEG 42/XB/Y/Z	Head On/Terminal Beach//Head On/Deviant Slice//Head On/I'm Glad I Never// Head On/In The Black (4 x 7" box set; each single sold separately)	25

(see also Acid Angels, Primal Scream)

JESUS JONES

89	Food FOOD 18	Info Freako/Broken Bones (p/s)	5
89	Food 12 FOOD 18	Info Freako/Broken Bones/Info Sicko (12", p/s)	8
89	Food CD FOOD 18	Info Freako/Broken Bones/Info Sicko (CD)	10
89	Food 12 FOODX 18	Info Psycho/Info Sicko/Info Freako (12", p/s)	12
89	Food FOOD 21	Never Enough/What's Going On (p/s)	4
89	Food FOODS 21	Never Enough/What's Going On (skateboard sticker pack)	6
89	Food 12 FOOD 21	Never Enough/Enough — Never Enough/It's The Winning That Counts (12", p/s)	7
89	Food CD FOOD 21	Never Enough/Enough — Never Enough/It's The Winning That Counts (CD)	7
89	Food 12 FOODP 22	Bring It Down/None Of The Answers/Cut And Dried/Beat It Down (12", poster pack)	7
89	Food 12 FOODX 22	Bring It Down (Liquidized Mix)/Cut And Dried/Info Sicko (12", p/s)	7
90	Food FOODS 24	Real Real Real (Rhythm 1)/Dead People's Lives (card pack)	4
90	Food 10 FOOD 25	Right Here Right Now/Are You Satisfied (Melvyn Mix)/Move Me (Metal House Mix)/Damn Good At This (10", box set with booklet)	5

JESUS LIZARD

93	Touch & Go TG 83	Puss/NIRVANA: Oh, The Guilt (p/s, blue vinyl, some with poster)	7/5

(see also Nirvana)

JESUS LOVES YOU

89	More Protein PRTX 12	After The Love (Fon Force Remix)/After The Love (Dub) (12", p/s)	15
90	More Protein JLY 1	One On One (12", withdrawn promo, as JLY Posse, black 'spunk' p/s)	20

(see also Culture Club)

JET

75	CBS 80699	JET (LP)	10

(see also Andy Ellison, Nice)

JETHRO TULL

68	MGM MGM 1384	Sunshine Day/Aeroplane (miscredited to 'Jethro Toe')	100
68	Island WIP 6043	A Song For Jeffrey/One For John Gee	18
68	Island WIP 6048	Love Story/A Christmas Song (2 different pink label designs)	5
68	Island WIP 6048	Love Story/A Christmas Song (mispressing, B-side or both sides credited to Ian Henderson)	each 10
69	Island WIP 6056	Living In The Past/Driving Song	6
69	Chrysalis WIP 6070	Sweet Dream/17 (most with large centre hole)	8/5
70	Chrysalis WIP 6077	The Witch's Promise/Teacher	5
70	Chrysalis WIP 6081	Inside/Alive And Well And Living In	10
71	Chrysalis WIP 6098	Lick Your Fingers Clean/Up To Me (withdrawn)	
71	Chrysalis WIP 6106	Life Is A Long Song/Up The Pool/Dr Bogenbroom/From Later/Nursie (EP)	4
74	Chrysalis CHS 2054	Bungle In The Jungle/Back Door Angels	5
75	Chrysalis CHS 2075	Minstrel In The Gallery/Summerday Sands	5
76	Chrysalis CHS 2086	Too Old To Rock'n'Roll/Rainbow Blues	4
76	Chrysalis CXP 2275	Ring Out Solstice Bells/March The Mad Scientist/A Christmas Song/ Pan Dance (EP)	7
77	Chrysalis CHS 2135	The Whistler/Strip Cartoon	7
78	Chrysalis CHS 2214	Moths/Life Is A Long Song (p/s)	5
78	Chrysalis CHS 2260	A Stitch In Time (4.20 Version)/Sweet Dream (p/s, white vinyl)	5
78	Chrysalis CHS 2260	A Stitch In Time (3.30 Version)/Sweet Dream (live) (p/s)	8
79	Chrysalis CHS 2378	North Sea Oil/Elegy (p/s)	8
79	Chrysalis CHS 2394	Home/King Henry's Madrigal (Theme From Mainstream)/ Warm Sporran (p/s)	12
79	Chrysalis CHS 2443	Ring Out Solstice Bells/March The Mad Scientist/A Christmas Song/ Pan Dance (EP)	7
79	Chrysalis CHS 2468	Working John, Working Joe/Flyingdale Flyer (p/s)	6
80	Chrysalis CHS 2619	Broadsword/Fallen On Hard Times (p/s)	6
80	Chrysalis CHSP 2619	Broadsword/Fallen On Hard Times (picture disc)	10
84	Chrysalis TULLD 1	Lap Of Luxury/Astronomy//Automotive Engineering/Tundra (double pack, gatefold p/s)	5

86	Chrysalis TULL 2	Coronach (with David Palmer)/Jack Frost And The Hooded Crow (p/s)	6
86	Chrysalis TULLX 2	Coronach (with David Palmer)/Jack Frost And The Hooded Crow/
		Living In The Past/Elegy (12", p/s)	20
87	Chrysalis TULLP 3	Steel Monkey/Down At The End Of Your Road (picture disc)	5
88	Chrysalis TULLP 4	Said She Was A Dancer/Dogs In Midwinter (shaped picture disc)	4
68	Island ILP 985	THIS WAS (LP, pink label, withdrawn mono issue, different mix to stereo)	50
68	Island ILPS 9085	THIS WAS (LP, pink label, stereo)	15
69	Island ILPS 9103	STAND UP (LP, pop-up sleeve, pink label)	15
70	Island ILPS 9123	BENEFIT (LP)	12
71	Island ILPS 9145	AQUALUNG (LP, with inner sleeve)	12
72	Chrysalis CHR 1003	THICK AS A BRICK (LP)	12
72	Chrysalis CJT 1	LIVING IN THE PAST (2-LP, with hard sleeve & booklet)	15
73	Chrysalis CHR 1040	A PASSION PLAY (LP, with booklet)	10
84	Chrysalis CDLP 1461	UNDER WRAPS (LP, picture disc)	12
	(see also Ian Anderson)

JETLINERS
| 66 | Blue Beat BB 367 | Nature Of Love/GIRL SATCHMO: Meditation | 8 |

JETS
| 79 | Decca F 13867 | Tearaway/Impossible | 4 |

JET SET
| 62 | Delta DW 5001 | VC 10/Cruising 600 (some in p/s) | 10/5 |

JET SET
| 64 | Parlophone R 5199 | You Got Me Hooked/True To You | 8 |

JETSET
80s	Shadows And Reflections	What Can I Say (Demo)/Christmas Greeting (flexidisc free with fanzine)	6/5
84	Dance Network NET 1	BEST OF THE JETSET (EP)	5
85	Dance Network WORK 1	THERE GOES THE NEIGHBOURHOOD (LP, pink sleeve)	10

JETSTREAMS
| 59 | Decca F 11149 | Bongo Rock/Tiger | 12 |

JOAN JETT (& BLACKHEARTS)
80	Ariola ARO 227	Make Believe/Call Me Lightning (poster p/s)	5
80	Ariola ARO 235	You Don't Know What You've Got/Abuse Me (p/s)	4
80	Ariola ARO 242	Jezebel/Bad Reputation (p/s)	4
82	Epic EPCA 2152	I Love Rock'n'Roll/Love Is Pain (picture disc)	4
82	Epic EPCA 2485	Crimson And Clover/Oh Woe Is Me (picture disc)	4
80	Ariola ARL 5058	BAD REPUTATION (LP, with "Hanky Panky")	10
82	Epic EPC 11 85686	I LOVE ROCK'N'ROLL (LP, picture disc, as Joan Jett & Blackhearts)	10
82	Cherry Red LAKER 1	I LOVE PLAYING WITH FIRE (LP, picture disc)	10
	(see also Runaways, Bangles)

JEWELS
| 64 | Colpix PX 11034 | Opportunity/Gotta Find A Way | 15 |
| 65 | Colpix PX 11048 | But I Do/Smokey Joe | 15 |

JIGSAW
68	Music Factory CUB 4	Mister Job/Great Idea	5
68	Music Factory CUB 6	Let Me Go Home/Tumblin'	50
68	MGM MGM 1410	One Way Street/Then I Found You	5
70	Philips 6006 112	One Way Street/Coffucious Confusion	10
70	Fontana 6007 017	Lollipop And Goody Man/Seven Fishes	12
71	Philips 6006 131	Jesu Joy Of Man's Desiring/No Questions Asked	6
71	Philips 6006 182	Keeping My Head Above Water/It's Nice But It's Wrong	6
74	BASF BA 1002	I've Seen The Film, I've Read The Book/Mention My Name	4
74	BASF BA 1010	You're Not The Only Girl/Face The Music	4
70	Philips 6308 033	LETHERSLADE FARM (LP)	50
71	Philips 6308 072	AURORA BOREALIS (LP)	35
74	BASF BAP 5051	I'VE SEEN THE FILM, I'VE READ THE BOOK (LP)	15

JIG-SAW BAND
| 68 | Polydor 56241 | I Need Your Love/I've Gotta Get Me Some Money | 5 |

JIH
88	Jungle JUNG 32T/BOV 3	Take Me To The Girl/Come Summer Come Winter/Wake Up (12",
		unissued white proof p/s with Mayking test pressings only)	20
88	Jungle JUNG 32T/BOV 3	Take Me To The Girl/Come Summer Come Winter/Wake Up
		(12", similar bluish or totally different p/s)	9/7
	(see also Associates)

JILL & BOULEVARDS
| 62 | Columbia DB 4823 | And Now I Cry/Eugene | 8 |

JILL & Y'VERNS
| 60s | Oak RGJ 503 | My Soulful Dress/Anything He Wants Me To Do | 25 |

JILTED JOHN
| 78 | Rabid TOSH 105 | Jilted John/Going Steady (p/s) | 4 |

JIM & JOE
| 64 | London HL 9831 | Fireball Mail/Daisy Mae | 12 |
| | *(see also James Burton)* |

JIM & MONICA
| 64 | Stateside SS 266 | Slippin' And Slidin'/Sing Along Without Jim & Monica | 15 |
| | *(see also Jimmy Gilmer & Fireballs)* |

JIMMIE & NIGHT HOPPERS
| 59 | London HLP 8830 | Cruising/Night Hop | 20 |
| 59 | London HLP 8830 | Cruising/Night Hop (78) | 18 |

JIMMY THE HOOVER
85	MCA MCA 996	Bandana Street/Smack In The Box//Tantalisa/Sing Sing (double pack)	4

JIVA
75	Dark Horse AMLH 22003	JIVA (LP)	10

JIV-A-TONES
58	Felsted AF 101	Flirty Gertie/Fire Engine Baby	160
58	Felsted AF 101	Flirty Gertie/Fire Engine Baby (78)	70

JIVE FIVE
61	Parlophone R 4822	My True Story/When I Was Single	125
62	Stateside SS 133	What Time Is It?/Begging You Please	25
65	United Artists UP 1106	I'm A Happy Man/Kiss Kiss Kiss	10

JIVERS (U.S.)
56	Vogue V 9060	Little Mama/Cherie	250
56	Vogue V 9060	Little Mama/Cherie (78)	40
57	Vogue V 9068	Ray Pearl/Dear Little One	250
57	Vogue V 9068	Ray Pearl/Dear Little One (78)	40

JIVERS (Jamaica)
68	Trojan TR 604	Wear My Crown/Down On The Beach	5

JIVING JUNIORS
60	Blue Beat BB 4	Lollipop Girl/Dearest Darling	10
60	Blue Beat BB 5	My Heart's Desire/I Love You	10
60	Starlite ST45 028	Lovers Line/Tu-Woo-Up-Tu-Woo	12
61	Starlite ST45 049	Slop & Mash/My Sweet Angel	10
61	Blue Beat BB 36	Over The River/Hip Rub	10
62	Island WI 003	Sugar Dandy/Valerie	10
62	Island WI 027	Andrea/Don't Leave Me	10
63	Island WI 129	Sugar Dandy/Valerie	10

J.J. ALLSTARS
69	Trojan TR 691	Memphis Underground Pts 1 & 2	4

DAMITA JO
(see under D)

JO BOXERS
83	RCA BOXX 1	Boxerbeat/Let's Talk About Love (picture disc)	4
83	RCA BOXX 2	Just Got Lucky/Forget Me Love (picture disc)	4
83	RCA BOXX 3	Johnny Friendly/Why Don't You Do Right (picture disc)	4

(see also Subway Sect)

JOBRIATH
73	Elektra EKS 75070	JOBRAITH (LP)	12
74	Elektra K 42163	CREATURES OF THE STREET (LP)	12

JO'BURG HAWK
73	Charisma CAS 1064	JO'BURG HAWK (LP, gatefold sleeve)	10

JODIMARS
56	Capitol CL 14518	Well Now, Dig This/Let's All Rock Together	40
56	Capitol CL 14518	Well Now, Dig This/Let's All Rock Together (78)	10
56	Capitol CL 14627	Lotsa Love/Rattle My Bones	35
56	Capitol CL 14627	Lotsa Love/Rattle My Bones (78)	10
56	Capitol CL 14641	Rattle Shakin' Daddy/Eat Your Heart Out Annie	35
56	Capitol CL 14641	Rattle Shakin' Daddy/Eat Your Heart Out Annie (78)	8
56	Capitol CL 14642	Dance To The Bop/Boom, Boom My Bayou Baby	35
56	Capitol CL 14642	Dance To The Bop/Boom, Boom My Bayou Baby (78)	8
56	Capitol CL 14663	Midnight/Clarabella	35
56	Capitol CL 14663	Midnight/Clarabella (78)	12
57	Capitol CL 14700	Cloud 99/Later	30
57	Capitol CL 14700	Cloud 99/Later (78)	18
60s	Ember SPE 6608	WELL NOW DIG THIS (LP)	15

(see also Bill Haley & Comets)

JODY GRIND
69	Transatlantic TRA 210	ONE STEP ON (LP)	25
70	Transatlantic TRA 221	FAR CANAL (LP)	25

AL T. JOE (& CELESTIALS)
62	Blue Beat BB 126	You Cheated On Me/This Heart Of Mine (as Al T. Joe & Celestials)	8
62	Dice CC 9	Rise Jamaica/I'm On My Own	8
63	Blue Beat BB 166	Goodbye Dreamboat/Please Forgive Me	8
63	Blue Beat BB 169	Fatso/Slow Boat	8
66	Blue Beat BB 368	Jacqueline/Please Come Home (as Al T. Joe & Celestials)	8

(see also Jamaica Fats)

JOE & ANN
65	Black Swan WI 468	Gee Baby/Wherever You May Be	6

JOE & EDDIE
59	Capitol CL 15038	Green Grass/And I Believed	4
64	Vocalion V 9215	There's A Meetin' Here Tonight/Lonesome Traveller	4
65	Vocalion V 9238	Gabrielle/He's Got The Whole World In His Hands	4
65	Vocalion V 9242	Depend On Yourself/With You In Mind	4
65	Vocalion V-N 9246	Farewell/Hey Nelly Nelly	4
65	Vocalion V-P 9250	Walkin' Down The Line/It Ain't Me Babe	8

BILLY JOEL
72	Philips 6078 001	She's Got A Way/Everybody Loves You Now	7

MINT VALUE £

73	Philips 6078 018	The Ballad Of Billy The Kid/If I Only Had The Words (To Tell You) 25
75	CBS 3183	Piano Man/You're My Home 4
75	CBS 3469	If I Only Had The Words/Stop In Nevada 4
77	CBS 4686	Say Goodbye To Hollywood/Stop In Nevada 4
79	CBS 7150	Honesty/Root Beer Rag (withdrawn) 20
78	CBS 6266	She's Always A Woman To Me/Everybody Has A Dream (gatefold p/s) 4
83	CBS A 3665	Tell Her About It/Easy Money (original "Innocent Man" p/s) 4
84	CBS GA 4884	This Night/I'll Cry Instead (gatefold p/s) 4
86	CBS DA 7247	Modern Woman/Sleep With The Television On//Up Town/All For Love (double pack) 4
72	Philips 6369 150	COLD SPRING HARBOUR (LP) 15
73	Philips 6369 160	PIANO MAN (LP, withdrawn) 25
73	Philips 6078 018	BALLAD OF BILLY THE KID (LP) 10
78	CBS H 82311	THE STRANGER (LP, half-speed master version) 15
79	CBS 66352	BILLY JOEL (3-LP box) 15

(see also Hassles)

JOE 9T & THUNDERBIRDS
80s	Gemme JOE 9T/LYN 6526	Joe 9T Theme/THEY MUST BE RUSSIANS: Psycho Analysis (p/s, white label) ...5

(see also They Must Be Russians)

JOE PUBLIC
80s	Capital CLA 55	Anti CND 6

(see also Long Tall Shorty)

JOE'S ALLSTARS
69	Joe DU 24	Hey Jude/Musical Feet 5
69	Joe/Duke DU 28	Battle Cry Of Biafra/Funky Reggae Part 1 5
69	Joe DU 50	Brixton Cat/Solitude 5
70	Joe JRS 9	Tony B's Theme/Skinhead Revolt 8

(see also Joe The Boss)

JOE SOAP
73	Polydor 2383 233	KEEP IT CLEAN (LP) 15

JOE (Mansano) THE BOSS
70	Joe JRS 6	Son Of Al Capone/All My Enemies 5

(see also Joe's Allstars)

JOEY & CONTINENTALS
70	Polydor 56520	Rudy Vadoo/She Rides With Me 6

JOEY & GENTLEMEN
64	Fontana TF 444	Like I Love You/I'll Never Let You Go 8
64	Fontana TF 485	Dummy Dum Song/Goodbye Little Girl 4

ALEKSANDER JOHN
74	Myrrh MYR 1010	DAYS GO BY (LP) 10

ANDREW JOHN
71	CBS 7017	Streets Of London/Rick Rack 4
71	CBS 64835	THE MACHINE STOPS (LP) 20

BASIL JOHN
70s	Planetone RC 12	Drink And Drive/MIKE ELLIOTT: J.K. Shuffle 5

CLIVE JOHN
75	United Artists UAS 29733	YOU ALWAYS KNOW WHERE YOU STAND WITH A BUZZARD (LP) 10

(see also Man)

DAVID JOHN & MOOD
64	Vocalion V 9220	To Catch That Man/Pretty Thing 150
65	Parlophone R 5255	I Love To See You Strut/Bring It To Jerome 100
65	Parlophone R 5301	Diggin' For Gold/She's Fine 125

(these singles do NOT feature David Bowie; see also Gagalactyca, Little Free Rock)

ELTON JOHN
68	Philips BF 1643	I've Been Loving You/Here's To The Next Time 100
69	Philips BF 1739	Lady Samantha/All Across The Heavens 35
69	DJM DJS 205	It's Me That You Need/Just Like Strange Rain (some in p/s) 60/20
71	DJM DJS 217	Border Song/Bad Side Of The Moon 6
70	DJM DJS 222	Rock And Roll Madonna/Grey Seal 10
71	DJM DJS 233	Your Song/Into The Dead Man's Shoes 5
71	DJM DJS 244	Friends/Honey Roll 6
72	DJM DJX 501	Rocket Man/Holiday Inn/Goodbye (gatefold p/s) 15
72	DJM DJS 269	Honky Cat/Lady Samantha/It's Me That You Need (p/s) 5
72	DJM DJS 271	Crocodile Rock/Elderberry Wine (p/s) 4
73	DJM DJS 275	Daniel/Skyline Pigeon (p/s) 4
73	DJM DJX 502	Saturday Night's Alright For Fighting/Jack Rabbit/Whenever You're Ready (We'll Go Steady Again) (p/s) 5
73	DJM DJS 285	Goodbye Yellow Brick Road/Screw You (p/s) 4
73	DJM DJS 290	Step Into Christmas/Ho! Ho! Ho! (Who'd Be A Turkey At Christmas) (p/s) 4
74	DJM DJS 297	Candle In The Wind/Bennie And The Jets (p/s) 4
74	DJM DJS 302	Don't Let The Sun Go Down On Me/Sick City (p/s) 4
74	DJM DJS 322	The Bitch Is Back/Cold Highway (p/s) 4
74	DJM DJS 340	Lucy In The Sky With Diamonds (featuring Dr. Winston O'Boogie & His Reggae Guitars)/One Day At A Time (p/s) 4
75	DJM DJS 354	Philadelphia Freedom/I Saw Her Standing There (as Elton John Band; B-side featuring John Lennon with Muscle Shoals Horns) (p/s) 7
75	DJM DJS 385	Someone Saved My Life Tonight/House Of Cards (p/s) 4
75	DJM DJS 610	Island Girl/Sugar On The Floor (p/s) 4
76	DJM DJS 629	Grow Some Funk Of Your Own/I Feel Like A Bullet (In The Gun Of Robert Ford) (p/s) 4

MINT VALUE £

76	DJM DJS 652	Pinball Wizard/Harmony (p/s) 4
76	Rocket ROKN 517	Sorry Seems To Be The Hardest Word/Shoulder Holster (p/s) 4
77	Rocket GOALD 1	The Goaldigger Song/Jimmy, Brian, Elton, Eric (mail-order, 500 only) 75
77	Rocket RU 1	Bite Your Lip (Remix)/KIKI DEE: Chicago (12", printed sleeve) 7
78	Rocket ROKN 538	Ego/Flintstone Boy (p/s) 4
78	DJM DJS 10901	Lady Samantha/Skyline Pigeon (p/s, reissue) 4
78	DJM DJS 10911	Philadelphia Freedom/Lucy In The Sky With Diamonds (p/s, reissue) 4
79	Rocket XPRES 1312	Are You Ready For Love/Three Way Love Affair/Mama Can't
		Buy You Love (12", p/s) 7
79	Rocket XPRES 20	Mama Can't Buy You Love/Strangers (p/s; withdrawn, misspelt "Mamma") 20
79	Rocket XPRES 21	The Victim Of Love/Strangers (p/s) 4
80	Rocket XPRES 45	Dear God/Tactics (p/s) 4
80	Rocket XPRES 45/ELTON1	Dear God/Tactics//Steal Away Child/Love So Cold (double pack) 6
81	DJM DJS 10965	I Saw Her Standing There/Whatever Gets You Thru The Night/Lucy In The
		Sky With Diamonds (EP, featuring John Lennon & Muscle Shoals Horns) 7
82	Rocket XPPIC 77	Empty Garden/Take Me Down To The Ocean (picture disc) 6
82	Rocket XPRPO 88	All Quiet On The Western Front/Where Have All The Good Times Gone
		(poster p/s) 6
83	Rocket EXPRES 91	I Guess That's Why They Call It The Blues/Lord Choc Ice Goes Mental ('raised' sl.)5
83	Rocket EJPIC 1	I'm Still Standing/Earn While You Learn (piano-shaped picture disc) 10
83	Rocket EJS 2/FREEJ 2	Kiss The Bridge/Dreamboat//Ego/Song For Guy (double pack) 4
83	Rocket EJS 3/2	Cold As Christmas/Crystal//Don't Go Breaking My Heart/Snow Queen
		(double pack, 2nd 45 with Kiki Dee) 4
84	Rocket PHPIC 7	Sad Songs (Say So Much)/Simple Man (hat-shaped picture disc) 10
85	Rocket EJS 8	Act Of War/(Version) (with Millie Jackson, 'concertina pack' of video stills) ...5
85	Rocket EJSR 812	Act Of War (Part 5)/Act Of War (Part 6) (Instrumental) (12", p/s) 7
85	Rocket EJSD 9	Nikita/The Man Who Never Died//Sorry Seems To Be The Hardest
		Word (live)/I'm Still Standing (live) (double pack, gatefold pop-up p/s) 8
85	Rocket EJSC 10	Wrap Her Up/Restless (live) (with George Michael, open-out 'cube' p/s) 7
85	Rocket EJPIC 10	Wrap Her Up/Restless (live) (with George Michael, shaped picture disc) 10
85	Rocket EJS 1012/EJS 912	Wrap Her Up (Extended)/Restless (live)/Nikita/The Man Who Never Died//
		Sorry Seems To Be The Hardest Word (live)/I'm Still Standing (live)
		(12", shrinkwrapped double pack) 7
86	Rocket EJSD 11	Cry To Heaven/Candy By The Pound//Rock'n'Roll Medley/Your Song
		(double pack) 4
86	Rocket EJSD 12	Heartache All Over The World/Highlander//Passengers/I'm Still Standing
		(double pack) 4
88	Rocket EJSP 15	Candle In The Wind/Sorry Seems To Be The Hardest Word (picture disc) 4
78	DJM EJ 12	THE ELTON JOHN SINGLES COLLECTION (12 x 7" box set) 50
77	DJM DJR 18001	FOUR FROM FOUR EYES (EP) 4
78	DJM DJT 15000	FUNERAL FOR A FRIEND (12" EP) 7
69	DJM DJMLP/DJLPS 403	EMPTY SKY (LP, mono/stereo) 15/12
70	DJM DJLPS 406	ELTON JOHN (LP, gatefold sleeve) 10
70	DJM DJLPS 410	TUMBLEWEED CONNECTION (LP, gatefold sleeve with booklet) 10
71	DJM DJLPS 414	17.11.70 (LP) 10
71	Paramount SPFL 269	FRIENDS (LP, soundtrack) 10
74	DJM ZCDJL 301	LADY SAMANTHA (cassette, original tape-only compilation) 10
75	DJM DJLPX 1	CAPTAIN FANTASTIC AND THE BROWN DIRT COWBOY (LP, 2,000 on
		brown vinyl; most with signed cover) 80/40
76	DJM DJE 29001	GOODBYE YELLOW BRICK ROAD (2-LP, yellow vinyl) 15
78	St. Michael 2094 0102	CANDLE IN THE WIND (LP, Marks & Spencer issue) 30
78	DJM DJV 2300	CAPTAIN FANTASTIC AND THE BROWN DIRT COWBOY (LP, picture disc) 12
78	DJM LSP 14512	ELTON JOHN (5-LP, box set) 30
83	Rocket HISPD 24	TOO LOW FOR ZERO (LP, with die-cut front cover) 10
83	DJM 8100 622	THE SUPERIOR SOUND OF ELTON JOHN (CD) 15
87	Rocket EJBXL 1	LIVE IN AUSTRALIA WITH THE MELBOURNE SYMPHONY ORCHESTRA
		(2-LP, 1,000 only) 15

(see also [Stu Brown &] Bluesology, Bread & Beer Band, John Lennon, George Michael, Millie Jackson, Neil Sedaka)

ELTON JOHN & CLIFF RICHARD

86	Rocket EJSP 13	Slow Rivers/ELTON JOHN: Billy & The Kids (picture disc) 6
86	Rocket EJSC 13	Slow Rivers/ELTON JOHN: Billy & The Kids (cassette) 5
86	Rocket EJS 13-12	Slow Rivers/ELTON JOHN: Billy & The Kids/Lord Of The Flies (12", p/s) 7

(see also Cliff Richard)

LITTLE WILLIE JOHN

56	Parlophone R 4209	Fever/Letter From My Darling 35
56	Parlophone R 4209	Fever/Letter From My Darling (78) 20
58	Parlophone R 4396	Uh, Uh, Baby/Dinner Date (With His Girl Friend) 22
58	Parlophone R 4396	Uh, Uh, Baby/Dinner Date (With His Girl Friend) (78) 20
58	Parlophone R 4432	Talk To Me, Talk To Me/Spasms 22
58	Parlophone R 4432	Talk To Me, Talk To Me/Spasms (78) 25
58	Parlophone R 4472	Let's Rock While The Rockin' Good/You're A Sweetheart 25
58	Parlophone R 4472	Let's Rock While The Rockin' Good/You're A Sweetheart (78) 30
59	Parlophone R 4571	Leave My Kitten Alone/Let Nobody Love You 20
60	Parlophone R 4674	Heartbreak (It's Hurtin' Me)/Do You Love Me 18
60	Parlophone R 4699	Sleep/There's A Difference 15
61	Parlophone R 4728	Walk Slow/HANK BALLARD: The Hoochie Coochie Coo 15
64	London HA 8126	COME ON AND JOIN LITTLE WILLIE JOHN (LP) 40

MABLE JOHN

66	Atlantic 584 022	It's Catching/Your Good Thing (Is About To End) 8
67	Stax 601 010	Same Time Same Place/Bigger And Better (dark blue or light blue label) 10/7
68	Stax 601 034	Able Mable/Don't Get Caught 7

ROBERT JOHN

| 68 | CBS 3436 | If You Don't Want My Love/Don't ....4 |
| 68 | CBS 3730 | Don't Leave Me/Children ....4 |

SAMMIE JOHN
67 Stateside SS 585   Little John/Boss Bag 5

STEVE JOHN
66 Fontana H 661   You Didn't Want To Know/Bitter Tears 4

JOHN & JOHNNY
63 Decca F 11719   I Want You To Be My Girl/It's You 4

JOHN & PAUL
65 London HLU 9997   People Say/I'm Walkin' 10

JOHNNIE & JACK
54 HMV 7MC 21   Honey, I Need You/Goodnight, Well It's Time To Go (export issue) 6
59 RCA RCA 1145   Sailor Man/Wild And Wicked World 4

JOHNNIE & JOE
58 London HLM 8682   Over The Mountain, Across The Sea/My Baby's Gone, On, On 150
58 London HLM 8682   Over The Mountain, Across The Sea/My Baby's Gone, On, On (78) 30

JOHNNY (Osborne) & ATTRACTIONS
67 Doctor Bird DB 1118   Young Wings Can Fly/DUDLEY WILLIAMSON: I'm Moving On 7

JOHNNY & CHAZ & GUNNERS
61 Decca F 11365   Bobby/Out Of Luck 20

JOHNNY & COPYCATS
60s Norco AB 102   I'm A Hog For You Baby/I Can Never See You 35

JOHNNY & HURRICANES
59	London HL 8899	Crossfire/Lazy (initially triangular-centre, later round centre) 25/8
59	London HL 8899	Crossfire/Lazy (78) 35
59	London HL 8948	Red River Rock/Buckeye (initially triangular-centre, later round centre) 10/5
59	London HL 8948	Red River Rock/Buckeye (78) 40
59	London HL 9017	Reveille Rock/Time Bomb (initially triangular-centre, later round centre) 10/5
59	London HL 9017	Reveille Rock/Time Bomb (78) 45
60	London HLI 9072	Beatnick Fly/Sand Storm 6
60	London HLI 9072	Beatnick Fly/Sand Storm (78) 50
60	London HLX 9134	Down Yonder/Sheba 6
60	London HLX 9134	Down Yonder/Sheba (78) 75
60	London HLX 9190	Rocking Goose/Revival 6
60	London HLX 9190	Rocking Goose/Revival (78) 100
60	London HL 7099	The Hep Canary/Catnip (export issue) 30
61	London HLX 9289	Ja-Da/Mr. Lonely 5
61	London HLX 9378	High Voltage/Old Smokie 5
62	London HLX 9491	Farewell, Farewell/Traffic Jam 6
62	London HLX 7116	You Are My Sunshine/Farewell, Farewell (export issue) 20
62	London HLX 9536	Salvation/Misirlou 7
62	London HLX 9617	Minnesota Fats/Come On Train 7
63	London HLX 9660	Whatever Happened To Baby Jane/Greens And Beans 7
68	London HLX 10199	Rocking Goose/Beatnik Fly (reissue) 4
64	Stateside SS 347	Money Honey/That's All 8
74	Contempo CS 9012	Red River Rock/Rockin' Goose (reissue) 4
75	Contempo CS 9022	Reveille Rock/Crossfire (reissue) 4
75	Contempo CS 9034	Beatnik Fly/Corn Bread 4
76	United Artists UPS 401	Red River Rock/Sheba/Reveille Rock/Beatnik Fly (p/s) 4
61	London REX 1284	ROCKING GOOSE (EP) 18
62	London REX 1347	JOHNNY AND THE HURRICANES (EP) 18
64	London REX 1414	JOHNNY AND THE HURRICANES VOL. 2 (EP) 20
60	London HA 2227	RED RIVER ROCK (LP, plum label; reissues on black label £12) 30
60	London HA-I 2269	STORMSVILLE (LP) 25
61	London HA-X 2322	THE BIG SOUND OF JOHNNY AND THE HURRICANES (LP) 25

JOHNNY & JACK
59 RCA RCA 1145   Sailor Man/Wild And Wicked World 4
59 RCA RCA 1145   Sailor Man/Wild And Wicked World (78) 5
50s RCA RCX 176   COUNTRY GUITAR VOL. 10 (EP) 7

JOHNNY & JAMMERS
79 Big Beat NS 55   School Day Blues/You Know I Love You 5
(see also Johnny Winter)

JOHNNY & JOHN
66 Polydor BM 56087   Bumper To Bumper/Scrape My Boot 12
(see also Johnny Gustafson, Big Three)

JOHNNY & JUDY
59 Vogue Pop V 9128   Bother Me Baby/Who's To Say 150
59 Vogue Pop V 9128   Bother Me Baby/Who's To Say (78) 40

JOHNNY & SELF ABUSERS
77 Chiswick NS 22   Saints And Sinners/Dead Vandals (p/s) 15
(see also Simple Minds)

JOHNNY & VIBRATIONS
63 Warner Bros WB 107   Bird Stompin'/Movin' The Bird 6

JOHNNY MOPED
76 Chiswick PROMO 3   BASICALLY, THE ORIGINAL JOHNNY MOPED TAPE (33rpm, no p/s) 15
77 Chiswick S 15   No-One/Incendiary Device (p/s) 6
78 Chiswick NS 27   Darling, Let's Have Another Baby/Something Else/It Really Digs (p/s) 5
78 Chiswick NS 41   Little Queenie/Hard Lovin' Man (p/s) 5
78 Chiswick WIK 8   CYCLEDELIC (LP, some with free single [PROMO 3]) 25/10
(see also Slime)

JOHNNY'S BOYS
59   Decca F 11156   Sleep Walk/Ciao Ciao Bambina 7

JOHNNY'S JAZZ
56   Decca FJ 10663   R.J. Boogie/Get Happy (featuring Johnny Hawksworth) 6
(see also Johnny Hawksworth)

BARRY JOHNS
58   HMV POP 472   Locked In The Arms Of Love/Are You Sincere 4

GLYN JOHNS
62   Decca F 11478   January Blues/Sioux Indian 5
63   Decca F 11753   Old Deceiver Time/Dancing With You 5
65   Immediate IM 013   Mary Anne/Like Grains Of Yellow Sand 12
65   Pye 7N 15818   I'll Follow The Sun/I'll Take You Dancing 6
60s Westcot LYN 827/828   Today You're Gone/Such Stuff Of Dreams (freebie with jeans offer) 6

GLYNIS JOHNS
54   Columbia SCM 5149   I Can't Resist Men/Always You 6

JOHN'S CHILDREN
66   Columbia DB 8030   The Love I Thought I'd Found/Strange Affair (very few in p/s) 175/60
67   Columbia DB 8124   Just What You Want — Just What You'll Get/But She's Mine 60
67   Track 604 003   Desdemona/Remember Thomas A'Beckett (some in p/s) 60/18
67   Track 604 005   Midsummer Night's Scene/Sara Crazy Child (withdrawn) 1000
67   Track 604 005   Come And Play With Me In The Garden/Sara Crazy Child (some in p/s) 80/18
67   Track 604 010   Go Go Girl/Jagged Time Lapse 30
(see also Marc Bolan, Andy Ellison, Radio Stars)

AL JOHNSON & JEAN CARN
80   CBS 8545   I'm Back For More/You Are My Personal Angel 6
(see also Jean Carn)

BETTY JOHNSON
56   London HLU 8307   I'll Wait/Please Tell Me Why 40
56   London HLU 8307   I'll Wait/Please Tell Me Why (78) 5
56   London HLU 8326   Honky Tonk Rock/Say It Isn't So, Joe 100
56   London HLU 8326   Honky Tonk Rock/Say It Isn't So, Joe (78) 35
57   London HLU 8365   I Dreamed/If It's Wrong To Love You 35
57   London HLU 8365   I Dreamed/If It's Wrong To Love You (78) 5
57   London HLU 8432   1492/Little White Lies 30
57   London HLU 8432   1492/Little White Lies (78) 5
58   London HLE 8557   Little Blue Man/Song You Heard When You Fell In Love 30
58   London HLE 8557   Little Blue Man/Song You Heard When You Fell In Love (78) 7
58   London HLE 8678   Dream/How Much 18
58   London HLE 8678   Dream/How Much (78) 5
58   London HLE 8701   There's Never Been A Night/Mr. Brown Is Out Of Town 35
58   London HLE 8701   There's Never Been A Night/Mr. Brown Is Out Of Town (78) 5
58   London HLE 8725   Hoopa Hoola/One More Time 30
58   London HLE 8725   Hoopa Hoola/One More Time (78) 5
59   London HLE 8839   Does Your Heart Beat For Me?/You And Only You 25
59   London HLE 8839   Does Your Heart Beat For Me?/You And Only You (78) 5
59   London REE 1221   DREAM (EP) 30
59   London HA-E 2163   THE SONG YOU HEARD WHEN YOU FELL IN LOVE (LP) 30

BLIND WILLIE JOHNSON
50s Square M-1   Dark was The Night — Cold Was The Ground/
                            Lord I Just Can't Keep From Crying (78) 50
58   Fontana TFE 17052   TREASURES OF NORTH AMERICAN NEGRO MUSIC NO. 2 (EP) 10

BOBBY JOHNSON & ATOMS
67   Ember EMB S 245   Do It Again A Little Bit Slower/Tramp 8

BRYAN JOHNSON
60   Decca F 11213   Looking High, High, High/Each Tomorrow 4
61   Decca DFE 6664   LOOKING HIGH (EP) 7

BUBBER JOHNSON
55   Parlophone R 4105   Let's Make Every Day A Christmas Day/It's Christmas Time (78) 5
56   Parlophone R 4161   Keep A Light In The Window For Me/A Wonderful Thing Happens (78) 5
57   Parlophone R 4259   Confidential/Have A Little Faith In Me 20
57   Parlophone R 4259   Confidential/Have A Little Faith In Me (78) 12

BUDDY JOHNSON
50   Mercury MB 3231   Upside Your Head/ELLA JOHNSON:
                            Crazy About A Saxophone (78) 8
59   Mercury ZEP 10009   BUDDY JOHNSON WAILS (EP, with Ella Johnson) 40
57   Mercury MPT 7515   ROCK AND ROLL (10" LP, with Ella Johnson) 50

BUNK JOHNSON (& HIS NEW ORLEANS BAND)
55   HMV 7M 141   When The Saints Go Marching In/Darktown Strutters' Ball 5
50s Melodisc EPM7 52   ONE YOU LOVE (EP) 10
54   Goodtime Jazz LDG 110 BUNK JOHNSON AND THE YERBA BUENA JAZZ BAND (10" LP) 12
54   Columbia 33SX 1015   BUNK JOHNSON AND HIS NEW ORLEANS BAND (LP) 12
50s Goodtime Jazz   SPIRITUALS AND JAZZ (10" LP) 10
62   Storyville SLP 152   BUNK JOHNSON'S BAND 1944 (LP) 12
63   Goodtime Jazz LAG 545 BUNK JOHNSON AND HIS SUPERIOR JAZZ BAND (LP) 10

CAREY JOHNSON
72   Banana BA 369   Correction Train/SOUL DEFENDERS: Version 5

DANIEL JOHNSON
65   Island WI 250   Come On My People/Brother Nation 7

DON JOHNSON
86	Epic EPCA 650203	Heartache Away/Love Roulette (picture disc)	4

GENERAL JOHNSON
73	Invictus INV 531	Only Time Will Tell/Only Time Will Tell (Instrumental Version)	4
76	Arista ARIST 45	All In The Family/Ready, Willing And Able	7

(see also Norman Johnson, Showmen, Chairmen Of The Board)

GIB JOHNSON
65	King KG 1023	Little Boy Lost/Kingdom Of A Fool	4
67	King KG 1057	The Last Time/Old Oak Chest	4

GINGER FOLORONS JOHNSON
60s	Melodisc MEL 1515	Africa Jazz Cha Cha/Egypt Bint Al Cha Cha	4
60s	Melodisc MEL 1520	Wee Tom Cha Cha/Won't You Cha Cha	4

HOWARD JOHNSON
71	Jay Boy BOY 47	The Slide/That Magic Touch Can Send You Flying	4

JAMES P. JOHNSON
54	Columbia SCM 5127	Feeling Blues/Riffs	8
56	HMV 7EG 8164	JAMES P. JOHNSON (EP)	10
57	HMV 7EG 8215	LOUISIANA SUGAR BABIES (EP, with Fats Waller)	12
57	Tempo EXA 65	JAMES P. JOHNSON (EP)	10
52	Brunswick LA 8548	DADDY OF THE PIANO (10" LP)	15
53	Brunswick LA 8622	FATS WALLER FAVOURITES (10" LP)	15
54	London AL 3511	EARLY HARLEM PIANO (10" LP)	20
55	London AL 3540	EARLY HARLEM PIANO VOLUME 2 (10" LP)	20

JAMES P. JOHNSON/LUCKEY ROBERTS
56	London HB-U 1057	HARLEM PARTY PIANO (10" LP, 1 side each)	20

JIMMY JOHNSON
65	Sue WI 387	Don't Answer The Door Pts 1 & 2	15

J.J. JOHNSON
55	Vogue LDE 124	J.J. JOHNSON SEXTET (10" LP)	12
55	Vogue LDE 162	J.J. JOHNSON QUINTET (10" LP)	12
60	Fontana TFL 5041	J.J. IN PERSON (LP)	10
61	Fontana TFL 5137	BLUE TROMBONE (LP, also stereo STFL 559)	10

(JOHNNY JOHNSON &) BANDWAGON
68	Direction 58-3520	Baby Make Your Own Sweet Music/On The Day We Fall In Love (as Bandwagon)	4
68	Direction 58-3670	Breaking Down The Walls Of Heartache/Dancin' Master (as Bandwagon)	4
69	Direction 58-3923	You/You Blew Your Cool And Lost Your Fool	4
69	Direction 58-4180	Let's Hang On/I Ain't Lying (withdrawn)	6
69	Direction 58-4180	Let's Hang On/Don't Let It In	4
72	Stateside SS 2207	Honey Bee/I Don't Know Why	5

JUDI JOHNSON
65	HMV POP 1399	How Many Times/A Way Out	7

LARRY JOHNSON
70	Blue Horizon 7-63851	PRESENTING THE COUNTRY BLUES (LP)	35

LAURIE JOHNSON ORCHESTRA
56	HMV 7MC 47	Buttercup/Lullaby Of The Leaves (export issue)	5
57	HMV POP 404	The Moonraker/Call Of The Casbah	4
64	Pye 7N 15599	Dr Strangelove Theme/Nevada	4
65	Pye 7N 17015	Avenger's Theme/Minor Bossa Nova (some in p/s)	15/8
71	Columbia DB 8826	The Jason King Theme/There Comes A Time	4
76	EMI EMI 2562	New Avengers Theme/Slaver Of The Avengers	4
80s	Unicorn Kanchani MCPS 5	The Professionals/The New Avengers (p/s)	4
67	Marble Arch MAL 695	THE AVENGERS (LP)	15
70	Columbia SCX 6412	LAURIE JOHNSON/LONDON JAZZ ORCHESTRA (LP)	12
71	Columbia SCX 6464	CONQUISTADORS (LP)	10

LINTON KWESI JOHNSON
79	Island WIP 6494	Want Fi Goh Rave/Reality Poem (p/s)	4

LONNIE JOHNSON
40s	Parlophone R 2259	Playing With The Strings/Stompin' 'Em Along Slow (78)	35
51	Vogue V 2015	Drunk Again/Jelly Roll Baker (78)	15
51	Vogue V 2079	Happy New Year/Little Rockin' Chair (78)	15
51	Melodisc MEL 1138	Rocks In My Bed/Solid Blues (78)	20
51	Melodisc MEL 1186	Blues For Everybody/In Love Again (78)	20
52	Melodisc MEL 1221	Blues In My Soul/Keep What You Got (78)	20
57	Parlophone GEP 8635	LONESOME ROAD (EP)	20
57	Parlophone GEP 8663	LONNIE'S BLUES (EP)	20
58	Parlophone GEP 8693	LONNIE'S BLUES NO. 2 (EP)	20
64	Storyville SLP 162	PORTRAITS IN BLUES VOL. 6 (LP)	15
60s	Xtra XTRA 1037	LONNIE JOHNSON (LP)	20

(see also Eddie Lang & Lonnie Johnson)

LONNIE JOHNSON & BLIND WILLIE BAND
40s	Parlophone R 1195	Two Tone Stomp/MAMIE SMITH: Jenny's Ball (78)	30

(see also Eddie Lang and Lonnie Johnson, Blind Willie Dunn's Gin Bottle Four)

LOU JOHNSON
63	London HLX 9805	Magic Potion/Reach Out For Me	20
64	London HLX 9917	Always Something There To Remind Me/Wouldn't That Be Something	15
64	London HLX 9929	Message To Martha/Last One To Be Loved	10
65	London HLX 9965	Please Stop The Wedding/Park Avenue	8

Lou JOHNSON

65	London HLX 9994	A Time To Love, A Time To Cry/Unsatisfied 25
69	London HLX 10269	Always Something There To Remind Me/Message To Martha 6
64	London REX 1438	THE MAGIC POTION OF LOU JOHNSON (EP) 30

LUTHER 'GEORGIA BOY SNAKE' JOHNSON

| 68 | Transatlantic TRA 188 | WITH THE MUDDY WATERS BLUES BAND (LP) ....10 |

MARGARET JOHNSON

24	Parlophone E 5187	If I Let You Get Away With It Once You'll Do It All The Time/
		E Flat Blues (78) 50
20s	Parlophone E 5300	Nobody Knows The Way I Feel Like This Morning/Absent Minded Blues (78) 50
52	Parlophone R 3506	Cushion Foot Stomp/Take Your Black Bottom Outside (78) 40

MARV JOHNSON

59	London HLT 8856	Come To Me/Whisper 60
59	London HLT 8856	Come To Me/Whisper (78) 28
59	London HLT 9013	You Got What It Takes/Don't Leave Me 8
59	London HLT 9013	You Got What It Takes/Don't Leave Me (78) 28
60	London HLT 9109	I Love The Way You Love/Let Me Love You 12
60	London HL 7095	I Love The Way You Love/Let Me Love You (export issue) 10
60	London HLT 9165	Ain't Gonna Be That Way/All The Love I've Got 12
60	London HLT 9187	(You've Got To) Move Two Mountains/I Need You 10
61	London HLT 9265	Happy Days/Baby, Baby 12
61	London HLT 9311	Merry-Go-Round/Tell Me That You Love Me 20
65	Tamla Motown TMG 525	Why Do You Want To Let Me Go/I'm Not A Plaything 60
69	Tamla Motown TMG 680	I'll Pick A Rose For My Rose/You Got The Love I Love 5
69	Tamla Motown TMG 713	I Miss You Baby (How I Miss You)/Bad Girl 4
70	Tamla Motown TMG 737	So Glad You Chose Me/I'm Not A Plaything 4
69	United Artists UP 35010	I Love The Way You Love/You Got What It Takes 4
60	London HA-T 2271	MARVELLOUS MARV JOHNSON (LP) 60
69	T. Motown (S)TML 11111	I'LL PICK A ROSE FOR MY ROSE (LP) 20

MATT JOHNSON

81	4AD CAD 113	BURNING BLUE SOUL (LP, original 'psychedelic eye' cover) 30
81	4AD CAD 113	BURNING BLUE SOUL (LP, reissue with 'Matt' picture
		& inner sleeve) 10

(see also Gadgets, The The)

MIRRIAM JOHNSON

| 61 | London HLW 9337 | Lonesome Road/Young And Innocent ....5 |

NORMAN JOHNSON & SHOWMEN

69	Action ACT 4529	You're Everything/Our Love Will Grow 15
69	Action ACT 4545	Take It Baby/In Paradise 15
71	Action ACT 4601	You're Everything/Our Love Will Grow (reissue) 8

(see also Chairmen Of The Board, Showmen, General Johnson)

PAUL JOHNSON

| 88 | CBS 450640 1 | PAUL JOHNSON (LP) ....15 |

PETE JOHNSON

39	Parlophone R 2717	Cherry Red/Baby Look At You (78) 20
44	Brunswick 03292	Death Ray Boogie/Basement Boogie (78) 15
51	Vogue V 2007	J.J. Boogie/Yancey Special (78) 12
51	Vogue V 2008	Swanee River Boogie/St. Louis Boogie (78) 12
56	Vogue V 2007	J.J. Boogie/Yancey Special 25
56	Vogue V 2008	Swanee River Boogie/St. Louis Boogie 25
55	Vogue EPV 1039	PETE JOHNSON (EP) 20
59	Top Rank JKR 8009	ROLL EM BOY (EP) 12
55	London AL 3549	JUMPIN' WITH PETE JOHNSON (10" LP) 30
55	Vogue Coral LRA 10016	BOOGIE WOOGIE MOOD (LP) 20

(see also Joe Turner & Pete Johnson, Albert Ammons & Meade Lux Lewis)

PLAS JOHNSON (ORCHESTRA)

57	Capitol CL 14772	The Big Twist/Come Rain Or Come Shine 12
57	Capitol CL 14816	Swanee River Rock/You Send Me 12
58	Capitol CL 14836	Popcorn/Hoppin' Mad 10
58	Capitol CL 14903	Little Rockin' Deacon/Dinah 12
59	Capitol CL 14973	Robbins Nest Cha Cha/Plaz Jazz 7
57	London HB-U 1078	BOP ME DADDY (10" LP) 30

PROFESSOR JOHNSON & HIS GOSPEL SINGERS

| 51 | Vocalion V 1013 | Give Me That Old Time Religion/Where Shall I Be (78) ....12 |
| 58 | Brunswick OE 9352 | PROFESSOR JOHNSON AND HIS GOSPEL SINGERS (EP) ....12 |

RAY JOHNSON

57	Vogue V 9073	If You Don't Want Me Baby/Calypso Joe 30
57	Vogue V 9073	If You Don't Want Me Baby/Calypso Joe (78) 5
58	Vogue V 9093	Calypso Blues/Are You There 25
58	Vogue V 9093	Calypso Blues/Are You There (78) 5

ROBERT JOHNSON

62	Philips BBL 7539	ROBERT JOHNSON (LP) 50
65	CBS BPG 62456	KING OF THE DELTA BLUES SINGERS (LP) 15
67	Kokomo K 1000	ROBERT JOHNSON (LP) 50
70	CBS 64102	KING OF THE DELTA BLUES SINGERS VOL. 2 (LP) 15
60s	Smokestack SS/LP 1	BLUES LEGEND 1936-1937 (LP) 30

ROY LEE JOHNSON

| 69 | Action ACT 4518 | So Anna Just Love Me/Boogaloo No. 3 ....7 |

RUBY JOHNSON

| 67 | Stax 601 020 | If I Ever Needed Love (I Sure Do Need It Now)/Keep On Keeping On ....7 |

SPIDER JOHNSON & POPEYE BAND
63	Riverside RIF 106904	Doin' The Popeye/The Gospel Truth	4

TEDDY JOHNSON
54	Columbia SCM 5098	Promise Me/Love Me	4
58	Pye 7N 15153	Merci Beaucoup/A Great Big Piece Of Chalk (with Polka Dots)	4

TEDDY JOHNSON & PEARL CARR
57	Pye 7N 15110	Tomorrow Tomorrow/Mandolin Serenade	4
58	Pye 7N 15123	Sweet Elizabeth/Never Let Me Go	4
59	Columbia DB 4260	Petite Fleur/Missouri Waltz	4
59	Columbia DB 4275	Sing Little Birdie/If Only I Could Live My Life Again	5
59	Columbia DB 4318	Tell Me, Tell Me/Viva Viva Amor	4
60	Columbia DB 4397	Pazzo Pazzo (Crazy Crazy)/The Five Pennies	4
59	HMV POP 697	Pickin' Petals/When The Tide Turns	4
59	Pye NEP 24112	MEET TEDDY AND PEARL (EP)	10

(see also Teddy & Pearl)

THEO JOHNSON
65	Aladdin WI 604	Masters Of War/Water Is Wide	5

WILKO JOHNSON & SOLID SENDERS
78	Virgin VS 214	Walking On The Edge/Dr. Dupree (p/s)	4
78	Virgin V 2105	SOLID SENDERS (LP, with free LP "Live" [VDJ 26])	10

(see also Dr. Feelgood)

JOHNSON ENGINEERING CO.
85	Gigantic G 103	Block Mania (die-cut company sleeve)	4

BRUCE JOHNSTON COMBO
63	London HL 9780	Pajama Party/Original Surfer Stomp	25

(see also Beach Boys, California Music)

SOPHIE & PETER JOHNSTON
85	Smash The Majors SPJ 1	Losing You/60 Second Blow (no p/s)	4

JOHNSTON BROTHERS
54	Decca F 10234	The Creep/Crystal Ball	8
54	Decca F 10286	I Get So Lonely/My Love, My Life, My Own	6
54	Decca F 10302	The Bandit/KEYNOTES: A Dime And A Dollar	6
54	Decca F 10364	Sh-Boom (Life Could Be A Dream)/Crazy 'Bout Ya Baby	12
54	Decca F 10401	Mambo In The Moonlight/Papa Loves Mambo (with Ted Heath Music)	6
54	Decca F 10414	"Join In And Sing" Medley (both sides)	6
55	Decca F 10451	Majorca/Heartbroken	6
55	Decca F 10490	The Right To Be Wrong/Hot Potato Mambo	6
55	Decca F 10513	Chee Chee-Oo Chee (Sang The Little Bird)/Hubble Bubble	6
55	Decca F 10526	Dreamboat/Jim, Johnny And Jonas	6
55	Decca F 10608	Hernando's Hideaway/Hey There	12
55	Decca F 10636	"Join In And Sing Again" Medley (both sides)	8
56	Decca F 10721	No Other Love/Flowers Mean Forgiveness	6
56	Decca F 10747	How Little We Know/The Street Musician	6
56	Decca F 10781	In The Middle Of The House (with Keynotes)/Stranded In The Jungle	12
56	Decca F 10814	"Join In And Sing, No. 3" Medley (both sides)	8
56	Decca F 10828	Give Her My Love (When You Meet Her)/A Rose And A Candy Bar	8
57	Decca F 10860	Whatever Lola Wants (Lola Gets)/Heart	6
57	Decca F 10915	All Star Hit Parade No. 2 (with other artists)	4
57	Decca F 10939	I Like Music — You Like Music/Seven Bar Blues	6
57	Decca F 10962	"Join In And Sing, No. 4" Medley (both sides)	5
58	Decca F 10996	A Very Precious Love/Yours, Yours, Yours	4
58	Decca F 11021	Scratch, Scratch/Little Serenade	4
58	Decca F 11083	Love Is All We Need/Clementine Cha-Cha	4
56	Decca DFE 6249	JOIN THE JOHNSTON BROTHERS (EP)	7
56	Decca DFE 6311	JOIN IN AND SING WITH THE JOHNSTON BROTHERS (EP)	7
57	Decca DFE 6458	JOIN AND SING AGAIN (EP)	7
58	Decca DFE 6503	EASY NO. 1 (EP)	7
58	Decca LK 4266	EASY (LP)	10

(see also Dennis Lotis, Vera Lynn, Edmundo Ros, Joan Regan, Lita Roza)

JOHNSTONS
66	Pye 7N 17144	Going Home/Travelling People	4
66	Pye 7N 17205	The Alamo/Life Of A Rover	4
67	Pye 7N 17205	The Curragh Of Kildare/Leaving London	4
67	Pye 7N 17430	I Never Will Marry/Banks Of Claudy	4
67	Transatlantic TRASP 17	They'll Never Get Their Man/Dublin Jack Of All Trades	4
68	Big T BIG 113	Both Sides Now/Urge For Going	4
68	Big T BIG 116	Give A Damn/Walking Out On Foggy Mornings	4
69	Big T BIG 121	My House/The Wherefore And The Why	4
70	Big T BIG 132	Streets Of London/The Spanish Lady	4
68	Transatlantic TRA 169	THE JOHNSTONS (LP)	10
68	Transatlantic TRA 184	GIVE A DAMN (LP)	10
68	Transatlantic TRA 185	THE BARLEYCORN (LP)	10
69	Marble Arch MAL 808	THE TRAVELLING PEOPLE (LP)	10
70	Transatlantic TRA 211	BITTER GREEN (LP)	10

JOHN THE POSTMAN
70s	Bent BIG BENT 2	PUERILE (12" EP, stamped brown paper bag p/s, with inserts)	12
70s	Bent BIG BENT 4	PSYCHEDELIC ROCK'N'ROLL FIVE SKINNERS (12" EP, white label, foldover p/s in bag)	12

JOINER, ARKANSAS, JUNIOR HIGH SCHOOL BAND
60	London HLG 9147	Big Ben/National City	6

MINT VALUE £

JO JO GUNNE (U.K.)
68	Decca F 12807	Every Story Has An End/Should Live Like That	6
69	Decca F 12906	Beggin' You Baby/Bad Penny	6

JO JO GUNNE (U.S.)
72	Asylum AYM 501	Run Run Run/Take It Easy (p/s)	4
72	Asylum AYM 507	Shake That Fat/I Make Love (p/s)	4
73	Asylum AYM 518	Ready Freddy/Wait A Lifetime (p/s)	4
74	Asylum AYM 528	I Wanna Love You/Neon City (p/s)	4
74	Asylum AYM 534	Where Is The Show/Single Man (p/s)	4

JOKERS
62	Salvo SLO 1806	Blue Moonbeam/Dog Fight	15

JOKER'S WILD
66	private pressing	JOKER'S WILD (mini-LP, 1-sided)	800

(see also Pink Floyd, Dave Gilmour)

GERARD JOLING
88	Mercury MER 267	Shangri-La (English)/Shangri-La (Dutch) (promo only)	5

JOLLY TINKERMEN
69	Page One POF 121	Hold On To Me Babe/Shavin' Cream	4

AL JOLSON
69	MCA MU 1092	Rockabye Your Baby With A Dixie Melody/Anniversary Song	4
54	Brunswick OE 9011	SONGS HE MADE FAMOUS VOL. 1 (EP)	7
55	Brunswick OE 9159	AL JOLSON MEMORIAL (EP)	7
57	Brunswick OE 9336	SONGS HE MADE FAMOUS PT. 1 (EP)	7
57	Brunswick OE 9337	SONGS HE MADE FAMOUS PT. 2 (EP)	7
59	Brunswick OE 9418	THEY SOLD A MILLION NO. 2 (EP)	8
59	Brunswick OE 9419	THEY SOLD A MILLION NO. 3 (EP)	8
58	Fontana TFE 17024	AL JOLSON (EP)	8
50	Brunswick LA 8502	JOLSON SINGS AGAIN (10" LP)	15
50	Brunswick LA 8509	AL JOLSON SOUVENIR (10" LP)	15
51	Brunswick LA 8512	JOLSON MEMORIES (10" LP)	15
53	Brunswick LA 8554	STEPHEN FOSTER SONGS (10" LP)	12
53	Brunswick LA 8575	AL JOLSON SOUVENIR ALBUM VOLUME 3 (10" LP)	12
53	Brunswick LA 8570	AL JOLSON SOUVENIR ALBUM VOLUME 4 (10" LP)	12
54	Brunswick LA 8655	AL JOLSON SOUVENIR ALBUM VOLUME 6 (10" LP)	12
57	Brunswick LAT 8220	THE JOLSON STORY — AMONG MY SOUVENIRS (LP)	10
58	Brunswick LAT 8267	THE IMMORTAL AL JOLSON (LP)	10
59	Brunswick LAT 8294	AL JOLSON OVERSEAS (LP)	10
60	Brunswick LAT 8322	THE WORLD'S GREATEST ENTERTAINER (LP)	10

JOLT
77	Polydor 2058 936	You're Cold/All I Can Do (p/s)	5
78	Polydor 2059 008	What'cha Gonna Do About It/Again And Again (die-cut p/s)	5
78	Polydor 2059 039	I Can't Wait/Route 66 (p/s)	6
79	Polydor 2229 215	Maybe Tonight/I'm In Tears/See Saw/Stop Look (p/s)	6
78	Polydor 2383 504	THE JOLT (LP)	10

JON
67	Parlophone R 5604	So Much For Mary/Polly Sunday (some in p/s)	25/10
67	Columbia DB 8249	Is It Love/Sing Out	40

JON & ALUN
63	Decca LK/SKL 4547	RELAX YOUR MIND (LP, mono/stereo)	20/25

JON & JEANNIE
68	Beacon 3-105	Lover's Holiday/Something You Got	5
71	Beacon BEA 113	Don't Sign The Papers/We Got Lovin'	4

JON & ROBIN & IN CROWD
67	Stateside SS 2027	Do It Again A Little Bit Slower/If I Need Someone It's You	6

JON & VANGELIS
81	Polydor POLD 5039	THE FRIENDS OF MR. CAIRO (LP, b&w sleeve, raised on left or in centre)	10

(see also Jon Anderson, Vangelis)

JONATHAN & CHARLES
69	Herald	ANOTHER WEEK TO GO (LP)	200

JONCUNO
71	Banana BA 361	The End/HORACE ANDY: See A Man's Face	4

AL JONES
58	HMV POP 451	Mad, Mad, World/Lonely Traveller	75
58	HMV POP 451	Mad, Mad, World/Lonely Traveller (78)	35

AL JONES
69	Parlophone PMC 7081	ALUN ASHWORTH JONES (LP, also stereo PCS 7081)	25
72	Village Thing VTS 19	JONESVILLE (LP)	20

(see also Anderson, Jones, Jackson)

ALLAN JONES
53	HMV 7M 111	Why Do I Love You/Make Believe	4
53	HMV 7M 135	I Believe/I Talk To The Trees	4
53	HMV 7M 161	Poppa Piccolino/Why?	4

BEVERLEY JONES
63	HMV POP 1109	The Boy I Saw With You/When It Comes To Love	6
63	HMV POP 1140	Why Do Lovers Break Each Other's Heart/I'm Just An In-Between	6
63	HMV POP 1201	Wait 'Til My Bobby Gets Home/A Boy Like You	6
64	Parlophone R 5189	Heatwave/Hear You Talking	8

B. LOU JONES & HIS JUPITERS
61	London HLU 9373	Anchors Aweigh/Anchors Aweigh (version)	4

BRENDA JONES & GROOVE HOLMES
76	RCA RCA 2688	This Is The Meme/Morning Children	4

BRENDA LEE JONES
75	UK USA 8	You're The Love Of My Life/Thread Your Needle	5

CAROL JONES
60	Triumph RGM 1012	The Boy With The Eyes Of Blue/I Gave Him Back His Ring	30

CASEY JONES & ENGINEERS
63	Columbia DB 7083	One Way Ticket/I'm Gonna Love	25

CURTIS JONES
66	RCA RCX 7184	R.C.A. VICTOR RACE SERIES VOL. 9 (EP)	12
64	Decca LK 4587	CURTIS JONES IN LONDON (LP)	20
68	Blue Horizon 7-63207	NOW RESIDENT IN EUROPE (LP)	35

DAVID JONES
65	Philips BF 1410	For Your Love/Love Bug	4

DAVIE JONES & KING BEES
64	Vocalion Pop V 9221	Liza Jane/Louie, Louie Go Home	450
78	Decca F 13807	Liza Jane/Louie, Louie Go Home (reissue)	5

(see also David Bowie, Davy Jones, Manish Boys, Calvin James)

DAVY JONES (U.S.)
60	Pye 7N 15254	Amapola/Mighty Man	4
61	Pye 7N 15318	Shenendoah/Scenery	4
61	Pye Intl. 7N 25072	Model Girl/Scarlet Woman	5
62	Piccadilly 7N 35038	Jezebel/Don't Come Crying To Me	4

DAVY JONES (U.K.)
65	Parlophone R 5315	You've Got A Habit Of Leaving/Baby Loves That Way	250

(see also David Bowie)

DAVY JONES (U.K.)
65	Colpix PX 784	What Are We Going To Do/This Bouquet	6
67	Pye 7N 17302	It Ain't Me Babe/Baby It's Me (some in p/s)	12/6
67	Pye 7N 17380	Theme For A New Love/Dream Girl (some in p/s)	12/6
67	Pye Intl. 7N 25432	Theme For A New Love/Dream Girl (reissue)	8
67	Pye NPL 18178	DAVY JONES (LP)	12

(see also Monkees)

DAVY JONES & LOWER THIRD/MANISH BOYS
79	EMI EMI 2925	You've Got A Habit Of Leaving/Baby Loves That Way/MANISH BOYS: I Pity The Fool/Take My Tip (p/s)	5
82	Charly CYM 1	You've Got A Habit Of Leaving/Baby Loves That Way/MANISH BOYS: I Pity The Fool/Take My Tip (12", p/s)	6

(see also David Bowie, Davie Jones & King Bees, Manish Boys, Calvin James)

DILL JONES TRIO
58	Pye Jazz 7NJ 2021	Little Rock Getaway/Carolina Shout	4
56	Polygon JTE 104	PIANO MOODS VOL. 2 (EP)	10

FLOYD JONES/EDDIE TAYLOR
60s	XX MIN 712	FLOYD JONES AND EDDIE TAYLOR (EP, 2 tracks each)	7

GAYNOR JONES
69	Morgan MR 16	Mum P T Dum P T/Memories Of Summertime	4
69	Decca F 12970	Peaches And Pears/Please Take My Hand	4

GEORGE JONES
59	Mercury AMT 1021	The Treasure Of Love/If I Don't Love You (Grits Ain't Groceries)	15
59	Mercury AMT 1021	The Treasure Of Love/If I Don't Love You (Grits Ain't Groceries) (78)	10
59	Mercury AMT 1036	White Lightning/Long Time To Forget	35
59	Mercury AMT 1058	Who Shot Sam/Into My Arms Again	18
59	Mercury AMT 1078	Big Harlan Taylor/Money To Burn	10
60	Mercury AMT 1100	Sparkling Brown Eyes/Accidentally On Purpose	10
61	Mercury AMT 1124	Candy Hearts/The Window Up Above	10
62	United Artists POP 1037	She Thinks I Still Care/Geronimo	10
63	United Artists UP 1015	I Saw Me/Not What I Had In Mind (as George Jones with Jones Boys)	8
69	Stateside SS 2145	If My Heart Had Windows/Taggin' Along	6
65	United Artists UP 1080	The Race Is On/She's So Lonesome Again	8
71	Pye Intl. 7N 25547	It's Been A Good Year For The Roses/Let A Little Come In	5
80	Epic EPC 8560	Stranger In The House (with Elvis Costello)/A Drunk Can't Be A Man	4
59	Mercury ZEP 10012	COUNTRY AND WESTERN (EP)	25
59	Mercury ZEP 10036	GEORGE JONES (EP)	50
60s	Melodisc EPM7 109	COUNTRY SONG HITS (EP)	25
64	Mercury 10009 MCE	C & W ACES (EP)	12
64	Ember EMB 4548	THE BEST OF AMERICAN COUNTRY MUSIC VOL. 4 (EP)	8
62	United Artists ULP 1007	THE NEW FAVOURITES OF GEORGE JONES (LP)	15
63	United Artists ULP 1014	MY FAVOURITES OF HANK WILLIAMS (LP)	15
63	Ember CW 101	THE CROWN PRINCE OF COUNTRY MUSIC (LP)	12
63	United Artists ULP 1037	HITS OF HIS COUNTRY COUSINS (LP)	15
64	United Artists ULP 1050	I WISH TONIGHT WOULD NEVER END (LP)	15
64	London HA-B 8125	GEORGE JONES SINGS HIS GREATEST HITS (LP)	20
64	United Artists ULP 1070	WHAT'S IN OUR HEARTS (LP, with Melba Montgomery)	12
64	Ember CW 109	THE FABULOUS COUNTRY MUSIC SOUND OF JONES (LP)	12
64	United Artists ULP 1074	MORE NEW FAVOURITES (LP)	15
65	United Artists ULP 1077	BLUE GRASS HOOTENANNY (LP, with Melba Montgomery)	12

George JONES

65	United Artists ULP 1091	I GET LONELY IN A HURRY (LP)	15
65	United Artists ULP 1082	JONES SINGS LIKE THE DICKENS (LP)	15
65	United Artists ULP 1101	TROUBLE IN MIND (LP)	15
65	Stateside SL 10147	GEORGE JONES AND GENE PITNEY (LP, with Gene Pitney)	12
65	Stateside SL 10157	MR. COUNTRY AND WESTERN MUSIC (LP)	12
66	London HA-B 8259	GEORGE JONES (LP, with Tommy Hill's Band)	20
66	United Artists (S)ULP 1136	THE GREAT GEORGE JONES (LP)	12
66	United Artists (S)ULP 1137	BLUE MOON OF KENTUCKY (LP, with Melba Montgomery)	12
66	Stateside SL 10173	IT'S COUNTRY TIME AGAIN (LP, with Gene Pitney)	12
66	Stateside S(S)L 10184	LOVE BUG (LP)	12
67	Stateside S(S)L 10195	WE FOUND HEAVEN RIGHT HERE ON EARTH AT '4033' (LP)	12
67	Mercury SMCL 20107	GREATEST HITS (LP)	12
67	London HA-B 8340	THE GEORGE JONES SONG BOOK (LP)	18
67	Stateside S(S)L 10215	VARIETY IS THE SPICE OF ... (LP)	12
68	Stateside S(S)L 10236	SINGS THE SONGS OF DALLAS FRAZIER (LP)	12
68	Hallmark HM 562	GEORGE JONES SINGS (LP)	10
68	Mercury SMWL 21003	C&W WINNERS (LP)	15
69	Stateside S(S)L 10256	IF MY HEART HAD WINDOWS (LP)	10
69	Stateside S(S)L 10283	MY COUNTRY (LP)	10
69	Fontana SFL 13202	THE GREAT GEORGE JONES (LP, reissue)	10
71	Pye Intl. NSPL 28150	THE BEST OF GEORGE JONES (LP)	10
72	Pye PKL 4412	THE BLUE SIDE OF LONESOME & OTHER COUNTRY FAVOURITES (LP)	12
72	Pye Intl. NSPL 28160	COUNTRY MUSIC '72 (LP)	12
73	Pye Intl. NSPL 28176	WRAPPED AROUND HER FINGERS (LP)	12
74	CBS EQ 30802	WE GO TOGETHER (LP, with Tammy Wynette, quadrophonic)	10

(see also Gene Pitney, Elvis Costello)

GLORIA JONES

66	Capitol CL 15429	Heartbeat Pts 1 & 2	15
66	Stateside SS 555	Finders Keepers/Run One Flight Of Stairs	20
74	Tamla Motown TMG 910	Tin Can People/So Tired	4
76	EMI EMI 2437	Get It On/Get It On (Version)	4
76	EMI EMI 2522	I Ain't Going Nowhere/Simplicity Blues	4
77	EMI EMI 2570	Go Now/Drive Me Crazy	4
77	EMI EMI 2720	Cry Baby/Bring On The Love	4
74	T. Motown STML 11254	SHARE MY LOVE (LP)	10

(see also Marc Bolan & Gloria Jones)

GRACE JONES

77	Polydor 2058 856	That's The Trouble/Sorry	4
77	Polydor 2058 898	I Need A Man/I Need A Man (Version)	4
83	Island ISP 103	My Jamaican Guy/Cry Now, Laugh Later (picture disc)	5
85	ZTT ISP 206	Slave To The Rhythm/Slave To The Rhythm (Annihilate Mix) (picture disc)	4
85	ZTT 12ISP 206	Slave To The Rhythm/Slave To The Rhythm (Annihilate Mix) (12", picture disc)	7
86	Island IPR 2004	La Vie En Rose/I Need A Man (12", promo-only)	10
86	Island ISP 240	Pull Up To The Bumper/La Vie En Rose (picture disc)	4
86	Island ISP 266	Love Is A Drug/Living My Life (picture disc)	4
87	Manhattan MTP 20	Party Girl (Remix)/White Collar Crime (shaped picture disc)	5

GRANDPA JONES

57	Brunswick 05676	Eight More Miles To Louisville/Dark As A Dungeon	25
59	Brunswick OE 9455	MOUNTAIN MUSIC VOL. 3 (EP)	20
64	London REU 1417	GRANDPA SINGS JIMMIE RODGERS (EP)	25
57	Parlophone GEP 8666	MEET GRANDPA JONES (EP)	25
58	Parlophone GEP 8766	COUNTRY AND WESTERN (EP)	30
59	Parlophone GEP 8781	COUNTRY ROUND UP (EP)	25
62	London HA-U/SH-U 8010	MAKE THE RAFTERS RING (LP)	25
64	London HA-U/SH-U 8119	YODELLING HITS (LP)	25

HOWARD JONES

83	WEA HOW 1/RISK 1	New Song/Change The Man//New Song/Don't Always Look At The Rain (double pack)	4
83	WEA HOW 2/SAM 183	What Is Love/It Just Doesn't Matter//What Can I Say (live)/Bounce Right Back (double pack with sticker)	10
84	WEA HOW 3PT	Hide And Seek/Tao Te Ching (square picture disc)	5
84	WEA HOW 3L	Hide And Seek/Tao Te Ching/China Dance (10", p/s)	5
84	WEA HOW 4P	Pearl In The Shell/Law Of The Jungle (shaped picture disc)	5
85	WEA HOW 6P	Things Can Only Get Better/Why Look For The Key (orange or green shaped discs)	6
85	WEA HOW 6P	Things Can Only Get Better/Why Look For The Key (blue/white shaped discs)	15
85	WEA HOW 7TE	Look Mama (Megamamamix) (12", p/s)	12
85	WEA HOW 8F	Life In One Day/Boom Bap Respite//Always Asking Questions/New Song (double pack, stickered gatefold p/s)	4
86	WEA HOW 11F (HOW 11/SAM 328)	You Know I Love You ... Don't You?/Dig This Well Deep//Hide And Seek (Orchestral) (double pack, stickered gatefold p/s, 2nd disc 1-sided)	4

JACK JONES

65	London HLR 9939	Dear Heart/Where Love Has Gone	4
65	London HLR 9956	The Race Is On/I Can't Believe I'm Losing You	4
66	London HLR 10088	Impossible Dream/A Day In The Life Of A Fool	4
67	London HLR 10108	Lady/Afraid Of Love	4
64	London HA-R 8167	WIVES AND LOVERS (LP)	10
64	London HA-R/SH-R 8191	SHE LOVES ME (LP)	10
65	London HA-R 8202	BEWITCHED (LP)	10
65	London HA-R/SH-R 8209	WHERE LOVE HAS GONE (LP)	10
65	London HA-R/SH-R 8222	SONGS OF LOVE (LP)	10
65	London HA-R/SH-R 8236	MY KIND OF TOWN (LP)	10
65	London HA-R/SH-R 8246	THE JACK JONES CHRISTMAS ALBUM (LP)	10

66	London HA-R/SH-R 8254	AND THERE'S LOVE (LP)	10

JANET JONES
74	Midas MR 005	SING TO ME LADY (LP)	50

JANIE JONES
65	HMV POP 1495	Witches Brew/Take-A My Tip	15
66	HMV POP 1514	Gunning For You/Go Go Away From Me	12
67	Columbia DB 8173	Tickle Me Tootsie Wootsies/High And Dry	6
68	Pye 7N 17550	Charlie Smith/Nobody's Perfect	5
68	Major Minor MM 577	Girl's Song/I've Never Met A Boy Like You	6
70	President PT 309	Back On My Feet Again/Psycho	6

JANIE JONES & LASH
83	Big Beat NS 91	House Of The Ju-Ju Queen/Sex Machine (p/s)	6
	(see also Clash)		

JERRY JONES
70	Bamboo BAM 65	Still Waters/SOUND DIMENSION: Wig Wam	5
70	Banana BA 316	Still Waters/SOUND DIMENSION: Wig Wam (reissue)	5
71	Bamboo BALPS 213	LIVE AT THE KINGSTON HOTEL, JAMAICA (LP)	25

JIMMY JONES
60	MGM MGM 1051	Handy Man/The Search Is Over	6
60	MGM MGM 1051	Handy Man/The Search Is Over (78)	60
60	MGM MGM 1078	Good Timin'/Too Long Will Be Too Late	6
60	MGM MGM 1078	Good Timin'/Too Long Will Be Too Late (78)	60
60	MGM MGM 1091	I Just Go For You/That's When I Cried	6
60	MGM MGM 1103	Ready For Love/For You	6
61	MGM MGM 1123	I Told You So/You Got It	5
61	MGM MGM 1133	Dear One/I Say Love	5
61	MGM MGM 1146	Mr Music Man/Holler Hey	5
62	MGM MGM 1168	You're Much Too Young/Nights Of Mexico	5
68	MGM MGM 1405	Good Timin'/Handy Man	5
60s	Cameo Parkway P 988	Don't You Just Know It	5
67	Stateside SS 2041	39-21-46/Personal Property	6
65	Columbia DB 7592	Walkin'/Pardon Me	20
60	MGM EP 745	JIMMY HANDYMAN JONES (EP)	30
61	MGM EP 787	ORIGINAL HITS (EP)	15
60	MGM C 832	GOOD TIMIN' (LP)	40

JO JONES TRIO
59	Top Rank 25/039	JO JONES (LP)	10

JOE JONES
60	Columbia DB 4533	You Talk Too Much/I Love You Still	10

JOHN PAUL JONES
64	Pye 7N 15637	A Foggy Day In Vietnam/Baja	60
	(see also Led Zeppelin, Tony Meehan)		

JOHNNY JONES & KING CASUALS
68	MCA MU 1031	Soul Poppin'/Blues For The Brothers	4
76	Cream CRM 5004	Purple Haze/Horsing Around	4
76	Brunswick BR 37	Purple Haze/FRED HUGHES: Baby Boy	4
80	Sonet SNTF 821	RARE RECORDINGS (LP)	10

JUGGY JONES
76	Contempo CS 2080	Inside America Pts 1 & 2	4

JUSTIN JONES
61	London HLU 9463	Dance By Yourself/Love	4

KEN JONES
61	Parlophone R 4763	Bluesville/On The Rebound	4
61	Parlophone R 4788	Just Rollin'/Joxsville	4
60s	Embassy	KEN JONES AND HIS ROCK AND ROLLERS (EP series)	each 10

LINDA JONES
67	Warner Bros WB 2070	Hypnotised/I Can't Stop Lovin' My Baby	35
72	London HLU 10368	For Your Precious Love/Don't Go	5
75	Warner Bros WB 16621	I Just Can't Live My Life/My Heart Will Understand	8

LOUIS JONES ROCK & ROLL BAND
50s	Vogue VE1 70111	ROCK AND ROLL (EP)	50

MAE JONES ENSEMBLE with MARGARET BOND
55	Decca F 10486	I Walked Into The Garden/Tenderly He Watches	4

MAGGIE JONES
70	VJM VLP 23	COLUMBIA RECORDINGS IN CHRONOLOGICAL ORDER VOL. 1 (LP)	15
70	VJM VLP 25	COLUMBIA RECORDINGS IN CHRONOLOGICAL ORDER VOL. 2 (LP)	15

NIC JONES
70	Trailer LER 2014	BALLADS AND SONGS (LP)	12
71	Trailer LER 2027	NIC JONES (LP)	10
73	Trailer LER 2083	SONGS OF THE CHANGING WORLD (LP)	10

NIGEL MAZLYN JONES
76	Isle Of Light IOL 666/1	SHIP TO SHORE (LP)	50
78	Avada AVA 105	SENTINEL (LP)	20
82	Isle Of Light IOL 0230	BREAKING COVER (LP)	20
	(see also Solstice)		

PALMER JONES
68	Direction 58-3603	The Great Magic Of Love/Dancing Master	6

MINT VALUE £

PAUL JONES

66	HMV POP 1554	High Time/I Can't On Much Longer	5
67	HMV POP 1576	I've Been A Bad Bad Boy/Sonny Boy Williamson	5
67	HMV POP 1602	Thinkin' Ain't For Me/Softly (La Vita)	4
67	Columbia DB 8303	Three Sisters/Sons And Lovers	4
68	Columbia DB 8379	And The Sun Will Shine/The Dog Presides	18
68	Columbia DB 8417	When I Was Six Years Old/You Have No Idea	6
69	Columbia DB 8514	Aquarius/Pisces	4
69	Columbia DB 8567	It's Getting Better/Hot Before Time	4
71	Vertigo 6059 053	Life After Death/The Mighty Ship	4
78	RSO RSO 003	Sheena Is A Punk Rocker/Pretty Vacant (p/s)	4
66	HMV 7EG 8974	PRIVILEGE (EP)	12
66	HMV CLP/CSD 3586	MY WAY (LP, mono/stereo)	18/20
67	HMV CLP/CSD 3602	LOVE ME, LOVE MY FRIENDS (LP, mono/stereo)	18/20
66	HMV CLP 3623	PRIVILEGE (LP, soundtrack, with George Bean Group & Mike Leander)	18
69	Columbia SCX 6347	COME INTO MY MUSIC BOX (LP)	20
71	Vertigo 6360 059	CRUCIFIX IN A HORSESHOE (LP, gatefold sleeve, spiral label)	30

(see also Manfred Mann, Blues Band)

PHILLY JOE JONES

70	Polydor 2460 142	TRAILWAYS EXPRESS (LP)	10

QUINCY JONES

59	Mercury AMT 1037	Tuxedo Junction/The Syncopated Clock	5
60	Mercury AMT 1111	Love Is Here To Stay/Moonglow	5
62	Mercury AMT 1195	Soul Bossa Nova/On The Street Where You Live	8
65	Mercury MF 844	Seaweed/Golden Boy Theme	5
69	A&M AMS 781	Killer Joe/Oh Happy Day	5
69	RCA RCA 1850	MacKenna's Gold/Soul Full Of Gold	4
72	Reprise K 14150	Money Runned	4
72	Atlantic K 10172	Listen To The Melody/Hot Rock Theme	4
60	Mercury ZEP 10047	BIG BAND BASH (EP)	10
61	Mercury ZEP 10109	THE BIRTH OF A BAND (EP, also stereo SEZ 19017)	7/8
61	Columbia SEG 8088	DOUBLE SIX MEET QUINCY JONES (EP)	7
61	Mercury ZEP 10119	THE BIRTH OF A BAND PT. 2 (EP, also stereo SEZ 19021)	7/8
60	Mercury MMC 14038	THE BIRTH OF A BAND (LP, also stereo CMS 18026)	12/14
60	Mercury MMC 14046	THE GREAT WORLD OF QUINCY JONES (LP, also stereo CMS 18031)	12/14
61	Mercury MMC 14080	I DIG DANCERS (LP, also stereo CMS 18055)	12
62	HMV CLP 1581	THE QUINTESSENCE (LP, also stereo CSD 1452)	12
62	Mercury MMC 14098	AROUND THE WORLD (LP, also stereo CMS 18064)	12
63	Mercury MMC 14125	BIG BAND BOSSA NOVA (LP, also stereo CMS 18080)	12
63	Mercury MMC 14128	PLAYS HIP HITS (LP)	10
64	Mercury MCL 20016	JONES EXPLORES THE MUSIC OF HENRY MANCINI (LP, also stereo SMCL 20016)	10
65	Columbia 33SX 1637	QUINCY'S HOME AGAIN (LP)	10
65	Mercury 20047MCL	GOLDEN BOY (LP)	10
66	Mercury 20072(S)MCL	"MIRAGE" (LP)	12
66	Mercury 20073(S)MCL	PLAYS FOR PUSSYCATS (LP)	10
66	Mercury 20078(S)MCL	QUINCY'S GOT A BRAND NEW BAG (LP)	15
66	Fontana FJL 127	FAB! (LP)	10
67	Mercury SMWL 30003	TRAVELLIN' ON THE QUINCY JONES BANDWAGON (LP)	10
70	United Artists	THEY CALL ME MISTER TIBBS (LP, soundtrack)	30
72	WEA K 44168	THE HEIST (LP, soundtrack)	10
72	Atlantic K 40371	HOW TO STEAL A DIAMOND (LP, soundtrack)	10

RONNIE JONES

64	Decca F 12012	I Need Your Loving/Let's Pin A Rose On You (with Night Timers)	10
65	Decca F 12066	My Love/It's All Over	12
65	Decca F 12146	Anyone Who Knows What Love Is/Nobody But You	10
65	Parlophone R 5326	You're Lookin' Good/I'm So Clean (with Blue Jays)	25
67	CBS 2699	Little Bitty Pretty One/Put Your Tears Away	6
67	Polydor 56222	In My Love Mind/Mama Come On Home	8
68	CBS 3304	Without Love (There Is Nothing)/Little Bitty Pretty One	8

SALENA JONES

66	Columbia DB 7818	Walk In The Black Forest/As Long As I Live	4
66	Columbia DB 7991	I Am Yours/I Only Know I Love You	4
67	Columbia DB 8212	When I Tell You (That I Love You)/Respect	4

SALINA JONES

65	Polydor BM 56012	Longing/Too Late	4

SAMANTHA JONES

65	United Artists UP 1072	It's All Because Of You/I Woke Up Crying	6
65	United Artists UP 1087	Don't Come Any Closer/Just Call And I'll Be There	4
65	United Artists UP 1105	Chained To A Memory/Just For Him	4
66	United Artists UP 1139	That Special Way/Somebody Else's Baby	4
67	United Artists UP 1185	Surrounded By A Ray Of Sunshine/How Do You Say Goodbye	35
67	United Artists UP 1200	Why Can't I Remember/Live For Life	4
68	United Artists UP 2248	Lonely Lonely Man/Doll On A Music Box	4
68	United Artists UP 2258	And Suddenly/Go Ahead And Love Me	20

SANDIE JONES

72	Polydor 2058 223	Music Of Love/Ceol An Ghra	15

SHIRLEY JONES

61	Pye Intl. 7N 25067	Pepe/Lovely Day	4

SPIKE JONES

53	HMV B 10482	I Went To Your Wedding/Lulu Had A Baby (78)	5

53	HMV 7M 121	Hot Lips/Hotter Than A Pistol (& His Country Cousins)	12
53	HMV 7M 160	I Saw Mommy Kissing Santa Claus/Winter (& His City Slickers)	8
54	HMV 7MC 3	Deep Purple/Dragnet (& His City Slickers, export issue)	6
54	HMV 7MC 17	I Wanna Go Back To West Virginia/Little Bo-Beep Has Lost Her Sheep (& His City Slickers, export issue)	6
55	HMV 7M 324	Secret Love/I'm In The Mood For Love (& His City Slickers)	8
61	Warner Bros WB 34	Monster Movie Babe/Teenage Brain Surgeon	4
57	HMV 7EG 8286	FUN IN HI FI (EP)	8
59	RCA RCX 1030	SPIKE JONES NO. 1 (EP)	8
59	RCA RCX 1037	SPIKE JONES NO. 2 (EP)	8
61	Warners W(S) EP 6044	SPIKE JONES IN HI FI (EP, mono/stereo)	7/10
60	Warner Bros WM 4004	THE BAND THAT PLAYS FOR FUN (LP, also stereo WS 8004)	10/12
60	London HA-G 2270	OMNIBUST — T.V. SCHEDULE (LP, also stereo SAH-G 6090)	10/12
61	London HA-G 2298	SIXTY YEARS OF MUSIC AMERICA HATES BEST (LP, also stereo SAH-G 6106)	10/12

TAMIKO JONES

| 75 | Arista ARIST 6 | Touch Me Baby/Creepin' On My Dreams | 5 |
| 76 | Contempo CS 2079 | I'm Spellbound/T.J.'s Magic | 4 |

THAD JONES

| 50s | Nixa Jazz NJL 13 | LEONARD FEATHER PRESENTS MAD THAD (LP) | 10 |

THELMA JONES

68	Sue WI 4047	Stronger/Never Leave Me	12
69	Soul City SC 110	The House That Jack Built/Give It To Me Straight	12
76	CBS 4711	Salty Tears/You're The Song	4

THUNDERCLAP JONES

| 56 | Oriole CB 1320 | Hurricane Boogie/The Laughing Rag (78) | 5 |
| 56 | Oriole CB 1328 | Sound Barrier Boogie/Ask For Joe (78) | 5 |

TOM JONES

64	Decca F 11966	Chills And Fever/Breathless	15
65	Decca F 12062	It's Not Unusual/To Wait For Love (Is To Waste Your Life Away)	4
65	Decca F 12121	Once Upon A Time/I Tell The Sea	5
65	Columbia DB 7566	Little Lonely One/That's What We'll All Do	12
65	Decca F 12191	With These Hands/Untrue	4
65	Decca F 12203	What's New Pussycat?/Rose	4
65	Columbia DB 7733	Lonely Joe/I Was A Fool	10
65	Decca F 12292	Thunderball/Key To My Heart	5
66	Decca F 12315	To Make A Big Man Cry/I'll Never Let You Go (export issue)	10
66	Decca F 12349	Stop Breaking My Heart/Never Give Away Love	8
66	Decca F 12461	This And That/City Girl	5
66	Decca F 22511	Green, Green Grass Of Home/Promise Her Anything	4
66	Decca F 12516	Green, Green Grass Of Home/If I Had You (export issue)	10
67	Decca F 22555	Detroit City/If I Had You	4
67	Decca F 22563	Detroit City/Ten Guitars (export issue)	10
67	Decca F 12599	Funny Familiar Forgotten Feelings/I'll Never Let You Go	4
68	Decca F 12747	Delilah/Smile Away Your Blues	4
71	Decca F 13183	Puppet Man/Every Mile	4
71	Decca FR 13237	Till/One Day Soon (export issue)	10
73	Decca F 13393	Letter To Lucille/Thank The Lord	4
73	Decca F 13434	Today I Started Loving You Again/I Still Love You Enough	4
73	Decca F 13471	Golden Days/Goodbye, God Bless You Baby	4
74	Decca F 13490	La La La (Just Having You Here)/Love Love Love	4
74	Decca F 13550	Somethin' 'Bout You Baby I Like/Keep A-Talking 'Bout Love	4
74	Decca F 13564	Pledging My Love/I'm Too Far Gone (To Turn Away)	4
75	Decca F 13575	Ain't No Love/When The Band Goes Home	4
75	Decca F 13590	I Got Your Number/The Pain Of Love	4
75	Decca F 13598	Memories Don't Leave Like People Do/My Helping Hand	4
70s	Decca F 12747/12062	Delilah/It's Not Unusual (double-A-side with different number each way)	4
82	Decca JONES 1	I'll Be Here Where The Heart Is/My Last Goodbye (p/s)	4
87	Epic OLE Q1	A Boy From Nowhere/I'll Dress You In Mourning (poster p/s)	4
65	Decca DFE 8617	ON STAGE (EP)	10
65	Columbia SEG 8464	TOM JONES (EP)	20
65	Decca DFE 8668	WHAT A PARTY (EP)	10
65	Decca LK 4693	ALONG CAME JONES (LP)	12
65	Decca LK/SKL 4743	A-TOM-IC JONES (LP, mono/stereo)	10/12
66	Decca LK 4814	FROM THE HEART (LP)	12
67	Decca LK/SKL 4855	GREEN, GREEN GRASS OF HOME (LP)	10
67	Decca LK/SKL 4874	LIVE! AT THE TALK OF THE TOWN (LP)	10
67	Decca LK/SKL 4909	13 SMASH HITS (LP)	10
68	Decca LK/SKL 4946	DELILAH (LP)	10
68	Decca LK/SKL 4982	HELP YOURSELF (LP)	10
69	Decca LK/SKL 5007	THIS IS TOM JONES (LP)	10
69	Decca LK/SKL 5032	LIVE IN LAS VEGAS (LP)	10
70	Decca LK/SKL 5045	TOM (LP)	10
70	Decca LK/SKL 5072	I, WHO HAVE NOTHING (LP)	10
71	Decca SKL 5089	SINGS SHE'S A LADY (LP)	10
71	Decca DKL 1 1/2	LIVE AT CAESAR'S PALACE, LAS VEGAS (2-LP)	14
72	Decca SKL 5132	CLOSE UP (LP)	10
73	Decca SKL 5162	THE BODY AND SOUL OF TOM JONES (LP)	10
74	Decca SKL 5197	SOMETHIN' 'BOUT YOU BABY I LIKE (LP)	10
75	Decca SKL 5214	MEMORIES DON'T LEAVE LIKE PEOPLE DO (LP)	10

U.K. JONES

| 69 | Deram DM 231 | Let Me Tell Ya/And The Rains Came Down | 5 |

MINT VALUE £

WIZZ JONES
63	United Artists SULP 1029	WIZZ JONES (LP)	100
70	Village Thing VTS 4	LEGENDARY ME (LP)	15
71	CBS 64809	RIGHT NOW (LP)	50
74	Village Thing VTS 24	WHEN I LEAVE BERLIN (LP)	15
77	Plant Life PLR 009	MAGICAL FLIGHT (LP, with insert)	15

(see also Pete Stanley & Wizz Jones)

JONES BOYS
57	Columbia DB 4046	Cool Baby/Rock-A-Hula Baby (Ukelele Lady)	7
58	Columbia DB 4170	A Certain Smile/Kathy-O	6
58	Columbia DB 4217	The Day The Rains Came/Hideaway	6
59	Columbia DB 4278	Dream Girl/Straight As An Arrow	5

(see also Four Jones Boys)

JONES GIRLS
82	Philadelphia Intl. PIR 2031	Nights Are Egypt/Love Don't Ever Say Goodbye	6
82	Phil. Intl. PIR 12-2031	Nights Are Egypt/Love Don't Ever Say Goodbye (12")	10
79	Phil. Intl. PIR 83831	THE JONES GIRLS (LP)	12

JONESY
72	Dawn DNS 1030	Ricochet/Every Day's The Same	5
72	Dawn DNLS 3042	NO ALTERNATIVE (LP, gatefold sleeve)	25
73	Dawn DNLS 3048	KEEPING UP (LP)	20
73	Dawn DNLS 3055	GROWING (LP, gatefold sleeve)	20

JON-MARK
65	Brunswick 05929	Baby I Got A Long Way To Go/Night Comes Down	4
66	Brunswick 05952	Paris Bells/Little Town Girl	4

HARLEM JONNS RESHUFFLE
68	Fontana TF 970	You Are The One I Love/Good Lovin'	8
69	Fontana TF 1004	Everything Under The Sun/Let Love Come Between Us	6
69	Fontana	HARLEM JONNS RESHUFFLE (LP)	10

JONSTON McPHILBRY
66	Fontana TF 663	She's Gone/Woke Up At Eight	40

JOOK
72	RCA RCA 2279	Alright With Me/Do What You Can	5
73	RCA RCA 2344	Shame/City And Suburban Blues	4
73	RCA RCA 2368	Oo Oo Rudi/Jook's On You	4
73	RCA RCA 2431	King Capp/Rumble	4
74	RCA RCA 5024	Bish Bash Bosh/Crazy Kids	4
78	Chiswick SW 30	Watch Your Step/La La Girl/Aggravation Place/Everything I Do (EP)	4

(see also John's Children)

JOOLZ
83	Abstract 12 ABS 018	Denise/The Latest Craze/War Of Attrition/Protection (12", p/s, with Jah Wobble)	8
84	Abstract 12 ABS 025	The Kiss/The Kiss (Club Mix)/Paved With Gold (12", p/s, with Jah Wobble)	7
85	EMI JLZ 1	Love Is (Sweet Romance)/Musket Fife & Drum (p/s)	4
85	EMI 12 JLZ 1	Love Is (Sweet Romance)/Musket Fife & Drum/Fury (12", p/s)	8
86	EMI EMI 5582	Mad Bad And Dangerous To Know/Legend (p/s)	4
86	EMI 12 EMI 5582	Mad Bad And Dangerous To Know/Legend/Babies (12", p/s)	7
85	Abstract ABS 011	NEVER NEVER LAND (mini-LP)	8
87	Columbia SCX 6711	HEX (LP)	12

(see also New Model Army, Jah Wobble)

JANIS JOPLIN
71	CBS 7019	Me And Bobby McGee/Half Moon	4
71	CBS 7217	Cry Baby/Mercedes Benz	4
72	CBS 8241	Down On Me/Bye Bye Baby	5
75	CBS 3683	Turtle Blues/Piece Of My Heart (withdrawn)	25
76	CBS 3960	Piece Of My Heart/Kozmic Blues (p/s)	6
71	CBS 9136	Move Over/Cry Baby/Try/Piece Of My Heart (EP)	7
69	CBS 63546	I GOT DEM OL' KOZMIC BLUES AGAIN, MAMA! (LP)	10
74	CBS CQ 30322/Q 64188	PEARL (LP, quadrophonic)	12

(see also Big Brother & Holding Company)

DANNY JORDAN
61	Mercury AMT 1159	Jeannie/Boom Ditty Boom	5

DICK JORDAN
60	Oriole CB 1534	Hallelujah, I Love Her So/Sandy	6
60	Oriole CB 1548	Little Christine/I'll Love You Forever	6
60	Oriole CB 1566	Alive, Alive Oh!/Garden Of Eden	4
60	Oriole CB 1591	Angel On My Shoulder/The Next Train Home	4
61	Piccadilly 7N 35035	Some Of These Days/I Want Her Back	4
62	Piccadilly 7N 35057	Fortune Teller/My Angel	4

JOHNNY JORDAN
57	HMV POP 349	It's Grand To Be In Love/Home At Last	4

LOUIS JORDAN (& HIS TYMPANY FIVE)
39	Vocalion S 243	Flat Face/Keep A Knockin' (78)	25
46	Brunswick 03696	Choo Choo Ch'boogie/That Chick's Too Young To Fry (78)	12
47	Brunswick 03778	Open The Door Richard/Ain't Nobody Here But Us Chickens (78)	12
47	Brunswick 03797	Let The Good Times Roll/Ain't That Just Like A Woman (78)	12
47	Brunswick 03834	Jack You're Dead/Boogie Woogie Blue Plate (78)	12
47	Brunswick 03848	Beware/Texas And Pacific (78)	12
47	Brunswick 03893	Salt Pork West Virginia/Reconversion Blues (78)	12

MINT VALUE £

48	Brunswick 03910	Barnyard Boogie/How Long Must I Wait For You (78)	12
48	Brunswick 03986	I Like 'Em Fat Like That/Don't Let The Sun Catch You Cryin' (78)	12
48	Brunswick 04019	Why'd You Do It Baby/Pettin' And Pokin' (78)	12
48	Brunsiwck 04041	Buzz Me/Caledonia (78)	10
49	Brunswick 04201	Ain't That Just Like A Woman/Have You Got The Gumption (78)	12
49	Brunswick 04325	What's The Use Of Gettin' Sober/The Chicks I Pick (78)	10
49	Brunswick 04326	Early In The Morning/Look Out (78)	10
49	Brunswick 04327	Lowdown Dirty Shame/Rusty Dusty Blues (78)	10
50	Brunswick 04402	Saturday Night Fish Fry Pts 1 & 2 (78)	10
50	Brunswick 04519	Push Ka Pee Shee Pie/Hungry Man (78)	8
51	Brunswick 04770	Three-Handed Woman/Is My Pop In There? (78)	8
54	Melodisc 1031	Dad Gum Ya Hide Boy/Whiskey Do Your Stuff (78)	15
56	Melodisc 1349	Messy Bessy/I Seen What'cha Done (78)	15
60	Downbeat CHA 3	Ooo-Wee/I'll Die Happy	20
50s	Melodisc EPM7 66	LOUIS JORDAN (EP, as Louis Jordon Tympany Five)	40
57	Mercury MPT 7521	SOMEBODY UP THERE DIGS ME (10" LP, with Tympany Five)	40
58	Mercury MPL 6541	MAN, WE'RE WAILIN' (LP, with Tympany Five)	30
65	Ace Of Hearts AH 85	LET THE GOOD TIMES ROLL (LP)	15
68	Coral CP 59	LET THE GOOD TIMES ROLL (LP, reissue)	12

LOUIS JORDAN & CHRIS BARBER'S BAND
| 50s | Melodisc 45-1616 | Is She Is Or Is She Ain't Your Baby/Fifty Cents | 8 |

(see also Chris Barber)

LOUIS JORDAN & ELLA FITZGERALD
| 49 | Brunswick 04274 | Baby It's Cold Outside/Don't Cry Baby (78) | 15 |

JORDANAIRES
57	Capitol CL 14687	Sugaree/Baby, Won't You Please Come Home?	30
57	Capitol CL 14687	Sugaree/Baby, Won't You Please Come Home? (78)	5
57	Capitol CL 14773	Summer Vacation/Each Day	12
57	Capitol CL 14773	Summer Vacation/Each Day (78)	5
58	Capitol CL 14921	Little Miss Ruby/All I Need Is You	12
63	Capitol CL 15281	Don't Be Cruel/Don't Worry	12
62	Capitol T 1742	SPOTLIGHT ON THE JORDANAIRES (LP)	25

(see also Elvis Presley, Patsy Cline, Don Gibson)

JORDAN BROTHERS
60	London HLW 8908	Never, Never/Please Tell Me Now	20
60	London HLW 8908	Never, Never/Please Tell Me Now (78)	8
60	London HLW 9235	Things I Didn't Say/Polly Plays Her Kettle Drum	6
61	London HLW 9308	No Wings On My Angel/Living For The Day	7

JOSEF K
80	Absolute ABS 1	Chance Meeting/Romance (p/s)	30
80	Postcard 80-3	Radio Drill Time/Crazy To Exist (live) (hand-coloured foldaround p/s, blue labels)	16
80	Postcard 80-3	Radio Drill Time/Crazy To Exist (live) (brown or cream/yellow sleeve &labels)	7/8
80	Postcard 80-5	It's Kinda Funny/Final Request (p/s in poly bag, some with picture insert)	12/7
81	Postcard 81-5	Chance Meeting/Pictures (Of Cindy) (die-cut sleeve, some with postcard)	8/6
81	Postcard 81-4/TWI 023	Sorry For Laughing/Revelation (p/s)	8
87	Supreme Intl. Edit. 87-7	Heaven Sent/Radio Drill Time/Heads Watch/Fun'n'Frenzy (12", p/s)	7
81	Postcard 81-1	SORRY FOR LAUGHING (LP, unreleased, a few with proof sleeve)	225/125
81	Postcard 81-7	THE ONLY FUN IN TOWN (LP)	18
87	Supreme Intl. Edit. 87-6	YOUNG AND STUPID (LP)	10

(see also Orange Juice, Paul Haig)

IRVING JOSEPH
| 60 | London HLT 9027 | I Left My Love/Lorena | 4 |

MARGIE JOSEPH (& BLUE MAGIC)
72	Stax 2025 052	Medicine Bend/Same Thing	4
74	Atlantic K 10460	Sweet Surrender/My Love	4
75	Atlantic K 10649	What's Come Over Me/You And Me (as Margie Joseph & Blue Magic)	4
72	Stax 2362 008	MAKES A NEW IMPRESSION (LP)	10

(see also Blue Magic)

JOSEPH & HELEN
| 72 | Rediffusion RS 001 | L'Imhabba/Gonna Be A Fun Day (export issue) | 6 |

JOSH
| 69 | Duke DU 41 | Judge/RON: Soul Of Joemel | 4 |

JOSH & HERBIE
| 60s | Kalypso AB 107 | I'm Nobody's Child/How Can I Believe In You | 4 |

JOSHUA
| 73 | Key KL 014 | JOSHUA (LP) | 100 |

MARVA JOSIE
| 66 | Polydor 56711 | Crazy Stockings/I'll Get By | 8 |

JOURNEY
78	CBS 6238	Wheel In The Sky/Can Do	4
78	CBS 6390	Lights/Open The Door	4
79	CBS 7890	Lovin', Touchin', Squeezin'/Daydream	4
82	CBS 11A 1728	Don't Stop Believin'/Natural Thing (12", picture disc)	7
85	CBS DA 7095	Be Good To Yourself/Only The Young//After The Fall/Rubicon (double pack)	4

JOURNEYMEN
| 67 | Ember EMB 3382 | INTRODUCING THE JOURNEYMEN (LP) | 12 |

RODDIE JOY
| 65 | Red Bird RB 021 | Come Back Baby/Love Hit Me With A Wallop | 40 |

JOY & DAVID

58	Parlophone R 4477	Whoopee!/My Oh My!	12
58	Parlophone R 4477	Whoopee!/My Oh My! (78)	8
59	Decca F 11123	Rocking Away The Blues/If You Pass Me By	18
60	Triumph RGM 1002	Let's Go See Gran'ma/Believe Me (as Joy & Dave)	15
60	Decca F 11291	My Very Good Friend The Milkman/Doopey Darling (as Joy & Dave)	12
61	Parlophone R 4855	They Tell Us Not To Love/Joe's Been A-Gittin' There (as Joy & Dave)	12

JOY DE VIVRE

81	Crass CR & SS ENVY 1	Our Wedding (flexidisc, white vinyl, no p/s)	20

(see also Crass)

JOY DIVISION

78	Enigma PSS 139	AN IDEAL FOR LIVING (EP, 14" x 14" foldout p/s)	100
78	Anonymous ANON 1	AN IDEAL FOR LIVING (12" EP, reissue)	65
80	Factory FAC 28	Komakino/Incubation (flexidisc)	5
80s	ICB 1	INTERVIEW WITH IAN CURTIS (picture disc)	4
81	Factory FACT 40	STILL (2-LP, hessian sleeve)	20

(see also New Order)

COL JOYE & JOYBOYS

59	Brunswick 05806	(Rockin' Rollin') Clementine/Bye Bye Baby Goodbye	8
59	Brunswick 05806	(Rockin' Rollin') Clementine/Bye Bye Baby Goodbye (78)	20
60	Top Rank JAR 529	Be My Girl/Yes Sir, That's My Baby	8

JOYFUL SINGERS & LYNN TAIT ON ORGAN

67	Master Time MT 001	Jesus Christ Is Risen/BELIEVERS: Money In The Rock	4
67	Master Time MT 002	Happy Days/He Watches Over Me	4

JOY OF LIFE

85	New European BADVC 62	ENJOY (12" EP)	8

JOYRIDE

69	RCA	FRIEND SOUND (LP)	20

JOY STRINGS

67	Regal Zonophone	CAROLS AROUND THE WORLD (LP)	20

JOY UNLIMITED

69	Page One POF 147	Daytime Night Time/Mister Pseudonym	5
69	Page One POF 160	Oh Darlin'/Feeling	5
70	Page One POLS 028	TURBULENCE (LP)	35

J.S.D. BAND

73	Cube BUG 29	Sarah Jane/Paddy Stacks (p/s)	4
71	Regal Zono. SRLZ 1018	COUNTRY OF THE BLIND (LP)	30
72	Cube HIFLY 11	J.S.D. BAND (LP)	12
73	Cube HIFLY 14	TRAVELLING DAYS (LP)	12

JUAN & JUNIOR

68	CBS 3223	To Girls/Andurina	8

JUDAS JUMP

70	Parlophone R 5828	Run For Your Life/Beer Drinking Woman	5
70	Parlophone R 5838	This Feelin' We Feel/Hangman's Playing	6
70	Parlophone R 5873	Beer Drinking Woman/I Have The Right	4
70	Parlophone PAS 1001	SCORCH (LP)	15

(see also Herd)

JUDAS PRIEST

74	Gull GULS 6	Rocka-Rolla/Never Satisfied	6
76	Gull GULS 31	The Ripper/Island Of Domination	6
77	CBS S CBS 5222	Diamonds And Rust/Dissident Aggressor	5
78	CBS S CBS 6077	Better By You, Better Than Me/Invader	5
78	CBS S CBS 6719	Evening Star/Starbreaker	5
78	CBS S CBS 6794	Before The Dawn/Rock Forever	4
79	CBS S CBS 6915	Take On The World/Starbreaker	4
79	CBS S CBS 12-6915	Take On The World/Starbreaker/White Heat Red Hot (12", p/s)	7
79	CBS S CBS 7312	Evening Star/Beyond The Realms Of Death	4
79	CBS 12-7312	Evening Star/The Green Manalashi/Beyond The Realms Of Death (12", clear vinyl 'picture disc')	7
79	Gull GULS 71	The Ripper/Victims Of Change	4
79	Gull GULS 71	The Ripper/Never Satisfied/Victims Of Change (12", p/s)	7
81	CBS A12 1153	Hot Rockin'/Steeler/You Don't Have To Be Old To Be Wise (12", no p/s)	7
82	CBS A 112611	You've Got Another Thing Comin'/Exciter (live) (picture disc)	4
82	CBS A 2822	(Take These) Chains/Judas Priest Audio File (p/s)	4
83	Gull GULS 7612	Tyrant/Rocka Rolla/Genocide (12", p/s, white vinyl)	12
86	CBS QTA 7144	Locked In (Extended)/Reckless/Desert Plains (live)/Freewheel Burning (live) (12", poster p/s)	7
91	Columbia 656589 0	A Touch Of Evil/Between The Hammer And The Anvil (shaped disc)	5
74	Gull GULP 1005	ROCKA ROLLA (LP, original)	10
76	Gull PGULP 1015	SAD WINGS OF DESTINY (LP, picture disc)	10
78	Gull PGULP 1026	THE BEST OF JUDAS PRIEST (LP, picture disc)	10
78	CBS 83135	KILLING MACHINE (LP, red vinyl)	10
79	CBS 83852	UNLEASHED IN THE EAST (LP, with free single "Rock Forever"/"Hell Bent For Leather"/"Beyond The Realms Of Death" [SJP 1])	10
79	CBS 66357	BOX SET (3-LP reissue of "Sin After Sin", "Stained Class" & Killing Machine")	20
86	Shanghai PGLP 1026	JUDAS PRIEST (LP, picture disc)	10

(see also Trapeze)

JUDD

70	Penny Farthing PEN 709	Snarlin' Mama Lion/Stronger Than A Man	5

| 70 | Penny Farthing PEL 504 | JUDD (LP) ....35 |

TERRY JUDGE & BARRISTERS
63	Oriole CB 1896	Hey Look At Her/Kind Of Girl You Can't Forget 6
64	Oriole CB 1938	I Don't Care/Try To Forget 6
65	Fontana TF 599	Come With Me And Love Me/Waitin' For The Night To Come 8

JUDGE DREAD
| 73 | Trojan TRLS 60 | DREADMANIA (LP) ....10 |
| 74 | Trojan TRLS 100 | WORKING CLASS 'ERO (LP) ....10 |

JUDGE HAPPINESS
| 85 | Mynah SCS 8501 | Hey Judge/Pig In Pink (very few with p/s) ....60/30 |

(see also Mock Turtles)

JUGGERNAUTS
| 84 | Supreme Int. Editions 84-2 | Come Throw Yourself/My First Million ....8 |

(see also Paul Haig)

JUG TRUST
| 70 | Parlophone R 5825 | Cat And Mouse/Goodbye Train ....4 |

JUICE ON THE LOOSE
| 81 | Juice JJOS 1 | JUICE ON THE LOOSE (LP) ....12 |

JUICY LUCY
70	Fontana TF 1068	Who Do You Love/Walking Down The Highway (unissued)
70	Vertigo V1/6059 001	Who Do You Love/Walking Down The Highway 4
70	Vertigo 6059 015	Pretty Woman/I'm A Thief 4
69	Vertigo VO 2	JUICY LUCY (LP, gatefold sleeve, spiral label) 20
70	Vertigo 6360 014	LIE BACK AND ENJOY IT (LP, spiral label, gatefold poster sleeve) 15
71	Bronze ILPS 9157	GET A WHIFF OF THIS (LP) 12
72	Polydor 2310 160	PIECES (LP) 12

(see also Misunderstood, Van Der Graaf Generator, Ray Owen)

JULIAN (Scott)
| 59 | Pye 7N 15236 | Sue Saturday/Can't Wait ....15 |

(see also Brian Bennett)

JULIAN KIRSCH
| 69 | Columbia DB 8541 | The Adventures Of A Young Cuckoo/Clever Little Man ....8 |

JULIAN'S TREATMENT
| 72 | Youngblood YB 1009 | Phantom City/Alda Dark Lady Of The Outer Worlds ....8 |
| 72 | Youngblood SYB 2 | A TIME BEFORE THIS (2-LP) ....80 |

(see also Julian Jay Savarin)

JULY
68	Major Minor MM 568	My Clown/Dandelion Seeds 70
68	Major Minor MM 580	Hello, Who's There?/The Way 60
68	M. Minor MMLP/SMLP 29	JULY (LP) 250

(see also Jade Warrior, Tom Newman)

JUMBLE LANE
| 71 | Holyground HG 115 | JUMBLE LANE (LP, 99 copies only) ....500 |

JUMPIN' JACKS
| 58 | HMV POP 440 | My Girl, My Girl/Tried And Tested ....15 |
| 58 | HMV POP 440 | My Girl, My Girl/Tried And Tested (78) ....5 |

JUMPING JACKS
| 56 | Capitol CL 14597 | About A Quarter To Nine/Lady, Play Your Mandoline ....6 |

(see also Danny Peppermint)

JUMPLEADS
| 82 | Ock OC 001 | THE STAG MUST DIE (LP, with insert) ....30 |

JUNCO PARTNERS
| 65 | Columbia DB 7665 | As Long As I Have You/Take This Hammer ....60 |
| 70 | Philips 6308 032 | JUNCO PARTNERS (LP) ....40 |

JUNCO PARTNERS
79	Rigid 15/JUNK/1028	Swinging Sixties Boys/Peepin' And Hidin' 7
81	Energy NRG 4	Tall Windows/Noizez In My Head (p/s) 5
81	Energy NRGX 4	Tall Windows (Extended)/Noizez In My Head (Extended) (12",
		stickered white label, plain sleeve) 8

JUNCTION 32
| 75 | Holyground HGS 119 | JUNCTION 32 (LP, 100 copies only) ....700 |

ROSANNE JUNE
| 56 | London HLU 8352 | The Charge Of The Light Brigade/Broken Windows ....18 |
| 58 | Oriole CB 1430 | When A Woman Cries/The Great Chicago Fire ....4 |

ROSEMARY JUNE
58	Fontana H 141	I'll Always Be In Love With You/Person To Person 7
59	Pye Intl. 7N 25005	I'll Be With You In Apple Blossom Time/Always A Bridesmaid 6
59	Pye Intl. 7N 25015	With You Beside Me/I Used To Love You, But It's All Over Now 5
59	London HLT 9014	The Village Of St. Bernadette/But Not For Me 5

JUNE BRIDES
84	Pink PINKY 1	In The Rain/Sunday To Saturday (p/s) 15
84	Pink PINKY 2	Every Conversation/Disneyland (die-cut sleeve, some with insert) 8/7
85	In Tape IT 024	No Place Called Home/We Belong (p/s) 4
85	In Tape ITTI 024	No Place Called Home/On The Rocks/Josef's Gone/We Belong (12", p/s) 7
86	In Tape IT 030	This Town/Cold/Just The Same (p/s 4
86	In Tape ITTI 030	This Town/Cold/Just The Same (12", p/s) 7

MINT VALUE £

86	Pink PINKY 9	In The Rain/Sunday To Saturday/Every Conversation/Disneyland (12", p/s)	7

(see also Phil Wilson)

JUNIOR
68	Giant GN 25	Come Cure Me/I Want Your Loving	4

JUNIORS
64	Columbia DB 7339	There's A Pretty Girl/Pocket Size	30

JUNIOR'S EYES
68	Regal Zono. RZ 3009	Mr. Golden Trumpet Player/Black Snake	12
69	Regal Zono. RZ 3018	Woman Love/White Light Part 2 (withdrawn)	12
69	Regal Zono. RZ 3018	Woman Love/Circus Days	8
69	Regal Zono. RZ 3023	Sink Or Swim/Star Child	10
69	Regal Zono. SLRZ 1008	BATTERSEA POWER STATION (LP)	30

(see also David Bowie)

JUNIOR SOUL
67	Doctor Bird DB 1112	Miss Cushie/LYNN TAITT: Doctor Paul	7
68	Big Shot BI 503	Chattie Chattie/Magic Touch	4

(see also Junior Murvin)

JUNIPER GREEN
71	Columbia DB 8809	Dreams In The Sky/Cascade Of Ice	5

LENA JUNOFF
68	Olga OLE 8	Yesterday Has Gone/Good Kind Of Hurt	20

ERIC JUPP & HIS ORCHESTRA
53	Columbia SCM 5070	Jog Trot/Doina Voda	4
54	Columbia SCM 5081	Ooop De Ooh (Lazy Mambo)/Footsteps In The Fog	6
54	Columbia DB 3465	Rock, Rock, Rock/Catwalk (78)	5
54	Columbia SCM 5140	They Were Doin' The Mambo/Skokaiian (with Coronets)	6
57	Columbia DB 4030	Bleep! Bleep!/Three-Two-One-Zero!	4
57	Columbia DB 4030	Bleep! Bleep!/Three-Two-One-Zero! (78)	5
55	Columbia SEG 7589	ERIC JUPP AND HIS ORCHESTRA (EP)	12
56	Columbia SEG 7603	RHYTHM AND BLUES (EP)	12
56	Columbia SEG 7621	THE PERFECT COMBINATION (EP)	8
56	Columbia 33S 1097	LET'S DANCE (10" LP)	12
58	Columbia 33SX 1072	MUSIC FOR SWEETHEARTS (LP)	10

MICKEY JUPP
77	Arista ARIST 136	Nature's Radio/Down At The Doctors	4
78	Stiff BUY 36	Old Rock'n'RollerS.P.Y.	4
78	Stiff UPP 1	My Typewriter/Nature's Radio (promo only, as Mickey Jupp & Legend)	5

(see also Legend)

CURT JURGENS
59	Top Rank JAR 151	Ferry To Hong Kong/Live For Love	4

SAMANTHA JUSTE
66	Go AJ 11402	No One Needs My Love Today/If Trees Could Talk	8

JUST FOUR MEN
64	Parlophone R 5186	That's My Baby/Things Will Never Be The Same (withdrawn, as Four Just Men)	50
64	Parlophone R 5208	That's My Baby/Things Will Never Be The Same	50
65	Parlophone R 5241	There's Not One Thing/Don't Come Any Closer	50

(see also Wimple Winch)

JUST FRANK
80	Rok ROK III/IV	You/SPLIT SCREENS: Just Don't Try (die-cut company sleeve)	5

JIMMY JUSTICE
60	Pye 7N 15301	I Understand Just How You Feel/Bloodshot Eyes (as Jimmy Justice & Jury)	12
61	Pye 7N 15351	When Love Has Left You/The Teacher	10
61	Pye 7N 15376	A Little Bit Of Soap/Little Lonely One	8
62	Pye 7N 15421	When My Little Girl Is Smiling/If I Lost Your Love	5
62	Pye 7N 15443	Ain't That Funny/One	5
62	Pye 7N 15457	Spanish Harlem/Write Me A Letter	4
62	Pye 7N 15469	Parade Of Broken Hearts/Dawning	4
63	Pye 7N 15502	The World Of Lonely People/I Wake Up Crying	4
63	Pye 7N 15509	Little Cracked Bell/Lighted Windows	4
63	Pye 7N 15528	The Guitar Player/Don't Let The Stars Get In Your Eyes	5
63	Pye 7N 15558	You're Gonna Need My Lovin'/Since You've Been Gone (with Exchequers)	4
69	Decca F 12899	Running Out Of Time/There Goes My World	4
65	Pye 7N 15963	Only Heartbreak For Me/Everything In The Garden	4
68	RCA Victor RCA 1681	I'm Past Forgetting You/Walking Away With My Heart	25
63	Pye NEP 24159	HIT PARADE (EP)	15
62	Pye NPL 18080	TWO SIDES OF JIMMY JUSTICE (LP)	25
62	Pye NPL 18085	SMASH HITS (LP)	20

JUSTIFIED ANCIENTS OF MU MU (J.A.M.s)
87	KLF Comm. JAMS 23	All You Need Is Love (Original) (12" white label, 1-sided, 500 only)	25
87	KLF Comm. JAMS 23(s)	All You Need Is Love (Me Ru Con Mix)/(Ibo Version) (1,000 only, plain sleeve)	15
87	KLF Comm. JAMS 23T	All You Need Is Love/Ivum Naya/Rap, Rhyme And Scratch Yourself (12", p/s)	20
87	KLF Comm. JAMS 24T	Whitney Joins The JAMs (120 bpm) (12", 1-sided, 'Scottish' issue)	15
87	KLF Comm. JAMS 25T	1987 — The 45 Edits (12", p/s)	12
88	KLF Comm. JAMS 26T	BURN THE BEAT (12" EP, 5,000 for export only)	15
87	KLF Comm. JAMS 27	Down Town (12", 1-sided white label, 500 only)	15
87	KLF Comm. JAMS 27(s)	Down Town (118 bpm edit)/Down Town (black sleeve, no p/s)	5

MINT VALUE £

87	KLF Comm. JAMS 27T	Down Town (118 bpm)/Down Town (12", p/s)	12
88	KLF Comm. JAMS 28T	It's Grim Up North (12", grey vinyl, 350 only)	70
87	KLF Comm. JAMS DS 1	Deep Shit (non-existent flexidisc, no copies pressed!)	
80s	Fierce FRIGHT 34(T)	20 GREATEST HITS (12" EP; not actually by JAMs!)	20
87	KLF Comm. JAMS LP 1	1987 (WHAT THE FUCK IS GOING ON?) (LP, withdrawn)	75
87	KLF Comm. JAMS LP 1	1987 (WHAT THE FUCK IS GOING ON?) (cassette, withdrawn)	30
88	KLF Comm. JAMS LP 2	WHO KILLED THE JAMS? (LP)	15

(see also KLF, Timelords, Disco 2000, Brilliant, Space, Orb, Bill Drummond)

JAY JUSTIN

| 60 | HMV POP 801 | Nobody's Darlin' But Mine/Sweet Sensation | 4 |
| 68 | Columbia DB 8439 | I Sell Summertime/Time (withdrawn) | 6 |

JUSTIN CASE

| 80 | Rok ROK XIX | TV/STRAIGHT UP: One Out All Out (die-cut company sleeve) | 5 |

JUSTINE

| 70 | Uni UNS 528 | She Brings Back The Morning With Her | 4 |
| 70 | Uni UNLS 111 | JUSTINE (LP) | 15 |

BILL JUSTIS & HIS ORCHESTRA

57	London HLS 8517	Raunchy/The Midnight Man	12
57	London HLS 8517	Raunchy/The Midnight Man (78)	8
58	London HLS 8614	College Man/The Stranger (B-side with Spinners)	15
58	London HLS 8614	College Man/The Stranger (B-side with Spinners) (78)	15
63	Mercury AMT 1201	I'm Gonna Learn To Dance	7

JUST PLAIN JONES

| 71 | CBS CBS 7480 | Crazy, Crazy/Should Have Stayed With Mary | 5 |

(see also Just Plain Smith, Micky Manchester, Dave Ballantyne, Mike Read)

JUST PLAIN SMITH

| 69 | Sunshine SUN 7702 | February's Child/Don't Open Your Mind (p/s) | 125 |

(see also Just Plain Jones, Micky Manchester)

JUST US

| 66 | CBS 202068 | I Can't Grow Peaches On A Cherry Tree/I Can Save You | 4 |

JUVENILES

| 66 | Pye Intl. 7N 25349 | Bo Diddley/Yes I Believe | 70 |

JYNX

| 64 | Columbia DB 7304 | How/Do What They Don't Say | 25 |

MICHAEL JACKSON

MINT VALUE £

CAROLINE K.
87 Earthly Delights EARTH 1   NOW WAIT FOR LAST YEAR (LP, 1,500 only) 15

KRISSIE K.
74 People PEO 110   Stick Up/Who Do You Think You Are 4

JOHNNY K. & SINGIN' SWINGIN' 8
63 Fontana H 408   Lemonade/Come Closer Melinda 5

MOSES K. & PROPHETS
65 Decca F 12244   I Went Out With My Baby Tonight/So Long 10

KADDO STRINGS
80 Grapevine GRP 146   Nothing But Love/Crying Over You 4
(see also Duke Browner, Tartans)

KADETTES
82 Blank GET 1   Fireball XL5/Mission Impossible 6

KAINE & ABEL
66 Philips BF 1472   Then You Must Know My Love/Crying In The Rain 4

KAJA
85 Parlophone R 6106   Shouldn't Do That/Charm Of A Gun//Hurricane/Whatever You Want (double pack) 4
(see also Kajagoogoo)

KAJAGOOGOO
83 EMI EMIP 5394   Hang On Now/Hang On Now (instrumental) (picture disc) 4
84 EMI EMIP 5449   The Lion's Mouth/Garden (picture disc) 4
(see also Limahl, Kaja)

KALA
73 Bradleys BRAD 302   Travelling Home/Still Got Time 4
73 Bradleys BRADL 1002   KALA (LP) 15
(see also Quintessence)

ALAN KALANI
59 Vogue V 9147   A Touch Of Pink/SURFERS: Mambo Jambo 6
59 Vogue V 9147   A Touch Of Pink/SURFERS: Mambo Jambo (78) 5

KALASANDRO!
60 Warner Bros WB 13   Chi Chi/Forbidden City 6

KALEIDOSCOPE (U.K.)
67 Fontana TF 863   Flight From Ashiya/Holidaymaker (some in p/s) 40/20
68 Fontana TF 895   A Dream For Julie/Please Excuse My Face 25
68 Fontana TF 964   Jenny Artichoke/Just How Much Are You 20
69 Fontana TF 1002   Do It Again For Jeffrey/Poem 20
69 Fontana TF 1048   If You So Wish/Balloon 60
67 Fontana (S)TL 5448   TANGERINE DREAM (LP, mono/stereo) 80/90
69 Fontana STL 5491   FAINTLY BLOWING (LP, gatefold sleeve; most have watermark
   on beginning of either side) 100/70
87 5 Hours Back TOCK 005   TANGERINE DREAM (LP, stereo reissue) 20
87 5 Hours Back TOCK 006   FAINTLY BLOWING (LP, reissue, single sleeve) 20
(see also Fairfield Parlour, I Luv Wight)

KALEIDOSCOPE (U.S.)
70 CBS 64005   BERNICE (LP, as American Kaleidoscope) 15
76 Island ILPS 9462   WHEN SCOPES COLLIDE (LP) 10

KALIN TWINS
58 Brunswick 05751   When/Three O'Clock Thrill 6
58 Brunswick 05751   When/Three O'Clock Thrill (78) 5
58 Brunswick 05759   Forget Me Not/Dream Of Me (some labels list "Dream Of You") 6
58 Brunswick 05759   Forget Me Not/Dream Of Me (78) 5
59 Brunswick 05775   Oh! My Goodness/It's Only The Beginning 10
59 Brunswick 05775   Oh! My Goodness/It's Only The Beginning (78) 5
59 Brunswick 05797   Cool/When I Look In The Mirror 7
59 Brunswick 05797   Cool/When I Look In The Mirror (78) 6
59 Brunswick 05803   Sweet Sugar Lips/Moody 6
59 Brunswick 05803   Sweet Sugar Lips/Moody (78) 8
59 Brunswick 05814   The Meaning Of The Blues/Who Don't You Believe Me? 7
59 Brunswick 05814   The Meaning Of The Blues/Who Don't You Believe Me? (78) 10
60 Brunswick 05826   Chicken Thief/Loneliness 7
60 Brunswick 05844   Zing! Went The Strings Of My Heart/No Money Can Buy 7
61 Brunswick 05848   Momma Poppa/You Mean The World To Me 6
61 Brunswick 05862   One More Time/I'm Forever Blowing Bubbles 6
58 Brunswick OE 9383   WHEN (EP) 20
59 Brunswick OE 9449   THE KALIN TWINS (EP) 20

KITTY KALLEN
54 Brunswick 05261   Are You Looking For A Sweetheart/In The Chapel In The Moonlight 12
54 Brunswick 05287   Little Things Mean A Lot/I Don't Think You Love Me Anymore 35
54 Brunswick 05357   Heartless Heart/The Spirit Of Christmas 10
54 Brunswick 05359   I Want You All To Myself/(Don't Let The) Kiddy Geddin' 10

55	Brunswick 05394	A Little Lie/Take Everything But You	8
55	Brunswick 05402	Polly Pigtails/I'm A Lonely Little Petunia (In A Potato Patch)	7
55	Brunswick 05431	Kitty Who?/By Bayou Bay	7
55	Brunswick 05447	Forgive Me/Lonely	7
55	Brunswick 05475	Let's Make The Most Of Tonight/Just Between Friends	7
55	Brunswick 05494	How Lonely Can I Get?/Sweet Kentucky Rose	7
56	Brunswick 05536	Go On With The Wedding (with Georgie Shaw)/Only Forever	8
56	Brunswick 05612	True Love/Will I Always Be Your Sweetheart?	6
57	Brunswick 05705	Long Lonely Nights/Lasting Love	6
58	Brunswick 05734	Crying Roses/I Never Was The One	5
59	Philips PB 971	If I Give My Heart To You/The Door That Won't Open	4
60	Philips PB 1028	Make Love To Me/Heaven Help Me	4
62	RCA RCA 1324	Call Me A Fool/My Colouring Book	4

(see also Georgie Shaw)

DICK KALLMAN

| 56 | Brunswick 05608 | Two Different Worlds/Love Me As Though There Were No Tomorrow | 4 |
| 60 | Vogue V 9162 | Born To Be Loved/Just Squeeze Me But Don't Teeze Me | 4 |

BOBBY KALPHAT

| 68 | Nu Beat NB 007 | Rhythm And Soul/BUNNY & RUDDY: True Romance | 6 |
| 70s | Faith FA 008 | Zion Hill/Dub Hill | 4 |

AMORY KANE

68	MCA MU 1036	Reflections Of Your Face/Four Ravens	5
70	UNI UNS 518	All The Best Songs And Marches/You Were On My Mind	4
70	CBS 5111	Him Or Me/Forever Waiting	4
68	MCA MUP(S) 348	MEMORIES OF TIME UNWOUND (LP)	30
70	CBS 63849	JUST TO BE THERE (LP)	25

EDEN KANE

60	Pye 7N 15284	Hot Chocolate Crazy/You Make Love So Well	12
61	Decca F 11353	Well I Ask You/Before I Lose My Mind	4
61	Decca F 11381	Get Lost/I'm Telling You	4
62	Decca F 11418	Forget Me Not/A New Kind Of Lovin'	4
62	Decca F 11460	I Don't Know Why/Music For Strings	4
62	Decca F 11504	House To Let/I Told You	5
63	Decca F 11568	Sounds Funny To Me/Someone Wants To Know	5
63	Fontana TF 398	Tomorrow Night/I Won't Believe You (some in p/s)	8/4
63	Fontana TF 413	Come Back (with Earl Preston's TTs)/Like I Love You	7
64	Fontana TF 438	Boys Cry/Don't Come Cryin' To Me	5
64	Fontana TF 462	Rain Rain Go Away/Guess Who It Is	4
64	Fontana TF 508	Hangin' Around/Gonna Do Something About You	4
65	Fontana TF 582	If You Want This Love/Have I Done Something Wrong	4
66	Decca F 12342	Magic Town/The Whole World Was Crying	12
69	Fontana TF 1023	Boys Cry/Don't Come Cryin' To Me (reissue)	4
62	Decca DFE 6696	WELL I ASK YOU! (EP)	18
62	Decca DFE 8503	HITS (EP)	18
64	Decca DFE 8567	SIX GREAT NEW SWINGERS (EP)	20
64	Fontana TFE 17424	IT'S EDEN (EP)	15
62	Ace Of Clubs ACL 1133	EDEN KANE (LP)	25
64	Fontana TL 5211	IT'S EDEN (LP)	35
66	Wing WL 1218	SMOKE GETS IN YOUR EYES (LP)	15

(see also Brothers Kane, Sarstedt Brothers)

GARY KANE

| 67 | Pye 7N 17334 | Too Good To Miss/Guilty Of Dreaming | 4 |

LEE KANE

| 55 | Capitol CL 14297 | Ev'ry Day/How Would You Have Me? | 6 |
| 55 | Capitol CL 14328 | Around And Around/Merci Beaucoup | 6 |

MARIA KANE

| 65 | Decca F 12184 | Love Is Slipping Away/Love Is Strange | 4 |

KANE GANG

| 85 | Kitchenware SKDP 20 | Gun Law (Edit)/Giving Up//Brother Brother (live)/Heaven Help Us All (live) (double pack, gatefold stickered p/s) | 4 |

KAN KAN

| 83 | Kabaret Music TRAIN 1 | Film Noir/The Watchmaker (no p/s, stickered plain sleeve) | 4 |

KANSAS

77	Kirshner S KIR 5820	Point Of Know Return/Closet Chronicles	4
78	Kirshner S KIR 4932	Carry On Wayward/Questions Of My Childhood	4
78	Kirshner S KIR 6205	Dust In The Wind/Paradox	4
82	Kirshner S KIR 2408	Play The Game Tonight/Play On	4

PAUL KANTNER

70	RCA SF 8163	BLOWS AGAINST THE EMPIRE (LP, gatefold sleeve with booklet, as Paul Kantner & Jefferson Starship)	12
71	Grunt FTR 1002	SUNFIGHTER (LP, gatefold sleeve with inner bag; as Paul Kantner, Grace Slick & Jefferson Starship)	12
73	Grunt BFL 1 0148	BARON VON TOLLBOOTH (LP, with Grace Slick & David Freiberg)	10

(see also Jefferson Airplane/Starship)

KAPLAN

| 68 | Philips BF 1636 | Do You Believe In Magic/I Like | 4 |
| 68 | Philips BF 1699 | I Love It/Trousers Down | 4 |

KAPT. KOPTER & FABULOUS TWIRLY BIRDS

| 72 | Epic EPC 65381 | KAPT. KOPTER & THE FABULOUS TWIRLY BIRDS (LP) | 10 |

(see also Randy California)

ANTON KARAS
60	Decca F 9235	The "Harry Lime" Theme/The Cafe Mozart Waltz	8
51	Decca LF 1053	ANTON KARAS (10" LP)	12

KARINA
68	Hispavox HXS 305	Romeo Y Julieta/Fortuna Y Le Poder	4
71	United Artists UP 35205	Tomorrow I'm Coming Your Way/Something	10

MIRIAM KARLIN
67	Columbia DB 8220	Celebration/Nose For Trouble	4

KARLINS
68	Columbia DB 8394	Everybody Wants To Go To Heaven/Stay On The Island	4

BILLY KARLOFF
78	Wanted CULT-45-001	Back Street Billy/Crazy Paving	4

BORIS KARLOFF
67	Brunswick LAT 8678	AN EVENING WITH BORIS KARLOFF AND FRIENDS (LP)	15

STEVE KARMEN BIG BAND
75	United Artists UP 35770	Breakaway/Breakaway (Vocal Version) (featuring Jimmy Radcliffe)	5

(see also Jimmy Radcliffe)

KARYN KARSH
68	RCA Victor RCA 1740	I Wasn't Born To Follow/Musty Dusty	4

KARYOBIN
(see under Spontaneous Music Ensemble)

KASENATZ-KATZ SINGING ORCHESTRAL CIRCUS
68	Pye Intl. 7N 25472	Down In Tennessee/Mrs. Green	4
68	Pye Intl. 7N 25476	Quick Joey Small (Run Joey Run)/Rumble '69 (unreleased)	
69	Pye Intl. 7N 25480	We Can Work It Out/Latin Shake	4
68	Buddah 201 022	Quick Joey Small (Run Joey Run)/Rumble '69	4
69	Buddah 201 041	Embrassee/I'm In Love With You	4
68	Pye Int. NSPL 28119	KASENATZ-KATZ SINGING ORCHESTRAL CIRCUS (LP)	12
69	Buddah 203 018	QUICK JOEY SMALL — I'M IN LOVE WITH YOU	
		(LP, as Kasenatz-Katz Super Circus)	10

AL KASHA
60	Coral Q 72410	Teardrops Are Falling/No Matter Where You Are	4
61	Coral Q 72420	Sing/One Of Them	4
61	Coral Q 72429	Where There's A Will There's A Way/My Arms, My Lips, My Heart	4

KATCH-22
66	Fontana TF 768	Major Catastrophe/Hold Me	25
67	Fontana TF 874	Makin' Up My Mind/While We're Friends	8
68	Fontana TF 930	The World's Gettin' Smaller/Don't Bother	8
68	Fontana TF 984	100,000 Years/Pumpkin Mini	8
69	Fontana TF 1005	Out Of My Life/Baby Love	8
69	CBS 4644	Missus Jones/It's The Sunshine	5
68	Saga EROS 8047	IT'S SOFT ROCK & ALLSORTS (LP)	10

KATE
68	CBS 3631	Strange Girl/I Don't Make A Sound	15
68	CBS 3815	Hold Me Now/Empty World	15
69	CBS 4123	Shout It/Sweet Little Thing	15

(see also Viv Prince, Pretty Things)

KATHYU
69	Morgan MR 14	Bonjour Monsieur/Long Night	4

KATZ
60s	Tetlour TET 118	LIVE AT THE RUM RUNNER (EP)	75

MICKEY KATZ & HIS ORCHESTRA
56	Capitol CL 14579	David Crockett (The Ballad Of Davy Crockett)/Keneh Hora	6
58	Capitol CL 14926	The Poiple Kishke Eater/Knish Doctor	6

ARTHUR KAY'S ORIGINALS
80	Red Admiral NYMPH 1	Ska Wars/Warska (p/s)	7
80	Red Admiral NYMPH 2	Sooty Was A Rudie/Play My Record (p/s)	6

JOHN KAY
73	Probe PRO 601	Easy Evil/Dance To My Song	4
72	Probe SPB 1054	FORGOTTEN SONGS AND UNSUNG HEROES (LP)	15
73	Probe SPBA 6274	MY SPORTIN' LIFE (LP)	15

(see also Steppenwolf)

KATHIE KAY(E)
55	HMV 7M 335	Suddenly There's A Valley/Teddy Bear	8
56	HMV 7M 363	Jimmy Unknown/Dreams Can Tell A Lie	8
56	HMV 7M 370	There Is Somebody Waiting For Me/Old Scotch Mother	5
56	HMV 7M 412	Bonnie Scotland/The Wee House 'Mang The Heather	4
56	HMV POP 265	A House With Love In It/To Be Sure	7
57	HMV POP 315	From The First Hello — To The Last/Every Day Is Mother's Day	5
57	HMV POP 352	We Will Make Love/Wind In The Willow	5
57	HMV POP 385	Tammy/Away From You	4
57	HMV POP 410	Be Content/My Last Love	4
58	HMV POP 485	The Secret Of Happiness/Summer Is A'Coming In	4
58	HMV POP 498	Hillside In Scotland/Tomorrow Is My Birthday	4
59	HMV POP 625	Goodbye Jimmy, Goodbye/Come Home To Loch Lomond And Me	5
61	HMV POP 878	In The Wee Small Hours Of The Morning/Come Home, My Darling	4

KATHIE KAY & BILLY COTTON
62	Columbia DB 4896	Til Tomorrow/Someone Nice Like You	4

CAB KAYE
50s	Melodisc M 1584	Everything Is Go/Don't You Go Away	4

DANNY KAYE
52	Brunswick 05023	Wonderful Copenhagen/Anywhere I Wander (78)	6
52	Brunswick 05031	The Ugly Duckling/The King's New Clothes (78)	6
54	Brunswick 05296	Knock On Wood/All About You	5
54	Brunswick 05344	The Best Things Happen While You're Dancing/Choreography (as Danny Kaye & Skylarks)	5
55	Brunswick 05414	Night Of My Nights/Not Since Ninevah (with Sonny Burke Orchestra)	5
55	Brunswick 05424	In My Neck O' The Woods/Manhattan Mambo	5
55	Brunswick 05499	I Love You Fair Dinkum (Dinky Di I Do)/Happy Ending	5
56	Brunswick 05524	Life Could Not Be Better/I'll Take You Dreaming	5
56	Brunswick 05525	Outfox The Fox/Pass The Bucket	5
56	Brunswick 05532	Little Child/Laugh It Off Upsy Daisy (as Danny & Dena Kaye)	5
56	Brunswick 05559	Delilah Jones/Molly-O	5
57	Capitol CL 14672	Love Me Do/Ciu Ciu Bella	4
58	Capitol CL 14907	The Square On The Hypotenuse/Everything Is Ticketty-Boo	4
59	Capitol CL 15061	Mommy, Gimme A Drinka Water!/Crazy Barbara	4
59	Brunswick 05023	Wonderful Copenhagen/Anywhere I Wander	4
59	Brunswick 05031	The Ugly Duckling/The King's New Clothes	4
60	London HL 7091	The Five Pennies/Lullaby In Ragtime (B-side with Eileen Wilson, export issue)	5
51	Brunswick LA 8507	DANNY KAYE (10" LP)	14
53	Brunswick LA 8572	HANS CHRISTIAN ANDERSON (10" LP)	14
54	Brunswick LA 8660	DANNY KAYE AT THE PALACE (10" LP)	14
54	Brunswick LA 8668	KNOCK ON WOOD (10" LP, soundtrack)	14
56	Brunswick LAT 8097	THE COURT JESTER (LP)	12
58	Fontana TFR 6008	PURE DELIGHT (10" LP)	12
58	Capitol T 937	MOMMY, GIMME A DRINKA WATER! (LP)	10
60	Brunswick LAT 8350	FOR CHILDREN (LP)	10

(see also Bing Crosby)

DANNY KAYE & LOUIS ARMSTRONG
60	London HLU 9346	The Five Pennies Saints/Bill Bailey Won't You Please Come Home	4
60	London HL 7092	The Five Pennies Saints/Bill Bailey Won't You Please Come Home (export)	4

(see also Louis Armstrong)

DAVE KAYE (& DYKONS)
64	Decca F 11866	A Fool Such As I/It's Nice Isn't It (as Davy Kaye)	15
65	Decca F 12073	In My Way/All The Stars In Heaven (as Dave Kaye)	15
69	Major Minor MM 641	Yesterday When I Was Young/Say You Love Me (as Dave Kaye & Dykons)	8

LINDA KAYE
66	Columbia DB 7915	I Can't Stop Thinking About You/When We Meet Again	15

PETER KAYE
60s	Windsor PS 116	Do Me A Favor/You Doll	4

SHIRLEY KAYE
68	Trojan TR 015	Make Me Yours/We Have Happiness	12

STUBBY KAYE
63	Parlophone R 4996	More Humane Mikado/Cool Mikado	4

THOMAS JEFFERSON KAYE
74	Anchor ABC 4004	American Heartbeat/L.A.	4
73	Probe SPB 1074	THOMAS JEFFERSON KAYE (LP)	12
74	ABC ABCL 5048	FIRST GRADE (LP)	10

TONY KAYE & HEARTBEATS
67	Pye Intl. 7N 25412	Hey, Hey Little Orphan Annie/Dream World	5

KAYES
67	Major Minor MM 515	It's No Secret/Remember Me	4

KAYE SISTERS
58	Philips PB 806	Are You Ready, Freddy?/The Pansy	10
58	Philips PB 832	Stroll Me/Torero	7
58	Philips PB 877	Calla, Calla (The Bride, The Bride)/Oho-Aha	4
59	Philips PB 892	Jerri-Lee (I Love Him So)/Deeply Devoted	4
59	Philips PB 925	Goodbye Jimmy, Goodbye/Dancing With My Shadow	4
59	Philips PB 970	True Love, True Love/Too Young To Marry	4
60	Philips PB 1024	Paper Roses/If Only You'd Be Mine (some in p/s)	8/4
60	Philips PB 1088	Come To Me/A Whole Lot Of Lovin'	4
61	Philips PB 1156	Palma De Majorca/I Just Wanna Be With You	4
61	Philips PB 1189	Little Soldier/Mistletoe Kisses	4
61	Philips PB 1208	If Only Tomorrow/Mistakes	4
63	Philips PB 1273	Nine Girls Out Of Ten Girls/I Forgot More Than You'll Never Know	4
66	Philips PB 1468	Life Goes On/I Should Never Know	4
62	Philips 326541	We Won't Say Goodbye/Seven Roses	4
63	Philips 326569	Big Wide World/I'm Forever Blowing Bubbles	4
57	Philips BBE 12166	PRESENTING THE KAYE SISTERS (EP)	10
59	Philips BBE 12256	THE KAYES AT THE COLONY (EP)	12

(see also Three Kayes/Three Kaye Sisters, Frankie Vaughan)

KAY GEES
76	Polydor 2310 467	HUSTLE WIT' EVERY MUSCLE (LP)	15

KITZA KAZACOS
56	MGM SP 1156	You Should Know/There's Always A First Time	4

K.C. & SUNSHINE BAND
77	T.K. XB 2167	I'm Your Boogie Man/Wrap Your Arms Around Me	4

ERNIE K-DOE
61	London HLU 9330	Mother-In-Law/Wanted, $10,000.00 Reward	10
61	London HLU 9390	Te-Ta-Te-Ta-Ta/Real Man	10
62	London HLU 9487	I Cried My Last Tear/A Certain Girl	12
65	Vocalion VP 9233	My Mother In Law (Is In My Hair Again)/Looking Into The Future	8
68	Action ACT 4502	Dancing Man/Later For Tomorrow	8
68	Action ACT 4512	Gotta Pack My Bags/How Sweet You Are	7

SHAKE KEANE
65	Decca SKL 4720	SHAKE KEANE WITH THE KEATING SOUND (LP)	10
66	Ace Of Clubs ACL 1219	THAT'S THE NOISE (LP)	10

JOHNNY KEATING ORCHESTRA
62	Piccadilly 7N 35032	Z-Cars Theme/The Lost Patrol	6
62	Piccadilly 7N 35071	We Three Kings/Three Beats To The Casbah	4
63	Piccadilly 7N 35113	The Preacher/Whoop Up (as Johnny Keating & Z Men)	4
63	Piccadilly 7N 35125	Getaway/A Little Waltzing	4
71	Fly BUG 17	Theme From The Onedin Line/Taransay Lullaby	4

KEEFERS KIDS
67	King KG 1068	Millions Of Hearts/KEEFERS: Lonely Hill	4

HOWARD KEEL
57	Columbia DB 3969	Love, Wonderful Love/Parisienne	4

(see also Kathryn Grayson & Howard Keel, Vic Damone)

JOHN KEEN
73	Track 2094 103	Old Fashioned Girl/That's The Way It Is	4
73	Track 2094 108	Let Us In/Keep On The Grass	4

(see also Speedy Keen, Thunderclap Newman)

SPEEDY KEEN
71	Track 2406 105	PREVIOUS CONVICTIONS (LP)	10

(see also John Keen, Thunderclap Newman)

MARION KEENE
56	HMV 7M 395	Fortune Teller/A Dangerous Age	5
57	HMV POP 375	In The Middle Of An Island/It's Not For Me To Say	5

NELSON KEENE
60	HMV POP 771	Image Of A Girl/Ocean Of Love	5
60	HMV POP 814	Keep Loving Me/Teenage Troubles	5
61	HMV POP 916	Miracles Are Happening To Me/Poor Little Rich Boy	5

(see also Guv'ners)

REX KEENE
56	Columbia DB 3831	Rebel In Town/Happy Texas Ranger	8

ACE KEFFORD STAND
69	Atlantic 584 260	For Your Love/Gravy Booby Jam	25

(see also Move, Cozy Powell, Young Blood, Big Bertha)

KEITH
66	Mercury MF 940	Ain't Gonna Lie/It Started All Over Again	5
67	Mercury MF 955	98.6/The Teeny Bopper Song	6
67	Mercury MF 968	Tell Me To My Face/I Can't Go Wrong	5
67	Mercury MF 989	Daylight Savin' Time/Happy Walking Around	7
67	Mercury MF 1002	Sugar Man/Easy As Pie (some in p/s)	7/4
67	Mercury MCL 20103	98.6/AIN'T GONNA LIE (LP)	15

BRIAN KEITH
68	Page One POF 072	The Shelter Of Your Arms/C'est La Vie	4
68	Page One POF 103	When The First Tear Shows/When My Baby Smiles At Me	6
69	Page One POF 152	Till We Meet Again/Lady Butterfly	4

BRYAN KEITH
63	London HLU 9707	Sad Sad Song/Mean Woman	10

RON KEITH
76	A&M AMS 7217	Party Music/Gotta Go By What You Tell Me	30

KEITH & BILLIE
(see under Keith Powell & Billie Davis; see also Keith Powell, Billie Davis)

KEITH (Stewart) & ENID (Cumberland)
60	Blue Beat BB 6	Worried Over You/Everything Will Be Alright	10
61	Blue Beat BB 11	Send Me/TRENTON SPENCE GROUP: People Will Say We're In Love	10
61	Starlite ST45 047	Never Leave My Throne/Only A Pity (as Keith & Enid with Caribs)	10
61	Starlite ST45 067	You're Gonna Break My Heart/What Have I Done	10
63	Dice CC 14	Sacred Vow/My Dreams	10
63	Dice CC 20	Just A Closer Walk/Don't Yield To Temptation	8
64	Black Swan BI 429	Lost My Love/I Cried	8
63	Island ILP 901	KEITH & ENID SING (LP)	40
70	Trojan TTL 37	KEITH & ENID SING (LP, reissue)	12
70	Trojan TBL 154	KEITH & ENID SING (LP, 2nd reissue)	10

KEITH (Lyn) & KEN (Lazarus)
65	London HA-R/SH-R 8229	YOU'LL LOVE JAMAICA (LP)	25

KEITH (Rowe) & TEX (Dixon)
67	Island WI 3085	Tonight/LYN TAIT & JETS: You Have Caught Me	12
68	Island WI 3091	Stop That Train/BOBBY ELLIS: Feeling Peckish	10

| 68 | Island WI 3137 | Hypnotizing Eyes/Lonely Man | 10 |
| 69 | Explosion EX 2008 | Tighten Up Your Gird/Look To The Sky | 5 |

JERRY KELLER

59	London HLR 8890	Here Comes Summer/Time Has A Way	5
59	London HLR 8890	Here Comes Summer/Time Has A Way (78)	15
59	London HLR 8980	If I Had A Girl/Lovable	5
59	London HLR 8980	If I Had A Girl/Lovable (78)	15
60	London HLR 9106	Now, Now, Now/Lonesome Lullaby	5
60	London HA-R 2261	HERE COMES JERRY KELLER (LP, also stereo SAH-R 6083)	35/45

PAT KELLEY & UNIQUES

| 68 | Giant GN 37 | Little Boy Blue/You Are Not Mine | 7 |
| | *(see also Pat Kelly)* | | |

MURRAY KELLUM

| 64 | London HLU 9830 | Long Tall Texan/GLEN SUTTON: I Gotta Leave This Town | 7 |

CHARLIE KELLY

| 68 | Island WI 3155 | So Nice Like Rice/STRANGER & GLADDY: Over Again | 8 |

DAVE KELLY

| 69 | Mercury SMCL 20151 | KEEPS IT IN THE FAMILY (LP) | 80 |
| 71 | Mercury 6310 001 | BLACK BLUE KELLY (LP) | 100 |

FRANK KELLY & HUNTERS

62	Fontana 267 242 TF	Send Me The Pillow That You Dream On/'Cept Me	5
63	Fontana 267 261 TF	I Saw Linda Yesterday/Good And True	5
63	Fontana 267 277 TF	What Do You Wanna Do/She Loves Me So	5
64	Fontana TF 454	Some Other Time/Why Baby Why	5
	(do NOT see also Hunters)		

GENE KELLY

53	MGM SP 1012	Singin' In The Rain/All I Do Is Dream Of You	10
53	MGM SP 1015	'S Wonderful (with Georges Guetary)/I Got Rhythm	6
57	MGM MGM 965	The Happy Road (Ca Ca C'est ...)/My Baby Just Cares For Me	4
58	RCA RCA 1068	A Very Precious Love/Uncle Samson	4
53	MGM D 117	SONG AND DANCE MAN (10" LP)	15
55	MGM D 133	S'WONDERFUL (10" LP)	15

GENE KELLY & GEORGE GUETARY

| 53 | MGM SP 1015 | I Got Rhythm (with Children's Choir)/S'Wonderful | 6 |

J. KELLY & PREMIERS

| 74 | People PEO 113 | She Calls Me Baby/Signed, Sealed And Delivered | 4 |

JO-ANN KELLY

60s	Halcyon HAL 1	NEW SOUNDS IN FOLK (EP, also listed as Harlequin HW 349, with other artists)	40
60s	GW EP 1	BLUES AND GOSPEL (EP, live at the Bridge House Club)	100
69	CBS 63841	JO-ANN KELLY (LP)	100
76	Red Rag RRR 006	DO IT (LP)	30

JO-ANN KELLY & TONY McPHEE

| 72 | Sunset SLS 50209 | THE SAME THING ON THEIR MINDS (LP) | 25 |
| | *(see also Tony McPhee)* | | |

JONATHAN KELLY

69	Parlophone R 5805	Denver/Son John	5
70	Parlophone R 5851	Don't You Believe It?/Billy	6
70	Parlophone R 5830	Make A Stranger Your Friend/Daddy Don't Take Me Down Fishing	5
70	Parlophone PCS 7114	JONATHAN KELLY (LP)	30
72	RCA SF 8262	TWICE AROUND THE HOUSES (LP)	10
73	RCA SF 8353	WAIT TILL THEY CHANGE THE BACKDROP (LP)	10
	(see also John Ledingham)		

KEITH KELLY

60	Parlophone R 4640	Ooh-La-La/(Must You Always) Tease Me	8
60	Parlophone R 4676	Listen Little Girl/Uh-Huh	8
60	Parlophone R 4713	With You/You'll Break My Heart	6
61	Parlophone R 4797	Cold White And Beautiful/When You First Fall In Love	4
65	CBS 201794	Save Your Love For Me/Laurie	4

MONTE KELLY ORCHESTRA

| 59 | London HLL 8777 | Willingly (Melodie Perdue)/The Blue Cha Cha | 4 |
| 60 | London HLL 9085 | Summer Set/Amalia | 4 |

PAT KELLY

68	Island WI 3121	Somebody's Baby/BEVERLY SIMMONS: Please Don't Leave Me	10
69	Gas GAS 110	The Workman Song/Never Give Up	4
69	Gas GAS 115	How Long/Try To Remember	4
71	Punch PH 88	Soulful Love/HUGH ROY & PARAGONS: One For All	4
69	Pama PMLP 12	PAT KELLY SINGS (LP)	20
71	Pama PMP 2013	COOL BREEZING (LP)	20
	(see also Pat Kelley & Uniques, Little Boy Blue)		

PAUL KELLY

65	Atlantic AT 4053	Chills And Fever/Only Your Love	15
67	Philips BF 1591	Sweet Sweet Lovin'/Cryin' For My Baby	10
72	Atlantic K 10272	Chills And Fever/Only Your Love (reissue)	5

PETE KELLY'S SOULUTION

| 68 | Decca F 12755 | Midnight Confessions/If Your Love Don't Swing | 12 |

| 68 | Decca F 22829 | Midnight Confessions/BERNIE & BUZZ BAND: The House That Jack Built (export issue) .... 12 |

(see also Bernie & Buzz Band)

SALLY KELLY
59	Decca F 11175	Little Cutie/Come Back To Me 5
60	Decca F 11238	He'll Have To Stay/Honey That's Alright 5
60s	Hit HIT 15	Believe In The Rain/So Much 4

SEYMOUR KELLY
| 68 | Columbia DB 8445 | Indian Scene/Worlds Apart .... 4 |

STAN KELLY
60s	Transatlantic TRASP 21	The Ballad Of Armagh Jail/Kelly The Boy From Killang 4
60	Topic TOP 27	STAN KELLY (EP) 7
61	Topic TOP 60	SONGS FOR SWINGING LANDLORDS (EP) 7

KELLY BROTHERS
67	Sue WI 4034	Falling In Love Again/Crying Days Are Over 30
68	President PT 143	You Put Your Touch On Me/Hanging In There 6
70	Blue Horizon 57-3177	That's What You Mean To Me/Comin' On In 10
68	President PTL 1019	SWEET SOUL (LP) 12

REV. (Samuel) KELSEY (& CONGREGATION)
52	Vocalion V 1014	Wedding Ceremony Of Sister Rosetta Tharpe And Russell Morrison Pts 1 & 2 (78) 12
52	Vocalion V 1020	Little Boy/Low Down The Chariot (78) 12
53	Vocalion V 1028	I'm A Royal Child/Where Is The Lion In The Tribes Of Judea (78) 12
56	Brunswick OE 9256	REV. KELSEY (EP) 15

(see also Sister Rosetta Tharpe)

PAUL KELVIN
| 69 | Morgan MR 2S | It's Easy/Anyone Can Move A Mountain .... 4 |

WAYNE KEMP
| 66 | Atlantic 584 006 | Watch That First Step/Little Home Wrecker .... 5 |

KEMPION
| 70s | Broadside BRO 123 | KEMPION (LP) .... 15 |
| 70s | Sweet Folk & Country | CAM YE O'ER FRAE FRANCE (LP) .... 15 |

RODD-KEN & CAVALIERS
| 60 | Triumph RGM 1001 | Magic Wheel/Happy Valley .... 18 |

JOHNNY KENDALL & HERALDS
| 64 | RCA RCA 1416 | St. James Infirmary/Little Girl .... 10 |

KENDALL SISTERS
| 58 | London HLM 8622 | Won't You Be My Baby/Yea, Yea .... 35 |
| 58 | London HLM 8622 | Won't You Be My Baby/Yea, Yea (78) .... 15 |

GRAHAM KENDRICK
| 73 | Key KL 011 | FOOTSTEPS ON THE SEA (LP) .... 30 |
| 73 | Key KL 016 | BRIGHT SIDE UP (LP) .... 25 |

LINDA KENDRICK
66	Polydor BM 56076	It's The Little Things/When Your Love Is Warm 20
66	Polydor BM 56146	I Fall Apart/Friend Of Mine 6
68	Philips BF 1660	Grey Sunny Day/In Need Of A Friend 4

NAT KENDRICK & SWANS
| 60 | Top Rank JAR 351 | (Do The) Mashed Potatoes Pts 1 & 2 .... 7 |
| 60 | Top Rank JAR 387 | Dish Rag Pts 1 & 2 .... 6 |

(see also James Brown)

EDDIE KENDRICKS
73	Tamla Motown TMG 845	If You Let Me/Just Memories 4
74	Tamla Motown TMG 916	Girl You Need A Change Of Mind Pts 1 & 2 4
75	Tamla Motown TMG 947	Shoe Shine Boy/Hooked On Your Love 4
71	T. Motown STML 11186	ALL BY MYSELF (LP) 10
73	T. Motown STML 11213	PEOPLE ... HOLD ON (LP) 10
73	T. Motown STML 12245	EDDIE KENDRICKS (LP) 10

(see also Temptations)

CHERYL KENNEDY
| 67 | Columbia DB 8271 | Thoroughly Modern Millie/Cradle Song .... 5 |
| 68 | Columbia DB 8347 | Love Is Blue/I Could Be Happy With You .... 5 |

DOUG KENNEDY
| 65 | Columbia DB 7707 | Julie/Jailbreak Man .... 4 |

GENE KENNEDY
| 65 | Hickory 45-1314 | You Better Take Home/Stand In Line .... 5 |

JOHN F. KENNEDY
| 64 | Stateside SL 10064 | THE PRESIDENTIAL YEARS 1960-1963 (LP) .... 10 |

LOU KENNEDY
| 55 | Columbia SCM 5198 | Stars Shine In Your Eyes/The Kentuckian Song .... 5 |
| 56 | Columbia SCM 5216 | Whisper/Sincerely Yours .... 5 |

KENNEDY EXPRESS
| 79 | Jet SJET 145 | Little Lolita/Stop Stop Stop .... 4 |
| 80 | Jet SJET 171 | IS THERE LIFE ON EARTH? (EP) .... 4 |

(see also Creation, Kenny Pickett)

CHRIS KENNER
61	London HLU 9410	I Like It Like That Pts 1 & 2	12
65	Sue WI 351	Land Of 1000 Dances/That's My Girl	18
66	Atlantic 587 008	LAND OF 1000 DANCES (LP)	15

JAMES KENNEY
58	Pye 7N 15150	The Shrine On The Second Floor/Expresso Party	4

TONY KENNY & SANDS SHOWBAND
67	Major Minor MM 555	Help Me Rhonda/Some Enchanted Evening	4
68	Major Minor MM 573	Yummy Yummy Yummy/Peanuts	4
60s	Hit HIT 1	Knock Three Times/See You In September	4

KENNY & CASH
65	Decca F 12283	Knees/The B Side	10

(see also Kenny Everett)

KENNY & CORKY
59	London HLX 9002	Nuttin' For Christmas/Suzy Snowflake	6

KENNY & DENNY
65	Decca F 12138	Try To Forget Me/Little Surfer Girl	5

KENNY & WRANGLERS
65	Parlophone R 5275	Doobie Doo/Moonshine	10
64	Parlophone R 5224	Somebody Help Me/Who Do You Think I Am?	10

AL KENT
67	Track 604 016	You Got To Pay The Price/Where Do I Go From Here	30
71	Mojo 2092 015	You Got To Pay The Price/Where Do I Go From Here (unreleased)	

ENOCH KENT
62	Topic TOP 81	SINGS THE BUTCHER BOY AND OTHER BALLADS (EP)	8

KLARK KENT
78	Kryptone KK 1	Don't Care/Thrills/Office Girls (p/s, green or rare black vinyl)	5/8
78	A&M AMS 7376	Don't Care/Thrills/Office Girls (reissue, p/s, green or black vinyl)	4
78	Kryptone KMS 7390	Too Kool To Kalypso/Theme For Kinetic Ritual (p/s, green vinyl)	5
80	A&M AMS 7532	Away From Home/Office Talk (p/s, green vinyl)	5
80	A&M AMS 7554	Rich In A Ditch/Grandelinquent (p/s, green vinyl)	5
80	A&M AMLE 68511	KLARK KENT (10" LP, green vinyl with inner sleeve)	10

(see also Police, Curved Air)

PAUL KENT
71	B&C CB 165	Do You/Helpless Harry	4
70	RCA SF 8083	P.C. KENT (LP)	20
71	B&C CAS 1044	PAUL KENT (LP)	15

RICHARD KENT STYLE
66	Columbia DB 7964	No Matter What You Do/Go, Go Children	40
66	Columbia DB 8051	You Can't Put Me Down/All Good Things	25
67	Columbia DB 8182	Marching Off To War/I'm Out	25
68	MCA MU 1032	Love Will Shake The World Awake/Crocodile Tears	18
69	Mercury MF 1090	A Little Bit O' Soul/Don't Tell Lies	15

SHIRLEY KENT
80	Tadpole TAD 001	My Dad/Marianne	5
66	Keele University 103	THE MASTER SINGERS AND SHIRLEY KENT SING FOR CHAREC 67 (EP)	20
89	Magic Spell 0001	FOREVER A WILLOW (LP)	12

(see also Ghost, Virginia Tree)

KENT (Brown) & DIMPLE (Hinds)
63	Island WI 046	Day Is Done/Linger A While	10

KENT (Brown) & JEANNIE
62	Blue Beat BB 98	Daddy/Hello Love	10

(see also Kent Brown & Rainbows)

RIK KENTON
74	Island WIP 6214	Bungalow Love/Lay It On You	4

(see also Roxy Music)

STAN KENTON & HIS ORCHESTRA
54	Capitol CL 14191	The Lady In Red/Skoot	6
55	Capitol CL 14247	Alone Too Long/Don't Take Your Love From Me	6
55	Capitol CL 14259	A-Ting-A-Ling/Malaguena (with Ann Richards)	8
55	Capitol CL 14269	23 Degrees North, 82 Degrees West/Falling (B-side with Ann Richards)	6
55	Capitol CL 14287	Lover Man/I've Got You Under My Skin	6
55	Capitol CL 14301	Casanova/Dark Eyes (with Ann Richards)	6
55	Capitol CL 14319	Freddy/The Handwriting's On The Wall	6
56	Capitol CL 14537	Winter In Madrid (with Ann Richards)/Baa-Too-Kee	4
56	Capitol CL 14539	Sunset Tower/Opus In Chartreuse	4
56	Capitol CL 14540	My Lady/Frank Speaking	4
56	Capitol CL 14541	Portrait Of A Count/Invention For Guitar And Trumpet	4
56	Capitol CL 14542	Cherokee/Limelight	5
57	Capitol CL 14707	His Feet Too Big For De Head (with June Christy)/Stardust — Boogie	5
57	Capitol CL 14806	Lemon Twist/Baby You're Tough	4
58	Capitol CL 14847	Tequila/Cuban Mumble	5
58	Capitol CL 14866	Reverie/More Love Than Your Love	4
59	Capitol CL 15029	Whistle Walk/Tamer-Lane	4
51	Capitol LC 6517	STAN KENTON'S MILESTONES (10" LP)	15
51	Capitol LC 6523	ENCORES (10" LP)	15
52	Capitol LC 6545	ARTISTRY IN RHYTHM (10" LP)	15
52	Capitol LC 6546	A CONCERT IN PROGRESSIVE JAZZ (10" LP)	15

MINT VALUE £

52	Capitol LC 6548	PRESENTS (10" LP)	15
52	Capitol LCT 6006	INNOVATIONS IN MODERN MUSIC (LP)	12
53	Capitol LC 6577	CITY OF GLASS (10" LP)	15
53	Capitol LC 6595	NEW CONCEPTS OF ARTISTRY IN RHYTHM (10" LP)	15
53	Capitol LC 6602	SKETCHES ON STANDARDS (10" LP)	15
54	Capitol LC 6667	THIS MODERN WORLD (10" LP)	15
54	Capitol LC 6676	CLASSICS (10" LP)	15
54	Capitol LCT 6009	KENTON SHOWCASE (LP)	12
55	Capitol LC 6697	PORTRAITS ON STANDARDS (10" LP)	15
56	Capitol LCT 6109	IN HI-FI (LP)	12
56	Capitol LCT 6118	CUBAN FIRE (LP)	12
56	Brunswick LAT 8122	THE FORMATIVE YEARS (LP)	10
57	Capitol LCT 6138	KENTON WITH VOICES (LP)	10
58	Capitol LCT 6157	THE KENTON ERA VOLUME ONE — PROLOGUE (LP)	10
58	Capitol LCT 6158	THE KENTON ERA VOLUME TWO — GROWING PAINS (LP)	10
58	Capitol LCT 6159	THE KENTON ERA VOLUME THREE — PROGRESSIVE JAZZ (LP)	10
58	Capitol LCT 6160	THE KENTON ERA VOLUME FOUR — CONTEMPORARY (LP)	10
58	Capitol (S)T 932	RENDEZVOUS WITH KENTON (LP)	10
58	Capitol T 995	BACK TO BALBOA (LP)	10
59	Capitol (S)T 1068	BALLAD STYLE OF STAN KENTON (LP)	10
59	Capitol T 1130	LUSH INTERLUDE (LP)	10
59	Capitol (S)T 1166	THE STAGE DOOR SWINGS (LP)	10

(see also June Christy)

KEN-TONES
| 56 | Parlophone MSP 6229 | Get With It/In Port Afrique | 7 |
| 57 | Parlophone R 4257 | I Saw Esau/Yaller, Yaller Gold | 6 |

(see also Benny Lee)

KENTUCKY BOYS
| 55 | HMV 7M 312 | Don't Fetch It/A Little Fella Like Me | 7 |

KENTUCKY COLONELS
| 74 | United Artists UAS 29514 | THE KENTUCKY COLONELS (LP) | 10 |

(see also Byrds)

BILL KENWRIGHT (& RUNAWAYS)
| 67 | Columbia DB 8239 | I Want To Go Back There Again/Walk Through Dreams (with Runaways) | 6 |
| 68 | MGM MGM 1430 | Giving Up/Love's Black And White (solo) | 5 |

WOODY KERN
| 69 | Pye 7N 17672 | Biography/Tell You I'm Gone | 6 |
| 67 | Pye NSPL 18273 | THE AWFUL DISCLOSURES OF MARIA MONK (LP) | 25 |

PATRICK KERR
| 65 | Decca F 12069 | Magic Potion/It's No Trouble To Love You | 10 |

RICHARD KERR
66	Decca F 12468	Concrete Jungle/You Got Nothing To Lose	4
66	Decca F 12538	Hard Lovin'/Auntie's Insurance Policy	4
67	Deram DM 138	Happy Birthday Blues/Mother's Blue Eyed Angel	4
72	Warners K 46206	FROM NOW UNTIL THEN (LP)	18

KERRIES
| 67 | Major Minor MM 541 | Coulters Candy/Gallon Of Whisky And A Barrel Of Beer | 4 |
| 67 | M. Minor MMLP/SMLP 9 | KERRIES (LP) | 20 |

CHRIS KERRY
| 65 | Mercury MF 957 | Seven Deadly Sins/The Place | 12 |
| 66 | Mercury MF 985 | Watermelon Man/I've Got My Pride | 8 |

DOUG KERSHAW
| 69 | Warner Bros WB 7304 | Feed It To The Fish/You Fight Your Fight (I'll Fight Mine) | 5 |
| 70 | Warner Bros WB 7413 | Orange Blossom Special/Swamp Rat | 4 |

NIK KERSHAW
83	MCA MCA 816	I Won't Let The Sun Go Down On Me/Dark Glasses (p/s)	4
84	MCA NIKD 5	Human Racing/Faces//Cloak And Dagger/Drum Talk (double pack, gatefold p/s)	4
84	MCA NIKP 5	Human Racing/Faces (picture disc)	4
84	MCA NIKX 5	Human Racing/Faces (12", picture disc)	7
84	MCA NIKP 6	The Riddle/Progress (picture disc)	4
85	MCA NIKP 8	Don Quixote/Don't Lie (picture disc)	4
86	MCA NIKP 11	Radio Musicola/Radio Musicola (Version) (picture disc)	4

KEN KESEY
| 83 | Psycho PSYCHO 4 | THE ACID TEST (LP, 300 only) | 30 |

BARNEY KESSEL
69	Polydor BM 56765	Frank Mills/Quail Bait	4
54	Vogue LDE 085	BARNEY KESSEL (10" LP)	12
55	Contemporary LDC 153	BARNEY KESSEL VOLUME 2 (10" LP)	12
77	Phil Spector Intl. 2307 011	SLOW BURN (LP)	15

(see also Rick Nelson)

JOHN KESTON
| 53 | MGM SP 1058 | Mardi Gras/There Was A Time | 4 |

KESTREL
| 75 | Cube HIFLY 19 | KESTREL (LP) | 80 |

KESTRELS
59	Pye 7N 15234	There Comes A Time/In The Chapel In The Moonlight	7
60	Pye 7N 15248	I Can't Say Goodbye/We Were Wrong	7
61	Decca F 11391	All These Things/That's It	5

62	Piccadilly 7N 35056	Wolverton Mountain/Little Sacka Sugar	4
62	Piccadilly 7N 35079	Don't Want To Cry/Love Me With All Your Heart	4
63	Piccadilly 7N 35104	Walk Right In/Moving Up The King's Highway	6
63	Piccadilly 7N 35126	There's A Place/Little Star	4
63	Piccadilly 7N 35144	Love Me With All Your Heart/Lazy River	4
63	Piccadilly NPL 38009	SMASH HITS (LP)	18

(see also Ivy League, Flowerpot Men)

ALLAN KEY
89	Diamond LOCK 1	Close The Window/There's Only One Per Room (p/s, with 'lawsuit' insert)	10

KEYBOARD RINGS
56	Oriole CB 1331	Rhapsody In Boogie/Rainbow Rag (78)	5

KEY CHAINS
66	London HLU 10055	Morgan's Song/Scruggs	4

EBONY KEYES
66	Piccadilly 7N 35358	Sitting In The Ring/If You Knew	7
67	Piccadilly 7N 35375	Cupid's House/If Our Love Should End	5
67	Piccadilly 7N 35390	Country Girl/How Many Times	5

KAROL KEYES
64	Fontana TF 517	You Beat Me To The Punch/No-One Can Take Your Place	8
67	Fontana TF 846	Can't You Hear The Music/The Sweetest Touch	6
66	Columbia DB 7899	A Fool In Love/The Good Love, The Bad Love	7
66	Columbia DB 8001	One In A Million/Don't Jump	30

TROY KEYES
68	Stateside SS 2087	Love Explosions/I'm Crying (Inside)	10
69	Stateside SS 2149	Love Explosions/I'm Crying (Inside) (reissue)	7

KEY LARGO
71	Blue Horizon 57-3178	Voodoo Rhythm/As The Years Go Passing By	12
70	Blue Horizon 7-63859	KEY LARGO (LP)	25

KEYMEN
59	HMV POP 584	Gazackstahagen/Miss You	6
62	Columbia DB 4902	Five Weeks In A Balloon/Secretly	4
57	Vogue Coral LVA 9048	THE VOCAL SOUNDS OF THE KEYMEN (LP)	10

KEYNOTES
54	Decca F 10302	A Dime And A Dollar/JOHNSTON BROTHERS: Bandit	6
55	Decca F 10643	Relax-Ay-Voo/Steam Heat	10
56	Decca F 10693	Scotland The Brave/Lewis Bridal Song	4
56	Decca F 10745	Let's Go Steady/Chincherinchee	5

(see also Bobbie Britton, Johnston Brothers, Dave King, Suzi Miller)

KEYS
64	Oriole CB 1968	Sleep Sleep My Baby/Colour Slides	5
65	CBS 201804	Go Get Her/My Everything	5

KEYS
81	White Dove RAWD 820	Captain Kirk's Disco Track/Star Lover	4

BOBBY KEYS
75	Ring O' 2017 102	Gimmie The Key/Honky Tonk (company sleeve)	4
72	Warner Bros K 46141	BOBBY KEYS (LP)	10

KGB
76	MCA MCF 2749	KGB (LP)	10

(see also Barry Goldberg, Mike Bloomfield)

KHAN
72	Deram SDL-R 11	SPACE SHANTY (LP)	25

(see also Steve Hillage, Egg, Nick Greenwood, Arzachel)

ASHISH KHAN
68	Liberty LBL 83083E	ASHISH KHAN (LP)	15

CHAKA KHAN
80	Warner Bros K 17617	Clouds/What You Did (p/s)	4
80	Warner Bros K 56713	NAUGHTY (LP)	10

(see also Rufus)

MICK KHAN
81	RPM RPM 5118	It Doesn't Matter Anymore/Wide Boy (p/s)	4

(see also Japan, Dali's Car)

USTAD ALI AKBAR KHAN
69	HMV ASD 2367	MUSIC FROM INDIA NO. 5 (LP)	12
69	Transatlantic TRA 183	DHUN PALAS KAFI (LP)	12
71	Mushroom 100 MR 14	THE PEACEFUL MUSIC OF USTAD ALI AKBAR KHAN (LP)	50

(see also Ravi Shankar)

USTAD VILAYET KHAN
70	Transatlantic TRA 239	RAGA TILAKKAMOD (LP)	15

KHANDARS
65	Blue Beat BB 332	Don't Dig A Hole For Me/BUSTER'S ALLSTARS: Skara	8

KHANS
62	London HLU 9555	New Orleans, 2 AM/Blue Mist	5

KHARTOMB
83	Whaam! WHA-AM 14	Swahili Lullaby/Teekon Warriors	7

KID CREOLE & COCONUTS

82	Island WIP 6480	Dear Addy/No Fish Today/Christmas On Riverside Drive (picture disc)	4
82	Island WIP 6756	I'm A Wonderful Baby/Table Manners (picture disc)	4
82	Island UWIP 6793	Stool Pigeon/In The Jungle//He's Not Such A Bad Guy/There But For The Grace Of God Go I (double pack, gatefold p/s)	4
83	Island IS 130	There's Something Wrong In Paradise/Fireside Story (picture disc)	4

JOHNNY KIDD (& PIRATES)

59	HMV POP 615	Please Don't Touch/Growl	10
59	HMV POP 674	Feelin'/If You Were The Only Girl In The World (solo)	10
59	HMV POP 698	You Got What It Takes/Longin' Lips	8
60	HMV POP 753	Shakin' All Over/Yes Sir, That's My Baby	7
60	HMV POP 790	Restless/Magic Of Love	8
61	HMV POP 853	Linda Lu/Let's Talk About Us	10
61	HMV POP 919	Please Don't Bring Me Down/So What	10
61	HMV POP 978	Hurry On Back To Love/I Want That	8
62	HMV POP 1088	A Shot Of Rhythm And Blues/I Can Tell	7
63	HMV POP 1173	I'll Never Get Over You/Then I Got Everything	4
63	HMV POP 1228	Hungry For Love/Ecstasy	6
64	HMV POP 1269	Always And Ever/Dr. Feelgood	6
64	HMV POP 1309	Jealous Girl/Shop Around	6
64	HMV POP 1353	Whole Lotta Woman/Your Cheatin' Heart	6
65	HMV POP 1397	The Birds And The Bees/Don't Make The Same Mistake As I Did	6
65	HMV POP 1424	Shakin' All Over '65/Gotta Travel On	8
65	HMV POP 1520	It's Got To Be You/I Hate Getting Up In The Morning (solo)	10
66	HMV POP 1559	The Fool/Send For That Girl	10
60	HMV 7EG 8628	SHAKIN' ALL OVER (EP)	25
64	HMV 7EG 8834	JOHNNY KIDD AND THE PIRATES (EP)	25
71	Regal Starline SRS 5100	SHAKIN' ALL OVER (LP)	12
78	EMI Nut NUTM 12	THE BEST OF JOHNNY KIDD AND THE PIRATES (LP)	10

(see also Pirates)

KIDS NEXT DOOR

65	London HLR 9993	Inky Dinky Spider/Goodbye Don't Cry	6

KIDZ NEXT DOOR

79	Warner Bros K 17492	What's It All About?/The Kidz Next Door (p/s)	8

REGINALD KILBEY & STRINGS STARLIGHT

66	HMV 7P 396	Exotica/Edelma	4

KILBURN & HIGH ROADS

74	Dawn DNS 1090	Rough Kids/Billy Bentley	5
75	Dawn DNS 1102	Crippled With Nerves/Huffety Puff	5
78	Warner Bros K 17225	Bentley/Pam's Moods	4
75	Dawn DNLS 3065	HANDSOME (LP)	12

(see also Ian Dury & Blockheads)

ROY KILDARE

63	Blue Beat BB 226	I Won't Leave/What About It	8

JUDY KILEEN

56	London HLU 8328	Just Walking In The Rain/A Heart Without A Sweetheart	20

MERLE KILGORE

54	London HL 8103	It Can't Rain All The Time/Seeing Double, Feeling Single	60
54	London HL 8103	It Can't Rain All The Time/Seeing Double, Feeling Single (78)	20
57	London HLP 8392	Ernie/Trying To Find (Someone Like You)	100
57	London HLP 8392	Ernie/Trying To Find (Someone Like You) (78)	28
60	Melodisc MEL 1545	Jimmie Bring Sunshine/Dear Mama	12
62	Mercury AMT 1193	42 In Chicago/A Girl Named Liz	10
65	London HA-B 8244	THERE'S GOLD IN THEM THAR HILLS (LP)	10

THEOLA KILGORE

67	Sue WI 4035	I'll Keep Trying/He's Coming Back To Me	12

LOUIS KILLEN

62	Topic TOP 75	NORTHUMBRIAN GARLAND (EP)	7
65	Topic 12T 126	BALLADS AND BROADSIDES (LP)	10

LOUIS KILLEN & JOHNNY HANDLE

62	Topic TOP 74	THE COLLIER'S RANT (EP)	7

(see also Johnny Handle)

KILLER EXPLODING WAR KING

89	Swordfish DICTATE 1	WRONG TELESCOPE (LP)	200

KILLERMETERS

79	Psycho P 2620	Why Should It Happen To Me/Cardiac Arrest (some in p/s)	50/20
80	Gem GEMS 22	Twisted Wheel/SX 225 (p/s)	15

KILLERS

77	Ariola ARL 5003	KILLER (LP)	10

JOHN KILLIGREW

71	Penny Farthing PELS 513	JOHN KILLIGREW (LP, with Pete Dello)	10

(see also Pete Dello)

KILLING FLOOR

70	Penny Farthing PEN 745	Call For The Politicians/Acid Bean	15
70	Spark SRLP 102	KILLING FLOOR (LP)	100
70	Penny Farthing PELS 511	OUT OF URANUS (LP)	100

| 73 | Spark Replay SRLM 2004 | ORIGINAL KILLING FLOOR (LP, reissue) ....40 |

KILLING JOKE

79	Malicious Damage MD 410	Nervous System/Turn To Red/Are You Receiving (10" EP in bag, some with picture & 4 cards) 15/10
80	Island WIP 6550	Turn To Red/Nervous System (p/s) 5
80	Island 12 WIP 6550	Almost Red/Nervous System/Are You Receiving/Turn To Red (12", p/s) 10
80	Malicious Damage MD 540	Wardance/Psyche (p/s, some with 'call up paper' insert) 8/5
80	EG EGMD 1.00	Requiem/Change (p/s) 4
80	EG EGMX 1.00	Requiem/Change/Change/Requiem (12", stamped sleeve, later in p/s) 12/10
81	EG EGMDS 1.01	Follow The Leaders/Tension (p/s) 4
81	EG EGMDX 1.01	Follow The Leaders/Follow The Leaders — Dub/Tension (10", p/s) 7
82	EG EGO 4	Empire Song/Brilliant (p/s) 4
82	EG EGO 7	Chop Chop/Good Samaritan (p/s) 4
82	EG EGO 10	Birds Of A Feather/Flock The B-Side (p/s) 4
82	EG EGOX 10	Birds Of A Feather/Flock The B-Side (12", p/s) 8
83	EG EGO 11	Let's All Go (To The Fire Dances)/Dominator (p/s) 4
83	EG EGOX 11	Let's All Go (To The Fire Dances)/The Fall Of Because (live)/ Dominator (Version) (12", p/s) 7
83	EG EGOD 14/KILL 1/2	Me Or You/Wilful Days//Feast Of Blaze (double pack, gatefold p/s) 5
83	EG EGOXD 14	Me Or You/Feast Of Blaze/Wilful Days//Let's All Go (To The Fire Dances)/ The Fall Of Because (live)/Dominator (Version) (12", sealed double pack) 15
84	EG EGO 16	Eighties/Eighties (Coming Mix) (p/s) 4
84	EG EGOX 16	Eighties (Serious Dance Mix)/Eighties/Eighties (Coming Mix) (12", p/s) 8
84	EG EGOX 17	A New Day (Dub Mix)/A New Day (12", p/s) 7
85	EG EGOY 20	Love Like Blood (Gestalt Mix)/Love Like Blood/Blue Feather (12", p/s) 10
85	EG EGOY 21	Kings And Queens (Knave Mix) (12", p/s) 10
85	EG EGOX 21	Kings And Queens (The Right Royal Mix)/The Madding Crowd/ Kings And Queens (12", p/s, with poster) 7
85	EG EGOX 21	Kings And Queens (The Right Royal Mix)/The Madding Crowd/ Kings And Queens (12", p/s, mispressing, withdrawn) 10
86	EG EGOD 27	Adorations/Exile//Ecstasy/Adorations (Instrumental Mix) (double pack) 4
86	EG EGO 30	Sanity/Goodbye To The Village (p/s, with "Wardance (Remix)" cassette & sticker) 12
88	EG EGOT 43	My Love Of This Land/Follow The Leaders (Dub)/Sun Goes Down (10", p/s, B-side matrix no. EGOT 43BE) 5
88	EG EGOT 43	My Love Of This Land/Follow The Leaders (Dub)/Sun Goes Down (10", p/s, B-side matrix no. EGOT 43B; last track plays "The Gathering") 5

(see also Youth, Brilliant, Peyr, Heavy Duty Breaks)

KILLJOYS

| 77 | Raw RAW 3 | Johnny Won't Get To Heaven/Naive (p/s, 4 different label designs) ....6 |

(see also Dexy's Midnight Runners)

KILOWATTS

| 68 | Doctor Bird DB 1140 | Bring It On Home/What A Wonderful World ....7 |

KILTIES

| 56 | Beltona BL 2666 | Teach You To Rock/Giddy-Up-A Ding Dong ....12 |

WILLIAM E. KIMBER

| 68 | Parlophone R 5735 | Kilburn Towers/Goodbye (withdrawn) ....6 |

(see also Couriers)

WILLIAM KIMBER

| 70s | EFDSS LP 1001 | WILLIAM KIMBER (LP, with booklet) ....15 |
| 74 | Topic 12T 249 | THE ART OF WILLIAM KIMBER (LP) ....10 |

STEVIE KIMBLE

| 66 | Decca F 12378 | Some Things Take A Little Time/All The Time In The World ....15 |

KING

84	CBS DA 4988	Love And Pride/Don't Stop//Love And Pride (Live)/I Kissed The Spikey Fridge (Live) (double pack) 4
85	CBS DA 6094	Won't You Hold My Hand Now (Remix)/Fish (Reprise) (live)//Won't You Hold My Hand Now (Encore) (live)/And As For Myself (Live) (double pack, gatefold p/s) 4
85	CBS QTA 6618	The Taste Of Your Tears/Crazy Party (poster p/s) 4
85	CBS WA 6618	The Taste Of Your Tears/Crazy Party (shaped picture disc) 4

(see also Reluctant Stereotypes)

AL KING

| 68 | Sue WI 4045 | Think Twice Before You Speak/The Winner ....18 |

ALBERT KING

67	Atlantic 584 099	Crosscut Saw/Down Don't Bother Me 10
67	Stax 601 015	Born Under A Bad Sign/Personal Manager 6
68	Stax 601 029	Cold Feet/You Sure Drive A Hard Bargain 6
68	Stax 601 042	(I Love) Lucy/You're Gonna Need Me 5
73	Stax 2025 162	Breaking Up Somebody's Home/Little Brother (Make A Way) 4
67	Polydor 2343 026	TRAVELLING TO CALIFORNIA (LP) 15
68	Stax (S)XATS 1002	LIVE WIRE — BLUES POWER (LP) 14
69	Atlantic 588 173	KING OF THE BLUES GUITAR (LP) 15
68	Stax SXATS 1017	KING DOES THE KING'S THINGS (LP) 12
70	Stax SXATS 1022	YEARS GONE BY (LP) 12
71	Stax 2363 003	LIVE WIRE — BLUES POWER (LP, reissue) 10
71	Stax 2325 042	LOVEJOY (LP) 10
72	Stax 2325 089	I'LL PLAY THE BLUES FOR YOU (LP) 10
74	Stax STX 1003	I WANNA GET FUNKY (LP) 10

ANNA KING

| 65 | Philips BF 1402 | If Somebody Told You/Baby, Baby, Baby (as Anna King & Bobby Byrd) ....8 |

Anna KING

| 65 | Philips BBE 12584 | BACK TO SOUL (EP) | 12 |
| 65 | Philips (S)BL 7655 | BACK TO SOUL (LP) | 20 |

(see also Bobby Byrd)

B.B. KING

62	HMV POP 1101	Tomorrow Night/Mother's Love	12
64	Ember EMB S 196	Rock Me Baby/I Can't Lose	12
65	Sue WI 358	The Letter/You Never Know	10
66	HMV POP 1568	Don't Answer The Door Pts 1 & 2	8
67	HMV POP 1580	Night Life/Waitin' On You	6
67	HMV POP 1594	I Don't Want You Cuttin' Your Hair/Think It Over	7
67	Polydor 56735	Jungle/Long Gone Baby	6
68	Stateside SS 2112	Paying The Cost To Be The Boss/Having My Say	5
68	Blue Horizon 57-3144	The Woman I Love/Blues For Me	12
69	Stateside SS 2141	Don't Waste My Time/Get Myself Somebody	5
69	Blue Horizon 57-3161	Everyday I Have The Blues/Five Long Years	10
70	Stateside SS 2161	The Thrill Is Gone/You're Mean	5
70	Stateside SS 2169	So Excited/Confessin' The Blues	4
70	Stateside SS 2176	Hummingbird/Ask Me No Questions	4
72	Probe PRO 573	Summer In The City/Found What I Need	4
65	HMV CLP 1870	LIVE AT THE REGAL (LP)	18
66	HMV CLP 3514	CONFESSIN' THE BLUES (LP)	18
67	HMV CLP 3608	BLUES IS KING (LP)	18
67	Ember EMB 3379	THE R&B AND SOUL OF B.B. KING (LP)	12
68	Stateside (S)SL 10238	BLUES ON TOP OF BLUES (LP)	15
68	Blue Horizon 7-63216	THE B.B. KING STORY CHAPTER 1 (LP)	35
69	Stateside (S)SL 10272	LUCILLE (LP)	15
69	Stateside SSL 10284	HIS BEST — THE ELECTRIC B.B. KING (LP)	15
69	Blue Horizon 7-63226	THE B.B. KING STORY CHAPTER 2 — BEALE STREET BLUES (LP)	35
70	Stateside SSL 10297	LIVE AND WELL (LP)	15
70	Stateside SSL 10299	COMPLETELY WELL (LP)	15
70	Probe SPBA 6255	INDIANOLA MISSISSIPPI SEEDS (LP)	12
70	Blue Horizon 2431 004	TAKE A SWING WITH ME (LP)	45
71	Probe SPB 1032	LIVE IN COOK COUNTY JAIL (LP)	12
71	Probe SPB 1041	IN LONDON (LP)	12
72	Probe SPB 1051	L.A. MIDNIGHT (LP)	10
73	Probe SPB 1063	GUESS WHO (LP)	10
73	Probe SPB 1083	TO KNOW YOU IS TO LOVE YOU (LP)	10

(see also U2)

B.B. KING & BOBBY BLAND

| 74 | ABC ABCD 605 | TOGETHER FOR THE FIRST TIME (2-LP) | 14 |

(see also Bobby Bland)

BEN E. KING

61	London HLK 9258	Spanish Harlem/First Taste Of Love	8
61	London HLK 9358	Stand By Me/On The Horizon	8
61	London HLK 9416	Amor, Amor/Souvenir Of Mexico	6
61	London HLK 9457	Here Comes The Night/Young Boy Blues	8
62	London HLK 9517	Ecstacy/Yes	6
62	London HLK 9544	Don't Play That Song (You Lied)/The Hermit Of Misty Mountain	6
62	London HLK 9586	Too Bad/My Heart Cries For You	6
63	London HLK 9631	I'm Standing By/Walking In The Footsteps Of A Fool	6
63	London HLK 9691	How Can I Forget/Gloria, Gloria	6
63	London HLK 9778	I (Who Have Nothing)/The Beginning Of Time	6
63	London HLK 9819	I Could Have Danced All Night/Gypsy	7
64	London HLK 9840	Around The Corner/Groovin'	7
64	Atlantic AT 4007	It's All Over/Let The Water Run Down	5
65	Atlantic AT 4018	Seven Letters/River Of Tears	5
65	Atlantic AT 4025	The Record (Baby I Love You)/The Way You Shake It	8
65	Atlantic AT 4043	Cry No More/(There's) No Place To Hide	8
66	Atlantic AT 4065	Goodnight My Love, Pleasant Dreams/Tell Daddy	5
66	Atlantic AT 4065	Goodnight My Love, Pleasant Dreams/I Can't Break The News To Myself (demos with blank label on B-side)	250
66	Atlantic 584 008	So Much Love/Don't Drive Me Away	5
66	Atlantic 584 046	I Swear By The Stars Above/Get In A Hurry	5
67	Atlantic 584 069	What Is Soul?/They Don't Give Medals To Yesterday's Heroes	5
67	Atlantic 584 090	Save The Last Dance For Me (as Ben E. King & Drifters)/Stand By Me	5
67	Atlantic 584 106	Tears, Tears, Tears/A Man Without A Dream	5
68	Atlantic 584 149	Seven Letters/Goodnight My Love	5
68	Atlantic 584 184	Don't Take Your Love From Me/Forgive This Fool	15
68	Atlantic 584 205	It's Amazing/Where's The Girl	4
69	Atlantic 584 238	'Till I Can't Take It Any More/It Ain't Fair	4
70	Crewe CRW 2	Goodbye My Old Girl/I Can't Take It Like A Man	5
71	Atlantic 2091 100	It's Amazing/Tears, Tears, Tears	4
71	CBS 7397	White Moon/All Of Your Sorrows	4
72	CBS 7785	Take Me To The Pilot/I Guess It's Goodbye	4
75	Atlantic K 10565	Supernatural Things Pts 1 & 2	4
75	Atlantic K 10618	Happiness Is Where You Find It/Drop My Heart Off	4
63	London REK 1361	HOW CAN I FORGET? (EP)	18
63	London REK 1386	I'M STANDING BY (EP)	18
64	Atlantic AET 6004	WHAT NOW MY LOVE (EP)	15
61	London HA-K 2395	SPANISH HARLEM (LP, also stereo SAH-K 6195)	25/30
62	London HA-K 8012	DON'T PLAY THAT SONG! (LP)	25
63	London HA-K/SH-K 8026	SONGS FOR SOULFUL LOVERS (LP, mono/stereo)	25/30
66	Atlantic 587/588 055	SONGS FOR SOULFUL LOVERS (LP, reissue)	12
67	Atlantic 590 001	SPANISH HARLEM (LP, reissue)	12
67	Atlantic 587 072	WHAT IS SOUL? (LP)	15

538　　Rare Record Price Guide

68	Atlantic 588 125	SEVEN LETTERS (LP)	15
70	Crewe CRWS 203	ROUGH EDGES (LP)	10
71	CBS 64570	THE BEGINNING OF IT ALL (LP)	10
75	Atlantic K 50118	SUPERNATURAL THING (LP)	10

(see also Drifters)

BOB KING
| 59 | Oriole CB 1497 | Hey Honey/My Petite Marie | 50 |
| 59 | Oriole CB 1497 | Hey Honey/My Petite Marie (78) | 30 |

BUZZY KING
| 60 | Top Rank JAR 278 | Schoolboy Blues/Your Picture | 8 |

CANNON BALL KING
| 69 | Camel CA 14 | Danny Boy/Reggae Happiness | 4 |
| 70s | Junior JR 103 | Reggay Got Soul/Land Of Love (actually by Soul Cats) | 5 |

(see also Carl Bryan, King Cannon)

CARL KING
| 66 | CBS 202407 | Out Of My Depth/Keep It Coming | 10 |
| 67 | CBS 202553 | You And Me/Satin Doll | 4 |

CAROLE KING
62	London HLU 9591	It Might As Well Rain Until September/Nobody's Perfect	8
66	London HLU 10036	Road To Nowhere/Some Of Your Lovin'	7
70	A&M AMLS 996	WRITER (LP)	10

CLAUDE KING
61	Philips BF 1173	Sweet Loving/Big River Big Man	6
61	Philips BF 1199	The Commancheros/I Can't Get Over The Way	6
62	CBS AAG 108	Wolverton Mountain/Little Bitty Heart	7
62	CBS AAG 119	Burning Of Atlanta/Don't The Moon Look Lonesome	7
65	CBS EP 6067	TIGER WOMAN (EP)	8

CLYDIE KING
| 69 | Minit MLF 11014 | One Part Two Part/Love Now Pay Later | 8 |
| 75 | UK USA 11 | Punish Me/Punish Me (Instrumental Version) | 5 |

(see also Jimmy Holiday & Clydie King, Raelets)

DANNY KING('S MAYFAIR SET)
64	Columbia DB 7276	Tossin' And Turnin'/Young Blood	15
65	Columbia DB 7456	Pretty Things/Outside Of My Room	25
65	Columbia DB 7792	Amen (My Teenage Prayer)/It's Such A Shame (as Danny King's Mayfair Set)	10

(see also Trevor Burton, Lemon Tree)

DAVE KING
56	Decca F 10684	Memories Are Made Of This (with Keynotes)/I've Changed My Mind A 1000 Times	10
56	Decca F 10720	You Can't Be True To Two/A Little Bit Independent	8
56	Decca F 10741	The Birds And The Bees/Hot Chocolatta (with Keynotes)	6
56	Decca F 10791	Christmas And You/You Make Nice	7
57	Decca F 10865	Love Is A Golden Ring/If Your Heart Wants To Dance	5
57	Decca F 10910	With All My Heart/Red Shutters	5
57	Decca F 10947	Shake Me I Rattle/Chances Are	6
58	Decca F 10973	The Story Of My Life/I'll Buy You A Star	7
58	Decca F 11012	I Suddenly/There's Only One Of You	4
58	Decca F 11061	The Story/Home	4
59	Pye Intl. 7N 25032	High Hopes/Night And Day	4
60	Pye 7N 15283	Many A Wonderful Moment/Goody Goody	4
61	Pye Intl. 7N 25076	Young In Love/C'est La Vie, C'est L'amour	4
56	Decca DFE 6385	A DAVE KING SELECTION (EP)	12
58	Decca DFE 6514	DAVE KING NO. 2 (EP)	12
62	Ace Of Hearts ACL 1095	MEMORIES ARE MADE OF THIS (LP)	10

DEE KING
| 66 | Piccadilly 7N 35316 | Sally Go Round The Roses/It's So Fine | 6 |

DON KING
| 85 | Doublevision DVR 14 | Revelry/Tanajura/The Don Goes On/Never Decide/Marco Polo (12", p/s) | 8 |

EDDIE KING
| 65 | Columbia DB 7572 | Always As A Distance/If You Wish | 4 |
| 65 | Columbia DB 7654 | I Wanna Love Her So Bad/If All You Need | 5 |

EVELYN KING
| 86 | Epic A 6671 | Give It Up/SPARKS: Armies Of The Night (p/s) | 4 |

(see also Sparks)

FREDDY/FREDDIE KING
61	Parlophone R 4777	Hideaway/I Love The Woman	20
65	Sue WI 349	Driving Sideways/Hideaway	18
69	Atlantic 584 235	Play It Cool/Funky	6
69	Atlantic 588 186	FREDDIE IS A BLUES MASTER (LP)	25
69	Polydor 2343 009	KING OF R&B VOL. 2 (LP)	12
69	Python KM 5	FREDDY KING VOLUME 1 (LP)	25
69	Python KM 7 (PLP 7)	FREDDY KING VOLUME 2 (LP)	25
71	A&M AMLS 65004	GETTING READY (LP)	15
71	Polydor 2343 047	HIS EARLY YEARS VOLUME 1 (LP)	10
72	A&M AMLS 68113	TEXAS CANNONBALL (LP)	10
72	Black Bear 904	LIVE PERFORMANCES VOLUME 1 (LP)	20
72	Black Bear 905	LIVE PERFORMANCES VOLUME 2 (LP)	20
73	A&M AMLS 68919	WOMAN ACROSS THE RIVER (LP)	10

Freddy/Freddie KING

73	Atlantic K 40496	FREDDIE IS A BLUES MASTER (LP, reissue)	10
73	Atlantic K 40497	MY FEELING FOR THE BLUES (LP)	10
75	RSO 2394 163	LARGER THAN LIFE (LP)	10

(pre-1970 releases are credited to Freddy King, post-1970 releases to Freddie King; see also Lulu Reed & Freddy King)

HANK KING
| 63 | Starlite STEP 41 | COUNTRY AND WESTERN (EP) | 15 |
| 66 | Starlite GRK 510 | COUNTRY AND WESTERN (EP, reissue) | 10 |

JAY W. KING
| 66 | Stateside SS 505 | I'm So Afraid/I Don't Have To Worry (Not Anymore) | 12 |

JONATHAN KING
65	Decca F 12187	Everyone's Gone To The Moon/Summer's Coming	4
65	Decca F 12237	Green Is The Grass/Creation	4
65	Decca F 12286	Where The Sun Has Never Shone/Don't Talk To Me Of Protest	4
66	Decca F 12457	Just Like A Woman/The Land Of The Golden Tree	4
66	Decca F 12517	Icicles/In A Hundred Years From Now	4
67	Decca LK/SKL 4908	OR THEN AGAIN... (LP)	12

MARK KING
84	Polydor MK 1	I Feel Free/There Is A Dog (p/s)	8
84	Polydor MKX 1	I Feel Free (Extended)/There Is A Dog (12", p/s)	10
84	Polydor MKX 2-DJ	Clocks Go Forward (Long Version)/Barcelona (12", promo-only)	15

(see also Level 42, Thunderthumbs & Toetsenman)

DR. MARTIN LUTHER KING
68	Pama PM 732	I Have A Dream/Top Of The Mountain	10
68	Tamla Motown TML 11076	THE GREAT MARCH TO FREEDOM (LP)	100
60s	Hallmark CHM 631	IN THE STRUGGLE FOR FREEDOM (LP)	10

PAUL KING
| 72 | Dawn DNS 1023 | Whoa Buck/Zoe | 4 |
| 72 | Dawn DNLS 3035 | BEEN IN THE PEN TOO LONG (LP, with insert) | 15 |

(see also King Earl Boogie Band, Mungo Jerry)

PEE WEE KING & HIS BAND
| 52 | HMV B 10229 | Bull Fiddle Boogie (with Golden Crest Cowboys)/Silver And Gold (78) | 7 |
| 54 | HMV 7MC 14 | Bimbo/Changing Partners (export issue) | 7 |

PETE KING CHORALE & ORCHESTRA
| 61 | London HLR 9437 | Hey! Look Me Over/Tall Hope | 4 |

PETER KING
| 68 | Crab CRAB 3 | Reggae Limbo/DERRICK MORGAN: River To The Bank | 5 |

RAMONA KING
| 64 | Warner Bros WB 125 | It's In His Kiss/It Couldn't Happen To A Nicer Guy | 6 |

RAY KING SOUL BAND
| 67 | Piccadilly 7N 35394 | Behold/Soon You'll Be Gone | 5 |

REG KING
| 71 | United Artists UAG 29157 | REG KING (LP) | 25 |

(see also Action, Andy Leigh)

SAMMY KING (& VOLTAIRS)
64	HMV POP 1285	What's The Secret/Great Balls Of Fire (as Sammy King & Voltairs)	7
64	HMV POP 1330	Rag Doll/We're Through	5
65	HMV POP 1384	Only You (And You Alone)/A Kiss, A Promise	4
66	HMV POP 1540	If You Can Find Someone To Love You/Past Caring (with Voltairs)	4

SID KING & FIVE STRINGS
| 56 | Philips PB 589 | Booger Red/Oobie-Doobie (78) | 25 |

SOLOMON KING
67	Columbia DB 8306	She Wears My Ring/Try Try (withdrawn)	10
67	Columbia DB 8325	She Wears My Ring/I Get That Feeling Over You	4
68	Columbia DB 8402	When We Were Young/Those Gentle Hands	4
68	Columbia DB 8454	Somewhere In The Crowd/Hava Nagila	4
68	Columbia DB 8508	Goodbye My Old Gal/Hundred Years Or More	4
69	Columbia DB 8554	Cry Softly/Time Alone Will Tell	4
69	Columbia DB 8586	For Each Question/If I Had Three Wishes	4
69	Columbia DB 8639	Bless Your Heart/Sugar Sweet As Candy	4
69	Columbia DB 8676	Say A Prayer For Me/This Beautiful Day	35
70	Columbia DB 8739	November Snow/Echoes Of A Million Kisses	4
71	Columbia DB 8771	Answer Me/Don't You Be A Sinner	4
68	Columbia S(C)X 6250	SHE WEARS MY RING (LP)	10
71	Columbia SCX 6458	YOU'LL NEVER WALK ALONE (LP)	10

(see also Levi Jackson)

TEDDI KING
56	Vogue Coral Q 72142	My Funny Little Lover/I'll Never Be The Same	5
55	Vogue LDE 142	MISS TEDDI KING WITH RUBY BRAFF (10" LP)	12
57	Vogue VA 160109	NOW IN VOGUE (LP)	10

(see also George Shearing)

TEDDY KING & BUSTER'S ALLSTARS
| 67 | Fab FAB 27 | Mexican Divorce/SOUL TOPS: Baby I Got News | 8 |

TOBY KING
| 75 | President PT 430 | The First Man To Die From The Blues/Country Blues | 4 |

TONY KING & HIPPY BOYS
| 69 | Trojan TR 667 | Proud Mary/My Devotion | 4 |

KING BROTHERS

57	Conquest CP 104	The Cradle Rock/Crazy Little Palace (78)	8
57	Conquest CP 109	Steamboat Railroad/Heart (78)	6
57	Parlophone R 4288	Marianne/Little By Little	8
57	Parlophone R 4288	Marianne/Little By Little (78)	5
57	Parlophone R 4310	A White Sport Coat (And A Pink Carnation)/Minne-Minnehaha!	7
57	Parlophone R 4310	A White Sport Coat (And A Pink Carnation)/Minne-Minnehaha! (78)	5
57	Parlophone R 4338	In The Middle Of An Island/Rockin' Shoes	6
57	Parlophone R 4338	In The Middle Of An Island/Rockin' Shoes (78)	5
57	Parlophone R 4367	Wake Up Little Susie/Winter Wonderland	6
57	Parlophone R 4367	Wake Up Little Susie/Winter Wonderland (78)	5
57	Parlophone R 4389	Put A Light In The Window/Miss Otis Regrets	6
58	Parlophone R 4410	Hand Me Down My Walking Cane/6-5 Jive	8
58	Parlophone R 4438	Torero/Moonlight And Roses	6
58	Parlophone R 4469	Sitting In A Tree House/Father Time	5
59	Parlophone R 4513	Leaning On A Lamp-Post/Thank Heaven For Little Girls	5
59	Parlophone R 4554	Hop, Skip And Jump/Civilization (Bongo, Bongo, Bongo)	8
59	Parlophone R 4577	Makin' Love/Caribbean	4
60	Parlophone R 4639	The Waiter And The Porter And The Upstairs Maid/Standing On The Corner	4
60	Parlophone R 4672	Mais Oui/Gotta Feeling	4
60	Parlophone R 4715	Doll House/Si Si Si	4
61	Parlophone R 4737	Seventy-Six Trombones/I Like Everybody	4
61	Parlophone R 4778	Goodbye Little Darling/Tuxedo Junction	4
61	Parlophone R 4825	The Next Train Out Of Town/Sabre Dance	4
64	Oriole CB 1978	Real Live Girls/Everytime It Rains	4
57	Parlophone GEP 8638	HARMONY KINGS (EP)	8
57	Parlophone GEP 8651	SING AL JOLSON (EP)	7
57	Parlophone GEP 8665	LULLABIES OF BROADWAY (EP)	7
58	Parlophone GEP 8726	THAT'S ENTERTAINMENT (EP)	7
58	Parlophone GEP 8760	KINGS OF SONG (EP)	8
61	Parlophone GEP 8838	KING SIZE HITS (EP)	7
58	Parlophone PMC 1060	THREE KINGS AND AN ACE (LP)	12

KING CANNON

69	Duke DU 13	Soul Pipe/Overproof (Little Darlin')	6
69	Trojan TR 663	Soul Scorcher/GLEN & DAVE: Lucky Boy	4
69	Trojan TR 664	Soul Special/TREVOR SHIELD: Moon Is Playing Tricks On Me	4
69	Crab CRAB 6	Mellow Trumpet/VAL BENNETT: Reggae City	4
71	Hillcrest HCT 2	Reggay Got Soul/SOUL CATS: Land Of Love	4
	(see also Cannon Ball King)		

KING CANNONBALL

68	Trojan TR 636	Thunderstorm/BERT WALTERS: Honey Love	4

KING COLE TRIO

(see under Nat 'King' Cole)

KING CRIMSON

69	Island WIP 6071	The Court Of The Crimson King Pts 1 & 2	12
70	Island WIP 6080	Cat Food/Groon (some in p/s)	10/5
74	Island WIP 6189	The Night Watch/The Great Deceiver	4
76	Island WIP 6274	21st Century Schizoid Man/Epitaph (some in p/s)	15/5
69	Island ILPS 9111	IN THE COURT OF THE CRIMSON KING (LP, pink label; later palm tree)	15/10
70	Island ILPS 9127	IN THE WAKE OF POSEIDON (LP, pink label; later palm tree label)	15/10
70	Island ILPS 9141	LIZARD (LP, pink label; later palm tree label)	15/10
71	Island ILPS 9175	ISLANDS (LP, with gatefold inner sleeve, palm tree label, pink label rumoured to exist)	10
72	Island HELP 6	EARTHBOUND (LP, black/pink label)	10
73	Island ILPS 9230	LARKS' TONGUE IN ASPIC (LP, with inner sleeve & palm tree label)	10
74	Island ILPS 9275	STARLESS AND BIBLE BLACK (LP, with inner sleeve & palm tree label)	10
74	Island ILPS 9308	RED (LP, palm tree label)	10
75	Island ILPS 9316	U.S.A. (LP, palm tree label)	10
76	Island ISLP 7	A YOUNG PERSON'S GUIDE (2-LP with booklet)	15
	(see also Giles Giles & Fripp, Robert Fripp, Gordon Haskell, Shame, McDonald & Giles, Emerson Lake & Palmer, Uriah Heep)		

KING CURTIS

62	London HLU 9547	Soul Twist/Twistin' Time (as King Curtis & Noble Knights)	12
64	Capitol CL 15346	Soul Serenade/More Soul	10
67	Atlantic 584 109	Good To Me/Hold On I'm Comin'	4
67	Atlantic 584 134	Memphis Soul Stew/Blue Nocturne	5
68	Ember SPE 1000	Wiggle Wobble/Night Train	8
69	Atlantic 584 287	Little Green Apples/La Jeanne	4
70	Atco 2091 012	Teasin'/Soulin' (as King Curtis & Delaney Bramlett, Eric Clapton & Friends)	4
60	London REK 1307	HAVE TENOR SAX, WILL BLOW (EP)	18
60	London HA-K 2247	HAVE TENOR SAX, WILL BLOW (LP)	25
62	RCA RD 27252	ARTHUR MURRAY'S MUSIC FOR DANCING - THE TWIST (LP)	20
62	Esquire 32-161	THE NEW SCENE OF KING CURTIS (LP)	20
67	Atlantic 587 067	PLAYS GREAT MEMPHIS HITS (LP)	14
68	Ember SPE/LP 6600	SOUL SERENADE (LP)	12
68	Atlantic 587 093	KINGSIZE SOUL (LP)	14
68	Atlantic 587 115	SWEET SOUL (LP)	12
69	Atlantic 228 027	INSTANT GROOVE (LP)	10
69	Atlantic 228 002	BEST OF KING CURTIS (LP)	10
70	Wand WNS 4	ETERNALLY SOUL (LP, as King Curtis & Shirelles)	10

KING CURTIS, OLIVER NELSON & JIMMY FORREST

63	Esquire 32-189	SOUL BATTLE (LP)	20

KINGDOM COME (U.K.)

MINT VALUE £

KINGDOM COME (U.K.)

71	Polydor 2001 234	General Messenger/I D Side To Be B Side The C Side	4
72	Polydor 2001 416	Spirit Of Joy/Come Alive	4
72	Polydor 2310 130	GALACTIC ZOO DOSSIER (LP, gatefold sleeve, some with poster)	35/18
73	Polydor 2310 178	KINGDOM COME (LP)	15
73	Polydor 2310 254	JOURNEY (LP)	15

(see also Arthur Brown)

KINGDOM COME (U.S.)

88	Polydor KCXP 1	Get It On/17 (picture disc)	4

KINGDOMS

84	Regard RG 114	Heartland/Stability (p/s)	10
84	Regard RGT 114	Heartland (Extended)/Stability (Extended) (12", p/s)	15

(see also House Of Love)

KING EARL BOOGIE BAND

72	Dawn DNS 1024	Plastic Jesus/If The Lord Don't Get You	4
72	Dawn DNS 1028	Starlight/Goin' The Germany	4
72	Dawn DNLS 3040	TROUBLE AT MILL (LP, with poster)	15

(see also Paul King, Mungo Jerry)

KING FIGHTER

60s	Jump Up JU 518	People Will Talk/Same Thing	6

KINGFISH

76	United Artists UAG 29922	KINGFISH (LP)	10
77	United Artists UAG 30080	LIVE AND KICKIN' (LP)	10

(see also Grateful Dead)

KING GEORGE

67	RCA RCA 1573	Drive On James/I'm Gonna Be Somebody Someday	12

KING HARVEST

73	Pye NSPL 28174	DANCING IN THE MOONLIGHT (LP)	10

KING HORROR

69	Joe/Duke DU 34	Dracula Prince Of Darkness/JOE'S ALL STARS: Honky	5
69	Grape GR 3003	Cutting Blade/Vampire	5
69	Grape GR 3006	The Hole/WINSTON GROOVY: Lover Come Back	5
69	Grape GR 3007	Lochness Monster/VISIONS: Zion I	5
69	Jackpot JP 713	Wood In The Fire/The Naked City	5
69	Jackpot JP 714	Police/PAMA DICE: Honky Tonk Popcorn	5
70	Nu Beat NB 051	Frankenstein/WINSTON GROOVY: I Can't Stand It	5

(see also Laurel Aitken)

KING KURT

82	Thin Sliced TSR 2	Zulu Beat/Rockin' Kurt (p/s, various coloured vinyls)	4-10
83	Stiff BUY 189	Destination Zululand/She's A Hairy (shaped picture disc)	10
84	Stiff PBUY 199	Mack The Knife/Wreck A Party Rock (shaped picture disc)	7
84	Stiff PBUY 199	Mack The Knife/Wreck A Party Rock (picture disc)	6
84	Stiff BUY 199	Mack The Knife/Wreck A Party Rock (p/s, with free flexidisc)	5
84	Stiff BUY 206	Banana Banana/Bo Diddley Goes East (scratch'n'sniff p/s)	4
84	Stiff PBUY 206	Banana Banana/Bo Diddley Goes East (shaped picture disc)	8
85	Stiff BUY 223	Billy/Back On The Dole (picture disc)	4
86	Polydor KURTP 1	America/High And Mighty (shaped picture disc)	6
87	Polydor KURTG 2	The Land Of Ring Dang Doo/Zulu Beat//Horatio/Gather Your Limb (double pack)	4
86	Stiff PSEEZ 62	BIG COCK (LP, picture disc)	10

KINGLY BAND

69	Decca F 12926	The Bitter And The Sweet/Standing At The Crossroads	7

KINGMAKER

91	Sacred Heart NONE 1	The Celebrated Working Man/Freewheeling (p/s, promo only)	15

KING OF MONTEGO BAY

64	Blue Beat BB 322	Burn/Independence '65	6

KING OF THE SLUMS

86	SLR SLR 001	Spider Psychiatry/The Lodge/Losing Ground (p/s)	15
89	Play Hard DEC 13	Bombs Away On Harphurey/Big Girl's Blouse (p/s)	6
80s	Gravity	Trouble At (flexidisc, free with 'Gravity' fanzine)	6
90	Midnight DING 63	It's Dead Smart (1-sided, die-cut company sleeve)	4
88	Play Hard DEC 08	ENGLAND'S FINEST HOPES (12" EP)	8
88	Play Hard DEC 14	VICIOUS BRITISH BOYFRIEND (12" EP)	7

KING OLIVER

53	London AL 3510	PLAYS THE BLUES (10" LP)	20

KINGPINS (U.S.)

58	London HLU 8658	Ungaua Pts 1 & 2	15
58	London HLU 8658	Ungaua Pts 1 & 2 (78)	5

KINGPINS (U.K.)

65	Oriole CB 1986	Two Right Feet/That's The Way It Should Be	15

(see also Orange Seaweed)

KINGPINS (U.K.)

67	Columbia DB 8146	Summer's Come And Gone/Another Tear Falls	4

KING ROCK & WILLOWS

67	Caltone TONE 111	You Are The One/ALVA LEWIS: Return Home	4

KING ROCKY
68	Studio One SO 2045	The King Is Back/THREE TOPS: Vex Till Yuh Buss	15

(see also Leroy & Rocky)

KINGS IV
59	London HLT 8914	Some Like It Hot/The World Goes On	8
59	London HLT 8914	Some Like It Hot/The World Goes On (78)	5

KING'S HENCHMEN
59	Coral FEP 2025	ALAN FREED PRESENTS VOL. 1 (EP)	100

KING SCRATCH
70s	Ethnic ETH 16	Spiritual Whip/Version	6
70s	Ethnic ETH 30	Mash Finger/Version	6

(see also Lee Perry/Upsetters)

KING SISTERS
57	Capitol CL 14711	While The Lights Are Low/In Hamburg (When The Nights ...)	4
57	Capitol CL 14729	Imagination/You're My Thrill	4
57	Capitol CL 14777	Easy To Love/That Old Feeling	4
58	Capitol CL 14865	Deep Purple/Unbelievable	4
58	Capitol CL 14893	What's New?/The Thrill Was New	4
58	Capitol CL 14934	The Guy In The Foreign Sports Car/Autumn In Pleasant Grove	4
59	Capitol CL 15012	Keep Smiling (Keep Laughin', Be ...)/The Maids Of Cadiz	4
59	Capitol CL 15069	Lovin' Up A Storm/What Would I Do Without You	4
59	Capitol CL 15096	Over The River (And Through The Woods)/Holiday Of Love (& Family)	4
57	Capitol T 808	ALOHA (LP)	10

CHARLES KINGSLEY CREATION
65	Columbia DB 7758	Summer Without Sun/Still In Love With You	30

EVELYN KINGSLEY
58	Capitol CL 14944	To Know Him Is To Love Him/FRANK PERRY: Let Me Be The One	6

KINGSMEN
58	London HLE 8735	Better Believe It/Week-End	20
58	London HLE 8735	Better Believe It/Week-End (78)	8
59	London HLE 8812	Conga Rock/The Cat Walk	25
59	London HLE 8812	Conga Rock/The Cat Walk (78)	10
59	London REE 1211	WEEK-END (EP)	45

(see also Bill Haley & Comets)

KINGSMEN
63	Pye International 7N 25231	Louie Louie/Haunted Castle	8
64	Pye International 7N 25262	Little Latin Lupe Lu/David's Mood	7
64	Pye International 7N 25273	Death Of An Angel/Searching For Love	8
65	Pye International 7N 25292	The Jolly Green Giant/Long Green	8
65	Pye International 7N 25311	The Climb/Waiting	6
65	Pye International 7N 25322	Annie Fanny/Something's Got A Hold On Me	6
66	Pye International 7N 25366	Little Latin Lupe Lu/Louie Louie	5
66	Pye International 7N 25370	Killer Joe/Little Green Thing	10
67	Pye International 7N 25406	Daytime Shadows/Trouble	8
64	Pye International NEP 44023	THE KINGSMEN (EP)	15
65	Pye International NEP 44040	MOJO WORKOUT (EP)	15
66	Pye International NEP 44063	FEVER (EP)	12
64	Pye International NPL 28054	THE KINGSMEN VOLUME II (LP)	15
65	Pye International NPL 28068	THE KINGSMEN ON CAMPUS (LP)	15
68	Marble Arch MAL 829	THE KINGSMEN'S GREATEST HITS (LP)	10
71	Wand WNS 6	UP AND AWAY (LP)	10

KINGS OF CARIBBEAN STEEL BAND
57	Melodisc MEL 1429	Rock 'N' Roll Susie/Down In Soho (78)	5

KING SPARROW
66	Island WI 285	Beggars Have No Choice/MARCIA GRIFFITHS: Funny	6
60s	Melodisc MEL 1475	Familysize Cokes/Clara Honey Bunch	4
60s	Melodisc MEL 1491	Goaty/I Confess	4

KING SPORTY
70	Banana BA 321	Inspiration/Choice Of Music	6
70	Banana BA 322	Lover's Version (as Sporty & Wilson)/DUDLEY SIBLEY: Having A Party	6
70	Banana BA 323	D.J. Special/RICHARD & MAD: Creation Version	6

KING STITT
(see under S)

KINGSTONIANS
67	Rio R 140	Winey Winey/I Don't Care	8
68	Coxsone CS 7066	Mother Miserable/I Make A Woman	12
68	Doctor Bird DB 1120	Put Down Your Fire/Girls Like Dirt	10
68	Doctor Bird DB 1123	Mummy And Daddy/False Witness	10
68	Doctor Bird DB 1126	Fun Galore/Crime Don't Pay	10
68	Trojan TR 627	Mix It Up/I'll Be Around	6
68	Big Shot BI 508	Sufferer/Kiss A Little Finger	5
69	Big Shot BI 526	Nice Nice/I'll Be Around	5
69	Trojan TR 770	I Need You/I'm Gonna Make It	5
69	Trojan TR 7708	I Need You/I'm Gonna Make It	4
69	Crab CRAB 19	Hold Down/BARRY YORK: Who Will She Be	4
69	Bullet BU 409	I Am Just A Minstrel/Yesterday	4
69	Songbird SB 1011	The Clip/BRUCE ANTHONY: Little Miss Muffett	4
70	Songbird SB 1019	Singer Man/CRYSTALITES: Version	4
70	Songbird SB 1041	Rumble Rumble/CRYSTALITES: Version	4

KINGSTONIANS

70	Duke DU 88	You Can't Wine/RUPIE EDWARDS ALLSTARS: Bee Sting 4
72	Duke DU 126	Lion's Den/Version 4
70	Trojan TBL 113	SUFFERER (LP) 10

KINGSTON JOE
64	Blue Beat BB 253	Time Is On My Friend/Wear And Tear (A-side actually by Lloyd Barnes, B-side actually by Lascelles Perkins) 8

KINGSTON PETE & BUSTER'S ALL STARS
67	Blue Beat BB 403	Little Boy Blue/I'm A Lover Try Me 6

(see also Larry Marshall)

KINGSTON TRIO
58	Capitol CL 14918	Scarlet Ribbons/Three Jolly Coachmen 5
58	Capitol CL 14951	Tom Dooley/Ruby Red 6
59	Capitol CL 14985	Raspberries, Strawberries/Sally 4
59	Capitol CL 15002	The Tijuana Jail/Oh Cindy 4
59	Capitol CL 15040	M.T.A./All My Sorrows 4
59	Capitol CL 15073	San Miguel/A Worried Man 4
60	Capitol CL 15113	Green Grasses/Coo Coo U 4
60	Capitol CL 15199	El Matador/Home From The Hill 4
60	Capitol CL 15138	Bad Man's Blunder/The Escape Of Old John Webb 4
60	Capitol CL 15161	This Mornin', This Evenin', So Soon/Everglades 4
65	Brunswick OE 9511	THE KINGSTON TRIO (EP) 8
59	Capitol EAP1 1119	M.T.A. (EP) 7
59	Capitol EAP1 1136	TOM DOOLEY (EP) 7
59	Capitol EAP1 1182	RASPBERRIES STRAWBERRIES (EP) 7
60	Capitol EAP1 1258	HERE WE GO AGAIN (EP, also stereo SEP1 1258) 7/8
60	Capitol EAP2 1258	HERE WE GO AGAIN (EP, also stereo SEP2 1258) 7/8
60	Capitol EAP3 1258	HERE WE GO AGAIN (EP, also stereo SEP3 1258) 7/8
60	Capitol EAP1 1322	A WORRIED MAN (EP) 7
62	Capitol EAP4 2011	TIME TO THINK (EP) 7
63	Capitol EAP1 20460	GREENBACK DOLLAR (EP) 7
64	Capitol EAP1 20655	LEMON TREE (EP) 7
58	Capitol T 996	THE KINGSTON TRIO (LP) 15
59	Capitol T 1107	FROM THE HUNGRY I (LP) 12
59	Capitol T 1199	AT LARGE (LP) 10
60	Capitol (S)T 1258	HERE WE GO AGAIN (LP) 10
60	Capitol (S)T 1352	SOLD OUT (LP) 10
60	Capitol (S)T 1407	STRING ALONG (LP) 12
60	Capitol ST 1183	STEREO CONCERT (LP) 15
60	Capitol (S)T 1446	LAST MONTH OF THE YEAR (LP) 10
61	Capitol (S)T 1474	MAKE WAY! (LP) 12
61	Capitol (S)T 1564	GOIN' PLACES (LP) 12
61	Capitol (S)T 1612	ENCORES (LP) 10
61	Capitol (S)T 1642	CLOSE UP (LP) 10
62	Capitol (S)T 1658	COLLEGE CONCERT (LP) 10
62	Capitol (S)T 1705	BEST OF THE KINGSTON TRIO (LP) 10
62	Capitol (S)T 1747	SOMETHING SPECIAL (LP) 10
63	Capitol (S)T 1809	NEW FRONTIER (LP) 10
63	Capitol (S)T 1871	NUMBER SIXTEEN (LP) 10
63	Capitol (S)T 1935	SUNNY SIDE (LP) 10
64	Capitol (S)T 2011	TIME TO THINK (LP) 10
64	Capitol (S)T 2081	BACK IN TOWN (LP) 10
64	Capitol (S)T 2180	FOLK ERA (LP) 12
65	Capitol (S)T 2280	BEST OF THE KINGSTON TRIO VOL. 2 (LP) 10
66	Capitol (S)T 2614	BEST OF THE KINGSTON TRIO VOL. 3 (LP) 10

KING TRIGGER
82	Chrysalis CHS 2623	The River/Punch Or Slide (picture disc) 4

KINKS
64	Pye 7N 15611	Long Tall Sally/I Took My Baby Home 35
64	Pye 7N 15636	You Still Want Me/You Do Something To Me 70
64	Pye 7N 15673	You Really Got Me/It's All Right 4
64	Pye 7N 15714	All Day And All Of The Night/I Gotta Move 4
65	Pye 7N 15759	Tired Of Waiting For You/Come On Now 4
65	Pye 7N 15813	Everybody's Gonna Be Happy/Who'll Be The Next In Line 5
65	Pye 7N 15854	Set Me Free/I Need You 4
65	Pye 7N 15919	See My Friend/Never Met A Girl Like You Before 4
65	Pye 7N 15981	Till The End Of The Day/Where Have All The Good Times Gone 4
66	Pye 7N 17064	Dedicated Follower Of Fashion/Sittin' On My Sofa 4
66	Pye 7N 17100	Well Respected Man/Milk Cow Blues (export only) 25
66	Pye 7N 17125	Sunny Afternoon/I'm Not Like Everybody Else 4
66	Pye 7N 17222	Dead End Street/Big Black Smoke 4
67	Pye 7N 17314	Mr. Pleasant/This Is Where I Belong (export only) 25
67	Pye 7N 17321	Waterloo Sunset/Act Nice And Gentle 4
67	Pye 7N 17400	Autumn Almanac/Mr. Pleasant 4
68	Pye 7N 17468	Wonderboy/Polly 5
68	Pye 7N 17573	Days/She's Got Everything (pink labels; later blue) 15/4
69	Pye 7N 17724	Plastic Man/King Kong 6
69	Pye 7N 17776	Drivin'/Mindless Child Of Motherhood 6
69	Pye 7N 17812	Shangri-La/Last Of The Steam-Powered Trains (withdrawn, demos may exist) ....75+
69	Pye 7N 17812	Shangri-La/This Man He Weeps Tonight 5
69	Pye 7N 17865	Victoria/Mr Churchill Says 5
70	Pye 7N 17961	Lola/Berkeley Mews 4
70	Pye 7N 45016	Apeman/Rats 4
71	Pye 7N 8001	God's Children/Moments (export issue) 15

MINT VALUE £

71	Pye 7NX 8001	PERCY (33rpm 4-track maxi-single, p/s)	8
72	RCA RCA 2211	Supersonic Rocket Ship/You Don't Know My Name	4
72	RCA RCA 2299	Celluloid Heroes/Hot Potatoes	4
73	RCA RCA 2387	Sitting In The Midday Sun/One Of The Survivors	4
73	RCA RCA 2418	Sweet Lady Genevieve/Sitting In My Hotel	4
74	RCA RCA 5015	Mirror Of Love/Cricket	4
74	RCA RCA 5042	Mirror Of Love/He's Evil	4
74	RCA RCA 2478	Holiday Romance/Shepherds Of The Nation	4
75	RCA RCA 2546	Ducks On The Wall/Rush Hour Blues	4
75	RCA RCA 2567	You Can't Stop The Music/Have Another Drink	4
76	RCA RCM 1	No More Looking Back/Jack The Idiot Dunce/ The Hard Way (p/s)	5
77	Arista ARIST 153	Father Christmas/Prince Of The Punks	4
78	Arista ARIST 210	Black Messiah/Misfits (p/s)	4
79	Arista ARIST 300	Moving Pictures/In A Space (p/s)	4
81	Arista ARIST 415	Better Things/Massive Reductions (p/s)	4
81	Arista ARIST 415/KINKS 1	Better Things/Massive Reductions//Lola (live)/David Watts (live) (double pack, gatefold p/s)	4
81	Arista ARIST 426	Predictable/Back To Front (picture disc)	5
	Music Week	How Are You (freebie with 'Music Week' magazine)	4
83	PRT KPD 1	You Really Got Me/Misty Water (picture disc)	4
84	PRT KIS 003	All Day And All Of The Night/I Gotta Move (picture disc)	4
87	PRT PYS 2	Sunny Afternoon/Tired Of Waiting For You (piture disc)	4
88	PRT PYS 7	Dedicated Follower Of Fashion/Autumn Almanac (picture disc)	4
64	Pye NEP 24200	KINKSIZE SESSION (EP)	12
64	Pye NEP 24203	KINKSIZE HITS (EP)	12
65	Pye NEP 24221	KWYET KINKS (EP)	15
66	Pye NEP 24258	DEDICATED KINKS (EP)	45
68	Pye NEP 24296	THE KINKS (EP)	175
75	Pye AMEP 1001	THE KINKS (EP, 'Yesteryear' export issue, red or blue vinyl)	10
83	PRT KBD 1	YOU REALLY GOT ME (EP, picture disc)	7
64	Pye NPL 18096	THE KINKS (LP, mono)	18
64	Pye NSPL 83021	THE KINKS (LP, stereo, possibly export only)	75
65	Pye NPL 18112	KINDA KINKS (LP)	18
66	Pye NPL 18131	THE KINKS KONTROVERSY (LP)	20
66	Pye N(S)PL 18149	FACE TO FACE (LP, mono/stereo)	20/30
67	Golden Guinea GGL 0357	THE KINKS (LP, reissue)	10
67	Pye N(S)PL 18191	LIVE AT KELVIN HALL (LP, mono/stereo)	20/25
67	Pye N(S)PL 18193	SOMETHING ELSE BY THE KINKS (LP, mono/stereo)	25/30
68	Pye N(S)PL 18233	THE KINKS ARE THE VILLAGE GREEN PRESERVATION SOCIETY (LP, unissued, 12-track version, test pressings only)	200
68	Pye N(S)PL 18233	THE KINKS ARE THE VILLAGE GREEN PRESERVATION SOCIETY (LP)	15
69	Pye NSPL 18317	ARTHUR (LP)	15
	(the above Pye LPs originally came with pink labels & laminated flipback sleeves)		
70	Pye NPL 18326	THE KINKS (2-LP)	15
70	Pye NSLP 18359	THE KINKS PT 1 — LOLA VS POWERMAN & THE MONEY-GO-ROUND (LP, gatefold sleeve)	10
71	Pye NSLP 18365	PERCY (LP, soundtrack)	10
71	RCA SF 8243	MUSWELL HILLBILLIES (LP)	10
72	RCA DPS 2035	EVERYBODY'S IN SHOWBIZ, EVERYBODY'S A STAR (2-LP)	14
73	RCA SF 8392	PRESERVATION ACT 1	10
73	Pye 11PP 100	ALL THE GOOD TIMES (4-LP boxed set)	45
74	RCA LPL2 5040	PRESERVATION ACT 2 (2-LP, gatefold sleeve)	14
75	RCA SF 8411	SOAP OPERA (LP)	10
75	RCA RS 1028	SCHOOLBOYS IN DISGRACE (LP)	10
76	RCA RS 1059	CELLULOID HEROES (LP)	10
77	Pye FILD 001	THE KINKS FILE (2-LP in flip-top sleeve)	10
83	PRT KINK 1	GREATEST HITS (LP, with free 10" "Dead End Street")	12
83	Arista 205 275	STATE OF CONFUSION (cassette, with "Once A Thief" listed on inlay card)	10

(see also Dave Davies, Maple Oak)

TONY KINSEY

55	Decca F 10548	She's Funny That Way/Fascinatin' Rhythm	4
55	Decca F 10606	Close Your Eyes/Pierrot	4
55	Decca F 10648	Hey! There/Ballet	4
56	Decca F 10708	Stompin' At The Savoy/China Boy (with Dill Jones)	4
56	Decca F 10709	Moonglow/One O'Clock Jump	4
56	Decca FJ 10725	Starboard Bow/Body And Soul	4
56	Decca FJ 10760	Lullaby Of The Leaves/Isolation	4
56	Decca FJ 10773	In A Ditch/A Smooth One	4
57	Decca FJ 10851	Mean To Me/Supper Party	4
57	Decca F 10952	The Midgets/Blue Eyes	4
56	Decca DFE 6282	PRESENTING THE TONY KINSEY QUARTET NO. 1 (EP)	7
56	Decca DFE 6283	PRESENTING THE TONY KINSEY QUARTET NO. 2 (EP)	7
50s	Parlophone SGE 2004	RED BIRD — JAZZ AND POETRY (EP, stereo)	7
50s	Parlophone SGE 2008	FOURSOME (EP, stereo)	7
63	Decca LK 4534	HOW TO SUCCEED (LP)	12

TONY KINSEY TRIO & JOE HARRIOTT

50s	Esquire EP 36	TONY KINSEY TRIO & JOE HARRIOTT (EP)	7
50s	Esquire EP 52	TONY KINSEY TRIO & JOE HARRIOTT (EP)	7
50s	Esquire EP 82	TONY KINSEY TRIO & JOE HARRIOTT (EP)	7
	(see also Joe Harriott)		

TOMMY KINSMAN & HIS ORCHESTRA

| 62 | Fontana 267 250 TF | Madison Time/Madison A Saint Tropez | 4 |

KINSMEN
| 68 | Decca F 22724 | Glasshouse Green, Splinter Red/It's Started To Rain Again | 12 |
| 68 | Decca F 22777 | It's Good To See You/Always The Loser | 8 |

(see also Four Kinsmen)

KIPPINGTON LODGE
67	Parlophone R 5645	Shy Boy/Lady On A Bicycle	20
68	Parlophone R 5677	Rumours/And She Cried	20
68	Parlophone R 5717	Tell Me A Story/Understand A Woman	20
68	Parlophone R 5750	Tomorrow Today/Turn Out The Light	20
69	Parlophone R 5776	In My Life/I Can See Her Face	22
78	EMI NUT 2894	KIPPINGTON LODGE (EP)	7

(see also Brinsley Schwartz, Nick Lowe)

KIRBY
76	Anchor ANC 1031	Love Letters/Flasher	12
78	Hot Wax WAX 1/ANCHO 1	Bottom Line/That's Some Dream	10
78	Hot Wax HW 2	COMPOSITION (LP)	100

(see also Curved Air, Stretch)

KATHY KIRBY
60	Pye 7N 15313	Love Can Be/Crush Me	6
61	Pye 7N 15342	Danny/Now You're Crying	5
62	Decca F 11506	Big Man/Slowly	4
63	Decca F 11682	Dance On/Playboy	4
63	Decca F 11759	Secret Love/You Have To Want To Touch Him	4
64	Decca F 11832	Let Me Go, Lover!/The Sweetest Sounds	4
64	Decca F 11892	You're The One/Love Me Baby	4
64	Decca F 11992	Don't Walk Away/No Regrets	4
65	Decca F 12087	I Belong/I'll Try Not To Cry	4
65	Decca F 12177	The Way Of Love/Oh Darling, How I Miss You	4
65	Decca F 12280	Where In The World?/That Wonderful Feeling Of Love	4
66	Decca F 12338	Spanish Flea/Till The End Of Time	4
66	Decca F 12432	The Adam Adamant Theme/Will I Never Learn?	4
67	Columbia DB 8139	No One's Gonna Hurt You Anymore/Mu Yiddishe Momme	6
67	Columbia DB 8192	In All The World/Time	6
67	Columbia DB 8302	Turn Around/Golden Days	6
68	Columbia DB 8400	I Almost Called Your Name/Let The Music Start	7
69	Columbia DB 8521	Come Back Here With My Heart/Antonio	7
69	Columbia DB 8559	I'll Catch The Sun/Please Help Me I'm Falling	7
69	Columbia DB 8634	Is That All There Is?/Knowing When To Leave	7
69	Columbia DB 8682	Wheel Of Fortune/Lucky	7
70	Columbia DB 8721	My Way/Little Green Apples	8
71	Columbia DB 8795	So Here I Go/Yes — I've Got (A-side titled "Here I Go Again" on demos)	8
72	Columbia DB 8910	Do You Really Have A Heart/Dream On, Dreamer	8
73	Columbia DB 8965	Little Song For You/Here, There And Everywhere	8
73	Orange OAS 216	Singer With The Band/Hello Morning	6
76	President PT 455	My Prayer/Nobody Loves Me Like You Do	4
63	Decca DFE 8547	KATHY KIRBY (EP)	7
65	Decca DFE 8596	KATHY KIRBY VOL. 2 (EP)	7
65	Decca DFE 8611	BBC TV'S SONG FOR EUROPE (EP)	7
65	Decca LK 4525	16 HITS FROM STARS AND GARTERS (LP)	12
67	Decca LK 4746	MAKE SOMEONE HAPPY (LP)	15
68	Ace Of Clubs ACL 1235	THE BEST OF KATHY KIRBY (LP)	12
68	Columbia S(C)X 6259	MY THANKS TO YOU (LP)	75

LARRY KIRBY & ENCORES
| 59 | Top Rank JAR 143 | My Baby Don't Love Me/My Rose Of Kentucky | 4 |
| 59 | Top Rank JAR 143 | My Baby Don't Love Me/My Rose Of Kentucky (78) | 15 |

BASIL KIRCHIN (BAND)
59	Parlophone R 4527	Rock-A-Conga/Skin Tight (as Basil Kirchin Band)	4
59	Parlophone R 4527	Rock-A-Conga/Skin Tight (as Basil Kirchin Band) (78)	5
71	Columbia SCX 6463	A WORLD WITHIN WORLDS (LP)	15

(IVOR & BASIL) KIRCHIN BAND
54	Parlophone MSP 6144	Mambo Macoco/Tangerine (as Kirchin Band)	6
55	Decca F 10434	Minor Mambo/Mother Goose Jumps (as Kirchin Band)	12
55	Parlophone R 4010	Mambo Rock/Tweedlee-Dee (78, as Kirchin Band)	7
56	Parlophone R 4140	Rock-A-Beatin' Boogie/Stone Age Mambo (78, as Ivor & Basil Kirchin Band)	7
56	Parlophone R 4222	The Roller/St. Louis Blues (as Ivor & Basil Kirchin)	6
56	Parlophone R 4237	Rockin' & Rollin' Thru The Darktown Strutters' Ball/Ambush	10
57	Parlophone R 4266	"Rock Around The World Medley" (with Shani Wallis)	8
57	Parlophone R 4284	Calypso!!/Jungle Fire Dance (as Ivor & Basil Kirchin)	8
57	Parlophone R 4335	Teenage World/So Rare (as Kirchin Band & Bandits)	5
57	Parlophone R 4335	Teenage World/So Rare (as Kirchin Band & Bandits) (78)	5
55	Parlophone GEP 8531	KIRCHIN BANDBOX (EP)	8
56	Parlophone GEP 8569	THE IVOR AND BASIL KIRCHIN BAND (EP)	10

(see also Basil Kirchin)

DEE KIRK
| 62 | Salvo SLO 1809 | I'll Cry/My Used To Be | 15 |

KEVIN KIRK
| 62 | Columbia DB 4909 | Sweet/Don't Waste Your Tears On Him | 4 |
| 62 | Columbia DB 4863 | Teenage Heartache/Midnight | 4 |

RICHARD H. KIRK
| 81 | Industrial IRC 34 | DISPOSABLE HALF TRUTHS (cassette) | 12 |

| 86 | Rough RTM 189 | UGLY SPIRIT (mini-LP) | 8 |

(see also Cabaret Voltaire, Peter Hope & Richard H. Kirk)

ROLAND KIRK

64	Mercury 10015 MCE	THE KIRK QUARTET MEETS THE BENNY GOLSON ORCHESTRA (EP)	7
65	Mercury 10016 MCE	ROLAND SPEAKS (EP, with Benny Golson Orchestra)	7
62	Esquire 32-164	KIRK'S WORK (LP, with Jack McDuff)	15
63	Mercury MMC 14126	WE FREE KINGS (LP)	15
64	Mercury 20002 MCL	THE KIRK QUARTET MEETS THE BENNY GOLSON ORCHESTRA (LP)	12
64	Mercury MCL 20021	KIRK IN COPENHAGEN (LP)	12
65	Mercury MCL 20037	WE FREE KINGS (LP, reissue)	10
65	Mercury MCL 20045	DOMINO (LP)	12
65	Fontana FJL 114	HIP! (LP)	10
66	Mercury (S)LML 4005	I TALK WITH THE SPIRITS (LP)	10
66	Mercury (S)LML 4015	RIP, RIG AND PANIC (LP)	10
67	Mercury (S)LML 4019	SLIGHTLY LATIN (LP)	10

KIRKBYS

| 66 | RCA RCA 1542 | It's A Crime/I've Never Been So Much In Love | 40 |

(see also 23rd Turnoff, Jimmy Campbell, Rockin' Horse, Merseybeats)

KEN KIRKHAM

| 56 | Columbia SCM 5244 | It's Almost Tomorrow/No Not Much | 4 |
| 58 | Columbia DB 4116 | Now And For Always/Cathy | 4 |

JOHN KIRKPATRICK & SUE HARRIS

| 72 | Trailer LER 2033 | JUMP AT THE SUN (LP) | 10 |

KISS

75	Casablanca CBX 503	Nothin' To Lose/Love Theme From Kiss	20
75	Casablanca CBX 510	Rock And Roll All Nite/Anything For My Baby	18
76	Casablanca CBX 516	Shout It Out Loud/Sweet Pain	12
76	Casablanca CBX 519	Beth/God Of Thunder	18
77	Casablanca CAN 102	Hard Luck Woman/Calling Dr Love/Beth (initially in p/s)	18/6
77	Casablanca CAN 110	Then She Kissed Me/Hooligan/Flaming Youth	12
77	Casablanca CANL 110	Then She Kissed Me/Hooligan/Flaming Youth (12")	12
78	Casablanca CAN 117	Rocket Ride/Love Gun (live)	7
78	Casablanca CANL 117	Rocket Ride/Detroit Rock City (live)/Love Gun (live) (12")	10
78	Casablanca CAN 126	Rock And Roll All Nite/C'Mon And Love Me (initially in p/s)	18/4
79	Casablanca CAN 152	I Was Made For Lovin' You/Hard Times	8
79	Casablanca CANL 152	I Was Made For Lovin' You/Charisma (12")	18
80	Casablanca NB 1001	2000 Man/I Was Made For Lovin' You/Sure Know Something (p/s)	15
80	Casablanca NBL 1001	2000 Man/I Was Made For Lovin' You/Sure Know Something (12", no p/s)	12
80	Casablanca MER 19	Talk To Me/She's So European (p/s)	10
80	Casablanca KISS 1	What Makes The World Go 'Round/Naked City (p/s)	10
81	Casablanca KISS 2	A World Without Heroes/Mr Blackwell (p/s)	6
82	Casablanca KISSP 2	A World Without Heroes/Mr Blackwell (picture disc)	8
82	Casablanca KISS 3	Killer/I Love It Loud (pull-out tongue) p/s	8
82	Casablanca KISS 312	Killer/I Love It Loud/I Was Made For Lovin' You (12", p/s)	15
83	Casablanca KISS 4	Creatures Of The Night/Rock And Roll All Nite (live) (p/s, pic or silver label)	8/7
83	Casablanca KISS 412	Creatures Of The Night/War Machine/Rock And Roll All Nite (live) (12", p/s)	15
83	Casablanca KISSD 4	Creatures Of The Night/Rock And Roll All Nite (live) (12", p/s, double groove, autographs engraved on 1 side)	18
83	Vertigo KISS 5	Lick It Up/Not For The Innocent (p/s)	4
83	Vertigo KISSP 5	Lick It Up/Not For The Innocent (poster p/s)	10
83	Vertigo KPIC 5	Lick It Up/Not For The Innocent (tank-shaped picture disc)	25
83	Vertigo KISS 512	Lick It Up/Not For The Innocent/I Still Love You (12", p/s)	7
84	Vertigo VER 12	Heaven's On Fire/Lonely Is The Hunter (p/s)	4
84	Vertigo VERX 12	Heaven's On Fire/Lonely Is The Hunter/All Hell's Breakin' Loose (12", p/s, with poster)	8
85	Vertigo KISS 6	Tears Are Falling/Heaven's On Fire (live) (p/s)	4
87	Vertigo KISSP 7	Crazy, Crazy Nights/No No No (poster p/s)	5
87	Vertigo KISSP 712	Crazy, Crazy Nights/No No No/Heaven's On Fire/Tears Are Falling (12", picture disc)	7
87	Vertigo KISS 8	Reason To Live/Thief In The Night (p/s, with patch)	4
87	Vertigo KISSP 812	Reason To Live/Thief In The Night/Who Wants To Be Lonely/Secretly Cruel (12", picture disc)	7
87	Vertigo KISSP 9	Turn On The Night/Hell Or High Water (poster p/s)	4
87	Vertigo KISSP 912	Turn On The Night/Hell Or High Water/King Of The Mountain/Any Way You Slice It (12", picture disc)	7
89	Vertigo KISP 1010	Hide Your Heart/Lick It Up/Heaven's On Fire (10", picture disc)	7
90	Vertigo KISXG 11	Forever (Remix)/The Street Giveth And The Street Taketh Away/Deuce (demo)/Strutter (demo) (12", gatefold p/s)	8
75	Casablanca CBC 4003	KISS (LP, blue label)	15
75	Casablanca CBC 4004	DRESSED TO KILL (LP, blue label, embossed sleeve)	15
77	Casablanca CBC 4008	DESTROYER (LP, blue label)	10
77	Casablanca CBSP 401	ALIVE! (2-LP, 'lovegun' label, gatefold sleeve; listed on records as CBC 4011/2)	14
77	Casablanca CALH 2001	ROCK AND ROLL OVER (LP, 'lovegun' label, red vinyl)	35
77	Casablanca CAL 2006	KISS (LP, reissue, 'lovegun' label, red vinyl)	35
77	Casablanca CAL 2007	HOTTER THAN HELL (LP, 'lovegun' label, red vinyl)	35
77	Casablanca CAL 2008	DRESSED TO KILL (LP, reissue, 'lovegun' label, red vinyl)	35
77	Casablanca CAL 2009	DESTROYER (LP, reissue, different sleeve with run-on, 'lovegun' label, red vinyl)	35
77	Casablanca CALD 5001	ALIVE! (2-LP, reissue, 'lovegun' label, red vinyl)	40
77	Casablanca CALH 2017	LOVE GUN (LP, 'lovegun' label, with picture inner sleeve)	10
77	Casablanca CALH 2017	LOVE GUN (LP, 'lovegun' label, red vinyl with picture inner sleeve)	35
77	Casablanca CALD 5004	KISS ALIVE II (2-LP, 'lovegun' label, with colour booklet & transfer sheet)	18
77	Casablanca CALD 5004	KISS ALIVE II (2-LP, 'lovegun' label, red vinyl, with colour booklet)	50

KISS

78	Casablanca CALD 5005	DOUBLE PLATINUM (2-LP, 'lovegun' label, silver foil embossed sleeve & insert;sleeve & insert pressed in U.S. with U.K. cat. no. sticker)	15
78	Casablanca CALD 5005	DOUBLE PLATINUM (2-LP, 'lovegun' label, red vinyl)	50+
79	Casablanca CALH 2051	DYNASTY (LP, 'lovegun' label, black vinyl, colour inner sleeve & poster)	12
79	Casablanca CALH 2051	DYNASTY (LP, 'lovegun' label, red vinyl)	50+

(it is not known if CALD 5005 & CALH 2051 were released on red vinyl in the U.K.)

81	Casablanca 6302 163	THE ELDER (LP, single sleeve)	10
82	Casa. CANL4/6302 219	CREATURES OF THE NIGHT (LP, 'make-up' sleeve)	10
87	Vertigo 832 903-1	CRAZY NIGHTS (LP, picture disc in stickered PVC wallet)	10

(see also Gene Simmons, Ace Frehley, Peter Criss, Paul Stanley)

KISSING THE PINK
81	Martyrwell Music MART 271	Don't Hide In The Shadows/Hand Held Cameras (p/s)	4
83	Magnet KTPP 4	Love Lasts Forever/Underage (picture disc)	4
83	Magnet KTP 36/KTP 0	Last Film/Shine//Water In My Eye (Instrumental)/Garden Parties (double pack)	4

KATIE KISSOON
69	Columbia DB 8525	Don't Let It Rain/Will I Never See The Sun	4

MAC KISSOON
70s	Boulevard (no cat. no.)	Wear It On Your Face/In A Dream	10
75	Youngblood YB 1005	Wear It On Your Face/In A Dream (reissue)	4

KITCHENS OF DISTINCTION
87	Gold Rush GRR 3	Escape/The Last Gasp Death Shuffle	12

KIT KATS
66	London HLW 10075	That's The Way/Won't Find Better Than Me	6

EARTHA KITT
53	HMV B 10584	I Want To Be Evil/Annie Doesn't Live Here Any More (78)	6
54	HMV 7M 191	Under The Bridges Of Paris/Lovin' Spree	12
54	HMV 7M 198	Somebody Bad Stole De Wedding Bell/Sandy's Tune	8
54	HMV 7M 234	Santa Baby/Let's Do It (Let's Fall In Love)	8
54	HMV 7M 246	Easy Does It/Mink Shmink	8
55	HMV 7M 282	Monotonous/African Lullaby	8
55	HMV 7M 288	C'est Si Bon/Senor	8
55	HMV B 10922	The Day That The Circus Left Town/I've Got That Lovin' (78)	5
56	HMV 7M 422	Honolulu Rock-A-Roll-A/Je Cherche Un Homme (I Want A Man)	18
56	MGM SP 1153	Please Do It/Lady Loves	5
56	MGM SP 1178	Diamonds Are A Girl's Best Friend/Good Little Girls	5
57	HMV POP 309	Just An Old-Fashioned Girl/If I Can't Take It With Me When I Go	8
57	HMV POP 346	There Is No Cure For L'Amour/Hey Jacque	6
58	RCA RCA 1037	Take My Love/Proceed With Caution	4
58	RCA RCA 1087	Just An Old-Fashioned Girl/If I Can't Take It With Me When I Go (reissue)	6
58	RCA RCA 1093	I Want To Be Evil/Oh John!	6
59	London HLR 8969	Love Is A Gamble/Sholem	6
59	London HLR 8969	Love Is A Gamble/Sholem (78)	5
60	RCA RCA 1180	There's No Cure For L'Amour/Let's Do It	4
63	London HL 7119	Shango/In The Evening (When The Sun Goes Down) (export issue)	8
55	HMV 7EG 8079	EARTHA KITT (EP)	7
57	HMV 7EG 8258	EARTHA KITT (EP)	7
50s	RCA SRC 7009	SAINT LOUIS BLUES (EP, stereo)	10
50s	RCA SRC 7015	THAT BLUE EARTHA (EP, stereo)	10
60	London RE-R 1266	REVISITED (EP)	8
63	MGM MGM-EP 772	BAD BUT BEAUTIFUL NO. 1 (EP)	7
63	MGM MGM-EP 774	BAD BUT BEAUTIFUL NO. 2 (EP)	7
63	MGM MGM-EP 777	BAD BUT BEAUTIFUL NO. 3 (EP)	7
55	HMV DLP 1067	THAT BAD EARTHA (10" LP)	15
55	HMV DLP 1087	DOWN TO EARTHA (10" LP)	15
57	HMV CLP 1104	THURSDAY'S CHILD (LP)	12
58	RCA RD 27067	THAT BAD EARTHA (LP, reissue)	10
58	RCA RD 27076	ST. LOUIS BLUES (LP)	10
58	RCA RD 27084	DOWN TO EARTHA (LP, reissue)	10
59	RCA RD 27099	THURSDAY'S CHILD (LP, reissue)	10
60	London HA-R 2207	THE FABULOUS EARTHA KITT (LP, also stereo SAH-R 6058)	10/12
60	London HA-R 2296	EARTHA KITT REVISITED (LP, also stereo SAH-R 6107)	10/12
62	MGM C 878	BAD BUT BEAUTIFUL (LP)	10

KITTENS
64	Decca F 12036	Round About Way/Don't Stop Now	4

MARK KJELDSEN
80	Back Door DOOR 2	Are You Ready/Something's Happening	4

KLAN
62	Palette PG 9052	Fifi The Fly/Already Mine	4

SUSIE KLEE
66	Polydor BM 56082	Mr Zero/Punch And Judy Girl	4

KLEEER
84	Atlantic 7801451	INTIMATE CONNECTION (LP)	12

KLEENEX
79	Rough Trade/Sunrise RT 9	Ain't You/Hedi's Head (poster p/s)	4
79	Rough Trade RT 014	Friendly/Angry (p/s)	4

ALAN KLEIN
62	Oriole CB 1719	Striped Purple Shirt/You Gave Me The Blues	15
62	Oriole CB 1737	Three Coins In The Sewer/Danger Ahead	15
65	Parlophone R 5292	It Ain't Worth The Lonely Road Back/I've Cried So Many Tears	5

548   Rare Record Price Guide

| 65 | Parlophone R 5370 | Age Of Corruption/I'm Counting On You ....5 |
| 69 | Page One POF 119 | Honey Pie/You Turned A Nightmare Into A Dream ....6 |

(see also New Vaudeville Band)

KLF

88	KLF Comm. KLF 002	Burn The Beat (II)/The Porpoise Song (p/s) 5
88	KLF Comm. KLF 002T	Burn The Beat (II)/Burn The Bastards (LP Edit) (12", p/s) 15
89	KLF Comm. KLF 004T	What Time Is Love? (Trance Mix)/(Mix 2) (12", 'Pure Trance 1', original issue with deep apple green p/s) 12
89	KLF Comm. KLF 004R	What Time Is Love? ('89 Primal Remix)/(Techno Slam)/(Trance Mix 1) (12", p/s) 15
89	KLF Comm. KLF 004M	What Time Is Love (Monster Attack Mix)/ (12", acetate only 1-sided, 3 pressed!) 100
90	KLF Comm. KLF 004Y	What Time Is Love? (Moody Boys Vs The KLF)/(Echo And The Bunnymen Mix)/ (Virtual Reality Mix) (12", p/s) 7
90	KLF Comm. KLF 004P	What Time Is Love (Live At Trancentral)/Wandafull Mix (12", w/l, 1,500 only) 40
90	KLF Comm. KLF 004X	What Time Is Love? (Live At Trancentral)/Techno Gate Mix (12", p/s, B-side actually plays "Wandafull Mix", matrix no. KLF 004X-B) 20
90	KLF Comm. KLF 004CD	What Time Is Love? (Radio)/(Live At Trancentral)/(Trance Mix 1) (CD , mispressing playing part of Knebworth 90 live CD) 10
91	KLF Comm. KLF 005R	3AM Eternal 'Single Edit'/Blue Danube Orbital Mix/Moody Boys Version/ 3PM Electro (12", original issue with stickered p/s) 7
91	KLF Comm. KLF 005S	3AM Eternal (Live At The S.S.L.) (Radio Freedom Edit) (white label, 500 only) 8
92	KLF Comm. KLF 5 TOTP	3AM Eternal (Xmas Top Of The Pops Version) (1-sided, with Extreme Noise Terror, mail order only, with insert & mailing envelope) 50
89	KLF Comm. KLF 008R	Last Train To Trancentral (Remixes 1 & 2) (12", p/s, 'Pure Trance 5', white label, 2,000 pressed but half badly warped) 30
89	KLF Comm. KLF 010(S)	Kylie Said To Jason (Edit)/Kylie Said Trance (p/s) 6
89	KLF Comm. KLF 010T	Kylie Said To Jason (Full Length)/Kylie Said Trance (12", p/s) 7
89	KLF Comm. KLF 010P	Kylie Said To Jason (Full Length)/Kylie Said Trance (12", stickered p/s with poster) 10
89	KLF Comm. KLF 010R	Kylie Said To Jason (Trance Kylie Express)/Kylie In A Trance/ Kylie Said Harder (12" remix, p/s, export issue) 20
89	KLF Comm. KLF 010RR	Kylie In A Trance/Kylie Said Mu (12", p/s, 500 only, shrinkwrapped with 010R) ..40
89	KLF Comm. KLF 010CD	Kylie Said To Jason (Full Length)/Madrugada Eterna/Kylie Said Trance (CD) 15
90	KLF Comm. KLF 11T	Madrugada Eterna (Club Mix)/(Edit)/(Ambient House Mix) (12", 20 only, beware of counterfeits!) 60
90	KLF Comm. ETERNA 1	Madrugada Eterna (Club Mix) (12", 1-sided, white label, 6 pressed, beware of counterfeits!) 100
91	KLF Comm. CHOC ICE 1	Justified And Ancient (All Bound For Mu Mu Land)/(Make Mine A '99') (12", white label) 12
91	KLF Comm. CHOC ICE 2	Justified And Ancient (Stand By The JAMs)/(Let Them Eat Ice Cream) (12", white label) 12
91	KLF Comm. CHOC ICE 3	Justified And Ancient (Anti-Acapella Version) (12", 1-sided, white label, 200 only)50
91	KLF Comm. LP PROMO 1	Make It Rain/No More Tears (promo-only, 1,729 only) 15
91	KLF Comm. 92PROMO 1	America: What Time Is Love/America No More (12", white label) 7
91	KLF Comm. 92PROMO 2	America: What Time Is January? (12", 1-sided, white label, 250 only) 100
92	KLF Comm. 92PROMO 3	What Time Is Love (Acid Mix) (12", 1-sided, white label, perhaps 20 only) 150
92	KLF USA 4X/CHOC ICE 2	Justified And Ancient/America: What Time Is Love? (12", picture disc, 4,000 only) 35
89	KLF Comm. JAMS LP 4	THE WHAT TIME IS LOVE STORY (LP) 30
89	KLF Comm. JAMS CD 4	THE WHAT TIME IS LOVE STORY (CD) 40
89	KLF Comm. JAMS LP 5	CHILL OUT (LP) 20
89	KLF Comm. JAMS CD 5	CHILL OUT (CD) 30
89	KLF Comm. JAMS MC 6	(TUNES FROM) THE WHITE ROOM (LP, unreleased, promo cassete only, beware of counterfeits) 60

(see also J.A.M.s, Timelords, Disco 2000, Brilliant, Bill Drummond, Space, Orb)

TONY KLINGER & MICHAEL LYONS

| 71 | Deram SML 1095 | EXTREEMS (LP) ....20 |

PETER KLINT (QUINTET)

| 66 | Mercury MF 997 | Walkin' Proud/Shake ....12 |
| 68 | Altantic 584 208 | Hey Diddle Diddle/Just Holding On (solo) ....5 |

ANNETTE KLOOGER

56	Decca F 10701	The Rock And Roll Waltz/Rock Around The Island (with Ted Heath Music) 8
56	Decca F 10733	The Magic Touch/We'll Love Again (with Four Jones Boys) 6
56	Decca F 10738	Why Do Fools Fall In Love?/Lovely One (with Four Jones Boys) 8
56	Decca F 10776	Mama, Teach Me To Dance/Mama, I Long For A Sweetheart (with Edmundo Ros Orchestra) 6
57	Decca F 10844	The Wisdom Of A Fool/Tra La La 6

(see also Four Jones Boys, Edmundo Ros)

EARL KLUGH

| 77 | United Artists UP 36251 | I Heard It Through The Grapevine/Kiko ....4 |
| 81 | Blue Note BNXW 642 | Living Inside Your Love/Dance With Me ....6 |

KNACK (U.K.)

65	Decca F 12234	Who'll Be The Next In Line/She Ain't No Good 25
65	Decca F 12278	It's Love Baby (24 Hours A Day)/Time Time Time 25
66	Piccadilly 7N 35315	Did You Ever Have To Make Up Your Mind?/Red Hearts 8
66	Piccadilly 7N 35322	Stop! (Before You Get Me Going)/Younger Girl 8
66	Piccadilly 7N 35347	Save All My Love For Joey/Take Your Love 8
67	Piccadilly 7N 35367	(Man From The) Marriage Guidance And Advice Bureau/Dolly Catch Her Man 8

(see also Gun, Adrian Gurvitz)

KNACK (U.S.)
| 79 | Capitol E-ST 11948 | GET THE KNACK (LP, limited white cover) | 10 |

BERNIE KNEE QUARTETTE
| 55 | HMV 7M 306 | Chocolate Whiskey And Vanilla Gin/Scrape Off De Bark | 5 |

(see also Bernie Nee)

KNEES
| 74 | United Artists UP 35773 | Day Tripper/Slow Down | 5 |

(see also Brinsley Schwartz)

KNICKERBOCKERS
66	London HLH 10013	Lies/The Coming Generation	12
66	London HLH 10035	One Track Mind/I Must Be Doing Something Right	12
66	London HLH 10061	High On Love/Stick With Me	12
66	London HLH 10093	Rumours, Gossip, Words Untrue/Love Is A Bird	12
67	London HLH 10102	Can You Help Me/Please Don't Love Him	12
73	Elektra K 12102	Lies/ELECTRIC PRUNES: I Had Too Much To Dream (Last Night)	5
66	London HA-H 8294	THE FABULOUS KNICKERBOCKERS (LP)	45

BAKER KNIGHT
| 66 | Reprise RS 20465 | Would You Believe It/Tomorrow's Good Time Girl | 8 |

CURTIS KNIGHT (& ZEUS)
69	RCA RCA 1888	Fancy Meeting You Here/Love In	8
74	Dawn DNS 1049	Devil Made Me Do It/Oh Rainbow	4
74	Dawn DNS 1065	People Places And Things/Mysterious Lady	4
74	Dawn DNLS 3060	ZEUS, SECOND COMING (LP)	15

(see also Jimi Hendrix & Curtis Knight)

GLADYS KNIGHT (& PIPS)
64	Stateside SS 318	Giving Up/Maybe Maybe Baby	12
64	Stateside SS 352	Lovers Always Forgive/Another Love	12
65	Sue WI 394	Letter Full Of Tears/You Broke Your Promise	15
66	Tamla Motown TMG 576	Just Walk In My Shoes/Stepping Closer To Your Heart	30
67	Tamla Motown TMG 604	Take Me In Your Arms And Love Me/Do You Love Me Just A Little Honey	7
67	Tamla Motown TMG 619	Everybody Needs Love/Stepping Closer To Your Heart (withdrawn, demos may exist)	25+
67	Tamla Motown TMG 619	Everybody Needs Love/Since I've Lost You	5
67	Tamla Motown TMG 629	I Heard It Through The Grapevine/It's Time To Go Now	6
68	Tamla Motown TMG 645	The End Of Our Road/Don't Let Her Take Your Love From Me	6
68	Tamla Motown TMG 660	It Should Have Been Me/You Don't Love Me No More	5
68	Tamla Motown TMG 674	I Wish It Would Rain/It's Summer	4
69	Tamla Motown TMG 714	The Nitty Gritty/Got Myself A Good Man	4
70	Tamla Motown TMG 728	Didn't You Know/Keep An Eye	4
70	Tamla Motown TMG 756	Friendship Train/You Need Love Like I Do, Don't You	4
71	Tamla Motown TMG 765	If I Were Your Woman/The Tracks Of My Tears	4
72	Tamla Motown TMG 805	Make Me The Woman That You Go Home	4
72	Ember EMB S 326	Every Beat Of My Heart/Room In Your Heart	4
72	Tamla Motown TMG 813	Just Walk In My Shoes/I'm Losing You	4
73	Buddah 2011 170	Where Peaceful Waters Flow/Perfect Love	4
73	Buddah 2011 181	Midnight Train To Georgia/Window Raising Granny	4
74	Buddah BDS 401	On And On/The Making Of You	4
74	Contempo CS 2021	Why Don't You Leave Me/Maybe Baby	6
75	Tamla Motown TMG 945	You've Lost That Loving Feeling/This Child Needs A Father	4
76	Buddah BDS 441	Silent Night/Do You Hear What I Hear	5
76	DJM DJS 681	Queen Of Tears/Every Beat Of My Heart	4
67	M. For Pleasure MFP 1187	GLADYS KNIGHT AND THE PIPS (LP)	10
67	T. Motown (S)TML 11058	EVERYBODY NEEDS LOVE (LP)	15
68	Bell MBLL 103	TASTIEST HITS (LP)	15
68	T. Motown (S)TML 11080	FEELIN' BLUESY (LP)	15
69	T. Motown (S)TML 11100	SILK'N'SOUL (LP)	12
69	T. Motown (S)TML 11135	THE NITTY GRITTY (LP)	12
70	T. Motown STML 11148	GREATEST HITS (LP)	10
75	Buddah BDLP 4038	2ND ANNIVERSARY (LP)	10
77	Buddah BDLP 5014	STILL TOGETHER (LP)	10
78	Buddah 11PP 602	COLLECTION (4-LP box set)	25
79	Buddah BDLP 4056	MISS GLADYS KNIGHT (LP, solo)	10

(see also Pips)

JASON KNIGHT
| 67 | Pye 7N 17399 | Our Love Is Getting Stronger/Standing In My Shoes | 35 |
| 73 | Pye 7N 45287 | Our Love Is Getting Stronger/Standing In My Shoes (reissue) | 4 |

JEAN KNIGHT
71	Stax 2025 049	Mr Big Stuff/Why Do I Keep Living These Memories	4
73	Stax 2025 161	Do Me/Save The Last Kiss For Me	4
71	Stax 2362 022	MR. BIG STUFF (LP)	10

MARIE KNIGHT
53	Brunswick 05071	The Old Rugged Cross/Satisfied With Jesus (78)	8
53	Brunswick 05165	Does Jesus Care?/Shaded Green Pastures (78)	8
61	Fontana H 354	Nothing/Come Tomorrow	8
65	Stateside SS 419	Cry Me A River/Comes The Night	6
85	Kent TOWN 102	That's No Way To Treat A Girl/JACK MONTGOMERY: Dearly Beloved	6
57	Brunswick OE 9283	GOSPEL SONGS VOL. 1 (EP, with Sam Price Trio)	7
50s	Mercury MCE 10034	SONG OF THE GOSPEL (EP)	7
50s	Mercury 10001 MCE	THE STORM IS PASSING OVER (EP)	7
58	Mercury MPL 6546	SONGS OF THE GOSPEL (LP)	10

(see also Sister Rosetta Tharpe & Sister Marie Knight)

PAULA KNIGHT
75	Ember EMB S 342	It's The Same Old Song/La-La Song	4

PETER KNIGHT ORCHESTRA/SINGERS
55	Parlophone MSP 6183	Twenty Minutes South (Medley) (both sides, as Peter Knight Singers)	5
67	Mercury SML 30023	SGT. PEPPER'S LONELY HEARTS CLUB BAND (LP)	10

PETER KNIGHT & KNIGHT RIDERS
64	Pye 7N 15687	Wonderful Day Like Today/It Isn't Enough	4

ROBERT KNIGHT
62	London HLD 9496	Free Me/The Other Half Of Man	5

ROBERT KNIGHT
68	Monument MON 1008	Everlasting Love/Somebody's Baby	6
68	Monument MON 1016	Blessed Are The Lonely/It's Been Worth It All	4
68	Monument MON 1017	The Power Of Love/Love On A Mountain Top	8
68	Bell BLL 1029	Isn't It Lonely Together/We'd Better Stop	4
68	Monument S/LMO 5015	EVERLASTING LOVE (LP)	12
71	Monument MNT 65956	LOVE ON A MOUNTAIN TOP (LP)	10

SONNY KNIGHT
57	London HLD 8362	Confidential/Jail Bird (possibly gold label, most on silver label)	150+/80
57	London HLD 8362	Confidential/Jail Bird (78)	18
57	London HL 7016	Confidential/Jail Bird (export issue)	50
59	Vogue Pop V 9134	But Officer/Dear Wonderful God	100

TERRY KNIGHT & PACK
66	Cameo Parkway C 102	I (Who Have Nothing)/Numbers	50

TONY KNIGHT
64	Decca F 11989	Did You Ever Hear The Sound?/I Feel So Blue (as Tony Knight & Live Wires)	20
65	Decca F 12109	How Sweet/Surfer Street (as Tony Knight's Chessmen)	20

KNIGHT BROTHERS
65	Chess CRS 8015	Sinking Low/Temptation 'Bout To Get Me	8
66	Chess CRS 8046	That'll Get It/She's A1	12

KNIGHTS OF ROUND TABLE
68	Pama PM 734	Lament To Bobby Kennedy/If You Were My Girl	5

K9's
85	Dog Breath WOOF 1	The K9 Hassle/Idi Amin/Sweeney Todd (numbered p/s, with insert)	12

KNOCKER JUNGLE
70	Ember NR 5052	KNOCKER JUNGLE (LP, gatefold sleeve)	50

KNOCKOUTS
60	Top Rank JAR 279	Darling Lorraine/Riot In Room 3C	20

DAVID KNOPFLER
83	Peach River BBPR 7	Soul Kissing/Come To Me (p/s)	8
83	Peach River BBPR 712	Soul Kissing/Come To Me/The Great Divide (12", p/s)	7
84	Fast Alley FAR 701	Madonna's Daughter/Hey Henry (p/s)	5

(see also Dire Straits)

MARK KNOPFLER
83	Vertigo DSTR 14	Going Home/Smooching or Wild Theme (p/s)	4
83	Vertigo DSTR 1412	Going Home/Wild Theme/Smooching (12", p/s)	7
84	Vertigo DSDJ 7	Joy (promo-only, 1-sided)	25
84	Vertigo DSTR 712	Comforts And Joy/Fistful Of Ice Cream (12", p/s)	30
84	Vertigo DSTR 8	Long Road/Irish Boy (p/s)	4
84	Vertigo DSTR 812	Long Road/Irish Boy (12", p/s)	7

(see also Dire Straits)

KNOPOV
80	white label	Misadventure/You're In The Army Now	6

(see also Mission)

KNOTT SISTERS
58	London HLX 8713	Undivided Attention/SHADES with KNOTT SISTERS: Sun Glasses	25

KNOX
80	Gem GEMS 46	She's So Good Looking/Love Is Burning (p/s)	4
80	Armageddon AS 003	Gigolo Aunt/Alligator Man (p/s)	4
83	Razor RA 27	PLUTONIUM EXPRESS (LP)	10

(see also Robyn Hitchcock, Vibrators, Fallen Angels, Soft Boys)

BUDDY KNOX
57	Columbia DB 3914	Party Doll/My Baby's Gone (gold label)	80
57	Columbia DB 3914	Party Doll/My Baby's Gone (78)	8
57	Columbia DB 3952	Rock Your Little Baby To Sleep/Don't Make Me Cry (gold label)	40
57	Columbia DB 3952	Rock Your Little Baby To Sleep/Don't Make Me Cry (78)	15
57	Columbia DB 4014	Hula Love/Devil Woman	25
57	Columbia DB 4014	Hula Love/Devil Woman (78)	10
58	Columbia DB 4077	Swingin' Daddy/Whenever I'm Lonely	25
58	Columbia DB 4077	Swingin' Daddy/Whenever I'm Lonely (78)	20
58	Columbia DB 4180	Somebody Touched Me/C'mon Baby	20
58	Columbia DB 4180	Somebody Touched Me/C'mon Baby (78)	20
59	Columbia DB 4302	To Be With You/I Think I'm Gonna Kill Myself	20
61	London HLG 9268	Lovey Dovey/I Got You	15
61	London HLG 9331	Ling Ting Tong/The Kisses (They're All Mine)	10
61	London HLG 9472	Three-Eyed Man/All By Myself	10
62	Liberty LIB 55411	Chi-Hua-Hua/Open Your Loving Arms	8

MINT VALUE £

62	Liberty LIB 55473	She's Gone/Now There's Only Me	8
63	Liberty LIB 55592	Shadaroom/Tomorrow Is Coming	7
64	Liberty LIB 55694	All Time Loser/Good Loving	7
69	United Artists UP 35019	God Knows I Love You/Night Runners	8
57	Columbia SEG 7732	ROCK-A-BUDDY KNOX (EP)	70
62	Liberty LBY 1114	GOLDEN HITS (LP)	30
71	Sunset SLS 50206	ROCK REFLECTIONS (LP)	12
78	Pye Intl. NPL 28243	PARTY DOLL (LP)	10

KRYSIA KOCJAN
| 74 | RCA LPL1 5052 | KRYSIA (LP) | 12 |

(see also Natural Acoustic Band)

KODIAKS
| 69 | Decca F 12942 | All Because You Wanna See Me Cry/Tell Me Rhonda | 8 |

SPIDER JOHN KOERNER
67	Elektra EKSN 45005	Won't You Give Me Some Love/Don't Stop	8
69	Elektra EKSN 45063	Friends And Lovers/Magazine Lady (with Willie Murphy)	8
68	Elektra EKL/EKS 4041	RUNNING JUMPING STANDING STILL (LP, with Willie Murphy)	18
71	Elektra K 42026	RUNNING JUMPING STANDING STILL (LP reissue, with Willie Murphy)	10

MOE KOFFMAN (QUARTET)
58	London HLJ 8549	Swingin' Shepherd Blues/Hambourg Bound	8
58	London HLJ 8633	Little Pixie/Koko-Mamey	6
59	London HLJ 8813	Shepherd's Cha-Cha/The Great Healer (solo)	6
62	Palette PG 9036	Cool Ghoul/Sapphire	4
68	CBS 3544	Mighty Peculiar/Archie Buckle Up	6
58	London REJ 1163	LITTLE PIXIE (EP)	12

KOKOMO, HIS PIANO & ORCHESTRA
| 61 | London HLU 9305 | Asia Minor/Roy's Tune | 5 |
| 62 | London HLU 9497 | Like Teen/Journey Home | 5 |

KOLETTES
| 64 | Pye Intl. 7N 25278 | Who's That Guy?/Just How Much | 12 |
| 73 | Chess 6145 021 | Who's That Guy?/Just How Much (reissue) | 4 |

JIMMIE KOMACK
54	Vogue Coral Q 2031	Cold Summer Blues/The Nic-Name Song	10
55	Vogue Coral Q 72061	Wabash 4-7473/An Old Beer Bottle	8
55	Vogue Coral Q 72087	Rock-A-Bye Your Baby With A Dixie Melody/This Is The Place	7

JOHN (T.) KONGOS
66	Piccadilly 7N 35341	I Love Mary/Goodtime Party Companion (as John T. Kongos)	6
69	Dawn DNS 1002	Flim Flam Pharisee/Blood	5
71	Fly BUG 8	He's Gonna Step On You Again/Sometimes It's Not Enough (p/s)	6
71	Fly BUG 14	Tokoloshe Man/Can Someone Please Direct Me Back To Earth	4
69	Dawn DNLS 3002	CONFUSIONS ABOUT A GOLDFISH (LP)	15
71	Fly HIFLY 7	KONGOS (LP)	10

(see also Scrugg)

KONRADS
| 65 | CBS 201812 | Baby It's Too Late Now/I'm Over You | 6 |

KONSTRUKTIVITS
| 80s | Third Mind TM 02 | PSYKO GENETIKA (LP) | 20 |
| 86 | Sterile SR 10 | GLENACAUL (LP) | 20 |

KOOBAS
65	Pye 7N 17012	Take Me For A Little While/Somewhere In The Night	25
66	Pye 7N 17087	You'd Better Make Up Your Mind/A Place I Know	15
66	Columbia DB 7988	Sweet Music/Face	20
67	Columbia DB 8103	Sally/Champagne And Caviar	15
67	Columbia DB 8187	Gypsy Fred/City Girl	30
68	Columbia DB 8419	The First Cut Is The Deepest/Walking Out	30
69	Columbia S(C)X 6271	THE KOOBAS (LP)	250

(see also Kubas, Van Der Graaf Generator)

KOOL
67	CBS 203003	Look At Me, Look At Me/Room At The Top	4
67	CBS 2865	Step Out Of Your Mind/Funny (What A Fool A Man Can Be)	5
69	MCA MU 1085	Lovin'/Baby's Out Of Reach	4

KOOL & GANG
70	London HLZ 10308	Kool And The Gang/Raw Hamburgers	7
71	Mojo 2027 005	Funky Man/Kool And The Gang/Let The Music Take Your Mind	6
72	Mojo 2027 006	Love The Life You Live/The Penguin	6
72	Mojo 2027 009	Music Is The Message Pts 1 & 2	5
73	Polydor 2001 474	Funky Stuff/More Funky Stuff	4
74	Polydor 2001 500	Jungle Boogie/North, South, East, West	4
74	Polydor 2001 530	Hollywood Swinging/Dujii	4
74	Polydor 2001 541	Higher Plane/Wild Is Love	4
75	Polydor 2001 558	Rhyme Tyme People/Father, Father	4
75	Polydor 2001 566	Spirit Of The Boogie/Jungle Jazz	6
76	Polydor 2058 645	Love And Understanding/Sunshine And Love	4
77	Contempo CS 1001	Super Band/Open Sesame	4
77	Contempo 12 CS 1001	Super Band/Open Sesame (12")	8
81	De-Lite GANG 11	Jones Vs Jones/Summer Madness//Funky Stuff/Hollywood Swinging (double pack)	4
81	De-Lite KOOL 11-12	Jones Vs Jones/Funky Stuff (12")	12
85	De-Lite GANG 20	Cherish/Celebration//Cherish (Instrumental)/Joanna (double pack)	4

87	Club JABXD 47	Stone Love/Dance Champion//Get Down On It/Ladies Night (double pack) 4
74	Polydor 2347 001	LIVE AT P.J.'S (LP) 40
74	Polydor 2347 002	THE BEST OF KOOL AND THE GANG (LP) 50
74	Polydor 2347 003	LIVE AT THE SEX MACHINE (LP) 20
74	Polydor 2347 004	MUSIC IS THE MESSAGE (LP) 25
74	Polydor 2310 299	WILD AND PEACEFUL (LP) 12
74	Polydor 2310 357	LIGHT OF WORLDS (LP) 10
75	Polydor 2310 416	SPIRIT OF THE BOOGIE (LP) 10
76	Polydor 2343 083	LIVE AT THE SEX MACHINE (LP, reissue) 12

AL KOOPER

65	Mercury MF 885	Parchman Farm/You're The Lovin' End (as Alan Kooper) 10
69	CBS 4011	You Never Know Who Your Friends Are/Soft Landing On The Moon 6
69	CBS 4160	Hey Western Union Man/I Stand Alone 8
71	CBS 5146	Brand New Lady/The Landlord (Love Theme From) 4
71	CBS 7376	John The Baptist/Back On My Feet 4
72	CBS 8084	Monkey Time/Bended Knees (Please Don't Let Me Down) 6
69	CBS 63538	I STAND ALONE (LP) 10
69	CBS 63651	YOU NEVER KNOW WHO YOUR FRIENDS ARE (LP) 10
70	CBS 63797	KOOPER SESSION — WITH SHUGGIE OTIS (LP) 12
70	CBS 66252	EASY DOES IT (2-LP) 14
71	United Artists UAS 29120	THE LANDLORD (LP, soundtrack, with Staple Singers & Lorraine Ellison) 10

(see also Blues Project, Blood, Sweat & Tears, Shuggie Otis)

AL KOOPER, MIKE BLOOMFIELD & STEPHEN STILLS

68	CBS 3770	Season Of The Witch/Albert's Shuffle 7
69	CBS 4094	The Weight/59th Street Bridge Song (as Mike Bloomfield & Al Kooper) 8
68	CBS 63396	SUPER SESSION (LP) 10
73	CBS CQ 30991	SUPER SESSION (LP, quadrophonic) 15

(see also Mike Bloomfield & Al Kooper, Stephen Stills)

KOPPYKATS

| 68 | Fontana SFT 13052/3 | BEATLES' BEST (2-LP) ....20 |

(see also Ian [Edward] & Zodiacs)

TOMMY KÖRBERG

| 69 | Sonet SON 2005 | Dear Mrs. Jones/Bird You Must Fly ....8 |

PAUL KORDA

66	Columbia DB 7994	Go On Home/Just Come Closer To Me 15
69	Parlophone R 5778	Seagull (West Coast Oil Tragedy Of '68)/Night Of The Next Day 5
71	MAM MAM 20	Between The Road/English Country Garden 4
71	MAM AS 1003	PASSING STRANGERS (LP) 18

(see also Tim Andrews & Paul Korda)

ALEXIS KORNER (BLUES INCORPORATED)

58	Tempo A 166	County Jail/I Ain't Gonna Worry No More (as Alexis Korner Skiffle Group) 20
60s	Lyntone LYN 299	Up-Town/Blaydon Races (flexidisc, as Blues Incorporated With Alexis Korner) 25
63	Parlophone R 5206	I Need Your Loving/Please Please Please (as Alexis Korner's Blues Inc.) 12
65	Parlophone R 5247	Little Baby/Roberta (as Alexis Korner's Blues Inc.) 15
65	King KG 1017	See See Rider/Blues A La King (as Alexis Korner's All Stars) 15
66	Fontana TF 706	River's Invitation/Everyday (I Have The Blues) 15
67	Fontana TF 817	Rosie/Rock Me 15
75	CBS 3520	Get Off Of My Cloud/Strange'n'Deranged 4
76	CBS 3877	Ain't That Peculiar/Tree Top Fever 4
58	Tempo EXA 76	ALEXIS KORNER SKIFFLE GROUP (EP) 30
59	Tempo EXA 102	ALEXIS KORNER BLUES INCORPORATED (EP) 30
70s	Collector CCSLP 150	ALEXIS KORNER AND ... (EP) 8
62	Ace of Clubs ACL 1130	R&B FROM THE MARQUEE (LP, live) 35
64	Transatlantic TRA 117	RED HOT FROM ALEX (LP) 70
64	Oriole PS 40058	AT THE CAVERN (live LP) 60
65	Ace of Clubs ACL 1187	ALEXIS KORNER'S BLUES INCORPORATED (LP) 40
65	Spot JW 551	SKY HIGH (LP, featuring Duffy Power) 300
67	Fontana TL 5381	I WONDER WHO (LP) 45
67	Polydor 236 206	BLUES INCORPORATED (LP) 40
68	Liberty LBL/LBS 83147	A NEW GENERATION OF BLUES (LP) 30
69	Transatlantic TRASAM 7	ALEXIS KORNER'S ALL STAR BLUES INCORPORATED (LP) ...12
71	Sunset SLS 50245	WHAT'S THAT SOUND I HEAR (LP, "A New Generation Of Blues" reissue) 12
71	Rak SRAK 501	ALEXIS (LP) 20
72	RAK SRAKSP 51	BOOTLEG HIM (2-LP) 25
73	Transatlantic TRA 269	ACCIDENTALLY BORN IN NEW ORLEANS (LP) 12
75	CBS 69155	GET OFF MY CLOUD (LP) 12

(see also Cyril Davies' All Stars, CCS, Bob Hall & Alexis Korner)

ALEXIS KORNER & DAVY GRAHAM

| 62 | Topic TOP 70 | 3/4 A.D. (EP, some copies credit 'Davy Graham with Alexis Korner') ....40 |

(see also Davy Graham)

ARTIE KORNFELD'S TREE

| 72 | Neighbourhood NBH 3 | Island Song/Feel ....4 |
| 70 | Probe SPB 1022 | A TIME TO REMEMBER (LP) ....15 |

KOROVA MILK BAR

| 88 | Smashing SMASH 1 | RONKO PRESENTS (EP, numbered p/s with raffle ticket, 2 different sleeve designs, 500 only) ....8 |

(see also Surf Drums)

KOSSOFF, KIRKE, TETSU & RABBIT
71	Island ILPS 9188	KOSSOFF, KIRKE, TETSU AND RABBIT (LP)	25

(see also Paul Kossoff, Rabbit, Free)

DAVID KOSSOFF
61	Pye 7N 15385	Alf's Blues/Please Sell No More Drink	4
61	Oriole CB 1597	I'm Shy, Mary Ellen, I'm Shy/When Father Papered The Parlour	4

PAUL KOSSOFF
73	Island ILPS 9264	BACK STREET CRAWLER (LP)	12
83	Street Tunes STLP 1002	CROYDON JUNE 15TH 1975 (2-LP)	15
83	St. Tunes SDLP 0012PD	MR. BIG/BLUE SOUL (LP, picture disc)	12

(see also Free, Kossoff Kirke Tetsu & Rabbit, Back Street Crawler)

CHIM KOTHARI
66	Deram DM 108	Sitar'N'Spice/Indian Bat	10
66	Deram DML 1002	SOUND OF THE SITAR (LP)	40

LEO KOTTKE
71	Capitol E-ST 682	MUDLARK (LP)	10
72	Sonet SNTF 629	LEO KOTTKE & HIS 12-STRING GUITAR (LP)	10
73	Capitol E-ST 11000	GREENHOUSE (LP)	10
73	Capitol E-ST 11164	MY FEET ARE SMILING (LP)	10
74	Capitol E-ST 11262	ICE WATER (LP)	10
75	Capitol E-ST 11335	DREAMS AND ALL THAT STUFF (LP)	10
75	Capitol E-ST 11446	CHEWING PINE (LP)	10

KRACKER
73	Rolling Stones RS 19106	A Song For Polly/Medicated Goo (company sleeve)	4
73	Rolling Stones COC 49102	KRACKER BRAND (LP)	12

KRAFTWERK
75	Vertigo 6147 012	Autobahn/Kometenmelodie 1	4
75	Vertigo 6147 015	Comet Melody 2/Kristallo	6
76	Capitol CL 15853	Radioactivity/Antenna (p/s)	5
77	Capitol CLX 104	Showroom Dummies/Europe Endless	6
77	Capitol CLX 104	Showroom Dummies/Europe Endless (12")	10
77	Capitol CL 15917	Trans-Europe Express/Europe Endless	5
78	Capitol CL 15981	The Robots/Spacelab (foldout p/s, 10,000 only)	6
78	Capitol CL 15981	The Robots (alternate mix)/Spacelab (normal p/s)	18
78	Capitol CL 15998	Neon Lights/Trans-Europe Express/The Model (p/s)	6
78	Capitol 12CL 15998	Neon Lights/Trans-Europe Express/The Model (12", luminous vinyl, dayglo sleeve & label)	10
78	Capitol 12CL 16098	Showroom Dummies/Europe Endless/Spacelab (12", p/s, reissue)	10
81	EMI TCEMI 5175	Pocket Calculator (Long & Short Versions)/Numbers (cassette)	15
81	EMI 12EMI 5175	Pocket Calculator/Numbers/Dentaku (12", p/s)	10
81	EMI 12EMI 5207	Computer Love/The Model (12", p/s, original issue)	8
81	EMI 12EMI 5207	The Model/Computer Love (12", p/s, 2nd issue)	7
84	Vertigo VER 3	Kometenmelodie 2/Vom Himmel Hoch (p/s)	7
84	EMI 12EMI 5413	Tour De France (Long, Short & Instrumental versions) (12", p/s)	15
86	EMI 12EMI 5588	Musique Non-Stop (6.15)/Musique Non-Stop (7" Version) (12", p/s)	10
87	EMI 12EMI 5602	The Telephone Call (Remix)/Housephone/Der Telefon Anruf (12", p/s)	10
73	Vertigo 6641 077	KRAFTWERK (2-LP, spiral label)	20
73	Vertigo 6360 616	RALF AND FLORIAN (LP, some with poster)	25/10
74	Vertigo 6360 620	AUTOBAHN (LP)	10
83	EMI EMC 3407	TECHNOPOP (LP, unissued)	

(see also Organisation)

KRAKEN
81	Knave	Fantasy Reality	15

BILLY J. KRAMER & DAKOTAS
63	Parlophone R 5023	Do You Want To Know A Secret/I'll Be On My Way	4
63	Parlophone R 5049	Bad To Me/I Call Your Name	4
63	Parlophone R 5073	I'll Keep You Satisfied/I Know	4
64	Parlophone R 5105	Little Children/They Remind Me Of You	4
64	Parlophone R 5156	From A Window/Second To None	4
65	Parlophone R 5234	It's Gotta Last Forever/Don't Do It No More	5
65	Parlophone R 5285	Trains And Boats And Planes/That's The Way I Feel	5
65	Parlophone R 5362	Neon City/I'll Be Doggone	5
66	Parlophone R 5408	We're Doing Fine/Forgive Me	6
66	Parlophone R 5482	You Make Me Feel Like Someone/Take My Hand	6
63	Parlophone GEP 8885	THE BILLY J. KRAMER HITS (EP)	15
64	Parlophone GEP 8895	I'LL KEEP YOU SATISFIED (EP)	15
64	Parlophone GEP 8907	LITTLE CHILDREN (EP)	15
64	Parlophone GEP 8921	FROM A WINDOW (EP)	18
65	Parlophone GEP 8928	BILLY J. PLAYS THE STATES (EP)	22
63	Parlophone PMC 1209	LISTEN (LP, also stereo PCS 3047)	16/20

(see also Dakotas)

BILLY J. KRAMER
67	Parlophone R 5552	Sorry/Going Going Gone	7
67	Reaction 591 014	Town Of Tuxley Toymakers/Chinese Girl	15
68	NEMS 56-3396	1941/His Love Is Just A Lie	5
68	NEMS 56-3635	A World Without Love/Going Through It	5
69	MGM 1474	The Colour Of My Love/I'm Running Away	6
73	Decca F 13426	A Fool Like You/I'll Keep You Satisfied	4
73	Decca F 13442	Darlin' Come To Me/Walking	4
74	BASF BA 1006	Stayin' Power/Blue Jean Queen	4

MINT VALUE £

77	EMI EMI 2661	San Diego/Warm Summer Rain	4
78	EMI EMI 2740	Ships That Pass In The Night/Is There Anymore At Home Like You	4
79	Hobo HOS 010	Blue Christmas/Little Love (p/s, blue vinyl)	6

SU KRAMER
| 76 | Decca F 13640 | You Got The Power Pts 1 & 2 | 4 |

WAYNE KRAMER
| 78 | Stiffwick DEA/SUK 1 | Ramblin' Rose/Get Some (numbered p/s) | 5 |
| 79 | Radar ADA 41 | The Harder They Come/East Side Girl (p/s) | 4 |
| *(see also MC5)* |

KRAY CHERUBS
| 88 | Fierce FRIGHT 014 | No (p/s, 1-sided) | 15 |
| 89 | Snakeskin SS 002 | Riot In Hell Mom/SAUCERMAN: Motor Drag (numbered, black or purple p/s, 300 only) | 8 |

BILL KRENZ & HIS RAGTIMERS
| 56 | London HLU 8258 | There'll Be No New Tunes On This Old Piano/Goofus | 15 |

KREW KATS
| 61 | HMV POP 840 | Trambone/Peak Hour | 7 |
| 61 | HMV POP 894 | Samovar/Jack's Good | 10 |
| *(see also Shadows, Brian Bennett)* |

KRIMSON KAKE
| 70 | Penny Farthing PEN 707 | Feelin' Better/Waiter | 5 |

DAVE KRISS
| 880s private pressing | EMIGRATING (2-LP) | 20 |

SONJA KRISTINA
68	Polydor 56299	Let The Sunshine In/Frank Mills	8
80	Chopper CHOP 101	St Tropez/Mr Skin (p/s)	6
80	Chopper CHOPE 5	SONJA KRISTINA (LP)	40
(see also Curved Air)

KROKODIL
| 69 | Liberty LBS 83306 | KROKODIL (LP) | 12 |
| 70 | Liberty LBS 83417 | SWAMP (LP) | 12 |

KROKUS
| 80 | Ariola ARO 225 | Bedside Radio/Back Seat Rock'n'Roll (p/s, clear vinyl) | 4 |
| 82 | Ariola ARO 254 | Rock City/Mr Sixty Nine/Mad Racket (p/s, red vinyl) | 4 |

KRONSTADT UPRISING
| 80s | Spider | The Unknown Revolution | 4 |
| 85 | Dog Rock SD 108 | Part Of The Game/The Horseman | 4 |

HARDY KRUGER
| 59 | Top Rank TR 5005 | Blind Date (I'm A Lonely Man)/PINEWOOD ORCHESTRA: Blind Date | 4 |

GENE KRUPA (& HIS ORCHESTRA)
60	HMV POP 750	Cherokee/Indiana "Montage"	4
55	Columbia 33S 1051	DRUMMIN' MAN (10" LP)	12
55	Columbia 33S 1064	RHYTHM PARADE (10" LP)	12
55	Columbia Clef 33C 9000	THE GENE KRUPA TRIO COLLATES (10" LP)	12
57	Columbia Clef 33C 9032	THE ROCKIN' MR. KRUPA (10" LP)	12

GENE KRUPA & BUDDY RICH
| 64 | Verve VS 503 | Perdida/Night Train | 4 |

KRYPTON TUNES
| 70s | Black & Red FIRE 1 | Behind Your Smile/Coming To See You | 4 |

BOB KUBAN & INMEN
66	Stateside SS 488	The Cheater/Try Me Baby	20
66	Stateside SS 514	The Teaser/All I Want	18
68	Bell BLL 1027	The Cheater/Try Me Baby (reissue)	6

KUBAS
| 65 | Columbia DB 7451 | I Love Her/Magic Potion | 20 |
| *(see also Koobas)* |

DAVID KUBINEC
| 79 | A&M AMS 7429 | Another Lone Ranger/On The Edge Of The Floor (blue vinyl) | 4 |
| 78 | A&M AMLH 68501 | SOME THINGS NEVER CHANGE (LP, red vinyl with inner sleeve) | 10 |
| *(see also Rainbow)* |

KUF-LINX
| 58 | London HLU 8583 | So Tough/What'cha Gonna Do | 125 |
| 58 | London HLU 8583 | So Tough/What'cha Gonna Do (78) | 30 |

LENNY KUHR
| 69 | Philips BF 1777 | The Troubadour/Oh No Monsieur | 15 |

KUKL
| 80s | Crass 1984/1 | THE EYE (LP, foldout sleeve) | 10 |
| 80s | Crass No. 4 | HOLIDAYS IN EUROPE (LP, with inner sleeve) | 10 |
| *(see also Sugarcubes)* |

KULT
| 69 | CBS 4276 | No Home Today/Mr No. 1 | 70 |

CHARLIE KUNZ
54	Decca F 10419	"Charlie Kunz Piano Medley, No. 114"	5
54	Decca F 10441	"Charlie Kunz Piano Medley, No. 115"	4
54	Decca F 10481	"Charlie Kunz Piano Medley, No. 116"	4

MINT VALUE £

FELA RANSOME KUTI (& AFRICA '70)

75	Creole CRLP 501	SHAKARA (LP, with Africa '70)	15
77	Creole CRLP 511	ZOMBIE (LP, with Africa '70)	12
78	Decca Phase 4 PFS 4412	YELLOW FEVER (LP)	10
79	Creole CRLP 502	GENTLEMEN (LP)	12
79	Creole CRLP 509	EVERYTHING SCATTER (LP)	10
81	Arista SPART 1167	BLACK PRESIDENT (LP)	12
	(see also Ginger Baker)		

DIXIE KWANKA

50s	Melodisc MEL 1573	I Left My Heart In Rhodesia/My Nyasaland Love	4

JIM KWESKIN JUG BAND

65	Fontana TFL 6036	JIM KWESKIN JUG BAND (LP)	12
67	Fontana (S)TFL 6080	SEE REVERSE SIDE FOR TITLE (LP)	10
68	Vanguard SVRL 19046	WHATEVER HAPPENED TO THOSE GOOD OLD DAYS AT CLUB 47 (LP)	12

CHARLES KYNARD

73	Mainstream MSL 1009	WOGA (LP)	10
73	Mainstream MSL 1017	YOUR MAMA WON'T DANCE (LP)	10

KYTES

66	Pye 7N 17136	Blessed/Call Me Darling	5
66	Pye 7N 17179	Frosted Panes/I'll Give You Better Love	15
68	Island WI 6027	Running In The Water/The End Of The Day	30

KISS

PATTI LA BELLE (& BLUEBELLES)

64	Sue WI 324	Down The Aisle/C'est La Vie (solo)	12
65	Cameo Parkway P 935	Danny Boy/I Believe	10
65	Atlantic AT 4055	All Or Nothing/You Forgot How To Love (as Patty La Belle & Her Belles)	10
66	Atlantic AT 4064	Over The Rainbow/Groovy Kind Of Love (as Patty La Belle & Her Belles)	6
66	Atlantic 584 007	Patti's Prayer/Family Man (as Patty La Belle & Her Belles)	5
67	Atlantic 584 072	Take Me For A Little While/I Don't Want To Go On Without You (as Patti La Belle)	7
66	Atlantic 587 001	OVER THE RAINBOW (LP)	15

(see also LaBelle, Bluebelles)

LABELLE

73	RCA RCA 2382	Open Up My Heart/Going On A Holiday	4
76	Track 2094 131	Miss Otis Regrets/Too Many Days	4
77	Epic EPC 4896	Lady Marmalade/Messin' With My Mind (coloured vinyl reissue)	4
74	Epic EPC 80566	NIGHT BIRDS (LP)	10
74	RCA Victor APL1 0205	PRESSURE COOKIN' (LP)	10
75	Epic EPC 69167	PHOENIX (LP)	10

LACE

| 68 | Columbia DB 8499 | People People/The Nun | 15 |
| 69 | Page One POF 135 | I'm A Gambler/Go Away | 6 |

(see also Universals, Pete Dello, Honeybus, Red Herring, Gary Walker & Rain)

DAVE LACEY & CORVETTES

| 65 | Philips BF 1419 | That's What They All Say/I've Had Enough | 6 |

LACKEY & SWEENEY

| 73 | Village Thing VTS 23 | JUNK STORE SONGS FOR SALE (LP) | 20 |

LADDERS

| 83 | Statik TAK 2 | Gotta See Jane/Krugerrands (p/s) | 6 |
| 83 | Statik TAK 2-12 | Gotta See Jane/Krugerrands (12", p/s) | 10 |

LADD'S BLACK ACES

| 56 | London AL 3556 | LADD'S BLACK ACES (10" LP) | 15 |

LA DE DA BAND

| 69 | Parlophone R 5810 | Come Together/Here Is Love | 7 |

LADIES OF THE 80'S

| 80s | Streetwave | Turned Onto You (12") | 15 |

TOMMY LADNIER

| 54 | London AL 3524 | BLUES AND STOMPS VOLUME ONE — TOMMY LADNIER (10" LP) | 25 |
| 55 | London AL 3548 | PLAYS THE BLUES WITH MA RAINEY & EDMONIA HENDERSON (10" LP) | 25 |

(see also Ma Rainey)

PATTIE LA DONNE

| 69 | Joe/Duke DU 23 | Friends And Lovers/JOE'S ALLSTARS: Hot Line | 5 |

LADYBIRDS

64	Columbia DB 7197	Lady Bird/I Don't Care Any More	4
64	Columbia DB 7250	The White Cliffs Of Dover/It's Not The Same Without A Boy	4
64	Columbia DB 7351	Memories/Try A Little Love	4
65	Columbia DB 7523	I Wanna Fly/O.K. Fred	4

LADY JANE & VERITY

| 59 | Pye Intl. 7N 25036 | The Slow Look/Cry Baby | 5 |

LADY JUNE

| 74 | Caroline C 1509 | LADY JUNE'S LINGUISTIC LEPROSY (LP, with perforated lyric sheet) | 20 |

(see also Kevin Ayers, Eno)

LADY LUCK & LULLABIES

| 62 | Philips PB 1245 | Young Stranger/Dance | 5 |

LAFAYETTES

| 62 | RCA RCA 1299 | Life's Too Short/Nobody But You | 4 |

LA HOST

| 85 | Quiet QU 001 | The Big Sleep/Just Breakin' Away (also listed as Orbitone ORB 010) | 4 |

LAIBACH

| 84 | East West 12 EWS 3 | Panorama/Decree (12", p/s) | 10 |
| 85 | Cherry Red 12CHERRY 91 | Die Liebe/Die Liebe 1st Grosste Kraft, Die Alles Schafft (12", p/s) | 7 |

CLEO LAINE

54	Parlophone MSP 6107	I Got Rhythm/I Know You're Mine (with Johnny Dankworth Orchestra)	4
55	Parlophone MSP 6147	Ain't Misbehavin'/I Got It Bad, And That Ain't Good (with Johnny Dankworth Orchestra)	4
57	Pye Jazz 7NJ 2013	I'm Beginning To See The Light/Jeepers Creepers	4
58	Pye 7N 15143	Hand Me Down Love/They Were Right	4
60	Fontana H 269	Let's Slip Away/Thieving Boy	4
61	Fontana H 326	You'll Answer To Me/I Only Have Eyes For You	4
65	Fontana TF 532	Little Boat/The Exciting Mr. Fitch	4
65	Fontana TF 622	If We Live On The Top Of A Mountain/Don't You Pass Me By	4

Cleo LAINE

66	Fontana TF 759	There Is Nothing Left To Say/Life Is A Wheel	4
57	Parlophone GEP 8613	I GOT RHYTHM (EP)	7
57	Pye Nixa Jazz NJE 1010	CLEO LAINE (EP)	7
57	Pye Nixa Jazz NJE 1026	THE APRIL AGE (EP, as Cleo Laine & Dave Lee Quintet)	7
50s	Esquire EP 102	CLEO LAINE (EP, as Cleo Laine & Keith Christie Quintet)	7
50s	Esquire EP 122	CLEO LAINE (EP, as Cleo Laine & Keith Christie Quintet)	7
61	Fontana TFE 17381	THE FABULOUS CLEO (EP)	7
64	Fontana TFE 17404	CLEO (EP)	7
55	Esquire 15-007	CLEO LAINE (10" LP)	12
58	Pye Nixa NPT 19024	CLEO'S CHOICE (10" LP)	12
58	MGM MGM-C 765	SHE'S THE TOPS (LP)	10
62	Fontana 680 992 TL	ALL ABOUT ME (LP, also stereo 886 159 TY)	10
66	Fontana (S)TL 5316	WOMAN TALK (LP)	10

(see also Tubby Hayes & Cleo Laine, Johnny Dankworth)

DENNY LAINE

67	Deram DM 122	Say You Don't Mind/Ask The People	6
68	Deram DM 171	Too Much In Love/Catherine's Wheel	10
69	Deram DM 227	Say You Don't Mind/Ask The People (reissue)	4
73	Wizard WIZ 104	Find A Way Somehow/Move Me To Another Place	4
73	Wizard SWZ 2001	AAH LAINE! (LP)	10

(see also Moody Blues, Paul McCartney/Wings, Balls, Trevor Burton, Incredible String Band)

FRANKIE LAINE

51	Columbia DB 2876	Jezebel/Rose, Rose, I Love You (78)	6
51	Columbia DB 2907	The Girl In The Wood/Wonderful, Wasn't It? (78)	5
52	Columbia DB 3113	High Noon/Rock Of Gibraltar (78)	5
53	Columbia SCM 5016	The Ruby And The Pearl/The Mermaid	18
53	Columbia SCM 5017	Jealousy/The Gandy Dancers' Ball	25
53	Columbia SCM 5031	I'm Just A Poor Bachelor/Tonight You Belong To Me	18
53	Columbia SCM 5064	September In The Rain/Chow Willy	15
53	Columbia SCM 5073	The Swan Song/My Ohio Home	15
54	Columbia SCM 5085	Tomorrow Mountain/I'd Give My Life	15
56	Mercury MT 109	The Cry Of The Wild Goose/Mule Train (78)	5
56	Philips PB 607	Champion, The Wonder Horse/Ticky Ticky Tick (I'm Gonna ...) (78)	5
56	Philips JK 1000	Moonlight Gambler/Only If We Love (jukebox issue)	12
57	Philips JK 1009	Love Is A Golden Ring (with Easy Riders)/There's Not A Moment To Spare	12
57	Philips JK 1017	Lonely Man/Without Him (jukebox issue)	12
57	Philips JK 1032	The Greater Sin/East Is East (jukebox issue)	12
58	Philips PB 797	Shine/Annabel Lee	6
58	Philips PB 821	The Lonesome Road/My Gal And A Prayer	6
58	Philips PB 836	Lovin' Up A Storm/A Kiss Can Change The World	7
58	Philips PB 848	Choombala Bay/I Have To Cry	5
58	Philips PB 886	When I Speak Your Name/Cottage For Sale	5
59	Philips PB 905	That's My Desire/In My Wildest Dreams	5
59	Philips PB 965	Rawhide/Journey's End	6
59	Philips PB 965	Rawhide/Journey's End (78)	12
60	Philips PB 997	Jelly Coal Man/Rocks And Gravel	5
60	Philips PB 1011	St. James Infirmary/Et Voila!	5
60	Philips PB 1064	And Doesn't She Roll/Seven Women	4
61	Philips PB 1135	Gunslinger/Wanted Man	4
63	CBS AAG 144	Don't Make My Baby Blue/The Moment Of Truth	4
63	CBS AAG 167	And She Doesn't Roll/I'm Gonna Be Strong	4
65	Capitol CL 15373	Go On With Your Dancing/Halfway	4
67	HMV POP 1573	Ev'ry Street's A Boulevard (In Old New York)/I'll Take Care Of Your Cares	5
67	HMV POP 1590	Making Memories/The Moment Of Truth	5
67	HMV POP 1597	You Wanted Someone To Play With/The Real True Meaning Of Love	4
67	HMV POP 1606	Laura/Sometimes	4
68	Stateside SS 2091	To Each His Own/I'm Happy To Hear You're Sorry	4
69	Stateside SS 2144	You Gave Me A Mountain/The Secret Of Happiness	5
73	CBS 1156	High Noon/Cool Water (p/s)	4
54	Columbia SEG 7505	JEZEBEL (EP, company die-cut sleeve)	15
54	Philips BBE 12005	FRANKIE LAINE (I BELIEVE) (EP)	12
56	Mercury MEP 9000	FRANKIE LAINE SINGS (EP)	14
56	Mercury MEP 9500	MORE HITS BY FRANKIE LAINE (EP)	14
56	Philips BBE 12087	FRANKIE LAINE No. 2 (EP)	14
56	Philips BBE 12103	JUBA JUBA JUBALEE (EP, as Frankie Laine & Four Lads)	12
57	Philips BBE 12130	FRANKIE LAINE No. 3 (EP)	14
57	Mercury MEP 9520	FRANKIE LAINE SINGS VOL. 2 (EP)	14
58	Philips BBE 12216	FRANKIE LAINE (PHILIPS TV SERIES) (EP)	12
60	Mercury ZEP 10062	FRANKIE LAINE'S ALL TIME HITS (EP)	12
61	Philips BBE 12447	WESTERN FAVOURITES (EP)	15
62	CBS AGG 20003	DEUCES WILD No. 1 (EP)	8
62	CBS AGG 20007	DEUCES WILD No. 2 (EP)	8
62	CBS AGG 20011	DEUCES WILD No. 3 (EP)	8
64	CBS AGG 20036	SONG OF THE OPEN ROAD (EP)	8
52	Oriole/Mercury MG 10001	MR RHYTHM SINGS (10" LP, stickered U.S. "Mr Rhythm" sleeve)	40
52	Oriole/Mercury MG 10002	FRANKIE LAINE SONGS (10" LP)	40
54	Mercury MG 25097	MR. RHYTHM SINGS (10" LP, reissue)	30
54	Mercury MG 25098	SONGS BY FRANKIE LAINE (10" LP)	30
54	Columbia 33S 1047	FRANKIE LAINE SINGS (10" LP)	30
54	Philips BBR 8014	THE VOICE OF YOUR CHOICE (10" LP)	30
55	Philips BBR 8068	MR. RHYTHM (10" LP)	25
56	Mercury MPT 7007	CRY OF THE WILD GOOSE (10" LP)	18
56	Philips BBL 7080	JAZZ SPECTACULAR (LP, with Buck Clayton & His Orchestra)	15
56	Philips BBL 7111	JUBA JUBA JUBILEE (LP, with Four Lads)	18
57	Philips BBL 7155	ROCKIN' (LP)	15

57	Mercury MPT 7513	THAT'S MY DESIRE (10" LP)	18
58	Philips BBL 7238	FOREIGN AFFAIR (LP)	16
58	Philips BBL 7260	TORCHING (LP)	12
58	Philips BBL 7263	SHOWCASE OF HITS (LP, flipback or non-flipback sleeve)	25/20
59	Philips BBL 7294	REUNION IN RHYTHM (LP, with Michel Legrand, also stereo SBBL 541)	14/16
60	Philips BBL 7357	FRANKIE LAINE BALLADEER (LP)	12
61	Philips BBL 7468	HELL BENT FOR LEATHER (LP, also stereo SBBL 616)	12/15
61	Ember EMB 3334	FRANKIE LAINE SINGS (LP)	10
62	Philips BBL 7535	DEUCES WILD (LP, also stereo SBBL 663)	12/15
62	CBS (S)BPG 62052	HELL BENT FOR LEATHER (LP, reissue)	10
62	CBS (S)BPG 62082	CALL OF THE WILD (LP, mono/stereo)	15
63	CBS (S)BPG 62126	WANDERLUST (LP)	15
60s	World Records SM 531/536	THE FRANKIE LAINE SONGBOOK (6-LP box set)	25

(see also Jo Stafford & Frankie Laine, Four Lads)

FRANKIE LAINE & JOHNNIE RAY

57	Philips JK 1026	Up Above My Head, I Hear Music In .../Good Evening Friends (jukebox issue)	18
57	Philips BBE 12153	FRANKIE AND JOHNNY (EP, 1 track each, 2 together)	15

(see also Johnnie Ray)

LINDA LAINE (& SINNERS)

64	Columbia DB 7204	Doncha Know, Doncha Know, Doncha Know/Ain't That Fun (solo)	7
64	Columbia DB 7370	Low Grades And High Fever/After Today (solo)	7
65	Columbia DB 7549	Don't Say It Baby/All I Want To Do Is Run (as Linda Laine & Sinners)	8

(see also Sinners)

SCOTT LAINE

63	Windsor WB 114	Tearaway Johnnie/John Silver	5

BONNIE LAKE & HER BEAUX

56	Brunswick 05622	The Miracle Of Love/Thirteen Black Cats	15

(see also Jack Pleis)

GREG LAKE

76	Manticore K 13511	I Believe In Father Christmas/Humbug (p/s)	5
77	Atlantic K 10990	C'est La Vie/Jeremy Bender (p/s)	5
78	Atlantic K 11061	Watching Over You/Hallowed Be Thy Name (p/s)	5

(see also Emerson Lake & Palmer, King Crimson)

LEE LEMAR & HIS ORCHESTRA

57	London HLB 8508	Sophia/Teenage Pedal Pushers	30
57	London HLB 8508	Sophia/Teenage Pedal Pushers (78)	10

CHRIS LAMB & UNIVERSALS

65	Decca F 12176	Mysterious Land/If You Ask Me	5

(see also Universals, Gidian)

KEVIN LAMB

70	Concord CON 23	Who Is The Hero?/The Road To Antibes	5
73	Birth RAB 1004	Who Is The Hero?/Who Stole The Ice	4
72	Birth RAB 4	WHO IS THE HERO? (LP)	12

JEANNIE LAMBE

67	CBS 202636	Miss Disc/Montano Blues (with Gordon Beck Orchestra)	15
67	CBS 2731	Day After Day After Day/City At Night	4
67	CBS 3000	This Is My Love/Where Have All The Endings Gone (as Jeanne Lam)	4

DAVE LAMBERT, JON HENDRICKS & ANNIE ROSS

60	Philips BBL 7368	DAVE LAMBERT, JON HENDRICKS & ANNIE ROSS (LP, stereo SBBL 562)	10

(see also Jon Hendricks, Annie Ross)

LAMBRETTAS

79	Rocket XPRES 23	Go Steady/Listen Listen/Cortinas (p/s; later in art sleeve)	5
80	Rocket XPRES 25	Poison Ivy/Runaround (with 2-Stroke sleeve & label)	5
80	Rocket XPRES 33	Da-a-a-ance/(Can't You) Feel The Beat (p/s)	4
80	Rocket XPRES 333	Da-a-a-ance/(Can't You) Feel The Beat (picture disc, 2 different shades)	4
80	Rocket XPRES 36	Another Day (Another Girl)/Steppin' Out (Of Line) (p/s)	4

LAMB STEW

72	Philips 6006 235	Sweet Summer Days/Got To Get Together (p/s)	4

LAMP SISTERS

68	Sue WI 4048	A Woman With The Blues/I Thought It Was All Over	25

LANA SISTERS

58	Fontana H 148	Ring-A My Phone/Chimes Of Arcady	15
58	Fontana H 148	Ring-A My Phone/Chimes Of Arcady (78)	5
59	Fontana H 176	Buzzin'/Cry, Cry, Baby	10
59	Fontana H 176	Buzzin'/Cry, Cry, Baby (78)	5
59	Fontana H 190	Mister Dee-Jay/Tell Him No	10
59	Fontana H 190	Mister Dee-Jay/Tell Him No (78)	5
59	Fontana H 221	(Seven Little Girls) Sitting In The Back Seat (with Al Saxon)/Sitting On The Sidewalk	8
59	Fontana H 221	(Seven Little Girls) Sitting In The Back Seat (with Al Saxon)/Sitting On The Sidewalk (78)	5
60	Fontana H 235	My Mother's Eyes/You've Got What It Takes	8
60	Fontana H 235	My Mother's Eyes/You've Got What It Takes (78)	8
60	Fontana H 252	Someone Loves You, Joe/Tinatarella Di Luna	6
60	Fontana H 283	Two-some/Down South	6
59	Fontana TFE 17146	DRUMBEAT (EP)	18

(see also Al Saxon, Dusty Springfield)

CYNTHIA LANAGAN
| 57 | Parlophone R 4316 | Jamie Boy/Silent Lips (as Cynthia Lanigan) | 5 |
| 57 | Parlophone R 4383 | (Don't Stop, Don't Stop) Tell Me More/I'm Available | 5 |

LANCASTRIANS
64	Pye 7N 15732	We'll Sing In The Sunshine/Was She Tall	6
65	Pye 7N 15791	Let's Lock The Door (And Throw Away The Key)/If You're Goin' To Leave Me	6
65	Pye 7N 15846	There'll Be No More Goodbyes/Never Gonna Come On Home	6
65	Pye 7N 15927	Lonely Man/I Can't Stand The Pain	6
66	Pye 7N 17043	The World Keeps Going Round/Not The Same Anymore	15
66	Pye 7N 17072	The Ballad Of The Green Berets/My Little Rose	5

MAJOR LANCE
63	Columbia DB 7099	The Monkey Time/Mama Didn't Know	25
63	Columbia DB 7168	Hey Little Girl/Crying In The Rain	12
64	Columbia DB 7205	Um, Um, Um, Um, Um, Um/Sweet Music	10
64	Columbia DB 7271	The Matador/Gonna Get Married	12
64	Columbia DB 7365	Rhythm/Please Don't Say No More	16
65	Columbia DB 7463	I'm So Lost/Sometimes I Wonder	10
65	Columbia DB 7527	Come See/You Belong To Me, My Love	10
65	Columbia DB 7609	I'm The One/Pride And Joy	12
65	Columbia DB 7688	Too Hot To Hold/Dark And Lonely	15
65	Columbia DB 7787	Everybody Loves A Good Time/I Just Can't Help It	12
66	Columbia DB 7967	Investigate/Little Young Lover	30
67	Columbia DB 8122	Ain't No Soul (Left In These Ole Shoes)/You'll Want Me Back	30
69	Atlantic 584 277	Follow The Leader/Since You've Been Gone	6
69	Atlantic 584 302	Sweeter As The Days Go By/Shadows Of A Memory	6
70	Soul City SC 114	The Beat/You'll Want Me Back	7
71	Buddah 2011 046	Stay Away From Me/Gypsy Woman	4
73	Contempo C 1	The Right Track/Um, Um, Um, Um, Um, Um	4
73	Contempo C 9	Ain't No Soul (Left In These Ole Shoes)/Investigate	4
73	Stax 2025 124	I Wanna Make Up/That's The Story Of My Life	6
73	Epic EPC 8404	Um, Um, Um, Um, Um, Um/Sweet Music (reissue)	4
73	Contempo C 26	Dark And Lonely/My Girl	4
73	Warner Bros K 16334	Sweeter/Wild & Free	5
74	Warner Bros K 16385	Without A Doubt/Open The Door To Your Heart	5
74	Contempo CS 2017	Gimme Little Sign/How Can You Say Goodbye	4
74	Contempo CS 9015	The Right Track/Ain't No Soul (Left In These Ole Shoes)	4
75	Contempo CS 2045	Don't You Know I Love You Pts 1 & 2	4
75	Pye 7N 45487	You're Everything I Need Pts 1 & 2	4
76	Pye Intl. 7N 25705	Nothing Can Stop Me/Follow The Leader	4
64	Columbia SEG 8318	UM UM UM UM UM UM (EP)	40
65	Columbia 33SX 1728	THE RHYTHM OF MAJOR LANCE (LP)	75
73	Contempo COLP 1001	GREATEST HITS LIVE AT THE TORCH (LP)	10

RICK LANCELOT & SEVEN KNIGHTS
| 66 | RCA RCA 1502 | Say Girl/Live Like A Lion | 6 |

LANCERS
54	London HL 8027	Stop Chasin' Me Baby/Peggy O'Neil	30
54	London HL 8027	Stop Chasin' Me Baby/Peggy O'Neil (78)	5
54	London HL 8079	So High, So Low, So Wide/It's You, It's You I Love	30
54	London HL 8079	So High, So Low, So Wide/It's You, It's You I Love (78)	5
54	Vogue Coral Q 2038	Mister Sandman/The Little White Light	15
54	Vogue Coral Q 2038	Mister Sandman/The Little White Light (78)	5
55	Vogue Coral Q 72062	Timberjack/C-r-a-z-y Music	10
55	Vogue Coral Q 72062	Timberjack/C-r-a-z-y Music (78)	5
55	Vogue Coral Q 72081	Get Out Of The Car (as Lancers & Georgie Auld)/Close Your Eyes	12
55	Vogue Coral Q 72081	Get Out Of The Car (as Lancers & Georgie Auld)/Close Your Eyes (78)	12
55	Vogue Coral Q 72100	Jo-Ann/The Bonnie Banks Of Loch Lomon'	10
56	Vogue Coral Q 72128	Alphabet Rock/Rock Around The Island	20
56	Vogue Coral Q 72128	Alphabet Rock/Rock Around The Island (78)	18
56	Vogue Coral Q 72157	Little Fool/A Man Is As Good As His Word	8
56	Vogue Coral Q 72157	Little Fool/A Man Is As Good As His Word (78)	5
56	Vogue Coral Q 72183	The First Travelling Saleslady/Free	6
56	Vogue Coral Q 72183	The First Travelling Saleslady/Free (78)	5
57	Vogue Coral Q 72220	Never Leave Me/I Came Back To Say I'm Sorry	6
57	Vogue Coral Q 72220	Never Leave Me/I Came Back To Say I'm Sorry (78)	5
57	Vogue Coral Q 72254	It Happened In Monterey/Ramona/Freckled-Face Sara Jane	4
57	Vogue Coral Q 72254	It Happened In Monterey/Ramona/Freckled-Face Sara Jane (78)	5
57	Vogue Coral Q 72282	Charm Bracelet/And It Don't Feel Bad	5
57	Vogue Coral Q 72282	Charm Bracelet/And It Don't Feel Bad (78)	5
58	Coral Q 72300	The Stroll/Don't Go Near The Water	6
58	Coral Q 72300	The Stroll/Don't Go Near The Water (78)	10
60	Coral Q 72398	Joey, Joey, Joey/JOHNNY DESMOND: The Most Happy Fella	4
61	Warner Bros WB 39	Young In Love/Lonesome Town	4
55	London REP 1027	PRESENTING THE LANCERS (EP)	16
54	London H-APB 1029	OH SWEET MAMA (10" LP)	18
61	London HA-P 2307	CONCERT IN CONTRASTS (LP)	10

ELSA LANCHESTER
| 58 | Vogue VA 160126 | SONGS FOR A SMOKE-FILLED ROOM (LP, with Charles Laughton) | 10 |
| 59 | Vogue VA 160139 | SONGS FOR A SHUTTERED PARLOUR (LP, with Charles Laughton) | 10 |

BILLY LAND
| 62 | Oriole CB 1750 | I Go Walking/You're Too Much | 5 |

BOB LANDER & SPOTNICKS
| 62 | Oriole CB 1756 | My Old Kentucky Home/Home On The Range (possibly unreleased on 7") | 15+ |

62	Oriole CB 1784	Midnight Special/My Old Kentucky Home	10

(see also Spotnicks)

BILL & BRETT LANDIS

59	Parlophone R 4516	Since You've Gone/Bright Eyes	4
59	Parlophone R 4551	By You, By You/Forgive Me	4
59	Parlophone R 4570	Baby Talk/Love Me True	6

JERRY LANDIS

62	Oriole CB 1390	Carlos Dominquez/He Was My Brother	15

(see also Paul Simon)

JOYA LANDIS

68	Trojan TR 620	Kansas City/Out The Light	7
68	Trojan TR 641	Moonlight Lover/I Love You True	7

(see also Jay & Joya)

NEIL LANDON

66	Decca F 12330	Waiting Here For Someone/I've Got Nothing To Lose	4
66	Decca F 12451	I'm Your Puppet/I Still Love You	4

HOAGY LANDS

67	Stateside SS 2030	The Next In Line/Please Don't Talk About Me When I'm Gone	125
68	Stateside SS 2085	I'm Yours/Only You	7
72	Action ACT 4605	Why Didn't You Let Me Know/Do You Know What Life Is All About	6
75	UK USA 13	Friends And Lovers Don't Go Together/True Love At Last	4
75	UK USA 14	The Next In Line/I'm Yours	5

LANDSCAPE

78	Event Horizon EVE 137	U2XME1X2MUCH/Don't Gimme No Rebop/Sixteen	5
78	Event Horizon EVE 139	Workers Playtime/Nearly Normal/Too Many Questions	5
79	RCA PB 5183	Japan/Gotham City	4
80	RCA PB 5259	Sonja Henie/Neddy Sindrum (p/s)	4
80	RCA EDM 1	European Man/Mechanical Bride (p/s)	4
80	RCA EDMT 1	European Man/Mechanical Bride (12", p/s)	12

DES(MOND) LANE

56	Decca F 10821	Penny-Whistle Rock/Penny-Whistle Polka	7
57	Decca F 10847	Rock Mister Piper/Plymouth Rock	7
59	Top Rank JAR 203	Moonbird/The Clanger March (as Des Lane Orchestra, with John Barry)	6
59	Top Rank JAR 203	Moonbird/The Clanger March (as Des Lane Orchestra, with John Barry) (78)	5
68	Pye 7N 17546	Sadie/No More Wild Oats (as Des Lane)	4

(see also Cyril Stapleton)

GARY LANE & GARRISONS

61	Fontana H 338	Start Walking Boy/How Wrong Can You Be	5
62	Fontana 267221 TF	I'm A Lucky Boy/A Love Like You	5

LOIS LANE

67	RCA RCA 1570	One Little Voice/Sing To Me	4
68	Mercury MF 1042	Punky's Dilemma/Lazy Summer Day	4
69	Mercury MF 1092	Brontasaurus Named Bert/Windmills Of Your Mind	4
69	Mercury MF 1115	Lovin' Time/Winds Of Heaven	4

(see also Caravelles)

MICKEY LEE LANE

64	Stateside SS 354	Shaggy Dog/Oo Oo	6
65	Stateside SS 456	Hey Sah-Lo-Ney/Of Yesterday	30

PENNY LANE

68	Columbia DB 8377	Loving Or Losing You/Deep Down Inside	4
68	CBS 3718	The Boy Who Never Grew Up/I'm Going Back	4

RONNIE LANE & SLIM CHANCE

73	GM GMS 011	The Poacher/How Come (p/s)	4
74	GM GMS 1024	ANYMORE FOR ANYMORE (LP)	10
75	Island ILPS 9321	RONNIE LANE'S SLIM CHANCE (LP)	12
76	Island ILPS 9366	ONE FOR THE ROAD (LP)	10

(see also Small Faces, Faces)

ROSEMARY LANE

60	Philips PB 1041	Down By The River/My First Love Letter	4
61	Philips BF 1127	Lyin' Kisses/The Nightingale Who Sang Off Key	4
61	Philips BF 1172	Who Does He Think He Is/What Is The Age	4
63	Oriole CB 1871	Like You Should/Baby Please Be Kind	4

TONY LANE & DELTONES

64	Sabre SA-45-5	It's Great/Now She's Mine	6

LANE BROTHERS

60	London HLR 9150	Mimi/Two Dozen And A Half	8

LANE SISTERS

61	Columbia DB 4671	Peek A Boo Moon/Birmingham Rag	4

DON LANG (& HIS "FRANTIC" FIVE)

55	HMV POP 115	Cloudburst/Seventeen (78)	6
56	HMV 7M 354	Four Brothers/I Want You To Be My Baby (solo)	20
56	HMV POP 150	Four Brothers/I Want You To Be My Baby (solo) (78)	5
56	HMV 7M 381	Rock Around The Island/Jumpin' To Conclusions (solo)	20
56	HMV POP 178	Rock Around The Island/Jumpin' To Conclusions (solo) (78)	5
56	HMV 7M 416	Rock And Roll Blues/Stop The World I Wanna Get Off (solo)	18
56	HMV POP 224	Rock And Roll Blues/Stop The World I Wanna Get Off (solo) (78)	5
56	HMV POP 260	Sweet Sue — Just You/Lazy Latin (solo)	12
56	HMV POP 260	Sweet Sue — Just You/Lazy Latin (solo) (78)	5

Don LANG

57	HMV POP 289	Rock Around The Cookhouse/Rock Mister Piper	20
57	HMV POP 289	Rock Around The Cookhouse/Rock Mister Piper (78)	5
57	HMV POP 335	Rock-A-Billy/Come Go With Me (B-side with Skifflers)	18
57	HMV POP 335	Rock-A-Billy/Come Go With Me (B-side with Skifflers) (78)	5
57	HMV POP 350	School Day (Ring! Ring! Goes The Bell)/Six-Five Special	15
57	HMV POP 350	School Day (Ring! Ring! Goes The Bell)/Six-Five Special (78)	10
57	HMV POP 382	White Silver Sands/Again 'N' Again 'N' Again	10
57	HMV POP 382	White Silver Sands/Again 'N' Again 'N' Again (78)	5
57	HMV POP 414	Red Planet Rock/Texas Tambourine	20
57	HMV POP 414	Red Planet Rock/Texas Tambourine (78)	10
58	HMV POP 434	Ramshackle Daddy/6-5 Hand Jive	15
58	HMV POP 434	Ramshackle Daddy/6-5 Hand Jive (78)	10
58	HMV POP 465	Tequila/Junior Hand Jive	12
58	HMV POP 465	Tequila/Junior Hand Jive (78)	5
58	HMV POP 488	Witch Doctor/Cool Baby Cool	7
58	HMV POP 488	Witch Doctor/Cool Baby Cool (78)	5
58	HMV POP 510	Hey Daddy!/The Bird On My Head	7
58	HMV POP 510	Hey Daddy!/The Bird On My Head (78)	5
58	HMV POP 547	Queen Of The Hop/La-Do-Da-Da (solo)	10
58	HMV POP 547	Queen Of The Hop/La-Do-Da-Da (solo) (78)	5
59	HMV POP 585	Wiggle Wiggle/(You Were Only) Teasin' (solo)	7
59	HMV POP 585	Wiggle Wiggle/(You Were Only) Teasin' (solo) (78)	5
59	HMV POP 623	Percy Green/Phineas McCoy (solo)	6
59	HMV POP 623	Percy Green/Phineas McCoy (solo) (78)	5
59	HMV POP 649	A Hoot An' A Holler/See You Friday	7
59	HMV POP 649	A Hoot An' A Holler/See You Friday (78)	5
59	HMV POP 682	Reveille Rock/Frankie And Johnny	7
60	HMV POP 714	Sink The Bismarck!/They Call Him Cliff (solo)	10
60	HMV POP 805	Time Machine/Don't Open That Door	7
62	Decca F 11483	Wicked Women/Play Money (as Don Lang & Boulder Rollers)	5
57	HMV 7EG 8208	ROCK 'N' ROLL (EP)	50
57	HMV DLP 1151	SKIFFLE SPECIAL (10" LP, by Don Lang & His Skiffle Group)	50
58	HMV DLP 1179	INTRODUCING THE HAND JIVE (10" LP)	100
62	Ace Of Clubs ACL 1111	TWENTY TOP-TWENTY TWISTS (LP)	18

(see also Gordon Langhorn)

EDDIE LANG & LONNIE JOHNSON

30s	Parlophone R 1496	Bull Frog Moan/A Handful Of Riffs (78)	35
67	Parlophone PMC 7019	BLUE GUITARS (LP)	40
70	Parlophone PMC 7106	BLUE GUITARS VOLUME 2 (LP)	40

(see also Blind Willie Dunn's Gin Bottle Four)

k.d. lang

87	Sire W 8465	Rose Garden/High Time For A Detour (unissued in U.K.)	
88	Sire W 7841	Sugar Moon/Honky Tonk Medley (p/s)	20
88	Sire W 7841T	Sugar Moon/Honky Tonk Medley/I'm Down To My Last Cigarette (12", p/s)	40
88	Sire W 7697	Our Day Will Come/Three Cigarettes In An Ashtray (live) (p/s)	20
88	Sire W 7697T	Our Day Will Come/Three Cigarettes In An Ashtray (live)/ Johnny Get Angry (live) (12", p/s)	40
90	Warner Bros W 9535	Ridin' The Rails/DARLENE LOVE: Mr Fix-It (p/s)	15
92	Sire W 0100	Constant Craving (Edit)/Barefoot (Rhythmic Version) (p/s)	4
92	Sire W 0100C	Constant Craving (Edit)/Barefoot (Rhythmic Version) (cassette)	4
92	Sire W 0100T	Constant Craving (Edit)/Barefoot (Rhythmic Version)/Season Of Hollow Soul (12", p/s)	7
92	Sire W 0100CD	Constant Craving (Edit)/Barefoot (Rhythmic Version)/Season Of Hollow Soul (CD)	7
92	Sire W 0135TW	Miss Chatalaine (St Tropez Mix)/Miss Chatalaine (St Tropez Edit)/Miss Chatalaine/Miss Chatalaine (Single Edit) (12", p/s, with poster)	8

k.d. lang & ROY ORBISON

89	Virgin VST 1166	Crying/ROY ORBISON: You Got It/The Only One (12", p/s)	10
89	Virgin VSCD 1166	Crying/ROY ORBISON: You Got It/The Only One (CD)	12
89	Virgin VS 1173	Crying/ROY ORBISON: She's A Mystery To Me (p/s)	5
89	Virgin VST 1173	Crying/ROY ORBISON: She's A Mystery To Me/Dream Baby (12", p/s)	8
89	Virgin VSCD 1173	Crying/ROY ORBISON: She's A Mystery To Me/Dream Baby (CD)	10
89	Virgin VS 1193	Blue Bayou (live)/ROY ORBISON: California Blue (p/s)	5
89	Virgin VSC 1193	Blue Bayou (live)/ROY ORBISON: California Blue (cassette)	5
89	Virgin VST 1193	Blue Bayou (live)/ROY ORBISON: California Blue/Leah (12", p/s)	8
89	Virgin VSCD 1193	Blue Bayou (live)/ROY ORBISON: California Blue/Leah/In Dreams (CD)	8
92	Virgin America VUS 63	Crying/ROY ORBISON: Falling (p/s)	4
92	Virgin America VUSC 63	Crying/ROY ORBISON: Falling (cassette)	4
92	Virgin America VUSCD 63	Crying/ROY ORBISON: Falling/Oh Pretty Woman (Edit)/ She's A Mystery To Me (CD)	7
92	Virgin America VUSCX 63	Crying/ROY ORBISON: Falling/Only The Lonely/It's Over (CD)	8

(see also Roy Orbison)

RAY LANG & JAMAICAN ROOM ORCHESTRA

57	Brunswick 05683	Last Train (Biddi-Biddi Bum-Bum)/Keetch (Hey! Bernice)	6

STEVIE LANGE

81	RCA RCA 152	Remember My Name/I Don't Want To Know (p/s)	12
81	RCA LIM 1	Remember My Name/I Don't Want To Know (p/s)	8
83	Jive JIVE 23	Remember My Name/Don't Want To Cry No More (no p/s)	8

LANGFORDS

60s	Torino TSP 341	Send Me An Angel/Candy (p/s, credited to Langford Boys on label)	4

GORDON LANGHORN

55	Decca F 10591	Give A Fool A Chance/Don't Stay Away Too Long	6

(see also Don Lang, Cyril Stapleton)

JERRY LANGLEY
65	Parlophone R 5325	Little Grey Man/Bitter Sweets	4
67	CBS 2935	Joanna Jones/How Long	4

(see also Langleys)

MARY LANGLEY
67	CBS 2862	Stay In My World/Summer Love	4
67	CBS 3032	It Always Rains On Sunday/All My Life Is You	4

(see also Perpetual Langley, Langleys)

PERPETUAL LANGLEY
66	Planet PLF 110	We Wanna Stay Home/So Sad	10
66	Planet PLF 115	Surrender/Two By Two	10

(see also Mary Langley, Langleys)

LANGLEYS
64	Fontana TF 483	Snakes And Ladders/I Wander Everywhere	4
65	Fontana TF 544	Green Island/You Know I Love You	4

(see also Jerry Langley, Mary Langley, Perpetual Langley)

HUW LLOYD LANGTON
83	Flicknife SHARP 015	OUTSIDE THE LAW (LP, with free 7" "Working Time"/"I See You" [FREE 001])	10

(see also Hawkwind)

PHIL LANGTON TRIO
60s	Holyground	PHIL LANGTON TRIO (LP)	20

LESTER LANIN & HIS ORCHESTRA
62	Columbia 33SX 1442	TWISTIN' IN HIGH SOCIETY! (LP)	10

SNOOKY LANSON
50	London L 555	The Old Master Painter/Did You Ever See A Dream Walking? (78)	10
50	London L 682	Roses/Where Are You Gonna Be When The Moon Shines (78)	8
56	London HLD 8223	It's Almost Tomorrow/Why Don't You Write	50
56	London HLD 8223	It's Almost Tomorrow/Why Don't You Write (78)	8
56	London HLD 8236	Last Minute Love/Stop (Let Me Off The Bus)	125
56	London HLD 8236	Last Minute Love/Stop (Let Me Off The Bus) (78)	20
56	London HLD 8249	Seven Days/Tippity Top	125
56	London HLD 8249	Seven Days/Tippity Top (78)	8
56	London HL 7005	Seven Days/Tippity Top (export issue)	20

(see also Eve Young & Snooky Lanson, Teresa Brewer)

MARIO LANZA
52	HMV 7R 130	Be My Love/The Bayou Lullaby	6
52	HMV 7R 131	Serenade/Serenade	6
52	HMV 7R 144	Because You're Mine/The Song Angels Sing	6
52	HMV 7R 147	O Come, All Ye Faithful/Oh! Little Town Of Bethlehem	4
53	HMV 7R 157	Granada/Lolita	4
57	RCA RCA 1026	A Night To Remember/Behold!	4
58	RCA RCA 1045	Seven Hills Of Rome/Come Dance With Me	4
58	RCA RCA 1080	Love In A Home/Do You Wonder	4
58	RCA RCA 1090	Drinking Song/Serenade (Romberg)	4
58	RCA RCA 1094	I'll Walk With God/The Lord's Prayer	4
60	RCA RCA 1166	Because You're Mine/The Donkey Serenade	4
53	HMV ALP 1071	THE GREAT CARUSO (LP, soundtrack)	15
54	HMV ALP 1202	OPERATIC ARIAS (LP)	15
55	HMV BLP 1071	SONGS OF ROMANCE (10" LP)	15
56	HMV ALP 1365	SERENADE (LP, soundtrack)	12
57	HMV BLP 1091	LANZA ON BROADWAY (10" LP)	15
57	HMV BLP 1094	THE TOUCH OF YOUR HAND (10" LP)	16
57	RCA RB 16002	IN A CAVALCADE OF SHOW TUNES (LP)	10
58	RCA RA 13001	THE SEVEN HILLS OF ROME (10" LP)	12
59	RCA RB 16085	SINGS A KISS AND OTHER LOVE SONGS (LP)	10
59	RCA RB 16112	THE GREAT CARUSO (LP, reissue)	10
59	RCA RB 16113	THE STUDENT PRINCE (LP, soundtrack)	10
59	RCA RB 16158	FOR THE FIRST TIME (LP, soundtrack)	10
59	RCA RB 16167	LANZA ON BROADWAY (LP, soundtrack)	10
59	RCA RB 16171/SB 2054	LANZA SINGS CHRISTMAS CAROLS (LP)	10
60s	Readers Digest RDS 6461-6	THE BEST OF MARIO LANZA (6-LP set)	30

GRAHAM LARKBEY
81	Dollar Ga$ DOG 2001	Deat Beat Town/Your Husband Didn't Like It/Make-up	4
81	Dollar Ga$ DOG 2002	Gotta Pull Myself Together/Ystalyfera/Hospital	4

(see also Aunt Fortiscue's Bluesrockers)

LARKS
64	Pye Intl. 7N 25284	The Jerk/Forget Me	18

SAM LARNER
60s	Folkways FG 3507	NOW IS THE TIME FOR FISHING (LP)	15
74	Topic 12T 244	A GARLAND FOR SAM (LP)	10

LARO
60s	Kalypso XX 21	Jamaican Referendum Calypso/Wrong Impressions Of A Soldier	5

WINSTON LARO
70	Downtown DT 461	Goodnight My Love/BOYSIE: I Don't Want To Be Hurt	4

JULIUS LA ROSA
55	London HL 8154	Mobile/Pass It On	18
55	London HLA 8170	Domani/Mama Rosa	18

Julius LA ROSA

55	London HLA 8193	Suddenly There's A Valley/Everytime I Kiss Carrie	18
56	HMV 7M 384	Lipstick And Candy And Rubber-Sole Shoe/Winter In New England	6
56	HMV POP 181	Lipstick And Candy And Rubber-Sole Shoe/Winter In New England (78)	5
56	London HLA 8272	No Other Love/Rosanne	12
56	London HLA 8353	Jingle Bells (Campanelle)/Jingle Dingle	12
58	RCA RCA 1063	Torero/Milano	6
58	Columbia DB 4218	Let Nature Take Its Course/Until He Gets A Girl	4
59	Columbia DB 4287	Where's The Girl/Protect Me	4
60	London HLR 9092	Green Fields/Caress Me	4
54	London RE-P 1005	SINGS (EP)	20
57	London HA-A 2031	JULIUS LA ROSA (LP)	20

LARRY (Marshall) & ALVIN

68	Coxsone CS 7081	Love Got Me/BOB ANDY: Lady With The Bright Light (both sides actually by Glen [Brown] & Dave [Barker])	12
68	Studio One SO 2065	Nanny Goat/ACTIONS: Wepp	12
68	Studio One SO 2067	Can't You Understand/Hush Up	12
69	Studio One SO 2080	Lonely Room (No One To Give Me Love)/You Mean To Me	12

LARRY & JOHNNY

65	Outasite 45 501	Beatle Time Pts 1 & 2	35

(see also Larry Williams & Johnny 'Guitar' Watson)

LARRY & TOMMY

68	Polydor 56741	You've Gotta Bend A Little/Yo-Yo	8

JACK LARSON

61	Top Rank JAR 573	I Love The Way She Laughs/The Hammer Bell Song	4

D.C. LARUE

76	Pye Intl. 7N 25719	Ca-The-Drals/Ca-The-Drals (Long Version)	4

LA'S

87	Go! Discs GOLAS 1	Way Out/Endless (p/s)	7
87	Go! Discs GOLAS 112	Way Out/Knock Me Down/Endless (12", red & silver p/s)	10
87	Go! Discs GOLAR 112	Way Out/Knock Me Down/Endless/Liberty Ship (Demo)/Freedom Song (Demo) (12", blue & silver stickered p/s)	15
88	Go! Discs GOLAS 2	There She Goes/Come In Come Out (red p/s)	4
88	Go! Discs GOLAR 2	There She Goes/Way Out/Who Knows/Come In Come Out (EP, blue p/s)	7
88	Go! Discs GOLAS 212	There She Goes/Come In Come Out/Who Knows/Man I'm Only Human (12", p/s)	8
88	Go! Discs LASCD 2	There She Goes/Come In Come Out/Who Knows/Man I'm Only Human (CD)	8
90	Go! Discs GOLAB 5	There She Goes/Freedom Song (numbered box set with badge & 3 stickers)	4
91	Go! Discs GOLAB 6	Feelin'/IOU (Alternate Version)/Feelin' (Alternate Version)/Doledrum (numbered box set with badge & 3 stickers)	4

DENISE LASALLE

73	Westbound 6146 102	Do Me Right/Your Man And Your Best Friend	5
73	Westbound 6146 105	Trapped By A Thing Called Love/I'm For You	4
74	Janus 6146 002	Trapped By A Thing Called Love/Keep It Coming	4

COUNT LASHER

60s	Kalypso 100 AB	Calypso Cha Cha Cha/Perseverance	4
60s	Kalypso 105 AB	Slide Mongoose/Miss Constance	4

LASSIES & RAY CHARLES SINGERS

56	Brunswick 05571	Sleepy Head/This I Offer You	6

LAST BANDITS

86	Hotwire HWLP 8504	THE LAST BANDITS IN THE WORLD (LP)	10

(see also Swell Maps, Nikki Sudden)

LAST CHANT

81	Chicken Jazz JAZZ 4	Run Of The Dove/Strength Alone/Tradition (p/s)	10

LAST EXIT

75	Wudwink WUD 01	Whispering Voices/Evensong	30

(see also Newcastle Big Band, Police, Sting)

LAST FEW DAYS

86	Touch TG-45	Too Much Is Not Enough/Solemn Warnings/If The Bonds Are Not To Burst (12", p/s)	7

LAST FLIGHT

81	Heavy Metal HEAVY 5	Dance To The Music/I'm Ready (p/s)	8

LAST POETS

71	Douglas DGL 69012	THIS IS MADNESS (LP)	12

LAST RESORT

78	Red Meat RMRS 01	Having Fun?/F.U.2 (die-cut printed paper sleeve)	8

LAST RESORT

80s	own label	Violence In Our Minds/Help Hostage/Soul Boys (p/s)	4

LAST RITES

83	Flicknife FLS 219	We Don't Care/Step Down (p/s)	4

LAST WORD

74	Polydor 2066 429	Keep On Bumping Before You Give Out Of Gas/Funky And Some	6

LAST WORDS

81	Armageddon ARM 2	THE LAST WORDS (LP)	10

YUSEF LATEEF

58	Esquire 32-069	THE SOUNDS OF YUSEF (LP)	15
58	Columbia Clef 33CX 10124	BEFORE DAWN (LP)	15
73	Prestige PR 24007	YUSEF LATEEF (LP)	12
70s	Atlantic K 40359	GENTLE GIANT (LP)	10
74	Atlantic K 50041	PART OF THE SEARCH (LP)	10
74	Milestone ML 47009	THE MANY FACES OF YUSEF LATEEF (LP)	10
75	Atlantic K 60102	10 YEARS HENCE (LP)	10
76	Vogue VJD 512	SAX MASTERS (LP)	10
76	Impulse IMPL 8013	CLUB DATE (LP)	10
76	Impulse IMPL 8036	THE GOLDEN FLUTE (LP)	10
78	CTI CTI 7082	AUTOPHYSIOPSYCHIC (LP)	10

LATIMORE

74	President PT 428	Let's Straighten It Out/Ain't Nobody Gonna Make Me Change	4

LATIN QUARTER

84	Ignition PUMA 8481	Radio Africa/Eddie (p/s)	4

GENE LATTER

66	Decca F 12364	Just A Minute Or Two/Dream Lover	5
66	Decca F 12397	Mother's Little Helper/Please Come Back To Me Again	10
67	CBS 202483	Something Inside Me Died/Don't Go	5
67	CBS 202655	Always/A Woman Called Sorrow	6
67	CBS 2843	A Little Piece Of Leather/Funny Face Girl	8
67	CBS 2986	With A Child's Heart/Ways	6
68	Direction 58-3245	A Tribute To Otis/Bring Your Love Home	4
69	Parlophone R 5800	Help Me Judy, Help Me/On The Highway	4
69	Parlophone R 5815	Tiger Bay/We Can Make Out	4
70	Parlophone R 5833	Someday You'll Need My Love	4
70	Spark SRL 1015	My Life Ain't Easy/Angie (as Gene Latter & Detours)	5
70	Spark SRL 1022	Sign On The Dotted Line/I Love You	8
71	Spark SRL 1031	The Old Iron Bell/Holding A Dream	4
71	Parlophone R 5896	Catch My Soul/Happiness	4
71	Spark SRL 1063	Sign On The Dotted Line/I Love You (reissue)	4
71	Parlophone R 5913	Sing A Song Of Freedom/Too Busy Thinking About My Baby	4
70s	Youngblood YB 1069	All Over Now/Annie's Place	4

STANLEY LAUDAN

58	Oriole CB 1434	Two Guitars/Blue Shawl	5

SIR HARRY LAUDER

59	HMV 7P 235	Harry Lauder Medley (both sides)	5
55	HMV DLP 1089	ROAMING IN THE GLOAMING (10" LP)	10

LAUGH

85	Debris DEB 01	Take Your Time Yeah!/TWANG: What's The Rub (flexidisc with 'Debris' magazine)	6/5

LAUGHING APPLE

81	Autonomy AUT 001	HA HA HEE HEE (EP)	10
81	Autonomy AUT 002	Participate!/Wouldn't You? (foldover p/s)	8
82	Essential ESS 001	Precious Feeling/Celebration (p/s)	10
83	Creation Artefact/Lyntone LYN 12903	Wouldn't You?/PASTELS: I Wonder Why! (live) (33rpm flexidisc, initially free with Legend 7" "'73 In '83" [CRE 001])	5

(see also Biff Bang Pow!)

LAUGHING CLOWNS

82	Pink Melon PM 020	Mad Flies Mad Flies/Mr Uddich (p/s)	6

LAUGHING GAS

70	RCA RCA 2006	All Shapes And Sizes/Opus No. 1	4

CYNDI LAUPER

84	Portrait WA 4290	Time After Time/I'll Kiss You (picture disc)	8
84	Portrait W 4620	She Bop/Witness (p/s)	4
84	Portrait WA 4620	She Bop/Witness (Cyndi-shaped picture disc)	7
85	Epic A 6009	Money Changes Everything/Money Changes Everything (live)/Extra Fun (p/s, reissue)	4
85	Epic TA 6009	Money Changes Everything/Money Changes Everything (live)/Extra Fun (12", p/s, reissue)	12
87	Portrait CYNP 1	What's Going On/What's Going On (Version) (picture disc)	6
89	Epic CYNC 6	Heading West/Insecurious/She Bop (live)/Money Changes Everything (live) (CD, picture disc)	8

(see also Blue Angel)

LAUREL & OWEN

(see under Laurel Aitken)

LAURELS

68	RCA Victor RCA 1741	Sunshine Thursday/Threepence A Tune	4
69	RCA Victor RCA 1836	Making It Groovy/Rainmaker	4

ROD LAUREN

59	RCA RCA 1165	If I Had A Girl/No Wonder	4
59	RCA RCA 1165	If I Had A Girl/No Wonder (78)	10

CHERISSE LAURENCE

86	Arista 108175	L'Amour De Ma Vie/The Love Of My Life (p/s)	4

ZACK LAURENCE (ORCHESTRA)

61	Parlophone R 4802	Teenage Concerto/Saratoga	4
63	Parlophone R 5000	Tempo Seven/Sleeve Shaker	4

MINT VALUE £

| 66 | HMV 7EG 8968 | BEATLE CONCERTO (EP) | 7 |

JOHN LAURENZ
| 55 | London HL 8138 | Goodbye, Stranger, Goodbye/Red Roses | 20 |

CY LAURIE JAZZ BAND
60s	Melodisc M 1479	You Make Me Love You/Dippermouth	4
61	Storyville A 45045	Don't Go Away Nobody/There'll Come A Day	5
55	Esquire 20-037	CY LAURIE JAZZ BAND (10" LP)	12
50s	Esquire 32-008	CY LAURIE JAZZ BAND (LP)	10

LINDA LAURIE
59	London HL 8807	Ambrose/Ooh, What A Lover	7
59	London HL 8807	Ambrose/Ooh, What A Lover (78)	5
60	Top Rank JAR 277	Stay With Me/All Winter Long	6

LAURIE SISTERS
| 60 | MGM MGM 1083 | Don't Forget (To Sign Your Name With ...)/I Surrender Dear | 4 |
| 61 | MGM MGM 1128 | Live It Up/Lonesome And Sorry | 4 |

MISS LAVELL
| 65 | Vocalion VP 9236 | Everybody's Got Somebody/The Best Part Of Me | 12 |

ROGER La VERN & MICRONS
| 63 | Decca F 11791 | Christmas Stocking/Reindeer Ride | 15 |
| 70s | SRT SRTS/CUS/042 | SING-A-LONG PIANO PARTY (maxi-single, p/s) | 5 |
| (see also Tornados) |

BETTY LAVETTE
67	Stateside SS 2015	I Feel Good All Over/Only Your Love Can Save Me	10
68	Pama PM 748	I Feel Good All Over/Only Your Love Can Save Me (reissue)	10
69	Polydor 56786	He Made A Woman Out Of Me/Nearer To You	8
72	Mojo 2092 030	Let Me Down Easy/I Feel Good All Over/What I Don't Know	4
73	Atlantic K 10299	Your Turn To Cry/Soul Tambourine	7
78	Atlantic K 11198	Doin' The Best I Can Pts 1 & 2	7

LAW & ORDER
| 81 | Fetal 110009 | ANYTHING BUT A CRITIC'S CHOICE (EP) | 5 |

AZIE LAWRENCE
60	Starlite ST45 022	West Indians In England/Jump Up (with Carib Serenaders)	6
61	Starlite ST45 041	No Dice/Love In Every Land	5
61	Melodisc M 1563	Jamaica Blues/Come Rumble & Tumble With Me	5
61	Melodisc M 1572	You Didn't Want To Know	5
64	Blue Beat BB 222	So Far Apart/Psalms Of Victory	8

DIANE LAWRENCE
| 67 | Doctor Bird DB 1075 | I Won't Hang Around Like A Hound Dog/Read It Over | 8 |
| 68 | Jolly JY 005 | Treat Me Nice/I'll Be Loving You | 5 |

EDDIE LAWRENCE
| 59 | Coral Q 72361 | The Salesman's Philosopher/Mother Philosopher | 4 |

ELLIOTT LAWRENCE BAND
51	Vogue V 9024	Sixty-Minute Man/Quick (78)	6
52	Vogue V 9032	Lovin' Machine/Don't Leave My Poor Heart Breakin' (78)	6
58	Vogue LAE 12057	PLAYS GERRY MULLIGAN ARRANGEMENTS (LP)	12

GENE LAWRENCE
| 67 | Jump Up JU 505 | Longest Day Meringue/Bachelor Boy | 4 |
| 67 | Jump Up JU 510 | Meringue Triniana/Devil Woman | 4 |

LARRY LAWRENCE (U.S.)
59	Pye Intl. 7N 25042	Goofin' Off/Bongo Boogie (as Larry Lawrence & Band Of Gold)	6
59	Pye Intl. N 25042	Goofin' Off/Bongo Boogie (as Larry Lawrence & Band Of Gold) (78)	10
60	Ember EMB S 106	Squad Car Theme/Jug-A-Roo (with Beatniks, some in art p/s)	10/6

LARRY LAWRENCE (Jamaica)
| 63 | Island WI 091 | Garden Of Eden/DERRICK MORGAN: I'm Sending This Message | 10 |

LEE LAWRENCE (& CORONETS)
53	Decca F 10177	Crying In The Chapel/To Live My Life With You (78)	5
54	Decca F 10285	The Little Mustard Seed/My Love For You	8
54	Decca F 10367	The Story of Tina/For You My Love	8
54	Decca F 10408	The Things I Didn't Do/You Still Mean The Same To Me	7
55	Decca F 10422	My Own True Love (Tara's Theme)/Beware Now!	7
55	Decca F 10438	Lights Of Paris/A Love Like Ours	6
55	Decca F 10485	Wedding Bells And Silver Horse-shoes/Will You Be Mine Alone?	6
55	Columbia SCM 5175	Beyond The Stars/Give Me Your Word	7
55	Columbia SCM 5181	My World Stood Still/Don't Worry	7
55	Columbia SCM 5190	More Than A Millionaire/Overnight	6
55	Columbia SCM 5201	Suddenly There's A Valley/Mi Muchacha (Little Girl)	12
56	Columbia SCM 5228	Young And Foolish/Don't Tell Me Not To Love You	7
56	Columbia SCM 5254	We Believe In Love/Welcome To My Heart	6
56	Columbia SCM 5283	Come Back, My Love/Valley Valparaiso	7
56	Columbia DB 3830	From The Candy Store On The Corner/High Upon A Mountain	10
57	Columbia DB 3855	Don't Nobody Move/Rock 'n' Roll Opera	18
57	Columbia DB 3855	Don't Nobody Move/Rock 'n' Roll Opera (78)	5
57	Columbia DB 3885	Your Love Is My Love/By You, By You, By You	7
57	Columbia DB 3922	Sold To The Man With The Broken Heart/Chapel Of The Roses	6
57	Columbia DB 3981	His Servant/Lonely Ballerina	6
59	Top Rank JAR 175	The Man I Could Be/Be My Love	4
53	Decca LF 1132	PRESENTING LEE LAWRENCE (10" LP)	12

STEVE LAWRENCE

53	Parlophone MSP 6038	Say It Isn't True/This Night (Madalena) (as Steve & Bernie Lawrence)	10
54	Parlophone MSP 6080	Remember Me (You Taught Me To Love)/Too Little Time	10
54	Parlophone MSP 6106	You Can't Hold A Memory In Your Arms/King For A Day	10
55	Vogue Coral Q 72114	Open Up The Gates Of Mercy/My Impression Of Janie	8
56	Vogue Coral Q 72133	Speedo/The Chicken And The Hawk	12
56	Vogue Coral Q 72133	Speedo/The Chicken And The Hawk (78)	18
57	Vogue Coral Q 72228	The Banana Boat Song/If You Would Say You're Mine	8
57	Vogue Coral Q 72243	Party Doll/Pum-Pa-Lum (The Bad Donkey)	8
57	Vogue Coral Q 72264	Fabulous/Can't Wait For The Summer (with Dick Jacobs Band)	8
57	Vogue Coral Q 72281	Fraulein/Blue Rememberin' You	8
57	Vogue Coral Q 72286	Never Mind/Long Before I Knew You	6
58	Coral Q 72304	Geisha Girl/I Don't Know	4
58	Coral Q 72335	Those Nights At The Round Table (with Guinevere)/Stranger In Mexico	4
59	Coral Q 72353	These Things Are Free/I Only Have Eyes For You	5
59	HMV POP 604	Only Love Me (Angelina)/Loving Is A Way Of Living	4
60	HMV POP 689	Pretty Blue Eyes/You're Nearer	6
60	HMV POP 689	Pretty Blue Eyes/You're Nearer (78)	35
60	HMV POP 726	Footsteps/You Don't Know	6
60	HMV POP 726	Footsteps/You Don't Know (78)	35
60	Top Rank JAR 416	Say It Isn't True/My Shawl	4
60	HMV POP 763	Why, Why, Why/You're Everything Wonderful	4
60	London HLT 9166	Girls, Girls, Girls/Little Boy Blue	4
60	HMV POP 795	Going Steady/Come Back, Silly Girl	4
61	HMV POP 914	In Time/Oh How You Lied	4
61	HMV POP 950	Somewhere Along The Way/While There's Still Time	4
62	CBS AAG 101	The Lady Wants To Twist/Tell Her I Said Hello	4
59	Coral FEP 2010	HERE'S STEVE LAWRENCE No. 1 (EP)	7
59	Coral FEP 2012	HERE'S STEVE LAWRENCE No. 2 (EP)	7
60	HMV CLP 1326	SWING SOFTLY WITH ME (LP)	10
60	Top Rank BUY 033	STEVE LAWRENCE (LP)	10
61	HMV CLP 1462	THE STEVE LAWRENCE SOUND (LP, also stereo CSD 1374)	12
62	HMV CLP 1504	PORTRAIT OF MY LOVE (LP, also stereo CSD 1404)	12
63	CBS (S)BPG 62088	COME WALTZ WITH ME (LP)	10
63	United Artists (S)ULP 1022	LAWRENCE GOES LATIN (LP)	10
63	CBS BPG 62124	WINNERS (LP)	10
64	Coral LVA 9219	SONGS EVERYBODY KNOWS (LP)	12

(see also Eydie Gorme & Steve Lawrence)

BILLY (M.) LAWRIE

69	Polydor 56363	Roll Over Beethoven/Come Back Joanna (as Billy M. Lawrie)	25
73	RCA RCA 2439	Rock And Roller/Shalee Shala	4
73	RCA SF 8395	SHIP IMAGINATION (LP)	10

DEBRA LAWS

81	Elektra K 12529	On My Own/As Long As We're Together (p/s)	4
81	Elektra K 12529T	On My Own/As Long As We're Together (12", p/s)	8
81	Elektra K 52281	VERY SPECIAL (LP)	10

ELOISE LAWS

69	CBS 4056	I'd Do It All Again/To Know Him Is To Love Him	4
70	CBS 4990	You Make Me Feel Like Someone/The Only Boy In My Life	5
77	Invictus INV 5247	Love Goes Deeper Than That/Camouflage	4

RONNIE LAWS

76	Blue Note BNXW 7004	Always There/Tidal Wave	7
79	Blue Note UP 36497	Always There/Tidal Wave (reissue)	4
79	Blue Note 12UP 36497	Always There/Tidal Wave (12")	7
75	Blue Note BNLA 452	PRESSURE SENSITIVE (LP)	12
76	Blue Note UAG 20002	PRESSURE SENSITIVE (LP, reissue)	10
76	Blue Note UAG 20007	FEVER (LP)	10
77	Blue Note UAG 30079	FRIENDS AND STRANGERS (LP)	10
78	Blue Note UAG 30204	FLAME (LP)	10

LAWSON-HAGGART ROCKIN' BAND

59	Brunswick OE 9451	BOPPING AT THE HOP (EP)	25
53	Brunswick LA 8576	JELLY ROLL'S JAZZ (10" LP)	15
53	Brunswick LA 8580	BLUES ON THE RIVER (10" LP)	15
53	Brunswick LA 8593	KING OLIVER'S JAZZ (10" LP)	15
54	Brunswick LA 8635	RAGTIME JAMBOREE (10" LP)	15
54	Brunswick LA 8639	WINDY CITY JAZZ (10" LP)	15
55	Brunswick LA 8703	SOUTH OF THE MASON-DIXON LINE (10" LP)	15
59	Brunswick STA 3010	BOPPING AT THE HOP (LP)	30

JULIET LAWSON

72	Sovereign SVNA 7257	BOO (LP)	30

(see also Trees)

SHIRLEY LAWSON

70	Soul City SC 108	The Star/One More Chance	20

JOHN LAWTON

75	Purple PUR 128	Little Chalk Blue/RONNIE DIO: Sitting In A Dream (featuring Roger Glover & Guests)	4

(see also Roger Glover, Ronnie Dio)

LOU LAWTON

67	Ember EMB S 232	Doin' The Philly Dog/I Am Searching	15
67	Speciality SPE 1005	I'm Just A Fool/Wrapped In A Dream	18

MINT VALUE £

LAXTON & OLIVER
69	Blue Cat BS 168	Wickeder/Stay In My Arms	6

LAY-A-BAHTS
60	Parlophone R 4641	Fings Ain't Wot They Used T'be/Layin' Abaht/The Ceiling	4

DEKE LAYNE
66	Fontana TF 774	Ringing Reindeer/Cross & Chain	4
67	Fontana TF 797	How Do You Think I Feel/I'll Be So Glad To Get Back Home	4

OSSIE LAYNE
65	R&B MRB 5006	Come Back/Never Answer That 'Phone	7

EDDIE LAYTON
58	Mercury 7MT 221	Over The Waves/Bright Lights Over Brussels	4
59	Mercury AMT 1064	Duck Walk/Doodles	6

TEDDY LAYTON JAZZ BAND
58	Parlophone R 4411	Down By The Riverside/Wooden Joe's Weary Blues	5

KEN LAZ(A)RUS (& CREW)
65	Island WI 220	Funny (as Ken Lazrus)/BYRON LEE & DRAGONAIRES: Walk Like A Dragon	8
70	London HLJ 10301	Monkey Man/Bongo Nyah	4
70	London HA-J 8412	REGGAE SCORCHER (LP, unissued)	

LAZY SMOKE
80s	Heyoka	CORRIDOR OF FACES (LP, reissue of U.S. LP)	15

BARBARA LEA
56	London HB-U 1058	A WOMAN IN LOVE (10" LP)	12

LEADBELLY (HUDDIE LEDBETTER)
40s	HMV MH 190	Alabama Bound/Pick A Bale Of Cotton (78)	20
50	Capitol CL 13282	Eagle Rock Rag/Backwater Blues (78)	12
50	Tempo R 11	Becky Deem, She Was A Gamblin' Gal/Pig Meat Papa (78)	8
50	Tempo R 13	Four Day Worry Blues/New Black Snake Moan (78)	8
5-	Tempo L 16	Diggin' My Potatoes/Defense Blues (78)	8
51	Melodisc 1140	How Long/Good Morning Blues (78)	10
51	Melodisc 1151	Goodnight Irene/Ain't You Glad (78)	10
51	Melodisc 1187	On A Monday/John Henry (78)	10
50s	Jazz Collector L 2	Packin' Trunk Blues/Honey I'm All Out And Down (78)	5
50s	Jazz Collector L 108	New Black Snake Moan/Fore Day Worry Blues (78)	5
50s	Jazz Collector L 124	Pig Meat Papa/Becky Beem (78)	5
56	Melodisc EPM7 63	HOW LONG BLUES (EP)	14
58	Melodisc EPM7 77	LEADBELLY (EP)	14
58	Melodisc EPM7 82	SEE SEE RIDER (EP)	14
59	Melodisc EPM7 87	PARTY PLAYS AND SONGS (EP)	12
59	RCA RCX 146	ROCK ISLAND LINE (EP)	10
61	Capitol EAP1 1821	HUDDIE LEDBETTER'S BEST No. 1 (EP)	10
61	Capitol EAP4 1821	HUDDIE LEDBETTER'S BEST No. 2 (EP)	10
61	Capitol EAP1 20111	LEADBELLY (EP)	10
60s	Storyville SEP 337	LEADBELLY (EP)	10
60s	Storyville SEP 387	STORYVILLE BLUES ANTHOLOGY VOL. 7 (EP)	10
53	Capitol LC 6597	LEADBELLY SINGS CLASSICS IN JAZZ (10" LP)	25
57	Melodisc MLP 511	LEADBELLY VOL. 1 (10" LP, green & silver labels)	20
57	Melodisc MLP 512	LEADBELLY VOL. 2 (10" LP, green & silver labels)	20
58	Melodisc MLP 515	LEADBELLY VOL. 3 (10" LP, green & silver labels)	20
58	Melodisc MLP 517	PLAYS PARTY SONGS (10" LP, green & silver labels)	20
58	Melodisc MLP 12-107	THE SAGA OF LEADBELLY (LP, green & silver or blue & black label)	20
59	Melodisc MLP 12-113	LEADBELLY'S LAST SESSIONS VOLUME 2 PART 1 (LP)	20
59	Melodisc MLP 12-114	LEADBELLY'S LAST SESSIONS VOLUME 2 PART 2 (LP)	20
62	Storyville SLP 124	A DEMON OF A MAN — BLUES ANTHOLOGY (LP)	15
60s	Storyville SLP 139	LEADBELLY 2 — T.B. BLUES (LP)	15
63	Capitol T 1821	HIS GUITAR, HIS VOICE, HIS PIANO: HUDDIE LEDBETTER'S BEST (LP)	12
63	RCA Victor RD 7567	GOOD MORNING BLUES (LP)	15
65	Verve (S)VLP 5002	TAKE THIS HAMMER (LP)	15
66	Elektra EKL 301/2	THE LIBRARY OF CONGRESS RECORDINGS (3-LP)	20
67	Verve (S)VLP 5011	KEEP YOUR HANDS OFF HER (LP)	15
69	Xtra XTRA 1046	LEADBELLY SINGS FOLK SONGS (LP)	20
69	Xtra XTRA 1126	SHOUT ON (LP)	20
70	CBS 64103	LEADBELLY (LP)	12
70s	Xtra XTRAD 1017	THE LEADBELLY BOX SET (2-LP)	15
70s	Storyville 616 003	IN THE EVENING WHEN THE SUN GOES DOWN (LP)	12
70s	Storyville 616 004	GOODNIGHT IRENE (LP)	12
70s	Ember CW 132	LEADBELLY (LP)	10

LEADBELLY/BLIND LEMON JEFFERSON
62	Jazz Collector JEL 124	THE MALE BLUES VOLUME 8 (EP)	10

(see also Blind Lemon Jefferson)

HARRY LEADER BAND
65	Parlophone R 5386	Dragon Fly/Rush Hour	5

LEADERBEATS
60	Top Rank JAR 405	Dance, Dance, Dance/Washington Square	4

LEADERS (U.K.)
65	Fontana TF 602	Night People/Love Will Find A Way	6

LEADERS (Jamaica)
68	Amalgamated AMG 804	Tit For Tat (actually by Lynn Taitt & Jets)/MARVETTS: You Take Too Long	8

LEADING FIGURES
67	Deram DML/SML 1006	OSCILLATION 67! (LP)	15
67	Ace Of Clubs SCL 1225	SOUND AND MOVEMENT (LP)	12

(see also Jon Lord, Deep Purple)

LEAF HOUND
71	Decca SKL-R 5094	GROWERS OF MUSHROOM (LP)	700

(see also Brunning Sunflower Blues Band, Black Cat Bones, Atomic Rooster, Cactus, Headbangers)

LEAGUE OF GENTLEMEN
65	Columbia DB 7666	Each Little Falling Tear/And I Do Now	15
66	Planet PLF 109	How Can You Tell/How Do They Know	25

(see also Giles Giles & Fripp)

LEAH
73	GM GMS 10	Arise Sir Henry/Uptight Basil	4

(see also Pete Dello, Red Herring)

JOE LEAHY (ORCHESTRA)
55	Parlophone MSP 6149	Desiree/Milano	4
55	Parlophone MSP 6168	Green Fire/Secretly Mine	4

MIKE LEANDER ORCHESTRA
64	Decca F 11849	The Heroes/Rang A Tang	4

ENRICO LEANDROS ORCHESTRA
59	Oriole CB 1487	Tristesse Dance/Take Me Dreaming	4

VICKY LEANDROS
72	Philips 6000 025	I Am/Love Tell Me Where Is Your Home	8
72	Philips 6000 049	Come What May (Apres Toi)/Take A Little Time	5
73	Philips 6000 066	Country Freedom/Mouth Organ Boy	12
73	Philips 6000 081	The Love In Your Eyes/You Answered My Prayer	4
73	Philips 6000 111	When Bouzoukis Played/Jacques	4
74	Philips 6000 129	Dreams Are Good Friends/Lovin' And Tenderness	12
74	Philips 6000 408	Danny, Teach Me To Dance/Love Me Tender	4
75	Philips 6000 169	More Than That/Papa's Knee	8
72	Philips 6303 019	I AM (LP)	10
74	Philips 6303 062	DREAMS ARE GOOD FRIENDS (LP)	10

BOB LEAPER
65	Pye 7N 15700	High Wire/The Lost World	6
64	Decca LK 4639	BIG BAND, BEATLE SONGS (LP)	10

LEAPERS CREEPERS SLEEPERS
66	Island WI 275	Ba Boo/Precious Words	8

KEVIN 'KING' LEAR
67	Polydor BM 56203	Count Me Out/Pretty Woman	15
68	Page One POF 087	Power Of Love/Mr. Pearly	7
68	Page One POF 109	Cry Me A River/Shoe Shine Sam	12
69	Page One POF 132	The Snake/Man In The Funnies	10

MIKE LEASE
66	Pye 7N 17174	The Many Faces Of Love/Morning	4

LEATHERCOATED MINDS
67	Fontana (S)TL 5412	A TRIP DOWN THE SUNSET STRIP (LP)	50

(see also J.J. Cale)

LEATHER NUN
79	Industrial IR 006	SIOW DEATH (EP)	12
84	Subterranean SUB 40	Prime Mover/F.F.A. (p/s)	4
87	Wire WRMS 014	I Can Smell Your Thoughts (Remix)/Falling Apart/Bonus Track: 506 (Re-visited) (12", p/s, with shrinkwrapped banned poster)	7

BILL LEATHERWOOD
60	Top Rank JAR 506	The Long Walk/My Foolish Heart	4

LEA VALLEY SKIFFLE GROUP
57	Esquire 10-508	Streamline Train/Railroad Bill (78)	5
58	Esquire 10-518	I'm Gonna Walk And Talk With Jesus/Oh Mary, Don't You ... (78)	5
58	Esquire EP 163	LEA VALLEY SKIFFLE GROUP (EP)	20

LEAVES
66	Fontana TF 713	Hey Joe/Funny Little World	20

OTIS LEAVILL
70	Atlantic 2091 015	I Love You/I Need You	4
70	Atlantic 2091 035	Love Uprising/Glad I Met You	4

JOHN LEDINGHAM
68	Pye 7N 17488	Love Is A Toy/Thank You Mrs. Gilbert	4

(see also Jonathan Kelly)

LED ZEPPELIN
69	Atlantic 584 269	Communication Breakdown/Good Times, Bad Times (unreleased)	200
69	Atlantic 584 309	Whole Lotta Love/Livin' Lovin' Maid (She's A Woman) (withdrawn)	350
70	Atlantic 2091 043	Immigrant Song/Hey, Hey What Can I Do? (unreleased)	
73	Atlantic K 10296	D'Yer Maker/Grunge (unreleased, promos only)	75
79	Swansong DC 1	Trampled Underfoot/Black Country Woman (promo freebie, company sleeve)	15
69	Atlantic 588 171	LED ZEPPELIN (LP, turquoise lettering on cover)	35
69	Atlantic 588 171	LED ZEPPELIN (LP, orange lettering on cover)	15
69	Atlantic 588 198	LED ZEPPELIN II (LP, light brown cover, original Polydor pressing)	15
70	Atlantic 2401 002	LED ZEPPELIN III (LP, rotating wheel cover, 'Do What Thou Wilt' in run-off)	15

LED ZEPPELIN

71	Atlantic 2401 012	LED ZEPPELIN IV (FOUR SYMBOLS) (LP, original Polydor pressing)	12

(all the above LPs originally came with red/plum labels)

76	Swansong SSK 59402	PRESENCE (LP, original shrinkwrapped package)	10
78	Atlantic K 50008	LED ZEPPELIN IV (FOUR SYMBOLS) (LP, lilac vinyl reissue)	30
78	Atlantic K 50008	LED ZEPPELIN IV (FOUR SYMBOLS) (LP, picture disc)	15
79	Swansong SSK 59410	IN THROUGH THE OUT DOOR (6-LP set, covers labelled A to F)	100
88	Atlantic K 50008/C 88 1-4	FOUR SYMBOLS (LP, HMV box set, numbered)	20
88	Atlantic K 50008/C 88 1-4	FOUR SYMBOLS (CD, HMV box set, numbered)	25

(see also Jimmy Page, Robert Plant, John Paul Jones, Band Of Joy, Listen)

ARTHUR LEE

72	A&M AMLS 64356	VINDICATOR (LP)	15
81	Beggars Banquet BEGA 26	ARTHUR LEE (LP)	10

(see also Love)

BENNY LEE (& KEN-TONES)

56	Parlophone MSP 6214	Love Plays The Strings Of My Banjo (with Ken-Tones)/Born To Sing The Blues	6
56	Parlophone MSP 6252	Sweet Heartaches/How Long Has This Been Going On?	6
56	Parlophone R 4245	Rock 'N' Rollin' Santa Claus/Life Was Made For Livin' (with Ken-Tones)	12

(see also Ken-Tones)

BRENDA LEE

56	Brunswick 05628	I'm Gonna Lasso Santa Claus/Christy Christmas (tri, as Little Brenda Lee)	90
56	Brunswick 05628	I'm Gonna Lasso Santa Claus/Christy Christmas (78)	20
57	Brunswick 05685	Love You Til I Die/Dynamite (tri-centre, with Anita Kerr Singers)	70
57	Brunswick 05685	Love You Til I Die/Dynamite (78)	20
57	Brunswick 05720	Ain't That Love/One Teenager To Another (tri, with Anita Kerr Singers)	75
57	Brunswick 05720	Ain't That Love/One Teenager To Another (78)	20
58	Brunswick 05755	Ring-A-My-Phone/Little Jonah (Rock On Your Little Steel Guitar) (triangular centre)	65
58	Brunswick 05755	Ring-A-My-Phone/Little Jonah (Rock On Your Little Steel Guitar) (78)	20
58	Decca BM 31186	Fairyland/One Step At A Time (tri-centre, export issue)	50
59	Brunswick 05780	Bill Bailey, Won't You Please Come Home/Hummin' The Blues Over You (triangular or round centre)	15/12
59	Brunswick 05780	Bill Bailey, Won't You Please Come Home/Hummin' The Blues Over You (78)	25
60	Brunswick 05819	Sweet Nuthin's/Weep No More My Baby (triangular or round centre)	20/8
60	Brunswick 05819	Sweet Nuthin's/Weep No More My Baby (78)	25
60	Brunswick 05823	Let's Jump The Broomstick/Rock-A-Bye Baby Blues	7
60	Brunswick 05833	I'm Sorry/That's All You Gotta Do	10
60	Brunswick 05839	I Want To Be Wanted/Just A Little	6
61	Brunswick 05847	Emotions/I'm Learning About Love	4
61	Brunswick 05849	You Can Depend On Me/It's Never Too Late	4
61	Brunswick 05854	Dum Dum/Eventually	4
61	Brunswick 05860	Fool No. 1/Anybody But Me	4
62	Brunswick 05864	Break It To Me Gently/So Deep	4
62	Brunswick 05867	Speak To Me Pretty/Lover, Come Back To Me	4
62	Brunswick 05871	Here Comes That Feeling/Everybody Loves Me But You	4
62	Brunswick 05876	It Started All Over Again/Heart In Hand	4
62	Brunswick 05880	Rockin' Around The Christmas Tree/Papa Noel	6
63	Brunswick 05882	All Alone Am I/Save All Your Lovin' For Me	4
63	Brunswick 05886	Losing You/He's So Heavenly	4
63	Brunswick 05891	I Wonder/My Whole World Is Falling Down	4
63	Brunswick 05896	Sweet Impossible You/The Grass Is Greener	4
64	Brunswick 05899	As Usual/Lonely Lonely Lonely Me	4
64	Brunswick 05903	Think/The Waiting Game	4
64	Brunswick 05911	Alone With You/My Dreams	4
64	Brunswick 05915	Is It True/What'd I Say	6
64	Brunswick 05921	Christmas Will Be Just Another Lonely Day/Winter Wonderland	4
65	Brunswick 05927	Thanks A Lot/Just Behind The Rainbow	4
65	Brunswick 05933	Truly, Truly True/I Still Miss Someone	4
65	Brunswick 05936	Too Many Rivers/No One	4
65	Brunswick 05943	Rusty Bells/If You Don't	4
66	Brunswick 05957	Too Little Time/Time And Time Again	4
66	Brunswick 05963	Ain't Gonna Cry No More/It Takes One To Know One	4
66	Brunswick 05967	Coming On Strong/You Keep Coming Back To Me	7
67	Brunswick 05970	Ride, Ride, Ride/Lonely People Do Foolish Things	4
67	Brunswick 05976	Where's The Melody/Born To Be By Your Side	7
68	Decca AD 1003	That's All Right/Baby, Won't You Please Come Home (export issue)	12
68	MCA MU 1001	That's All Right/Baby, Won't You Please Come Home	4
68	MCA MU 1021	Let's Jump The Broomstick/All Alone Am I	4
69	MCA MU 1063	Johnny One Time/I Must Have Been Out Of My Mind	4
70	MCA MU 1115	Johnny One Time/Bring Me Sunshine	4
72	MCA MU 1155	Everybody's Reaching Out For Someone/If This Is Our Last Time	4
73	MCA MU 1189	Nobody Wins/We Had A Good Thing Going	4
73	MCA MU 1219	Sunday Sunrise/Must I Believe	4
59	Brunswick OE 9462	ROCK THE BOP (EP, green p/s & tri centre or blue p/s & round centre)	40/30
62	Brunswick OE 9482	PRETEND (EP)	20
62	Brunswick OE 9488	SPEAK TO ME PRETTY (EP)	15
63	Brunswick OE 9492	ALL ALONE AM I (EP)	15
64	Brunswick OE 9499	BRENDA LEE'S TRIBUTE TO AL JOLSON (EP)	15
65	Brunswick OE 9510	FOUR FROM '64 (EP)	15
58	Brunswick LAT 8319	GRANDMA WHAT GREAT SONGS YOU SANG (LP)	40
60	Brunswick LAT 8347	MISS DYNAMITE (LP)	30
61	Brunswick LAT 8360	THIS IS BRENDA (LP)	20
61	Brunswick LAT 8376	EMOTIONS (LP, also stereo STA 3044)	18/22
61	Brunswick LAT 8383	ALL THE WAY (LP, also stereo STA 3048)	15/18
61	Brunswick LAT 8396	SINCERELY (LP, also stereo STA 3056)	18/20
62	Brunswick LAT/STA 8516	BRENDA, THAT'S ALL (LP, mono/stereo)	18/20

MINT VALUE £

62	Brunswick LAT/STA 8530	ALL ALONE AM I (LP, mono/stereo)	12/15
63	Ace of Hearts AH 59	LOVE YOU (LP)	20
63	Brunswick LAT/STA 8548	LET ME SING (LP, mono/stereo)	15/18
64	Brunswick LAT/STA 8576	BY REQUEST (LP, mono/stereo)	18/20
64	Brunswick LAT/STA 8590	MERRY CHRISTMAS FROM BRENDA (LP, mono/stereo)	20/25
65	Brunswick LAT/STA 8603	TOP TEEN HITS (LP, mono/stereo)	18/20
65	Brunswick LAT 8614	THE VERSATILE BRENDA LEE (LP)	15
65	Brunswick LAT/STA 8622	TOO MANY RIVERS (LP, mono/stereo)	18/20
66	Brunswick LAT/STA 8649	BYE BYE BLUES (LP, mono/stereo)	15/18
67	Brunswick LAT/STA 8672	COMING ON STRONG (LP, mono/stereo)	18/20
68	MCA MUP(S) 306	REFLECTIONS IN BLUE (LP)	15
68	MCA MUP(S) 321	CALL ME (LP)	15
68	MCA MUP(S) 322	THE GOOD LIFE (LP)	10
68	MCA MUP(S) 330	MERRY CHRISTMAS FROM BRENDA LEE (LP)	12
68	MCA MUP(S) 332	BRENDA AND PETE — FOR THE FIRST TIME (LP, with Pete Fountain)	10
70	MCA MUP(S) 396	JOHNNY ONE TIME (LP)	12
71	MCA MUPS 423	MEMPHIS PORTRAIT (LP)	10
72	MCA MUPS 460	A WHOLE LOTTA BRENDA LEE (LP)	10
73	MCA MUPS 485	BRENDA (LP)	10

BYRON LEE & DRAGONAIRES

60	Blue Beat BB 2	Dumplin's/BUDDY DAVIDSON: Kissin' Gal	10
61	Blue Beat BB 28	Mash Mr. Lee/KEITH LYNN: Help Me Forget	10
61	Starlite ST45 045	Joy Ride/Over The Rainbow	8
64	Parlophone R 5124	River Bank/Musical Communion	7
64	Parlophone R 5125	Sour Apples/Hanging Up My Heart	7
64	Parlophone R 5140	Sammy Dead/Say Bye Bye (both sides actually by Eric Morris with Byron Lee)	7
64	Parlophone R 5177	Beautiful Garden/Too Late	7
64	Parlophone R 5182	Come Back/Jamaica Ska	7
64	MGM MGM 1256	Night Train From Jamaica/Ska Dee Wah	7
65	Island WI 222	Dan Is The Man/BLUES BUSTERS: Wings Of A Dove	10
66	Doctor Bird DB 1003	Sloopy/Gold Finger	10
67	Pyramid PYR 6015	Sloopy/Gold Finger (reissue)	6
68	Trojan TR 624	Soul Limbo/The Whistling Song	5
68	Trojan TR 631	Mr Walker/Sunset Jump Up	4
69	Duke DU 39	Elizabethan Reggae/Soul Serenade	4
69	Major Minor MM 615	Every Day Will Be Like A Holiday/Oh What A Feeling	4
71	Dynamic DYN 409	My Sweet Lord/Shock Attack	4
71	Dynamic DYN 414	Way Back Home/Version	4
72	Dynamic DYN 435	Make It Reggae/DENNIS ALCAPONE: Go Johnny Go	4
73	Dragon DRA 1008	In The Mood/Black On	4
65	Atlantic AET 6014	SKA TIME (EP, as Byron Lee Ska Kings)	15
64	Island ILP 905	CARIBBEAN JOY RIDE (LP)	35
69	Trojan TTL 5	ROCKSTEADY EXPLOSION (LP)	10
70	Trojan TBL 110	REGGAE BLAST OFF (LP)	10
71	Trojan TRL 26	REGGAY SPLASHDOWN (LP)	10
72	Trojan TRL 40	REGGAY HOT COOL AND EASY (LP)	10

CURTIS LEE

60	Top Rank JAR 317	With All My Heart (I Love You)/Pure Love	25
61	London HLX 9313	Pledge Of Love/Then I'll Know	10
61	London HLX 9397	Pretty Little Angel Eyes/Gee How I Wish You Were Here	10
61	London HLX 9445	Under The Moon Of Love/Beverly Jean	12
62	London HLX 9533	A Night At Daddy Gee's/Just Another Fool	10
67	CBS 2717	Get My Bag/Everybody's Going Wild (as Curtis Lee & K.C.P.s)	20
72	Stateside SS 2208	Under The Moon Of Love/Beverly Jean (reissue)	4

DAVE LEE (& STAGGERLEES)

63	Decca F 11600	Take Four/Five To Four On	6
63	Oriole CB 1864	Dance Dance Dance/Love Me (as Dave Lee & Staggerlees)	5
63	Oriole CB 1907	Sweet & Lovely/Forever And Always (as Dave Lee & Staggerlees)	5
66	Fontana TF 723	Adam Adamant/Georgie's Theme (as Dave Lee & His Orchestra)	7

DAVID H. LEE

| 69 | Morgan MR 1 | Johnny's Eyes/You're The Only One | 4 |

DEREK LEE

| 66 | Parlophone R 5468 | Girl/You've Done Something To My Heart | 6 |

DICK LEE

53	Columbia SCM 5066	All I Want Is A Chance/The Show Is Ended	4
53	Columbia SCM 5078	I Thought You Might Be Lonely/Happy Bells	4
54	Columbia SCM 5094	Book/Stay In My Arms Cinderella	4

DICKIE LEE

59	MGM MGM 1013	A Penny A Kiss — A Penny A Hug/Bermuda	25
62	Mercury AMT 1190	Patches/More Or Less	5
62	Mercury AMT 1196	I Saw Linda Yesterday/The Girl I Can't Forget	8
62	Mercury AMT 1200	Don't Wanna Think About Paula/Just A Friend	5
65	Stateside SS 433	Laurie (Strange Things Happen)/Party Doll (as Dickey Lee)	4
65	Stateside SS 464	The Girl From Peyton Place/A Girl I Used To Know (as Dickey Lee)	4

DINAH LEE

| 65 | Aladdin WI 606 | I'll Forgive You Then Forget You/Nitty Gritty | 6 |
| 65 | Aladdin WI 608 | I Can't Believe What You Say/Pushin' A Good Thing Too Far | 7 |

DON (TONY) LEE

67	Island WI 3081	Lee's Special (as Don Lee)/UNIQUES: Never Let Me Go	7
68	Big Shot BI 504	It's Reggae Time (as Don Tony Lee)/ERROL DUNKLEY: The Clamp Is On	6
68	Doctor Bird DB 1106	Lee's Special (as Don Tony Lee)/LLOYD & GROOVERS: My Heart And Soul	10

Don (Tony) LEE

| 68 | Island WI 3160 | It's Reggae Time (as Don Tony Lee)/ERROL DUNKLEY: The Clamp Is On ......8 |
| 69 | Unity UN 519 | Peyton Place/Red Gal In The Ring (as Don Tony Lee) ....4 |

EDNA LEE
| 68 | President PT 175 | I Really Think I'm Crying 'Cause I Love You/Don't Let My Friends See What You Do ....4 |

(Freddie) 'FINGERS' LEE (& UPPER HAND)
65	Fontana TF 619	The Friendly Undertaker/Little Bit More (as 'Fingers' Lee) 15
66	Fontana TF 655	I'm Gonna Buy Me A Dog/I Can't Drive (as 'Fingers' Lee) 12
66	Columbia DB 8002	Bossy Boss/Don't Run Away (as Fingers Lee & Upper Hand) 7

(see also At Last The 1958 Rock & Roll Show)

GEORGE LEE
| 69 | Downtown DT 443 | Talking Boss/Jungle Fever ....4 |

JACK LEE
| 82 | Disclexia DXL 002 | Hangin' On The Telephone/Women (p/s) ....4 |

JACKIE LEE (U.K.)
| 55 | Decca F 10550 | I Was Wrong/For As Long As I Live ....4 |

JACKIE LEE (U.K.)
65	Decca F 12068	I Cry Alone/Cause I Love Him 4
67	Decca F 12663	Born To Lose/Saying Goodbye 4
65	Columbia DB 7685	Lonely Clown/Love Is Gone 4
66	Columbia DB 7860	I Know, Know, Know I'll Never Love/So Love Me 4
66	Columbia DB 8052	The Town I Live In/You Too 4

(see also Jacky, Jackie Lee & Raindrops)

JACKIE LEE & RAINDROPS (U.K.)
62	Oriole CB 1702	I Was The Last One To Know/There's No One In The Whole World 5
62	Oriole CB 1757	Party Lights/Midnight 5
63	Oriole CB 1800	End Of The World/Goodbye Is Such A Lonely Word 5
63	Philips BF 1283	Down Our Street/My Heart Is Your Heart (as Jackie & Raindrops) 4
64	Philips BF 1328	Here I Go Again/Come On Dream Come On (as Jackie & Raindrops) 4

(see also Jacky, Jackie Lee [U.K.], Raindrops)

JACKIE LEE (U.S.)
| 60 | Top Rank JAR 286 | Rancho/Like Sunset ....6 |

JACKIE LEE (U.S.)
65	Fontana TF 646	The Duck/Let Your Conscience Be Your Guide 12
68	London HLM 10233	The Duck/Dancing In The Street 6
70	Jay Boy BOY 26	Do The Temptation Walk/The Shotgun And The Duck 4
70	Jay Boy BOY 28	Would You Believe/You're Everything 4
72	Jay Boy BOY 66	Oh! My Darlin'/Don't Be Ashamed 4
73	Jay Boy BOY 76	African Boo-Ga-Loo/Bring It Home 4
73	Contempo C 5	The Duck Pts 1 & 2 4
85	Kent TOWN 107	Darkest Days/EDDIE BISHOP: Call Me 4
67	London HA-M 8336	THE DUCK (LP) 15
71	Joy JOYS 192	THE DUCK (LP, reissue) 10

(see also Bob & Earl, Earl Nelson, Jackie Lee & Delores Hall)

JACKIE LEE & DELORES HALL
| 69 | B&C CB 105 | Whether It's Right Or Wrong/Baby I'm Satisfied ....7 |
| 72 | Jay Boy BOY 52 | Whether It's Right Or Wrong/Baby I'm Satisfied (reissue) ....4 |

(see also Jackie Lee [U.S.], Delores Hall)

JAMIE LEE & ATLANTICS
| 63 | Decca F 11571 | In The Night/Little Girl In Blue ....20 |

JIMMY LEE
| 61 | Starlite ST45 059 | All My Life/Chicago Jump ....18 |

JOHN LEE'S GROUNDHOGS
| 66 | Planet PLF 104 | Over You Baby/I'll Never Fall In Love Again ....40 |

(see also Groundhogs, Tony McPhee)

JOHNNIE LEE
59	Pye 7N 15201	It's-a Me, It's-a Me, It's-a Me My Love/Echo 4
59	Pye 7N 15233	I'm Finally Free/I Fell 4
60	Fontana H 257	They're Wrong/Cindy Lou 4
60	Fontana H 280	Poetry In Motion/Let It Come True 4
61	Fontana H 306	Lonely Joe/Nobody 4
67	CBS 202591	Kiss Tomorrow Goodbye/Love No Longer Sounds 7
67	CBS 2802	I Forgot What It Was Like/Lonely Is The Willow 4
67	CBS 3112	Because You're Mine/I'll Not Forget 4

JULIA LEE & HER BOYFRIENDS
| 51 | Capitol LC 6535 | PARTY TIME (10" LP) ....40 |

LAURA LEE (U.K.)
60	Triumph RGM 1030	Tell Tommy I Miss Him/I'm Sending Back Your Roses 20
62	Decca F 11513	Too Young To Be In Love/Brand New Heartbeat 8
68	Columbia DB 8495	Love In Every Room/Master Jack 5

LAURA LEE (U.S.)
67	Chess CRS 8062	Dirty Man/It's Mighty Hard 7
68	Chess CRS 8070	As Long As I Got You/A Man With Some Backbone 7
72	Tamla Motown TMG 831	To Win Your Heart/So Will I 4
72	Hot Wax HWX 115	Rip Off/Two Lovely Pillows 4
73	Hot Wax HWX 118	Wedlock Is A Padlock/Since I Fell For You 4
73	Hot Wax HWX 119	You've Got The Love To Save Me/Crumbs Off The Table 4
74	Invictus INV 2654	I Need It Just As Bad As You/If I'm Good Enough To Love 4

Laura LEE (U.S.)

MINT VALUE £

71	Hot Wax SHW 5006	WOMEN'S LOVE RIGHTS (LP)	10
72	Hot Wax SHW 5009	TWO SIDES OF LAURA LEE (LP)	10

LEAPY LEE
65	Pye 7N 17001	It's All Happening/In The Meantime	4
66	Decca F 12369	King Of The Whole Wide World/Shake Hands (features Kinks)	25
67	CBS 202550	The Man On The Flying Trapeze/My Mixed-Up Mind	4
68	MCA MU 1028	Little Arrows/Time Will Tell	4
68	Pye 7N 17619	It's All Happening/It's Great	4

LITTLE MR. LEE & CHEROKEES
66	Vocalion VP 9268	Young Lover/I Don't Want To Go	20

MANDY LEE
50s	Poydras 76	I'm A Harmony Baby/If Your Man Is Like My Man (78)	10

MARILYN LEE
64	Embassy WB 636	My Guy/DAVE CHARLES: Hello, Dolly	5

MICHELLE LEE
68	CBS 3350	L. David Sloan/Everybody Loves My Baby	4

NICKIE LEE
70	Deep Soul DS 9103	And Black Is Beautiful/Faith Within	7

NORMA LEE
67	CBM CBM 002	Hurt/Rollin' On	4

PEGGY LEE
54	Brunswick 05286	Johnny Guitar/I Didn't Know What Time It Was	9
54	Brunswick 05345	Love, You Didn't Do Right By Me/Sisters	7
55	Brunswick 05360	Let Me Go, Lover/Bouquet Of Blues	9
55	Brunswick 05368	Straight Ahead/It Must Be So (with Mills Brothers)	7
55	Brunswick 05421	Baubles, Bangles And Beads/Summer Vacation	6
55	Brunswick 05435	I Belong To You/How Bitter, My Sweet	6
55	Brunswick 05461	Ooh That Kiss/Oh! No! (Please Don't Go)	6
55	Brunswick 05471	Sugar/What Can I Say After I Say I'm Sorry	6
55	Brunswick 05472	He Needs Me/Sing A Rainbow	6
55	Brunswick 05482	He's A Tramp (with Pound Hounds)/The Siamese Cat Song (with Oliver Wallace)	8
55	Brunswick 05483	Bella Notte/La La Lu	6

(the above singles originally came with gold writing on labels, silver label reissues are worth two-thirds the value)

56	Brunswick 05549	Three Cheers For Mister Magoo/Mister Magoo Does The Cha Cha Cha (with Jim Backus)	6
56	Brunswick 05554	The Come Back/You've Got To See Mama Every Night	5
56	Brunswick 05593	That's All Right Honey/Love You So	5
56	Brunswick 05625	We Laughed At Love/They Can't Take That Away From Me	5
57	Brunswick 05671	Mr. Wonderful/The Gypsy With Fire In His Shoes	7
57	Brunswick 05714	I Don't Know Enough About You/Where Flamingo's Fly	5
57	Capitol CL 14741	Baby, Baby Wait For Me/Every Night	4
57	Capitol CL 14795	Uninvited Dreams/Listen To The Rockin' Bird	4
58	Capitol CL 14902	Fever/You Don't Know	6
58	Capitol CL 14955	Light Of Love/Sweetheart	4
59	Capitol CL 14984	Alright, Okay, You Win/My Man	4
59	Brunswick 05798	It Ain't Necessarily So/Swing Low, Sweet Chariot	5
59	Capitol CL 15025	Hallelujah, I Love Him So/I'm Lookin' Out The Window	4
59	Capitol CL 15058	You Came A Long Way From St. Louis/I Lost My Sugar In ... (with George Shearing Quintet)	4
59	Capitol CL 15103	You Deserve/Things Are Swingin'	4
61	Capitol CL 15184	Till There Was You/Bucket Of Tears	4
61	Capitol CL 15214	Manana/The Folks Who Live On The Hill	4
63	Capitol CL 15313	Doodlin' Song/Got That Magic	4
65	Capitol CL 15376	Pass Me By/That's What It Takes	4
65	Capitol CL 15413	I Go To Sleep/Stop Living In The Past	6
69	Capitol CL 15614	I'm A Woman/Me And My Shadow	4
69	Capitol CL 15614	Is That All There Is?/I'm A Woman	4
74	Warner Bros K 10527	Let's Love/Always	5
55	Brunswick OE 9153	PETE KELLY'S BLUES No. 1 (EP)	7
55	Brunswick OE 9154	PETE KELLY'S BLUES No. 2 (EP)	7
56	Brunswick OE 9282	PRESENTING PEGGY LEE (EP)	7
58	Brunswick OE 9400	SEA SHELLS PT. 1 (EP)	7
58	Brunswick OE 9401	SEA SHELLS PT. 2 (EP)	7
58	Philips BBE 12172	PEGGY WITH BENNY (EP, with Benny Goodman)	8
59	Capitol EAP1 1052	FEVER (EP)	7
59	Capitol EAP1 1213	ALRIGHT OKAY YOU WIN (EP)	7
61	Capitol EAP1 1857	I'M A WOMAN (EP)	7
53	Capitol LC 6584	CAPITOL PRESENTS PEGGY LEE (10" LP)	20
53	Brunswick LA 8629	BLACK COFFEE (10" LP)	20
55	Brunswick LA 8717	SONGS IN AN INTIMATE STYLE (10" LP)	20
55	Brunswick LAT 8078	PETE KELLY'S BLUES (LP, with Ella Fitzgerald)	16
56	Brunswick LA 8731	SONGS FROM 'LADY AND THE TRAMP' (10" LP)	20
56	Capitol LC 6817	MY BEST TO YOU (10" LP)	20
56	Capitol T 864	THE MAN I LOVE (LP)	14
57	Brunswick LAT 8171	DREAM STREET (LP)	16
58	Capitol (S)T 979	JUMP FOR JOY (LP)	14
58	Brunswick LAT 8266	SEA SHELLS (LP)	12
59	Capitol T 1049	THINGS ARE SWINGIN' (LP)	12
59	Capitol (S)T 1131	I LIKE MEN! (LP)	12
59	Brunswick LAT 8287	MISS WONDERFUL (LP)	12
60	Capitol (S)T 1219	BEAUTY AND THE BEAT! (LP, with George Shearing Quintet, mono/stereo)	10/12

Rare Record Price Guide   573

Peggy LEE

60	Capitol (S)T 1290	LATIN ALA LEE (LP, mono/stereo)	10/12
60	Capitol (S)T 1401	PRETTY EYES (LP, mono/stereo)	12/14
61	Brunswick LAT 8355	THE BEST OF PEGGY LEE VOL. 1 (LP)	10
61	Brunswick LAT 8356	THE BEST OF PEGGY LEE VOL. 2 (LP)	10
61	Capitol T 1366	ALL AGLOW AGAIN! (LP)	12
61	Capitol (S)T 1423	CHRISTMAS CAROUSEL (LP)	14
61	Ace Of Hearts AH 5	BLACK COFFEE (LP, reissue)	12
62	Capitol (S)T 1520	BASIN STREET EAST PRESENTS PEGGY LEE (LP, mono/stereo)	10/12
62	Capitol (S)T 1630	IF YOU GO (LP, mono/stereo)	12/14
62	Ace Of Hearts AH 26	PEGGY LEE (LP)	10
62	Capitol (S)T1 1671	BLUES CROSS COUNTRY (LP, mono/stereo)	12/14
63	Capitol T 1743	BEWITCHING-LEE! (LP)	10
63	Ace Of Hearts AH 44	DREAM STREET (LP, reissue)	10
63	Capitol (S)T 1857	I'M A WOMAN (LP)	10
64	Capitol (S)T 1850	MINK JAZZ (LP, mono/stereo)	12/14
64	Capitol (S)T 1969	IN LOVE AGAIN (LP, mono/stereo)	10/12
64	Ace Of Hearts AH 75	SEA SHELLS (LP, reissue)	10
64	Capitol (S)T 2096	IN THE NAME OF LOVE (LP, mono/stereo)	10/12
65	Capitol (S)T 2320	PASS ME BY (LP)	10
66	Capitol (S)T 1475	OLE A LA LEE! (LP)	14
66	Ace Of Hearts AH 107	THE FABULOUS PEGGY LEE (LP)	10
66	Capitol (S)T 2388	THEN WAS THEN, NOW IS NOW! (LP)	10
66	Brunswick LAT 8629	BLACK COFFEE (LP, 2nd reissue)	10
67	Capitol (S)T 2469	GUITARS A LA LEE (LP)	10
67	Capitol (S)T 2475	BIG SPENDER (LP)	10
69	Capitol (S)T 21141	IS THAT ALL THERE IS? (LP)	12

(see also Bing Crosby)

ROBERTA LEE

53	Brunswick 05076	Sixty Minute Man (with Hardrock Gunter)/RED FOLEY: Hot Toddy (78)	8
54	HMV 7M 261	True Love And Tender Care/When The Organ Played At Twilight	6
55	Brunswick 05388	Ridin' To Tennessee/I'll Be There If Ever You Want Me	6

(see also Red Foley, Hardrock Gunter)

ROBIN LEE

62	Reprise R 20068	Gamblin' Man/An Angel With A Broken Wing	10

ROY LEE

61	Decca F 11406	Two Initials/Honey Lies	4

TONY LEE

68	Doctor Bird DB 1106	Lee's Special/LLOYD & GROOVERS: My Heart My Soul	7

VANESSA LEE (& OLIVE GILBERT)

52	HMV 7P 133	Someday My Heart Will Awake (solo)/Coronation Scene & Finale	4

VINNY LEE & RIDERS

61	HMV POP 856	Mule Train/Gambler's Guitar	10

WILMA LEE & STONEY COOPER

64	Hickory 45-1257	Big John's Wife/Pirate King	4

LEE & CLARENDONIANS

72	Green Door GD 4038	Night Owl/Night Owl Version	4

LEE & PAUL

59	Philips PB 912	The Chick/Valentina, My Valentina	4

BOBBIE LEECAN'S NEED-MORE BAND

30	HMV B 5398	Washboard Cut Out/DIXIELAND JUG BLOWERS: Skit Skat Skoodle Do (78)	35
30	HMV B 5430	Apaloosa Blues/BENNIE MOTEN: Sugar (78)	35

(see also Dixie Jazzers Washboard Band)

BRAD LEEDS

60	Pye Intl. 7N 25050	A Teenage Love Is Born/I'm Walking Behind You	5

PHIL LEEDS

66	London HLR 10044	Would You Believe It?/FRANK GALLOP: The Ballad Of Irving	5

MARK LEEMAN FIVE

65	Columbia DB 7452	Portland Town/Gotta Get Myself Together	15
65	Columbia DB 7648	Blow My Blues Away/On The Horizon	20
66	Columbia DB 7812	Forbidden Fruit/Goin' To Bluesville	15
66	Columbia DB 7955	Follow Me/Gather Up The Pieces	15

THOMAS LEER

78	Oblique ER 101	Private Plane/International (folded photocopied p/s, hand-stamped labels)	10
78	Company/Oblique OBCO 1	Private Plane/International (reissue, printed p/s)	6
84	Arista LEER 1	International/Easy Way (p/s)	4
84	Arista LEER 121	International/Easy Way (12", p/s)	7
84	Arista LERPD 121	International/Easy Way (12", picture disc)	8
82	Cherry Red CHERRY 52	All About You/Saving Grace (p/s)	4
82	Cherry Red 12CHERRY 52	All About You/Saving Grace (12", p/s)	7
82	Cherry Red ERED 26	CONTRADICTIONS (12", double pack)	7
79	Industrial IR 0007	THE BRIDGE (LP, with Robert Rental)	14

(see also Act, Robert Rental)

JOHN LEES

74	Polydor 2058 513	Best Of My Love/You Can't Get It	7
77	Harvest HAR 5132	Child Of The Universe/Kes (A Major Fancy)	5
77	Harvest SHSM 2018	A MAJOR FANCY (LP)	10

(see also Barclay James Harvest)

69	Apple APPLES 1002	You Know My Name (Look Up The Number)/What's The New Mary Jane (as Plastic Ono Band, unreleased; type-written Apple 'Custom Recording' test pressings only, handwritten catalogue number) 1500
70	Apple APPLES 1003	Instant Karma!/Who Has Seen The Wind? (p/s, as Lennon/Ono with Plastic Ono Band) 10
71	Apple R 5892	Power To The People/YOKO ONO/PLASTIC ONO BAND: Open Your Box (p/s, full apple label both sides) 10
71	Apple R 5892	Power To The People/YOKO ONO/PLASTIC ONO BAND: Open Your Box 2nd pressing, full/half apple label) 4
72	Apple R 5970	Happy Xmas (War Is Over) (as John & Yoko/Plastic Ono Band with Harlem Community Choir)/YOKO ONO/PLASTIC ONO BAND: Listen, The Snow Is Falling (p/s, green or black vinyl) 12/7
72	Apple R 5953	Woman Is The Nigger Of The World/Sisters O Sisters (unreleased, demos only) 250
73	Apple R 5994	Mind Games/Meat City (p/s) 8
74	Apple R 5998	Whatever Gets You Thru' The Night/Beef Jerky (company sleeve) 5
75	Apple R 6003	# 9 Dream/What You Got (company sleeve) 4
75	Apple R 6005	Stand By Me/Move Over Ms. L (company sleeve) 6
75	Apple R 6009	Imagine/Working Class Hero (p/s) 10
81	Geffen K 79195M	Woman/YOKO ONO: Beautiful Boys (cassette, cigarette pack-style box) 7
81	Geffen K 79207M	Watching The Wheels/Yes, I'm Your Angel (cassette, cigarette pack-style box) ...8
84	Polydor POSPG 701	Borrowed Time/YOKO ONO: Your Hands (poster p/s) 6
84	Polydor POSPX 701	Borrowed Time/YOKO ONO: Your Hands (12", poster p/s) 7
84	Polydor POSP 712	Every Man Has A Woman Who Loves Him/SEAN ONO LENNON: It's Alright (p/s, with free poster) 6
88	Parlophone RP 6199	Imagine/Jealous Guy (picture disc) 4
68	Apple APCOR 2	UNFINISHED MUSIC NO. 1: TWO VIRGINS (LP, with Yoko Ono, mono) 750
68	Apple SAPCOR 2/ Track 613 012	UNFINISHED MUSIC NO. 1: TWO VIRGINS (LP, with Yoko Ono, stereo with brown paper outer sleeve) 150
69	Zapple ZAPPLE 01	UNFINISHED MUSIC NO. 2: LIFE WITH THE LIONS (LP, with Yoko Ono, with inner sleeve) 60
69	Apple SAPCOR 11	WEDDING ALBUM (LP, with Yoko Ono, box set with booklet & inserts) 150
69	Apple CORE 2001	LIVE PEACE IN TORONTO 1969 (LP, some sealed with stapled calendar, as Plastic Ono Band) 60/10
70	Apple PCS 7124	JOHN LENNON/PLASTIC ONO BAND (LP, with inner sleeve) 10
71	Apple PAS 10004	IMAGINE (LP, with Plastic Ono Band, with inner sleeve, poster & postcard) ...15
72	Apple PCSP 716	SOMETIME IN NEW YORK CITY (2-LP, as John & Yoko/Plastic Ono Band, with Elephant's Memory, Invisible Strings & Frank Zappa, with inner sleeves) ..12
74	Apple PCTC 253	WALLS AND BRIDGES (LP, with inner sleeve, booklet & foldout cover) 10
74	Apple Q4 PAS 10004	IMAGINE (LP, quadrophonic, with inner sleeve, poster & postcard) 50
81	Parlophone JLB 8	THE JOHN LENNON BOX (9-LP set) 55
84	Polydor POLH P5	MILK AND HONEY (LP, picture disc, 2,000 only) 25

(see also Beatles, Yoko Ono, Bill Elliott/Elastic Oz Band, Elephants Memory, Musketeer Gripweed, Elton John)

JOHN LENNON & BLEECHERS (Jamaica)
70	Punch PH 23	Ram You Hard/UPSETTERS: Soul Stew 5

JULIAN LENNON
84	Charisma JLY 1	Too Late For Goodbyes/Well I Don't Know (picture disc) 10
84	Charisma JLS 2	Valotte/Let Me Be (arch-shaped picture disc with stand) 12
84	Charisma JL 212	Valotte/Let Me Be/Bebop (12" poster p/s) 7

LENNON SISTERS
56	Vogue Coral Q 72176	Graduation Day/Toy Tiger 6
57	Vogue Coral Q 72259	Young And In Love/Teenage Waltz 6
57	Vogue Coral Q 72285	Shake Me I Rattle/Pocohontas 8
61	London HLD 9417	Sad Movies/I Don't Know Why 5
64	London HA-D/SH-D 8154	GREAT FOLK SONGS (LP, as Lennon Sisters & Cousins) 10

J.B. LENOIR (& AFRICAN HUNCH)
65	Sue WI 339	I Sing Um The Way I Feel/I Feel So Good (as J.B. Lenoir & African Hunch) 15
65	Bootleg 503	Man Watch Your Woman/Mama Talk To Your Daughter 25
66	Blue Horizon 45-1004	Mojo Boogie/I Don't Care What Nobody Say 30
70	Polydor 2482 014	CRUSADE (LP) 10
72	Python PLP 25	J.B. LENOIR (LP) 25
75	Rarity LP 2	J.B. LENOIR (LP) 20
70s	CBS 62593	ALABAMA BLUES (LP) 25

ROBIN LENT
71	Nepentha 6347 002	SCARECROW'S JOURNEY (LP, gatefold sleeve, with Focus) 35

(see also Focus)

VAN LENTON
65	Immediate IM 008	Gotta Get Away/You Don't Care 15

LEON (Silvera) & OWEN (Gray)
62	Blue Beat BB 117	Murder/ROY PANTON: Forty Four 8
64	Island WI 146	Nextdoor Neighbour/ROLAND ALPHONSO: Feeling Fine 10

CHARLES LEONARD
71	Jay Boy BOY 39	Funky Driver On A Funky Bus Pts 1 & 2 4

DEKE LEONARD
73	United Artists UP 35494	Diamond Road/Circles And Squares 4
73	United Artists UP 35556	Nothing Is Happening/She's A Cow (demo only) 8
73	United Artists UP 35556	A Hard Way To Live/The Aching Is So Sweet 4
74	United Artists UP 35668	Louisiana Hoedown/She's A Cow 4
79	United Artists UP 36488	Map Of India/Hey There! (Lady In The Black Tuxedo) (gatefold p/s) 4
73	United Artists UAG 29464	ICEBURG (LP) 10
74	United Artists UAG 29544	KAMIKAZE (LP) 10

(see also Man, Marty Wilde, Help Yourself, Pete Brown's Piblokto)

MINT VALUE £

ANN LEONARDO
57	Capitol CL 14723	Straws In The Wind/Travelling Stranger	4
57	Capitol CL 14755	Lottery/One And Only	4
57	Capitol CL 14797	Three Time Loser/I'll Wait Till Monday	4

TOMMY LEONETTI
54	Capitol CL 14199	That's What You Made Me/I Love My Mama	6
55	Capitol CL 14272	Ever Since You Went Away/Untied	6
56	Capitol CL 14556	Heartless/Sometime	4
56	Capitol CL 14598	It's Wild/Free	4
56	Capitol CL 14654	Too Proud/Wrong	4
58	RCA RCA 1107	Dream Lover/Moonlight Serenade	6

LEONIE & JOE NOLAN BAND
| 68 | Jolly JY 015 | Move And Groove/Don't Let Me Do It | 4 |

LE ORME
| 73 | Charisma CAS 1072 | FELONA AND SERONA (LP) | 12 |

LEO'S SUNSHIPP
| 79 | Grapevine RED 3 | Give Me The Sunshine/I'm Back For More | 4 |
| 79 | Grapevine REDC 3 | Give Me The Sunshine/I'm Back For More (12") | 15 |

LE RITZ
| 77 | Breaker BS 2001 | Punker/What A Sucker | 6 |

LEROY & ROCKY (Ellis)
| 68 | Studio One SO 2042 | Love Me Girl/WRIGGLERS: Reel Up | 15 |

(see also King Rocky)

LE ROYS
64	HMV POP 1274	Gotta Lotta Love (Ciribiribin)/Don't Cry Baby	6
64	HMV POP 1312	Chills/Lost Out On Love	8
64	HMV POP 1368	I Came Smiling On Through/California GL 903	4
64	Give A Disc LYN 504/5	Money/Swinging On A Star (flexidisc)	10

(see also Mike Sarne, Simon Scott, John Leyton, Mike Berry, Grazina, Billie Davis, Billy Boyle)

LEROYS & INNOCENTS
| 64 | Regal Zonophone RZ 502 | HOT SIX (maxi-single, plain sleeve) | 6 |

(see also Innocents)

LES FLAMBEAUX
| 65 | HMV POP 1456 | Cachita/Greensleeves | 4 |
| 71 | Mushroom 100 MR 13 | LES FLAMBEAUX (LP, 2 different sleeve designs) | 40 |

LES HOBEAUX
57	HMV POP 377	Oh, Mary Don't You Weep/Toll The Bell Easy	10
57	HMV POP 403	Mama Don't Allow/Hey, Hey, Daddy Blues	10
58	HMV POP 444	Dynamo/Two Ships	12
57	HMV 7EG 8297	SOHO SKIFFLE (EP)	20

LORNE LESLEY
59	Parlophone R 4518	Some Of These Days/When Love Has Let You Down	5
59	Parlophone R 4567	Warm/You Ought To Be Mine	4
59	Parlophone R 4581	So High, So Low/I Don't Know	6
60	Polydor NH 66928	Take All My Love/Ritroviamoci (Till We Meet Again)	4
60	Polydor NH 66956	Bloodshot Eyes/We're Gonna Dance	8
66	Parlophone R 5538	Little Snowflakes/Would You	4

MICHAEL LESLEY
65	Pye 7N 15835	Momma Didn't Know/I Don't Wanna Know	4
65	Pye 7N 15908	Penny Arcade/Bye Bye Baby	4
65	Pye 7N 15959	Make Up Or Break Up/She Can't See Me	10
66	Decca F 12531	Right Or Wrong/Office Girl	4

LES MYSTERES DES VOIX BULGARES
| 86 | 4AD AD 603 | Prïtourïtze Planinata/Polegnala E Todora (promo-only, no p/s) | 7 |

LES SAUTERELLES
(see under Sauterelles)

HEDDY LESTER
| 77 | Sonet SON 2013 | The World Keeps Turning/Never Saw Him Laughing (p/s) | 6 |

KETTY LESTER
62	London HLN 9527	Love Letters/I'm A Fool To Want You	6
62	London HLN 9574	But Not For Me/Moscow Nights	5
62	London HLN 9608	You Can't Lie To A Liar/River Of Salt	5
62	London HLN 9635	This Land Is Your Land/Love Belongs To Everyone	5
63	London HLN 9698	A Warm Summer Day/I'll Never Stop Loving You	4
64	RCA Victor RCA 1394	Some Things Are Better Left Unsaid/The House Is Haunted	20
64	RCA Victor RCA 1403	Roses Grow With Thorns/Please Don't Cry Anymore	20
65	RCA Victor RCA 1421	"The Luck Of Ginger Coffey" Theme/I Trust You Baby	4
65	RCA Victor RCA 1460	Looking For A Better World/Pretty Eyes	6
65	Capitol CL 15427	West Coast/I'll Be Looking Back	15
66	Capitol CL 15447	When A Woman Loves A Man/We'll Be Together Again	5
62	London RE-N 1348	KETTY LESTER (EP)	15
63	London HA-N 2455	LOVE LETTERS (LP)	18
64	RCA Victor RD 7669	THE SOUL OF ME (LP)	12
65	RCA Victor RD 7712	WHERE IS LOVE (LP)	12
67	Stateside S(S)L 10196	WHEN A MAN LOVES A WOMAN (LP)	10

LAZY LESTER
| 64 | Stateside SS 277 | I'm A Lover Not A Fighter/Sugar Coated Love | 10 |

71	Blue Horizon 2431 007	MADE UP MY MIND (LP)	75
77	Flyright FLYLP 526	THEY CALL ME LAZY (LP)	10
79	Flyright FLYLP 544	POOR BOY BLUES (LP)	10

ROBIE LESTER
62	Polydor NH 66963	Ballad Of Cheating John/Miracle Of Love	4

LES YPER SOUND
67	Fontana TF 880	Too Fortiche/Psyche Rock	50

LES ZARJAZ
85	Creation CRE 014	One Charming Nyte/My Baby Owns A Fallout Zone (foldover p/s, poly bag)	8

(see also Tronics)

LET'S ACTIVE
84	Bucketfull Of Brains BOB 10	I Feel Funny/Wild Wild Women (flexidisc with 'Bucketfull Of Brains' issue 16)	5/4

LETTERMEN
61	Capitol CL 15222	The Way You Look Tonight/That's My Desire	4
65	Capitol CL 15405	Theme From A Summer Place/Sealed With A Kiss	4
68	Capitol CL 15526	Goin' Out Of My Head/Can't Take My Eyes Off You — I Believe	4
69	Capitol CL 15609	Hurt So Bad/Traces	4
61	Capitol EAP 41669	THE LETTERMEN (EP)	7

LETTERMEN
74	Stag SG 10075	FIRST CLASS (LP, private pressing)	175

LETTERS
79	Heartbeat PULSE 9	Nobody Loves Me/Don't Want You Back (p/s)	5

DON LETTS & JAH WOBBLE
79	Virgin VS 239	Steel Leg: Stratetime & The Wide Man/Electric Dread: Haile Unlikely (p/s)	10

(see also Jah Wobble, PiL, B.A.D.)

LEVEE BREAKERS
65	Parlophone R 5291	Babe I'm Leaving You/Wild About My Loving	18

LEVEE CAMP MOAN
69	County	LEVEE CAMP MOAN (LP, private pressing)	400
69	County	PEACOCK FARM (LP, private pressing)	450

LEVEL 42
80	Elite DAZZ 4	Sandstorm/POWERLINE: Journey To The Powerline (12", promo only)	100
80	Elite DAZZ 5	Love Meeting Love/Instrumental Love (7", unreleased)	
80	Elite DAZZ 5	Love Meeting Love/Instrumental Love (12", company die-cut stickered sleeve)	50
80	Polydor POSP 170	Love Meeting Love/Instrumental Love (no p/s)	5
80	Polydor POSPX 170	Love Meeting Love/Instrumental Love (12", company sleeve)	10
80	Polydor POSP 200	(Flying On The) Wings Of Love/Wings Of Love (no p/s)	8
80	Polydor POSPX 200	(Flying On The) Wings Of Love (US Mix)/(UK Mix) (12", white stickered sleeve)	15
81	Polydor POSPX 200	(Flying On The) Wings Of Love ('81 Remix)/Love Meeting (12", white stickered sleeve)	20
81	Polydor POSP 234	Love Games/42 (no p/s)	4
81	Polydor POSPX 234	Love Games (Extended Mix)/42 (12")	7
81	Polydor POSP 286	Turn It On/Beezer One (no p/s)	4
81	Polydor POSPX 286	Turn It On (Extended Mix)/Beezer One (12", blue company sleeve)	8
81	Polydor POSP 343	Starchild/Foundation And Empire Part 1 (p/s)	4
81	Polydor POSPX 343	Starchild (Extended Mix)/Foundation And Empire Pts 1 & 2 (12", p/s)	7
82	Polydor POSP 396	Are You Hearing (What I Hear)?/The Return Of The Handsome Rugged Man (p/s)	4
82	Polydor POSPX 396	Are You Hearing (What I Hear)? (Full Length)/The Return Of The Handsome Rugged Man (12", p/s)	7
82	Polydor POSPX 500	You Can't Blame Louis/Dune Tune (Live)/Love Games (live) (12", unreleased, white label test pressings only, no p/s)	50
82	Polydor POSPX 500	Weave Your Spell (Extended Mix)/Love Games (live)/Dune Tune (live) (12", p/s)	7
83	Polydor POSPX 538	The Chinese Way (Extended Mix)/88 (live) (12", p/s, yellow vinyl)	25
83	Polydor POSPX 538	The Chinese Way (Extended Mix)/88 (live)//Weave Your Spell (Extended Mix)/Dune Tune (live)/Love Games (live) (12", double pack)	12
83	Polydor POSPP 570	Out Of Sight Out Of Mind/You Can't Blame Louis (picture disc)	7
83	Polydor POSPX 570	Out Of Sight Out Of Mind (Extended Mix)/You Can't Blame Louis (Extended Remix) (12", p/s)	10
83	Polydor POPPX 570	Out Of Sight Out Of Mind (Extended Mix)/You Can't Blame Louis (Extended Remix) (12", picture disc)	25
83	Polydor POSP 622	The Sun Goes Down (Living It Up)/Can't Walk You Home (p/s, with promo cassette: "Love Games" & excerpts from LP "Standing In The Light")	7
83	Polydor POSPPX 622	The Sun Goes Down (Living It Up)/Can't Walk You Home/Love Games (Extended Mix)/Forty Two (12", p/s, white or blue titles on sleeve)	7
83	Polydor POSPX 643	Micro-Kid (Extended Mix)/Turn It On (Live) (12", p/s, with free cassette)	12
83	Polydor POSPX 643/ LEVEL 643	Micro-Kid (Extended Mix)/Turn It On (Live)//The Chinese Way (New York Remix)/The Chinese Way (Dub Mix) (12", double pack)	20
84	Polydor POSPX 697	Hot Water (Master Mix)/Standing In The Light (Extended Version) (12", p/s)	7
84	Polydor POSPX 697	Hot Water (Master Mix)/Standing In The Light (Extended Version)/Micro-Kid (Specially Remixed U.S. Version) (12", p/s, mispress with extra track, matrix: POSPA 697)	35
84	Polydor POSP 710	The Chant Has Begun (Edited Version)/Almost There (Edited Version) (p/s, with free cassette from "True Colours" LP [LEVEL 710])	8
85	Polydor POSPG 759	Something About You/Coup D'Etat (Version) (poster p/s)	6
85	Polydor POSPT 759	Something About You/The Chinese Way/Follow Me (live) (10", p/s)	12
85	Polydor POSPA 759	Something About You (Sisa Mix)/Coup D'Etat (Version)/Hot Water/The Sun Goes Down (12", p/s)	7
85	Polydor POSPP 776	Leaving Me Now (Remix)/I Sleep On My Heart (poster p/s)	7
85	Polydor POSPD 776	Leaving Me Now (Remix)/I Sleep On My Heart//Something About You/Coup D'Etat (shrinkwrapped double pack)	5
85	Polydor POSPT 776	Leaving Me Now/I Sleep On My Heart (Remix) (10", p/s)	10

LEVEL 42

85	Polydor POSPX 776	Leaving Me Now (Remix)/I Sleep On My Heart//Something About You/ Coup D'Etat (12", p/s) 8
86	Polydor POSA 790	Lessons In Love/Something About You (U.S. Remix Edit) (p/s) 6
87	Polydor POSXX 842	Running In The Family (Extended)/Dream Crazy/Running In The Family (7" Version)//World Machine (Shep Pettibone Remix)/World Machine (Dub) (12", double pack) 8
87	Polydor POSPP 855	To Be With You Again/Micro Kid (live) (picture disc) 6
87	Polydor POSPG 900	It's Over (Remix)/Physical Presence (live) (envelope pack, 4 cards & sticker) 5
87	Polydor POSPP 911	Children Say (Remix)/Starchild (Remix) (picture disc) 6
88	Polydor PZX 14	Heaven In My Hands (U.S. Remix)/(7" Version)/Gresham Blues (12", p/s) 7
88	Polydor POG 24	Take A Look (Remix)/Man (envelope pack with 4 postcards) 4
82	Lyntone LYN 12914	Love Games (live) (white flexidisc with 'Melody Maker' magazine) 6/5
81	Elite LEV LP 1	STRATEGY (LP, unreleased, 6 white label test pressings only) 450
85	Polydor POLHC 25	WORLD MACHINE (cassette with bonus tracks) 12

(see also Thunderthumbs & Toetsenman, Mark King)

GERRY LEVENE (& AVENGERS)

| 64 | Decca F 11815 | It's Driving Me Wild (solo)/Dr. Feelgood ....25 |

(see also Moody Blues)

ANNABEL LEVENTON

| 69 | Morgan MR 20 | Easy To Be Hard/My Dear Friend ....4 |

LEVIATHAN

68	Elektra EKSN 45052	Remember The Times/Second Production 25
69	Elektra EKSN 45057	The War Machine/Time 25
69	Elektra EKSN 45075	Flames/Just Forget Tomorrow 20

(see also Mike Stuart Span)

HANK LEVINE ORCHESTRA

| 61 | HMV POP 947 | Image Pts 1 & 2 ....7 |
| 65 | HMV POP 1390 | Image Pts 1 & 2 (reissue) ....5 |

LEVON & HAWKS

| 65 | Atlantic AT 4054 | The Stones I Throw/He Don't Love You ....25 |

(see also Band)

BEN LEVY

| 66 | Ska Beat JB 245 | Doren/Never Knew Love ....7 |
| 66 | Ska Beat JB 255 | I'll Make You Glad/Keep Smiling ....7 |

CARL LEVY & CIMARRONS

| 70s | Hot Rod HR 100 | Walk The Hot Street/PEGGY & CIMARRONS: You Say You Don't Love Me ....4 |

JONA LEWIE

74	Sonet SON 2048	Piggy Back Sue/Papa Don't Go 4
75	Sonet SON 2056	The Swan/Custer's Last Stand 4
76	Sonet SON 2081	Hallelujah Europe Pts 1 & 2 4
77	Sonet SON 2117	Rocking Yobs/After We Swum 4
78	Stiff SEEZ P8	ON THE OTHER HAND THERE'S A FIST (LP, picture disc) 15
78	Stiff SEEZ 8	ON THE OTHER HAND THERE'S A FIST (LP, black or yellow vinyl) 15/10

ALVA LEWIS

| 67 | Caltone TONE 111 | Return Home/KING ROCK & WILLOWS: You Are The One ....6 |

BARBARA LEWIS

63	London HLK 9724	Hello Stranger/Think A Little Sugar 12
63	London HLK 9779	Straighten Up Your Heart/If You Love Her 14
64	London HLK 9832	Snap Your Fingers/Puppy Love 12
64	Atlantic AT 4013	Pushin' A Good Thing Too Far/Come Home 10
65	Atlantic AT 4031	Baby I'm Yours/Hello Stranger 10
65	Atlantic AT 4041	Make Me Your Baby/Love To Be Loved 10
66	Atlantic AT 4068	Don't Forget About Me/It's Magic 10
66	Atlantic 584 037	Make Me Belong To You/Girls Need Loving Care 6
67	Atlantic 584 061	Baby What You Do To Me/I Remember The Feeling 20
68	Atlantic 584 153	Hello Stranger/Baby I'm Yours 5
68	Atlantic 584 174	Sho Nuff (It's Got To Be Your Love)/Thankful For What I Got 7
71	Atlantic 2091 143	Someday We're Gonna Love Again/Baby I'm Yours 6
72	Atlantic K 10128	Someday We're Gonna Love Again/Baby I'm Yours (reissue) 4
65	Atlantic AET 6015	SNAP YOUR FINGERS (EP) 25
66	Atlantic ATL 5042	BABY I'M YOURS (LP) 15
66	Atlantic 587 002	IT'S MAGIC (LP) 15

BOB LEWIS

| 57 | Parlophone R 4309 | Far Away/The Mayflower Song ....5 |

BOBBY LEWIS

61	Parlophone R 4794	Tossin' And Turnin'/Oh Yes I Love You 12
61	Parlophone R 4831	One Track Mind/Are You Ready 10
62	Stateside SS 126	I'm Tossin' And Turnin' Again/Nothin' But The Blues 10

CAPPY LEWIS

| 61 | Vogue V 9184 | Bullfight/OLYMPICS: Little Pedro ....12 |

(see also Olympics)

CLIVE LEWIS

| 71 | Rediffusion | WHERE ARE YOU CLIVE LEWIS (LP) ....15 |

DAVE LEWIS

| 66 | Pye Intl. NEP 44057 | GIVIN' GAS (EP) ....15 |

DAVID LEWIS

| 70 | AX 1 | SONGS OF DAVID LEWIS (LP, private pressing) ....450 |

(see also Andwella['s Dream], David Baxter)

FURRY LEWIS

69	Blue Horizon 7-63228	PRESENTING THE COUNTRY BLUES (LP)	40
70	Matchbox SDR 190	IN MEMPHIS (LP)	12
71	Xtra XTRA 1116	FURRY LEWIS (LP)	15
71	Spokane SPL 1004	THE EARLY YEARS 1927-1929 (LP)	40

(see also John Estes)

GARY LEWIS & PLAYBOYS

65	Liberty LIB 10187	This Diamond Ring/Tijuana Wedding	6
65	Liberty LIB 55778	Count Me In/Little Miss Go-Go	10
65	Liberty LIB 55809	Save Your Heart For Me/Without A Word Of Warning	5
65	Liberty LIB 55818	Everybody Loves A Clown/Time Stands Still	5
66	Liberty LIB 55846	She's Just My Style/I Won't Make That Mistake Again	5
66	Liberty LIB 55865	Sure Gonna Miss Her/I Don't Wanna Say Goodnight	5
66	Liberty LIB 55880	Green Grass/I Can Read Between The Lines	5
66	Liberty LIB 55898	My Heart's Symphony/Tina	10
66	Liberty LIB 55914	(You Don't Have To) Paint Me A Picture/Looking For The Stars	5
67	Liberty LIB 55933	Where Will The Words Come From/The Best Man	5
67	Liberty LIB 55949	Loser (With A Broken Heart)/Ice Melts In The Sun	5
67	Liberty LIB 55971	Girls In Love/Let's Be More Than Friends	5
67	Liberty LBF 15025	Jill/Needles And Pins	8
68	Liberty LBF 15131	Sealed With A Kiss/Pretty Thing	5
70	Liberty LBF 15335	Orangutan/Something Is Wrong	4
65	Liberty LBY 1259	THIS DIAMOND RING (LP)	25
66	Liberty LBY 1322	JUST OUR STYLE (LP)	15

GEORGE LEWIS & HIS NEW ORLEANS STOMPERS/BAND

56	Vogue V 2051	Climax Rag/Deep Bayou Blues	5
56	Vogue V 2052	Millenberg Joys/Two Jim Blues	5
56	Vogue V 2053	Just A Closer Walk With Thee/Just A Little While To ...	5
56	Vogue V 2054	Fidgety Feet/Dauphine Street Blues	5
56	Vogue V 2055	Don't Go 'Way Nobody/Careless Love Blues	5
60	HMV POP 707	South Rampart Street Parade/Chinatown My Chinatown (with Band)	8
55	Vogue EPV 1066	GEORGE LEWIS AND HIS NEW ORLEANS STOMPERS (EP)	8
55	Vogue EPV 1081	GEORGE LEWIS AND HIS NEW ORLEANS STOMPERS (EP)	8
56	Tempo EXA 15	GEORGE LEWIS AND HIS NEW ORLEANS STOMPERS (EP)	7
57	Tempo EXA 62	GEORGE LEWIS (EP)	7
57	Tempo EXA 66	GEORGE LEWIS (EP)	7
57	Tempo EXA 70	GEORGE LEWIS' RAGTIME BAND (EP)	7
58	Tempo EXA 97	GEORGE LEWIS (EP)	7
59	Tempo EXA 101	GEORGE LEWIS (EP)	7
59	Vogue EPV 1220	GEORGE LEWIS IN HI FI (EP)	8
59	Vogue EPV 1252	GEORGE LEWIS IN HI FI (EP)	8
50s	Good Time Jazz EPG 1182	NEW ORLEANS MUSIC (EP)	7
50s	Esquire EP 125	NEW ORLEANS RAGTIME BAND VOL. 1 (EP)	7
50s	Esquire EP 135	NEW ORLEANS RAGTIME BAND VOL. 2 (EP)	7
50s	Esquire EP 155	NEW ORLEANS RAGTIME BAND VOL. 3 (EP)	7
50s	Esquire EP 175	NEW ORLEANS RAGTIME BAND VOL. 4 (EP)	7
50s	Esquire EP 209	NEW ORLEANS RAGTIME BAND VOL. 5 (EP)	7
60s	Esquire EP 211	NEW ORLEANS RAGTIME BAND VOL. 6 (EP)	7
60s	Esquire EP 215	NEW ORLEANS RAGTIME BAND VOL. 7 (EP)	7
60s	Esquire EP 219	NEW ORLEANS RAGTIME BAND VOL. 8 (EP)	7
60	Esquire EP 225	NEW ORLEANS RAGTIME BAND VOL. 9 (EP)	7
60	HMV 7EG 8540	SOUNDS OF NEW ORLEANS (EP)	8
50s	Storyville SEP 315	ICE CREAM (EP)	7
50s	Storyville SEP 321	PANAMA (EP)	7
50s	Storyville SEP 322	LOUISIANA (EP)	7
50s	Storyville SEP 325	WILLIE THE WEEPER (EP)	8
60	Storyville SEP 349	JAZZ FROM NEW ORLEANS (EP)	8
61	Storyville SEP 361	TILL WE MEET AGAIN (EP)	8
61	Storyville SEP 365	ISLE OF CAPRI (EP)	8
61	Storyville SEP 369	MUSKRAT RUMBLE (EP)	8
60s	Storyville SEP 503	HIGH SOCIETY (EP)	8
60s	Storyville SEP 504	DALLAS BLUES (EP)	8
52	Vogue LDE 012	GEORGE LEWIS AND HIS NEW ORLEANS ALLSTARS (10" LP)	20
54	Vogue LDE 082	GEORGE LEWIS JAM SESSION (10" LP)	20
55	Vogue LAE 12005	GEORGE LEWIS AND HIS NEW ORLEANS STOMPERS (LP)	15
55	London H-APB 1041	VOL. 1 JAZZ BAND (10" LP, with New Orleans Jazz Band & Quartet)	25
56	London HB-U 1045	VOL. 2 ALL STARS (10" LP, with New Orleans All Stars & Quartet)	25
57	Tempo TAP 13	GEORGE LEWIS RAGTIME BAND (LP)	12
50s	Esquire 20-067	GEORGE LEWIS RAGTIME BAND (10" LP)	15
50s	Esquire 20-073	GEORGE LEWIS RAGTIME BAND (10" LP)	15
50s	'77' LA 12/28	SMILE DARN YA SMILE (LP, as George Lewis with Barry Martyn's Band)	18
59	Columbia Clef 33C 9042	RAGGIN' AND STOMPIN' (10" LP)	15
60	HMV CLP 1371/CSD 1309	BLUES FROM THE BAYOU (LP, mono/stereo)	10/12
61	HMV CLP 1413/CSD 1337	DOCTOR JAZZ (LP, mono/stereo)	10/12
64	London HA-K/SH-K 8165	JAZZ AT PRESERVATION HALL VOL. 4 (LP, with Band Of New Orleans)	20

GEORGE LEWIS/FREDDIE KOHLMAN

53	Brunswick LA 8627	NEW ORLEANS JAZZ CONCERT (10" LP)	15

HOPETON LEWIS

67	Island WI 3054	Rock Steady/Cool Cool Collie	10
67	Island WI 3055	Finder's Keepers/ROLAND ALPHONSO: Shanty Town Curfew	10
67	Island WI 3056	Let Me Come On Home/Hardships Of Life	10
67	Island WI 3057	Run Down/Pick Yourself Up	10
67	Island WI 3059	Let The Little Girl Dance/This Music Got Soul	10
67	Island WI 3068	Rock A Shacka/I Don't Want Trouble	10

MINT VALUE £

68	Island WI 3076	Everybody Rocking/Stars Shining So Bright	10
68	Fab FAB 43	Skinny Leg Girl/Live Like A King (as Hopetown Lewis & Glenmore Brown)	5
70	Duke Reid DR 2505	Boom Shaka Lacka/TOMMY McCOOK QUINTET: Dynamite	6
70	Duke Reid DR 2516	Testify/TOMMY McCOOK: Super Soul	6
71	Treasure Isle TI 7060	To The Other Man/TOMMY McCOOK: Stampede	6
72	Treasure Isle TI 7071	Judgement Day(actually by Hopeton Lewis & Dennis Alcapone)/ EARL LINDO: Version Day	6
67	Island ILP 957	TAKE IT EASY (LP)	70
71	Trojan TRL 36	GROOVING OUT ON LIFE (LP)	10

(see also Glenmore Brown & Hopeton Lewis)

HUEY LEWIS (& NEWS)

82	Chrysalis CHS 2589	Do You Believe In Love/Is It Me (p/s)	4
82	Chrysalis CHS 2620	Tattoo (Giving It All Up For Love)/Do You Believe In Love/Some Of My Lies Are True (EP, newspaper p/s)	6
82	Chrysalis CHSP 2620	Tattoo (Giving It All Up For Love)/Do You Believe In Love/Some Of My Lies Are True (EP, picture disc)	6
84	Chrysalis CHSP 2798	Heart Of Rock'n'Roll/Do You Believe In Love (star-shaped picture disc)	6
84	Chrysalis CHSD 2803	If This Is It/Change Of Heart//Walkin' On A Thin Line (live)/Workin' For A Living (live) (double pack)	4
85	Chrysalis HUEY 1	The Power Of Love/Bad Is Bad//I Want A New Drug (Called Love) (live)/ It's All Right (live) (double pack, gatefold p/s)	4
85	Chrysalis HUEY P2	Heart And Soul/Back In Time (Short Version) ('The Heart And Soul EP', picture disc, 33rpm)	4
85	Chrysalis HUEY P3	The Power Of Love/Do You Believe In Love (picture disc)	4
86	Chrysalis HUEY D4	The Heart Of Rock'n'Roll/Hope You Love Me Like You Say You Do//Tattoo (Giving It All Up For Love)/Bad Is Bad (double pack, gatefold p/s)	4
86	Chrysalis HUEY P4	The Heart Of Rock'n'Roll (Extended)/Hope You Love Me Like You Say You Do/Tattoo (Giving It All Up For Love)/Bad is Bad (12", picture disc)	7
87	Chrysalid HUEY D7	Simple As That/Walking On A Thin Line//The Power Of Love/Do You Believe In Love (double pack)	4

(see also Clover, American Express)

HUGH X. LEWIS

66	London HLR 10032	Looking In The Future/Too Late	4
66	London HA-R 8293	THE HUGH X. LEWIS ALBUM (LP)	12
67	London HA-R 8303	JUST BEFORE DAWN (LP)	12

JENNIFER LEWIS

| 65 | Columbia DB 7662 | Bring It To Me/You Know | 4 |
| 66 | Columbia DB 7814 | I've Heard It All Before/Bad Storm Coming (with Angela Strange) | 4 |

JERRY LEWIS

56	Capitol CL 14559	I Keep Her Picture Hanging Upside Down/I Love A Murder Mystery	5
56	Capitol CL 14626	Buckskin Beauty/Pardners (B-side with Dean Martin)	5
57	Brunswick 05636	Rock-a-bye Your Baby With A Dixie Melody/Come Rain Or Come Shine	6
57	Brunswick 05672	Let Me Sing And I'm Happy/It All Depends On You	4
57	Brunswick 05693	With These Hands/My Mammy	4
57	Brunswick 05710	By Myself/No One	4
58	Brunswick 05727	Sad Sack/Shine On Your Shoes	4
58	Brunswick 05756	Dormi, Dormi, Dormi/Love Is A Lonely Thing	4
59	Brunswick 05777	Song From "The Geisha Boy"/The More I See You	4
53	Capitol LC 6591	CAPITOL PRESENTS JERRY LEWIS (10" LP)	12

JERRY LEE LEWIS

57	London HLS 8457	Whole Lotta Shakin' Goin' On/It'll Be Me	25
57	London HLS 8457	Whole Lotta Shakin' Goin' On/It'll Be Me (78)	10
57	London HLS 8529	Great Balls Of Fire/Mean Woman Blues	20
57	London HLS 8529	Great Balls Of Fire/Mean Woman Blues (78)	10
58	London HLS 8559	You Win Again/I'm Feelin' Sorry	25
58	London HLS 8559	You Win Again/I'm Feelin' Sorry (78)	20
58	London HLS 8592	Breathless/Down The Line	15
58	London HLS 8592	Breathless/Down The Line (78)	15
58	London HLS 8700	Break-Up/I'll Make It All Up To You	15
58	London HLS 8700	Break-Up/I'll Make It All Up To You (78)	20
59	London HLS 8780	High School Confidential/Fools Like Me	18
59	London HLS 8780	High School Confidential/Fools Like Me (78)	20
59	London HLS 8840	Lovin' Up A Storm/Big Blon' Baby	12
59	London HLS 8840	Lovin' Up A Storm/Big Blon' Baby (78)	20
59	London HLS 8941	Let's Talk About Us/The Ballad Of Billy Joe	10
59	London HLS 8941	Let's Talk About Us/The Ballad Of Billy Joe (78)	25
59	London HLS 8993	Little Queenie/I Could Never Be Ashamed Of You	12
59	London HLS 8993	Little Queenie/I Could Never Be Ashamed Of You (78)	30

(all the above 45s originally had triangular centres, later round centre pressings are worth around two thirds the value)

60	London HLS 9083	I'll Sail My Ship Alone/It Hurt Me So	8
60	London HLS 9131	Baby, Baby, Bye Bye/Old Black Joe	10
60	London HLS 9202	John Henry/Hang Up My Rock And Roll Shoes	8
61	London HLS 9335	What'd I Say/Livin' Lovin' Wreck	5
61	London HLS 9414	It Won't Happen With Me/Cold Cold Heart	7
61	London HLS 9446	As Long As I Live/When I Get Paid	7
62	London HLS 9526	I've Been Twistin'/Ramblin' Rose	7
62	London HLS 9584	Sweet Little Sixteen/How's My Ex Treating You	6
63	London HLS 9688	Good Golly Miss Molly/I Can't Trust Me (In Your Arms Anymore)	6
63	London HLS 9722	Teenage Letter/Seasons Of My Heart (B-side with Linda Gail Lewis)	6
63	Mercury AMT 1216	Hit The Road Jack/Pen And Paper	6
64	Philips BF 1324	I'm On Fire/Bread And Butter Man	8
64	London HLS 9867	Lewis Boogie/Bonnie B	10
65	Philips BF 1371	Hi-Heel Sneakers/You Went Back On Your Word	5
65	Philips BF 1407	Baby Hold Me Close/I Believe In You	6

65	Philips BF 1425	Rockin' Pneumonia And The Boogie Woogie Flu/This Must Be The Place	6
65	London HLS 9980	I Know What It Means/Carry Me Back To Old Virginia	8
66	Philips BF 1521	Memphis Beat/If I Had It All To Do Over	6
67	Philips BF 1594	It's A Hang-Up Baby/Holdin' On	6
67	Philips BF 1615	Turn On Your Love Light/Shotgun Man	6
68	Mercury MF 1020	Another Place, Another Time/Walking The Floor Over You	6
68	Mercury MF 1024	Great Balls Of Fire/Whole Lotta Shakin' Goin' On	5
68	London HLS 10193	What'd I Say/I've Been Twistin'	5
68	Mercury MF 1045	What's Made Milwaukee Famous (Has Made A Loser Out Of Me)/ All The Good Is Gone	4
69	Mercury MF 1088	To Make Love Sweeter For You/Let's Talk About Us	4
69	Mercury MF 1105	Long Tall Sally/Jenny, Jenny	7
69	Mercury MF 1110	Great Balls Of Fire/Whole Lotta Shakin' Goin' On	6
72	Mercury 6052 141	Chantilly Lace/Think About It Darlin'	5

(the below singles are all export issues)

58	London HL 7050	High School Confidential/Fools Like Me	18
62	London HL 7117	Save The Last Dance For Me/Hello Josephine	35
63	London HL 7120	Good Golly Miss Molly/I Can't Trust Me (In Your Arms Anymore)	15
63	London HL 7123	In The Mood/I'm Feelin' Sorry	35
58	London RE-S 1140	JERRY LEE LEWIS — No. 1 (EP, initially with triangular centre)	30/20
59	London RE-S 1186	JERRY LEE LEWIS — No. 2 (EP, initially with triangular centre)	30/20
59	London RE-S 1187	JERRY LEE LEWIS — No. 3 (EP)	25
61	London RE-S 1296	JERRY LEE LEWIS — No. 4 (EP)	25
62	London RE-S 1336	JERRY LEE LEWIS — No. 5 (EP)	20
63	London RE-S 1351	JERRY LEE LEWIS — No. 6 (EP)	20
63	London RE-S 1378	FOUR MORE FROM JERRY LEE LEWIS (EP)	25
66	Philips BE 12599	COUNTRY STYLE (EP)	14
70s	Sun JLL EP 001	THE FABULOUS JERRY LEE LEWIS VOL. 1 (EP, Fan Club issue)	12
70s	Sun JLL EP 002	THE FABULOUS JERRY LEE LEWIS VOL. 2 (EP, Fan Club issue)	12
59	London HA-S 2138	JERRY LEE LEWIS (LP)	40
62	London HA-S 2440	JERRY LEE LEWIS VOL. 2 (LP)	30
64	Philips BL 7622	GOLDEN HITS (LP)	15
65	Philips BL 7646	LIVE AT THE STAR CLUB, HAMBURG (LP, with Nashville Teens)	15
64	Philips BL 7650	THE GREATEST LIVE SHOW ON EARTH (LP)	15
67	Philips BL 7668	THE RETURN OF ROCK (LP)	16
65	London HA-S 8251	WHOLE LOTTA SHAKIN' GOIN' ON (LP)	35
66	Philips BL 7688	COUNTRY SONGS FOR CITY FOLKS (LP)	14
66	Philips BL 7706	MEMPHIS BEAT (LP)	15
66	Ember NR 5038	SUNSTROKE (LP, shared with Carl Perkins)	15
67	Philips (S)BL 7746	BY REQUEST — MORE GREATEST LIVE SHOW ON EARTH (LP, m/s)	14/16
67	London HA-S 8323	BREATHLESS (LP)	35

(all the above London LPs originally had plum labels; later black label reissues are worth £15-£20)

68	Mercury 20117 MCL	SOUL MY WAY (LP)	16
68	Fontana SFJL 964	GOT YOU ON MY MIND (LP)	12
69	Mercury SMWL 21011	ANOTHER TIME, ANOTHER PLACE (LP)	12
69	Mercury SMCL 21047	SHE STILL COMES AROUND (LP)	12
69	Mercury SMCL 20156	I'M ON FIRE (LP)	12
69	Mercury SMCL 20157	COUNTRY MUSIC HALL OF FAME HITS VOL. 1 (LP)	10
69	Mercury SMCL 20158	COUNTRY MUSIC HALL OF FAME HITS VOL. 2 (LP)	10
70	Mercury SMCL 20172	TOGETHER (LP, with Linda Gail Lewis)	12
70	Mercury 6338 010	SHE EVEN WOKE ME UP TO SAY GOODBYE (LP)	10
71	Mercury 6338 045	THERE MUST BE MORE TO LOVE THAN THIS (LP)	10
72	Mercury 6338 071	WOULD YOU TAKE ANOTHER CHANCE ON ME? (LP)	10
72	Mercury 6336 300	ROCKIN' WITH JERRY LEE LEWIS (LP)	10
72	Mercury 6338 088	THE KILLER ROCKS ON (LP)	10
73	Mercury 6672 008	THE SESSION (2-LP)	16
73	Mercury 6338 148	LIVE AT THE INTERNATIONAL HOTEL, LAS VEGAS (LP)	10
74	Mercury 6338 452	SOUTHERN ROOTS (LP)	10
74	Mercury 6338 496	FAN CLUB CHOICE (LP)	10
84	Sun SUN 102	THE SUN YEARS (12-LP, box set with booklet)	50

JIMMY LEWIS

| 68 | Minit MLF 11002 | The Girl From Texas/Let Me Know | 20 |

JOE 'CANNONBALL' LEWIS

| 51 | MGM MGM 430 | Train Whistle Nightmare/Trust Me Again (78) | 7 |

JOHN LEWIS

| 60 | London Jazz LTZ-K 15186 | IMPROVISED MEDITATIONS AND EXCURSIONS (LP) | 12 |
| 61 | London LTZ-K 15218 | MUSIC FOR BRASS — THE GOLDEN STRIKER (LP, also stereo SAH-K 6152) | 10 |

(see also Modern Jazz Quartet)

LEW LEWIS (REFORMER)

76	Stiff BUY 5	Caravan Man/Boogie On The Street (p/s, with Dr. Feelgood)	4
77	United Artists UP 36217	Out For A Lark/Watch Yourself	4
78	Lew Lewis LEW 1	Lucky Seven/Night Talk (500 only, plain white sleeve)	8
79	Stiff LEW 1	Lucky Seven/Night Talk (p/s, reissue)	4
79	Stiff BUY 48	Win Or Lose/Photo Finish (p/s, as Lew Lewis Reformer)	4

(see also Oil City Shieks, Dr. Feelgood)

LINDA LEWIS

| 67 | Polydor 56173 | You Turned My Bitter Into Sweet/Do You Believe | 40 |

MARGARET LEWIS

| 62 | Starlite ST45 081 | Sometin's Wrong Baby/John De Lee | 12 |

MEADE 'LUX' LEWIS

40s	Parlophone R 2187	Honky Tonk Train Blues/JEFF STACY: Barrelhouse (78)	15
40s	HMV B 8579	Honky Tonk Train/Whistlin' Blues (78)	20
40s	Brunswick 02187	Mr Freddy's Blues/I'm In The Mood (78)	15

Meade 'Lux' LEWIS

40s	Brunswick 02243	Yancey Special/Celeste Blues (78)	12
50s	Melodisc 1130	Boogie Tidal/Yancey's Pride (78)	8
50s	Melodisc 1136	Glendale Glide/Denapas Parade (78)	8
50s	Melodisc 1153	Randini's Boogie/Lux's Boogie (78)	8
55	Vogue EPV 1065	MEADE 'LUX' LEWIS (EP)	25
56	Melodisc EPM7 107	BOOGIE WOOGIE AND BLUES (EP)	25
56	Columbia Clef SEB 10030	BOOGIE WOOGIE PIANO AND DRUMS No. 1 (EP)	10
56	Columbia Clef SEB 10052	BOOGIE WOOGIE PIANO AND DRUMS No. 2 (EP)	10
57	Columbia Clef 33CX 10094	YANCEY'S LAST RIDE (LP)	20
57	HMV DLP 1176	OUT OF THE ROARING TWENTIES (10" LP)	20
60s	Philips 652 014 BL	HOUSE PARTY (LP)	20

MEADE 'LUX' LEWIS & SLIM GAILLARD

56	Columbia Clef 33C 9021	JAZZ AT THE PHILHARMONIC (10" LP)	20

(see also Slim Gaillard)

MEADE 'LUX' LEWIS, PETE JOHNSON & ALBERT AMMONS

40s	Parlophone R 2947	Café Society Rag/Lovin' Mama (78)	20
55	Columbia SEG 7528	ALBERT AMMONS, PETE JOHNSON & MEADE 'LUX' LEWIS SHOUT FOR JOY (EP)	15

(see also Albert Ammons, Pete Johnson)

MIA LEWIS

65	Decca F 12117	Wish I Didn't Love Him/This Is The End	4
65	Decca F 12240	It's Goodbye Now/The Luckiest Girl	4
66	Parlophone R 5526	Nothing Lasts Forever/(Baby) I'm Feeling Good	12
67	Parlophone R 5585	No Time For Lovin'/Onion	4
67	Parlophone R 5617	Woman's Love/You Won't Get Away	4

PATTI LEWIS

56	Columbia DB 3825	Earthbound/Happiness Street (Corner Sunshine Square)	5
57	Columbia DB 3923	Your Wild Heart/A Poor Man's Roses (Or A Rich Man's ...)	4
57	Columbia DB 3967	Pull Down De Shade/Speak For Yourself John	4

RAMSEY LEWIS (TRIO)

65	Chess CRS 8020	The 'In' Crowd/Since I Fell For You (as Ramsey Lewis Trio)	6
65	Chess CRS 8024	Hang On Sloopy/Movin' Easy (as Ramsey Lewis Trio)	5
66	Chess CRS 8029	A Hard Day's Night/'Tout A Doubt (as Ramsey Lewis Trio)	5
66	Chess CRS 8031	Hi-Heel Sneakers Pts 1 & 2 (as Ramsey Lewis Trio)	6
66	Chess CRS 8041	Wade In The Water/Ain't That Peculiar (as Ramsey Lewis Trio)	7
66	Chess CRS 8044	Uptight (Everything's Alright)/Money In The Pocket	6
67	Chess CRS 8051	Day Tripper/Hurt So Bad	10
67	Chess CRS 8055	1-2-3/Down By The Riverside	4
67	Chess CRS 8058	Function At The Junction/Hey Mrs. Jones	6
67	Chess CRS 8060	Saturday Night After The Movies/China Gate	4
67	Chess CRS 8061	Girl Talk/Dancing In The Street	6
67	Chess CRS 8064	Soul Man/Struttin' Lightly	5
69	Chess CRS 8096	Cry Baby Cry/Wade In The Water	4
70	Chess CRS 8104	Julia/Do What You Wanna	4
72	CBS 8280	Slipping Into Darkness/Collage	5
66	Chess CRE 6019	A HARD DAY'S NIGHT (EP, as Ramsey Lewis Trio)	7
65	Pye Jazz NJL 55	AT THE BOHEMIAN CAVERNS (LP)	12
65	Chess CRL 4511	THE IN CROWD (LP)	10
65	Chess CRL 4518	CHOICE! THE BEST OF RAMSEY LEWIS (LP)	10
66	Chess CRL 4520	HANG ON RAMSEY! (LP)	10
66	Chess CRL 4522	WADE IN THE WATER (LP)	10
67	Chess CRL 4528	GOIN' LATIN (LP)	10
67	Chess CRL 4531	THE MOVIE ALBUM (LP)	12
68	Chess CRL(S) 4533	DANCIN' IN THE STREET (LP)	12
68	Chess CRLS 4535	UP POPS RAMSEY LEWIS (LP)	10
68	Chess CRLS 4539	MAIDEN VOYAGE (LP)	10
68	Fontana SFJL 962	DOWN TO EARTH (LP)	10
73	CBS CQ 31096	UPENDO NI PAMOJA (LP, quadrophonic)	10

(see also Young-Holt Unlimited)

REGGIE LEWIS

72	Upsetter US 391	Natty Natty/UPSETTERS: Version	5

RICHARD LEWIS BAND

60	Downbeat CHA 1	Hey Little Girl/Hey, Little Boy	15

SMILEY LEWIS

53	London L 1189	Big Mamou/Play Girl (78)	75
56	London HLU 8312	One Night/Ain't Gonna Do It	400
56	London HLU 8312	One Night/Ain't Gonna Do It (78)	40
56	London HLU 8337	Down Yonder We Go Ballin'/Don't Be That Way (Please Listen To Me)	400
56	London HLU 8337	Down Yonder We Go Ballin'/Don't Be That Way (Please Listen To Me) (78)	40
57	London HLP 8367	Shame, Shame, Shame/No, No	275
57	London HLP 8367	Shame, Shame, Shame/No, No (78)	30
70	Liberty LBF 15337	I Hear You Knocking/Playgirl	6
70	Liberty LBS 83308	SHAME, SHAME, SHAME (LP)	15

STEVIE LEWIS

65	Mercury MF 871	Take Me For A Little While/My Whole World Seems To Be Tumbling Down	12
65	Mercury MF 919	Sometimes When You're Lonely/Under The Smile Of Love	5
65	Polydor 56003	Heard It All Before/Wild	4
69	RCA RCA 1840	I Can Try/Take A Little Warning	4

TAMALA LEWIS

79	Destiny DS 1010	You Won't Say Nothing/If You Can Stand Me	4

TINY LEWIS
60   Parlophone R 4617   Too Much Rockin'/I Get Weak 70

WEBSTER LEWIS
78   Epic EPC 84283   8 FOR THE 80'S (LP) 10

LEWIS & CLARKE EXHIBITION
67   RCA Victor RCA 1633   I Feel Good/Blue Revelations 4

LEWIS SISTERS
65   Tamla Motown TMG 536   You Need Me/Moonlight On The Beach 45

MONIQUE LEYRAC
68   SNB 55-3309   Time Time/Love Is Blue 5

JOHN LEYTON
60   Top Rank JAR 426   Tell Laura I Love Her/Goodbye To Teenage Love 30
60   HMV POP 798   The Girl On The Floor Above/Terry Brown's In Love With Mary Dee 60
61   Top Rank JAR 577   Johnny Remember Me/There Must Be 6
61   Top Rank JAR 585   Wild Wind/You Took My Love For Granted 6
61   HMV POP 956   Son This Is She/Six White Horses 5
62   HMV POP 992   Lone Rider/Heart Of Stone 8
62   HMV POP 1014   Lonely City/It Would Be Easy 5
62   HMV POP 1054   Down The River Nile/I Think I'm Falling In Love 6
62   HMV POP 1076   Lonely Johnny/Keep On Loving You 7
63   HMV POP 1122   Cupboard Love/Land Of Love 5
63   HMV POP 1175   I'll Cut Your Tail Off/The Great Escape 6
63   HMV POP 1204   On Lover's Hill/Lovers Lane 7
63   HMV POP 1230   I Guess You Are Always On My Mind/Beautiful Dreamer 6
64   HMV POP 1264   Make Love To Me/Missing You (as John Leyton & Le Roys) 6
64   HMV POP 1338   Don't Let Her Go Away/I Want A Love I Can See 8
64   HMV POP 1374   All I Want Is You/Every Day Is A Holiday (with Grazina Frame & Mike Sarne) 8
73   York SYK 551   Dancing In The Graveyard/Riversong 5
73   York YR 210   Rock 'N' Roll/Highway Song 5
62   Top Rank JKP 3016   JOHN LEYTON (EP) 25
62   HMV 7EG 8747   HIT PARADE (EP) 20
64   HMV 7EG 8843   BEAUTIFUL DREAMER (EP) 25
64   HMV 7EG 8854   TELL LAURA I LOVE HER (EP) 30
61   HMV CLP 1497   THE TWO SIDES OF JOHN LEYTON (LP) 30
62   HMV CLP 1664   ALWAYS YOURS (LP, with Charles Blackwell's Orchestra) 45
73   York FYK 416   JOHN LEYTON (LP) 12
(see also Le Roys)

LIAISON
82   Catweazle CR 001   Play It With A Passion/Caught In A ... (p/s) 6
83   Liaison LIC 101   LOOKING AFTER NUMBER ONE (EP) 5
84   Liaison LSN 0020   Only Heaven Knows/Ease The Pain Away (p/s) 4

LIAR
79   Bearsville K 55524   SET THE WORLD ON FIRE (LP) 10
79   Bearsville K 55524   SET THE WORLD ON FIRE (LP, picture disc) 12

LIBERACE
56   Columbia DB 3834   I Don't Care (As Long As You Care For Me)/As Time Goes By 6

LIBERATORS
65   Stateside SS 424   It Hurts So Much/You Look So Fine 4
(see also Pinkerton's Assorted Colours)

EVE LIBERTENE & CRASS
80s   Crass 1984/4   ACTS OF LOVE (LP, with book) 10
(see also Crass)

LIBERTY BELLES
71   Jay Boy BOY 40   Shing-A-Ling Time/Just Try Me 4

PEPE LIENHARD BAND
77   EMI EMI 2597   Swiss Lady/Shiny Red Balloon 4

LIEUTENANT PIGEON
73   Decca SKL 5154   MOULDY OLD MUSIC (LP) 10
74   Decca SKL 5174   PIGEON PIE (LP) 10
74   Decca SKL 5196   PIGEON PARTY (LP) 10
(see also Shel Naylor)

LIFE
73   Philips 6006 280   Cats Eyes/Death In The Family (paper or moulded label) 12/4

LIFE
69   Polydor 56778   Hands Of The Clock/Ain't I Told You Before 6
74   Polydor 2058 500   Woman/Bless My Soul 4
74   Polydor 2383 295   LIFE AFTER DEATH (LP) 35

LIFE AFTER LIFE
84   private pressing   LIFE AFTER LIFE (LP) 200

LIFE 'N' SOUL
67   Decca F 12659   Ode To Billy Joe/Peacefully Asleep 8
68   Decca F 12851   Here Comes Yesterday Again/Dear Paul 7

LIFETIME
69   Polydor 583 574   EMERGENCY (2-LP) 25
70   Polydor 2425 019   TURN IT OVER (LP) 15
(see also Tony Williams)

MINT VALUE £

JOE LIGGINS & HONEYDRIPPERS

40s	Parlophone R 3124	The Honeydripper Parts 1 And 2 (78)	45
40s	Parlophone R 3000 series	Pink Champagne/I've Got A Right To Cry (78)	45
50	Parlophone R 3309	I've Got The Right To Cry/Blue Moods (78)	20
76	Speciality SDN 5006	Pink Champagne/Honey Dripper	6

LEN LIGGINS

85	AAZ AAZ 4	A REMEDY FOR BAD NERVES (EP)	4

BEN LIGHT

56	HMV 7M 350	Bring Me A Bluebird/You	5

ENOCH LIGHT

59	Top Rank JAR 134	With My Eyes Wide Open/I Cried For You (as Enoch Light & Light Brigade)	4
59	Top Rank JAR 234	Scarlet Ribbons/Greensleeves (as Enoch Light & His Vibrant Strings)	4

LIGHT FANTASTIC

73	RCA RCA 2331	Jeanie/You Don't Care	20

GORDON LIGHTFOOT

62	Decca F 11527	(Remember Me) I'm The One/Daisy-Doo (as Gord Lightfoot)	5
63	Fontana 267 275TF	Negotiations/It's Too Late, He Wins (as Gordie Lightfoot)	5
63	Fontana TF 405	The Day Before Yesterday/Take Care Of Yourself (as Gordie Lightfoot)	5
65	United Artists UP 1109	Just Like Tom Thumb's Blues/Ribbon Of Darkness	6
66	Warner Bros WB 5621	I'm Not Sayin'/For Lovin' Me	4
68	President PT 138	Adios Adios/Is My Baby Blue Tonight	5
68	United Artists UP 2216	Black Day In July/Pussy Willow's Cat Tails	4
69	United Artists UP 2272	The Circle Is Small/Does Your Mother Know	4
69	United Artists UP 35020	Bitter Green/May I	4
69	United Artists UP 35036	Early Morning Rain/The Gypsy	4
72	Reprise K 14210	If You Could Read My Mind/Me And Bobby McGee/Summer Side/ Talking In Your Sleep (p/s)	4
68	United Artists SULP 1199	DID SHE MENTION MY NAME (LP)	10
69	United Artists SULP 1239	BACK HERE ON EARTH (LP)	10

PADDY LIGHTFOOT

50s	Melodisc EPM7 100	PADDY LIGHTFOOT (EP)	7

PAPA (GEORGE) LIGHTFOOT

69	Liberty LBF 15176	Wine Whiskey And Woman/SLIM HARPO: Something Inside Me	12
60s	Jan & Dil JR 451	MORE DOWN HOME BLUES (EP)	12
69	Liberty LBS 83353	NATCHEZ TRACE (LP, as Papa George Lightfoot)	12

TERRY LIGHTFOOT'S (NEW ORLEANS) JAZZMEN

57	Columbia DB 4032	I Saw Mommy Kissing Santa Claus/Winter Wonderland	4
58	Pye Jazz 7NJ 2018	My Bucket's Got A Hole In It/Good Time Swing	4
60	Columbia DB 4519	The Preacher/The Onions	4
56	Nixa Jazz NJT 503	JAZZ GUMBO VOLUME ONE (10" LP)	12
58	Columbia 33SX 1073	TRADITION IN COLOUR (LP)	12
61	Columbia 33SX 1290	TRAD PARADE (LP, with New Orleans Jazzmen, also stereo SCX 3354)	10/12
65	Columbia 33SX 1721	ALLEYCAT (LP, as Terry Lightfoot's Jazzmen)	10

LIGHTHOUSE

69	RCA RCA 1884	Eight Miles High/If There Ever Was A Time	6
72	Philips 6073 152	One Fine Morning/Little Kind Words	4
72	Philips 6073 153	Take It Slow/Sweet Lullaby	4
71	Vertigo 6342 010	ONE FINE MORNING (LP, gatefold sleeve, spiral label)	30
71	Vertigo 6342 011	THOUGHTS OF MOVIN' ON (LP, gatefold sleeve, spiral label)	30
70	RCA SF 8103	SUITE FEELING (LP)	15
70	RCA SF 8121	PEACING IT ALL TOGETHER (LP)	12

LIGHTNIN' SLIM

72	Blue Horizon 2096 013	Just A Little Bit/You're Old Enough To Understand/Mind Your Own Business	15
65	Stateside SL 10135	A LONG DRINK OF BLUES (LP, with Slim Harpo)	35
69	Python PLP 8	THE DOWNHOME BLUES PART 1 (LP)	25
70	Blue Horizon 7-63863	ROOSTER BLUES (LP)	40
72	Blue Horizon 2931 005	LONDON GUMBO (LP)	50
78	Flyright FLYLP 533	TRIP TO CHICAGO (LP)	10
79	Flyright FLYLP 583	THE FEATURE SIDES 1954 (LP)	10
80	Flyright FLYLP 612	WE GOTTA ROCK TONIGHT (LP)	10
	(see also Slim Harpo)		

LIGHTNING LEON

60s	Jan & Dil JR 450	DOWN HOME BLUES — SIXTIES STYLE (EP)	12

LIGHTNING RAIDERS

80	Arista ARIST 341	Psychedelik Music/Views (p/s)	5
81	Revenge REVS 200	Criminal World/Citizens (p/s)	12

LIGHTNING SEEDS

(see also Big In Japan, Care)

LIGHT OF THE WORLD

80	Ensign ENY 43	London Town/Pete's Crusade	4
80	Ensign ENY 4312	London Town/Pete's Crusade (12")	8
82	EMI EMI 5319	No. 1 Girl/Don't Run	5
82	EMI 12EMI 5319	No. 1 Girl/Don't Run (12")	8
79	Ensign ENVY 7	LIGHT OF THE WORLD (LP)	12
80	Ensign ENVY 14	ROUND TRIP (LP)	12
82	EMI EMC 3410	CHECK US OUT (LP)	15

LIKE A SONG

73	De Wolfe	LIKE A SONG (LP, library issue)	15

LILAC TIME
88	Swordfish LILAC 1	Return To Yesterday/Trumpets From Montparnasse (no p/s)	8
88	Swordfish 12 LILAC 1	Return To Yesterday/Railway Bazaar/Trumpets From Montparnasse/	
		Reunion Ball (12", p/s)	12
88	Swordfish SWF LP 6	THE LILAC TIME (LP, original)	12

(see also Hawks, Stephen Duffy, Tin Tin)

LIMAHL
83	EMI LMLP 1	Only For Love/O.T.T. (picture disc)	4

(see also Kajagoogoo)

LIMELIGHT
72	Deram DM 363	Baby Don't Get Hooked On Me/I'll See You On Sunday	4

LIMELIGHT
75	United Artists UP 35779	I Should Have Known Better/Tell Me Why	12

(see also Brinsley Schwarz)

LIMELIGHT
80	Future Earth FER 006	Metal Man/Hold Me Touch Me (p/s)	8
82	Future Earth FER 010	Ashes To Ashes/Knife In Your Back (p/s)	8
80	Future Earth FER 008	LIMELIGHT (LP)	30
81	Avatar	LIMELIGHT (LP, some with single)	30/15

LIMELIGHTERS
63	RCA Victor RD/SF 7581	FOURTEEN 14K FOLK SONGS (LP)	10

LIMEYS
65	Pye 7N 15820	I Can't Find My Way Through/Don't Cry (My Love)	6
65	Pye 7N 15909	Some Tears Fall Dry/Half Glass Of Wine	6
66	Decca F 12382	Cara-Lin/Feel So Blue	25
66	Decca F 12466	The Mountain's High/Lovin' Yourself	6

PETER LINCOLN
67	Major Minor MM 520	In The Day Of My Youth/My Monkey Is A Junkie	8

(see also Peter Sarstedt, Sarstedt Brothers, Brothers Kane)

PHILAMORE LINCOLN
68	NEMS 56-3711	Running By The River/Rainy Day	4

LINCOLNS
66	Parlophone R 5418	Mister Loneliness/Only Love Will Break Your Heart	4

LINCOLN X
63	Oriole CB 1823	Heartaches And Happiness/Stand In For Her Past	4

BOB LIND
66	Fontana TF 670	Elusive Butterfly/Cheryl's Goin' Home	4
66	Fontana TF 702	Remember The Rain/Truly Julie's Blues (I'll Be There)	4
66	Fontana TF 750	San Francisco Woman/Oh Babe Take Me Home	4
67	Verve VS 1501	Hey Nellie Nellie/Wandering	4
66	Fontana (S)TL 5340	DON'T BE CONCERNED (LP)	12
67	Fontana (S)TL 5395	PHOTOGRAPHS OF FEELINGS (LP)	10

DADDY LINDBERG
67	Columbia DB 8138	Shirl/Wade In The Shade	4

ANITA LINDBLOM
62	Fontana 267223 TF	Uptown/Mr Big Wheel	4

DENNIS LINDE
73	Elektra K 42149	DENNIS LINDE (LP)	10
74	Elektra K 52013	TRAPPED IN THE SUBURBS (LP)	10

KATHY LINDEN
58	Felsted AF 102	Billy/If I Could Hold You In My Arms	7
58	Felsted AF 105	You'd Be Surprised/Why Oh Why	7
58	Felsted AF 108	Oh! Johnny, Oh! Johnny!/Georgie	5
58	Felsted AF 111	Kissin' Conversation/Just A Sandy Haired Boy Called ...	7
59	Felsted AF 122	Goodbye Jimmy, Goodbye/Heartaches At Sweet Sixteen	5
59	Felsted AF 124	So Close To My Heart/You Don't Know Girls	6
60	Felsted AF 130	Think Love/Mary Lou Wilson And Johnny Brown	7
59	Felsted GEP 1001	KATHY (EP)	12
59	Felsted GEP 1002	KATHY'S IN LOVE VOLUME ONE (EP)	12
59	Felsted GEP 1004	KATHY'S IN LOVE VOLUME TWO (EP)	12

LINDISFARNE
70	Charisma CB 137	Clear White Light Pt II/Knacker's Yard Blues	10
71	Charisma CB 153	Lady Eleanor/Nothing But The Marvellous Is Beautiful (p/s)	6
72	Charisma CB 173	Meet Me On The Corner/Scotch Mist/No Time To Lose (p/s)	5
72	Charisma CB 191	All Fall Down/We Can Swing Together (live) (p/s)	5
74	Charisma CB 228	Taking Care Of Business/North Country Boy	4
85	LMP FOG 3	I Remember The Lights (Acappella Version)/Day Of The Jackal (p/s)	4
85	LMP FOG 4	CHRISTMAS (EP, sold at Christmas concerts)	6
88	River City LIND 2A	Save Our Ales/Save Our Ales (Sub Mix) (p/s)	4
90	Best ZA 44207	Fog On The Tyne (Revisited)/Fog On The Tyne (Revisited) (Instrumental)	
		(picture disc, by Gazza [Paul Gascoigne] & Lindisfarne)	4
70	Charisma CAS 1025	NICELY OUT OF TUNE (LP, pink label)	10

(see also Alan Hull)

MARK LINDSAY
71	CBS 7330	Been Too Long On The Road/All I Really See Is You	4
71	CBS 7551	Are You Old Enough/Don't You Know	4

(see also Paul Revere & Raiders)

TERRY LINDSAY
69	President PT 232	It's Over	5

VIRNA LINDT
81	Compact Org. ACT 1	Attention Stockholm/Episode 1 (p/s, yellow/purple or beige/black label)	4
81	Compact Org. ACT 3	Young And Hip/The Dossier Of Virna Lindt (p/s)	4

DAVID LINDUP ORCHESTRA
66	Columbia DB 7979	Informer Theme/Blue Mountain	4

LINDYS
60	Decca F 11253	The Train Of Love/You Know How Things Get Around	8
60	Decca F 11272	Boy With The Eyes Of Blue/Someone Else's Roses	6

LINES
78	Linear SJP 782	White Night/Barbican (p/s)	6
79	Illegal ILS 0011	White Night/Barbican (p/s, reissue)	4

BUZZY LINHART
69	Philips SBL 7885	BUZZY (LP)	10

LINKMEN
85	Kitchenware SK 17	Every Inch A King/Manic Depression (p/s)	4

ELMO LINN
63	Starlite ST45 101	Another Man's Arms/Sam Houston	10

LINN COUNTY
68	Mercury SMCL 20142	PROUD FLESH SOOTHSEER (LP)	15
69	Mercury SMCL 20165	FEVER SHOT (LP)	15
70	Philips SBL 7923	TILL THE BREAK OF DAWN (LP)	15

JOE LINTHECOME
50s	Poydras 87	Pretty Mama Blues/Hummingbird Blues (78)	12

LIONHEART
85	Epic A 5001	Die For Love/Dangerous Games	5
84	Epic EPC 26214	HOT TONIGHT (LP)	10

LIONS
69	Polydor 56757	Twisted Nerve/My Friend The Blackbird	4

LIONS OF JUDAH
69	Fontana TF 1016	Our Love's A Growin' Thing/Katja	8

JOE LIPMAN ORCHESTRA
54	MGM SP 1108	Looking Back To See/Stop	4

LIP MOVES
79	Tichonderoga HP 1	Guest/What Is (p/s with insert, stickered white labels, some signed)	8

LIQUID SMOKE
69	Avco 33005	LIQUID SMOKE (LP)	45

LISTEN
65	CBS 202456	You'd Better Run/Everybody's Gonna Say	125
	(see also Robert Plant, Led Zeppelin)		

LITTER
69	Probe CLPS 4504	EMERGE (LP)	20

'BIG' TINY LITTLE
57	Vogue Coral Q 72263	School Day/That's The Only Way To Live	25
57	Vogue Coral Q 72263	School Day/That's The Only Way To Live (78)	20
60	Coral FEP 2058	HONKY TONK PIANO VOL. 1 (EP)	7
60	Coral FEP 2059	HONKY TONK PIANO VOL. 2 (EP)	7

KENNY LITTLE & LITTLE PEOPLE
65	United Artists UP 1074	A Shot In The Dark/Never On A Sunday	4

MARIE LITTLE
72	Argo ZFB 19	FACTORY GIRL (LP)	100
73	Trailer LER 2084	MARIE LITTLE (LP)	20
87	private pressing	MY ELDORADO (LP)	10

LITTLE ABNER
57	Oriole CB 1380	Not Here, Not There/You Mean Everything To Me (78)	6

LITTLE ANGELS
87	Little Angels LAN 001	LITTLE AGELS 87 (12" EP)	35
88	Polydor LTL 1	90 Degrees In The Shade/England Rocks (live) (p/s)	6
88	Polydor LTLD 1	90 Degrees In The Shade/England Rocks (live) (poster p/s)	12
88	Polydor LTLX 1	90 Degrees In The Shade/Big Bad World/England Rocks (live) (12", p/s)	10
88	Polydor LTLXP 1	90 Degrees In The Shade/England Rocks (live) (shaped picture disc)	15
89	Polydor LTL 2	She's A Little Mover/Better Than The Rest (p/s)	6
89	Polydor LTLEP 2	THE BIG BAD EP (12")	10
89	Polydor LTLCD 2	THE BIG BAD EP (CD)	10
89	Polydor LTLXV 3	Do You Wanna Riot/Move In Slow/Some Kind Of Alien (live)/Snatch (10", p/s, red vinyl)	8
89	Polydor LTLXP 4	Don't Pray For Me (live)/She's A Little Angel (live)/Pleasure Pyre (live)/ Tie Your Mother Down (live) (12", poster p/s)	8
90	Polydor LTLB 5	Kickin' Up Dust/Kickin' Up Dust (live) (box set with poster)	4
90	Polydor LTLXP 5	Kickin' Up Dust (live)/Sex In Cars (live)/When I Get Out Of Here (live)/ Kick Hard (live) (12", picture disc)	7
90	Polydor LTLB 6	Radical Your Lover/Don't Love You No More (box set with poster)	7
90	Polydor LTLXP 6	GET RADICAL (12" EP, picture disc)	7
90	Polydor LTLT 7	She's A Little Angel/Sex In Cars (live) (in numbered tin)	5

90	Polydor APLTL 7	She's A Little Angel/Down On My Knees (poster p/s) 4
91	Polydor LTLXB 10	Young Gods (12", box set with poster, stencil & sticker) 7
91	Polydor LTLXG 11	I Ain't Gonna Cry (12", black metal tin) 8
87	Powerstation AMP 14	TOO POSH TO MOSH (mini-LP) 35

LITTLE ANTHONY & IMPERIALS

58	London HLH 8704	Tears On My Pillow/Two People In The World 30
58	London HLH 8704	Tears On My Pillow/Two People In The World (78) 20
59	London HL 8848	So Much/Oh Yeah 25
59	London HL 8848	So Much/Oh Yeah (78) 25
59	Top Rank JAR 256	Shimmy, Shimmy, Ko-Ko Bop/I'm Still In Love With You 15
60	Top Rank JAR 366	My Empty Room/Bayou, Bayou, Baby 15
64	United Artists UP 1065	I'm On The Outside Looking In/Please Go 8
64	United Artists UP 1073	Goin' Out Of My Head/Make It Easy On Yourself 6
65	United Artists UP 1083	Hurt So Bad/Reputation 10
65	United Artists UP 1098	Take Me Back/Our Song 6
65	United Artists UP 1112	I Miss You/Get Out Of My Life 6
66	United Artists UP 1126	Hurt/Never Again 6
66	United Artists UP 1137	Better Use Your Head/The Wonder Of It All 25
66	United Artists UP 1151	Gonna Fix You Good (Every Time You're Bad)/You Better Take It Easy Baby 30
67	United Artists UP 1189	My Love Is A Rainbow/You Only Live Twice 5
68	United Artists UP 2260	Let The Sunshine In/The Gentle Rain 4
69	United Artists UP 35017	Anthem/Goodbye Goodtimes 4
72	United Artists UP 35345	Gonna Fix You Good (Every Time You're Bad)/You Better Take It Easy Baby (reissue) 5
74	Janus 6146 005	Father Father/Each One Teach One 4
74	Janus 6146 012	Where Do I Begin/There's An Island 4
74	Avco 6105 031	La La La At the End/I Don't Have Time To Worry 4
76	United Artists UP 36118	Better Use Your Head/Gonna Fix You Good (Every Time You're Bad) 4
76	United Artists REM 405	Goin' Out Of My Head/I'm On The Outside Looking In/Hurt So Bad/ Gonna Fix You Good (Every Time You're Bad) 5
65	United Artists UEP 1004	LITTLE ANTHONY AND THE IMPERIALS (EP) 35
64	United Artists ULP 1089	I'M ON THE OUTSIDE LOOKING IN (LP) 30
66	United Artists ULP 1100	GOIN' OUT OF MY HEAD (LP) 20

LITTLE ARCHIE

| 68 | Atlantic 584 209 | I Need You/I Am A Carpet ....4 |

LITTLE BEN'S BANJOS

| 60 | Columbia DB 4467 | There Are Just Two I's In Dixie/Silly Little Tune ....4 |

LITTLE BEVERLEY

| 68 | Pama PM 731 | What A Guy/You're Mine ....6 |

LITTLE BILL & BLUE NOTES

| 59 | Top Rank JAR 176 | I Love An Angel/Bye, Bye Baby ....8 |

LITTLE BO BITCH

79	Cobra COB 1	It's Only Love/I'm Confused 5
80	Cobra COB 4	Take It Easy (Lights Out Over London)/Lorraine, Lorraine (p/s) 5
79	Cobra CBR 1002	LITTLE BO BITCH (LP) 12

LITTLE BOY BLUE

| 69 | Jackpot JP 701 | Dark End Of The Street (actually by Pat Kelly) ....5 |
| | *(see also Pat Kelly)* | |

LITTLE DARLING

| 67 | Blue Beat BB 325 | No One/BUSTER'S ALLSTARS: Congo Revolution ....8 |

LITTLE DARLINGS

| 65 | Fontana TF 539 | Little Bit O' Soul/Easy To Cry ....50 |

LITTLE DIPPERS

| 60 | Pye Intl. 7N 25051 | Forever/Two By Four ....6 |
| 61 | London HLG 9269 | Lonely/I Wonder, I Wonder, I Wonder ....7 |

LITTLE ESTHER

(see under Little Esther Phillips)

LITTLE EVA

62	London HL 9581	The Locomotion/He Is The Boy 5
62	London HLU 9633	Keep Your Hands Off My Baby/Where Do I Go 6
63	London HLU 9687	Let's Turkey Trot/Old Smokey Locomotion 6
63	Colpix PX 11013	The Trouble With Boys/What I Gotta Do (To Make You Jealous) 6
63	Colpix PX 11019	Please Hurt Me/Let's Start The Party Again 6
64	Colpix PX 11035	Run To Her/Making With The Magilla 7
65	Stateside SS 477	Stand By Me/That's My Man 10
63	London HA-U 8036	L-L-L-L-LOCO-MOTION (LP, original with plum label & laminated sleeve) 30
72	London SH-U 8437	L-L-L-L-LOCO-MOTION (LP, stereo reissue, plum label, boxed label logo) 10
	(see also Big Dee Irwin & Little Eva, Luther & Little Eva)	

LITTLE FREE ROCK

| 69 | Transatlantic TRA 608 | LITTLE FREE ROCK (LP) ....70 |
| | *(see also David John & Mood)* | |

LITTLE GEORGE

| 64 | Rio R 45 | Mary Anne/EDWARDS ALLSTARS: Blue Night ....8 |

LITTLE GRANTS & EDDIE (Grant)

67	President PT 159	Rudy's Dead/Everything's Alright 5
67	President PT 172	Rock Steady '67/Bingo 5
	(see also Equals)	

LITTLE HANK
66	London HLU 10090	Mr. Bang Bang Man/Don't You Know (withdrawn)	35
70	Monument MON 1045	Mr. Bang Bang Man/Don't You Know	8

LITTLE HELEN
79	Destiny DS 1015	You're Ready Now/CHICO REVILLE: This Beautiful Day	4

LITTLE JOE (& THRILLERS)
60	Fontana H 281	Stay (as Little Joe & Thrillers)/Cherry	12
63	Reprise R 20142	Peanuts/No No I Can't Stop	4

LITTLE JOEY & FLIPS
62	Pye Intl. 7N 25152	Bongo Stomp/Lost Love	7

LITTLE JOHN
67	Pama PM 702	Let's Get Married/Around The World	5

LITTLE JOHNNY & THREE TEENAGERS
58	Decca F 10990	Baby Lover/Rickety Rackety Rendezvous	10

LITTLE LUMAN
64	Rio R 44	Hurry Harry/R. ALPHONSE: Hucklebuck (B-side actually by Roland Alphonso)	8

LITTLE LUTHER
64	Pye Intl. 7N 25266	Eenie Meenie Minie Moe/Twirl	35

LITTLE MACK & BOSS SOUNDS
66	Atlantic 584 031	In The Midnight Hour/You Can't Love Me (In The Midnight Hour)	7

LITTLE MILTON
65	Pye Intl. 7N 25289	Blind Man/Blues In The Night	8
65	Chess CRS 8013	We're Gonna Make It/Can't Hold Back The Tears	10
65	Chess CRS 8018	Who's Cheating Who?/Ain't No Big Deal On You	12
69	Chess CRS 8087	Grits Ain't Groceries/I Can't Quit You Baby	10
69	Chess CRS 8101	Let's Get Together/I'll Always Love You	10
73	Stax 2025 095	That's What Love Will Make You Do/I'm Living Off The Love You Give	5
74	Stax STXS 2003	Behind Closed Doors/Bet You I Win	6
75	Stax STA 100	If That Ain't A Reason/Mr. Mailman	4
69	Chess CRLS 4552	GRITS AND GROCERIES (LP)	12
74	Stax STX 1013	BLUES 'N' SOUL (LP)	10

(see also Roy Milton)

LITTLE NORMA & LAUREL (Aitken)
64	Dice CC 26	Ten Commandments Of Woman/BUSTER'S ALLSTARS: The Hunter	7

LITTLE RED SCHOOLHOUSE
80S	Waterfall WFL 3	Aged Bee/HURT: Take My Breath (free with 'Jump Away' fanzine)	5/4

LITTLE RICHARD
56	London HLO 8336	Rip It Up/Ready Teddy (gold lettering on labels, later silver lettering)	85/40
56	London HLO 8336	Rip It Up/Ready Teddy (78)	10
57	London HLO 8366	Long Tall Sally/Tutti Frutti (gold lettering on labels, later silver lettering)	75/35
57	London HLO 8366	Long Tall Sally/Tutti Frutti (78)	10
57	London HLO 8382	The Girl Can't Help It/She's Got It (gold lettering on labels, later silver)	80/45
57	London HLO 8382	The Girl Can't Help It/She's Got It (78)	10

(the above three 45s were later pressed with silver-top labels & round centres, which are worth £18 each)

57	London HLO 8446	Lucille/Send Me Some Lovin' (as Little Richard & His Band)	22
57	London HLO 8446	Lucille/Send Me Some Lovin' (as Little Richard & His Band) (78)	10
57	London HLO 8470	Jenny, Jenny/Miss Ann (as Little Richard & His Band)	20
57	London HLO 8470	Jenny, Jenny/Miss Ann (as Little Richard & His Band) (78)	10
57	London HLO 8509	Keep A Knockin'/Can't Believe You Wanna Leave	22
57	London HLO 8509	Keep A Knockin'/Can't Believe You Wanna Leave (78)	10
58	London HLU 8560	Good Golly Miss Molly/Hey-Hey-Hey-Hey	18
58	London HLO 8560	Good Golly Miss Molly/Hey-Hey-Hey-Hey (78)	12
58	London HLO 8647	Ooh! My Soul/True, Fine Mama	15
58	London HLO 8647	Ooh! My Soul/True, Fine Mama (78)	12
58	London HLU 8770	Baby Face/I'll Never Let You Go	8
58	London HLU 8770	Baby Face/I'll Never Let You Go (78)	15
59	London HLU 8831	By The Light Of The Silvery Moon/Early One Morning	8
59	London HLU 8831	By The Light Of The Silvery Moon/Early One Morning (78)	18
59	London HLU 8868	Kansas City/She Knows How To Rock	12
59	London HLU 8868	Kansas City/She Knows How To Rock (78)	20

(the above 45s originally had triangular centres, round centre pressings are worth half to two-thirds the value)

60	London HLU 9065	Baby/I Got It	10
60	London HLU 9065	Baby/I Got It (78)	40
61	Mercury AMT 1165	Joy Joy Joy (Down In My Heart)/He's Not Just A Soldier	6
62	Mercury AMT 1189	He Got What He Wanted (But He Lost What He Had)/Why Don't You Change Your Ways?	6
63	London HLK 9708	Crying In The Chapel/Hole In The Wall	8
63	London HLK 9756	Travelin' Shoes/It Is No Secret	8
64	London HL 9896	Bama Lama Bama Loo/Annie's Back	8
64	Fontana TF 519	Blueberry Hill/Cherry Red	8
64	Stateside SS 340	Whole Lotta Shakin' Goin' On/Goodnight Irene	8
64	Mercury MF 841	Joy, Joy, Joy (Down In My Heart)/Peace In The Valley	5
66	Fontana TF 652	I Don't Know What You've Got But It's Got Me Pts 1 & 2	8
66	Stateside SS 508	Holy Mackerel/Baby, Don'tcha Want A Man Like Me?	8
66	Sue WI 4001	Dance What You Wanna/Without Love	15
66	Sue WI 4015	It Ain't Watcha Do/Crossover	15
66	Columbia DB 7974	Poor Dog/Well	18
66	Columbia DB 8058	I Need Love/The Commandments Of Love	12
67	Columbia DB 8116	Get Down With It/Rose Mary	30
67	Columbia DB 8240	A Little Bit Of Something/Money	30

67	Columbia DB 8263	Hurry Sundown/I Don't Want To Discuss It	18
68	MCA MU 1006	She's Together/Try Some Of Mine	5
68	London HLU 10194	Good Golly Miss Molly/Lucille	4
68	President PT 201	Whole Lotta Shakin' Goin' On/Lawdy Miss Clawdy	4
69	Action ACT 4528	Baby What Do You Want Me To Do Pts 1 & 2	8
70	Reprise RS 20907	Dew Drop In/Freedom Blues	4
71	President PT 329	Without Love/Talkin' 'Bout Soul	4
71	Reprise K 14124	Green Power/Dancing In The Street	4
72	Reprise K 14150	Money Is/Money Runner	4

(the below singles are all export issues)

57	London HL 7022	Jenny, Jenny/Miss Ann (as Little Richard & His Band)	12
58	London HL 7049	Ooh! My Soul/True, Fine Mama	8
58	London HL 7056	Baby Face/I'll Never Let You Go	7
59	London HL 7074	She Knows How To Rock/Early One Morning	12
59	London HL 7079	By The Light Of The Silvery Moon/Kansas City	10
59	London HL 7085	Whole Lotta Shakin' Goin' On/All Around The World	30
68	Decca AD 1006	She's Together/Try Some Of Mine	12
57	London RE-O 1071	LITTLE RICHARD AND HIS BAND VOL. 1 (EP, gold tri centre, later silver)	20/12
57	London RE-O 1074	LITTLE RICHARD AND HIS BAND VOL. 2 (EP, gold tri centre, later silver)	20/12
57	London RE-O 1103	LITTLE RICHARD AND HIS BAND VOL. 3 (EP)	15
57	London RE-O 1106	LITTLE RICHARD AND HIS BAND VOL. 4 (EP)	15
59	London RE-U 1208	LITTLE RICHARD AND HIS BAND VOL. 5 (EP)	18
60	London RE-U 1234	LITTLE RICHARD AND HIS BAND VOL. 6 (EP)	20
60	London RE-U 1235	LITTLE RICHARD AND HIS BAND VOL. 7 (EP)	22

(the above EPs originally came with tri centres, later round centre reissues are worth two-thirds of silver label values)

62	Summit LSE 2049	FOUR DYNAMIC NUMBERS (EP, 2 each by Little Richard & Brock Peters)	10
63	London REK 1400	HE'S BACK (EP)	12
64	Vocalion VEP 170155	MEMPHIS SLIM AND LITTLE RICHARD (EP)	45
66	Stateside SE 1042	DO YOU FEEL IT (EP)	15
57	London HA-O 2055	HERE'S LITTLE RICHARD (LP, flipback, rear sleeve initially in gloss red)	45/35
57	London HA-O 2055	HERE'S LITTLE RICHARD (LP, small flipback or non-flipback sleeve)	30/25
58	London HA-U 2126	LITTLE RICHARD VOL. 2 (LP, flipback or non-flipback sleeve)	35/30
59	RCA Camden CDN 125	LITTLE RICHARD (LP, 8 tracks only; others by Buck Ram Orchestra)	20
59	London HA-U 2193	THE FABULOUS LITTLE RICHARD (LP, flipback or non-flipback sleeve)	35/30
60	Top Rank 25/025	PRAY ALONG WITH LITTLE RICHARD VOL. 1: A CLOSER WALK WITH THEE (LP, plain white sleeve, mail-order only)	40
60	Top Rank 25/026	PRAY ALONG WITH LITTLE RICHARD VOL. 2: I'M QUITTING SHOW BUSINESS (LP, plain white sleeve, mail-order only)	60
62	Egmont EGM 9207	SINGS FREEDOM SONGS (LP, reissue of Top Rank 25/025)	15
63	Egmont EGM 9270	PRAY ALONG WITH LITTLE RICHARD (LP)	15
64	Stateside SL 10054	SINGS GOSPEL (LP)	18
64	Coral LVA 9220	COMING HOME (LP)	18
65	Fidelio ATL 4124	SINGS GOSPEL (LP, 4 tracks by Brock Peters but credited to Little Richard)	12
65	Summit ATL 4124	SINGS GOSPEL (LP, 4 tracks by Brock Peters, overprinted front cover)	10
65	Dial DLP 4124	SINGS GOSPEL (LP, 4 tracks by Brock Peters, correctly credited)	10
65	Mercury MCL 20036	IT'S REAL (LP)	12
65	Fontana TL 5235	IS BACK! (LP)	15
65	Ember NR 5022	REALLY MOVIN' GOSPEL (LP, 3 tracks by Sister Rosetta Tharpe)	12
66	Fontana TL 5314	GREAT HITS (LP)	12
67	Columbia S(C)X 6136	THE EXPLOSIVE LITTLE RICHARD (LP)	20
67	Polydor 236 202	THE INCREDIBLE LITTLE RICHARD (LP)	10
68	Fontana SFL 13010	KING OF THE GOSPEL SINGERS (LP)	10
70	Reprise RSLP 6406	THE RILL THING (LP)	10
70	Specialty SNTF 5001	ROCK HARD, ROCK HEAVY (LP)	10
71	Epic EPC 66285	CAST A LONG SHADOW (LP)	10
71	Reprise K 44156	THE KING OF ROCK AND ROLL (LP)	10

(see also Canned Heat)

LITTLE ROOSTERS

79	Pye 7P 152	She Cat Sister Floozie/Roostering With Intent (no p/s)	5
80	Ami AIS 101	That's How Strong My Love Is/Suspicious (no p/s)	4
80	Ami AIS 107	I Need A Witness/The Age Of Reason (no p/s)	4

(see also Cocksparrer)

LITTLE SAL with DANDY & SUPERBOYS

68	Giant GN 19	I'm In The Mood/I'm A Lover	5

(see also Dandy & Superboys, Superboys)

LITTLE SISTERS

63	MGM MGM 1192	Goin' To Boston/Where Does It Lead	4

LITTLE SONNY

71	Stax 2363 005	NEW KING OF THE BLUES HARMONICA (LP)	10

LITTLE SUZIE

61	Warner Bros WB 35	Young Love/The Boy I Left Behind	4

LITTLE TONY & HIS BROTHERS

58	Durium DRS 54008	Let Her Go/What Did I Do	6
59	Durium DC 16639	Who's That Knockin'/The Beat	12
59	Durium DC 16657	Four An' Twenty Thousand Kisses/Bella Marie	7
59	Decca F 11164	I Can't Help It/Arrivederci Baby	6
59	Decca F 11169	The Hippy Hippy Shake/Hey Little Girl	8
59	Decca F 11190	Too Good/Foxy Little Mama	6
60	Decca F 21218	I Love You/The Magic Of Love	6
60	Decca F 21223	Princess/I Love You	7
60	Decca F 21247	Kiss Me, Kiss Me/Teddy Girl	8
58	Durium U 20058	PRESENTING LITTLE TONY AND HIS BROTHERS (EP)	25
50s	Durium	LITTLE TONY (LP)	25

LITTLE RED WALTERS

LITTLE RED WALTERS
60s	XX MIN 706	DARK MUDDY BOTTOM (EP)	7

LITTLE WALTER
60	London HLM 9175	My Babe/Blue Midnight	25
64	Pye Intl. 7N 25263	My Babe/You Better Watch Yourself	10
56	London REU 1061	LITTLE WALTER AND HIS JUKES (EP)	70
64	Pye Intl. NPL 28043	LITTLE WALTER (LP)	25
67	Chess CRL 4529	SUPER BLUES (LP, with Bo Diddley & Muddy Waters)	15
68	Marble Arch MAL 815	LITTLE WALTER (LP, reissue)	10
69	Python PLP-KM 20	LITTLE WALTER AND HIS DUKES (LP)	25

LITTLE WILBUR (& PLEASERS)
57	Vogue V 9091	Plaything/I Don't Care	125
57	Vogue V 9091	Plaything/I Don't Care (78)	45
58	Vogue V 9097	Heart To Heart/Alone In The Night (solo)	125
58	Vogue V 9097	Heart To Heart/Alone In The Night (solo) (78)	45

(see also Wilbur Whitfield)

LIVELY ONES
63	London HA 8082	SURF DRUMS (LP)	25
63	London HA 8107	SURF RIDER (LP)	25

LIVELY SET
65	Pye 7N 15880	Don't Call My Name/What Kind Of Love	4
66	Capitol CL 15472	Let The Trumpets Sound/The Green Years	4

LIVERPOOL FISHERMEN
71	Mushroom 150 MR 9	SWALLOW THE ANCHOR (LP)	150

(see also Brian Jacques & Brigantine)

LIVERPOOL SCENE
68	RCA RCA 1762	Son Son/Baby	4
69	RCA RCA 1816	The Woo Woo/Love Is	4
67	CBS 63045	THE INCREDIBLE NEW LIVERPOOL SCENE (LP)	18
68	RCA SF 7995	THE AMAZING ADVENTURES OF LIVERPOOL SCENE (LP)	12
69	RCA SF 8057	BREAD ON THE NIGHT (LP)	12
70	RCA SF 8100	ST. ADRIAN CO. BROADWAY & 3RD (LP)	12
70	RCA SF 8134	HEIRLOON (LP)	12

(see also Clayton Squares, Adrian Henri, Brian Patten, Mike Hart, Andy Roberts, Grimms)

KERRY LIVGREN('S AD)
84	CBS	TIME LINE (LP)	12
85	Kerygma	ART OF THE STATE (LP, as Kerry Livgren's Ad)	12

RICKY LIVID & TONE DEAFS
64	Parlophone R 5136	Tomorrow/Nuts And Bolts	4

LIVING COLOUR
88	Epic LCLP 1	Middle Man/Desperate People (shaped picture disc)	5
88	Epic LCLG 2	Glamour Boys/Which Way To America (PVC 'glitter' p/s)	4
88	Epic CTLCL 2	Glamour Boys/Which Way To America (picture disc)	4
88	Epic LCLB 3	Cult Of Personality/Open Letter To A Landlord (box set)	4
88	Epic CDLCL 3	Cult Of Personality/Open Letter To A Landlord/Middle Man (live) (CD)	7
89	Epic LCLQ 4	Open Letter (To A Landlord)/Cult Of Personality (live) (poster p/s)	4
89	Epic LCLP 5	Cult Of Personality/Open Letter To A Landlord (reissue, picture disc)	4

LIVING DAYLIGHTS
67	Philips BF 1561	Let's Live For Today/I'm Real (B-side actually "It's Real")	15
67	Philips BF 1613	Always With Him/Baila Maria	25

(see also Greatest Show On Earth)

LIVING IN TEXAS
83	Rhythmic RMNS 2	And David Cried/And Dem Bahnhoff (p/s)	8
83	Rebirth RB 20	My End Of Heaven/Awaken/Soul & The Silent Gods/Julia's Child (12", p/s)	8

LIZA & JET SET
65	Parlophone R 5248	How Can I Know?/Dancing Yet	10

LIZZIE & DELROY WILSON
71	Jackpot JP 771	Double Attack/AGGRAVATORS: The Sniper	4

LIZZY
73	Duke DU 161	Love Is A Treasure/FREDDIE McKAY: Love Is A Treasure	5

LIZZY & DENNIS (Alcapone)
70	Ackee ACK 114	Happy Go Lucky Girl/BOBBY & DAVE: Sammy	5

LIZZY & PARAGONS
70	Ackee ACK 118	On The Beach/DAVE BARKER: Maria	5

LLAN
66	CBS 202405	Realise/Anytime	20

(see also Vogues)

A.L. LLOYD
60	Topic 12T 51	OUTBACK BALLADS (LP)	12
65	Topic 12T 135	BIRD IN THE BUSH (LP)	12

(see also Peggy Seeger)

CHARLES LLOYD (QUARTET)
67	Atlantic 584 125	Sombrero Sam Pts 1 & 2	6
67	Atlnatic 587/588 077	LOVE-IN (LP)	15
68	Atlantic 587/588 101	JOURNEY WITHIN (LP)	15
68	Atlantic 588 108	CHARLES LLOYD IN EUROPE (LP)	12

FRED LLOYD
65 Polydor 56055   Girl From Chelsea/You Kissed Him 4

JERRY LLOYD
60 Top Rank JAR 411   Be Faithful, Be True/Sooner Or Later 4

JIMMY LLOYD
58 Philips PB 795   The Prince Of Players/Ever Since I Met Lucy 6
58 Philips PB 827   Witch Doctor/For Your Love 8
58 Philips PB 871   The End/Street In The Rain 4
59 Philips PB 909   I Kneel At Your Throne/Sapphire 4
60 Philips PB 1010   Teenage Sonata/Falling 6
60 Philips PB 1055   I Double Dare You/Just For A Thrill 4
61 Philips PB 1120   Pony Time/Three Handed Woman 5
61 Philips PB 1157   Yellow Bird/Without The Sun 5
61 Philips PB 1201   I'm Coming Home/You Are My Sunshine 5
62 Philips 326 527 BF   True Love/Mother Nature And Father Time 4
63 Philips 326 568 BF   Call On Me/Humma Humma Humma Humming Bird 6
59 Philips BBE 12186   FOCUS ON JIMMY LLOYD (EP) 7
62 Philips BBE 12509   YOU ARE MY SUNSHINE (EP) 7

KATHY LLOYD
54 Decca F 10386   It Worries Me/Tomorrow Night 4
54 Decca F 10418   Teach Me Tonight/It's A Woman's World 4
55 Decca F 10464   Our Future Has Only Begun/Unsuspecting Heart 4
55 Decca F 10567   Experience Unnecessary/This Must Be Wrong (with Ted Heath Music) 4

PEGGY LLOYD
55 London REP 1017   DIXIELAND HONKY TONK (EP) 12

LLOYD (Robinson) & DEVON (Russell)
67 Punch PH 14   Love Is The Key/VIRTUES: High Tide 4
68 Blue Cat BS 151   Out Of The Fire/Can't Understand (B-side actually by Austin Faithful) 6

LLOYD (Robinson) & GLEN (Brown)
67 Coxsone CS 7011   That Girl/You Got Me Wrong 12
67 Doctor Bird DB 1058   Jezebel/TOMMY McCOOK & SUPERSONICS: Jam Session 10
67 Doctor Bird DB 1071   Keep On Pushing/BOBBY AITKEN & CARIBBEATS: You Won't Regret
                                 (B-side actually by Lloyd & Glen) 10

LLOYD (Jackson) & GROOVERS
67 Caltone TONE 108   Do It To Me Baby/DIPLOMATS: Meet Me At The Corner 8
68 Caltone TONE 109   My Heart My Soul/DIPLOMATS, with TOMMY McCOOK/
                                 SUPERSONICS: Going Along 8
68 Caltone TONE 112   Listen To The Music/DIPLOMATS: Strong Man 8
    (see also Groovers)

LLOYD & JOHNNY
68 Island WI 3158   My Argument/GEORGE DEKKER: Foey Man 8

LLOYD'S ALLSTARS
69 Doctor Bird DB 1178   Love Kiss Blue/UNIQUES: Secretly 10

LLOYDIE & LOWBITES
71 Lowbite LOW 001   CENSORED! (LP) 15
    (see also Lloyd Tyrell/Charmers)

LLYGOD FFYRNIG
78 Pwdwr PWDWR 1   N.C.B./Sais/Cariad Y Bus Stop (p/s) 20

LOADED FORTY-FOURS
81 X-S TL 44/1   Thunderbirds (Are Go!)/T.V. Child (p/s) 4

DICKIE LOADER
61 Palette PG 9015   Heatwave/Happiness 15

JOSEF LOCKE
53 Columbia SCM 5008   My Heart And I/Goodbye 6
53 Columbia SCM 5009   Hear My Song, Violetta/The Soldier's Dream 6

LOCKETS
63 Pye Intl. 7N 25232   Don't Cha Know/Little Boy 10

LOCKJAW
77 Raw RAW 8   Radio Call Sign/The Young Ones (p/s) 6
78 Raw RAW 19   Journalist Jive/I'm A Virgin/A Doonga Doonga (p/s) 8
    (see also Cure)

HANK LOCKLIN
60 RCA RCA 1188   Please Help Me, I'm Falling/My Old Home Town 5
60 RCA RCA 1188   Please Help Me, I'm Falling/My Old Home Town (78) 30
61 RCA RCA 1252   You're The Reason/Happy Birthday To Me 4
62 RCA RCA 1273   From Here To There To You/This Song Is Just for You 4
62 RCA RCA 1305   Welcome Home, Mr. Blues/We're Gonna Go Fishin' 4
63 RCA RCA 1336   Flyin' South/Behind The Footlights 4
63 RCA RCA 1370   Wooden Soldier/Kiss On The Door 4
64 RCA RCA 1391   You Never Want To Love Me/Followed Closely By My Teardrops 4
65 RCA RCA 1458   Faith And Truth/Forty Nine, Fifty One 4
66 RCA RCA 1510   I Feel A Cry Coming On/Insurance 5
66 RCA RCA 1548   The Last Thing On My Mind/The Best Part Of Loving You 4
67 RCA RCA 1575   It Is Love/The Upper Room 4
67 RCA RCA 1610   Wishing On A Star/Hasta Luego 4
67 RCA RCA 1641   The Country Hall Of Fame/Evergreen 4
68 RCA RCA 1678   Love Song For You/Little Geisha Girl 4

Hank LOCKLIN

68	RCA RCA 1729	Everlasting Love/I'm Slowly Going Out Of Your Mind	4
58	RCA RCX 115	COUNTRY GUITAR VOL. 3 (EP)	10
62	RCA RCX 217	SEVEN DAYS (EP)	10
63	Parlophone GEP 8875	ENCORES (EP)	15
63	RCA RCX 7116	WALTZ OF THE WIND (EP)	10
64	RCA RCX 7150	IRISH SONGS COUNTRY STYLE (EP)	8
61	RCA RD 27201	PLEASE HELP ME, I'M FALLING (LP)	15
64	RCA RD 7623	IRISH SONGS COUNTRY STYLE (LP)	12
65	Fontana FJL 305	BORN TO RAMBLE (LP)	10

GERRY LOCKRAN

69	Decca F 12873	Hey Jude/This Train	4
69	Decca F 12919	Standing On Your Own/You're Not There	4
67	Planet PLL 1002	HOLD ON, I'M COMING (LP)	50
68	Waverley ZLP 2091	BLUES VENDETTA (LP)	20
69	Saga FID 2165	BLUES AT SUNRISE (LP)	12
69	Spark SRLP 104	THE ESSENTIAL (LP)	15
72	Polydor 2383 122	WUN (LP)	10
76	Decca SKL-R 5257	RAGS TO GLADRAGS (LP)	10

GERRY LOCKRAN, REDD SULLIVAN, DAVE TRAVIS

| 69 | Fidelity FID 2165 | BLUES AT SUNRISE (LP) | 10 |

MALCOLM LOCKYER ORCHESTRA

54	Decca F 10304	I'm Gonna Rock, Rock, Rock/Changing Partners (78, as Malcolm Lockyer & His Strict Tempo Music For Dancing)	5
61	HMV POP 929	"The Pursuers" T.V. Theme/Stranger Than Fiction	4
65	Columbia DB 7552	The Intelligence Men/Brighton Run	4
65	Columbia DB 7663	The Eccentric Dr. Who/Daleks And Thals	10

LOCOMOTIVE

67	Direction 58-3114	Rudy A Message To You/Broken Heart	7
68	Parlophone R 5718	Rudi's In Love/Never Set Me Free	6
69	Parlophone R 5758	Mr. Armageddon/There's Got To Be A Way	10
69	Parlophone R 5801	I'm Never Gonna Let You Go/You Must Be Joking	10
70	Parlophone R 5835	Movin' Down The Line/Roll Over Mary	8
71	Parlophone R 5915	Rudi's In Love/You Must Be Joking	5
69	Parlophone PCS 7093	WE ARE EVERYTHING YOU SEE (LP)	120

(see also Brumbeats, Norman Haines Band)

NILS LOFGREN

76	CBS 4339	Soft Fun/Slippery Fingers	4
79	A&M AMS 7455	Shine Silently/Kool Skool (p/s, coloured vinyl)	4
85	Towerbell TOWG 68	Secrets In The Street/From The Heart//Message/Little Bit Of Time (double pack)	5
85	Towerbell TOWTX 73	Flip Ya Flip/Message (12", picture disc)	7

(see also Grin, Crazy Horse, Bruce Springsteen)

LOFT

84	Creation CRE 009	Why Does The Rain/Like (foldaround p/s in poly bag)	14
85	Creation CRE 015	Up The Hill And Down The Slope/Lonely Street (foldaround p/s in poly bag)	12
85	Creation CRE 015T	Up The Hill And Down The Slope/Your Door Shines Just Like Gold/Time/Lonely Street (12", p/s)	8

(see also Weather Prophets, Caretaker Race)

CRIPPLE CLARENCE LOFTON

59	Vogue EPV 1209	CRIPPLE CLARENCE LOFTON (EP)	18
54	London AL 3531	A LOST RECORDING DATE (10" LP)	30
55	Vogue LDE 122	JAZZ IMMORTALS NO. 1 (10" LP)	30

JOHNNY LOGAN

| 87 | Epic LOGQ 1 | Hold Me Now/Living A Lie (poster p/s) | 4 |

CHRISTOPHER LOGUE & TONY KINSEY

| 58 | Parlophone GEP 8765 | RED BIRD JAZZ AND POETRY (EP) | 8 |

LOK

| 81 | Fetish FET 1 | Fun House/Starlet Love/Tell Me (p/s) | 5 |

LOLLIPOPS

| 71 | Atlantic 2091 114 | Nothing's Gonna Stop Our Love/I Believe In Love | 4 |

LAURIE LOMAN

| 54 | London HL 8101 | Whither Thou Goest/I Was The Last One To Know | 25 |

ALAN LOMAX (& RAMBLERS)

56	Decca F 10787	Dirty Old Town/Hard Case (as Alan Lomax & Ramblers)	8
56	Decca DFE 6367	OH LULA (EP)	8
58	Pye Jazz NJE 1055	ALAN LOMAX SINGS (EP, with Dave Lee's Bandits)	12
58	Pye Jazz NJE 1062	MURDERER'S HOME PT 1 (EP)	8
58	Pye Jazz NJE 1063	MURDERER'S HOME PT 2 (EP)	8
58	Pye Jazz NJE 1064	MURDERER'S HOME PT 3 (EP)	8
58	Pye Jazz NJE 1065	MURDERER'S HOME PT 4 (EP)	8
59	Melodisc EPM7 88	SONGS FROM TEXAS (EP)	10
57	Nixa Jazz NJL 8	BLUES IN THE MISSISSIPPI NIGHT (LP)	10
57	Nixa Jazz NJL 11	MURDERER'S HOME (LP)	10
58	Pye Nixa NPL 18013	ALAN LOMAX PRESENTS AMERICAN SONG TRAIN VOLUME ONE (LP)	10
58	HMV CLP 1192	GREAT AMERICAN BALLADS (LP, with Guy Carawan)	10

JACKIE LOMAX

68	CBS 2554	Genuine Imitation Life/One Minute Woman	8
68	Apple APPLE 3	Sour Milk Sea/The Eagle Laughs At You (company sleeve)	12
69	Apple APPLE 11	New Day/I Fall Inside Your Eyes (company sleeve)	15
70	Apple APPLE 23	How The Web Was Woven/Thumbin' A Ride (some with p/s)	15/5

| 69 | Apple (S)APCOR 6 | IS THIS WHAT YOU WANT (LP, with inner sleeve, mono/stereo) | 25/20 |

(see also Badger, Undertakers, Takers, Lomax Alliance, Heavy Jelly)

LOMAX ALLIANCE

| 67 | CBS 2729 | Try As You May/See The People | 8 |

(see also Jackie Lomax)

GUY LOMBARDO (& ROYAL CANADIANS)

55	Brunswick 05372	No More/Pupalina	5
55	Brunswick 05412	Softly Softly/(I'm Always Hearing) Wedding Bells	5
55	Brunswick 05413	Hey, Mr. Banjo/Blue Mirage	5
55	Brunswick 05443	Cherry Pink And Apple Blossom White/Marty	6
56	Capitol CL 14563	Our Melody/You Couldn't Help But Be Wonderful	4
56	Capitol CL 14585	Rinka Tinka Man/Charleston Parisien	4

AL LOMBARDY & HIS ORCHESTRA

| 54 | London HL 8076 | The Blues/The Boogie | 25 |
| 55 | London HL 8127 | In A Little Spanish Town/Flying Home | 25 |

LONDON

77	MCA MCA 305	Everyone's A Winner/Handcuffed (p/s)	4
77	MCA MCA 319	SUMMER OF LOVE (EP)	5
77	MCA 12 MCA 319	SUMMER OF LOVE (12" EP)	7
77	MCA MCA 336	Animal Games/Us Kids Cold (p/s)	4
78	MCA MCF 2823	ANIMAL GAMES (LP)	10

EDDIE LONDON & CHIMES

| 57 | Decca F 10859 | Song Of The Moonlight/I'll Thank You | 4 |

JIMMY LONDON

71	Randy's RAN 514	Shake A Hand/CARL MURPHY: Lick I Pipe	4
71	Randy's RAN 517	Bridge Over Troubled Water/RANDY'S ALLSTARS: War	4
71	Randy's RAN 518	Hip Hip Hooray/IMPACT ALLSTARS: Version	4
71	Randy's RAN 520	A Little Love/IMPACT ALLSTARS: Version	4
71	Randy's RAN 521	It's Now Or Never/IMPACT ALLSTARS: Version	4
72	Trojan TRL 39	BRIDGE OVER TROUBLED WATERS (LP)	15

JOE LONDON

| 59 | London HLW 9008 | It Might Have Been/Lonesome Whistle | 6 |

JULIE LONDON

56	London HLU 8240	Cry Me A River/S'Wonderful (gold lettering on labels, later silver)	35/20
56	London HLU 8240	Cry Me A River/S'Wonderful (78)	5
56	London HLU 8279	Baby, Baby All The Time/Shadow Woman (gold lettering on labels)	25
56	London HLU 8279	Baby, Baby All The Time/Shadow Woman (78)	5
57	London HLU 8394	The Meaning Of The Blues/Now! Baby, Now! (gold lettering, later silver)	20/12
57	London HLU 8394	The Meaning Of The Blues/Now! Baby, Now! (78)	5
57	London HLU 8414	The Boy On A Dolphin/Tall Boy	12
57	London HLU 8414	The Boy On A Dolphin/Tall Boy (78)	5
58	London HLU 8602	Saddle The Wind/It Had To Be You	10
58	London HLU 8602	Saddle The Wind/It Had To Be You (78)	5
58	London HLU 8657	My Strange Affair/It's Easy	8
58	London HLU 8657	My Strange Affair/It's Easy (78)	5
58	London HLU 8769	Man Of The West/Blue Moon	7
58	London HLU 8769	Man Of The West/Blue Moon (78)	5
59	London HLU 8891	Must Be Catchin'/Come On-A My House	10
59	London HLU 8891	Must Be Catchin'/Come On-A My House (78)	10
61	London HLG 9360	Sanctuary/Every Chance I Get	6
63	Liberty LIB 10078	There'll Be Some Changes Made/Love On The Rocks	4
63	Liberty LIB 55605	I'm Coming Back To You/When Snowflakes Fall In The Summer	8
64	Liberty LIB 55666	I Want To Find Out For Myself/Guilty Heart	4
65	Liberty LIB 10189	Send For Me/Bye Bye Blackbird	4
65	Liberty LIB 10205	Charade/Wives And Lovers	4
67	Liberty LIB 10274	Girl Talk/The Mickey Mouse March	4
83	Edsel PE 5004	Cry Me A River/February Brings The Rain (picture disc)	4
57	London RE-U 1076	JULIE SINGS FILM SONGS (EP, gold lettering label)	15
57	London RE-N 1092	LONDON'S GIRL FRIENDS VOL. 1 (EP)	16
58	London RE-U 1151	MAKE LOVE TO ME — PART ONE (EP)	14
58	London RE-U 1152	MAKE LOVE TO ME — PART TWO (EP)	14
58	London RE-U 1153	MAKE LOVE TO ME — PART THREE (EP)	14
59	London RE-U 1180	JULIE — PART ONE (EP)	12
59	London RE-U 1181	JULIE — PART TWO (EP)	12
59	London RE-U 1182	JULIE — PART THREE (EP)	12
63	Liberty LEP 2103	DESAFINADO (EP)	10
66	Liberty LEP 2260	ALL THROUGH THE NIGHT (EP)	10
56	London HA-U 2005	JULIE IS HER NAME (LP)	25
57	London HA-U 2038	CALENDAR GIRL (LP)	20
58	London HA-U 2083	MAKE LOVE TO ME (LP)	18
58	London HA-U 2091	ABOUT THE BLUES (LP)	18
58	London HA-U 2112	JULIE (LP)	18
59	London HA-U 2171	LONDON BY NIGHT (LP)	15
59	London HA-U 2186	JULIE IS HER NAME VOL. 2 (LP, also stereo SAH-U 6042)	18/22
60	London HA-W 2225	SWING ME AN OLD SONG (LP)	15
60	London HA-W 2229	YOUR NUMBER PLEASE (LP)	15
60	London HA-G 2280	JULIE AT HOME (LP, also stereo SAH-G 6097)	15/18
61	London HA-G 2299	AROUND MIDNIGHT (LP)	15
61	London HA-G 2353	SEND FOR ME (LP, also stereo SAH-G 6154)	15/18
62	London HA-G 2405	WHATEVER JULIE WANTS (LP, also stereo SAH-G 6205)	15/18
62	Liberty LBY 1023	THE BEST OF JULIE LONDON (LP)	12
62	Liberty (S)LBY 1083	LOVE LETTERS (LP)	12

Julie LONDON

63	Liberty (S)LBY 1113	LOVE ON THE ROCKS (LP)	12
63	Liberty (S)LBY 1136	SINGS LATIN IN A SATIN MOOD (LP)	12
64	Liberty (S)LBY 1185	THE WONDERFUL WORLD OF JULIE LONDON (LP)	12
65	Liberty LBY 1222	IN PERSON AT THE AMERICANA (LP)	12
65	Liberty (S)LBY 1251	OUR FAIR LADY (LP)	12
66	Liberty (S)LBY 1281	FEELING GOOD (LP, with Gerald Wilson Big Band)	12
66	Liberty (S)LBY 1300	ALL THROUGH THE NIGHT (LP)	12
67	Liberty (S)LBY 1334	FOR THE NIGHT PEOPLE (LP)	12
67	Liberty (S)LBY 1364	NICE GIRLS DON'T STAY FOR BREAKFAST (LP)	12
68	Liberty LBL/LBS 83049	GREAT PERFORMANCES (LP)	10
69	Liberty LBL/LBS 83183E	YUMMY, YUMMY, YUMMY (LP)	10

LAURIE LONDON

57	Parlophone R 4359	He's Got The Whole World In His Hands/The Cradle Rock	6
57	Parlophone R 4359	He's Got The Whole World In His Hands/The Cradle Rock (78)	5
57	Parlophone R 4388	Handed Down/She Sells Sea Shells	5
57	Parlophone R 4388	Handed Down/She Sells Sea Shells (78)	5
58	Parlophone R 4408	The Gospel Train/Boomerang	5
58	Parlophone R 4408	The Gospel Train/Boomerang (78)	5
58	Parlophone R 4426	I Gotta Robe/Casey Jones	5
58	Parlophone R 4426	I Gotta Robe/Casey Jones (78)	5
58	Parlophone R 4450	Basin Street Blues/Joshua (Fit The Battle Of Jericho)	5
58	Parlophone R 4450	Basin Street Blues/Joshua (Fit The Battle Of Jericho) (78)	5
58	Parlophone R 4474	My Mother/Darktown Strutters' Ball	5
58	Parlophone R 4474	My Mother/Darktown Strutters' Ball (78)	5
58	Parlophone R 4499	Up Above My Head/Three O'Clock	5
58	Parlophone R 4499	Up Above My Head/Three O'Clock (78)	5
59	Parlophone R 4557	Pretty-Eyed Baby (with Gitte)/Boom-Ladda-Boom-Boom	5
59	Parlophone R 4557	Pretty-Eyed Baby (with Gitte)/Boom-Ladda-Boom-Boom (78)	5
59	Parlophone R 4601	Old Time Religion/God's Little Acre	5
60	Parlophone R 4635	I'm Afraid/Roll On Spring	5
60	Parlophone R 4662	Hear Them Bells/Banjo Boy	4
61	Parlophone R 4747	Today's Teardrops/Darling Sue	4
61	Parlophone R 4801	Down By The Riverside/I'll Make Her Forget Him	4
67	CBS 202461	The Bells Of St. Mary's/Sad Songs	4
57	Parlophone GEP 8664	LAURIE LONDON (EP)	15
58	Parlophone GEP 8689	LITTLE LAURIE LONDON No. 2 (EP)	15

MARK LONDON

65	Pye 7N 15825	Stranger In The World/Moanin'	10

MICHAEL LONDON

62	HMV POP 1026	Miracles Sometimes Happen/Stranger On The Shore (with Acker Bilk)	4
62	HMV POP 1085	Mutiny On The Bounty Love Song/For The Very Young	4

PETER LONDON

65	Pye 7N 15957	Bless You/Baby I Like The Look Of You	18

(see also Peter Cook)

LONDON & BRIDGES

66	CBS 202056	It Just Ain't Right/Leave Her Alone	25

LONDON JAZZ FOUR

67	Polydor 56214	It Strikes A Chord/Song For Hilary	4
67	Polydor 582 005	TAKE A NEW LOOK AT THE BEATLES (LP)	10

LONDON JAZZ QUARTET

60	Tempo TAP 28	LONDON JAZZ QUARTET (LP, with Tubby Hayes & Tony Crombie)	20

(see also Tubby Hayes, Tony Crombie)

LONDON JAZZ QUARTET

66	Polydor 56092	Norwegian Wood/I Feel Fine	4

(see also London Jazz Four)

LONDON POPS ORCHESTRA

68	Pye 7N 17630	Eleanor Rigby/If I Only Had Time	4

LONDON PX

82	New Puritan NP 1	Orders/Eviction (p/s)	5
82	Terrapyn SYD 1	Arnold Layne/Indian Summer (1-sided flexidisc)	4

LONDON UNDERGROUND

81	Situation 2 SIT 9	Train Of Thought/All Too Many (p/s)	6
82	On-U Sound ON-U 3	Between The Lines/Rise And Fall (p/s)	4
82	On-U Sound ON-U 4	WATCHING WEST INDIANS IN THE COLD (10" EP)	6
83	On-U Sound ON-U 5	STRANGE (10" EP)	6

LONDON WAITS

66	Immediate IM 030	Softly Softly/Serenadio	15

LONE JUSTICE

87	Geffen GEF 18F	I Found Love/If You Don't Like Rain//Sweet Jane (live)/Don't Toss Us Away (live) (double pack)	4
87	Geffen GEF 18TP	I Found Love (Extended Remix)/I Found Love/If You Don't Like Rain (12", picture disc)	7

JOHNNY LONESOME

61	HMV POP 837	Marie Marie/Doctor Heartache	6

LONESOME NO MORE

81	Rage RAGE 3	Turned Insane/Do Ya Think I Care (p/s)	6

(see also Cult)

LONESOME STONE
73   Reflection RL 306   LONESOME STONE (LP, stage production recording) 22
(see also Sheep)

LONESOME SUNDOWN
70   Blue Horizon 7-63864   LONESOME LONELY BLUES (LP) 40
70s Flyright LP 529   BOUGHT ME A TICKET (LP) 10
70s Flyright LP 587   LONESOME WHISTLER (LP) 10

LONESOME TRAVELLERS
70s Nebula NEB 100   THE LOST CHILDREN (LP) 15

FITZROY D. LONG & BUSTER ALL STARS
68   Fab FAB 32   Get A New Girl/BUSTER'S ALL STARS: Come And Do It With Me 4

JOHNNY LONG ORCHESTRA
55   Parlophone MSP 6176   Silver Dollar/We'll Build A Mountain 5

SHORTY LONG
65   Tamla Motown TMG 512   Out To Get You/It's A Crying Shame 40
66   Tamla Motown TMG 573   Function At The Junction/Call On Me (narrow print issue; 2nd pressing £10) 18
67   Tamla Motown TMG 600   Chantilly Lace/Your Love Is Amazing (narrow print issue; 2nd pressing £6) 10
68   Tamla Motown TMG 644   Night Fo' Last (Vocal)/Night Fo' Last (Instrumental) 10
68   Tamla Motown TMG 663   Here Comes The Judge/Sing What You Wanna 8
68   T. Motown (S)TML 11086 HERE COMES THE JUDGE (LP) 20
70   T. Motown (S)TML 11144 THE PRIME OF SHORTY LONG (LP) 15
(see also Art Mooney)

LONG & SHORT
64   Decca F 11964   The Letter/Love Is A Funny Thing 10
64   Decca F 12043   Choc Ice/Here Comes The Fool 10

LONGBOATMEN
66   Polydor 56115   Take Her Any Time/Only In Her Home Town 175

LONGDANCER
73   Rocket PIG 1   If It Was So Simple/Silent Emotions 5
74   Rocket PIG 11   Puppet Man/Cold Love 4
73   Rocket PIGL 1   IF IT WAS SO SIMPLE (LP) 10
74   Rocket PIGL 6   TRAILER FOR A GOOD LIFE (LP, gatefold sleeve) 10
(see also Tourists, Eurythmics)

LONG HELLO
73   private pressing   THE LONG HELLO (LP, mail-order only, numbered white sleeve) 20
(see also Van Der Graaf Generator)

LONG RYDERS
85   Island ISD 237   Looking For Lewis And Clarke/Southside Of The Story//Child Bride/
                      If I Were A Bramble (double pack) 4
85   Island 10IS 237   Looking For Lewis And Clarke/Child Bride/Southside Of The Story/
                      If I Were A Bramble (10", p/s) 5
(see also Spinning Wighats)

LONG TALL SHORTY
79   Warner Bros K 17491   By Your Love/1970's Boy (p/s, withdrawn) 30
81   Ramkup CAC 007   Win Or Lose/Ain't Done Wrong (p/s) 35
81   Dr Creation LYN 9904   If I Was You/That's What I Want (flexidisc) 8
85   Diamond DIA 002   On The Streets Again/I Fought The Law/Promises
                      (p/s, some with poster) 8/6
86   Diamond DIA 005   What's Going On/Steppin' Stone/Win Or Lose/England (p/s) 6
(see also Joe Public)

LOOKING GLASS
87   Dreamworld DREAM 12   Mirror Man/Through The Looking Glass (For Tea) (p/s) 6
87   Dreamworld DREAM 12T Mirror Man/Through The Looking Glass (For Tea)/Coming Down (12", p/s) 7

LOOP
87   Head HEAD 5   16 Dreams/Head On/Burning World (12", p/s) 18
87   Head HEAD 7L   Spinning Pts 1 & 2 (large centre, plain black die-cut sleeve) 8
87   Head HEAD 7   Spinning/Deep Hit/I'll Take You There (12", p/s) 16
88   Chapter 22 LCHAP 27   Collision/Crawling Heart (large centre, plain black die-cut sleeve) 7
88   Chapter 22 12 CHAP 27 Collision/Crawling Heart/Thief Of Fire/Thief (Motherfucker) (12", p/s) 8
88   Chapter 22 12 CHAP 32 Black Sun/Circle Grave/Mother Sky (12", p/s) 6
88   Cheree CHEREE 1   Soundhead (live)/TELESCOPES: Forever Close Your Eyes (flexidisc, p/s) 10
89   Situation 2 SIT 64   Arc-Lite (Sonar)/Arc-Lite (Radiated) (large centre, plain black sleeve) 5
87   Head HEADLP 1   HEAVEN'S END (LP, with inner sleeve) 10
88   Chapter 22 CHAPLLP 34 FADE OUT (LP, 2 x 45rpm 12", gold stickered gatefold sleeve, some signed) .15/10
90   Situation 2 SITU 27   A GILDED ETERNITY (LP, as 2 x 45rpm 12" with free 7" [Shot With A
                      Diamond/The Nail Will Burn (Burn Out), no p/s] & foldaround sticker) 10

LOOSE ENDS
66   Decca F 12437   Send The People Away/I Ain't Gonna Eat My Heart Out Anymore 15
66   Decca F 12476   Taxman/That's It 15

LOOT
66   Page One POF 013   Baby Come Closer/Baby Come Closer (Version) 8
67   Page One POF 026   I've Just Gotta Love You/You Need Someone To Love 12
67   CBS 2938   Whenever You're Ready/I Got What You Want 10
68   Page One POF 095   She's A Winner/Save Me (withdrawn) 15
68   Page One POF 095   She's A Winner/Radio City 12
68   CBS 3231   Don't Turn Around/You Are My Sunshine Girl 7
69   Page One POF 115   Try To Keep It A Secret/Radio City 15
(see also Soul Agents, Hookfoot)

LINDA LOPEZ MAMBO ORCHESTRA
55	Parlophone MSP 6179	Limehouse Blues/Nursery Mambo	5

TRINI LOPEZ
63	London HL 9808	Jeanie Marie/Love Me Tonight	6
63	Reprise R 20198	If I Had A Hammer/Unchain My Heart	4
63	Reprise R 20236	Kansas City/Lonesome Traveller	4
63	Reprise R 20260	Jailer Bring Me Water/You Can't Say Goodbye	4
63	Reprise R 20276	Ya Ya/What Have I Got Of My Own	4
66	Reprise R 20455	I'm Coming Home Cindy/The 32nd Of May	4
66	Reprise R 20480	La Bamba/Trini's Tune	4
72	Reprise K 14205	America/If I Had A Hammer (p/s)	4
63	Reprise R 6093	LOPEZ AT P.J.'s (LP)	12
64	London HA 8132	TEENAGE LOVE SONGS (LP)	20
64	London HA 8160	MORE OF TRINI LOPEZ (LP)	15

DENISE LOR
54	Parlophone MSP 6120	If I Give My Heart To You/Hallo Darling	6
55	Parlophone MSP 6148	Every Day Of My Life/And One To Grow On	5

KENNY LORAN
59	Capitol CL 15081	Mama's Little Baby/Magic Star	25

L'ORANGE MECHANIK
86	Art Pop POP 44	Symphony/Intermezzo (Sprechstimme)/Scherzo (p/s)	8

(see also Times)

BOBBY LORD
64	Hickory 45-1232	Life Can Have Meaning/Pickin' White Gold	4
64	Hickory 45-1259	Take The Bucket To The Well/A Man Needs A Woman	4
65	Hickory 45-1310	That Room In The Corner Of The House/I'm Going Home Next Summer	4

BOBBY LORD/BOB LUMAN
64	Hickory LPE 1501	HICKORY SHOWCASE VOL. 2 (EP, 1 side each)	10
64	Hickory LPE 1504	HICKORY SHOWCASE VOL. 3 (EP, 1 side each)	10

(see also Bob Luman)

JON LORD
76	Purple PUR 131	Bouree/Aria	5
82	Harvest HAR 5220	Bach Onto This/Going Home (p/s)	4
71	Purple TPSA 7501	GEMINI SUITE (LP)	10
74	Purple TPSA 7513	WINDOWS (LP)	10
76	Purple TPSA 7516	SARABANDE (LP, die-cut sleeve)	10

(see also Artwoods, Deep Purple, Ashton & Lord, Paice Ashton & Lord, Bernie Marsden, Wizard's Convention)

TONY LORD
66	Planet PLF 102	World's Champion/It Makes Me Sad	10

JERRY LORDAN
59	Parlophone R 4588	I'll Stay Single/Can We Kiss	6
60	Parlophone R 4627	Who Could Be Bluer?/Do I Worry?	6
60	Parlophone R 4653	Sing Like An Angel/Ev'ry Time	6
60	Parlophone R 4695	Ring, Write Or Call/I've Still Got You	6
61	Parlophone R 4748	You Came A Long Way From St. Louis/Let's Try Again	6
62	Parlophone R 4903	One Good Solid 24 Carat Reason/Second Hand Dress	4
70	CBS 5057	The Old Man And The Sea/Harlequin Melodies	5
61	Parlophone PMC 1133	ALL MY OWN WORK (LP, also stereo PCS 3014)	50/60

(see also Lee & Jay Elvin)

LORD BEGINNER
60s	Melodisc CAL 1	Victory Test Match	6

LORD BRISCO
64	Black Swan WI 447	Spiritual Mambo/BABA BROOKS BAND: Fly Right	10
64	Black Swan WI 450	My Love Has Come/BABA BROOKS BAND: Sweet Eileen	10
64	Black Swan WI 454	Trojan/I Am The Least	10
65	Island WI 187	Jonah (The Master)/Mr. Cleveland	10

LORD BRYNNER & SHEIKS
66	Island WI 266	Congo War/Teach Me To Ska	8

LORD BUCKLEY
60s	Fontana	IN CONCERT (LP)	15
60s	other labels	LPs	10

LORD BURGESS & HIS SUN ISLANDERS
68	Pye Intl. NPL 28109	CALYPSO AU GO-GO (LP)	15

LORD CHARLES & HIS BAND
70s	Sound Of Jamaica JA 1	Jamaican Bits And Pieces/JA Island Soul	5

LORD COMIC
70	Bamboo BAM 66	Rhythm Rebellion/ROY RICHARDS: Reggae Children	6
70	Pressure Beat PB 5507	Jack Of My Trade/CYNTHIA RICHARDS: United We Stand	4

LORD CREATOR
62	Island WI 001	Independent Jamaica/Remember Your Mother And Father	15
64	Port-O-Jam PJ 4005	Rhythm Of The Blues/Simple Things	7
64	Port-O-Jam PJ 4119	Jamaica's Anniversary/Mother's Love	7
64	Blue Beat BB 292	Evening News/Good For Creator	8
64	National Calypso NC 2001	Drive With Care/Sweet Jamaica	5
65	Black Swan WI 463	Wicked Lady/MAYTALS: My Little Ruby	7
66	Doctor Bird DB 1029	Obeah Wedding/BERTRAM ENNIS COMBO: Part Two	7
67	Jump Up JU 503	Jamaica Jump Up/Laziest Man	6

MINT VALUE £

67	Jump Up JU 524	Big Bamboo/Marjorie And Harry	6
60s	Kalypso XX 24	Peeping Tom/Second Hand Piano	5
70	Clan Disc CLA 224	Kingston Town/FABULOUS FLAMES: Holly Holy	4

(see also Kentrick Patrick)

LORD CRISTO

| 67 | Jump Up JU 515 | Dumb Boy And The Parrot/General Hospital | 5 |
| 67 | Jump Up JU 517 | Election War Zone/Bad Luck Man | 5 |

LORD DANIEL

| 60s | Kalypso XX 26 | Small Island Gal | 5 |

LORD FLEA & HIS CALYPSONIANS

| 57 | Capitol CL 14704 | The Naughty Little Flea/Shake Shake Sonora | 4 |

LORD GANDA

| 57 | Melodisc 1417 | Everybody Is Rockin' & Rollin'/Landlady Don't Steal My ... (78) | 10 |

LORD INVADER & HIS CALYPSO RHYTHM BOYS

| 59 | Pye N 15162 | Teddy Boy Calypso/Reincarnation (The Bed Bug) (78) | 5 |

LORD KITCHENER

56	Melodisc 1400	Rock 'n' Roll Calypso/Life Begins At Forty (78)	6
63	Melodisc CAL 2	Kitch/Rebound Wife	5
63	Melodisc CAL 3	Muriel And The Bug/Nora And The Yankee	5
63	Melodisc CAL 4	Kitch Take It Easy/Redhead	5
63	Melodisc CAL 5	Drink A Rum/Your Wife	5
63	Melodisc CAL 6	Too Late Kitch/Saxophone Number Two	5
63	Melodisc CAL 7	Wife And Mother/Mango Tree	5
64	Melodisc CAL 10	Kitch Mambo Calypso/Ghana	5
64	Melodisc CAL 11	Life Begins At Forty/Short Skirts	5
64	Melodisc CAL 12	Romeo/Kitch Calypso Medley	5
64	Melodisc CAL 14	Federation/Alfonso In Town	5
64	Melodisc CAL 19	Black Pudding/Piccadilly	5
64	Melodisc CAL 21	Come Back In The Morning/If You Brown	5
64	Melodisc CAL 22	Jamaica Turkey/Edna What You Want	5
64	Melodisc CAL 23	Carnival	5
60s	Jump Up JU 504	Love In The Cemetery/Jamaica Woman	5
60s	Jump Up JU 506	Road/Neighbour	5
64	Jump Up JU 511	Dr. Kitch/Come Back Home Meh Boy	4
60s	Jump Up JU 530	Kitch You So Sweet/Ain't That Fun	5
60s	Aladdin WI 612	Dr. Kitch/Come Back Home Meh Boy (reissue)	6
55	Melodisc MLP 500	KITCH — KING OF CALYPSO (10" LP)	20
60s	Melodisc 12-129	CALYPSOS TOO HOT TO HANDLE (LP)	20
60s	Melodisc 12-130	CALYPSOS TOO HOT TO HANDLE VOL. 2 (LP)	20
60s	Melodisc 12-199	CALYPSOS TOO HOT TO HANDLE (LP, reissue with extra tracks)	15
60s	Melodisc 12-200	CALYPSOS TOO HOT TO HANDLE VOL. 2 (LP, reissue with extra tracks)	15

LORD LEBBY

| 60 | Starlite ST45 018 | Caldonia/One Kiss For My Baby | 50 |
| 60s | Kalypso XX 05 | Sweet Jamaica/Mama Want No Rice No Peas | 6 |

LORD MELODY

60	Kalypso XX 14	Rock 'N' Roll Calypso/Bo Bo Man	5
60s	Melodisc MEL 1440	The Devil/No, No	5
60s	Melodisc MEL 1449	Robbery/Men Company	5
60s	Melodisc MEL 1474	Do Able/Happy Holiday	5
60s	Melodisc CAL 16	Happy Holiday/Do Able	5

LORD NELSON

63	Stateside SS 189	I Got An Itch/Problems On My Mind	5
64	Stateside SS 281	It's Delinquency/Proud West Indian	5
68	Direction 58-3909	Michael/No Hot Summer	4
64	Stateside SE 1024	PROUD WEST INDIAN (EP)	10

LORD POWER

| 68 | Coxsone CS 7079 | Temptation/AL & VIBRATORS: Change Everything | 12 |

LORD ROCKINGHAM'S XI

58	Decca F 11024	The Squelch/Fried Onions	8
58	Decca F 11059	Hoots Mon/Blue Train	5
59	Decca F 11104	Wee Tom/Lady Rockingham, I Presume?	8
59	Decca F 11139	Ra-Ra Rockingham/Farewell To Rockingham	7
62	Decca F 11426	Newcastle Twist/Rockingham Twist	6
58	Decca DFE 6555	OH BOY! (EP)	25
68	Columbia SCX 6291	THE RETURN OF LORD ROCKINGHAM'S XI (LP)	15

LORD ROSE

| 60s | Kalypso XX 25 | Independent Jamaica/Twistin' Uncle | 4 |

LORDS

| 67 | Columbia DB 8121 | Don't Mince Matters/No One Knows | 40 |
| 68 | Columbia DB 8367 | Gloryland/Gypsy Boy | 8 |

LORD SITAR

| 68 | Columbia SCX 6256 | LORD SITAR (LP) | 10 |

LORDS OF NEW CHURCH

82	Illegal ILS 0028	New Church/Livin' On Livin' (p/s)	6
82	Illegal ILS 0030	Open Your Eyes/Girls Girls Girls (p/s)	4
82	Illegal ILS 0033	Russian Roulette/Young Don't Cry (p/s)	4
82	Illegal ILSP 0033	Russian Roulette/Young Don't Cry (picture disc)	6
83	IRS PFSX 1022	Dance With Me/I'm Not Running Hard Enuff (12", picture disc)	9

LORDS OF NEW CHURCH

83	IRS PFSX 1022	Dance With Me/I'm Not Running Hard Enuff (12", p/s, coloured vinyl)	8
84	IRS IRSY 113	M Style/Sorry For The Man//Dance With Me/I'm Not Running Hard Enuff (double pack)	4
85	Illegal LORDSP 1	Like A Virgin/Method To My Madness (picture disc)	5

(see also Brian James, Stiv Bators, Wanderers)

LORD TANAMO
64	Rio R 21	I Had A Dream/OSBOURNE GRAHAM: Be There	10
64	Ska Beat JB 177	Night Food Ska/My Business	10
65	Ska Beat JB 217	Mattie Rag/BABA BROOKS BAND: Mattie Rag	10
65	Ska Beat JB 224	I'm In The Mood For Ska/You Never Know	10
66	Ska Beat JB 243	Mother's Love/Downtown Gal	10
60s	Caribou CRC 3	I Love You Truly/If You Were Only Mine	8

LORD'S TAVENERS
56	Decca F 10752	ALL STAR HIT PARADE (p/s, various artists)	4
57	Decca F 10915	ALL STAR HIT PARADE No. 2 (p/s, various artists)	4
58	Decca F 10915	STAR BAND HIT PARADE (p/s, various artists)	4

SOPHIA LOREN
58	Philips PB 857	Love Song From "Houseboat"/Bing! Bang! Bong!	4

(see also Peter Sellers & Sophia Loren)

LORI & CHAMELEONS
78	Zoo CAGE 006	Touch/Love On The Ganges (p/s)	6
79	Sire SIR 4025	Touch/Love On The Ganges (p/s, reissue)	4
80	Korova KOW 5	The Lonely Spy/Peru (p/s)	4
81	Korova KOW 20	Touch/The Lonely Spy (p/s)	4
81	Korova KOW 20T	Touch/The Lonely Spy/Love On The Ganges (12", p/s)	7

(see also Teardrop Explodes, Bill Drummond)

MYRNA LORRIE
55	London HLU 8187	Underway/I'm Your Man, I'm Your Gal (B-side with Buddy DeVal)	30
55	London HLU 8187	Underway/I'm Your Man, I'm Your Gal (B-side with Buddy DeVal) (78)	5
56	London HLU 8294	Life's Changing Scene/Listen To My Heartstrings	18
56	London HLU 8294	Life's Changing Scene/Listen To My Heartstrings (78)	5

LORRIES
79	Redball RR 016	The Night/Steal You Anyway/Pushover/Idiot Dances (p/s)	4

LORRIES
87	Red Rhino REDD 76	Crawling Mantra/All The Same//Hang Man/Shout At The Sky (live) (double pack)	4

(see also Red Lorry Yellow Lorry)

DICK LORY
56	London HLD 8348	Cool It Baby/Ball Room Baby	175
56	London HLD 8348	Cool It Baby/Ball Room Baby (78)	45
61	London HLG 9284	My Last Date/Broken Hearted	10
62	Liberty LIB 55415	The Pain Is Here/Handsome Guy	6
63	Liberty LIB 55529	I Got Over You/Welcome Home Again	6

LOS BRAVOS
66	Decca F 22419	Black Is Black/I Want A Name	4
66	Decca F 22484	I Don't Care/Don't Be Left Out In The Cold	4
66	Decca F 22529	Going Nowhere/Brand New Baby	4
67	Decca F 22615	I'm All Ears/You'll Never Get The Chances Again	4
67	Decca F 22682	Like Nobody Else/Wearing A Smile	4
68	Decca F 22765	Bring A Little Lovin'/Make It Last	4
69	Decca F 22853	Save Me, Save Me/Baby I Love You Because I Need You	4
70	Decca F 13064	People Talking Around/Every Dog Has His Night	4
66	Decca LK 4822	BLACK IS BLACK (LP)	15
68	Decca LK/SKL 4905	LOS BRAVOS (LP)	12

LOS BRINCOS
67	Page One POF 023	Lola/Passport	30
67	Page One POF 031	Nobody Wants You Now/Train	10

LOS CANARIOS
67	Major Minor MM 502	Three Two One Ah/What Can I Do For You	5
67	Major Minor MM 532	Get On Your Knees/Keep On The Right Side	10

LOS CINCOS RICARDOS
65	Philips BF 1436	One Big Kiss/Something	4
65	Philips BF 1461	La Yenka/Too Big For Her Boots	4
66	Philips BF 1525	Most Exclusive Residence For Sale/It's All Over Now	5

LOS INDIOS TABAJARAS
63	RCA RCA 1365	Maria Elena/Jungle Dream	4
64	RCA RCA 1388	Always In My Heart/Moonlight And Shadows	4
64	RCA RCX 7135	A LA ORILLA DEL LAGO (EP)	7
60s	RCA	LOS INDIOS TABAJARAS (LP)	10

LOS LOBOS
85	Slash LASHT 4	Will The Wolf Survive/Don't Worry Baby (10", p/s)	5

LOS MARCELLOS FERIAL
50s	Durium DB 16665	Quando Calienta El Sol/Llorando Me	4
50s	Durium DRS 54002	Sel Deventata Nera/Da Stasera E Per Sempre	4

JOE LOSS (& HIS ORCHESTRA)
55	HMV 7M 329	Have You Ever Been Lonely/Remember	4
55	HMV 7M 330	Button Up Your Overcoat/Wake The Town And Tell The People	4
56	HMV 7M 341	Love Is A Many Splendoured Thing/I'll Come When You Call	4

56	HMV 7M 342	Malaguena/Autumn Leaves	4
56	HMV 7M 355	Babette/Moments To Remember	4
56	HMV 7M 377	You're The Cream In My Coffee/Young And Foolish	4
56	HMV 7M 378	The Tender Trap/April In Paris	4
56	HMV 7M 386	Zambesi/The Rose Tattoo	4
56	HMV 7M 387	Memories Are Made Of This/Who's Sorry Now	4
56	HMV 7M 398	Fortune Teller/If You Knew Susie	4
56	HMV 7M 399	The Great Pretender/Dear Love My Love	4
56	HMV 7M 409	Tear Fell/It's D'Lovely	4
56	HMV 7M 425	Laura/Monglow & Theme From "Picnic"	4
58	HMV 7M 430	I'll Buy You A Star/At Last	4
58	HMV 7M 431	Parlez Moi D'Amour/My Darling My Darling	4
61	HMV POP 959	Twistin' The Mood/Everybody Twist	4
61	HMV POP 995	The Maigret Theme/Along The Bouvelard	5
63	HMV POP 1192	Steptoe And Son/Phase Four	5
64	HMV POP 1351	March Of The Mods/Tango '65	4
65	HMV POP 1389	A Shot In The Dark/Drum Diddley	4
65	HMV POP 1470	Let's Kick/Just For Kicks	4
66	HMV POP 1500	"Thunderbirds" Theme/"The Avengers" Theme	8
66	HMV POP 1517	The World Cup March/Auld Lang Syne (March)	4

LOS SENORS
| 63 | Cameo Parkway C 290 | Amapola/Acapulco | 4 |

LOST CHERRIES
| 83 | Riot RIOT 3 | NO FIGHTING NO WAR (EP) | 4 |
| 84 | Mortarhate MORT 3 | MAN'S DUTY (EP) | 4 |

LOST JOCKEY
| 82 | Operation Twilight OPT 11 | Professor Slack/Rise And Fall/Animal/Behaviour And Crude Din (p/s) | 8 |

LOTHAR & HAND PEOPLE
| 69 | Capitol CL 15610 | Sdrawkcab (Backwards)/Today Is Only Yesterday's Tomorrow | 10 |
| 69 | Capitol ST 247 | SPACE HYMN (LP) | 40 |

DENNIS LOTIS
54	Decca F 10287	Such A Night/Cuddle Me (with Ted Heath Music & Johnston Brothers)	10
54	Decca F 10392	Honey Love/Manhattan Mambo (with Ted Heath Music)	8
55	Decca F 10469	Face Of An Angel, Heart Of A Devil/The Golden Ring	6
55	Decca F 10471	Chain Reaction/Go, Go, Go (with Ted Heath Music)	6
56	Pye 7N 15053	Green Grows The Grass/No Other Love Can Take Your Place	4
57	Columbia DB 3993	Tammy/I Complain	4
57	Columbia DB 4056	Valentina/Good Mornin' Life	4
58	Columbia DB 4090	I May Never Pass This Way Again/Gretna Green	4
58	Columbia DB 4158	The Only Man On The Island/Guessing What The Neighbours'll Say	4
58	Columbia DB 4182	Safe In The Arms Of My Darling/Belonging To Someone	4
59	Columbia DB 4277	Moonlight Serenade/Danger Within	4
59	Columbia DB 4339	Who Is? You Are!/Too Much	4
60	Columbia DB 4432	I Wish It Were You/Love Me A Little	4
60	Columbia DB 4507	Strangers When We Meet/Two Wrongs Don't Make A Right	4
56	Pye NEP 24017	THERE'S A TIME AND A PLACE (EP)	7
57	Pye NEP 24043	LET'S BE HAPPY (EP)	7
57	Pye NEP 24046	HOW ABOUT YOU (EP)	7
57	Pye NEP 24053	HOW ABOUT YOU PT. 2 (EP)	7
57	Pye NEP 24055	HOW ABOUT YOU PT. 3 (EP)	7
59	Columbia SEG 7955	HALLELUJAH IT'S DENNIS LOTIS (EP)	7
57	Nixa NPL 18002	HOW ABOUT YOU (LP)	15
58	Columbia 33SX 1089	BIDIN' MY TIME (LP)	15

PETER LOTIS
| 60 | Ember EMB S 110 | Doo-Dah/You're Singing Our Love Song To Somebody Else | 4 |

LOTUS EATERS
83	Arista/Sylvan SYL 1	The First Picture Of You/The Lotus Eater (picture disc)	4
84	Arista/Sylvan SYL 2	You Don't Need Someone New/Two Virgins Tender (picture disc)	4
84	Arista/Sylvan SYL 4	Out Of Your Own/Endless (picture disc)	4
85	Arista FS 5	It Hurts/Evidence//The Soul In Sparks/Church At Llanbadrig (double pack)	4

(see also Wild Swans, Care)

BONNIE LOU
53	Parlophone MSP 6021	Seven Lonely Days/Dancin' With Someone	30
53	Parlophone MSP 6036	Hand-Me-Down Heart/Scrap Of Paper	30
53	Parlophone MSP 6048	Tennessee Wig Walk/Just Out Of Reach	35
53	Parlophone R 3730	Tennessee Wig Walk/Just Out Of Reach (78)	5
53	Parlophone MSP 6051	Since You Said Goodbye/Pa-Paya Mama	25
54	Parlophone MSP 6072	The Texas Polka/No Heart At All	15
54	Parlophone MSP 6095	Don't Stop Kissing Me Goodnight/The Welcome Mat	15
54	Parlophone MSP 6108	No One/Huckleberry Pie	15
54	Parlophone MSP 6117	Blue Tennessee Rain/Wait For Me, Darling	15
54	Parlophone MSP 6132	Two Step — Side Step/Please Don't Laugh When I Cry	15
55	Parlophone MSP 6151	Tennessee Mambo/Train Whistle Blues	16
55	Parlophone MSP 6157	Tweedle Dee/The Finger Of Suspicion Points At You	18
55	Parlophone R 4012	A Rusty Old Halo/Danger! Heartbreak Ahead (78)	5
55	Parlophone MSP 6173	Drop Me A Line/Old Faithful And True Love	12
55	Parlophone MSP 6178	The Barnyard Hop/Tell The World	12
55	Parlophone MSP 6188	Dancin' In My Socks/Daddy-O	18
55	Parlophone R 4096	Dancin' In My Socks/Daddy-O (78)	5
56	Parlophone MSP 6223	Darlin' Why/Miss The Love (That I've Been Dreaming Of)	10
56	Parlophone MSP 6234	Bo Weevil (A Country Song)/Chaperon	12
56	Parlophone MSP 6253	Lonesome Lover/Little Miss Bobby Sox	18

56	Parlophone R 4194	Lonesome Lover/Little Miss Bobby Sox (78)	5
56	Parlophone R 4215	No Rock 'N' Roll Tonight/One Track Love	12
56	Parlophone R 4215	No Rock 'N' Roll Tonight/One Track Love (78)	5
57	Parlophone R 4350	Teenage Wedding/Runnin' Away	12
57	Parlophone R 4350	Teenage Wedding/Runnin' Away (78)	5
50s	Parlophone DP 545	I'm Available/Waiting In Vain (export issue)	20

BONNIE LOU & RUSTY YORK
| 58 | Parlophone R 4409 | Let The School Bell Ring Ding-A-Ling/La Dee Dah | 50 |
| 58 | Parlophone R 4409 | Let The School Bell Ring Ding-A-Ling/La Dee Dah (78) | 18 |

(see also Rusty York)

JOHN D. LOUDERMILK
61	RCA RCA 1269	The Language Of Love/Darling Jane	5
62	RCA RCA 1287	Thou Shalt Not Steal/Mister Jones	5
62	RCA RCA 1323	Angela Jones/Road Hog	8
68	RCA RCA 1761	Sidewalks/The Odd Folks Of Okracoke	6
62	RCA RD 27248	THE LANGUAGE OF LOVE (LP, also stereo SF 5123)	20
62	RCA Victor RD/SF 7515	TWELVE SIDES OF JOHN D. LOUDERMILK (LP)	20
67	RCA Victor RD/SF 7890	SINGS A BIZARRE COLLECTION OF SONGS (LP)	15

(see also Johnny Dee)

LOUDEST WHISPER
| 70s | Polydor | CHILDREN OF LIR (LP, Ireland only) | 400 |

JOE HILL LOUIS
| 65 | Bootleg 502 | Heartache Baby/I Feel Like A Million | 25 |

JOE HILL LOUIS
| 74 | Polydor 2383 214 | BLUE IN THE MORNING (LP) | 15 |

(see also Willie Nix)

LOUISIANA RED
64	Columbia DB 7270	Keep Your Hands Off My Woman/Don't Cry	10
64	Sue WI 337	I Done Woke Up/I Had A Feeling	15
64	Columbia 33SX 1612	LOWDOWN BACK PORCH BLUES (LP)	30
72	Atlantic K 40436	SINGS THE BLUES (LP)	12
70s	Polydor 2941 002	THE SEVENTH SON (LP)	15

LOUISIANA SUGAR BABIES
| 57 | HMV 7EG 8215 | LOUISIANA SUGAR BABIES (EP, with Fats Waller & James P. Johnson) | 12 |

JACQUES LOUSSIER
| 66 | Decca F 22383 | Air On A G String/Prelude No. 16 (Bach) | 4 |

LOUVIN BROTHERS
59	Capitol CL 14989	Knoxville Girl/I Wish It Had Been A Dream	7
59	Capitol CL 15078	You're Learning/My Curly Headed Baby	6
56	Capitol EAP1 769	TRAGIC SONGS OF LIFE (EP)	12
58	Capitol EAP1 910	IRA AND CHARLIE (EP)	12
59	Capitol EAP1 1106	COUNTRY LOVE BALLADS (EP)	8

LOVABLES
| 68 | Stateside SS 2108 | You're The Cause Of It/Beautiful Idea | 12 |

LOVE
66	London HLZ 10053	My Little Red Book/Hey Joe	15
66	London HLZ 10073	7 And 7 Is/No. Fourteen	15
67	Elektra EKSN 45010	She Comes In Colours/Orange Skies	10
67	Elektra EKSN 45016	Softly To Me/The Castle	8
68	Elektra EKSN 45024	Alone Again Or/Bummer In The Summer	7
68	Elektra EKSN 45026	Andmoreagain/The Daily Planet	8
68	Elektra EKSN 45038	Laughing Stock/Your Mind And We Belong Together	10
70	Elektra EKSN 45086	I'm With You/Robert Montgomery	6
70	Harvest HAR 5014	Stand Out/Doggone	7
70	Harvest HAR 5030	The Everlasting First/Keep On Shining	8
71	Elektra 2101 019	Alone Again Or/Bummer In The Summer (reissue)	4
75	RSO 2090 151	Time Is Like A River/You Said You Would	4
66	Elek. EKL 4001/EKS 74001	LOVE (LP, gold label, sleeve printed in U.S.)	25
66	Elek. EKL 4001/EKS 74001	LOVE (LP, orange label, sleeve printed in U.S. or U.K.)	25
67	Elek. EKL 4005/EKS 74005	DA CAPO (LP, orange label, sleeve printed in U.S. or U.K.)	25
67	Elek. EKL 4013/EKS 74013	FOREVER CHANGES (LP, orange label, mono/stereo)	25/22
69	Elektra EKS 74049	FOUR SAIL (LP, orange label)	20
70	Harvest SHDW 3/4	OUT HERE (2-LP, gatefold sleeve)	20
70	Elektra 2469 009	LOVE REVISITED (LP, gatefold sleeve)	12
70	Harvest SHVL 787	FALSE START (LP, gatefold sleeve)	15
72	Elektra K 42068	LOVE (LP, reissue, butterfly label)	10
72	Elektra K 42030	FOUR SAIL (LP, reissue, butterfly label)	10
73	Elektra K 32002	LOVE MASTERS (LP)	10
74	RSO 2394 145	REEL TO REAL (LP)	10

(see also Arthur Lee)

CHRISTOPHER LOVE
| 69 | London HLU 10263 | The Curse Goes On/You May Be The Next | 8 |

DARLENE LOVE
63	London HLU 9725	The Boy I'm Gonna Marry/Playing For Keeps	15
63	London HLU 9765	Wait 'Till My Bobby Gets Home/Take It From Me	15
63	London HLU 9815	A Fine Fine Boy/Marshmallow World	15
69	London HLU 10244	Wait 'Till My Bobby Gets Home/The Boy I'm Gonna Marry	10
74	Warner Bros/Spector K 19011	Christmas (Baby Please Come Home)/Wait Till My Bobby Comes Home (coloured vinyl)	4
77	Phil Spector Intl. 2010 019	Lord If You're A Woman/Johnny Baby	4

| 77 | Phil Spector Intl. 2010 019 | Lord If You're A Woman/Johnny Baby (10") | 7 |
| 64 | London RE-U 1411 | WAIT TILL MY BOBBY GETS HOME (EP) | 100 |

(see also Bob B. Soxx & Blue Jeans, Crystals, Phil Spector)

GARFIELD LOVE & JIMMY SPRUILL

| 69 | Blue Horizon 57-3150 | Next Time You See Me/Part Time Love | 15 |

GEOFF LOVE ORCHESTRA

56	MGM SP 1175	Theme From Mutiny On The Bounty/Love Song From Mutiny On The Bounty	5
57	Columbia DB 3977	Me Belle/You Are My Heart's Delight	4
58	Columbia DB 4169	Brazil/Patricia	4
59	Columbia DB 4352	The Sabre Dance/Mambo Jambo	4
61	Columbia DB 4627	Coronation Street Theme/Sophia	4
62	Columbia DB 4881	Steptoe And Son/Over The Backyard Fence	4
74	EMI EMI 2105	Match Of The Day/Bless This House	4

JILL BABY LOVE

| 76 | Black Magic BM 116 | My Way Or Hit The Highway Pts 1 & 2 | 4 |

MARY LOVE

65	King KG 1024	You Turned My Bitter Into Sweet/I'm In Your Hands	50
67	Stateside SS 2009	Lay This Burden Down/Think It Over Baby	35
68	Stateside SS 2135	The Hurt Is Just Beginning/If You Change Your Mind	20
82	Kent TOWN 501	You Turned My Bitter Into Sweet/SWEETHEARTS: This Couldn't Be Me	4

RONNIE LOVE

| 61 | London HLD 9272 | Chills And Fever/Pledging My Love | 10 |
| 78 | Grapevine GRP 108 | Let's Make Love/Nothing To Do | 4 |

WILLIE LOVE/WILLIE NIX

| 66 | Highway 51 H 700 | THE TWO WILLIES FROM MEMPHIS (LP) | 50 |

(see also Willie Nix)

LOVE AFFAIR

67	Decca F 12558	She Smiled Sweetly/Satisfaction Guaranteed	20
69	CBS 3125	Everlasting Love/Gone Are The Songs Of Yesterday	4
68	CBS 3366	Rainbow Valley/Someone Like Us (some in p/s)	8/4
68	CBS 3674	A Day Without Love/I'm Happy	4
69	CBS 3994	One Road/Let Me Know	4
69	CBS 4300	Bringing On Back The Good Times/Another Day	4
69	CBS 4631	Baby I Know/Accept Me For What I Am	4
70	CBS 4780	Lincoln County/Sea Of Tranquility	4
70	CBS 5017	Speak Of Peace Sing Of Joy/Brings My Whole World Tumbling Down	4
70	Pye 7N 45218	Let Me Dance/Love's Looking Out At You	4
68	CBS	EVERLASTING LOVE AFFAIR (LP)	15
70	CBS 64109	NEW DAY (LP)	10

(see also Elastic Band, Widowmaker)

LOVE & ROCKETS

| 85 | Beggars Banquet BEG 132 | Ball Of Confusion/Inside The Outside (p/s) | 4 |

(see also Bauhaus, Bubblemen)

LOVE CHILDREN

| 69 | Deram DM 268 | Easy Squeezy/Every Little Step | 4 |
| 70 | Deram DM 303 | Paper Chase/My Turkey Snuffed It | 5 |

LOVE GENERATION (U.S.)

| 67 | Liberty LBF 15018 | She Touched Me/The Love In Me | 6 |
| 68 | Liberty LBS 83121E | LOVE GENERATION (LP) | 10 |

LOVE GENERATION (Jamaica)

| 73 | Grape GR 3046 | Money Raper/HEPTONES: The Magnificent Heptones 3 In One | 4 |

LOVE/HATE

| 90 | Columbia | LIVE (EP, with 'Kerrang!' magazine) | 4 |

JOY LOVEJOY

| 72 | Chess 6145 010 | In Orbit/Uh! Hum | 5 |

LOVELITES

| 78 | Grapevine GRP 107 | Get Him Off My Conscience/Oh, What A Day | 4 |

TONY LOVELLO

| 59 | Top Rank JAR 200 | Amore Mio/Dreamy Serenade | 4 |

LOVE OF LIFE ORCHESTRA

| 80 | Infidelity JMB 227 | EXTENDED NICETIES (12" EP) | 7 |

(see also David Byrne)

JOHNNY LOVER

| 70 | Amalgamated AMG 871 | Pumpkin Eater/Version | 4 |
| 70 | Amalgamated AMG 873 | Two Edged Sword/Version | 4 |

LOVERS

| 58 | Vogue Pop V 9111 | Let's Elope/I Wanna Be Loved | 150 |
| 58 | Vogue Pop V 9111 | Let's Elope/I Wanna Be Loved (78) | 50 |

LOVE SCULPTURE

68	Parlophone R 5664	River To Another Day/Brand New Woman	15
68	Parlophone R 5731	Wang-Dang-Doodle/The Stumble	12
68	Parlophone R 5744	Sabre Dance/Think Of Love	4
69	Parlophone R 5807	Seagull/Farandole	8
70	Parlophone R 5831	In The Land Of The Few/People People	8
68	Parlophone PMC/PCS 7059	BLUES HELPING (LP, mono/stereo)	25/20

LOVE SCULPTURE

69	Parlophone PCS 7090	FORMS AND FEELINGS (LP)	20

(see also Human Beans, Dave Edmunds)

EDDIE LOVETTE
69	Big Shot BI 519	You're My Girl/Let Them Say	4
70	London HA-J 8413	TOO EXPERIENCED (LP, unissued)	

LOVE UNLIMITED
72	Uni UNLS 124	LOVE UNLIMITED (LP)	12
73	Pye NSPL 28179	UNDER THE INFLUENCE OF ... (LP)	10
74	Pye NSPL 28191	RHAPSODY IN WHITE (LP)	10
74	MCA MCF 2681	LOVE UNLIMITED (LP)	10
74	20th Century BT 443	IN HEAT (LP)	10
74	20th Century BT 458	WHITE GOLD (LP)	10

LOVEY AUSTIN BLUE SERENADERS
60S	Collector JE 123	SMALL JAZZ BAND VOL. 1 (EP, shared with State Street Ramblers)	7

LENE LOVICH
76	Polydor 2058 812	I Saw Mommy Kissing Santa Claus/The Christmas Song (Merry Christmas To You)/Happy Christmas	15
78	Stiff BUY 32	I Think We're Alone Now/Lucky Number (p/s, 5,000 only)	4
78	Stiff BUYJ 32	I Think We're Alone Now (Japanese)/Lucky Number (promo only)	10
80	Stiff BUY 69	What Will I Do Without You?/Joan//Monkey Talk/The Night/Too Tender/You Can't Kill Me (p/s, with free live EP)	6
81	Stiff ZBUY 97	New Toy/Cat's Away/New Toy (Extended Version) (cassette)	4
82	Stiff BUYP 164	It's You, Only You/Blue (picture disc)	4
78	Stiff SEEZ 7	STATELESS (LP, original pressing on black [2,000 only] or red vinyl) ..... each 10
78	Stiff SEEZ 7	STATELESS (LP, picture disc, 5,000 only)	12

(see also Diversions)

LOVIN'
67	Page One POF 035	Keep On Believing/I'm In Command	25
67	Page One POF 041	All You've Got/Do It Again	30

(see also Nerve)

LOVING AWARENESS
76	More Love ML 001	LOVING AWARENESS (LP)	12

(see also Glencoe, Skip Bifferty, Ian Dury)

LOVING KIND
66	Piccadilly 7N 35299	Accidental Love/Nothing Can Change This Love	8
66	Piccadilly 7N 35318	I Love The Things You Do/Treat Me Nice	10
66	Piccadilly 7N 35342	Ain't That Peculiar/With Rhyme And Reason	12

(see also Noel Redding Band)

LOVIN' SPOONFUL
65	Pye Intl. 7N 25327	Do You Believe In Magic?/On The Road Again	7
66	Pye Intl. 7N 25344	You Didn't Have To Be So Nice/My Gal	7
66	Pye Intl. 7N 25361	Daydream/Night Owl Blues	4
66	Kama Sutra KAS 200	Summer In The City/Bald Headed Lena	4
66	Kama Sutra KAS 201	Rain On The Roof/Warm Baby	4
67	Kama Sutra KAS 204	Nashville Cats/Full Measure	4
67	Kama Sutra KAS 207	Darling Be Home Soon/Darlin' Companion	4
67	Kama Sutra KAS 208	Six O'Clock/The Finale	5
67	Kama Sutra KAS 210	She Is Still A Mystery/Only Pretty, What A Pity	4
67	Kama Sutra KAS 211	Money/Close Your Eyes	4
68	Kama Sutra KAS 213	Never Going Back/Forever	6
66	Kama Sutra KEP 300	DID YOU EVER HAVE TO MAKE UP YOUR MIND (EP)	10
66	Kama Sutra KEP 301	JUG BAND MUSIC (EP)	10
66	Kama Sutra KEP 302	SUMMER IN THE CITY (EP)	10
67	Kama Sutra KEP 303	DAY BLUES (EP)	10
67	Kama Sutra KEP 304	NASHVILLE CATS (EP)	10
67	Kama Sutra KEP 305	LOVIN' YOU (EP)	10
67	Kama Sutra KEP 306	SOMETHING IN THE NIGHT (EP)	10
65	Pye Intl. NPL 28069	DO YOU BELIEVE IN MAGIC? (LP)	12
66	Pye Intl. NPL 28078	DAYDREAM (LP)	15
67	Kama Sutra KLP 401	HUMS OF THE LOVIN' SPOONFUL (LP)	12
67	Kama Sutra KLP 402	YOU'RE A BIG BOY NOW (LP, soundtrack)	12
67	Kama Sutra KLP 403	THE BEST OF THE LOVIN' SPOONFUL (LP)	10
68	Kama Sutra KLP 404	EVERYTHING PLAYING (LP)	12
68	Kama Sutra K(S)LP 405	THE BEST OF THE LOVIN' SPOONFUL VOL. 2 (LP)	10
69	Kama Sutra 602 009	REVELATION: REVOLUTION '69 (LP)	10

(see also John Sebastian, Mugwumps, Zalman Yanovsky)

BRUCE LOW
56	HMV JO 464	Just Walking In The Rain/Cindy Oh Cindy (export issue)	10

DENNIS LOWE
70	Downtown DT 465	What's Your Name/MUSIC DOCTORS: Mr Locabe	4
70	Downtown DT 468	Stand Up For The Sound/OWEN & DENNIS: Old Man Trouble	4

JIM LOWE
55	London HLD 8171	Close The Door/Nueva Laredo (gold lettering on label)	40
55	London HLD 8171	Close The Door/Nueva Laredo (78)	5
56	London HLD 8276	Blue Suede Shoes/Maybellene (silver lettering on label)	60
56	London HLD 8276	Blue Suede Shoes/Maybellene (78)	10
56	London HLD 8288	Love Is The $64,000 Dollar Question/Rene La Rue (gold lettering on label)	40
56	London HLD 8288	Love Is The $64,000 Dollar Question/Rene La Rue (78)	5
56	London HLD 8317	The Green Door/The Little Man In Chinatown (as Jim Lowe & High Fives, gold lettering on label, later silver)	30/18

56	London HLD 8317	The Green Door/The Little Man In Chinatown (78)	5
57	London HLD 8368	By You, By You, By You/I Feel The Beat (gold lettering label, later silver)	25/18
57	London HLD 8368	By You, By You, By You/I Feel The Beat (78)	5
57	London HLD 8431	Four Walls/Talkin' To The Blues	25
57	London HLD 8431	Four Walls/Talkin' To The Blues (78)	5
58	London HLD 8538	Roc-A-Chicka/The Bright Light (with Billy Vaughan's Orchestra)	85
58	London HLD 8538	Roc-A-Chicka/The Bright Light (with Billy Vaughan's Orchestra) (78)	20
60	London HLD 9043	He'll Have To Go/(This Life Is Just A) Dress Rehearsal	12
65	United Artists UP 1096	Mr Moses/Make Your Back Strong	4
58	London HA-D 2108	SONGS THEY SING BEHIND THE GREEN DOOR (LP)	35
59	London HA-D 2146	WICKED WOMEN (LP)	25

NICK LOWE

76	Stiff BUY 1	So It Goes/Heart Of The City (p/s)	4
77	Stiff LAST 1	BOWI (EP)	4
77	Stiff BUY 22	Halfway To Paradise/I Don't Want The Night To End (p/s)	4
78	Radar ADA 26	American Squirm/(What's So Funny 'Bout) Peace, Love And Understanding (p/s)	4
82	F-Beat XX 23F/SAM 147	My Heart Hurts/Pet You And Hold You//Cracking Up/(What's So Funny 'Bout) Peace, Love And Understanding (double pack)	4

(see also Kippington Lodge, Brinsley Schwartz, Tartan Horde, Disco Brothers, Rockpile, Elvis Costello, Ernie Graham)

PETER LOWE

56	Parlophone R 4199	Hear My Song Of Love/Toula	7
57	Parlophone R 4270	The Banana Boat Song/The Wisdom Of A Fool	6
57	Parlophone R 4380	Tingle/Ca, C'Est L'Amour	5

SAMMY LOWE

| 61 | RCA RCA 1239 | Hey Lawdy Lawdy Mary | 10 |

LOW NOISE

| 81 | Happy Birthday UR 5 | Jungle Line/Urban Tribal/Jungle Line (Instrumental) (p/s) | 6 |
| 81 | Happy Birthday UR 5 | Jungle Line/Urban Tribal/Jungle Line (Instrumental) (12", p/s) | 8 |

(see also Thomas Dolby)

LOW NUMBERS

| 79 | Warner Bros K 17493 | Keep In Touch/Nine All Out (p/s) | 6 |

LOWRELL

| 79 | AVI AVIS 108 | Mellow Mellow Right On/You're Playing Dirty | 4 |
| 79 | AVI AVISL 108 | Mellow Mellow Right On/You're Playing Dirty (12") | 8 |

HENRY LOWTHER BAND

| 70 | Deram SML 1070 | CHILD SONG (LP) | 60 |

(see also Manfred Mann, John Mayall & Blues Breakers, Keef Hartley Band)

MARK LOYD

65	Parlophone R 5277	I Keep Thinking About You/Will It Be The Same	5
65	Parlophone R 5332	Everybody Tries/She Said No	4
66	Parlophone R 5423	When Evening Falls/When I'm Gonna Find Her	25

L.T.D.

| 76 | A&M AMS 7265 | Love Ballad/Let The Music Keep Playing | 4 |

JEREMY LUBBOCK

58	Parlophone R 4399	Catch A Falling Star/The Man Who Invented Love	4
58	Parlophone R 4421	Lemon Twist/Tonight	4
58	Parlophone R 4473	Odd Man Out/Too Bad You're Not Around	4
58	Parlophone GEP 8745	JUST FOR THE FUN OF IT (EP)	7

LUCAS & MIKE COTTON SOUND

67	Pye 7N 17313	Step Out Of Line/Ain't Love Good, Ain't Love Proud	15
68	MGM MGM 1398	Soul Serenade/We Got A Thing Going Baby	12
68	MGM MGM 1427	Jack And The Beanstalk/Mother-In-Law	6

(see also Mike Cotton Sound, Artwoods)

BUDDY LUCAS BAND

53	London L 1181	Organ Grinder's Swing/Laura (78, as Buddy Lucas & His Orchestra)	40
60	Pye International 7N 25045	I Want To Know/Deacon John	6
60	Pye International 7N 25045	I Want To Know/Deacon John (78)	10

FRED LUCAS

| 57 | Columbia DB 3861 | Friendly Persuasion (Thee I Love)/A Thing Of Beauty | 4 |

TREVOR LUCAS

| 66 | Reality RE 505 | Waltzing Matilda/It's On | 25 |
| 66 | Reality RY 1002 | OVERLANDER (LP) | 250 |

(see also Fairport Convention, Bronco)

LUCIFER

71	Lucifer L 001	Don't Care/Hypnosis	8
72	Lucifer L 003/004	Fuck You/Bad	8
72	Lucifer L 005/006	Prick/Want It (some housed in black box with L 003/004 £20)	8
72	Lucifer LLP 1	BIG GUN (LP, private pressing, with poster/inserts, sold through 'Oz' mag)	60
72	Lucifer LLP 2	EXIT (LP, private pressing, with poster, sold through 'Oz' magazine)	90

JOHNNY LUCK

| 58 | Fontana H 110 | Play Rough/Buzz, Buzz, Buzz (78) | 6 |

LUCKY MILLINDER & HIS ORCHESTRA

51	Vogue V 9007	I'm Waiting Just For You/Bongo Boogie (78)	10
51	Vogue V 9021	The Grape Vine/No One Else Could Be (78)	10
52	Vogue V 2138	Ram-Bunk-Shush/Let It Roll Again (78)	10

TOM LUCY

82	Bridgehouse BHS 15	Paris, France/Man Found Dead In Graveyard (no p/s)	6

(see also Wasted Youth)

LUCY SHOW

83	Shout XS 007	Leonardo Da Vinci/Kill The Beast (p/s)	5

LUDLOWS

65	Pye 7N 15946	The Last Thing On My Mind/Kisses Sweeter Than Wine	4
66	Pye 7N 17050	The Sea Around Us/The Butcher Boys	4
66	Pye 7N 17123	The Winds Thro' The Rafters/That's My Song	4
66	Pye 7N 17221	Johnny Lad/Pack Up Your Sorrows	4
67	Pye 7N 17319	Enniskillen Dragoons/Foggy Dew	4
67	Pye 7N 17384	Plaisir D'Amour/Yesterday's Dream	4
66	Pye NPL 18150	THE WIND AND THE SEA (LP)	12

(see also Jim McCann)

LUDUS

80	New Hormones ORG 4	The Visit/Lullaby Cheat/Unveil (12", p/s, with insert)	8
81	New Hormones ORG 8	My Cherry Is In Sherry/Anatomy Is Not Destiny (p/s)	5
81	New Hormones CAT 1	PICKPOCKET (C-30 cassette pack with A4 book & button in PVC bag)	12
81	New Hormones ORG 12	Mother's Hour/Patient (with poster)	5
81	New Hormones ORG 16	THE SEDUCTION (2 x 12" EP, each 12" in p/s all in bag)	12
80s	New Hormones	LINDER SINGS BARDOT (cassette)	10
82	New Hormones ORG 20	DANGER CAME SMILING (LP)	10

ROBIN LUKE

58	London HLD 8676	Susie Darlin'/Living's Loving You	8
58	London HLD 8676	Susie Darlin'/Living's Loving You (78)	8
58	London HLD 8771	Chicka Chicka Honey/My Girl	12
58	London HLD 8771	Chicka Chicka Honey/My Girl (78)	10
59	London RED 1222	ROBIN LUKE (EP)	50

LULU (& LUVERS)

64	Decca F 11884	Shout/Forget Me Baby (as Lulu & Luvers)	6
64	Decca F 11965	Can't Hear You No More/I Am In Love	5
64	Decca F 12017	Here Comes The Night/That's Really Some Good	4
65	Decca F 12128	Satisfied/Surprise Surprise (as Lulu & Luvers)	6
65	Decca F 12169	Leave A Little Love/He Don't Want Your Love Anymore	4
65	Decca F 12214	Try To Understand/Not In This Whole World	4
65	Decca F 12254	Tell Me Like It Is/Stop Fooling Around	4
66	Decca F 12326	Call Me/After You	4
66	Decca F 12491	What A Wonderful Feeling/Tossin' And Turnin'	4
67	Columbia DB 8169	The Boat That I Row/Dreary Days And Nights	4
67	Columbia DB 8221	Let's Pretend/To Sir With Love	5
67	Columbia DB 8295	Love Love's To Love Love/You And I	4
68	Columbia DB 8358	Me, The Peaceful Heart/Lookout	4
68	Columbia DB 8425	Boy/Sad Memories	4
68	Columbia DB 8500	I'm A Tiger/Without Him	4
69	Columbia DB 8550	Boom Bang-A-Bang/March!	4
69	Atco 226 008	Oh Me, Oh My (I'm A Fool For You Baby)/Sweep Around Your Own Back Door	4
70	Atco 2091 014	Hum A Song (From Your Heart)/Mr Bojangles	4
71	Atco 2091 049	Got To Believe In Love/Move To My Rhythm	5
71	Atlantic 2091 083	Everybody Clap/After The Feeling Is Gone	5
72	Atlantic K 10185	Even If I Could Change/You Ain't Wrong You Just Ain't Right	4
74	Polydor 2001 490	The Man Who Sold The World/Watch That Man	4
74	Chelsea 2005 015	The Man With The Golden Gun/A Boy Like You	7
75	Chelsea 2005 022	Take Your Mama For A Ride Pts 1 & 2	4
75	Chelsea 2005 031	Boy Meets Girl/Mama's Little Corner Of The World	4
75	Chelsea 2001 048	Heaven And Earth And The Stars/A Boy Like You	4
65	Decca DFE 8597	LULU (EP)	15
65	Decca LK 4719	SOMETHING TO SHOUT ABOUT (LP)	18
67	Ace Of Clubs ACL 1232	LULU! (LP)	12
67	Fontana STL 5446	TO SIR WITH LOVE (LP, soundtrack, with Mindbenders)	12
67	Columbia S(C)X 6201	LOVE LOVES TO LOVE LULU (LP)	12
68	Columbia S(C)X 6265	LULU'S ALBUM (LP)	12
69	Atco 228 031	NEW ROUTES (LP)	10

(see also Luvvers)

BOB LUMAN

60	Warner Bros WB 12	Dreamy Doll/Buttercup	6
60	Warner Bros WB 18	Let's Think About Living/You've Got Everything	6
60	Warner Bros WB 28	Why, Why, Bye, Bye/Oh, Lonesome Me	6
61	Warner Bros WB 37	The Great Snow Man/The Pig Latin Song	5
61	Warner Bros WB 49	Private Eye/You Turned Down The Lights	5
62	Warner Bros WB 60	Louisiana Man/Rocks Of Reno (unissued)	
62	Warner Bros WB 75	Hey Joe/The Fool	6
64	Hickory 45 1238	Bigger Men Than I/File	5
64	Hickory 45 1266	Run On Home Baby Brother/Lonely Room	5
64	Hickory 45 1277	Fire Engine Red/Old George Dickel	6
65	Hickory 45 1289	Bad Bad Day/Tears From Out Of Nowhere	8
65	Hickory 45 1410	Come On And Sing/It's A Sin	6
68	CBS 3602	Ain't Got Time To Be Unhappy/I Can't Remember To Forget	12
61	Warner Bros WEP 6046	LET'S THINK ABOUT LIVING (EP, also stereo WSEP 2046)	25/35
62	Warner Bros WEP 6055	LET'S THINK ABOUT LIVING NO. 2 (EP, also stereo WSEP 2055)	25/35
62	Warner Bros WEP 6102	LET'S THINK ABOUT LIVING NO. 3 (EP, also stereo WSEP 2102)	25/35
60	Warner Bros WM 4025	LET'S THINK ABOUT LIVING (LP, also stereo WS 8025)	50/60
64	Hickory LPM 124	LIVIN' LOVIN' SOUNDS (LP)	20
71	London ZGE 115	LIVIN' LOVIN' SOUNDS (LP, reissue)	10

77	DJM DJM 22057	BOB LUMAN ROCKS (LP)	10

(see also Sue Thompson & Bob Luman)

BOB LUMAN/BOBBY LORD

64	Hickory LPE 1501	HICKORY SHOWCASE VOL. 2 (EP, 1 side each)	10
64	Hickory LPE 1504	HICKORY SHOWCASE VOL. 3 (EP, 1 side each)	10
64	Hickory LPM 121	CAN'T TAKE THE COUNTRY FROM THE BOYS (LP, 1 side each)	15

(see also Bobby Lord)

RUFUS LUMLEY

66	Stateside SS 516	I'm Standing/Let's Hide Away	55
78	EMI International INT 556	I'm Standing/Let's Hide Away (reissue)	4

LUNACHICKS

89	Blast First BFFP 44	Sugar Luv/Get Off The Road//Makin' It (With Other Species)/Jan Brady (double pack)	5

LUNAR TWO

60s	Spot JWS 551	Get It Take It/Don't Ever Leave Me	6

LUNATIC FRINGE

82	Resurrection ERECT 1	WHO'S IN CONTROL (EP, with BUAV insert)	4

LYDIA LUNCH

93	Clawfist X-PIG 19	Unearthly Delights/Busted (p/s)	4
82	Situation 2 SITU 6	13.13 (LP, with inner sleeve)	10
84	Doublevision DVR 5	IN LIMBO (LP, red vinyl with inner sleeve)	10
86	Widowspeak SWP 01/07	THE INTIMATE DIARIES OF THE SEXUALLY INSANE (signed box set with book & cassette)	8

(see also Eight-Eyed Spy, Roland S. Howard)

ART LUND

53	MGM SP 1042	If I Were A Bell/JOHNNY DESMOND: A Bushel And A Peck	6
65	United Artists UP 1100	Branded/Gonna Have A Little Talk	4
57	Vogue Coral LVA 9056	THIS IS ART (LP)	10

LARRY LUREX

73	EMI EMI 2030	I Can Hear Music/Goin' Back (beware of convincing counterfeits!)	100

(see also Queen)

LURKERS

77	Beggars Banquet BEG 1	Free Admission Single: Shadow/Love Story (p/s, black vinyl; reissued on red, blue or white vinyl)	5/8
77	Beggars Banquet BEG 2	Freak Show/Mass Media Believer (p/s)	4
78	Beggars Banquet BEG 6	Ain't Got A Clue/Ooh Ooh I Love You (p/s, 15,000 with gold flexidisc, 'Chaos Brothers Fulham Fallout Forty Free' [BEG 6 1/2])	6/4
78	Beggars Banquet BEG 6	Ain't Got A Clue/Ooh Ooh I Love You (reissue, diff. p/s, with clear vinyl pic flexi)	5
79	Beggars Banquet BACK 1	Shadow/Love Story//Freak Show/Mass Media Believer (reissue double pack)	4
79	Beggars Banquet BACK 3	I Don't Need To Tell Her/Pills//Just Thirteen/Countdown (double pack)	4
82	Clay CLAY 17P	Drag You Out/Heroin (It's All Over) (picture disc)	4

(see also Pete Stride & John Plain)

DON LUSHER BAND

55	Decca F 10560	Rock 'n' Roll/On With The Don	6
56	Decca F 10740	Fast And Furious/Let's Do It	4

LUSTMØRD

82	Sterile SR 3	LUSTMØRD (LP, with odorous label)	50

NELLIE LUTCHER

49	Capitol CL 13026	The Song Is Ended/Sleepy Lagoon (78)	15
49	Capitol CL 13049	Come And Get It/The Lady's In Love With You (78)	15
54	Brunswick 05352	Blues In The Night/Breezin' Along With The Breeze	10
55	Brunswick 05437	It's Been Said/Please Come Back	7
55	Brunswick 05497	Whose Honey Are You?/If I Didn't Love You Like I Do	7
60	Capitol CL 15106	My Mother's Eyes/The Heart Of A Clown	5
60	Capitol EAP 20066	REAL GONE (EP)	20
56	Philips BBE 12045	NELLIE LUTCHER (EP)	18
51	Capitol LC 6500	REAL GONE! (10" LP)	40
57	London HA-U 2036	OUR NEW NELLIE (LP)	20
66	Music For Pleasure 1038	REAL GONE (LP)	12

CLAUDE LUTER ORCHESTRA

59	Vogue V 9132	The Day That The Rains Came/La Grande Coco	4

LUTHER

76	Cotillion K 10781	It's Good For The Soul Pts 1 & 2	20

FRANK LUTHER

60	Decca F 9050	The Little Red Hen (Song Story) (both sides)	4
60	Decca F 9051	The Three Billy Goats Gruff (Song Story) (both sides)	5

LUTHER & LITTLE EVA

57	Parlophone R 4292	Love Is Strange/Ain't Got No Home	150
57	Parlophone R 4292	Love Is Strange/Ain't Got No Home (78)	50

(see also Little Eva)

LUV BUG

86	Roxy!-Ritz TEASE 2	You Can Count On Me/You Can't Have It (p/s)	7

LUV MACHINE

71	Polydor 2460 102	LUV MACHINE (LP)	100

LUVVERS

66	Parlophone R 5459	The House On The Hill/Most Unlovely	25

(see also Lulu)

MINT VALUE £

GARY LUX
85	Global LUX 2	Children Of The World/Movies (p/s)	5

L-VOAG
81	Axis No. 9	THE WAY OUT (LP, with booklet & poster)	15

(see also Homosexuals)

ARTHUR LYMAN GROUP
59	Vogue V 9153	Taboo/Dahil Sayo	4
59	Vogue V 9153	Taboo/Dahil Sayo (78)	5
59	Vogue VA 160142	TABOO VOL. 1 (LP)	10
59	Vogue VA 160149	MORE EXOTIC SOUNDS — BWANA A (LP)	10
60	Vogue VA 160166	BAHIA (LP)	10
61	Vogue VA 160171	HAWAIIAN SUNSET (LP)	10
61	Vogue VA 160174	TABOO VOL. 2 (LP, also stereo SAV 8003)	10

FRANKIE LYMON (& TEENAGERS)
56	Columbia SCM 5265	Why Do Fools Fall In Love?/Please Be Mine	40
56	Columbia DB 3772	Why Do Fools Fall In Love?/Please Be Mine (78)	8
56	Columbia SCM 5285	I Want You To Be My Girl/I'm Not A Know It All	30
56	Columbia DB 3797	I Want You To Be My Girl/I'm Not A Know It All (78)	8
56	Columbia DB 3819	Who Can Explain?/I Promise To Remember	25
56	Columbia DB 3819	Who Can Explain?/I Promise To Remember (78)	8
56	Columbia DB 3858	Share/The A.B.C.'s Of Love	25
56	Columbia DB 3858	Share/The A.B.C.'s Of Love (78)	8
57	Columbia DB 3878	I'm Not A Juvenile Delinquent/Baby, Baby	25
57	Columbia DB 3878	I'm Not A Juvenile Delinquent/Baby, Baby (78)	8
57	Columbia DB 3910	Teenage Love/Paper Castles	25
57	Columbia DB 3910	Teenage Love/Paper Castles (78)	10
57	Columbia DB 3942	Miracle In The Rain/Out In The Cold Again	25
57	Columbia DB 3942	Miracle In The Rain/Out In The Cold Again (78)	10
57	Columbia DB 3983	Goody Goody/Creation Of Love	12
57	Columbia DB 3983	Goody Goody/Creation Of Love (78)	10
57	Columbia DB 4028	My Girl/So Goes My Love	18
57	Columbia DB 4028	My Girl/So Goes My Love (78)	8
58	Columbia DB 4073	Thumb Thumb/Footsteps	15
58	Columbia DB 4073	Thumb Thumb/Footsteps (78)	15
58	Columbia DB 4134	Mama Don't Allow It/Portable On My Shoulder	12
58	Columbia DB 4134	Mama Don't Allow It/Portable On My Shoulder (78)	8
59	Columbia DB 4245	Melinda/The Only Way To Love	10
59	Columbia DB 4245	Melinda/The Only Way To Love (78)	10
59	Columbia DB 4295	Up Jumped A Rabbit/No Matter What You've Done	15
60	Columbia DB 4499	Little Bitty Pretty One/Creation Of Love	15
66	King KG 1042	Why Do Fools Fall In Love?/I'm Not A Juvenile Delinquent	8
57	Columbia SEG 7662	TEENAGE ROCK (EP)	30
57	Columbia SEG 7694	I'M NOT A JUVENILE DELINQUENT (EP)	30
57	Columbia SEG 7734	FRANKIE LYMON AND THE TEENAGERS (EP)	30
58	Columbia 33S 1127	FRANKIE LYMON IN LONDON (10" LP)	100
58	Columbia 33S 1134	ROCKIN' WITH FRANKIE LYMON (10" LP)	300
78	Pye NSPL 28251	WHY DO FOOLS FALL IN LOVE? (LP)	10

LEWIS LYMON & TEENCHORDS
58	Oriole CB 1419	Too Young/Your Last Chance	200
58	Oriole CB 1419	Too Young/Your Last Chance (78)	35

DERMOTT LYNCH
68	Blue Cat BS 101	Hot Shot/I've Got Your Number	10
68	Blue Cat BS 122	I Got Everything/Echo	8
68	Doctor Bird DB 1115	Adults Only/Cool It	8

KENNY LYNCH
60	HMV POP 751	Mountain Of Love/Why Do You Treat Me This Way?	4
60	HMV POP 786	Slowcoach/You Make Love So Well	4
61	HMV POP 841	So/Love Me	4
61	HMV POP 900	The Story Behind My Tears/Steady Kind	4
61	HMV POP 985	There's Never Been A Girl/Doll Face	4
62	HMV POP 1005	It Would Take A Miracle/Strolling Blues	4
62	HMV POP 1057	Puff/Happy That's Me	4
62	HMV POP 1090	Up On The Roof/Jump On Your Broomstick	4
63	HMV POP 1136	Misery/Shut The Door	5
63	HMV POP 1165	You Can Never Stop Me Loving You/Crazy Crazes	4
63	HMV POP 1229	For You (There's Not A Thing I Wouldn't Do)/With Somebody	4
63	HMV POP 1260	Shake And Scream/Harlem Library	4
64	HMV POP 1280	Stand By Me/Baby It's True	4
64	HMV POP 1321	That's What Little Girls Are Made For/What Am I To You?	4
64	HMV POP 1367	My Own Two Feet/So Much To Love You For	8
65	HMV POP 1430	For Loving You Baby/I'll Stay By You	4
65	HMV POP 1476	Nothing But The Real Thing/Don't Ask Me To Stop Loving You	5
65	HMV POP 1496	Get Out Of My Way/One Look At You	4
66	HMV POP 1534	The World I Used To Know/Come On Come On	4
67	HMV POP 1577	I Just Wanna Love You/It's Too Late	7
67	HMV POP 1604	Movin' Away/Could I Count On You	10
68	Columbia DB 8329	Mister Moonlight/The Other Side Of Dreamland	4
68	Columbia DB 8498	Along Came Love/Sweet Situation	4
69	Columbia DB 8599	The Drifter/Did I Stay Too Long?	5
70	Columbia DB 8703	Loving You Is Sweeter Than Ever/In Old Kentucky	4
63	HMV 7EG 8820	HEY GIRL (EP)	12
64	HMV 7EG 8855	KENNY LYNCH (EP)	12
65	HMV 7EG 8881	WHAT AM I TO YOU (EP)	12

| 63 | HMV CLP 1635 | UP ON THE ROOF (LP, also stereo CSD 1489) | 35/50 |
| 66 | Music For Pleasure 1022 | WE LIKE KENNY (LP) | 10 |

LEE LYNCH (& BLUE ANGELS)
66	Decca F 12375	You Won't See Me/You Know There's Me (as Lee Lynch & Blue Angels)	4
69	Ember EMB 262	Stay Awhile/Bad Time To Stop Loving Me (p/s)	4
70	Ember EMB 271	Sweet Woman/Can't Take My Eyes Off You (p/s)	4
70	Ember EMB 282	Joe Poor Loves Daphne E Rich/It's Over (p/s)	4

LINDA LYNDELL
| 70 | Stax 601 041 | Bring Your Love Back To Me/Here I Am | 20 |

BARBARA LYNN
64	London HLW 9918	Oh! Baby (We Got A Good Thing Goin)/Unfair	8
65	Immediate IM 011	You Can't Buy My Love/That's What A Friend Will Do	20
66	London HLU 10094	You Left The Water Running/Until I'm Free	12
67	Sue WI 4028	Letter To Mommy And Daddy/Second Fiddle Girl	12
67	Sue WI 4038	You'll Lose A Good Thing/Lonely Heartaches	15
71	Atlantic 2091 133	Until Then I Suffer/Take Your Love And Run	8
75	Oval OVAL 1006	Letter To Mommy And Daddy/You'll Lose A Good Thing	4
67	Sue ILP 949	THE BARBARA LYNN STORY (LP)	50

BOBBI LYNN
| 68 | Stateside SS 2088 | Earthquake/Opportunity Street | 20 |
| 71 | Bell BLL 1168 | Earthquake/Opportunity Street (reissue) | 6 |

CHERYL LYNN
| 84 | Streetwave KHAN 23 | Encore/Got To Be Real | 4 |
| 84 | Streetwave MKHAN 23 | Encore/Got To Be Real (12") | 8 |

KARI LYNN
| 61 | Oriole CB 1632 | Yo Yo/Summer Day | 4 |
| 61 | Oriole CB 1644 | You've Got To See Mamma Every Night/Lonesome And Sorry | 4 |

PATTI LYNN
62	Fontana H 370	I See It All Now/Someone Else's Valentine	5
62	Fontana H 391	Johnny Angel/Tonight You Belong To Me	5
62	Fontana 267247 TF	Tell Me Telstar/Big Big Love	5
62	Fontana TFE 17392	PATTI (EP)	12

TAM(M)I LYNN
66	Atlantic AT 4071	I'm Gonna Run Away From You/The Boy Next Door	25
71	Mojo 2092 001	I'm Gonna Run Away From You/The Boy Next Door (reissue)	4
72	Mojo 2916 007	LOVE IS HERE AND NOW YOU'RE GONE (LP)	10

VERA LYNN
54	Decca F 10253	Two Easter Sunday Sweethearts/Du Bist Mein Liebeshoen	6
54	Decca F 10290	The Homecoming Waltz/Humble People	6
54	Decca F 10372	My Son, My Son/Our Heaven On Earth (with Frank Weir & His Saxophone)	15
55	Decca F 10463	Addio Amore (with Johnston Brothers)/I Do	5
55	Decca F 10535	Doonaree/Show Me The Way	4
55	Decca F 10566	Ev'ry Day Of My Life/My Lonely Lover	4
55	MGM SP 1142	From Tomorrow/Each Moment I Live	4
56	Decca F 10688	Last Love/Such A Day	4
56	Decca F 10715	Who Are We?/I'll Be True To You	7
56	Decca F 10799	A House With Love In It/Little Lost Dog	7
57	Decca F 10846	The Faithful Hussar (Don't Cry My...)/The One Beside You	7
57	Decca F 10903	Travellin' Home/Dear To Me	7
59	Decca F 9927	Auf Wiederseh'n, Sweetheart/From The Time You Say Goodbye	7
52	Decca LF 1022	SINCERELY YOURS, VERA LYNN (10" LP)	10
53	Decca LF 1102	SINCERELY YOURS, VERA LYNN VOL. 2 (10" LP)	10
53	Decca LF 1183	SINCERELY YOURS, VERA LYNN VOL. 3 (10" LP)	10

GLORIA LYNNE
64	London HLY 9846	I Wish You Love/Through A Long And Sleeping Night	4
64	London HLY 9888	I Should Care/Indian Love Call	4
60	Top Rank BUY 031	LONELY AND SENTIMENTAL (LP)	10
64	London HA-Y 8112	AT THE LAS VEGAS THUNDERBIRD (LP, with Herman Foster Trio)	10

JEFF LYNNE
| 77 | Jet UP 36281 | Doin' That Crazy Thing/Goin' Down To Rio (p/s) | 5 |
(see also Nightriders, Idle Race, E.L.O., Move, Traveling Wilburys)

SUE LYNNE
68	RCA Victor RCA 1724	Reach For The Moon/All Alone	4
69	RCA Victor RCA 1822	You/Don't Pity Me	75
69	RCA Victor RCA 1874	Baby Baby Baby/You Lose Again	4

PHIL LYNOTT
80	Vertigo SOLO 1	Dear Miss Lonely Hearts/Solo In Soho (p/s)	4
80	Vertigo SOLO 112	Dear Miss Lonely Hearts/Solo In Soho (12, p/s)	7
81	Vertigo SOLO 3	Yellow Pearl/Girls (p/s, yellow vinyl)	4
85	Polydor POSPD 777	19/19 (Dub Version)//THIN LIZZY: Whiskey In The Jar (live) (double pack with 1-sided bonus disc)	5
80	Vertigo PHIL 1	SOLO IN SOHO (LP, picture disc)	12
(see also Thin Lizzy, Gary Moore & Phil Lynott, John Sykes)

JACKIE LYNTON
61	Piccadilly 7N 35012	Over The Rainbow/High In The Sky	4
62	Piccadilly 7N 35055	Don't Take Away Your Love/Wishful Thinking	4
62	Piccadilly 7N 35064	All Of Me/I'd Steal	8
63	Piccadilly 7N 35107	I Believe/The Girl In The Wood	4
63	Piccadilly 7N 35140	Jeannie With The Light Brown Hair/Teddy Bear's Picnic	4

Jackie LYNTON

63	Piccadilly 7N 35156	I'm Talkin' About You/Lawdy Miss Clawdy	4
64	Piccadilly 7N 35177	Little Child/Never A Mention	4
64	Piccadilly 7N 35190	Laura/Ebb Tide	4
65	Decca F 12052	Three Blind Mice/Corrina Corrine	4
67	Columbia DB 8097	He'll Have To Go/Only You	4
67	Columbia DB 8180	Decision/Sporting Life	4
67	Columbia DB 8224	Answer Me/I Never Loved A Girl Like You	4
74	WWA WWA 012	THE JACKIE LYNTON ALBUM (LP)	10

(see also Savoy Brown Blues Band)

LYNYRD SKYNYRD

74	MCA MCA 136	Don't Ask Me No Questions/Take Your Time	5
74	MCA MCA 160	Sweet Home Alabama/Take Your Time	5
75	MCA MCA 199	Saturday Night Special/Made In The Shade	4
76	MCA MCA 229	Double Trouble/Roll Gypsy Roll	4
76	MCA MCA 251	Free Bird/Sweet Home Alabama/Double Trouble (p/s)	7
76	MCA MCA 275	Free Bird (Edit)/Gimme Three Steps (p/s)	7
78	MCA MCEP 101	DOWN SOUTH JUKIN' (EP, p/s)	6
78	MCA MCA 342	What's Your Name/I Know A Little	4
82	MCA MCA 799	I've Been Your Fool/Gotta Go (p/s)	5
82	MCA MCATP 251	Free Bird//Sweet Home Alabama/Double Trouble (12" picture disc)	8
74	MCA MCG 3502	PRONOUNCED LEH-NERD SKIN-NERD (LP, gatefold sleeve)	10
74	MCA MCG 3525	STREET SURVIVORS (LP, with tour dates on inner sleeve)	10

BARBARA LYON

55	Columbia SCM 5186	I Love To Dance With You/Yes You Are	6
55	Columbia SCM 5207	Whisper/Where You Are	6
56	Columbia SCM 5232	Band Of Gold/Such A Day	6
56	Columbia SCM 5276	Puppy Love/The Birds And The Bees	6
56	Columbia DB 3826	It's Better In The Dark/A Heart Without A Sweetheart	6
56	Columbia DB 3865	Falling In Love/Letter To A Soldier	8
57	Columbia DB 3931	C'est La Vie/Fire Down Below	4
57	Columbia DB 4026	Thanks For The Loan Of A Dream/Third Finger — Left Hand	4
58	Columbia DB 4137	Red Was The Moon/Ring On A Ribbon	4
60	Triumph RGM 1027	My Charlie/Tell Me	15
56	Columbia SEG 7640	MY FOUR FRIENDS (EP)	12

PATTI LYON

| 62 | Fontana H 370 | I See It All Now/Someone Else's Valentine | 4 |

RICHARD LYON

| 59 | Fontana H 206 | All My Own/Private Eye | 4 |

LYONS & MALONE

| 69 | Jay Boy BOY 9 | Doctor Gentle/She's Alright | 4 |

LYON ST.
(see under Associates)

LYRICS

67	Coxsone CS 7003	A Get It/KEN PARKER: How Strong	12
68	Coxsone CS 7067	Music Like Dirt/TONETTES: I Give It To You	12
70	Randy's RAN 504	Give Thanks And Praises/TOMMY McCOOK: Get Ready	4

JIMMY LYTELL

| 59 | London HL 8873 | Hot Cargo/A Blues Serenade | 7 |

JOHNNY LYTLE

| 68 | Minit MLF 11006 | Gonna Get That Boat Pts 1 & 2 | 8 |

HUMPHREY LYTTELTON (& HIS BAND)

53	Parlophone MSP 6001	Out Of The Gallion/The Old Grey Mare	6
53	Parlophone MSP 6023	Muskrat Ramble/Mamzelle Josephine (as Lyttelton Paseo Band, B-side with George Brown)	6
53	Parlophone MSP 6033	Maryland, My Maryland/Blue For Waterloo	6
53	Parlophone MSP 6034	Shake It And Break It/Jail Break	6
53	Parlophone MSP 6045	Red For Piccadilly/Kater Street Rag	6
54	Parlophone MSP 6061	Martiniquen Song (Last Year)/Ain't Cha Got Music	6
54	Parlophone MSP 6076	East Coast Trot/Breeze	6
54	Parlophone MSP 6093	Just Once For All Time/Joshua, Fit The Battle Of Jericho	6
54	Parlophone MSP 6097	Mainly Traditional/Oh! Dad (with 'Melody Maker' All Stars)	6
54	Parlophone MSP 6128	Mezzy's Tune/Jelly Bean Blues	6
56	Tempo A 10	When The Saints Go Marching In/Careless Love	6
56	Parlophone R 4184	Bad Penny Blues/Close Your Eyes (78)	5
56	Parlophone R 4212	Love, Love, Love/Echoing The Blues	6
56	Esquire 10-491	The Thin Red Line/Melancholy Blues (78)	5
56	Esquire 10-494	First Of Many/Blues For Two (78)	5
57	Parlophone R 4262	It's Mardi Gras/Sweet And Sour	4
57	Parlophone R 4277	Baby Doll/Red Beans And Rice	4
57	Esquire 10-501	Elizabeth/Blue For Waterloo (78)	5
57	Parlophone R 4333	Early Call (Bermondsey Bounce)/Creole Serenade	4
57	Parlophone R 4368	Dixie Theme/Blues At Dawn	4
57	Esquire 10-511	Cake Walkin' Babies/If You See Me Comin' (78)	5
58	Parlophone CMSP 41	Bad Penny Blues/Baby Doll (export issue)	25
58	Parlophone R 4392	Buona Sera/Blues In The Afternoon	4
58	Parlophone R 4428	Hand Me Down Love/Here And Gone (Blues In 1890)	4
58	Decca F 11058	La Paloma/Bodega	4
59	Parlophone R 4519	Saturday Jump/The Bear Steps Out	4
59	Parlophone R 4578	Summertime/Manhunt	4
50s	Storyville A 45041	The Thin Red Line/Ole Miss	4
57	Parlophone GEP 8645	HUMPH'S BLUES NO. 2 (EP)	8

PEGGY LEE

M
| 78 | Do It 640 147 | Moderne Man/Satisfy Your Lust (p/s) | 6 |
| 79 | MCA MCAT 413 | Pop Musik/M Factor (12", p/s, double groove) | 7 |

(see also Comic Romance, Robin Scott)

MABEL
| 78 | Sonet SON 2147 | Boom Boom/FBI On The Nail (p/s) | 6 |

MABEL JOY
| 75 | Real | MABEL JOY (LP) | 30 |

MOMS MABLEY
| 69 | Mercury MF 1127 | Abraham, Martin And John/Sunny | 4 |

WILLIE MABON
64	Sue WI 320	Got To Have Some/Why Did It Happen To Me	12
65	Sue WI 331	Just Got Some/That's No Big Thing	12
65	Sue WI 382	I'm The Fixer/Some More	12

NEIL MacARTHUR
69	Deram DM 225	She's Not There/World Of Glass	6
69	Deram DM 262	Don't Try To Explain/Without Her	5
69	Deram DM 275	It's Not Easy/12.29	5

(see also Colin Blunstone, Zombies)

DAVID MACBETH
59	Pye 7N 15231	Mr. Blue/Here's A Heart	4
60	Pye 7N 15250	Tell Her From Me/Livin' Dangerously	4
60	Pye 7N 15274	Unhappy/Once Upon A Star	4
60	Pye 7N 15291	Blue Blue Blue/Pigtails In Paris	4
61	Pye 7N 15325	The Puppet Song/Angel On My Shoulder	4

MACC LADS
90	FM Revolver VHF 42	Barrels Round/Jingle Bells (p/s)	4
82	Hectic House	ONE GALLON DEMO (cassette)	10
82	Hectic House	MINGE PIES AND MISTLETOE (cassette)	8
83	Hectic House	EH UP! MACC LADS (cassette)	7
85	Hectic House HH 1A	BEER AND SEX AND CHIPS'N'GRAVY (promo cassette)	8
86	Hectic House HHS 1	EH UP! MACC LADS (EP)	5
86	Hectic House HH 2	ONE GALLON DEMO (EP)	4
86	Hectic House HH 3	MINGE PIES AND MISTLETOE (EP)	4
86	Hectic House HH 5	MACC LADDS FIVE (cassette EP)	4
87	Hectic House HH 6	FILTHY, FAT AND FLATULENT (cassette EP)	4
88	Hectic House HH 10A	LIVE AT LEEDS — THE MACC LADS (THE WHO?) (promo cassette)	8
88	Hectic House HH 12A	FROM BEER TO ETERNITY (promo cassette)	8
85	FM Revolver FMLP 56	BEER AND SEX AND CHIPS'N'GRAVY (LP, white vinyl)	10

EWAN MacCOLL
60	Topic 12T 41	STREETS OF SONG (LP, with Dominic Behan)	10
61	Topic 12T 16	CHORUS FROM THE GALLOWS (LP)	10
61	PRE 13004	THE BEST OF EWAN MacCOLL (LP)	10
62	Topic 12T 79	JACOBITE SONGS (LP)	10
65	Topic 12T 103	ENGLISH AND SCOTTISH FOLK BALLADS (LP, with A.L. Lloyd)	10
67	Topic 12T 130	BUNDOOK BALLADS (LP)	10
67	Argo ZBF 12	SOLO FLIGHT (LP)	10
68	Argo ZBF 67	WANTON MUSE (LP)	10

EWAN MacCOLL & PEGGY SEEGER (& CHARLES PARKER)
60s	AUEW AUEW 1	We Are The Engineers/I'm Gonna Be An Engineer (p/s)	6
60s	Argo RG 502	SINGING THE FISHING (LP)	20
65	Argo RG 474	THE BALLAD OF JOHN AXON (LP, by Ewan MacColl & Charles Parker)	25
67	Topic 12T 147	THE MANCHESTER ANGEL (LP)	10
67	Argo (Z)DA 66	LONG HARVEST 1 (LP)	12
67	Argo (Z)DA 67	LONG HARVEST 2 (LP)	12
67	Argo (Z)DA 68	LONG HARVEST 3 (LP)	12
67	Argo (Z)DA 69	LONG HARVEST 4 (LP)	12
68	Argo (Z)DA 70	LONG HARVEST 5 (LP)	10
68	Argo (Z)DA 71	LONG HARVEST 6 (LP)	10
68	Argo (Z)DA 72	LONG HARVEST 7 (LP)	10
68	Argo (Z)DA 73	LONG HARVEST 8 (LP)	10
68	Argo (Z)DA 74	LONG HARVEST 9 (LP)	10
68	Argo (Z)DA 75	LONG HARVEST 10 (LP)	10
68	Argo (Z)DA 84	THE ANGRY MUSE (LP)	15
68	Argo (Z)DA 85	THE AMOROUS MUSE (LP)	15
69	Argo (Z)DA 98	THE PAPER STAGE 1 (LP)	10
69	Argo (Z)DA 99	THE PAPER STAGE 2 (LP)	10
69	Argo DA 133	TRAVELLING PEOPLE (LP, with Peggy Seeger & Charles Parker)	20
71	Argo DA 140	THE BIG HEWER — A RADIO BALLAD BY EWAN MacCOLL, PEGGY SEEGER, CHARLES PARKER (LP, documentary with music)	30

(see also Peggy Seeger)

KIRSTY MacCOLL
| 79 | Stiff BUYPD 47 | They Don't Know/Turn My Motor On (picture disc) | 5 |

MINT VALUE £

79	Stiff BUY 57	You Caught Me Out/Boys (with Boomtown Rats, unreleased, demos only)	10+
85	Stiff BUYPD 225	He's On The Beach/Please Go To Sleep (picture disc)	4

(see also Drug Addix)

BIG MACEO
62	RCA RCX 203	KINGS OF THE BLUES (EP)	10

MACEO & ALL KING'S MEN
72	Pye Intl. 7N 25571	Got To Get 'Cha/Thank You For Letting Me Be Myself Again	6
72	Mojo 2916 017	FUNKY MUSIC MACHINE (LP)	60
75	Contempo CRM 114	FUNKY MUSIC MACHINE (LP, reissue)	30

MACEO & MACKS
87	Urban URB 1	Cross The Tracks (We Better Go Back)/Soul Power (company sleeve)	6
87	Urban URBX 1	Cross The Tracks (We Better Go Back) (Extended Version)/Party Pt 1/ Soul Power (12", company die-cut sleeve)	12
74	Polydor 2391 122	US (LP)	30
88	Urban URBLP 8	US (LP, reissue)	15

(see also Maceo & All King's Men, James Brown)

MACHINE
69	Polydor 56760	Spooky's Day Off/Nobody Wants You	5

(see also Swinging Soul Machine)

ALURA MACK
50s	Poydras 84	Everybody's Man Is Mine/Monkey Blues (78)	8

FREDDIE MACK EXTRAVAGANZA
73	Contempo C 21	People Pts 1 & 2	4

JOHNNY MACK
70	Col. Blue Beat DB 116	Reggae All Night Long/A Million Marvellous Feelings	6

LONNIE MACK
63	Stateside SS 207	Memphis/Down In The Dumps	8
63	Stateside SS 226	Wham!/Susie-Q	10
64	Stateside SS 312	Lonnie On The Move/Say Something Nice To Me	7
65	Stateside SS 393	Sa-Ba-Hoola/Chickin' Pickin'	12
67	President PT 127	Where There's A Will/Baby What's Wrong?	6
67	President PT 142	Save Your Money/Snow On The Mountain	6
68	President PT 198	Soul Express/I Found A Love	6
69	Elektra EKSN 45044	Memphis/Why (Edited Version)	6
69	Elektra EKSN 45060	Save Your Money/In The Band	5
71	Elektra EKSN 45715	Lay It Down/She Even Woke Me Up To Say Goodbye	4
79	Lightning OG 9011	Memphis/CHRIS MONTEZ: Let's Dance (picture disc)	5
67	President PTL 1004	THE WHAM OF THAT MEMPHIS MAN (LP)	15
69	Elektra EKL/EKS 74040	GLAD I'M IN THE BAND (LP)	12
69	Elektra EKS 74050	WHATEVER'S RIGHT (LP)	12
70	Elektra 2410 007	FOR COLLECTORS ONLY (LP, reissue of "The Wham Of That Memphis Man")	15
72	Elektra K 42097	THE HILLS OF INDIANA (LP)	10

WARNER MACK
58	Brunswick 05728	Roc-A-Chicka/Since I Lost You (with Anita Kerr Quartet)	90
58	Brunswick 05728	Roc-A-Chicka/Since I Lost You (with Anita Kerr Quartet) (78)	20
58	Decca	Roc-A-Chicka/Since I Lost You (export issue, with Anita Kerr Quartet)	50
62	London HA-R/SH-R 8002	GOLDEN COUNTRY HITS (LP)	15
63	London HA-R/SH-R 8025	GOLDEN COUNTRY HITS VOL. 2 (LP)	15
66	Brunswick LAT 8658	COUNTRY TOUCH (LP)	15
67	Brunswick LAT 8684	DRIFTING APART (LP)	15

ANDY MACKAY
74	Island WIP 6197	Ride Of The Valkyries/Time Regained	4
75	Island WIP 6243	Wild Weekend/Walking The Whippet (DJ versions in p/s £10	5
78	Bronze BRO 64	A Song Of Friendship/Skill And Sweat	5
74	Island ILPS 9278	IN SEARCH OF EDDIE RIFF (LP, 2 different versions)	10

(see also Roxy Music, Rock Follies)

MAHNA MACKAY
69	Parlophone R 5808	Mah Na Mah Na/Daydream	6

RABBIT MacKAY
68	MCA MU 1041	Hard Time Woman/Candy	4
68	MCA MUPS 351	BUG CLOTH (LP)	12

GISELE MacKENZIE
55	HMV 7M 318	Hard To Get/Boston Fancy	4

MACKENZIES
87	Ron Johnson ZRON 9	New Breed/Dog's Breakfast	4

MACKERAL
66	Columbia DB 8013	Funny Fish/This Is Mine	4
68	Columbia DB 8388	Trying Again/White Man's Burden	4

KEN MACKINTOSH (& HIS ORCHESTRA)
56	HMV 7M 343	Creeping Tom/Lovers In The Dark	5
56	HMV 7M 359	Start Walking/Curtain Call	5
56	HMV 7M 379	Blues In The Night/Come Next Spring (B-side with Kenny Bardell)	5
56	HMV POP 197	Rock Jangle Boogie/Touch And Go (78)	5
56	HMV 7M 403	Sleepwalker/The Berkeley Hunt	5
56	HMV 7M 417	Dizzy Fingers/The Policeman's Holiday	5
56	HMV POP 270	Soft Summer Breeze/Highway Patrol	4
57	HMV POP 287	The Buccaneers/Regimental Rock	8

Ken MACKINTOSH

57	HMV POP 300	Slow Walk/Apple-jack	12
57	HMV POP 327	Almost Paradise/Rock Man Rock	12
57	HMV POP 327	Almost Paradise/Rock Man Rock (78)	5
57	HMV POP 358	Poni Tail/Keep It Movin'	6
57	HMV POP 396	Marching Along To The Blues/Six-Five Blues	6
57	HMV POP 426	Raunchy/Mojo	6
57	HMV POP 426	Raunchy/Mojo (78)	5
58	HMV POP 441	The Stroll/The Swingin' Shepherd Blues	6
58	HMV POP 441	The Stroll/The Swingin' Shepherd Blues (78)	5
58	HMV POP 464	Big Guitar/Squatty	6
58	HMV POP 506	The Swivel/Muchacha	4
59	HMV POP 592	Rock-A-Conga/Hampden Park	4
59	HMV POP 656	Sleep Walk/Morgen (One More Sunrise)	4
60	HMV POP 713	No Hiding Place/Tally Ho!	4
56	HMV 7EG 8170	TEENAGER'S SPECIAL (EP)	12
58	HMV 7EG 8468	DANCING TO THE ROARING TWENTIES (EP)	7
55	HMV DLP 1093	KEN MACKINTOSH (10" LP)	15
58	HMV DLP 1178	ONE NIGHT STAND (10" LP)	15

MACK SISTERS
56	London HLU 8331	Long Range Love/Stop What You're Doing	25

PETE MacLAINE & CLAN
63	Decca F 11699	Yes I Do/U.S. Mail	8

SHIRLEY MacLAINE
69	MCA MU 1062	My Personal Property/Where Am I Going	4

DOLINA MACLENNAN & ROBIN GRAY
64	Topic TOP 68	BY MORMOND BRAES (EP)	7

JOHN MacLEOD'S FIRST XI
66	Fontana TF 696	Don't Shoot The Ref/Tomato Crisps	6

JOHN MacLEOD SOUND
60s	Transatlantic TRASP 12	Russian Roulette/West Wind	4

ANGUS MacLISE
87	Fierce FRIGHT 010	Trance (1-sided, with Dopechoc & badge)	10

PATRICK MacNEE & HONOR BLACKMAN
64	Decca F 11843	Kinky Boots/Let's Keep It Friendly	8
	(see also Honor Blackman)		

UNCLE DAVE MACON
63	RCA RCX 7112	UNCLE DAVE MACON NO. 1 (EP)	12
63	RCA RCX 7113	UNCLE DAVE MACON NO. 2 (EP)	12
66	Ace Of Hearts AH 135	UNCLE DAVE MACON (LP)	10

GILLIAN MacPHERSON
71	RCA Victor SF 8220	POETS AND PAINTERS AND PERFORMERS OF THE BLUES (LP)	15

GORDON MacRAE
54	Capitol CL 14168	How Do You Speak To An Angel?/C'est Magnifique	8
54	Capitol CL 14193	Count Your Blessings Instead Of Sheep/Never In A Million Years	8
55	Capitol CL 14222	Here's What I'm Here For/Love Can Change The Stars	8
55	Capitol CL 14276	Stranger In Paradise/High On A Windy Hill	8
55	Capitol CL 14293	You Forget (To Tell Me That You Love Me)/Tik-A-Tee, Tik-A-Tay	8
55	Capitol CL 14334	Jim Bowie/Why Break The Heart That Loves You	8
55	Capitol CL 14361	Bella Notte/Blame It On My Youth	8
56	Capitol CL 14526	Follow Your Heart/Fate	5
56	Capitol CL 14548	Never Before And Never Again/Don't Blame Me	5
56	Capitol CL 14576	Who Are We/There's A Lull In My Life	5
56	Capitol CL 14606	One Misty Morning/I Asked The Lord	5
56	Capitol CL 14613	People Will Say We're In Love/The Surrey With The Fringe On Top (with Ray Anthony)	5
56	Capitol CL 14622	Woman In Love/I Don't Want To Walk Without You	5
56	Capitol CL 14650	Without Love/Obey	5
57	Capitol CL 14743	Endless Love/When You Kiss Me	4
58	Capitol CL 14818	Lonely/Sayonora	4
58	Capitol CL 14841	Now/Till We Meet Again	4
58	Capitol CL 14864	I've Grown Accustomed To Her Face/Never Till Now	4
58	Capitol CL 14920	The Secret/A Man Once Said	4
59	Capitol CL 14983	Little Do You Know/Fly Little Bluebird	4
59	Capitol CL 15021	Palace Of Love/The Stranger	4
62	Capitol CL 15256	Sail Away/Face To Face	4
63	Capitol CL 15315	Lovely/Warmer Than A Whisper	4
52	Capitol LC 6564	THE MERRY WIDOW (10" LP, with Lucille Norman)	12
53	Capitol LC 6592	CAPITOL PRESENTS GORDON MACRAE (10" LP)	12
53	Capitol LC 6599	BY THE LIGHT OF THE SILVERY MOON (10" LP, with June Hutton)	12
53	Capitol LC 6606	THE DESERT SONG (10" LP, with Lucille Norman)	12
53	Capitol LC 6613	THE STUDENT PRINCE (10" LP, with Dorothy Warenskjold)	12
54	Capitol LC 6663	NAUGHTY MARIETTA (10" LP, with Lucille Norman)	12
54	Capitol LC 6666	ROBERTA (10" LP, with Lucille Norman)	12
56	Capitol LC 6805	ROMANTIC BALLADS (10" LP)	12
60	Capitol (S)T 1251	SONGS FOR AN EVENING AT HOME (LP)	10
60	Top Rank 25/006	GORDON MACRAE (LP)	10
	(see also Jo Stafford, Ray Anthony)		

JOSH MACRAE
60	Top Rank JAR 290	Talkin' Army Blues/Talkin' Guitar Blues	6
60	Pye 7N 15306	Original Talkin' Blues (Talkin' Southern Blues)/Talkin' Thro' The Mill	4

60	Pye 7N 15307	Let Ramensky Go/Sky High Joe	4
60	Pye 7N 15308	Wild Side Of Life/Dear John	6
61	Pye 7N 15319	High Class Feeling/Messing About On The River	4
61	Pye 7N 15360	Arkansas Rambler/Never Never Man	4
61	Pye 7N 15384	Do It Yourself/Special Place Of Yorn	4
60	Pye NEP 24131	WALKIN', TALKIN', SINGIN' (EP)	10
60	Top Rank JKP 2061	JOSH MACRAE (EP)	7
66	Golden Guinea GGL 0335	MESSING ABOUT ON THE RIVER (LP)	10

M.A.D.

| 84 | Crim. Damage CRI 12121 | Sunfeast/Craving (12") | 7 |

JOHNNY MADARA

| 57 | HMV POP 389 | Be My Girl/Lovesick | 6 |

MAD CATS

| 69 | Coxsone CS 7099 | Losing You (actually by Winston Jarrett & Flames)/WINSTON JARRETT: Peck Up A Pagan | 15 |

MADCAPS

| 53 | Brunswick LA 8631 | HARMONICATERS (10" LP) | 10 |

MADCAPS/HARMONICATS

| 54 | London H-APB 1016 | HARMONICA RHYTHMS (10" LP, 1 side each) | 10 |

MAD DOG

| 74 | Chappell LPC 1053 | POP SOUNDS (LP, library edition) | 50 |

(there is a whole series of Mad Dog albums!)

JOHNNY MADDOX (& HIS ORCHESTRA)

53	Vogue V 9047	Johnny Maddox Boogie/Little Grass Shack (78)	5
55	London HL 8134	The Crazy Otto — Medley/Humoresque	18
55	London HLD 8203	Do, Do/When You Wore A Tulip (And I Wore A Big Red Rose)	18
56	London HLD 8277	Hands Off/Hop Scotch Boogie	18
56	London HLD 8347	Dixieland Band/Heart And Soul	12
58	London HLD 8540	Yellow Dog Blues/Sugar Train	6
59	London HLD 8826	The Hurdy Gurdy Song/Old Fashioned Love	5
55	London RE-P 1020	PRESENTING JOHNNY MADDOX AND THE RHYTHMASTERS (EP)	8
55	London RE-P 1040	PRESENTING JOHNNY MADDOX AND THE RHYTHMASTERS NO. 2 (EP)	8
58	London RE-D 1150	HONKY TONK JAZZ (EP)	7
61	London RE-D 1270	OLD FASHIONED LOVE (EP)	7
56	London HB-D 1060	JOHNNY MADDOX PLAYS (10" LP, with His Rhythmasters)	12
58	London HA-D 2101	MY OLD FLAMES (LP)	10

ROSE MADDOX

| 59 | Capitol CL 15023 | Gambler's Love/What Makes Me Hang Around | 6 |

MADE IN SHEFFIELD

| 67 | Fontana TF 871 | Amelia Jane/Right Satisfied | 15 |

MADE IN SWEDEN

69	Sonet SLP 71	MADE IN SWEDEN (LP)	15
69	Sonet SLP 2504	SNAKES IN A HOLE (LP)	15
70	Sonet SLP 2506	LIVE AT THE GOLDEN CIRCLE (LP)	15
70	Sonet SLP 2512	MADE IN ENGLAND (LP)	15
71	Sonet SNTF 621	MAD RIVER (LP)	15

BETTY MADIGAN

54	MGM SP 1109	Always You/That Was My Heart You Heard!	4
55	MGM SP 1119	And So I Walked Home/Be A Little Darlin'	4
55	MGM SP 1131	Salute/The Wheels Of Love	4
55	MGM SP 1137	I Had A Heart/Wonderful Words	4
55	MGM SP 1138	Teddy Bear/Strangers	4
69	MGM MGM 1492	I'm Gonna Make You Love Me/Goodnight	5
58	Coral FEP 2009	JEROME KERN SONGBOOK VOL. 1 (EP)	7
59	Coral FEP 2011	JEROME KERN SONGBOOK VOL. 2 (EP)	7

MAD JOCKS & ENGLISHMEN

| 80 | Wild Dog | TONGUE IN CHEEK (LP) | 10 |

MAD LADS

65	Atlantic AT 4051	Don't Have To Shop Around/Tear Maker	10
66	Atlantic AT 4083	I Want Someone/Nothing Can Break Through	10
66	Atlantic 584 038	Sugar Sugar/Get Out Of My Life Woman	8

MADNESS

79	2-Tone TT 3	The Prince/Madness (paper label, later plastic; company die-cut sleeve)	10/4
79	Stiff BUYIT 56	One Step Beyond/Mistakes/Nutty Theme (12", p/s)	7
79	Stiff MAD 1	Don't Quote Me On That/Swan Lake (12", promo only)	30
79	Stiff BUY 62	My Girl/Stepping Into Line (p/s)	4
80	Stiff BUY 71	WORK, REST & PLAY (EP)	6
80	Stiff BUY 102	Embarrassment/Crying Shame (p/s)	4
81	Stiff BUY 108	The Return Of The Los Palmas 7/That's The Way To Do It ('cartoon' p/s)	4
81	Stiff BUYIT 108	The Return Of The Los Palmas 7/My Girl (Demo)/That's The Way To Do It/Swan Lake (live) (12", p/s, with comic)	15
81	Stiff BUY 112	Grey Day/Memories (p/s)	7
81	Stiff ZBUY 112	Grey Day/Memories (cassette)	7
82	Stiff PBUY 146	House Of Fun/Don't Look Back (picture disc)	5
82	Stiff BUY 153	Driving In My Car/Animal Farm (poster p/s)	4
82	Stiff PBUY 153	Driving In My Car/Animal Farm (picture disc)	5
82	Stiff PBUY 163	Our House/Walking With Mr Wheeze (picture disc)	5
83	Stiff PBUY 169	Tomorrow's (Just Another Day)/Madness (Is All In The Mind) (picture disc)	5
83	Stiff BUY 181	Wings Of A Dove/Behind The 8 Ball (picture disc)	5

83	Stiff PBUY 192	The Sun And The Rain/Fireball XL5 (picture disc)	5
84	Stiff PBUY 196	Michael Caine/If You Think There's Something (picture disc)	5
84	Stiff PBUY 201	One Better Day/Guns (picture disc)	5
85	Zarjazz JAZZ D5	Yesterday's Men/All I Knew (square picture disc)//Yesterday's Men (Harmonica Mix)/It Must Be Love (live) (double pack in gold PVC wallet)	8
85	Zarjazz JAZZY 7	Uncle Sam/Please Don't Go/Inanity Over Christmas (picture disc)	4
85	Zarjazz JAZZ F7	Uncle Sam/Please Don't Go ('flag bag')	5
86	Zarjazz JAZZ D8	Sweetest Girl/Jennie (A Portrait Of)//Tears You Can't Hide/Call Me (double pack)	7
86	Zarjazz JAZZ Y 8	Sweetest Girl/Jennie (A Portrait Of) (1-sided picture disc)	4
86	Zarjazz JAZZ S9	(Waiting For) The Ghost-Train/Maybe In Another Life (square picture disc)	4
86	Zarjazz JAZZ B9-12	(Waiting For) The Ghost-Train/Maybe In Another Life/Seven Year Scratch (12", p/s, with 8-page booklet)	7
88	Virgin VSX 1054	I Pronounce You/4BF/Patience/11th Hour (box set with 4-track EP, enamel badge, 2 postcards & sticker)	4
88	Virgin VSS 1078	What's That/Be A Good Boy (jigsaw picture disc)	4
88	Virgin VSJ 1078	What's That/Flashings (jigsaw picture disc)	4
80s	Stiff/Lyntone LYN 8680	Patches Brings You A Few Minutes Of Madness (flexi with 'Patches' mag)	6/4
81	Lyntone LYN 11546	My Girl (Ballad) (green vinyl flexidisc with 'Flexipop' magazine issue 19)	8/6
82	Lyntone LYN 10208	Take It or Leave It (square flexidisc free with 'Event' magazine)	10/8
82	Lyntone LYN 10719	CAROLS ON 45 (flexidisc)	8
84	Lyntone LYN 15280/1	Inanity Over Christmas/Visit To Dracstein Castle (fan club flexidisc)	6
85	Lyntone LYN 16676	From Us ... To You (Mad Not Mad tour flexidisc)	5
85	Lyntone LYN 16981	Live From The Mad Not Mad Tour (flexidisc with tour programme)	8/5
86	Lyntone LYN 18251	(Waiting For) The Ghost Train (Demo) (fan club flexidisc)	5
82	Stiff GRAB 1	THE MADNESS PACK (6 x 7" in clear plastic folder)	25
80s	fan club	30 MINUTES OF CULTURE (cassette)	10
84	Stiff PSEEZ 53	KEEP MOVING (LP, picture disc, U.S. running order)	10
80s	Madness Info Service	THE M.I.S. PLAYERS PRESENT 30 MINUTES OF CULTURE (fan club cassette)	10

(see also Fink Brothers, Argonauts, Voice Of The Beehive)

MADONNA

82	Sire W 9899	Everybody/(Dub Version) (p/s)	45
82	Sire W 9899T	Everybody/(Dub Version) (12", p/s)	60
83	Sire W 9522	Lucky Star (Edit)/I Know It ('sunglasses' p/s)	35
83	Sire W 9522T	Lucky Star (Full Length Version)/I Know It (12", 'sunglasses' p/s)	30
83	Sire W 9522T	Lucky Star (Full Length Version)/I Know It (12", stickered 'TV screen' p/s, some with poster)	30/15
83	Sire W 9522TV	Lucky Star (U.S Remix)/I Know It (12", stickered plain white die-cut sleeve)	50
83	Sire W 9405	Holiday/Think Of Me ('train' p/s)	10
83	Sire W 9405T	Holiday (Full Length Version)/Think Of Me (12", 'train' p/s, some with 'Copyright Control' wording on label)	18
84	Sire W 9260	Borderline (Edit)/Physical Attraction (p/s)	4
84	Sire W 9260T	Borderline (U.S. Remix)/Borderline (Dub Remix)/Physical Attraction (12", p/s, with '9-' LP catalogue numbers on rear of sleeve)	8
84	Sire W 9210	Like A Virgin/Stay (p/s)	4
84	Sire W 9210T	Like A Virgin (U.S. Dance Remix)/Stay (12", p/s, some with poster)	18/7
85	Sire W 9083	Material Girl/Pretender (initially in poster p/s)	40/4
85	Sire W 9083T	Material Girl (Jellybean Dance Mix)/Pretender (12", p/s, some with poster)	25/7
85	Geffen A 6323	Crazy For You/I'll Fall In Love Again (p/s)	5
85	Geffen WA 6323	Crazy For You/I'll Fall In Love Again (Madonna-shaped picture disc)	65
85	Sire W 8934P	Into The Groove/Shoo-Be-Doo (heart-shaped picture disc)	20
85	Sire W 8934T	Into The Groove/Shoo-Be-Doo (12", p/s, initially with free poster)	15/7
85	Sire W 9405	Holiday (Edit)/Think Of Me (reissue, 'cross earring' p/s)	4
85	Sire W 9405T	Holiday (Full Length Version)/Think Of Me (12", p/s, reissue)	7
85	Sire W 9405P	Holiday (Full Length Version)/Think Of Me (12", picture disc)	25
85	Sire W 8881P	Angel (Edit)/Burning Up (shaped pic disc, some with cardboard plinth)	25/18
85	Geffen A 6585	Gambler/BLACK 'N' BLUE: Nature Of The Beast (p/s)	5
85	Geffen QA 6585	Gambler/BLACK 'N' BLUE: Nature Of The Beast (poster p/s)	20
85	Geffen TA 6585	Gambler (Extended Dance Mix)/Gambler (Instrumental Remix)/BLACK 'N' BLUE: Nature Of The Beast (12", p/s)	15
85	Sire W 8848TF	Dress You Up (12" Formal Mix)/(Casual Instrumental)/I Know It (12", poster p/s, '4 Track Studio' or 'Live Like A Virgin Tour' rear video advert)	20
85	Sire W 8848P	Dress You Up/I Know It (star-shaped picture disc)	25
86	Sire W 9260F	Borderline (Edit)/Physical Attraction//Holiday/Think Of Me (p/s, reissue, 'map' p/s, shrinkwrapped double pack with sticker)	40
86	Sire W 9260T	Borderline (U.S. Remix)/Borderline (Dub Remix)/Physical Attraction (12", p/s, reissue, with 'WX' LP catalogue numbers on rear of sleeve)	7
86	Sire W 9260P	Borderline/Physical Attraction (Madonna-shaped picture disc)	30
86	Sire W 8717T	Live To Tell (LP Version)/Live To Tell (Edit)/(Instrumental) (12", p/s)	7
86	Sire W 8717TW	Live To Tell (LP Version)/(Edit)/(Instrumental) (12", p/s, with poster)	15
86	Sire W 8636T	Papa Don't Preach (Extended Version)/Papa Don't Preach (LP Version)/Ain't No Big Deal (12", p/s, initially with free poster)	15/7
86	Sire W 8636P	Papa Don't Preach (Extended Remix)/Ain't No Big Deal (LP Version) (12", picture disc)	20
86	Sire W 8550P	True Blue (Extended Dance Version)/Holiday (Extended Dance Mix) (12", picture disc)	20
86	Sire W 8480P	Open Your Heart (Extended Version)/Open Your Heart (Dub Mix)/Lucky Star (Full Length Version) (12", picture disc)	15
87	Sire W 8378P	La Isla Bonita (Extended Remix)/(Extended Instrumental) (12", picture disc)	20
87	Sire W 8341TX	Who's That Girl (Extended Version)/Who's That Girl (Dub Mix)/White Heat (12" Remix) (12", p/s)	8
87	Sire W 8341TP	Who's That Girl (Extended Version)/White Heat (12", picture disc)	35
87	Sire W 8224	Causing A Commotion (Silver Screen Single Mix)/Jimmy Jimmy (p/s, with free button badge shrinkwrapped to p/s)	14
87	Sire W 8224TP	Causing A Commotion (Silver Screen Mix)/Causing A Commotion (Movie House Mix)/Jimmy Jimmy (Fade) (12", picture disc)	18

87	Sire W 8115P	The Look Of Love/Love Don't Live Here Anymore/I Know It (12", picture disc) . . .15
89	Sire W 7539	Like A Prayer/Act Of Contrition (p/s, with free Virgin Megastore poster) 6
89	Sire W 7539TP	Like A Prayer (12" Extended Remix)/Like A Prayer (Club Mix)/Act of Contrition (12", picture disc) 10
89	Sire W 7539TX	Like A Prayer (12" Dance Mix)/(Churchapella Mix)/(7" Remix Edit) (12", p/s) 12
89	Sire W 2948X	Express Yourself (7" Remix)/The Look Of Love (LP) (poster p/s) 6
89	Sire W 2948W	Express Yourself (7" Remix)/The Look Of Love (LP) ('jeans zipper' p/s) 12
89	Sire W 2948TP	Express Yourself/(Non-Stop Express Mix)/(Stop And Go Dubs) (12", 'nude' picture disc) 15
89	Sire W 2883TP	Cherish (Extended Version)/(7" Version)/Supernatural (12", picture disc) 10
89	Sire W 2883TP	Cherish (Extended Version)/(7" Version)/Supernatural (12", misspressed picture disc, plays "Cherish" but picture features Fish's "State Of Mind") 15
89	Sire W 2883 CD	Cherish (extended)/Cherish/Supernatural (3" CD) 7
89	Sire W 2668P	Dear Jessie/Till Death Do Us Part (picture disc) 6
89	Sire W 2668T	Dear Jessie/Till Death Do Us Part/Holiday (12" Version) (12", poster p/s) 10
89	Sire W 2268CDX	Dear Jessie/Till Death Do Us Part/Holiday (12" Version) (CD, picture disc) 20
90	Sire W 9851P	Vogue (Single Version)/Keep It Together (Single Remix) (picture disc) 7
90	Sire W 9851TW	Vogue (12" Version)/Keep It Together (12", p/s, with 'Face of the 80s' poster) . . .7
90	Sire W 9851TX	Vogue (12" Version)/(Strike-A-Pose Dub)/Keep It Together (12", p/s, with free 'X-rated' 30" x 20" poster) 10
90	Sire W 9851TP	Vogue (12" Version)/Keep It Together (12" Remix) (12", picture disc) 12
90	Sire W 9789TP	Hanky Panky (Bare Bottom 12" Mix)/Hanky Panky (Bare Bones Single Mix)/ More (LP Version) (12", picture disc with gatefold insert & poster) 10
90	Sire W 9000TP	Justify My Love (12" picture disc, with insert) 10
91	Sire W 0008P	Crazy For You (Remix)/Keep It Together (shaped picture disc with plinth & insert) 6
91	Sire W 0008CD	Crazy For You (Remix)/Keep It Together/Into The Groove (CD, picture disc) 7
92	Receiver RRSP 1007	Shine A Light (picture disc, withdrawn) 5
92	Receiver RRSPT 1007	Shine A Light (12", p/s, withdrawn) 7
92	Sire W 0138TP	Erotica (Album Version)/(Intrumental)/(Radio Edit) (12", withdrawn picture disc, with gold insert) 500
85	Sire WX 20P	LIKE A VIRGIN (LP, picture disc in die-cut sleeve) 30
86	Sire WX 54	TRUE BLUE (LP, with tour poster) 10
87	Sire WX 76	YOU CAN DANCE (LP, with free poster) 10
90	Sire 7599 264932	ROYAL BOX (box set with "Immaculate Collection" CD in satin Digipak, video, poster & postcards) 60

MADRIGAL

71	Decca F 12110	Blues Eyes In Paradise/Wendy 4
71	Decca F 13184	You Hear What You Wanna Hear/Guadalajara City 4
72	Sovereign SOV 107	Time Of The Season/Tapestry 4

MADRIGAL

73	MAD 100	BENEATH THE GREENWOOD TREE (LP, private press) .120

MAD RIVER

68	Capitol (S)T 2985	MAD RIVER (LP) 25

MAD ROY

70	Banana BA 324	Nannie (Goat) Version/BIGGER D: Freedom (Blues) Version (both sides actually by Dennis Alcapone) 7
71	Banana BA 326	Home Version/SOUND DIMENSION: One Time (both actually by Dennis Alcapone) 7
71	Banana BA 328	Duppy Serenade/Sunshine Version (both sides actually by Dennis Alcapone) 7

(see also Dennis Alcapone)

JOHNNY MAESTRO

61	HMV POP 875	What A Surprise/The Warning Voice 20
61	HMV POP 909	Mr. Happiness/Test Of Love 20
64	United Artists UP 1004	Before I Love Her/Fifty Million Heartbeats 12

(see also Crests)

MAGAZINE

78	Virgin VS 200	Shot By Both Sides/My Mind Ain't So Open (card or paper p/s) 5/4
78	Virgin VS 207	Touch And Go/Goldfinger (p/s) 4
78	Virgin VS 237	Give Me Everything/I Love You, You Big Dummy (p/s) 4
79	Virgin VS 251	Rhythm Of Cruelty/T.V. Baby (p/s) 4
80	Virgin VS 368	Sweetheart Contract/Feed The Enemy//Twenty Years Ago/Shot By Both Sides (shrinkwrapped double pack) 6
83	Virgin VS 592-12	SHOT BY BOTH SIDES (12" EP) 7

(see also Buzzcocks)

MAGENTA

78	Cottage	CANTERBURY MOON (LP) 85

MAGGIE

68	Columbia DB 8389	L. David Sloane/Too Young To Get Married 4

MAGIC CARPET

71	Mushroom 200 MR 20	MAGIC CARPET (LP) 80

(see also Clem Alford)

MAGIC CHRISTIANS

70	Major Minor MM 673	Come And Get It/Nats 8
70	Major Minor MM 673	If You Want It/Nats (reissue) 6

MAGICIANS

66	Decca F 12361	Wet Your Whistle/Take The A Train 4
66	Decca F 12374	The Liars/Poggy Goes Pop 6
67	Decca F 12602	The Tarzan March/What A Day For A Metamorphosis 6
68	MCA MU 1046	Painting On Wood/Slow Motion 4

MAGIC LANTERNS

66	CBS 202094	Excuse Me Baby/Greedy Girl	5
66	CBS 202250	Rumplestiltskin/I Stumbled	20
67	CBS 202459	Knight In Rusty Armour/Simple Things	5
67	CBS 202637	Auntie Grizelda/Time Will Tell (If I'm A Loser)	6
67	CBS 2750	We'll Meet Again/What Else Can It Be But Love?	4
69	Camp 602 007	Shame Shame/Baby I Gotta Go Now	5
69	Camp 602 009	Melt All Your Troubles Away/Bossa Nova 1940 — Hello You Lovers	5
67	CBS 62935	LIT UP WITH THE MAGIC LANTERNS (LP)	12

MAGIC MICHAEL

80	Atomic MAGIC 1	Millionaire/My Friend And I (p/s)	4

(see also Damned, Captain Sensible)

MAGIC MIXTURE

68	Saga FID 2125	THIS IS MAGIC MIXTURE (LP)	60

MAGIC MUSHROOM BAND

85	Magick Eye MUSH 001	THE MAGIC MUSHROOM BAND (cassette EP)	15
85	Magick Eye MUSH 002	FEED YOUR HEAD (cassette)	15
86	Magick Eye MUSH 003	THE POLITICS OF ECSTASY (cassette)	10
86	Pagan PM 003	THE POLITICS OF ECSTASY (LP, with A3 insert, 500 only, 100 with A1 poster) 80/60
87	Aftermath AFT 3	BOMSHAMKAR (LP)	10
89	Magick Eye MUSH 004	LIVE '89 (live cassette)	10
90	Fungus FUN 003	PROCESS OF ILLUMINATION (LP, signed with insert & foldaround sleeve & comic in printed PVC sleeve)	18
91	Fungus FUN 005	SPACED OUT (LP, foldout sleeve with A4 booklet)	15

MAGIC NOTES

61	Blue Beat BB 9	Album Of Memory/Why Did You Leave	10
61	Blue Beat BB 51	Rosabel/I'm Not Worthy	10

MAGIC ROUNDABOUT

80s	BBC RBT 8	MAGIC ROUNDABOUT (LP, from TV programme)	10

MAGIC SAM

69	Python PEN 701	Twenty One Days In Jail/Easy Baby	25
69	Rooster 707	MEAN MISTREATER (EP)	8
69	Blue Horizon 7-63223	1937-1969 (LP)	60
73	Delmark DS 615	WEST SIDE SOUL (LP, blue label)	15
74	Delmark DS 620	BLACK MAGIC (LP, blue label)	15

MAGIC SHOP

80s	Sha La La 008	It's Time/VISITORS: Goldmine (flexidisc)	5

MAGIC VALLEY

69	Penny Farthing PEN 701	Taking The Heart Out Of Love/Uptight Basil	8

MAGISTRATES

68	MGM MGM 1425	Here Comes The Judge/Girl	7
68	MGM MGM 1437	After The Fox/Tear Down The Walls (with Jane Hillery)	6

(see also Jane Hillery)

MAGITS

79	Outer Hammilayan SRTS/79/CUS/401	Fragmented/Disconnected/Disjointed/Detached (p/s)	5

(see also Rudimentary Peni)

MAGMA

74	A&M AMS 7119	Mekanik Machine/Mekanik Machine (Version)	8
70	Philips 6359 051/2	MAGMA (2-LP)	15
71	Philips 6397 031	1001 CENTIGRADE (LP)	12
74	A&M AMLH 64397	MEKANIK DESTRUCTIW KOMMANDOH (LP)	10
74	A&M AMLH 68260	KOHN TARKOSZ (LP)	10

MAGNA CARTA

69	Fontana TF 1060	Romeo Jack/7 O'Clock Hymn	8
69	Mercury MF 1096	Mid Winter/Spinning Wheels Of Time	8
72	Vertigo 6059 073	All My Life/Falkland Green	4
73	Vertigo 6059 092	Give Me Luv/Song Of Evening	4
69	Mercury SMCL 20166	MAGNA CARTA (LP)	45
70	Vertigo 6360 003	SEASONS (LP, gatefold sleeve, spiral label)	15
71	Vertigo 6360 040	SONGS FROM WASTIES ORCHARD (LP, gatefold sleeve, spiral label)	15
72	Vertigo 6360 068	IN CONCERT (LP, gatefold sleeve, spiral label)	12
73	Vertigo 6360 093	LORD OF THE AGES (LP, gatefold sleeve, spaceship label)	12

MAGNA JAZZ BAND

57	Parlophone R 4387	Buddy's Habits/Flat Foot	4

MAGNIFICENT MEN

66	Capitol CL 15462	Peace Of Mind/All Your Lovin's Gone To My Head	18
68	Capitol CL 15530	Sweet Soul Medley (both sides)	5
68	Capitol CL 15570	Save The Country/So Much Love Waiting	6

MAGNUM

75	CBS S CBS 2959	Sweets For My Sweet/Movin' On	4

MAGNUM

78	Jet SJET 116	Kingdom Of Madness/In The Beginning	5
78	Jet SJET 128	Invasion/Universe	4
79	Jet JET 155	Changes/Lonesome Star (silver p/s)	5
79	Jet JET 163	Foolish Heart/Baby Rock Me (p/s)	4
80	Jet JET 175	Magnum Live [All Of My Life (live)/Great Adventure (live)//Invasion (live)/ Kingdom Of Madness (live)] (double pack, stickered p/s)	6

80	Jet JET 188	Changes (live Remix)/Everybody Needs/Changes (live) (black p/s) 4
81	Jet JET 7007	Black Nights (promo only?) 4
82	Jet JET 7020	The Lights Burned Out/Long Days Black Nights (p/s) 4
82	Jet JET 7027	Back To Earth (live)/Hold Back Your Love (live)//Soldier Of The Line (live)/ Sacred Hour (live) (double pack) 5
86	Polydor POSPG 798	Lonely Night/Les Morts Dansant (live)//All England's Eyes (live)/ Hit And Run (live) (double pack) 5
86	Polydor POSPP 833	Midnight (Remix)/Back Street Kid/Kingdom Of Madness (live) (12", picture disc) . 8
88	Polydor POSPG 910	Days Of No Trust/Maybe Tonight ('oct-o-pack', gatefold p/s) 4
88	Polydor POSPP 910	Days Of No Trust/Maybe Tonight (p/s, with sew-on patch) 4
88	Polydor POSPG 920	Start Talking Love/C'est La Vie (gatefold pop-up p/s) 4
88	Polydor POSPP 920	Start Talking Love/Days Of No Trust (10", shaped picture disc) 6
88	Polydor POSPG 930	It Must Have Been Love/Crying Time ('prismatic' pack) 4
85	FM WKFM LP 34	ON A STORYTELLER'S NIGHT (LP, with free single) 10
89	FM WKFM PD 34	ON A STORYTELLER'S NIGHT (LP, picture disc reissue) 10

MAGPIES
| 68 | Doctor Bird DB 1129 | Lulu/Must I Be Lonely . . . . 8 |
| 68 | Doctor Bird DB 1132 | Blue Boy/I Guess I'm Crazy . . . . 8 |

MAGUS
| 80 | Northern Sound NSR 200 | BREEZIN' AWAY (LP, private pressing) . . . . 100 |

(see also Blue Epitaph)

TAJ MAHAL
68	Direction 58-3547	Everybody's Got To Change Sometime/Statesboro Blues 4
69	Direction 58-4044	Ee Zee Rider/You Don't Miss Your Water 4
69	Direction 58-4586	Give Your Woman What She Wants/Further On Down The Road 4
67	Direction 8-63279	TAJ MAHAL (LP) 15
68	Direction 8-63397	THE NATCH'L BLUES (LP) 15
69	Direction 8-66226	GIANT STEP/DE OLE FOLKS AT HOME (2-LP) 15
71	CBS 66288	THE REAL THING (2-LP) 14
71	CBS 64447	HAPPY JUST TO BE LIKE I AM (LP) 10
72	CBS 65090	RECYCLING THE BLUES AND OTHER RELATED STUFF (LP) 10

MAHAVISHNU ORCHESTRA
| 75 | CBS 3007 | Can't Stand Your Funk/Eternity's Breath Pt 1 . . . . 4 |

MITCH MAHON & EDITIONS
| 69 | Pye 7N 17844 | You Got What I Need/I've Thrown Our Love Away . . . . 4 |

MAIL
| 71 | Parlophone R 5916 | Omnibus/Life Goes On . . . . 4 |

MAINEEAXE
84	Powerstation OHM 6	Gonna Make You Rock 7
84	Powerstation AMP 3	SHOUT IT OUT (LP) 10
85	Powerstation MINIAMP 7	THE HOUR OF THUNDER (mini-LP) 10

MAINFRAME
86	Polydor MAINA 1	5 Minutes On.../Eric's Revenge (p/s) 4
86	Polydor MAINX 1	5 Minutes On...(7.01)/He Said It/Eric's Revenge (12", p/s) 8
86	Polydor MAINF 1	5 Minutes On.../He Said It (131 bpm)/Eric's Revenge (131 bpm) (12", p/s) 7

MAINHORSE
| 71 | Polydor 2383 049 | MAINHORSE (LP) . . . . 15 |

MAIN INGREDIENT
| 74 | RCA PB 0305 | Happiness Is Just Around The Bend/Why Can't We All Unite . . . . 4 |

MAINLAND
| 79 | Christy ACML 0200 | EXPOSURE (LP) . . . . 20 |

MAIN T. POSSEE
| 83 | Respond KOB 703 | Fickle Public Speakin'/(Version) (promo-only p/s) . . . . 4 |

(see also Guns For Hire)

DEXTER MAITLAND
| 69 | United Artists UP 35006 | Take Ten Terrific Girls (But Only Nine Costumes)/RUDY VALLEE: Night They Raided Minsky's . . . . 4 |

MAJAMOOD
| 66 | Doc. Bird/W.I.R.L. DB 1052 | Two Hundred Million Red Ants/Faces Amassed . . . . 30 |

MAJOR ACCIDENT
82	M. Melodies MAME 10001	Warboots/Terrorist Gang (unissued, test pressings only) 20
83	Step Forward SF 23	Mr. Nobody/That's You (p/s) 5
83	Flicknife FLS 216	Fight To Win/Free Man (p/s) 5
83	Flicknife FLS 023	Leaders Of Tomorrow/Dayo/Breakaway (p/s) 4
84	Flicknife FLS 026	Respectable/Man On The Wall (p/s) 5
83	Step Forward SFLP 9	MASSACRED MELODIES (LP) 10
84	Syndicate SYNLP 9	TORTURED TUNES LIVE (LP) 10

MAJORITY
65	Decca F 12186	Pretty Little Girl/I Don't Wanna Be Hurt No More 5
65	Decca F 12271	A Little Bit Of Sunlight/Shut 'Em Down In London Town 6
66	Decca F 12313	We Kiss In A Shadow/Ring The Bells 4
66	Decca F 12453	Simplified/One Third 4
66	Decca F 12504	To Make Me A Man/Tears Won't Help 4
67	Decca F 12573	I Hear A Rhapsody/Wait By The Fire 4
67	Decca F 12638	Running Away With My Baby/Let The Joybells Ring 6
68	Decca F 12727	All Our Christmases/People 4

MAJORS
| 62 | London HLP 9602 | A Wonderful Dream/Time Will Tell . . . . 12 |

MINT VALUE £

62	London HLP 9627	She's A Troublemaker/A Little Bit Now	15
63	London HLP 9693	What In The World/Tra La La	12
64	Liberty LBF 66009	Ooh Wee Baby/I'll Be There	18
63	London REP 1358	MEET THE MAJORS (EP)	60
63	London HA-P 8068	MEET THE MAJORS (LP)	75

MAKADOPOULOS & HIS GREEK SERENADERS
60	Palette PG 9002	In The Streets Of Athens/Festival A La Greca	4
61	Palette PG 9005	Never On Sunday/Yasou (some in p/s)	6/4

PETER MAKANA & HIS RHYTHM BOYS
58	Oriole CB 1445	Baboon Shepherd (with Black Duke)/Black John	4
58	Oriole CB 1446	Cool Mood/Sweet Baby	4

MIRIAM MAKEBA
63	London HL 9747	Click Song/Mbube	5
61	London HA 2332	MIRIAM MAKEBA (LP)	10

MAKIN' TIME
86	Countdown VAIN 1	Here Is My Number/Nothing Else (picture disc)	4

MALAGON SISTERS & CHA CHA RHYTHM BOYS
59	Pye Intl. 7N 25008	In A Little Spanish Town/Lessons In Cha-Cha-Cha	5

MAL & PRIMITIVES
65	Pye 7N 15915	Every Minute Of Every Day/Pretty Little Face	50

(see also Primitives, Mal Ryder & Spirits)

MALARIA!
82	Jungle JUNG 3	NEW YORK PASSAGE (12" EP)	7

CARLOS MALCOLM & AFRO JAMAICAN RHYTHMS
65	Island WI 173	Bonanza Ska/Papa Luigi	10

GEORGE MALCOLM
53	Parlophone MSP 6058	Bach Goes To Town/Bach Before The Mast	6

HUGH MALCOLM
68	Amalgamated AMG 827	Good Time Rock/LYNN TAITT & JETS: Sleepy Ludy	8
68	Amalgamated AMG 829	Mortgage/CANNONBALL BRYAN TRIO: Man About Town	8

MALLARD
77	Virgin VS 168	Harvest/Green Coyote	4
76	Virgin V 2045	MALLARD (LP)	12
77	Virgin V 2077	IN A DIFFERENT CLIMATE (LP)	10

(see also Captain Beefheart & His Magic Band)

STEPHEN MALLINDER
81	Fetish FE 12	Temperature Drop/Cool Down (12")	8
82	Fetish FM 2010	POW-WOW (LP)	10

(see also Cabaret Voltaire)

SIW MALMKVIST
59	Oriole CB 1486	Sermonette/The Preacher	5
61	Parlophone R 4765	Wedding Cake/Red Roses And Little White Lies	4
64	Columbia DB 7411	Sole Sole Sole/Sabato Sera (as Siw Malmkvist & Umberto Marcato)	4
68	Atlantic 584 229	The Man Who Took The Valise Off/Sadie The Cleaning Lady	4

CINDY MALONE
61	RCA RCA 1254	Weird Beard/Young Marriage	4

WIL MALONE
70	Fontana STL 5541	WIL MALONE (LP)	45

(see also Motherlight)

RICHARD MALTBY
61	Columbia DB 4606	The Rat Race/Walkie Talkie	12

MAMA LION
75	Philips 6078 002	Ain't Too Proud To Beg/Me Invitation	4
72	Philips 6369 153	MAMA LION PRESERVE WILDLIFE (LP)	10
70s	Philips	GIVE IT EVERYTHING I'VE GOT (LP)	10

MAMAS & PAPAS
66	RCA Victor RCA 1503	California Dreamin'/Somebody Groovy	5
66	RCA Victor RCA 1516	Monday Monday/Got A Feelin'	4
66	RCA Victor RCA 1525	You've Got To Hide Your Love Away/BARRY McGUIRE: Cloudy Summer Afternoon	10
66	RCA Victor RCA 1533	I Saw Her Again/Even If I Could	4
66	RCA Victor RCA 1551	Look Through My Window/Once There Was I Time I Thought	5
67	RCA Victor RCA 1564	Words Of Love/I Can't Wait	4
67	RCA Victor RCA 1576	Dedicated To The One I Love/Free Advice	4
67	RCA Victor RCA 1613	Creeque Alley/No Salt On Her Tail	4
67	RCA Victor RCA 1630	12.30/Straight Shooter	4
67	RCA Victor RCA 1649	Glad To Be Unhappy/Hey Girl	4
68	RCA Victor RCA 1710	Safe In My Garden/Too Late	4
68	RCA Victor RCA 1726	Dream A Little Dream Of Me/Midnight Voyage	4
68	RCA Victor RCA 1744	For The Love Of Ivy/Strange Young Girls	4
69	Stateside SS 8009	You Baby/My Girl	4
70	Stateside SS 8058	Go Where You Wanna Go/No Salt On Her Tail	4
72	Probe PRO 552	Shooting Star/No Dough	4
66	RCA Victor RD 7803	IF YOU CAN BELIEVE YOUR EYES AND EARS (LP)	12
66	RCA Victor RD/SF 7834	CASS, JOHN, MICHELLE, DENNY (LP)	12
67	RCA Victor RD/SF 7880	DELIVER (LP)	12
68	RCA Victor RD/SF 7960	PRESENTED BY THE PAPAS AND THE MAMAS (LP)	12

MINT VALUE £

68	Stateside (S)SL 5002	THE MAMAS AND THE PAPAS GOLDEN ERA VOL. 2 (LP) 10
70	Probe SPB 1013/14	A GATHERING OF FLOWERS (2-LP) 14
72	Probe SPB 1048	PEOPLE LIKE US (LP) 10
78	M&S MO 101225	CALIFORNIA DREAMIN' (LP, available only through Marks & Spencers) 15

(see also Mama Cass (Elliot), John Phillips, Michelle Phillips, Scott McKenzie, Barry McGuire, Mugwumps)

MAMA'S BOYS
81	Pussy	Silence Is Out Of Fashion (p/s) 12
82	Scoff DT 015	Belfast City Blues/Reach For The Top (p/s) 6
82	Ultra-Noise ION 1038	In The Heat Of The Night (p/s) 4
84	Jive JIVE 71	Mama We're All Crazee Now/Crazy Daisy's House Of Dreams//
		Runaway Rogues/Gentlemen Rogues (double pack) 4
83	Spartan SPLP 001	TURN IT UP/TOO LITTLE OF YOU TO LOVE (LP, with free live bootleg LP) 18
85	Jive HIP 24	POWER AND PASSION (LP, with free 12" picture disc) 10

MAMMATH
| 84 | Neat NEAT 42 | Rock Me/Rough 'N' Ready (p/s) ....5 |

MAN
69	Pye 7N 17684	Sudden Life/Love 12
71	Liberty LBF 15448	Daughter Of The Fireplace/Country Girl 10
74	United Artists UP 35643	Don't Go Away (possibly unissued) ....15+
74	United Artists UP 35703	Taking The Easy Way Out Again/California Silks And Satins 6
74	United Artists UP 35739	Day And Night/A Hard Way To Live 5
76	MCA MCA 236	Out Of Your Head/I'm A Love Taker 4
76	United Artists REM 408	BANANAS (EP) 5
69	Pye N(S)PL 18275	REVELATION (LP, mono/stereo) 20/18
69	Dawn DNLS 3003	2 OZ'S OF PLASTIC WITH A HOLE IN THE MIDDLE (LP, orange label) 15
69	Dawn DNLS 3003	2 OZ'S OF PLASTIC WITH A HOLE IN THE MIDDLE
		(LP, later pressings with red & blue or purple labels) 10
70	Liberty LBG 83464	MAN (LP) 15
71	United Artists UAS 29236	DO YOU LIKE IT HERE NOW, ARE YOU SETTLING IN? (LP) 15
72	United Artists USP 100	LIVE AT THE PADGET ROOMS, PENARTH (LP) 20
72	United Artists UAG 29417	BE GOOD TO YOURSELF AT LEAST ONCE A DAY
		(LP, 'map' sleeve with 'family tree' inner) 12
73	Utd Artists UAD 60053/4	BACK INTO THE FUTURE (2-LP) 14
74	United Artists UAG 29631	RHINOS, WINOS & LUNATICS (LP) 10
74	United Artists UAG 29675	SLOW MOTION (LP, with inner sleeve) 10
75	United Artists UAG 29872	MAXIMUM DARKNESS (LP, with poster) 10

(see also Bystanders, Eyes Of Blue, Ancient Grease, Big Sleep, Clive John, Alkatraz, Help Yourself, Martin Ace, Deke Leonard)

(STEPHEN STILLS') MANASSAS
| 72 | Atlantic K 60021 | MANASSAS (2-LP) ....14 |
| 73 | Atlantic K 40440 | DOWN THE ROAD (LP) ....10 |

(see also Stephen Stills)

JUNIOR MANCE
| 60 | HMV CLP 1342 | JUNIOR (LP) ....10 |

STEVE MANCHA/J.J. BARNES
| 73 | Stax SXATS 1012 | RARE STAMPS (LP) ....12 |

(see also J.J. Barnes)

MICKY MANCHESTER
| 75 | Rainbow RBW 2001 | Have You Seen Your Daughter Mrs. Jones/Chamberlain Said ....4 |

(see also Just Plain Smith, Just Plain Jones, Trainspotters)

MANCHESTER MEKON
| 79 | Newmarket NEW 102 | No Forgetting/Have A Go-Go/Jonathan Livingstone Seafood |
| | | (hand-painted p/s with insert, 1,000 only) ....10 |

MANCHESTER MOB
| 67 | Parlophone R 5552 | Bony Maronie At The Hop/Afro Asian ....20 |

(see also High Society, 10cc)

MANCHESTERS
| 66 | Ember | TRIBUTE TO THE BEATLES (LP) ....15 |

MANCHESTER'S PLAYBOYS
| 66 | Fontana TF 745 | I Feel So Good/I Close My Eyes ....35 |

HENRY MANCINI & HIS ORCHESTRA
59	RCA RCA 1134	Peter Gunn Theme/The Brothers Go To Mother's 6
59	RCA RCA 1134	Peter Gunn Theme/The Brothers Go To Mother's (78) 5
63	RCA RCX 7136	THE PINK PANTHER (EP) 10

MANDALA BAND
| 75 | Chrysalis CHR 1095 | MANDALA BAND (LP) ....12 |
| 78 | Chrysalis CHR 1181 | THE EYE OF WENDOR: PROPHECIES (LP, with booklet) ....12 |

MANDARIN KRAZE
| 70 | Carnaby CNS 4008 | How Long Does It Take To Explain/Magazine Cottage ....4 |

HARVEY MANDEL
74	Janus 6146 024	Uno Ino/Shangrenade 4
68	Philips SBL 7873	CRISTO REDENTOR (LP) 15
69	Philips SBL 7904	RIGHTEOUS (LP) 12
70	Philips SBL 7915	GAMES GUITARS PLAY (LP) 12
71	Dawn DNLS 3015	BABY BATTER (LP) 12
72	London SH-O 8426	GET OFF IN CHICAGO (LP) 10
72	Janus 6310 210	THE SNAKE (LP) 10
73	Janus 6499 831	SHANGRENADE (LP) 10

MINT VALUE £

MANDINGO
73	EMI EMI 2014	Medicine Man/Black Rite	7

MANDRAKE
60	Philips PB 1093	Mandrake/The Witch's Twist	5
61	Philips BF 1153	Thank Goodness It's Friday/Queen Of Sheba	4

MANDRAKE MEMORIAL
69	RCA SF 8028	MEDIUM (LP)	25
70	RCA/Poppy PYS 11003	PUZZLE (LP)	30

MANDRAKE PADDLE STEAMER
69	Parlophone R 5780	Strange Walking Man/Steam	60
88	Bam Caruso NRIC 033	Strange Walking Man/Steam (reissue, gatefold p/s)	4

MANDRILL
73	Polydor 2066 320	Mandrill/Hang Loose	4
73	Polydor 2066 357	Fencewalk/Polk Street Carnival	4
70	Polydor 2489 028	MANDRILL (LP)	10
72	Polydor 2391 030	MANDRILL IS (LP)	10
73	Polydor 2391 061	COMPOSITE TRUTH (LP)	10
73	Polydor 2391 092	JUST OUTSIDE OF TOWN (LP)	10

MANEATERS
82	Editions EG EGO 8	Nine To Five/SUZI PINNS: Jerusalem (withdrawn 'Adam & Toyah' p/s)	40
82	Editions EG EGO 8	Nine To Five/SUZI PINNS: Jerusalem (title p/s)	5
	(see also Adam & Ants, Toyah)		

MAN FROM DELMONTE
87	Ugly Man UGLY 3	Drive Drive Drive/Twenty Two And Still In Love With You/Sun Serious (p/s)	8
87	Ugly Man UGLY 5	Water In My Eyes/Bred By You (p/s)	7
87	Ugly Man UGLY 5T	Water In My Eyes/Bred By You (12", p/s)	12
88	Ugly Man UGLY 7	Will Nobody Save Louise/Good Things In Life (p/s)	4
88	Ugly Man UGLY 7T	Will Nobody Save Louise/Good Things In Life/Like A Millionaire (12", p/s)	7

MANHATTANS
65	Sue WI 384	I Wanna Be (Your Everything)/Searchin' For My Baby	12
66	Carnival CAR 100	Baby I Need You/Teach Me	8
66	Carnival CAR 101	That New Girl/Can I	8
74	CBS 2117	Soul Train/I'm Not A Run Around	4
76	CBS 81513	THE MANHATTANS (LP)	10
78	CBS 81828	IT FEELS GOOD (LP)	10
79	CBS 35693	LOVE TALK (LP)	10

MANIACS
77	United Artists UP 36327	Chelsea 1977/Ain't No Legend	5
	(see also Rings, Physicals)		

MANIAX
60s	White Label WLR 101/102	Out Of Reach/The Devil's Home	10

MANIC STREET PREACHERS
89	SBS SBS 002	Suicide Alley/Tennessee (I Feel So Low) (300 only, 150 with p/s)	80/60
90	Hopelessly Devoted 1	UK Channel Boredom/LAURENS: I Don't Know What The Trouble Is (p/s flexidisc, some free with 'Hopelessly Devoted' fanzine)	12/8
91	Heavenly HVN8 12	Motown Junk/Sorrow 16/We Her Majesty's Prisoners (12")	10
91	Heavenly HVN8 CD	Motown Junk/Sorrow 16/We Her Majesty's Prisoners (CD)	10
90	Damaged Goods YUBB 4	NEW ART RIOT (12" EP, black & white or black-on-yellow label)	10/8
90	Damaged Goods YUBB 4P	NEW ART RIOT (12" EP, reissue on pink vinyl)	12
91	Caff CAFF 15	FEMININE IS BEAUTIFUL (500 only)	25

MANICURED NOISE
80	Pre PRE 003	Metronome/Moscow (die-cut p/s with postcard)	4
80	Pre PRE 006	Faith/Free Time	4
	(see also Steve Walsh & Weathermen)		

BARRY MANILOW
82	Arista ARIPD 464	Stay (live)/Nickels And Dimes (picture disc)	5
83	Arista ARILE 542	You're Lookin' Hot Tonight (live)/Let's Get On With It (p/s)	6
83	Arista ARISD 551	Read 'Em And Weep/One Voice (live) (picture disc)	4

MANISH BOYS
65	Parlophone R 5250	I Pity The Fool/Take My Tip	250
	(see also David Bowie)		

MANISH BOYS/DAVY JONES & LOWER THIRD
79	EMI EMI 2925	I Pity The Fool/Take My Tip/DAVY JONES & LOWER THIRD: You've Got A Habit Of Leaving/Baby Loves That Way (p/s)	5
82	Charly CYM 1	I Pity The Fool/Take My Tip/DAVY JONES & LOWER THIRD: You've Got A Habit Of Leaving/Baby Loves That Way (10", p/s)	6
	(see also David Bowie, Davy Jones, Davie Jones & King Bees, Calvin James)		

MANITOBA
70	RCA RCA 2016	You'll Never Get Back/Something In You	5

BARRY MANN
61	HMV POP 911	Who Put The Bomp/Love True Love	12
61	HMV POP 949	Little Miss U.S.A./Find Another Fool	7
62	HMV POP 1084	Hey Baby I'm Dancin'/Like I Don't Love You	7
63	HMV POP 1108	Bless You/Teenage Has Been	6
64	Colpix PX 776	Talk To Me Baby/Amy	7
66	Capitol CL 15463	Angelica/Looking At Tomorrow	6
68	Capitol CL 15538	The Young Electric Psychedelic Hippy Flippy Folk And Funky Philosophic Turned On Groovy 12 String Band/Take Your Love	6

63	HMV CLP 1559	WHO PUT THE BOMP IN THE BOMP BOMP BOMP? (LP)	150

CARL MANN

59	London HLS 8935	Mona Lisa/Foolish One	20
59	London HLS 8935	Mona Lisa/Foolish One (78)	45
59	London HLS 9006	Pretend/Rockin' Love	15
59	London HLS 9006	Pretend/Rockin' Love (78)	50
60	London HLS 9170	South Of The Border/I'm Comin' Home	18
60	London HA-S 2277	LIKE MANN — CARL MANN SINGS (LP)	100

CHARLES MANN

73	Probe PRO 585	Say You Love Me Too/I Can Feel It	4

DONNY MANN

70s	Avalanche AV 67327	Things/Is There A Missing Piece	4

GLORIA MANN

56	Brunswick 05569	Why Do Fools Fall In Love/Partners For Life	12
56	Brunswick 05610	It Happened Again/My Secret Sin	6

HERBIE MANN

66	Atlantic 584 052	Philly Dog/DAVE PIKE: Sunny	10
66	Atlantic 584 058	Love Theme From Paris Burning/Happy Brass	5
67	Atlantic 584 112	And The Beat Goes On/Free For All	5
68	A&M AMS 719	Unchain My Heart/Glory Of Love	6
69	Atlantic 584 297	Memphis Underground/New Orleans	5
75	Atlantic K 10580	Hijack/Orient Express	4
56	London EZN 19006	EAST COAST JAZZ NO. 4 PT. 1 (EP)	8
58	Fontana TFE 17113	HERBIE MANN (EP)	10
59	Columbia Clef SEB 10102	MAGIC FLUTE OF HERBIE MANN (EP)	10
58	Fontana TFL 5013	SALUTE TO THE FLUTE (LP)	15
60	Top Rank 25/015	FLUTE FOR ETERNITY (10" LP, with Buddy Collette)	15
63	London HA-K/SH-K 8043	RIGHT NOW (LP)	15
64	Atlantic ATL 5008	HERBIE MANN AT NEWPORT (LP)	15
65	Atlantic ATL/SAL 5035	THE ROAR OF THE GREASE PAINT (LP)	15
66	CBS (S)BPG 62585	LATIN MANN (LP)	12
66	Atlantic ATL/SAL 5038	STANDING OVATION AT NEWPORT (LP)	15
66	Atlantic 587/588 003	MONDAY NIGHT AT THE VILLAGE GATE (LP)	15
66	Atlantic 587/588 028	NIRVANA (LP, with Bill Evans)	15
67	Atlantic 1471	NEW MANN AT NEWPORT (LP)	12
67	Atlantic 587/588 054	HERBIE MANN AT THE VILLAGE GATE (LP)	12
68	Atlantic 590 013	FREE FOR ALL (LP)	12
68	Atlantic 1475	IMPRESSIONS OF THE MIDDLE EAST (LP)	15
68	Atlantic 1490	THE HERBIE MANN STRING ALBUM (LP)	12
69	Solid State USS 7007	ST. THOMAS (LP)	15
69	Atlantic 588 156	INSPIRATION I FEEL (LP)	12
69	A&M AMLS 944	GLORY OF LOVE (LP)	10
69	Atlantic 588 200	MEMPHIS UNDERGROUND (LP)	12
69	SRCP 3002	AFRO-JAZZIAC (LP)	12
70	Polydor 2465 005	CONCERTO GROSSO IN D BLUES (LP)	12
70	Polydor 2465 008	STONE FLUTE (LP)	12
71	Atco 2400 022	MUSCLE SHOALS NITTY GRITTY (LP)	12
71	Atco 2400 121	MEMPHIS TWO-STEP (LP)	12
72	Atco 2400 191	PUSH, PUSH (LP, with Duane Allman)	15
72	Atlantic K 40385	MISSISSIPI GAMBLER (LP)	10
73	Atlantic K 40467	HOLD ON I'M COMING (LP)	10
73	Atlantic K 60020	EVOLUTION OF MANN (2-LP)	14
74	Atlantic K 50020	TURTLE BAY (LP)	10
74	Atlantic K 50032	LONDON UNDERGROUND (LP)	10
75	Atlantic K 50053	REGGAE (LP)	10
75	Atlantic K 50128	DISCOTHEQUE (LP)	10
75	Atlantic K 50174	WATER BED (LP)	10

(see also Buddy Collette & Herbie Mann Group)

LORIE MANN

59	Top Rank JAR 116	A Penny A Kiss, A Penny A Hug/Dream Lover	4
59	Top Rank JAR 148	Just Keep It Up/You Made Me Care	4
59	Top Rank JAR 237	So Many Ways/I Wonder	4

MANFRED MANN

63	HMV POP 1189	Why Should We Not/Brother Jack	12
63	HMV POP 1225	Cock-A-Hoop/Now You're Needing Me	12
64	HMV POP 1252	5-4-3-2-1/Without You	5
64	HMV POP 1282	Hubble Bubble (Toil And Trouble)/I'm Your Kingpin	5
64	HMV POP 1320	Do Wah Diddy Diddy/What You Gonna Do?	4
64	HMV POP 1346	Sha La La/John Hardy	4
65	HMV POP 1381	Come Tomorrow/What Did I Do Wrong?	4
65	HMV POP 1413	Oh No Not My Baby/What Am I Doing Wrong	4
65	HMV POP 1466	If You Gotta Go, Go Now/Stay Around	4
66	HMV POP 1523	Pretty Flamingo/You're Standing By	4
66	HMV POP 1541	You Gave Me Somebody To Love/Poison Ivy	8
66	Fontana TF 730	Just Like A Woman/I Wanna Be Rich	4
66	Fontana TF 757	Semi-Detached, Suburban Mr. James/Morning After The Party	4
67	Fontana TF 812	Ha! Ha! Said The Clown/Feeling So Good (some in p/s)	8/4
67	Fontana TF 828	Sweet Pea/One Way	7
67	Fontana TF 862	So Long, Dad/Funniest Gig	7
68	Fontana TF 897	Mighty Quinn/By Request — Edwin Garvey	4
68	Fontana TF 908	Up The Junction/Sleepy Hollow (some in p/s)	10/5
68	Fontana TF 943	My Name Is Jack/There Is A Man	4
68	Fontana TF 985	Fox On The Run/Too Many People	4

MANFRED MANN

69	Fontana TF 1013	Ragamuffin Man/A 'B' Side	4
64	HMV 7EG 8848	MANFRED MANN'S COCK-A-HOOP WITH 54321 (EP)	15
65	HMV 7EG 8876	GROOVIN' WITH MANFRED MANN (EP)	12
65	HMV 7EG 8908	THE ONE IN THE MIDDLE (EP)	10
65	HMV 7EG 8922	NO LIVING WITHOUT LOVING (EP)	10
66	HMV 7EG 8942	MACHINES (EP)	12
66	HMV 7EG 8949	INSTRUMENTAL ASYLUM (EP)	12
66	HMV 7EG 8962	AS WAS (EP)	15
66	Fontana TE 17483	INSTRUMENTAL ASSASSINATION (EP)	7
68	Philips MCF 5002	THE HITS OF MANFRED MANN (cassette EP)	12
68	Philips MCF 5005	THE HITS OF MANFRED MANN AND DDDBM&T (cassette EP)	12
64	HMV CLP 1731	THE FIVE FACES OF MANFRED MANN (LP)	15
65	HMV CLP 1911/CSD 1628	MANN MADE (LP, mono/stereo)	15/18
66	HMV CLP 3559	MANN MADE HITS (LP)	15
66	Fontana (S)TL 5377	AS IS (LP, 'alcove' or 'locomotive' cover)	15/20
67	HMV CLP/CSD 3594	SOUL OF MANN (LP, mono/stereo)	18/20
68	Fontana (S)TL 5460	UP THE JUNCTION — ORIGINAL SOUNDTRACK RECORDING (LP)	15
68	Fontana SFL 13003	WHAT A MANN (LP)	12
68	Fontana (S)TL 5470	MIGHTY GARVEY! (LP, mono/stereo)	14/12
70	Fontana 6852 005	UP THE JUNCTION — ORIGINAL SOUNDTRACK RECORDING (LP, reissue)	10

(see also Paul Jones, Blues Band, Mike Hugg, Henry Lowther, Mike D'Abo, McGuinness Flint)

MANFRED MANN & MIKE HUG(G)

| 71 | Ski SKI 1 | Ski 'Full-Of-Fitness' Theme/Baby Jane (some in p/s) | 15/7 |
| 71 | Michelin MIC+01 | The Michelin Theme (Go Radial, Go Michelin) (1-sided, gatefold p/s) | 12 |

MANFRED MANN'S CHAPTER III

70	Vertigo 6059 012	Happy Being Me/Devil Woman	4
69	Vertigo VO 3	MANFRED MANN CHAPTER 3 (LP, gatefold sleeve, spiral label)	15
70	Vertigo 6360 012	MANFRED MANN CHAPTER 3 VOL. 2 (LP, gatefold sleeve, spiral label)	15

MANFRED MANN'S EARTH BAND

70	Lyntone LYN 1981	The Maxwell House Shake (1-sided flexidisc)	5
71	Philips 6006 122	Living Without You/Tribute (as Manfred Mann)	4
71	Philips 6006 159	Mrs Henry/Prayer (as Manfred Mann)	4
72	Philips 6006 251	Meat/Glorified Magnified	4
72	Vertigo 6059 078	Get Your Rocks Off/Sadjoy (as Earth Band)	4
79	Bronze BPO 77	Don't Kill It Carol/Blinded By The Light (picture disc)	5
72	Philips 6308 086	MANFRED MANN'S EARTH BAND (LP)	12
72	Philips 6308 125	GLORIFIED MAGNIFIED (LP)	12
73	Vertigo 6360 087	MESSIN' (LP, spiral label)	18

SHADOW MANN

| 68 | Roulette RO 504 | Come Live With Me/One By One | 6 |

SHELLY MANNE

68	Atlantic 584 180	Daktari/Out On A Limb	4
54	Vogue LDE 072	SHELLY MANNE AND HIS MEN VOL. 1 (10" LP)	15
55	Contemporary LDC 143	SHELLY MANNE VOL. 2 (10" LP)	15
56	Contemporary LDC 190	SHELLY MANNE, SHORTY ROGERS AND JIMMY GIUFFRE — THE THREE (10" LP)	15
56	Contemporary LDC 192	SHELLY MANNE AND RUSS FREEMAN (10" LP)	15
61	Contemporary LAC 12250	AT THE BLACK HAWK VOL. 1 (LP, also stereo SCA 5015)	12
61	Contemporary LAC 12255	AT THE BLACK HAWK VOL. 2 (LP, also stereo SCA 5016)	12
61	Contemporary LAC 12260	AT THE BLACK HAWK VOL. 3 (LP, also stereo SCA 5017)	12
61	Contemporary LAC 12265	AT THE BLACK HAWK VOL. 4 (LP, also stereo SCA 5018)	12
65	Stateside SL 10125	SHELLY MANNE AND CO. (LP)	10

(see also Gerry Mulligan & Shelly Manne, Jimmy Giuffre)

BOB MANNING

54	Capitol CL 14190	I'm A Fool For You/It's All Right With Me	6
55	Capitol CL 14220	The Very Thought Of You/Just For Laughs	6
55	Capitol CL 14256	Majorca (Isle Of Love)/It's My Life	6
55	Capitol CL 14234	My Love Song To You/After My Laughter Came Tears	6
55	Capitol CL 14288	The Mission San Michel/You Are There	6
55	Capitol CL 14318	What A Wonderful Way To Die/Why Didn't You Tell Me?	6

MARTY MANNING & CHEETAHS

| 67 | CBS 2721 | Tarzan March/Sunny | 6 |

EDDIE MANNION

| 60 | HMV POP 804 | Just Driftin'/Quiet Girl | 6 |

WINGY MANONE ORCHESTRA

| 57 | Brunswick 05655 | Party Doll/Real Gone | 12 |
| 57 | Brunswick 05655 | Party Doll/Real Gone (78) | 5 |

MAN ON THE MOON

| 69 | Philips 88457 DE | Man On The Moon (spoken word, 2-part tri-foldout p/s with insert, 'historic souvenir' available via 'News Of The World' newspaper) | 4 |

JOE MANSANO

| 68 | Blue Cat BS 150 | Life On Reggae Planet/RECO & RHYTHM ACES: Z.Z. Beat | 5 |

TONY MANSELL

54	Parlophone MSP 6130	The High And The Mighty/Hold My Hand (with Johnny Dankworth Orchestra)	4
56	Parlophone MSP 6222	Zambesi (Sweet African)/11th Hour Melody (with Johnny Dankworth Orch.)	5
58	Parlophone R 4471	Impossible/Who Are They To Say	4

(see also Johnny Dankworth)

JAYNE MANSFIELD

| 67 | London HL 10147 | As The Clouds Drift By/Suey (demos more common, £12) | 18 |

(see also Jimi Hendrix)

CHARLES MANSON

86	Fierce FRIGHT 006	Rise/Sick City (p/s, 1-side etched, handdone labels) 12
88	Fierce FRIGHT 012	It's Comin' Down Fast (Helter Skelter) (p/s, 1-side etched, handdone labels) 12
80s	Fierce FRIGHT 001	LOVE AND TERROR CULT (LP) 30

EDDY MANSON

55	HMV 7M 325	Oh! No!/The Lovers 5

JEANE MANSON

79	CBS SCBS 7222	I've Already Seen It In Your Eyes/J'ai Deja Vu Ca Dans Tes Yeux 15

JOHN MANTELL

65	CBS 201783	Remember Child/I'll See You Around 20

MIKE MANTLER

74	Virgin JD 3001	JAZZ COMPOSERS' ORCHESTRA (2-LP) 15

BOB MANTON

81	Mainstreet MS 101	No Trees In Brixton Prison/Brixton Walkabout (p/s) 5
	(see also Purple Hearts)	

MANTOVANI (ORCHESTRA)

53	Decca F 10168	Swedish Rhapsody/Jamaican Rumba 6
54	Decca F 10233	Luxembourg Polka/Music Box Tango 4
54	Decca F 10250	Shadow Waltz/Moonlight Serenade 4
54	Decca F 10292	Bewitched/Dream, Dream, Dream 4
54	Decca F 10395	Lonely Ballerina/Lazy Gondolier 6
60	Decca F 9696	Charmaine/Diane 5
67	Decca F 12630	You Only Live Twice/Puppet On A String (as Mantovani Orchestra) 4

MANUFACTURED ROMANCE

81	Fresh FRESH 16	The Time Of My Life/Room To Breathe (various colours of p/s) 4

PHIL MANZANERA (& 801)

77	Polydor 2001 733	Flight 19/Car Rhumba 5
78	Polydor 2001 800	Island/Diamond Head 4
78	Polydor 2001 835	Remote Control/K Scope 5
78	Polydor PB 10	Remote Control/K Scope 5
	(see also Roxy Music, Quiet Sun)	

MAPLE OAK

70	Decca F 13008	Son Of A Gun/Hurt Me So Much 15
71	Decca SKL 5085	MAPLE OAK (LP) 150
	(see also Kinks)	

LUCILLE MAPP

57	Columbia DB 3916	Mangos/On Treasure Island 6
57	Columbia DB 3949	Jamie Boy/Moonlight In Vermont 4
57	Columbia DB 4040	I'm Available/Lovin' Ya, Lovin' Ya, Lovin' Ya 6
58	Columbia DB 4071	Love Is/The Early Birdie 4
58	Columbia DB 4168	Remember When/I'm A Dreamer, Aren't We All? 4
59	Columbia DB 4261	Chinchilla/Follow Me 4
57	Columbia SEG 7726	STREET OF DREAMS (EP) 7
57	Columbia SEG 7773	LUCILLE MAPP (EP) 7

TOMMY MARA

55	MGM SP 1128	Pledging My Love/Honey Bunch 6
55	MGM SP 1128	Pledging My Love/Honey Bunch (78) 10
58	Felsted AF 109	Where The Blues Of The Night/What Makes You So Lonely 6
59	Felsted AF 116	You Don't Know/Marie 5
59	Felsted AF 123	Until I Hear From You/Now Is The Hour 5

(JOSEPH) MARAIS & MIRANDA

53	Columbia SCM 5025	Old Johnnie Goggabie/The Zulu Warrior 4
59	Fontana H 225	I-Ha-She/The Queen Bee (as Marais & Miranda) 4

MIKE MARAN

72	Bronze ILPS 9221	FAIR WARNING (LP) 10

MARATHONS

61	Pye Intl. 7N 25088	Peanut Butter/Down In New Orleans 8
61	Vogue V 9185	Peanut Butter/Talkin' Trash 15

MARAUDERS

63	Decca F 11695	That's What I Want/Hey What'd You Say 6
63	Decca F 11748	Always On My Mind/Heart Full Of Tears 6
64	Decca F 11836	Lucille/Little Egypt 6
65	Fontana TF 609	Baby I Wanna Be Loved/Somebody Told My Girl 7
	(see aldo Danny Davis)	

MARBLES

68	Polydor 56272	Only One Woman/By The Light Of A Burning Candle 5
69	Polydor 56310	The Walls Fell Down/Love You 4
	(see also Graham Bonnet, Fut)	

MARBLE STAIRCASE

83	Whaam! WHA-AM 11	Still Dreaming/Dark Ages (p/s) 7

MARC & MAMBAS

82	Some Bizzare BZS 512	Fun City/Sleaze (Take It, Shake It)/Taking It And Shaking It (12", p/s, fan club issue, mail-order only) 20
82	Lyntone LYN 12505	Discipline (flexidisc) 8
82	Some Bizzare BZS 15	Big Louise/Empty Eyes (withdrawn, any copies pressed?) ....10+
82	Some Bizzare BZS 1512	Big Louise/Empty Eyes/The Dirt Behind The Neon (Sleaze Revisited) (12", withdrawn, any copies pressed?) ....25+

MARC & MAMBAS

83	Some Bizzare BZS 19	Black Heart/Your Aura (p/s, with postcard)	7
83	Some Bizzare BZS 1912	Black Heart/Your Aura/Mamba (12", p/s)	15
83	Some Bizzare BZSDJ 21	Torment/You'll Never See On Sunday (promo-only, no p/s)	20
83	Some Bizzare BZS 2112	Torment/First Time/You'll Never See Me On A Sunday (12", p/s)	18
82	Some Bizzare BZS 13	UNTITLED (LP, with 12")	12
83	Some Bizzare BZSL 4	TORMENT AND TOREROS (2-LP, black inner sleeves)	14
84	Gutterheart GH 1	BITE BLACK AND BLUES (fan club LP)	25

(see also Soft Cell, Marc Almond)

LYDIA MARCELLE
66	Sue WI 4025	Another Kind Of Fellow/I've Never Been Hurt Like This Before	20

MUZZY MARCELLINO
56	London HLU 8355	Mary Lou/MR. FORD & MR. GOON-BONES: Ain't She Sweet	20

MARCELS
61	Pye Intl. 7N 25073	Blue Moon/Goodbye To Love	7
61	Pye Intl. 7N 25083	Summertime/Teeter Totter Love	6
61	Pye Intl. 7N 25105	You Are My Sunshine/Find Another Fool	7
61	Pye Intl. 7N 25114	Heartaches/My Love For You	8
62	Pye Intl. 7N 25124	My Melancholy Baby/Really Need Your Love	7
63	Pye Intl. 7N 25201	I Wanna Be The Leader/Give Me Back Your Love	6
61	Pye Intl. NPL 28016	BLUE MOON (LP)	60

GLORIA MARCH
58	London HLB 8568	Baby Of Mine/Nippon Wishing Well	12

HAL MARCH
58	London HLD 8534	Hear Me Good/One Dozen Roses	20
58	London HLD 8534	Hear Me Good/One Dozen Roses (78)	5

JO MARCH
58	London HLR 8696	Dormi, Dormi, Dormi (Sleep, Sleep, Sleep)/Fare Thee Well, Oh Honey	6
58	London HLR 8763	The Virgin Mary Had One Son/I, Said The Donkey	6

(LITTLE) PEGGY MARCH
63	RCA RCA 1338	I Will Follow Him/Wind Up Doll (as Little Peggy March)	5
63	RCA RCA 1350	My Teenage Castle/I Wish I Were A Princess (as Little Peggy March)	5
63	RCA RCA 1362	Hello Heartache, Goodbye Love/Boy Crazy (as Little Peggy March)	5
64	RCA RCA 1426	Watch What You Do With My Baby/Can't Stop (as Little Peggy March)	5
65	RCA RCA 1472	Let Her Go/Your Girl	5
68	RCA RCA 1687	If You Loved Me/Thinking Through My Tears	25
68	RCA RCA 1752	I've Been Here Before/Time And Time Again	5
69	RCA RCA 1809	What Am I Gonna Do With You/Lilac Skies	5
65	RCA	IN OUR FASHION (LP)	15

BOBBY MARCHAN
68	Atlantic 584 155	Get Down With It/Half A Mind	5
69	Action ACT 4533	Ain't No Reason For Girls To Be Lonely Pts 1 & 2	5

VICTOR MARCHESE
53	MGM SP 1018	Fandango/Flamingo	4

MARCH HARE
68	Chapter One CH 101	Cry My Heart/With My Eyes Closed	6
69	Deram DM 258	I Could Make It There With You/Have We Got News For You	4

MARCHING GIRLS
81	Pop:Aural POP 011	True Love/First In Line (p/s)	4

MARCH VIOLETS
82	Merciful Release MR 013	Religious As Hell/Fodder/Children On Stun/Bon Bon Babies (p/s)	12
83	Merciful Release MR 017	Grooving In Green/Stream (p/s)	12
84	Rebirth RB 18	Crow Baby/One Two I Love You (p/s)	5
85	Rebirth RB 18-12	Crow Baby/One Two I Love You/Long Pig/Crow Bait (12", p/s)	8
84	Rebirth RB 21	Snake Dance/Slow Drip Lizard (snakeskin-embossed stickered p/s with insert)	4
84	Rebirth RB 21-12	Snake Dance/It's Hot/Slow Drip Lizard/Snake Dance (Extended) (12", p/s)	7
84	Rebirth VRB 24	Walk Into The Sun/Lights Go Out (p/s)	4
84	Rebirth VRB 24-12	Walk Into The Sun/Essence (12", p/s, with lyric insert)	7
84	Rebirth VRB 25	NATURAL HISTORY (LP)	10

(see also Batfish Boys)

MARCIA & JEFF
68	Studio One SO 2047	Words/SHARKS: How Could I Live	12

MARCUS
76	United Artists UAS 30000	MARCUS (LP)	20

GUY MARDEL
65	Vogue VRS 7000	V'Avoue Jamais (actually "N'Avoue Jamais")/Si Tu N'y Crois Pas	5

JANIE MARDEN
55	Decca F 10600	Soldier Boy/Hard To Get	6
55	Decca F 10605	I'll Come When You Call/Thank You For The Waltz (with Frank Weir & His Saxophone)	5
55	Decca F 10673	You Are My Love/A Teen Age Prayer	6
56	Decca F 10765	Allegheny Moon/Magic Melody	4

ERNIE MARESCA
62	London HLU 9531	Shout Shout/Crying Like A Baby Over You	10
62	London HLU 9579	Mary Jane/Down On The Beach	12
63	London HLU 9720	Love Express/Lorelei	8
64	London HLU 9834	Rovin' Kind/Please Be Fair	8
65	London HLU 10008	It's Their World/I Can't Dance	5
66	Stateside SS 560	Rockin' Boulevard Street/Am I Better Off Than Them	10

MARGO, Franck Oliver, Diane Solomon, Malcolm Roberts etc.
85	Sonet SON 2281	Children, Kinder, Enfants (English)/(International)/(French)	5

MARGO & MARVETTES
64	Parlophone R 5154	Cherry Pie/Say You Will	8
64	Parlophone R 5227	Copper Kettle/So Fine	5
67	Piccadilly 7N 35387	Seven Letters/That's How Love Goes	5
67	Pye 7N 17423	When Love Slips Away/I'll Be Home (When You Call)	6

MARGUERITA
64	Black Swan WI 431	Woman Come/ERIC MORRIS: Number One	10

CHARLES MARGULIS
59	London HLL 8774	Gigi/Malaguena	6

MARIANE
68	Columbia DB 8420	As For Marionettes/You Know My Name	6
68	Columbia DB 8456	You Had Better Change Your Evil Ways/Like A See Saw	4

MARIANNE & MIKE
64	Vocalion V 9218	As He Once Was Mine/Go On (B-side by Marianne)	4
64	Vocalion V 9225	You're The Only One/One Good Turn Deserves Another	4

(see also Friday Brown. These records do NOT feature Mick Jagger or Marianne Faithfull)

MARIAS & MIRANDA
59	Fontana TF 225	I He She/The Queen Bee	4

MARIBELLE
84	Ariola 106 235	In Love With You/Ik Hou Van Jou	5

ANNE MARIE
65	Fontana TF 523	Runaround/There Must Be A Reason	4

TINA MARIE
82	Motown TMGT 1251	Portuguese Love/The Ballad Of Cradle Rob And Me (12")	8

MARIE CELESTE
71	private press	AND THEN PERHAPS (LP)	200

MARILLION
82	EMI EMI 5351	Market Square Heroes/Three Boats Down From The Candy (p/s)	5
82	EMI 12 EMI 5351	Market Square Heroes/Three Boats Down From The Candy/Grendel (12", p/s)	7
82	EMI 12 EMIP 5351	Market Square Heroes/Three Boats Down From The Candy/Grendel (12", picture disc, 3,000 only)	40
83	EMI EMI 5362	He Knows, You Know/Charting The Single (p/s, originally with blue plastic label & paper sleeve)	5
83	EMI 12 EMI 5362	He Knows, You Know/Charting The Single/He Knows, You Know (Full Length Version) (12", p/s)	8
83	EMI 12 EMIP 5362	He Knows, You Know/Charting The Single/He Knows, You Know (Full Length Version) (12", picture disc, unreleased)	
83	EMI EMI 5393	Garden Party/Margaret (live) (p/s)	4
83	EMI EMIP 5393	Garden Party/Margaret (live) ('jester'-shaped picture disc)	15
83	EMI 12 EMIS 5393	Garden Party (Extended Version)/Charting The Single (live)/Margaret (Extended Live Version) (12", p/s, with poster)	12
83	EMI 12 EMI 5393	Garden Party (Extended Version)/Charting The Single (live)/Margaret (Extended Live Version) (12", p/s)	7
84	EMI 12 MARILP 1	Punch And Judy/Market Square Heroes (New Version)/Three Boats Down From The Candy (New Version) (12", picture disc)	15
84	EMI 12 MARILP 2	Assassing (Full Length Version)/Cinderella Search (Full Length Version) (12", picture disc)	15
85	EMI MARILP 3	Kayleigh/Lady Nina (picture disc)	10
85	EMI 12 MARILP 3	Kayleigh (Alternative Mix)/Kayleigh (Extended Version)/Lady Nina (Extended Version) (12", picture disc)	12
85	EMI 12 MARILP 4	Lavender (Remix)/Freaks/Lavender (12", picture disc)	10
85	EMI 12 MARILP 5	Heart Of Lothian (Full Length Version)/Chelsea Monday (live)/Heart Of Lothian (7" Version) (12", picture disc)	10
87	EMI 12MARILP 6	Incommunicado (LP Version)/(Alternative Mix)/Going Under (12", picture disc)	8
87	EMI CD MARIL 6	Incommunicado (LP Version)/(Alternative Mix)/Going Under (CD, gatefold p/s)	7
87	EMI MARILP 7	Sugar Mice (Radio Edit)/Tux On (picture disc with poster)	8
87	EMI 12MARILP 7	Sugar Mice (Extended Version)/(Album Version)/Tux On (12", picture disc)	12
87	EMI CD MARIL 7	Sugar Mice (Extended Version)/(Radio Edit)/Tux On (CD, 3,000 only, withdrawn)	12
87	EMI 12MARILP 8	Warm Wet Circles (Full Version)/White Russian (live at Loreley)/Incommunicado (live at Loreley) (12", picture disc)	10
87	EMI CD MARIL 8	Warm Wet Circles (Full Version)/White Russian (live at Loreley)/Incommunicado (live at Loreley)/Up On Top Of A Rainbow (CD)	7
88	EMI MARIL 9	Freaks (live)/Kayleigh (live) (p/s)	4
88	EMI MARILP 9	Freaks (live)/Kayleigh (live) ('jester'-shaped picture disc)	4
89	EMI 12MARIL 10P	Hooks In You (Meaty Mix)/Hooks In You/After Me (12", with poster)	7
89	EMI MARIL PD 11	Uninvited Guests/The Bell In The Sea (shaped picture disc)	4
90	EMI MARILP 12	Easter/The Release (picture disc)	4
91	EMI MARILS 14	No One Can/A Collection (box set with 4 colour pictures & badge)	4
84	EMI EMCP 3429	SCRIPT FOR A JESTER'S TEAR (LP, picture disc)	35
84	EMI MRLP 1	FUGAZI (LP, picture disc)	25
85	EMI JESTP 1	REAL TO REEL (LP, picture disc, die-cut sleeve)	15
85	EMI MRLP 2	MISPLACED CHILDHOOD (LP, picture disc, in die-cut sleeve)	20
87	EMI EMDP 1002	CLUTCHING AT STRAWS (LP, picture disc in sleeve)	12
89	EMI EMDPD 1011	SEASON'S END (LP, picture disc, with insert)	10

(see also Fish)

MINT VALUE £

MARILYN SISTERS

55	Decca F 10518	Bubbles/No Chance	4
55	Decca F 10552	Genuine Love/Everything Is Big Way Down In Texas	4
55	Decca F 10604	D-a-r-l-i-n'/The Kinkajou	4

(see also Suzi Miller)

MARINE GIRLS

82	In Phaze COD 2	On My Mind/The Lure Of The Rockpools (p/s, with insert)	12
82	Cherry Red CHERRY 40	On My Mind/The Lure Of The Rockpools (reissue, different p/s)	5
83	Cherry Red CHERRY 54	You Must Be Mad/Don't Come Back (p/s)	4
81	In Phaze COD 1	BEACH PARTY (cassette with inserts)	15
81	Whaam! COD 1	BEACH PARTY (LP, with inserts)	12

(see also Tracey Thorn, Everything But The Girl, Jane)

MARINERS

55	London HLA 8201	I Love You Fair Dinkum/(At The) Steamboat River Ball	20
58	Fontana H 127	I Heard Ya The First Time/I Live For You	5
56	London HA-A 2007	SPIRITUALS (LP)	10

MARINO MARINI & HIS QUARTET

58	Durium DC 16631	Guitar Boogie/Armen's Theme	6
58	Durium DC 16632	Come Prima/Volare (Nel Blu Dipinto Di Blu)	6
58	Durium DC 16635	Stella Stella (Star Of Love)/Lazzarella	6
59	Durium DC 16636	Ciao Ciao Bambina/Avevamo La Stessa Eta'	6
55	Durium DLU 96012	HAPPY MUSIC FROM ITALY (10" LP)	10
59	Durium DLU 96039	IN SOHO (10" LP)	12
60	Durium TLU 97028	MARINO MARINI QUARTET (LP)	10

MARION (Finland)

73	Columbia DB 8987	Tom Tom Tom/My Son John	15

MARION (U.K.)

67	Page One POF 042	I Go To Sleep/Abyssinian Secret	4

MARIONETTES

65	Decca F 12056	Whirlpool Of Love/Nobody But You	4
65	Parlophone R 5300	Was It Me?/Under The Boardwalk	4
65	Parlophone R 5356	Raining It's Pouring/Pick Up Your Feet (withdrawn)	6
65	Parlophone R 5374	At The End Of The Day/Pick Up Your Feet	4
66	Parlophone R 5416	Like A Man/Tonight It's Going To Storm	6

(see also Rag Dolls)

JON MARK

69	Philips BF 1772	All Neat In Black Stockings/Run To Me	4

(see also John Mayall, Mark-Almond)

MARK-ALMOND

71	Harvest SHSP 4011	MARK-ALMOND (LP)	10
72	Harvest SHVL 809	RISING (LP)	10

(see also Johnny Almond Music Machine)

MARK & JOHN

64	Decca F 12044	Walk Right Back/Karen	5

MARKETTS

62	Liberty LIB 55401	The Surfer Stomp/Start	8
62	Liberty LIB 55443	Balboa Blue/Stompede	6
64	Warner Bros WB 120	Out Of Limits/Bella Delana	10
64	Warner Bros WB 130	Vanishing Point/Borealis	4
66	Warner Bros WB 5696	The Batman Theme/Richie's Theme	8
67	Warner Bros WB 5847	Tarzan's March/Stirrin' Up Some Soul	30
63	Warner Bros WM 8140	TAKE TO WHEELS (LP)	18
66	Warner Bros W 1642	BATMAN (LP)	16

MAR-KEYS

61	London HLK 9399	Last Night/Never On Sunday	8
61	London HLK 9449	Morning After/Diana	6
62	London HLK 9510	Foxy/One Degree North	6
66	Atlantic AT 4079	Philly Dog/Honey Pot	8
67	Atlantic 584 074	Last Night/Night Before	6
69	Stax STAX 132	Black/Jive Man	4
62	London HA-K 8011	DO THE POP-EYE (LP)	25
66	Atlantic 587/588 024	THE GREAT MEMPHIS SOUND (LP)	12
68	Atlantic 587/588 135	MELLOW JELLY (LP)	12

(see also Booker T. & MGs)

MARK II

60	Columbia DB 4549	Night Theme/Confusion	6

MARK IV

59	Mercury AMT 1025	I Got A Wife/Aah-Oo-Gah	10
59	Mercury AMT 1025	I Got A Wife/Aah-Oo-Gah (78)	8
59	Mercury AMT 1045	Move Over Rover/Dante's Inferno	8
59	Mercury AMT 1060	Ring, Ring, Ring Those Bells/Mairzy Doats	6

MARK FOUR

64	Mercury MF 815	Rock Around The Clock/Slow Down	25
64	Mercury MF 825	Crazy Country Hop/Try It Baby	25
65	Decca F 12204	Hurt Me If You Will/I'm Leaving	30
66	Fontana TF 664	Work All Day (Sleep All Night)/Going Down Fast	35
85	Bam Caruso OPRA 037	LIVE AT THE BEAT SCENE CLUB (EP)	10

(see also Creation)

MARK FIVE
64	Fontana TF 513	Baby What's Wrong/Tango	30

PIGMEAT MARKHAM
68	Chess CRS 8077	Here Comes The Judge/The Trial	5
68	Chess CRS 8085	Sock It To 'Em Judge/The Hip Judge	5

ALFRED MARKS
68	RCA RCA 1777	My Young Visitors And Me/When I Wed Miss Ethel Montiche	4

GUY MARKS
68	Stateside SS 2107	Loving You Has Made Me Bananas/Forgive Me My Love	4

MARKSMEN
63	Parlophone R 5075	Smersh/Orbit Three	10

(see also Mark Rogers & Marksmen, Houston Wells & Marksmen)

BOB MARLEY/WAILERS
63	Island WI 088	Judge Not/Do You Still Love Me (as Robert Marley)	100
63	Island WI 128	ERNEST RANGLIN: Exodus/ROBERT MARLEY: One Cup Of Coffee	60
65	Island WI 188	It Hurts To Be Alone/Mr. Talkative	30
65	Island WI 206	Playboy/Your Love	30
65	Island WI 211	PETER ROSH: Hoot Nanny Hoot (actually by Peter Tosh)/BOB MARLEY: Do You Remember	30
65	Island WI 212	Maga Dog/Hooligan	30
65	Island WI 215	Shame And Scandal/The Jerk (as Peter Tosh & Wailers)	35
65	Island WI 216	Donna/Don't Ever Leave Me	30
65	Island WI 254	What's New Pussycat/Where Will I Find	30
65	Ska Beat JB 186	Simmer Down/I Don't Need Your Love	30
65	Ska Beat JB 211	Lonesome Feelings/There She Goes	30
65	Ska Beat JB 226	I Made A Mistake/SOUL BROTHERS: Train To Skaville	30
66	Ska Beat JB 228	Love And Affection/Teenager In Love	30
66	Ska Beat JB 230	And I Love Her/Do It Right	30
66	Ska Beat JB 249	Lonesome Tracks/Sinner Man	30
66	Island WI 260	Jumbie Jamboree/SKATALITES: Independent Anniversary Ska (Girl Like You)	30
66	Island WI 268	Put It On (Feel The Spirit)/Love Won't Be Mine	30
66	Island WI 3001	He Who Feels It Knows It/Sunday Morning	30
66	Island WI 3009	Let Him Go (Rude Boy Get Bail)/Sinner Man (B-side matrix WI-3009B+)	30
66	Island WI 3009	Let Him Go (Rude Boy Get Bail)/BABA BROOKS track (B-side matrix WI-3009 B+2)	30
66	Rio R 116	Dancing Shoes/Don't Look Back	25
66	Doctor Bird DB 1013	Rude Boy/ROLANDO AL & SOUL BROTHERS: Ringo's Theme (This Boy)	30
66	Doctor Bird DB 1021	Good Good Rudie (Jailhouse)/CITY SLICKERS: Oceans II	30
66	Doctor Bird DB 1039	Rasta Put It On/ROLAND AL & SOUL BROTHERS: Ska With Ringo	25
67	Island WI 3035	Baby I Need You/KEN BOOTHE: I Don't Want To See You Cry	25
67	Island WI 3042	PETER TOUCH & WAILERS: I Am The Toughest/MARCIA GRIFFITHS: No Faith	25
67	Island WI 3043	Bend Down Low/Freedom Time	30
67	Coxsone CS 7021	Oh My Darling/HAMLINS: Trying To Keep A Good Man Down	25
67	Doctor Bird DB 1091	Nice Time/Hypocrite	30
67	Studio One SO 2010	Have Faith In The Lord (as Bob Marley & Heavenly Sisters)/JOE HIGGS: Dinah	30
67	Studio One SO 2024	NORMA FRAZER: Come By Here/I Stand Predominate (as Bob Marley/Wailers)	30
68	Fab FAB 41	Burial/Bus Them Shut (white label only)	60
68	Trojan TR 617	Stir It Up/This Train	25
70	Bamboo BAM 55	JOHN HOLT: A Stranger In Love/WAILERS: Jailhouse (Good Rudy)	15

(all the above singles are credited to Wailers unless stated)

70	Trojan TR 7759	Soul Shake Down Party/BEVERLY ALLSTARS: Version	15
70	Escort ERT 842	Run For Cover/To The Rescue	15
70	Upsetter US 340	My Cup/LEE PERRY & WAILERS: Son Of Thunder	15
70	Upsetter US 342	Version Of Cup (as Bob Marley)/UPSETTERS: Version Of Cup	15
71	Upsetter US 348	Duppy Conqueror (some copies play Dave Barker's "Upsetting Station", £8)/UPSETTERS: Dig Your Grave	15
71	Upsetter US 354	Mr Brown/UPSETTERS: Dracula	15
71	Upsetter US 356	Kaya/UPSETTERS: Version	15
71	Upsetter US 357	Small Axe/All In One	15
71	Upsetter US 368	Picture On The Wall (as Rass Dawkins & Wailers)/UPSETTERS: Version	12
71	Upsetter US 369	More Axe (as Bob Marley)/UPSETTERS: Axe Man	15
71	Upsetter US 371	Dreamland (as Wailers)/UPSETTERS: Version	15
71	Upsetter US 372	More Axe (as Bob Marley, different version)/UPSETTERS: Axe Man	15
71	Jackpot JP 730	Mr Chatterbox/Walk Through The World	12
71	Bullet BU 464	Soultown/Let The Sun Shine On Me	15
71	Bullet BU 493	Lick Samba/Samba	15
71	Punch PH 69	Small Axe/DAVE BARKER: What A Confusion	15
71	Punch PH 77	Down Presser (as Wailers)/JUNIOR BYLES: Got The Tip	15
71	Summit SUM 8526	Stop The Train/Caution (as Wailers)	15
71	Green Door GD 4005	Trench Town Rock/Grooving Kingston 12	15
71	Green Door GD 4022	Lively Yourself Up/TOMMY McCOOK: Lively	15
72	Upsetter US 392	Keep On Moving/African Herbsman	15
72	CBS 8114	Reggae On Broadway/Oh Lord, I Got To Get There (as Wailers)	10
72	Green Door GD 4025	Guava Jelly/Redder Than Red	15
72	Unity UN 562	Duppy Conqueror/UPSETTERS: Duppy Conqueror (Version)	15
73	Punch PH 101	Screw Face/Face Man	15
73	Punch PH 102	Lively Up Yourself/TOMMY McCOOK: Version	15
73	Supreme SUP 216	I Like It Like This (as Bob Marley)/(other artist)	40
73	Blue Mountain 1021	Baby We've Got A Date/Stop That Train	8

Bob MARLEY/WAILERS

73	Island WIP 6164	Concrete Jungle/Reincarnated Soul (as Wailers) 5
73	Island WIP 6167	Get Up, Stand Up/Slave Driver (as Wailers) 5
74	Trojan TR 7911	Soul Shake Down Party/Caution 6
74	Trojan TR 7926	Mr Brown/Version 6
75	Island WIP 6212	Natty Dread/So Jah Seh 5
75	Island WIP 6265	Jah Live/Concrete 5
75	Island WIP 6296	Johnny Was (Woman Hang Her Head Up And Cry)/Cry To Me 4
76	Island WIP 6309	Roots Rock Reggae/Stir It Up 4
76	Island WIP 6478	Stir It Up/Rat Race (withdrawn, demos only) 15
76	Trojan TR 7979	Mr Brown/Trench Town Rock 5

(all the above singles are credited to Bob Marley & Wailers unless stated)

71	Trojan TBL 126	SOUL REBEL (LP) 35
73	Trojan TRL 62	AFRICAN HERBSMAN (LP) 30
72	Island ILPS 9241	CATCH A FIRE (LP) 25
73	Island ILPS 9256	BURNIN' (LP) 20
74	Trojan TRLS 89	RASTA REVOLUTION (LP, reissue of TBL 126 with 2 extra tracks) 20
78	Island ISLD 11	BABYLON BY BUS (2-LP with free live 12" single "War"/"No More Trouble"/
		"Exodus" [Island IPR 2026]) 15
84	Island PBMW 1	LEGEND — THE BEST OF BOB MARLEY (LP, picture disc) 10

(see also Peter Tosh, Rita Marley, Ernest Ranglin, Interns)

RITA MARLEY

67	Rio RIO 108	Pied Piper/It's Alright 10

(see also Soulettes)

MICKI MARLO

54	Capitol CL 14086	Loves Like That/I'm Gonna Rock-Rock-Rock (78) 8
55	Capitol CL 14271	Prize Of Gold/Foolish Notion 8
57	London HL 8481	That's Right/What You've Done To Me (B-side with Paul Anka) 20
57	London HL 8481	That's Right/What You've Done To Me (B-side with
		Paul Anka) (78) 5

(see also Paul Anka)

MARLON

74	Purple PUR 120	Let's Go To The Disco/Broken Man 4

JOHN MARLON

81	Situation 2 SIT 12	Sister Soul/Turn The Lights Out (p/s) 4

MARION MARLOWE

56	London HLA 8306	The Hands Of Time/Ring, Phone, Ring (withdrawn) 50

MARMALADE

66	CBS 202340	It's All Leading Up To Saturday Night/Wait A Minute Baby 5
67	CBS 202643	Can't Stop Now/There Ain't No Use In Hangin' On 4
67	CBS 2948	I See The Rain/Laughing Man 8
67	CBS 3088	Man In A Shop/Cry 5
68	CBS 3412	Lovin' Things/Hey Joe 4
68	CBS 3708	Wait For Me Mary Anne/Mess Around 4
68	CBS 3892	Ob-La-Di, Ob-La-Da/Chains 4
69	CBS 4287	Baby Make It Soon/Time Is On My Side 4
69	CBS 4615	Butterfly/I Shall Be Released 4
68	CBS 63414	THERE'S A LOT OF IT ABOUT (LP) 12
70	Decca LK/SKL 5047	REFLECTIONS OF THE MARMALADE (LP) 10
71	Decca SKL 5111	SONGS (LP) 10

(see also Dean Ford & Gaylords, Gaylords)

MARQUIS DE SADE

82	Out Of Town HOOT 8	Crystal Grieff/Vampire Affair (p/s) 5

MARQUIS OF KENSINGTON

67	Immediate IM 052	Changing Of The Guard/Reverse Thrust 15

HANK MARR

60	Blue Beat BB 26	Tonk Game/Hob-Nobbin 7

STEVE MARRIOTT

63	Decca F 11619	Give Her My Regards/Imaginary Love 60
75	Aura AUS 145	Wha'cha Gonna Do About It/All Shook Up 4
76	A&M AMS 7230	Star In My Life/Midnight Rollin' 4
76	A&M AMLH 64572	MARRIOTT (LP) 10

(see also Small Faces, Humble Pie)

M/A/R/R/S

87	4AD BAD 707R	Pump Up The Volume (Remix)/Anitina (The First Time I See She Dance)
		(Remix) (12", p/s) 7
87	4AD CAD 707R	Pump Up The Volume (Remix)/Anitina/Pump Up The Volume/Anitina
		(The First Time I See She Dance) (Remix) (CD, gatefold p/s) 8

(see also A.R. Kane, Colourbox)

BETTY MARS

72	Columbia DB 8879	Come-Comedie/Mon Café Russe (LP) 7

JOHNNY MARS

81	Ace NS 73	Born Under A Bad Sign/Horses And Places/Mighty Mars (p/s, unissued) 5
72	Polydor 2460 168	BLUES FROM MARS (LP) 12

BERNIE MARSDEN

81	Parlophone R 6047	Sad Clown/You And Me (p/s) 4
81	Parlophone R 6050	Look At Me Now/Always Love You So (p/s) 4
81	Parlophone R 6052	Shakey Ground/After All This Madness (p/s) 4
82	Parlophone R 6053	Thunder And Lightning/Bylbo's Shack (p/s) 4

(see also Jon Lord, Whitesnake, Cozy Powell, Jack Bruce)

BERYL MARSDEN

63	Decca F 11707	I Know/I Only Care About You 6
64	Decca F 11819	When The Lovelight Starts Shining Through His Eyes/Love Is Going To Happen To Me 8
65	Columbia DB 7718	Who You Gonna Hurt?/Gonna Make Him My Baby 7
65	Columbia DB 7797	Music Talk/Break-A-Way 8
66	Columbia DB 7888	What's She Got/Let's Go Somewhere 7

(see also Shotgun Express, She Trinity)

GERRY MARSDEN

67	CBS 2784	Please Let Them Be/I'm Not Blue 8
67	CBS 2946	Gilbert Green/What Makes Me Love You 8
68	CBS 3575	Liverpool/Charlie Girl (as Gerry Marsden & Derek Nimmo) 8
68	NEMS 56-3831	In The Year Of April/Every Day 4
69	NEMS 56-4229	Every Little Minute/In Days Of Old 4
71	Decca F 13172	I've Got My Ukelele/What A Day 4

(see also Gerry & Pacemakers)

MARSEILLE

78	Mountain BON 1	The French Way/Cold Steel 4
79	Mountain BON 2	Over And Over/You're A Woman/Can Can 4
79	Mountain TOP 39	Kiss Like Rock'n'Roll/Can Can 4
79	Mountain TOP 49	Bring On The Dancing Girls/Rock Me Tonight 4
80	Mountain TOP 51	Kites/Some Like It Hot 4
84	Ultra Noise WALK 1	Walking On A Highwire/Too Late 4
76	Mountain TOPC 5012	RED WHITE AND SLIGHTLY BLUE (LP) 10
79	Mountain TOPS 125	MARSEILLE (LP) 10
84	Ultra Noise ULTRA 3	TOUCH THE NIGHT (LP) 10

(see also Paul Dale)

STEVIE MARSH

59	Decca F 11181	If You Were The Only Boy In The World/Leave Me Alone 6
60	Decca F 11209	You Don't Have To Tell Me (I Know)/Wish 4
60	Decca F 11244	A Girl In Love/Over And Done With 4
62	Ember EMB S 139	I Shouldn't Be Kissing You/Time And Time Again 4

JACK MARSHALL ORCHESTRA & CHORUS

58	Capitol CL 14888	Thunder Road Chase/Finger Poppin' 10

JOY MARSHALL

66	Decca F 12422	The More I See You/Taste Of Honey 4

LARRY MARSHALL

67	Doctor Bird DB 1008	Snake InThe Grass/ROLAND ALPHONSO: V.C. 10 10
67	Blue Beat BB 374	Move Your Feet/Find A New Baby 10
67	Blue Beat BB 380	Suspicion/Broken Heart 10
68	Caltone TONE 126	No One To Give Me Love/PHIL PRATT: Safe Travel 10
70	Bamboo BAM 22	Girl Of My Dreams/SOUND DIMENSON: Give It Away 5
70	Bamboo BAM 52	Man From Galilee/Give It Away (as Larry Marshall & Enid Cumberland) .. 5
70	Bamboo BAM 61	Let's Make It Up/BURNING SPEAR: Free 5
70	Banana BA 300	Stay A Little Longer/MAYTALLS: He'll Provide 5
71	Banana BA 364	Maga Dog/OSSIE ROBINSON: Ecomomical Heatwave 5

(see also Larry & Alvin)

LOIS MARSHALL

59	HMV ALP 1671	BRITISH FOLK SONGS (LP) 10

MARSHALL-HAIN

78	Harvest SHSP 4087	FREE RIDE (LP) 10

MARSHMALLOW WAY

69	United Artists UP 35031	C'mon Kitty Kitty/Michigan Mints 4

MARSHMELLOW HIGHWAY

68	London HLR 10204	I Don't Wanna Live This Way/Loving You Makes Everything Alright .. 4

MARSUPILAMI

70	Transatlantic TRA 213	MARSUPILAMI (LP) 40
71	Transatlantic TRA 230	ARENA (LP) 55

LENA MARTELL

61	HMV POP 958	Love Can Be/The Night The Sky Fell Down 4
62	HMV POP 1049	The Reasons Why/To This Man 4
63	HMV POP 1152	Let The Music Play/One Boy 4
63	HMV POP 1214	I Wish You Well/Arriverderci Not Addio 4
64	Decca F 11978	I'm A Fool To Want You/All Cried Out 4

PIERA MARTELL

74	CBS SCBS 2293	My Ship Of Love/Mein Ruf Nach Dir 12

MARTELLS

66	Decca F 12463	Time To Say Goodnight/The Cherry Song 7

RALPH MARTERIE & HIS ORCHESTRA

53	Oriole CB 1199	Crazy Man, Crazy/Go Away (78) 8
54	Mercury MB 3176	Dig That Crazy Santa Claus/Rock, Rock (78) 8
54	Mercury MB 3186	Kiss Crazy Baby/Bongo Guitar (78) 6
55	Mercury MB 3220	Chicken Boogie/Silver Moon (78) 6
57	Mercury 7MT 138	Guaglione/Carla 6
57	Mercury 7MT 158	Tricky/Shish-Kebab 6
58	Mercury 7MT 204	Tequila/Pop Corn 6
58	Mercury 7MT 213	Night Stroll/Trombone Blues 6
58	Mercury 7MT 232	Cha-Hua-Hua/Torero 6

Ralph MARTERIE & HIS ORCHESTRA

58	Mercury AMT 1009	Pretend Cha Cha/Flighty	4
59	Mercury AMT 1042	Compulsion/Words Of Love	4
59	Mercury AMT 1056	Wampum/Cleopatra's Dream	4
59	Mercury AMT 1074	In The Mood/Bwana	4
57	Mercury MEP 9510	HIT PARADE VOL. 2 (EP)	12
57	Mercury MEP 9517	PRESENTING RALPH MARTERIE (EP)	15
58	Mercury MEP 9532	YOUR CHOICE NO. 2 (EP)	12
59	Mercury ZEP 10001	IT'S CHA CHA TIME (EP)	8
60	Mercury ZEP 10068	MUSIC FOR A PRIVATE EYE (EP)	7

MARTHA & MUFFINS

79	DinDisc DIN 4	Insect Love/Cheesies And Gum (gatefold p/s in bag)	4
80	DinDisc DIN 19	About Insomnia/1 4 6 (p/s, green vinyl)	4

MARTHA (REEVES) & VANDELLAS

63	Oriole CBA 1814	I'll Have To Let Him Go/My Baby Won't Come Back	250
63	Oriole CBA 1819	Come And Get These Memories/Jealous Lover	80
63	Stateside SS 228	Heatwave/A Love Like Yours (Don't Come Knockin' Every Day)	35
64	Stateside SS 250	Quicksand/Darling, I Hum Our Song	35
64	Stateside SS 272	Livewire/Old Love (Let's Try It Again)	18
64	Stateside SS 305	In My Lonely Room/A Tear For The Girl	35
64	Stateside SS 345	Dancing In The Street/There He Is (At My Door)	12
65	Stateside SS 383	Wild One/Dancing Slow	15
65	Tamla Motown TMG 502	Nowhere To Run/Motoring	8
65	Tamla Motown TMG 530	You've Been In Love Too Long/Love (Makes Me Do Foolish Things)	15
66	Tamla Motown TMG 549	My Baby Loves Me/Never Leave Your Baby's Side	10
66	Tamla Motown TMG 567	What Am I Going To Do Without Your Love/Go Ahead And Laugh	10
66	Tamla Motown TMG 582	I'm Ready For Love/He Doesn't Love Her Anymore	7
67	Tamla Motown TMG 599	Jimmy Mack/Third Finger, Left Hand	5
67	Tamla Motown TMG 621	Love Bug Leave My Heart Alone/One Way Out	7
68	Tamla Motown TMG 636	Honey Chile/Show Me The Way	5
68	Tamla Motown TMG 657	I Promise To Wait, My Love/Forget Me Not	7
68	Tamla Motown TMG 669	I Can't Dance To That Music You're Playing/I Tried	6
69	Tamla Motown TMG 684	Dancing In The Street/Quicksand	4
69	Tamla Motown TMG 694	Nowhere To Run/Livewire	4
71	Tamla Motown TMG 762	Forget Me Not/I Gotta Let You Go	4
71	Tamla Motown TMG 794	Bless You/Hope I Don't Get My Heart Broke	4
65	Tamla Motown TME 2009	MARTHA AND THE VANDELLAS (EP)	50
66	Tamla Motown TME 2017	HITTIN' (EP)	50
63	Oriole PS 40052	COME AND GET THESE MEMORIES (LP)	75
65	Tamla Motown TML 11005	HEATWAVE (LP)	30
65	Tamla Motown TML 11013	DANCE PARTY (LP)	45
67	T. Motown (S)TML 11040	GREATEST HITS (LP)	12
67	T. Motown (S)TML 11051	WATCH OUT! (LP)	25
68	T. Motown (S)TML 11078	RIDIN' HIGH (LP)	12
69	T. Motown (S)TML 11099	DANCING IN THE STREET (LP)	12
70	T. Motown (S)TML 11134	SUGAR N' SPICE (LP)	10
70	T. Motown STML 11166	NATURAL RESOURCES (LP)	10

(see also Martha Reeves)

MARTIKA

89	CBS 6552947	I Feel The Earth Move/Alibis (p/s, with 2 badges)	4
89	CBS 6552940	I Feel The Earth Move/Alibis (picture disc)	4
90	CBS 6555260	MORE THAN YOU KNOW (EP, foldout poster p/s)	4

MARTIN

68	Coxsone CS 7056	I Second That Emotion (actually by Martin Riley)/ROY TOMLINSON: I Stand For I	12

ALAN MARTIN

63	Rio R 3	The Party/Indeed	7
63	Rio R 6	You Came Late/Dreaming	7
63	Rio R 9	Secretly/Fame And Fortune	7
63	Rio R 10	Mother Brother/Tell Me	7
65	Rio R 66	Must Know I Love You/VIC BROWN'S COMBO: Rio Special	7
65	Rio R 67	Sweet Rosemarie/HONEY DUCKERS: Banjo Man	7
65	Rio R 68	Why Must I Cry/Shirley I Love You	7
65	Rio R 74	Since I Married Dorothy/You Promised Me	7
66	Rio R 94	Days Are Lonely/My Baby	7
66	Rio R 96	Rome Wasn't Built In A Day/I'm Hurt	7

BARRY MARTIN

61	RCA RCA 1234	Little Lonely One/Are You Sure	5

BILL MARTIN

68	Page One POF 067	Private Scotty Grant/Singing Vietnam Blues	4

CHRIS MARTIN

59	HMV POP 664	Lonely Street/Swing A Little Lover	4
60	HMV POP 692	I Don't Regret A Thing/Point Of No Return	4

DAVE MARTIN

64	Port-O-Jam PJ 4112	Let Them Fight/OSSIE IRVING SIX: Why I Love You	7
64	Port-O-Jam PJ 4115	All My Dreams/Take Your Belongings	7

DEAN MARTIN

52	Vogue V 9040	Santa Lucia/Hold Me (78)	8
53	Capitol CL 13893	Kiss/There's My Lover (78)	5
53	Capitol CL 14008	That's Amore/You're The Right One (78)	5
54	Capitol CL 14123	Hey Brother Pour The Wine/I'd Cry Like A Baby	16
54	Capitol CL 14138	Sway/Pretty As A Picture	18
54	Capitol CL 14150	Ev'ry Street's A Boulevard (with Jerry Lewis)/How Do You Speak To An Angel?	12

54	Capitol CL 14170	The Peddlar Man (Ten I Loved)/Try Again	12
54	Capitol CL 14180	One More Time/If I Could Sing Like Bing	12
55	Capitol CL 14215	Long, Long Ago/Open Up The Doghouse (Two Cats Are Trying To Get In) (with Nat 'King' Cole)	14
55	Capitol CL 14226	Let Me Go, Lover/The Naughty Lady Of Shady Lane	15
55	Capitol CL 14227	Mambo Italiano/That's All I Want From You	15
55	Capitol CL 14253	Belle From Barcelona/Confused	12
55	Capitol CL 14255	Under The Bridges Of Paris/What Could Be More Beautiful	12
55	Capitol CL 14311	Chee Chee-Oo (Sang The Little Bird)/Ridin' Into Love	12
55	Capitol CL 14356	Relax-Ay-Voo/Two Sleepy People (as Dean Martin & Line Renaud)	12
55	Capitol CL 14367	Simpatico/Love Is All That Matters	12
55	Capitol CL 14370	In Napoli/I Like Them All	12
		(all the above singles originally came with triangular centres, round centre reissues are worth around half the value)	
56	Capitol CL 14505	When You Pretend/The Lucky Song	6
56	Capitol CL 14507	Innamorata/You Look So Familiar	8
56	Capitol CL 14519	Young And Foolish/Just One More Chance	8
56	Capitol CL 14523	Memories Are Made Of This/Change Of Heart	12
56	Capitol CL 14586	Watching The World Go By/The Lady With The Big Umbrella	6
56	Capitol CL 14624	The Test Of Time/I'm Gonna Steal You Away	5
56	Capitol CL 14625	Me 'N' You 'N' The Moon/The Wind, The Wind	5
56	Capitol CL 14626	Buckskin Beauty/Pardners (B-side with Jerry Lewis)	5
56	Capitol CL 14656	Give Me A Sign/Mississippi Dreamboat	4
57	Capitol CL 14690	The Man Who Plays The Mandolino/I Know I Can't Forget	6
57	Capitol CL 14714	Bamboozled/Only Trust Your Heart	5
57	Capitol CL 14737	I Never Had A Chance/I Can't Give You Anything But Love	4
57	Capitol CL 14758	Beau James/Write To Me From Naples	4
57	Capitol CL 14782	The Triche Trache/Promise Her Anything	4
57	Capitol CL 14801	The Look/Just Kiss Me	4
57	Capitol CL 14813	Good Mornin' Life/Makin' Love Ukelele Style	4
58	Capitol CL 14844	Return To Me/Forgetting You	6
58	Capitol CL 14890	I'll Gladly Make The Same Mistake Again/Angel Baby	4
58	Capitol CL 14910	Volare (Nel Blu Dipinto Di Blu)/Outta My Mind	6
58	Capitol CL 14943	The Magician/Once Upon A Time (It Happened)	4
59	Capitol CL 14990	You Were Made For Love/It Takes So Long (To Say Goodbye)	4
59	Capitol CL 15015	Rio Bravo/My Rifle, My Pony And Me	7
59	Capitol CL 15039	You Can't Love 'Em All/On An Evening In Roma	4
59	Capitol CL 15064	Maybe/Ain't Gonna Lead This Life	4
59	Capitol CL 15102	(Love Is A) Career/For You	4
60	Capitol CL 15127	Love Me, My Love/Who Was That Lady?	4
60	Capitol CL 15145	Napoli/Buttercup A Golden Hair	4
60	Capitol CL 15155	Just In Time/Humdinger	4
60	Capitol CL 15172	Sogni D'Oro (Golden Dreams)/How Sweet It Is	4
61	Capitol CL 15188	Sparklin' Eyes/Tu Sei Bella, Signoria	4
61	Capitol CL 15198	Bella Bella Bambina/All In A Night's Work	4
61	Capitol CL 15209	The Story Of Life/Giuggiola	4
61	Capitol CL 15294	Cha Cha Cha D'Amour/I Wish You Love	4
64	Capitol CL 15363	Somebody Loves You/Hundred Years From Today	4
64	Reprise R 20281	Everybody Loves Somebody Sometime/Little Voice	4
70	Reprise R 20893	Down Home/Come On Down	4
55	Capitol EAP7 9123	DEAN MARTIN (EP)	15
56	Capitol EAP 1007	SWINGING DOWN YONDER NO. 1 (EP)	8
56	Capitol EAP 1022	SWINGING DOWN YONDER NO. 2 (EP)	8
56	Capitol EAP 1033	DEAN MARTIN AND JERRY LEWIS (EP, with Jerry Lewis)	7
56	Capitol EAP 1037	SWINGING DOWN YONDER NO. 3 (EP)	8
55	Capitol EAP1 481	SUNNY ITALY (EP)	10
57	Capitol EAP1 806	HOLLYWOOD OR BUST — FILM SELECTION (EP)	8
57	Capitol EAP1 840	TEN THOUSAND BEDROOMS — FILM SELECTION (EP)	8
57	Capitol EAP1 939	RETURN TO ME (EP)	7
58	Capitol EAP1 1027	VOLARE (EP)	7
60	Capitol EAP1 1285	A WINTER ROMANCE (EP)	8
60	Capitol EAP2 1285	A WINTER ROMANCE (EP)	8
60	Capitol EAP3 1285	A WINTER ROMANCE (EP)	8
61	Capitol EAP1 20072	RELAXING WITH DEAN MARTIN (EP)	8
61	Capitol EAP1 20124	DEAN MARTIN IN MOVIELAND (EP)	10
61	Capitol EAP1 20152	I'M YOURS (EP)	10
62	Capitol EAP6 1702	SOMEBODY LOVES YOU (EP)	7
62	Capitol EAP7 1702	CHA CHA D'AMOUR (EP)	7
60s	Reprise	EPs	5-6
53	Capitol LC 6590	CAPITOL PRESENTS (10" LP)	40
56	Britone LP 1002	DEAN MARTIN SINGS/NICOLINI LUCCHESI PLAYS (10" LP)	50
57	Capitol T 849	PRETTY BABY (LP)	15
58	Capitol T 1047	THIS IS DEAN MARTIN! (LP)	14
59	Capitol (S)T 1150	SLEEP WARM (LP, orchestra conducted by Frank Sinatra, mono/stereo)	12/14
61	Capitol (S)T 1442	THIS TIME I'M SWINGIN'! (LP, mono/stereo)	12/14
62	Capitol (S)T 1659	DINO (LP, mono/stereo)	12/14
62	Reprise R(9) 6021	FRENCH STYLE (LP, mono/stereo)	12/14
63	Reprise R 6061	DEAN (TEX) MARTIN COUNTRY STAR (LP)	15
64	Reprise R 6085	DEAN (TEX) MARTIN RIDES AGAIN (LP)	15
60s	Reprise	other LPs	10-12
67	Stateside S(S)L 10201	LOVE IS A CAREER (LP)	12
		(see also Line Renaud & Dean Martin)	

DEREK MARTIN

64	Sue WI 308	Daddy Rolling Stone/Don't Put Me Down Like This (credited as Derak Martin)	15
65	Columbia DB 7694	You Better Go/You Know	18
68	Stax 601 039	Soul Power/Sly Girl	15

DON MARTIN & DANDY (& SUPERBOYS)
67	Giant GN 6	Got A Feelin'/CONNECTIONS: At The Junction	5
68	Giant GN 24	Keep On Fighting/Rock Steady Boogie (with Superboys)	4

(see also Dandy & Superboys)

GEORGE MARTIN & HIS ORCHESTRA
64	Parlophone R 5135	I Saw Her Standing There/All My Loving	7
64	Parlophone R 5166	And I Love Her/Ringo's Theme (This Boy)	8
65	Parlophone R 5222	All Quiet On The Mersey Front/Out Of The Picture	5
65	Parlophone R 5256	I Feel Fine/The Niagara Theme	6
65	Parlophone R 5375	Yesterday/Another Girl	6
66	United Artists UP 1154	By George! — It's The David Frost Theme/Double Scotch	5
66	United Artists UP 1165	Love In The Open Air/Theme From "The Family Way"	15
67	United Artists UP 1194	Theme One/Elephants And Castles	10
65	Parlophone GEP 8930	MUSIC FROM "A HARD DAY'S NIGHT" (EP)	18
64	Parlophone PMC 1227	OFF THE BEATLE TRACK (LP, also stereo PCS 3057)	25
65	Columbia SX 1775	PLAYS HELP! (LP, mono)	15
65	Studio Two TWO 102	PLAYS HELP! (LP, stereo)	15
66	United Artists (S)ULP 1157	INSTRUMENTALLY SALUTES THE BEATLES GIRLS (LP)	20
66	Studio Two TWO 141	AND I LOVE HER (LP)	15
67	Decca (S)KL 4847	THE FAMILY WAY (LP)	70
68	United Artists (S)ULP 1196	BRITISH MAID (LP)	15
70	Sunset SLS 50182	BY GEORGE! (LP)	10
73	United Artists UAS 29475	LIVE AND LET DIE (LP, soundtrack)	10
74	Polydor Super 2383 304	BEATLES TO BOND AND BACH (LP)	10
78	St. Michael IMP 105	BEATLES TO BOND AND BACH (LP, available through Marks & Spencer)	20

(see also Beatles)

GRADY MARTIN & SLEWFOOT FIVE
56	Brunswick 05535	Nashville/Don't Take Your Love From Me	12

HONEYBOY MARTIN & VOICES
67	Caltone TONE 103	Dreader Than Dread/DANDY: In The Mood	10

IRVING MARTIN
(see under Martin's Magic Sounds)

JANIS MARTIN
60	Palette PG 9000	Here Today And Gone Tomorrow Love/Hard Times Ahead	25

JEAN MARTIN
63	Decca F 11751	Ain't Gonna Kiss Ya/Three Times Three Is Love	4
64	Decca F 11897	Save The Last Dance For Me/Will You Still Love Me Tomorrow	4

JERRY MARTIN
63	London HLU 9692	Shake-A Take-A/Exchange Student	5

KERRY MARTIN
58	Parlophone R 4449	Stroll Me/Cold Hands, Warm Heart	6

LINDA MARTIN
84	CBS A 4456	Terminal 3/(Feels Like) Walking In My Sleep (p/s)	4

LUCIA MARTIN
62	Parlophone R 4915	Big Jim/Star From Heaven	10

MARILYN MARTIN
86	Atlantic A 9465P	Night Moves/Wildest Dreams (shaped picture disc with plinth)	6

(see also Phil Collins & Marilyn Martin)

MARK MARTIN
67	Page One POF 020	Extraordinary Girl/Love Could Be Like Hell	6

MILES MARTIN FOLK GROUP
71	Amber	MILES MARTIN FOLK GROUP (LP, private pressing)	100

MILLICENT MARTIN
58	Columbia DB 4171	Our Language Of Love/Seriously	4
60	Columbia DB 4466	Tintarella Di Luna/I Can Dream, Can't I?	4

MOON MARTIN
79	Capitol 12CL 16076	Victim Of Romance (live)/Hot Night In Dallas (12")	7

(see also Southwind)

PAUL MARTIN
67	Sue WI 4041	Snake In The Grass/I've Got A New Love	15

RAY MARTIN (& HIS) CONCERT ORCHESTRA
53	Columbia SCM 5001	Blue Tango/Belle Of The Ball	8
53	Columbia SCM 5002	The Waltzing Cat/The Marching Strings	6
53	Columbia SCM 5063	Swedish Rhapsody/Hi-Lili, Hi-Lo	8
54	Columbia SCM 5107	Strings On Parade/"Story Of Three Loves" Theme	4
56	Columbia SCM 5240	Lisbon Antigua/Glamorous Night	6
56	Columbia SCM 5264	The Carousel Waltz/Port Au Prince	6
59	Columbia SCD 2123	The Carousel Waltz/Port Au Prince (reissue)	5
56	Columbia SEG 7639	IT'S GREAT TO BE YOUNG — FILM MUSIC (EP)	8
53	Columbia 33S 1011	MUSIC IN THE RAY MARTIN MANNER VOL. 1 (10" LP)	10
54	Columbia 33S 1021	MUSIC IN THE RAY MARTIN MANNER VOL. 2 (10" LP)	10

(see also Ray Burns)

RICKY MARTIN & TYME MACHINE
68	Olga OLE 4	Something Else/Blue Suede Shoes	6

RODGE MARTIN
67	Polydor 56725	When She Touches Me/Lovin' Machine	8

RON MARTIN & JUBILEE STOMPERS
| 68 | Doctor Bird DB 1151 | Give Your Love To Me/I Cry My Heart .... 6 |

SARAH MARTIN
24	Parlophone E 5235	Graveyard Dream Blues/A Green Gal Can't Catch On Blues (78) 50
30s	Parlophone R 3506	Cushion Foot Stomp/Take Your Black Bottom Outside (78) 40
50s	Jazz Collector L 105	Death String Blues/Mistreating Man Blues (as Margaret Johnson) (78) 8

SETH MARTIN
| 68 | Page One POF 073 | Another Day Goes By/Look At Me ....6 |
| 69 | Page One POF 134 | What A Lovely Way To Spend Forever ....4 |

SHANE MARTIN
| 68 | CBS 2894 | You're So Young/I Need You ....120 |

SKIP MARTIN VIDEO ALL-STARS
| 60 | Golden Guinea GGL 0060 | TV JAZZ THEMES (LP, also stereo GGLS 10060) ....10 |

STEVE MARTIN
56	Columbia SCM 5212	Only You/Lola 6
58	Philips PB 820	Stairway Of Love/Chanson D'Amour 4
58	Philips PB 853	The Man Inside/Blue-Eyes Sue 4

TONY MARTIN
53	HMV 7M 105	Tenement Symphony (both sides) 10
53	HMV 7M 136	The Golden Years/April In Portugal 8
53	HMV 7M 137	Please, Please/You're So Dangerous 8
53	HMV 7M 158	Unfair/Sorta On The Border 8
54	HMV 7M 203	Here/I Could Write A Book 7
54	HMV 7M 210	That's What A Rainy Day Is For/Look Out, I'm Romantic 6
54	HMV 7M 254	Uno/Let's Try Again 6
54	HMV 7M 258	I Love Paris/Boulevard Of Nightingales 6
55	HMV 7M 283	My Bambina/Angels In The Sky 6
55	HMV 7M 302	Stranger In Paradise/Vera Cruz 12
55	HMV 7M 320	Domani/What's The Time In Nicaragua 6
56	HMV 7M 376	Just A Gigolo/Love, You Funny Thing 6
56	HMV 7M 414	Walk Hand In Hand/Flamenco Love 8
56	HMV 7MC 41	Walk Hand In Hand/Flamenco Love (export issue) 10
56	HMV POP 257	It's Better In The Dark/Your Place In The Sun 6
57	HMV POP 282	All Of You/Moderation 6
57	HMV POP 319	The Rainmaker/My Budapest 5
57	RCA RCA 1002	The Man From Idaho/One Is A Lonely Number 4
59	RCA RCA 1101	She Is Not Thinking Of Me/GOGI GRANT: Say A Prayer For Me Tonight 4
63	HMV 7P 314	Tenement Symphony (both sides, reissue) 4
65	Stateside SS 394	Talkin' To Your Picture/Our Rhapsody 60
65	Tamla Motown TMG 537	The Bigger Your Heart Is (The Harder You'll Fall)/The Two Of Us 40
67	RCA RCA 1582	This Year/Sand Pebbles 4
54	HMV 7EG 8006	TONY MARTIN (EP) 7
55	HMV 7EG 8124	TENEMENT SYMPHONY (EP) 7
57	HMV 7EG 8205	THE DESERT SONG — SOUNDTRACK EXCERPTS (EP) 7
58	RCA RCX 130	SONGS FROM CINDERELLA (EP) 7
55	Brunswick LA 8713	TONY MARTIN SINGS VOL. 1 (10" LP) 20
56	Mercury MPT 7005	TONY MARTIN FAVOURITES (10" LP) 20
57	Mercury MPT 7516	DREAM MUSIC (10" LP) 18
57	HMV DLP 1137	SPEAK TO ME OF LOVE (10" LP) 15
57	RCA RD 27003	A NIGHT AT THE COPACABANA (LP) 10
61	London HA-D 2341	TONY MARTIN'S GREATEST HITS (LP) 10
65	Stateside SL 10113	AT CARNEGIE HALL (LP) 10
	(see also Gogi Grant)	

TRADE MARTIN
| 63 | London HL 9662 | Hula Hula Dancin' Doll/Something In The Wind ....6 |

VINCE MARTIN (& TARRIERS)
| 56 | London HLN 8340 | Cindy, Oh Cindy/Only If You Praise The Lord (with Tarriers) ....25 |
| 59 | HMV POP 594 | Old Grey Goose (Aunt Rhodie)/Goodnight, Irene (solo) ....4 |

MARTIN & BROWNSHIRTS
| 78 | Lightning GIL 507 | Taxi Driver/Boring ....5 |

MARTIN & DERRICK
61	Blue Beat BB 48	Times Are Going/I Love You Baby 10
62	Island WI 024	Come On/MONTY & CYCLONES: Organisation 10
	(see also Derrick Morgan)	

MARTIN & FINLEY
| 73 | Tamla Motown TMG 867 | It's Another Sunday/Best Friends (withdrawn, demos only) ....80 |

MARTINAS & HIS MUSIC
| 58 | Columbia DB 4223 | Cha Cha Momma Brown/My Bonnie Lies Over The Ocean ....4 |

WINK MARTINDALE
59	London HLD 8962	Deck Of Cards/Now You Know How It Feels 6
59	London HLD 8962	Deck Of Cards/Now You Know How It Feels (78) 10
60	London HLD 9042	Life Gits Tee-Jus Don't It?/I Never See Maggie Alone 5
61	London HLD 9419	Black Land Farmer/Make Him Happy 5
67	Dot DS 26753	The Shifting Whispering Sands/Trees 4
63	London RED 1370	DECK OF CARDS (EP) 15
65	Dot DEP 20000	DECK OF CARDS (EP) 8
60	London HA-D 2240	WINK MARTINDALE (LP) 25

RAY MARTINE
| 63 | Piccadilly NPL 38007 | EAST END — WEST END (LP) ....10 |

TONY MARTINEZ QUINTET

| 54 | HMV 7M 264 | Cucusa Tune Mambo/Bernie's Tune Mambo | 4 |

MIA MARTINI

| 77 | CBS SCBS 5178 | Freedom Is Today/Libera | 5 |

AL MARTINO

52	Capitol CL 13769	Take My Heart/I Never Cared (78)	5
52	Capitol CL 13779	Here In My Heart/I Cried Myself To Sleep (78)	5
52	Capitol CL 13835	Now/Say You'll Wait For Me (78)	5
53	Capitol CL 13879	Rachel/One Lonely Night (78)	5
54	Capitol CL 14128	Wanted/There'll Be No Teardrops Tonight	25/20
54	Capitol CL 14148	On And On (In Love With You)/Give Me Something To Go With The Wine	25/20
54	Capitol CL 14163	The Story Of Tina/Destiny (No One Can Change)	25/20

(prices for the above 45s are first for green labels with triangular centres, then later copies with purple labels)

54	Capitol CL 14192	I Still Believe/When?	18
54	Capitol CL 14202	Not As A Stranger/No One But You	18
55	Capitol CL 14224	Don't Go To Strangers/Say It Again	18
55	Capitol CL 14284	The Snowy, Snowy Mountains/Love Is Eternal	18
55	Capitol CL 14343	The Man From Laramie/To Please My Lady	20
55	Capitol CL 14379	Come Close To Me/Small Talk	15

(all the above 45s originally came with triangular centres, round centre reissues are worth around half these values)

56	Capitol CL 14550	Journey's End/Sound Advice	10
56	Capitol CL 14614	The Girl I Left In Rome/Some Cloud Above	10
57	Capitol CL 14680	I'm Sorry/A Love To Call My Own	10
59	Top Rank JAR 108	I Can't Get You Out Of My Heart/Two Hearts Are Better Than One	8
59	Top Rank JAR 187	Darling I Love You/The Memory Of You	8
60	Top Rank JAR 312	Summertime/I Sold My Heart	6
60	Top Rank JAR 337	Mama/Dearest (Cara)	6
60	Top Rank JAR 418	Why Do I Love You/Sunday	5
60	Ember EMB S 119	Our Concerto/It's All Over But The Crying	5
62	Ember EMB S 147	Darling I Love You/There's No Tomorrow	5
62	Capitol CL 15260	Because You're Mine/Make Me Believe	5
63	Capitol CL 15300	I Love You Because/Merry-Go-Round	5
63	Capitol CL 15314	Painted, Tainted Rose/That's The Way It's Got To Be	5
63	Capitol CL 15324	Living A Lie/I Love You Truly	4
64	Capitol CL 15337	I Love You More And More Each Day/I'm Living My Heaven With You	4
64	Capitol CL 15349	Tears And Roses/A Year Ago Tonight	4
64	Capitol CL 15362	Always Together/Thank You For Loving Me	4
64	Capitol CL 15368	We Could/Sunrise To Sunrise	4
65	Capitol CL 15383	My Heart Would Know/Hush, Hush Sweet Charlotte	4
65	Capitol CL 15390	Somebody Else Is Taking My Place/With All My Heart	4
65	Capitol CL 15406	My Cherie/Ramona	4
65	Capitol CL 15421	Forgive Me/What Now, My Love	4
66	Capitol CL 15430	Spanish Eyes/Melody Of Love (original label)	4
66	Capitol CL 15442	Think I'll Go Somewhere And Cry Myself To Sleep/My Love, Forgive Me (Amore, Scusami)	4
66	Capitol CL 15449	Wiederseh'n/The Minute You're Gone	4
66	Capitol CL 15464	Just Yesterday/By The River Of The Roses	4
66	Capitol CL 15479	The Wheel Of Hurt/Somewhere In This World	4
67	Capitol CL 15490	Daddy's Little Girl/Devolution	4
67	Capitol CL 15504	Mary In The Morning/I Love You And You Love Me	4
67	Capitol CL 15516	More Than The Eye Can See/Red Is Red	4
68	Capitol CL 15528	Glory Of Love/The Voice In The Choir	4
55	Capitol EAP1 405	AL MARTINO SINGS (EP)	18
61	Capitol EAP1 20153	TO PLEASE MY LADY (EP)	10
63	Ember EMB 4528	DARLING I LOVE YOU (EP)	10
63	Capitol EAP4 2107	MARTINO SINGS OF LOVE (EP)	8
64	Capitol EAP1 20590	LOSING YOU (EP)	8
60	Top Rank BUY 030	AL MARTINO (LP)	12
60	Top Rank 25/025	SWING ALONG WITH AL MARTINO (LP)	12
63	Capitol (S)T 1774	THE EXCITING VOICE OF AL MARTINO (LP, mono/stereo)	10/12
63	Capitol (S)T 1914	I LOVE YOU BECAUSE (LP, mono/stereo)	10/12
64	Capitol (S)T 1975	PAINTED, TAINTED ROSE (LP, mono/stereo)	10/12
64	Capitol (S)T 2040	LIVING A LIE (LP, mono/stereo)	8/10
64	Capitol (S)T 2107	AL MARTINO (LP, mono/stereo)	8/10
65	Capitol (S)T 2200	WE COULD (LP, mono/stereo)	8/10
65	Capitol (S)T 2312	SOMEBODY ELSE IS TAKING MY PLACE (LP, mono/stereo)	8/10
66	Capitol (S)T 2362	MY CHERIE (LP, mono/stereo)	8/10
66	Capitol (S)T 2435	SPANISH EYES (LP, mono/stereo)	8/10

MARTIN'S MAGIC SOUNDS

| 67 | Deram DM 141 | Mon Amour, Mon Amour/Midem Melody | 4 |
| 67 | Deram DML/SML 1014 | MARTIN'S MAGIC SOUNDS (LP) | 12 |

JOHN MARTYN

71	Island WIP 6116	May You Never/Just Now	5
77	Island WIP 6385	Over The Hill/Head And Heart	4
78	Island WIP 6414	Dancing/Dealer (Version)	4
80	Island WIP 6547	Johnny Too Bad/Johnny Too Bad (Version)	4
81	Island IPR 2046	Johnny Too Bad (Extended Dub Version)/Big Muff (Extended Mix) (12", promo)	8
82	WEA K 259987-7	Gun Money (US Remix)/Hiss On the Tape (live)	4
86	Island CID 265	Angeline/Tight Connection To My Heart/May You Never/Solid Air/Glistening Glyndebourne (CD, foldout sleeve)	20
67	Island ILP 952	LONDON CONVERSATION (LP, pink or 'palm' label)	20/10
68	Island ILP 991/ILPS 9091	THE TUMBLER (LP, mono/stereo)	14/12
75	Island ILPS 9343	LIVE AT LEEDS (LP, mail-order only, some numbered & signed)	30/20

JOHN & BEVERLEY MARTYN

69	Island WIP 6076	John The Baptist/The Ocean	5
70	Island ILPS 9113	STORMBRINGER (LP)	12
70	Island ILPS 9133	THE ROAD TO RUIN (LP)	12

(see also Beverley)

KID MARTYN

62	77 77LA 12/20	IN NEW ORLEANS WITH KID SHEIK'S BAND (LP)	12

MARVELETTES

61	Fontana H 355	Please Mr Postman/So Long Baby	30
62	Fontana H 386	Twistin' Postman/I Want A Guy	35
62	Oriole CBA 1764	Beechwood 4-5789/Someday Someway	70
63	Oriole CBA 1817	Locking Up My Heart/Forever	250
64	Stateside SS 251	As Long As I Know He's Mine/Little Girl Blue	20
64	Stateside SS 273	He's A Good Guy (Yes He Is)/Goddess Of Love	35
64	Stateside SS 334	You're My Remedy/A Little Bit Of Sympathy, A Little Bit Of Love	25
65	Stateside SS 369	Too Many Fish In The Sea/Need For Love	15
65	Tamla Motown TMG 518	I'll Keep Holding On/No Time For Tears	35
65	Tamla Motown TMG 535	Danger Heartbreak Dead Ahead/Your Cheating Ways	20
66	Tamla Motown TMG 546	Don't Mess With Bill/Anything You Wanna Do	25
66	Tamla Motown TMG 562	You're The One/Paper Boy	20
67	Tamla Motown TMG 594	The Hunter Gets Captured By The Game/I Think I Can Change You	15
67	Tamla Motown TMG 609	When You're Young And In Love/The Day You Take One, You Have To Take The Other	7
68	Tamla Motown TMG 639	My Baby Must Be A Magician/I Need Someone	12
68	Tamla Motown TMG 659	Here I Am Baby/Keep Off, No Trespassing	8
69	Tamla Motown TMG 701	Reachin' For Something I Can't Have/Destination Anywhere	6
73	Tamla Motown TMG 860	Reachin' For Something I Can't Have/Here I Am Baby	4
75	Tamla Motown TMG 1000	Finders Keepers, Losers Weepers/KIM WESTON: Do Like I Do	15
65	Tamla Motown TMG 2003	THE MARVELETTES (EP)	75
65	Tamla Motown TML 11008	THE MARVELLOUS MARVELETTES (LP)	140
67	T. Motown (S)TML 11052	THE MARVELETTES (LP)	40
69	T. Motown (S)TML 11090	SOPHISTICATED SOUL (LP)	25
70	T. Motown (S)TML 11145	IN FULL BLOOM (LP)	20

MARVELOWS

65	HMV POP 1433	I Do/My Heart	12

MARVELS

68	Columbia DB 8341	Keep On Searching/Heartache	8

MARVELS FIVE

65	HMV POP 1423	Bye Bye Baby Bunting/In Front Of Her House	4
65	HMV POP 1452	Don't Play That Song/Forgive	4

MARVETTES

68	Amalgamated AMG 804	Tit For Tat (actually by Lyn Taitt & Jets)/You Take So Long To Know	8
68	Sacred Sound SS 001	We Are Not Divided/He Is So Real To Me	4
68	Sacred Sound SS 002	We Shall Have A Grand Time/Let The Power Fall On Me	4
68	Sacred Sound SS 003	I Was Once Lost In Sin/What A Wonderful Thing	4
60s	Tabernacle TS 1001	I Want A Revival/Tell It	6
60s	Tabernacle TS 1003	Sweet Jesus/When I Look Back	6
60s	Coxsone TLP 1002	IT'S REVIVAL TIME (LP)	70

BRETT MARVIN & THUNDERBOLTS

74	Sonet SON 2011	Standing On The Platform/Too Many Hot Dogs	4
74	Sonet SON 2015	Thoughts Of You/Coming Back	4
74	Sonet SON 2017	Southbound Lane/Little Red Caboose	4
70	Sonet SNTF 616	BRETT MARVIN AND THE THUNDERBOLTS (LP)	15
71	Sonet SNTF 619	12 INCHES OF BRETT MARVIN & THE THUNDERBOLTS (LP)	10
71	Sonet SNTF 620	BEST OF FRIENDS (LP)	10
72	Sonet SNTF 630	ALIAS TERRY DACTYL AND THE DINOSAURS (LP)	12
73	Sonet SNTF 651	TEN LEGGED FRIEND (LP)	10

HANK (B.) MARVIN

68	Columbia DB 8326	London's Not Too Far/SHADOWS: Running Out Of World	8
69	Columbia DB 8552	Goodnight Dick/Wahine	8
69	Columbia DB 8601	Sacha/Sunday For Seven Days	8
69	Columbia DB 8628	Midnight Cowboy/SHADOWS: Slaughter On Tenth Avenue	10
70	Columbia DB 8693	Break Another Dawn/Morning Star	8
78	EMI EMI 2744	Flamingo/Syndicated (as Hank Marvin Guitar Syndicate)	8
69	Columbia S(C)X 6352	HANK MARVIN (LP, blue/black label, mono/stereo)	18/15

(see also Shadows, Marvin & Farrar, Marvin, Welch & Farrar, Bruce Welch & Hank Marvin, Cliff Richard, Spaghetti Junction)

MARVIN & FARRAR

73	EMI EMI 2044	Music Makes My Day/Skin Deep (with Olivia Newton-John)	8
75	EMI EMI 2335	Small And Lonely Light/Galadriel (Spirit Of Starlight)	7
73	EMI EMA 755	HANK MARVIN AND JOHN FARRAR (LP, with Olivia Newton-John)	12

(see also Shadows, Hank Marvin, Marvin Welch & Farrar)

MARVIN & JOHNNY

57	Vogue V 9074	Yak Yak/Pretty Eyes	150
57	Vogue V 9074	Yak Yak/Pretty Eyes (78)	45
58	Vogue V 9099	Smack, Smack/You're In My Heart	125
58	Vogue V 9099	Smack, Smack/You're In My Heart (78)	45
65	Black Swan WI 467	Cherry Pie/Ain't That Right	15

MARVIN, WELCH & FARRAR

71	Regal Zono. RZ 3030	Faithful/Mr Sun	6
71	Regal Zono. RZ 3035	Lady Of The Morning/Tiny Robin	6

MARVIN, WELCH & FARRAR

72	Regal Zono. RZ 3048	Marmaduke/Strike A Light	7
71	Regal Zono. SRZA 8502	MARVIN, WELCH AND FARRAR (LP)	15
71	Regal Zono. SRZA 8504	SECOND OPINION (LP)	18
71	Regal Zono. 4SRZA 8504	SECOND OPINION (LP, quadrophonic)	25

(see also Shadows, Marvin & Farrar, Bruce Welch [& Hank Marvin])

RICHARD MARX
| 88 | Manhattan MTP 39 | Endless Summer Nights/Have Mercy (picture disc) | 4 |

MARY JANE with BARRY GRAY & SPACEMAKERS
| 63 | Philips 326587 | Robot Man/Just The Same As I Do (some in p/s) | 15/8 |

(see also Barry Gray)

MARZIPAN
| 70 | Trend 6099 007 | My Kind Of Music/Sweet Water Mary | 4 |

MASAI
| 74 | Contempo CS 2007 | Cross The Tracks (We Better Go Back) Pts 1 & 2 | 10 |

MASCOTS
| 63 | Pye Intl. 7N 25189 | Hey Little Angel/Once Upon A Love | 6 |

HUGH MASEKELA
68	Uni UN 504	Grazing The Grass/Bajabula Bonke	4
68	Uni UN 510	I Haven't Slept/Where Has All The Grass Gone	4
68	Uni UNL(S) 101	ALIVE AND WELL AT THE WHISKEY (LP)	10
69	Fontana SFL 13056	HUGH MASEKELA (LP)	10
71	Rare Earth SRE 3002	AND THE UNION OF SOUTH AFRICA (LP)	10

SPOKES MASHIYANE
| 58 | Oriole CB 1441 | Jika Spokes (with Ben Nkosi)/Boys Of Jo'burg (with France Pilane) | 4 |

MASKED PHANTOM
| 66 | Parlophone R 5437 | These Clogs Are Made For Waltzing/Fried Scampi | 4 |

MASKMAN & AGENTS
| 69 | Direction 58-4059 | One Eye Open/Y'awll | 4 |

MASON
| 74 | Dawn DNLS 3050 | MASON (LP, export issue) | 15 |

BARBARA MASON
65	London HL 9977	Yes, I'm Ready/Keep Him	20
68	Direction 58-3382	Oh How It Hurts/Ain't Got Nobody	8
69	Action ACT 4542	Slipping Away/Half A Love	12
72	Buddah 2011 154	Give Me Your Love/You Can be With The One You Don't Love	6
75	Buddah BDS 425	From His Woman To You/When You Wake Up In Georgia	4
69	Action ACLP 6002	OH HOW IT HURTS (LP)	15
75	Buddah BDLP 4027	TRANSITION (LP)	12
75	Buddah BDLP 4032	LOVE'S THE THING (LP)	12

BARRY MASON
66	Decca F 12401	Misty Morning Eyes/Take Your Time	4
66	Deram DM 104	Over The Hills And Far Away/A Collection Of Recollections	40
69	Decca F 12895	I'm In Love With You, Pom Pom/Mister D.J. Play Me A Sad Song	4

CURTISS MASON
| 71 | Columbia DB 8800 | Monkberry Moon Delight/Lot Of Lovin' | 4 |

DAVE MASON
68	Island WIP 6032	Just For You/Little Woman	12
70	Harvest HAR 5017	World In Changes/Can't Stop Worrying, Can't Stop Lovin'	5
70	Harvest HAR 5024	Only You Know And I Know/Sad And Deep As You	5
70	Harvest SHTC 251	ALONE TOGETHER (LP)	10
71	Island ILPS 9203	HEAD KEEPER (LP)	10

DAVE MASON & CASS ELLIOT
| 71 | Probe PRO 513 | Something To Make You Happy/Next To You | 4 |
| 71 | Probe SPBA 6259 | DAVE MASON AND CASS ELLIOT (LP) | 10 |

(see also Heilions, Revolution, Traffic; Mama Cass Elliot)

GLEN MASON
56	Parlophone MSP 6240	Hot Diggity (Dog Ziggity Boom)/Baby Girl Of Mine	10
56	Parlophone R 4203	Love, Love, Love/Glendora	8
56	Parlophone R 4244	The Green Door/Why Must You Go, Go, Go	8
57	Parlophone R 4271	Don't Forbid Me/Amore	7
57	Parlophone R 4291	Round And Round/Walking And Whistling	6
57	Parlophone R 4334	Crying My Heart Out For You/Why Don't They Understand	6
57	Parlophone R 4357	By My Side/By The Fireside	5
58	Parlophone R 4390	What A Beautiful Combination/I'm Alone Because I Love You	4
58	Parlophone R 4415	I May Never Pass This Way Again/A Moment Ago	5
58	Parlophone R 4451	I Know Where I'm Going/Autumn Souvenir	5
58	Parlophone R 4485	The End/Fall In Love	5
59	Parlophone R 4562	The Battle Of New Orleans/I Don't Know	6
60	Parlophone R 4626	You Got What It Takes/If There's Someone	6
60	Parlophone R 4723	That's What I Want!/I Like It When it Rains	5
61	Parlophone R 4834	Don't Move/Shadrack	5
62	Parlophone R 4900	St. Louis Blues/That's Life	5

MARLIN MASON
| 56 | Vogue Coral Q 72168 | Don't Throw My Love Away/The Mystery Of Love | 6 |

NICK MASON & RICK FENN
| 85 | Harvest HAR 5238 | Lie For A Lie/And The Address (p/s) | 4 |
| 85 | Harvest 12 HAR 5238 | Lie For A Lie/And The Address/Mumbo Jumbo (12", p/s) | 8 |

81	Harvest SHSP 4116	FICTITIOUS SPORTS (LP, with inner sleeve)	10

(see also Pink Floyd)

SANDY MASON

80s	Boot BOS 7234	ONLY LOVE (LP)	10

SPENCER MASON

67	Parlophone R 5555	Flugel In Carnaby Street/Albuferia	6

TINA MASON

60s	Capitol	TINA MASON (LP)	10

MASQUERADERS

68	Bell BLL 1023	I Ain't Got To Love Nobody Else/I Got It	4
70s	Now! NOW 1001	Love Peace And Happiness/Tell Me You Love Me	4

MASS

80	4AD AD 14	You And I/Cabbage (some with poster insert in die-cut sleeve)	8/5
81	4AD CAD 107	LABOUR OF LOVE (LP)	15

MASS PRODUCTION

77	Cotillion K 11021	I Believe In Music/Cosmic Lust	4

MASSED ALBERTS

64	Parlophone R 5159	Blaze Away/Goodbye Dolly (Gray)	5

MASTERMINDS

65	Immediate IM 005	She Belongs To Me/Taken My Love	15

SAMMY MASTERS

60	Warner Bros WB 10	Rockin' Red Wing/Lonely Weekend	20
60	Warner Bros WB 10	Rockin' Red Wing/Lonely Weekend (78)	50
65	London HLR 9949	Big Man Cried/I Fought The Law (And The Law Won)	7

VALERIE MASTERS

58	Fontana H 132	Sharing/The Secret Of Happiness	4
58	Fontana H 145	(Well-a, Well-a) Ding-Dong/Merci Beaucoup	4
59	Fontana H 175	Dreams End At Dawn/Wonder	4
59	Fontana H 195	Jack O'Diamonds/Say When	4
59	Fontana H 224	If There Are Stars In My Eyes/Just Squeeze Me	4
60	Fontana H 238	Oh, Gee/No One Understands	4
60	Fontana H 253	Cow Cow Boogie/Banjo Boy	6
60	Fontana H 268	Sweeter As The Day Goes By/Fools Fall In Love	4
61	Fontana H 293	Too Late For Tears/I Got Rhythm	4
61	Fontana H 322	Birmingham Rag/All The Days Of My Life	4
62	Fontana H 367	African Waltz/All Night Long	4
64	Columbia DB 7426	Christmas Calling/He Didn't Fool Me	15
65	Polydor 56056	It's Up To You/Next Train Out	4
69	Columbia DB 8629	I Don't Wanna Play House/Just Wait A Little While (as Val Masters)	4

MASTER'S APPRENTICES

71	Regal Zono. RX 3031	I'm Your Satisfier/Because I Love You	15
70	Regal Zono. SLRZ 1016	MASTER'S APPRENTICES (LP)	100
71	Regal Zono. SLRZ 1022	A TOAST TO PANAMA RED (LP)	80

DOROTHY MASUKA

50s	Melodisc M 1518	Zoo Lake/Khauleza	4

MATATA (AIR-FIESTA)

72	President PT 380	I Wanna Do My Thing	7
73	President PT 406	I Feel Funky/I Want You	10
74	President PT 417	Return To You/Something On My Mind	4
75	President PT 438	Good Good Understanding/Gimme Some Lovin'	7
74	President PTLS 1052	MATATA (LP)	15
75	President PTLS 1057	INDEPENDENCE (LP)	50

MATCHBOX

75	Dawn DNS 1104	Rock 'n' Roll Band/Born To Rock & Roll	4
77	Raw RAW 9	Troublesome Bay/Rock Rollin' Boogie (p/s)	4

MATCHING MOLE

72	CBS 8101	O Caroline/Signed Curtain	7
72	CBS 64850	MATCHING MOLE (LP)	12
73	CBS 65260	MATCHING MOLE'S LITTLE RED RECORD (LP)	12

(see also Robert Wyatt, Caravan, Hatfield & North)

JODI MATHEWS

75	Capitol CL 15827	Mama/Don't You Care Anymore	5

COUNTRY JOHNNY MATHIS

60	Top Rank JKP 2064	COUNTRY AND WESTERN EXPRESS NO. 5 (EP)	20

JOHNNY MATHIS

57	Philips JK 1029	The Twelfth Of Never/Chances Are (jukebox issue)	15
57	Fontana H 103	Wild Is The Wind/No Love (But Your Love)	7
57	Fontana H 103	Wild Is The Wind/No Love (But Your Love) (78)	5
58	Fontana H 117	Come To Me/When I Am With You	5
58	Fontana H 117	Come To Me/When I Am With You (78)	5
58	Fontana H 130	Teacher, Teacher/Easy To Love	6
58	Fontana H 130	Teacher, Teacher/Easy To Love (78)	5
58	Fontana H 142	A Certain Smile/Let It Rain	6
58	Fontana H 142	A Certain Smile/Let It Rain (78)	5
58	Fontana H 163	Call Me/Stairway To The Sea	4
58	Fontana H 163	Call Me/Stairway To The Sea (78)	5
58	Fontana H 165	Winter Wonderland/Sleigh Ride	5

Johnny MATHIS

58	Fontana H 165	Winter Wonderland/Sleigh Ride (78)	5
59	Fontana H 186	Let's Love/You'd Be Nice To Come Home To	4
59	Fontana H 186	Let's Love/You'd Be Nice To Come Home To (78)	5
59	Fontana H 199	Someone/They Say It's Wonderful	4
59	Fontana H 199	Someone/They Say It's Wonderful (78)	5
59	Fontana H 218	The Best Of Everything/Cherie	5
59	Fontana H 218	The Best Of Everything/Cherie (78)	5
59	Fontana H 219	Misty/The Story Of Our Love	5
59	Fontana H 219	Misty/The Story Of Our Love (78)	5
59	Fontana H 220	It's Not For Me to Say/Warm And Tender	4
59	Fontana H 220	It's Not For Me to Say/Warm And Tender (78)	5
60	Fontana H 234	You Are Beautiful/Very Much In Love	4
60	Fontana H 248	The Twelfth Of Never/Get Me To The Church On Time	4
60	Fontana H 254	Starbright/All Is Well	4
60	Fontana H 267	My Love For You/Oh That Feeling (some in p/s)	7/4
61	Fontana H 272	Maria/Hey Love	4
61	Fontana H 316	You Set My Heart To Music/Jenny	4
61	Fontana H 328	Laurie, My Love/Should I Wait (Or Should I Run To Her)	4
61	Fontana H 335	Love Look Away/When My Sugar Walks Down The Street	4
62	Fontana H 372	Sweet Thursday/One Look	4
60s	Fontana	other 45s	3
62	CBS AAG 117	Gina/I Love Her, That's Why (with picture insert)	5
63	HMV POP 1217	Your Teenage Dreams/Come Back	4
63	HMV POP 1217	Your Teenage Dreams/Come Back (export-only p/s)	12
63	HMV POP 1267	Bye Bye Barbara/A Great Night For Crying	4
64	HMV POP 1294	The Fall Of Love/No More	4
64	HMV POP 1318	Taste Of Tears/White Roses From A Blue Valentine	4
64	HMV POP 1365	Listen Lonely Girl/All I Wanted	4
65	HMV POP 1467	Sweetheart Tree/Mirage	4
65	HMV POP 1491	Danny Boy/This Is Love	4
66	HMV POP 1503	On A Clear Day You Can See Forever/Come Back To Me	4
66	HMV POP 1527	Moment To Moment/The Glass Mountain	4
66	HMV POP 1550	The Impossible Dream/Hurry It's Lovely Up Here	4
69	CBS Special Prod. WB 731	Up Up And Away/ARETHA FRANKLIN: Mockingbird (p/s)	4
57	Philips BBE 12156	JOHNNY MATHIS (EP)	10
58	Fontana TFE 17011	JOHNNY MATHIS (EP)	8
58	Fontana TFE 17025	LET ME LOVE YOU (EP)	8
58	Fontana TFE 17039	COME TO ME (EP)	8
58	Fontana TFE 17047	WHILE WE'RE YOUNG (EP)	8
58	Fontana TFE 17056	THE TWELFTH OF NEVER (EP)	8
58	Fontana TFE 17064	AVE MARIA (EP)	8
58	Fontana TFE 17088	THERE GOES MY HEART (EP)	8
58	Fontana TFE 17089	SWING LOW (EP)	8
58	Fontana TFE 17091	A HANDFUL OF STARS (EP)	8
58	Fontana TFE 17162	CHRISTMAS WITH JOHNNY MATHIS (EP)	8
59	Fontana TFE 17177	MEET MISTER MATHIS (EP)	7
59	Fontana TFE 17194	IT'S DE LOVELY (EP, also stereo STFE 8001)	7/10
60	Fontana TFE 17215	SO NICE (EP, also stereo STFE 8000)	7/10
60	Fontana TFE 17275	FOUR HITS (EP)	7
60	Fontana TFE 17281	TENDERLY (EP)	7
60	Fontana TFE 17282	ELI ELI (EP)	7
60	Fontana TFE 17283	I'LL BE SEEING YOU (EP)	7
60	Fontana TFE 17285	LIKE SOMEONE IN LOVE (EP, also stereo STFE 8018)	7/8
61	Fontana TFE 17316	MOONLIGHT AND MATHIS (EP)	7
61	Fontana TFE 17317	FOUR SHOW HITS (EP)	7
61	Fontana TFE 17318	CALL ME (EP)	7
61	Fontana TFE 17319	IT'S LOVE (EP)	7
61	Fontana TFE 17334	MY LOVE FOR YOU (EP)	7
61	Fontana TFE 17354	I AM IN LOVE (EP)	7
61	Fontana TFE 17355	LET'S DO IT (EP)	7
61	Fontana TFE 17356	SECRET LOVE (EP)	7
62	Fontana TFE 17393	RING THE BELL (EP)	7
62	Fontana TFE 17394	THE PARTY'S OVER (EP)	7
62	CBS AGG 20001	LIVE IT UP VOL. 1 (EP)	7
62	CBS AGG 20006	LIVE IT UP VOL. 2 (EP)	7
62	CBS AGG 20012	LIVE IT UP VOL. 3 (EP)	7
63	CBS AGG 20028	RAPTURE (EP)	7
64	CBS AGG 20032	MATHIS ON BROADWAY (EP)	7
57	Fontana TFL 5003	WONDERFUL, WONDERFUL (LP)	20
58	Fontana TFL 5011	JOHNNY MATHIS (LP)	20
58	Fontana TFL 5015	WARM (LP, also stereo STFL 510)	15/18
58	Fontana TFL 5023	HEAVENLY (LP)	15
58	Fontana TFL 5031	MERRY CHRISTMAS (LP, also stereo STFL 506)	15/18
59	Fontana TFL 5039	SWING SOFTLY (LP, also stereo STFL 500)	14/18
59	Fontana TFL 5050	OPEN FIRE, TWO GUITARS (LP, also stereo STFL 515)	14/18
59	Fontana TFL 5058	JOHNNY'S GREATEST HITS (LP)	14
60	Fontana TFL 5061	RIDE ON A RAINBOW (LP, also stereo STFL 516)	14/18
60	Fontana TFL 5083	MORE OF JOHNNY'S GREATEST HITS (LP, also stereo STFL 517)	14/18
60	Fontana TFL 5084	FAITHFULLY (LP, also stereo STFL 522)	14/18
60	Fontana SET(S) 101	THE RHYTHMS AND BALLADS OF BROADWAY (2-LP, mono/stereo)	18/22
61	Fontana TFL 5117	JOHNNY'S MOOD (LP, also stereo STFL 545)	14/16
61	Fontana TFL 5134	I'LL BUY YOU A STAR (LP, also stereo STFL 557)	14/16
61	Fontana TFL 5153	PORTRAIT OF JOHNNY (LP, also stereo STFL 571)	14/16
62	Fontana TFL 5177	LIVE IT UP (LP, also stereo STFL 589)	12/14
62	CBS (S)BPG 62077	PORTRAIT OF JOHNNY (LP, reissue, mono/stereo)	10/12
62	CBS (S)BPG 62072	JOHNNY'S MOOD (LP, reissue, mono/stereo)	10/12

63	CBS (S)BPG 62106	RAPTURE (LP)	10
63	CBS (S)BPG 62147	JOHNNY'S NEWEST HITS (LP)	10
63	CBS (S)BPG 62172	JOHNNY (LP)	10
63	HMV CLP 1696	SOUNDS OF CHRISTMAS (LP, also stereo CSD 1521)	12/15
64	CBS (S)BPG 62202	ROMANTICALLY (LP)	10
64	HMV CLP 1721	TENDER IS THE NIGHT (LP, also stereo CSD 1535)	12/15
64	CBS (S)BPG 62270	I'LL SEARCH MY SECRET HEART & OTHER GREAT HITS (LP)	10
65	HMV CSD 1553	THE WONDERFUL WORLD OF MAKE BELIEVE (LP, stereo only)	25
65	HMV CSD 1578	OLE (LP, stereo; mono copies [CLP 1818] unconfirmed)	50
65	HMV CSD 1600	THIS IS LOVE (LP, stereo; mono copies [CLP 1859] unconfirmed)	18
66	HMV CLP 1926	AWAY FROM HOME (LP, also stereo CSD 1638)	40
66	CBS (S)BPG 62062	SWING SOFTLY (LP, reissue, mono/stereo)	10/12
66	CBS (S)BPG 62569	JOHNNY'S GREATEST HITS (LP, reissue)	10
66	CBS (S)BPG 62063	OPEN FIRE, TWO GUITARS (LP, reissue, mono/stereo)	10/12
66	CBS (S)BPG 62064	RIDE ON A RAINBOW (LP, reissue, mono/stereo)	10/12
66	CBS (S)BPG 62067	FAITHFULLY (LP, reissue, mono/stereo)	10/12
66	CBS (S)BPG 62105	LIVE IT UP (LP, reissue)	10
66	HMV CLP/CSD 3522	LOVE IS EVERYTHING (LP)	15
66	HMV CLP/CSD 3556	THE SHADOW OF YOUR SMILE (LP)	15
73	CBS CQ 30740	YOU'VE GOT A FRIEND — TODAY'S GREAT HITS (LP, quadrophonic)	10
73	CBS GQ 30979	JOHNNY MATHIS IN PERSON (LP, quadrophonic)	10
73	CBS CQ 31342	THE FIRST TIME EVER (I SAW YOUR FACE) (LP, quadrophonic)	10
73	CBS CQ 31626	SONG SUNG BLUE (LP, quadrophonic)	10
73	CBS CQ 32114	ME AND MRS JONES (LP, quadrophonic)	10
74	CBS CQ 32435	I'M COMING HOME (LP, quadrophonic)	10
75	CBS 66415	THE BEST OF JOHNNY MATHIS (3-LP box set, mail-order only)	20
79	CBS 66355	JOHNNY MATHIS (3-LP box set)	16
81	Readers Digest 034	THE BEST OF JOHNNY MATHIS (4-LP box set, mail-order only)	18
83	OPEN 1	THE ULTIMATE JOHNNY MATHIS (2-LP, mail-order only)	14

TONY MATOS

62	Salvo SLO 5520-LP	CHA CHA! WITH TONY MATOS (LP, no sleeve)	10

BRIAN MATTHEW

61	Pye 7N 15403	Trad Mad/Sing With Me, Mates	4

BRIAN MATTHEW & PETE MURRAY

60	Decca F 11305	What's It All About Eh?/Gee Ma, I Wanna Go Home	4

IAN MATTHEWS

71	Vertigo 6360 034	IF YOU SAW THRU MY EYES (LP, gatefold sleeve, spiral label)	15
72	Vertigo 6360 056	TIGERS WILL SURVIVE (LP, gatefold sleeve, spiral label)	15
73	Elektra K 42144	VALLEY HI (LP)	10
74	Elektra K 42160	SOME DAYS YOU EAT THE BEAR, SOME DAYS THE BEAR EATS YOU (LP)	10

(see also Pyramid, Fairport Convention, Matthews Southern Comfort, Plainsong, Hi-Fi, Tim Hollier)

JOE MATTHEWS

68	Sue WI 4046	Sorry Ain't Good Enough/You Better Mend Your Ways	30

MILT MATTHEWS

75	London HLF 10479	All These Changes/When Kids Rule The World	4

WINSTON MATTHEWS

71	Banana BA 329	Sun Is Shining/INN KEEPERS: My Friend (B-side actually "The Pressure Is On" by Purpleites)	6

MATTHEWS SOUTHERN COMFORT

70	Uni UNS 513	Colorado Springs Eternal/The Struggle	4
70	Uni UNS 521	Ballad Of Obray Ramsey/Parting	4
70	Uni UNS 526	Woodstock/Scion	4
70	Uni UNLS 108	MATTHEWS SOUTHERN COMFORT (LP)	12
70	Uni UNLS 112	SECOND SPRING (LP)	12
70	MCA MKPS 2015	LATER THAT SAME YEAR (LP)	10

(see also Ian Matthews)

HARVEY MATUSOW'S JEWS HARP BAND

69	Head HEAD 4004	Afghan Red/Wet Socks	7
69	Head HDLS 6001	WAR BETWEEN THE FATS & THE THINS (LP)	30

MAUDS

67	Mercury MF 1000	Hold On/C'mon And Move	8
68	Mercury MF 1062	Soul Drippin'/Forever Gone	6

SUSAN MAUGHAN

62	Philips 326 533BF	I Didn't Mean What I Said/I've Got To Learn To Forget	4
62	Philips 326 544BF	Bobby's Girl/Come A Little Closer	4
63	Philips 326 562BF	Hand A Handkerchief To Helen/I'm A Lonely One Too	4
63	Philips 326 586BF	She's New To You/Don't Get Carried Away	4
61	Philips BF 1216	Mama Do The Twist/Blue Night In Yokohama	4
62	Philips BF 1236	Some Of These Days/Baby Doll	4
63	Philips BF 1266	The Verdict Is Guilty/Bachelor Girl	4
64	Philips BF 1301	Hey Lover/Stop Your Foolin'	4
64	Philips BF 1336	Kiss Me Sailor/Call On Me	4
64	Philips BF 1363	Little Things Mean A Lot/That Other Place	10
64	Philips BF 1382	South American Joe/Make Him Mine	4
65	Philips BF 1399	You Can Never Get Away From You/Don't Be Afraid	4
65	Philips BF 1417	When She Walks Away/Come Along Down And See	4
65	Philips BF 1445	Poor Boy/Your Girl	4
66	Philips BF 1495	Come And Get Me/Don't Love Him Too Much	4
66	Philips BF 1518	Where The Bullets Fly/I'll Never Stop Loving You	4
67	Philips BF 1564	Don't Go Home (My Little Darlin')/Somebody To Love	4
71	Spark SRL 1049	I Can't Make You Love Me/I'm Gonna Get That Guy	6

Susan MAUGHAN

62	Philips BBE 12525	HI, I'M SUSAN MAUGHAN AND I SING (EP)	12
63	Philips BBE 12549	FOUR BEAUX AND A BELLE (EP)	15
62	Philips 433 621 BE	EFFERVESCENT MISS MAUGHAN (EP)	12
63	Philips 433 641 BE	MORE OF MAUGHAN (EP)	15
63	Philips 632 300 BL	I WANNA BE BOBBY'S GIRL BUT ... (LP)	25
64	Philips BL 7577	SWINGIN' SUSAN (LP)	15
65	Philips BL 7637	SENTIMENTAL SUSAN (LP)	15
67	Wing WL 1105	BOBBY'S GIRL (LP)	10

MAU-MAUS

82	Pax PAX 6	SOCIETY'S REJECTS (EP)	5
82	Pax PAX 8	No Concern/Clampdown/Why Do We Suffer (p/s)	4
83	Pax/Paragon PAX 12	FACTS OF WAR (EP)	4
85	Rebel REBEL 01	TEAR DOWN THE WALLS (EP)	4

MAUREENY WISHFULL

| 68 | Moonshine WO 2388 | THE MAUREENY WISHFULL ALBUM (LP, 300 copies only) | 75 |

(see also Jimmy Page, Big Jim Sullivan)

MAURICE & MAC

| 68 | Chess CRS 8074 | You Left The Water Running/You're The One | 6 |
| 68 | Chess CRS 8081 | Why Don't You Try Me/Lean On Me | 8 |

MAX & ELAINE

| 73 | Ackee ACK 516 | I'm Leaving/Version | 4 |

(see also Max Romeo)

MAX & GREGORY

| 73 | Ackee ACK 525 | My Jamaican Collie/Push It Down, Rub It Up | 4 |

(see also Max Romeo)

JOE S. MAXEY

| 72 | Action ACT 4607 | Sign Of The Crab/May The Best Man Win (actually plays Packers' "Hole In The Wall"/"Go Ahead On") | 5 |

MAXI

| 73 | Decca F 13394 | Do I Dream/Here Today And Gone Tomorrow | 8 |

MAXI, DICK & TWINK

| 69 | Columbia DB 8663 | Things You Hear About Me/Catch The Bride's Bouquet | 4 |

(this single does NOT feature Twink from Pink Fairies!)

MAXIMILIAN

| 61 | London HLX 9356 | The Snake/The Wanderer | 30 |

(see also Del Shannon)

MAXIM'S TRASH

| 79 | Gimp GIMP 1 | Disco Girls/Blu Shoes (plastic p/s & inner, hand-stamped white labels) | 40 |

(see also Sunset Boys, Captain Sensible)

MAXIMUM BAND

| 68 | Fab FAB 51 | Cupid/Hold Me Tight | 4 |

MAXIMUM BREED

| 69 | Revolution REV 1 | Sitting In The Park/You've Got It | 4 |

ERNEST MAXIN ORCHESTRA

| 57 | Parlophone R 4319 | Four Walls/The Star You Wished Upon Last Night | 5 |

MAXINE

| 70 | Smash SMA 2301 | My Boy Lollipop/Everybody Needs Love | 4 |

MAX WEBSTER (BAND)

79	Capitol CLP 16079	Paradise Skies/The Party (picture disc)	4
81	Mercury MER 59	Battlescar/April In Toledo	4
79	Capitol EST 11937	A MILLION VACATIONS (LP)	10
80	Mercury 6337 144	UNIVERSAL JUVENILES (LP)	10

BILLY MAY & HIS ORCHESTRA

55	Capitol CL 14210	Loop-De-Loop Mambo/Rudolph The Red-Nosed Reindeer Mambo	6
55	Capitol CL 14266	How Important Can It Be?/Let It Happen	6
55	Capitol CL 14308	Shaner Maidel/The Cha Cha Cha	6
55	Capitol CL 14353	Hernando's Hideaway/Just Between Friends	6
56	Capitol CL 14514	Street Of Dreams/Por Favor	5
56	Capitol CL 14551	Main Title From "The Man With The Golden Arm"/Suzette	6
56	Capitol CL 14558	Oklahoma/Our Melody	4
56	Capitol CL 14609	Nightmare/The Beat	8
56	Capitol CL 14671	Floater/Christopher Columbus	4
57	Capitol CL 14713	Whatever Lola Wants/Mad About The Boy	4
56	Capitol EAP 1013	IT'S BILLY MAY TIME (EP)	7
56	Capitol EAP3 677	SWINGING DRUMS (EP)	8
55	Tempo EXA 4	BILLY MAY'S DIXIELAND BAND (EP)	7
53	Capitol LC 6571	CAPITOL PRESENTS BILLY MAY AND HIS ORCHESTRA (10" LP)	10
53	Capitol LC 6623	BIG BAND BASH (10" LP)	10
54	Capitol LC 6644	BACCHANALIA (10" LP)	10
54	Capitol LC 6659	NAUGHTY OPERETTA (10" LP)	10

BRIAN MAY

83	EMI EMI 5436	Starfleet/Son Of Starfleet (p/s)	8
83	EMI SFLT 1078061	STARFLEET PROJECT (mini-LP)	15
89	Odeon ODO 112	Who Want To Live Forever (p/s, as Ian & Belinda with Brian May)	8
89	Odeon 12ODO 112	Who Want To Live Forever (12", p/s, as Ian & Belinda with Brian May)	18
93	Parlophone 12RPD 6351	Resurrection (12" picture disc, with insert)	7

(see also Queen, Eddie Howell)

JOHN MAYALL & BLUESBREAKERS

64	Decca F 11900	Crawling Up The Hill/Mr. James (as John Mayall & Blues Breakers)	25
65	Decca F 12120	Crocodile Walk/Blues City Shakedown	20
65	Immediate IM 012	I'm Your Witchdoctor/Telephone Blues	20
66	Purdah 45-3502	Lonely Years/Bernard Jenkins (as John Mayall & Eric Clapton)	60
66	Decca F 12490	Parchman Farm (solo)/Key To Love (B-side with Bluesbreakers)	10
66	Decca F 12506	Looking Back/So Many Roads (as John Mayall's Bluesbreakers & Peter Green)	8
67	Decca F 12545	Sitting In The Rain/Out Of Reach (as John Mayall's Bluesbreakers)	8
67	Decca F 12588	Curly/Rubber Duck (as Bluesbreakers)	8
67	Decca F 12621	Double Trouble/It Hurts Me Too (as John Mayall's Bluesbreakers)	8
67	Immediate IM 051	I'm Your Witchdoctor/Telephone Blues (reissue, as John Mayall & Bluesbreakers with Eric Clapton)	20
67	Decca F 12684	Suspicions Pts 1 & 2 (as John Mayall's Bluesbreakers)	7
68	Decca F 12732	Picture On The Wall/Jenny (as John Mayall)	6
68	Decca F 12792	No Reply/She's Too Young (as John Mayall's Bluesbreakers)	6
68	Decca F 12846	The Bear/2401	6
70	Polydor 56544	Don't Waste My Time/Don't Pick A Flower	8
71	Polydor 2066 021	Thinking Of My Woman/Plan Your Revolution	8
79	DJM DJS 10918	Bottom Line/Dreamboat (p/s)	4
67	Decca DFE-R 8673	THE BLUESBREAKERS WITH PAUL BUTTERFIELD (EP)	15
65	Decca LK 4680	PLAYS JOHN MAYALL — LIVE AT KLOOKS KLEEK (LP)	30
65	Decca LK 4804	BLUESBREAKERS WITH ERIC CLAPTON (LP, flipback cover, original label)	20
69	Decca LK/SKL 4804	BLUESBREAKERS WITH ERIC CLAPTON (LP, boxed Decca logo on label)	10
67	Decca LK/SKL 4853	A HARD ROAD (LP, featuring Peter Green)	15/12
67	Decca LK/SKL 4890	CRUSADE (LP, featuring Mick Taylor, mono/stereo)	15/12
67	Ace of Clubs ACL 1243	THE BLUES ALONE (LP, also stereo SCL 1243)	15
68	Decca LK/SKL 4918	THE DIARY OF A BAND VOL. 1 (LP)	15
68	Decca LK/SKL 4919	THE DIARY OF A BAND VOL. 2 (LP)	15
68	Decca LK/SKL 4945	BARE WIRES (LP)	15
69	Decca LK/SKL 4972	BLUES FROM LAUREL CANYON (LP, featuring Mick Taylor)	15
70	Decca LK/SKL 5010	LOOKING BACK (LP)	12
70	Polydor 583 571	THE TURNING POINT (LP)	12
70	Polydor 583 580	EMPTY ROOMS (LP)	12
70	Polydor 2425 020	U.S.A. UNION (LP)	10
71	Polydor 2657 005	BACK TO THE ROOTS (2-LP)	15
71	Polydor 2483 016	BEYOND THE TURNING POINT (LP)	12
71	Decca SKL 5086	THRU THE YEARS (LP)	10
71	Polydor 2425 085	MEMORIES (LP)	10
72	Polydor 2425 103	JAZZ-BLUES FUSION (LP)	10
73	Polydor 2391 047	MOVING ON (LP)	10

(see also Paul Butterfield, Eric Clapton, Jack Bruce, Peter Green, McGuinness Flint, Johnny Almond Music Machine, Alan Skidmore, Mick Taylor, Dick Heckstall-Smith, Keef Hartley, Paul Williams, Ray Warleigh, Colosseum, Henry Lowther, Jon Mark)

MAY BLITZ

| 70 | Vertigo 6360 007 | MAY BLITZ (LP, gatefold sleeve, spiral label) | 40 |
| 71 | Vertigo 6360 037 | THE 2ND OF MAY (LP, gatefold sleeve, spiral label) | 65 |

MAYDAY

| 80 | Reddingtons R.R. DAN 2 | Day After Day (p/s) | 8 |

JOHN MAYER

66	Columbia DB 8037	Acka Raga (as John Mayer's I-J-7)/Gana (as John Mayer & Joe Harriott)	7
67	Columbia SX 6122	INDO-JAZZ FUSIONS (LP)	30
68	Columbia SCX 6215	INDO-JAZZ FUSIONS II (LP)	30
69	Sonet SNTF 603	ETUDES (LP, as John Mayer Indo-Jazz Fusions)	20
71	Columbia	RADHA KRISHNA (LP)	35

NATHANIEL MAYER & TWILIGHTS

| 62 | HMV POP 1041 | Village Of Love/I Want A Woman | 20 |

CURTIS MAYFIELD

70	Buddah 2011 055	(Don't Worry) If There's A Hell Below We're All Going To Go (Edit)/The Makings Of You	5
71	Buddah 2011 080	Move On Up/Give It Up/Beautiful Brother Of Mine (maxi-single)	5
71	Buddah 2011 101	We Got To Have Peace/People Get Ready	5
72	Buddah 2011 119	Keep On Keeping On/Stone Junkie	4
72	Buddah 2011 141	Freddie's Dead (Theme From "Superfly")/Underground	4
72	Buddah 2011 156	Superfly/Give Me Your Love (Love Song)	4
73	Buddah 2011 187	Back To The World (edit)/The Other Side Of Town	4
74	Buddah BDS 402	Kung Fu/Right On For The Darkness	4
74	Buddah BDS 410	Move On Up/Give It Up	4
75	Buddah BDS 426	Mother's Son/Love Me Right In The Pocket	4
71	Buddah 2318 015	CURTIS (LP, gatefold sleeve)	20
71	Buddah 2659 004	CURTIS/LIVE (2-LP)	20
72	Buddah 2318 045	ROOTS (LP, gatefold sleeve)	15
72	Buddah 2318 065	SUPERFLY (LP, soundtrack)	10
73	Buddah 2318 085	BACK TO THE WORLD (LP, gatefold sleeve)	10
74	Buddah 2318 091	CURTIS IN CHICAGO (LP, gatefold sleeve)	10
74	Buddah 2318 099	SWEET EXORCIST (LP)	15
74	Buddah BDLP 2001	CURTIS/LIVE (2-LP, reissue)	14
74	Buddah BDLH 5001	SWEET EXORCIST (LP, reissue)	10
74	Buddah BDLH 5005	CURTIS (LP, reissue)	10
74	Buddah BDLH 5006	ROOTS (LP, reissue)	10
74	Buddah BDLP 4015	MOVE ON UP (THE BEST OF CURTIS MAYFIELD) (LP)	10
74	Buddah BDLP 4029	GOT TO FIND A WAY (LP)	10

Curtis MAYFIELD

75	Buddah BDLP 4033	THERE'S NO PLACE LIKE AMERICA TODAY (LP)	10
76	Buddah BDLP 4042	GIVE GET TAKE AND HAVE (LP)	10

(see also Impressions, Blow Monkeys)

PERCY MAYFIELD

63	HMV POP 1185	The River's Invitation/Baby Please	6
76	Speciality SPE 5007	Please Send Me Someone To Love/The River's Invitation	4
67	HMV CLP/CSD 3572	MY JUG AND I (LP)	15

MAYFIELD'S MULE

69	Parlophone R 5817	Double Dealing Woman/(Drinking My) Moonshine	18
70	Parlophone R 5843	I See A River/"Queen" Of Rock'n'Roll	10
70	Parlophone R 5858	We Go Rollin'/My Way Of Living	8

(see also Elastic Band, Sweet, Amen Corner)

MAYHEM

82	Riot City RIOT 13	GENTLE MURDER (EP)	4
83	Riot City RIOT 24	PULLING PUPPET STRINGS (EP)	4

MAYHEM

85	Vigilante VIG 1	Bloodrush/Addictive Risk (p/s)	6
85	Vigilante VIG 1T	Bloodrush/Addictive Risk (12", p/s)	10

(TOOTS &) MAYTALS

63	Blue Beat BB 176	Hallelujah/Helping Ages Past	10
64	Blue Beat BB 215	He Is Real/Domino	10
64	Blue Beat BB 220	Pain In My Belly/BUSTER'S ALLSTARS: City Riot	10
64	Blue Beat BB 231	Dog War/RECO & CREATORS: I'll Be Home	10
64	Blue Beat BB 245	Little Flea/Pain In My Belly	10
64	Blue Beat BB 255	Judgement Day/Goodbye Jane	10
64	Blue Beat BB 270	You've Got Me Spinning/Lovely Walking	10
64	R&B JB 130	Hurry Up/Love Divide	10
64	R&B JB 141	Another Chance/FRANKIE ANDERSON: Always On A Sunday	10
64	R&B JB 153	Give Me Your Love/He Will Provide	10
64	R&B JB 174	Christmas Feelings/Let's Kiss	10
65	Blue Beat BB 281	Looking Down The Street/BUSTER'S ALLSTARS: Blues Market	10
65	Blue Beat BB 299	Light Of The World/Lovely Walking	10
65	Blue Beat BB 306	Ska War (actually "Treating Me Bad")/SKATALITES: Perhaps	10
65	Ska Beat JB 202	Let's Jump/Joy And Jean	10
65	Island WI 200	Never You Change/What's On Your Mind	10
65	Island WI 213	My New Name/It's No Use	10
65	Black Swan WI 464	John James/THEO BECKFORD: Sailing On	10
66	Doctor Bird DB 1019	If You Act This Way/SIR LORD COMIC & HIS COWBOYS: Ska-ing West	8
66	Doctor Bird DB 1038	Bam Bam/So Mad In Love	8
68	Pyramid PYR 6030	54-46, That's My Number/ROLAND ALPHONSO: Dreamland	10
68	Pyramid PYR 6043	Struggle/ROLAND ALPHONSO: Stream Of Life	10
68	Pyramid PYR 6048	Just Tell Me/Reborn	10
68	Pyramid PYR 6050	Bim Today, Bam Tomorrow/Hold On	10
68	Pyramid PYR 6052	We Shall Overcome/DESMOND DEKKER & ACES: Fu Manchu	10
68	Pyramid PYR 6055	Schooldays/Big Man	10
68	Pyramid PYR 6057	Do The Reggay/BEVERLEY'S ALLSTARS: Motoring	10
68	Pyramid PYR 6064	Scare Him/In My Heart	10
69	Pyramid PYR 6066	Don't Trouble Trouble/BEVERLEY'S ALLSTARS: Double Action	8
69	Pyramid PYR 6070	Aldina/Hold On	8
69	Pyramid PYR 6073	Pressure Drop/BEVERLEY'S ALLSTARS: Express	8
69	Pyramid PYR 6074	Sweet And Dandy/Oh Yeah	8
69	Trojan TR 7709	Pressure Drop/BEVERLEY'S ALLSTARS: Smoke Screen	5
69	Trojan TR 7711	Monkey Man/Night And Day	5
69	Trojan TR 7726	Sweet And Dandy/54-46, That's My Number	5
70	Trojan TR 7741	Bla Bla Bla/Reborn	5
70	Trojan TR 7757	Water Melon/She's My Scorcher	5
70	Trojan TR 7768	Doctor Lester/Sun, Moon And Star	4
70	Summit SUM 8510	Peeping Tom/BEVERLEY'S ALLSTARS: Version	4
71	Trojan TR 7808	54-46 Was My Number/BEVERLEY'S ALLSTARS: Version	4
71	Summit SUM 8513	Monkey Girl/BEVERLEY'S ALLSTARS: Version	4
71	Summit SUM 8520	One Eye Enos/BEVERLEY'S ALLSTARS: Version	4
71	Summit SUM 8527	It's You/BEVERLEY'S ALLSTARS: Version	4
71	Summit SUM 8529	Walk With Love/BEVERLEY'S ALLSTARS: Version	4
72	Summit SUM 8536	Thy Kingdom Come/BEVERLEY'S ALLSTARS: Version	4
72	Summit SUM 8537	It Must Be True Love/BEVERLEY'S ALLSTARS: Version	4
72	Dynamic DYN 438	Redemption Song	5
73	Dragon DRA 1007	Sit Right Down/Screwface Underground/Pomps & Pride (as Toots & Maytals)	4
73	Dragon DRA 1013	Country Road/Funky Kingston (as Toots & Maytals)	4
73	Dragon DRA 1016	In The Dark/Sailing On (as Toots & Maytals)	4
74	Dragon DRA 1021	Fever/It Was Written Down	4
74	Dragon DRA 1024	Time Tough/Time Tough Version	4
74	Dragon DRA 1026	Sailing On/If You Act This Way (as Toots & Maytals)	4
64	Ska Beat JBL 1113	PRESENTING THE MAYTALS (NEVER GROW OLD) (LP)	80
66	Doctor Bird DLM 5003	THE SENSATIONAL MAYTALS (LP)	70
70	Trojan TBL 107	MONKEY MAN (LP)	15
73	Trojan TRLS 65	FROM THE ROOTS (LP)	12
73	Dragon DRLS 5002	FUNKY KINGSTON (LP)	10
74	Dragon DRLS 5004	IN THE DARK (LP)	10
74	Prince Buster PB 11	ORIGINAL GOLDEN OLDIES VOLUME 3 (LP)	18

MAYTONES

68	Blue Cat BS 149	Billy Goat/Call You Up	6
69	Blue Cat BS 152	Loving Reggae/Musical Beat	6
69	Blue Cat BS 166	Copper Girl/Love	6

MINT VALUE £

69	Blue Cat BS 173	We Nah Tek You Lick/Dig Away De Money	6
69	Camel CA 27	Sentimental Reason/Lover Girl	4
70	Punch PH 35	Serious Love/CHARLIE ACE: Musical Combination	4

MAZE (U.K.)
| 66 | Reaction 591 009 | Hello Stranger/Telephone | 60 |
| 67 | MGM MGM 1368 | Catari Catari/Easy Street | 25 |

(see also M.I. Five, Deep Purple)

MAZE (U.S.)
82	Capitol 12CL 211	Joy And Pain/Happy (12")	8
82	Capitol 12CL 244	Before I Let Go/Golden Time Of Day (12")	8
77	Capitol E-ST 11607	MAZE FEATURING FRANKIE BEVERLY (LP)	10

JACKIE McAULEY
| 71 | Dawn DNS 1020 | Rocking Shoes/One Fine Day | 5 |
| 71 | Dawn DNLS 3023 | JACKIE McAULEY (LP) | 35 |

(see also Them, Trader Horne, Wand)

JIMMY McBEATH
| 67 | Topic 12T 173 | WILD ROVER NO MORE (LP) | 10 |

NICKO McBRAIN
| 91 | EMI NICKOPD 1 | Rhythm Of The Beast/McBrain Damage Interview (shaped pic disc, insert & plinth) | 5 |

(see also Iron Maiden)

DAN McCAFFERTY
75	Mountain TOP 1	Out Of Time/Cinnamon Girl	4
75	Mountain TOP 5	Watcha Gonna Do About It/Nightingale	4
78	Mountain DAN 1	Stay With Me Baby/Out Of Time/Watcha Gonna Do About It (p/s)	6
76	Mountain TOP 18	The Honky Tonk Downstairs/Trouble	4
79	Mountain TOP 47	Watcha Gonna Do About It/Boots Of Spanish Leather	4
75	Mountain TOPS 102	DAN McCAFFERTY (LP, with inner sleeve)	10

(see also Nazareth, Sensational Alex Harvey Band)

JERRY McCAIN
| 69 | Python 02 | Homogenised Love/728 Texas | 25 |

CASH McCALL
63	Ember EMB S 173	Anytime/From The Very First Rose	10
65	Ember EMB S 204	Many Are The Words (I've Left Unspoken)/Buenos Noches	10
67	Chess CRS 8056	It's Wonderful (To Be In Love)/Let's Try It Over	8

DARRELL McCALL
61	Capitol CL 15196	My Kind Of Lovin'/Beyond Imagination	6
63	Philips BF 1259	No Place To Hide/Hud	4
63	Philips 304 002 BF	Dear One/I've Been Known	4

TOUSSAINT McCALL
| 67 | Pye Intl. 7N 25420 | Nothing Takes The Place Of You/Shimmy | 12 |
| 72 | Mojo 2092 035 | Nothing Takes The Place Of You/Shimmy (reissue) | 4 |

NOEL McCALLA
| 80 | Direction 58 8731 | Beggin'/Ain't That Peculiar/One More Heartache/Shake Me, Wake Me | 4 |

DAVID McCALLUM
66	Capitol CL 15439	Communication/My Carousel	5
66	Capitol CL 15474	In The Garden/The House On Breckenridge Lane	5
66	Capitol (S)T 2432	MUSIC ... A PART OF ME (LP)	15
66	Capitol (S)T 2498	MUSIC ... A BIT MORE OF ME (LP)	15

JIM McCANN
| 73 | Polydor 2489 053 | McCANNED! (LP) | 50 |

(see also Ludlows)

LES McCANN (LTD)
60	Vogue V 2417	Fish This Week/Vakushna (as Les McCann Ltd)	5
66	Mercury MF 973	Bucket O'Grease/All	8
69	Atlantic 584 284	With These Hands/Burnin' Coal	4
60	Vogue LAE 12238	THE TRUTH (LP)	12
69	Atlantic 588 176	MUCH LES (LP)	10

McCARTHY
86	Wall Of Salmon MAC 001	In Purgatory/The Comrade Era/Something Wrong Somewhere (foldover p/s in poly bag, white labels)	20
86	Pink PINKY 12	Red Sleeping Beauty/From The Damned (p/s)	5
86	Pink PINKY 12T	Red Sleeping Beauty/The Comrade Era/From The Damned/For The Fat Lady (12", p/s, with foldover insert)	8
87	Pink PINKY 17	Frans Hals/The Fall (p/s)	5
87	Pink PINKY 17T	Frans Hals/The Fall (Remix)/Kill Kill Kill Kill/Frans Hals (Version) (12", p/s)	8
87	September SEPT 1	The Well Of Loneliness/Antiamericancretin/Unfortunately (p/s)	5
87	September SEPT 1T	The Well Of Loneliness/Bad Dreams/Someone Worse Off/Antiamericancretin/Unfortunately (12", p/s)	7

(see also Stereolab)

KEITH McCARTHY
| 67 | Coxsone CS 7014 | Everybody Rude Now/BASES: Beware | 12 |

LYN & GRAHAM McCARTHY
65	Columbia DB 7584	Seven Doves/Out After Ale	4
66	Columbia DB 7921	I Can't Help But Wonder/There's Got To Be Love	4
66	Columbia DB 8087	The Turkey's Trial/Bitty Withy	4
68	Columbia DB 8422	I Think It's Going To Rain/Once I Was	6
68	RCA RCA 1759	Sacrborough Fair — Canticle/Wild Berries	4

CECIL McCARTNEY

68	Columbia DB 8474	Hey Aleuthia I Want You/Liquid Blue	4
68	Columbia S(C)X 6283	OM (LP)	15

PAUL McCARTNEY/WINGS

71	Apple R 5889	Another Day/Oh Woman, Oh Why (company sleeve)	4
71	Apple R 5914	The Back Seat Of My Car/Heart Of The Country (as Paul & Linda McCartney, company sleeve)	4
72	Apple R 5932	Love Is Strange/I Am Your Singer (unreleased)	
72	Apple R 5936	Give Ireland Back To The Irish/(Version) (as Wings, yellow 'shamrock' die-cut sleeve)	8
72	Apple R 5949	Mary Had A Little Lamb/Little Woman Love (p/s, as Wings)	6
72	Apple R 5973	Hi Hi Hi/C Moon (as Wings, plain red sleeve)	5
73	Apple R 5985	My Love/The Mess (as Paul McCartney & Wings)	4
73	Apple R 5987	Live And Let Die/I Lie Around (as Wings, company sleeve)	4
73	Apple R 5993	Helen Wheels/Country Dreamer (as Paul McCartney & Wings)	4
74	Apple R 5996	Jet/Let Me Roll It (as Paul McCartney & Wings, yellow die-cut sleeve)	4
74	Apple R 5997	Band On The Run/Zoo Gang (as Paul McCartney & Wings, company sleeve)	4
74	Apple R 5999	Junior's Farm/Sally G (as Paul McCartney & Wings, company sleeve)	4
75	Apple R 5999	Sally G/Junior's Farm (reversed sides, demo only)	100
75	Capitol R 6006	Listen To What The Man Said/Love In Song (p/s, as Wings)	5
75	Capitol R 6008	Letting Go/You Gave Me The Answer (no p/s, as Wings)	4
75	Capitol R 6010	Venus And Mars; Rock Show/Magneto And Titanium Man (no p/s, as Wings)	4
77	Capitol R 6018	Mull Of Kintyre/Girls' School (p/s, as Wings)	6
78	Parlophone R 6020	I've Had Enough/Deliver Your Children (p/s, as Wings)	8
79	Parlophone R 6023	Goodnight Tonight/Daytime Nightime Suffering (no p/s, as Wings)	4
79	Parlophone 12R 6023	Goodnight Tonight (Long Version)/Daytime Nightime Suffering (12" p/s, as Wings, with die-cut inner sleeve [later sold without p/s])	7
79	Parlophone R 6026	Old Siam Sir/Spin It On (as Wings, die-cut 'Wings' sleeve)	6
79	Parlophone R 6027	Getting Closer/Baby's Request (p/s, as Wings)	6
79	Parlophone R 6029	Wonderful Christmastime/Rudolph The Red-Nose Reggae (p/s)	5
80	Parlophone R 6035	Coming Up/Coming Up (live at Glasgow)/Lunch Box — Odd Sox (p/s, B-side as Paul McCartney & Wings)	4
80	Parlophone R 6037	Waterfalls/Check My Machine (p/s)	4
80	Parlophone R 6039	Temporary Secretary/Secret Friend (7" demo only, no p/s)	25
80	Parlophone 12R 6039	Temporary Secretary/Secret Friend (12", p/s)	20
82	Epic A 2729	The Girl Is Mine (with Michael Jackson)/MICHAEL JACKSON: Can't Get Outta The Rain (p/s)	4
82	Epic A 11-2729	The Girl Is Mine (with Michael Jackson)/MICHAEL JACKSON: Can't Get Outta The Rain (picture disc)	15
84	Parlophone R 6080	No More Lonely Nights (Ballad)/(Playout Version) (laminated p/s)	4
84	Parlophone R 6080	No More Lonely Nights (Ballad)/(Playout Version) (misspelt as 'Lonley')	4
84	Parlophone 12RA 6080	No More Lonely Nights (Arthur Baker Remix)/Silly Love Songs/No More Lonely Nights (Ballad) (12", p/s)	40
84	Parlophone 12RP 6080	No More Lonely Nights (Extended Version)/Silly Love Songs/No More Lonely Nights (Ballad) (12", picture disc)	10
84	Parlophone RP 6086	We All Stand Together/We All Stand Together (Humming Version) (with Frog Chorus, shaped picture disc, printed PVC sleeve)	10
85	Parlophone R 6118	Spies Like Us/My Carnival (laminated p/s)	4
85	Parlophone RP 6118	Spies Like Us/My Carnival (shaped picture disc)	12
85	Parlophone 12RP 6118	Spies Like Us (Party Mix)/Spies Like Us (Alternative Mix)/Spies Like Us (DJ Version)/My Carnival (Party Mix) (12", picture disc)	10
86	Parlophone R 6133	Press/It's Not True (laminated p/s)	4
86	Parlophone R 6133	Press (Video Edit)/It's Not True (p/s)	4
86	Parlophone 10R 6133	Press/It's Not True (Video Edit) (10", circular foldout sleeve)	7
87	Parlophone TCR 6145	Pretty Little Head/Write Away (cassette)	8
86	Parlophone R 6148/ R 6018	Only Love Remains/Tough On A Tightrope//Mull Of Kintyre/Girls' School (p/s, stickered double pack in PVC sleeve, no p/s on R 6018)	7
87	Parlophone 12R 6170	Once Upon A Long Ago (Long Version)/Back On My Feet/Midnight Special Don't Get Around Much Anymore (12", brown p/s)	7
87	Parlophone 12RX 6170	Once Upon A Long Ago (Extended Version)/Back On My Feet/Lawdy Miss Clawdy/Kansas City (12", blue stickered p/s)	15
87	A&M FREE 21	Long Tall Sally (live)/I Saw Her Standing There (live) (p/s, free with "The Prince's Trust 10th Anniversary Birthday Party" LP [AMA 3906])	4
89	Parlophone RX 6223	This One/The Long And Winding Road (p/s, envelope pack with 6 postcards)	8
89	Parlophone 12RX 6223	This One/The First Stone/Good Sign (12", embossed p/s)	8
89	Parlophone 12RS 6235	Figure Of Eight/Ou Est Le Soleil? (12" with stickered p/s, 1 side etched)	7
89	Parlophone 12RX 6235	Figure Of Eight/Ou Est Le Soleil?/Ou Est Le Soleil (Tub Dub Mix) (12", p/s)	7
89	Parlophone CD3R 6235	Figure Of Eight/Rough Ride/Ou Est Le Soleil? (3" CD, card gatefold p/s)	7
89	Parlophone CDRS 6235	Figure Of Eight (edit)/The Long And Winding Road/Loveliest Thing (5" CD, card gatefold p/s)	7
90	Parlophone CDRX 6278	All My Trials/Strawberry Fields Forever-Help!-Give Peace A Chance (live medley) (CD)	8
90	Parlophone 2034136	Ou Est Le Soleil?/(Tub Dub Mix)/(Instrumental Mix) (12", p/s)	7
70s	MPL MPL 1	We've Moved (with other artists, promo-only MPL Publishing sampler)	75
70	Apple PCS 7102	McCARTNEY (LP)	10
73	Apple PCTC 252	RED ROSE SPEEDWAY (LP, as Paul McCartney & Wings, gatefold sleeve with booklet)	10
73	Apple PAS 10007	BAND ON THE RUN (LP, as Paul McCartney & Wings, inner sleeve & photos)	10
75	Capitol PCTC 254	VENUS AND MARS (LP, as Wings, gatefold sleeve with inner, 2 posters & 2 stickers)	10
79	Parlophone PCTCP 257	BACK TO THE EGG (LP, as Wings, MPL in-house picture disc; die-cut sleeve, matrix numbers YEX 987-2 & YEX 988-4, beware of counterfeits!)	1200
79	Parlophone PCTC 257	BACK TO THE EGG (LP, promo box set with badge, T-shirt, booklet, sticker, postcard & 5 cigarette cards)	250
79	Capitol (no cat. no.)	MPL PRESENTS (6-LP box set, hand-numbered, 25 only)	250

Rare Record Price Guide

MINT VALUE £

89	Parlophone PCSDX 106	FLOWERS IN THE DIRT — WORLD TOUR PACK (LP, with etched 7" "Party Party" [R 6238], with postcards, family tree & poster)	10
89	Parlophone CDPCSDX 106	FLOWERS IN THE DIRT — WORLD TOUR PACK (CD, with 3" picture CD "Party Party" [CD3R 6238], with postcards, family tree & poster)	15

(see also Beatles, Country Hams, Percy 'Thrills' Thrillington, Mike McGear, Suzy & Red Stripes, George Martin)

ENOS McCLEOD
68	Blue Cat BS 135	You Can Never Get Away/ENOS & SHEILA: La La La Bamba	7

DELBERT McCLINTON
62	Decca F 11541	Hully Gully/Baby Heartbreak	8

BOBBY McCLURE
66	Chess CRS 8048	Peak Of Love/You Got Me Baby	20

(see also Fontella Bass & Bobby McClure)

CHRIS McCLURE
66	Decca F 12346	The Dying Swan/The Land Of The Golden Tree	4
68	Polydor 56227	Hazy People/I'm Just A Country Boy	8
68	Polydor 56259	Answer To Everything/Meditation	4
69	RCA RCA 1849	Our Song Of Love/Weather Vane	4

McCLUSKY BROTHERS
88	DDT DISP 15T	She Said To The Driver/Upstreet Downfall/Silent Journey (12", p/s)	7

(see also Bluebells)

BRIAN McCOLLOM FOLK GROUP
66	Pye 7N 17198	This Dusty Road/Henry Joy McCraken	4

TOMMY McCOOK (& SUPERSONICS)
63	Island WI 102	Adam's Apple/MAYTALS: Every Time (B-side actually by Tonettes)	10
63	Island WI 118	Below Zero/LEE PERRY: Never Get Weary	10
63	Island WI 124	Junior Jive/HORACE SEATON: Power	10
64	R&B JB 139	Sampson/ROY & ANNETTE: My Arms Are Waiting	10
64	R&B JB 163	Bridge View/NAOMI & CO: What Can I Do (B-side actually by Naomi & Clive)	10
64	Port-O-Jam PJ 4001	Exodus (& His Group)/LEE PERRY: Help The Weak	10
64	Black Swan WI 422	Two For One/LASCELLES PERKINS: I Don't Know	8
65	Island WI 232	Rocket Ship/JUSTIN HINDS & DOMINOES: Turn Them Back	10
66	Rio R 100	Jerk Time (with Supersonics)/UNIQUES: The Journey	8
66	Rio R 101	Out Of Space (with Supersonics)/UNIQUES: Do Me Good	8
66	Rio R 103	Ska Jam/Smooth Sailing (with Supersonics)	8
66	Rio R 104	Riverton City/HEPTONES: Gunmen Coming To Town	8
66	Doctor Bird DB 1032	Naked City (with Supersonics)/NORMA FRASER: Heartaches	10
66	Doctor Bird DB 1047	Spanish Eyes (with Lynn Taitt)/STRANGER & HORTENSE: Loving Wine	10
66	Doctor Bird DB 1051	A Little Bit Of Heaven (& His Band)/LLOYD WILLIAMS: Sad World	10
66	Doctor Bird DB 1053	Indian Love Call (with Supersonics)/OWEN & LEON: How Would You Feel	10
66	Doctor Bird DB 1056	Danger Man (with Supersonics)/ERIC MORRIS: If I Didn't Love You	10
67	Doctor Bird DB 1058	Jam Session (with Supersonics)/LLOYD & GLEN: Jezebel	10
67	Island WI 3047	One Two Three Kick/TREASURE ISLE BOYS: What A Fool (B-side actually by Silvertones)	10
67	Island WI 3049	Saboo/MOVIN BROTHERS: Darling I Love You	10
67	Treasure Isle TI 7018	Saboo (with Supersonics)/MOVING BROTHERS: Darling I Love You	10
68	Treasure Isle TI 7032	Venus/Music Is My Occupation (with Supersonics)	10
68	Treasure Isle TI 7039	Our Man Flint (with Supersonics)/SILVERTONES: Old Man River	10
68	Treasure Isle TI 7042	Moving (with Supersonics)/SILVERTONES: Slow And Easy	10
68	Trojan TR 642	Breaking Up/Supersonic (with Supersonics)	5
69	Trojan TR 657	The Saints/SOUL OFROUS: Ease Me Up Officer (B-side actually by Righteous Flames)	5
69	Trojan TR 7706	Black Coffee (with Supersonics)/VIC TAYLOR: Heartaches	5
69	Unity UN 506	The Avengers/LAUREL AITKEN: Donkey Man	5
69	Unity UN 534	Dream Boat/Tommy's Dream	4
69	Unity UN 535	Peanut Vendor/100,000 Tons Of Rock	4
70	Duke DU 76	The Rooster (with Supersonics) (actually by Jeff Barnes)/PHYLLIS DILLION: Walk Through This World	5
70	Duke DU 77	Open Jaw (with Supersonics)/JOHN HOLT: The Working Kind	5
73	Duke DU 161	Love Is A Treasure/(Version) (as Tommy McCook Stars)	4
73	Technique TE 927	Rub It Down/Rub It Down (Version) (as Tommy McCook Stars)	4
70	Trojan TBL 111	GREATER JAMAICA (MOONWALK REGGAE) (LP, actually by various artists)	20

JOHN McCORMACK & EDWARD SCHNEIDER
60	HMV 7P 276	Believe Me If All Those Endearing/O Mary Dear	4

GAYLE McCORMICK
72	Probe PRO 535	Gonna Be Alright Now/Save Me	4

McCORMICK BROTHERS
63	Polydor NH 66986	Red Hen Boogie/Blue Grass Express	40
66	Hickory LPE 1509	AUTHENTIC BLUEGRASS HITS (EP)	12

BUDD McCOY
58	RCA RCA 1106	Hiawatha/The Midnight Ride Of Paul Revere	6

CLYDE McCOY
57	Mercury MEP 9513	DANCING TO THE BLUES (EP)	10

JOE McCOY
59	Collector JDL 81	One In A Hundred/One More Greasing	25

JOHN McCOY
83	Legacy LGY 9	Oh Well! (Edit)/Because You Lied	4
83	Legacy	MINI ALBUM (mini-LP)	10
84	Mausoleum SKULL 8373	THINK HARD (LP)	10

(see also Gillan, Samson, Zzebra, Split Knee Loons)

Van McCOY

VAN McCOY
75	Avco 6105 037	The Hustle/Get Dancin'	7
75	Avco 6105 038	The Hustle/Hey Girl Come And Get It	4

VIOLA McCOY
24	Actuelle 10693	Do Right Blues/I've The World In A Jug (78)	60
25	Edison 51478	Memphis Bound/ROSA HENDERSON: Don't Advertise Your Man (78)	50
40s	Oriole CB 1002	South Street Blues/Charleston Blues (78)	40
50s	Ristic LP 27	VIOLA McCOY 1923-1927 (10" LP)	50

(see also Amanda Brown, Daisy Cliff)

McCOYS
65	Immediate IM 001	Hang On Sloopy/I Can't Explain It	4
65	Immediate IM 021	Fever/Sorrow	5
66	Immediate IM 028	Don't Worry Mother, Your Son's Heart Is Pure/Ko-Ko	6
66	Immediate IM 029	Up And Down/If You Tell A Lie	6
66	Immediate IM 034	Runaway/Come On Let's Go	6
66	Immediate IM 037	(You Make Me Feel) So Good/Every Day I Have To Cry	5
67	Immediate IM 046	I Got To Go Back/Dynamite	8
67	London HLZ 10154	Say Those Magic Words/I Wonder If She Remembers Me	15
68	Mercury MF 1067	Jesse Brady/Resurrection	5
69	Immediate IM 076	Hang On Sloopy/This Is Where We Came In	4
66	Immediate IMEP 002	HITS VOL. 1 (EP)	20
66	Immediate IMEP 003	HITS VOL. 2 (EP)	20
65	Immediate IMLP 001	HANG ON SLOOPY (LP)	25
68	Mercury (S)MCL 20128	THE INFINITE McCOYS (LP)	12
71	Joy JOYS 196	HANG ON SLOOPY (LP, reissue)	10

JIMMY McCRACKLIN
58	London HLM 8598	The Walk/I'm To Blame (as Jimmy McCracklin & His Band)	40
58	London HLM 8598	The Walk/I'm To Blame (as Jimmy McCracklin & His Band) (78)	15
58	London HL 7035	The Walk/I'm To Blame (export issue, as Jimmy McCracklin & His Band)	20
62	Top Rank JAR 617	Just Got To Know/The Drag	15
65	R&B MRB 5001	I Got Eyes For You/I'm Gonna Tell Your Mother	15
66	Outasite 45 120	Christmas Time Pts 1 & 2	30
65	Liberty LIB 66094	Every Night, Every Day/Can't Raise Me	7
66	Liberty LIB 66129	Think/Steppin' Up In Class	7
68	Minit MLF 11003	How Do You Like Your Love/Get Together	8
68	Minit MLF 11009	Pretty Little Sweet Thing/A And I	8
65	Vocalion VEP 170160	JIMMY McCRACKLIN (EP)	60
68	Minit MLL/MLS 40003	A PIECE OF JIMMY McCRACKLIN (LP)	10

GWEN McCRAE
74	President PT 416	It's Worth The Hurt/90% Of Me Is You	6
82	Atlantic FLAM 1	Keep The Fire Burning/Funky Sensation	4
82	Atlantic FLAM 1T	Keep The Fire Burning/Funky Sensation (12")	8
75	President	GWEN McCRAE (LP)	10

GWEN & GEORGE McCRAE
75	President PTLS 1070	TOGETHER (LP)	10

DANNY McCULLOCH
69	Capitol CL 15607	Blackbird/Time Of Man	4
70	Pye Intl. 7N 25514	Colour Of The Sunset/Smokeless Zone	4
69	Capitol E-(S)T 174	WINGS OF A MAN (LP)	12

HENRY McCULLOUGH
75	Dark Horse AMLH 22005	MIND YOUR OWN BUSINESS! (LP)	10

GEORGE McCURN
63	London HLH 9705	I'm Just A Country Boy/In My Little Corner Of The World	6

LUKE McDANIEL
55	Parlophone CMSP 29	The Automobile Song/I Can't Steal Another's Bride (export issue)	6

GENE McDANIELS
61	London HLG 9319	A Hundred Pounds Of Clay/Take A Chance On Love	6
61	London HLG 9396	A Tear/She's Come Back	6
61	London HLG 9448	Tower Of Strength/Secret	6
62	Liberty LIB 55405	Chip Chip/Another Tear Falls	5
62	Liberty LIB 55480	Point Of No Return/Warmer Than A Whisper	6
63	Liberty LIB 55510	Spanish Lace/Somebody's Waiting	5
63	Liberty LIB 55541	Cry Baby Cry/The Puzzle	5
63	Liberty LIB 55597	It's A Lonely Town/False Friends	8
63	Liberty LIB 10130	Anyone Else/New Love In Old Mexico	5
64	Liberty LIB 55723	In Times Like These/Make Me A Present Of You	8
65	Liberty LIB 55805	Walk With A Winner/A Miracle	50
62	Liberty LEP 2054	A CHANGE OF MOOD (EP)	14
61	London REG 1298	GENE McDANIELS (EP)	30
61	London HA-G 2384	A HUNDRED POUNDS OF CLAY (LP, also stereo SAH-G 6184)	30/35
62	Liberty LBY 1003	... SOMETIMES I'M HAPPY (LP)	25
62	Liberty LBY 1021	TOWER OF STRENGTH (LP)	25
63	Liberty (S)LBY 1128	SPANISH LACE (LP)	25
68	Sunset SLS 50017E	FACTS OF LIFE (LP)	10

BILL McDAVID
61	Starlite ST45 63	Kiss Me For Christmas/Little Shepherd Boy	4

CHAS McDEVITT (SKIFFLE GROUP)
57	Oriole CB 1352	Freight Train (with Nancy Whiskey)/The Cotton Song	12
57	Oriole CB 1352	Freight Train (with Nancy Whiskey)/The Cotton Song (78)	5
57	Oriole CB 1357	It Takes A Worried Man/The House Of The Rising Sun	10

MINT VALUE £

57	Oriole CB 1371	Green Back Dollar (with Nancy Whiskey)/I'm Satisfied	12
57	Oriole CB 1386	Face In The Rain (with Nancy Whiskey)/Sporting Life (with Tony Kohn)	8
57	Oriole CB 1395	Sing, Sing, Sing/My Old Man	8
58	Oriole CB 1403	Johnny-O (with Nancy Whiskey)/Bad Man Stack-O-Lee	8
58	Oriole CB 1405	Across The Bridge (with Shirley Douglas)/Deep Down	8
58	Oriole CB 1457	Real Love (with Shirley Douglas)/Juke-Box Jumble	8
58	Oriole CB 1457	Real Love (with Shirley Douglas)/Juke-Box Jumble (78)	5
59	Oriole CB 1511	Teenage Letter (with Shirley Douglas)/SHIRLEY DOUGLAS: Sad Little Girl	6
60	Top Rank JAR 338	Dream Talk/Forever (with Shirley Douglas)	6
61	HMV POP 845	One Love/Can It Be Love (with Shirley Douglas)	5
61	HMV POP 928	Mommy Out De Light/I've Got A Thing About You (with Shirley Douglas)	4
62	HMV POP 999	Happy Family/Throwing Pebbles In A Pool (with Shirley Douglas)	4
65	Columbia DB 7955	The Most Of What Is Least/Don't Blame Me (with Shirley Douglas)	4
68	Fontana TF 957	City Smoke/One Man Band	4
57	Oriole EP 7002	CHAS AND NANCY (EP, with Nancy Whiskey)	15
57	Oriole MG 10018	THE INTOXICATING MISS WHISKEY (10" LP, with Nancy Whiskey)	30

(see also Nancy Whiskey)

AIMI McDONALD

| 67 | Polydor 56191 | Thoroughly Modern Millie/Jimmy | 4 |

GAVIN McDONALD

| 72 | Regal Zono. SLRZ 1027 | LINES (LP) | 15 |

(COUNTRY) JOE McDONALD

69	Vanguard (S)VRL 19057	THINKING OF WOODY GUTHRIE (LP)	10
70	Vanguard 6359 004	TONIGHT I'M SINGING JUST FOR YOU (LP)	10
71	Sonet SNTF 622	QUIET DAYS IN CLICHY (LP, film soundtrack)	10
71	Vanguard VSD 79314	HOLD ON — IT'S COMING (LP)	10
71	Vanguard VSD 79315	WAR WAR WAR (LP)	10
72	Vanguard VSD 79316	INCREDIBLE! LIVE! (LP)	10

(see also Country Joe & Fish)

SHELAGH McDONALD

| 70 | B&C CAS 1019 | THE SHELAGH McDONALD ALBUM (LP) | 15 |
| 71 | B&C CAS 1043 | STAR GAZER (LP) | 15 |

SKEETS McDONALD

56	Capitol CL 14566	Fallen Angel/It'll Take Me A Long, Long Time	25
56	Capitol CL 14566	Fallen Angel/It'll Take Me A Long, Long Time (78)	7
59	Capitol EAP1 1040	GOING STEADY WITH THE BLUES (EP)	35

McDONALD & GILES

| 70 | Island ILPS 9126 | McDONALD AND GILES (LP, pink label) | 15 |

(see also King Crimson)

ROSE McDOWALL

| 88 | Rio Digital 7RDS 3 | Don't Fear The Reaper/Crystal Days (p/s) | 5 |
| 88 | Rio Digital 12RDS 3 | Don't Fear The Reaper/Crystal Days (12", p/s) | 8 |

(see also Strawberry Switchblade)

(MISSISSIPPI) FRED McDOWELL

66	Bounty BY 6022	MY HOME IS IN THE DELTA (LP)	15
66	Fontana 688 806 ZL	MISSISSIPPI DELTA BLUES (LP)	15
69	CBS 63735	LONG WAY FROM HOME (LP)	15
69	Polydor 236 278	GOING DOWN SOUTH (LP)	12
70	Capitol E-ST 409	I DO NOT PLAY NO ROCK & ROLL (LP)	15
70	Transatlantic TRA 194	LONDON 1 (LP)	10
71	Transatlantic TRA 203	LONDON 2 (LP)	10
71	Revival RVS 1001	EIGHT YEARS RAMBLING (LP)	12
72	Polydor 2460 193	MISSISSIPPI DELTA BLUES (LP)	10
74	Xtra XTRA 1136	MISSISSIPPI FRED McDOWELL 1904-1972 (LP)	15

BROTHER JACK McDUFF

64	Stateside SS 275	Sanctified Samba/Whistle While You Work	5
64	Stateside SS 302	Rock Candy/Real Good 'Un	5
64	Stateside SS 328	Carpetbaggers (Main Theme)/The Pink Panther (Theme)	5
66	Atlantic 584 036	Down In The Valley/A Change Is Gonna Come	5
64	Stateside SL 10060	BROTHER JACK McDUFF LIVE! (LP)	15
64	Stateside SL 10101	THE DYNAMIC JACK McDUFF (LP, as Brother Jack McDuff Quartet)	15
65	Stateside SL 10121	BROTHER JACK McDUFF QUARTET LIVE! AT THE JAZZ WORKSHOP (LP)	15
65	Stateside SL 10142	PRELUDE (LP)	15
66	Stateside SL 10165	THE CONCERT McDUFF (LP)	12
66	Atlantic 587 030	A CHANGE IS GONNA COME (LP)	12
67	Transatlantic PR 7404	SILK AND SOUL (LP)	12
69	Blue Note BST 84322	DOWN HOME STYLE (LP)	10

(see also Roland Kirk, Kenny Burrell)

JOHNNY McEVOY

| 70s | Hawk HALPX 117 | SOUNDS LIKE JOHNNY McEVOY (LP) | 18 |

(see also The Rambler)

BOB McFADDEN & DOR

| 59 | Coral Q 72378 | The Mummy/The Beat Generation | 5 |

MC5

68	Elektra EKSN 45056	Kick Out The Jams/Motor City Is Burning	15
69	Elektra EKSN 45067	Ramblin' Rose/Borderline	15
69	Elek. EKL 4042/EKS 74042	KICK OUT THE JAMS (LP, red label, gatefold sleeve)	20
70	Atlantic 2400 016	BACK IN THE U.S.A. (LP)	15
71	Atlantic 2400 123	HIGH TIME (LP)	15

(see also Wayne Kramer, Destroy All Monsters, Rob Tyner & Hot Rods)

MIKE McGEAR

72	Island WIP 6131	Woman/Kill	4
74	Warner Bros K 16446	Leave It/Sweet Baby (p/s)	6
75	Warner Bros K 16520	Sea Breezes/Givin' Grease A Ride	4
75	Warner Bros K 16573	Dance The Do/Norton	5
75	Warner Bros K 16658	Simply Love You/What Do We Really Know	4
76	EMI EMI 2485	Doing Nothing All Day/A To Z	4
72	Island ILPS 9191	WOMAN (LP)	10
74	Warner Bros K 56051	*McGEAR (LP, gatefold sleeve with insert)	12
80s	Centre Labs	*McGEAR (LP, 6-track reissue, 500 only, numbered & signed)	30

(see also Grimms, Scaffold, McGough & McGear, Paul McCartney)

FRANCINE McGEE

78	RCA PC 9126	Delerium/Feelin' Good (12")	8

PAT McGEEGAN

68	Emerald MD 1096	Chance Of A Lifetime/Don't Laugh At Me (If I Cry)	7

BROWNIE McGHEE

51	Melodisc 1127	Secret Mojo Blues/Me And My Dog (78)	15
63	Columbia SEG 8226	BLUES ON PARADE NO. 1 (EP)	12
78	Magpie PY 1805	LET'S HAVE A BALL (LP)	10

BROWNIE McGHEE & DAVE LEE

57	Pye Jazz NJE 1060	THE BLUEST (EP)	8

(see also Sonny Terry & Brownie McGhee)

(Roger) McGOUGH & (Mike) McGEAR

68	Parlophone PCS 7047	McGOUGH AND McGEAR (LP, beware of counterfeits)	200

(see also Scaffold, Adrian Henri, Mike McGear, Jimi Hendrix)

ROGER McGOUGH & BRIAN PATTEN

75	Argo ZPL 1190	READ THEIR OWN VERSE — BRITISH POETS OF OUR TIME (LP)	15

LETHER McGRAW

40s	Vocalion S 238	Do Your Duty/Low Down Dirty Groundhog (78)	25

CHRIS McGREGOR('S BROTHERHOOD OF BREATH)

63	Gallojazz	AFRICAN SOUND (LP)	80
68	Polydor 184 137	VERY URGENT (LP, as Chris McGregor Group)	40
68	Polydor 583 072	UP TO EARTH (LP, unreleased, test pressings only)	150
70	RCA Neon NE 2	CHRIS McGREGOR'S BROTHERHOOD OF BREATH (LP, gatefold sleeve)	25
72	RCA SF 8260	BROTHERHOOD (LP, g/f sleeve, as Chris McGregor's Brotherhood Of Breath)	25

(see also Brotherhood Of Breath)

FREDDIE McGREGOR

70s	Fab FAB 261	Wise Words/NEW ESTABLISHMENT: Version	4

EDNA McGRIFF

60s	Gala 45XP 1014	EDNA McGRIFF'S THE NAME (EP)	10

JIMMY McGRIFF

63	Sue WI 303	All About My Girl/M.G. Blues	15
64	Sue WI 310	Last Minute Pts 1 & 2	12
64	Sue WI 317	I've Got A Woman Pts 1 & 2	15
64	Sue WI 333	Round Midnight/Lonely Avenue	12
66	United Artists UP 1170	See See Rider/Hallelujah	6
69	United Artists UP 35025	The Worm/What's That	8
64	Sue ILP 907	I'VE GOT A WOMAN (LP)	35
64	Sue ILP 908	GOSPEL TIME (LP)	35
65	London HA-C 8247	BLUES FOR MISTER JIMMY (LP)	20
66	London HA-C 8242	AT THE APOLLO (LP)	20
66	United Artists (S)ULP 1158	A BAG FULL OF SOUL (LP)	12
68	United Artists (S)ULP 1170	THE BIG BAND (LP)	12
69	Solid State USS 7012	I'VE GOT A NEW WOMAN (LP)	10
70	Blue Note BST 84350	ELECTRIC FUNK (LP)	20
75	Blue Note BST 84364	SOMETHING TO LISTEN TO (LP)	10

BILL McGUFFIE TRIO

53	Parlophone MSP 6040	Concerto For Boogie/Begin The Beguine	6

ROGER McGUINN

74	CBS 2649	Peace On You/Without You	4
77	CBS 5231	American Girl/Russian Hill	4
73	CBS 65214	ROGER McGUINN (LP)	10
74	CBS 81071	PEACE ON YOU (LP)	10
75	CBS 80877	ROGER McGUINN AND BAND (LP)	10
76	CBS 81369	CARDIFF ROSE (LP)	10

(see also Byrds)

McGUINNESS FLINT

70	Capitol CL 15662	When I'm Dead And Gone/Lazy Afternoon	4
70	Capitol EA-ST 22625	McGUINNESS FLINT (LP)	10

(see also Manfred Mann, Blues Band, John Mayall & Blues Breakers, Gallagher & Lyle)

BARRY McGUIRE

65	Ember EMB S 208	So Long Stay Well/Far Side Of The Hill	5
65	RCA Victor RCA 1469	Eve Of Destruction/What Exactly Is The Matter With Me	4
65	RCA Victor RCA 1493	Child Of Our Times/Upon A Painted Ocean	4
66	RCA Victor RCA 1497	This Precious Time/Don't You Wonder Where It's At	4
66	RCA Victor RCA 1508	Walking My Cat Named Dog/I'd Have To Be Outta My Mind	4
66	RCA Victor RCA 1525	Cloudy Summer Afternoon/MAMAS & PAPAS: You've Got To Hide Your Love Away	10

66	Ember EMB S 224	Greenback Dollar/One By One	4
67	RCA Victor RCA 1638	Masters Of War/Why Not Stop And Dig It While You Can	4
65	Envoy VOY 9153	HERE AND NOW (LP, with New Christy Minstrels)	10
65	RCA Victor RD 7751	SINGS EVE OF DESTRUCTION (LP)	12
66	Ember EMB 3362	THE EVE OF DESTRUCTION MAN (LP, with New Christy Minstrels)	10
71	A&M AMLS 2008	BARRY McGUIRE AND THE DOCTOR (LP, with Eric Hord)	10

(see also Mamas & Papas)

McGUIRE SISTERS

54	Vogue Coral Q 2028	Lonesome Polecat/Muskrat Ramble	8
55	Vogue Coral Q 72050	Sincerely/No More	12
55	Vogue Coral Q 72050	Sincerely/No More (78)	5
55	Vogue Coral Q 72052	Melody Of Love/Open Up Your Heart	7
55	Vogue Coral Q 72082	Something's Gotta Give/It May Sound Silly	7
55	Vogue Coral Q 72108	Christmas Alphabet/He	7
56	Vogue Coral Q 72117	Young And Foolish/Doesn't Anybody Love Me?	7
56	Vogue Coral Q 72145	Missing/Be Good To Me (Baby, Baby)	7
56	Vogue Coral Q 72161	Delilah Jones/Picnic	10
56	Vogue Coral Q 72188	Weary Blues/In The Alps	6
56	Vogue Coral Q 72201	My Baby's Got Such Lovin' Ways/Endless	6
56	Vogue Coral Q 72209	Tip Toe Through The Tulips With Me/Do You Remember When?	6
56	Vogue Coral Q 72216	Goodnight My Love, Pleasant Dreams/Mommy	6
57	Vogue Coral Q 72238	Heart/Sometimes I'm Happy	6
57	Vogue Coral Q 72249	Kid Stuff/Without Him	6
57	Vogue Coral Q 72265	Rock Bottom/Beginning To Miss You	6
57	Vogue Coral Q 72272	He's Got Time/Interlude	6
57	Vogue Coral Q 72296	Forgive Me/Kiss Them For Me	6
58	Coral Q 72305	Sugartime/Banana Split	8
58	Coral Q 72327	Ding Dong/Since You Went Away To School	6
58	Coral Q 72334	Volare/Do You Love Me Like You Kiss Me?	5
59	Coral Q 72356	May You Always/Achoo-Cha-Cha	5
59	Coral Q 72370	Summer Dreams/Peace	4
59	Coral Q 72379	Red River Valley/Compromise	4
60	Coral Q 72387	Lovers' Lullaby/Livin' Dangerously	4
60	Coral Q 72399	"The Unforgiven" Theme (The Need For Love)/I Give Thanks	4
60	Coral Q 72406	Nine O'Clock/The Last Dance	4
60	Coral Q 72415	I Don't Know Why/To Be Loved	4
61	Coral Q 72427	Really Neat/Just For Old Time's Sake	4
61	Coral Q 72435	Will There Be Space In The Spaceship/Tears On My Pillow	4
61	Coral Q 72441	Just Because/I Do, I Do, I Do	4
62	Coral Q 72446	I Can Dream, Can't I/Old Devil Moon	4
62	Coral Q 72452	Sugartime Twist/More Hearts Are Broken That Way	4
64	Reprise R 20338	I'll Walk Alone/Ticket To Anywhere	4
58	Coral FEP 2001	THE McGUIRE SISTERS (EP)	15
58	Coral FEP 2006	VOLARE (EP)	15
59	Coral FEP 2033	MAY YOU ALWAYS (EP)	15
56	Vogue Coral LVA 9024	DO YOU REMEMBER WHEN? (LP)	18
57	Vogue Coral LVA 9072	CHILDREN'S HOLIDAY (LP)	18
58	Coral LVA 9073	TEENAGE PARTY (LP)	18
58	Coral LVA 9082	WHILE THE LIGHTS ARE LOW (LP)	16
59	Coral LVA 9115	MAY YOU ALWAYS (LP)	18
60	Coral LVA 9133	GOLDEN FAVORITES (LP)	16
61	Coral LVA 9140	HIS AND HERS (LP)	16

JIM McHARG'S SCOTSVILLE JAZZ BAND

| 62 | Pye Jazz 7NJ 2053 | Forgotten Dreams/St Thomas | 4 |
| 62 | Pye Jazz 7NJ 2055 | Look For A Sky Of Blue/Once In A Blue Moon | 4 |

JOHN McHUGH

| 65 | Columbia SCD 2245 | When The Stars/Strange Harmony | 4 |
| 65 | Columbia SCD 2252 | Goldsmith Of Toledo Serenade/O Vision Entrancing | 4 |

FREDDIE McKAY

71	Banana BA 348	Picture On The Wall/SOUND DIMENSION: Version	5
71	Banana BA 358	Sweet You, Sour You/High School Dance	5
72	Banana BA 370	Drunken Sailor/SOUND DIMENSION: Version	5
71	Banana BALPS 01	PICTURE ON THE WALL (LP)	25
73	Attack ATLP 1013	PICTURE ON THE WALL (LP, reissue)	12
74	Dragon DRLS 5005	LONELY MAN (LP)	10

(see also Freddie McLean)

SCOTT McKAY

| 67 | Columbia DB 8147 | I Can't Make Your Way/Take A Giant Step | 25 |

SCOTTY McKAY

| 64 | London HLU 9885 | Cold Cold Heart/What You Wanna | 6 |

LONETTE McKEE

| 75 | Sussex SXX 4 | Save It/Do It To Me | 5 |

KENNETH McKELLAR

| 66 | Decca F 12341 | A Man Without Love/As Long As The Sun Shines | 4 |

McKENDREE SPRING

69	MCA MUPS 277	McKENDREE SPRING (LP)	10
71	MCA MUPS 433	SECOND THOUGHTS (LP)	10
72	MCA MUPS 454	THREE (LP)	10
73	MCA MUPS 476	TRACKS (LP)	10
75	Dawn DNLS 3067	GET ME TO THE COUNTRY (LP)	12

MAE McKENNA
75 Transatlantic TRA 297   MAE McKENNA (LP) 10

VAL McKENNA
65 Piccadilly 7N 35237   Baby Do It/I Believe In Love 4
65 Piccadilly 7N 35256   Mixed Up Shook Up Girl/Now That You've Made Up Your Mind 6
66 Piccadilly 7N 35286   I Can't Believe What You Say/Don't Hesitate 4
69 Spark SRL 1005   House For Sale/I'll Be Satisfied 4

McKENNA FOLK
69 Pye 7N 17676   Blowing Green/High Germany 4

McKENNA MENDELSON MAINLINE
69 Liberty LBF 15235   You Better Watch Out/She's Alright 6
69 Liberty LBF 15276   Don't Give Me No Goose For Christmas/Beltmaker 5
69 Liberty LBS 83251   STINK (LP) 22

GISELE McKENZIE
55 HMV 7M 318   Hard To Get/The Boston Fancy 4

JUDY McKENZIE
70 Key KL 005   JUDY (LP) 25
71 Key KL 009   PEACE AND LOVE AND FREEDOM (LP, with poster) 30

MARLENE McKENZIE
68 Double D DD 106   Left Me For Another/BOBBY AITKEN & CARIBBEATS:
    Cell Block Eleven 8

SCOTT McKENZIE
67 CBS 2816   San Francisco (Be Sure To Wear Some Flowers In Your Hair)/
    What's The Difference 4
67 Capitol CL 15509   Look Into Your Eyes/All I Want Is You 5
67 CBS 3009   Like An Old-Time Movie/What's The Difference Chapter II 5
68 CBS 3393   Holy Man/What's The Difference (Chapter 3) 4
67 CBS (S)BPG 63157   THE VOICE OF SCOTT McKENZIE (LP) 12
(see also Mamas & Papas)

TOMMY McKENZIE
68 Pama PM 720   Fiddle Sticks/Please Stay 5

McKENZIE, DOUG & BOB
82 Mercury HOSER 1   Take Off/Elron McKenzie (p/s) 15
(see also Rush)

RAY McKINLEY & HIS ORCHESTRA
56 Brunswick 05541   Flaggin' The Train (To Tuscaloosa)/Airizay 4
58 RCA RCA 1034   Falling Leaves/So Sweet (with New Glenn Miller Orchestra) 4

McKINLEYS
64 Columbia DB 7230   Someone Cares For Me/Million Miles Away 6
64 Columbia DB 7310   When He Comes Along/Then I'll Know It's Love 6
65 Columbia DB 7583   Give Him My Love/Once More 10

ROD McKUEN
57 London HLU 8390   Happy Is A Boy Named Me/Jaydee 20
60 Brunswick 05828   Two Brothers/Time After Time 12
64 Capitol CL 15348   The World I Used To Know/Someplace Green 4
66 Ember EMB 223   Soldiers Who Want To Be Heroes/Wayfarin' Stranger 4
68 RCA Victor RCA 1734   Cat Named Sloopy/Where Are We Now 4
71 Buena Vista DF 482   Pastures Green/Theme From Scandalous John/Train To Quivira (p/s) .. 4
67 RCA Victor RD 7897   THROUGH EUROPEAN WINDOWS (LP) 10
69 Warner Bros   LONESOME CITIES (LP) 12

HAL McKUSICK SEXTET/QUINTET
57 Vogue Coral Q 72258   Kelly And Me (as Sextet)/When I Fall In Love (as Quintet) 4

TOMMY McLAIN
66 London HL 10065   Sweet Dreams/I Need You So 10
66 London HL 10091   Think It Over/I Can't Take No More 8

MALCOLM McLAREN
84 Charisma MALC 5   Madame Butterfly/First Couple Out (shaped picture disc) 4

JOHN McLAUGHLIN
69 Marmalade 608 007   EXTRAPOLATION (LP) 18
70 Marmalade 2343 012   EXTRAPOLATION (LP, reissue) 12
71 Douglas DGL 69014   MY GOAL'S BEYOND (LP) 12
71 Douglas DGL 65075   DEVOTION (LP) 12
71 Dawn DNLS 3018   WHERE FORTUNE SMILES (LP, with insert, with John Surman) 10

DON McLEAN
72 United Artists UP 35359   Vincent/Castles In The Air (p/s) 4

FREDDIE McLEAN
67 Blue Beat BB 386   Go On Girl/Giving You A Try Girl 10

NANA McLEAN
71 Banana BA 355   A Little Love/SOUND DIMENSION: Heavy Beat 5

PHIL McLEAN
61 Top Rank JAR 597   Small Sad Sam/Chicken 6
62 Top Rank JAR 613   Big Mouth Bill/Come With Us 6

ENOS McLEOD
68 Blue Cat BS 135   You Can Never Get Away/ENOS & SHEILA: La La La Bamba 8
(see also Enos & Sheila)

OSCAR McLOLLIE & HIS HONEYJUMPERS
| 55 | London HL 8130 | Love Me Tonight/Take Your Shoes Off, Pop | 150 |
| 55 | London HL 8130 | Love Me Tonight/Take Your Shoes Off, Pop (78) | 25 |

EDDIE McLOYD
| 75 | Brunswick BR 27 | Once You Fall In Love/Baby Get Down | 5 |

ROSS McMANUS
64	HMV POP 1279	Patsy Girl/I'm The Greatest	4
66	HMV POP 1543	Stop Your Playing Around/Girlie Girlie	4
67	Decca F 12618	Can't Take My Eyes Off Of You/If I Were A Rich Man	4
60s	Golden Guinea	SINGS ELVIS PRESLEY'S GOLDEN HITS (LP)	10

(see also Day Costello)

BARBARA McNAIR
| 66 | Tamla Motown TMG 544 | You're Gonna Love My Baby/The Touch Of Time | 150 |

(see also Billy Williams & Barbara McNair)

HAROLD McNAIR
68	RCA Victor RCA 1742	The Hipster/Indecision	10
65	Island ILP 926	AFFECTIONATE FUNK (LP, with Ornette Coleman's Sidemen)	30
68	RCA SF 7969	HAROLD McNAIR (LP)	30
70	B&C CAS 1016	THE FENCE (LP)	25
71	B&C CAS 1045	HAROLD McNAIR (LP)	40

JOSEPH McNALLY
| 56 | Oriole CB 1325 | The March Hare/I'm A Sentimental One | 4 |

JOHN McNALLY
| 69 | CBS 4517 | Mary In The Morning/My Love Forgive Me | 4 |

(this is NOT John McNally of the Searchers)

BIG JAY McNEELY
59	Top Rank JAR 169	There Is Something On Your Mind/...Back...Shac ...Track	12
65	Sue WI 373	There Is Something On Your Mind/...Back...Shac ...Track (reissue)	15
64	Warner Bros WM 8143	BIG JAY'S PARTY (LP)	20

AARON McNEIL
| 73 | Action ACT 4619 | Soul Of A Black Man/Reap What You Sow | 5 |

DAVID McNEIL
| 68 | President PT 212 | Don't Let Your Chance Go By/Space Plane | 12 |

PAUL McNEIL
| 66 | Decca LK 4803 | TRADITIONALLY AT THE TROUBADOUR (LP) | 20 |

PAUL McNEIL & LINDA PETERS
| 68 | MGM MGM 1408 | You Ain't Goin' Nowhere/I'll Show You How To Sing | 4 |

(see also Richard & Linda Thompson)

RONNIE McNEIR
| 75 | London HLA 10494 | Wendy Is Gone/Give Me A Sign | 5 |

McPEAKE FOLK GROUP
| 60s | Evolution Z 1002 | McPEAKE (LP) | 50 |

CLYDE McPHATTER
56	London HLE 8250	Seven Days/I'm Not Worthy Of You	250
56	London HLE 8250	Seven Days/I'm Not Worthy Of You (78)	25
56	London HL 7006	Seven Days/I'm Not Worthy Of You (export issue)	75
56	London HLE 8293	Treasure Of Love/When You're Sincere	150
56	London HLE 8293	Treasure Of Love/When You're Sincere (78)	10
57	London HLE 8462	Just To Hold My Hand/No Matter What	120
57	London HLE 8462	Just To Hold My Hand/No Matter What (78)	15
57	London HLE 8476	Long Lonely Nights/Heartaches	80
57	London HLE 8476	Long Lonely Nights/Heartaches (78)	15
57	London HLE 8525	Rock And Cry/You'll Be There	70
57	London HLE 8525	Rock And Cry/You'll Be There (78)	15
58	London HLE 8707	Come What May/Let Me Know	50
58	London HLE 8707	Come What May/Let Me Know (78)	15
58	London HLE 8755	A Lover's Question/I Can't Stand Up Alone	30
58	London HLE 8755	A Lover's Question/I Can't Stand Up Alone (78)	15
59	MGM MGM 1014	I Told Myself A Lie/(I'm Afraid) The Masquerade Is Over	15
59	London HLE 8878	Lovey Dovey/My Island Of Dreams	25
59	London HLE 8878	Lovey Dovey/My Island Of Dreams (78)	20
59	London HLE 8906	Since You've Been Gone/Try Try Baby	25
59	London HLE 8906	Since You've Been Gone/Try Try Baby (78)	20
59	MGM MGM 1040	Twice As Nice/Where Did I Make My Mistake	12
59	London HLE 9000	You Went Back On Your Word/There You Go	30
59	London HLE 9000	You Went Back On Your Word/There You Go (78)	22
59	MGM MGM 1048	Bless You/Let's Try Again	12
60	London HLE 9079	Just Give Me A Ring/Don't Dog Me	25
60	MGM MGM 1061	Think Me A Kiss/When The Right Time Comes Along	12
60	Mercury AMT 1108	Ta Ta/I Ain't Givin' Up Nothin' (If I Can't Get Something)	10
60	Mercury AMT 1120	You're For Me/I Just Want To Love You	10
61	Mercury AMT 1136	Tomorrow Is A-Comin'/I'll Love You Till The Cows Come Home	10
62	Mercury AMT 1174	Lover Please/Let's Forget About The Past	15
62	Mercury AMT 1181	Little Bitty Pretty One/Next To Me	12
62	Ember JBS 705	Harbour Lights/JACKIE WILSON: Tenderly	175
66	Stateside SS 487	Everybody's Somebody's Fool/I Belong To You	7
66	Stateside SS 567	A Shot Of Rhythm And Blues/I'm Not Going To Work Today	8
67	Stateside SS 592	Lavender Lace/Sweet And Innocent	6
68	Deram DM 202	Only A Fool/Thank You Love	4

Clyde McPHATTER

69	Deram DM 223	Baby I Could Be So Good At Loving You/Baby You've Got It	4
69	Pama PM 775	A Shot Of Rhythm And Blues/I'm Not Going To Work Today (reissue)	6
69	B&C CB 106	Denver/Tell Me	4
59	London RE-E 1202	CLYDE McPHATTER (EP)	80
59	MGM MGM-EP 705	TWICE AS NICE (EP)	50
60	MGM MGM-EP 739	THIS IS NOT GOODBYE (EP)	50
63	Mercury MMC 14120	LOVER PLEASE (LP)	40
64	Atlantic ATL 5001	THE BEST OF CLYDE McPHATTER (LP)	40
71	MCA MUPS 418	WELCOME HOME (LP)	10
73	Atlantic K 30033	A TRIBUTE TO CLYDE McPHATTER (LP)	12

(see also Drifters, Billy Ward & Dominoes)

CLYDE McPHATTER/JACKIE WILSON

62	Ember JBS 705	Tenderly/CLYDE McPHATTER: Harbour Lights	175
62	Ember NR 5001	McPHATTER AND WILSON MEET THE DOMINOES (LP, 1 side each)	100

(see also Jackie Wilson, Dominoes)

TONY (T.S.) McPHEE

66	Purdah 45-3501	Someone To Love Me/Ain't Gonna Cry No Mo' (as T.S. McPhee)	80
80s	TS 001	Time Of Action/Born To Be With You (sold only at gigs)	10
68	Liberty LBL/LBS 83190	ME AND THE DEVIL (LP)	60
73	World Wide Artists WWA 1	THE TWO SIDES OF TONY (T.S.) McPHEE (LP, with insert)	22

TONY McPHEE & JO-ANN KELLY

71	Sunset SLS 50209	THE SAME THING ON THEIR MINDS (LP)	25

(see also Groundhogs, Champion Jack Dupree; Jo-Ann Kelly)

CHARLES McPHERSON

65	Stateside SL 10151	BEBOP REVISITED (LP)	15

KEVIN McQUINN

62	Top Rank JAR 598	Every Step Of The Way/Keep Me On Your Mind	5

CARMEN McRAE

55	Brunswick 05502	Love Is Here To Stay/This Will Make You Laugh	6
56	Brunswick 05588	You Don't Know Me/Never Loved Him Anyhow	5
56	Brunswick 05632	Star Eyes/I'm A Dreamer (Aren't We All)	5
57	Brunswick 05652	Whatever Lola Wants (Lola Gets)/Ooh (What 'Cha Doin' To Me) (with Dave Lambert Quartet)	6
57	Brunswick 05723	It's Like Getting A Donkey To Gallop/The Party's Over	5
58	Brunswick 05738	As I Love You/Passing Fancy	4
58	Brunswick 05761	Namely You/I'll Love You (Till I Die)	4
59	Brunswick 05789	Come On, Come In/I Love The Ground You Walk On	4
59	London HLR 8837	Play For Keeps/Which Way Is Love	8
60	Mercury AMT 1122	The Very Thought Of You/Oh! Look At Me Now	4
75	Blue Note BNXW 7002	Who Gave You Permission/The Trouble With Hello Is Goodbye	4
57	London REN 1094	LONDON'S GIRL FRIENDS (EP)	12
56	Brunswick LAT 8104	BY SPECIAL REQUEST (LP)	15
56	Brunswick LAT 8133	TORCHY (LP)	15
56	Brunswick LAT 8147	BLUE MOON (LP)	15
58	Brunswick LAT 8257	AFTER GLOW (LP)	15
59	London HA-R 2185	BOOK OF BALLADS (LP)	15

(see also Sammy Davis Jnr.)

CARMEN McRAE & DAVE BRUBECK FIVE

62	Fontana H 379	Take Five/It's A Raggy Waltz	4

(see also Dave Brubeck)

JAY McSHANN

55	Brunswick LA 8735	KANSAS CITY MEMORIES (10" LP)	20

BLIND WILLIE McTELL

67	Storyville 670 816	BLIND WILLIE McTELL 1940 (LP)	15
73	Atlantic K 40400	ATLANTA TWELVE STRING GUITAR (LP)	15

RALPH McTELL

69	Big T BIG 125	Summer Comes Along	4
70	Big T BIG 131	Kew Gardens/Father Forgive Him	4
70	Big T BIG 134	Spiral Staircase/Terminus	4
71	Famous FAM 105	First And Last Man	4
71	Famous FAM 111	Teacher Teacher	4
72	Reprise K 14225	Zimmerman Blues	4
74	Reprise K 14380	Streets Of London/Summer Lightning (p/s)	4
68	Transatlantic TRA 165	8 FRAMES A SECOND (LP)	10
69	Transatlantic TRA 177	SPIRAL STAIRCASE (LP, with insert)	10
69	Transatlantic TRA 209	MY SIDE OF YOUR WINDOW (LP)	10
71	Famous SFMA 5753	YOU, WELL MEANING, BROUGHT ME HERE (LP)	10
77	Warner Bros K2 56296	RIGHT SIDE UP (LP, quadrophonic)	10

McTELLS

87	Frank TRUFFAUT 303	Jesse Man Rae/If Only/Rotten/M.T.B. (p/s in bag)	5

RAY McVAY SOUND

65	Pye 7N 15777	Raunchy/Revenge	25
65	Pye 7N 15816	Kinda Kinky/Kinkdom Come	15
66	Parlophone R 5460	Genesis/House Of Clowns (as Ray MacVay Band)	6
69	Mercury MF 1121	Destination Moon/Mexican Scavenger	4

CHRISTINE McVIE

84	Warner Bros W 9372PT	Got A Hold On Me/Who's Dreaming This Dream (12", picture disc)	7

CARL McVOY

58	London HLU 8617	Tootsie/You Are My Sunshine	150

58	London HLU 8617	Tootsie/You Are My Sunshine (78)	40

DAVID McWILLIAMS

66	CBS 202348	God And My Country/Blue Eyes	6
67	Major Minor MM 533	The Days Of Pearly Spencer/Harlem Lady	7
68	Major Minor MM 561	This Side Of Heaven/Mister Satisfied	5
69	Major Minor MM 592	The Stranger/Follow Me	6
69	Major Minor MM 616	Oh Mama Are You My Friend?/I Love Susie In The Summer	5
67	Major Minor MMLP 2	SINGING SONGS BY DAVID McWILLIAMS (LP, also stereo SMLP 2)	15
67	Major Minor MMLP 10	DAVID McWILLIAMS VOL. 2 (LP, also stereo SMLP 10)	15
68	Major Minor MMLP 11	VOLUME III (LP, also stereo SMLP 11)	15
67	Major Minor MCP 5026	THE DAYS OF PEARLY SPENCER (LP)	15
72	Dawn DNLS 3039	LORD OFFALY (LP)	12
73	Dawn DNLS 3047	THE BEGGAR AND THE PRIEST (LP)	10
74	Dawn DNLS 3059	LIVING'S JUST A STATE OF MIND (LP)	10

VAUGHN MEADER

63	MGM MGM 1239	No Hiding Place/The Elephant Song	4

ME & THEM

64	Pye 7N 15596	Feels So Good/I Think I'm Gonna Kill Myself	8
64	Pye 7N 15631	Everything I Do Is Wrong/Show You Mean It Too	7
64	Pye 7N 15683	Get Away/Tell Me Why	7

MEANIES

79	Vendetta VD 002	Waiting For You/It's True (p/s)	4

MEAN STREET DEALERS

80	Graduate GRAD 5	Japanese Motorbikes/Tight (p/s)	7
79	Graduate GRADLP 1	BENT NEEDLES (LP)	25

MEASLES

65	Columbia DB 7531	Casting My Spell/Bye Birdie Fly	20
65	Columbia DB 7673	Night People/Dog Rough Dan	15
66	Columbia DB 7875	Kicks/No Baby At All	15
66	Columbia DB 8029	Walkin' In/Looking For Love	18

MEATBEAT MANIFESTO

87	Sweatbox SOX 023	Suck Hard (I Got The Fear)/Kick That Man/Kneel And Buzz (12", p/s)	12
88	Sweatbox SOX 023R	I Got The Fear (Titanium Mix)/I Got The Fear (Without Fuck) (12", p/s)	10
88	Sweatbox OX 032	Strap Down/Wall To Wall (p/s)	4
88	Sweatbox OX 032R	Strap Down (The Sound Defence Policy Remix)/Wall To Wall (p/s)	5

MEATLOAF

78	Epic EPC 5890	You Took The Words Right Out Of My Mouth/For Crying Out Loud (p/s)	4
78	Epic EPC 6281	Two Out Of Three Ain't Bad/For Crying Out Loud (p/s)	4
78	Epic EPC 6797	All Revved Up With No Place To Go/Paradise By A Dashboard Light (p/s)	4
79	Epic SEPC 12-7018	Bat Out Of Hell/Heaven Can Wait (12", p/s, red vinyl)	7
81	Epic EPCA 1697	Dead Ringer/More Than You Deserve (picture disc)	5
82	Epic EPCA 2012	Read 'Em And Weep/Everything Is Permitted (12", with interview disc)	10
83	Epic WA 3357	If You Really Want To/Keep Driving (picture disc)	4
83	Epic WA 3511	Razor's Edge/You Can Never Be Too Sure About The Girl (picture disc)	4
83	Epic DA 3748	Midnight At The Lost And Found/Fallen Angel//Bat Out Of Hell (live)/ Dead Ringer (live) (double pack)	5
84	Arista ARISD 585	Modern Girl/Take A Number (shaped picture disc in poster)	6
84	Arista ARIPD 585	Modern Girl/Take A Number (12", picture disc)	7
85	Arista ARISG 600	Nowhere Fast/Clap Your Hands (gatefold p/s with booklet)	4
85	Arista ARISD 600	Nowhere Fast/Clap Your Hands (shaped picture disc)	5
85	Arista ARISD 603	Piece Of The Action/Sailor To A Siren (shaped picture disc)	4
86	Arista ARIST 666P	Rock'N'Roll Mercenaries/Revolutions Per Minute (with John Parr, guitar-shaped picture disc)	5
86	Arista ARIST 666XP	Rock'N'Roll Mercenaries/Revolutions Per Minute (with John Parr, 12" picture disc)	7
86	Arista ARIST 683P	Getting Away With Murder/Rock'n'Roll Hero (shaped picture disc)	5
86	Arista ARIST 10683	Getting Away With Murder/Scot Free (Remix)/Rock'n'Roll Hero (10", p/s)	6
83	Epic EPCA 40 2621	GREATEST ORIGINAL HITS (cassette EP)	4
82	Epic SEPC 11 82419	BAT OUT OF HELL (LP, picture disc)	15
82	Epic SEPC 82419	BAT OUT OF HELL (LP, half-speed mastered audiophile pressing)	15
85	Epic SEPC 11 83645	DEADRINGER FOR LOVE (LP, picture disc)	10

(see also Stoney & Meatloaf, Jim Steinman)

MEAT WHIPLASH

85	Creation CRE 020	Don't Slip Up/Here It Comes (foldaround p/s in poly bag; 1st press has rear photo of band by fence, 2nd press has band in field)	12/8

MECHANICAL HORSETROUGH

70s	Kap KAPS 96	Dogshit On Your Shoes/Jeremy Germoline/Horsetrough Hoedown (p/s)	5
75	Sonet SON 2068	When Santa Lost His Trousers/The Ballad Of Big Bruce	4

MEDALLION STRINGS

60	London HLR 9218	Green Leaves Of Summer/Spellbound	5
60	London HLR 9242	Loria's Theme/Suzie Wong	5
61	London HA-R 2331	THE SOUND OF HOLLYWOOD (LP, also stereo SAHR 6130)	10/12

MEDDY EVILS

65	Pye 7N 15941	Find Somebody To Love/A Place Called Love	60
66	Pye 7N 17091	It's All For You/Ma's Place	60

MEDIA

80	Takeaway TA 001	TV Kids/Don't Sit Back/Just For You/Rose And Crown	5

MEDICINE HEAD

70	Dandelion S 4661	HIs Guiding Hand/This Love Of Old	10

MINT VALUE £

70	Dandelion S 5075	Coast To Coast/All For Tomorrow	6
71	Dandelion DAN 7003	(And The) Pictures In The Sky/Natural Sight (also listed as K 19002)	4
72	Dandelion 2001 276	Kum On/On The Land	6
72	Dandelion 2001 325	Only To Do What Is True/Sittin' In The Sun	4
72	Dandelion 2001 383	How Does It Feel/Morning Light	4
70	Dandelion 63757	NEW BOTTLES, OLD MEDICINE (LP)	20
71	Dandelion DAN 8005	HEAVY ON THE DRUM (LP, gatefold sleeve, also listed as K 49005)	22
71	Dandelion 2310 166	DARK SIDE OF THE MOON (LP, with insert)	15
72	Polydor 2310 248	ONE & ONE IS ONE (LP)	10
74	Polydor 2383 272	THRU' A FIVE (LP)	10

(see also Ashton, Gardner & Dyke)

MEDITATIONS
| 68 | Liberty LBF 15045 | Transcendental Meditation/Beautiful Experience | 6 |

MEDIUM
| 68 | CBS 3404 | Edward Never Lies/Colours Of The Rainbow | 10 |

MEDIUM MEDIUM
| 80 | APT SAP-01 | Them Or Me/Freeze (p/s) | 4 |
| 81 | Cherry Red BRED 19 | THE GLITTERHOUSE (LP) | 10 |

BILL MEDLEY
67	Verve VS 564	That Lucky Old Sun/My Darling Clementine	4
68	MGM MGM 1418	I Can't Make It Alone/One Day Girl	5
68	MGM MGM 1432	Brown Eyed Woman/Let The Good Times Roll	5
68	MGM MGM 1456	Peace Brother Peace/Winter Won't Come This Year	7
69	MGM MGM 1475	This Is A Love Song/Something's So Wrong	4
70	MGM MGM 1491	Someone Is Standing Outside/Reaching Back	4
71	A&M AMS 898	You've Lost That Lovin' Feelin'/We've Only Just Begun	4
68	MGM C(S) 8091	BILL MEDLEY 100% (LP)	10

(see also Righteous Brothers, Garnet Mimms)

JOE MEDLIN
| 59 | Mercury AMT 1032 | I Kneel At Your Throne/Out Of Sight, Out Of Mind | 6 |

MICHAEL MEDWIN
| 58 | HMV POP 490 | The Army Game/What Do We Do In The Army? (with Bernard Bresslaw, Alfie Bass & Leslie Fyson) | 8 |
| 59 | HMV POP 645 | Blankety-Blankety-Blank/Do It Yourself (with Norman Rossington) | 4 |

KEITH MEEHAN
| 69 | Marmalade 598 016 | Darkness Of My Life/TONY MEEHAN: Hooker Street | 8 |

TONY MEEHAN
| 64 | Decca F 11801 | Song Of Mexico/Kings Go Fifth | 6 |

(see also Shadows, Jet Harris & Tony Meehan, Keith Meehan, John Paul Jones)

JOE MEEK ORCHESTRA
| 63 | Decca F 11801 | The Kennedy March/The Theme Of Freedom | 25 |

MEGA CITY FOUR
88	Primitive PRIME 009	Miles Apart/Running In Darkness (p/s)	15
88	Mega City MEGA 1	Miles Apart/Running In Darkness (with Decoy sticker on rear of p/s)	7
88	Mega City MEGA 1	Miles Apart/Running In Darkness (Decoy printed on rear of p/s)	4
91	Big Life MEGA R2	Words That Say/Untouchable/Lipscar/Mansion (p/s, green vinyl, 33rpm)	4

(see also Capricorn)

MEGADETH
87	Capitol CLP 476	Wake Up Dead/Black Friday (picture disc)	8
87	Capitol 12CL 476	Wake Up Dead/Black Friday/Devil's Island//Wake Up Dead/Black Friday (12", p/s, some shrink-wrapped with 7" picture disc)	12/7
87	Capitol 12CL 476	Wake Up Dead/Black Friday/Devil's Island (12", p/s, with 'Deth' certificate)	7
88	Capitol CLP 480	Anarchy In The U.K./Liar (picture disc)	6
88	Capitol 12CL 480	Anarchy In The U.K./Liar/502 (12", p/s)	7
88	Capitol CLP 489	Mary Jane/Hook In Mouth (picture disc)	5
88	Capitol 12CL 489	Mary Jane/Hook In Mouth/My Last Words (12", p/s)	7
90	Capitol 12CLP 588	Holy Wars ... The Punishment Due/(13-minute interview) (12" picture disc)	8
91	Capitol 12CLP 604	Hangar 18/The Conjuring (live)/Hangar 18 (live)/Hook In Mouth (live) (12" picture disc)	7
92	Capitol CLPD 662	Symphony For Destruction/In My Darkest Hour (live) (picture disc)	4
92	Capitol 12CLS 662	Symphony For Destruction/Breakpoint/Go To Hell (12", p/s, clear vinyl)	7
92	Capitol CDCL 662	Symphony For Destruction/Breakpoint/Go To Hell (CD)	7
86	Capitol ESTP 2022	PEACE SELLS ... BUT WHO'S BUYING? (LP, picture disc)	12
88	Capitol ESTP 2053	SO FAR ... SO GOOD ... SO WHAT (LP, picture disc)	10
88	M. For Nations MFN 46P	KILLING IS MY BUSINESS ... AND BUSINESS IS GOOD (LP, picture disc)	10

MEGATON
| 69 | Songbird SB 1009 | I've Been Loving You/Memphis Reggae | 6 |
| 69 | Songbird SB 1010 | Ging Gong Gollie/I'm Thirsty | 6 |

MEGATON
| 71 | Deram DM 331 | Out Of Your Own Little World/Niagara | 20 |
| 71 | Deram SML-R 1086 | MEGATON (LP) | 300 |

MEGATON
| 81 | Hot Metal HMM 69 | Aluminium Lady/Diehard (p/s) | 4 |

MEGATONS (U.S.)
| 65 | Sue WI 325 | Shimmy Shimmy Walk Pts 1 & 2 | 15 |

(see also Billy Lee Riley)

MEGATONS (Jamaica)
| 70 | Downtown DT 464 | Take It Easy/Funk The Beat | 4 |

| 70 | Downtown DT 469 | Militant Man/MUSIC DOCTORS: Reggae Jeggae Version | 4 |

MEGATRONS
| 59 | Top Rank JAR 146 | Velvet Waters/The Merry Piper | 6 |
| 59 | Top Rank JAR 236 | Tootie Flootie/Whispering Winds | 6 |

JOHN MEHEGAN TRIO
| 56 | London EZC 19005 | THE FIRST MEHEGAN VOLUME ONE (EP) | 8 |
| 56 | London EZC 19015 | THE FIRST MEHEGAN VOLUME TWO (EP) | 8 |

MEKONS
78	Fast Products FAST 1	Never Been In A Riot/32 Weeks/Heart And Soul (p/s)	5
78	Fast Products FAST 7	Where Were You?/I'll Have To Dance Then (On My Own) (p/s)	4
80	Virgin SV 101	Teeth/Guardian//Kill/Stay Cool (double pack, gatefold p/s)	4
82	CNT CNT 1	This Sporting Life (6.12)/Frustration (6.21)/(mystery live track) (12", p/s)	8
82	CNT CNT 008	This Sporting Life/Fight The Cuts (p/s)	4
82	CNT CNT 014	THE ENGLISH DANCING MASTER (12" EP)	8
80s	Catalogue CAT 075/3	Griller/MEKONS: Amnesia (square flexidisc with 'The Catalogue' magazine)	4

(George) MELACHRINO ORCHESTRA
| 56 | HMV B 10958 | Autumn Concerto/A Woman In Love | 8 |

MEL & DAVE
| 70 | Upsetter US 330 | Spinning Wheel/Version | 5 |

MEL & TIM
73	Stax 2025 125	Starting All Over Again/It Hurts To Want It So Bad	4
73	Stax 2025 171	What's Your Name/Free For All	5
74	Concord CON 004	Backfield In Motion/Do It Right (pink or brown label)	5/4
73	Stax 2325 090	STARTING ALL OVER AGAIN (LP)	10

MELANIE
68	Buddah 201 027	Mr. Tambourine Man/Christopher Robin	4
69	Buddah 201 028	Bobo's Party/I'm Back In Town	4
69	Buddah 201 063	Tuning My Guitar/Beautiful People (withdrawn, demos may exist)	10+
69	Buddah 201 066	Beautiful People/Uptown And Down	4
70	Buddah 2011 013	Lay Down (Candles In The Rain)/Animal Crackers	4
71	Buddah 2011 039	Peace Will Come (According To Plan)/Close To It All	4
71	Buddah 2011 064	Stop! I Don't Wanna Hear It Any More/Beautiful People	4
71	Buddah 2011 093	Alexander Beetle/Christopher Robin/Animal Crackers	4
70s	Lyntone LYN 2673/4	A Gift From Honey (flexidisc, p/s)	5
72	Neighbourhood NBH 6	Bitter Bad/Do You Believe	4
73	Neighbourhood NBH 8	Seeds/Some Say (I Got Devil)	4
75	Neighbourhood SNBH3789	Almost Like Being In Love/Beautiful People	4
83	Neighbourhood NBP 1	Every Breath Of The Way/Lover's Lullaby (picture disc)	4
69	Buddah 203 019	BORN TO BE (LP, gatefold sleeve)	15
69	Buddah 203 028	AFFECTIONATELY MELANIE (LP, with inner lyric sheet)	12
70	Buddah 2318 009	CANDLES IN THE RAIN (LP, gatefold sleeve)	12
70	Buddah 2318 011	LEFTOVER WINE (LP, gatefold sleeve)	12
71	Buddah 2318 034	ALL THE RIGHT NOISES (LP, soundtrack)	14
71	Buddah 2322 001	THE GOOD BOOK (LP, gatefold sleeve, with booklet)	12
71	Buddah 2322 002	GATHER ME (LP, gatefold sleeve)	12
72	Buddah 2318 054	GARDEN IN THE CITY (LP, scratch'n'sniff sleeve)	12
72	Neighbourhood NHTC 251	STONEGROUND WORDS (LP, gatefold sleeve, with lyric inner & poster)	10
74	Buddah 2659 013	THE FOUR SIDES OF MELANIE (2-LP)	15

GIL MELLE QUINTET
| 55 | Vogue LDE 141 | GIL MELLE QUINTET (10" LP) | 12 |

SUSAN MELLEN
| 75 | MAM MAMAS 1014 | THE MELLEN BIRD (LP, with insert) | 30 |

JOHN COUGAR MELLENCAMP
79	Riva RIVA 20P	Miami/Do You Think It's Fair (picture disc)	6
83	Riva JCM 38P	Hand To Hold On To/Hurt So Good (picture disc)	5
86	Riva JCMDP 5	Small Town/(Version)//Hurt So Good/The Kind Of Fella I Am (double pack)	4
86	Riva JCMXD 5	Small Town/(Version)//Pink Houses/Small Town (Acoustic) (12", double pack)	7

MELLODITIES
| 64 | R&B JB 179 | Vacation/TOMMY McCOOK: Music Is My Occupation | 10 |

MELL(O)TONES
68	Amalgamated AMG 812	Fat Girl In Red/VERSATILES: Trust The Book	10
68	Amalgamated AMG 817	Feel Good (maybe actually by Bleechers)/Soulful Mood (actually by Tommy McCook & Supersonics)	10
68	Doctor Bird DB 1136	None Such/VAL BENNETT: Popeye On The Shore	10
68	Trojan TR 612	Uncle Charlie/What A Botheration	10
68	Pyramid PYR 6060	Let's Join Together/BEVERLEY'S ALLSTARS: I Don't Know	8
69	Camel CA 18	Facts Of Life/TERMITES: I'll Be Waiting	5
70s	Escort ERT 344	Work It/SOUL MAN: Good Lover	4

MELLOW CANDLE
68	SNB 55-3645	Feeling High/Tea With The Sun	35
72	Deram DM 357	Dan The Wing/Silversong	30
72	Deram SDL 7	SWADDLING SONGS (LP)	350

MELLOW CATS
| 61 | Blue Beat BB 68 | Rock A Man Soul/MONTO & THE CYCLONES: Lazy Lou (B-side actually by Monty [Alexander] & Cyclones) | 10 |

(see also Melo Cats)

MELLOW LARKS
| 60 | Blue Beat BB 16 | Time To Pray (Allelujah)/Love You Baby (with Clue J. & His Blues Busters) | 10 |

GEORGE MELLY & MICK MULLIGAN BAND

51	Tempo A 96	Rock Island Line/Send Me To The 'Lectric Chair (78)	8
52	Tempo A 104	Kitchen Man/Jazzbo Brown From Memphis Town (78)	5
55	Decca F 10457	Frankie And Johnny/I'm Down In The Dumps	6
56	Tempo A 144	Jenny's Ball/Muddy Water	6
56	Tempo A 147	Death Letter/Cemetery Blues	6
56	Decca F 10763	Kingdom Coming/I'm A Ding Dong Daddy	6
56	Decca FJ 10779	Waiting For A Train/Railroadin' Man	6
56	Decca FJ 10806	My Canary Has Circles Under His Eyes/Heebie Jeebies	6
57	Decca FJ 10840	Black Bottom/Magnolia	6
59	Decca F 11115	Abdul Abuldul Amir/Get Away, Old Man, Get Away	4
60	Pye 7N 15253	Ise A Muggin'/Run Come See Jerusalem	4
75	Warner Bros WB 16532	Ain't Misbehavin'/My Canary Has Circles Under His Eyes (p/s)	4
57	Tempo EXA 41	GEORGE MELLY WITH MICK MULLIGAN'S JAZZ BAND (EP)	10
57	Tempo EXA 47	GEORGE MELLY (EP)	10
58	Decca DFE 6552	MICHIGAN WATER BLUES (EP)	7
58	Decca DFE 6557	ABDUL ABULBUL AMIR (EP)	7
61	Columbia SEG 8093	PSYCHOLOGICAL SIGNIFICANCE OF ANIMAL SYMBOLISM IN AMERICAN NEGRO FOLK MUSIC AND ALL THAT JAZZ (EP)	7

(see also Mick Mulligan Band)

MELO CATS

| 61 | Blue Beat BB 54 | Another Moses/ROLAND ALPHONSO & ALLEY CATS: Hully Gully Rock | 10 |

(see also Mellow Cats)

MELODIANS

66	Island WI 3014	Lay It On/Meet Me	10
67	Coxsone CS 7004	I Should Have Made It Up/JOE HIGGS: Neighbour Neighbour	12
67	Treasure Isle TI 7006	You Don't Need Me/I Will Get Along	10
67	Treasure Isle TI 7022	You Have Caught Me/I Know Just How She Feels	10
67	Treasure Isle TI 7023	Last Train To Expo. '67/TOMMY McCOOK & SUPERSONICS: Expo	10
68	Treasure Isle TI 7028	Come On, Little Girl/TOMMY McCOOK & SUPERSONICS: Got Your Soul	10
68	Doctor Bird DB 1125	Little Nut Tree/You Are My Only Love	10
68	Doctor Bird DB 1139	Swing And Dine/I Could Be King	10
68	Fab FAB 61	Sweet Rose/It Comes And Goes	10
69	Gas GAS 108	Ring Of Gold/You've Got It	4
69	Gas GAS 116	Personally Speaking/LLOYD ROBINSON: Trouble Trouble	4
69	Crab CRAB 15	When There Is You/UNIQUES: My Woman's Love	5
69	Trojan TR 660	Everybody Bawlin' /TOMMY McCOOK: Kilowatt	7
69	Trojan TR 695	Sweet Sensation/It's My Delight	5
69	Trojan TR 7720	A Day Seems So Long/BEVERLEY'S ALLSTARS: Project	5
70	Trojan TR 7762	Say Darling Say/Come Rock It With Me	5
70	Summit SUM 8505	Walking In The Rain/Rivers Of Babylon	4
70	Summit SUM 8512	It Took A Miracle/BEVERLEY'S ALLSTARS: Version	4
70	High Note HS 044	Love Is A Good Thing/No Nola	4

(see also Gentiles)

JOHNNY MELODY

| 68 | Island WI 3158 | Soey Man/LLOYD CHARMERS: My Argument (Conversation Version) | 8 |
| 69 | Pyramid PYR 6023 | Govern Your Mouth (actually by George Dekker) | 6 |

MELODY ENCHANTERS

| 63 | Island WI 049 | Enchanter's Ball/I'll Be True | 8 |
| 63 | R&B JB 117 | Gone Gone/Blueberry Hill | 10 |

MELODY FAIR

| 68 | Decca F 12801 | Something Happened To Me/Sittin', Watchin', Waitin' | 4 |

'MELODY MAKER' ALLSTARS

(see under Humphrey Lyttleton)

MELO'S MARITIME

| 67 | Philips BF 1602 | Blow The Man Up/Maneater | 4 |

KANSAS CITY MELROSE/CASINO SIMPSON

| 72 | Chicago Piano 12-001 | KANSAS CITY MELROSE/CASINO SIMPSON (LP) | 15 |

MONIQUE MELSEN

| 71 | Decca F 23170 | The Love Beat/Pomme Pomme Pomme | 12 |

JOE MELSON

61	Polydor NH 66959	Oh Yeah!/What's The Use I Still Love You	40
61	Polydor NH 66961	Hey Mister Cupid/No One Really Cares	35
64	Hickory 45-1229	Stay Away From Her/His Girl	5

MELTING BEER

| 85 | Beggars Banquet BEG 144 | It Makes No Difference (unreleased, white label test pressings only) | 10 |

(see also Icicle Works)

MELTON CONSTABLE

| 70s | SIS private pressing | MELTON CONSTABLE (LP) | 250 |

HAROLD MELVIN & BLUE NOTES

72	CBS 8291	I Miss You Pts 1 & 2	4
72	CBS 8496	If You Don't Know Me By Now/Let Me Into My World	4
75	Route RT 06	Get Out/You May Not Love Me	5
77	ABC 4161	Reaching For The World/Stay Together	4
63	CBS Q 65859	BLACK AND BLUE (LP, quadrophonic)	10

MELVINS

| 90 | Tupelo TUPEP 10 | Sweet Young Thing Ain't Sweet No More/STEELPOLE BATH TUB: I Dreamed I Dream (12", p/s, green vinyl, 600 only) | 8 |

MEMBERS

78	Stiff/One Off OFF 3	Solitary Confinement/Rat Up A Drainpipe (p/s) 7
79	Virgin VS 242	The Sound Of The Suburbs/Handling The Big Jets (clear vinyl, window sleeve) 5
80	Virgin VS 352	Flying Again/Disco Oui Oui//Live In A Lift/Rat Up A Drainpipe (double pack) 4

MEMBRANES

80	Vinyl Drip VD 005	Flexible Membrane: Fashionable Junkies/Almost China (flexidisc, p/s) 5
82	Vinyl Drip VD 007	Muscles/All Roads Lead To Norway 4

MEMOS

59	Parlophone R 4616	The Biddy Leg/My Type Of Girl 50

MEMPHIS BEND

76	United Artists UP 36132	Ubangi Stomp/Tennessee 8
77	United Artists UAS 30036	GOOD ROCKIN' TONITE (LP) 10

MEMPHIS HORNS

71	Atlantic 2091 080	Wooly Bully/I Can't Turn You Loose 4
77	RCA PB 0836	Get Up And Dance/Don't Abuse It 6
73	Polydor 2466 010	MEMPHIS HORNS (LP) 10

MEMPHIS JUG BAND

37	Regal Zono. MR 2331	Kansas City/KC Moan (78) 65
55	HMV 7EG 8073	MEMPHIS JUG BAND (EP, withdrawn) 100
70s	Saydisc Matchbox RL 33	MEMPHIS JUG BAND (LP) 15
71	Saydisc Matchbox RL 337	MEMPHIS JUG BAND VOLUME 2 (LP) 15

MEMPHIS MINNIE

64	Heritage H 103	MEMPHIS MINNIE (EP) 20
69	Limited Edition (no cat no)	MEMPHIS MINNIE 1934-1936 (LP) 30
69	Limited Edition (no cat no)	MEMPHIS MINNIE 1934-1941 (LP) 30
69	Sunflower ET 1400	MEMPHIS MINNIE 1941-1949 (LP) 30
74	Flyright LP 108	MEMPHIS MINNIE 1934-1941 (LP, reissue) 12
74	Flyright LP 109	MEMPHIS MINNIE 1941-1949 (LP, reissue) 12

MEMPHIS SLIM

53	Esquire 10-319	Harlem Bound/ST. LOUIS JIMMY R&B BAND: Holiday For Boogie (78) ..8
60	Collector JDN 102	Pinetop's Blues/How Long 6
62	Storyville A 45055	Big City Girl/El Capitan 12
61	Collector JEN 5	GOING TO KANSAS CITY (EP) 12
62	Storyville SEP 385	STORYVILLE BLUES ANTHOLOGY VOL. 5 — BOOGIE WOOGIE AND THE BLUES (EP) 12
63	Vocalion VEP 170155	MEMPHIS SLIM AND LITTLE RICHARD (EP) 45
63	Summit LSE 2041	WORLD'S FOREMOST BLUES SINGERS (EP) 7
61	Collector JGN 1004	MEMPHIS SLIM IN THE U.S.A. (LP) 18
61	Collector JGN 1005	MEMPHIS SLIM (VOL. 2) (LP) 18
62	Bluesville BV 1018	JUST BLUES (LP) 20
62	Storyville SLP 118	MEMPHIS SLIM (LP) 12
62	Fontana 688 302 ZL	NO STRAIN (LP) 18
63	United Artists ULP 1042	BROKEN SOUL BLUES (LP) 18
64	Storyville SLP 118	TRAVELLIN' WITH THE BLUES (LP, reissue of "Memphis Slim") 15
64	Xtra XTRA 1008	MEMPHIS SLIM (LP) 15
65	Fontana TL 5254	CLAP YOUR HANDS (LP) 15
66	Fontana 688 315 ZL	FRISCO BAY BLUES (LP) 22
67	Polydor 623 211	PINETOP'S BLUES (LP) 15
68	Polydor 623 263	BLUESINGLY YOURS (LP, with Mickey Baker) 15
69	Xtra XTRA 1085	CHICAGO BLUES (LP) 15
69	Joy JOYS 143	AT THE GATE OF HORN (LP) 10
73	Sonet SNTF 647	LEGACY OF THE BLUES: 7 (LP) 10
73	Polydor 2460 155	ROCK ME BABY (LP) 10
73	Ember EMB 3422	SOUL BLUES (LP) 10
72	Barclay 920 214	BLUE MEMPHIS (LP, with Peter Green) 40
73	Barclay 920 332-3	OLD TIMES NEW TIMES (2-LP) 15
74	Barclay 920 407	CLASSIC ALL AMERICAN MUSIC (LP) 10
70s	Xtra XTRA 5063	ALL KINDS OF BLUES (LP) 15

MEMPHIS THREE

68	Page One POF 070	Wild Thing/She's A Yum Yum 4

MEN

79	Virgin VS 269	I Don't Depend On You/Cruel (p/s) 10
79	Virgin VS 269 12	I Don't Depend On You/Cruel (12", p/s) 10

(see also Human League, Philip Oakey & Giorgio Moroder)

MENACE

77	Illegal IL 004	Screwed Up/Insane Society (p/s) 5
77	Illegal IL 004	Screwed Up/Insane Society (12", p/s) 7
78	Illegal IL 008	I Need Nothing/Electrocutioner (p/s) 5
78	Small Wonder SMALL 5	G.L.C./I'm Civilized (p/s) 5
79	Small Wonder SMALL 16	Final Vinyl: Last Year's Youth/Carry No Banners (p/s) 4
78	Fresh FRESH 14	The Young Ones/Tomorrow's World/Live For Today (p/s) 4

(see also Aces, Vermilion & Aces)

MEN AT WORK

83	Epic EPCA 1980	Down Under/Crazy (Australia-shaped picture disc) 7
84	Epic DA 4119	Be Good Johnny/Who Can It Be Now//Settle Down/Upstairs At My House (double pack) 4

CARLOS MENDES

72	Pye Intl. 7N 25581	Shadows/Glow Worm 8

SERGIO MENDES
68	A&M AMS 739	Scarborough Fair — Canticle/Canto Triste (p/s)	4

MENDES PREY
83	MP AM 076	On To The Borderline/Runnin' For You	4
86	Wag WAG 2	Wonderland/Can You Believe It (p/s)	8
86	Wag 12 WAG 2	Wonderland/Can You Believe It (12", p/s)	8

ENOCH & CHRISTY MENSAH
60s	Melodisc M 1569	Rebecca/Dakuku Dum	4

MENTATZ
81	Naff N 001	Never Trust A Russian/Dead To The World	4

IAN MENZIES
58	Pye Jazz 7NJ 2027	Polly Wolly Doodle/In A Persian Market (with His New Stompers)	4
58	Pye Jazz 7NJ 2028	Bill Bailey Won't You Please Come Home/Hot Time In The Old Town Tonight (as Ian Menzies & Clyde Valley Stompers)	4
59	Pye Jazz 7NJ 2031	The Fish Man/Salty Dog (as Ian Menzies & Clyde Valley Stompers)	4
58	Pye Jazz NJE 1049	MELODY MAKER ALL STARS (EP)	8
60	Pye Jazz NJL 23	HAVE TARTAN, WILL TRAD (LP, with Lonnie Donegan)	12
60	Pye Jazz NJL 26	IAN MENZIES AND THE CLYDE VALLEY STOMPERS (LP)	10

JOHNNY MERCER
53	Capitol LC 6633	CAPITOL PRESENTS JOHNNY MERCER (10" LP)	10
54	Capitol LC 6640	CAPITOL PRESENTS JOHNNY MERCER VOL. 2 (10" LP)	10
54	Capitol LC 6648	CAPITOL PRESENTS JOHNNY MERCER VOL. 3 (10" LP)	10
54	Capitol LC 6655	CAPITOL PRESENTS JOHNNY MERCER VOL. 4 (10" LP)	10

MARY MAE MERCER
65	Decca DFE 8599	MARY MAE MERCER (EP)	12

FREDDIE MERCURY
84	CBS A 4735	Love Kills/GEORGIO MORODER: Rot Wang's Party (p/s)	7
84	CBS WA 4735	Love Kills/GEORGIO MORODER: Rot Wang's Party (picture disc)	25
84	CBS TA 4375	Love Kills (Extended)/GEORGIO MORODER: Rot Wang's Party (12", p/s)	15
85	CBS A 6019	I Was Born To Love You/Stop All The Fighting (p/s)	6
85	CBS DA 6019	I Was Born To Love You/Stop All The Fighting//Love Kills/Stop All The Fighting (Extended) (double pack)	18
85	CBS TA 6019	I Was Born To Love You (7.03)/Stop All The Fighting (12", p/s)	12
85	CBS A 6413	Made In Heaven (Remix 3.59)/She Blows Hot And Cold (p/s)	7
85	CBS WA 6413	Made In Heaven (Remix)/She Blows Hot And Cold (shaped picture disc)	25
85	CBS TA 6413	Made In Heaven (Extended Remix 4.43)/Made In Heaven (Remix 3.59)/She Blows Hot And Cold (Extended) (12", p/s)	15
85	CBS A 6555	Living On My Own/My Love Is Dangerous (p/s)	6
85	CBS TA 6555	Living On My Own (Ext. 6.38)/My Love Is Dangerous (Ext. 6.25) (12", p/s)	10
85	CBS GTA 6555	Living On My Own (Ext. 6.38)/My Love Is Dangerous (Ext. 6.25) (12", gatefold p/s)	15
85	CBS A 6725	Love Me Like There's No Tomorrow/Let's Turn It On (p/s)	5
85	CBS TA 6725	Love Me Like There's No Tomorrow (Extended Mix)/Let's Turn It On (Extended Mix) (12", p/s)	12
86	EMI EMI 5559	Time (From The Musical)/Instrumental (p/s)	5
86	EMI 12EMI 5559	Time (From The Musical) (Extended)/Time (Instrumental) (12", p/s)	10
87	Parlophone R 6151	The Great Pretender/Exercises In Free Love (p/s)	5
87	Parlophone RP 6151	The Great Pretender/Exercises In Free Love (shaped pic disc with plinth)	25
87	Parlophone 10R 6151	The Great Pretender/Exercises In Free Love (10", white label only)	30
87	Parlophone 12R 6151	The Great Pretender (Extended)/(7")/Exercises In Free Love (12", p/s)	10
87	Polydor POSP 887	Barcelona/Exercises In Free Love (with Montserrat Caballe, gatefold p/s)	5
87	Polydor POSPX 887	Barcelona/Exercises In Free Love (Version 2)/Barcelona (Extended) (12", gatefold p/s)	12
87	Polydor POSPP 887	Barcelona/Exercises In Free Love (Version 2)/Barcelona (Extended) (12" picture disc)	20
87	Polydor POCD 887	Barcelona/Exercises In Free Love (Version 2)/Barcelona (Extended) (CD, card p/s)	10
87	Polydor POCD 887	Barcelona/Exercises In Free Love (Version 2)/Barcelona (Extended) (CD, autographed card p/s)	75
88	Polydor POSP 23	The Golden Boy/The Fallen Priest (p/s)	5
88	Polydor POSPX 23	The Golden Boy/The Fallen Priest/The Golden Boy (Instrumental) (12", p/s)	12
88	Polydor POCD 23	The Golden Boy/The Fallen Priest/The Golden Boy (Instrumental) (CD)	12
88	Polydor POSX 29	How Can I Go On/Overture Piccante (with Montserrat Caballe, picture disc)	15
89	Polydor POSPX 29	How Can I Go On/Guide Me Home/Overture Piccante (12", p/s)	12
89	Polydor PZ 29	How Can I Go On/Guide Me Home/Overture Piccante (CD)	10
85	CBS 86312	MR. BAD GUY (LP, with inner sleeve)	10
85	CBS 40-86312	MR. BAD GUY (cassette)	10
85	CBS CD 86312	MR. BAD GUY (CD)	20

(see also Queen, Larry Lurex)

MERCY
69	London HLZ 10273	Love (Can Make You Happy)/Fireball	5
69	Warner Bros WB 7291	Love (Can Make You Happy)/Fireball (reissue)	4

BURGESS MEREDITH
63	Colpix PX 690	Home In The Meadow/No Goodbye	4

MERION
67	Page One POF 041	I Go To Sleep/Abyssinian Secrets	6

LOTTIE MERLE
72	Flyright 001	Howling In The Moonlight/Catfish	5

ETHEL MERMAN
54	Brunswick 05346	A Husband — A Wife (with Jimmy Durante)/The Lake Song (with Ray Bolger)	6

55	Brunswick 05381	(There's No Business Like) Show Business/Play A Simple Melody	
		(B-side with Dan Dailey)	6
58	RCA RCA 1039	A New-Fangled Tango/Mutual Admiration Society	4
52	Brunswick LAT 8016	SONGS FROM "CALL ME MADAM" (LP)	10
52	Brunswick LA 8539	CALL ME MADAM (LP, with Dick Haymes)	10
54	Brunswick LA 8636	SONGS SHE HAS MADE FAMOUS (10" LP)	10
54	Brunswick LA 8638	DUET FROM FORD 50TH ANNIVERSARY TV SHOW (LP, with Mary Martin)	10

RAY MERRELL

60	Ember EMB S 113	Why Did You Leave Me?/Teenage Love	4
60s	Windsor PS 115	Battle Of Waterloo/Not Any More	4
64	Pye 7N 15709	Where In The World/Share A Dream With Me	4
65	Pye 7N 15793	Almost There/Only In A Dream	4
67	Columbia DB 8204	Chiquita Mia/Lazy Miss Hazy	4
69	Columbia DB 8643	Memories/Red Summer Roses	4
70	Jay Boy BOY 22	Tears Of Joy/Searchin' (withdrawn)	120

TONY MERRICK

66	Columbia DB 7913	Lady Jane/Michelle	5
66	Columbia DB 7995	Wake Up/It's For You	5

BOB MERRILL

58	Columbia DB 4086	Nairobi/Jump When I Say Frog	6
58	Columbia DB 4086	Nairobi/Jump When I Say Frog (78)	5

BUDDY MERRILL

66	Vocalion VN 9261	Sweet September/Sherk	10

MERRITTS

70s	Hot Rod HR 113	I Don't Want To/HOT ROD ALL STARS: Version	5

MERRYMEN

66	Doctor Bird DB 1004	Big Bamboo/Island Woman	8
68	Island ILP 984	CARIBBEAN TREASURE CHEST (LP)	25

MERSEYBEATS

63	Fontana TF 412	It's Love That Really Counts/The Fortune Teller	6
63	Fontana TF 431	I Think Of You/Mister Moonlight	4
64	Fontana TF 459	Don't Turn Around/Really Mystified	4
64	Fontana TF 482	Wishin' And Hopin'/Milkman	4
64	Fontana TF 504	Last Night (I Made A Little Girl Cry)/Send Me Back	4
65	Fontana TF 568	Don't Let It Happen To Us/It Would Take A Long Long Time	6
65	Fontana TF 607	I Love You, Yes I Do/Good Good Lovin'	5
65	Fontana TF 645	I Stand Accused/All My Life	5
69	Fontana TF 1025	I Think Of You/Wishin' And Hopin'	4
81	Tudor CR 23	This Is Merseybeat (both sides) (p/s)	5
64	Fontana TE 17422	ON STAGE (EP)	20
64	Fontana TE 17423	I THINK OF YOU (EP)	20
64	Fontana TE 17432	THE MERSEYBEATS (EP)	15
64	Fontana TL 5210	THE MERSEYBEATS (LP)	50
65	Wing WL 1163	THE MERSEYBEATS (LP)	20

(see also Merseys, Rockin' Horse, Tony Crane, Kirkbys, Quotations)

MERSEYBOYS

64	Ace Of Clubs ACL 1169	15 GREAT SONGS BY JOHN, PAUL AND GEORGE (LP)	12

MERSEYS

66	Fontana TF 694	Sorrow/Some Other Day	5
66	Fontana TF 732	So Sad About Us/Love Will Continue	6
66	Fontana TF 776	Rhythm Of Love/Is It Love?	6
67	Fontana TF 845	The Cat/Change Of Heart	5
68	Fontana TF 916	Penny In My Pocket/I Hope You're Happy	5
68	Fontana TF 955	Lovely Loretta/Dreaming	5
73	Philips 6006 258	Sorrow/I Think Of You	4

(see also Merseybeats, Crackers)

TEDDY MERTEN'S TRUMPET

63	Oriole CB 1925	This Is My Prayer/My River Of Memories	4

MERTON PARKAS

79	Beggars Banquet BEG 22	You Need Wheels/I Don't Want To Know You (b&w p/s with patch)	6
79	Beggars Banquet BEG 22	You Need Wheels/I Don't Want To Know You (coloured p/s)	4
79	Beggars Banquet BEG 25	Plastic Smile/The Man With The Disguise (p/s)	4
79	Beggars Banquet BEG 30	Give It To Me Now/Gi's It (p/s)	4
80	Beggars Banquet BEG 43	Put Me In The Picture/In The Midnight Hour (p/s)	5
83	Well Suspect BLAM 002	Flat 19/Band Of Gold (p/s)	10
79	Beggars Banquet BEGA 11	FACE IN THE CROWD (LP)	10

(see also Style Council)

JUNIOR MERVIN

69	Big Shot BI 527	Hustler/Magic Touch	4

MESH

88	Castalia STAB 001	Meet Every Situation Head On (p/s)	4
88	Castalia TAB 001	Meet Every Situation Head On (12", p/s)	7

(see also Psychic TV)

MESSENGERS

64	Columbia DB 7344	I'm Stealin' Back/This Little Light Of Mine	5
65	Columbia DB 7495	When Did You Leave Heaven/More Pretty Girls Than One	4

MESSENGERS

83	Chrysalis CHS 2663	I Turn In (To You)/The Semi Professionals (Theme No. 1) (p/s)	4
83	Chrysalis CHS 12-2663	I Turn In (To You)/The Semi Professionals (Theme No. 1) (12", p/s)	7

84	Chrysalis MUST 1	Great Institutions/Here Come The Heroes (p/s) 4
84	Chrysalis MUSTX 1	Great Institutions/Here Come The Heroes/Strawboy (12", p/s) 7
84	Chrysalis MUST 2	Frontiers/Plane To Siberia (p/s) 4
84	Chrysalis MUSTX 2	Frontiers/Plane To Siberia/Andy Warhol (12", p/s) 7

METABOLIST

| 79 | Drömm DRO 1 | Drömm/Slaves/Eulam's Beat (p/s, 2 different pressings) .... 10-12 |
| 79 | Drömm DRO 3 | Identity/Tiz Hoz Nam (p/s) .... 8 |

METALLICA

84	Music For Nations 12 KUT 105	Jump In The Fire/Seek And Destroy (live)/Phantom Lord (live) (12", p/s, red vinyl) 10
84	Music For Nations PKUT 105	Jump In The Fire/Seek And Destroy (live)/Phantom Lord (live) (shaped picture disc) 15
87	M. F. Nations 12 KUT 112	Creeping Death/Am I Evil/Blitzkrieg (12", p/s, red or green vinyl, original label) 35
87	M. F. Nations P12 KUT 112	Creeping Death/Am I Evil/Blitzkrieg (12", picture disc) 12
87	M. F. Nat. GV12 KUT 112	Creeping Death/Am I Evil/Blitzkrieg (12", p/s, gold vinyl) 15
87	M. F. N. CV12 KUT 112	Creeping Death/Am I Evil/Blitzkrieg (12", p/s, blue vinyl) 10
87	Vertigo METAL 112	$5.98 EP — GARAGE DAYS (12", p/s) 7
88	Vertigo METAL 2	Harvester Of Sorrow (Radio Edit) (promo, p/s) 25
88	Vertigo METAL 212	Harvester Of Sorrow/Breadfan/The Prince (12", promo in special sleeve) 20
88	Vertigo METAL CD 2	Harvester Of Sorrow/Breadfan/The Prince (CD) 12
88	Vertigo MET CD 100	THE WHIPLASH SAMPLER (CD, promo only) 20
89	Vertigo METDJ 5	One (Radio Edit)/Seek And Destroy (live) (promo p/s) 25
89	Vertigo MET 512	One (Demo Version)/For Whom The Bell Tolls (live)/Welcome Home (Sanitarium) (live) (12", p/s) 7
89	Vertigo METG 512	One (Demo Version)/For Whom The Bell Tolls (live)/Welcome Home (Sanitarium) (live) (12", gatefold p/s) 12
89	Vertigo METPD 510	One/Seek And Destroy (live) (10", picture disc with card) 12
89	Vertigo METCD 5	One/For Whom The Bell Tolls (live)/Welcome Home (Sanitarium) (live) (CD) ... 7
90	Vertigo 875 487 1	THE GOOD, THE BAD AND THE LIVE — THE 6½ YEARS ANNIVERSARY COLLECTION (6 x 12", with live anniversary EP) 40
91	Vertigo METAL 7	Enter Sandman/Stone Cold Crazy (picture disc in p/s) 6
91	Vertigo METAL 712	Enter Sandman/Stone Cold Crazy/Holier Than Thou' (12", p/s) 7
91	Vertigo METBX 712	Enter Sandman/Stone Cold Crazy/Holier Than Thou' (12", box with 4 prints) ... 12
91	Vertigo METCD 7	Enter Sandman/Stone Cold Crazy/Holier Than Thou' (CD, box set) 20
91	Vertigo METAP 812	The Unforgiven/Killing Time (picture disc) 5
91	Vertigo METAL 812	The Unforgiven/Killing Time/So What (12", p/s) 7
91	Vertigo METCD 8	The Unforgiven (CD, 3-track) 7
92	Vertigo METAL 1012	Nothing Else Matters/Enter Sandman (live)/Harvester Of Sorrow (live)/ Nothing Else Matters (Demo) (12", p/s) 7
92	Vertigo METCD 10	Nothing Else Matters/Enter Sandman (live)/Harvester Of Sorrow (live)/ Nothing Else Matters (Demo) (CD) 7
92	Vertigo METCL 10	Nothing Else Matters — Live (CD, 4-track live at Wembley) 10
86	M. For Nations MFN 7P	KILL 'EM ALL (LP, picture disc) 15
86	M. For Nations MFN 27P	RIDE THE LIGHTNING (LP, picture disc) 15
86	M. For Nations MFN 60P	MASTER OF PUPPETS (2-LP, picture disc) 15

METAL MIRROR

| 80s private pressing | | METAL MIRROR (EP) .... 10 |

METAL URBAIN

| 78 | Radar ADA 20 | Hysterie Connective/Pas Poubelle .... 5 |
| 79 | Rough Trade RT 001 | Paris Maquis/Cle De Contact (p/s) .... 6 |

(see also Doctor Mix & Remix)

METEORS

| 64 | Polydor NH 52263 | Get A Load Of This/Ruby Ann .... 4 |

METEORS

| 79 | EMI EMI 5000 | My Balls Ache/Action (p/s) .... 4 |

METEORS

81	Ace SW 65	METEOR MADNESS (EP, some on blue vinyl) 8/5
81	Ace SWT 65	METEOR MADNESS (10" EP, white label test pressings only, custom p/s) 30
81	Chiswick CHIS 147	Radioactive Kid/Graveyard Stomp (p/s) 6
81	Lost Soul LOST 101	The Crazed/Attack Of The Zorch Men (p/s) 8
81	Ace NS 74	Radioactive Kid/Graveyard Stomp (p/s, reissue, some clear or blue vinyl) 7/4
82	WXYZ ABCD 5	Mutant Rock/The Hills Have Eyes (p/s) 4
82	ID EYE 1	Johnny Remember Me/Fear Of The Dark/Wreckin' Crew (p/s) 4
83	ID EYE 1P	Johnny Remember Me/Fear Of The Dark/Wreckin' Crew (picture disc) 6
86	ID EYE 10	MUTANT ROCK (EP, green vinyl) 4
86	ID EYET 10	MUTANT ROCK (12" EP, green or blue vinyl) 7
83	Lyntone LYN 12647	METEORS: Mutant Rock (Instrumental)/ANTI NOWHERE LEAGUE: World War Three/DEFECTS: Dance (red flexidisc with 'Flexipop' mag. issue 26) 6/5
81	Ace MAD 1	THE METEORS MEET SCREAMIN' LORD SUTCH (mini-LP, stickered cartoon on plain card sleeve) 30
81	Lost Soul LOSTLP 3001	IN HEAVEN (LP) 10

(see also Tall Boys, Clapham South Escalators, Screaming Lord Sutch)

METERS

69	Stateside SS 2140	Sophisticated Cissy/Sehorns Farms 8
70	Direction 58 4751	Look Ka-Py-Py/This Is My Last Affair 5
74	Reprise K 14367	People Say/Africa 4
75	Reprise K 14405	Fire On The Bayou/They All Asked For You 4
72	Reprise K 44242	CABBAGE ALLEY (LP) 15
74	Reprise K 54027	REJUVENATION (LP) 25
74	Island ILPS 9250	CISSY STRUT (LP) 20
75	Reprise K 54044	FIRE ON THE BAYOU (LP) 25

76	Reprise K 54076	BEST OF THE METERS (LP)	10
76	Reprise K 54078	TRICK BAG (LP)	20
77	Reprise K 56378	NEW DIRECTIONS (LP)	10
79	Pye PKL 5578	GOOD OLD FUNKY MUSIC (LP)	10

METHUSELAH
69	Elektra EKS 74052	MATTHEW, MARK, LUKE & JOHN (LP)	40

(see also Amazing Blondel)

FRANK METIS ORCHESTRA
56	London REN 1048	SHOW BUSINESS — SELECTION (EP)	10

METROPAK
80	Metropak PAK 001	You're A Rebel/OK Let's Go/Run Run Run (numbered p/s)	5
80	Metropak PAK 002	Here's Looking At You/Walking (foldout card p/s)	5

METROPHASE
79	Neo London MS 01	In Black/Neo Beauty/Cold Rebellion (photocopied p/s with lyric insert)	8
79	Neo London MS 02	New Age/Frames Of Life (foldout p/s, stamped white labels)	8
81	Fresh FRESH 6	In Black/Neo Beauty/Cold Rebellion (reissue, better quality p/s with insert)	6

(see also Swell Maps)

M.E.V.
69	Polydor 583 769	MUSICA ELETTRONICA VIVA (LP)	15

ANNA MEYERS
40s	Davega 5067	That Da-Da Strain/Ain't Nobody's Biz-ness If I Do (78)	60

LEE MEZA
67	Stateside SS 589	If It Happens/One Good Thing Leads To Another	25

MEZZ MEZZROW
62	Storyville SEP 394	KING JAZZ STORY (EP)	8
55	Vogue LAE 12007	PLAYEL CONCERT (LP)	10
56	Vogue LAE 12017	THE MEZZROW-BECHET QUINTET (LP)	10

(see also Sidney Bechet)

M.F.Q.
(see under Modern Folk Quartet)

M.F.S.B.
81	Phil. Intl. PIR 12-9501	Mysteries Of The World/Manhattan Skyline (12")	8
81	Phil. Intl. PIR 84251	MYSTERIES OF THE WORLD (LP)	12

M-G-M STUDIO ORCHESTRA
54	MGM SP 1099	Peddler Song/Antonia/Fisherman's Song	4
55	MGM SP 1144	Rock Around The Clock/"Blackboard Jungle" Love Theme	6
55	MGM MGM 861	Rock Around The Clock/"Blackboard Jungle" Love Theme (78)	5

MIAMI SOUND MACHINE
84	Epic A 4800	Prisoner Of Love/Toda Tuya (Toda Dia Eva Dia De Indio) (p/s)	4
84	Epic TX 4800	Prisoner Of Love/Toda Tuya (Toda Dia Eva Dia De Indio)/ Prisoner Of Love (Instrumental) (12", p/s)	7
85	Epic A 6537	Bad Boy (Shep Pettibone Remix)/Movies (p/s)	5
85	Epic QTA 6537	Bad Boy (Club Mix)/Bad Boy (Rubber-Club-Dub Mix)/Movies (12", p/s)	7
85	Epic TA 6361	Conga! (Dance Mix)/Conga! (Instrumental) (12", p/s)	7
86	Epic A 6956	Falling In Love (Uh-Oh)/Surrender Paradise (p/s)	4
86	Epic 650251 7	Falling In Love (Uh-Oh) (Remix)/Surrender Paradise (p/s)	4
86	Epic TA 6956	Falling In Love (Uh-Oh)/Conga (The Stronga-Conga Remix)/Surrender Paradise (12", p/s)	7
84	Epic EPC 26167	EYES OF INNOCENCE (LP)	10
85	Epic EPC 26491	PRIMITIVE LOVE (LP)	10

(see also Gloria Estefan [& Miami Sound Machine])

MIAOW
85	Venus VENUS 1	Belle Vue/Fate (p/s)	4
85	Venus VENUS 1T	Belle Vue/Fate/Grocer's Devil Daughter (12", p/s)	7

MICHA
65	Pye 7N 15982	Protest Singer/Serpent	4

GEORGE MICHAEL
84	Epic A 4603	Careless Whisper/Careless Whisper (Instrumental) (poster p/s)	15
84	Epic QTA 4603	Careless Whisper/Careless Whisper (Wexler Mix) (12", p/s)	40
84	Epic WA 4603	Careless Whisper/Careless Whisper (Instrumental) (12" picture disc clear or black rim)	35/25
86	Epic GTA 7033	A Different Corner (Extended)/A Different Corner (Instrumental) (12", gatefold p/s)	7
87	Epic LUSTC 1	I Want Your Sex (Monogamy Mix)/I Want Your Sex (Instrumental) (cassette)	4
87	Epic QT 1	I Want Your Sex/I Want Your Sex (Instrumental) (12" gatefold p/s)	10
87	Epic CDLUST 1	I Want Your Sex (Monogamy Mix)/Rhythm 1 Lust/Rhythm 2 Brass In Love/ Rhythm 3 A Last Request (CD)	10
87	Epic EMUP 3	Faith/Hand To Mouth/Faith (Instrumental) (12" picture disc)	10
87	Epic CD EMU 3	Faith/Hand To Mouth/Faith (Instrumental) (CD)	7
88	Epic EMUP 4	Father Figure (Extended)/Love's In Need Of Love Today/Father Figure (Instrumental) (shaped picture disc in wallet)	8
88	Epic CD EMU 4	Father Figure (Extended)/Love's In Need Of Love Today/Father Figure (Instrumental) (CD)	7
88	Epic EMU B5	One More Try/Look At Your Hands (p/s, with free badge)	5
88	Epic EMU T5	One More Try/Look At Your Hands (12" p/s, with poster)	8
88	Epic EMU G6	Monkey/Monkey (Version) (gatefold p/s)	4
91	Epic XPC 4060	WEMBLEY (4-track gig cassette)	25

(see also Elton John & George Michael)

CODY MICHAELS
79	Grapevine GRP 121	7 Days — 52 Weeks/VIRTUE ORCHESTRA: Don't Look Back	4

LEE MICHAELS
68	A&M AMS 763	Heighty Hi/Want My Baby	4
72	A&M AMS 882	Can I Get A Witness/You Are What You Do	5
69	A&M AMLS 928	RECITAL (LP)	10
69	A&M AMLS 956	LEE MICHAELS (LP)	10

MARILYN MICHAELS
60	RCA RCA 1208	Tell Tommy I Miss Him/Everyone Was There But You	7

MICHIGAN RAG
72	Blue Horizon 2096 009	Don't Run Away/She's Looking Good	10

MICHIGANS
63	Vogue V 9207	Intermission Riff/Tea For Two	4

MICK & MALCOLM
66	Piccadilly 7N 35344	Little Venice/In A Game Of Chess	4
67	Piccadilly 7N 35372	Big Black Smoke/Two Or Three Minutes Of My Time	4

MICKEY (Baker) & KITTY (Noble)
60	London HLE 9054	Buttercup/My Reverie	12

MICKEY (Baker) & SYLVIA
57	HMV POP 331	Love Is Strange/I'm Going Home	175
57	HMV POP 331	Love Is Strange/I'm Going Home (78)	35
58	RCA RCA 1064	Rock And Stroll Room/Bewildered	25
58	RCA RCA 1064	Rock And Stroll Room/Bewildered (78)	30
60	RCA RCA 1206	Sweeter As The Day Goes By/Mommy Out De Light	15
65	RCA Victor RCA 1487	Love Is Strange/Dearest	20
65	RCA Camden CDN 5133	LOVE IS STRANGE (LP)	100

MICKEY FINN
65	Columbia DB 7510	The Sporting Life/Night Comes Down	40
66	Polydor BM 56719	I Do Love You/If I Had You Baby	40
67	Direction 58-3086	Garden Of My Mind/Time To Start Loving You	35
	(DON'T see also Micky Finn & Blue Men under 'F')		

MICROBE
69	CBS 4158	Groovy Baby/Your Turn Now	4

MICRODISNEY
82	Kabuki KAMD 2	Hello Rascals/The Helicopter Of The Holy Ghost	6
83	Kabuki KAMD 4	Pink Skinned Man/Fiction Land	5

TONY MIDDLETON
65	London HLR 9983	My Little Red Book (as Burt Bacharach Orchestra with Tony Middleton)/ BURT BACHARACH ORCHESTRA: What's New Pussycat	15
66	Polydor BM 56704	Don't Ever Leave Me/To The Ends Of The Earth	200
78	Grapevine GRP 115	Paris Blues/Out Of This World	4

MIDNIGHT MOVERS
73	Contempo C 7	Follow The Wind Pts 1 & 2	6

MIDNIGHT OIL
83	CBS A 3343	U.S. Forces/Some Kids/Knife Edge (p/s)	5
83	CBS A 3176	The Power And The Passion/Glitch Baby Glitch (p/s)	5
85	CBS A 6383	Best Of Both Worlds/Kosciusko (p/s)	4
85	CBS TA 6383	Best Of Both Worlds/Kosciusko/The Power And The Passion (12", p/s)	7
85	CBS A 6583	When The Generals Talk/Who Can Stand In The Way (p/s)	4
90	CBS CD OIL 6	FORGOTTEN YEARS (CD EP)	8

MIDNIGHT RAGS
80	Ace ACE 005	Public Enemy/Alcatraz/Mamma Said	8
80	Velvet Moon VM 1	The Cars That Ate New York/Oscar Automobile (p/s) (withdrawn)	10
	(see also Paul Roland, Weird Strings)		

MIDNIGHTS
66	Ember EMB S 220	(Won'tcha) Show Me Around/Only Two Can Play	6
60s	private pressing	MIDKNIGHTS (EP)	125+

MIDNIGHT SHIFT
66	Decca F 12487	Saturday Jump/Living Fast	10

MIDNIGHT SUN
71	MCA MK 5081	Nickels And Dimes/King Of The Sun	4
72	MCA MKPS 2019	MIDNIGHT SUN (LP)	18
72	MCA MKPS 2024	WALKING CIRCLES (LP)	18
73	MCA MCF 2687	MIDNIGHT SUN (LP, reissue)	12
73	MCA MCF 2691	WALKING CIRCLES (LP, reissue)	12

M.I. FIVE
66	Parlophone R 5486	You'll Never Stop Me Loving You/Only Time Will Tell	30
	(see also Maze, Deep Purple)		

MIGHTY AVENGERS
64	Decca F 11891	Hide Your Pride/Hey Senorita	10
64	Decca F 11962	So Much In Love/Sometime They Say	10
65	Decca F 12085	Blue Turns To Grey/I'm Lost Without You	10
65	Decca F 12198	(Walkin' Thru The) Sleepy City/Sir Edward And Lady Jane	15
	(see also Andrew Oldham)		

MIGHTY BABY
71	Blue Horizon 2096 003	Devil's Whisper/Virgin Spring	20

69	Head HDLS 6002	MIGHTY BABY (LP)	55
71	Blue Horizon 2931 001	A JUG OF LOVE (LP)	80
84	Psycho PSYCHO 31	EGYPTIAN TOMB (LP, reissue of "Mighty Baby")	15

(see also Action, Robin Scott, Habibiyya, Keith Christmas)

MIGHTY CAESARS

| 86 | Empire LWC 604 | Ten Bears Of The Comanches/Baby What's Wrong | 4 |
| 88 | Swag SWG 001 | She's Just Fifteen Years Old/The Swag (flexi with 'Pandora's Box' fanzine) | 8/6 |

(see also Milkshakes, Prisoners)

MIGHTY CLOUDS OF JOY

75	ABC ABC 4036	Mighty Clouds Of Joy/Everything Is Going Up	4
76	ABC ABC 4102	Mighty High/Touch My Soul	4
75	ABC ABCL 5097	IT'S TIME (LP)	10

MIGHTY DOUGLAS

60s	Jump Up JU 501	Laziest Man/Dance Me Lover	5
60s	Jump Up JU 508	Teacher Teacher/Split Me In Two	5
60s	Jump Up JU 509	Ugliness/My Wicked Boy Child	5

MIGHTY FLEA & MICKEY BAKER

| 72 | Polydor 2058 328 | Bloodshot Eyes/Charley Stone | 4 |
| 72 | Polydor 2460 185 | LET THE GOOD TIMES ROLL (LP) | 10 |

MIGHTY LEMON DROPS

85	Dreamworld DREAM 5	Like An Angel/Something Happens/Sympathise With Us (12", p/s)	8
86	Dreamworld DREAM 006	Like An Angel/Now She's Gone (p/s)	6
86	Blue Guitar AZURS 3	My Biggest Thrill/Open Mind//Rollercoaster/Wait And See (double pack, gatefold p/s)	5
87	Blue Guitar AZURG 4	The Out Of Hand EP: Out Of Hand/Going Under//Splash #1 (Now I'm Home)/Count Me Out (double pack, gatefold stickered p/s)	4
87	Tardis 004/LYN 18687	The Happy Head Demos: Uptight/Behind Your Back (flexidisc, stickered plain sleeve, free with 'The Beast' fanzine)	8/6
89	fan club	Fall Down (Original Demo)/Breaking Down (Original Arrangement) (fan club issue, 200 copies only)	10
90	Lyntone	Sometimes Good Guys Don't Wear White (live at the Dominion) (p/s gig freebie flexi; blue or black p/s)	each 6
85	private cassette	SOME OF MY BEST FRIENDS ARE SONGS (8-song cassette, 150 only)	15

(see also Wild Flowers, Active Restraint, Another Dream)

MIGHTY MEN

| 62 | Salvo SLO 1804 | No Way Out/You Too Much | 12 |

MIGHTY MIGHTY

| 86 | Girlie GAYE 001 | Everybody Knows The Monkey/You're On My Mind (foldover p/s in poly bag) | 5 |
| 86 | Sha La La 001 | Throwaway/CLOUDS: Jenny Nowhere (p/s flexi free with various fanzines) | 6 |

MIGHTY MO

| 72 | Columbia DB 8851 | Ape Call/Heavy Bear | 5 |

MIGHTY POWER

| 67 | Jump Up JU 513 | You're Wasting Your Time/Smart Barbarian | 5 |

MIGHTY SAM

66	Stateside SS 534	Sweet Dreams/That Good Humour Man	8
66	Stateside SS 544	Fannie Mae/Badmouthin'	8
68	Stateside SS 2076	When She Touches Me/Just Like Old Times	7
70	Soul City SC 115	Papa True Love/I Need A Lot Of Lovin'	8
70	Soul City SCM 004	MIGHTY SOUL (LP)	30

MIGHTY SPARROW

60s	Jump Up JU 523	Village Ram/Pull Pistle Gang	5
60s	Kalypso XX 22	Mr. Herbert/Simpson	6
68	NEMS 56-3558	Mr. Walker/Carnival In '68	6
60s	Kalypso XXEP 1	MIGHTY SPARROW (EP)	10
63	Island ILP 902	THE SLAVE (LP)	30
72	Trojan TRL 49	HOTTER THAN EVER (LP)	10

MIGHTY SPARROW/BYRON LEE & DRAGONAIRES

| 69 | Trojan TRL 8 | THE SPARROW MEETS THE DRAGON (LP) | 10 |

(see also Byron Lee & Dragonaires)

MIGHTY VIKINGS

| 67 | Island WI 3060 | Do Re Mi/The Sound Of Music | 8 |
| 67 | Island WI 3074 | Rockitty Fockitty/Give Me Back My Gal (actually by Sammy Ismay & Mighty Vikings) | 8 |

MIGIL FIVE

64	Pye 7N 15597	Mockingbird Hill/Long Ago And Far Away	4
64	Pye 7N 15645	Near You/Don't Wanna Go On Shaking	4
64	Pye 7N 15677	Boys And Girls/I Saw Your Picture	4
65	Pye 7N 15757	Just Behind The Rainbow/Seven Lonely Days	4
65	Pye 7N 15874	One Hundred Years/I'm In Love Again	4
66	Pye 7N 17023	Pencil And Paper/Nevertheless (I'm In Love With You)	4
67	Columbia DB 8196	Together/Superstition	10
69	Jay Boy BOY 4	If I Had My Way/Somebody's Stolen The Moon	5
64	Pye NEP 24191	MEET THE MIGIL FIVE (EP)	10
64	Pye NPL 18093	MOCKING BIRD HILL (LP)	15

(see also Migil Four)

MIGIL FOUR

| 63 | Pye 7N 15572 | Maybe/Can't I? | 6 |

(see also Migil Five)

MIKE & MECHANICS

85	WEA U 8908	Silent Running/I Get The Feeling (p/s, original sleeve without Paul Carrack)	5
85	WEA U 8908T	Silent Running/I Get The Feeling (12", p/s, original sleeve)	8
85	WEA 8908P	Silent Running/I Get The Feeling (engine-shaped picture disc)	10
85	WEA U 8765TP	All I Need Is A Miracle/You Are The One/A Call To Arms (12" picture disc)	10
91	Virgin VCCDX 1351	A Time And Place/Yesterday Tomorrow/Word Of Mouth (East West Mix) (CD, in photo wallet with 5 prints)	7

(see also Mike Rutherford, Genesis)

MIKE & MODIFIERS

62	Oriole CB 1775	I Found Myself A Brand New Baby/It's Too Bad	450

MIKI & GRIFF

59	Pye 7N 15213	Hold Back Tomorrow/Deedle Dum Doo Die Day	5
60	Pye 7N 15266	Long Time To Forget/Someday You'll Call My Name	5
60	Pye 7N 15296	I'm Here To Get My Baby Out Of Jail/Rockin' Alone	4
61	Pye 7N 15346	Have I Stayed Away Too Long/You Don't Ever Write Or Call	4
61	Pye 7N 15362	I Wish It Had Been A Dream/My Baby's Gone	4
61	Pye 7N 15386	Tennessee Waltz/Whispering Hope	4
62	Pye 7N 15412	Little Bitty Tear/I Missed Me	4
62	Pye 7N 15432	I Wonder Where You Are Tonight/Tears Break Out	4
62	Pye 7N 15449	This Time I Would Know/It's Just The Idea	4
62	Pye 7N 15490	Madd Madd World/Are You Wasting My Time	4
64	Pye 7N 15614	Here Today Gone Tomorrow/Changing Partners (p/s)	5
60	Pye NEP 24116	THIS IS MIKI THIS IS GRIFF (EP)	7
60	Pye NEP 24129	HIT PARADE (EP)	7
61	Pye NEP 24145	TWO'S COMPANY (EP)	7
62	Pye NEP 24153	HIT PARADE (EP)	7
65	Pye NEP 24207	OLD ROCKING CHAIR (EP)	7
66	Pye NEP 24268	IT'S MY WAY (EP)	7
61	Pye NPL 18058	MIKI AND GRIFF (LP)	10
62	Pye NPL 18074	COUNTRY STYLE (LP)	12

BOBBY MILANO

55	Capitol CL 14252	A King Or A Slave/If You Cared	6
55	Capitol CL 14309	If Tears Could Bring You Back/Make Me A Present Of You	6

AMOS MILBURN

57	Vogue V 9064	Every Day Of The Week/Girl Of My Dreams (triangular or round centre)	....80/30
57	Vogue V 9064	Every Day Of The Week/Girl Of My Dreams (78)	25
57	Vogue V 9069	Rum And Coca Cola/Soft Pillow	90
57	Vogue V 9069	Rum And Coca Cola/Soft Pillow (78)	25
57	Vogue V 9080	Thinking Of You Baby/If I Could Be With You (One Hour Tonight)	80
57	Vogue V 9080	Thinking Of You Baby/If I Could Be With You (One Hour Tonight) (78)	25
60	Vogue V 9163	One Scotch, One Bourbon, One Beer/Bad, Bad Whiskey	90
57	Vogue VE 170102	ROCK AND ROLL (EP)	140
78	United Artists UAS 30203	CHICKEN SHACK BOOGIE (LP)	12

AMOS MILBURN JNR

63	London HLU 9795	Gloria/Look At Me Fool	6

PERCY MILEM

66	Stateside SS 566	Crying Baby, Baby, Baby/Call On Me	10

BUDDY MILES (EXPRESS)

68	Mercury MF 1065	Train Pts 1 & 2	4
69	Mercury MF 1098	Miss Lady/'69 Freedom Special	4
71	Mercury 6052 036	Them Changes/Your Feeling Is Mine (solo)	4
72	Mercury 6052 127	Give Away None Of My Love/Take It Off Him And Put It On Me (solo)	4
69	Mercury SMCL 20137	EXPRESSWAY TO YOUR SKULL (LP)	15
69	Mercury SMCL 20163	ELECTRIC CHURCH (LP)	15
70	Mercury 6338 016	THEM CHANGES (LP)	12
70	Mercury 6338 028	WE GOT TO LIVE TOGETHER (LP)	10
70	Mercury 6338 048	A MESSAGE TO THE PEOPLE (LP)	10
75	Casablanca CBC 4006	MORE MILES PER GALLON (LP)	10

(see also Electric Flag)

GARRY MILES

60	London HLG 9155	Look For A Star/Afraid Of Love	8
60	London REG 1264	LOOK FOR A STAR (EP)	35

JOHN MILES

71	Amity OTS 508	Why Don't You Love Me?/If I Could See Through	4
71	Decca F 13196	Jose/You Make It So Hard	4
72	Orange OAS 207	Come Away Melinda/Walking With My Head Held High	4
72	Orange OAS 208	Yesterday (Was Just The Beginning)/Road To Freedom	4
73	Orange OAS 209	Hard Road/You're Telling Me Lies	4
73	Orange OAS 211	Jacqueline/Keep On Tryin'	4
73	Orange OAS 213	One Minute Every Hour/Hollywood Queen	4
74	Orange OAS 220	Fright Of My Life/Good Time Woman	4
74	Orange OAS 223	What's On Your Mind/Rock'n'Roll Band	4
74	Orange OAS 224	What's On Your Mind/To Be Grateful	5
83	EMI EMI 5386	The Right To Sing/Back To The Magic (picture disc)	4

(see also Influence)

JOSIE MILES

40s	Edison 51476	Sweet Man Joe/ROSA HENDERSON: Undertaker's Blues (78)	50
40s	Edison 51477	Temper'Mental Papa/Mad Mama's Blues (78)	50
60s	Poydras 103	JOSIE MILES (EP)	8

LENNY MILES
61	Top Rank JAR 546	Don't Believe Him Donna/Invisible	10

LIZZIE MILES
23	HMV B 1703	You're Always Messin' 'Round With My Man/EDNA HICKS: I'm Going Away Just To Wear You Off My Mind (78)	50
50s	Melodisc EPM7 55	NEW ORLEANS BOYS (EP)	18
57	Capitol T 792	A NIGHT IN NEW ORLEANS (LP)	12

LIZZIE MILES/BILLY YOUNG
56	HMV 7EG 8178	THE BLUES THEY SANG (EP, 1 side each)	12

MILESTONES & BUTCH BAKER
75	Black Magic BM 111	The Joker Pts 1 & 2	5

MILKSHAKES
82	Bilko BILK-O	Please Don't Tell My Baby/It's You (p/s)	7
83	Upright UP 6	Soldiers Of Love/Shimmy Shimmy (p/s)	5
84	Big Beat NS 94	Brand New Cadillac/Commanche/Jezebel/Jaguar And Thunderbird (p/s)	4
84	Big Beat SW 105	The Ambassadors Of Love/No More/Gringles And Groyles Again/ Remarkable (p/s)	4
86	Empire UXF 228	Let Me Love You/She Tells Me She Loves Me (p/s)	4
83	Big Beat NED 4	14 RHYTHM AND BEAT GREATS (LP)	10
83	Upright UPLP 1	AFTER SCHOOL SESSIONS (LP)	10
84	Milkshake HARP-O	NOTHING CAN STOP THESE MEN (LP)	10
85	Big Beat WIK 30	THEY CAME, THEY SAW, THEY CONQUERED (LP)	10
86	Milkshake MILK-O	TALKING 'BOUT MILKSHAKES (LP)	10

(see also Thee Mighty Caesars, Prisoners/Milkshakes)

MILKWOOD
72	Warner Bros K 16141	Watching You Go/Here I Stand	4
73	Warner Bros K 16283	I'm A Song (Sing Me)/Patterson's Brewery	4
74	Warner Bros K 16418	What Can I Do To Make You Love Me/Now And Then	4

MILLER
65	Oak RGJ 190	Baby I've Got News For You/The Girl With The Castle	150
65	Columbia DB 7735	Baby I Got News For You/The Girl With The Castle	100

(see also Big Boy Pete)

ANN MILLER
54	MGM SP 1076	Too Darn Hot/KATHRYN GRAYSON & HOWARD KEEL: So In Love	4

ANN MILLER & KATHRYN GRAYSON
54	MGM SP 1078	Always True To You In My Fashion/I Hate Men	5

(see also Kathryn Grayson & Howard Keel)

BETTY MILLER
59	Top Rank JAR 115	Pearly Gates/Old Time Religion	5
59	Top Rank JAR 127	Jack O'Diamonds/(It Took) One Kiss	5

BOB MILLER & MILLERMEN
59	Fontana TF 181	Dig This!/The Poacher	4
59	Fontana TF 192	Little Dipper/The Keel Row	4
59	Fontana TF 228	In The Mood/Joey's Song	4
60	Fontana TF 236	The Busker's Tune/My Guy's Come Back	4
60	Fontana TF 245	77 Sunset Strip/Manhunt	4
60	Fontana TF 284	Night Theme/Last Date	4
61	Parlophone R 4779	Trouble Shooter/Hootin'	4
61	Parlophone R 4854	The "Oliver" Twist/That's It	4
65	Mercury MF 947	Uptown And Downtown/Carnaby Street Parade	6
65	Polydor 56005	6-5 Special/Dick Van Dyke Theme	4
66	Columbia DB 7877	Get Smart/Bony's Blues (as Bob Miller & His Millermen)	4

BOBBIE MILLER
65	Decca F 12064	What A Guy/You Went Away	30
65	Decca F 12252	Every Beat Of My Heart/Tomorrow	5
66	Decca F 12354	Everywhere I Go/IAN STEWART & RAILROADERS: Stu-Ball	50

(see also Mongrels, Rolling Stones)

CHUCK MILLER
56	Capitol CL 14543	Rogue River Valley/No Baby Like You	12
57	Mercury MT 157	Bye, Bye Love/Rang Tang Ding Dong (78)	6
57	Mercury MT 181	Plaything/After Yesterday (78)	5
58	Mercury 7MT 153	The Auctioneer/Me Head's In De Barrel	20
58	Mercury MT 153	The Auctioneer/Me Head's In De Barrel (78)	5
58	Mercury 7MT 215	Down The Road A-Piece/Mad About Her Blues	35
58	Mercury MT 215	Down The Road A-Piece/Mad About Her Blues (78)	5
59	Mercury AMT 1026	The Auctioneer/Baby Doll	12
59	Mercury AMT 1026	The Auctioneer/Baby Doll (78)	5
60	Mercury ZEP 10058	GOING GOING GONE (EP)	40

FRANKIE MILLER (U.S.)
59	Melodisc MEL 1519	True Blue/Black Land Farmer	12
59	Melodisc MEL 1519	True Blue/Black Land Farmer (78)	10
59	Melodisc MEL 1529	Poppin' Johnnie/Family Man	8
59	Melodisc MEL 1529	Poppin' Johnnie/Family Man (78)	10
60	Melodisc MEL 1552	Rain, Rain/Baby Rocked Her Dolly	8
62	Top Rank JKP 3013	COUNTRY MUSIC (EP)	20

FRANKIE MILLER (U.K.)
78	Chrysalis CHS 2221	Stubborn Kind Of Fellow/Good Time Love (p/s, coloured vinyl)	4

Gary MILLER

MINT VALUE £

GARY MILLER

58	Pye 7N 15120	The Story Of My Life/Put A Light In The Window	6
58	Pye 7N 15136	Lollipop/Dancing With My Shadow	6
58	Pye 7N 15140	On The Street Where You Live/That's For Me	4
58	Pye 7N 15151	A Couple Of Crazy Kids (with Marion Ryan)/Ivanhoe Of England	5
58	Pye 7N 15164	The First Christmas Day/Nearest And Dearest	4
59	Pye 7N 15188	Jezebel/The Railroad Song	4
59	Pye 7N 15207	Sing Along/Someone To Come Home To	4
59	Pye 7N 15239	Marina/Hold Me, Thrill Me, Kiss Me	4
60	Pye 7N 15277	Mission Bell/Happy Together	4
61	Pye 7N 15338	Goodnight Sweetheart/Dream Harbour	4
61	Pye 7N 15368	The Story Behind The Tears/Some Enchanted Evening	4
61	Pye 7N 15404	There Goes That Song Again/The Night Is Young	4
62	Pye 7N 15425	If You Were The Only Girl/Dancing In The Park	4
62	Pye 7N 15452	If I Had My Way/Moonlight Becomes You	4
62	Pye 7N 15474	Mister Lonely/Sunday	4
63	Pye 7N 15497	I've Heard That Song Before/You Are Beautiful	4
64	Pye 7N 15592	Maria Elena/Amor	4
64	Pye 7N 15651	The Way You Look Tonight/Dear Friend	4
64	Pye 7N 15698	Stingray/Aqua Marina	12
56	Pye NEP 24013	YELLOW ROSE OF TEXAS (EP)	18
57	Pye NEP 24047	HIT PARADE VOL. 1 (EP)	15
57	Pye NEP 24057	MEET MISTER MILLER PT. 1 — ON STAGE (EP)	10
57	Pye NEP 24058	MEET MISTER MILLER PT. 2 — FOR THE YOUNG IN LOVE (EP)	10
57	Pye NEP 24059	MEET MISTER MILLER PT. 3 — FOR THE YOUNG IN LOVE (EP)	10
58	Pye NEP 24072	HIT PARADE VOL. 2 (EP)	12
60	Pye NEP 24123	FLOWER DRUM SONG (EP)	7
57	Nixa NPL 18008	MEET MISTER MILLER (LP)	20
61	Pye NPL 18059	GARY ON THE BALL (LP)	12

GLEN MILLER

67	Doctor Bird DB 1089	Where Is The Love/Funky Broadway	7
68	Doctor Bird DB 1128	Rocksteady Party/Book Of Memories	7

GLENN MILLER & HIS ORCHESTRA

46	HMV BD 5942	Moonlight Serenade/American Patrol (78)	5
54	Columbia SCM 5086	Sleepy Time Gal/I Got Rhythm	8
54	HMV 7M 195	Don't Sit Under The Apple Tree/Little Brown Jug	12
58	RCA RCA 1034	Falling Leaves/So Sweet (as Glenn Miller New Orchestra)	4
58	RCA RCA 1096	American Patrol/Little Brown Jug	6
59	Top Rank JAR 114	Boom Shot/You Say The Sweetest Things, Baby	6
59	Top Rank TR 5003	Chattanooga Choo Choo/Serenade In Blue	6
65	Columbia DB 7550	Pennsylvania 6-5000/The Girl From Ipanema	6
54	HMV 7EG 8031	GLENN MILLER AND HIS ORCHESTRA (EP)	7
54	HMV 7EG 8043	GLENN MILLER AND HIS ORCHESTRA (EP)	7
54	HMV 7EG 8055	GLENN MILLER AND HIS ORCHESTRA (EP)	7
55	HMV 7EG 8067	GLENN MILLER AND HIS ORCHESTRA (EP)	7
55	HMV 7EG 8077	GLENN MILLER AND HIS ORCHESTRA (EP)	7
55	HMV 7EG 8097	THAT MILLER MUSIC (EP)	7
55	Brunswick OE 9169	COLLECTOR'S ITEMS (EP)	7
57	HMV 7EG 8204	GLENN MILLER SPECIAL (EP)	7
59	Top Rank JKR 8019	GOLDEN MILLER (EP)	7
53	HMV DLP 1012	GLENN MILLER CONCERT VOL. 1 (10" LP)	14
53	HMV DLP 1013	GLENN MILLER CONCERT VOL. 2 (10" LP)	14
53	HMV DLP 1021	GLENN MILLER CONCERT VOL. 3 (10" LP)	14
54	HMV DLP 1024	THE GLENN MILLER STORY (10" LP)	12
54	HMV DLP 1049	TIME FOR MELODY (10" LP)	12
54	HMV DLP 1059	ORCHESTRA WIVES (10" LP)	12
54	HMV RLS 599	GLENN MILLER LIMITED EDITION (5-LP, in album, 'snakeskin' cover)	50
55	HMV DLP 1062	SUNRISE SERENADE (10" LP)	12
55	HMV DLP 1081	GLENN MILLER CONCERT VOL. 4 (10" LP)	12
55	Philips BBR 8072	GLENN MILLER (10" LP)	12
56	HMV CLPC 6-10/RLS 598	GLENN MILLER LIMITED EDITION VOL. 2 (5-LP, in album)	50
56	HMV RLS 637	GLENN MILLER & THE ARMY AIRFORCE BAND (5-LP, presentation box, [CLP 1077-CLP 1081])	30
56	HMV DLP 1122	MILLER MAGIC (10" LP)	12
56	Philips BBR 8092	GLENN MILLER (10" LP)	12
57	HMV DLP 1145	POLKA DOTS AND MOONBEAMS (10" LP)	12
58	RCA RD 27057	THE GLENN MILLER CARNEGIE HALL CONCERT (LP)	10
58	RCA RD 27068	THE GLENN MILLER STORY (LP)	10
58	RCA RD 27090	THE MARVELLOUS MILLER MEDLEYS (LP)	10
58	RCA RD 27096	MARVELLOUS MILLER MOODS (LP)	10
58	RCA RD 27135	GLENN MILLER ARMY AIRFORCE BAND VOL. 1 (LP)	10
59	Top Rank RX 3004	GLENN MILLER AND HIS ORCHESTRA VOL. 1 (LP)	10
59	Top Rank 35/023	GLENN MILLER AND HIS ORCHESTRA VOL. 2 (LP)	10
60	RCA RD 27146/RD 27147	FOR THE VERY FIRST TIME (2-LP)	14

JIMMY MILLER & (NEW) BARBECUES

57	Columbia DB 4006	Sizzlin' Hot/Free Wheelin' Baby (as Jimmy Miller & Barbecues)	35
57	Columbia DB 4006	Sizzlin' Hot/Free Wheelin' Baby (as Jimmy Miller & Barbecues) (78)	15
58	Columbia DB 4081	Jelly Baby/Cry, Baby, Cry (as Jimmy Miller & New Barbecues)	30
58	Columbia DB 4081	Jelly Baby/Cry, Baby, Cry (as Jimmy Miller & New Barbecues) (78)	6

JODY MILLER

64	Capitol CL 15335	He Walks Like A Man/Looking At The World Through A Tea Cup	4
64	Capitol CL 15356	The Fever/In My Room	4
65	Capitol CL 15393	Queen Of The House/The Greatest Actor	4
65	Capitol CL 15404	Silver Threads And Golden Needles/Melody For Robin	4

668 Rare Record Price Guide

| 65 | Capitol CL 15415 | Home Of The Brave/This Is The Life | 4 |
| 66 | Capitol CL 15482 | If You Were A Carpenter/Let Me Walk With You | 4 |

KENNY MILLER
| 65 | Stateside SS 405 | Restless/Take My Tip | 25 |

MANDY MILLER
| 56 | Parlophone R 4219 | Nellie The Elephant/It's Time To Dream | 6 |
| 58 | Parlophone GEP 8776 | CHILDREN'S CHOICE (EP) | 7 |

MAX MILLER
58	Pye 7N 15141	With A Little Bit Of Luck/Be Sincere	4
59	HMV 7EG 8558	THE CHEEKY CHAPPIE (EP)	7
61	Pye NEP 25154	MAX AT THE MET (EP)	7
62	Pye NEP 25162	MAX AT THE MET VOL. 2 (EP)	7
58	Pye NPT 19026	MAX AT THE MET (10" LP)	12

(see also Lonnie Donegan)

MITCH MILLER ORCHESTRA
| 53 | Columbia SCM 5058 | Just Dreaming/Without My Lover | 4 |
| 56 | Philips BBE 12043 | LISBON ANTIGUA (EP) | 8 |

(see also Guy Mitchell)

NED MILLER
63	Capitol CL 15301	Dark Moon/Go On Back You Fool	5
63	London HL 9658	From A Jack To A King/Parade Of Broken Hearts	5
63	London HL 9728	Just Before Dawn/Mona Lisa	5
63	London HL 9766	Another Fool Like Me/Magic Moon	5
64	London HL 9838	Big Love/Sunday Morning Tears	5
64	London HL 9873	Invisible Tears/Old Restless Ocean	5
64	London HL 9937	Do What You Do Do Well/Dusty Guitar	5
63	Capitol CL 15301	Go On Back, You Fool/Dark Moon	4
63	Capitol EAP1 20492	NED MILLER (EP)	12
63	London RE 1382	NED MILLER (EP)	15
63	London HA 8072	FROM A JACK TO A KING (LP)	20

ROGER MILLER
64	Philips BF 1354	Dang Me/Got 2 Again	4
64	Philips BF 1365	Chug-A-Lug/Reincarnation	4
65	Philips BF 1390	Do-Wacka-Do/Love Is Not For Me	4
65	Philips BF 1397	King Of The Road/Atta Boy Girl	4
65	Philips BF 1416	Engine Engine No. 9/The Last Word In Lonesome Is Me	4
65	Philips BF 1437	Kansas City Star/One Dyin' And Buryin'	4
65	Philips BF 1456	England Swings/The Good Old Days	4
66	Philips BF 1475	Husbands And Wives/I've Been A Long Time Leavin'	4
66	Philips BF 1498	You Can't Roller Skate In A Buffalo Herd/Train Of Life	4
66	Philips BF 1516	My Uncle Used To Love Me But She Died/You're My Kingdom	4
67	Philips BF 1560	Walkin' In The Sunshine/Home	4
69	Mercury MF 1108	England Swings/King Of The Road (p/s)	4
65	Philips BE 12578	KING OF THE ROAD (EP)	7
65	Camden CDN 5121	SONGS I HAVE WRITTEN (LP)	12
65	Philips BL 7667	ROGER AND OUT! (LP)	12
66	Philips BL 7669	THE RETURN OF ROGER MILLER (LP)	12
66	Philips BL 7676	THE 3RD TIME AROUND (LP)	12
66	Philips BL 7748	WORDS AND MUSIC (LP)	12
67	Philips (S)BL 7822	WALKING IN THE SUNSHINE (LP)	10
67	Philips (S)BL 7833	SINGS THE MUSIC & TELLS THE TALE OF WATERHOLE 3 (LP)	10

RUSS MILLER
| 57 | HMV POP 391 | I Sit In My Window/Wait For Me, My Love | 25 |
| 57 | HMV POP 391 | I Sit In My Window/Wait For Me, My Love (78) | 5 |

STEPHEN MILLER & LOL COXHILL
| 74 | Caroline C 1503 | COXHILL MILLER (LP) | 12 |
| 74 | Caroline C 1507 | THE STORY SO FAR ... OH REALLY? (LP) | 12 |

STEVE MILLER BAND
68	Capitol CL 15539	Sittin' In Circles/Roll With It	7
68	Capitol CL 15564	Living In The U.S.A./Quicksilver Girl	6
69	Capitol CL 15604	My Dark Hour/Song For Our Ancestors	6
69	Capitol CL 15618	Little Girl/Don't Let Nobody Turn You Around	6
70	Capitol CL 15656	Going To The Country/Never Kill Another Man	5
72	Capitol CL 15712	My Dark Hour/The Gangster Is Back/Song For Our Ancestors (33rpm)	4
73	Capitol CL 15765	The Joker/Something To Believe In	4
74	Capitol CL 15786	Living In The U.S.A./Kow Kow Calqulator	4
68	Capitol (S)T 2920	CHILDREN OF THE FUTURE (LP, 'rainbow rim' label)	12
69	Capitol (S)T 2984	SAILOR (LP)	10
69	Capitol E-(S)T 184	BRAVE NEW WORLD (LP)	10
70	Capitol E-ST 331	YOUR SAVING GRACE (LP)	10
82	Mercury HS 9919 916	GREATEST HITS 1974-1978 (LP, half-speed master audiophile pressing)	12

SUZI MILLER
54	Decca F 10264	The Tennessee Wig Walk/Bimbo (B-side with Johnston Brothers) (78)	5
54	Decca F 10389	Happy Days And Lonely Nights/Tell Me, Tell Me (with Johnston Brothers)	12
54	Decca F 10423	Two Step, Side Step (with Johnston Brothers)/Hang My Heart On A Christmas Tree (with Keynotes)	6
55	Decca F 10475	Tweedlee-Dee (with Johnston Brothers)/That's All I Want From You	10
55	Decca F 10512	Dance With Me Henry (Wallflower) (with Johnston Brothers)/Butterfingers (with Marilyn Sisters)	8
55	Decca F 10593	The Banjo's Back In Town/Go On By	6
56	Decca F 10677	Ay-Ay-Senores/Reckless	6

Suzi MILLER

| 56 | Decca F 10722 | Get Up! Get Up! (You Sleepy Head)/The Key To My Heart | 6 |
| 57 | Decca F 10848 | I Love My Baby/The Money Tree | 6 |

(see also Marilyn Sisters)

MILLIE (SMALL)

63	Fontana TF 425	Don't You Know/Until You're Mine	6
64	Fontana TF 449	My Boy Lollipop/Something's Gotta Be Done	5
64	Fontana TF 479	Sweet William/Oh Henry	6
64	Fontana TF 502	I Love The Way You Love/Bring It On Home To Me	6
65	Fontana TF 515	I've Fallen In Love With A Snowman/What Am I Living For	5
65	Fontana TF 529	See You Later Alligator/Chilly Kisses	5
65	Fontana TF 591	My Street/It's Too Late	5
65	Fontana TF 617	Bloodshot Eyes/Tongue Tied	5
65	Brit WI 1002	My Street/Mixed Up Fickle Moody Self-Centred Spoiled Kind Of Boy	7
66	Fontana TF 740	Killer Joe/Carry Go Bring Home (as Millie Small)	7
67	Fontana TF 796	Chicken Feed/Wings Of A Dove (as Millie Small)	6
67	Island WIP 6021	You Better Forget/I Am In Love	5
68	Fontana TF 948	When I Dance With You/Hey Mr. Love	4
69	Decca F 12948	Readin' Writin' Arithmetic/I Want You Never To Stop	4
70	Pyramid PYR 6080	My Love And I/Tell Me About Yourself	4
61	Blue Beat BBEP 302	MILLIE (EP)	20
64	Fontana TE 17425	MY BOY LOLLIPOP (EP)	15
66	Island IEP 705	MILLIE AND HER BOYFRIENDS (EP)	25
64	Fontana (S)TL 5220	MORE MILLIE (LP)	25
65	Fontana TL 5276	MILLIE SINGS FATS DOMINO (LP)	35
67	Island ILP 953	THE BEST OF MILLIE SMALL (LP)	35
69	Trojan TTL 17	MILLIE AND HER BOYFRIENDS (LP)	15
69	Trojan TTL 49	THE BEST OF MILLIE SMALL (LP, reissue)	15
70	Trojan TBL 108	TIME WILL TELL (LP)	10

(see also Jackie & Millie, Roy & Millie, Owen & Millie)

SPIKE MILLIGAN

58	Parlophone R 4406	Wish I Knew/Will I Find My Love Today?	5
61	Parlophone R 4839	I'm Walking Out With A Mountain/The Sewers Of The Strand	4
62	Parlophone R 4891	Wormwood Scrubs Tango/Postman's Knock	4
64	Pye 7N 15720	The Olympic Team/Epilogue (with John Bluthal)	4
66	Parlophone R 5513	Purple Aeroplane/Nothing At All	4
66	Parlophone R 5543	Tower Bridge/Silent Night	4
69	Parlophone R 5771	The Q5 Piano Tune/Ning Nang Nong	4
61	Parlophone PMC 1148	MILLIGAN PRESERVED (LP)	15
65	Decca LK 4701	MUSES WITH MILLIGAN (LP)	15
69	Pye NPL 18271	THE WORLD OF THE BEACHCOMBER (LP)	12

(see also Goons, Famous Eccles, Peter Sellers)

LUCKY MILLINDER & ORCHESTRA

40s	Brunswick 03519	Apollo Jump/Are You Ready (78)	10
51	Vogue V 9007	I'm Waiting Just For You/Bongo Boogie (78)	12
51	Vogue V 9021	No One Else Could Be/The Grape Vine (78)	12
52	Vogue V 2138	Ram-Bunk-Shush/Let It Roll Again (78)	10

MILLIONAIRES (Ireland)

| 66 | Decca F 12468 | Wishing Well/Chatterbox | 35 |

MILLIONAIRES (U.S.)

| 73 | Mercury 6052 301 | Never For Me/If I Had You Babe (paper label) | 7 |

MILLIONS OF DEAD CHILDREN

| 85 | Radical MDC 3 | Chickensquawk (poster p/s) | 4 |

BARBARA MILLS

65	Hickory 45-1323	Queen Of Fools/Make It Last, Take Your Time	85
65	Hickory 45-1392	Try/Let's Make A Memory	8
75	London HLE 10491	Queen Of Fools/Make It Last, Take Your Time (reissue)	8

GARRY MILLS

59	Top Rank JAR 119	Hey Baby (You're Pretty)/You Alone	10
59	Top Rank JAR 219	Seven Little Girls Sitting In The Back Seat/The Night You Became 17	6
59	Oriole CB 1529	Living Lord/Big Story Breaking	5
59	Oriole CB 1530	I Am The Great I Am/Rhythm In Religion	5
60	Top Rank JAR 301	Running Bear/Teen Angel	6
60	Top Rank JAR 336	Look For A Star/Footsteps	6
60	Top Rank JAR 393	Comin' Down With Love/I'm Gonna Find Out	6
60	Top Rank JAR 500	Top Teen Baby/Don't Cheat Me Again (some in p/s)	10/6
61	Top Rank JAR 542	Who's Gonna Take You Home Tonight?/Christina	5
61	Decca F 11358	I'll Step Down/Your Way Is My Way	6
61	Decca F 11383	Bless You/Footprints In The Sand	6
61	Decca F 11415	Treasure Island/Sad Little Girl	6
62	Decca F 11471	Never Believed In Love/Save A Dream For Me	6
61	Top Rank JKP 3001	LOOK FOR A STAR (EP)	25

GORDON MILLS

| 65 | Ace Of Clubs ACL 1191 | DO IT YOURSELF (LP) | 12 |

(see also Viscounts)

HAYLEY MILLS

| 61 | Decca F 21396 | Let's Get Together/Cobbler Cobbler | 4 |
| 60s | Decca | POLLY ANNA (LP) | 10 |

HAYLEY MILLS & EDDIE HODGES

| 63 | HMV POP 1179 | Flitterin'/Beautiful Beulah | 4 |

(see also Eddie Hodges)

MAUDE MILLS
60s	Vintage Jazz VEP 34	MAUDE MILLS (EP) 12

RUDY MILLS
67	Island WI 3092	A Long Story/BOBBY ELLIS: Now We Know 10
68	Island WI 3136	I'm Trapped/BOBBY ELLIS & CRYSTALLITES: Dollar A Head 10
68	Big Shot BI 509	John Jones/A Place Called Happiness 6
69	Explosion EX 2007	Lemi Li/Goody Goody 6
69	Crab CRAB 20	Tears On My Pillow/I'm Trapped 5
69	Crab CRAB 24	A Heavy Load/Wholesale Love 4
69	Pama SECO 12	REGGAE HITS (LP) 25

STEPHANIE MILLS
74	Paramount PARA 3050	I Knew It Was Love/The Passion And The Pain 4
76	Tamla Motown TMG 1020	This Empty Place/I See You For The First Time (demo only) 25
76	T. Motown STML 12017	FOR THE FIRST TIME (LP) 10

MILLS BROTHERS
52	Brunswick 05007	The Glow Worm/After All (78) 5
54	Brunswick 05325	How Blue?/Why Do I Keep Lovin' You? 10
55	Brunswick 05390	Paper Valentine/The Urge 8
55	Brunswick 05439	Smack Dab In The Middle/Opus One 12
55	Brunswick 05452	You're Nobody Till Somebody Loves/Yes You Are 8
55	Brunswick 05487	Mi Muchacha (Little Girl)/Gum Drop 18
55	Brunswick 05488	Suddenly There's A Valley/That's All I Ask Of You 8
56	Brunswick 05522	I've Changed My Mind A Thousand Times/All The Way 'Round The World 8
56	Brunswick 05550	Dream Of You/In A Mellow Tone 7
56	Brunswick 05600	Ninety-Eight Cents/King Porter Stomp 6
56	Brunswick 05606	That's Right/Don't Get Caught (Short On Love) 8
56	Brunswick 05631	That's All I Need/Tell Me More 5
57	Brunswick 05664	In De Banana Tree/The Knocked Out Nightingale 4
57	Brunswick 05680	My Troubled Mind/Queen Of The Senior Prom 5
58	London HLD 8553	Get A Job/I Found A Million Dollar Baby 15
58	London HLD 8553	Get A Job/I Found A Million Dollar Baby (78) 5
60	London HLD 9169	I Got You/Highways Are Happy Ways 5
54	Brunswick OE 9014	PRESENTING THE MILLS BROTHERS (EP) 12
55	Brunswick OE 9060	THE MILLS BROTHERS NO. 2 (EP) 8
56	Brunswick OE 9239	SINGING AND SWINGING PT. 1 (EP) 8
59	Brunswick OE 9427	THEY SOLD A MILLION NO. 11 (EP) 12
59	London RED 1215	THE MILLS BROTHERS (EP) 10
54	Brunswick LA 8664	MEET THE MILLS BROTHERS (10" LP) 20
55	Brunswick LA 8702	FOUR BOYS AND A GUITAR (10" LP) 16
59	London HA-D 2192	THE MILLS BROTHERS' GREATEST HITS (LP, also stereo SAH-D 6046) 12
60	London HA-D 2250	THE MILLS BROTHERS SING (LP, also stereo SAH-D 6074) 12
61	London HA-D 2319	THE MILLS BROTHERS' GREATEST HITS (LP) 12
61	London HA-D 2383	SAN ANTONIO ROSE (LP, also stereo SAH-D 6183) 12
63	London HA-D/SH-D 8058	BEER BARREL POLKA (LP) 10
63	London HA-D/SH-D 8092	THE END OF THE WORLD (LP) 12

MILLTOWN BROTHERS
89	Big Round BIGR 101	Roses/We've Got Time (p/s) 10
89	Big Round BIGR 101T	COMING FROM THE MILL 1989 (12" EP) 15
89	Big Round BIGR 101CD	COMING FROM THE MILL 1989 (CD EP) 15
89	Big Round BIGR 104	Which Way Should I Jump/Silvertown (p/s) 7
89	Big Round BIGR 104T	Which Way Should I Jump/Silvertown/Why Should I (12", p/s) 10
90	Suburban MTOWN 001	Seems To Me/Natural (p/s) 5
90	Suburban MTOWN 001T	Seems To Me (Extended)/Natural/Seems To Me (Take 2) (12", p/s) 8
91	A&M AMX 711	Which Way Should I Jump/Diplomat (10" box, numbered with poster & card) 5

JIM MILNE (& TRACTOR)
77	Polydor 2058 942	No More Rock & Roll/Northern Lights (as Jim Milne & Tractor) 4
79	Birds Nest BN 122	Who Am I/Trick Of The Light (solo) 4
	(see also Tractor, The Way We Live)	

RONNIE MILSAP
66	Pye Intl. 7N 25392	Ain't No Soul (Left In These Old Shoes)/Another Branch From The Same Old Tree 20
69	Pye Intl. 7N 25490	Denver/Nothing Is As Good As It Used To Be 5
72	Wand WN 26	Ain't No Soul (Left In These Old Shoes)/Another Branch From The Same Old Tree (reissue) 4

RONNIE MILSAP/ROSCOE ROBINSON
66	Pye Intl. NEP 44078	SOUL SENSATIONS (EP) 12

JOHNNY MILTON & CONDORS
61	Oriole CB 1588	Charleston Cocktail (medley) (as Johnny Milton Band) 4
64	Decca F 11862	A Girl Named Sue/Somethin' Else (as Johnny Milton & Condors) 7
64	Fontana TF 488	Cry Baby/Hurt 5
	(see also Symbols)	

ROY MILTON
66	Sue WI 4021	Early In The Morning/Bless Your Heart 20
	(see also Little Milton)	

MILVA
63	Oriole CB 1899	I Can't Believe You're Leaving Me/Loneliness Of Autumn 5
64	Oriole CB 1952	I'll Set My Love To Music/Come Sempre 5

MILWAUKEE COASTERS
68	Pama PM 733	Treat Me Nice/Sick And Tired (Oh Babe) 5
68	Pama PMLP 2	WEST COAST ROCK'N'ROLL 1968 (LP) 10

GARNET MIMMS (& ENCHANTERS)

63	United Artists UP 1033	Cry Baby/Don't Change Your Heart (with Enchanters)	8
63	United Artists UP 1038	For Your Precious Love/Baby Don't You Weep (with Enchanters)	8
64	United Artists UP 1048	Tell Me Baby/Anytime You Want Me (with Enchanters)	8
65	United Artists UP 1090	It Was Easier To Hurt Her/So Close	12
66	United Artists UP 1130	I'll Take Good Care Of You/Looking For You	40
66	United Artists UP 1147	It's Been Such A Long Way Home/Thinkin'	10
66	United Artists UP 1153	My Baby/It Won't Hurt Half As Much	7
66	United Artists UP 1172	All About Love/The Truth Hurts	10
67	United Artists UP 1181	Roll With The Punches/Only Your Love	10
67	United Artists UP 1186	As Long As I Have You/Yesterday	8
68	Verve VS 569	I Can Hear My Baby Crying/Stop And Think It Over	8
68	Verve VS 569	I Can Hear My Baby Crying/BILL MEDLEY: That Lucky Old Sun (mispress)	8
68	Verve VS 574	We Can Find That Love/Can You Top This	8
76	United Artists REM 403	REMEMBER GARNET MIMMS (EP)	7
63	United Artists ULP 1067	CRY BABY AND 11 OTHER HITS (LP, with Enchanters)	40
66	United Artists (S)ULP 1145	WARM AND SOULFUL (LP)	35
67	United Artists (S)ULP 1174	LIVE (LP, as Garnet Mimms & Senate)	30

MINDBENDERS

66	Fontana TF 644	A Groovy Kind Of Love/Love Is Good	4
66	Fontana TF 697	Can't Live With You, Can't Live Without You/One Fine Day	5
66	Fontana TF 731	Ashes To Ashes/You Don't Know About Love	5
66	Fontana TF 780	I Want Her, She Wants Me/The Morning After	6
67	Fontana TF 806	We'll Talk About It Tomorrow/Far Across Town	5
67	Fontana TF 869	The Letter/My New Day And Age	5
67	Fontana TF 877	Schoolgirl/Coming Back	6
68	Fontana TF 910	Blessed Are The Lonely/Yellow Brick Road	6
68	Fontana TF 961	Uncle Joe, The Ice Cream Man/The Man Who Loved Trees	7
66	Fontana (S)TL 5324	THE MINDBENDERS (LP, mono/stereo)	18/22
67	Fontana (S)TL 5403	WITH WOMAN IN MIND (LP)	35
68	Fontana SFL 13045	THE MINDBENDERS (LP, reissue)	12

(see also Wayne Fontana & Mindbenders, Hotlegs, Lulu)

SAL MINEO

57	Philips JK 1024	Start Movin' (In My Direction)/Love Affair (jukebox issue)	25
57	Philips PB 707	Start Movin' (In My Direction)/Love Affair (78)	5
57	Philips PB 733	Lasting Love/You Shouldn't Do That (78)	5
57	Philips PB 764	Party Time/The Words That I Whisper (78)	5
58	Fontana H 118	Little Pigeon/Cuttin' In	25
58	Fontana H 118	Little Pigeon/Cuttin' In (78)	6
58	Fontana H 135	Seven Steps To Love/A Couple Of Crazy Kids	18
58	Fontana H 135	Seven Steps To Love/A Couple Of Crazy Kids (78)	10
58	Fontana TFL 5004	SAL (LP)	45

MINERS SONG

60s	Holyground	single	5

CORINA MINETTE

60	HMV POP 752	He'll Have To Stay/TOMMY THOMAS ORCHESTRA: Young At Cha Cha	4

CHARLES/CHARLIE MINGUS

60	Philips BBE 12399	CHARLES MINGUS (EP)	8
61	Philips BBE 12451	MINGUS DYNASTY (EP, as Charles Mingus Jazz Groups, also stereo SBBE 9050)	8/10
61	Philips BBE 12453	THINGS AIN'T WHAT THEY USED TO BE (EP, as Charles Mingus Jazz Groups, also stereo SBBE 9052)	8/10
63	Parlophone GEP 8786	SCENES IN THE CITY (EP)	10
65	Mercury 10021MCE	JAZZ MAKERS (EP, as Charlie Mingus Orchestra)	8
56	Vogue LDE 178	CHARLIE MINGUS PRESENTS JAZZ WORKSHOP VOL. 2 (10" LP)	18
59	Parlophone PMC 1092	EAST COASTING (LP)	15
60	London Jazz LTZ-K 15194	BLUES AND ROOTS (LP, also stereo SAH-K 6087)	15
62	Atlantic SD 8005	CHARLES MINGUS PRESENTS CHARLES MINGUS (LP, U.K. issue of U.S. LP)	15
62	United Artists ULP 1004	JAZZ PORTRAITS (LP)	15
62	London HA-K/SH-K 8007	OH YEAH (LP, by Charlie Mingus & Jazz Group)	15
63	RCA RD/SF 7514	TIJUANA MOODS (LP)	15
63	Vocalion LAE 543	CHAZZ (LP)	15
64	HMV CLP 1694	THE BLACK SAINT AND THE SINNER LADY (LP)	15
65	United Artists ULP 1068	TOWN HALL CONCERT (LP)	15
65	Vocalion LAEF/SEAF 591	CHARLIE MINGUS QUINTET WITH MAX ROACH (LP)	15
65	HMV CLP 1742	MINGUS, MINGUS, MINGUS (LP, also stereo CSD 1545)	15
65	HMV CLP 1796	MINGUS PLAYS PIANO (LP, as Charlie Mingus)	15
65	Atlantic ATL/SAL 5019	CHARLIE MINGUS (LP)	15
66	Realm RM 211	JAZZ COMPOSERS WORKSHOP (NO. 1) (LP)	12
66	CBS (S)BPG 62261	MINGUS DYNASTY (LP)	12
68	Polydor 623 215	CHARLIE MINGUS (LP)	12
68	Atlantic 587 131	PITHECANTHROPUS ERECTUS (LP, as Charlie Mingus Jazz Workshop)	15
69	CBS 52346	MINGUS AH-UM! (LP, as Charlie Mingus)	12
69	Atlantic 587 166	REINCARNATION OF A LOVEBIRD (LP, as Charlie Mingus jazz Workshop)	15
69	Mercury SMWL 21056	MINGUS REVISITED (LP, as Charlie Mingus)	12
70	Atlantic 545 111	DUKE'S CHOICE (LP, as Charlie Mingus Jazz Workshop)	12
70	Liberty LBS 83346	MY FAVOURITE QUINTET (LP, as Charlie Mingus)	12
72	Ember CJS 832	INTRUSIONS (LP, as Charlie Mingus)	10
72	CBS 24010	CHARLES MINGUS (2-LP)	14
73	RCA LSA 3117	TIJUANA MOODS (LP, reissue)	10
74	Atlantic K 60039	THE ART OF CHARLIE MINGUS: THE ATLANTIC YEARS (2-LP)	14

MINIM

67	Polydor 582 011	WRAPPED IN A UNION JACK (LP)	50

MINISTRY
82	Situation 2 SIT 17T	Cold Life/I'm Falling/Cold Life Dub (12", p/s)	10
83	Arista ARIST 510	Work For Love/For Love (some with free cassette)	7/4
83	Arista ARIST 12510	Work For Love/For Love (12", p/s)	7
83	Arista ARIST 533	I Wanted To Tell Her/A Walk In The Park (p/s)	4
83	Arista ARIST 12533	I Wanted To Tell Her/(Tongue Tied Mix)/A Walk In The Park (12", p/s)	7
83	Arista ARIST 549	Revenge (You Did It Again)/Effigy (p s)	4
83	Arista ARIST 12549	Revenge (You Did It Again)/Effigy/Work For Love (12", p/s)	7

MINISTRY OF SOUND
66	Decca F 12449	White Collar Worker/Back Seat Driver	12

MINK DeVILLE
78	Capitol CL 16005	Soul Twist/Rolene (lurid magenta vinyl, special sleeve & label)	4

LIZA MINNELLI
66	Capitol CL 15483	The Middle Of The Street/I (Who Have Nothing)	7

KYLIE MINOGUE
88	PWL PWLT 8R	I Should Be So Lucky (Bicentennial Mix)/(Instrumental) (12", p/s)	10
88	PWL PWLT 12R	Got To Be Certain (Extra Beat Boys Mix)/Got To Be Certain (7" Mix)/Got To Be Certain (Out For A Duck Bill Platter Plus Dub Mix) (12", p/s)	12
88	PWL PWCD 12	Got To Be Certain (Extended Mix)/Got To Be Certain (Instrumental)/I Should Be So Lucky (6.03) (CD)	10
88	PWL PWLT 14R	The Loco-Motion (Sankie Mix)/I'll Still Be Loving You (12", p/s)	10
88	PWL PWLP 21	Je Ne Sais Pas Pourquoi/Made In Heaven (poster p/s)	12
88	PWL PWLT 21R	Je Ne Sais Pas Pourquoi (Revolutionary Mix)/Made In Heaven (Maid In England Mix) (12", p/s)	8
88	PWL PWCD 21	Je Ne Sais Pas Pourquoi (Moi Non Plus Mix)/Made In Heaven (Maid In England Mix)/The Loco-Motion (Sankie Mix) (CD)	7
88	PWL PWCD 24	Especially For You (7" Mix)/(Extended)/All I Wanna Do (Extended) (CD)	7
89	PWL PWLT 35R	Hand On Your Heart (Heartache Mix)/Hand On Your Heart (Dub Mix)/Just Wanna Love You (12", p/s)	15
89	PWL PWMC 42	Wouldn't Change A Thing/It's No Secret (cassette)	4
89	PWL PWLT 42R	Wouldn't Change A Thing (Espagna Mix)/Wouldn't Change A Thing (7" Mix)/It's No Secret (Extended) (12", p/s)	12
90	PWL PWMC 56	Better The Devil You Know/I'm Over Dreaming (Remix) (cassette, orange)	4
90	PWL PWMC 64	Step Back In Time (Edit)/(Instrumental) (cassette, initially green)	4
90	PWL PWLP 72	What Do I Have To Do (New Mix)/(Instrumental) (p/s, with postcards)	4
90	PWL PWL P81	Shocked (DNA Mix)/Shocked (Harding & Curnow Mix) (picture disc)	6

MINORBOPS
58	Vogue V 9110	Need You Tonight/Want You For My Own	150
58	Vogue V 9110	Need You Tonight/Want You For My Own (78)	50

MINSTRELS
67	Studio One SO 2036	People Get Ready/HAMLINS: Everyone's Got To Be There	12
68	Studio One SO 2050	Miss Highty Tighty/WESTMORELITES: Let Me Be Yours Until Tomorrow	12

MINTS
57	London HLP 8423	Night Air/KEN COPELAND: Pledge Of Love	175
57	London HLP 8423	Night Air/KEN COPELAND: Pledge Of Love (78)	35

MINUTE MEN
61	Capitol CL 15206	Yankee Diddle/Blue Pearl	6

MINUTEMEN
83	SST SST 002	PARANOID TIME (8-track EP)	10
84	SST SST 016	BUZZ OR HOWL UNDER THE INFLUENCE OF THE HEAT (12" EP)	10
85	Homestead REFLEX-L	TOUR SPIEL (live 4-track EP)	6

(SMOKEY ROBINSON &) MIRACLES
61	London HL 9276	Shop Around/Who's Lovin' You	40
61	London HL 9366	Ain't It Baby/The Only One I Love	60
62	Fontana H 384	What's So Good About Goodbye/I've Been So Good To You	80
63	Oriole CBA 1795	You've Really Got A Hold On Me/Happy Landing	65
63	Oriole CBA 1863	Mickey's Monkey/Whatever Makes You Happy	40
64	Stateside SS 263	I Gotta Dance To Keep From Crying/Such Is Love, Such Is Life	35
64	Stateside SS 282	(You Can't Let The Boy Overpower) The Man In You/Heartbreak Road	25
64	Stateside SS 324	I Like It Like That/You're So Fine And Sweet	20
64	Stateside SS 353	That's What Love Is Made Of/Would I Love You	20
65	Stateside SS 377	Come On Do The Jerk/Baby Don't You Go	20
65	Tamla Motown TMG 503	Ooo Baby Baby/All That's Good	25
65	Tamla Motown TMG 522	The Tracks Of My Tears/A Fork In The Road	30
65	Tamla Motown TMG 540	My Girl Has Gone/Since You Won My Heart	15
66	Tamla Motown TMG 547	Going To A Go-Go/Choosey Beggar	12
66	Tamla Motown TMG 569	Whole Lotta Shakin' In My Heart/Oh Be My Love	15
66	Tamla Motown TMG 584	(Come 'Round Here) I'm The One You Need/Save Me	8
(all the above singles were credited to Miracles)			
67	Tamla Motown TMG 598	The Love I Saw In You Was Just A Mirage/Swept For You Baby	15
67	Tamla Motown TMG 614	More Love/Come Spy With Me (withdrawn)	80
67	Tamla Motown TMG 614	More Love/Swept For You Baby	10
67	Tamla Motown TMG 631	I Second That Emotion/You Must Be Love	6
68	Tamla Motown TMG 648	If You Can Want/When The Words From Your Heart Get Caught Up In Your Throat	6
68	Tamla Motown TMG 661	Yester Love/Much Better Off	6
68	Tamla Motown TMG 673	Special Occasion/Give Her Up	5
69	Tamla Motown TMG 687	Baby Baby Don't Cry/Your Mother's Only Daughter	5
69	Tamla Motown TMG 696	The Tracks Of My Tears/Come On Do The Jerk (reissue)	4

MINT VALUE £

70	Tamla Motown TMG 745	The Tears Of A Clown/You Must Be Love	30
70	Tamla Motown TMG 745	The Tears Of A Clown/Who's Gonna Take The Blame	4
71	Tamla Motown TMG 761	(Come 'Round Here) I'm The One You Need/We Can Make It, We Can	4
71	Tamla Motown TMG 774	I Don't Blame You At All/That Girl	4
72	Tamla Motown TMG 811	My Girl Has Gone/Crazy 'Bout The La La La	4

(the above singles were credited to Smokey Robinson & MIracles)

76	Tamla Motown TMG 1023	Nightlife/The Miracle Workers: Overture (as Miracles)	4
61	London RE 1295	SHOP AROUND (EP, as Miracles)	80
83	Tamla Motown CTME 2028	TEARS OF A CLOWN (cassette EP, as Smokey Robinson & Miracles)	7
63	Oriole PS 40044	HI! WE'RE THE MIRACLES (LP)	75
64	Stateside SL 10099	THE FABULOUS MIRACLES (LP)	70
65	Tamla Motown TML 11003	I LIKE IT LIKE THAT (LP)	45
66	Tamla Motown TML 11024	GOIN' TO A GO-GO (LP, as Smokey Robinson & Miracles)	35
66	T. Motown (S)TML 11031	THE MIRACLES FROM THE BEGINNING (LP)	35
67	T. Motown (S)TML 11044	AWAY WE A-GO-GO (LP)	30

(the above albums are credited to Miracles unless otherwise stated)

68	T. Motown (S)TML 11067	MAKE IT HAPPEN (LP)	15
68	T. Motown (S)TML 11072	GREATEST HITS (LP)	12
69	T. Motown (S)TML 11089	SPECIAL OCCASION (LP)	12
69	T. Motown (S)TML 11107	LIVE (LP)	10
70	T. Motown STML 11129	TIME OUT FOR SMOKEY ROBINSON & MIRACLES (LP)	10
70	T. Motown STML 11151	FOUR IN BLUE (LP)	10
71	T. Motown STML 11172	POCKETFUL OF MIRACLES (LP)	10
73	T. Motown STMA 8008	1957-1972 (LP, gatefold sleeve)	10

(see also Smokey Robinson)

MIRAGE

65	CBS 201772	It's In Her Kiss/What Ye Gonna Do 'Bout It	15
65	CBS 202007	Go Away/Just A Face	15
66	Philips BF 1534	Tomorrow Never Knows/You Can't Be Serious	25
67	Philips BF 1554	Hold On/Can You Hear Me	10
67	Philips BF 1571	The Wedding Of Ramona Blair/Lazy Man	20
68	Page One POF 078	Mystery Lady/Chicago Cottage	6
69	Page One POF 111	Carolyn/World Goes On Around You	6

(see also Caleb)

MIRETTES

68	Uni UN 501	In The Midnight Hour/To Love Somebody	5
68	Uni UN 505	The Real Thing/Take Me For A Little While	5
69	MCA Soul Bag BAG 8	Whirlpool/Ain't You Trying To Cross Over	4
72	Jay Boy BOY 65	Now That I've Found You Baby/He's Alright With Me	4
69	MCA MUP(S) 344	IN THE MIDNIGHT HOUR (LP)	10

(see also Ikettes)

MIRKWOOD

| 71 | Flams Ltd PR 1067 | MIRKWOOD (LP) | 500 |

MIRO

| 90 | Sacred Heart SH 30008 | GREETINGS FROM THE GOLBORNE RD (EP, handmade coloured p/s) | 5 |
| 90 | Sacred Heart SH 4008 | The World In Maps/Great Dominions (handmade p/s with mini-booklet) | 4 |

MIRROR

| 68 | Philips BF 1666 | Gingerbread Man/Faster Than Light | 40 |

MISFITS (U.K.)

| 60s | PRI 101 | You Won't See Me/Hanging Around (Aberdeen Students Charities Campaign) | 10 |

MISFITS (U.S.)

| 81 | Plan 9/Cherry Red PLP 9 | BEWARE (12" EP) | 60 |

MISSING PRESUMED DEAD

| 80s | Sequel PART 4 | MISSING PRESUMED DEAD (LP) | 12 |
| 80s | Sequel PART 5 | REVENGE (LP) | 10 |

MISSING SCIENTISTS

| 80 | Rough Trade RT 057 | Big City, Bright Lights/Discotheque X (p/s) | 10 |

(see also Television Personalities, Slaughter)

MISSION

86	Chapter 22 CHAP 6/7	Serpent's Kiss/Wake (p/s)	5
86	Chapter 22 CHAP 6	Serpent's Kiss/Naked And Savage/Wake (12", p/s)	8
86	Chapter 22 CHAP 7	Garden Of Delight/Like A Hurricane (p/s)	5
86	Chapter 22 12 CHAP 7	Like A Hurricane/Garden Of Delight/Over The Hills And Far Away/The Crystal Ocean (12", p/s)	8
86	Chapter 22 L12 CHAP 7	Like A Hurricane/Garden Of Delight/Dancing Barefoot/The Crystal Ocean (12", autographed p/s)	15
86	Mercury MYSG 1	Stay With Me/Blood Brother (autographed, gatefold p/s)	8
87	Mercury MYTHB 2	Wasteland/Shelter From The Storm (edited live version)/Serpent's Kiss (live)/1969 (live) (box set, with 5 photos)	8
87	Mercury MYTHX 22	Wasteland (Anniversary Mix)/Shelter From The Storm (live)/1969 (live)/Wake (live) (12", p/s)	10
87	Mercury MYTHP 3	Severina/Tomorrow Never Knows (p/s, with poster & numbered wraparound paper strip)	5
87	Mercury MYTHL 3	Severina/Wishing Well/Tomorrow Never Knows (12", p/s, with poster)	7
88	Mercury MYTHX 4	Tower Of Strength (Extended)/Fabienne/Dream On/Breath (Instrumental) (12", p/s)	7
88	Mercury MYTHX 6	Beyond The Pale (Armageddon Mix)/Tadeusz (1912-1988)/Love Me To Death/Forever More (12", p/s)	7
88	Mercury MYTHCD 6	Beyond The Pale (Armageddon Mix)/Tadeusz (1912-1988)/Love Me To Death/Forever More (CD)	10

90	Mercury MYCDB 8	Butterfly On A Wheel (CD, picture disc in 12" x 12" box)	7
86	Mercury MERH 102	GOD'S OWN MEDICINE (LP, gatefold sleeve)	10

(see also Sisters Of Mercy, Dead Or Alive, Pauline Murray & Invisible Girls, Artery, Red Lorry Yellow Lorry, Guthrie Handley & Wayne Hussey)

MISSION BELLES
65	Decca F 12154	Sincerely/When A Girl Really Loves You	6

MISS JANE
68	Pama PM 704	Bad Mind People/My Heart Is Aching (B-side actually by Coolers' "Witch Doctor")	5

MISS X (Joyce Blair)
63	Ember EMB S 175	Christine/S-E-X	6

MISTER MOST
69	Downtown DT 409	Reggae Train/Pushwood	4

MISTER VERSATILE
69	Jackpot JP 701	Apple Blossom/LITTLE BOY BLUE: Dark End Of The Street	4
69	Jackpot JP 702	Devil's Disciples/ERROL DUNKLEY: Having A Party	4

(see also Lester Sterling)

MISTURA
76	Route RT 30	The Flasher/Life Is A Song Worth Singing	4

MISTY
77	Cottage	MISTY (LP)	40

MISUNDERSTOOD
66	Fontana TF 777	I Can Take You To The Sun/Who Do You Love	20
69	Fontana TF 998	Children Of The Sun/I Unseen (small or large centre hole)	25/20
69	Fontana TF 1028	You're Tuff Enough/Little Red Rooster (some in p/s)	30/15
69	Fontana TF 1041	Never Had A Girl (Like You Before)/Golden Glass (as Misunderstood featuring Glenn "Fernando" Campbell)	25
81	Cherry Red CHERRY 22	Children Of The Sun/Who Do You Love/I'll Take You To The Sun (p/s)	4
80s	Bucketful Of Brains BOB 2	You're My Girl (flexidisc with 'Bucketfull Of Brains' magazine)	6/4

(see also Juicy Lucy, High Tide, Van Der Graaf Generator)

CHAD MITCHELL
62	London HLR 9509	Lizzie Borden/Super Skier	5

DENNY MITCHELL SOUNDSATION
64	Decca F 11848	I've Been Crying/For Your Love	4

GROVER MITCHELL
68	London HLU 10221	Turned On/Blue Over You	4

GUY MITCHELL
51	Columbia DB 2800	My Heart Cries For You/Me And My Imagination (78)	5
51	Columbia DB 2816	The Roving Kind/You're Not In My Arms Tonight (78)	5
51	Columbia DB 2831	Sparrow In The Tree Top/Christopher Columbus (78)	5
51	Columbia DB 2885	My Truly, Truly Fair/Who Knows Love (78)	5
51	Columbia DB 2908	Belle, Belle, My Liberty Belle/Sweetheart Of Yesterday (78)	5
52	Columbia DB 3056	There's A Pawnshop On The Corner/The Doll With A Sawdust Heart (78)	5
52	Vogue V 9033	Cabaret/I've Got A Frame Without A Picture (with Satisfiers) (78)	8
52	Columbia DB 3151	Feet Up (Pat Him On The Po-Po)/Angels Cry (78)	5
53	Columbia SCM 5018	Feet Up (Pat Him On The Po-Po)/Jenny Kissed Me	20
53	Columbia SCM 5022	'Cause I Loved Ya, That's A-Why/Train Of Love (with Mindy Carson)	18
53	Columbia SCM 5032	She Wears Red Feathers/Why Should I Cry Now?	20
53	Columbia SCM 5037	Pretty Little Black-Eyed Susie/MITCH MILLER HORNS: Horn Belt Boogie	20
56	Philips JK 1001	Singing The Blues/Crazy With Love (jukebox issue)	20
57	Philips JK 1005	Knee Deep In The Blues/Take Me Back Baby (jukebox issue)	18
57	Philips JK 1015	Rock-A-Billy/Got A Feeling (jukebox issue)	18
57	Philips JK 1023	Sweet Stuff/In The Middle Of A Dark, Dark Night (jukebox issue)	12
57	Philips JK 1027	Call Rosie On The Phone/Cure For The Blues (jukebox issue)	12
58	Philips PB 766	The Unbeliever/C'mon Let's Go	8
58	Philips PB 798	Wonderin' And Worryin'/If Ya Don't Like It, Don't Knock It	6
58	Philips PB 830	Honey Brown Eyes/Hangin' Around	6
58	Philips PB 858	Let It Shine, Let It Shine/Butterfly Doll	6
58	Philips PB 885	Till We're Engaged/My Heart Cries For You	6
59	Philips PB 915	Alias Jesse James/Pride O' Dixie	6
59	Philips PB 964	Heartaches By The Number/Two	5
59	Philips PB 964	Heartaches By The Number/Two (78)	8
60	Philips PB 998	The Same Old Me/Build My Gallows High	5
60	Philips PB 1026	Cry Hurtin' Heart/Symphony Of Spring	5
60	Philips PB 1050	My Shoes Keep Walking Back To You/Silver Moon Upon The Golden Sands	6
60	Philips PB 1084	One Way Street/Sunshine Guitar	4
61	Philips PB 1131	Follow Me/Your Goodnight Kiss	4
61	Philips PB 1183	I'll Just Pretend/Divorce	4
61	Philips PB 1202	Soft Rain/Big Big Change	4
63	Pye Intl. 7N 25179	Go Tiger Go/If You Ever Go Away	12
63	Pye Intl. 7N 25185	Have I Told You Lately That I Love You/Blue Violets	5
66	CBS 202238	Singing The Blues/Rock-A-Billy	12
67	London HLB 10173	Traveling Shoes/Every Night Is A Lifetime	5
68	London HLB 10190	Alabam/Goodbye Road, Hello Home	5
68	London HLB 10218	Before You Take Your Love From Me/Singing The Blues	5
68	London HLB 10234	Just Wish You'd Maybe Change Your Mind/If You Could Cry Me My Tears	5
54	Columbia SEG 7513	PRETTY LITTLE BLACK EYED SUSIE (EP, plain sleeve)	12
55	Columbia SEG 7581	MY TRULY TRULY FAIR (EP, plain sleeve)	12
55	Columbia SEG 7598	JENNY KISSED ME (EP, plain sleeve)	12
55	Philips BBE 12008	GUY MITCHELL (EP)	12

56	Philips BBE 12093	GUY MITCHELL NO. 2 (EP) 15
57	Philips BBE 12112	SINGING THE BLUES WITH GUY MITCHELL (EP) 12
58	Philips BBE 12215	GUY MITCHELL PHILIPS TV SERIES (EP) 15
54	Columbia 33S 1028	GUY MITCHELL SINGS (10" LP) 40
55	Philips BBR 8031	THE VOICE OF YOUR CHOICE (10" LP) 30
58	Philips BBL 7246	A GUY IN LOVE (LP) 25
58	Philips BBL 7265	A SHOWCASE OF HITS (LP) 25
61	Philips BBL 7465	SUNSHINE GUITAR (LP) 25
66	CBS Realm RM 52336	THE BEST OF GUY MITCHELL (LP) 15
68	London HA-B 8364	TRAVELLING SHOES (LP, also stereo SH-B 8364) 15

JONI MITCHELL

68	Reprise RS 20694	Night In The City/I Had A King 5
72	Asylum AYM 511	You Turn Me On, I'm A Radio/Urge For Going 5
83	Geffen DA 3122	Chinese Cafe/Ladies Man (double pack, with free interview 7") 5
68	Reprise RSLP 6293	SONGS TO A SEAGULL (LP) 10
69	Reprise RSLP 6341	CLOUDS (LP) 10
70	Reprise RSLP 6376	LADIES OF THE CANYON (LP) 10
82	Asylum/Numbus K 53018	THE HISSING OF SUMMER LAWNS (LP, audiophile press, sold via mag) ..15

MALCOLM MITCHELL

| 54 | Parlophone MSP 6084 | The Jones Boy/Granada ....4 |

McKINLEY 'SOUL' MITCHELL

| 68 | President PT 125 | The Town I Live In/No Love Like Your Love ....5 |
| 68 | President PTL 1005 | McKINLEY 'SOUL' MITCHELL (LP) ....10 |

PHILIP MITCHELL

| 71 | Jay Boy BOY 37 | I'm Gonna Build California/The World Needs More People Like You ......4 |
| 72 | Jay Boy BOY 57 | Free For All/Flower Child ....6 |

RONNIE MITCHELL

| 60 | London HLU 9220 | How Many Times/The Only Love ....6 |

SINX MITCHELL

| 64 | Hickory 45-1248 | Weird Sensation/Love Is All I'm Asking For ....8 |
| | *(see also Crickets)* | |

WILLIE MITCHELL

64	London HLU 9926	20-75/Secret Home 6
65	London HLU 10004	Everything Is Gonna Be Alright/That Driving Beat 12
66	London HLU 10039	Bad Eye/Sugar T. 6
66	London HLU 10085	Mercy/Sticks And Stones 6
68	London HLU 10186	Soul Serenade/Buster Browne 5
68	London HLU 10215	Prayer Meetin'/Rum Daddy 5
68	London HLU 10224	Up Hard/Beale Street Mood 4
69	London HLU 10246	Everything Is Gonna Be Alright/Mercy 4
69	London HLU 10282	Young People/Kitten Korner 4
70	London HLU 10313	Robbin's Nest/Six To Go 4
73	London HLU 10407	Last Tango In Paris/Six To Go 4
67	London HA-U 8319	THE HIT SOUND OF WILLIE MITCHELL (LP) 12
68	London HA-U/SH-U 8365	SOUL SERENADE (LP) 10
68	London HA-U/SH-U 8368	LIVE (LP) 10
69	London HA-U/SH-U 8372	SOLID SOUL (LP) 10
69	London HA-U/SH-U 8388	ON TOP (LP) 10
70	London HA-U/SH-U 8408	SOUL BAG (LP) 10

ROBERT MITCHUM

57	Capitol CL 14701	What Is This Generation Coming To?/Mama Looka Boo Boo 6
62	Capitol CL 15251	The Ballad Of Thunder Road/My Honey's Lovin' Arms 5
67	Monument MON 1007	Little Ole Wine Drinker Me/Walker's Woods 4
55	Brunswick OE 9197	RACHEL AND THE STRANGER (EP) 12
67	Monument LMO 5011	THAT MAN (LP) 10

JACKIE MITTO(O)

66	Island WI 293	Killer Diller (as Jackie Mitto & Soul Brothers)/PATRICK HYTTON: Oh Lady 10
67	Rio R 123	Got My Buglaoo/ETHIOPIANS: What To Do 10
67	Coxsone CS 7002	Somebody Help Me/GAYLADS & SOUL VENDORS: The Sound Of Silence 15
67	Coxsone CS 7009	Ba Ba Boom/SLIM SMITH & FREEDOM SINGERS: Mercy Mercy 15
67	Coxsone CS 7019	Ram Jam/SUMMERTAIRES: You're Gonna Leave 15
67	Coxsone CS 7026	Something Stupid/LYRICS: Money Lover 15
68	Coxsone CS 7040	Norwegian Wood/GAYLADS: Most Peculiar Man 15
68	Coxsone CS 7042	Sure Shot/OCTAVES: The Bottle 15
68	Coxsone CS 7046	Man Pon Shot/BOP & BELTONES: Not For A Moment 15
68	Coxsone CS 7050	Napoleon Solo/CANNON BALL BRYAN: You're My Everything 15
68	Coxsone CS 7075	Mission Impossible/HEPTONES: Giddy Up (B-side actually by Actions) 15
68	Studio One SO 2043	Put It On/SOUL VENDORS: Chinese Chicken 15
68	Studio One SO 2056	Race Track/BASES: I Don't Mind 15
69	Studio One SO 2082	Hi-Jack/TREVOR CLARKE: Sufferer 15
69	Doctor Bird DB 1177	Dark Of The Sun/MATADOR ALL STARS: Bridge View 10
69	Bamboo BAM 6	Our Thing (with Sound Dimension)/C. MARSHALL: Tra La La Sweet '69 6
69	Bamboo BAM 15	Clean Up/Spring Time (as Jackie Mittoo & Sound Dimension) 6
70	Bamboo BAM 17	Dark Of The Moon/Moon Walk (as Jackie Mittoo and Sound Dimension) 6
70	Bamboo BAM 20	Gold Dust/SUPERTONES: Real Gone Loser 6
70	Bamboo BAM 31	Can I Change My Mind/BRENTFORD ALLSTARS: Early Duckling 6
70	Bamboo BAM 51	Dancing Groove/BLACK & GEORGE: Peanut Butter 6
70	Bamboo BAM 315	Holly Holy/LARRY MARSHALL: I've Got To Make It 6
70	Bamboo BAM 320	Peenie Wallie/ROY RICHARDS: Can't Go On 6
67	Coxsone CSL 8009	IN LONDON (LP) 70
68	Coxsone CSL 8014	EVENING TIME (LP, with Soul Vendors) 70

| 69 | Coxsone CSL 8020 | KEEP ON DANCING (LP) ....70 |
| 70 | Bamboo BDLP 209 | NOW (LP) ....25 |

MIXED BAG
| 69 | Decca F 12880 | Potiphar/Million Dollar Bash ....4 |
| 69 | Decca F 12907 | Round And Round/Have You Ever Been In Love ....4 |

MIXTURE
| 65 | Fontana TF 640 | One By One/Monkey Jazz ....4 |
| 69 | Parlophone R 5755 | Sad Old Song/Never Trust In Tomorrow ....4 |

BILLY MIZE ORCHESTRA
| 60 | Top Rank JAR 391 | Little Coco Palm/The Windward Castle ....4 |

VIC MIZZY, HIS ORCHESTRA & CHORUS
| 65 | RCA RCA 1440 | Addams Family Main Theme/Kentucky Jones Main Theme ....6 |

M.J.6
| 60 | Decca F 11212 | Tracy's Theme/Private Eye ....4 |

M.J.Q.
(see under Modern Jazz Quartet)

MO & STEVE
| 66 | Pye 7N 17175 | Oh What A Day It's Going To Be/Reach Out For Your Lovin' Touch ......5 |

MOB
68	Mercury MF 1026	Disappear/I Wish You Would Leave Me Alone 5
71	Polydor 2001 127	I Dig Everything About You/Love's Got A Hold On Me 6
73	MGM 2006 278	Tear The House Down/One Way Ticket To Nowhere 4

MOB
80	All The Madmen MAD 1	Youth/Crying Again (p/s) 6
80	All The Madmen MAD 002	Witch Hunt/Shuffling Souls/What's Going On (EP, handwritten white labels with sticker & foldout, stapled, gatefold sleeve) 5
81	All The Madmen MAD 6	The Mirror Breaks/Stay (p/s, with lyric insert) 4
82	Crass 321984/7	No Doves Fly Here/I Hear You Laughing (foldout p/s) 4

MOMS MOBLEY
| 70 | Mercury MF 1127 | Sunny/Abraham, Martin And John ....6 |

MOBY GRAPE
67	CBS 2953	Omaha/Hey Grandma 8
68	CBS 3555	Can't Be So Bad/Murder In My Heart For The Judge 6
69	CBS 3945	Trucking Man/Ooh Mama Ooh 7
67	CBS (S)BPG 63090	MOBY GRAPE (LP) 15
68	CBS 63271	WOW (LP) 15
69	CBS 63430	'69 (LP) 15
70	CBS 63698	TRULY FINE CITIZEN (LP) 15
72	Reprise K 44152	20 GRANITE CREEK (LP) 10
74	CBS 64743	GREAT GRAPE (LP) 10

MOCEDADES
| 73 | Bell BELL 1303 | Touch The Wind/Eres Tu ....6 |

MOCKINGBIRDS
65	Columbia DB 7480	That's How It's Gonna Stay/I Never Should Have Kissed You 30
65	Columbia DB 7565	I Can Feel We're Parting/The Flight Of The Mockingbird 30
65	Immediate IM 015	You Stole My Love/Skit Skat 60
66	Decca F 12434	One By One/Lovingly Yours 25
66	Decca F 12510	How To Find A Lover/My Story 25
(see also 10cc, Graham Gouldman, Whirlwinds)

MOCK TURTLES
87	Imaginary MIRAGE 003	POMONA (12" EP) 18
89	Imaginary MIRAGE 009	Wicker Man/The Willow Song/Another Jesus Walks On Water/Fionnuala (12", p/s) 12
89	Imaginary MIRAGE 015	And Then She Smiles/Calm Before The Storm/Shangri-La (12", p/s, 1st issue with pink small type; 2nd with b&w type & girl's face in pink) 10/8
90	Imaginary MIRAGE 017	Lay Me Down/Can You Dig It? (fully autographed, sold at gigs) 5
90	Imaginary MIRAGE 019	Are You Experienced?/(Extended Mix) (12", no p/s, 500 autographed) 8
91	Imaginary FREE 001	Pale Blue Eyes/ECHO & BUNNYMEN: Foggy Notion (promo only) 7
80s	Bucketfull Of Brains BOB 26	Croppies Lie Down/SAINTS: I Dreamed Of Marie Antoinette (free with 'Bucketfull Of Brains', issue 32) 6/4
(see also Judge Happiness)

M.O.D.
| 79 | Vertigo 6059 233 | M.O.D./M.O.D. (Version) (p/s) ....8 |
(see also David Essex)

MODE
| 80s | private pressing | THE MODE (EP) ....200 |

MODELS
| 77 | Step Forward SF 3 | Freeze/Man Of The Year (p/s) ....5 |
(see also Adam & Ants)

MODERATES
| 80 | Open Eye OEEP 1001 | FETISHES (12" EP) ....7 |

MODERNAIRES
54	Vogue Coral Q 2024	Teach Me Tonight/Mood Indigo (with Georgie Auld) 8
54	Vogue Coral Q 2035	New Juke Box Saturday Night/Bugle Call Rag 8
55	Vogue Coral Q 72069	Birds And Puppies And Tropical Fish/Mine! Mine! Mine! 8
55	Vogue Coral Q 72084	Wine, Women And Gold/Sluefoot (with Bob Crosby Bob Cats) 8
55	Vogue Coral Q 72112	At My Front Door/Alright, Okay, You Win 10

MINT VALUE £

56	Vogue Coral Q 72135	"Let's Dance" Medley (Benny Goodman Story)	6
56	Vogue Coral Q 72158	Go On With The Wedding/Ain't She Sweet	6
56	Vogue Coral Q 72169	April In Paris/Hi-Diddlee-I-Dee	4
55	Vogue Coral LVC 10012	STOP, LOOK AND LISTEN (10" LP)	20
58	Coral LVA 9080	HERE COMES THE MODERNAIRES (LP)	15

(see also Four Guys)

MODERN ART

85	Color Disc COLORS 1	Dreams To Live/Beautiful Truth	25
80s	Color Disc COLORS 5	Penny Valentine/One Way Ticket (flexidisc)	12
87	Color Disc COLOR 3	STEREOLAND (LP, hand-stencilled with insert, 300 only)	45

(see also Sun Dial)

MODERN ENGLISH

79	Limp LMP 2	Drowning Man/Silent World (p/s)	18
80	4AD AD 6	Swans On Glass/Incident (p/s)	9
80	4AD AD 15	Gathering Dust/Tranquillity Of A Summer Moment (p/s)	8
81	4AD AD 110	Smiles And Laughter/Mesh And Lace (p/s)	7
82	4AD BAD 208	Life In The Gladhouse/The Choicest View (12", p/s)	7
82	4AD AD 212	I Melt With You/The Prize (p/s)	5

MODERN EON

80	Modern Eon EON 001	PIECES (EP)	20
81	Inevitable INEV 3	Euthenics/Waiting For The Cavalry (p/s)	8
81	Dinsales 2	Euthenics/Choreography/Waiting For The Cavalry/The Real Hymn (12", white label LP sampler)	30
81	DinDisc DIN 30	Euthenics (New Version)/Cardinal Signs (tri-gatefold folder p/s)	5
81	DinDisc DID 11	FICTION TALES (LP)	10

MODERN FOLK QUARTET (M.F.Q.)

64	Warner Bros WB 147	The Love Of A Clown/If You All Think	4
66	RCA RCA 1514	Night Time Girl/Lifetime (as M.F.Q.)	12
63	Warner Bros WM/WS 8135	THE MODERN FOLK QUARTET (LP)	12

MODERN JAZZ QUARTET (M.J.Q.)

50s	Esquire EP 106	MODERN JAZZ QUARTET (EP)	7
50s	Esquire EP 109	MODERN JAZZ QUARTET (EP)	7
50s	Esquire EP 116	GERSHWIN BALLAD MEDLEY (EP)	7
50s	Esquire EP 166	FIVE WAYS OF PLAYING LA RONDE (EP)	7
50s	Fontana 469 204TE	ALL OF YOU (EP)	7
57	London EZC 19019	THE QUARTET (EP, as The Quartet)	7
59	London EZK 19046	ONE NEVER KNOWS (EP)	7
59	London EZK 19047	THE MODERN JAZZ QUARTET (EP)	7
61	London REK 1314	MODERN JAZZ QUARTET (EP)	8
61	London REK 1320	MODERN JAZZ QUARTET AT MUSIC INN (EP)	8
62	London REK 1319	MODERN JAZZ QUARTET — EUROPEAN CONCERT (EP)	8
55	Esquire 20-069	MODERN JAZZ QUARTET (10" LP)	15
55	Esquire 20-038	MODERN JAZZ QUARTET VOL. 2 (10" LP)	15
58	London Jazz LTZK 15140	PLAYS ONE NEVER KNOWS (LP)	12
59	Columbia Clef 33CX 11028	MODERN JAZZ QUARTET AND OSCAR PETERSON AT THE OPERA HOUSE(LP)	10
60	London Jazz LTZ-K 15193	PYRAMID (LP, also stereo SAH-K 6086)	12
61	London Jazz LTZ-K 15207	THIRD STREAM MUSIC (LP, with Beaux Arts String Quartet & Jimmy Giuffre Three)	12
61	Esquire 32-124	LOOKING BACK AT THE MODERN JAZZ QUARTET (LP)	10
63	London HA-K/SH-K 8016	LONELY WOMAN (LP)	12
63	London HA-K/SH-K 8046	THE COMEDY SUITE (LP)	12
64	London HA-K/SH-K 8161	THE SHERIFF (LP)	12
65	Stateside SL 10141	THE BEST OF THE MODERN JAZZ QUARTET (LP)	10
66	Atlantic 587 044	A QUARTET IS A QUARTET IS A QUARTET (LP)	10
68	Apple (S)APCOR 4	UNDER THE JASMINE TREE (LP, mono/stereo)	35/30
69	Apple SAPCOR 10	SPACE (LP, gatefold sleeve)	40

(see also John Lewis, Milt Jackson, Sonny Rollins)

MODERN JAZZ SEXTET

| 56 | Columbia Clef 33CX 10048 | MODERN JAZZ SEXTET (LP) | 10 |

MODERN JAZZ SOCIETY

| 56 | Columbia Clef 33CX 10038 | A CONCERT OF CONTEMPORARY MUSIC (LP) | 10 |

MO-DETTES

79	Mode/R. TradeMODE 1	White Mice/Masochistic Opposite (pink [card or paper] or white p/s)	4/6
80	Deram DET-R-1/MODE 1½	Twist And Shout (gig freebie flexidisc, different label design to later issue)	4
80	Sound For industry SFI 550/MODE 1½	Paint It Black/Bitta Truth (with flexidisc "Twist And Shout" with insert, black & white or blue & white p/s)	5/6

MODS

| 64 | RCA RCA 1399 | Something On My Mind/You're Making Me Blue | 7 |

MODS 79

| 79 | Casino Classics CC 13 | Green Onions/High On Your Love (no p/s) | 4 |

DOMENICO MODUGNO

58	Oriole ICB 5000	Volare (Nel Blu Dipinto Di Blu)/Nisciuno Po' Sape'	6
58	Oriole CB 1460	Volare (Nel Blu Dipinto Di Blu)/Nisciuno Po' Sape'	6
59	Oriole CB 1475	Come Prima (More Than Ever)/Mariti In Citta	4
59	Oriole CB 1489	Ciao, Ciao Bambina (Piove)/Resta Cu 'Mme	6

MODULATIONS

| 74 | Buddah BDS 406 | I Can't Fight Your Love/Your Love Has Locked Me Up | 4 |

PETER MOESSER'S MUSIC

| 70 | Stateside SS 2182 | Hello/Bye Bye (withdrawn) | 4 |

MOFFAT ALL STARS
| 69 | Jackpot JP 719 | Riot/IMPERSONATORS: Girls And Boys | 6 |

MOGUL THRASH
| 70 | RCA RCA 2030 | Sleeping In The Kitchen/St. Peter | 4 |
| 71 | RCA SF 8156 | MOGUL THRASH (LP) | 18 |

ESSRA MOHAWK
| 75 | Mooncrest CREST 24 | ESSRA MOHAWK (LP, with insert) | 15 |

MOHAWKS
68	Pama PM 719	The Champ/Sound Of The Witchdoctors	12
68	Pama PM 739	Baby Hold On Pts 1 & 2	8
68	Pama PM 751	Sweet Soul Music/Hip Jigger	8
68	Pama PM 757	Mony Mony/Pepsi	8
69	Pama PM 758	Ride Your Pony/Western Promise	8

MOIST
| 86 | Debris DEB 9/LYN 19589 | The Cut Up #1/KING OF THE SLUMS: Haemophiliacs On Tacks (33rpm flexidisc free with 'Debris' magazine) | 8/6 |

MOJO HANNAH
| 71 | Kingdom KVL 9001 | SIX DAYS ON THE ROAD (LP) | 18 |

MOJO MEN
65	Pye Intl. 7N 25336	Dance With Me/The Loneliest Boy In Town	8
66	Reprise RS 20486	Hanky Panky/She's My Baby	25
67	Reprise RS 20539	Sit Down I Think I Love You/Don't Leave Me Crying Like Before	8
67	Reprise RS 20580	Me About You/When You're In Love	10

MOJOS
63	Decca F 11732	Forever/They Say	6
64	Decca F 11853	Everything's Alright/Give Your Lovin' To Me	4
64	Decca F 11918	Why Not Tonight/Don't Do It Any More	4
64	Decca F 11959	Seven Daffodils/Nothin' At All	5
65	Decca F 12127	Comin' On To Cry/That's The Way It Goes	7
67	Decca F 12557	Goodbye Dolly Gray/I Just Can't Let Her Go	8
68	Liberty LBF 15097	Until My Baby Comes Home/Seven Park Avenue	25
64	Decca DFE 8591	THE MOJOS (EP)	40
	(see also Stu James & Mojos)		

MOLES
| 68 | Parlophone R 5743 | We Are The Moles Pts 1 & 2 | 25 |
| | *(see also Simon Dupree & Big Sound)* | | |

MOMENTS
63	London HLN 9656	Walk Right In/Walk Right In (Instrumental)	6
74	London HL 10449	Sexy Mama/Where Can I Find Her	6
75	All Platinum 6146 309	Look At Me/French Version	4
75	All Platinum 9109 302	SHARP (LP)	10

MOMUS
| | *(see also Happy Family)* | | |

MONARCHS
| 64 | London HLU 9862 | Look Homeward Angel/What's Made You Change Your Mind | 15 |

JULIE MONDAY
| 66 | London HLU 10080 | Come Share The Good Times With Me/Time Is Running Out For Me | 4 |

PAUL MONDAY
68	MCA MU 1024	Musical Man/Wait For Me	12
69	MCA MK 5008	Here Comes The Sun/Musical Man	10
	(see also Paul Raven, Gary Glitter)		

MONEY
| 69 | Major Minor MM 620 | Come Laughing Home/Power Of The Rainbow | 5 |
| 70 | Major Minor MM 669 | Breaking Of Her Heart/Welcome My Love | 4 |

MONEY
79	Gull GULL 64	Aren't We All Searching/Where Have All The Dancers Gone	4
79	Gull GULP 1031	FIRST INVESTMENT (LP)	10
	(see also Iron Maiden)		

ZOOT MONEY'S BIG ROLL BAND
64	Decca F 11954	The Uncle Willie/Zoot's Suit (as Zoot Money)	15
65	Columbia DB 7518	Good/Bring It On Home To Me	12
65	Columbia DB 7600	Please Stay/You Know You'll Cry	12
65	Columbia DB 7697	Something Is Worrying Me/Stubborn Kind Of Fellow	12
65	Columbia DB 7768	The Many Faces Of Love/Jump Back (as Paul Williams & Zoot Money Band)	12
66	Columbia DB 7876	Let's Run For Cover/Self-Discipline	12
66	Columbia DB 7975	Big Time Operator/Zoot's Sermon	10
66	Columbia DB 8090	The Star Of The Show (The La La Song)/The Mound Moves	12
67	Columbia DB 8172	I Really Learnt How To Cry/Nick Knack (as Zoot Money)	10
70	Polydor 2058 020	No One But You/Prisoner	5
66	Columbia SEG 8519	BIG TIME OPERATOR (EP)	45
66	Columbia S(C)X 6075	ZOOT! — LIVE AT KLOOK'S KLEEK (LP, mono/stereo)	25/30
65	Columbia 33SX 1734	IT SHOULD'VE BEEN ME (LP)	50
68	Direction 8-63231	TRANSITION (LP)	30
70	Polydor 2482 019	ZOOT MONEY (LP)	15
	(see also Paul WIlliams & Big Roll Band, Dantalion's Chariot, Eric Burdon & Animals, Ellis, Grimms, John Rostill)		

MONGREL
| 73 | Polydor 2383 182 | GET YOUR TEETH INTO THIS (LP) | 30 |

MONGRELS

64	Decca F 12003	I Long To Hear/Everywhere	25
65	Decca F 12086	My Love For You/Stewball	25

(see also Bobbie Miller)

MONITORS

69	T. Motown (S)TML 11108	GREETINGS WE'RE THE MONITORS (LP)	45

THELONI(O)US MONK

63	CBS AAG 172	Hackensack/Bye Ya	5
56	Vogue EPV 1115	THELONIOUS MONK (EP)	10
50s	Esquire EP 75	THELONIOUS MONK TRIO (EP)	8
50s	Esquire EP 148	SONNY ROLLINS AND THELONIOUS MONK (EP)	8
61	Esquire EP 236	NUTTY MONK (EP)	8
62	Esquire EP 246	BLUE MONK (EP)	8
60s	Riverside REP 3214	NUTTY (EP, as Thelonious Monk & John Coltrane)	8
60s	Riverside REP 3217	RUBY MY DEAR (EP, as Thelonious Monk & John Coltrane)	8
55	Esquire 20-039	THELONIOUS MONK QUINTET (10" LP)	18
55	Esquire 20-049	THELONIOUS MONK (10" LP)	18
56	Esquire 20-075	THELONIOUS MONK PLAYS (10" LP)	18
60	Esquire 32-109	THELONIOUS MONK QUINTETS (LP)	15
61	Esquire 32-115	WORK! (LP, with Art Blakey & Sonny Rollins)	15
61	Esquire 32-119	MONK'S MOODS (LP)	15
61	Riverside RLP 12-201	MONK PLAYS ELLINGTON (LP)	15
61	Philips BBL 1510	THELONIOUS MONK VOL. 1 (LP)	15
61	Riverside RLP 12-226	BRILLIANT CORNERS (LP)	15
61	Riverside RLP 12-262	MONK IN ACTION (LP)	15
62	Riverside RLP 12-300	AT THE TOWN HALL (LP)	15
62	Riverside RLP 12-323	AT THE BLACK HAWK (LP, also stereo RLP 1171)	15
62	Philips BBL 1511	THELONIOUS MONK VOL. 2 (LP)	15
62	Riverside RLP 12-242	MONK'S MUSIC (LP)	15
63	Riverside RLP 201	MONK PLAYS ELLINGTON (LP, reissue)	10
63	CBS (S)BPG 62135	MONK'S DREAM (LP)	15
63	Riverside RLP 12-235	THELONIOUS HIMSELF (LP)	15
63	Riverside JLP (9)46	THELONIOUS MONK AND JOHN COLTRANE (LP)	15
64	Riverside RLP 002	IN EUROPE (VOL. 1)	15
64	CBS (S)BPG 62173	CRISS-CROSS (LP)	15
64	Blue Note (B)BLP 1510	THE GENIUS OF MODERN MUSIC (VOL. 1) (LP)	15
64	Blue Note (B)BLP 1511	THE GENIUS OF MODERN MUSIC (VOL. 2) (LP)	15
64	Riverside RLP 279	MISTERIOSO (LP)	15
64	CBS (S)BPG 62248	THELONIOUS MONK (LP)	15
65	CBS (S)BPG 62391	IT'S MONK'S TIME (LP)	15
65	Riverside RLP 305	FIVE BY MONK BY FIVE (LP)	15
65	Riverside RLP 003	IN EUROPE (VOL. 2) (LP)	15
65	CBS (S)BPG 62497	MONK (LP)	15
65	Riverside RLP 312	ALONE IN SAN FRANCISCO (LP)	15
65	Fontana FJL 113	WAY OUT! (LP)	15
65	Realm RM 52223	NICA'S TEMPO (LP, with Gigi Gryce)	12
65	CBS (S)BPG 62549	SOLO (LP)	15
65	Stateside SL 10152	THE GOLDEN MONK (LP)	15
66	Riverside RLP 004	IN EUROPE (VOL. 3)	12
66	CBS (S)BPG 62620	MISTERIOSO (LP, reissue)	10
67	CBS (S)BPG 63009	STRAIGHT, NO CHASER (LP)	12
67	Transatlantic PR 7169	WORK (LP)	12
69	CBS 63609	MONK'S BLUES (LP)	10
69	Storyville 673 014	THELONIOUS MONK PLAYS DUKE (LP)	10
69	Storyville 673 022	IN CONCERT (LP)	10
70	Storyville 673 024	*THE* THELONIOUS MONK (LP)	10
72	Polydor 2460 152	SOMETHING IN BLUE (LP)	10
73	CBS PR 24006	THELONIUS MONK (2-LP)	14
74	Polydor 2460 197	THE MAN I LOVE (LP)	10
75	DJM DJSLM 2017	PURE MONK (LP)	10
75	CBS 88034	WHO'S AFRAID OF BIG BAD MONK (LP)	10

(see also John Coltrane, Sonny Rollins)

MONKEES

66	RCA Victor RCA 1547	Last Train To Clarksville/Take A Giant Step	4
66	RCA Victor RCA 1560	I'm A Believer/(I'm Not Your) Stepping Stone	4
67	RCA Victor RCA 1580	A Little Bit Me, A Little Bit You/The Girl I Knew Somewhere	4
67	RCA Victor RCA 1604	Alternate Title/Forget That Girl	4
67	RCA Victor RCA 1620	Pleasant Valley Sunday/Words	4
67	RCA Victor RCA 1645	Daydream Believer/Goin' Down	4
68	RCA Victor RCA 1673	Valleri/Tapioca Tundra	4
68	RCA Victor RCA 1706	D.W. Washburn/It's Nice To Be With You	4
69	RCA RCA 1802	Teardrop City/A Man Without A Dream	5
69	RCA RCA 1824	Someday Man/Listen To The Band	5
69	RCA RCA 1862	The Porpoise Song/Daddy's Song	6
69	RCA RCA 1887	Mommy And Daddy/Good Clean Fun	6
70	RCA RCA 1958	Oh My My/Love You Better	6
67	RCA Victor RD/SF 7844	THE MONKEES (LP, mono/stereo)	10/12
67	RCA Victor RD/SF 7868	MORE OF THE MONKEES (LP, mono/stereo)	10/12
67	RCA Victor RD/SF 7886	HEADQUARTERS (LP, mono/stereo)	10/12
67	RCA Victor RD/SF 7912	PISCES, AQUARIUS, CAPRICORN AND JONES LTD. (LP, mono/stereo)	10/12
68	RCA Victor RD/SF 7948	THE BIRDS, THE BEES & THE MONKEES (LP, mono/stereo)	10/12
69	RCA RD/SF 8016	INSTANT REPLAY (LP, mono/stereo)	18/15
69	RCA RD/SF 8051	HEAD (LP, soundtrack, mono/stereo)	40/35

70s	Reader's Digest	THE MONKEES (LP, free with various artists box set) 15

(see also Mickey Dolenz, Davy Jones, Michael Nesmith)

BOB MONKHOUSE
69	CBS 3958	I Remember Natalie/In My Dream World 4
69	CBS 4607	Another Time Another Place Another World/When I Found You 4

MONOCHROME SET
79	Rough Trade RT 005	Alphaville/He's Frank (p/s) 5
79	Rough Trade RT 019	Eine Symphonie Des Grauens/Lester Leaps In (p/s) 4
79	Rough Trade RT 028	The Monochrome Set/Mr Bizarro (p/s) 4
79	Disquo Bleu BL 1	He's Frank (Slight Return)/Silicon Carne/Fallout (all cuts live) (no p/s) 5
80	DinDisc DID 8	LOVE ZOMBIES (LP, with lithograph) 10

(see also Art Attacks)

MONOGRAMS
59	Parlophone R 4515	Juke Box Cha Cha/The Greatest Mistake Of My Life 6
59	Parlophone R 4515	Juke Box Cha Cha/The Greatest Mistake Of My Life (78) 5
59	Parlophone R 4545	Crystal/Teach Me 4

MONOPOLY
67	Polydor 56164	House Of Lords/Magic Carpet 5
67	Polydor 56188	We're All Going To The Seaside/It Isn't Easy 5
70	Pye 7N 17940	We Belong Together/Gone Tomorrow 4

MONOTONES (U.S.)
58	London HLM 8625	Book Of Love/You Never Loved Me 40
58	London HLM 8625	Book Of Love/You Never Loved Me (78) 15

MONOTONES (U.K.)
64	Pye 7N 15608	What Would I Do/Is It Right 5
64	Pye 7N 15640	It's Great/Anymore 5
65	Pye 7N 15761	No Waiting/Like A Lover Should 5
65	Pye 7N 15814	Something's Hurting Me/A Girl Like That 5

MATT MONRO
56	Decca F 10816	Ev'rybody Falls In Love With Someone/Out Of Sight, Out Of Mind 12
57	Decca F 10839	Gone With The Wind/My Old Flame (unreleased)
57	Decca F 10845	The Garden Of Eden/Love Me Do 12
57	Decca F 10870	My House Is Your House/The Bean Song 12
58	Fontana H 115	I'll Never Have A Sweetheart/The Golden Age (78) 5
58	Fontana H 122	The Story Of Ireland/Another Time Another Place 10
58	Fontana H 167	Prisoner Of Love/Have Guitar, Will Travel 10
60	Parlophone R 4638	Love Walked In/I'll Know Her 4
60	Parlophone R 4714	Portrait Of My Love/You're The Top Of My Hit Parade .4
63	Parlophone R 5068	From Russia With Love/Here And Now 4
63	Parlophone GEP 8889	SINGS THE THEME FROM THE FILM 'FROM RUSSIA FROM LOVE' (EP) 12
57	Decca LF 1276	BLUE AND SENTIMENTAL (10" LP) 25
61	Ace Of Clubs ACL 1069	PORTRAIT (LP) 10
61	Parlophone PMC 1151	LOVE IS THE SAME ANYWHERE (LP, also stereo) 10
62	Parlophone PMC 1185	MATT MONRO SINGS HOAGY CARMICHAEL (LP, also
		stereo PCS 3034) 10
65	Parlophone PMC 1250	I HAVE DREAMED (LP, also stereo PCS 3067) 10
66	Capitol (S)T 2540	THIS IS THE LIFE! (LP) 10
67	Capitol (S)T 2608	HERE'S TO MY LADY (LP) 10
67	Capitol (S)T 2683	INVITATION TO BROADWAY (LP) 10
67	Capitol (S)T 2730	INVITATION TO THE MOVIES (LP) 10
68	Capitol (S)T 2801	THESE YEARS (LP) 10
68	Capitol (S)T 2919	THE LATE, LATE SHOW (LP) 10
69	Fontana SFL 13161	TONY BLACKBURN MEETS MATT MONRO (LP) 10

BARRY MONROE
66	Polydor 56088	Never Again/World Of Broken Hearts 6

BILL MONROE (& HIS BLUE GRASS BOYS)
56	Brunswick 05567	New John Henry Blues/Put My Little Shoes Away 8
56	Brunswick 05567	New John Henry Blues/Put My Little Shoes Away (78) .5
57	Brunswick 05681	Four Walls/A Fallen Star 8
57	Brunswick 05681	Four Walls/A Fallen Star (78) 5
59	Brunswick 05776	Gotta Travel On/No One But My Darlin' 8
59	Brunswick 05776	Gotta Travel On/No One But My Darlin' (78) 5
66	Brunswick 05960	Blue Ridge Mountain Blues/John Hardy (solo) 5
55	Brunswick OE 9160	COUNTRY DATE (EP) 18
55	Brunswick OE 9195	COUNTRY WALTZ (EP) 18
63	RCA RCX 7105	COUNTRY GUITAR VOL. 16 (EP, 2 tracks by Monroe Brothers) 8
61	Brunswick LAT 8338	I SAW THE LIGHT (LP) 12
63	Brunswick LAT 8511	BLUEGRASS RAMBLE (LP, also stereo STA 8511) 12
65	Brunswick LAT/STA 8579	BLUEGRASS SPECIAL (LP) 12

(see also Monroe Brothers)

GERRY MONROE
70	Chapter One CHS 806	SALLY — PRIDE OF OUR ALLEY (LP) 10
71	Chapter One CHS 809	GERRY MONROE (LP) 10

MARILYN MONROE
53	MGM MGM 663	Diamonds Are A Girl's Best Friend/Bye Bye Baby (78) .8
54	HMV 7M 232	I'm Gonna File My Claim/The River Of No Return 20
54	HMV B 10723	I'm Gonna File My Claim/The River Of No Return (78) 20
55	HMV B 10847	After You Get What You Want/Heat Wave (78) 20
59	London HLT 8862	I Wanna Be Loved By You/I'm Thru' With Love 15
59	London HLT 8862	I Wanna Be Loved By You/I'm Thru' With Love (78) 20
87	Zuma ZOOMP 6	When I Fall In Love/Heat Wave (picture disc) 5

Marilyn MONROE

55	HMV 7EG 8090	THERE'S NO BUSINESS LIKE SHOW BUSINESS	
		— SOUNDTRACK EXCERPTS (EP)	20
60	London RET 1231	SOME LIKE IT HOT (EP, soundtrack)	30
60	Philips BBE 12414	LET'S MAKE LOVE — FILM SOUNDTRACK (EP, with Yves Montand & Frankie Vaughan; also stereo SBBE 9031)	18/25
53	MGM MGM-D 116	GENTLEMEN PREFER BLONDES (10" LP, soundtrack with other artists)	50
59	London HA-T 2176	SOME LIKE IT HOT (LP, s/track with other artists, stereo SAH-T 6040)	45/50
60	Philips BBL 7414	LET'S MAKE LOVE (LP, soundtrack, with Yves Montand & Frankie Vaughan)	35
63	Stateside S(S)L 10048	MARILYN (LP, soundtrack, mono/stereo)	15/18
83	Liberty UASP 30226	SOME LIKE IT HOT (LP, picture disc)	10
	(see also Frankie Vaughan)		

VAUGHN MONROE (& HIS ORCHESTRA)

53	HMV 7M 144	Less Than Tomorrow (But More Than Yesterday)/Ruby	6
53	HMV 7M 148	Small World/Don't You Care	6
53	HMV 7M 165	(All Roads Lead To) The Fiesta/I Know For Sure	6
54	HMV 7M 247	They Were Doin' The Mambo/Mister Sandman	7
55	HMV 7M 287	Goodnight, Mrs. Jones/The Butterscotch Mop	6
56	HMV 7M 332	Black Denim Trousers And Motorcycle Boots/All By Myself	18
57	HMV POP 354	Wringle Wrangle/Westward Ho The Wagons!	5
59	RCA RCA 1124	The Battle Of New Orleans/Hercules	4
60	London HLT 9123	Ballerina/Love Me Forever	5
59	RCA RCX 1043	VAUGHAN MONROE'S GREATEST HITS (EP)	12
57	RCA RD 27049	FAMILY SING-SONG (LP)	10
50s	HMV	LPs	12

MONROE BROTHERS

63	RCA RCX 7103	COUNTRY GUITAR VOL. 14 (EP)	10
63	RCA RCX 7104	COUNTRY GUITAR VOL. 15 (EP)	10
63	RCA RCX 7105	COUNTRY GUITAR VOL. 16 (EP, 2 tracks by Bill Monroe & Bluegrass Boys)	8
	(see also Bill Monroe)		

MONSOON

81	Indipop IND 1	Ever So Lonely/Sunset Over The Ganges/The Mirror Of Your Mind/ Shout! (Till You're Heard) (in plastic sleeve with insert)	4

MONTANAS

65	Piccadilly 7N 35262	All That Is Mine Can Be Yours/How Can I Tell	8
66	Pye 7N 17183	That's When Happiness Began/Goodbye Little Girl	30
67	Pye 7N 17282	Ciao Baby/Anyone There	5
67	Pye 7N 17338	Take My Hand/Top Hat	8
67	Pye 7N 17394	You've Got To Be Loved/Difference Of Opinion	8
68	Pye 7N 17499	A Step In The Right Direction/Someday (You'll Be Breaking My Heart Again)	8
68	Pye 7N 17597	You're Making A Big Mistake/Run To Me	8
69	Pye 7N 17697	Roundabout/Mystery	8
69	Pye 7N 17729	Ciao Baby/Someday (You'll Be Breaking My Heart Again)	5
70	MCA MK 5036	Let's Get A Little Sentimental/Hey Diddle Diddle	4

MONTCLAIRS

74	Contempo CS 2008	Make Up For Lost Time/How Can One Man Live	4
75	Contempo CS 2036	Hung Up On Your Love/I Need You More Than Ever	8

LOU MONTE

54	HMV 7M 176	A Baby Cried/One Moment More	5
54	HMV 7M 190	Darktown Strutters' Ball/I Know How You Feel	6
54	HMV 7M 217	Won't You Forgive Me?/Somewhere There Is Someone	5
54	HMV 7M 249	Chain Reaction/Vera's Veranda	4
54	HMV 7M 276	In My Dreams/When I Hold You In My Arms	4
58	RCA RCA 1048	Lazy Mary (Luna Mezzo Mare)/Angelique-o	4
59	RCA RCA 1161	Santa Nicola/All Because It's Christmas	4
60	Columbia DB 4500	Oh! Oh! Rosie/(The New) Darktown Strutters' Ball	4

VINNIE MONTE

59	London HL 8947	Summer Spree/I'll Walk You Home	10
59	London HL 8947	Summer Spree/I'll Walk You Home (78)	18
63	Stateside SS 156	Joanie Don't Be Angry/Take Good Care Of Her	6

MONTEGO JOE

66	Stateside SL 10159	JARRIBA! CON MONTEGO JOE (LP)	10

HUGO MONTENEGRO ORCHESTRA

62	Oriole CB 1765	Palm Canyon Drive/Dark Eyes	5
63	Oriole CB 1792	Get Off The Moon/Sherry	20
65	RCA RD 7758	THE MAN FROM U.N.C.L.E. (LP, soundtrack)	20
66	RCA RD 7832	MORE MUSIC FROM THE MAN FROM U.N.C.L.E. (LP, soundtrack)	25

BOBBY MONTEZ

60	Vogue V 9165	Holiday In Havana/Jungle Stars	4

CHRIS MONTEZ

62	London HLU 9596	Let's Dance/You're The One	5
63	London HLU 9650	Some Kinda Fun/Tell Me	5
63	London HLU 9764	My Baby Loves To Dance/In An English Towne	6
66	Pye Intl. 7N 25348	Call Me/Go 'Head On	5
66	Pye Intl. 7N 25369	The More I See You/You, I Love You	5
66	Pye Intl. 7N 25381	There Will Never Be Another You/You Can Hurt The One You Love	5
66	Pye Intl. 7N 23599	Time After Time/Keep Talkin'	5
67	Pye Intl. 7N 25415	Because Of You/Elena	4
68	London HLU 10205	Let's Dance/Some Kinda Fun	4
63	London REU 1392	LET'S DANCE (EP)	20
66	Pye Intl. NEP 44071	THE MORE I SEE YOU (EP)	12
66	Pye Intl. NEP 44080	CHRIS MONTEZ (EP)	10

63	London HA-U 8079	LET'S DANCE AND HAVE SOME KINDA FUN!!! (LP)	25
66	Pye Intl. NPL 28080	THE MORE I SEE YOU (LP)	12
67	Pye Intl. N(S)PL 28087	TIME AFTER TIME (LP)	12
68	A&M AML 906	FOOLIN' AROUND (LP)	10
68	A&M AML(S) 925	WATCH WHAT HAPPENS (LP)	10

JACK MONTGOMERY

| 85 | Kent TOWN 102 | Dearly Beloved/MARIE KNIGHT: That's No Way To Treat A Girl | 6 |

LITTLE BROTHER MONTGOMERY

50s	Jazz Collector L 44	No Special Rider Blues/Vicksburg Blues (78)	8
61	Columbia DB 4595	Pinetop's Boogie Woogie/Cow Cow Blues	12
61	Columbia 33SX 1289	LITTLE BROTHER MONTGOMERY (LP)	20
62	'77' 77LA 12/21	LITTLE BROTHER MONTGOMERY/SUNNYLAND SLIM (LP)	10
65	Decca LK 4664	LITTLE BROTHER MONTGOMERY (LP)	15
60s	Xtra XTRA 1115	FARRO ST. JIVE (LP)	10
71	Saydisc SDR 213	LITTLE BROTHER MONTGOMERY 1930-1969 (LP)	15

MARIAN MONTGOMERY

65	Capitol CL 15375	When Sunny Gets Blue/Teach Me Tonight	4
67	Reaction 591 018	Love Make Two People Sing/Monday Thru Saturday	8
68	Pye 7N 17533	Why Say Goodbye/Love Today — Cry Tomorrow	4

MONTROSE

| 74 | Warner Bros K 16382 | Bad Motor Scooter/One Thing On My Mind | 4 |
| 74 | Warner Bros K 16428 | Rock The Nation/One Thing On My Mind | 4 |

(see also Sammy Hagar)

MONTY, DEREK & PATSY

| 64 | Blue Beat BB 280 | Stir The Pot/Mercy | 7 |

(see also Monty Morris, Derrick Morgan, Patsy Todd)

MONTY (Morris) & ROY

| 61 | Blue Beat BB 61 | In And Out The WIndow/Tra La La Boogie | 10 |
| 61 | Blue Beat BB 63 | Sweetie Pie/ROLAND ALPHONSO'S GROUP: Green Door | 10 |

(see also Monty Morris)

MONTY PYTHON('S FLYING CIRCUS)

70	BBC	Flying Sheep/Man With Three Buttocks	10
72	Charisma CB 192	Spam Song/The Concert	4
72	Charisma CB 200	Eric The Half A Bee (Extended)/The Yangtse Song (with Neil Innes)	4
74	NME/Charisma SFI 1259	Monty Python's Tiny Black Round Thing (The Election Special) (flexidisc free with 'NME' magazine; with/without mag)	7/4
70s	Zig Zag	Monty Python (flexidisc free with 'Zig Zag' magazine)	7/5
80	Charisma CB 374	I Like Chinese/I Bet You They Don't Play This/Finland (p/s)	4
83	CBS WA 3495	Galaxy Song/Every Sperm Is Sacred (goldfish bowl-shaped picture disc)	4
75	Charisma MP 001	PYTHON ON SONG (double pack EP [CBS 268/PY 2])	8
70	BBC REB 73M	MONTY PYTHON'S FLYING CIRCUS (LP)	10
71	Charisma CAS 1049	ANOTHER MONTY PYTHON RECORD (LP, with 'great actor kit': printed inner sleeve, cut-outs sheet, cue sheet & script)	10
72	Charisma CAS 1063	MONTY PYTHON'S PREVIOUS RECORD (LP, with free p/s flexidisc, "Teach Yourself Health" & inner sleeve)	10
77	Charisma CAS 1134	THE MONTY PYTHON INSTANT RECORD COLLECTION (LP, foldout sleeve)	10
80	Charisma CAS 1152	CONTRACTUAL OBLIGATION ALBUM (LP, with inner sleeve & "Farewell To John Denver")	12

(see also John Cleese, Rutles)

MONUMENT

| 71 | Beacon BEAS 15 | THE FIRST MONUMENT (LP) | 60 |

(see also Zior)

MOOCHE

| 69 | Pye 7N 17735 | Hot Smoke And Sasafrass/Seen Through A Light | 20 |

AMEIL MOODIE

| 68 | Blue Cat BS 143 | Mello Reggae/Lifeline | 7 |
| 69 | Blue Cat BS 164 | Ratchet Knife/Bend The Tree | 7 |

MOODISTS

| 85 | Creation CRE 023T | Justice And Money Too/You've Got Your Story/Take Us All Home (12", p/s) | 7 |

MOOD MOSAIC

66	Columbia DB 7801	A Touch Of Velvet, A Sting Of Brass/Bond Street P.M.	10
67	Columbia DB 8149	Chinese Chequers/The Real Mr. Smith	8
68	Parlophone R 5716	The Yellow Spotted Capricorn/ELMER HOCKETT'S HURDY GURDY: Fantastic Fair	4
69	Columbia DB 8618	A Touch Of Velvet, A Sting Of Brass/Bond Street P.M. (reissue)	6
67	Columbia SX 6153	MOOD MOSAIC (LP, also stereo Studio Two TWO 160)	10

(see also Mark Wirtz Orchestra & Chorus, Keith West)

MOOD OF HAMILTON

| 67 | Columbia DB 8304 | Why Can't There Be More Love?/King's Message | 10 |

MOOD REACTION

| 60s | Pama | MOOD REACTION (LP) | 12 |

MOODS

| 63 | Starlite ST45 098 | Duckwalk/Easy Going | 15 |

MOOD SIX

82	EMI EMI 5300	Hanging Around/Mood Music (p/s)	5
82	EMI EMI 5336	She's Too Far/Venus (unreleased; white label copies exist with p/s)	30
85	Psycho PSYCHO 2001	Plastic Flowers/It's Your Life (p/s)	5
85	Psycho PSYCHO 4001	PLASTIC FLOWERS (12" EP)	10

85	Psycho PSYCHO 33	THE DIFFERENCE IS... (LP)	10

(see also VIPs)

RON MOODY

61	Decca F 11371	You've Gotta Pick A Pocket Or Two/Reviewing The Situation	4
64	Parlophone R 5205	Rinkety Tink/Bringing Home My Darling	4

MOODY BLUES

64	Decca F 11971	Steal Your Heart Away/Loose Your Money (But Don't Lose Your Mind) (as Moodyblues)	30
64	Decca F 12022	Go Now!/It's Easy Child	4
65	Decca F 12095	I Don't Want To Go On Without You/Time Is On My Side	5
65	Decca F 12166	From The Bottom Of My Heart (I Love You)/And My Baby's Gone	5
65	Decca F 12266	Everyday/You Don't (All The Time)	6
66	Decca F 12498	Boulevard De La Madelaine/This Is My House (But Nobody Calls)	6
67	Decca F 12543	Life's Not Life/He Can Win (withdrawn)	30
67	Decca F 12607	Fly Me High/Really Haven't Got The Time	10
67	Decca F 12670	Love And Beauty/Leave This Man Alone	10
67	Deram DM 161	Nights In White Satin/Cities (1st issue, darker labels than later copies)	4
68	Deram DM 196	Voices In The Sky/Doctor Livingstone, I Presume	4
68	Deram DM 213	Ride My See-Saw/A Simple Game	5
69	Deram DM 247	Never Comes The Day/So Deep Within You	4
69	Threshold TH 1	Watching And Waiting/Out And In	6
70	Threshold TH 4	Question/Candle Of Life	4
72	Threshold TH 9	Isn't Life Strange/After You Came	4
81	Threshold THPD 29	Talking Out Of Turn/Veteran Cosmic Rocker (picture disc)	7
65	Decca DFE 8622	THE MOODY BLUES (EP, original label or reissue with boxed Decca logo)	15/8
65	Decca LK 4711	THE MAGNIFICENT MOODIES (LP, original label)	14
67	Deram DML/SML 707	DAYS OF FUTURE PASSED (LP, mono/stereo)	12/10
68	Deram DML/SML 711	IN SEARCH OF THE LOST CHORD (LP, mono/stereo)	14/10
69	Deram DML/SML 1035	ON THE THRESHOLD OF A DREAM (LP with stapled booklet, mono/stereo)	14/10
69	Threshold THM/THS 1	TO OUR CHILDREN'S CHILDREN'S CHILDREN (LP, with insert, mono/stereo)	18/10
78	Decca TXS 129	OCTAVE (LP, blue vinyl)	12

(see also Justin Hayward, Denny Laine, Gerry Levene & Avengers)

MOON

68	Liberty LBF 15076	Someday Girl/Mothers And Fathers	5
70	Liberty LBF 15333	Pirate/Not To Know	4
68	Liberty LBL/LBS 83146	WITHOUT EARTH (LP)	15

KEITH MOON

75	Polydor 2058 584	Don't Worry Baby/Together	5
75	Polydor 2442 134	TWO SIDES OF THE MOON (LP)	15

(see also Who)

LARRY MOON

63	Ember EMB 171	Tia Juana Ball/Bouquet Of Roses	4

MOON BOYS

69	Amalgamated AMG 846	Apollo 11/PIONEERS: Love Love Everyday	6

(see also Hippy Boys)

MOONDANCE

68	A&M AMS 792	Lazy River/Anna St Claire	4

MOONDOG

54	London REP 1010	ON THE STREETS OF NEW YORK (EP)	20
69	CBS 63906	MOONDOG (LP, gatefold sleeve)	15

MOONDOGS

79	Good Vibrations GOT 10	She's Nineteen/Ya Don't Do Ya (foldout p/s)	4
80	Real ARE 13	Who's Gonna Tell Mary/Overcaring Parents (p/s)	4
81	Real ARE 14	Talking In The Canteen/Make Her Love Me (p/s, with neckerchief)	6
81	Real ARE 16	Imposter/Baby Snatcher (p/s)	4

ART MOONEY (& HIS ORCHESTRA)

52	MGM MGM 503	The Blacksmith Blues/SHORTY LONG: Move It On Over (78)	5
53	MGM SP 1037	I Played The Fool/I Just Couldn't Take It, Baby (with Cathy Ryan)	5
53	MGM SP 1045	Baby Don't Do It/Believe In Me (with Cathy Ryan)	5
54	MGM SP 1088	Oh Boy What Joy We Had/Silhouette D'Amour	4
55	MGM SP 1134	No Regrets/Honey Babe	4
56	MGM SP 1166	Memories Of You/I'm Looking Over	5
56	MGM MGM 899	Tutti Frutti/OCIE SMITH & CLOVERLEAFS: Our Melody (78)	5
57	MGM MGM 923	"Rebel Without A Cause" Theme/"East Of Eden" Theme	10
57	MGM MGM 923	"Rebel Without A Cause" Theme/"East Of Eden" Theme (78)	5
57	MGM MGM 943	Giant/There's Never Been Anyone Else But You	10
57	MGM MGM 943	Giant/There's Never Been Anyone Else But You (78)	5
57	MGM MGM 951	Rock And Roll Tumbleweed/Is There A Teenager In The House (with Ocie Smith)	18
57	MGM MGM 951	Rock And Roll Tumbleweed/Is There A Teenager In The House (with Ocie Smith) (78)	15

(see also Ocie Smith, Shorty Long)

HAL MOONEY ORCHESTRA

62	Oriole CB 1782	Small World/Let Us Entertain You	4

MOONGLOWS

57	London HLN 8374	I Knew From The Start/Over And Over Again	250
57	London HLN 8374	I Knew From The Start/Over And Over Again (78)	40

(see also Harvey & Moonglows)

MOONKYTE
71	Mother SMOT 1	COUNT ME OUT (LP, with insert, spiral sleeve)	110

MOONLIGHTERS
63	Island WI 043	Going Out/Hold My Hands	10

MICKY MOONSHINE
74	Decca F 13555	Baby Blue/Name It You Got It	7
75	Decca F 13555	Baby Blue/Name It You Got It (reissue, with inverted matrix number)	4

MOONSHINERS
65	Stateside SL 10137	THE MOONSHINERS BREAKOUT! (LP)	10
67	Page One POLS 004	HOLD UP (LP)	20

MOONSTONES
65	Parlophone R 5331	Heaven Fell Last Night/Little Roses	4
66	Parlophone R 5497	Violets Of Dawn/Power Of Decision	4
67	Mercury MF 1011	Louisville/How Many Times	4

MOON'S TRAIN
67	MGM MGM 1333	Deed I Do/It's In My Mind	10

MOONTREKKERS
61	Parlophone R 4814	Night Of The Vampire/Melodie d'Amour	15
62	Parlophone R 4888	There's Something At The Bottom Of The Well/Hatashiai	15
63	Decca F 11714	Moondust/The Bogey Man	10

MICHAEL MOORCOCK (DEEP FIX)
80	Flicknife FLEP 200	Dodgem Dude/Star Cruiser (p/s)	8
82	Flicknife	Brothel In Rosenstrasse/Time Centre (500 only, with insert)	30
75	United Artists UAG 29732	NEW WORLD'S FAIR (LP, with inner sleeve)	40

(see also Hawkwind)

ADA MOORE & JIMMY RUSHING
57	Philips BBE 12150	CAT MEETS CHICK (EP)	12

(see also Jimmy Rushing)

ANTHONY MOORE
76	Virgin VS 144	Catch A Falling Star/Back To The Top	4
71	Polydor 2310 062	PIECES FROM THE CLOUDLAND BALLROOM (LP)	40
72	Polydor 2310 079	SECRETS OF THE BLUE BAG (LP)	40

(see also Slapp Happy)

ALICE MOORE
50s	Poydras MC 66	Prison Blues/My Man Blues (78)	10

BOBBY MOORE & RHYTHM ACES
66	Chess CRS 8033	Searching For My Love/Hey Mr D.J.	8
75	Pye Intl. 7N 25691	Call Me Your Anything Man/(Disco Version) (solo)	4
66	Chess CRL 4521	SEARCHIN' FOR MY LOVE (LP)	20

BOB MOORE ORCHESTRA
61	London HLU 9409	Mexico/Hot Spot	5
63	London HLU 9736	Kentucky/Flowers Of Florence	5

BUTCH MOORE
65	Pye 7N 15832	Walking The Streets In The Rain/I Stand Still	7

CHRISTY MOORE
69	Mercury 20170 SMCL	PADDY ON THE ROAD (LP)	50
75	Polydor 2383 344	WHATEVER TICKLES YOUR FANCY (LP)	10

DUDLEY MOORE (TRIO)
61	Parlophone R 4772	Strictly For The Birds (solo)/Duddly Dell (B-side as Dudley Moore Trio)	5
68	Decca F 12850	30 Is A Dangerous Age Cynthia/The Real Stuff (solo)	4
69	Decca F 12882	Keep it Up/Gently (as Dudley Moore Trio)	4
66	Decca LK 4788	GENUINE DUD (LP, as Dudley Moore Trio)	10
68	Decca LK/SKL 4923	BEDAZZLED (LP)	10
69	Decca LK/SKL 4976	THE DUDLEY MOORE TRIO (LP)	25
69	Decca SKL 4980	THE MUSIC OF DUDLEY MOORE (LP)	10

(see also Peter Cook & Dudley Moore)

GARY MOORE
78	MCA MCA 386	Back On The Streets/Track Nine (some in p/s)	25/5
79	MCA MCA 419	Parisienne Walkways/Fanatical Fascists (p/s)	10
79	MCA MCA 534	Spanish Guitar/Spanish Guitar (instrumental) (p/s)	10
81	Jet JET 12016	Nuclear Attack/Don't Let Me Be Misunderstood/Run To Your Mama (12", company sleeve, as Gary Moore & Friends)	8
82	Virgin VSY 528	Always Gonna Love You/Cold Hearted (picture disc)	6
83	Virgin VSY 564	Falling In Love With You/Falling In Love With You (Instrumental) (picture disc)	6
83	Virgin VS 564	Falling In Love With You/Falling In Love With You (Instrumental) (poster p/s)	4
83	Virgin VS 564	Falling In Love With You/(Instrumental) (p/s, with comic)	6
84	10 TEN 13	Hold On To Love/Devil In Her Heart (poster p/s)	4
84	10 TENS 13	Hold On To Love/Devil In Her Heart (shaped picture disc)	10
84	10 TEN 19	Shapes Of Things/Blinder (p/s, with patch)	4
84	10 TENS 19	Shapes Of Things/Blinder (explosion-shaped picture disc)	10
84	10 TEN 25	Empty Rooms/Empty Rooms (live) (poster p/s)	4
84	10 TEN 25-12	Empty Rooms (Ext. Mix)/Empty Rooms//Nuclear Attack (live)/Empty Rooms (live)/Rockin' Every Night (live) (12" double pack, gatefold p/s with poster)	8
85	10 TEND 58	Empty Rooms ('85 Version)/Out Of My System//Parisienne Walkways (live)/Murder In The Skies (live) (double pack, gatefold p/s)	5
86	10 TENS 134	Over The Hills And Far Away/Crying In The Shadows (guitar-shaped pic disc)	7
86	10 TEND 134	Over The Hills And Far Away/Crying In The Shadows//Out In The Fields (live with Phil Lynott)/All Messed Up (live) (double pack, gatefold p/s)	5

Gary MOORE

86	10 TENG 134	Over The Hills And Far Away (Extended Mix)/Over The Hills And Far Away (7" Version)/Crying In The Shadows/All Messed Up (live) (12", gatefold p/s)	7
87	10 TEND 159	Wild Frontier/Run For Cover (live)//Wild Frontier (live)/Murder In The Skies (live) (double pack, gatefold p/s)	.5
87	10 TENP 164	Friday On My Mind/Reach For The Sky (live) (picture disc)	.5
87	10 TEND 190	Take A Little Time/Out In The Fields//All Messed Up (live)/Thunder Rising (live) (double pack, gatefold p/s)	.5
89	Virgin GMSY 1	After The War/This Thing Called Love (picture disc, stickered PVC sleeve)	.5
82	Virgin V 2245	CORRIDORS OF POWER (LP, with free live EP [VDJ 34])	10
86	10 DIXP 16	RUN FOR COVER (LP, picture disc, die-cut sleeve)	10
87	10 DIXG 56	WILD FRONTIER (2-LP)	15

GARY MOORE & PHIL LYNOTT

85	10 TENS 49	Out In The Fields/Military Man (interlocking shaped picture disc, 2 designs)	each 12
85	10 TEND 49	Out In The Fields/Military Man//Still In Love With You/Stop Messin' Around (live) (double pack)	.5
85	10 TEN 49-12	Out In The Fields/Military Man/Still In Love With You (12", gatefold p/s)	.7

(see also Skid Row, G-Force, Thin Lizzy, Phil Lynott)

JACKIE MOORE

71	Jay Boy BOY 35	Dear John/Here Am I	4
71	Atlantic 2091 095	Sometimes It's Got To Rain (In Your Love Life)/Wonderful, Marvellous (with Dixie Flyers)	4
74	Atlantic K 10481	Both Ends Against The Middle/Willpower	4

JOHNNY MOORE

67	Caltone TONE 101	Sound And Soul/ROY SHIRLEY: Get On The Ball	8
69	Doctor Bird DB 1180	Big Big Boss/CARL CANNONBALL BRYON: Reggae This Reggae	10

MERRILL E. MOORE

54	Capitol CL 14057	Bell Bottom Boogie/The House Of Blue Lights (78)	12
54	Capitol CL 14130	Nola/Fly Right Boogie (78)	12
55	Capitol CL 14369	Five Foot Two, Eyes Of Blue/Hard Top Race (as Merrill Moore)	100
55	Capitol CL 14369	Five Foot Two, Eyes Of Blue/Hard Top Race (as Merrill Moore) (78)	10
68	Ember EMB S 253	Down The Road A-Piece/Buttermilk Baby	12
69	B&C CB 100	Sweet Mama Tree Top Tall/Little Green Apples	.6
67	Ember EMB 3392	BELLYFUL OF BLUE-THUNDER (LP)	12
68	Ember EMB 3394	ROUGH-HOUSE 88 (LP)	12
69	B&C CAS 1001	TREE TOP TALL (LP)	10

MONETTE MOORE

50s	Vocalion S 200	Rhythm For Sale/Two Old Maids In A Folding Bed (78)	20

OSCAR MOORE TRIO

55	London H-APB 1035	KENYA (10" LP)	10

ROGER MOORE

65	CBS 202014	Where Does Love Go/Tomorrow After Tomorrow	4

SHELLEY MOORE (& MOORE SESSIONEERS)

55	Columbia SCM 5197	In The Wee Small Hours Of The Morning/When You Lose The One You Love	.4
58	Starlite ST45 002	You've Tied Me Up/Gone On The Guy	4
58	Starlite ST45 003	Where Is The Bluebird?/Everything Is Gonna Be All Right	4

(as Shelley Moore & Moore Sessioneers)

THURSTON MOORE, KIM GORDON & EPIC SOUNDTRACKS

92	Imaginary FREE 003	Sitting On A Barbed Wire Fence/BLUEBIRDS: Tom Thumb's Blues (promo)	8

(see also Sonic Youth, Epic Soundtracks)

WHISTLING ALEX MOORE

63	'77' LA 12-6	WHISTLING ALEX MOORE (LP)	25

BIG MOOSE (Walker)

68	Python PKM 1	Puppy Howl Blues/Rambling Woman	20

MOPEDS

68	Col. Blue Beat DB 108	Whiskey And Soda/Do It	5

(see also Cindy Starr & Mopeds)

MOQUETTES

64	Columbia DB 7315	Right String, But The Wrong Yo-Yo/You Came Along	30

SANTOS MORADOS

68	Island WIP 6034	Tonopah/Anytime	4

MORE

80	Atlantic K 11561	We Are The Band/Atomic Rock (p/s)	4
80	Atlantic K 11561T	We Are The Band/Atomic Rock (12", p/s, some with patch)	8/7
82	Atlantic K 11744	Trickster/Hey Joe	4
81	Atlantic K 50775	WARHEAD (LP)	10
82	Atlantic	BLOOD AND THUNDER (LP)	10

MORECAMBE & WISE

61	HMV POP 957	We're The Guys/Me And My Shadow	4
63	HMV POP 1240	Boom Oo Yatta Ta Ta/Why Did I Let You Go	4
64	HMV POP 1373	Was Sailing/The Happiest Christmas Of All	4
66	HMV POP 1518	Now That You're Here/That Riviera Touch	4
67	Pye 7N 17436	Twelve Days Of Christmas/Bingle Jells	4
69	Columbia DB 8646	Bring Me Sunshine/Just Around The Corner	4
64	HMV CLP 1682	MR. MORECAMBE MEETS MR. WISE (LP, also stereo CSD 1522)	10

MORGAN

73	RCA SF 8321	NOVA SOLIS (LP, with insert)	30

(see also Mott The Hoople)

MORGAN & MARK SEVEN

| 66 | Polydor BM 56083 | I'm Gonna Turn My Life Around/Undercover Man | 7 |

AL MORGAN

49	London L 500	Jealous Heart/Turnabout Is Fair Play (78)	5
58	London HLU 8741	Jealous Heart/Foolish Tears	8
51	London H-APB 1001	JEALOUS HEART (10" LP)	15
51	London H-APB 1003	LITTLE RED BOOK (10" LP)	15

P.C. ALEXANDER MORGAN

| 66 | Columbia DB 8095 | Sussex By The Sea/METROPOLITAN POLICE BAND: Thunderbirds March | 10 |

DAVID/DAVY MORGAN

| 65 | Columbia DB 7624 | Tomorrow I'll Be Gone/Ain't Got Much More To See (as Davy Morgan) | 20 |
| 68 | Parlophone R 5692 | True To Life/Dawning (as David Morgan) | 10 |

DERRICK MORGAN

60	Blue Beat BB 7	Fat Man/I'm Gonna Leave You	10
60	Blue Beat BB 12	Don't Cry/I Pray For You (as Derrick Morgan & Ebonies)	10
60	Blue Beat BB 18	Lover Boy/Oh My!	10
61	Blue Beat BB 31	Now We Know/Nights Are	10
61	Blue Beat BB 35	Leave Earth/Wee Wigger Shuffle	10
61	Blue Beat BB 62	Shake A Leg/Golden Rule (as Derrick & Drumbago Orchestra)	10
62	Blue Beat BB 76	Be Still/Sunday Morning	10
62	Blue Beat BB 82	Don't You Know Little Girl (as Derrick & Basil)/BASIL GABBIDON: Hully Gully Miss Molly	10
62	Blue Beat BB 85	Come On Over/Come Back My Darling	10
62	Blue Beat BB 94	Meekly Wait/Day In Day Out (both sides with Yvonne Harrison)	8
62	Blue Beat BB 130	Should Be Ashamed/Marjorie	10
62	Blue Beat BB 141	Joybells (with Duke Reid Group)/Going Down To Canaan (with Denzil Dennis)	10
62	Blue Beat BB 148	Jezebel/Burnette	10
62	Island WI 004	Travel On/Teach My Baby	10
62	Island WI 006	The Hop/Tell It To Me	10
62	Island WI 011	Forward March/Please Don't Talk About Me (with Eric Morris)	10
62	Island WI 013	Cherry Home/See And Blind	10
63	Blue Beat BB 177	Patricia My Dear/The Girl I Left Behind	10
63	Blue Beat BB 187	Tears On My Pillow/You Should Have Known	10
63	Blue Beat BB 196	Telephone/Tough Man Tough	10
63	Island WI 037	Dorothy/Leave Her Alone	10
63	Island WI 051	Blazing Fire/I'm In A Jam (B-side with Patsy Todd)	10
63	Island WI 053	No Raise, No Praise/Loving Baby	10
63	Island WI 080	Angel With Blue Eyes/Corner Stone	10
63	Rio R 1	Balzing Fire/Edmarine	10
64	Blue Beat BB 261	The Soldier Man/BUSTER'S ALLSTARS: Jet 707	10
64	Blue Beat BB 268	Katy Katy/Call On Me	10
64	Black Swan WI 402	Street Girl/Edmarine	10
64	Black Swan WI 425	Cherry Pie (actually by Frederick Hibbert)/BOB WALLS: Beware	10
65	Blue Beat BB 276	Weep No More/I Want A Girl	10
65	Blue Beat BB 280	Stir The Pot/Mercy	10
65	Blue Beat BB 283	Johnny Grave/BUSTER'S ALLSTARS: Yeah Yeah	10
65	Blue Beat BB 311	Throw Them Away/Baby Face	10
65	Blue Beat BB 329	Sweeter Than Honey/You Never Know (with Prince Buster)	10
65	Ska Beat JB 218	Don't Call Me Daddy/BABA BROOK'S BAND: Girl's Town Ska	7
65	Island WI 225	Starvation/I Am A Blackhead Again	10
66	Island WI 277	It's Alright/I Need Someone	10
66	Island WI 288	I Found A Queen/It's True My Darling	10
66	Island WI 289	Ameletia (actually by Frank Cosmo)/Don't You Worry (B-side with Patsy Todd)	10
66	Island WI 3010	Gather Together Now (Jamaican Independence Song)/So Hard	10
66	Rio R 122	Cool Off Rudies/Take It Easy	8
67	Island WI 3079	Someone (actually Derrick & Pauline Morgan)/Do You Love Me (with Pauline)	10
67	Pyramid PYR 6010	Tougher Than Tough/ROLAND ALPHONSO: Song For My Father	8
67	Pyramid PYR 6013	Greedy Gal/SOUL BROTHERS: Marcus Junior	8
67	Pyramid PYR 6014	Court Dismiss/FREDERICK McCLEAN: Fine Fine Fine	8
67	Pyramid PYR 6019	Judge Dread In Court/Last Chance	8
67	Pyramid PYR 6021	Kill Me Dead/Don't Be A Fool	8
67	Pyramid PYR 6024	No Dice/I Mean It	8
67	Pyramid PYR 6025	Do The Bang Bang/Revenge	8
68	Island WI 3094	Conquering Ruler/LLOYD & DEVON: Red Rum Ball	10
68	Island WI 3101	Gimme Back/VICEROYS: Send Requests	10
68	Island WI 3159	Hold You Jack/One Day In May	8
68	Pyramid PYR 6029	I Am The Ruler/I Mean It	8
68	Pyramid PYR 6039	Woman A Grumble/Don't Be A Fool	8
68	Pyramid PYR 6040	Want More/ROLAND ALPHONSO: Goodnight My Love	8
68	Pyramid PYR 6045	Try Me/I'm Leaving (B-side with Pauline)	8
68	Pyramid PYR 6046	King For Tonight (with Pauline)/Last Chance	8
68	Pyramid PYR 6053	Me Now Give Up/BEVERLEY'S ALLSTARS: Dreadnaught	8
68	Pyramid PYR 6056	Ben Johnson Day/MAYTALS: Ain't Got No Tip	8
68	Pyramid PYR 6061	What's Your Grouse/BEVERLEY'S ALLSTARS: I Don't Know	8
68	Pyramid PYR 6063	Johnny Pram Pram/Don't Say (B-side with Pauline Morgan)	8
68	Amalgamated AMG 824	I Want To Go Home/JACKIE ROBINSON: Let The Little Girl Dance	4
68	Crab CRAB 3	River To The Bank/PETER KING: Reggae Limbo	6
68	Trojan TR 626	Fat Man/VAL BENNETT: South Parkway Rock	7
68	Nu Beat NB 016	I Love You/JUNIOR SMITH: Searching	5
68	Big Shot BS 506	Shower Of Rain/VAL BENNETT: It Might As Well Be Spring	6
69	Crab CRAB 8	Seven Letters/TARTANS: Lonely Heartaches (B-side actually by Clarendonians)	6
69	Crab CRAB 11	My First Taste Of Love/TARTANS: Dance All Night	4
69	Crab CRAB 18	Don't Play That Song/How Can I Forget You?	4

Derrick MORGAN

69	Crab CRAB 23	Send Me Some Loving/Come What May	4
69	Jackpot JP 700	Seven Letters/Too Bad	5
69	Unity UN 507	Belly Woman/PAULETT & LOVERS: Please Stay	5
70	Unity UN 546	Return Of Jack Slade/Fat Man	4
70	Unity UN 569	The Conquering Ruler/Bedweight	5
63	Island ILP 903	FORWARD MARCH (LP)	70
69	Doctor Bird DLMB 5014	BEST OF DERRICK MORGAN (LP)	70
69	Island ILP 990	DERRICK MORGAN AND HIS FRIENDS (LP)	60
69	Pama ECO 10	DERRICK MORGAN IN LONDON (LP)	30
69	Pama PSP 1006	MOON HOP (LP)	25
69	Trojan TTL 5	SEVEN LETTERS (LP)	15
70	Trojan TTL 38	FORWARD MARCH (LP, reissue)	10
70s	Magnet MGT 004	IN THE MOOD (LP)	10

(see also Derrick & Lloyd, [Monty] Derrick & Patsy, Derrick & Naomi, Derrick & Paulett, Derrick & Pauline, Derrick Patsy & Basil)

FREDDY MORGAN

59	London HL 7077	Side Saddle/64 Rue Blondell (export issue)	8

GEORGE MORGAN

68	London HLB 10197	Barbara/Sad Bird	4
57	Philips BBE 12149	COUNTRY AND WESTERN SPECTACULAR (EP)	12

JANE MORGAN (& TROUBADORS)

55	London HL 8148	Why — Oh Why/The Heart You Break (May Be Your Own)	25
57	London HLR 8395	From The First Hello To The Last Goodbye/Come Home, Come Home, Come Home	20
57	London HLR 8436	Around The World/It's Not For Me To Say	12
57	London HLR 8468	Fascination (with Troubadors)/Why Don't They Leave Us Alone	10
58	London HLR 8539	I'm New At The Game Of Romance/It's Been A Long Long Time (with Troubadors)	10
58	London HLR 8611	I've Got Bells On My Heart/Only One Love	10
58	London HLR 8649	Enchanted Island/Once More, My Love, Once More	8
58	London HLR 8751	The Day The Rains Came/Le Jour Ou La Pluie Viendra	6
58	London HL 7064	The Day The Rains Came/I May Never Pass This Way Again (export issue)	10
59	London HLR 8810	If I Could Only Live My Life Again/To Love And Be Loved	6
59	London HLR 8925	With Open Arms/I Can't Begin To Tell You	5
59	London HLR 8999	Happy Anniversary/C'est La Vie, C'est L'Amour	5
60	London HLR 9087	My Love Doesn't Love Me At All/The Bells Of St. Mary's	5
60	London HLR 9120	Romantica/I Am A Heart	5
60	London HLR 9210	Lord And Master/Where's The Boy (I Never Met)	5
60	London HLR 9249	Somebody/The Angry Sea	5
61	London HLR 9421	It Takes Love/Homesick For Old England	5
62	London HLR 9528	What Now My Love/Forever My Love	5
63	London HLR 9683	Theme From Carnival (Love Makes The World Go 'Round)/The Second Time Around	5
63	Colpix PX 700	Red Sails In The Sunset/My Special Dream	4
64	Colpix PX 713	Bless 'Em All/Does Goodnight Mean Goodbye	4
67	Columbia DB 8177	The Three Bells (Jimmy Brown Song)/I Want To Be With You	5
68	Stateside SS 2082	Masquerade/Smile	4
58	London RER 1161	ALL THE WAY PART 1 (EP, with Troubadours)	12
58	London RER 1162	ALL THE WAY PART 2 (EP, with Troubadours)	12
59	London RER 1204	THE DAY THAT THE RAINS CAME (EP)	15
61	London RER 1331	JANE MORGAN (EP)	15
57	London HA-R 2086	FASCINATION (LP)	20
58	London HA-R 2110	ALL THE WAY (LP, with Troubadors)	18
58	London HA-R 2133	SOMETHING OLD, SOMETHING NEW, SOMETHING BORROWED, SOMETHING BLUE (LP)	18
59	London HA-R 2136	GREAT SONGS FROM THE GREAT SHOWS OF THE CENTURY VOL. 1 (LP)	15
59	London HA-R 2137	GREAT SONGS FROM THE GREAT SHOWS OF THE CENTURY VOL. 2 (LP)	15
59	London HA-R 2158	THE DAY THE RAINS CAME (LP)	18
60	London HA-R 2244	JANE IN SPAIN (LP)	16
60	London HA-R 2316	THE BALLADS OF LADY JANE (LP)	16
61	London HA-R 2371	JANE MORGAN TIME (LP)	16
61	London HA-R 2377	THE SECOND TIME AROUND (LP, also stereo SAH-R 6177)	16/18
62	London HA-R 2430	AT THE COCOANUT GROVE (LP, also stereo SAH-R 6226)	15/17
62	London HA-R/SH-R 8042	WHAT NOW MY LOVE (LP, mono/stereo)	14/16
63	London HA-R/SH-R 8069	LOVE MAKES THE WORLD GO ROUND (LP, mono/stereo)	14/16
63	Colpix PXL 460	JANE MORGAN SERENADES THE VICTORS (LP)	12
65	Columbia SX 6010	IN MY STYLE... (LP)	10

(see also Troubadors, Roger Williams)

JAYE P. MORGAN

55	HMV 7M 327	The Longest Walk/Swanee	7
56	HMV 7M 348	If You Don't Want My Love/Pepper Hot Baby	18
56	HMV 7M 365	Not One Goodbye/My Bewildered Heart	6
56	Brunswick 05519	Have You Ever Been Lonely?/Baby Don't Do It	8
57	RCA RCA 1014	You, You Romeo/Graduation Ring	5
59	MGM MGM 1005	Are You Lonesome Tonight?/Miss You	6
59	MGM MGM 1005	Are You Lonesome Tonight?/Miss You (78)	5
59	MGM MGM 1021	(It Took) One Kiss/My Reputation	5
59	MGM MGM 1039	Somebody Loses, Somebody Wins/Somebody Else Is Taking My Place	5
60	MGM MGM 1093	I Walk The Line/Wondering Where You Are	5
62	MGM MGM 1182	Heartache Named Johnny/He Thinks I Still Ache	4
62	MGM MGM 1190	Brotherhood Of Man/Nobody's Sweetheart	4
54	London REP 1013	JAYE P. SINGS (EP)	15
59	MGM MGM-C 793	SLOW AND EASY (LP)	10
50s	RCA	JUST YOU, JUST ME (LP)	12

Rare Record Price Guide

JOHN MORGAN

72	Carnaby 6302 010	KALEIDOSCOPE (LP)	45
70s	SWP 1007	LIVE AT DURRANT HOUSE (LP, private pressing)	120

(see also Spirit Of John Morgan)

LEE MORGAN

61	Columbia 33SX 1399	THE BIRDLAND STORY VOL. 1 (LP)	15
62	Stateside SL 10016	EXPOOBIDENT (LP)	15
65	Blue Note (B)BLP 4157	THE SIDEWINDER (LP)	15
65	Blue Note (B)BLP 4034	LEEWAY (LP)	15
66	Blue Note BLP 4199	THE RUMPROLLER (LP, also stereo BST 84199)	15
66	Blue Note BLP 4169	SEARCH FOR THE NEW LAND (LP, also stereo BST 84169)	15
69	Blue Note BST 84289	CARAMBA (LP)	12
69	Blue Note BST 84312	CHARISMA (LP)	12

MACE MORGAN THUNDERBIRDS

63	Starlite STEP 36	SHAKE AND SWING (EP)	20

MARY MORGAN

56	Parlophone MSP 6204	Jimmy Unknown/You Are My Love	5
56	Parlophone R 4227	From The Candy Store On The Corner/No-One Was There But You	5
57	Parlophone R 4348	A Call To Arms/One For Sorrow, Two For Joy	4

RUSS MORGAN ORCHESTRA

55	Brunswick 05464	Alabamy Bound/SCRANTON 7: The Popcorn Song	4
55	Brunswick 05493	Dog Face Soldier/Don't Cry Sweetheart	4
56	Brunswick 05537	The Poor People Of Paris (Poor John)/Silver Moon	4
56	Brunswick 05602	Lay Down Your Arms/My Best You You	4
55	Brunswick OE 9068	MOONLIGHT MUSIC (EP)	7

MORGAN BROTHERS

59	MGM MGM 1007	Nola/Guiding Star	8
59	MGM MGM 1026	Kissin' On The Red Light/Milk From The Coconut	6

MORGAN TWINS

58	RCA RCA 1083	T.V. Hop/Let's Get Going	70
58	RCA RCA 1083	T.V. Hop/Let's Get Going (78)	25

(Ron Paul) MORIN & WILSON

72	Sovereign SVNA 7252	PEACEFUL COMPANY (LP)	20

JOHNNY MORISETTE

62	Stateside SS 107	Meet Me At The Twistin' Place/Any Time Any Day Any Where	6

MORNING

70	Liberty LBS 83463	MORNING (LP)	12
74	United Artists UAS 29337	STRUCK LIKE SILVER (LP)	10

MORNING GLORY

73	Island ILPS 9237	MORINING GLORY (LP)	12

(see also John Surman)

GIORGIO MORODER

66	Polydor 56101	Run Run/Girl Without A Heart	4
66	Page One POF 003	Full Stop/Believe Me	4
67	Page One POF 028	How Much Longer Must I Wait/Bla Bla Diddley	4

(see also Phil Oakey & Giorgio Moroder)

ENNIO MORRICONE ORCHESTRA

67	RCA Victor RCA 1596	A Fistful Of Dollars/The Man With No Name	4
67	RCA Victor RCA 1634	For A Few Dollars More/La Resi Dei Conti	4
70	Stateside SSL 10307	THE SICILIAN CLAN (LP, soundtrack)	12
70	RCA Camden CDS 1052	FISTFUL OF DOLLARS/FEW DOLLARS MORE (LP)	10

ERIC MORRIS

61	Starlite ST45 052	Search The World/Busters Shack	10
61	Blue Beat BB 53	Humpty Dumpty/Corn Bread And Butter	10
62	Blue Beat BB 74	My Forty-Five/I've Tried Everybody	10
62	Blue Beat BB 81	Sinners Repent And Pray/ALTON ELLIS: Now And Forever More	10
62	Blue Beat BB 83	Money Can't Buy Life/ALTON ELLIS: True Love	10
62	Blue Beat BB 105	Pack Up Your Troubles/Oh What A Smile Can Do	10
62	Blue Beat BB 115	G.I. Lady/Going To The River	8
62	Blue Beat BB 128	Over The Hills/Lazy Woman	8
62	Blue Beat BB 137	Miss Peggy's Grandmother/BUSTER'S ALLSTARS: Aegaton	8
62	Blue Beat BB 140	Seven Long Years/For Your Love	8
63	Blue Beat BB 153	Lonely Blue Boy/PRINCE BUSTER: Oh We	8
63	Blue Beat BB 184	Country Girl/Sweet Love	8
64	Blue Beat BB 218	Love Can Break A Man/Worried People	8
64	Blue Beat BB 273	A Stitch In Time/Forever	8
64	Black Swan WI 414	Solomon Gundie/BABA BROOKS' BAND: Key To The City	10
64	Black Swan WI 433	Supper In The Gutter/Words Of My Mouth	10
64	Black Swan WI 439	River Come Down/Seek And You'll Find	10
64	Black Swan WI 445	Home Sweet Home/LESTER STERLING: '64 Special	10
64	Island WI 142	Penny Reel/DOTTY & BONNIE: Darling When	8
64	Island WI 147	Mama No Fret/FRANKIE ANDERSON: Santa Lucia	8
64	Island WI 150	Drop Your Sword/BABA BROOKS: Catch A Fire	8
64	Island WI 151	What A Man Doeth/DUKE REID'S GROUP: Rude Boy	8
64	Port-O-Jam PJ 4006	Oh My Dear/Lena Belle	8
64	Rio R 39	Little District/True And Just	8
64	Rio R 48	Live As A Man/Man Will Rule	8
65	Rio R 72	By The Sea/I Wasn't Around	8
65	Island WI 183	Love Can Make A Mansion/Ungodly People	8

Eric MORRIS

65	Island WI 185	Suddenly/Many Long Years	8
65	Island WI 199	Fast Mouth/The Harder They Come	8
65	Island WI 234	Children Of Today/BABA BROOKS: Greenfield Ska	8
65	Blue Beat BB 298	Those Teardrops/DON DRUMMOND: Ska Town	8
65	Blue Beat BB 349	I'm The Greatest/BUSTER'S ALL STARS: Picket Line	8
67	Fab BB 30	Humpty Dumpty (as Eric Humpty Dumpty Morris & Buster All Stars)/	
		FOLKS BROTHERS: Carolina	5

(see also Monty Morris)

HAINSLEY MORRIS
68	Pama PM 720	Stay Loose	6

HELMSLEY MORRIS
67	Caltone TONE 104	Love Is Strange/DON D. JUNIOR: Sir Pratt Special	8

JOE MORRIS & ORCHESTRA
54	London HL 8088	I Had A Notion/Just Your Way Baby (78)	60
54	London HL 8098	Travelin' Man/No, It Can't Be Done (78)	12

LIBBY MORRIS
56	Parlophone R 4225	When Liberace Winked At Me/None Of That Now	6

MILTON MORRIS
69	Upsetter US 318	No Bread And Butter/UPSETTERS: Soulful One	6

MONTY MORRIS
67	Doctor Bird DB 1067	Play It Cool/BABA BROOKS' BAND: Open The Door	10
67	Doctor Bird DB 1081	Put On Your Red Dress/BABA BROOKS' BAND: Faberge	10
68	Doctor Bird DB 1162	Last Laugh/You Really Got A Hold On Me	10
68	Pama PM 721	Say What You're Saying/Tears In Your Eyes	6
68	Nu Beat NB 007	True Romance/BUNNY & RUDDY: Rhythm And Soul	4
68	Nu Beat NB 011	Simple Simon/BUNNY & RUDDY: On The Town	4
69	Doctor Bird DB 1176	Same Face/A Little Bit Of This	10
69	Big Shot BI 513	Deportation/Say I'm Back	7
69	Camel CA 12	Can't Get No Peace/UPSETTERS: For A Few Dollars More	6
69	Camel CA 28	No More Teardrops/Love Me Or Leave Me (as Monty Morris	
		& Maples)	4

(see also Eric Morris, Monty Derek & Patsy)

ROGER MORRIS
72	Regal Zono. SRZA 8509	FIRST ALBUM (LP)	25

RUSSELL MORRIS
69	Decca F 22964	The Real Thing/It's Only A Matter Of Time	30
70	Decca F 23066	Rachel/Slow Joey	5

VICTOR MORRIS
68	Amalgamated AMG 813	Now I'm Alone/Rise And Fall	7

MORRIS & MINORS
80	Round MOR 1	STATE THE OBVIOUS (EP)	8

MORRIS & MITCH
57	Decca F 10900	Cumberland Gap/I'm Not A Juvenile Delinquent	8
57	Decca F 10929	What Is A Skiffler?/The Tommy Rot Story	8
58	Decca F 11086	Highway Patrol/Bird Dog	8
68	Trend TRE 1010	The Magical Musherishi Tourists/Mister D.J. Man	5
58	Decca DFE 6486	SIX FIVE NOTHING SPECIAL (EP)	15

MORRIS FAMILY & GOSPEL JUBILEERS
60	Top Rank JAR 322	Wake Up Jonah/He Never Complained	6

MORRIS ON
72	Island HELP 5	MORRIS ON (LP, actually by various folk artists)	12

(see also Fairport Convention, Steeleye Span)

CURLEY JIM MORRISON
61	Starlite ST45 065	Air Force Blues/Didn't I Tell You	100

DOROTHY MORRISON
69	Elektra EKSN 45070	All God's Children Got Soul/Put A Little Love In Your Heart	4

PROFESSOR MORRISON'S LOLLIPOP
68	London HLU 10228	You Got The Love/Gypsy Lady	4
69	London HLU 10254	Oo Poo Pah Susie/You Take It	4

TOM MORRISON
60	MGM MGM EP709	THE ADVENTURES OF MIGHTY MOUSE AND HIS PALS (EP)	8

VAN MORRISON
67	London HLZ 10150	Brown-Eyed Girl/Goodbye Baby (Baby Goodbye)	12
70	Warner Bros WB 7383	Come Running/Crazy Love	4
70	Warner Bros WB 7434	Domino/Sweet Jannie	4
70	President PT 328	Brown-Eyed Girl/Goodbye Baby (Baby Goodbye) (reissue)	4
72	Warner Bros K 16210	Jackie Wilson Said/You've Got The Power	5
74	London HLM 10453	Brown-Eyed Girl/Goodbye Baby (Baby Goodbye) (reissue)	4
74	Warner Bros K 16392	Caldonia/What's Up, Crazy Pup	6
77	Warner Bros K 16986	Joyous Sound/Mechanical Bliss	4
67	London HA-Z 8346	BLOWIN' YOUR MIND (LP)	18
68	Warner Bros WS 1768	ASTRAL WEEKS (LP, green label)	12
70	Warner Bros WS 1835	MOONDANCE (LP, green label)	10
70	Warner Bros WS 1884	HIS BAND AND STREET CHOIR (LP, green label)	10
71	Warner Bros K 46114	TUPELO HONEY (LP, gatefold sleeve, green label)	10
72	Warner Bros K 46172	ST. DOMINIC'S PREVIEW (LP, green label)	10
73	Warner Bros K 46242	HARD NOSE THE HIGHWAY (LP)	10

MINT VALUE £

74	Warner Bros K 86007	IT'S TOO LATE TO STOP NOW (2-LP, gatefold sleeve)	14

(see also Them)

MORRISONS
87	Morrisons MOR 1	Listen To Your Heart/Everytime I Open The Bottle (33rpm p/s flexi)	4

MORRISSEY
88	HMV 12 POP 1618	Suedehead/I Know Very Well How I Got My Name/Hairdresser On Fire (12", p/s)	8
88	HMV TC POP 1618	Suedehead/I Know Very Well How I Got My Name/Hairdresser On Fire/ Oh Well, I'll Never Learn (cassette)	7
88	HMV TC POP 1618	Suedehead/I Know Very Well How I Got My Name/(Ordinary Girl)/ Oh Well, I'll Never Learn (mispressed withdrawn cassette)	15
88	HMV CD POP 1618	Suedehead/I Know Very Well How I Got My Name/Hairdresser On Fire/ Oh Well, I'll Never Learn (CD)	10
88	HMV 12 POP 1619	Everyday Is Like Sunday/Sister I'm A Poet/Disappointed (12", p/s)	7
88	HMV CD POP 1619	Everyday Is Like Sunday/Sister I'm A Poet/Disappointed/Will Never Marry (CD)	8
89	HMV CD POP 1620	The Last Of The Famous International Playboys/Lucky Lips/Michael's Bones (CD)	7
89	HMV 12 POPS 1621	Interesting Drug/Such A Little Thing Makes Such A Big Difference (12", p/s, 1 side etched)	7

(see also Smiths, Durutti Column)

MORRISSEY-MULLEN
79	Harvest SHSP 4098	CAPE WRATH (LP)	10

BUDDY MORROW & HIS ORCHESTRA
51	HMV B 10199	The Boogie Woogie March/On The Old Potato Farm (78)	7
52	HMV B 10347	Night Train/Vereda Tropical (78)	5
53	HMV 7M 145	Heap Big Beat/I Can't Get Started	5
53	HMV 7M 151	I Can't Get Started/Heap Big Beat	5
53	HMV 7M 162	Dragnet/Your Mouth's Got A Hole In It	6
54	HMV 7M 216	Knock On Wood (with Shaye Cogan)/All Night Long	6
54	Mercury MB 3170	Rock-A-Beatin' Boogie/Mr. Sandman (78)	5
56	Mercury MT 119	Theme From "The Proud Ones" (with Whistling Elmo Tanner)/Paradise Lost (78)	5
57	Mercury MT 166	Easy Does It/Midnight March (78)	5
60	RCA RCA 1167	Staccato's Theme/Scraunchy	6
56	Mercury MPT 7003	SHALL WE DANCE (10" LP)	10

ELLA MAE MORSE
52	Capitol CL 13666	Tennessee Saturday Night/A Little Further Down The Road (78)	12
52	Capitol CL 13754	Oakie Boogie/Love Ya' Like Mad (78)	12
53	Capitol CL 13853	Jump Back Honey/Greyhound (78)	8
53	Capitol CL 13930	Big Mamou/Is It Any Wonder (78)	8
53	Capitol CL 13960	Forty Cups Of Coffee/Oh! You Crazy Moon (78)	8
54	Capitol CL 14037	T'Ain't What You Do, It's The Way That You Do It/It Ain't Necessarily So (78)	5
54	Capitol CL 14044	The Guy Who Invented Kissin'/Good (78)	5
54	Capitol CL 14116	Goodnight, Well It's Time To Go/Sensational (78)	5
54	Capitol CL 14176	(We've Reached) The Point Of No Return/Give A Little Time (78)	8
55	Capitol CL 14223	Bring Back My Baby To Me/Lovey Dovey	35
55	Capitol CL 14223	Bring Back My Baby To Me/Lovey Dovey (78)	5
55	Capitol CL 14303	Smack Dab In The Middle/Yes, Yes I Do	25
55	Capitol CL 14303	Smack Dab In The Middle/Yes, Yes I Do (78)	5
55	Capitol CL 14332	Heart Full Of Hope/Livin', Livin', Livin'	25
55	Capitol CL 14332	Heart Full Of Hope/Livin', Livin', Livin' (78)	5
55	Capitol CL 14341	Razzle-Dazzle/Ain't That A Shame (with Big Dave & His Music)	60
55	Capitol CL 14341	Razzle-Dazzle/Ain't That A Shame (with Big Dave & His Music) (78)	5
55	Capitol CL 14362	Seventeen/Piddily Patter Song (with Big Dave & His Music)	40
55	Capitol CL 14362	Seventeen/Piddily Patter Song (with Big Dave & His Music) (78)	5
55	Capitol CL 14376	Birmin'ham/An Occasional Man	25
55	Capitol CL 14376	Birmin'ham/An Occasional Man (78)	5

(the above 45s originally came with triangular centres; round centre re-pressings are worth around two-thirds the value)

56	Capitol CL 14508	When Boy Kiss Girl (It's Love)/Sing-Ing-Ing-Ing	15
56	Capitol CL 14508	When Boy Kiss Girl (It's Love)/Sing-Ing-Ing-Ing (78)	5
56	Capitol CL 14572	Down In Mexico/Rock And Roll Wedding	25
56	Capitol CL 14572	Down In Mexico/Rock And Roll Wedding (78)	5
57	Capitol CL 14726	What Good'll It Do Me/Mister Money Maker	12
57	Capitol CL 14726	What Good'll It Do Me/Mister Money Maker (78)	5
57	Capitol CL 14760	I'm Gone/Sway Me	12
57	Capitol CL 14760	I'm Gone/Sway Me (78)	5
55	Capitol EAP1 513	BARRELHOUSE BOOGIE AND THE BLUES (EP)	35
54	Capitol LC 6687	BARRELHOUSE BOOGIE AND THE BLUES (10" LP)	60

ELLA MAE MORSE & FREDDIE SLACK
67	Ember SPE 6605	ROCKIN' BREW (LP)	10

MORTIMER
68	Philips BF 1664	Dedicated Music Man/To Understand Someone	4

AZIE MORTIMER
60	London HLX 9237	Lips/Wrapped Up In A Dream	6

JELLY ROLL MORTON('S RED HOT PEPPERS)
53	HMV 7M 132	The Chant/Tank Town Bump	8
54	HMV 7M 178	Fat Frances/Pep (solo)	8
54	HMV 7M 187	Wild Man Blues/Smoke-House Blues	8
54	HMV 7M 207	Harmony Blues/Jungle Blues	8
54	HMV 7M 256	Fussy Mabel/Burnin' The Iceberg	8
50s	Vogue EPV 1126	JELLY ROLL MORTON (EP)	15
50s	Collector JE 120	JAZZ ORIGINATORS VOL. 3 (EP)	12
55	HMV 7EG 8178	THE BLUES THEY SANG (EP)	12
59	RCA RCX 168	JELLY ROLL MORTON (EP)	10
60	RCA RCX 207	JELLY ROLL MORTON NO. 2 (EP)	10

MINT VALUE £

60	Fontana TFE 17263	TREASURES OF NORTH AMERICAN NEGRO MUSIC VOL. 4 (EP)	10
61	Storyville SEP 379	JELLY ROLL MORTON (EP)	10
53	HMV DLP 1016	JELLY ROLL MORTON AND HIS RED HOT PEPPERS (10" LP)	15
54	HMV DLP 1044	MORTON'S RED HOT PEPPERS (10" LP)	15
54	Vogue LDE 080	NEW ORLEANS MEMORIES (10" LP)	15
54	London AL 3519	JELLY ROLL MORTON SOLOS (10" LP)	15
54	London AL 3520	JELLY ROLL MORTON'S KINGS OF JAZZ (10" LP)	15
54	London AL 3534	CLASSIC JAZZ PIANO VOL. 1 (10" LP)	15
55	HMV DLP 1071	MORTON'S RED HOT PEPPERS NO. 3 (10" LP)	15
56	London AL 3559	CLASSIC JAZZ PIANO VOL. 2 (10" LP)	15
59	RCA RD 27113	THE KING OF NEW ORLEANS JAZZ (LP)	10
61	RCA RD 27184	THE KING OF NEW ORLEANS JAZZ VOL. 2 (LP)	10
61	Riverside RLP 12-132	MR. JELLY LORD (LP)	10
62	Riverside RLP 12-111	CLASSIC PIANO SOLOS (LP)	10
65	Fontana TL 5261	JELLY ROLL MORTON (LP)	10
67	Fontana TL 5415	MORTON SIXES AND SEVENS (LP)	10

MANDY MORTON (BAND)

79	Banshee BANS 791	Song For Me (Music Prince)/Little Inbetween (no p/s, with Spriguns)	15
78	Banshee BAN 1001	MAGIC LADY (LP, with insert, 1,000 only)	150
78	Banshee BAN 1001	MAGIC LADY (LP, with insert, blue vinyl, 20 only)	200
80	Polydor 2382 101	SEA OF STORMS (LP, solo)	10
83	Banshee	VALLEY OF THE LIGHT (LP, private pressing)	40

(see also Spriguns [Of Tolgus])

MIKE MORTON

68	Plexium PXM 5	I Can't Take You To The Dance/It's Been So Long (as Mike Morton 8)	4
68	Plexium PXM 7	Jennifer Jennifer/See You Around (as Mike Morton Sound)	4
68	Plexium PXM 11	The Cokey Cokey/Time For Living (as Mike Morton Sound)	4
68	Plexium PXM 15	Butlin Shrug/Butlin Rock (as Mike Morton Sound)	4
69	Plexium PXM 19	Burning Bridges/You Gotta Be Mine (as Mike Morton Combination)	4

MOSAICS

66	Columbia DB 7990	Let's Go Drag Racing/Now That You're Here	12

MOSES & JOSHUA (DILLARD)

67	Stateside SS 2059	My Elusive Dreams/What's Better Than Love (as Moses & Joshua Dillard)	8
68	Bell BLL 1018	Get Out Of My Heart/They Don't Want Us Together (as Moses & Joshua)	7
72	Mojo 2092 054	My Elusive Dreams/Get Out Of My Heart	4

MOSKOW

82	Moskow SRS 2103	Man From UNCLE/White Black (p/s)	8
84	T.W. HIT 103	Man From UNCLE/White Black (reissue in different p/s)	5

BILL MOSS

69	Pama PM 765	Sock It To 'Em Soul Brother Pts 1 & 2	5
70	Pama PM 796	Number One	5

BUDDY MOSS

60s	Kokomo K 1003	GEORGIA BLUES VOLUME 2 (LP)	50

JENNY MOSS

63	Columbia DB 7061	Hobbies/Big Boys	25

STIRLING MOSS

61	Redemption RLP 5004	THE STIRLING MOSS STORY (LP)	10

TEDDY MOSS/JOSH WHITE

62	Jazz Collector JEL 5	THE MALE BLUES (EP)	8

(see also Josh White)

MOST

79	SRT SRTS/CUS/570	Carefree/In And Out (no p/s with insert)	5

ABE MOST OCTET

55	London REP 1028	PRESENTING THE ABE MOST OCTET (EP)	10

MICKIE MOST (& GEAR)

63	Decca F 11664	Mr. Porter/Yes Indeed I Do	8
63	Columbia DB 7117	The Feminine Look/Shame On You Boy	8
63	Columbia DB 7180	Sea Cruise/It's A Little Bit Hot	8
64	Columbia DB 7245	Money Honey/That's Alright (as Mickey Most & Gear)	8

(see also Most Brothers)

MR MOST

69	Downtown DT 408	Push Wood/Reggae Train	4

MOST BROTHERS

57	Decca F 10968	Whistle Bait/I'm Comin' Home	10
58	Decca F 10998	Whole Lotta Woman/Teen Angel	10
58	Decca F 11040	Don't Go Home/Dottie	7

(see also Mickie Most, Alex Murray)

MOTELS

80	Capitol CLP 16149	Days Are OK/Slow Town (picture disc, 7,000 only)	4
82	Capitol CLP 245	Take The L Out Of Lover/Change My Mind (picture disc)	4

BENNY MOTEN'S KANSAS CITY ORCHESTRA

54	HMV DLP 1057	BENNIE MOTEN PLAYS KAY-CEE JAZZ (10" LP)	15

MOTHER EARTH

69	Mercury MF 1081	Goodnight Melda Grebe The Telephone Company Has Cut Us Off/ I Did My Part	8
72	Reprise K 14089	Temptation Took Control/I'll Be Long Gone	4
68	Mercury SMCL 20143	LIVING WITH THE ANIMALS (LP)	15

69	Mercury SMCL 20173	MAKE A JOYFUL NOISE (LP)	15
69	Mercury SMCL 20179	TRACY NELSON COUNTRY (LP)	15
70	Mercury 6338 023	SATISFIED (LP)	15
71	Reprise K 44133	BRING ME HOME (LP)	12

MOTHERLIGHT

| 69 | Morgan Bluetown BT 5003 | BOBAK JONS MALONE (LP) | 120 |

(see also Wil Malone, Orange Bicycle)

MOTHERLODE

| 69 | Buddah 201 064 | When I Die/Hard Life | 4 |
| 69 | Buddah 2318 043 | WHEN I DIE (LP) | 10 |

MOTHERS OF INVENTION

(see under Frank Zappa/Mothers Of Invention)

MOTHER'S RUIN

81	Spectra SPC 1	Streetfighters/Leaving You (p/s)	4
82	Spectra SPC 6	Street Lights/Turn A Corner (p/s)	8
82	Spectra SPC 7	Say It's Not True/It's Illogical (p/s)	8
80s	Off Course 7901	Dany Hot Dog/No More Superstars (p/s)	4
82	Spectra SPA 1	ROAD TO RUIN (LP)	10

MOTHER'S SONS

| 70s | J-Dan JDN 4415 | I Want To Tell The World/Underground Man | 4 |

MOTHMEN

79	Absurd ABSURD 6	Does It Matter Irene?/Please Let Go (p/s)	5
81	Do It DUN 12	Show Me Your House And Car/People People (p/s, deleted after 1 day)	8
81	Do It DUNIT 12	Show Me Your House And Car/People People (12", p/s, deleted after 1 day)	10

(see also Alberto Y Los Trios Paranoias)

MOTHS

| 69 | Deroy | MOTHS (LP, private press in plain white sleeve) | 450 |

MOTIONS

| 66 | Pye Intl. 7N 25390 | Stop Your Crying/Every Step I Take | 6 |

MOTIONS

| 60s | Hallmark | THE MOTIONS (LP) | 50 |

MOTIVATION

| 68 | Direction 58-3248 | Come On Down/Little Man | 4 |

MÖTLEY CRÜE

84	Elektra E 9756	Looks That Kill/Piece Of The Action (p/s)	10
84	Elektra E 9756T	Looks That Kill/Piece Of The Action/Live Wire (12", p/s, with free tattoo)	12
84	Elektra E 9756TP	Looks That Kill/Piece Of The Action/Live Wire (12" picture disc)	20
84	Elektra E 9732	Too Young To Fall In Love/Take Me To The Top (p/s)	10
84	Elektra E 9732T	Too Young To Fall In Love/Take Me To The Top (12", p/s, some with poster)	12/7
86	Elektra EKR 16TP	Smokin' In The Boys' Room/Use It Or Lose It (mask-shaped picture disc with sticker)	18
86	Elektra EKR 33P	Smokin' In The Boys' Room/Home Sweet Home (mask-shaped picture disc)	18
86	Elektra EKR 33P	Smokin' In The Boys' Room/Home Sweet Home (interlocking picture discs)	35
86	Elektra EKR 33T	Smokin' In The Boys' Room/Home Sweet Home/Shout At The Devil (12", p/s, with poster)	12
87	Elektra EKR 59P	Girls, Girls, Girls/Sumthin' For Nuthin' (poster sleeve)	8
87	Elektra EKR 59	Girls, Girls, Girls/Sumthin' For Nuthin' ('X-rated' stickered p/s, 3,000 only)	8
87	Elektra EKR 59B	Girls, Girls, Girls/Sumthin' For Nuthin'/Smokin' In The Boys' Room (12" box set with patch)	12
87	Elektra EKR 59T	Girls, Girls, Girls/Sumthin' For Nuthin'/Smokin' In The Boys' Room (12", p/s, with patch)	8
87	Elektra EKR 59TP	Girls, Girls, Girls/Sumthin' For Nuthin'/Smokin' In The Boys' Room (12", picture disc)	12
88	Elektra EKR 65TP	You're All I Need/Wild Side/Home Sweet Home/Looks That Kill (12", picture disc)	10
88	Elektra EKR 65TB	You're All I Need/Wild Side/Home Sweet Home/Looks That Kill (12", box set with poster, tour pass & patch)	10
89	Elektra EKR 97P	Dr Feelgood/Sticky Sweet (shaped picture disc)	8
83	Elektra 9602 891	SHOUT AT THE DEVIL (LP, picture disc with poster)	20

MOTOR BOYS MOTOR

| 80 | Silent SSH 4 | Drive Friendly/Fast'n'Bulbous/Grow Fins (p/s) | 4 |

(see also Screaming Blue Messiahs)

MOTORHEAD

77	Stiff BUY 9	White Line Fever/Leaving Here (p/s, "Stiff Boxed Set" 45, later mail-order)	15
79	Chiswick S 13	Motorhead/City Kids (p/s)	8
79	Chiswick S 13	Motorhead/City Kids (12", p/s)	12
78	Bronze BRO 60	Louie Louie/Tear Ya Down (p/s)	8
79	Bronze BRO 67	Overkill/Too Late, Too Late (p/s, initially with 'Overkill' badge)	7/5
79	Bronze 12 BRO 67	Overkill/Too Late, Too Late (12", p/s)	8
79	Bronze BRO 78	No Class/Like A Nightmare (3 different sleeves)	each 7
79	Bronze BRO 85	Bomber/Over The Top (p/s, some on blue vinyl)	8/5
79	Big Beat NS 13	Motorhead/City Kids (p/s, black, pink, blue, orange vinyl [10 only on white vinyl, £50+])	5-6
80	Big Beat NSP 13	Motorhead/City Kids (p/s, black & white or blue & white picture disc)	8
80	Bronze BRO 92	THE GOLDEN YEARS (EP)	5
80	Bronze 12 BRO 92	THE GOLDEN YEARS (12" EP)	8
80	Big Beat NS 61	BEER DRINKERS EP (p/s, black or pink vinyl)	4
80	Big Beat NS 61	BEER DRINKERS EP (p/s, blue or orange vinyl)	5
80	Big Beat SWT 61	BEER DRINKERS EP (12", p/s, black, pink or scarcer blue or orange vinyl)	7-10

MOTORHEAD

80	Bronze BRO 106	Ace Of Spades/Dirty Love (p/s)	6
80	Bronze BROX 106	Ace Of Spades/Dirty Love (12", in 'Xmas' sleeve)	10
81	Bronze BRO 116	ST. VALENTINES DAY MASSACRE (EP, with Girlschool)	4
81	Bronze BROX 116	ST. VALENTINES DAY MASSACRE (10" EP, with Girlschool)	10
81	Lyntone LYN 9661	The Train Kept-A Rollin' (live) (blue flexi free with 'Flexipop' mag, issue 7)	7/6
81	Bronze BRO 124	Motorhead (live)/Over The Top (live) (p/s)	5
81	Bronze BROP 124	Motorhead (live)/Over The Top (live) (picture disc)	10
82	Bronze BRO 146	Iron Fist/Remember Me I'm Gone (p/s, red or blue vinyl)	8/12
82	Bronze BRO 146	Iron Fist/Remember Me I'm Gone (p/s, black vinyl)	5
82	Bronze BRO 151	Stand By Your Man/No Class/Masterplan (p/s, with Wendy O. Williams)	7
83	Bronze BRO 165	I Got Mine/Turn You Round Again (p/s)	6
83	Bronze BROX 165	I Got Mine/Turn You Round Again (12", p/s)	8
83	Bronze BRO 167	Shine/Hoochie Coochie Man (live) (p/s)	6
83	Bronze BROX 167	Shine/Hoochie Coochie Man (live)/Don't Need Religion (12", p/s)	8
83	Bronze BROX 167/	Shine/Hoochie Coochie Man (live)/Don't Need Religion//	
	BROX 92	THE GOLDEN YEARS (12", double pack)	14
83	Lyntone LYN 4383	In Their Own Words/BRONZ: Taken By Storm (flexi free with 'Kerrang!')	6/5
84	Bronze BRO 185	Killed By Death (Edited Version)/Under The Knife (p/s)	6
84	Bronze BROP 185	Killed By Death/Under The Knife (logo skull-shaped picture disc)	15
84	Bronze BROX 185	Killed By Death (Full Length Version)/Under The Knife (12", p/s, with poster)	8
86	GWR GWR 2	Deaf Forever/On The Road (live) (p/s, some with competition form)	6/5
87	GWR GWR 6	Eat The Rich/Cradle To The Grave (p/s)	4
88	Castle CD3-10	MOTORHEAD (CD, 5,000 only)	6
88	Sounds WAVES 1	Killed By Death (live) (p/s, with others, free with 'Sounds' magazine)	4
88	GWR GWR 15	Ace Of Spades/Dogs/Traitor (sold at concerts & through fan club)	15
90	Epic 656578 0	The One To Sing The Blues/Dead Man's Hand (shaped picture disc)	6
77	Chiswick WIK 2	MOTORHEAD (LP, silver sleeve & inner, 600 only)	30
77	Chiswick WIK 2	MOTORHEAD (LP, black & white sleeve & inner)	12
77	Big Beat WIK 2	MOTORHEAD (LP, reissue, red or clear vinyl)	12
79	Bronze BRON 515	OVERKILL (LP, green vinyl)	15
79	Bronze BRON 523	BOMBER (LP, blue vinyl)	15
80	Bronze BRONG 531	ACE OF SPADES (LP, gold vinyl)	15
81	Chiswick CWK 3008	MOTORHEAD (LP, white vinyl reissue)	15
81	Bronze BRONG 535	NO SLEEP 'TIL HAMMERSMITH (LP, gold vinyl)	15
84	Bronze/PRO MOTOR 1	NO REMORSE (2-LP, leather sleeve with inners)	18
86	Castle CLACD 121	NO REMORSE (CD, leather sleeve)	15

(see also Sam Gopal, Hawkwind, Girlschool, Wild Horses, Philthy Phil & Fast Eddie)

MOTORS

77	Virgin VS 186	Dancing The Night Away/Whisky And Wine (p/s)	4
77	Virgin VS 186-12	Dancing The Night Away (Mix)/Whisky And Wine (12", p/s)	7
77	Virgin VS 194	Be What You Gotta Be/You Beat The Hell Outta Me (p/s)	4
78	Virgin VS 206	Sensation/The Day I Found I Fiver (p/s, some with £5 note offer)	6/4
78	Virgin VS 219	Airport/Cold Love (live) (p/s)	4
78	Virgin VS 219-12	Airport/Cold Love (live) (12", blue vinyl, company sleeve)	7
78	Virgin VS 222-12	Forget About You/Picturama/The Middle Bit/Soul Surrender (12", red vinyl, company die-cut sleeve with sticker)	7
79	Virgin VS 263	Love And Loneliness/Time For Make Up (10", red, green, blue or yellow vinyl, die-cut p/s)	7
78	Virgin V 2089	APPROVED BY THE MOTORS (LP, red vinyl with withdrawn group photo)	10

(see also Ducks Deluxe, Heroes, Nick Garvey, Bram Tchaikovsky, Martin Ace)

MOTOWN SPINNERS
(see under Detroit Spinners)

MOTT THE HOOPLE

69	Island WIP 6072	Rock And Roll Queen/Road To Birmingham	12
71	Island WIP 6105	Midnight Lady/The Debt (some in p/s)	10/5
71	Island WIP 6112	Downtown/Home (Is Where I Want To Be)	8
72	CBS 8271	All The Young Dudes/One Of The Boys	4
73	CBS 1530	Honaloochie Boogie/Rose	4
73	CBS 1764	All The Way From Memphis/Ballad Of Mott The Hoople	4
73	CBS 1895	Roll Away The Stone/Where Do You All Come From?	4
76	CBS 3963	All The Young Dudes/Roll Away The Stone (p/s)	4
69	Island ILPS 9108	MOTT THE HOOPLE (LP, pink label; a few with "Road To Birmingham")	30/20
70	Island ILPS 9119	MAD SHADOWS (LP, pink label, gatefold sleeve)	15
71	Island ILPS 9144	WILD LIFE (LP, pink label)	15
71	Island ILPS 9178	BRAIN CAPERS (LP, pink label & inner sleeve, some with mask)	35/15
72	CBS 65184	ALL THE YOUNG DUDES (LP, with inner sleeve)	10
72	Island ILPS 9215	ROCK AND ROLL QUEEN (LP)	10

(see also Ian Hunter, At Last The 1958 Rock & Roll Show, Mick Ralphs, Mick Ronson, British Lions)

MATTIE MOULTRIE

| 67 | CBS 202547 | That's How Strong My Love Is/The Saddest Story Ever Told | 7 |

MOUND CITY BLUE BLOWERS

| 50s | Collector JEL 1 | BLUES BLOWING JAZZ VOL. 1 (EP) | 10 |
| 55 | HMV 7EG 8096 | MOUND CITY BLUE BLOWERS (EP) | 8 |

MOUNTAIN

70	Bell BLL 1078	Dreams Of Milk And Honey/Wheels On Fire	8
70	Bell BLL 1112	Mississippi Queen/The Laird	5
70	Bell BLL 1125	Sittin' On A Rainbow/My Friend	5
72	Island WIP 6119	Roll Over Beethoven/Crossroader	4
70	Bell SBLL 133	MOUNTAIN CLIMBING (LP)	18
71	Island ILPS 9148	NANTUCKET SLEIGHRIDE (LP)	18
71	Island ILPS 9179	FLOWERS OF EVIL (LP)	12
72	Island ILPS 9199	LIVE — THE ROAD GOES ON FOREVER (LP)	10

(see also West Bruce & Laing, Leslie West)

VALERIE MOUNTAIN
61	Columbia DB 4660	Go It Alone/Gentle Christ	6
62	Pye 7N 15450	Some People/Yes You Did	5
62	Pye NEP 24158	SOME PEOPLE — SOUNDTRACK (EP, with Eagles)	10

(see also Eagles)

MOUNTAIN ASH
75	Witches Bane LKLP 6036	THE HERMIT (LP, private press with insert)	250

MOUNTAIN LINE
74	Xtra XTRA 1140	MOUNTAIN LINE (LP)	10
75	Xtra XTRA 1147	HORSEPOWER (LP)	10

MOUNT RUSHMORE
68	Dot DOT 115	Stone Free/She's No Good To Me	5

MOURNING PHASE
71	private press	MOURNING PHASE (LP)	600
80s	private press	EDEN (LP, reissue of "Mourning Phase")	25

MOUSE
73	Sovereign SOV 122	We Can Make It/It's Happening To Me And You	15
74	Sovereign SOV 127	All The Fallen Teen Angels/Just Came Back	15
74	Sovereign SVNA 7262	LADY KILLER (LP)	140

MOUSE & TRAPS
68	President PT 174	L.O.V.E. Love/Beg Borrow And Steal	15
68	President PT 210	Sometimes You Just Can't Win/Crying Inside	8

MOUSEFOLK
88	Tea Time Surf's Up 01	Don't Let It Slip Away/Spinning Round (flexidisc, initially with p/s)	10/5
80s	Tea Time Surf's Up 02	Devil In The Deep Blue Sea (p/s)	4
80s	Flowerpot 001	Motorcycle Boy/RISK: This Year's Model (p/s flexi, foldaround p/s)	4

NANA MOUSKOURI
63	Fontana 261 365TF	The One That Got Away/No Moon At All	10

ALPHONSE MOUZON
76	United Artists UAG 20005	THE MAN INCOGNITO (LP)	10

ALPHONSE MOUZON & LARRY CORYELL
77	Atlantic K 50382	BACK TOGETHER AGAIN (LP)	10

(see also Larry Coryell)

MOVE
66	Deram DM 109	Night Of Fear/The Disturbance	5
67	Deram DM 117	I Can Hear The Grass Grow/Wave The Flag And Stop The Train	4
67	Regal Zono. RZ 3001	Flowers In The Rain/(Here We Go Round) The Lemon Tree	5
68	Regal Zono. RZ 3005	Fire Brigade/Walk Upon The Water	5
68	Regal Zono. RZ 3012	Wild Tiger Woman/Omnibus	7
68	Regal Zonophone	Cherry Blossom Clinic/Vote For Me (unissued, test pressings may exist)	50+
69	Regal Zono. RZ 3015	Blackberry Way/Something	5
69	Regal Zono. RZ 3021	Curly/This Time Tomorrow	5
70	Regal Zono. RZ 3026	Brontosaurus/Lightnin' Never Strikes Twice	4
70	Fly BUG 2	When Alice Comes Back To The Farm/What?	4
71	Harvest HAR 5036	Ella James/No Time (unissued)	
71	Harvest HAR 5038	Tonight/Don't Mess Me Up	4
71	Harvest HAR 5043	Chinatown/Down On The Bay	4
72	MagniFly ECHO 104	Fire Brigade/I Can Hear The Grass Grow/Night Of Fear (p/s)	6
72	Harvest HAR 5050	California Man/Do Ya/Ella James	4
74	Harvest HAR 5086	Do Ya/No Time	4
68	Regal Zono. TRZ 2001	SOMETHING ELSE FROM THE MOVE (6-track EP/"mini-LP", 33rpm)	30
68	Regal Zono. (S)LRZ 1002	THE MOVE (LP)	20
70	Regal Zono. SLRZ 1012	SHAZAM (LP)	18
70	Fly HIFLY 1	LOOKING ON (LP)	12
71	Harvest SHSP 4013	MESSAGE FROM THE COUNTRY (LP)	12
72	Cube TOOFA 5/6	THE MOVE/SHAZAM (2-LP reissue)	14
74	Harvest SHSP 4035	CALIFORNIA MAN (LP)	10

(see also Roy Wood, Jeff Lynne, ELO, Idle Race, Trevor Burton, Nicky James Movement, Ace Kefford Stand)

MOVEMENT
68	Pye 7N 17443	Something You've Got/Tell Her	70
68	Big T BIG 112	Head For The Sun/Mister Mann	40

MOVERS
65	Ska Beat JB 191	Jo-Anne/DON DRUMMOND: Don De Lion	10

MOVIES
75	A&M AMLH 33002	PLAY THE MOVIES (LP)	10

(see also Ora, Public Foot The Roman)

MOVIN BROTHERS
67	Island WI 3049	Darling I Love You/TOMMY McCOOK: Saboo	10

MOVING FINGER
68	Mercury MF 1051	Jeremy The Lamp/Pain Of My Misfortune	15
69	Mercury MF 1077	Higher And Higher/Shake And Fingerpop	8
73	Decca F 13406	So Many People/We're Just As Happy As We Are	8

(see also Anglians)

MOVING FINGERS
69	Polydor 583 045	REALITY (LP)	20

(see also Second Hand)

MOXY
77	Power Exchange PXL 011	MOXY II (LP)	10
77	Power Exchange PXL 022	RIDING HIGH (LP)	10
78	Polydor 2480 400	UNDER THE LIGHTS (LP)	10

ALISON MOYET
84	CBS A 4497	Love Resurrection/Baby I Do (p/s, original with black labels)	4
85	CBS DA 6044	That Ole Devil Called Love/Don't Burn Down The Bridge//That Ole Devil Called Love (live)/Twisting The Knife (live) (double pack, gatefold sleeve)	4
87	CBS MOYET 2	Weak In The Presence Of Beauty/To Work On You//Is This Love/ Blow Wind Blow (double pack, gatefold sleeve)	4

(see also Yazoo, Little Red Roosters)

MICKEY MOZART QUINTET
59	Columbia DB 4308	Little Dipper/Mexican Hop	6

MR. DYNAMITE
67	Sue WI 4027	Sh'mon Pts 1 & 2	25

MR. FLOOD'S PARTY
70	Ember EMBS 312	Compared To What/Unbreakable Toy	12
75	Bull Dog BD 6	Compared To What/Unbreakable Toy (reissue)	8

MR. FORD & MR. GOON-BONES
56	London HLU 8355	Ain't She Sweet/MUZZY MARCELLINO: Mary Lou	20

MR. FOUNDATION
67	Studio One SO 2001	Have A Good Time/KEN PARKER: See Them A Come	15
67	Studio One SO 2003	All Rudies In Jail (by Zoot Simms)/HORTENSE & ALTON: Easy Squeeze	15
68	Studio One SO 2061	Time-Oh/DUDLEY SIBLEY & PETER AUSTIN: Hole In Your Soul	15
68	Studio One SO 2069	Reggae Rumble/MARCIA GRIFFITHS: You Keep Me On The Move	15
69	Supreme SUP 201	Time To Pray (actually by Lloyd Robinson)/Young Budd (by Leonard Dillon)	5

MR. FOX
70	Big T BIG 135	Little Woman/Join Us In Our Game	4
70	Transatlantic TRA 226	MR FOX (LP)	25
71	Transatlantic TRA 236	THE GIPSY (LP)	35
75	Transatlantic TRA 303	THE COMPLETE MR FOX (2-LP, reissue of "Mr Fox" & "The Gypsy")	25

(see also Bob Pegg, Bob & Carolanne Pegg)

MR. MO'S MESSENGERS
67	Columbia DB 8133	Feelin' Good/The Handyman	8

MR. RUBBISH
84	Rubbish R 2	Modern Art By Mr. Rubbish/Dog-Loo Art Group	4
85	L.E.N. 001	FROM THE WOLF'S LAIR (cassette in deluxe 'bouffant' packaging)	15
92	MP 001	THE SEMIOTICS OF THE CRIMINAL MIND (LP, 100 only)	20

(see also Breadwinner)

MR. TWISTER & TORNADOS
63	Starlite ST45 099	Big Twist Pts 1 & 2	5

MRS. B, ESSEX
87	Shopping Tipps SAVE 99p	The Best Fuck I Ever Had/You Never Guess What (perforated coupon p/s)	8

MU
74	United Artists UAG 29709	LEMURIAN MUSIC (LP)	15

(see also Captain Beefheart, Fapardokly)

MUCKY DUCK
70	Deram DM 314	Jefferson/Psycho's On The Run	4

MUD
67	CBS 203002	Flower Power/You're My Mother (some in p/s)	30/15
68	CBS 3355	Up The Airy Mountain/Latter Days	12
69	Philips BF 1775	Shangri-La/House On The Hill	12
70	Philips 6006 022	Jumping Jehosaphat/Won't Let It Go	8
72	Rak RR 6	Tiger Feet/Oh Boy/Dynamite (p/s)	4
74	Rak RAK 187	Lonely This Christmas/I Can't Stand It (p/s)	6
79	Carrere CAR 117	Drop Everything And Run/Taking The Easy Way Out (picture disc)	4

(see also Dum)

MARY MUDD
58	Columbia DB 4144	Stroll Me/Learning To Love (unreleased)	

(see also Mudlarks)

MUD HUTTERS
79	Defensive NATO ONE	INFORMATION (EP, foldout p/s, also listed as SRTS/79/CUS 263)	5
79	Defensive NATO TWO	THE DECLARATION (EP, also listed SRTS/79/CUS 496)	4
81	Defensive NATO 3	FACTORY FARMING (LP)	10

MUDLARKS
58	Columbia DB 4064	A New Love/Mutual Admiration Society	7
58	Columbia DB 4099	Lollipop/Young Dove's Calling	8
58	Columbia DB 4133	Book Of Love/Yea, Yea	8
58	Columbia DB 4190	There's Never Been A Night/Light'nin' Never Strikes Twice	6
58	Columbia DB 4210	Which Witch Doctor/My Grandfather's Clock	6
59	Columbia DB 4250	Abdul The Bulbul Amer Cha Cha/The Love Game	6
59	Columbia DB 4291	Time Flies/Tell Him No	4
59	Columbia DB 4331	Waterloo/Mary	4
59	Columbia DB 4374	Tennessee/True Love, True Love	5
60	Columbia DB 4417	Never Marry A Fishmonger/Candy	4
60	Columbia DB 4513	(You've Got To) Move Two Mountains/You're Free To Go	4
61	Columbia DB 4636	When Mexico Gave Up The Rumba/Toy Balloon	4

61	Columbia DB 4708	The Mountain's High/Don't Gamble With Love	4
62	Columbia DB 4788	Them Twistin' Bones/Coney Island Washboard	4
62	Columbia DB 4861	Manana Pasado Manana/March Of The Broken Hearts	4
62	Decca F 11537	I've Been Everywhere/Just The Snap Of Your Fingers	4
63	Decca F 11601	The Little Cracked Bell San Raquel/La De Da	4
64	Fontana TF 495	Walk Around/Here's Another Day	4
58	Columbia SEG 7854	MUDLARKS (EP)	15

(see also Mary Mudd)

MUGWUMPS

64	Warner Bros WB 144	I'll Remember Tonight/I Don't Wanna Know	8
67	Warner Bros W 1697	THE MUGWUMPS — AN HISTORICAL RECORDING (LP)	20
70	Valiant VS 134	THE MUGWUMPS — AN HISTORICAL RECORDING (LP, reissue)	12

(see also Mamas & Papas, Mama Cass Elliot, Lovin' Spoonful)

BOBBY MUIR & BLUEBEATS

60	Blue Beat BB 20	Baby What You Done Me Wrong/Go Pretty Baby Go (as Bobby Muir)	7
61	Blue Beat BB 44	Honey Please/That's My Girl	7
61	Blue Beat BB 77	Brand New Automobile/Spanish Town Twist	7

LINDSAY MUIR'S UNTAMED

| 66 | Planet PLF 113 | Daddy Long Legs/Trust Yourself A Little Bit | 30 |

(see also Untamed)

MULCAYS

54	Polygon P 1118	My Happiness/Near You (78)	7
55	London HLF 8188	Harbour Lights/Dipsy Doodle	20
54	London REP 1016	MERRY CHRISTMAS (EP)	12
56	London REF 1046	HARMONICS BY THE MULCAYS (EP)	12

MULDOONS

| 65 | Decca F 12164 | I'm Lost Without You/Come Back Now Baby | 25 |

MULESKINNERS

| 65 | Fontana TF 527 | Back Door Man/Need Your Lovin' | 80 |
| 60s | Keepoint KEE-EP-7104 | MULESKINNERS (EP, private press, no p/s) | 500 |

MOON MULLICAN

51	Vogue V 9013	Cherokee Boogie/Love Is The Light That Leads Me Home (78)	15
56	Parlophone MSP 6254	Honolulu Rock-A Roll-A/Seven Nights To Rock (with Boyd Bennett & His Rockets)	300
56	Parlophone R 4195	Honolulu Rock-A Roll-A/Seven Nights To Rock (with Boyd Bennett & His Rockets) (78)	50
59	Parlophone GEP 8794	COUNTRY ROUND UP (EP)	35
50s	Parlophone CGEP 15	PIANO BREAKDOWN (EP, export issue, company sleeve)	25

(see also Boyd Bennett & His Rockets)

GERRY MULLIGAN

56	Vogue V 2157	Frenesi/Nights At The Turntable	4
56	Vogue V 2158	Bernie's Tune/Freeway	4
56	Vogue V 2159	Carioca/My Funny Valentine	4
56	Vogue V 2225	Lullaby Of The Leaves/Walkin' Shoes	4
56	Vogue V 2257	Darn That Dream/I'm Beginning To See The Light	4
56	Vogue V 2258	Swing House/I May Be Wrong	4
56	Vogue V 2259	Jeru/Love Or Leave Me	4
56	Vogue V 2260	Bark For Barksdale/Moonlight In Vermont	4
56	Vogue V 2304	Carson City Stage/Cherry	4
56	Vogue V 2305	I Can't Believe That You're In Love With Me/Lady Be Good (with Lee Konitz)	4
56	Vogue V 2306	Motel/Makin' Whopee	4
56	Vogue V 2324	Soft Shoe/Aren't You Glad You're You?	4
56	Vogue V 2337	Line For Lyons/Limelight	4
57	Vogue V 2358	I May Be Wrong/Swing House	4
59	London HLT 8901	I Want To Live — Theme/Black Nightgown (as Gerry Mulligan Combo)	6
60	HMV POP 734	Line For Lyons/Standstill (with Paul Desmond Quartet)	4
60	HMV POP 769	I'm Gonna Go Fishin' (both sides)	4
60	Philips JAZ 102	News From Blueport/Utter Chaos	4
55	Capitol EAP1 439	PRESENTING GERRY MULLIGAN AND HIS TENTETTE (EP)	7
55	Capitol EAP2 439	PRESENTING GERRY MULLIGAN AND HIS TENTETTE (EP)	7
58	Emarcy ERE 1553	PRESENTING THE GERRY MULLIGAN SEXTET (EP)	7
58	Emarcy ERE 1556	PRESENTING THE GERRY MULLIGAN SEXTET VOL. 2 (EP)	7
58	Emarcy ERE 1560	PRESENTING THE GERRY MULLIGAN SEXTET VOL. 3 (EP)	7
58	Emarcy ERE 1574	MAINSTREAM VOL. 1 (EP)	7
58	Emarcy ERE 1575	MAINSTREAM VOL. 2 (EP)	7
60	Mercury ZEP 10071	MULLIGAN MANIA (EP)	7
53	Capitol LC 6621	THE GERRY MULLIGAN TENTETTE — ROCKER (10" LP)	18
53	Vogue LDE 029	THE GERRY MULLIGAN QUARTET VOL. 1 (10" LP)	15
53	Vogue LDE 030	THE GERRY MULLIGAN QUARTET VOL. 2 (10" LP)	15
53	Vogue LDE 031	THE GERRY MULLIGAN QUARTET VOL. 3 (10" LP)	15
54	Vogue LDE 075	THE GERRY MULLIGAN QUARTET (10" LP)	15
54	Vogue LDE 083	THE GERRY MULLIGAN QUARTET VOL. 4 (10" LP)	15
54	Esquire 20-032	GERRY MULLIGAN ALLSTARS — MULLIGAN'S TOO (10" LP)	15
55	Vogue LDE 156	GERRY MULLIGAN QUARTET WITH LEE KONITZ (10" LP)	15
56	Esquire 32-014	GERRY MULLIGAN ALLSTARS (LP)	12
56	Vogue LAE 12006	THE GERRY MULLIGAN QUARTET (LP)	12
56	Vogue LAE 12015	THE GERRY MULLIGAN QUARTET (LP)	12
56	Emarcy EJL 101	PRESENTING THE GERRY MULLIGAN SEXTET (LP)	12
57	Emarcy EJL 1259	MAINSTREAM OF JAZZ (LP, by Gerry Mulligan Sextet)	12
58	Columbia Clef 33CX 10113	GERRY MULLIGAN AND PAUL DESMOND QUARTET (LP)	12
58	HMV CLP 1204	PHIL SUNKEL'S "JAZZ CONCERTO GROSSO" (LP, with Bob Brookmeyer)	10
59	Philips SBBL 552	WHAT IS THERE TO SAY? (LP, stereo)	12

Gerry MULLIGAN

59	Vogue SEA 5006	GERRY MULLIGAN SONGBOOK (LP, stereo)	12
59	Vogue SEA 5007	REUNION WITH CHET BAKER (LP, stereo, as Gerry Mulligan Quartet)	12
59	London Jazz LTZT 15161	I WANT TO LIVE (LP, as Gerry Mulligan & Shelly Manne)	10
60	HMV CLP 1373	GERRY MULLIGAN MEETS BEN WEBSTER (LP)	10
61	HMV CLP 1432	THE CONCERT JAZZ BAND (LP, also stereo CSD 1351)	10
61	Vocalion LAE 12268	THE GENIUS OF GERRY MULLIGAN (LP)	10
62	HMV CLP 1465	GERRY MULLIGAN MEETS JOHNNY HODGES (LP, also stereo CSD 1372)	10
62	HMV CLP 1488	AT THE VILLAGE VANGUARD (LP, also stereo CSD 1396)	10
62	Riverside RLP 12-247	MULLIGAN MEETS MONK (LP, with Thelonious Monk)	10
62	HMV CLP 1549	A CONCERT IN JAZZ (LP, also stereo CSD 1432)	10
62	HMV CLP 1585	ON TOUR (LP, with Zoot Sims)	10

(see also Paul Desmond & Gerry Mulligan, Chet Baker, Shelly Manne)

MICK MULLIGAN'S JAZZ BAND

56	Tempo A 139	In A Shanty In Old Shanty Town/Snag It	4
56	Tempo A 143	Oriental Strut/Big House Blues	4
56	Tempo A 152	Beale Street Blues/Raver's Edge	4
57	Tempo A 155	St. James' Infirmary/After A While	4
57	Tempo A 164	Old Stack-O-Lee Blues/Double Dee	4
55	Tempo EXA 25	MICK MULLIGAN'S JAZZ BAND (EP)	7
56	Tempo EXA 41	GEORGE MELLY WITH MICK MULLIGAN'S JAZZ BAND (EP)	10
57	Tempo TAP 14	JAZZ AT THE RAILWAY ARMS (LP, with George Melly)	12
59	Pye Jazz NJL 21	MEET MICK MULLIGAN (LP)	10
59	Parlophone PMC 1103	THE SAINTS MEET THE SINNERS (LP, with George Melly & Saints Jazz Band)	10

(see also George Melly)

GENE MUMFORD

58	Philips PB 862	More Than You Know/Please Give Me One More Chance	6
58	Philips PB 862	More Than You Know/Please Give Me One More Chance (78)	5

MUNGO JERRY

70	Dawn DNX 2502	In The Summertime/Mighty Man/Dust Pneumonia Blues (p/s)	5
71	Dawn DNX 2505	Baby Jump/The Man Behind The Piano/Live From Hollywood: Maggie/Midnight Special/Mighty Man (p/s)	5
71	Dawn DNX 2510	Lady Rose/Have A Whiff On Me/Milk Cow Blues/Little Louis (p/s)	7
71	Dawn DNX 2510	Lady Rose/She Rowed/Milk Cow Blues/Little Louis (p/s)	5
71	Dawn DNX 2513	You Don't Have To Be In The Army To Fight In The War/The Sun Is Shining/O'Reilly/We Shall Be Free (p/s)	5
72	Dawn DNX 2514	Open Up/Going Back Home/I Don't Wanna Go Back To School/No Girl Reaction (p/s)	5
72	Dawn DNX 2515	My Girl And Me/46 And On/It's A Goodie Boogie Woogie/Summer's Gone (p/s)	5
70	Dawn DNLS 3008	MUNGO JERRY (LP)	10
71	Dawn DNLS 3020	ELECTRONICALLY TESTED (LP)	10
74	Dawn DNLS 3501	LONG LEGGED WOMAN (LP)	10

(see also Ray Dorset, King Earl Boogie Band)

CAROLINE MUNRO

85	Numa NU 5	Pump Me Up/The Picture (p/s)	5
85	Numa NUM 5	Pump Me Up (Extended 6.09)/The Picture/Pump Me Up (4.00 7" Version) (12", p/s)	7

(see also Gary Numan)

HAL MUNRO

58	Embassy WB 284	Breathless/Wear My Ring Around Your Neck	6
59	Embassy WB 336	C'mon Everybody/It's Late	6

(see also Neville Taylor)

JANET MUNRO & SEAN CONNERY

59	Top Rank JAR 163	Pretty Irish Girl/Ballamaquilty's Band	4

LEE MUNRO

86	Numa NU 20	Stereo Headphones/Give Me Your Love (p/s)	5
86	Numa NUM 20	Stereo Headphones (Extended Version)/Give Me Your Love/Stereo Headphones (7" Version) (12", p/s)	8

PATRICE MUNSEL

53	HMV 7M 152	Is This The Beginning Of Love/The Melba Waltz	4

JERRY MURAD'S HARMONICATS

59	Mercury ZEP 10001	IT'S CHA CHA TIME (EP)	8

MURDER THE DISTURBED

79	Small Wonder SMALL 17	GENETIC DISRUPTION (EP)	4

BILLY MURE (ORCHESTRA)

60	Top Rank JAR 344	Jambalaya/Kaw Liga (as Billy Mure Orchestra)	5
59	RCA RCX 158	SUPERSONICS IN FLIGHT (EP, also stereo SRC 7032)	12/20
59	Felsted GEP 1006	THE VERSATILE BILLY MURE (EP)	8
60	MGM C 800	SUPERSONIC GUITARS (LP)	10
60	MGM C 835/CS 5011	SUPERSONIC GUITARS VOL. 2 (LP, mono/stereo)	10/12

(see also Supersonic Guitars)

MURMAIDS

63	Stateside SS 247	Popsicles And Icicles/Comedy And Tragedy	10

MICHAEL MURPHEY

72	Regal Zono. RZ 3062	Boy From The Country/Geronimo's Cadillac	4
72	Regal Zono. SRZA 8512	GERONIMO'S CADILLAC (LP)	12

ARTHUR MURPHY

59	Parlophone R 4523	Sixteen Candles/Molly Malone	4
59	Parlophone R 4523	Sixteen Candles/Molly Malone (78)	5

ELLIOT MURPHY

74	Polydor 2391 100	AQUASHOW (LP)	10

MARK MURPHY

57	Brunswick 05701	Goodbye Baby Blues/The Right Kind Of Woman	4
58	Capitol CL 14962	Belong To Me/Don't Cry My Love	4
60	Capitol CL 15117	Send For Me/Come To Me	4
63	Riverside RIF 106905	Like Love/Fly Away My Sadness	4
63	Riverside RIF 106908	Fly Me To The Moon/Why Don't You Do Right	4
65	Fontana TF 572	High On Windy Hill/Broken Heart	4
67	Fontana TF 803	(Ain't That) Just Like A Woman/Do You Wonder If I Love You	4
69	Pye 7N 17672	Come Back To Me/Dear Heart	4
57	Brunswick LAT 8172	MEET MARK MURPHY (LP)	10
60	Capitol (S)T 5011	HIT PARADE (LP)	10
64	Fontana (S)TL 5217	MARK TIME! (LP)	10
66	Immediate IMLP/IMSP 004	WHO CAN I TURN TO (LP)	40

NOEL MURPHY

67	Fontana TL 5450	NYA-A-A-H! (LP)	10
73	Village Thing VTS 25	MURF (LP)	10

PETER MURPHY

88	B. Banquet BEGB 210	Indigo Eyes/God Sends (box set)	4
	(see also Bauhaus)		

ROSE MURPHY

50	HMV B 9901	Busy Line/Girls Were Made To Take Care Of Boys (78)	10
53	London L 1176	Little Red Monkey/Time On My Hands (78)	10
52	Oriole/Mercury MG 10004	SONGS BY ROSE MURPHY (10" LP)	15

ALEX MURRAY

60	Decca F 11203	Teen Angel/Paper Doll	6
60	Decca F 11225	All On My Own/String Along	4
61	Decca F 11345	When You Walked Out/Send For Me	4
	(see also Most Brothers)		

LADY MURRAY

66	Clan 597 002	Mister Abercrombie Taught Me/In My Imagination	4

MISTER MURRAY

65	Fontana TF 623	Down Came The Rain/Whatever Happened To Music?	6
66	Fontana TF 674	I Drink To Your Memory/I Was A Good Song	4
	(see also Mitch Murray Clan)		

MITCH MURRAY CLAN

66	Clan 597 001	Skyliner/Cherokee	6
	(see also Mister Murray)		

PAULINE MURRAY & INVISIBLE GIRLS

80	Illusive IVE 1	Dream Sequences (One)/Dream Sequences (Two) (p/s)	5
80	Illusive IVEX 1	Dream Sequences (One)/Dream Sequences (Two) (10", p/s)	7
80	Illusive IVE 2	Mr. X/Two Shots (p/s)	4
81	Illusive IVE 3	Searching For Heaven/Animal Crazy (p/s)	4
81	Illusive IVEX 3	Searching For Heaven/Animal Crazy/The Visitor (10", p/s)	7
87	Polestar PSTR 002	HONGKONG (12" EP, as Pauline Murray & Saint)	7
80	Illusive/RSO 2934 277	PAULINE MURRAY & THE INVISIBLE GIRLS (LP)	10
	(see also Penetration, Walkie Talkies, Dead Or Alive, Only Ones)		

PETE MURRAY

60s	A.T.V. ATV 1	T.V. THEMES (EP, marketed by Pascal Fruits)	7

RUBY MURRAY

54	Columbia DB 3542	Heartbeat/He's A Pal Of Mine (78)	5
55	Columbia SCM 5162	Softly, Softly/What Could Be More Beautiful	18
55	Columbia DB 3577	Let Me Go Lover/Happy Days And Lonely Nights (78)	5
55	Columbia SCM 5165	Spring, Spring, Spring/Goin' Co'tin (with Ray Burns, Diana Decker & Ronnie Harris)	8
55	Columbia SCM 5169	If Anyone Finds This, I Love You (with Anne Warren)/Before We Know It	12
55	Columbia SCM 5180	Evermore/Bambino	12
56	Columbia SCM 5222	Two Rivers/Boy Meets Girl (with Norman Wisdom)	10
56	Columbia SCM 5225	For Now, For Ever/Oh, Please Make Him Jealous	10
56	Columbia DB 3810	Teddy O'Neil/It Only Hurts For A Little While	10
57	Columbia DB 3849	Knock On Any Door/True Love	8
57	Columbia DB 3852	In Love/O'Malley's Tango	8
57	Columbia DB 3911	From The First Hello — To The Last Goodbye/Heart	8
57	Columbia DB 3933	Mr. Wonderful/Pretty, Pretty	8
57	Columbia DB 3955	Scarlet Ribbons/Macushla Mine	8
57	Columbia DB 3994	Little White Lies/Passing Strangers	6
57	Columbia DB 4042	Ain't That A Grand And Glorious Feeling/I'll Remember Today	6
58	Columbia DB 4075	Forgive Me My Darling/Keep Smiling At Trouble	6
58	Columbia DB 4108	In My Life/Nora Malone (Call Me By 'Phone)	6
58	Columbia DB 4192	Real Love/Little One	6
59	Columbia DB 4266	Nevertheless (I'm In Love With You)/Who Knows	5
59	Columbia DB 4305	Goodbye Jimmy, Goodbye/The Humour Is On Me Now	6
59	Columbia DB 4326	A Pretty Irish Girl/Connemara (with Brendan O'Dowde)	4
59	Columbia DB 4379	A Message From Jimmy/A Voice In The Choir	4
60	Columbia DB 4426	Forever/Congratulations	4
60	Columbia DB 4497	My Little Corner Of The World/Sweetheart Of All My Dreams	4
61	Columbia DB 4575	Goodbye Is The Loneliest Word/Living For The Day	4
61	Columbia DB 4701	Tammy, Tell Me True/The Faith Of A Child	4
62	Columbia DB 4771	Pianissimo/The Diamond	4

Ruby MURRAY

62	Columbia DB 4944	How Did He Look?/As Simple As That	4
63	Columbia DB 7028	I'm In Love With The Boy Next Door/I'll Walk The Rest Of The Way	4
63	Columbia DB 7152	Hurry Home/Something Old — Something New	4
65	Decca F 12291	The Little Pine Tree/Silent Night	4
55	Columbia SEG 7588	RUBY IS A GEM (EP)	15
56	Columbia SEG 7620	EVERYBODY'S SWEETHEART NO. 1 (EP)	8
56	Columbia SEG 7631	EVERYBODY'S SWEETHEART NO. 2 (EP)	8
56	Columbia SEG 7636	EVERYBODY'S SWEETHEART NO. 3 (EP)	10
57	Columbia SEG 7748	MUCUSHLA MINE (EP)	7
59	Columbia SEG 7952	ENDEARING YOUNG CHARMS (EP)	8
60	Columbia SEG 8052	LOVE'S OLD SWEET SONG (EP, also stereo ESG 7830)	8/12
55	Columbia 33S 1079	WHEN IRISH EYES ARE SMILING (10" LP)	18
58	Columbia 33S 1135	ENDEARING YOUNG CHARMS (10" LP)	25
60	Columbia 33SX 1201	RUBY (LP, also stereo SCX 3289)	15/17

(see also Norman Wisdom & Ruby Murray, Ray Burns)

JUNIOR MURVIN
(see under Junior Soul)

MUSCLE SHOALS HORNS
76	Bang BANG 002	Breakdown/Get It Up	4

MUSHROOM
73	Hawk HASP 320	Devil Among The Tailors/Sun Ni Dhuibir/King Of Ireland's Daughter	25
73	Hawk HALPX 116	EARLY ONE MORNING (LP, some with poster inner)	350/275

(see also Joe O'Donnell)

MUSHROOM BIRIANI
88	Yak MIN 102	Straight Through You/Ring Of Fire (p/s, with perfumed insert)	6
88	Yak MIN 105	Japanese Flag/Windy (no p/s)	8
88	Yak MAX 1	HOTTER THAN EVER (LP, with free pepper saché)	50

(see also Mushroom Soup)

MUSHROOM SOUP
70	Button BUTTON 1	Frodo's Green Trip Machine/Open The Tin	20
71	Button BUTTON 3	Pogoing With The Penguins/Push It	18
69	Roll & Butter PAT 1	... AND OTHER RECIPES (LP)	200
70	Roll & Butter PAT 2	PSYCHEDELIC SOUP (LP, withdrawn)	300
72	Wynd Up APRIL 1	MAGIC (LP, private press, 7 1/2 copies only)	800
92	14th Circle SOOP 1	PSYCHEDELIC SOUP (reissue LP, withdrawn)	100

MUSICAL THEATRE
70	Pye NSPL 28128	A REVOLUTIONARY REVELATION (LP)	10

MUSIC BOX
72	Westwood MRS 013	SONGS OF SUNSHINE (LP)	15

MUSIC DOCTORS
69	Downtown DT 447	Music Doctor Pts 1 & 2	4
71	Downtown DT 479	The Pliers Pts 1 & 2	4
70s	J-Dan JDN 4403	Bush Doctor/Lick Your Stick	4
70s	J-Dan JDN 4411	The Wild Bunch/ISRAELITES: Born To Be Strong	4
70s	J-Dan JDN 4417	Discretion Version/Doctor Dan, Boy Friday And Friend	4
70	Trojan TBL 117	REGGAE IN THE SUMMERTIME (LP)	10

MUSIC EMPORIUM
83	Psycho PSYCHO 11	MUSIC EMPORIUM (LP)	20

MUSIC EXPLOSION
67	Stateside SS 2028	A Little Bit O' Soul/I See The Light	7
67	Stateside SS 2054	Sunshine Games/Can't Stop Now	5
67	Philips BF 1547	Little Black Egg/Stay By My Side	6
69	London HLP 10272	Little Bit O' Soul/Everybody	4
67	London HA-P/SH-P 8352	A LITTLE BIT O' SOUL (LP)	15

MUSIC FOR PLEASURE
81	Rage RAGE 1	The Human Factor/Madness At The Mission (p/s)	4
81	Rage RAGE 2	Fuel To The Fire/Debris (p/s)	4

MUSICIANS
66	King KG 1055	Jaunty Joe/The Chelsea Set	5

MUSIC MACHINE
67	Pye Intl. 7N 25407	Talk Talk/Come On In	25
67	Pye Intl. 7N 25414	The People In Me/Masculine Intuition (demo only)	20

MUSIC THROUGH SIX
68	Domain D3	Riff Raff/ROY DOCKER: Mellow Moonlight	5

(see also Jason Sims & Music Through Six)

MUSKETEER GRIPWEED & THIRD TROOP
66	United Artists UP 1196	How I Won The War/Aftermath	50

(see also John Lennon)

CHARLIE MUSSELWHITE BLUES BAND
68	Vanguard SVRL 19012	STONE BLUES (LP)	10

VIDO MUSSO & HIS ORCHESTRA
54	London HL 8077	Vido's Boogie/Blue Night (78)	7

BOOTS MUSSULLI QUARTET
54	Capitol KC 65002	Diga Diga Doo/Lullaby In Rhythm	6
55	Capitol KPL 106	THE BOOTS MUSSULLI QUARTET (10" LP)	10

MUSTANG
67	Parlophone R 5579	Why/Here, There And Everywhere	20

MUS-TWANGS
61   Mercury AMT 1140   Roch Lomond/Marie 8

MUTANTS
78   Rox ROX 002   Boss Man/Back Yard Boys 4
79   Rox ROX 005   School Teacher/Hard Time/Lady (p/s, red vinyl) 4

MUTE DRIVERS
80s Mute Drivers MD 001   MUTE DRIVERS (LP, with insert in handmade painted sleeve, 300 only) 15
    (see also Anonymes)

MUTT 'N' JEFF
66   Decca F 12335   Don't Nag Me Ma/Strolling The Blues 7

MX-80
80s Island   HARD ATTACK (LP) 10

MY BLOODY VALENTINE
86   Fever FEV 5X   No Place To Go/Moonlight (p/s) 12
86   Fever FEV 5   GEEK! (12" EP) 18
86   Kaleid. Sound KS 101   THE NEW RECORD BY MY BLOODY VALENTINE (12" EP) 30
87   Lazy LAZY 04   Sunny Sundae Smile/Paint A Rainbow (p/s) 18
87   Lazy LAZY 04T   Sunny Sundae Smile/Paint A Rainbow/Kiss The Eclipse/Sylvie's Head
    (12", p/s) 22
87   Lazy LAZY 07   Strawberry Wine/Never Say Goodbye/Can I Touch You (12", p/s) 20
88   Creation CRE 055   You Made Me Realise/Slow (die-cut company sleeve) 8
88   Creation CRE 061   Feed Me With Your Kiss/Emptiness Inside (plays "I Believe") (die-cut co. sleeve) .8
80s Lyntone   Sugar/PACIFIC: December, With The Day (square flexi w/'The Catalogue') 6/4
87   Lazy LAZY 08   ECSTACY (LP, 3,000 only) 30
88   Creation CRELP 040   ISN'T ANYTHING (LP, initial 3,000 copies with free 7", "Instrumental"/
    "Instrumental" [CRE FRE 4, no p/s]) 15

MY CAPTAINS
86   4AD AD 103   FALL (EP) 8

MY DEAR WATSON
68   Parlophone R 5687   Elusive Face/The Shame Just Drained 15
68   Parlophone R 5737   Make This Day Last/Stop, Stop, I'll Be There 15
70   DJM DJS 224   Have You Seen Your Saviour/White Line Road 8

BILLY MYLES
57   HMV POP 423   Honey Bee/The Joker (That's What They Call Me) 20
57   HMV POP 423   Honey Bee/The Joker (That's What They Call Me) (78) .10

MEG MYLES
56   Capitol CL 14555   Sing On, Baby/Will You Shed A Tear For Me? 4

MYLESTONES
76   Black Magic BM 111   The Joker/Juicie Brucie 4
    (see also Butch Barker)

MY LORDE SHERIFFE'S COMPANIE
79   private pressing   MY LORDE SHERIFFE'S COMPANIE (LP) 30

MYRTELLES
63   Oriole CB 1805   Don't Wanna Cry Again/Just Let Me Cry 6
    (see also Sue & Sunshine, Sue & Sunny)

MYSTERE FIVE'S
84   Flicknife FLS 001   No Message/Shake Some Action 4
82   Flicknife FLS 202   Never Say Thank You/Heart Rules The Head 4
    (see also Wayne County & Electric Chairs)

MYSTERIES
64   Decca F 11919   Give Me Rhythm And Blues/Teardrops 20

WILLIAM MYSTERIOUS
82   Mezzanine MEZ 1   Security Of Noise/Alright (p/s, with Fay Fife & Revettes) 4
    (see also Rezillos)

MYSTERY GIRLS
80   Strange HAM 001   SOUNDS LIKE (EP) 5
81   Strange HAM 002   I'M A BELIEVER (EP) 4

MYSTERY GIRLS
88   Mystery Girls MGS 2   I Promise To Rock You Forever/Nuthin' To Do (stickered white label, promo-only) 6

MYSTERY GUESTS
80   Boys Own/Heater   Wurlitzer Junction/The Merry Shark You Are
    Vol. BO 1   (handmade stickered white labels) 5
81   Boys Own BO 3   The Sparrow That Ate New York/The Nude (p/s) 4

MYSTERY MAKER
77   Caves UHC 3   MYSTERY MAKER (LP, private press with booklet) 175

MYSTIC NUMBER NATIONAL BANK
69   Probe SPB 1001   MYSTIC NUMBER NATIONAL BANK (LP) 10

MYSTICS
59   HMV POP 646   Hushabye/Adam And Eve 30
59   Top Rank JAR 243   Don't Take The Stars/So Tenderly 12

MYTHRA
80   Streetbeat LAMP 2   Killer/Death And Destiny/U.F.O. (p/s) 10
80   Streetbeat LAMP 2T   Killer/Death And Destiny/U.F.O. (12", p/s) 40
82   Guardian GRM 16   DEATH AND DESTINY (EP, 4-track, no p/s) 6

MUD

METALLICA

Rare Record Price Guide

NAAFI SANDWICH
80   Absurd ABSURD 8   Slice One/Slice Two (p/s) 4
NABAY
79   Grapevine GRP 143   Believe It Or Not/Believe It Or Not (Instrumental) 4
RICKY NADIR
79   Charisma CB 339   The Polaroid/PETER HAMMILL: The Old School Tie 10
     (see also Peter Hammill)
NAKED LUNCH
81   Ramkup CAC 003   Rabies/Slipping Again (p/s) 4
NAKED TRUTH
70   Deram DM 287   Two Little Rooms/Rag Doll Boy 5
NAMES
81   Factory FAC 29   Nightshift/I Wish I Could Speak Your Language (p/s) 4
N & Y
90   IRS ADRENT 1   Adrenalin (Extended Mix)/Love Is The Doctor/Adrenalin (Edit) (12", p/s) 7
     (see also Yen, Gary Numan)
NANETTE
70   Columbia SCX 6398   NANETTE (LP) 20
ED NANGLE
68   Blue Cat BS 120   Good Girl/ENFORCERS: Musical Fever 10
68   Coxsone CS 7038   Whipping The Prince (actually by Ed Nangle & Alton Ellis & Soul Vendors)/
                            HEPTONES: If You Knew 10
NICK NANTOS & HIS FIREBALLERS
64   Summit ATL 4114   GUITARS ON FIRE (LP) 15
     (see also Bill Haley & Comets)
NAPALM DEATH
89   Earache 7 MOSH 008   promo single (p/s) 4
89   Earache 7 MOSH 14   Mentally Murdered (p/s) 4
90   Earache 7 MOSH 24L   Suffer The Children (p/s, with stickers) 4
90s RISE 001   LIVE (EP, poster p/s) 7
NAPOLEON XIV
66   Warner Bros WB 5831   They're Coming To Take Me Away Ha-Haa!/!Aah-Ah Yawa Em Ekat Ot
                            Gnimoc Er'Yeht 4
66   Warner Bros WB 5853   I'm In Love With My Little Red Tricycle/Doin' The Napoleon 10
66   Warner Bros W 1661   THEY'RE COMING TO TAKE ME AWAY HA-HA-A! (LP) 50
     (see also Jerry Samuels, Kim Fowley)
MARTY NAPOLEON
56   London EZN 19001   MARTY NAPOLEON SWINGS AND SINGS (EP) 7
NARNIA
74   Myrrh MYR 1007   NARNIA — ASLAN IS NOT A TAME LION (LP) 100
     (see also After The Fire)
BILLY NASH COMBO
61   Philips PB 1181   Sunset/Nobody Loves Me Like You 4
BILLY NASH ROCK BAND
63   Philips 370 406 BF   The Madison Step/Madison Rhythm 4
GENE NASH
59   Capitol CL 15042   I'm An Eskimo Too/Ja, Ja, Ja (Deutsche Rock 'N Roll) 12
GRAHAM NASH
71   Atlantic 2091 096   Chicago/Simple Man 4
71   Atlantic 2091 135   Military Madness/I Used To Be A King 4
71   Atlantic 2401 011   SONGS FOR BEGINNERS (LP) 10
     (see also Hollies, Crosby, [Stills,] Nash [& Young], Fool)
JOHNNY NASH
57   HMV POP 402   Ladder Of Love/I'll Walk Alone 6
58   HMV POP 435   Won't You Let Me Share My Love With You?/A Very Special Love 5
58   HMV POP 475   It's Easy To Say/My Pledge To You 5
58   HMV POP 553   Almost In Your Arms/Midnight Moonlight 4
59   HMV POP 597   Walk With Faith In Your Heart/Roots Of Heaven 4
59   HMV POP 620   As Time Goes By/Voice Of Love 4
59   HMV POP 651   And The Angels Sing/Baby, Baby, Baby 4
59   HMV POP 673   Take A Giant Step/Imagination 4
60   HMV POP 746   A Place In The Sun/Goodbye 4
60   HMV POP 822   Somebody/Kisses 4
62   Warner Bros WB 65   Don't Take Away Your Love/Mom 4
62   Warner Bros WB 76   Ol' Man River/My Dear Little Sweetheart 4
63   Warner Bros WB 93   Cigareets, Whiskey And Wild, Wild Women/I'm Moving On 4
64   Chess CRS 8005   Strange Feelin'/Raining In My Heart 8
64   Pye Intl. 7N 25250   Love Ain't Nothin'/Talk To Me 12
66   Pye Intl. 7N 25353   Let's Move And Groove (Together)/Understanding 4

Johnny NASH

66	Pye Intl. 7N 25363	One More Time/Tryin' To Find Her	4
68	Regal Zono. RZ 3010	Hold Me Tight/Let's Move And Groove Together	4
69	MGM MGM 1480	(I'm So) Glad You're My Baby/Stormy	10
68	Major Minor MM 586	You Got Soul/Don't Cry	4
69	Major Minor MM 603	Cupid/People In Love	4
64	RCA RCX 7163	PRESENTING JOHNNY NASH (EP)	30
59	HMV CLP 1251	JOHNNY NASH (LP)	12
59	HMV CLP 1299	QUIET HOUR WITH JOHNNY NASH (LP)	12
60	HMV CLP 1325/CSD 1288	I GOT RHYTHM (LP, mono/stereo)	12/14
62	Encore ENC 2005	LET'S GET LOST (LP)	12
69	Major Minor SMLP 47	YOU GOT SOUL (LP)	12
69	Major Minor SMLP 54	JOHNNY NASH AND KIM WESTON (LP)	12
69	Major Minor SMLP 56	SOUL FOLK (LP)	12
69	Major Minor MMLP 63	PRINCE OF PEACE (LP, also stereo SMLP 63)	12
73	CBS Q 56449	MY MERRY GO ROUND (LP, quadrophonic)	10

(see also Kim Weston)

TONY NASH

70s	Hot Rod HR 110	Keep On Trying/WINSTON JAMES: Just Can't Do Without Your Love	4

NASH THE SLASH

81	DinDisc DIN 28	Deadman's Curve/Reactor No. 2 (p/s)	4
81	DinDisc DIN 29	19th Nervous Breakdown/Danger Zone (p/s)	4
81	Smash Hits (no cat. no.)	Swing-Shift (Flexi-Version)/ORCHESTRAL MANOEUVRES IN THE DARK: Pretending To See The Future (live) (blue flexidisc with 'Smash Hits')	5/4

NASHVILLE FIVE

62	Decca F 11427	Stand Up And Say That/Like Nashville	5
62	Decca F 11484	Some Other Love/Brainwave	5
62	Decca DFE 6706	LIKE NASHVILLE (EP)	20

NASHVILLE TEENS

64	Decca F 11930	Tobacco Road/I Like It Like That	5
64	Decca F 12000	Goggle Eye/T.N.T.	4
65	Decca F 12089	Find My Way Back Home/Devil-In-Law	5
65	Decca F 12143	This Little Bird/Whatcha Gonna Do?	5
65	Decca F 12255	I Know How It Feels To Be Loved/Soon Forgotten	4
66	Decca F 12316	The Hard Way/Upside Down	5
66	Decca F 12458	Forbidden Fruit/Revived 45 Time	5
66	Decca F 12542	That's My Woman/Words	10
67	Decca F 12580	I'm Coming Home/Searching	6
67	Decca F 12657	The Biggest Night Of Her Life/Last Minute	6
68	Decca F 12754	All Along The Watchtower/Sun-Dog	6
69	Major Minor MM 599	The Lament Of The Cherokee Reservation Indian/Looking For You	8
69	Decca F 12929	Tobacco Road/All Along The Watchtower	4
71	Parlophone R 5925	Ella James/Tennessee Woman	8
72	Enterprise ENT 001	Lawdy Miss Clawdy/Let It Rock: Break Up	4
65	Decca DFE 8600	THE NASHVILLE TEENS (EP)	30
75	New World NW 6002	THE NASHVILLE TEENS (LP)	30

(see also Jerry Lee Lewis)

NATCHBAND

78	Far In FARS 01	Cadillac (Made In USA)/Being From The Sky	4

NATIONAL-ELLS

67	Parlophone R 5609	Mr. Moon/Dance, Dance	4

NATIONAL HEAD BAND

71	Warner Bros K 46094	ALBERT I (LP)	12

NATIONAL HEALTH

78	Affinity AFF 6	NATIONAL HEALTH (LP)	10
78	Charly CRL 5010	OF QUEUES AND CURES (LP)	10

(see also Hatfield & North)

NATIONAL LAMPOON

78	Island HELP 8	RADIO DINNER (LP)	10

NATIONAL PINION POLE

66	Planet PLF 111	Make Your Mark Little Man/I Was The One You Came In With	10

NATURAL ACOUSTIC BAND

73	RCA RCA 2324	Echoes/Is It True Blue	4
72	RCA SF 8272	LEARNING TO LIVE (LP)	10
74	RCA SF 8314	BRANCHING IN (LP)	10

(see also Krysia Kocjan)

NATURAL BRIDGE BUNCH

69	Atlantic 584 231	Pig Snoots Pts 1 & 2	4

NATURAL FOUR

75	Atlantic K 56142	HEAVEN RIGHT HERE ON EARTH (LP)	10

NATURAL GAS

76	Private Stock PVT 71	The Right Time/Miracle Mile	4
76	Private Stock PSS 1	NATURAL GAS (EP, promo-only)	7
76	Private Stock PVLP 1007	NATURAL GAS (LP)	10

(see also Badfinger, Blue Goose, Humble Pie, Uriah Heep, Quiver)

NATURALS (U.S.)

55	MGM SP 1123	The Finger Of Suspicion Points At You/You Forgot To Remember	5
57	MGM MGM 939	The Buccaneers/The Ballad Of Sir Lancelot	4

(see also Debbie Reynolds)

NATURALS (U.K.)
64	Parlophone R 5116	Daisy Chain/That Girl	5
64	Parlophone R 5165	I Should Have Known Better/Didn' I?	5
64	Parlophone R 5202	It Was You/Look At Me Now	5
65	Parlophone R 5257	Blue Roses/Shame On You	8

NATURALS (U.K.)
| 82 | Logo GO 414 | Six Girls And Alice/Your Bravery (p/s) | 4 |

NATURE ZONE
| 76 | London HLU 10537 | Porcupine/Rhythm Will Keep Us Together | 4 |

NAUGHTIEST GIRL WAS A MONITOR
| 80 | Aardvark STEAL 4 | All The Naked Heroes/Wax Museum/West Street (p/s) | 4 |
| 81 | Illuminating/KSUNGWAM 1 | Front/Sensation — No Sensation/Synthesizer, The Story So Far (p/s) | 4 |

JERRY NAYLOR
| 61 | Top Rank JAR 591 | Stop Your Crying/You're Thirteen | 10 |
| 67 | Stateside SS 2029 | Sweet Violets/Temptation Leads Me | 4 |

SHEL NAYLOR
| 63 | Decca F 11776 | How Deep Is The Ocean/La Bamba | 10 |
| 64 | Decca F 11856 | One Fine Day/It's Gonna Happen Soon | 70 |

(see also Lieutenant Pigeon, Stavely Makepiece)

NAZARETH
72	Pegasus PGS 2	Dear John/Friends	18
72	Pegasus PGS 4	Morning Dew/Spinning Top	20
72	Pegasus PGS 5	If You See My Baby/Hard Luck	20
73	Mooncrest MOON 1	Broken Down Angel/Witchdoctor Woman	6
73	Mooncrest MOON 9	Bad Bad Boy/Hard Living/Spinning Top (some in p/s)	8/4
73	Mooncrest MOON 14	This Flight Tonight/Called Her Name	5
74	Mooncrest MOON 22	Shang'hai'd In Shang'hai/Love, Now You're Gone	5
74	Mooncrest MOON 37	Love Hurts/Down	5
75	Mooncrest MOON 44	Hair Of The Dog/Too Bad, Too Bad	6
75	Mooncrest MOON 47	My White Bicycle/Miss Misery	4
75	Mountain TOP 3	Holy Roller/Railroad Boy	4
76	Mountain TOP 8	Carry Out Feelings/Lift The Lid	4
76	Mountain TOP 14	You're The Violin/Loretta	4
76	Mountain TOP 21	I Don't Want To Go On Without You/Good Love	4
77	Mountain TOP 22	Somebody To Roll/Vancouver Shakedown	4
77	Mountain NAZ 1	HOT TRACKS (EP, p/s)	5
78	Mountain NAZ 2	Gone Dead Train/Greens/Desolation Road (p/s)	6
78	Mountain TOP 37	Place In Your Heart/Kentucky Fried Blues	4
79	Mountain NAZ 3	May The Sunshine/Expect No Mercy (p/s)	5
79	Mountain NAZ 4	Whatever You Want Babe/Telegram (p/s, some on purple vinyl)	10/5
79	Mountain TOP 45	Star/Born To Love (p/s)	5
80	Mountain TOP 50	Holiday/Ship Of Dreams	4
81	NEMS BSD 1	LIVE (double pack, gatefold p/s)	6
81	NEMS NES 301	Dressed To Kill/Pop The Silo (p/s)	5
81	NEMS NES 302	Morning Dew (Live)/Juicy Lucy (p/s)	5
82	NEMS Int. NIS 101	Love Leads To Madness/Take The Rap (p/s)	4
83	NEMS Int. NIS 102	Games/You Love Another (p/s)	5
83	NEMS Int. NIS 103	Dream On/Juicy Lucy (p/s)	4
83	Mountain NEP 2	HOT TRACKS (reissue, picture disc)	4
84	Vertigo VER 13	Ruby Tuesday/Sweetheart Tree (p/s)	5
84	Vertigo VERX 13	Ruby Tuesday/Sweetheart Tree/This Month's Messiah/Do You Think (12", p/s)	8
71	Pegasus PEG 10	NAZARETH (LP)	20
72	Pegasus PEG 14	EXERCISES (LP, gatefold sleeve)	16
72	Mooncrest CREST 10	NAZARETH (LP, reissue)	12
72	Mooncrest CREST 14	EXERCISES (LP, reissue in gatefold sleeve)	10

(see also Dan McCafferty, Sensational Alex Harvey Band, Spirit)

NAZIS AGAINST FASCISM
| 80 | Truth TRUTH 1 | Sid Did It (Intelligible)/Sid Did It (Radio Version) (p/s, 2 different issues) | 6 |

NAZZ
68	Atlantic 584 224	Open My Eyes/Hello It's Me (withdrawn, promos may exist £40+)	
68	Screen Gems SGC 219001	Open My Eyes/Hello It's Me	10
69	Screen Gems SGC 219002	Hello It's Me/Crowded	8
69	Screen Gems SGC 219003	Not Wrong Long/Under The Ice	10
68	Screen Gems SGC 221001	NAZZ (LP)	25

(see also Todd Rundgren)

N' BETWEENS
(see under In-Be-Tweens)

CHRIS NEAL
| 71 | Fly BUG 15 | Blame It All On Eve/All The Time In The World (p/s) | 5 |

JOHNNY NEAL & STARLINERS
| 65 | Pye 7N 15388 | And I Will Love You/Walk Baby Walk | 40 |
| 70 | Parlophone R 5870 | Put Your Hand In The Hand/Now | 4 |

TOMMY NEAL
| 68 | Vocalion VL 9290 | Goin' To A Happening/Tee Ta | 10 |

NEARLY NORMAL
| 82 | Insurrection Now! IN 1 | Bedtime/Die Baby Die (p/s) | 5 |

NEAT CHANGE
| 68 | Decca F 12809 | I Lied To Auntie May/Sandman (some copies maybe in foldout p/s) | 30/15 |

(see also Peter Banks)

NECROMANDUS
90   Reflection MM 09   QUICKSAND DREAM (LP, 500 only) 15

NED'S ATOMIC DUSTBIN
90   Chapter 22 CHAP 48   Kill Your Television (p/s) 4

BERNIE NEE
58   Philips PB 794   Lend Me Your Comb/Medal Of Honour 12
     (see also Bernie Knee)

LOUIS NEEFS
69   Columbia DB 8561   Jennifer Jennings/I Love You 15

ELGIN NEELY
65   Vogue V 9240   Four Walls/I Could Be 6

NEGATIVES
80   Aardvark STEAL 1   Electric Waltz/Money Talk (p/s) 4

NEIL
84   WEA YZP 10   Hole In My Shoe/Hurdy Gurdy Mushroom Man (picture disc) 4

FRED NEIL
68   Elektra EKSN 45036   Candy Man/The Water Is Wide 4
69   Capitol CL 15616   Everybody's Talkin'/Badi Da 4
65   Elektra EKS 7293   BLEECKER AND MacDOUGAL (LP) 10

DON NEILSON
60   Philips BF 1058   The House Is Haunted/For All We Know 4
63   Piccadilly 7N 35103   I Will Live My Life For You/How Do You Keep From Crying 4

NEKTAR
73   United Artists NEK 1   What Ya Gonna Do?/Day In The Life Of A Preacher Pt. One (Edit) (p/s) 5
74   United Artists UP 35706   Fidgety Queen/Little Boy 4
75   United Artists UP 35853   Astral Man/Nelly The Elephant 4
73   U. Artists UAD 60041/2   SOUNDS LIKE THIS (2-LP) 15
74   United Artists UAS 29499   A TAB IN THE OCEAN (LP, gatefold sleeve) 10
74   United Artists UAS 29545   REMEMBER THE FUTURE (LP) 10
74   United Artists UAG 29680   DOWN TO EARTH (LP) 12
76   Decca SKL-R 5250   RECYCLED (LP) 10

BILL NELSON('S RED NOISE)
79   Harvest HAR 5176   Furniture Music/Wondertoys That Last Forever/Acquitted By Mirrors
                              (p/s, red vinyl) 4
79   Harvest HAR 5183   Revolt Into Style/Out Of Touch (p/s, blue vinyl) 4
80   Cocteau COQ 1   DO YOU DREAM IN COLOUR (EP) 4
82   Mercury WILL 22   Youth Of Nation On Fire/Be My Dynamo//Rooms With Brittle Views/All My
                              Wives Were Iron (double pack, gatefold p/s) (solo) 5
82   Mercury WILL 44   Eros Arriving/Haunting In My Head//Flesh/He And Sleep Were Brothers
                              (double pack) (solo) 5
84   Cocteau COQP 15   Acceleration/Hard Facts From The Fiction Department/Acceleration (Short)/
                              Acceleration (Long) (12" picture disc) (solo) 7
85   Cocteau JEAN 1   PERMANENT FLAME SINGLES BOX (box set of 5 singles) 10
71   Smile LAF 2182/HG 116   NORTHERN DREAM (LP, 250 only in gatefold sleeve & booklet, some no'd) 70
71   Smile LAF 2182/HG 116   NORTHERN DREAM (LP, repressing, gatefold sleeve) 12
85   Cocteau JEAN 2   TRIAL BY INTIMACY (LP, box set) 30
86   Butt BUTT 002   NORTHERN DREAM (LP, reissue, different sleeve) 10
     (see also Astral Navigations, Be Bop Deluxe)

CLARE NELSON
59   MGM MGM 1025   The Valley Of Love/You Are My Sunshine 5

DAVID NELSON
64   Philips BF 1321   Somebody Loves Me/Well I Have 8

EARL NELSON
59   London HLW 8950   No Time To Cry/Come On 10
59   London HLW 8950   No Time To Cry/Come On (78) 15

OZZIE & HARRIET NELSON
59   London HA-P 2145   OZZIE AND HARRIET NELSON (LP) 25

RICK(Y) NELSON
57   HMV POP 355   I'm Walkin'/A Teenager's Romance (gold or silver label) 100/60
57   HMV POP 355   I'm Walkin'/A Teenager's Romance (78) 40
57   HMV POP 390   You're My One And Only Love/BARNEY KESSEL: Honey Rock 60
57   HMV POP 390   You're My One And Only Love/BARNEY KESSEL: Honey Rock (78) 35
57   London HLP 8499   Have I Told You Lately That I Love You/Be-Bop Baby 25
57   London HLP 8499   Have I Told You Lately That I Love You/Be-Bop Baby (78) 15
58   London HLP 8542   Stood Up/Waitin' In School 18
58   London HLP 8542   Stood Up/Waitin' In School (78) 15
58   London HLP 8594   Believe What You Say/My Bucket's Got A Hole In It 15
58   London HLP 8594   Believe What You Say/My Bucket's Got A Hole In It (78) 12
58   London HLP 8670   Poor Little Fool/Don't Leave Me This Way 8
58   London HLP 8670   Poor Little Fool/Don't Leave Me This Way (78) 15
58   London HLP 8732   Someday/I Got A Feeling 6
58   London HLP 8732   Someday/I Got A Feeling (78) 15
58   London HLP 8738   Lonesome Town/My Babe 10
58   London HLP 8738   Lonesome Town/My Babe (78) 15
59   London HLP 8817   It's Late/Never Be Anyone Else But You (silver top label) 8
59   London HLP 8817   It's Late/Never Be Anyone Else But You (78) 18
     (the above 45s originally came with triangular centres; later round centre pressings are worth half to two thirds the value)
59   London HLP 8894   Just A Little Too Much/Sweeter Than You (unreleased)

59	London HLP 8927	Just A Little Too Much/Sweeter Than You	6
59	London HLP 8927	Just A Little Too Much/Sweeter Than You (78)	20
59	London HL 7081	Just A Little Too Much/Sweeter Than You (export issue)	8
60	London HLP 9021	I Wanna Be Loved/Mighty Good	7
60	London HLP 9021	I Wanna Be Loved/Mighty Good (78)	30
60	London HLP 9121	Young Emotions/Right By My Side	6
60	London HLP 9121	Young Emotions/Right By My Side (78)	40
60	London HLP 9188	Yes, Sir, That's My Baby/I'm Not Afraid	6
60	London HLP 9188	Yes, Sir, That's My Baby/I'm Not Afraid (78)	50
61	London HLP 9260	You Are The Only One/Milk Cow Blues	10
61	London HLP 9347	Hello Mary Lou/Travelin' Man	6
61	London HLP 9440	Everlovin'/A Wonder Like You	6

(the above singles were credited to Ricky Nelson; all subsequent singles were credited to Rick Nelson unless stated)

62	London HLP 9524	Young World/Summertime	6
62	London HLP 9583	Teen Age Idol/I've Got My Eyes On You (And I Like What I See)	6
63	London HLP 9648	It's Up To You/I Need You	6
63	Brunswick 05885	I Got A Woman/You Don't Love Me Anymore	6
63	Brunswick 05889	String Along/Gypsy Woman	7
63	Brunswick 05895	Fools Rush In/Down Home	6
64	Brunswick 05900	For You/That's All She Wrote	6
64	Liberty LIB 66004	Today's Teardrops/Thank You Darling	8
64	Brunswick 05908	The Very Thought Of You/I Wonder	6
64	Brunswick 05918	Lonely Corner/There's Nothing I Can Say	6
64	Brunswick 05924	A Happy Guy/Don't Breathe A Word	6
65	Brunswick 05939	Come Out Dancin'/Yesterday's Love	8
66	Brunswick 05964	You Just Can't Quit/Louisiana Man (as Ricky Nelson)	10
66	Liberty LIB 12033	I Need You/Wonder Like You	5
69	MCA MU 1106	She Belongs To Me/Promises	4
70	MCA MU 1124	Red Balloon/I Shall Be Released	5
71	MCA MU 1135	Life/California (with Stone Canyon Band)	5
72	MCA MU 1147	Love Minus Zero: No Limit/Gypsy Pilot (with Stone Canyon Band)	4
72	MCA MU 1165	Garden Party/So Long Mama	5
73	MCA MUS 1181	Palace Guard/A Flower Opens Gently By Itself	4
73	MCA MUS 1225	Lifestream/Evil Woman Child	4
74	MCA MCA 126	Windfall/Legacy (with Stone Canyon Band)	4
74	MCA MCA 144	One Night Stand/Lifestream (with Stone Canyon Band)	4
75	MCA MCA 198	Try (Try To Fall In Love)/Louisiana Belle (with Stone Canyon Band)	4
77	Epic S EPC 5821	You Can't Dance/It's Another Day	4
58	London REP 1141	RICKY PART 1 (EP)	25
58	London REP 1142	RICKY PART 2 (EP)	25
58	London REP 1143	RICKY PART 3 (EP)	25
58	London REP 1144	RICKY PART 4 (EP)	25
59	London REP 1168	RICKY NELSON PART 1 (EP)	25
59	London REP 1169	RICKY NELSON PART 2 (EP)	25
59	London REP 1170	RICKY NELSON PART 3 (EP)	25
59	London REP 1200	RICKY SINGS AGAIN PART 1 (EP)	25
59	London REP 1201	RICKY SINGS AGAIN PART 2 (EP)	25
60	London REP 1238	I GOT A FEELING (EP)	25
60	London REP 1249	RICKY SINGS SPIRITUALS (EP)	22
61	London REP 1300	RICKY NELSON PART 4 (EP)	30

(the above EPs were credited to Ricky Nelson; all subsequent EPs were credited to Rick Nelson)

62	London REP 1339	IT'S A YOUNG WORLD (EP)	20
63	London REP 1362	IT'S UP TO YOU (EP)	20
63	Brunswick OE 9502	ONE BOY TOO LATE (EP)	20
64	Liberty LEP 4001	SINGS FOR YOU (EP)	20
64	Liberty LEP 4019	THAT'S ALL (EP)	30
65	Liberty LEP 4028	I'M IN LOVE AGAIN (EP)	35
65	Brunswick OE 9512	HAPPY GUY (EP)	20
57	London HA-P 2080	RICKY (LP)	40
58	London HA-P 2119	RICKY NELSON (LP)	40
59	London HA-P 2159	RICKY SINGS AGAIN (LP)	35
59	London HA-P 2206	SONGS BY RICKY (LP)	35
60	London HA-P 2290	MORE SONGS BY RICKY (LP, gatefold sleeve, also stereo SAH-P 6102)	30/40
61	London HA-P 2379	RICK IS 21 (LP, also stereo SAH-P 6179)	30/40

(the above LPs were credited to Ricky Nelson; all subsequent LPs were credited to Rick Nelson)

62	London HA-P 2445	ALBUM SEVEN (LP, also stereo SAH-P 6236)	30/35
63	London HA-P 8066	IT'S UP TO YOU (LP)	30
63	Brunswick LAT 8545	FOR YOUR SWEET LOVE (LP, also stereo STA 8545)	25/30
64	Brunswick LAT/STA 8562	RICKY SINGS "FOR YOU" (LP, mono/stereo)	25/30
64	Liberty LBY 3027	MILLION SELLERS (LP)	20
64	Brunswick LAT/STA 8581	THE VERY THOUGHT OF YOU (LP)	25
64	Brunswick LAT/STA 8596	SPOTLIGHT ON RICK (LP)	25
65	Brunswick LAT/STA 8615	BEST ALWAYS (LP)	25
65	Brunswick LAT/STA 8630	LOVE AND KISSES (LP)	25
66	Brunswick LAT/STA 8657	BRIGHT LIGHTS, COUNTRY MUSIC (LP)	25
67	Brunswick LAT/STA 8680	COUNTRY FEVER (LP)	30
68	Liberty LBL 83020	MILLION SELLERS (LP, reissue)	10
68	MCA MUP(S) 302	ANOTHER SIDE OF RICK (LP)	15
70	MCA MUPS 409	IN CONCERT (LP, with Stone Canyon Band)	14
71	MCA MUPS 422	RICK SINGS NELSON (LP, with Stone Canyon Band)	12
72	MCA MUPS 440	RUDY THE FIFTH (LP, with Stone Canyon Band)	12
73	MCA MDKS 8009	GARDEN PARTY (LP, gatefold sleeve, with Stone Canyon Band)	10
74	MCA MCG 3516	WINDFALL (LP)	10
77	Epic EPC 81102	INTAKES (LP)	10

SANDY NELSON

| 59 | Top Rank JAR 197 | Teen Beat/Big Jump | 6 |

Sandy NELSON

59	London HLP 9015	Drum Party/The Big Noise From Winnetka	8
60	London HLP 9214	I'm Walkin'/Bouncy (as Sandy Nelson & His Combo)	7
61	London HLP 9377	Get With It/Big Noise From The Jungle	7
61	London HLP 9466	Let There Be Drums/Quite A Beat (as Sandy Nelson On The Drums)	4
62	London HLP 9521	Drums Are My Beat/My Girl Josephine	5
62	London HLP 9558	Drummin' Up A Storm/Drum Stomp	5
62	London HLP 9612	... And Then There Were Drums/Live It Up	5
63	London HLP 9717	Ooh Poo Pah Doo/Feel So Good	6
64	Liberty LIB 66060	Teen Beat '65/Kitty's Theme	5
66	Liberty LIB 12062	Hey Joe/Come On Let's Go	5
60	Top Rank JKP 2060	RUSHING FOR PERCUSSION (EP, 2 tracks by Preston Epps)	15
62	London REP 1337	LET THERE BE DRUMS (EP)	15
63	London REP 1371	IN THE MOOD (EP)	15
65	Liberty LEP 4033	PLAYS ROCKHOUSE (EP)	12
60	London HA-P 2260	TEEN BEAT (LP, also stereo SAH-P 6082)	20/25
61	London HA-P 2425	LET THERE BE DRUMS (LP, also stereo SAH-P 6221)	20/25
62	London HA-P 2446	DRUMS ARE MY BEAT! (LP, also stereo SAH-P 6237)	18/22
62	London HA-P/SH-P 8009	DRUMMIN' UP A STORM (LP)	18/22
63	London HA-P/SH-P 8029	COMPELLING PERCUSSION (LP)	15
63	London HA-P/SH-P 8051	TEENAGE HOUSE PARTY (LP)	20
65	Liberty LBY 3007	SANDY NELSON PLAYS (LP)	12
65	Liberty LBY 3035	LIVE IN LAS VEGAS (LP)	12
66	Liberty LBY 3061	DRUMS A GO-GO (LP)	12
66	Liberty (S)LBY 3080	SUPERDRUMS (LP)	12
67	Liberty LBL/LBS 83043E	THE BEAT GOES ON (LP)	10
68	Liberty LBL/LBS 83094E	SOUL DRUMS (LP)	10
68	Liberty LBL/LBS 83110E	BOOGALOO BEAT (LP)	10
68	Liberty LBL/LBS 83131E	SUPERDRUMS (LP, reissue, different sleeve)	10
69	Liberty LBL/LBS 83165E	ROCK'N'ROLL REVIVAL (LP)	10
70	Liberty LBS 83302E	GROOVY (LP)	10

TERRY NELSON (& FIREBALLS)

63	Dice CC 23	Run Run Run/Bonita (as Terry Nelson & Fireballs)	7
64	Dice CC 25	Bulldog Push/Pretty Little Girl (as Terry Nelson & Fireballs)	7
64	Dice CC 27	Tomorrow Will Soon Be Here/My Blue Eyed Baby	7
67	Blue Beat BB 326	Help, Nobody Wants To Know/PRINCE BUSTER: Johnny Dollar	8
70s	Halagala HG 19	That True Love Must Be Me/Bulldog Walk	5

WILLIE NELSON

63	Liberty LIB 55532	Half A Man/The Last Letter	6
64	Liberty LIB 55697	Opportunity To Cry/River Boy	6
69	RCA RCA 1867	My Own Peculiar Way/Natural To Be Gone	4
66	RCA Victor RD 7749	COUNTRY WILLIE (LP)	12
66	Liberty (S)LBY 1240	AND THEN I WROTE (LP)	16
69	RCA RD 7997	TEXAS IN MY SOUL (LP)	12

NELSON TRIO

57	Oriole CB 1360	Tear It Up/Roll The Carpet Up	6
60	London HLL 9019	All In Good Time/The Town Crier	7

CHIITRA NEOGY

68	Gemini GMX 5030	THE PERFUMED GARDEN (LP)	20

NEO MAYA

67	Pye 7N 17371	I Won't Hurt You/U.F.O.	40

NEON HEARTS

77	Neon Hearts NEON 1	Venus Eccentric/Regulations (8" p/s)	8

NEPTUNE'S EMPIRE

71	Polymax PXX 01	NEPTUNE'S EMPIRE (LP, private press)	80

NERO & GLADIATORS

61	Decca F 11329	Entry Of The Gladiators/Boots	8
61	Decca F 11367	In The Hall Of The Mountain King/The Trek To Rome	8
61	Decca F 11413	Czardas/That's A Long Time Ago	8
	(see also Laurie Jay, Gladiators, State Of Mickey & Tommy)		

NERVE

67	Page One POF 019	No. 10 Downing Street/Georgie's March	6
68	Page One POF 055	Magic Spectacles/Come The Day	12
68	Page One POF 081	It Is/Mystery Lady	12
68	Page One POF 097	Piece By Piece/Satisfying Kind	8
	(see also Lovin')		

NERVES

78	Lightning GIL 520	TV Adverts/Sex Education	4
81	Good Vibrations BIG 3	NOTRE DEMO (LP, official bootleg, foldover sleeve; [matrix A1])	12

NERVOUS CHOIR

89	Cathexis CRN 5407	O'David/Tonight We Start On Witches/Alsations/Introducing (p/s, with inserts)	4

NERVOUS NORVUS

56	London HLD 8338	Ape Call/Wild Dog Of Kentucky (gold label lettering, later silver)	75/50
56	London HLD 8338	Ape Call/Wild Dog Of Kentucky (78)	5
57	London HLD 8383	Dig/Bullfrog Hop (gold or silver label)	100/50
57	London HLD 8383	Dig/Bullfrog Hop (78)	7
62	Salvo SLO 1812	Does A Chinese Chicken Have A Pigtail/ROD BARTON: Dear Old San Francisco	20

JIM NESBIT

65	Vocalion V 9241	Tiger In My Tank/I Can't Stand This Living Alone	5

MICHAEL NESMITH & FIRST NATIONAL BAND

68	Dot DOT 111	Don't Cry Now/Tapioca Tundra (unissued)	
70	RCA RCA 2001	Joanne/The Crippled Lion	5
71	RCA RCA 2053	Silver Moon/Lady Of The Valley	5
71	RCA RCA 2086	Nevada Fighter/Here I Am	5
76	RCA RCA 2692	Silver Moon/Lady Of The Valley (reissue)	4
76	Island IEP 4	I Fall To Pieces/Silver Moon/Some Of Shelley's Blues/Joanne (solo, p/s)	5
70	RCA SF 8136	MAGNETIC SOUTH (LP)	15
71	RCA SF 8209	NEVADA FIGHTER (LP)	15
72	RCA SF 8276	TANTAMOUNT TO TREASON VOLUME ONE (LP)	15
73	RCA APL1-0164	PRETTY MUCH YOUR STANDARD RANCH STASH (LP, solo)	10
75	Island ILPS 9428	THE PRISON (LP, boxed with book, unreleased in U.K.)	
77	Island ILPS 9439	AND THE HITS JUST KEEP ON COMIN' (LP, as Michael Nesmith)	10
77	Island ILPS 9486	FROM A RADIO ENGINE TO A PHOTON WING (LP, as Michael Nesmith)	10

(see also Monkees, Wichita Train Whistle)

NEU

73	United Artists UP 35485	Super/Neuschnee	4
75	United Artists UP 35874	Isi/After Eight	4
72	United Artists UAS 29396	NEU (LP)	10
73	United Artists UAS 29500	NEU II (LP)	10
75	United Artists UAS 29782	NEU '75 (LP)	10

NEUTRONS

74	United Artists UP 35704	Dance Of The Psychedelic Lounge Lizard/Suzy And The Wonder Boy	4
74	United Artists UAG 29652	BLACK HOLE STAR (LP)	12
75	United Artists UAG 29726	TALES FROM THE BLUE COCOONS (LP)	12

(see also Man)

AARON NEVILLE

67	Stateside SS 584	Tell It Like It Is/Why Worry	12
69	B&C CB 107	Tell It Like It Is/Why Worry (reissue)	6
74	Contempo CS 9009	Tell It Like It Is/Why Worry (reissue)	4
67	Liberty LBY 3089	HERE 'TIS (LP)	20

MR. NEW & MR. WU

56	Oriole CB 1343	"Rock 'N Roll Party" Medley (both sides) (78)	5

NEW AGE STEPPERS

80	On-U Sound ONU 1	Fade Away/LONDON UNDERGROUND: Learn A Language (p/s)	7
80	On-U Sound ONULP 1	NEW AGE STEPPERS (LP)	10

NEW-ASIA

82	Situation 2 SIT 2	Central Position/Here + There, Now + Then (p/s)	4

NEWBEATS

64	Hickory 45-1269	Bread And Butter/Tough Little Buggy	5
64	Hickory 45-1282	Everything's Alright/Pink Dally Rue	5
65	Hickory 45-1290	Break Away/Hey O Daddy O	5
65	Hickory 45-1305	The Birds Are For The Bees/Better Watch Your Step	5
65	Hickory 45-1320	I Can't Hear You No More/Little Child	5
65	Hickory 45-1332	My Yesterday Love/Patent On Love	6
66	Hickory 45-1366	Shake Hands (And Come Out Crying)/Too Sweet To Be Forgotten	10
66	Hickory 45-1387	Crying My Heart Out/Short Of Love	15
66	Hickory 45-1422	My Yesterday Love/Patent On Love	6
65	Hickory LPE 1503	NEWBEATS (EP)	10
65	Hickory LPE 1506	AIN'T THAT LOVIN' YOU BABY (EP)	12
66	Hickory LPE 1510	OH GIRLS GIRLS (EP)	15
65	Hickory LPM 120	BREAD AND BUTTER (LP)	12

(see also Dean & Mark)

PHINEAS NEWBORN

61	Columbia 33SX 1311	I LOVE A PIANO (LP, also stereo SCX 3370)	10

NEW BREED

65	Decca F 12295	Friends And Lovers Forever/Unto Us	20

MICKEY NEWBURY

76	Elektra K 12047	American Trilogy/San Francisco Mable Joy	4

NEWBY & JOHNSON

71	Mercury 6052 027	Sweet Happiness/I Want To Give You Everything	4

NEWCASTLE BIG BAND

72	Impulse ISS NBB 106	NEWCASTLE BIG BAND (LP, white labels, 2000 only)	175

(see also Last Exit, Police, Sting)

NEW CHRISTY MINSTRELS

65	CBS EP 6057	THREE WHEELS ON MY WAGON (EP)	7
66	CBS EP 6072	EVERYBODY LOVES SATURDAY NIGHT (EP)	7

(see also Barry McGuire)

NEW COLONY SIX

66	London HLZ 10033	I Confess/Dawn Is Breaking	35
66	Stateside SS 522	I Lie Awake/At The River's Edge	60
68	Mercury MF 1030	I Will Always Think About You/Hold Me With Your Eyes	5
69	Mercury MF 1086	Things I'd Like To Say/Come And Give Your Love To Me	5

NEWCOMERS

72	Stax 2025 063	Pin The Tail On The Donkey/Mannish Boy	4
75	Stax STXS 2023	Keep An Eye On Your Close Friends/(Instrumental Version)	4

NEW CROSS

70s	New Cross Skyline NC 1	No One At All/Cruzin' Downtown (p/s)	4

NEW DREAM
| 72 | Parlophone R 5946 | Turn 21/Someone Like You .... 4 |

DENNIS NEWEY
61	Philips PB 1134	Checkpoint/Title Unknown 5
61	Philips PB 1198	Border Patrol/Yes Yes 4
62	Philips 326588 F	The Nightriders/The Pied Piper 4

NEW FAST AUTOMATIC DAFFODILS
| 90 | Playtime AMUSE 7 | Big (1-sided, die-cut sleeve) .... 4 |

NEW FORMULA
67	Piccadilly 7N 35381	Do It Again A Little Bit Slower/I'm On The Outside Looking In 4
67	Piccadilly 7N 35401	I Want To Go Back There Again/Can't You See That She Loves Me 4
68	Pye 7N 17552	My Baby's Coming Home/Burning In The Background 4
69	Pye 7N 17818	Stay Indoors/Hare Krishna 20

NEW GENERATION
69	Spark SRL 1000	Sadie And Her Magic Mister Garland/Digger 5
69	Spark SRL 1007	Smokey Blues Away/She's A Soldier Boy 8
70	Spark SRL 1019	Police Is Here/Mister C. 4

BOB NEWHART
60	Warner Bros WM 4010	THE BUTTON-DOWN MIND OF BOB NEWHART (LP, also stereo WS 8010) 10
61	Warner Bros WM 4032	THE BUTTON-DOWN MIND STRIKES BACK (LP) 10
62	Warner Bros WM 4055	BEHIND THE BUTTON-DOWN MIND OF BOB NEWHART (LP) 10
63	Warner Bros WM/WS 8110	THE BUTTON-DOWN MIND ON TV (LP) 10
64	Warner Bros WM 8148	NEWHART FACES BOB NEWHART (LP) 10
65	Warner Bros W(W) 1588	THE WINDMILLS ARE WEAKENING (LP) 10

NEW HEARTS
77	CBS 5800	Just Another Teenage Anthem/Blood On The Knife (p/s) 5
78	CBS 6381	Plain Jane/My Young Teacher (p/s) 6
	(see also Secret Affair)	

NEW JERSEY CONNECTION
| 82 | Nitelife LIFE 1 | Love Don't Come Easy/Love Don't Come Easy (Instrumental) (12") .... 8 |

NEW JUMP BAND
| 68 | Domain D 1 | The Only Kind Of Girl/Seven Kinds Of Sweet Lovin' .... 5 |

NEW KIDS ON THE BLOCK
88	CBS 652992-7	Please Don't Go Girl/Whatcha Gonna Do About It (p/s) 4
88	CBS 652992-6	Please Don't Go Girl (Extended)/Please Don't Go Girl (7")/Whatcha Gonna Do About It (12", p/s) 7
88	CBS 652992-2	Please Don't Go Girl (Extended)/Please Don't Go Girl (7")/Whatcha Gonna Do About It (3" CD) 10
89	CBS 653169-7	You Got It (The Right Stuff)/Whatcha Gonna Do About It (p/s) 4
89	CBS 653169-6	You Got It (The Right Stuff) (Extended)/You Got It (The Right Stuff) (Remix)/Whatcha Gonna Do About It (12", p/s) 7
89	CBS 653169-2	You Got It (The Right Stuff) (Extended)/You Got It (The Right Stuff) (Remix)/Whatcha Gonna Do About It (CD) 8
89	CBS XPS 240	HANGIN' TOUGH (flexidisc sampler, red vinyl in A4 card cover) 4

ANTHONY NEWLEY
59	Decca F 11127	I've Waited So Long/Sat'day Night Rock-A-Boogie 6
59	Decca F 11137	Idle On Parade/Idle Rock-A-Boogie 8
59	Decca F 11142	Personality/My Blue Angel 6
59	Decca F 11163	Someone To Love/It's All Over 4
60	Decca F 11194	Why/Anything You Wanna Do 4
60	Decca F 11220	Do You Mind/Girls Were Made To Love And Kiss 4
60	Decca F 11254	If She Should Come To You/Lifetime Of Happiness 4
60	Decca F 11295	Strawberry Fair/A Boy Without A Girl 4
61	Decca F 11331	And The Heavens Cried/Lonely Boy And Pretty Girl 4
61	Decca F 11362	Pop Goes The Weasel/Bee Bom 4
61	Decca F 11376	What Kind Of Fool Am I/Once In A Lifetime 4
62	Decca F 11419	D-Darling/I'll Walk Beside You 4
62	Decca F 11486	That Noise/The Little Golden Clown 4
63	Decca F 11636	There's No Such Thing As Love/She's Just Another Girl 4
63	Decca F 11767	The Father Of Girls/I Love Everything About You 4
64	Decca F 11818	Tribute/Lament To A Hero 4
59	Decca DFE 6566	SINGS FOUR SONGS FROM IDLE ON PARADE (EP) 10
60	Decca DFE 6629	TONY'S HITS (EP) 7
60	Decca DFE 6655	MORE HITS FROM TONY (EP) 7
61	Decca DFE 6687	THIS TIME THE DREAM'S ON ME (EP) 7
60	Decca LK 4343	LOVE IS A NOW AND THEN THING (LP) 12
61	Decca LK 4406	TONY (LP) 10
64	Decca LK 4600	IN MY SOLITUDE (LP) 10
65	Decca LK 4654	NEWLEY DELIVERED (LP) 12
66	RCA Victor RD/SF 7737	WHO CAN I TURN TO (LP, mono/stereo) 10/12
67	RCA Victor RD/SF 7837	NEWLEY RECORDED (LP) 12

ANDY NEWMAN
| 71 | Track 2406 103 | RAINBOW (LP) .... 12 |
| | *(see also Thunderclap Newman)* | |

BRAD NEWMAN
62	Fontana H 357	Somebody To Love/This Time It's Love 5
62	Fontana H 369	Get A Move On/Here And Now And Evermore 5
62	Fontana 267 220TF	Stay By Me/Candy Lips 5
62	Fontana 267 243TF	Point Of No Return/Now I've Lost You 5
63	Fontana 267 273TF	I'll Find You Another Baby/No Man Should Ever Be Alone 4

MINT VALUE £

64	Piccadilly 7N 35174	Please Don't Cry/Every Hour Of Living	4

COLIN NEWMAN
80	Beggars Banquet BEG 48	B/Classic Remains/Alone On Piano (p/s)	5
81	Beggars Banquet BEG 52	Inventory/This Picture (p/s)	5
82	4AD AD 209	We Means We Starts/Not To (Remix) (p/s)	7

(see also Wire)

JIMMY (C.) NEWMAN
57	London HLD 8460	A Fallen Star/I Can't Go On This Way	20
57	London HLD 8460	A Fallen Star/I Can't Go On This Way (78)	8
59	MGM MGM 1009	What'cha Gonna Do/So Soon	8
59	MGM MGM 1009	What'cha Gonna Do/So Soon (78)	15
59	MGM MGM 1037	Grin And Bear It/The Ballad Of Baby Doe	7
60	MGM MGM 1085	A Lovely Work Of Art/What About Me	6
61	MGM MGM 1112	Now That You're Gone/Wanting You With Me Tonight	4
59	MGM MGM EP 706	GRIN AND BEAR IT — COUNTRY AND WESTERN STYLE (EP)	25

JOE NEWMAN SEXTET
57	Vogue Coral Q 72244	Cocktails For Two/Later For The Happenings	4
57	Vogue Coral LVA 9052	HAPPY CATS (LP)	10

LIONEL NEWMAN ORCHESTRA
58	Columbia DB 4150	Hey! Eula/Two Butterflies	6
58	Columbia DB 4150	Hey! Eula/Two Butterflies (78)	5

PAUL NEWMAN
66	Mercury MF 969	Ain't You Got A Heart	10

RANDY NEWMAN
68	Reprise RS 20692	Love Story/I Think It's Going To Rain Today	5
70	Reprise RS 20945	Gone Dead Train/JACK NITZSCHE: Harry Flowers	5
72	Reprise K 14155	Lonely At The Top/My Old Kentucky Home	4
72	Reprise K 14190	Sail Away/Political Science	4
68	Reprise R(S)LP 6286	RANDY NEWMAN CREATES SOMETHING NEW UNDER THE SUN (LP)	12
70	Reprise RSLP 6373	12 SONGS (LP)	10

(see also Harry Nilsson)

TOM NEWMAN
68	Decca F 12795	Soul Thing/Let The Good Times Roll	6
75	Virgin VS 130	Don't Treat Your Woman Bad	4
76	Virgin VS 133	Sleep/Darling Corey	4
76	Virgin VS 141	Ebony Eyes/Draught Guinness	4
77	Decca F 13735	Dance Of The Theena Shee/The Unseelie Court (as Faerie Symphony)	4
75	Virgin V 2022	FINE OLD TOM (LP)	15
75	Virgin V 2042	LIVE AT THE ARGONAUT (LP, unreleased, test pressings only)	80
77	Decca TXS 123	FAERIE SYMPHONY (LP)	18

(see also July)

TONY NEWMAN
68	Decca F 12795	Soul Thing/Let The Good Times Roll	8
70	Decca F 13041	Soul Thing/Let The Good Times Roll (reissue)	5

NEW MODEL
83	Mr. Clean MERC 001	Chilean Warning/The World Thru Our Eyes/Totalitarian Terror (p/s, some in 7" x 10"folder)	10/6

NEW MODEL ARMY
83	Shout QS 002/QF 001	Bittersweet/Betcha/Tension (p/s, some with flexi "Fashion"/"The Cause")	15/6
83	Abstract ABS 0020	Great Expectations/Waiting (p/s)	25
84	Abstract ABS 0028	The Price/1984 (p/s)	12
85	EMI NMA 1	No Rest/Heroin (p/s)	4
85	EMI TC NMA 1	No Rest/Heroin (cassette)	6
85	EMI 12 NMA 1	No Rest/Heroin (12", p/s)	7
85	EMI 12 NMAD 1/PSLP 387	No Rest/Heroin//Vengeance (live)/The Price (live)/No Greater Love (live) (12", double pack)	15
85	EMI NMA 2	Better Than Them/No Sense/Adrenalin/Trust (p/s)	5
85	EMI NMAD 2/NMA 22	The Acoustic EP: Better Than Them/No Sense/Adrenalin/Trust (double pack, gatefold sleeve)	8
85	EMI 12 NMA 2	The Acoustic EP: Better Than Them/No Sense/Adrenalin/Trust (12", p/s)	15
85	EMI NMA 3	Brave New World/R.I.P. (p/s)	6
85	EMI 12 NMA 3	Brave New World (Extended)/R.I.P. (Alternative Mix)/Brave New World 2 (12", p/s)	8
85	EMI 12 NMAD 3/PSLP 395	Brave New World (Extended)/R.I.P. (Alternative Mix)/Brave New World 2// Young, Gifted & Skint (live)/Sex (The Black Angel) (live) (12", double pack)	15
86	EMI NMA 4	51st State/Ten Commandments (p/s)	5
86	EMI 12 NMA 4	51st State/Ten Commandments/Liberal Education (live)/No Rest (live)/ No Man's Land (live) (12", p/s)	8
86	EMI 12 NMAD 4/PSLP 348	51st State/Ten Commandments//Liberal Education (live)/No Rest (live)/ No Man's Land (live) (12", double pack)	15
86	Abstract ABS 090	Great Expectations/Waiting (p/s, blue vinyl, reissue)	4
87	EMI NMA 5	Poison Street/Courage (p/s, red vinyl)	20
87	EMI NMA 5	Poison Street/Courage (p/s, black vinyl)	4
87	EMI 12 NMA 5	Poison Street (Extended)/Poison Street (7" Mix)/Courage (12", p/s)	8
87	EMI 12 NMAD 5/ PSLP 1002	Poison Street (Extended)/Poison Street (7" Mix)/Courage//All Of This (live)/ My Country (live) (12", double pack)	15
87	EMI NMA 6	White Coats/The Charge/Chinese Whispers/My Country (p/s, black vinyl)	4
87	EMI 12 NMAG 6	White Coats (Full Version)/The Charge/Chinese Whispers/ My Country (live) (12", poster sleeve)	8
89	EMI NMAG 7	Stupid Questions/Nothing Touches (gatefold p/s)	4
89	EMI 12 NMAP 7	Stupid Questions/Nothing Touches/Stupid Questions (Stupid Mix)/ Betcha (live) (12", poster p/s)	7

NEW MODEL ARMY

89	EMI NMAG 8	Vagabonds (Edit)/Deadeye (gatefold p/s, shrinkwrapped with free badge) 4
89	EMI NMAP 8	Vagabonds (Edit)/Deadeye (picture disc) 4
89	EMI NMAPD 9	Green And Grey/The Charge (live) (picture disc) 4
90	EMI 10 NMA 10	Get Me Out (12" Mix)/Prison/Get Me Out (7")/Waiting (live)
		(10", numbered p/s) 6
80s	House Of Dolls HOD 007	125mph (Special Remix) (free with 'House Of Dolls' magazine, issue 21) 8/5
81	private	ARIES ENTERPRISES (various artists cassette) .... 25+

(see also Joolz)

NEW MONITORS
71	Buddah 2011 118	Fence Around Your Heart/Have You Seen Her 4

NEW MUSIK
79	GTO GT 255	Straight Lines/On Islands (10") 7

NEW ORDER (U.K.)
81	Factory FAC 3312	Ceremony (Re-recording)/In A Lonely Place (Extended) (12", p/s) 8
81	Factory FAC 53	Procession/Everything's Gone Green (p/s with white writing) 5
82	Factory FAC 51B	Rocking Carol/Ode To Joy (flexidisc given away at Hacienda, 4,000 only) 10
83	Factory FAC 93	Confusion (Edit)/(Same) (DJ only) (p/s) 18
84	Factory FAC 103	Thieves Like Us (Edit)/Lonesome Tonight (Edit) (DJ only) (p/s) 12
88	Factory FAC 73RD	Blue Monday 1988/Blue Monday (DJ-only mix) (12", p/s, DJ only) 10
89	Factory FAC 263DJ	Round & Round (Ben Grosse Mix)/(12" Mix)/(Detroit Mix) (12", p/s, DJ only) ... 10
89	Factory FAC 273/7	Run 2 (Edit)/MTO (Edit) (DJ only, p/s, 500 only) 12
89	Factory FAC 273	Run 2/Run 2 (Extended Version)/MTO/MTO (Minus Mix) (12" p/s,
		with inner sleeve, 20,000 only) 14
87	Strange Fruit SFPSC 001	PEEL SESSIONS 1.6.82 (cassette) 7
85	Factory FACTUS 12C	POWER, CORRUPTION & LIES (cassette with 2 extra tracks) 10
86	Factory FACT 150SP	BROTHERHOOD (LP, limited metallic sleeve) 10
87	Factory FACT 200	THE GATEFOLD SUBSTANCE (LP, numbered gatefold sleeve, 1,000 only) ... 25
87	Factory FACT 200C	SUBSTANCE (cassette, 200 only in box set with insert) 25
87	Factory FACD 150SP	BROTHERHOOD (CD, with "State Of The Nation" & metallic booklet) 15

(see also Joy Division)

NEW ORDER
80s	Come Organisation	BRADFORD RED LIGHT DISTRICT (LP) .... 20+

(see also Come)

NEW ORLEANS ALL STAR BAND
56	Vogue V 2380	Struttin' With Some Barbecue/Basin Street Blues 4
56	Vogue V 2368	Christopher Columbus/Bugle Call Rag 4

NEW ORLEANS BOOTBLACKS
54	Columbia SCM 5090	Flat Foot/Mad Dog 6

NEW ORLEANS WILD CATS
62	Storyville A 45048	Roll Along Prairie Moon/Well Well Well 4

NEWPORT JAZZ FESTIVAL ALL STARS
61	London Jazz LTZ-K 15202	NEWPORT JAZZ FESTIVAL ALL STARS (LP, also stereo SAH-K 6116) 10

NEW RELIGION
72	Bamboo BAM 70	In The Black Caribbean/Black Is Black 5
73	Ackee ACK 526	Walk Away Renee/What's It All About 4

NEWS
66	Decca F 12356	The Entertainer/I Count The Tears 6
66	Decca F 12477	This Is The Moment/Ya Ya Da Da 6

(see also Patto)

NEWS FROM BABEL
86	Recommended RÉ 6116	NEWS FROM BABEL (LP, hand-screened sleeve) 10

WAYNE NEWTON
63	Capitol CL 15319	Danke Schoen/Better Now Than Later 4
65	Capitol CL 15380	Comin' On Too Strong/Red Roses For A Blue Lady 4

OLIVIA NEWTON-JOHN
66	Decca F 12396	Till You Say You'll Be Mine/For Ever 100
76	EMI EMI 2519	Don't Stop Believin'/Greensleeves (p/s) 5
77	EMI EMI 2616	Sam/Changes (p/s) 5
80	Jet JET 185	Xanadu/Fool Country (gatefold p/s, with ELO) 6
80	Jet JET 10-185	Xanadu/Fool Country (10" pink vinyl, die-cut p/s, with ELO) 10
80	Jet JETP 196	Magic/Whenever You're Away From Me (picture disc) 6
77	EMI (no cat. no.)	Please Mr. Please/PILOT: Love Is (flexidisc free with 'Record Mirror') 4
71	Pye Int. NSPL 28155	OLIVIA NEWTON-JOHN (LP) 15
72	Pye Int. NSPL 28168	OLIVIA (LP) 12
74	Pye Int. NSPL 28185	MUSIC MAKES MY DAY (LP, blue/black or white/black label) 12
74	EMI EMC 3055	FIRST IMPRESSION (LP) 10
77	EMI EMC 3193	MAKING A GOOD THING BETTER (LP) 10
78	EMI EMAP 789	TOTALLY HOT (LP, picture disc) 15

(see also Toomorrow, Marvin & Farrar)

OLIVIA NEWTON-JOHN & CLIFF RICHARD
80	Jet JET 7002	Suddenly/You Made Me Love You (p/s) 4

(see also Cliff Richard)

NEWTOWN NEUROTICS
79	No Wonder A 45	Hypocrite/You Said No (no p/s, also listed as SRTS-79/CUS/363) 10
80	No Wonder NOW 4	When The Oil Runs Out/Oh No (no p/s, some with sticker & insert) 8/5
82	CNT 4/No Wonder NOW 56	Kick Out The Tories!/Mindless Violence! (p/s) 4
82	CNT CNT 010	Licensing Hours/No Sanctuary (p/s) 5
83	Razor RZS 107	Blitzkrieg Bop/Hypocrite (New Version)/I Remember You (p/s) 4
83	Razor RAZ 6	BEGGARS CAN BE CHOOSERS (LP) 12

NEW VAUDEVILLE BAND

68	Fontana TF 909	Bonnie And Clyde/Uncle Gabriel	4
67	Fontana TFE 17497	NEW VAUDEVILLE BAND (EP)	7
67	Fontana (S)TL 5386	WINCHESTER CATHEDRAL (LP)	10
67	Fontana (S)TL 5430	FINCHLEY CENTRAL (LP)	10

(see also Bonzo Dog Doo Dah Band, Alberts, Alan Klein)

NEW WANDERERS

79	Grapevine GRP 144	This Man In Love/Adam And Eve	4

NEW YORK BLONDES featuring MADAME X

79	London/Bomp HLZ 10574	Little GTO/RODNEY & BRUNETTES: Holocaust On Sunset Boulevard (p/s)	8

(see also Blondie, Debbie Harry)

NEW YORK DOLLS

73	Mercury 6052 402	Jet Boy/Vietnamese Baby	7
74	Mercury 6052 615	Stranded In The Jungle/Who Are The Mystery Girls	7
77	Mercury 6160 008	Jet Boy/Babylon/Who Are The Mystery Girls	5
85	Antler DOLLS 1	Personality Crisis/Subway Train (picture disc)	4
85	Antler DOLLS 2	Looking For A Kiss/Bad Girl (picture disc)	4
73	Mercury 6338 270	NEW YORK DOLLS (LP)	12
74	Mercury 6338 498	TOO MUCH TOO SOON (LP)	12

(see also Johnny Thunders, Heartbreakers, Sylvain Sylvain)

NEW YORK PORT AUTHORITY

77	Invictus INV 5312	I Got It/I Got It (Version)	4

NEW YORK PUBLIC LIBRARY

66	Columbia DB 7948	I Ain't Gonna Eat Out My Heart Anymore/Rejected	20
68	MCA MU 1025	Gotta Get Away/Time Wastin'	8
68	MCA MU 1045	Love Me Two Times/Which Way To Go	8

NEW YORK ROCK & ROLL ENSEMBLE

71	CBS 5292	Running Down The Highway/Law And Order	4
69	Atco 228 932	FAITHFUL FRIENDS (LP)	12
71	CBS 64126	ROLL OVER (LP)	10
72	CBS 64324	FREEDOMBURGER (LP)	10

NIADEM'S GHOST

80s	Hide HIDE 001	IN SHELTERED WINDS (LP)	25

NICE

67	Immediate IM 059	The Thoughts Of Emerlist Davjack/Angel Of Death	5
68	Immediate IM 068	America (2nd Amendment)/The Diamond Hard Blue Apples Of The Moon (some in p/s)	10/4
68	Immediate IM 072	Brandenburger/Happy Freuds	5
71	Charisma CB 132	Country Pie/One Of Those People	4
67	Immediate IMLP/IMSP 016	THE THOUGHTS OF EMERLIST DAVJACK (LP)	12
68	Immediate IMSP 020	ARS LONGA VITA BREVIS (LP)	12
69	Immediate IMSP 026	THE NICE (LP)	10
70	Charisma CAS 1014	THE FIVE BRIDGES SUITE (LP, pink label, gatefold sleeve)	10
71	Charisma CAS 1030	ELEGY (LP, pink label)	10

(see also Keith Emerson, Emerson, Lake & Palmer, Habits, Brian Davison, Refugee, Attack, Jet)

NICK NICELY

80	Voxette VOX 1001	D.C.T. Dreams/Treeline (p/s)	10
81	EMI EMI 5256	Hillyfields (1892)/49 Cigars (p/s)	10

ALBERT NICHOLAS & AL FAIRWEATHER

56	Tempo A 129	How Long Blues/Rose Room	5

PAUL NICHOLAS

68	Polydor 56285	Where Do I Go/Here Comes The Clown	4
69	Polydor 56322	Who Can I Turn To/Sing A Sad Song For Sammy	4
70	Polydor 56374	Freedom City/Run Shaker Life	4

(see also Oscar)

BILLY NICHOLLS

68	Immediate IM 063	Would You Believe/Daytime Girl	10
73	Track 2094 109	Forever's No Time At All/This Song Is Green (with Pete Townshend)	4
67	Immediate IMCP 009	WOULD YOU BELIEVE (LP)	120

JANICE NICHOLLS

63	Decca F 11586	I'll Give It Five/The Wednesbury Madison	6

RED NICHOLS & HIS PENNY SYMPHONY

55	Capitol CL 14365	The Viennese Lantern (Lights Of Vienna)/While You're Away	6
56	Capitol CL 14544	Glory, Glory/Bugler's Lament	4
56	Capitol CL 14560	Corky/The Wail Of The Winds	4
56	Capitol CL 14596	The Beautiful Girls Of Vienna/Speak Easy	4
56	Capitol CL 14617	Cool Tango/Indiana	4
51	Capitol LC 6534	JAZZ TIME (10" LP)	10

STEVIE NICKS

81	WEA K 79231	Stop Draggin' My Heart Around/Kind Of Woman (p/s, with Tom Petty & Heartbreakers)	5
81	WEA K 79265	Leather And Lace/Outside The Rain (p/s)	6
82	WEA K 79264	Edge Of Seventeen/Outside The Rain (p/s)	4
83	WEA U 9870	Stand Back/Garbo (p/s)	4
83	WEA U 9870T	Stand Back/Garbo/Wild Heart (12", p/s)	12
83	WEA X 9590	If Anyone Falls/Gate & Garden (p/s)	4
84	WEA U 9690	Nightbird/Nothing Ever Changes (p/s)	5
86	Parlophone R 6124	Talk To Me/One More Big Time Rock'n'Roll Star (p/s)	4

Stevie NICKS

86	Parlophone 12R 6124	Talk To Me/One More Big Time Rock'n'Roll Star/Imperial Hotel (12", p/s)	8
86	Parlophone R 6110	I Can't Wait/Rock A Little (p/s)	4
86	Parlophone 12R 6110	I Can't Wait/Rock A Little (12", p/s)	10
86	EMI EMI 5574	Has Anyone Ever Written Anything For You?/I Can't Wait (p/s)	4
86	EMI 12EMI 5574	Has Anyone Ever Written Anything For You?/I Can't Wait/ No Spoken Word (12", p/s)	8
89	EMI 12EMP 90	Rooms On Fire/Alice/Has Anyone Ever Written Anything For You? (live) (12", poster p/s)	8
89	EMI CDEM 90	Rooms On Fire/Alice/Has Anyone Ever Written Anything For You? (live) (CD)	8
89	EMI 12EMG 97	Long Way To Go/Real Tears/Long Way To Go (Remix) (12", gatefold p/s)	7
89	EMI CDEM 97	Long Way To Go/Real Tears/No Spoken Word + 1 (3" CD)	7
89	EMI 12EMP 114	Whole Lotta Trouble/Edge Of Seventeen/Beauty & The Beast (Live) (12", poster p/s)	8
91	EMI EMP 203	Sometimes It's A Bitch/Desert Angel (portrait pack)	4
91	EMI 12EMS 214	I Can't Wait (Time Space Mix)/I Can't Wait Dub/Sleeping Angel (12", with photos)	7
89	EMI EMD 1008	THE OTHER SIDE OF THE MIRROR (LP, with hologram)	10
89	EMI CDEMC 1008	THE OTHER SIDE OF THE MIRROR (CD, with hologram)	15

(see also Fleetwood Mac, Buckingham-Nicks)

NICO

65	Immediate IM 003	I'm Not Sayin'/The Last Mile	20
81	Flicknife FLS 206	Vegas/Saeta (p/s)	8
82	Immediate IMS 003	I'm Not Saying/The Last Mile (p/s reissue)	4
82	Half 1/2 1	Procession/All Tomorrow's Parties (p/s)	4
68	Elektra EKL 4029	THE MARBLE INDEX (LP, orange label, also stereo EKS 74029)	20/18
71	Reprise RSLP 6424	DESERTSHORE (LP, with John Cale)	15
71	MGM Select 2353 025	CHELSEA GIRL (LP)	15
74	Island ILPS 9311	THE END (LP)	12
81	Aura AUL 715	DRAMA OF EXILE (LP, colour cover)	10

(see also John Cale, Velvet Underground, Ayers, Cale, Nico & Eno)

JIMMY NICOL (& SHUBDUBS)

64	Pye 7N 15623	Humpty Dumpty/Night Train	12
64	Pye 7N 15666	Husky/Don't Come Back (solo)	10
64	Pye 7N 15699	Baby Please Don't Go/Shub Dubbery (possibly unissued)	20+
65	Decca F 12107	Clementine/Bim Bam (solo)	10

(see also Georgie Fame)

NICOLE

82	CBS A 2365	A Little Peace/Thank You, Merci (art sleeve without photo of artist)	4

NICRA

77	Ogun	LISTEN/HEAR (LP)	20

NIGHTBIRDS

59	Oriole CB 1490	Cat On A Hot Tin Roof/The Square	6

NIGHTBLOOMS

90	Fierce FRIGHT 041	Crystal Eyes/Never Dream At All (p/s)	12

NIGHTCRAWLERS

67	London HLR 10109	The Little Black Egg/You're Running Wild	25

ROBERT NIGHTHAWK

60s	XX MIN 718	ROBERT NIGHTHAWK (EP)	7

NIGHT-HAWKS

58	Fontana H 120	Cool For Cats/Time Will Tell (78)	5

NIGHTIME FLYER

81	Red Eye EYE 2	Out With A Vengeance/Heavy Metal Rules (p/s)	5

MAXINE NIGHTINGALE

69	Pye 7N 17798	Don't Push Me Baby/Thru' Loving You	6
70	Pye 7N 45046	Love On Borrowed Time/It's A Hurtin' Thing	4
75	United Artists UP 36015	Right Back Where We Started From/Believe In What You Do	4

NIGHTINGALES

81	Rough Trade RT 075	Idiot Strength/Seconds (p/s)	4
82	Cherry Red CHERRY 34	USE YOUR LOAF (EP)	4
85	Vindaloo VILP2X	THIS PACKAGE (12" with flexi, 12", booklet, card & lyric sheet, envelope p/s)	12

(see also Prefects)

NIGHTMARES IN WAX

79	Inevitable INEV 0002	BIRTH OF A NATION (EP, with wraparound p/s)	20
84	KY KY 9	Black Leather/Shangri-La (12", p/s)	18
85	KY KY 9 1/2	Black Leather/Shangri-La/Girls Song (12", different p/s, 3,000 only)	18

(see also Dead Or Alive)

NIGHTRIDERS

66	Polydor 56116	It's Only The Dog/Your Friend	45
66	Polydor	Love Me Right Now (promo only)	60

(see also Mike Sheridan & Nightriders, Mike Sheridan's Lot, Idle Race, Jeff Lynne)

NIGHTSHIFT

65	Piccadilly 7N 35243	Corrine Corrina/Lavender Tree	10
65	Piccadilly 7N 35264	Stormy Monday Blues/That's My Story	12

NIGHT-TIMERS

65	Parlophone R 5355	The Music Played On/Yield Not To Temptation (featuring Herbie Goins)	20

(see also Herbie Goins & Night-Timers)

NIGHTWING

80	Ovation OVS 1209	Barrel Of Pain/Nightwing (p/s)	5

MINT VALUE £

84	Gull GULS 75	Treading Water/Call Your Name (p/s) 4
84	Gull GULS 77	Night Of Mystery/Dressed To Kill (p/s) 4
84	Gull GULS 77T	Night Of Mystery/Dressed To Kill (12", p/s) 8
85	Gull GULS 80	Strangers Are Welcome/Games To Play//The Devil Walks Behind You/
		Cell 151 (double pack, gatefold p/s) 6
79	Ovation OV 1757	SOMETHING IN THE AIR (LP) 10
82	Gull GULP 1036	BLACK SUMMER (LP) 10
83	Gull GULP 1038	STAND UP AND BE COUNTED (LP) 10
83	Gull PGULP 1038	STAND UP AND BE COUNTED (LP, picture disc) 10
85	Gull GULP 1043	NIGHT OF MYSTERY (LP) 10

NIHILIST SPASM BAND
| 85 | United Dairies UD 016 | 1X - X = X (LP) ....15 |

BILL NILE (& HIS GOODTIME BAND)
| 67 | Decca F 12661 | Pashionella Grundy/Bric A Brac Man ....4 |
| 70 | Deram DM 290 | I Try Not To Laugh/Nobody Knows The Trouble ....5 |

WILLY NILLY
| 84 | Ad Hoc AH 1 | On The Spur Of The Moment/Half A Job (p/s, with 'time-table' insert) ....15 |

(HARRY) NILSSON
67	RCA Victor RCA 1632	You Can't Do That/Ten Little Indians 4
68	RCA Victor RCA 1675	One/Sister Marie 4
68	RCA RCA 1707	Everybody's Talkin'/Don't Leave Me 4
68	RCA RCA 1764	Mourning Glory/Rainmaker 4
69	RCA RCA 1864	Maybe/The Puppy Song 4
74	RCA RCA 2459	Many Rivers To Cross/Don't Forget Me 4
75	RCA RCA 2504	Save The Last Dance For Me/All My Life 4
70s	RCA Record Year LB 2	Without You/(other artist) 4
68	RCA Victor RD/SF 7928	PANDEMONIUM SHADOW SHOW (LP) 10
68	RCA RD/SF 7973	AERIAL BALLET (LP) 10
70	RCA SF 8091	NILSSON SINGS NEWMAN (LP, with Randy Newman) 10
72	RCA SF 8166	THE POINT (LP, gatefold sleeve with book) 10
74	Rapple APL1 0220	SON OF DRACULA (LP, soundtrack with Ringo Starr, fold-out sleeve) 10
74	RCA APL 1-0570	PUSSY CATS (LP, features John Lennon, gatefold sleeve) 10
	(see also Randy Newman, Ringo Starr, Cher)	

NILSSON TWINS
| 57 | Capitol CL 14698 | Rain On My Window/I Dance When I Walk ....4 |

LEONARD NIMOY
| 68 | Dot (S)LPD 511 | PRESENTS MR. SPOCK'S MUSIC FROM OUTER SPACE (LP) ....15 |

NINA
| 70 | CBS 4681 | Do You Know How Christmas Trees Are Grown?/The More Things Change .....12 |

NINE BELOW ZERO
| 80 | M&L ML 1 | PACK FAIR AND SQUARE (EP) ....5 |
| 81 | A&M AMS 8110 | Three Times Enough/Doghouse (p/s, yellow vinyl) ....4 |

NINE DAYS WONDER
| 71 | Harvest SHSP 4014 | NINE DAYS WONDER (LP) ....30 |
| | (see also Kilburn & High Roads) | |

999
77	Labritain LAB 999	I'm Alive/Quite Disappointing (p/s) 8
77	United Artists UP 36299	Nasty Nasty/No Pity (p/s, green vinyl) 6
77	United Artists FREE 7	Nasty Nasty/No Pity (78rpm promo) 30
78	Labritain 12 FREE 10	Waiting/Action (12", mail order freebie) 10
78	United Artists UP 36399	Emergency/My Street Stinks (p/s) 5
78	United Artists UP 36376	Me And My Desire/Crazy (p/s) 4
78	United Artists UP 36435	Feelin' Alright With The Crew/Titanic (My Over) Reaction (p/s) 4
78	United Artists UP 36467	Homicide/Soldier (p/s, some on green vinyl) 6/5
79	United Artists UP 36519	I'm Alive/Quite Disappointing (p/s, reissue) 5
79	Radar ADA 46	Found Out Too Late/Lie Lie Lie (p/s) 4
80	Polydor POSP 99	Trouble/Love Made A Fool Of You (p/s) 4
81	Albion INO 1011	Obsessed/Change/Lie, Lie, Lie (live) (p/s, with patch; some shrinkwrapped) 4/5
81	Albion ION 1017	Li'l Red Riding Hood/Waiting For Your Number To Be Called/I Ain't Gonna
		Tell Ya (live) (p/s, with stencil; some shrinkwrapped) 4/5
81	Albion ION 1023	Indian Reservation/So Greedy (Remixed)/Taboo (Remix)
		(p/s, with sticker, clear vinyl) 4
82	Albion ION 1033	Wild Sun/Scandal City/Bongos On The Nile (p/s, yellow vinyl) 4
82	Albion CION 1033	Wild Sun/Scandal City/Bongos On The Nile (cassette) 6
78	United Artists UAG 30199	999 (LP, with inner sleeve) 10

1910 FRUITGUM CO.
68	Pye Intl. 7N 25447	Simon Says/Reflections From The Looking Glass 4
68	Pye Intl. 7N 25458	May I Take A Giant Step (Into Your Heart)/(Poor Old) Mr. Jensen 4
68	Pye Intl. 7N 25468	1,2,3, Red Light/Sticky, Sticky 4
68	Pye Intl. 7N 25478	Pop Goes The Weasel/The Year 2001 4
69	Buddah 201 049	Special Delivery/No Good Annie 4
68	Pye Intl. N(S)PL 28115	SIMON SAYS (LP) 12
69	Buddah 203 014	GOODY GOODY GUMDROPS (LP) 10
70	Buddah 2359 006	HARD RIDE (LP) 12
	(see also Lemon Pipers & 1910 Fruitgum Co.)	

9.30 FLY
| 72 | Ember NR 5062 | 9.30 FLY (LP) ....120 |

NINEY (& DESTROYERS/OBSERVERS)
| 70 | Amalgamated AMG 856 | Niney Special/Danger Zone ....5 |
| 70 | Pressure Beat PB 5501 | Honey No Money/INSPIRATIONS: This Message To You ....4 |

71	Big Shot BI 568	Blood And Fire/Mud And Water	4
71	Big Shot BI 575	Brimstone And Fire/Lightning And Thunder	4
71	Big Shot BI 586	Message To The Ungodly/Message To The Ungodly Version	4
71	Big Shot BI 588	Keep Pushing/Hot Tip	4
72	Big Shot BI 607	Hiding By The Riverside/The Red Sea	4
72	Big Shot BI 609	Beg In The Gutter/Beg In The Gutter Version	4
72	Big Shot BI 610	Everyday Music/Observing The Av	4
72	Downtown DT 494	Get Out My Life/Get Out My Life Version	4
72	Downtown DT 495	Hi Diddle/Hi Diddle Version	4

NING
| 71 | Decca F 23114 | Machine/More Ning | 6 |

NINO & EBBTIDES
| 61 | Top Rank JAR 572 | Those Oldies But Goodies/Don't Run Away | 30 |

NIPPLE ERECTORS
| 78 | Soho SH$^1/_2$ | King Of The Bop/Nervous Wreck (originally glossy p/s, later matt) | 18/12 |

(see also Nips, Pogues)

NIPS
78	Soho SH 4	All The Time In The World/Private Eyes (foldover p/s)	20
79	Soho SH 9	Gabrielle/Vengeance (no p/s)	8
79	Soho SH 9	Gabrielle/Vengeance (tour copy with 'licensed to cool' stamp)	30
79	Chiswick CHIS 119	Gabrielle/Vengeance (reissue, p/s)	10
81	Test Pressing TP 5	Happy Song/Nobody To Love (p/s)	15
80	Soho HOHO 1	ONLY AT THE END OF THE BEGINNING (LP, with insert, white labels)	20

(see also Nipple Erectors, Pogues)

NIRVANA (U.K.)
67	Island WIP 6016	Tiny Goddess/I Believe In Magic	12
67	Island WIP 6020	Pentecost Hotel/Feelin' Shattered	8
68	Island WIP 6029	Rainbow Chaser/Flashbulb	10
68	Island WIP 6038	Girl In The Park/C Side In Ocho Rios	10
68	Island WIP 6045	All Of Us (The Touchables)/Trapeze	8
68	Island WIP 6052	Wings Of Love/Requiem To John Coltrane	10
69	Island WIP 6057	Oh! What A Performance/Darling Darlene	8
70	Pye 7N 25525	The World Is Cold Without You/Christopher Lucifer	12
70	Vertigo 6059 035	The Saddest Day Of My Life/(I Wanna Go) Home	10
71	Philips 6006 127	Pentecost Hotel/Lazy Day Drift	6
72	Philips 6006 166	Stadium/Please Believe Me	6
88	Bam Caruso OPRA 45	Black Flower/WIMPLE WINCH: Save My Soul (jukebox issue, die-cut sleeve)	4
67	Island ILP 959/ILPS 9059	THE STORY OF SIMON SIMOPATH (LP, pink label, mono/stereo)	50/40
68	Island ILP 987/ILPS 9087	ALL OF US (LP, pink label)	30
70	Pye NSPL 28132	DEDICATED TO MARKOS III (LP)	55
71	Vertigo 6360 031	LOCAL ANAESTHETIC (LP, gatefold sleeve, spiral label)	25
72	Philips 6308 089	SONGS OF LOVE AND PRAISE (LP)	40

(see also Patrick Campbell-Lyons, Ray Singer, Pica, Hat & Tie)

NIRVANA (U.S.)
89	Tupelo TUP EP8	Blew/Love Buzz/Been A Son/Stain (p/s)	12
89	Tupelo TUP CD8	Blew/Love Buzz/Been A Son/Stain (CD)	12
91	Tupelo TUP 25	Sliver/Dive (gatefold p/s, 2,000 on green vinyl)	15
91	Tupelo TUP EP25	Sliver/Dive/About A Girl (live) (12", black vinyl)	7
91	Geffen DGCTP 5	Smells Like Teen Spirit/Drain You (LP Version)/Aneurysm (12", picture disc)	7
93	Touch & Go TG83	Oh, The Guilt/JESUS LIZARD: Puss (blue vinyl with/without poster, p/s)	7/5
89	Tupelo TUP LP6	BLEACH (LP, 300 on white vinyl, 2,000 on green vinyl)	60/30
89	Tupelo TUP CD6	BLEACH (CD)	15

NITAE DASGUPTA
| 72 | Mushroom 100 MR 22 | SONGS OF INDIA (LP) | 40 |

NITE PEOPLE
66	Fontana TF 747	Sweet Tasting Wine/Nobody But You	10
67	Fontana TF 808	Trying To Find Another Man/Stay As Sweet As Your Are	8
67	Fontana TF 885	Summertime Blues/In The Springtime	30
68	Fontana TF 919	Morning Sun/Where You There	12
69	Page One POF 149	Love, Love, Love/Hot Smoke And Sassafras (some with insert)	10/6
69	Page One POF 159	Is This A Dream/Cream Song	6
70	Page One POF 174	Season Of The Rain/P.M.	6
69	Page One POLS 025	P.M. (LP)	125

NITE ROCKERS
| 58 | RCA RCA 1079 | Nite Rock (Lonely Train)/Oh! Baby | 75 |
| 58 | RCA RCA 1079 | Nite Rock (Lonely Train)/Oh! Baby (78) | 40 |

NITE SHADES
| 65 | CBS 201763 | Be My Guest/I Must Reveal | 4 |
| 65 | CBS 201817 | Fell So Fast/I'm Not Gonna Worry | 4 |

NITRO FUNCTION
(see under Billy Cox)

NITTY GRITTY DIRT BAND
67	Liberty LIB 55948	Buy Me For The Rain/Candy Man	5
68	Liberty LBF 15099	Collegiana/End Of Your Line	5
70	Liberty LBF 15358	Rave On/The Cure	4
72	United Artists UP 35357	Jambalaya/Hoping To Say	4
71	United Artists UP 35282	Some Of Shelley's Blues/The Cure	4
68	Liberty LBL/LBS 83122	PURE DIRT (LP)	15
69	Liberty LBS 83286	DEAD AND ALIVE (LP)	15
70	Liberty LBG 83345	UNCLE CHARLIE AND HIS DOG TEDDY (LP)	10

NITZER EBB

85	Power Of Voice NEP 1	Isn't It Funny How Your Body Works/The Way You Live/Crane/Cold War (12", p/s, with insert)	8
85	Power Of Voice NEP 2	Warsaw Ghetto/So Bright, So Strong (12", p/s, with insert)	7
86	Power Of Voice NEP/ NEBX 2	Warsaw Ghetto/So Bright, So Strong (Dub Mix)/(Rap Mix)/ So Bright, So Strong (Radio Mix) (12", reissue double pack)	14

JACK NITZSCHE

63	Reprise R 20202	The Lonely Surfer/Song For A Summer Night	10
63	Reprise R 20237	Night Walker/Green Grass Of Texas	7
78	MCA MCA 366	Hard Workin' Man (featuring Captain Beefheart)/Coke Machine	4
74	Warner Bros K 41211	ST GILES CRIPPLEGATE (LP)	15

(see also Captain Beefheart, Mick Jagger, Randy Newman)

NIVENS

88	Woosh WOOSH 1	Let Loose Of My Knee/HOLIDAYMAKERS: Everyday (flexidisc with 'Woosh' fanzine, foldaround p/s in poly bag)	10
89	Woosh WOOSH 5	Yesterday/I Hope You'll Always Be My Friend	5

REV A.W. NIX

40s	Decca F 3850	Black Diamond Express To Hell Pts 1 & 2 (78)	35

WILLIE NIX

(see under Willie Love, Joe Hill Louis)

NIX-NOMADS

64	HMV POP 1354	You're Nobody (Till Somebody Loves You)/She'll Be Sweeter Than You (demos wrongly credited to Nix-Nomands)	60

MEL NIXON

75	Alaska ALA 26	Every Beat Of Your Heart/ASTRA NOVA ORCHESTRA: Soul Sleeper	4

RAB NOAKES

78	Ring O' 2017 115	Waiting Here For You/Restless (p/s)	5
78	Ring O' 2017 117	I Won't Let You Down/Long After Dark (company sleeve)	4
70	Decca SKL 5061	DO YOU SEE THE LIGHTS (LP)	202
72	A&M AMLS 68119	RAB NOAKES (LP, with Stealers Wheel)	10
78	Ring O' 2339 201	RESTLESS (LP)	10

(see also Steelers Wheel)

LISA NOBLE

58	Decca F 11006	Maggie! — Yes Ma!/Who's Sorry Now	4
58	Decca F 11051	It's A Boy/The Saints	4

NICK NOBLE

57	Mercury MT 165	Fallen Star/Let Me Hold You In My Arms (78, with Dick Noel Singers)	8
60	Coral Q 72403	The Tip Of My Fingers/Sweet Love	5
60	Coral Q 72413	Island Farewell/Excuse Me (I Think I've Got A Heartache)	4

PATSY ANN NOBLE

61	HMV POP 980	Good Looking Boy/The Guy Who Can Mend A Broken Heart	5
63	Columbia DB 4956	Don't You Ever Change Your Mind/Sour Grapes	5
63	Columbia DB 7008	Heartbreak Avenue/I'm Nobody's Baby	5
63	Columbia DB 7060	I Was Only Foolin' Myself/Ordinary Love	5
63	Columbia DB 7088	Accidents Will Happen/He Tells Me With His Eyes	5
63	Columbia DB 7148	It's Better To Cry Today/Don't Tell Him I Told You	5
64	Columbia DB 7258	I Did Nothing Wrong/Better Late Than Never	5
64	Columbia DB 7318	Private Property/Crack In The Door	5
64	Columbia DB 7386	Tied Up With Mary/Green Eyed People	5
65	Columbia DB 7472	Then You Can Tell Me Goodbye/If You Wanna Be More Than Friends	5
65	Polydor BM 56054	He Who Rides A Tiger/City Of Night	4

NOBLEMEN

59	Top Rank JAR 155	Thunder Wagon/Dragon Walk	7
59	Top Rank JAR 155	Thunder Wagon/Dragon Walk (78)	18

CLIFF NOBLES (& CO.)

68	Direction 58-3518	The Horse/Love Is Alright	4
68	Direction 58-3738	Judge Baby, I'm Back/Horse Fever (solo)	4
69	Direction 58-4205	Switch It On/Burning Desire (solo)	4
69	Direction 8-63477	THE HORSE (LP)	10

NOCTURNAL EMISSIONS

84	Sterile SR 6	NO SACRIFICE (12", p/s, 2,000 only)	15
84	CFC LP 2	CHAOS — LIVE AT THE RITZY (LP)	50
84	Illuminated JAMS LP 33	VIRAL SHEDDING (LP)	20
84	Sterile EMISS 001	TISSUE OF LIES (LP, 1st batch numbered, later in blue sleeve)	80/40
84	Sterile ION 2	FRUITING BODY (LP)	50
84	Sterile SR 4	DROWNING IN A SEA OF BLISS (LP)	70
84	Sterile SR 5	BEFEHLSNOTSTAND (LP)	50
85	Sterile SRC 003	DEATHDAY (cassette)	10
85	Sterile SR 7	SONGS OF LOVE AND REVOLUTION (LP)	20
86	Sterile SR 9	SHAKE THOSE CHAINS, RATTLE THOSE CAGES (LP)	15
87	Earthly Delights EARTH 02	THE WORLD IS MY WOMB (LP)	20
88	Earhtly Delights EARTH 04	SPIRITFLESH (LP)	25
89	Earthly Delights EARTH 05	BEYOND LOGIC (LP)	15
90	Earthly Delights EARTH 06	MOUTH OF THE BABES (LP)	15

NOCTURNES

55	MGM SP 1120	Whodat? (Buck Dance)/Hey Punchinello	5
55	MGM SP 1148	Birmin'ham/Toodle-oo Igaloo	5
64	Solar SRP 102	Troilka/Rawhide	5

MINT VALUE £

NOCTURNES
67	Columbia DB 8158	Wish You Would Show Me Your Mind/I Do, I Do	5
67	Columbia DB 8219	Why (Am I Treated So Bad?)/Save The Last Dance For Me	5
68	Columbia DB 8332	A New Man/Suddenly Free	4
68	Columbia DB 8453	Carpet Man/Look At Me	4
68	Columbia DB 8493	Montage/Fairground Man	4
68	Columbia S(C)X 6223	THE NOCTURNES (LP)	12
68	Columbia S(C)X 6315	WANTED ALIVE (LP)	15

NOCTURNS
64	Decca F 12002	Carryin' On/Three Cool Cats	6

PROFESSOR ERNEST NODE & HIS MUG & JUG BAND
67	Columbia DB 8100	The Egg Plant That Ate Chicago/I'm In The Doghouse	5

NO DICE
79	EMI EMI 2927	Come Dancing/Bad Boys (picture disc)	4

NOEL
88	Virgin VP 2126	IS THERE MORE TO LIFE THAN DANCING (LP, picture disc)	10

DICK NOEL
56	London HLH 8295	(The Same Thing Happens With) The Birds And The Bees/Birth Of The Blues	20

NOIR
71	Dawn DNLS 3029	WE HAD TO LET YOU HAVE IT (LP, with insert)	20

NO KIDDING
74	Wave	NO KIDDING (LP)	20

COLEEN NOLAN
78	Target TGT 142	Andy/Thanks For Calling	6

(see also Nolan Sisters)

DENISE NOLAN
79	Pye 7P 126	Sorry Seems To Be The Hardest Word/Holding You	4
82	Mercury MER 103	Girls Do It, Boys Do It/Just Can't Stop The Feeling (p/s)	4
82	Mercury MER 125	In Love With Love/My Mind's Made Up On You (p/s)	5

(see also Nolan Sisters)

TERRY NOLAND
58	Coral Q 72311	Oh Baby! Look At Me/Puppy Love	80
58	Coral Q 72311	Oh Baby! Look At Me/Puppy Love (78)	30

NOLAN SISTERS/NOLANS
72	Nevis NEVS 007	Blackpool/Apple Pie	15
72	Nevis NEVEP 005	SILENT NIGHT (EP)	8
74	EMI EMI 2209	But I Do/Now I'm Stuck On You	12
75	Target TGT 103	Make A Little Sunshine Shine/Have Love Will Travel	6
76	Target TGT 108	Rain/Oh My Darling	7
76	Target TGT 116	Thanks For Calling/Oh My Darling	6
76	Target TGT 121	When You Are A King/Hey What A Day	6
77	Target TGT 132	Love Transformation/Oh My Darling	4
77	Target TGT 137	Love Bandit/Don't Take Your Love Away	4
78	Target TGT 140	Don't It Make My Brown Eyes Blue/Something Tells Me (p/s)	4
78	Target SAM 84	Medley (sampler for "20 Giant Hits")	8
79	Epic EPC 7197	Harry My Honolulu Lover/Out Of Love With Love	4
79	Epic EPC 8068	I'm In The Mood For Dancing/Let's Make Love (p/s)	5
80	Epic EPC 8349	Don't Make Waves/Don't Let Me Be The Last To Know (p/s)	7
82	Epic EPCA 11-1927	Don't Love Me Too Hard/A Simple Case Of Loving You (picture disc)	4
82	Epic EPCA 11-2378	Crashing Down/It Takes All Night (picture disc)	4
82	Epic EPCA 2625	GREATEST ORIGINAL HITS (EP)	4
82	Epic EPCA 40-2625	THE NOLANS (EP, cassette)	4
82	Lyntone LYN 11073	Konica Pop Flexi (flexi)	4
84	Scoop 33 75R 5032	THE NOLANS (EP, label also listed as Pickwick)	4
72	Nevis NEVR 009	THE SINGING NOLANS (LP)	20
77	Hanover Grand HG 19751	THE NOLAN SISTERS (LP, sold only at London Room Club, Drury Lane)	30

(see also Coleen Nolan, Denise Nolan)

PIERRE NOLES
63	Oriole CB 1791	Jacqueline/Marilyn	4

NAZ NOMAD & NIGHTMARES
84	Big Beat NS 93	I Had Too Much To Dream (Last Night)/Cold Turkey (p/s)	4
84	Big Beat WIK 21	GIVE DADDY THE KNIFE CINDY (LP, purple vinyl)	10

(see also Damned)

NOMADS
70	Pye 7N 17906	The Singer Sang His Song/Lovin' Him	4

NON/SMEGMA
80	Mute MUTE 7	I Can't Look Straight/Flash Cards (p/s, with 2 playing holes, 1 side each)	5

PETER NOONE
71	Rak RAK 114	Oh You Pretty Thing/Together Forever	4
71	Rak RAK 121	Right On Mother/Walnut Whirl	6
72	Rak RAK 129	Shoo Be Doo Ah/Because You're There	4
72	Rak RAK 136	Should I/Each And Every Minute	4

(see also Herman's Hermits)

NO QUARTER
83	Reel REEL 1	Survivors/Time And Space/Racing For Home (12", foldout p/s)	10

KEN NORDINE
57	London RED 1091	KEN NORDINE READS (EP, with Billy Vaughn Orchestra)	25

| 59 | London Jazz EZD 19040 | WORD JAZZ (EP) | ....15 |

(see also Billy Vaughn & His Orchestra)

NORKS
| 92 | Big Jug NIP 1 | A NICE PAIR (2-LP, with free size 36-D bra) | ....40 |

NORMAL
| 78 | Mute MUTE 001 | T.V.O.D./Warm Leatherette (p/s) | ....4 |

GENE NORMAN (JUST JAZZ)
50s	Vogue V 2022	Hot House Pts 1 & 2 (solo)	4
56	Vogue V 2047	Blue Lou Pts 1 & 2	4
50s	Vogue V 2272	Four O'Clock Jump/Three O'Clock Jump	4

LARRY NORMAN
| 69 | Key KL 010/Dove DOVE 64 | UPON THIS ROCK (LP) | ....12 |

MONTY NORMAN
55	HMV 7M 349	The Shifting, Whispering Sands/Bonnie Blue Gal	5
57	HMV POP 281	The Garden Of Eden/Priscilla	8
57	HMV POP 281	The Garden Of Eden/Priscilla (78)	5
65	United Artists UEP 1010	DOCTOR NO SOUNDTRACK (EP)	18
65	United Artists (S)ULP 1097	DR NO (LP, soundtrack, mono/stereo)	............15/18

OLIVER NORMAN
| 67 | Polydor 56176 | Down In The Basement/Drowning In My Own Despair | ....6 |
| 68 | Polydor 56247 | People People/You'll Find It Will Come | ....4 |

NORMAN & INVADERS
64	United Artists UP 1031	Our Wedding Day/Stacey	5
64	United Artists UP 1058	Our Wedding Day/Stacey (reissue)	4
65	United Artists UP 1077	Night Train To Surbiton/Likely Lads	12

NORMAN CONQUEST
| 67 | MGM MGM 1376 | Two People/Upside Down | ....40 |

(see also Factory, Peter & Wolves, John Panty)

FREDDIE NORTH
| 72 | Mojo 2916 012 | FRIEND (LP) | ....10 |

ROY NORTH
| 63 | Oak RGJ 107 | Blues In Three/Blues In Five | ....20 |

NORTHERN LIGHTS
| 66 | United Artists UP 1123 | No Time/Time To Move Along | ....25 |
| 66 | United Artists UP 1161 | Through Darkness, Light/Baby Those Are The Rules | ....25 |

(see also Hootenanny Singers, Abba)

NORTH STARS
| 65 | Fontana TF 581 | For My True Love/Nothing But The Best | ....4 |
| 66 | Fontana TF 726 | She's So Far Out She's In/Eeenie Meenie Minee Mo | ....12 |

NORTHWIND
| 71 | Regal Zono. SLRZ 1020 | SISTER, BROTHER, LOVER (LP) | ....150 |

(see also Elastic Band)

NOSEBLEEDS
| 77 | Rabid TOSH 12 | Ain't Bin To No Music School/Fascist Pigs (p/s) | ....5 |

(see also Durutti Column, Ed Banger, Blue Orchids)

NOSMO
| 74 | Pye 7N 45383 | Goodbye/Teenage Love | ....8 |

NO SWEAT
| 79 | Rip Off RIP 4 | Start All Over Again/You Should Be So Lucky (p/s) | ....4 |

NOTATIONS
74	Chapter One SCH 174	Need Your Love/Just Nothing Left To Give	12
76	Curtom K 16696	Think Before You Stop/I'm Losing	5
76	Curtom K 56212	NOTATIONS (LP)	25

FREDDIE NOTES & RUDIES
69	Downtown DT 427	I Don't Wanna Lose That Girl/Train From Vietnam	4
69	Grape GR 3010	Guns Of Navarone/Yester Me Yester You	4
69	Grape GR 3011	Babylon Girl/Girl I've Got A Date	4
69	Trojan TR 7713	Shanghai/Rome Wasn't Built In A Day	4
69	Trojan TR 7724	Rocco/Don't Tell Your Mama	4
70	B&C CB 125	It Came Out The Sky/Well Oh Well (p/s)	4
70	Trojan TR 7734	Down On The Farm/Easy Street	4
70	Trojan TBL 109	UNITY (LP)	12
70	Trojan TBL 152	MONTEGO BAY (LP)	12

NOTORIOUS
90	Bronze BYZ 1	The Swalk/Eyes Of The World (square picture disc)	5
90	Bronze BYZ 1T	The Swalk/Eyes Of The World (12", p/s)	7
90	Bronze	NOTORIOUS (LP, withdrawn)	10

NOTSENSIBLES
79	Redball RR 02	(I'm In Love With) Margaret Thatcher/Little Boxes/Gary Bushell's Band Of The Week (p/s)	8
80	Bent SMALL BENT 5	Death To Disco/Coronation Street Hustle/Lying On The Sofa (p/s)	5
80	Snotty Snail NELCOL 1	(I'm In Love With) Margaret Thatcher/Little Boxes/Gary Bushell's Band Of The Week (p/s, reissue)	5
80	Snotty Snail NELCOL 3	I Thought You Were Dead/I Make A Balls Of Everything I Do/Teenage Revolution (p/s)	5
81	Snotty Snail NELCOL 6	I Am The Bishop/The Telephone Rings Again (p/s)	5

80	Bent/Snotty Snail	INSTANT CLASSICS (LP, 2 different issues)	15/10

NOVA LOCAL
69	MCA MUPS 377	NOVA 1 (LP)	12

NOVAS
63	RCA RCA 1360	Push A Little Harder/Oh, Gee Baby!	5

(see also Avons)

NOVAS
65	London HLU 9940	The Crusher/Take 7	20

NOW
78	Ultimate ULT 401	Development Corporations/Why (p/s, some on blue vinyl)	10/6
78	Raw RAW 31	Into The 1980s/Nine O'Clock (p/s)	5

NOYES BROTHERS
80	Object OBJ 0009/0010	SHEEP FROM GOATS (2-LP)	20

NOYS OF US
60s	KRS Sound Stud. KPS 502	He's Alright Jill/What Can I Do	30

N.R.B.Q. (New Rhythm & Blues Quintet)
69	CBS 4290	Stomp/I Didn't Know Myself	4
69	CBS 4501	C'mon Everybody/Rocket Number 9	4
73	Kama Sutra 2013 056	Ain't It All Right/Only You	4
69	CBS 63653	N.R.B.Q. (LP)	12
72	Buddah 2319 018	SCRAPS (LP)	10

(see also Carl Perkins)

N.S.U.
69	Stable SLE 8002	TURN ON OR TURN ME DOWN (LP)	120

GUITAR NUBBIT
64	Bootleg 501	Georgia Chain Gang/Hard Road	25
60s	XX MIN 705	GUITAR NUBBIT (EP)	7

NUCHA
90	CBS 655885 7	Together/Ha Sempre Alguem	4

NUCLEAR SOCKETTS
81	Subversive SUB 001	HONOR BEFORE GLORY (EP, folded p/s, 33rpm)	6
81	Subversive SUB 002	Play Loud/Shadow On The Map	5

NUCLEUS
70	Vertigo 6360 008	ELASTIC ROCK (LP, gatefold sleeve, spiral label, later spaceship label)	18/10
70	Vertigo 6360 027	WE'LL TALK ABOUT IT LATER (LP, g/fold sl., spiral or spaceship label)	20/10
73	Vertigo 6360 091	LABYRINTH (LP, spaceship label)	12
73	Vertigo 6360 100	ROOTS (LP, spaceship label)	10
74	Vertigo 6360 110	UNDER THE SUN (LP, spaceship label)	10
75	Vertigo 6360 119	SNAKE HIPS ETCETERA (LP, spaceship label)	10
75	Vertigo 6360 124	ALLEY CAT (LP, spaceship label)	10
76	Vertigo 9286 019	DIRECT HITS (LP, spaceship label)	10
80	Mood 24000	AWAKENING (LP)	30

(see also Ian Carr, Don Rendell)

TED NUGENT (& AMBOY DUKES)
73	Discreet K 19200	Sweet Revenge/Ain't It The Truth (as Ted Nugent & Amboy Dukes)	5
76	Epic EPC 3900	Storm Troopin'/Hey Baby (yellow label)	4
76	Epic EPC 4796	Dog Eat Dog/Love You So I Told You A Lie	4
77	Epic EPC 5482	Cat Scratch Fever/A Thousand Nights	4
75	Discreet K 59203	CALL OF THE WILD (LP)	10

(see also [American] Amboy Dukes)

NUGGETS
55	Capitol CL 14216	Quirl Up In My Arms/So Help Me, I Love You	15
55	Capitol CL 14216	Quirl Up In My Arms/So Help Me, I Love You (78)	5
55	Capitol CL 14267	Shtiggy Boom/Anxious Heart	12
55	Capitol CL 14267	Shtiggy Boom/Anxious Heart (78)	5

GARY NUMAN
79	Beggars Banquet BEG 23	Cars/Asylum (p/s, 'mispressed' on dark red vinyl)	7
79	Beggars Banquet BEG 29	Complex/Bombers (Live Version)	4
79	Beggars Banquet BEG 29T	Complex/Bombers (Live Version)/Me I Disconnect From You (Live) (12", p/s)	8
80	Beggars Banquet BEG 26	I Die, You Die/Down In The Park (Piano Version) (p/s, dark red vinyl 'mispress')	7
80	Beggars Banquet BEG 26	I Die, You Die/Down In The Park (Piano Version) (p/s, mispress, plays "Remember I Was A Vapour" & "On Broadway" [SAM 126])	12
81	Beggars Banquet BEG 62	She's Got Claws/I Sing Rain (p/s, mispress, plays Dollar's "Hand Held In Black And White")	12
81	Beggars Banquet BEG 68T	Love Needs No Disguise/Take Me Home/Face To Face (12", with Dramatis)	7
82	Beggars Banquet BEG 70T	Music For Chameleons/Noise Noise/Bridge, What Bridge (12", p/s)	7
82	Beggars Banquet BEG 77T	We Take Mystery (To Bed)/The Images/We Take Mystery (Early Version) (12", p/s)	7
82	Beggars Banquet BEG 81T	White Boys And Heroes/War Games/Glitter And Ash (12", p/s)	7
83	Beggars Banquet BEG 95P	Warriors/My Car Slides (aeroplane-shaped picture disc)	20
85	Numa NU 7	THE LIVE EP (black, blue or white vinyl)	6/4/4
85	Numa NUM 7	THE LIVE EP (12", black, blue or white vinyl)	8/7/7
85	Numa NU 9	Your Fascination/We Need It (picture disc)	6
85	Numa NUMP 9	Your Fascination (Extended)/We Need It/Anthem (12", picture disc)	10
85	Numa NU 13	Miracles/Fear (p/s, black, red or white vinyl)	6/4/4
85	Numa NUM 13	Miracles/Fear (12", p/s, black, red or white vinyl)	8/7/7
86	Numa NU 16	This Is Love/Survival (p/s, with interview flexidisc)	4
86	Numa NUP 16	This Is Love/Survival (picture disc)	4
86	Numa NUM 16	This Is Love/Survival (12", p/s, with interview flexidisc)	7

86	Numa NUMX 16	This Is Love/Survival//Call Out The Dogs (Extended)/No Shelter/
		This Ship Comes Apart (12", stickered double pack, shrinkwrapped) 10
86	Numa NUMP 16	This Is Love/Survival (12", picture disc) 8
86	Numa NU 17	I Can't Stop/Faces (p/s, autographed, with interview flexidisc) 4
86	Numa NUP 17	I Can't Stop/Faces (plane-shaped picture disc) 8
86	Numa NUDJ 17	I Can't Stop (Club Mix)/Faces (10", p/s, with interview flexidisc) 10
86	Numa NUM 17	I Can't Stop/Faces (12", p/s, autographed, with interview flexidisc) 7
86	Numa NUMP 17	I Can't Stop (Picture Mix)/Faces (12", picture disc) 8
86	Numa NUP 21	I Still Remember (Remix)/Puppets (picture disc) 4
86	Numa NUMP 21	I Still Remember/Puppets (12", picture disc) 7
87	B. Banquet BEG 199P	Cars ('E' Reg Model)/Are Friends Electric? (picture disc) 7
87	Beggars Banquet	Cars ('E' Reg Extended Model)/Are Friends Electric?/Cars
	BEG 199TR	('E' Reg Model 7" Mix)/Cars (Motorway Mix) (12", p/s) 8
88	IRS ILSP 1003	New Anger/I Don't Believe (poster p/s) 4
88	IRS ILSG 1003	New Anger/I Don't Believe/Children (12", gatefold p/s) 7
88	IRS ILSCD 1003	New Anger/I Don't Believe/Creatures (live)/I Can't Stop (live) (CD) 12
88	IRS ILPD 1004	America/Respect (live) (picture disc) 7
88	IRS ILPD 1004	America/Respect (live) (mispressed picture disc, 'Gary' picture both sides) 20
91	IRS NUMAN CV 1	Heart/Shame (p/s, red vinyl, picture labels) 5
80	Beggars Banquet BEGA 19	TELEKON (LP, with live 7" "Remember I Was A Vapour"/"On Broadway"
		[SAM 126]) 12
80	Beggars Banquet BEGA 19	TELEKON (LP, with poster) 10
80	Beggars Banquet BEGA 19	TELEKON (LP, dark red vinyl 'mispressing') 15
82	TV TVA 7	NEW MAN NUMAN (LP) 10
84	B. Banquet BEGA 55P	THE PLAN (LP, picture disc) 12
86	Numa NUMA 1003	THE FURY (LP, with pink inner sleeve) 12
86	Numa NUMAP 1003	THE FURY (LP, picture disc) 10
86	Numa NUMAP 1003	THE FURY (LP, mispress pic. disc, with "Your Fascination" 12" photo on A-side) 35
86	Numa CDNUMA 1003	THE FURY (CD) 35
86	Numa CDNUMA 1005	STRANGE CHARM (CD) 40
88	IRS ILP 035	METAL RHYTHM (LP, gatefold sleeve) 10
88	IRS ILPX 035	METAL RHYTHM (LP, picture disc) 15
86	Numa GNFCDA 1	IMAGES 1 & 2 (2-LP, Fan Club issue, with photo inserts, mail-order only) 25
87	Numa GNFCDA 2	IMAGES 3 & 4 (2-LP, Fan Club issue, with photo inserts, mail-order only) 25
87	Numa GNFCDA 3	IMAGES 5 & 6 (2-LP, Fan Club issue, with photo inserts, mail-order only) 20
87	Numa GNFCDA 4	IMAGES 7 & 8 (2-LP, Fan Club issue, with photo inserts, mail-order only) 20
87	Numa NUMAD 1007	GHOST (2-LP, Fan Club issue, mail-order only) 20
89	Numa GNFCDA 5	IMAGES 9 & 10 (2-LP, Fan Club issue, with photo inserts, mail-order only) 15

*(see also Tubeway Army, Sharpe & Numan, Paul Gardiner, Dramatis,
Claire Hamill, Radio Heart, Nicky Robson, Caroline Munro, Paper Toys,
N & Y, West Won, Hohokam)*

NUMBER NINE BREAD STREET
| 67 | Holy Ground HG 112/1109 | NUMBER NINE BREAD STREET (LP, 250 copies only) ....450 |

NUMBERS
| 79 | Blasto SRTS 79/CUS/358 | ROCK STARS (EP, with insert) ....4 |

NU NOTES
| 63 | HMV POP 1232 | Hall Of Mirrors/Fury ....35 |
| 64 | HMV POP 1311 | Kathy/Sunset ....8 |

(see also Russ Sainty & Nu Notes)

NURSE WITH WOUND
87	Crystal/Wisewound WW 01	Crank/TERMITE QUEEN: Wisecrack (no'd, with printed band, 500 only) ...12
88	Yankhi YANKHI 02	FAITH'S FAVOURITES (12", with Current 93) 10
88	Idle Hole 003	Cooloorta Moon/Great Empty Space 7
90	Harbinger 001	Burial Of The Stoned Sardine/CURRENT 93: No Hiding From The Blackbird 5
90	United Dairies UD 031CD	SORESUCKER (CD EP) 7
90	Shock SX 004	Sinister Senile: Human Human Human/Psychedelic Underground (45/33rpm) 5
79	United Dairies UD 01	CHANCE MEETING ON A DISSECTING TABLE OF A SEWING MACHINE
		AND UMBRELLA (LP, 500 only) 100
80	United Dairies UD 03	TO THE QUIET MEN FROM A TINY GIRL (LP, 500 only) 70
80	United Dairies UD 04	MERZBILD SCHWET (LP, 500 only) 70
81	United Dairies UD 08	INSECT AND INDIVIDUAL SILENCED (LP, 1,000 only) 50
84	Third Mind YMR 03	OSTRANENIE 1913 (LP, 3,000 only) 35
85	United Dairies UD 012	HOMOTOPY TO MARIE (LP, 5,000 only) 35
86	United Dairies UD 019	AUTOMATING VOL. 1 (LP, 3,000 only) 15
86	United Dairies UD 020	A MISSING SENSE (LP, 1 side only, other side by Organum) 15
87	United Dairies UD 025	DRUNK WITH THE OLD MAN OF THE MOUNTAINS (LP, handmade
		custom sleeves, 100 or so only) 50
88	United Dairies UD 027	ALAS THE MADONNA DOES NOT FUNCTION (mini-LP, 45/33rpm) ...12
88	Idle Hole MIRROR ONE	SOLILOQUY FOR LILITH (3-LP box set) 40
89	United Dairies UD 030	AUTOMATING II (LP) 15
89	United Dairies UD 032	A SUCKED ORANGE (LP, some with full colour insert) 10
89	Idle Hole MIRROR TWO	PRESENTS THE SISTERS OF PATAPHYSICS (LP, 1,000 only) 10

(see also Current 93)

NU TORNADOS
| 58 | London HLU 8756 | Philadelphia U.S.A./Magic Record ....12 |
| 58 | London HLU 8756 | Philadelphia U.S.A./Magic Record (78) ....5 |

NUTRONS
| 60s | Melodisc M 1593 | The Very Best Things/Stop For The Music ....15 |

MAY'F NUTTER
| 66 | Vocalion VL 1282 | Head Shrinker/Don't Know What To Do ....6 |

NUTTY SQUIRRELS
| 59 | Pye Intl. 7N 25044 | Uh! Oh! Pts 1 & 2 ....6 |

MINT VALUE £

NUTZ

NYAH SHUFFLE

JUDY NYLON

(see also John Cale, Snatch)

LAURA NYRO

NIRVANA

OAK
71 Topic 12TS 212   WELCOME TO OUR FAIR (LP) 40
(see also Peta Webb)

OAKENSHIELDS
85 Acorn OAK 1   ACROSS THE NARROW SEAS (LP) 15
87 Acorn OAK 2   AGAINST THE GRAIN (LP) 15

PHILIP OAKEY & GIORGIO MORODER
84 Virgin VSY 713   Together In Electric Dreams/(Instrumental) (picture disc) 6
(see also Human League, Men)

OBERON
70s Acorn (no cat. no.)   A MIDSUMMER NIGHT'S DREAM (LP, private press) 300

HUGH O'BRIAN
58 HMV POP 539   Legend Of Wyatt Earp/Down In The Meadow 4
58 Oriole CB 1480   I'm Looking For A Girl/Ain't Got A Nickel 4
58 HMV DLP 1189   TV'S WYATT EARP SINGS (10" LP) 12

OBTAINERS
79 Dance Fools Dance   Yeh Yeh Yeh/Pussy Wussy/MAG-SPYS: Lifeblood/Bombs
    (no cat. no.)   (stickered plain sleeve, 100 only) 70
(see also Cure)

DIERDRE O'CALLAGHAN
59 Top Rank JAR 164   The Bridal Path/I'll Walk With My Love 4

SEAN O'CASEY, Ó'RIADA & CEOLTOIRI CUALANN
60s Gael-Linn CEF 010   THE PLAYBOY OF THE WESTERN WORLD (LP) 10

OCCASIONALLY DAVID
79 Oven Ready OD 77901   TWIST AND SHOUT (EP) 8
80 Oven Ready OD 1/98002 I Can't Get Used To Losing You (So I'm Coming Back)/Will You Miss Me
                         Tonight? (foldout p/s) 6

OCCASIONAL WORD ENSEMBLE
69 Dandelion 63753   THE YEAR OF THE GREAT LEAP SIDEWAYS (LP) 15

OCCULT CHEMISTRY
80 Bikini Girl   Water Earth Fire Air (Rough Version) (5" clear flexidisc in stamped
                         envelope with 'Bikini Girl' magazine) 10
81 Dining Out TUX 4   Water Earth Fire Air/Fire Air Water Earth (p/s) 4

PHIL OCHS
65 Elektra EKSN 45002   I Ain't Marchin' Anymore/That Was The President 8
67 A&M AMS 716   Outside Of A Small Circle Of Friends/Miranda 4
65 Elektra EKL 269   ALL THE NEWS THAT'S FIT TO SING (LP) 18
65 Elektra EKL 287   I AIN'T MARCHIN' ANYMORE (LP) 18
66 Elektra EKL 310   PHIL OCHS IN CONCERT (LP) 18
67 A&M AML(S) 913   PLEASURES OF THE HARBOR (LP) 12
68 A&M AMLS 919   TAPE FROM CALIFORNIA (LP) 12
69 A&M AMLS 934   REHEARSALS FOR RETIREMENT (LP) 12
70 A&M AMLS 973   GREATEST HITS (LP) 12
74 A&M AMLM 64599   CHORDS OF FAME (2-LP) 15

DES O'CONNOR
57 Columbia DB 4011   Moonlight Swim/Sailing Down The Chesapeake Bay 6

HAZEL O'CONNOR
79 Albion DEL 2   Ee-I-Adio/Time Is Free (p/s) 4
81 Lyntone   Men Of Good Fortune/D Days (yellow flexi with 'Flexipop' mag, issue 9) 5/4
84 RCA RCAP 387   Don't Touch Me/Bring It On Home To Me (picture disc) 4

SINÉAD O'CONNOR
87 Ensign ENY 610   Troy/Still Listening (p/s) 5
87 Ensign ENYX 610   Troy/Still Listening (12", p/s) 7
87 Ensign ENY 611   Mandinka/Drink Before The War (gatefold p/s) 4
87 Ensign ENYX 611   Mandinka (Extended)/Mandinka (Instrumental Dub)/Drink Before The War
                         (12", p/s) 7
87 Ensign ENYXR 611   Mandinka (Jake's Remix)/Mandinka/A Drink Before The War (12", p/s) 10
87 Ensign ENYCD 611   Mandinka/Drink Before The War/Mandinka (Instrumental Dub) (CD) 12
88 Ensign ENYCD 618   Jump In The River (Duet with Karen Finley)/Jump In The River/
                         Never Get Old (live) (CD) 8
90 Ensign ENYB 630   Nothing Compares 2 U/Jump In The River (box set with poster & badge) 4
90 Ensign ENYB 633   The Emperor's New Clothes/What Do You Want (box with poster & 3 cards) 4
(see also World Party, Edge & Sinéad O'Connor)

GENE OCTOBER
83 Illegal ILS 034   Suffering In The Land/Suffering Dub (p/s) 4
84 Slipped Discs SPLAT 001 Don't Quit/Burning Sounds (p/s) 4
(see also Chelsea)

JOHNNY OCTOBER
59 Capitol CL 15070   Growin' Prettier/Young And In Love 6

MINT VALUE £

60	Capitol CL 15121	So Mean/There'll Always Be A Feeling	6

OCTOPUS
70	Penny Farthing PEN 705	Laugh At The Poor Man/Girl Friend	15
70	Penny Farthing PEN 716	The River/Thief	15
73	Mooncrest MOON 7	Hey Na Na/Future Feelings	6
69	Penny Farthing PELS 508	RESTLESS NIGHT (LP)	175

(see also Cortinas)

MARTIN O'CUTHBERT
78	Esoteric EE 1	BEMS (Bug Eyed Monsters)/Fragments Of A Possessed Ego (p/s)	4
79	Eso EE 2/SRT/78/CUS 186	Serene Machines/Space Shall Weave Our Destiny (foldover p/s)	4

(see also Futurythm)

ANITA O'DAY
56	HMV POP 245	You're The Top/Honeysuckle Rose	4
60	HMV POP 821	Tea For Two/Sweet Georgia Brown	4
56	HMV CLP 1085	ANITA (LP)	12
56	Columbia Clef 33C 9020	ANITA O'DAY COLLATES (10" LP)	12
57	Columbia Clef 33CX 10068	AN EVENING WITH ANITA O'DAY (LP)	12
58	Columbia Clef 33CX 10125	ANITA SINGS THE MOST (LP)	12
58	HMV DLP 1169	PICK YOURSELF UP (10" LP)	12
59	HMV DLP 1203	ANITA AT MISTER KELLY'S (10" LP)	12
60	HMV CLP 1332	ANITA O'DAY SWINGS COLE PORTER WITH BILLY MAY (LP)	10

PAT O'DAY
55	MGM SP 1129	Earth Angel (Will You Be Mine?)/A Rusty Old Halo	15
55	MGM MGM 823	Earth Angel (Will You Be Mine?)/A Rusty Old Halo (78)	5
55	MGM SP 1142	Soldier Boy/Annie Oakley	10
60	Pye Intl. 7N 25048	I'll Build A Stairway To Your Paradise/No One Understands	5

BILL ODDIE
65	Parlophone R 5346	Knitting Song/Ain't Got Rhythm	4
66	Parlophone R 5433	I Can't Get Through/Because She Is My Love	4
69	Decca F 12903	We Love Jimmy Young/Irish Get Out (as Bill Oddie & Average Mothers)	4
70	Dandelion S 4786	On Ilkla Moor Baht'at/Harry Khrishna	4

ODDS
80	Double R RED 001	Saturday Night/Not Another Love Song (p/s)	6
81	JSO EAT 1	Yesterday Man/So You Think (p/s)	4
81	JSO EAT 7	Dread In My Bed/Spare Rib (p/s)	4

ODDSOCKS
75	Sweet Folk & C. SFA 030	MEN OF THE MOMENT (LP)	15

ANN ODELL
73	DJM DJS 10280	Swing Song/Everything's Fine Sunshine	4
73	DJM DJLPS 434	A LITTLE TASTE (LP)	18

MAC ODELL
54	Parlophone CMSP 25	The Stone Has Rolled Away/Heaven Bound Gospel Train (export issue)	10

RONNIE O'DELL & HIS ORCHESTRA
57	London HLD 8439	Melody Of Napoli/Struttin' Down Jane Street	10

ODIN'S PEOPLE
67	Major Minor MM 501	From A Distance/I Need You	5
67	Major Minor MM 506	Tommy Jones/I Need Your Hand In Mine	5

JOE O'DONNELL
77	EMI International INT 540	Golden Earrings/Omega	5
77	Polydor 2058 930	Poets And Story Tellers/The Great Banqueting Hall	5
77	Polydor 2383 465	GAODHAL'S VISION (LP)	30

(see also Mushroom, Rory Gallagher)

ROCK O'DOODLE
73	Decca F 13450	Queen Of Rock & Roll/Woman	4

(see also Patrick Campbell-Lyons)

ODYSSEY (U.K.)
66	Strike JH 312	How Long Is Time/Beware	7

(see also Sons Of Fred)

ODYSSEY (U.S.)
73	Mowest MWS 7002	ODYSSEY (LP)	25

OEDIPUS COMPLEX
68	Philips BF 1716	Holding My Hands Out/Brought Me Such Confusion	5
69	Philips BF 1771	Up Down Round And Round/Empty Highway	5

(JOHN) O'HARA (& PLAYBOYS)
68	Fontana TF 924	In The Shelter Of My Heart/Goodnight Mr. Nightfall (as O'Hara's Playboys)	4
68	Fontana TF 974	I Started A Joke/Show Me (as John O'Hara & Playboys)	5
77	President PT 465	Starsky And Hutch/Sister Rae	4
68	Fontana (S)TL 5461	GET READY (LP, as O'Hara's Playboys)	20

OHIO EXPRESS
68	Pye Intl. NSPL 28117	OHIO EXPRESS (LP)	10
69	Buddah 203 015	CHEWY CHEWY (LP)	10

OHIO PLAYERS
69	Capitol CL 15587	Here Today And Gone Tomorrow/Bad Bargain	5
74	Janus 6146 009	Pain Pts 1 & 2	4
74	Janus 6146 017	Got Pleasure/I Wanna Hear From You	4
74	Westbound 6146 100	Funky Worm/Paint Me	4
74	Mercury 6167 012	Skin Tight/Heaven Must Be Like This	4

75	Mercury 6167 058	Fire/Together	4
74	Mercury 6338 497	SKIN TIGHT (LP)	10

OIL CITY SHIEKS
79	United Artists UP 36514	Don't Take But A Few Minutes/Blues Jam	5

(see also Dr. Feelgood, Lew Lewis)

OINKLETTS
80s	In Tape IT 032	The Oink Song/UNCLE PIGG: Oink Rapp (flexidisc, free with 'Oink' mag)	4

O'JAYS
65	Liberty LIB 66102	Lipstick Traces/Think It Over Baby	30
66	Liberty LIB 66197	Stand In For Love/Friday Night	12
67	Stateside SS 2073	I'll Be Sweeter Tomorrow/I Dig Your Act	35
68	Bell BLL 1020	I'm So Glad I Found You/Look Over Your Shoulder	8
68	Bell BLL 1033	The Choice/Going Going Gone	4
70	Now! NOW 1002	Don't You Know A True Love/That's Alright (p/s)	6
72	United Artists UP 35337	Working On Your Case/Hold On	4
73	Mojo 2092 052	I Dig Your Act/I'll Be Sweeter Tomorrow (reissue)	4
73	CBS 1546	Time To Get Down/Shifty Shadey Jealous Kind Of People	4
74	Power Exchange PX 101	Peace/Little Brother	4
69	Sunset SLS 50038	FULL OF SOUL (LP)	10
73	CBS 65257	BACKSTABBERS (LP)	12
73	Epic EPC 65469	IN PHILADELPHIA (LP)	10

O'KAYSIONS
68	Stateside SS 2126	Girl Watcher/Deal Me In	20

JOHNNY O'KEEFE (& DEE JAYS)
58	Coral Q 72330	Shake Baby Shake/Real Wild Child (as Johnny O'Keefe & Dee Jays)	75
58	Coral Q 72330	Shake Baby Shake/Real Wild Child (as Johnny O'Keefe & Dee Jays) (78)	40
60s	Zodiac ZR 0016	Tell The Blues So Long/Sing	12

(ROGER) EARL OKIN
67	Parlophone R 5644	Yellow Petals/I Can't Face The Animals (as Roger Earl Okin)	4
68	CBS 4495	Stop And You'll Become Aware (as Earl Okin)	8

OLA (& JANGLERS)
67	Decca F 12646	I Can Wait/Eeny Meeny Miney Moe	8
68	Big T BIG 108	What A Way To Die/That's Why I Cry (solo)	6

OLATUNJI
73	Paramount PARA 3038	Soul Makossa Pts 1 & 2	4

OLD & IN THE WAY
75	Round RX 103	OLD AND IN THE WAY (LP)	10

(see also Jerry Garcia, Seatrain, Rowan Brothers)

MIKE OLDFIELD
74	Virgin VS 101	Mike Oldfield's Single (Tubular Bells Theme)/Froggy Went A-Courtin'	8
74	Virgin VS 112	Hergest Ridge excerpt/Spanish Tune (promo-only, no p/s)	50
75	Virgin VS 117	Don Alfonso/In Dulci Jubilo (For Maureen) (some in p/s)	10/4
75	Virgin VS 131	In Dulci Jubilo/On Horseback	5
76	Virgin VS 163	Portsmouth/Speak (Tho' You Only Say Farewell) (Roger Dean or blue/red label, later in brown wraparound p/s)	4
77	Virgin VS 167	The William Tell Overture/Algiers	6
77	Virgin VS 198	The Cuckoo Song/Pipe Song	5
78	Virgin VS 238	TAKE 4 (EP)	4
78	Virgin VS 238-12	TAKE 4 (12", white vinyl, stickered p/s)	7
79	Virgin VS 245-12	Guilty (Extended Mix)/Guilty/Excerpt From Incantations (12", blue vinyl)	7
82	Virgin VSY 464	Five Miles Out/Live Punkadiddle (picture disc)	6
82	Virgin VSY 489	Family Man/Mount Teidi (picture disc)	6
82	Virgin VSY 541	Mistake/Waldberg (The Peak) (picture disc)	6
83	Virgin VSY 586	Moonlight Shadow/Rite Of Man (picture disc)	6
85	Virgin VSD 836	Pictures In The Dark/Legend//Moonlight Shadow/Rite Of Man (double pack in PVC gatefold p/s)	6
86	Virgin VSS 863	Shine/The Past (with Jon Anderson, shaped picture disc)	15
86	Virgin CDEP 6	Islands/When The Night's On Fire/The Wind Chimes (promo-only CD, white gatefold sleeve)	8
74	Virgin QV 2001	TUBULAR BELLS (LP, quadrophonic mix, 2 different mixes)	15
74	Virgin V 2020	STAR'S END (LP, with David Bedford)	10
76	Virgin QV 2043	OMMADAWN (LP, quadrophonic mix)	18
76	Virgin VBOX 1	BOXED (4-LP box set with booklet)	20
78	Virgin VP 2001	TUBULAR BELLS (LP, picture disc in sleeve, stereo remix of quad; 2 versions)	15
79	Tellydisc TELLY 4	IMPRESSIONS (LP, mail order-only)	25
85	Virgin CDBOX 1	BOXED (2-CD set)	25

(see also Sallyangie, David Bedford, Kevin Ayers & Whole World, Jon Anderson)

ANDREW OLDHAM (ORCHESTRA)
64	Decca F 11878	365 Rolling Stones/Oh I Do Like To See Me On The 'B' Side	15
64	Decca F 11987	We Don't All Wear D'same Size Boots/Right Of Way	15
64	Ace Of Clubs ACL 1180	16 HIP HITS (LP)	35
64	Decca LK 4636	LIONEL BART'S MAGGIE MAY (LP)	15
66	Decca LK/SKL 4796	THE ROLLING STONES SONGBOOK (LP)	35

(see also Aranbee Pop Symphony, Rolling Stones, Cleo, Bo & Peep, Jeannie & Her Redheads, Gulliver's Travels, Mighty Avengers)

OLD TIMERS SKIFFLE GROUP
58	Fontana H 105	The Woman Who Loved A Swine/The Lynching Of Jeff Buckner (78)	5

JOHNNY OLENN & HIS BAND
57	London HLU 8388	My Idea Of Love/I Ain't Gonna Cry No More	150

Johnny OLENN

| 57 | London HLU 8388 | My Idea Of Love/I Ain't Gonna Cry No More (78) | 35 |
| 59 | Mercury AMT 1050 | Born Reckless/You Lovable You (as Johnny Olenn & Blockbusters) | 40 |

O-LEVEL
| 78 | Psycho PSYCHO 2 | East Sheen/Pseudo Punk ('map' or 'schoolboy' p/s) | 20/25 |
| 78 | Kings Road KR 002 | THE MALCOLM EP (photocopied wraparound or printed p/s) | 18/10 |

(see also Teenage Filmstars, Times, Television Personalities)

OLIVER
| 74 | Olive OL 1 | STANDING STONE (LP, private press) | 200 |

JOHNNY OLIVER
| 56 | MGM SP 1165 | Chain Gang/These Hands | 8 |
| 60 | Mercury AMT 1095 | What A Kiss Won't Do/That's All I'm Living For | 6 |

SY OLIVER & HIS ORCHESTRA
58	London HL 7067	The Mardi Gras March/One More Time (export issue)	5
59	London HLJ 8776	In A Little Spanish Town Cha-Cha/The Mardi Gras March	6
53	Brunswick LA 8586	FOR DANCERS ONLY (10" LP)	10

OLIVERS
| 57 | Columbia DB 3995 | Ma Curly Headed Baby/Beautiful Dreamer | 5 |

OLLIE & NIGHTINGALES
| 69 | Stax STAX 109 | You're Leaving Me/Showered With Love | 8 |

NIGEL OLSSON
| 72 | DJM DJLPS 417 | DRUM ORCHESTRA (LP) | 10 |

OLYMPICS
58	HMV POP 528	Western Movies/Well!	12
58	HMV POP 528	Western Movies/Well! (78)	10
58	HMV POP 564	(I Wanna) Dance With The Teacher/Everybody Needs Love	15
58	HMV POP 564	(I Wanna) Dance With The Teacher/Everybody Needs Love (78)	20
59	Columbia DB 4346	Private Eye/(Baby) Hully Gully	15
60	Vogue Pop V 9174	I Wish I Could Shimmy Like My Sister Kate/Workin' Hard	10
61	Vogue Pop V 9181	Dance With A Dolly/Dodge City	10
61	Vogue Pop V 9184	Little Pedro/CAPPY LEWIS: Bullfight	12
62	Vogue Pop V 9196	The Twist/Everybody Likes To Cha Cha Cha	10
62	Vogue Pop V 9198	The Stomp/Mash Them 'Taters	10
62	Vogue Pop V 9204	Baby It's Hot/The Scotch	10
63	HMV POP 1155	Nothing/Sidewalk Serenade	7
64	Sue WI 348	The Bounce/Fireworks	15
65	Warner Bros WB 157	Good Lovin'/Olympic Shuffle	12
66	Fontana TF 678	We Go Together (Pretty Baby)/Secret Agents	12
66	Fontana TF 778	Baby, Do The Philly Dog/Western Movies	12
69	Action ACT 4539	Baby, Do The Philly Dog/Mine Exclusively	8
69	Action ACT 4556	I'll Do A Little Bit More/Same Old Thing	7
70	Jay Boy BOY 27	Hully Gully/Big Boy Pete	4
72	Jay Boy BOY 56	Baby, Do The Philly Dog/Secret Agents	4
73	Jay Boy BOY 74	I'll Do A Little Bit More/Same Old Thing (reissue)	4
61	Vocalion VAH 8059	DANCE BY THE LIGHT OF THE MOON (LP)	35
67	London HA-M 8327	SOMETHING OLD, SOMETHING NEW (LP, unissued)	
67	Fontana TL 5407	SOMETHING OLD, SOMETHING NEW (LP)	20
72	Jay Boy JSX 2008	THE OLYMPICS (LP)	10

(see also Cappy Lewis)

PATRICK O'MAGICK
| 74 | Chrysalis CHS 2041 | You're A Winner/The Proposal | 4 |

(see also Patrick Campbell-Lyons)

O.M.D.
(see under Orchestral Manoeuvres In The Dark)

OMEGA
| 76 | Decca SKL 5219 | HALL OF FLOATERS IN THE SKY (LP) | 10 |
| 76 | Decca SKL 5243 | TIME ROBBERS (LP) | 10 |

OMEGA
| 85 | Rock Machine MACH 1 | THE PROPHET (LP) | 20 |

OMEGA TRIBE
| 83 | Crass 221984/10 | ANGRY SONGS (EP) | 4 |

OMEN SEARCHER
| 82 | OCS | Teacher Of Sin (p/s) | 30 |
| 82 | OCS | Too Much (p/s) | 40 |

ONDIOLINE BAND
| 66 | London HL 10022 | Last Bicycle To Brussels/Lovers Of Cologne | 4 |

ONE
| 70 | Fontana STL 5539 | ONE (LP) | 70 |

ONE & ONE
| 64 | Decca F 11948 | I'll Give You Lovin'/It's Me | 4 |

(see also Ivy League, Flowerpot Men)

ONE HAND CLAPPING
| 80s | Curve Of Earth COTE 1 | The Rich Get Rich/Running Down Greek (poster p/s) | 4 |

101'ERS
76	Chiswick S 3	Keys To Your Heart/5 Star Rock & Rock Petrol (p/s)	10
76	Chiswick NS 3	Keys To Your Heart/5 Star Rock & Rock Petrol (reissue, p/s)	6
76	Big Beat NS 3	Keys To Your Heart/5 Star Rock & Rock Petrol (2nd reissue, p/s)	4
80	Big Beat NS 63	Sweet Revenge/Rabies (From The Dogs Of Love) (p/s)	5

| 81 | Andalucia AND 101 | ELGIN AVENUE BREAKDOWN (LP) | 15 |

(see also Clash, Alvaro)

100% PROOF
| 72 | Hot Wax HWX 120 | Never My Love/Since You've Been Gone | 4 |
| 70s | Hot Wax | 100% PROOF (LP) | 12 |

MATTY O'NEIL
51	London L 1037	Don't Sell Daddy Any More Whiskey/Little Rusty (78)	5
51	London L 1095	Whiskey Took My Daddy Away/What's This World Coming To? (78)	5
54	London L 1037	Don't Sell Daddy Any More Whiskey/Little Rusty (gold label, tri-centre)	30
54	London L 1037	Don't Sell Daddy Any More Whiskey/Little Rusty (silver label, tri-centre)	18
54	London L 1037	Don't Sell Daddy Any More Whiskey/Little Rusty (silver top, round centre)	12

JOHNNY O'NEILL
| 59 | RCA RCA 1114 | Wagon Train/Somebody, Just Like You | 6 |

ONE IN A MILLION
| 67 | CBS 202513 | Use Your Imagination/Hold On | 50 |
| 68 | MGM MGM 1370 | Fredereek Hernando/Double Sight | 150 |

ONE MILLION FUZZTONE GUITARS
| 82 | Monsters In Orbit TVEYE 3 | Heaven/Annuese (foldover p/s, at least 2 different designs) | 6 |
| 83 | M'ters In Orbit TVEYE 10 | 26 (LP) | 10 |

ONENESS OF JUJU
| 79 | Buddah BDS 497 | Everyway But Loose/Make A Change | 4 |
| 79 | Buddah BDS 497 | Everyway But Loose/Make A Change (12") | 8 |

1,000 MEXICANS
| 83 | Whaam! WHA-AM 12 | The Art Of Love/News For You (p/s, 1,500 only) | 7 |

1,000 VIOLINS
85	Dreamworld DREAM 2	Halcyon Days/I Remember When Everybody Used To Ride Bikes ... Now We All Drive Cars (12", p/s, 1,000 only)	10
86	Dreamworld DREAM 8	Please Don't Sandblast My House/Time I Broke Down (p/s, 2,000 only)	5
86	Dreamworld DREAM 8T	Please Don't Sandblast My House/You Ungrateful Bastard/Though It Poured The Next Day, I Never Noticed The Rain (12", p/s)	8
87	Dreamworld DREAM 14	Locked Out Of The Love-in/Why Is It Always December? (p/s)	4
87	Dreamworld DREAM 14T	Locked Out Of The Love-in/Why Is It Always December?/I Was Depending On You To Be My Jesus/No-one Was Saving The World (12", p/s)	7
86	Lyntone	You Ungrateful Bastard (fanzine flexidisc)	6

(see also Page Boys)

ONE TWO & THREE
| 65 | Decca F 12093 | Black Pearl/Bahama Lullaby | 8 |
| 65 | Decca LK 4682 | BLACK PEARLS AND GREEN DIAMONDS (LP) | 80 |

ONE WAY SYSTEM
| 82 | Lightbeat WAY 1 | Stab The Judge/Beat The System (p/s) | 5 |
| 82 | Anagram ANA 1 | Just Another Hero/Give Us A Future (p/s) | 4 |

ONLOOKERS
| 82 | Demon D 1012 | You And I/Understand/Julia (p/s) | 15 |

ONLY ONES
77	Vengeance VEN 001	Lovers Of Today/Peter And The Pets (p/s)	10
77	Vengeance VEN 001	Lovers Of Today/Peter And The Pets (12", stickered white sleeve)	12
78	CBS S CBS 6228	Another Girl, Another Planet/Special View (p/s)	8
78	CBS S CBS 6576	Another Girl, Another Planet/As My Wife Says (promo-only, no p/s)	10
78	CBS S CBS 12-6576	Another Girl, Another Planet/As My Wife Says (12", p/s)	10
79	CBS S CBS 7086	You've Got To Pay/This Ain't All (It's Made Out To Be) (p/s)	4
79	CBS S CBS 7285	Out There In The Night/Lovers Of Today (p/s, possibly promo-only)	7
79	CBS S CBS 12-7285	Out There In The Night/Lovers Of Today/Peter And The Pets (12", p/s, blue vinyl, 2 slight sleeve variations)	7
79	CBS S CBS 7963	Trouble In The World/Your Chosen Life (withdrawn 'group' black & red p/s)	60
79	CBS S CBS 7963	Trouble In The World/Your Chosen Life (normal p/s)	5
80	CBS S CBS 8535	Fools/Castle Built On Sand (p/s, with Pauline Murray)	5
83	Vengeance VEN 002	Baby's Got A Gun/PETER PERRETT: Silent Night (no p/s)	4
78	CBS 82830	THE ONLY ONES (LP, orange label)	15
79	CBS 83451	EVEN SERPENTS SHINE (LP, orange label)	15
80	CBS 84089	BABY'S GOT A GUN (LP, orange label)	15

(see also England's Glory)

YOKO ONO
71	Apple APPLE 38	Mrs. Lennon/Midsummer New York (company sleeve)	12
72	Apple APPLE 41	Mind Train/Listen, The Snow Is Falling (p/s)	22/8
73	Apple APPLE 47	Death Of Samantha/Yang Yang	18
73	Apple APPLE 48	Run Run Run/Men Men Men	18
81	Geffen K 79202M	Walking On Thin Ice/It Happened/Hard Times Are Over (cassette, cigarette-pack style box)	8
70	Apple SAPCOR 17	YOKO ONO/PLASTIC ONO BAND (LP, with inner sleeve)	30
71	Apple SAPTU 101/2	FLY (2-LP, with inner sleeves, poster & postcard)	40
73	Apple SAPDO 1001	APPROXIMATELY INFINITE UNIVERSE (2-LP, with inner sleeves)	25
73	Apple SAPCOR 26	FEELING THE SPACE (LP)	35

(see also John Lennon, Bill Elliott & Elastic Oz Band)

ONSLAUGHT
| 83 | Complete Control TROL 1 | First Strike/State Control/No More (p/s) | 6 |

ONYX
68	Pye 7N 17477	You've Gotta Be With Me/It's All Put On	10
68	Pye 7N 17622	My Son John/Step By Step	10
69	Pye 7N 17668	Tamaris Khan/So Sad Inside	25

69	CBS 4635	Time Off/Movin' In	15
71	Parlophone R 5888	Air/Our House	8
71	Parlophone R 5906	The Next Stop Is Mine/What's That You Say	8

OPAL BUTTERFLY
68	CBS 3576	Beautiful Beige/Speak Up	25
69	CBS 3921	Mary Anne With The Shakey Hand/My Gration Or?	60
70	Polydor 2058 041	You're A Groupie Girl/Gigging Song	15

(see also Hawkwind)

JACKIE OPEL
64	Black Swan WI 421	You're No Good/King Liger	10
64	R&B JB 138	Stand By Me (as Jackie Opel & Hortense Ellis)/Solid Rock	10
64	R&B JB 160	Pity The Fool/The Day Will Come	10
65	King KG 1011	Cry Me A River/Eternal Love	10
65	Island WI 203	Wipe Those Tears/Don't Take Your Love	10
65	Island WI 209	Go Away/Shelter The Storm	10
65	Island WI 227	Old Rockin' Chair/SKATALITES: Song Of Love	10
65	Ska Beat JB 190	More Wood In The Fire/Done With A Friend	10
65	Ska Beat JB 227	A Little More/The Lord Is With Thee	10
66	Island WI 264	A Love To Share/ROLAND ALPHONSO: Devoted To You	10
66	Rio R 117	I Am What I Am/JACKIE MITTOO & SKATALITES: Devil's Bug	8

(see also Jackie & Doreen, Doreen & Jackie, Hortense & Jackie)

OPEN MIND
69	Philips BF 1790	Horses And Chariots/Before My Time	35
69	Philips BF 1805	Magic Potion/Cast A Spell	80
69	Philips SBL 7893	OPEN MIND (LP)	250
86	Antar ANTAR 2	OPEN MIND (LP, reissue)	15

OPEN ROAD
| 72 | Greenwich GSS 102 | Swamp Fever/Lost And Found | 6 |
| 71 | Greenwich GSLP 1001 | WINDY DAZE (LP) | 25 |

(see also Warm Sounds, Denny Gerrard, Donovan)

OPERATING THEATRE
| 86 | Mother MUM 4 | Queen Of No Heart/Spring Is Coming With A Strawberry In The Mouth (p/s) | 4 |
| 86 | Mother 12MUM 4 | Queen Of No Heart/Spring Is Coming With A Strawberry In The Mouth/Part Of My Make-up/Atlantean Satanosa (12", p/s) | 7 |

OPPRESSED
| 83 | Firm NICK 1 | NEVER SAY DIE (EP) | 6 |
| 83 | Jungle OPPO 1 | Work Together/Victims (p/s) | 5 |

OPUS
| 69 | Columbia DB 8675 | Baby, Come On/Angela Grey | 15 |

GENE O'QUIN
| 51 | Capitol CL 13600 | Boogie Woogie Fever/RAMBLIN' JIMMY DOLAN: Wine, Women, And Pink Elephants (78) | 10 |

ORA
| 69 | Tangerine OPLOP 0025 | ORA (LP) | 180 |

(see also Byzantium, Movies)

ORAL SEX
| 85 | Conquest QUEST 6 | ORAL SEX (LP) | 10 |

ORANGE BICYCLE
67	Columbia DB 8259	Hyacinth Threads/Amy Peate	15
67	Columbia DB 8311	Laura's Garden/Lavender Girl	15
68	Columbia DB 8352	Early Pearly Morning/Go With Goldie	15
68	Columbia DB 8413	Jenskadajka/Nicely	15
68	Columbia DB 8483	Sing This All Together/Trip On An Orange Bicycle	15
69	Parlophone R 5789	Tonight I'll Be Staying Here With You/Last Cloud Home	8
69	Parlophone R 5811	Carry That Weight/You Never Give Me Your Money/Want To B Side	8
70	Parlophone R 5827	It's Not My World/Take Me To The Pilot	8
70	Parlophone R 5854	Jelly On The Bread/Make It Rain	8
71	Regal Zono. RZ 3029	Goodbye Stranger/Country Comforts	10
70	Parlophone PCS 7108	ORANGE BICYCLE (LP)	40

(see also Motherlight)

ORANGE DISASTER
| 80s | Neuter OD 1 | Something's Got To Give/Out Of The Room/Hiding From Frank | 6 |

(see also Varicose Veins, Architects Of Disaster, Perfect Disaster)

ORANGE JUICE
80	Postcard 80-1	Falling And Laughing/Moscow Olympics/Moscow (foldaround p/s in poly bag, with flexidisc "Felicity (live)" [I Wish I Was A Postcard 1], some with postcard)	60/50
80	I Wish I Was A Postcard 1	Felicity (live) (flexidisc with fanzines)	15
80	Postcard 80-2	Blue Boy/Lovesick (hand-coloured p/s in poly bag, blue labels)	20
80	Postcard 80-2	Blue Boy/Lovesick (brown labels/die-cut sleeve or yellow labels/cream slv)	7/8
80	Postcard 80-6	Simply Thrilled Honey/Breakfast Time (p/s, with picture insert & card in bag)	18
80	Postcard 80-6	Simply Thrilled Honey/Breakfast Time (brown die-cut sleeve)	7
81	Postcard 81-2	Poor Old Soul/Poor Old Soul Pt 2 (die-cut sleeve, some with postcard)	10/7
81	Postcard 81-6	Wan Light/You Old Eccentric (unreleased)	
83	Polydor POSP 547/OJ 2	Rip It Up/Snake Charmer//Love Sick/Sad Lament (double pack, poster p/s)	6
83	Polydor OJ 4	Flesh Of My Flesh/Lord John White And The Bottleneck Train (picture disc)	4
84	Polydor OJ 5	Bridge/Out For The Count (p/s, with free flexidisc "Poor Old Soul [live]")	5
84	Polydor OJ 6/OJC 6	What Presence/A Place In My Heart//Nutshell/Simply Thrilled Honey/Dying Day (p/s, with free cassette)	5

(see also Edwyn Collins, Fun Four, Josef K)

ORANGE MACHINE
68	Pye 7N 17559	Three Jolly Little Dwarfs/Real Life Permanent Dream	40
69	Pye 7N 17680	You Can All Join In/Dr. Crippen's Waiting Room	40

ORANGE PEEL
70	Reflection RS 5	I Got No Time/Searching For A Place To Hide	10

ORANGE SEAWEED
68	Pye 7N 17515	Stay Awhile/Pictures In The Sky	20

(see also Kingpins)

ORB
89	Wau! Mr Modo MWS 010T	KISS (12" EP, 949 only, die-cut company sleeve)	40
90	Wau! Mr Modo MWS 017T	A Huge Ever Growing Pulsating Brain That Rules From The Centre Of The Ultraworld: Loving You (Orbital Mix)/(Bucket And Spade Mix)/Why Is 6 Scared Of 7 (12" p/s, B-side matrix states 'MWS 016T')	25
90	Wau! Mr Modo MWS 017T	A Huge Ever-Growing Pulsating Remix/From One Ear To Another/Why Is 6 Scared Of 7? (12" white label promo, 100 only)	40
90	Wau! Mr Modo MWS 017R	A Huge Ever-Growing Pulsating Brain That Rules From The Centre Of The Ultraworld (Orbital Dance Mix)/(Orbital Radio Mix)/(Aubrey Mix Mk II) (12", 1000 only, stamped white label promos)	40
90	Big Life BLR 270T	A Huge Ever-Growing Pulsating Brain That Rules From The Centre Of The Ultraworld : Loving You (edited)/(Bucket And Spade Mix)/Why Is 6 Scared Of 7 (12" p/s, 8000 only, B-side matrix states 'MWS 016T')	20
90	Big Life BLR 270CD	A Huge Ever-Growing Pulsating Brain That Rules From The Centre Of The Ultraworld : Loving You (Original Ambient House Mix) (CD)	20
90	Big Life BLR 27T	A Huge Ever-Growing Pulsating Remix (Orbital Dance Mix)/(9am Radio Mix)/(Aubrey Mix I) (12" p/s, 8000 only)	25
90	Big Life BLR 27CD	A Huge Ever-Growing Pulsating Remix (Orbital Dance Mix)/(9am Radio Mix)/(Aubrey Mix I) (CD)	25
90	Big Life BLR 33	Little Fluffy Clouds/Ambient Mix Mk 1 (p/s)	4
90	Big Life BLR 33T	Little Fluffy Clouds (Dance Mk 2)/Into The Fourth Dimension (Essenes Beyond Control)/Little Fluffy Clouds (Ambient Mk 1) (12", p/s)	15
90	Big Life BLR 33CD	Little Fluffy Clouds (Dance Mk 2)/Into The Fourth Dimension (Essenes Beyond Control)/Little Fluffy Clouds (Ambient Mk 1) (CD)	15
90	Big Life BLR 33R	Little Fluffy Clouds (Drum & Vox Version)/(Seven Inch Mk 1)/Into The Fourth Dimension (12" remix, p/s)	18
91	Big Life BLR 46	Perpetual Dawn: Solar Youth/Star 6&789 (Phase II) (p/s)	5
91	Big Life BLRT 46	Perpetual Dawn: Solar Flare Extended Mix/Star 6&789 (Phase II)/Perpetual Dawn: Ultrabass (12", p/s)	12
91	Big Life BLR 46CD	Perpetual Dawn: Solar Youth/Star 6&789 (Phase II)/Perpetual Dawn: Solar Flare (CD)	12
91	Big Life BLR R46	Orb In Dub: Towers Of Dub (Ambient Mix)/Perpetual Dawn (Ultrabass II) (12" remix, stickered p/s, with Jah Wobble)	25
92	Big Life BLRDA 75	Blue Room (CD card pack with postcard. gatefold sleeve)	7
90	Big Life ORB PROMO 1	A Huge Ever-Growing Pulsating Remix (Orbital Dance Mix)/(9am Radio Mix)/(Aubrey Mix Mk 1) (12" promo)	15
90	Big Life ORB PROMO 2	Little Fluffy Clouds (Dance Mk 1)/Into The Fourth Dimension/Little Fluffy Clouds (Ambient Mk 1) (12" promo)	15
91	Big Life ORB PROMO 3	Perpetual Dawn: Ultrabass/Perpetual Dawn: Solar Flare (12" promo)	12
91	Big Life ORB PICTURE 3	Perpetual Dawn: Ultrabass II (12" 1-sided promo picture disc, 400 only, stickered PVC sleeve)	30
91	Big Life ORB PICTURE 3	Perpetual Dawn: Ultrabass II (12" 1-sided picture disc, mispress, plays "Towers Of Dub (Ambient)", 400 pressed but 300 allegedly destroyed)	40
91	Big Life	THE ORB SAMPLER (4-track promo)	25
92	Big Life ORB PROMO 4	Blue Room (Part One)/(Part Two) (12" promo)	8
92	Big Life BLR 81D	Blue Room (Radio 7)/Assassin (Radio 7) (jukebox 7", 1000 only)	15
92	Big Life ORB PROMO CD 5	Assassin (Radio 7 Edit)/(Another Live Version)/(Chocolate Hills Of Bohol Mix) (CD promo)	7
92	Big Life ORB PROMO 5	Assassin (The Oasis Of Rhythms Mix)/(Another Live Version) (12" promo, turquoise vinyl)	12
91	Big Life BLRDLP 5	THE ORB'S ADVENTURES BEYOND THE UNDERWORLD (2-LP with inner sleeve, 'classical pressing')	14
91	Big Life BLRLP 14	THE ORB AUBREY MIXES: THE ULTRAWORLD EXCURSIONS (LP, with inner sleeve)	16
91	Big Life BLRC 14	THE ORB AUBREY MIXES: THE ULTRAWORLD EXCURSIONS (cassette)	10
91	Big Life BLRCD 14	THE ORB AUBREY MIXES: THE ULTRAWORLD EXCURSIONS (CD)	20
92	Big Life BLRLP 18	UFORB (3-LP, with inner sleeves & 2 art prints in sealed green pack)	25
92	Big Life BRLLP 18	UFORB (2-LP, with inner sleeves & 2 art prints in sealed black pack)	16

(see also System 7, KLF, JAMs, Jah Wobble)

ORBIDÖIG
81	Situation 2 SIT 15	Nocturnal Operation/Down Periscope (p/s)	8

(see also Associates)

ROY ORBISON
60	London HLU 9149	Only The Lonely (Know How I Feel)/Here Comes That Song Again	6
60	London HLU 9149	Only The Lonely (Know How I Feel)/Here Comes That Song Again (78)	150
60	London HLU 9207	Blue Angel/Today's Teardrops	6
61	London HLU 9307	I'm Hurtin'/I Can't Stop Loving You	6
61	London HLU 7108	I'm Hurtin'/I Can't Stop Loving You (export issue)	15
61	London HLU 9342	Runnin' Scared/Love Hurts	5
61	London HLU 9405	Cryin'/Candy Man	5
62	London HLU 9511	Dream Baby/The Actress	5
62	London HLU 9561	The Crowd/Mama	5
62	London HLU 9607	Workin' For The Man/Leah	6
63	London HLU 9676	In Dreams/Shahdaroba	5
63	London HLU 9727	Falling/Distant Drums	5

Roy ORBISON

MINT VALUE £

63	London HLU 9777	Blue Bayou/Mean Woman Blues	5
64	London HLU 9845	Borne On The Wind/What'd I Say	5
64	London HLU 9882	It's Over/Indian Wedding	4
64	Ember EMB S 197	You're My Baby/Rock House	7
64	Ember EMB S 200	This Kind Of Love/I Never Knew (some in p/s)	12/7
64	London HLU 9919	Oh, Pretty Woman/Yo Te Amo Maria	4
64	London HLU 9930	Pretty Paper/Summersong	5
65	London HLU 9951	Goodnight/Only With You	5
65	Ember EMB S 209	Sweet And Easy To Love/You're Gonna Cry (some in p/s)	12/7
65	London HLU 9978	(Say) You're My Girl/Sleepy Hollow	4
65	London HLU 9986	Ride Away/Wondering	4
65	London HLU 10000	Crawling Back/If You Can't Say Something Nice	5
66	London HLU 10015	Breakin' Up Is Breakin' My Heart/Wait	5
66	London HLU 10034	Twinkle Toes/Where Is Tomorrow	5
66	London HLU 10051	Lana/House Without Windows	5
66	London HLU 10067	Too Soon To Know/You'll Never Be Sixteen Again	5
66	London HLU 10096	There Won't Be Many Coming Home/Going Back To Gloria	5
67	London HLU 10113	So Good/Memories	5
67	London HLU 10143	Cry Softly Lonely One/Pistolero	5
67	London HLU 10159	She/Here Comes The Rain Baby	5
68	London HLU 10176	Born To Be Loved By You/Shy Away	5
68	London HLU 10206	Walk On/Flowers	6
68	London HLU 10222	Heartache/Sugar Man	6
69	London HLU 10261	My Friend/Southbound Jerico Pathway	7
69	London HLU 10285	Penny Arcade/Tennessee Owns My Soul	10
69	London HLU 10294	Break My Heart (by Roy Orbison & Art Movement)/How Do You Start Over	7
70	London HLU 10310	So Young/If I Had A Woman Like You	7
71	London HLU 10339	(Love Me Like You Did It) Last Night/Close Again	7
72	Sun 6094 001	Ooby Dooby/Devil Doll	4
72	London HLU 10358	God Love You/Changes	7
72	London HLU 10388	Memphis Tennessee/I Can Read Between The Lines	7
72	London HLU 10388	Memphis Tennessee/I Can Read Between The Lines (export copies with alternate take of A-side: matrix no. MSC-8474-T2-IL)	15
85	ZTT DZTAS 9	Wild Hearts/Wild Hearts (Voiceless)//Ooby Dooby/Crying (double pack)	25
57	London RES 1089	HILLBILLY ROCK (EP, orange p/s, mauve/gold label, triangular centre)	80
57	London RES 1089	HILLBILLY ROCK (EP, orange p/s, mauve/silver label, round centre)	60
57	London RES 1089	HILLBILLY ROCK (EP, re-pressing, yellow p/s, silver-top, round centre)	40
60	London REU 1274	ONLY THE LONELY (EP)	12
63	London REU 1354	ROY ORBISON (EP)	12
63	London REU 1373	IN DREAMS (EP)	12
64	Ember EP 4546	SWEET AND EASY TO LOVE (EP)	30
64	Ember EP 4563	TRYIN' TO GET TO YOU (EP)	30
64	London REU 1435	IT'S OVER (EP)	12
64	London REU 1437	OH PRETTY WOMAN (EP)	12
65	London REU 1439	ROY ORBISON'S STAGE SHOW HITS (EP)	12
65	Ember EP 4570	DEVIL DOLL (EP)	30
65	London REU 1440	LOVE HURTS (EP)	15
61	London HA-U 2342	LONELY AND BLUE (LP)	25
62	London HA-U 2437	CRYIN' (LP, also stereo SAH-U 6229)	20/25
63	London HA-U/SH-U 8108	IN DREAMS (LP, mono/stereo)	18/22
64	London HA-U 8207	OH, PRETTY WOMAN (LP)	16
64	Ember NR 5013	THE EXCITING SOUNDS OF ROY ORBISON (LP)	14
65	London HA-U/SH-U 8252	THERE IS ONLY ONE ROY ORBISON (LP, mono/stereo)	18/22
65	Ember FA 2005	ROY ORBISON AND OTHERS (LP, with 4 tracks by Orbison)	10
66	London HA-U/SH-U 8279	THE ORBISON WAY (LP, mono/stereo)	18/22
67	Monument LMO/SMO 5004	ORBISONGS (LP)	16
66	London HA-U/SH-U 8297	THE CLASSIC ROY ORBISON (LP, black label mono/blue label stereo)	16/18
67	Monument LMO/SMO 5007	ROY ORBISON'S GREATEST HITS (LP)	12
67	London HA-U/SH-U 8318	SINGS DON GIBSON (LP, black label mono/blue label stereo)	16/18

(unless stated, the above London LPs originally had plum labels [mono] or blue labels [stereo]; later pressings had black labels [mono] or plum labels [stereo] with a boxed London logo and are worth around two-thirds the value)

68	London HA-U/SH-U 8357	CRY SOFTLY, LONELY ONE (LP)	18
68	London HA-U/SH-U 8358	SONGS FROM "THE FASTEST GUITAR ALIVE" FILM SOUNDTRACK (LP)	25
68	Monument LMO/SMO 5013	EARLY ORBISON (LP)	15
68	Monument LMO/SMO 5014	MORE OF ROY ORBISON'S GREATEST HITS (LP)	12
70	London HA-U/SH-U 8406	THE BIG "O" (LP)	16
72	London SH-U 8435	ROY ORBISON SINGS (LP)	14
72	Ember NR 5013	THE EXCITING SOUND OF ROY ORBISON (LP)	10
73	London SH-U 8445	MEMPHIS (LP)	20
79	Asylum K 53092	LAMINAR FLOW (LP)	12

(see also K.D. Lang & Roy Orbison)

ORBIT FIVE

| 68 | Decca F 12799 | I Wanna Go To Heaven/Walking (some in p/s) | 25/10 |

ORCHESTRAL MANOEUVRES IN THE DARK (O.M.D.)

79	Factory FAC 6	Electricity/Almost (black 'braille' p/s)	15
79	Din Disc DIN 2	Electricity (Version)/Almost (p/s, reissue)	5
79	Din Disc DIN 2	Electricity (LP Version)/Almost (version) (2nd reissue, different rear sleeve)	5
80	Din Disc DIN 6	Red Flame White Heat/I Betray My Friends (p/s)	6
80	Din Disc DIN 15-10	Messages (Extended)/Waiting For The Man/Taking Sides Again (10", p/s)	6
80	Din Disc DIN 22-12	Enola Gay (Extended)/Annex (12", p/s, shrinkwrapped)	7
80	Din Disc DIN 24-10	Souvenir (Extended)/Motion And Heart (Amazon Version)/Sacred Heart (10", p/s)	6
81	Flexi/Smash Hits (no cat. no.)	Pretending To See The Future (Live Version)/NASH THE SLASH: Swing-Shift (Flexi-Version) (blue 33rpm 1-sided flexidisc free with 'Smash Hits')	5/4

730 Rare Record Price Guide

82	Din Disc DIN 40-12	Maid Of Orleans (The Waltz Joan Of Arc)/Navigation/Of All Things We've Made (12", 'coin' cover; incorrectly lists "Experiments In Vertical Take-Off")	8
82	Virgin VSY 527	Genetic Engineering/4-Neu (picture disc)	5
83	Virgin VSY 580	Telegraph/66 And Fading (picture disc)	5
83	Virgin VS 580-12	Telegraph (Extended)/66 And Fading (12", p/s)	7
84	Virgin VSS 660	Locomotion/Her Body In My Soul (train-shaped picture disc)	7
84	Virgin VSY 685	Talking Loud And Clear/Julia's Song (picture disc)	6
84	Virgin VSY 727	Never Turn Away/Wrappup (picture disc)	6
85	Virgin VS 766-13	So In Love (Extended Remix)/Concrete Hands (Extended)/Maria Gallante (12"; p/s, record listed as VS 766-12)	7
85	Virgin VSY 766-14	So In Love (Extended Remix)/Concrete Hands (Extended)/Maria Gallante (12", picture disc)	7
85	Virgin VS 796-12	Secret (Extended)/Drift//Red Frame — White Light/I Betray My Friends (12", double pack)	8
85	Virgin VSS 811	La Femme Accident/Firegun (shaped picture disc)	7
85	Virgin VSD 811-12	La Femme Accident/Firegun/La Femme Accident (12" Mix)/Locomotion (live)/ Enola Gay (12", double pack)	7
86	Virgin VSY 888	(Forever) Live And Die/This Town (picture disc)	5
86	Virgin VSD 911	We Love You/(Dub)//If You Leave/88 Seconds In Greensboro' (double pack)	4
86	Virgin VSC 911	We Love You/We Love You (Dub)//Souvenir/Electricity/Enola Gay/ Joan Of Arc/We Love You/We Love You (Dub) (with free cassette)	8
86	Virgin VS 911-12	We Love You (Extended)/We Love You/We Love You (Dub) (12", p/s)	7
87	Virgin MIKE 938-12	Shame (Extended Re-recorded Version)/Goddess Of Love/ (Forever) Live And Die (12" Mix) (CD, gatefold p/s)	10
88	Virgin VSY 987-12	Dreaming (Extended)/Satellite/Gravity Never Failed (12", picture disc with poster)	7
88	Virgin VS 987-10	Dreaming (The William Orbit Remix)/Dreaming/Messages/Secret (10", numbered p/s)	7
88	Virgin VSCDX 987	Dreaming (Extended)/Satellite/Gravity Never Failed/Dreaming (CD, trifold digipak)	10
88	Virgin TRICD 4	Dreaming/Satellite/Gravity Never Failed (3" CD with adaptor)	7
88	Virgin CDT 12	The Locomotion/Her Body In My Soul/The Avenue (3" CD)	7
88	Virgin CDT 27	Maid Of Orleans (The Waltz Joan Of Arc)//Navigation/Joan Of Arc/ Of All Things We've Made (3" CD)	8
91	Virgin VSCDX 1310	Sailing On The Seven Seas (Extended)/Burning/Dancing On The Seven Seas/Big Town (CD, in foldout box)	12
80	Din Disc DID 6	ORGANISATION (LP, with free 7" "Introducing Radios"/"Distance Fades Between Us"/"Progress"/"Once When I Was Six" [DEP 2])	10
84	Virgin V 2310	JUNK CULTURE (LP, with free 7" "Angels Keep Turning The Wheels Of The Universe" [JUNK 1])	10

ORCHIDS

63	Decca F 11743	Gonna Make Him Mine/Stay At Home	10
63	Decca F 11785	Love Hit Me/Don't Make Me Mad	10
64	Decca F 11861	I've Got The Feeling/Larry	10

ORCHIDS

88	Sarah SARAH 002	I've Got A Habit/Give Me Some Peppermint Freedom/Apologies (foldover p/s with poster, 1,000 only)	15
88	Sha La La BaBaBaBaBa 5	From This Day/SEA URCHINS: Summertime (flexidisc, p/s, 2,500 only)	8

ORE

82	Bandit BR 003	Your Time Will Come/Yellow River (p/s)	20

CHARLES ORGANAIRE

64	R&B JB 149	Little Village/It Happens On A Holiday	8
64	Rio R 28	Little Village/It Happens On A Holiday (reissue)	8

ORGANISATION

70	RCA SF 8111	TONE FLOAT (LP)	80
	(see also Kraftwerk)		

ORGANISERS

66	Pye 7N 17022	Lonesome Road/The Organiser	50

ORGANUM/NEW BLOCKADERS

80s	Aeroplane AR 7	Pulp Pts 1 & 2 (gatefold p/s)	30
	(see also Nurse With Wound)		

ORIGINAL BARMSTORMERS SPASM BAND

50s	Tempo A 168	That's All There Is/Stormin' The Barn	6

ORIGINAL BLIND BOYS OF ALABAMA

65	Fontana 688 520 ZL	OLD TIME RELIGION (LP)	10

ORIGINAL CHECKMATES

62	Pye 7N 15428	Hot Toddy/Tuxedo Junction	8
62	Pye 7N 15442	Checkmate Stomp/Begin The Beguine	10
63	Decca F 11688	Union Pacific/The Spy	18
	(see also Checkmates)		

ORIGINAL DIXIELAND JAZZ BAND

56	HMV DLP 1065	HISTORIC RECORDS OF THE FIRST RECORDED JAZZ (10" LP)	20
56	Columbia 33S 1087	ORIGINAL DIXIELAND JAZZ BAND IN ENGLAND (1919) (10" LP)	20
56	Columbia 33S 1133	ORIGINAL DIXIELAND JAZZ BAND IN ENGLAND NO. 2 (1919-20) (10" LP)	20

ORIGINAL DYAKS

67	Columbia DB 8184	Got To Get A Good Thing Going/Would You Love Me Too	8

ORIGINAL NEW ORLEANS RHYTHM KINGS

54	Columbia SCM 5113	Golden Leaf Strut/She's Crying For Me	7

ORIGINALS

59	London HL 8783	Sleepless Nights/Anna (unissued)	
62	Top Rank JAR 600	Gimme A Little Kiss, Will Ya, Huh/At Times Like This	12

ORIGINALS

67	Tamla Motown TMG 592	Goodnight Irene/Need Your Lovin', Want You Back	35
69	Tamla Motown TMG 702	Green Grow The Lilacs/You're The One	6
70	Tamla Motown TMG 733	Baby I'm For Real/The Moment Of Truth	6
72	Tamla Motown TMG 822	God Bless Whoever Sent You/I Like Your Style/Baby I'm For Real	5
76	T. Motown TMGT 1038	Down To Love Town/Just To Be Closer To You (12")	10
76	Tamla Motown TMG 1066	Six Million Dollar Man/Mother Nature's Best (unreleased)	
69	T. Motown (S)TML 11116	GREEN GROW THE LILACS (LP)	15

ORIGINAL TORNADOES

65	SRT SRTS 75350	Telstar/Red Rocket	8

ORIGINELLS 4

64	Columbia DB 7259	My Girl/Kathy (as Origenells)	10
64	Columbia DB 7388	Nights/I Can Make You Mine	8

ORIOLES

53	London L 1180	Hold Me, Thrill Me, Kiss Me/Teardrops On My Pillow (78)	60
53	London L 1201	Crying In The Chapel/Don't You Think I Ought To Know (78)	60
54	London HL 8001	In The Mission Of St. Augustine/Write And Tell Me Why (78)	60

ORION THE HUNTER

84	Portrait PRT 25906	ORION THE HUNTER (LP)	10

ORLANDO

69	NEMS 56-4159	Am I The Same Guy/Poor Little Me	6

TONY ORLANDO

61	Fontana H 308	Halfway To Paradise/Lonely Tomorrows	10
61	Fontana H 330	Bless You/Am I The Guy	7
61	Fontana H 350	Happy Times (Are Here To Stay)/Lonely Am I	7
62	Fontana H 366	Talkin' About You/My Baby's A Stranger	6
62	Columbia DB 4871	Chills/At The Edge Of Tears	6
63	Columbia DB 4954	Beautiful Dreamer/The Loneliest	6
63	Columbia DB 4991	Shirley/Joanie	6
64	Columbia DB 7288	Tell Me What Can I Do/She Doesn't Know It	6
63	Columbia SEG 8238	BLESS YOU (EP)	35
63	Fontana TFL 5167	BLESS YOU (LP, also stereo STFL 582)	40/50

ORLONS

62	Columbia DB 4865	The Wah Watusi/Holiday Hill	10
62	Cameo Parkway C 231	The Conservative/Don't Hang Up	6
63	Cameo Parkway C 243	South Street/Them Terrible Boots	7
63	Cameo Parkway C 257	Not Me/My Best Friend	7
63	Cameo Parkway C 273	Crossfire/It's No Big Thing	8
63	Cameo Parkway C 287	Bon Doo Wah/Don't Throw Your Love Away	10
63	Cameo Parkway C 295	Shimmy Shimmy/Everything Nice	7
64	Cameo Parkway C 319	Rules Of Love/Heartbreak Hotel	10
64	Cameo Parkway C 332	Knock Knock (Who's There)/Goin' Places	10
66	Planet PLF 117	Spinnin' Top/Anyone Who Had A Heart	40
72	Mojo 2092 029	Spinnin' Top/Anyone Who Had A Heart (reissue)	6
62	Cameo Parkway C 1033	ALL THE HITS (LP)	30
63	Cameo Parkway C 1061	BIGGEST HITS (LP)	25

CYRIL ORNANDEL (ORCHESTRA)

55	MGM SP 1141	King Of Kings (Theme From)/El Cid (Theme From)	6

ORPHAN

86	Swoop RTLS 013	Nervous/Little England (p/s)	4

ORPHEUS

66	Red Bird RB 10-041	My Life/Music Minus Orpheus	10

ORPHEUS

68	MGM MGM 1413	I've Never Seen Love Like This/Lesley's World	4
68	MGM C(S) 8072	ORPHEUS (LP)	12

ORSON FAMILY

83	Orson Enterprises OE 1	Heartbeat/(Be My) Ball And Chain/You Shake My Soul (gatefold p/s)	6

KID ORY & HIS CREOLE JAZZ/DIXIELAND BAND

53	Columbia SCM 5047	Mahogany Hall Stomp/At A Georgia Camp Meeting	4
53	Columbia SCM 5069	Tiger Rag/The World's Jazz Crazy, Lawdy So Am I	4
56	Tempo A 106	Dippermouth Blues/Savoy Blues	4
56	Tempo A 107	High Society/Ballin' The Jack	4
56	Vogue V 2011	Tiger Rag/Eh, La-Bas	4
56	Vogue V 2012	12th Street Rag/Savoy Blues	4
56	Good Time Jazz GV 2322	When The Saints Go Marching In/Muskrat Rumble	4
56	Good Time Jazz GV 2339	St. James Infirmary/Bill Bailey, Won't You Please Come Home	4
50s	Storyville SEP 317	KID ORY (EP)	7
50s	Tempo EXA 5	KID ORY'S CREOLE JAZZ BAND (EP)	7
55	Vogue EPV 1035	KID ORY'S CREOLE JAZZ BAND (EP)	7
50s	Good Time Jazz EPG 1006	KID ORY'S CREOLE JAZZ BAND (EP)	7
59	Philips BBE 12275	KID ORY (EP)	7
60	Collector JE 117	IN THE BEGINNING (EP)	7
54	Goodtime Jazz LDG 055	KID ORY'S CREOLE JAZZ BAND 1944-1945 (10" LP)	14
54	Goodtime Jazz LDG 093	KID ORY'S CREOLE JAZZ BAND 1944-1945 VOL. 2 (10" LP)	14
56	Goodtime Jazz LDG 184	KID ORY'S CREOLE JAZZ BAND 1944-1945 VOL. 3 (10" LP)	14
58	Columbia Clef 33CX 10116	KID ORY IN EUROPE (LP)	12

MINT VALUE £

59	Columbia Clef 33CX 10134	SONG OF THE WANDERER (LP)	12
59	HMV CLP 1303	A KID FROM NEW ORLEANS — ORY, THAT IS (LP)	10
50s	Capitol T 389	SONG OF THE WANDERER (LP, reissue)	10
60	HMV CLP 1329	IN THE MOOD (LP)	10
60	HMV CLP 1364	KID ORY PLAYS W.C. HANDY (LP)	10
60	HMV CLP 1395/CSD 1325	DANCE WITH KID ORY — OR JUST LISTEN (LP)	10
61	HMV CLP 1422	WE'VE GOT RHYTHM (LP, with Red Allen)	10

MIKE OSBORNE
71	Turtle TUR 300	OUTBACK (LP)	40

OSBORNE BROTHERS
62	MGM MGM 1184	The Banjo Boys/Poor Old Cora	8
59	MGM MGM-EP 691	COUNTRY PICKING AND HILLSIDE SINGING (EP)	20

JOHNNY OSBOURNE & SENSATIONS
70	Trojan TTL 29	COME BACK DARLING (LP)	15

OZZY OSBOURNE
80	Jet JET 197	Crazy Train/You Looking At Me Looking At You (p/s)	5
80	Jet JET 7003	Mr. Crowley (live)/You Said It All (live) (p/s)	8
80	Jet JET 12003	Mr. Crowley (live)/You Said It All (live)/Suicide Solution (live) (12", p/s)	8
80	Jet JETP 12003	Mr. Crowley (live)/You Said It All (live)/Suicide Solution (live) (12", picture disc)	15
81	Jet JET 7017	Over The Mountain/I Don't Know (p/s)	4
81	Jet JET 12017	Over The Mountain/I Don't Know (12", p/s)	7
82	Jet JET 7030	Symptom Of The Universe/N.I.B. (p/s)	4
82	Jet JETP 7030	Symptom Of The Universe/N.I.B. (picture disc)	10
82	Jet JET 12030	Symptom Of The Universe/N.I.B./Children Of The Grave (12", p/s)	8
83	Epic TA 3915	Bark At The Moon/One Up The B-Side (12", p/s, silver vinyl)	20
83	Epic WA 3915	Bark At The Moon/One Up The B-Side (12", picture disc)	15
84	Epic DA 4452	So Tired/Bark At The Moon (live)//Waiting For Darkness/Paranoid (live) (double pack)	6
84	Epic TA 4452	So Tired/Bark At The Moon (live)/Waiting For Darkness/Suicide Solution/Paranoid (live) (12", p/s, with patch)	7
84	Epic WA 4452	So Tired/Bark At The Moon (live)/Waiting For Darkness/Suicide Solution (live) (12", p/s, gold vinyl)	12
86	Epic A 6859	Shot In The Dark/Rock'n'Roll Rebel (p/s, with signature card)	5
86	Epic QA 6859	Shot In The Dark/Rock'n'Roll Rebel (poster p/s)	6
86	Epic A 7311	The Ultimate Sin/Lightning Strikes (p/s, with free patch)	4
88	Epic 653063-9	Miracle Man/Crazy Babies (head-shaped picture disc)	8
88	Spieal Scratch 2/Ozzy 1	An Interview With (free with 'Spiral Scratch' magazine issue 2, 5000 only)	4
86	Epic EPC 11-26404	THE ULTIMATE SIN (LP, picture disc)	10
	(see also Black Sabbath)		

BOB OSBURN
64	London HLD 9869	Bound To Happen/Think Of Me	10

OSCAR
66	Reaction 591 003	Club Of Lights/Waking Up	15
66	Reaction 591 006	Join My Gang/Days Gone By	15
67	Reaction 591 012	Over The Wall We Go/Every Day Of My Life	15
67	Reaction 591 016	Holiday/Give Her All She Wants	15
68	Polydor 56257	Open Up The Skies/Wild Ones	15
	(see also Ivor Bird, Paul Nicholas, David Bowie)		

OSCAR
74	Buk BULP 2001	OSCAR (LP)	12

OSCAR BICYCLE
68	CBS 3237	On A Quiet Night/The Room Revolves Around Me	20

WAVIS O'SHAVE
80s	Company CR 3	DENNIS SMOKES TABS (EP)	4
80s	Anti-Pop AP 2	ANNA FORD'S BUM (LP)	10

OSIBISA
71	MCA MKS 5079	Music For Gong Gong/Woyaya	5
73	Buddah 2011 179	Superfly Man/Prophets	4
71	MCA MDKS 8001	OSIBISA (LP)	12
71	MCA MDKS 8005	WOYOYA (LP)	12
73	Buddah 2318 087	SUPER FLY T.N.T. (LP, soundtrack)	10

DONNY OSMOND
72	MGM 2006 071	Go Away Little Girl/Time To Ride	4
72	MGM 2006 087	Hey Girl/I Knew You When	4
73	MGM 2006 300	Young Love/Million To One (p/s)	4
	(see also Osmond Brothers, Osmonds)		

OSMOND BROTHERS
63	MGM MGM 1208	Be My Little Baby Bumble Bee/I Wouldn't Know	20
63	MGM MGM 1245	Travels Of Jamie McPheeters/Aura Lee	15
	(see also Osmonds)		

OSMONDS
72	MGM 2006 021	One Bad Apple/He Ain't Heavy He's My Brother	4
72	MGM 2006 043	Sweet And Innocent/Motown Special (Medley)	4
	(see also Osmond Brothers, Donny Osmond)		

OSSIAN
79	Iona IR 001	ST. KILDA WEDDING (LP)	10
81	Iona IR 002	SEALSONG (LP)	10
83	Springthyme SPR 1004	OSSIAN (LP)	10

OSSIE & UPSETTERS
66	Doctor Bird DB 1018	Turn Me On/True Love	10

(see also Upsetters)

GILBERT O'SULLIVAN
(see under Gilbert)

OTHER BROTHERS
69	Pama PM 785	Let's Get Together/Little Girl	6

OTHERS
64	Fontana TF 501	Oh Yeah/I'm Taking Her Home	50

(see also Sands; note this single does NOT include Brian May)

OTHER TWO
64	Decca F 11911	I Wanna Be With You/Grumbling Guitar	8
65	RCA RCA 1465	Don't You Wanna Love Me/Hold Back The Light Of Dawn	4
66	RCA RCA 1531	I'll Never Let You Go/Hot At Night	4

CLYDE OTIS ORCHESTRA
61	Mercury AMT 1143	Jungle Drums/Peanut Vendor	5

JOHNNY OTIS SHOW
50	Parlophone R 3291	Harlem Nocturne (solo)/SLIM GAILLARD: Jam Man (78)	25
57	Capitol CL 14794	Ma (He's Makin' Eyes At Me)/Romance In The Dark	8
58	Capitol CL 14817	Bye Bye Baby (as Johnny Otis Show with Marie Adams)/Good Golly	12
58	Capitol CL 14837	The Light Still Shines In My Window/All I Want Is Your Love (as Johnny Otis Show with Marie Adams)	8
58	Capitol CL 14854	Well, Well, Well, Well!/You Just Kissed Me Goodbye (as Johnny Otis Show with Mel Williams)	8
58	Capitol CL 14875	Ring-A-Ling/The Johnny Otis Hand Jive	12
58	Capitol CL 14941	Crazy Country Hop/Willie Did The Cha Cha	12
59	Capitol CL 15008	You/My Dear (as Johnny Otis Show with Mel Williams)	8
59	Capitol CL 15018	Castin' My Spell/Telephone Baby (as Johnny Otis Show with Marci Lee)	8
59	Capitol CL 15057	Three Girls Named Molly Doin' The Hully Gully/I'll Do The Same Thing For You	8
60	Capitol CL 15112	Mumblin' Mosie/Hey Baby, Don't You Know?	8
59	Capitol EAP1 1134	THE JOHNNY OTIS SHOW (EP)	35
65	Vocalion VEP 170162	JOHNNY OTIS (EP)	60
58	Capitol T 940	THE JOHNNY OTIS SHOW (LP)	40
60s	Ember SPE 6604	FORMIDABLE (LP)	15
69	Sonet SNTF 613	COLD SHOT (LP)	10
71	Epic EPC 66295	LIVE AT MONTEREY (2-LP)	10
73	Starline SRS 5129	PIONEERS OF ROCK VOLUME 3 (LP)	12

(see also Marie Adams)

SHUGGIE OTIS
70	CBS 63996	HERE COMES SHUGGIE OTIS (LP)	15

(see also Al Kooper & Shuggie Otis)

NOIT OTNI & PITS
80s	Automotive AERS 107	A Heart Can Only Be Broken Once/Moving Target (p/s)	5

KNUCKLES O'TOOLE
59	Top Rank JAR 125	If You Knew Susie/Yes, We Have No Bananas	4

NATALINO OTTO
59	Oriole CB 1515	Carina/Questo Nostro Amore	4

JOHN OTWAY (& WILD WILLY BARRETT)
72	County COUN 215	Gypsy/Misty Mountain (private pressing, with lyric sheet)	25
73	Track 2094 111	Murder Man/If I Did	8
75	Viking (no cat. no.)	Beware Of The Flowers/Louisa On A Horse (private pressing)	25
76	Track 2094 133	Louisa On A Horse/Misty Mountain (as John Otway, no p/s)	6
77	Polydor 2058 916	Racing Cars (Jet Spotter Of The Track)/Running From The Law (p/s)	5
77	Polydor 2058 951	Really Free/Beware Of The Flowers (Cos I'm Sure They're Going To Get You Yeh) (p/s)	4
78	Polydor 2059 001	Geneve/It's A Long Time Since I Heard Homestead On The Farm (p/s, solo)	4
78	Polydor 2059 060	Baby's In The Club/Julie Julie Julie (p/s, solo)	4
79	Polydor 2059 105	Frightened And Scared/Are You On My Side? (p/s, solo)	4
79	Polydor 2059 105	Frightened And Scared/Are You On My Side? (p/s, instrumentals, allegedly only 3 copies pressed!)	50+
79	Polydor POSP 143	Birthday Boy/Wow, What A Woman (no p/s)	4
80	Polydor 2059 250	DK 50-80/JOHN OTWAY: It's A Long Time Since I Heard Homestead On The Farm/WILD WILLY BARRETT: The Homestead On The Farm (p/s)	4
80	Stiff BUY 101	Green Green Grass Of Home/Wednesday Club (p/s)	4
81	Stiff BUY 115	Turning Point/Too Much Air, Not Enough Oxygen (die-cut p/s)	4
82	Stiff Indie STIN 1	Headbutts/Live Version (p/s)	4
77	Extracted EXLP 1	JOHN OTWAY AND WILD WILLY BARRETT (LP, handmade sleeve)	15
77	white label	LIVE AT THE ROUNDHOUSE (LP)	15
77	Polydor Super 2383 453	JOHN OTWAY AND WILD WILLY BARRETT (LP, reissue)	10
78	Polydor Super 2383 501	DEEP AND MEANINGLESS (LP, some with free 7" "Racing Cars (Jet Spotter Of The Track) (live)"/"Down The Road (live)" [OT 1])	15/10

(see also Johnny Japes & His Jesticles)

OUIDA & NUMBERS
80	Modern STP 1	Runaway/Yeah, Yeah, Yeah, Yeah (p/s)	4

(see also Hugh Cornwell)

OUR PLASTIC DREAM
67	Go AJ 11411	A Little Bit Of Shangrila/Encapsulated Marigold	60

OUT
82	Rabid TOSH 113	Who Is Innocent/Linda's Just A Statue (p/s)	4

OUTCASTS
78	It IT 4	Frustration/Don't Want To Be No Adult/You're A Disease (p/s)	10
79	Good Vibrations GOT 3	Just Another Teenage Rebel/Love Is For Sops (poster p/s, various colours; 'band' p/s or 'type' p/s)	10/8
79	Good Vibrations GOT 17	Self Conscious Over You/Love You For Never (p/s)	5
81	GBH GBH 001	Magnum Force/Gangland Warfare (p/s)	6
81	Outcasts Only 0001	Programme Love/Beating And Screaming Pts 1 & 2/Mania (p/s)	4
79	Good Vibrations BIG 1	SELF CONSCIOUS OVER YOU (LP)	12

OUTER LIMITS
67	Elephant LUR 100	When The Work Is Thru'/5 MAN CARGO: What A Wonderful Feeling (Leeds Students Charity Rag)	30
67	Deram DM 125	Just One More Chance/Help Me Please	15
68	Instant IN 001	Great Train Robbery/Sweet Freedom (Immediate label demos £60)	15
71	Decca F 13176	The Dark Side Of The Moon/Black Boots	8

OUTLAW BLUES BAND
69	Stateside SSL 10290	BREAKING IN (LP)	12

OUTLAWS
61	HMV POP 844	Swingin' Low/Spring Is Near	10
61	HMV POP 877	Ambush/Indian Brave	10
61	HMV POP 927	Valley Of The Sioux/Crazy Drums	12
62	HMV POP 990	Ku-pow!/Last Stage West	12
62	HMV POP 1074	Sioux Serenade/Fort Knox	12
63	HMV POP 1124	The Return Of The Outlaws/Texan Spiritual	10
63	HMV POP 1195	That Set The Wild West Free/Hobo	12
63	HMV POP 1241	Law And Order/Do-Da-Day	12
64	HMV POP 1277	Keep-A-Knockin'/Shake With Me	25
61	HMV CLP 1489	DREAM OF THE WEST (LP)	80

(see also Mike Berry, Charles Hodges, Ritchie Blackmore, Bobbie Graham)

OUT OF DARKNESS
70	Key KL 006	OUT OF DARKNESS (LP)	250

OUTPATIENTS
81	Albion ION 1014	New Japanese Hairstyles/Children (p/s)	4

OUTRAGE
70	Kama Sutra 618 027	The Letter/The Way I See It	4

OUTSIDERS (U.K.)
65	Decca F 12213	Keep On Doing It/Songs We Sang Last Summer	12

OUTSIDERS (U.S.)
66	Capitol CL 15435	Time Won't Let Me/Was It Really Real?	18
66	Capitol CL 15450	Girl In Love/What Makes You So Bad, You Weren't Brought Up That Way	15
66	Capitol CL 15468	Respectable/Lost In My World	15
66	Capitol CL 15480	Help Me Girl/You Gotta Look	10
67	Capitol CL 15495	I'll Give You Time/I'm Not Tryin' To Hurt You	12

OUTSIDERS (U.K.)
77	Raw Edge RER 002	ONE TO INFINITY (EP)	8
78	Xciting Plastic	Vital Hours/Take Up (unissued)	
77	Raw Edge RER 001	CALLING ON YOUTH (LP)	15
78	Raw Edge RER 003	CLOSE UP (LP)	15

(see also Sound)

OUTSKIRTS OF INFINITY
87	Woronzow WOO 7	LORD OF THE DARK SKIES (LP)	15

OVALTINEES
80s	BAA 021	BRITISH JUSTICE (EP)	15

OVARY LODGE
73	RCA SF 8372	OVARY LODGE (LP)	30
76	Ogun OG 600	OVARY LODGE (LP)	12

(see also Keith Tippett)

OVERLANDERS
63	Pye 7N 15544	Summer Skies And Golden Sands/Call Of The Wild	4
63	Pye 7N 15568	Movin'/Rainbow	4
64	Pye 7N 15619	Yesterday's Gone/Gone In The Rainbow	4
64	Pye 7N 15678	Sing A Song Of Sadness/Don't It Make You Feel Good	4
64	Pye 7N 15712	If I Gave You/I Wonder Why	4
64	Pye 7N 15719	The Leaves Are Falling/Delia's Gone	4
65	Pye 7N 15804	Along Came Jones/Walking The Soles Off My Shoes	4
65	Pye 7N 15883	Freight Train/Take The Bucket To The Well	4
65	Pye 7N 15967	Room Enough For You And Me/January	4
66	Pye 7N 17034	Michelle/Cradle Of Love	4
66	Pye 7N 17068	My Life/The Girl From Indiana	4
66	Pye 7N 17159	Go Where You Wanna Go/Don't Let It Happen Again	4
66	Pye NEP 24245	MICHELLE (EP)	15
66	Pye NPL 18138	MICHELLE (LP)	20

OVERLOAD
80	MCA MCA 618	Into Overload/Follow The Lines (p/s)	6
81	MCA MCA 656	Who Are You/Drift Away	4

OVERLORD
79	Airebeat	Lucy	7

MINT VALUE £

RUNE OVERMAN
| 63 | Decca F 11605 | Big Bass Boogie/Madison Piano | 5 |

OVERTAKERS
| 68 | Amalgamated AMG 803 | That's The Way You Like It/The Big Take-Over | 10 |
| 68 | Amalgamated AMG 809 | Girl You Ruff/KEITH BLAKE: Woo Oh Oh | 10 |

OWEN & LEON
64	Island WI 163	My Love For You/How Many Times	10
64	Island WI 164	Fits Is On Me/SKATALITES: Good News	10
64	Island WI 165	Running Around/SKATALITES: Around The World	10
65	Ska Beat JB 189	Woman/BABA BROOKS with DON DRUMMOND: Doctor Deck	10

(see also Leon & Owen)

OWEN & MILLIE
| 62 | Blue Beat BB 96 | Sit And Cry/Do You Know | 10 |
| 62 | Island WI 014 | Sugar Plum/OWEN GRAY: Jezebel | 10 |

(see also Millie, Owen & Leon, Leon & Owen)

RAY OWEN
| 69 | Fontana TF 1045 | Tonight I'll Be Staying Here With You/Down, Don't Bother Me | 4 |
| 71 | Polydor 2325 061 | RAY OWEN'S MOON (LP) | 15 |

(see also Juicy Lucy)

REG OWEN & HIS ORCHESTRA
56	Parlophone R 4217	Comin' Thru' The Rye Bread/Harlem Swing	4
57	Parlophone R 4303	Easy Now/Sweeping The Floor	4
59	Pye Intl. 7N 25009	Manhattan Spiritual/Ritual Blues	6
59	Pye Intl. 7N 25040	Ginchy/Kazoo	4
60	Palette PG 9004	Obsession/Sunday Morn	4
61	Palette PG 9013	Payroll/Swing A Ling-Ling	4
61	Palette PG 9022	Teen Dreams/Bye Bye Blackbird (as Reg Owen Strings)	4
62	Palette PG 9030	Hula Twist/Gonna High Life	4
56	Parlophone PMD 1045	SWING ME HIGH (10" LP)	10
59	Pye Intl. NPL 28000	MANHATTAN SPIRITUAL (LP, also stereo NSPL 93000)	10/12

BUCK OWENS (& BUCKAROOS)
59	Capitol CL 15009	Everlasting Love/Second Fiddle	6
60	Capitol CL 15123	Above And Beyond/Til These Dreams Come True	5
60	Capitol CL 15162	Excuse Me (I Think I've Got A Heartache)/I've Got A Right To Know	4
61	Capitol CL 15187	Foolin' Around/High As The Mountain	4
63	Capitol CL 15321	Love's Gonna Live Here/Getting Used To Losing You	4
64	Capitol CL 15364	Together Again/Ain't It Amazin' Gracie (as Buck Owens & Buckaroos)	4
65	Capitol CL 15379	I've Got A Tiger By The Tail/Cryin' Time	4
65	Capitol CL 15402	Before You Go/(I Want) No One But You	4
66	Capitol CL 15437	Waitin' In Your Welfare Line/In The Palm Of Your Hand	4
66	Capitol CL 15452	Think Of Me/Heart Of Glass (as Buck Owens & Buckaroos)	4
67	Capitol CL 15501	Sam's Place/Don't Ever Tell Me Goodbye (as Buck Owens & Buckaroos)	4
63	Capitol EAP1 1550	FOOLIN' AROUND (EP)	12
65	Capitol EAP1 20602	ACT NATURALLY (EP)	12
64	Capitol (S)T 2105	THE BEST OF BUCK OWENS (LP)	12
65	Capitol T 2135	TOGETHER AGAIN/MY HEART SKIPS A BEAT (LP)	12
66	Capitol (S)T 2353	BEFORE YOU GO/NO ONE BUT YOU (LP)	12
66	Capitol (S)T 2443	ROLL OUT THE RED CARPET (LP)	12
66	Fontana FJL 307	BUCK OWENS WITH FERLIN HUSKY & FARON YOUNG (LP)	12
66	Capitol (S)T 2283	I'VE GOT A TIGER BY THE TAIL (LP)	12
66	Capitol (S)T 20861	YOURS, COUNTRY STYLE (LP)	15
67	Capitol (S)T 2556	CARNEGIE HALL CONCERT (LP)	12
68	Capitol (S)T 2760	YOUR TENDER LOVING CARE (LP, with His Buckaroos)	12
68	Capitol (S)T 2841	IT TAKES PEOPLE LIKE YOU TO MAKE PEOPLE LIKE ME (LP)	12
68	Capitol (S)T 2897	THE BEST OF BUCK OWENS VOL. 2 (LP)	10
69	Capitol (S)T 2994	THE GUITAR PLAYER (LP)	10
69	Capitol E-(S)T 131	I'VE GOT YOU ON MY MIND AGAIN (LP)	10
69	Capitol E-(S)T 232	BUCK OWENS IN LONDON (LP)	10
70	Capitol E-ST 212	TALL DARK STRANGER (LP)	10
71	Capitol E-ST 628	I WOULDN'T LIVE IN NEW YORK CITY (LP)	10
71	Capitol E-ST 685	BRIDGE OVER TROUBLED WATER (LP)	10
72	Capitol E-ST 795	BUCK OWENS' RUBY (LP)	10
72	Capitol E-ST 11039	BUCK OWENS LIVE AT THE NUGGET (LP)	10
73	Capitol E-ST 11136	IN THE PALM OF YOUR HAND (LP)	10
73	Capitol E-ST 11180	AIN'T IT AMAZING, GRACIE (LP)	10

DONNIE OWENS
58	London HLU 8747	Need You/If I'm Wrong	12
58	London HLU 8747	Need You/If I'm Wrong (78)	5
59	London HLW 8897	Ask Me Anything/Between Midnight And Dawn (unissued)	

GWEN OWENS
| 75 | Casablanca CBX 509 | You Better Watch Out/Everybody Needs Love | 5 |

OWL
| 68 | United Artists UP 2240 | Run To The Sun/Shades Of Blue And Green Water Flies | 15 |

TONY OXLEY (QUARTET)
69	CBS 52664	THE BAPTISED TRAVELLER (LP)	30
70	CBS 64071	4 COMPOSITIONS FOR SEXTET (LP)	30
71	RCA SF 8215	ICHNOS (LP)	30

OXY & MORONS
| 81 | Music For The Deaf MFD 1 | Dirty Harry In The Falls Road/Nice To Be Back (printed brown paper bag p/s) | 5 |
| 82 | Music For The Deaf MFD 2 | Work/The Good Life (no p/s) | 4 |

OXYM

OZRIC TENTACLES

OZZ II

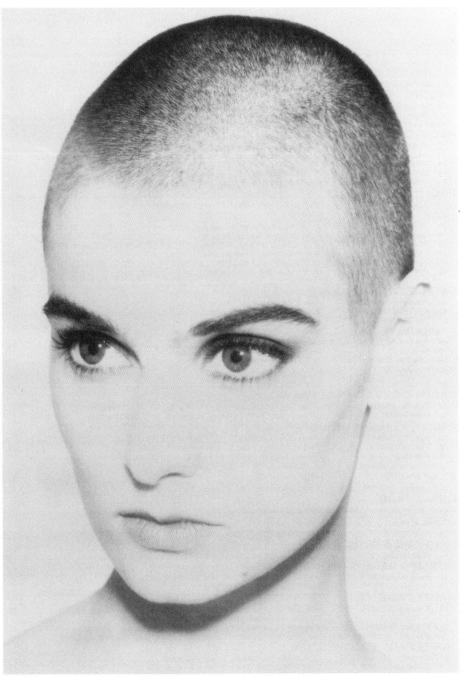

SINEAD O'CONNOR

AUGUSTUS PABLO
71	Ackee ACK 134	Still Yet/AQUARIANS: Version	6
71	Ackee ACK 138	Snowball And Pudding/AQUARIANS: Version	6
71	Big Shot BI 579	East Of The River Nile/HERMAN: Version	6
71	Duke DU 122	Reggae In The Fields/TOMMY McCOOK: Love Brother	6
75	Island WIP 6226	King Tubby Meets The Rockers Uptown/Baby I Love You So	4
78	Rough Trade RT 002	Pablo Meets Mr. Bassie/Mr. Bassie Special (with Rockers All Stars)	4

AUGUSTUS PABLO & FAY
| 73 | Randy's RAN 536 | Bedroom Mazurka/Melodica Version | 6 |

PACIFIC DRIFT
| 70 | Deram DM 304 | Water Woman/Yes You Do | 6 |
| 70 | Deram Nova (S)DN 13 | FEELIN' FREE (LP) | 25 |

(see also Wimple Winch, Just Four Men)

PACIFIC GAS & ELECTRIC
70	CBS 5039	Are You Ready/Staggolee	5
69	B&C CAS 1003	GET IT ON (LP)	12
69	CBS 63822	PACIFIC GAS & ELECTRIC (LP)	10
70	CBS 64026	ARE YOU READY (LP)	10
71	CBS 64295	HARD BURN (LP)	10

PACK
| 65 | Columbia DB 7702 | Do You Believe In Magic?/Things Bring Me Down | 25 |

PACK
79	SS PAK 1	Brave New Soldiers/Heathen (p/s, 2,500 only)	12
79	Rough Trade RT 025	King Of Kings/Number 12 (p/s)	9
80	SS SS 1N2/SS 2N1	KIRK BRANDON AND THE PACK OF LIES (EP, with printed inner sleeve)	15
81	Escape ESC 102	Muchos Gracias/Limelight (p/s)	5
82	Cyclops CYCLOPS 1	LONG LIVE THE PAST (EP)	7
82	Donut DONUT 2	THE PACK LIVE, 1979 (cassette)	12

(see also Theatre Of Hate, Spear Of Destiny)

PACKABEATS
61	Parlophone R 4729	Gypsy Beat/Big Man	6
62	Pye 7N 15480	Evening In Paris/The Traitors	10
63	Pye 7N 15549	Dream Lover/Packabeat	10

PACKERS
66	Pye Intl. 7N 25343	Hole In The Wall/Go 'Head On	12
70	Soul City SC 111	Hole In The Wall/Go 'Head On (reissue)	8
70	Soul City SCM 003	HOLE IN THE WALL (LP)	25

PACKEYS
| 60s | Speciality SPE 1003 | Stone Fox/Diggin' | 8 |

PADDY GOES TO HOLLYWOOD
| 87 | Jackeen PAD 1 | Green Green Grass Of Home/(Telling Me) All Those Lies (p/s) | 5 |
| 87 | Rage PADDY 1 | Green Green Grass Of Home/(Telling Me) All Those Lies (p/s) | 4 |

PADDY, KLAUS & GIBSON
65	Pye 7N 15906	I Wanna Know/I Tried	10
66	Pye 7N 17060	No Good Without You Baby/Rejected	20
66	Pye 7N 17112	Teresa/Quick Before They Catch Us	10

(see also Manfred Mann, Big Three, Rory Storm & Hurricanes, Kingsize Taylor)

BILLY PAGE
| 65 | London HLU 10006 | It's Pop/American Girl | 4 |

CHRIS PAGE
| 66 | Cameo Parkway C 751 | Wait And See/Mine Mine Mine | 4 |

GENE PAGE
| 75 | Atlantic K 10574 | Satin Soul/Cream Corner | 4 |

HAL PAGE & WHALERS
| 60 | Melodisc MEL 1553 | After Hours Blues/Going Back To My Home | 25 |

HOT LIPS PAGE & HIS ORCHESTRA
| 55 | Parlophone MSP 6172 | Ain't Nothing Wrong With That Boy/The Cadillac Song | 5 |
| 55 | Parlophone MSP 6172 | Ain't Nothing Wrong With That Boy/The Cadillac Song (78) | 6 |

JIMMY PAGE
65	Fontana TF 533	She Just Satisfies/Keep Moving	250
88	Geffen GEF 41	Wasting My Time/Writes Of Winter (p/s, withdrawn)	8
91	Fontana TFCD 533	She Just Satisfies/Keep Moving (CD, in 'Led Zeppelin Celebration' pack)	10

(see also Led Zeppelin, Yardbirds, Paul, Brian Auger, Carter-Lewis & Southerners, Neil Christian & Crusaders)

LARRY PAGE (ORCHESTRA)
57	Columbia DB 3965	Cool Shake/Start Movin' (In My Direction)	12
57	Columbia DB 3965	Cool Shake/Start Movin' (In My Direction) (78)	5
58	Columbia DB 4012	That'll Be The Day/Please Don't Blame Me	12
58	Columbia DB 4012	That'll Be The Day/Please Don't Blame Me (78)	5
58	Columbia DB 4080	Under Control/This Is My Life	8

58	Columbia DB 4080	Under Control/This Is My Life (78)	5
59	Saga SAG 45-2902	I Vibrate/Big Blon' Baby	8
60	Saga SAG 45-2903	How'm I Doing, Hey Hey/Throw All Your Lovin' My Way	7
60	Saga SAG 45-2904	Little Old Fashioned You/Marylin	5
66	Decca F 12320	Waltzing To Jazz/Jo Jo (as Larry Page Orchestra)	4
66	Decca F 12368	Peyton Place Theme/Leanda's Theme (as Larry Page Orchestra)	4
68	Page One POF 068	Take Five/Michelle	4
68	Page One POF 096	Hey Jude/Those Were The Days (as Larry Page Orchestra)	4
60	Saga STP 1024	SINGS HIS PERSONAL CHOICE (EP)	7
65	Decca LK 4692	KINKY MUSIC (LP, as Larry Page Orchestra)	70
68	Page One POL(S) 002	EXECUTIVE SUITE (LP, as Larry Page Orchestra)	10
68	Page One POLS 004	FROM LARRY, WITH LOVE (LP)	10
69	Page One POLS 601	LARRY PAGE ORCHESTRA (LP)	10

MALLY PAGE

66	Pye 7N 17105	The Life And Soul Of The Party/You Can Be Wrong About Boys	6

PATTI PAGE

51	Oriole CB 1046	The Tennessee Waltz/Long, Long Ago (78)	5
52	Oriole CB 1129	I Went To Your Wedding/You Belong To Me (78)	5
58	Mercury 7MT 184	I'll Remember Today/My, How The Time Goes	5
58	Mercury 7MT 200	Bring Us Together/Belonging To Someone	5
58	Mercury 7MT 206	Another Time, Another Place/These Worldly Goods	5
58	Mercury 7MT 223	Left Right Out Of Your Heart/Longing To Hold You Again	7
58	Mercury AMT 1000	Fibbin'/You Will Find Your Love (In Paris)	4
59	Mercury AMT 1022	Trust In Me/Under The Sun Valley Moon	4
59	Mercury AMT 1038	The Walls Have Ears/My Promise	4
59	Mercury AMT 1054	My Mother's Eyes/With My Eyes Wide Open I'm Dreaming	4
60	Mercury AMT 1089	Promise Me Thomas/2,000, 200, 23 Miles	4
60	Mercury AMT 1102	One Of Us (Will Weep Tonight)/What Will My Future Be	4
60	Mercury AMT 1112	I Wish I'd Never Been Born/I Need You	4
56	Mercury MEP 9502	PATTI PAGE (EP)	8
59	Mercury ZEP 10006	PATTI PAGE ONE (EP)	8
59	Mercury ZEP 10017	PATTI PAGE TWO (EP)	8
59	Mercury ZEP 10032	PATTI PAGE THREE (EP)	8
59	Mercury ZEP 10045	PATTI PAGE NO. 4 (EP)	8
54	Mercury MG 25101	FOLK SONG FAVOURITES (10" LP)	16
55	Mercury MG 25197	PATTI'S SONGS (10" LP)	16
56	Mercury MPT 7510	CHRISTMAS WITH PATTI PAGE (10" LP)	14
57	Mercury MPT 7531	I'M GETTING SENTIMENTAL OVER YOU (10" LP)	14
57	Mercury MPT 7535	PATTI'S SONGS (10" LP, reissue)	14
57	Emarcy EJL 1252	PATTI PAGE IN THE LAND OF HI-FI (LP)	12
57	Mercury MPL 6506	MANHATTAN TOWER (LP)	10
58	Mercury MPL 6521	YOU GO TO MY HEAD (LP)	10
58	Mercury MPL 6524	PAGE 1 — A COLLECTION OF HER MOST FAMOUS SONGS (LP)	10
59	Mercury MMC 14000	LET'S GET AWAY FROM IT ALL (LP)	10
59	Mercury MMC 14007	I'VE HEARD THAT SONG BEFORE (LP)	10
59	Mercury MMC 14013	I'LL REMEMBER APRIL (LP)	10
59	Mercury MMC 14017	INDISCRETION (LP)	10
59	Mercury CMS 18004	PATTI PAGE IN THE LAND OF HI-FI (LP, stereo reissue)	10
60	Mercury MMC 14036	THREE LITTLE WORDS (LP)	10
61	Mercury MMC 14064	ROMANCE IN RHYTHM (LP)	10

PAGEBOYS (U.S.)

65	London HLU 9948	When I Meet A Girl Like You/I Have Love	5

PAGE BOYS (U.K.)

83	Whaam! WHAAM 10	You're My Kind Of Girl/In Love With You (p/s, 1,000 copies only)	8

(see also 1,000 Violins)

PAGE FIVE

66	Parlophone R 5426	Let Sleeping Dogs Lie/I Know All About Her	20

PAGE TEN

65	Decca F 12248	Boutique/Colour Talk	10

CARLOS PAIAO

81	EMI EMI 5174	Playback (English)/Playback (Portuguese)	7

PAICE, ASHTON & LORD

77	Polydor/Oyster 2391 269	MALICE IN WONDERLAND (LP, with inner sleeve)	10

(see also Deep Purple, Jon Lord, Ashton & Lord, Ashton, Gardner & Dyke, Elf)

ELAINE PAIGE

86	RCA CHESS 7D	Nobody's Side (Remix)/Embassy Lament//I Know Him So Well/Chess (Theme) (double pack)	5

JOEY PAIGE

65	Fontana TF 554	Cause I'm In Love With You/Yeah Yeah Yeah	15

ROSALIND PAIGE

55	London HL 8120	When The Saints Go Marching In/Nobody's Sweetheart Now	15
57	MGM MGM 937	Love, Oh Careless Love/That Funny Melody	7

PAINTBOX

72	Young Blood YB 1013	Get Ready For Love/Can I Get To Know You	5
71	Young Blood YB 1029	Get Ready For Love/Can I Get To Know You (reissue)	4

(see also Easybeats, Haffy's Whiskey Sour)

PAINTED SHIP

67	Mercury MF 988	Frustration/I Told Those Little White Lies	40

PAINTED WORD
86	Mother MUM 5	Independence Day/Letter From Jackie (p/s)	4
86	Mother 12 MUM 5	Independence Day/Letter From Jackie/State Of Mind (12", p/s)	7

PAISLEYS
83	Psycho PSYCHO 7	COSMIC MIND AT PLAY (LP, reissue)	15

PALACE COURT BRIGADE
69	CBS 4643	Whistlin' In The Sunshine/Girls Grow Up	4

PALADIN
71	Bronze WIP 6108	Anyway/Giving All My Love	4
73	Bronze BRO 3	Sweet Sweet Music/Get One Together	4
71	Bronze ILPS 9150	PALADIN (LP)	20
72	Bronze ILPS 9190	CHARGE (LP, gatefold sleeve)	30

(see also Glass Menagerie, McGuinness Flint)

PALE FOUNTAINS
82	Operation Twilight OPT 09	Just A Girl/(There's Always) Something On My Mind	4
85	Virgin VS 750	From Across The Kitchen Table/Bicycle Thieves//Thank You/ Just A Girl (double pack)	4

PALE SAINTS
80s	Panic Recordings	Children Break/SAVLONS: ...And What's More/KERRY FIDDLES: Shiver Me Timbers (33rpm flexidisc, stickered card sleeve with insert)	15
92	4AD CAD 2004	IN RIBBONS (LP, with free 7" "A Thousand Stars Burst Open"/ "A Revelation" [RIB 1])	10

TOM PALEY
69	Argo ZFB 3	SUE COW (LP)	10

PALEY BROTHERS
78	Sire SRE 4005	Come On Let's Go/Magic Power	6

(see also Ramones)

PALI GAP
82	Synister	Under The Sun	45

MORTY PALITZ & ACES
59	London HLJ 8778	The Grocer's Cha Cha Cha/Eso Es El Amor (This Is Love)	4

PALLAS
78	Sue-i-cide PAL 101	PALLAS (EP)	50
82	Granite Wax GWS 1	Arrive Alive/Stranger (On The Edge Of Time)	35
83	Cool King CK 010	Paris Is Burning/The Hammer Falls (p/s)	6
83	Cool King 12 CK 010	Paris Is Burning/The Hammer Falls/Stranger At The Edge Of Time (12", p/s)	10
84	EMI Harvest PLS 1	Eyes In The Night (Arrive Live)/East West (p/s)	4
84	EMI Harvest PLSP 1	Eyes In The Night (Arrive Live)/East West (picture disc)	5
84	EMI Harvest 12 PLS 1	Eyes In The Night (Arrive Live)/East West/Crown Of Thorns (12", p/s)	8
84	EMI Harvest 12 PLSP 1	Eyes In The Night (Arrive Live)/East West/Crown Of Thorns (12", picture disc, possibly unissued)	15+
84	EMI Harvest PLS 2	Shock Treatment/March On Atlantis (poster p/s)	4
84	EMI Harvest 12 PLS 2	Shock Treatment/March On Atlantis/Heart Attack (12", p/s)	7
85	Harvest PLS 3	Strangers/Nightmare/Sanctuary (p/s)	4
85	Harvest 12 PLS 3	THE KNIGHTMOVES EP (Strangers/Nightmare/Sanctuary) (12", p/s)	7
85	Harvest 12 PLSP 3	THE KNIGHTMOVES EP (12", picture disc)	8
85	Harvest 12 PLSD 3	THE KNIGHTMOVES EP (12", with free 7" "Mad Machine"/"Stitch In Time" in sealed plastic sleeve)	20
86	Harvest 12 PLS 4	Throwing Stones At The Wind/Cut And Run (live)/Crown Of Thorns (live) (12", p/s)	7
83	Cool King CKLP 002	ARRIVE ALIVE (LP)	15
84	Harvest SHSP 2400 121	THE SENTINEL (LP, some with poster)	12/10

PALMER JONES
68	Direction 58-3603	The Great Music Of Love/Dancing Master	4

EARL PALMER & HIS TEN PIECE ROCKIN' BAND
58	Capitol CL 14859	Drum Village Pts 1 & 2	8

EDDIE PALMER
57	Decca F 10873	The Sky/The Twilight Theme	4

RICK PALMER
59	London HLL 8900	You Threw A Heart/My Greatest Wish (unreleased)	

ROBERT PALMER
75	Island WIP 6250	Which Of Us Is The Fool/Get Outside	4
76	Island WIP 6272	Gimme An Inch Girl/Pressure Drop	4
76	Island WIP 6345	Man Smart, Woman Smarter/From a Whisper To A Scream	4
78	Island WIP 6425	Every Kinda People/Keep In Touch	4
78	Island WIP 6445	Best Of Both Worlds/Where Can It Go	4
79	Island WIP 6481	Bad Case Of Loving You (Doctor Doctor)/Love Can Run Faster (p/s)	4
81	Island WIP 6678	Not A Second Time/Woke Up Laughing (p/s)	4
82	Island PWIP 6754	Some Guys Have All The Luck/Too Good To Be True (picture disc)	5
82	Island 12PWIP 6754	Some Guys Have All The Luck/Style Kills/Si Chatouillieux/ What Do You Care (12", picture disc)	7
82	Island PWIP 6833	Pride/Pride (Instrumental) (picture disc)	5
83	Island ISP 121	You Can Have It (Take My Heart)/The Silver Gun (picture disc)	5
85	Island ISD 256	Riptide/Johnny And Mary//Trick Bag/No Not Much/Back In My Arms (double pack)	4
86	Island ISP 270	Addicted To Love/More (shaped picture disc)	5

| 86 | Island CID 283 | I Didn't Mean To Turn You On/Addicted To Love/Get It Through/ You Are in My System/Johnny And Mary (CD, withdrawn) ....20 |

(see also Alan Bown [Set], Dada, Vinegar Joe, Power Station)

ROY PALMER & STATE STREET RAMBLERS
| 54 | London AL 3518 | A CHICAGO SKIFFLE SESSION (10" LP) ....20 |

PALMETTO KINGS
| 60 | Starlite ST45 021 | Ten Rum Bottles/Home Cookin' Mama ....5 |

PAMA DICE
69	Jackpot JP 715	Bongo Man/Bear De Pussy 5
69	Jackpot JP 716	Sin, Sun And Sex/Reggae Popcorn 5
70s	Reggae REG 3001	Brixton Fight/OPENING: Tea House 5

PAN
| 89 | Ton Son Ton SON 14 | Bana Bana (After Midnight Mix)/Bana Nana (Before Midnight Mix) (p/s) ....6 |
| 89 | Ton Son Ton SONL 14 | Bana Bana (After Midnight 12" Club Mix)/Bana Nana (Before Midnight 12" Club Mix)/Bana Nana (Original Version) (12", p/s) ....8 |

PANAMA FRANCIS BLUES BAND
| 64 | Stateside SL 10070 | TOUGH TALK!! (LP) ....10 |

PANAMA LIMITED (JUG BAND)
69	Harvest HAR 5010	Lady Of Shallot/Picture Blues 8
70	Harvest HAR 5022	Round And Round/Rotting Wooden In A White Collar's Grave 8
69	Harvest SHVL 753	PANAMA LIMITED JUG BAND (LP) 35
70	Harvest SHVL 779	INDIAN SUMMER (LP, as Panama Limited) 45

GENE PANCHO (alias Gene Rondo)
| 68 | Giant GN 21 | I Like Sweet Music/Seven Days (with Sandy & Superboys) ....5 |

PANDAMONIUM
67	CBS 202462	Season Of The Witch/Today I'm Happy 40
67	CBS 2664	No Presents For Me/Sun Shines From His Eyes 60
68	CBS 3451	Chocolate Buster Dam/Fly With Me Forever 40

PANDIT PRANNATH
| 69 | Transatlantic TRA 193 | EARTH GROOVE (LP) ....20 |

PANHANDLE
| 72 | Decca SKL 5105 | PANHANDLE (LP) ....25 |

(see also Chris Spedding)

PANIK
| 77 | Rainy City SHOT 1 | IT WON'T SELL (EP) ....5 |

JAN PANTER
65	Oriole CB 1938	My Two Arms Minus You Equals Tears/Does My Heart Show 5
65	CBS 201810	Stand By And Cry/Let It Be Me 5
66	Pye 7N 17097	Scratch My Back/Put Yourself In My Place 25

PANTHER BURNS
| 81 | Rough Trade RT 077 | Train Kept A Rollin'/Red Headed Woman (p/s) ....6 |

(see also Tav Falco's Panther Burns, Alex Chilton)

ROY PANTON
| 64 | Rio R 19 | Cherita/Seek And You Shall Find ....10 |
| 64 | Rio R 33 | You Don't Know Me/KING EDWARD'S ALLSTARS: Doctor No ....10 |

(see also Roy & Annette, Roy & Millie, Roy & Paulette)

JOHN PANTRY
| 72 | Philips 6308 129 | JOHN PANTY (LP) ....12 |

(see also Factory, Peter & Wolves, Norman Conquest)

PANZA DIVISION
| 82 | Panza Trax PTO 1 | We'll Rock The World/Standing On The Outside (p/s) ....12 |

PAOLA
| 69 | Decca F 22916 | Bonjour Bonjour/Valse D'Amour ....7 |

NIKKI PAPAS
| 59 | Parlophone R 4590 | 49 State Rock/Try Again ....10 |
| 60 | Parlophone R 4652 | By The River/Don't Leave Me Alone ....8 |

PAPER BLITZ TISSUE
| 67 | RCA RCA 1652 | Boy Meets Girl/Grey Man ....80 |

PAPER BUBBLE
| 70 | Deram DML/SML 1059 | SCENERY (LP) ....25 |

PAPER DOLLS
68	Pye 7N 17456	Something Here In My Heart/All The Time In The World 5
68	Pye 7N 17547	My Life Is In Your Hands/There's Nobody I'd Sooner Love 4
68	Pye 7N 17655	Someday/Any Old Time You're Lonely And Sad 4
70	RCA RCA 1919	My Boyfriend's Back/Mister Good Time Friday 4
70	RCA RCA 2007	Remember December/Same Old Story 5
68	Pye N(S)PL 18226	PAPER DOLLS HOUSE (LP) 10

PAPER TOYS
| 90 | Armada ARMAP 003 | Cold Surrender (Winston Club Mix)/Cold Surrender (D-Day 7" Radio Mix)/ Cold Surrender (Outland Mix) (numbered p/s, 500 only) ....8 |

(see also Gary Numan)

PARADE
| 67 | A&M AMS 701 | Sunshine Girl/This Old Melody ....4 |
| 67 | A&M AMS 720 | Radio Song/I Can See Love ....4 |

Vanessa PARADIS

VANESSA PARADIS
88	Polydor POSPG 902	Joe Le Taxi/Varvara Pavlovna (poster p/s)	15
88	Polydor 080 466 2	Joe Le Taxi/Varvara Pavlovna/Joe Le Taxi (Extended Mix) (CD)	8
89	Polydor PZ 38	Maxou (Remix)/Le Bon Dieu (12", p/s)	7

PARADONS
60	Top Rank JAR 514	Diamonds And Pearls/I Want Love	35

PARADOX
68	Polydor 56275	Ring The Changes/The Wednesday Theme	70

(see also David Walker)

PARAFFIN JACK FLASH LTD
68	Pye NSPL 18252	MOVERS AND GROOVERS (LP)	12

PARAGONS
66	Doctor Bird DB 1060	Happy-Go-Lucky Girl/Love Brings Pain	10
67	Island WI 3039	So Depressed/We Were Meant To Be	10
67	Island WI 3045	On The Beach/TOMMY McCOOK: Sweet And Gentle	10
67	Island WI 3067	Talikng Love/If I Were You	10
67	Treasure Isle TI 7009	Only A Smile/The Tide Is High	10
67	Treasure Isle TI 7011	Mercy, Mercy, Mercy/Riding On A High And Windy Day	10
67	Treasure Isle TI 7013	The Same Song/TOMMY McCOOK & SUPERSONICS: Soul Serenade	10
67	Treasure Isle TI 7025	Wear You To The Ball/You Mean The World To Me	10
68	Treasure Isle TI 7034	Silver Bird/My Best Girl	10
68	Duke DU 7	Left With A Broken Heart/I've Got To Get Away	8
68	Island WI 3138	Memories By The Score/The Number One For Me	10
69	Studio One SO 2081	Have You Ever Been In Love/Change Your Style	12
67	Doctor Bird DLM 5010	ON THE BEACH (LP)	70

(see also Rosalyn Sweat & Paragons)

PARALEX
80	Reddingtons R.R.E	Travelling Man	7
80	Reddingtons R.R.	White Lightning (12", p/s, green vinyl)	25

NORRIE PARAMOR & HIS ORCHESTRA
53	Columbia SCM 5023	Cotton Reel/Pink Plank Plonk	4
53	Columbia SCM 5034	Fandango/Penny Whistle	4
53	Columbia SCM 5051	April In Portugal/Where Is Your Heart	4
53	Columbia SCM 5065	Melba Waltz/Melodia	4
53	Columbia SCM 5068	Man Between/Callaghan's Monkey	4
54	Columbia SCM 5082	Mon Pays/My First Romance	4
54	Columbia SCM 5126	Johnny Guitar/Paramambo	4
54	Columbia SCM 5136	High And Mighty/Rip Van Twinkle	4
54	Columbia SCM 5157	Gina/Midinette	4
56	Columbia SCM 5251	Theme From The Threepenny Orchestra/Poor John	4
56	Columbia SCM 5271	Charleston/Ask For Joe	4
60	Columbia DB 4419	Summer Place (Theme)/Half Pint	4
62	Columbia DB 4789	Z Cars (Theme)/Ballad Of A Soldier (Theme)	6
65	Columbia DB 7446	Dance Of The Warriors/Dragon Dance	4
70	Polydor 56375	Randall And Hopkirk (Deceased)/A Summer Place	12
55	Columbia 33S 1076	JUST WE TWO (10" LP)	10
66	Columbia SX 6012	SHADS IN LATIN (LP, also stereo Studio Two TWO 107)	10/15
67	Studio Two TWO 172	PLAYS THE HITS OF CLIFF RICHARD (LP)	10

(see also Big Ben Banjo Band)

PARAMOUNT ALL STARS
50	Tempo R 20	Hometown Skiffle (both sides) (78)	7

PARAMOUNTS
63	Parlophone R 5093	Poison Ivy/I Feel Good All Over	7
64	Parlophone R 5107	Little Bitty Pretty One/A Certain Girl	10
64	Parlophone R 5155	I'm The One Who Loves You/It Won't Be Long	12
64	Parlophone R 5187	Bad Blood/Do I	8
65	Parlophone R 5272	Blue Ribbons/Cuttin' In	10
65	Parlophone R 5351	You Never Had It So Good/Don't Ya Like My Love	10
64	Parlophone GEP 8908	THE PARAMOUNTS (EP)	160

(see also Procol Harum)

PARAMOUNT ALL-STARS
50s	Tempo R 20	Hometown Skiffle Parts 1 And 2 (78)	12

(see also Blind Blake, Will Ezell, Georgia Tom, Alex Hill, Papa Charlie Jackson, Blind Lemon Jefferson, Charlie Spand)

PARCHMENT
72	Pye 7N 45178	Light Up The Fire/Let There Be Light (p/s)	5
72	Pye 7N 45214	Where Can I Find You/Working Man	4
73	Pye 7N 45233	You Were On My Mind/Rock'n'Roll Part Time	4
72	Pye NSPL 18388	LIGHT UP THE FIRE (LP with insert)	25
73	Pye NSLP 18409	HOLLYWOOD SUNSET (LP)	20
75	Myrrh MYR 1028	SHAMBLEJAM (LP)	25
77	Pilgrim Grapevine	REHEARSAL FOR A REUNION (LP)	20

PAULA PARFITT
71	Beacon BEA 135	Love Is Wonderful/I'm Gonna Give You Back Your Ring	35

TINY PARHAM
50s	Audubon AAC	TINY BARHAM (10" LP)	25

PARIS
70s	Avalanche AV 67312	I've Lost The Way/Long Time	5
84	Bluebird BR 9	I Choose You/Punkin' Funkin' (p/s)	5
84	Bluebird BRT 9	I Choose You/Punkin' Funkin' (12", p/s)	8

BOBBY PARIS
68	Polydor 56747	Per So Nal Ly/Tragedy	50
79	Capitol CL 16067	I Walked Away/H.B. BARNUM: Heartbreaker	7
77	London HLU 10553	Night Owl/YVONNE BAKER: You Didn't Say A Word	4

PARIS ANGELS
90	Sheer SHEER 002/T	All On You (Perfume)/Muffin 2/Perfume (Version) (12", p/s)	7

PARIS SISTERS
61	Top Rank JAR 588	I Love How You Love Me/I'll Be Crying Tomorrow	40
64	MGM MGM 1240	Dream Lover/Lonely Girl	20

PARISH HALL
70	Liberty LBS 83374	PARISH HALL (LP)	15

ALAN PARKER
70	Aristocrat AR 1022	GUITAR FANTASY (LP)	10

(see also Hungry Wolf, Ugly Custard)

BENNY PARKER & DYNAMICS
64	Decca F 11944	Boys And Girls/You'll Be On Your Way	25

BILLY PARKER
63	Decca F 11668	Thanks A Lot/Out Of Your Heart	4

BOBBY PARKER
61	London HLU 9393	Watch Your Step/Steal Your Heart Away	15
64	Sue WI 340	Watch Your Step/Steal Your Heart Away (reissue)	15
69	Blue Horizon 57-3151	It's Hard But It's Fair/I Couldn't Quit My Baby	20

CHARLIE PARKER
60	HMV POP 747	Kim/Cosmic Eyes (as Charlie Parker Quartet)	4
55	Vogue EPV 1011	CHARLIE PARKER PLAYS (EP)	7
55	Columbia Clef SEB 10002	THE MAGNIFICENT CHARLIE PARKER NO. 1 (EP)	7
56	Columbia Clef SEB 10026	NOW'S THE TIME (EP)	7
56	Columbia Clef SEB 10032	PLAYS SOUTH OF THE BORDER (EP)	7
56	Columbia Clef SEB 10038	THE MAGNIFICENT CHARLIE PARKER NO. 2 (EP, as Charlie Parker Group)	7
57	Columbia Clef SEB 10053	THE MAGNIFICENT CHARLIE PARKER NO. 3 (EP)	7
50s	Esquire EP 57	CHARLIE PARKER QUINTET (EP)	7
60	Vogue EPV 1264	ALL STAR QUINTET/SEXTET (EP)	7
60	HMV 7EG 8626	CHARLIE PARKER BIG BAND (EP)	7
64	Realm REP 4008	PARKER'S MOOD (EP, as Charlie Parker All Stars)	7
52	Vogue LDE 004	CHARLIE PARKER VOLUME ONE (10" LP)	18
53	Vogue LDE 016	CHARLIE PARKER VOLUME TWO (10" LP)	18
55	Melodisc MLP 12-105	BIRD AT ST. NICK'S (LP)	15
55	Columbia Clef 33CX 10004	CHARLIE PARKER BIG BAND (LP)	15
56	Columbia Clef 33C 9026	BIRD AND DIZ (10" LP, with Dizzy Gillespie)	18
57	Columbia Clef 33CX 10081	APRIL IN PARIS (LP, as Charlie Parker With Strings)	15
57	Columbia Clef 33CX 10090	CHARLIE PARKER PLAYS COLE PORTER (LP)	15
58	Columbia Clef 33CX 10117	CHARLIE PARKER JAZZ PERENNIAL (LP)	15
58	London Jazz LTZ-C 15104	THE IMMORTAL CHARLIE PARKER VOL. 1 (LP)	15
58	London Jazz LTZ-C 15105	THE IMMORTAL CHARLIE PARKER VOL. 2 (LP)	15
58	London Jazz LTZ-C 15106	THE IMMORTAL CHARLIE PARKER VOL. 3 (LP)	15
58	London Jazz LTZ-C 15107	THE IMMORTAL CHARLIE PARKER VOL. 4 (LP)	15
58	Mercury MPL 12-105	BIRD AT NICK'S (LP)	12
60	Collector JGN 1002	CHARLIE PARKER IN SWEDEN (LP)	12
61	HMV CLP 1538	THE ESSENTIAL CHARLIE PARKER (LP)	12
62	Storyville SLP 27	IN SWEDEN 1950 (LP)	15
62	Esquire 32-157	'BIRD' IS FREE (LP)	15
62	Eros ERL 50054	MEMORIAL VOL. 1 (LP)	10
62	Eros ERL 50057	MEMORIAL VOL. 2 (LP)	10
62	Eros ERL 50060	MEMORIAL VOL. 3 (LP)	10
62	Eros ERL 50065	MEMORIAL VOL. 4 (LP)	10
63	Realm RM 131	MEMORIAL VOL. 5 (LP)	10
63	Columbia 33SX 1555	PORTRAIT OF THE BIRD (LP)	12
64	MGM C 986	HISTORICAL MASTERPIECES VOL. 1 (LP)	10
64	MGM C 987	HISTORICAL MASTERPIECES VOL. 2 (LP)	10
64	MGM C 988	HISTORICAL MASTERPIECES VOL. 3 (LP)	10
65	Realm RM 214	MEMORIAL VOL. 6 (LP)	10

(see also Dizzy Gillespie & Charlie Parker)

DAVID PARKER
71	Polydor 2460 101	DAVID PARKER (LP)	40

DEAN PARKER & REDCAPS
62	Decca F 11555	Stormy Evening/Blue Eyes And Golden Hair	25

EDDIE PARKER (U.K.)
55	Columbia SCM 5211	Far Away From Everybody/Bella Notte	4
56	Columbia DB 3804	Love Me As Though There Were No Tomorrow/Rich In Love	4

EDDIE PARKER (U.S.)
79	Grapevine GRP 119	I Love You Baby Pts 1 & 2	4

EULA PARKER
58	Oriole CB 1411	Silhouettes/Hedgehopper	8
58	Oriole CB 1411	Silhouettes/Hedgehopper (78)	8

(see also Frank Weir)

FESS PARKER
57	Oriole CB 1378	Wringle Wrangle/Ballad Of John Colter	6
57	Philips PB 654	Yaller Yaller Gold/King Of The River	4

GRAHAM PARKER (& RUMOUR)

77	Vertigo PARK 001	THE PINK PARKER (EP, double pack, pink vinyl) 5
80	Stiff BUY 82	Love Without Greed/Mercury Poisoning (envelope p/s) 5
85	Elektra EKR 6/SAM 239	Break Them Down/Everyone's Hand Is On The Switch//Bricks And Mortar/
		Too Much To Think (double pack, as Graham Parker & Shot) 4
76	Vertigo 6360 129	HOWLIN' WIND (LP, with free live 7", "Kansas City"/"Silly Thing" [GPS 1],
		5,000 only) 10
77	Vertigo GP 1	LIVE AT MARBLE ARCH (LP, promo only, red or beige label, 500 only) 15

JIMMY PARKER

| 62 | Top Rank JAR 608 | We Gonna/No Word From Betty ....6 |

(LITTLE) JUNIOR PARKER

61	Vogue V 9179	Stand By Me/I'll Forget About You (as Little Junior Parker) 15
62	Vogue V 9193	Mary Jo/Annie Get Your Yo-Yo (as Little Junior Parker) 12
66	Vocalion VP 9256	These Kind Of Blues Pts 1 & 2 15
66	Vocalion VP 9275	Goodbye Little Girl/Walking The Floor Over You 10
67	Mercury SMCL 20097	LIKE IT IS (LP) 15
72	Groove Merchant GM 502	BLUE SHADOWS FALLING (LP) 10
73	Groove Merchant GM2205	GOOD THINGS DON'T HAPPEN EVERY DAY (LP) 10
73	Vogue LDM 30163	MEMORIAL (LP) 12
74	People PLEO 4	YOU DON'T HAVE TO BE BLACK TO LOVE THE BLUES (LP) 10
(see also Howlin' Wolf)		

KEN PARKER

67	Island WI 3082	How Could I/SONNY BURKE: Choo Choo Train 12
67	Studio One SO 2001	See Them A Come/MR FOUNDATION: Have A Good Time 15
68	Island WI 3096	Down Low/Sad Mood 10
68	Island WI 3105	Lonely Man/ERROL DUNKLEY: I Am Going Home One Day Tomorrow ...10
68	Giant GN 34	Change Is Gonna Come/VAL BENNETT: Jumping With Val 10
69	Bamboo BAM 1	My Whole World Is Falling Down/The Chokin' Kind 6
69	Amalgamated AMG 847	It's Alright/COBBS: One One 5
69	Amalgamated AMG 853	Only Yesterday/COBBS: Joe Gibbs Mood 5
70	Duke DU 79	I Can't Hide/TOMMY McCOOK: Kansas City 5
71	Duke Reid DR 2521	Jimmy Brown/Version 5
72	Treasure Isle TI 7073	Help Me Make It Through The Night/TOMMY McCOOK &
		ALLSTARS (Version) 7
74	Trojan TRLS 80	JIMMY BROWN (LP) 12

RAY PARKER JUNIOR

84	Arista ARIPD 580	Ghostbusters Pts 1 & 2 (picture disc) 4
84	Arista ARISD 580	Ghostbusters Pts 1 & 2 (shaped picture disc) 4
84	Arista ARIPD 12 580	Ghostbusters Pts 1 & 2 (12" picture disc, p/s, luminous vinyl) 12

RAYMOND PARKER

| 66 | Sue WI 4024 | Ring Around The Roses/She's Coming Home ....15 |

ROBERT PARKER

66	Island WI 286	Barefootin'/Let's Go Baby 8
66	Island WI 3008	Happy Feet/The Scratch 10
66	Island ILP 942	BAREFOOTIN' (LP) 35

SONNY PARKER

56	Vogue V 2392	My Soul's On Fire/Disgusted Blues 150
56	Vogue V 2392	My Soul's On Fire/Disgusted Blues (78) 12
(see also Lionel Hampton)		

WILLIE PARKER

| 67 | President PT 171 | You Got Your Finger In My Eye/I Love The Life I Live ....5 |

PARKING LOT

69	Parlophone R 5779	Carpet Man/World Spinning Sadly 20
88	Bam Caruso OPRA 060	World Spinning Sadly/NICK HAEFFNER: Sneaky Mothers
		(jukebox issue, die-cut sleeve) 4

JIMMY PARKINSON

56	Columbia SCM 5236	The Great Pretender/Hand In Hand 15
56	Columbia SCM 5267	Walk Hand In Hand/Cry Baby 12
56	Columbia DB 3808	Gina/A Lover's Quarrel 12
56	Columbia DB 3833	In The Middle Of The House/You To Me 12
57	Columbia DB 3876	But You/Together (You And I) 5
57	Columbia DB 3912	Round And Round/Whatever Lola Wants (Lola Gets) 5
57	Columbia 33S 1109	SOLO (10" LP) 18

BERNICE PARKS

| 55 | Coral Q 72056 | Lovin' Machine/Only Love Me ....10 |

LLOYD PARKS

| 70 | Harry J HJ 6603 | Feel A Little Better/I'll Be Your Man ....4 |

SONNY PARKS

| 63 | Warner Bros WB 100 | New Boy In Town/Us Kids Have Got To Make Up Our Minds ....6 |

VAN DYKE PARKS

| 66 | MGM MGM 1301 | Number Nine/Do What You Wanta ....4 |
| 68 | Warner Bros W(S) 1727 | SONG CYCLE (LP) ....10 |

PARLET

| 79 | Casablanca CAL 2052 | INVASION OF THE BOOTY SNATCHERS (LP) ....20 |
| *(see also Parliament)* | | |

PARLIAMENT

| 71 | Invictus INV 513 | The Silent Boatman/Livin' The Life ....8 |
| 72 | Invictus INV 522 | Come In Out Of The Rain/Little Old Country Boy ....8 |

MINT VALUE £

75	Casablanca CBX 505	Up On The Down Stroke/Presence Of A Brain	5
76	Casablanca CBX 518	Tear The Roof Off The Sucker (Give Up The Funk)/P. Funk	6
77	Casablanca CAN 103	Tear The Roof Off The Sucker (Give Up The Funk)/Dr. Funkenstein/ P. Funk	4
78	Casablanca CAN 115	Bop Gun/I've Been Watching You	4
78	Casablanca CANL 115	Bop Gun/I've Been Watching You (12")	8
78	Casablanca CAN 136	Aqua Boogie/Water Sign	4
79	Casablanca CAN 154	Deep/Flashlight	4
79	Casablanca CANL 154	Deep/Flashlight (12")	8
80	Casablanca CANL 188	Theme From Black Hole/Big Bang Theory (12")	8
81	Casablanca CAN 223	Agony Of De Feet/The Freeze	4
81	Casablanca CANL 223	Agony Of De Feet/The Freeze (12")	7
71	Invictus SVT 1004	OSMIUM (LP)	60
74	Casablanca NBLP 7002	UP ON THE DOWN STROKE (LP)	25
75	Casablanca NBLP 7014	CHOCOLATE CITY (LP)	15
76	Casablanca CBC 4009	MOTHERSHIP CONNECTION (LP)	15
76	Casablanca CAL 2003	THE CLONES OF DR. FUNKENSTEIN (LP)	12
74	Casablanca CAL 2011	UP ON THE DOWN STROKE (LP, reissue)	10
75	Casablanca CAL 2012	CHOCOLATE CITY (LP, reissue)	10
77	Casablanca CAL 2013	MOTHERSHIP CONNECTION (LP, reissue)	10
77	Casablanca CALD 5002	PARLIAMENT LIVE — P. FUNK EARTH TOUR (2-LP, with poster & transfer)	12
78	Casablanca CALH 2021	FUNKENTELECHY VS. THE PLACEBO SYNDROME (LP, with poster)	12
79	Casablanca CALN 2044	MOTOR BOOTY AFFAIR (LP)	15
79	Casablanca CALN 2044	MOTOR BOOTY AFFAIR (LP, picture disc)	15

(see also Parliaments, Funkadelic, Parlet, Brides Of Funkenstein, Bootsy's Rubber Band, P-Funk Allstars)

PARLIAMENTS
| 67 | Track 604 013 | I Wanna Testify/I Can Feel The Ice Melting | 12 |
| 69 | Track 604 032 | I Wanna Testify/I Can Feel The Ice Melting (reissue) | 6 |

(see also Parliament, Funkadelic)

PARLOPHONE POPS ORCHESTRA
| 56 | Parlophone R 4250 | Giddy Up A Ding Dong/(We're Gonna) Rock Around The Clock | 6 |

PARLOUR BAND
| 72 | Deram SDL 10 | IS A FRIEND? (LP) | 90 |

JACK PARNELL ORCHESTRA
53	Parlophone MSP 6009	Waltzing The Blues/Catherine Wheel	6
53	Parlophone MSP 6031	Night Train/Hawk Talks	6
53	Parlophone MSP 6041	Topaz/Flying Down To Rio	5
53	Parlophone MSP 6046	Cotton Tail/April In Paris	5
53	Parlophone MSP 6054	Dragnet/Fuller Bounce	5
54	Parlophone MSP 6066	Route 66/The Creep	5
54	Parlophone MSP 6078	Skin Deep/Devil's Eyes (B-side with Dennis Hale)	4
54	Parlophone MSP 6094	Knock Out/Blowin' Wild (B-side with Dennis Hale)	4
54	Parlophone MSP 6102	The Bandit (with Dennis Hale)/Annie's Blues (with Annie Ross)	4
54	Parlophone MSP 6122	Kick Off/Sure Thing	4
54	Parlophone MSP 6138	Trip To Mars/Sky Blue Shirt And Rainbow Tie	4
55	Parlophone R 3986	Shake Rattle And Roll/Fanfare Boogie (78)	5
58	Parlophone R 4500	Topsy/Cha Cha Rock	4
59	HMV POP 630	Kansas City/The Golden Stalker	7
60	Philips PB 1005	77 Sunset Strip/Teen Ride	4
55	Parlophone GEP 8532	JACK PARNELL AND HIS ORCHESTRA (EP)	7
52	Decca LF 1065	THE JACK PARNELL QUARTET (10" LP)	12
58	Parlophone PMD 1053	TRIP TO MARS (10" LP)	10

(see also Dennis Hale)

CATHERINE PARR
| 65 | Decca F 12210 | You Belong To Me/He's My Guy | 8 |

DEAN PARRISH
66	Stateside SS 531	Tell Her/Fall On Me	25
66	Stateside SS 550	Determination/Turn On Your Lovelight	35
67	Stateside SS 580	Skate Pts 1 & 2	20
75	UK USA 2	I'm On My Way/Watch Out	4

PARRISH & GURVITZ
| 71 | Regal Zono. SRZA 8506 | PARRISH & GURVITZ (LP) | 12 |

(see also Baker Gurvitz Army, Three Man Army, Adrian Gurvitz)

SAM PARRY
| 73 | Argo ZDA 155 | IF SADNESS COULD SING (LP) | 20 |

ALAN PARSONS PROJECT
76	Charisma CB 293	(The System Of) Doctor Tarr And Professor Fether/ A Dream Within A Dream	4
76	Charisma CB 298	The One In Paradise/The Cask Of Amontillado	4
84	Arista ARISD 553	Don't Answer Me/You Don't Believe (shaped picture disc)	5

BILL PARSONS & HIS ORCHESTRA
| 59 | London HL 8798 | The All American Boy/Rubber Dolly | 10 |
| 59 | London HL 8798 | The All American Boy/Rubber Dolly (78) | 8 |

(see also Bobby Bare)

GENE PARSONS
| 74 | Warner Bros K 46257 | KINDLING (LP) | 10 |

(see also Byrds)

GRAM PARSONS
| 73 | Reprise K 14245 | The New Soft Shoe/She | 4 |
| 73 | Reprise K 44228 | G.P. (LP, gatefold sleeve) | 10 |

MINT VALUE £

74	Reprise K 54018	GRIEVOUS ANGEL (LP)	10

(see also Byrds, Flying Burrito Brothers)

PARTICULAR PEOPLE

68	Big T BIG 105	Boys Cry/What's The Matter With Julliet	4

PARTISANS

82	No Future OI 2	Police Story/Killing Machine (p/s, with lyric insert)	5
82	No Future OI 12	17 Years Of Hell/The Power And The Greed/Bastards In Blue (p/s)	5
83	Cloak & Dagger PART 1	Blind Ambition/Come Clean (p/s)	4
83	No Future PUNK 4	PARTISANS (LP)	10
84	Cloak & Dagger PARTLP 1	THE TIME WAS RIGHT (LP)	10

PARTISANS

88	Hotwire HWS 863	Open Your Eyes/Partisan (p/s)	4

(see also Blades)

PARTNERS IN CRIME

84	Epic A 4803	Hold On/She's Got Eyes For You (p/s)	5
84	Epic TX 4803	Hold On/She's Got Eyes For You (12", p/s)	8
85	Epic A 5040	Miracles/What You Gonna Do? (p/s)	4
85	Epic A 6170	Hollywood Dream/She's Got Eyes For You (p/s)	4

MR. PARTRIDGE

80	Virgin V 2145	TAKEAWAY — THE LURE OF THE SALVAGE (LP)	10

(see also XTC, Three Wise Men, Duke Of Stratosphere, Johnny Japes & His Jesticles, Colonel)

DON PARTRIDGE

60s	CFP CFP 001/002	SINGING SOHO STYLE (EP)	10
68	Columbia S(C)X 6280	DON PARTRIDGE (LP)	10

PARTRIDGE FAMILY

72	Bell MABEL 1	Breaking Up Is Hard To Do/I'll Meet Halfway (p/s)	4

(see also David Cassidy)

FRANCOISE PASCAL

68	SNB 55-3634	When It Comes To Love/Got It Badly	4

JEAN CLAUDE PASCAL

61	HMV POP 861	Nous Les Amoureux/Les Oubliettes	6

PASCAL FRUITS

60s	A.T.V. ATV 1	T.V. THEMES (EP, presented by Pete Murray)	7

PASCALIS, MARIANNA, ROBERT & BESSY

77	Power Exchange PX 254	A Music Lesson/Mathema Solfege	8

PASHA

68	Liberty LBF 15199	Someone Shot The Lollipop Man/Pussy Willow Dragon	70

(see also Searchers)

PASSAGE

78	Object Music OM 02	NEW LOVE SONGS (EP)	4
79	Object Music OM 08	ABOUT TIME (EP)	4
81	Lyntone LYN 1183/84	Born Every Minute/BLANCMANGE: Living On The Ceiling/Sad Day (excerpt) (clear black 33rpm flexidisc free with 'Melody Maker' magazine)	5/4
80	Object Music OBJ 11	PINDROP (LP)	10

(see also Contact)

PASSIONS (U.S.)

58	Capitol CL 14874	My Aching Heart/Jackie Brown	20
59	Top Rank JAR 224	Just To Be With You/Oh Melancholy Me	25
60	Top Rank JAR 313	I Only Want You/This Is My Love	25

PASSIONS (U.K.)

78	Soho SH 5	Needles And Pills/Body And Soul (p/s)	5
82	Polydor POSP 384	Africa Mine/Feel Cheap And The Square//Why Me/Snow/ (I'm In Love With A) German Film Star (double pack)	4

PASSMORE SISTERS

85	Sharp CAL 3	Three Love Songs: Dance This House Down (p/s)	5

PAST SEVEN DAYS

86	4AD AD 102	Raindance/So Many Others/Nothing (p/s)	7

PASTELS

82	Whaam! WHA-AM 005	Songs For Children: Heavens Above!/Tea Time Tales	25
83	Rough Trade RT 137	I Wonder Why/Supposed To Understand (p/s)	20
83	Creation Artefact/Lyntone LYN 12903	I Wonder Why! (live)/LAUGHING APPLE: Wouldn't You? (33rpm flexidisc, initially free with Legend 7" "'73 In '83" [CRE 001])	5
84	Creation CRE 005	Something Going On/Stay With Me Till Morning (foldaround p/s in poly bag)	20
84	Creation CRE 011T	A Million Tears/Baby Honey/Surprise Me (12", p/s)	8
85	Villa 21 VILLA 3	Heavens Above!/Tea Time Tales/I Wonder Why (live)/ Tea Time Tales (live) (p/s)	30
85	Creation CRE 023T	I'm Alright With You/Couldn't Care Less/What It's Worth (12", p/s)	10
86	Glass GLASS 048	Truck Train Tractor/Breaking Lines (p/s)	6
86	Glass GLASS 12 048	Truck Train Tractor/Truck Train Tractor (2)/Breaking Lines (12", green p/s)	7
87	Glass GLASS 053	Comin' Through/Sit On It Mother (p/s, with print)	4
87	Glass PASTEL 001	Truck Train Tractor/Truck Train Tractor (2)/Breaking Lines//Crawl Babies/ Empty House/The Day I Got Certified (double 12")	10
90	Overground OVER 06	Heavens Above!/Tea Time Tales/Something Going On (demo)/Until Morning Comes (demo) (p/s)	4

(see also Vaselines, Buba & Shop Assistants, Laughing Apple)

PASTEL SIX
63   London HLU 9651   The Cinnamon Cinder/Bandido 6

PASTORAL SYMPHONY
68   President PT 202   Love Machine/Spread A Little Love Around 7

PAT & MARIE
66   Ska Beat JB 234   I Try Not To Tell You/PAT RHODEN: Don't Blame It On Me 8
66   Ska Beat JB 235   You're Really Leaving/PAT RHODEN: Broken Heart 8
(see also Pat Rhoden)

PAT & ROXIE
65   Caribou CRC 2   Sing To Me/Things I Used To Do 7

PATCHES
72   Warner Bros K 16201   Living In America 8

JOHNNY PATE ORCHESTRA
58   Parlophone R 4404   Swinging Shepherd Blues/The Elder 4
58   Parlophone R 4437   Muskeeta/Pretty One 4
59   Parlophone PMD 1057   JAZZ GOES IVY LEAGUE (10" LP) 10
59   Parlophone PMD 1072   SWINGIN' FLUTE (10" LP) 10
73   Probe SPB 1077   SHAFT IN AFRICA (LP, soundtrack, with Four Tops) 15
60s MGM   OUTRAGEOUS (LP) 25

PATHETIX
78   No Records NO 001   Aleister Crowley/Don't Touch My Machine/Snuffed It (p/s with insert) 8
79   TJM TJM 12   THE PATHETIX (EP) 4

PATHFINDERS
64   Decca F 12038   I Love You Caroline/Something I Can Always Do 6

PATHFINDERS
65   Parlophone R 5372   Don't You Believe It/Castle Of Love 6
(see also [White] Trash, Poets)

PATHWAY TO YOUR MIND
68   Major Minor SMLP 19   PREPARING THE MIND AND BODY FOR MEDITATION (LP, spoken word) 50

PATIENCE & PRUDENCE
56   London HLU 8321   Tonight You Belong To Me/A Smile And A Ribbon 20
57   London HLU 8369   Gonna Get Along Without Ya Now/The Money Tree 18
57   London HL 7017   Gonna Get Along Without Ya Now/The Money Tree (export issue) 7
57   London HLU 8425   Dreamer's Bay/We Can't Sing Rhythm And Blues 12
57   London HLU 8493   You Tattletale/Very Nice Is Bali Bali 10
58   London HLU 8773   Tom Thumb's Tune/Golly Oh Gee 8
57   London REU 1087   A SMILE AND A SONG (EP) 25

BOBBY PATRICK BIG SIX
64   Decca F 11898   Shake It Easy Baby/Wildwood Days 15
64   Decca F 12030   Monkey Time/Sweet Talk Me Baby 12
64   Decca DFE 8570   TEENBEAT FROM STAR CLUB HAMBURG (EP) 60
(see also Beat Brothers, Tony Sheridan & Beat Brothers)

DAN PATRICK
67   Stateside SS 2004   Tiger Lee/Call Of The Wild 8

KENTRICK PATRICK
63   Island WI 066   Man To Man/ROLAND ALPHONSO: Hit And Run 10
63   Island WI 079   Don't Stay Out Late/Forever And Ever 10
63   Island WI 104   The End Of The World/Little Princess 10
63   Island WI 119   Golden Love/Beyond 10
64   Island WI 131   Take Me To The Party/I'm Sorry 10
64   Island WI 137   Goodbye Peggy Darling/BABA BROOKS & HIS BAND:
                              Portrait Of My Love 10
64   Island WI 140   I Am Wasting Time/RANDY'S GROUP: Royal Charley 10
(see also Lord Creator)

PATRIOTS
66   Fontana TF 650   Prophet/I'll Be There 8

PATRON OF THE ARTS
66   Page One POF 012   Eleanor Rigby/The True Patron Of The Arts 15

PATSY
68   Doctor Bird DB 1122   Little Flea/The Retreat Song 7
(see also Patsy Todd, Derrick & Patsy, Stranger & Patsy)

PATSY & PEGGY
70s Hot Rod HR 107   Strictly Invitation/Dog Your Woman 5

BRIAN PATTEN
70   Caedmon TC 1300   BRIAN PATTEN (LP) 10
71   Tangent TGS 116   VANISHING TRICK (LP) 35
77   Argo ZSW 607   SLY CORMORANT (LP) 10
(see also Liverpool Scene, Roger McGough & Brian Patten)

BOBBY PATTERSON (& MUSTANGS)
68   Pama PM 735   Broadway Ain't Funky No More/I Met My Match (with Mustangs) 6
68   Pama PM 743   The Good Ol' Days/Don't Be So Mean 5
68   Pama PM 754   Busy Busy Bee/Sweet Taste Of Love (with Mustangs) 5
69   Pama PM 763   T.C.B. Or T.Y.A./What A Wonderful Night For Love (with Mustangs) 8
69   Pama PM 773   My Thing Is Your Thing/Keep It In The Family 5
72   Action ACT 4604   I'm In Love With You/Married Lady 10
72   Mojo 2092 037   How Do You Spell Love/She Don't Have To See You 6

Ottilie PATTERSON

OTTILIE PATTERSON
55	Decca F 10472	I Hate A Man Like You/Reckless Blues (with Chris Barber's Jazz Band)	5
55	Decca F 10621	Weeping Willow Blues/Nobody Knows You When You're Down And Out	5
57	Pye 7N 15109	Kay-Cee Rider/I Love You Baby	4
58	Pye Jazz 7NJ 2015	Jailhouse Blues/Beale Street Blues	4
58	Pye Jazz 7NJ 2025	Trombone Cholly/Lawdy, Lawdy Blues	4
63	Columbia DB 7208	Baby Please Don't Go/I Feel So Good (with Sonny Boy Williamson)	20
56	Decca DFE 6303	BLUES (EP)	7
56	Polygon Jazz T. JTE 102	THAT PATTERSON GIRL (EP)	12
56	Pye Jazz Today NJE 1012	THAT PATTERSON GIRL (EP, reissue)	7
56	Pye Jazz Today NJE 1023	THAT PATTERSON GIRL VOL. 2 (EP)	7
59	Pye NPL 18028	OTTILIE'S IRISH NIGHT (LP)	10
69	Marmalade 608 011	3000 YEARS WITH OTTILIE (LP)	10

(see also Chris Barber)

ROBERT PATTERSON SINGERS
60s	United Artists UAS 2903	THE SOUL OF GOSPEL (LP)	10
65	Fontana 688 516 ZL	I'M SAVED (LP)	10

PATTERSON'S PEOPLE
66	Mercury MF 913	Shake Hands With The Devil/Deadly Nightshade	12

HUBERT PATTISON
66	Pye 7N 17207	Bare Back Rider/The Baby 1 & 2 Problem	4
67	Fontana TF 859	My Home's In My Pocket/Saturday Morning Bride	4

(MIKE) PATTO
66	Columbia DB 8091	Can't Stop Talking About My Baby/Love (as Mike Patto)	50
74	Goodear EAR 106	Sitting In The Park/Get Up And Dig It (as Mike Patto)	4
70	Vertigo 6360 016	PATTO (LP, gatefold sleeve, spiral label)	30
71	Vertigo 6360 032	HOLD YOUR FIRE (LP, spiral label, foldout sleeve)	80
72	Island ILPS 9210	ROLL 'EM SMOKE 'EM PUT ANOTHER LINE OUT (LP)	25

(see also Bo Street Runners, Breakaways, Boxer, News, Chicago Line Blues Band, Timebox, Felder's Orioles)

ALEXANDER PATTON
66	Capitol CL 15461	A Li'l Lovin' Sometimes/No More Dreams	70

CHARLIE PATTON
50s	Heritage REU 4	CHARLIE PATTON (EP)	20

JOHN PATTON
64	Blue Note 45-1889	I'll Never Be Free/Along Came John	5

PATTY & EMBLEMS
64	Stateside SS 322	Mixed Up Shook Up Girl/Ordinary Guy	15

PAUL
65	Polydor BM 56045	Will You Follow Me/Head Death	10

(see also Jimmy Page)

ANDY PAUL
84	Proto ENA 117	Anna Mari-Elena (Greek)/Anna Mari-Elena (English)/Bistepsememe (p/s, all copies mispressed with Greek version of A-side included twice)	12

BILLY PAUL
73	Epic EPC 1055	Me And Mrs. Jones/Your Song	4
70s	Epic 65351	360 DEGREES OF BILLY PAUL (LP)	12
73	Phil. Intl. PIR 65930	360 DEGREES OF BILLY PAUL (LP, reissue)	10
73	Phil. Intl. PIR 65931	EBONY WOMAN (LP)	10
74	Phil. Intl. PIR 65861	WAR OF THE GODS (LP, gatefold sleeve)	10
76	Phil. Intl. PIR 69207	WHEN LOVE IS NEW (LP)	10

BUNNY PAUL
54	Columbia SCM 5102	New Love/You'll Never Leave My Side	7
54	Columbia DB 3454	New Love/You'll Never Leave My Side (78)	5
54	Columbia SCM 5112	Such A Night/I'm Gonna Have Some Fun	10
54	Columbia DB 3469	Such A Night/I'm Gonna Have Some Fun (78)	5
54	Columbia SCM 5131	Lovey Dovey/Answer The Call	8
54	Columbia DB 3510	Lovey Dovey/Answer The Call (78)	15
54	Columbia SCM 5151	You Came A Long Way From St. Louis/You Are Always In My Heart	6
54	Columbia DB 3540	You Came A Long Way From St. Louis/You Are Always In My Heart (78)	5
55	Capitol CL 14279	Please Have Mercy (On A Fool ...)/These Are The Things We'll Share	8
55	Capitol CL 14279	Please Have Mercy (On A Fool ...)/These Are The Things We'll Share (78)	5
55	Capitol CL 14304	Leave My Heart Alone/Two Castanets	6
55	Capitol CL 14304	Leave My Heart Alone/Two Castanets (78)	5
55	Capitol CL 14368	Song Of The Dreamer/For The Very First Time	6
55	Capitol CL 14368	Song Of The Dreamer/For The Very First Time (78)	5

CLARENCE PAUL
75	London HLU 10492	I'm In Love Again/Blue Tuesday	4

DARLENE PAUL
64	Capitol CL 15344	Act Like Nothing Happened/Little Bit Of Heaven	12

JOHN E. PAUL
67	Decca F 12685	Prince Of Players/I Wanna Know	10

LES PAUL (& MARY FORD)
51	Brunswick 04798	Guitar Boogie/Steel Guitar Rag (as Les Paul & His Trio) (78)	8
53	Capitol CL 13943	Vaya Con Dios/Deep In The Blues (78)	5
54	Brunswick 05311	Guitar Boogie/Steel Guitar Rag (as Les Paul & His Trio) (78, reissue)	6
54	Capitol CL 14185	Mandolino/Whither Thou Goest	15

748   Rare Record Price Guide

55	Capitol CL 14212	Mister Sandman/That's What I Like	25
55	Capitol CL 14233	Someday Sweetheart/Song In Blue	15
55	Capitol CL 14300	No Letter Today/Genuine Love	15
55	Capitol CL 14342	Goodbye My Love/Hummingbird	15
56	Capitol CL 14502	Alabamy Bound/Texas Lady	10
56	Capitol CL 14521	Magic Melody/Amukiriki (The Lord Willing)	8
56	Capitol CL 14534	Theme From "The Threepenny Opera" (Moritat)/Nuevo Laredo	8
56	Capitol CL 14577	Send Me Some Money/Say The Words I Love To Hear	7
56	Capitol CL 14593	San Antonio Rose/Cimarron (Roll On)	7
56	Capitol CL 14665	Runnin' Wild/Blow The Smoke Away	8
57	Capitol CL 14710	Cinco Robles (Five Oaks)/Ro-Ro-Robinson	7
57	Capitol CL 14738	Hummin' And Waltzin'/Tuxedos And Flowers	6
57	Capitol CL 14776	Strollin' Blues/I Don't Want You No More	8
57	Capitol CL 14809	(I'm Keeping My Heart Away From) Fire/A Pair Of Fools	8
58	Capitol CL 14839	Bewitched/The Night Of The Fourth (as Les Paul solo)	7
58	Capitol CL 14858	More And More Each Day/Small Island	6
58	Philips PB 873	Put A Ring On My Finger/Fantasy	7
58	Philips PB 882	Jealous Heart/Big Eyed Girl	7
59	Philips PB 906	All I Need Is You/At The Sav-A-Penny Super Store	7
61	Philips PB 1155	Jura/It's Been A Long Long Time	5
55	Capitol EAP1 9121	PRESENTING LES PAUL AND MARY FORD (EP)	10
55	Capitol EAP1 540	SITTING ON TOP OF THE WORLD (EP)	12
60	Capitol EAP1 20048	MR AND MRS MUSIC (EP)	12
61	Capitol EAP1 20145	NOLA (EP)	8
65	Capitol EAP1 20540	JAZZ ME BLUES (EP)	10
51	Capitol LC 6514	THE NEW SOUND (10" LP)	20
53	Capitol LC 6581	THE NEW SOUND VOL. 2 (10" LP)	20
55	Capitol LC 6701	LES AND MARY (10" LP)	20
55	Capitol LC 6704	LES AND MARY PART 2 (10" LP)	20
56	Capitol LC 6806	BYE BYE BLUES! (10" LP)	18
50s	Capitol T 416	HIT MAKERS (LP)	12
57	Capitol T 802	TIME TO DREAM (LP)	12
50s	Capitol T 1276	LOVER (LP)	12
59	Philips BBL 7306	LOVER'S LUAU (LP)	10
61	Capitol T 1476	HITS OF LES AND MARY (LP)	12
68	Decca LK 4924	LES PAUL NOW (LP, also stereo Phase 4 PFS 4138)	10

RIM D. PAUL
| 68 | Philips BF 1737 | Thousand Hours/Downstairs To Meet Her | 4 |

SHELLEY PAUL
| 69 | Jay Boy BOY 10 | Clowns Are Coming In/Take Me To You Heart | 4 |

PAUL & PAULA
63	Philips 304 012 BF	Hey Paula/Bobby Is The One	5
63	Philips 304 016 BF	Young Lovers/Da Hey Be	4
63	Philips BF 1256	First Quarrel/School Is Thru	4
63	Philips BF 1269	Something Old, Something New/Flipped Over You	4
63	Philips BF 1281	First Day Back At School/A Perfect Pair	4
64	Philips BF 1380	No Other Baby/Too Dark To See	4
63	Philips BBE 12639	YOUNG LOVERS (EP)	18
63	Philips 652 026BL	SING FOR YOUNG LOVERS (LP)	16
63	Philips BL 7573	WE GO TOGETHER (LP)	15
63	Philips BL 7587	HOLIDAY FOR TEENS (LP)	15

PAUL & RITCHIE & CRYING SHAMES
| 66 | Decca F 12483 | September In The Rain/Come On Back | 70 |

(see also Cryin' Shames, Gary Walker & Rain)

PAUL & JETLINERS
| 66 | Rainbow RAI 102 | The Great Pretender/The Legend Of The Man From U.N.C.L.E. | 5 |
| 66 | Rainbow RAI 105 | I Know Someday/Something On My Mind | 5 |

PAULETTE
| 68 | Major Minor MM 565 | One Love In My Heart/Must We Say Goodbye | 4 |

PAULETTE SISTERS
55	Capitol CL 14294	Dream Boat/Leave My Honey Be	10
55	Capitol CL 14310	Ring-A-Dang-A-Doo/Lonely One	10
55	Capitol CL 14347	You Win Again/Mama, El Baion	10

PAUL'S DISCIPLES
| 65 | Decca F 12081 | See That My Grave Is Kept Clean/Sixteen Tons | 20 |

PAUL'S TROUBLES
| 67 | Ember EMB S 233 | You'll Find Out/You've Got Something | 20 |

PAUPERS
68	Verve Forecast VS 1514	Think I Care/White Song	5
69	Verve Forecast VS 1520	Southdown Road/Numbers	5
68	Verve Forecast SVLP 6017	ELLIS ISLAND (LP)	12

PAX EXTERNAL
| 71 | Decca F 13167 | A Second Chance Mr Jones/You See Him As Your Brother | 6 |

GARY PAXTON
| 62 | Liberty LIB 55485 | Stop Twisting Baby/Alley Oop Was A Two Dab Man | 5 |

TOM PAXTON
67	Elektra EPK 802	TOM PAXTON (EP)	7
66	Elektra EKL 277/EKS 7277	RAMBLIN' BOY (LP, U.K. pressing in U.S. sleeve)	12
66	Elektra EKL 298/EKS 7298	AIN'T THAT NEWS (LP, U.K. pressing in U.S. sleeve)	12

66	Elektra EKL 317/EKS 7317	OUTWARD BOUND (LP) 10
68	Elek. EKL 4019/EKS 74019	MORNING AGAIN (LP) 10
69	Elek. EKS 74043	THINGS I NOTICE NOW (LP) 10
71	Reprise K 44129	HOW COME THE SUN (LP) 10

DAVEY PAYNE & MEDIUM WAVE

| 69 | Ember EMB S 265 | Walk In The Sunshine/Looking Towards The Sky (p/s) ....4 |

FREDA PAYNE

62	HMV POP 1091	He Who Laughs Last/Slightly Out Of Tune 10
70	Invictus INV 502	Band Of Gold/The Easiest Way To Fall 4
70	Invictus INV 505	Deeper And Deeper/Unhoked Generation 4
71	Invictus INV 509	Cherish What Is Dear To You (While It's Near To You)/The World Don't
		Owe You A Thing 4
71	Invictus INV 512	Rock Me In The Cradle (Of Your Lovin' Arms)/Now Is The Time
		To Say Goodbye 4
71	Invictus INV 515	Bring Home The Boys/Odds And Ends 4
71	Invictus INV 518	You've Got To Love Somebody/Mama's Gone 4
72	Invictus INV 520	You Brought Me Joy/Suddenly It's Yesterday 4
72	Invictus INV 526	Unhooked Generation/Come Back 4
73	Invictus INV 529	I Shall Not Be Moved/Thru' The Memory Of My Mind 4
73	Invictus INV 533	Band Of Gold/The Easiest Way To Fall (withdrawn reissue) 8
75	ABC ABC 4087	You/Lost In Love 4
78	Capitol 12CL 15959	Love Magnet/Bring Back The Joy (12", promo only) 7
71	Invictus SVT 1001	BAND OF GOLD (LP) 12
72	Invictus SVT 1005	CONTACT (LP) 12
73	Invictus SVT 1007	THE BEST OF FREDA PAYNE (LP) 10
78	Capitol E-ST 11864	SUPERNATURAL HIGH (LP) 10

LEON PAYNE

| 64 | London HA-B 8136 | AMERICANA (LP) ....10 |

PAZ

83	Spotlight SPJ 507	KANDEEN LOVE SONG (LP) 12
83	Spotlight SPJ 518	PAZ ARE BACH (LP) 10
83	Paladin PALP 001	LOOK INSIDE (LP) 10

DAVE PEACE QUARTET

| 69 | Saga FID 2155 | GOOD MORNING MR. BLUES (LP) ....20 |
| | *(see also Birmingham)* | |

PEACEFUL COMPANY

| 73 | Sovereign SVNA 7252 | PEACEFUL COMPANY (LP) ....25 |

PEACHES & HERB

67	CBS 202509	Let's Fall In Love/We're In This Thing Together 15
67	CBS 2711	Close Your Eyes/I Will Watch Over You 6
67	CBS 2866	For Your Love/I Need Your Love So Desperately 15
67	Direction 58-3096	Love Is Strange/Two Little Kids 5
68	Direction 58-3415	Let It Be Me/I Need Your Love So Despeartely 5
68	Direction 58-3548	United/Thank You 4
68	Direction 58-3829	Let's Make A Promise/Me And You 4
69	Direction 58-4085	When He Touches Me/Touch Me 4
70	Direction 58-5249	Soothe Me With Your Love/We're So Much In Love 8
77	Epic EPC 4903	Soothe Me With Your Love/Satisy My Hunger (coloured vinyl) 4
67	CBS 62966	LET'S FALL IN LOVE (LP) 12
67	CBS 63119	FOR YOUR LOVE (LP) 12
68	Direction 8-63263	GOLDEN DUETS (LP) 12

ANNETTE PEACOCK

72	RCA SF 8255	I'M THE ONE (LP) 12
78	Aura AUL 702	X DREAMS (LP) 10
78	Aura AUL 707	PERFECT DREAMS PERFECT RELEASE (LP) 10
70s	Aura	LIVE IN PARIS (LP) 25
83	Aura AUL 722	THE COLLECTION (LP) 10

ANNETTE PEACOCK & PAUL BLEY

| 74 | Polydor 2383 105 | DUAL UNITY (LP) ....20 |
| | *(see also Paul Bley, Bley-Peacock Synthesiser Show, Annette Peacock)* | |

TREVOR PEACOCK

| 61 | Decca F 11414 | I Didn't Figure On Him To Come Back/Can I Walk You Home ....4 |

PEAK FOLK

| 70s | Folk Heritage | PEAK FOLK (LP) ....25 |

PEANUT

65	Pye 7N 15901	Thank You For The Rain/I'm Not Sad 4
65	Pye 7N 15963	Home Of The Brave/I Wanna Hear It Again 8
66	Columbia DB 8032	I'm Waiting For The Day/Someone's Gonna Be Sorry 4
67	Columbia DB 8104	I Didn't Love Him Anyway/Come Tomorrow 4

PEANUT BUTTER CONSPIRACY

67	CBS 2981	It's A Happening Thing/Twice Is Life 6
68	CBS 3543	Turn On A Friend/Captain Sandwich 6
69	London HLH 10290	Back In L.A./Have A Little Faith 7
68	CBS 63277	THE GREAT CONSPIRACY (LP) 18

BOB PEARCE BLUES BAND

68	Avenue BEV 1054	BLUES CRUSADE (EP, credited to Brother Bung) 15
74	Westwood WRS 040	LET'S GET DRUNK AGAIN (LP) 10
79	Forest Tracks FT 3015	COLOUR BLIND (LP) 10

PEARL JAM
92	Epic 468884 0	TEN (LP, picture disc)	12
92	Epic 468884 5	TEN (CD, metallic yellow digipack)	15

PEARLS
62	Embassy EMB 564	He's So Fine/BUD ASHTON: Scarlett O'Hara	4

PEARLS BEFORE SWINE
68	Fontana STL 5503	BALAKLAVA (LP, with poster)	20
68	Fontana STL 5505	ONE NATION UNDERGROUND (LP)	18
69	Reprise RSLP 6364	THESE THINGS TOO (LP)	12
70	Reprise RSLP 6405	THE USE OF ASHES (LP)	14
71	Reprise RSLP 6442	CITY OF GOLD (LP)	14
71	Reprise RSLP 6467	BEAUTIFUL LIES YOU COULD LIVE (LP)	12

BUSTER PEARSON BAND
73	Action ACT 4612	Big Funky/Pretty Woman	5

JOHNNY PEARSON
66	Columbia DB 7851	Rat Catcher's Theme/Weaver's Green Theme	8

KEITH PEARSON'S RIGHT HAND BAND
76	Eron ER 014	KEITH PEARSON'S RIGHT HAND BAND (LP)	12

RONNIE PEARSON
58	HMV POP 489	Flippin' Over You/Teen-Age Fancy	200
58	HMV POP 489	Flippin' Over You/Teen-Age Fancy (78)	50

PEASANTS
65	Columbia DB 7642	Got Some Lovin' For You Baby/Let's Get Together	60

PEBBLES
68	Major Minor MM 574	40 Miles Inside Your Heart/Get Around	4
69	Decca F 22944	Incredible George/Playing Chess	7
70	Deram DM 305	Stand Up And Be Counted/May In The Morning	5
71	Parlophone R 5900	Goodnight Ma/Sadness Of A Summer's Afternoon	5
71	Parlophone R 5921	First Time Loving/Party	5

PEBBLES & BAMM BAMM
66	Pye Intl. 7N 25382	Daddy/The World Is Full Of Joys	4

PEDDLERS
64	Philips BF 1375	Let The Sunshine In/True Girl	5
65	Philips BF 1404	Whatever Happened To The Good Times/Song For The Blues	5
65	Philips BF 1455	Over The Rainbow/You Must Be Having Me On	5
66	Philips BF 1504	Adam's Apple/Anybody's Fool	5
66	Philips BF 1530	I've Got To Hold On/Gassin'	5
67	Philips BF 1557	What'll I Do/Delicious Lady	5
67	CBS 2947	Irresistable You/Murry's Mood	4
67	CBS 3055	You're The Reason I'm Living/Nine Miles High	4
68	CBS 3333	Handel With Care/Horse's Collar	4
68	CBS 3734	Comin' Home Baby/Empty Club Blues	4
69	CBS 4045	That's Life/Wasting My Time	4
69	CBS 4449	Birth/Steel Mill	4
70	CBS 4720	Girlie/P.S. I Love You	4
67	Philips (S)BL 7768	LIVE AT THE PICKWICK (LP)	15
67	CBS (S)BPG 63183	FREE WHEELERS (LP)	10
68	CBS 63411	THREE IN A CELL (LP)	10
68	Fontana SFL 13016	THE FANTASTIC PEDDLERS (LP)	10
70	CBS 63682	BIRTHDAY (LP)	10
70	Philips 6308 028	THREE FOR ALL (LP)	10
71	Philips 6386 066	GEORGIA ON MY MIND (LP)	10
72	Philips 6308 102	SUITE LONDON (LP, with London Symphony Orchestra)	10

MIKE PEDICIN QUINTET
62	HMV POP 1001	When Cats Come Twistin' In/Gotta Twist	5

BOBBY PEDRICK
58	London HLX 8740	White Bucks And Saddle Shoes/Stranded	30
58	London HLX 8740	White Bucks And Saddle Shoes/Stranded (78)	12

ANN PEEBLES
70	London HLU 10322	Part Time Love/I Still Love You	4
71	London HLU 10328	I Pity The Fool/Heartaches, Heartaches	4
71	London HLU 10346	Slipped, Tripped And Fell In Love/99 Lbs	4
72	London HLU 10361	Breaking Up Somebody's Home/Troubles, Heartaches And Sadness	4
72	London HLU 10385	Somebody's On Your Case/I've Been There Before	4
73	London HLU 10405	I'm Gonna Tear Your Playhouse Down/One Way Street	4
74	London HLU 10428	I Can't Stand The Rain/I've Been There Before	4
75	London HLU 10484	Beware/You Got To Feed The Fire	5
75	London HLU 10508	Come On Mama/I'm Leaving You	4
72	London SHU 8434	STRAIGHT FROM THE HEART (LP)	10
74	London SHU 8468	I CAN'T STAND THE RAIN (LP)	10
76	London SHU 8490	TELLIN' IT (LP)	10

PAUL PEEK
61	Pye Intl. 7N 25102	Brother In Law/Through The Teenage Years	4
66	CBS 202073	Rockin' Pneumonia/Pin The Tail On The Donkey	4

(see also Gene Vincent & Blue Caps)

DAVID PEEL (& LOWER EAST SIDE)
68	Elek. EKL 4032/EKS 74032	HAVE A MARIJUANA (LP)	15

David PEEL (& LOWER EAST SIDE)

70	Elektra 2401 001	AMERICAN REVOLUTION (LP)	12

PEELERS
72	Polydor 2460 165	BANISHED MISFORTUNE (LP)	175

PEELS
66	Stateside SS 513	Juanita Banana/Fun	5
60s	Audio Fidelity AFSP 527	Time Marches On/Scrooey Mooey	12

PEENUTS
67	Ember EMB S 242	The Theme For "The Monkees"/The World's Been Good To Me Tonight (some in p/s)	10/6

PEEPS
65	Philips BF 1421	Now Is The Time/Got Plenty Of Love	8
65	Philips BF 1443	What Can I Say?/Don't Talk About Love	10
66	Philips BF 1478	Gotta Get A Move On/I Told You Before	7
66	Philips BF 1509	Tra La La/Loser Wins	7

(see also Martin Cure & Peeps, Sabres)

PEEP SHOW
67	Polydor BM 56196	Mazy/Your Servant, Steven	60
68	Polydor BM 52226	Esprit De Corps/Mino In A Mix Up	15

DONALD PEERS
53	HMV B 10411	Barrels 'N' Barrels Of Roses/Lulu Had A Baby (78, B-side with Tanner Sisters)	5
58	Oriole CB 1431	Oh! Oh! I'm Falling In Love Again/I Need Somebody	4

BEV PEGG (& HIS GOIN' NOWHERE BAND)
70s	Beaujangle DB 0007	NOSTALGIA IS A THING OF THE PAST (LP, private pressing, with booklet, 100 only; as Bev Pegg & His Goin' Nowhere Band)	12
70s	Beaujangle DB 0008	THE FOUNDRY DITTY AND THE INDUSTRIAL AIR (LP, private pressing, 500 only)	10

(see also David Cartwright, Away From The Sand, Brindley Brae)

BOB PEGG
74	Transatlantic TRA 280	THE SHIPBUILDER (LP)	15
75	Transatlantic TRA 299	ANCIENT MAPS (LP)	12

BOB & CAROLANNE PEGG
71	Trailer LER 3016	HE CAME FROM THE MOUNTAIN (LP, red label)	18

(see also Carolanne Pegg, Mr. Fox)

BOB PEGG & NICK STRUTT
73	Transatlantic TRA 265	BOB PEGG & NICK STRUTT (LP)	12

CAROLANNE PEGG
73	Transatlantic TRA 266	CAROLANNE PEGG (LP)	15

(see also Bob & Carolanne Pegg, Albert Lee)

PEGGY & JIMMY
70s	Hot Rod HR 101	Remember Easter Monday/CARL LEVY: Pum Pum Lover	6

PEGGY'S LEG
73	Bunch	William Tell Overture	30
73	Bunch BAN 2001	GRINILLA (LP, insert)	500

(see also Skid Row, Jimi Slevin)

PEG LEG SAM
74	Flyright LP 507/8	THE LAST MEDICINE SHOW (2-LP)	15

TRACY PENDARVIS
60	London HLS 9059	A Thousand Guitars/Is It Too Late	15
60	London HLS 9213	Is It Me/South Bound Line	15

PENDLEFOLK
70	Folk Heritage FHR 007	PENDLEFOLK (LP)	20

PENDRAGON
87	Awareness AWS 101	Red Shoes/Searching/Contact (p/s)	4
87	Awareness AWSX 101	Red Shoes/Searching/Contact (12", p/s)	7
87	Awareness	Saved By You (12")	7
84	Elusive ARRMP 001	FLY HIGH FALL FAR (12" mini-LP)	8
85	Elusive ARRLP 100	FIRE IN HARMONY (LP)	10
85	Elusive ARRLP 101	THE JEWEL (LP)	10

PENDULUMS
64	Pye 7N 15701	The Weaver/The Slow Weaver	4

PENETRATION
77	Virgin VS 192	Don't Dictate/Money Talks (p/s)	6
78	Virgin VS 213	Firing Squad/Never (p/s)	5
78	Virgin VS 226	Life's A Gamble/V.I.P. (p/s)	4
79	Virgin VS 257	Danger Signs/Stone Heroes (live) (p/s)	4
79	Virgin VS 268	Come Into The Open/Lifeline (p/s)	4
78	Virgin V 2109	MOVING TARGETS (LP, 15,000 on luminous vinyl)	10
79	Virgin V 2131	COMING UP FOR AIR (LP)	10
79	Virgin/Clifdayn PEN 1	RACE AGAINST TIME (LP, official bootleg)	12

(see also Pauline Murray & Invisible Girls)

PENGUINS
55	London HL 8114	Earth Angel/Hey Senorita (gold lettering label, later silver)	1000/400
55	London HL 8114	Earth Angel/Hey Senorita (78)	60

DAWN PENN
66	Rio R 113	Long Days Short Night/Are You There	10
67	Studio One SO 2030	You Don't Love Me/SOUL VENDORS: Portobello Road	15
68	Island WI 3097	I'll Never Let You Go/MARK BROWN: Brown Low Special	10

TONY PENN
62	Starlite ST45 083	That's What I Like/I Won't Cry Anymore	25

PENNSYLVANIA SIXPENCE
67	Pye 7N 17326	Love Of The Common People/Midweek Excursion	4

PENNY
61	Piccadilly 7N 35009	Who Does He Think He Is/Sparks	4
62	Piccadilly 7N 35045	Shall I Take My Heart And Go/What'd I Do?	4

GEORGE A. PENNY
68	Trojan TR 625	Win Your Love/VAL BENNETT: All In The Game	10

HANK PENNY
56	Parlophone MSP 6202	Bloodshot Eyes/Wham! Bam! Thank You Ma'am	30
56	Parlophone R 4120	Bloodshot Eyes/Wham! Bam! Thank You Ma'am (78)	6

PENNY PEEPS
68	Liberty LBF 15053	Little Man With A Stick/Model Village	40
68	Liberty LBF 15114	I See The Morning/Curly, The Knight Of The Road	10

LYDIA PENSE & COLD BLOOD
70s	ABC ABC 4109	I Get Off On You/We Came Down Here/Cold Blood Smoking	6

PENTAD
65	Parlophone R 5288	Silver Dagger/Nothing But Love	15
65	Parlophone R 5368	Don't Throw It All Away/Too Many Ways	8
66	Parlophone R 5424	Something Other People Call Love/It Better Be Me	8

PENTAGONS
61	London HLU 9333	To Be Loved Forever/Down At The Beach	30

PENTANGLE
68	Big T BIG 109	Travellin' Song/Mirage (some in title sleeve)	7/4
69	Big T BIG 124	Once I Had A Sweetheart/I Saw An Angel	4
70	Big T BIG 128	Light Flight/Cold Mountain	4
68	Transatlantic TRA 162	THE PENTANGLE (LP)	15
68	Transatlantic TRA 178	SWEET CHILD (2-LP)	18
69	Transatlantic TRA 205	BASKET OF LIGHT (LP, gatefold sleeve)	15
70	Transatlantic TRA 228	CRUEL SISTER (LP)	12
71	Transatlantic TRA 240	REFLECTIONS (LP)	12
72	Reprise K 44197	SOLOMON'S SEAL (LP, with lyric insert)	18
72	Transatlantic TRASAM 23	HISTORY BOOK (LP)	10
73	Transatlantic TRASAM 29	PENTANGLING (LP)	10

(see also Bert Jansch, Jon Renbourn)

PEOPLE
69	Capitol CL 15553	I Love You/Somebody Tell Me My Name	8
69	Capitol CL 15599	Ulla/Turnin' Me In	6
71	Deram DM 346	In Ancient Times/Glastonbury	6

PEOPLE'S BAND
70	Transatlantic TRA 214	PEOPLE'S BAND (LP, with Charlie Watts)	30

(see also Charlies Watts)

PEOPLE'S CHOICE
71	Mojo 2092 024	I Like To Do It/Big Ladies Man	8

PEPPER
68	Pye 7N 17569	We'll Make It Together/I'm On The Way Down	8

ART PEPPER
54	Vogue LDE 067	ART PEPPER QUARTET (10" LP)	12
60	Contemporary LAC 12229	MODERN JAZZ CLASSICS (LP, as Art Pepper Eleven)	10

(see also Chet Baker)

JIM PEPPER
71	Atlantic 2400 149	PEPPER'S POW WOW (LP)	20

KEN PEPPER
61	Top Rank JAR 535	Just A Little At A Time/I Get The Blues When It Rains	4

PEPPERMINT CIRCUS
67	Olga OLE 007	All The King's Horses/It Didn't Take Long	6
68	Polydor 56288	I Won't Be There/Keeping My Head Above Water	5
69	Polydor 56312	Please Be Patient/Take My Love	5
69	A&M AMS 765	One Thing Can Lead To Another/It's So Easy	4
70	A&M AMS 778	Let Me Go/School Days	4

DANNY PEPPERMINT (& JUMPING JACKS)
61	London HLL 9478	The Peppermint Twist/Somebody Else Is Taking My Place (with Jumping Jacks)	6
62	London HLL 9516	One More Time/La Dee Dah	5
62	London HLL 9614	Maybe Tomorrow But Not Today/Passing Parade	6
62	London HA-L 2438	TWIST WITH DANNY PEPPERMINT (LP)	12

(see also Jumping Jacks)

PEPPERMINT RAINBOW
68	MCA MU 1034	Walking In Different Circles/Pink Lemonade	5
69	MCA MU 1076	Will You Be Staying After Sunday/And I'll Be There	5
69	MCA MU 1091	Rosemary/Don't Wake Up In The Morning	5

PEPPERMINT TROLLEY COMPANY
68	Dot DOT 110	Baby You Come Rolling 'Cross My Mind/Nine O'Clock Business Man	4

PEPPI
62	Decca F 11520	Stories/When I Think Of You	4
63	Decca F 11638	Can You Waddle/I Never Danced Before	6
64	Decca F 11991	Pistol Packin' Mama/Roll On Baby	7
65	Decca F 12055	The Skip/Do The Skip	6

PERCELLS
63	HMV POP 1154	Cheek To Cheek/What Are Boys Made Of?	4

LANCE PERCIVAL
77	Parlophone R 5517	End Of The Season/Our Jim	4

NORMAN PERCIVAL
67	United Artists UP 1197	Theme From "Billion Dollar Brain"/Shades Of Green	4

PERCY PAVILION
83	Pavil. In Splendour PIS 1	CRICKET (EP)	7
84	Dead Good Dolly P. DMS 2	Gower Power/You're An Extra Baby (p/s)	4

(see also Captain Sensible, Dolly Mixture)

PERET
74	Pye Intl. 7N 25645	Canta Y Se Feliz/Tocale Las Palmas	5

PERE UBU
79	Chrysalis CHS 2372	The Fabulous Sequel (Have Shoes Will Walk)/Humour Me (live)/The Book Is On The Table (p/s)	8
80	Rough Trade RT 049	Final Solution/My Dark Ages (p/s)	4
81	Rough Trade RT 066	Not Happy/Lonesome Cowboy Dave (p/s)	4
78	Radar RDR 1	DATAPANIK IN THE YEAR ZERO (12" EP)	8
78	Blank BLANK 001	THE MODERN DANCE (LP)	15
80	Rough Trade ROUGH 14	THE ART OF WALKING (LP, original with "Miles" & "Arabia")	12
88	Fontana SFCD 3	THE MODERN DANCE (CD, 1000 only, numbered)	14

(see also David Thomas)

PEREGRINE
70s	Westwood	SONGS OF MINE (LP)	50

PERENNIAL DIVIDE
88	Sweatbox SOX 020	Bee Head (1-sided, promo only)	5

CHRISTINE PERFECT
69	Blue Horizon 57 3165	When You Say/No Road Is The Right Road	6
70	Blue Horizon 57 3172	I'm Too Far Gone (To Turn Around)/Close To Me	8
70	Blue Horizon 7 63860	CHRISTINE PERFECT (LP)	40

(see also Fleetwood Mac, Illusive Dream)

PERFECT DISASTER
87	Glass GLAEP 107	Hey Hey Hey/The Night Belongs To Charlie/That's What The Doctor Says/Elusive Dreams (12", p/s)	7

(see also Varicose Veins, Orange Disaster, Architects Of Disaster)

PERFECT PEOPLE
69	MCA MU 1079	House In The Country/Polyanna	10

PERFORMERS
69	Action ACT 4552	I Can't Stop/L.A. Stomp	8

PERISHERS
68	Fontana TF 965	How Does It Feel/Bye Bye Baby	20

(see also Seftones)

NICK PERITO ORCHESTRA
60	London HLT 9221	Green Leaves Of Summer/Jennifer	4

CARL PERKINS
56	London HLU 8271	Blue Suede Shoes/Honey Don't	125
56	London HLU 8271	Blue Suede Shoes/Honey Don't (78)	20
57	London HLS 8408	Matchbox/Your True Love	125
57	London HLS 8408	Matchbox/Your True Love (78)	20
57	London HLS 8527	Glad All Over/Forever Yours	80
57	London HLS 8527	Glad All Over/Forever Yours (78)	20
58	London HLS 8608	Lend Me Your Comb/That's Right	80
58	London HLS 8608	Lend Me Your Comb/That's Right (78)	20
59	Philips PB 983	One Ticket To Loneliness/I Don't See Me In Your Eyes Anymore	12
59	Philips PB 983	One Ticket To Loneliness/I Don't See Me In Your Eyes Anymore (78)	35
61	Philips PB 1179	Anyway The Wind Blows/The Unhappy Girls	12
64	Brunswick 05905	Help Me Find My Baby/I Wouldn't Have You	8
64	Brunswick 05909	Big Bad Blues/Lonely Heart	7
64	Brunswick 05923	The Monkey Shine/Let My Baby Be	10
67	Stateside SS 599	A Country Boy's Dream/If I Could Come Back	8
68	London HLP 7125	A Country Boy's Dream/Shine Shine Shine (export issue)	15
68	Spark SRL 1009	Lake County, Cotton Country/It's You	8
68	London HLS 10192	Blue Suede Shoes/Dixie Fried (unissued)	
68	London HLS 10192	Blue Suede Shoes/Matchbox	7
69	CBS 3932	Restless/11.43	7
70	CBS 4991	All Mama's Children/Step Aside	5
78	Jet UP 36365	Blue Suede Shoes/That's All Right/Rock On Around The World (p/s)	4
78	Jet SJET 117	Mustang Wine/The Whole World Misses You (p/s)	4

80	Jet JET 182	Love Sick Blues/Turn Around/Miss Misunderstood/	
		Blue Suede Shoes (p/s)	4
59	London HA-S 2202	THE DANCE ALBUM OF CARL PERKINS (LP)	70
66	CBS Realm 52305	WHOLE LOTTA CARL PERKINS (LP)	15
68	CBS 63309	KING OF ROCK (LP)	12
68	London HA-P/SH-P 8366	COUNTRY BOY'S DREAM (LP)	15
69	CBS 63676	CARL PERKINS' GREATEST HITS (LP)	10
70	CBS 63826	BOPPIN' THE BLUES (LP, with NRBQ)	12
66	Ember NR 5038	SUNSTROKE (LP, shared with Jerry Lee Lewis)	12
82	Sun BOX 101	THE SUN YEARS (3-LP box set with booklet)	20
	(see also NRBQ)		

JOE PERKINS
63	London HLU 9794	Little Eeefin Annie/Encle Eeef	4

LASCELLES PERKINS
61	Blue Beat BB 41	Creation/Lonely Robin	10
63	Island WI 038	Tango Lips (with Yvonne Harrison)/My Ideal	8
64	R&B JB 175	I Am So Grateful/When I Survey	8
70	Banana BA 317	Tell It All Brothers/SOUND DIMENSION: Polkadots	5
70	Escort ES 814	Please Stay/MATADORS: Voyage From The Moon	4

POLLY PERKINS
63	Decca F 11583	The Girls Are At It Again/I Reckon You	6
	(see also Academy)		

TONY PERKINS
57	RCA RCA 1018	Moonlight Swim/First Romance	4
57	RCA RCA 1018	Moonlight Swim/First Romance (78)	10

PAT PERRIN
68	Island WI 3115	Over You/LLOYD TERRELL: Lost Without You	10

PERRI'S
63	Oriole CB 1481	Jerri-Lee/Ballad Of A Happy Heart	6

GREG PERRY
78	Casablanca CBX 511	Boogie Man/Will She Meet The Train In The Rain	4

JEFF PERRY
76	Arista ARIST 51	Love Don't Come No Stronger/I've Got To See You Right Away	7

LEE 'SCRATCH' PERRY (& UPSETTERS)
63	R&B JB 102	Prince In The Black/Don't Copy	10
63	R&B JB 104	Old For New/Prince And Duke	10
63	R&B JB 106	Mad Head/Man And Wife	10
63	R&B JB 135	Royalty/Can't Be Wrong	10
64	Port-O-Jam PJ 4003	Bad Minded People/TOMMY McCOOK & HIS GROUP: Jam Rock	10
64	Port-O-Jam PJ 4010	Chatty Chatty Woman/TOMMY McCOOK & HIS GROUP: Road Block	10
65	Island WI 210	Please Don't Go/Bye, St. Peter (with Upsetters)	10
65	Island WI 223	Country Girl/Strange Country (with Upsetters)	10
65	Ska Beat JB 201	Roast Duck/Hand To Hand, Man To Man	10
65	Ska Beat JB 203	Trail And Crosses/Jon Tom	10
65	Ska Beat JB 212	Wishes Of The Wicked/Hold Down	10
65	Ska Beat JB 215	Open Up/ROLAND ALPHONSO: Twin Double	10
66	Ska Beat JB 251	The Woodman/Give Me Justice	10
66	Island WI 292	Doctor Dick (as King Perry)/SOUL BROTHERS: Magic Star	10
66	Island WI 298	Rub And Squeeze (as King Perry & Soulettes)/SOUL BROTHERS: Here Comes The Minx	10
67	Doctor Bird DB 1073	Run For Cover/Something You've Got (as Lee 'King' Perry & Sensations)	10
67	Doctor Bird DB 1098	Whop Whop Man/Wind-Up Doll (with Dynamites)	10
68	Amalgamated AMG 808	The Upsetter/Thank You Baby	12
68	Doctor Bird DB 1146	People Funny Boy/BURT WALTERS: Blowing In The Wind	10
68	Trojan TR 644	Uncle Desmond/Bronco (with Upsetters)	8
69	Upsetter US 324	Yakety Yak/Tackio (with Upsetters)	6
70	Upsetter US 325	Kill Them All/Soul Walk (with Upsetters)	6
71	Bullet BU 461	All Combine Pts 1& 2 (as Lee Perry & Upsetters)	5
72	Upsetter US 385	French Connection (with Upsetters)/UPSETTERS: Version	5
72	Upsetter US 389	Back Biter (with Dennis Alcapone)/UPSETTERS: Version	5
73	Upsetter US 397	Jungle Lion/Freakout Skank	5
73	Upsetter US 398	Cow Thief Skank (actually by Lee Perry & Charlie Ace)/Seven And Three Quarters Skank	5
73	Bread BR 1111	Station Underground/CARLTON & SHOES: Better Days	5
73	Downtown DT 513	Bucky Skank/Mid East Rock	5
73	Jackpot JP 812	Justice To The People/UPSETTERS: Version	5
79	Cactus CTLP 112	REVOLUTION DUB (LP)	12
79	Trojan TRL 166	AFRICAN BLOOD (LP)	10
	(see also Upsetters, Defenders)		

MAL PERRY
58	Fontana H 125	Lollipop/Love Me Again (78)	6
58	Fontana H 133	That's When Your Heartaches Begin/Make Me A Miracle	5
58	Fontana H 133	That's When Your Heartaches Begin/Make Me A Miracle (78)	5
58	Fontana H 149	Too Young To Love/Who Are They To Say	4
58	Fontana H 149	Too Young To Love/Who Are They To Say (78)	5
58	Fontana H 157	Things I Didn't Say/The Girl Next Door	5
59	Fontana H 172	Richer Than I/Willingly	4

STEVE PERRY
60	HMV POP 745	Step By Step/Because They're Young	5

Steve PERRY

62	Decca F 11462	Ginny Come Lately/Two Of A Kind	4
62	Decca F 11526	Young And In Love/Let It Come True	4
63	Decca F 11656	Find Me A Girl/My Dad	4
64	Decca F 11895	Crooked Little Man/Day Dreams	4

PERRY SISTERS

59	Brunswick 05802	Willie Boy/Fabian	20
59	Brunswick 05802	Willie Boy/Fabian (78)	12

PERSIAN RISK

83	Neat NEAT 24	Ridin' High/Hurt You (p/s)	4
86	Metal Masters METALLP 2	RISE UP (LP)	12

PERSIANS

69	Pama PM 772	I Only Have Eyes For You	5
72	Capitol CL 15726	Baby Come Back Home/I Want To Go Home	4

PERSIMMON'S PECULIAR SHADES

68	Major Minor MM 554	Watchmaker/Coplington	15

PERSONALITIES

65	Blue Beat BB 35	Push It Down/BUSTER'S ALLSTARS: Blues Market	8
65	Dice CC 30	I Remember/Suffering	7

PERSUASIONS (U.K.)

65	Columbia DB 7560	I'll Go Crazy/Try Me	15
65	Columbia DB 7700	Big Brother/Deep Down Love	20
66	Columbia DB 7859	La, La, La, La, La/Opportunity	20

PERSUASIONS (U.S.)

69	Minit MLF 11017	Party In The Woods/It's Better To Have Loved And Lost	8
70	Straight STS 1062	ACAPPELLA (LP)	40
72	Island ILPS 9201	STREET CORNER SYMPHONY (LP)	10

MORRIS PERT

75	Chantry ABM 21	LUMINOS/CHROMOSPHERE/4 JAPANESE VERSES (LP)	40
80s	Chantry CHT 001	LUMINOS/CHROMOSPHERE/4 JAPANESE VERSES (LP, reissue)	30
82	Chantry CHT 007	BOOK OF LOVE/FRAGMENTI I/ULTIMATE DECAY (LP)	30

JON PERTWEE

72	Purple PUR 111	Who Is The Doctor/Pure Mystery	10
85	Safari DOCTOR 1	Who Is The Doctor/Doctor Blood Donor (p/s)	4

PESKY GEE!

69	Pye 7N 17708	Where Is My Mind/Place Of Heart Break	15
69	Pye NSPL 18293	EXCLAMATION MARK (LP)	50
	(see also Black Widow, Agony Bag)		

PETALS

63	Decca F 11650	Let's Do The Tamoure/Look At Me	4

PETER & GORDON

64	Columbia DB 7225	A World Without Love/If I Were You	4
64	Columbia DB 7292	Nobody I Know/You Don't Have To Tell Me	4
64	Columbia DB 7356	I Don't Want To See You Again/I Would Buy	4
64	Columbia DB 7407	I Go To Pieces/Love Me Baby	4
65	Columbia DB 7524	True Love Ways/If You Wish	4
65	Columbia DB 7617	To Know You Is To Love You/I Told You So	4
65	Columbia DB 7729	Baby I'm Yours/When The Black Of Your Eyes Turns To Grey	4
66	Columbia DB 7834	Woman/Wrong From The Start	5
66	Columbia DB 7951	Don't Pity Me/To Show I Love You	4
66	Columbia DB 8003	Lady Godiva/Morning's Calling	5
66	Columbia DB 8075	Knight In Rusty Armour/The Flower Lady	5
67	Columbia DB 8159	Sunday For Tea/Start Trying Someone Else	5
67	Columbia DB 8198	The Jokers/Red, Cream And Velvet	4
68	Columbia DB 8398	I Feel Like Going Out/The Quest For The Holy Grail	5
68	Columbia DB 8451	You've Had Better Times/Sipping My Wine	5
69	Columbia DB 8585	I Can Remember (Not Too Long Ago)/Hard Time Rainy Day	5
64	Columbia SEG 8337	JUST FOR YOU (EP)	10
64	Columbia SEG 8348	NOBODY I KNOW (EP)	12
64	Columbia 33SX 1630	PETER AND GORDON (LP, also stereo SCX 3518)	15/18
64	Columbia 33SX 1660	IN TOUCH WITH PETER AND GORDON (LP, also stereo SCX 3532)	16/20
65	Columbia 33SX 1761	HURTIN' 'N' LOVIN' (LP, also stereo SCX 3565)	15/18
66	Columbia S(C)X 6045	PETER AND GORDON (LP, mono/stereo)	15/18
66	Columbia S(C)X 6097	SOMEWHERE... (LP, mono/stereo)	15/18
65	Columbia SCXC 25	I GO TO PIECES (LP, export issue)	25
66	Columbia SCXC 29	WOMAN (LP, export issue)	25
66	Columbia SCXC 33	LADY GODIVA (LP, export issue)	25
	(see also Gordon Waller)		

PETER & GORDON/FREDDIE & DREAMERS

64	Columbia SEG 8349	JUST FOR YOU (EP, 2 tracks each)	8

PETER & HEADLINES

64	Decca F 11980	Don't Cry Little Girl/It Was Love	12
64	Decca F 12035	Tears And Kisses/I've Got My Reasons	12
	(see also Count Downe & Zeros)		

PETER & PAUL

65	Blue Beat BB 364	Hosana Hallelujah/Schoolgirl	7

PETER & PAVEL

69	Page One POF 112	Laska/Wenceslas Square	4

PETER & PERSUADERS
60s	Oak RGJ 197	The Wanderer/Wine Glass Rock/Oh My Soul/Cross My Heart (EP)	25

PETER & WOLVES
67	MGM MGM 1352	Little Girl/Lost And Found	7
68	MGM MGM 1374	Lantern Light/Break Up, Break Down	6
68	MGM MGM 1397	Julia/Birthday	5
69	UPC UPC 104	Something In The Way She Moves/The Lady And Me	4

(see also Factory, Norman Conquest, John Pantry)

PETER B's
66	Columbia DB 7862	If You Wanna Be Happy/Jodrell Blues	40

(see also Tony Colton)

PETER, JAN & JOHN
65	HMV POP 1442	Mountain Boy/I'm Lookin' Out	4

PETER, PAUL & MARY
63	Warner Bros WB 95	Puff The Magic Dragon/Pretty Mary	4
63	Warner Bros WSE 6119	MOVING (EP, stereo)	7
63	Warner Bros WSE 6122	PETER, PAUL AND MARY (EP, stereo)	7
63	Warner Bros WM 4064	PETER, PAUL AND MARY (LP, also stereo WS 9064)	12
63	Warner Bros WM/WS 8124	MOVING (LP)	12
64	Warner Bros WM/WS 8142	IN THE WIND (LP)	10
65	Warner Bros WM/WS 8158	IN CONCERT VOL. 1 (LP)	12
65	Warner Bros WM/WS 8159	IN CONCERT VOL. 2 (LP)	12
65	Warner Bros (W)W 1589	A SONG WILL RISE (LP)	10
66	Warner Bros (W)W 1615	SEE WHAT TOMORROW BRINGS	10
66	Warner Bros W(S) 1648	PETER, PAUL & MARY ALBUM (LP)	10
67	Warner Bros W(S) 1700	ALBUM 1700 (LP)	10
68	Warner Bros W(S) 1751	LATE AGAIN (LP)	10

PETER'S FACES
64	Piccadilly 7N 35178	Why Did You Bring Him To The Dance/She's In Love	5
64	Piccadilly 7N 35205	Wait/Just Like Romeo And Juliet	8
65	Piccadilly 7N 35225	De-Boom-Lay-Boom/Suzie Q	5

JANICE PETERS & PLAYBOYS
58	Columbia DB 4222	This Little Girl's Gone Rockin'/Kiss Cha Cha	20
58	Columbia DB 4222	This Little Girl's Gone Rockin'/Kiss Cha Cha (78)	20
59	Columbia DB 4276	A Girl Likes/You're The One	15
59	Columbia DB 4276	A Girl Likes/You're The One (78)	30

JOHNNY PETERS
65	Decca F 12172	When You Ask About Love/People Say	4

LENNIE PETERS
63	Oriole CB 1887	And My Heart Cried/For A Lifetime	4
64	Oriole CB 1956	Let The Tears Begin/Love Me, Love Me	4

MARK PETERS & SILHOUETTES
63	Oriole CB 1836	Fragile (Handle With Care)/Janie	15
64	Oriole CB 1909	Cindy's Gonna Cry/Show Her	15
64	Piccadilly 7N 35207	Don't Cry For Me/I Told You So	6

(see also Rats)

WENDY PETERS
68	Saga OPP 1	Morning Dew/I Don't Understand	12

PAUL PETERSEN
62	Pye Intl. 7N 25153	Keep Your Love Locked/Be Everything To Anyone You Love	4
62	Pye Intl. 7N 25163	Lollipops And Roses/Please Mr Sun	4
63	Pye Intl. 7N 25173	My Dad/Little Boy Sad	4
63	Pye Intl. 7N 25196	Amy/Goody Goody	4
68	Tamla Motown TMG 670	A Little Bit For Sandy/Your Love Gets Me Burning Alive	10

PAUL PETERSEN & SHELLEY FABARES
62	Pye 7N 25133	She Can't Find Her Keys/Very Unlikely	7

(see also Shelley Fabares)

BOBBY PETERSON (QUINTET)
59	Top Rank JAR 232	The Hunch/Love You Pretty Baby (as Bobby Peterson Quintet)	15
64	Sue WI 342	Rockin' Charlie Pts 1 & 2 (solo)	12
65	Sue WI 346	Piano Rock/One Day (solo)	12

OSCAR PETERSON
57	HMV POP 366	Soft Sands/Echoes	4
60	HMV POP 706	Jive At Five/Blues For Basie	4
61	HMV POP 850	Woody 'N' You/Liza	4
55	Columbia Clef SEB 10005	OSCAR PETERSON (EP)	7
56	Columbia Clef SEB 10022	OSCAR PETERSON NO. 2 (EP)	7
55	Columbia 33C 1037	PLAYS PRETTY (10" LP)	15
55	Columbia Clef 33C 9012	PLAYS PRETTY (10" LP, reissue)	12
55	Columbia 33C 1038	THE OSCAR PETERSON QUARTET (10" LP)	15
55	Columbia Clef 33C 9013	THE OSCAR PETERSON QUARTET (10" LP, reissue)	12
55	Columbia Clef 33C 1039	OSCAR PETERSON SINGS (10" LP)	15
55	Columbia Clef 33C 9014	OSCAR PETERSON SINGS (10" LP, reissue)	12
55	Columbia Clef 33CX 10012	PLAYS DUKE ELLINGTON (LP)	10
55	Columbia Clef 33CX 10016	PLAYS COLE PORTER (LP)	10
55	Columbia Clef 33CX 10028	PLAYS RICHARDS RODGERS (LP)	10
55	Columbia Clef 33CX 10039	PLAYS COUNT BASIE (LP)	10
56	Columbia Clef 33C 9025	O LADY BE GOOD (10" LP)	12
56	HMV CLP 1086	IN ROMANTIC MOOD (LP)	10

Oscar PETERSON

57	Columbia Clef 33CX 10062	KEYBOARD (LP)	10
57	Columbia Clef 33CX 10073	PLAYS HAROLD ARLEN (LP)	10
58	Columbia Clef 33CX 10096	STRATFORD (CANADA SHAKESPEAREAN FESTIVAL) (LP)	10
59	Columbia Clef 33CX 10135	A NIGHT ON THE TOWN (LP)	10
59	HMV CLP 1278	THE OSCAR PETERSON TRIO SWINGS "MY FAIR LADY" (LP)	10
59	HMV CLP 1317	OSCAR PETERSON AT THE CONCERTGEBOUW (LP)	10
60	HMV CLP 1403/CSD 1326	SWINGING BRASS (LP)	10
61	HMV CLP 1429	THE JAZZ SOUL OF OSCAR PETERSON (LP)	10
63	Verve VLP 9052	NIGHT TRAIN (LP)	10

(see also Louis Armstrong)

RAY PETERSON

59	RCA RCA 1131	The Wonder Of You/I'm Gone	10
59	RCA RCA 1131	The Wonder Of You/I'm Gone (78)	22
59	RCA RCA 1154	Shirley Purley/Come And Get It	10
59	RCA RCA 1154	Shirley Purley/Come And Get It (78)	35
60	RCA RCA 1175	Answer Me/Goodnight My Love, Pleasant Dreams	8
60	RCA RCA 1195	Tell Laura I Love Her/Wedding Day	8
60	London HLX 9246	Corrine, Corrina/Be My Girl	7
61	London HLX 9332	Sweet Little Cathy/You Didn't Care	8
61	London HLX 9379	Missing You/You Thrill Me	7
62	London HLX 9489	I Could Have Loved You So Well/Why Don't You Write Me	7
62	London HLX 9569	You Didn't Care/You Know Me Much Too Well	7
63	London HLX 9746	Without Love/Give Us Your Blessing	8
64	MGM MGM 1249	Oh No/If You Were Here	4
64	MGM MGM 1258	Across The Street/When I Stop Dreaming	4
65	MGM MGM 1273	House Without Windows/Wish I Could Say No To You	4
65	MGM MGM 1288	Don't Fight It/It's All Over	4
66	MGM MGM 1303	Everybody/Love Hurts	4
61	London REX 1293	CORRINE CORRINA (EP)	35

PETER, SUE & MARC + PFURI, GORPS & KNIRL

79	EMI EMI 2940	Second Hand Company/Troedler & Co.	6

PET HATE

84	Heavy Metal 12 VHF 2	Roll Away The Stone (12", p/s)	7
85	Heavy Metal VHF 8	Girls Grow Up Too Fast (p/s)	4
84	Heavy Metal HMRLP 17	THE BRIDE WORE RED (LP)	10
84	Heavy Metal HMRLP 23	BAD PUBLICITY (LP)	10
84	Heavy Metal HMRLP 23W	BAD PUBLICITY (LP, white vinyl)	12

(see also Silverwing)

PETITES

60	Philips PB 1035	Get Your Daddy's Car Tonight/Sun Showers	6

MARY PETTI

61	RCA RCA 1239	Gee, But It Hurts/Hey, Lawdy Lawdy	20

PETS

58	London HL 8652	Cha-Hua-Hua/Cha-Kow-Ski	20
58	London HL 8652	Cha-Hua-Hua/Cha-Kow-Ski (78)	5
59	Pye Intl. 7N 25004	(You Wandered) Beyond The Sea/Wow-ee!!!	6

(see also Seph Acre & Pets)

PET SHOP BOYS

84	Epic A 4292	West End Girls/Pet Shop Boys (p/s)	30
84	Epic TA 4292	West End Girls (Extended)/Pet Shop Boys (12", p/s)	45
85	Parlophone R 6097	Opportunities (Let's Make Lots of Money)/In The Night (Extended) (1st mix) (p/s, matrix: A-3-1-2)	22
85	Parlophone R 6097	Opportunities (Let's Make Lots of Money)/In The Night (2nd mix, white p/s, matrix: A-1U-1-1-1)	18
85	Parlophone 12R 6097	Opportunities (Let's Make Lots of Money) (Dance Mix)/In The Night (Extended) (12", white p/s)	25
85	Parlophone 12RA 6097	Opportunities (Let's Make Lots of Money) (Version Latina)/Opportunities (Dub For Money Remix)/In The Night (Extended Mix) (2nd 12", large picture labels, die-cut p/s)	40
85	Parlophone 12R 6097	Opportunities (Let's Make Lots of Money) (Dance Mix)/In The Night (Ext.) (12", p/s, mispress, B-side plays "Opportunities [Dub For Money Remix]")	50
85	Parlophone 12R 6097	Opportunities (Let's Make Lots of Money)/In The Night (Extended) (12", p/s, 2nd mispress, A-side plays "Opportunities [Let's Make Lots of Money] [Version Latina]")	35
85	Parlophone R 6115	West End Girls/A Man Could Get Arrested (4.36 Mix) (glossy or paper p/s)	6/4
85	Parlophone 10R 6115	West End Girls (Untitled Mix)/A Man Could Get Arrested (4.09 Mix)/West End Girls (7" Mix) (10", foldout round stickered p/s, sealed with free p/s 7")	50
85	Parlophone 10R 6115	West End Girls (Untitled Mix)/A Man Could Get Arrested (4.09 Mix)/West End Girls (7" Mix) (10", foldout round p/s — no sticker or 7")	30
85	Parlophone 12R 6115	West End Girls (Dance Mix)/A Man Could Get Arrested (4.36 Mix)/West End Girls (7" Mix) (12", standard p/s, standard labels)	7
85	Parlophone 12R 6115	West End Girls (Dance Mix)/A Man Could Get Arrested (4.09 Mix)/West End Girls (7" Mix) (2nd 12", p/s, with 4" die-cut hole, 4" labels)	12
85	Parlophone 12R 6115	West End Girls (Dance Mix)/A Man Could Get Arrested (4.09 Mix)/West End Girls (7" Mix) (3rd 12", p/s, with 6" die-cut hole, 6" picture labels)	12
86	Parlophone 12RA 6115	West End Girls (Shep Pettibone Mastermix)/West End Dub/A Man Could Get Arrested (4.09 Mix) (4th 12", black, blue & red p/s, standard labels)	20
86	Parlophone 12RA 6115	West End Girls (Shep Pettibone Mastermix)/West End Dub/A Man Could Get Arrested (4.09 Mix) (5th 12", black, blue & red p/s with 6" yellow circle, standard labels)	15
86	Parlophone 12RA 6115	West End Girls (Shep Pettibone Mastermix)/West End Dub/A Man Could Get Arrested (4.09 Mix) (6th 12", stickered black, blue & red 6" die-cut p/s, 6" yellow picture labels)	15

86	Parlophone R 6116	Love Comes Quickly/That's My Impression (glossy p/s) 6
86	Parlophone 10R 6116	Love Comes Quickly (Dance Mix)/That's My Impression (Disco Mix) (10" with poster, PVC sleeve) 45
86	Parlophone 12R 6116	Love Comes Quickly (Dance Mix)/That's My Impression (Disco Mix) (12", standard p/s) 10
86	Parlophone 12R 6116	Love Comes Quickly (Dance Mix)/That's My Impression (Disco Mix) (2nd 12", large picture labels, die-cut white p/s) 15
86	Parlophone 12R 6129	Opportunities (Let's Make Lots of Money) (7.18 Shep Pettibone Mastermix)/ (4.27 Reprise)/(6.44 Original Dance Mix)/Was That What It Was (12", stickered silver p/s) 8
86	Parlophone RD 6140	Suburbia/Paninaro//Love Comes Quickly (Shep Pettibone Remix)/Jack The Lad/Suburbia Part Two (double-pack, gatefold p/s) 12
86	Parlophone TR 6140	Suburbia/Paninaro/Jack The Lad/Love Comes Quickly (Shep Pettibone Remix) (1st cassette) 10
86	Parlophone TCR 6140	Suburbia (The Full Horror)/Paninaro/Jack The Lad/Love Comes Quickly (Shep Pettibone Remix) (2nd cassette) 12
	(some "Suburbia" cassettes were misprinted with reversed numbers, so both TCR 6140 & TR 6140 exist with different mixes)	
86	Parlophone 12R 6140	Suburbia (The Full Horror)/Paninaro/Jack The Lad (12", with inner sleeve) 12
87	Parlophone RS 6158	It's A Sin/You Know Where You Went Wrong (p/s, with inner p/s) 5
87	Parlophone TCR 6158	It's A Sin (7" version)/You Know Where You Went Wrong/It's A Sin (Disco Mix) (cassette) 10
87	Parlophone 12R 6158	It's A Sin (Disco Mix)/You Know Where You Went Wrong (7" Version) (12", with inner sleeve) 12
87	Parlophone 12RX 6158	It's A Sin (Ian Levine Remix)/You Know Where You Went Wrong (Rough Mix) (2nd 12", different p/s) 15
87	Parlophone CDR 6158	It's A Sin (7" Version)/You Know Where You Went Wrong/It's A Sin (Disco Mix) (CD, in pouch) 10
87	Parlophone TCR 6163	What Have I Done To Deserve This? (Extended Mix) (with Dusty Springfield)/ A New Life/What Have I Done To Deserve This? (Disco Mix) (cassette) 8
87	Parlophone 12R 6163	What Have I Done To Deserve This? (Extended Mix) (with Dusty Springfield)/ A New Life/What Have I Done To Deserve This? (Disco Mix) (12", p/s) 8
87	Parlophone CDR 6163	What Have I Done To Deserve This? (Extended Mix) (with Dusty Springfield)/ A New Life/What Have I Done To Deserve This? (Disco Mix) (CD in pouch) 12
87	Parlophone TCR 6168	Rent (Extended)/Rent (Dub)/I Want A Dog (cassette) 8
87	Parlophone 12R 6168	Rent (Extended)/Rent (Dub)/I Want A Dog (12", p/s) 8
87	Parlophone CDR 6168	Rent (Extended)/Rent (Dub)/I Want A Dog (CD) 12
87	Parlophone RS 6171	Always On My Mind/Do I Have To? (p/s, with inner sleeve) 6
87	Parlophone TCR 6171	Always On My Mind (Extended Dance Mix)/Do I Have To?/ Always On My Mind (Edit) (cassette) 7
87	Parlophone 12RS 6171	Always On My Mind (Extended Dance Mix)/Do I Have To?/ Always On My Mind (Edit) (12", p/s, with inner sleeve) 15
87	Parlophone 12RX 6171	Always On My Mind (Phil Harding Remix)/Do I Have To?/ Always On My Mind (Dub) (2nd 12", different p/s) 15
87	Parlophone CDR 6171	Always On My Mind (Extended Dance Mix)/Do I HaveTo?/ Always On My Mind (Edit) (CD) 10
88	Parlophone R 6177	Heart/I Get Excited (You Get Excited Too) (Neil or Chris p/s) . . . . each 6
88	Parlophone TCR 6177	Heart (Disco Mix)/I Get Excited (You Get Excited Too)/Heart (Dance Mix) (cassette) 6
88	Parlophone 12R 6177	Heart (Disco Mix)/I Get Excited (You Get Excited Too)/Heart (Dance Mix) (12", Neil or Chris p/s) . . . . each 10
88	Parlophone 12RX6177	Heart (Julian Mendelsohn Remix)/Heart (Dub Mix)/I Get Excited (You Get Excited Too) (2nd 12", p/s) 15
88	Parlophone CDR 6177	Heart (Disco Mix)//I Get Excited (You Get Excited Too)/Heart (Dance Mix) (CD) 10
88	Parlophone RS 6190	Domino Dancing/Don Juan (p/s, with inner sleeve) 4
88	Parlophone TCR 6190	Domino Dancing (Disco Mix)/Don Juan (Disco Mix)/Domino Dancing (Alternative Mix) (cassette) 6
88	Parlophone 12RS 6190	Domino Dancing (Disco Mix)/Don Juan (Disco Mix)/Domino Dancing (Alternative Mix) (12", p/s, with inner sleeve) 7
88	Parlophone 12RX 6190	Domino Dancing (Remix)/Don Juan (Demo)/Domino Dancing (Demo) (2nd 12", different p/s) 15
88	Parlophone CDR 6190	Domino Dancing (Disco Mix)/Don Juan (Disco Mix)/Domino Dancing (Alternative Mix) (CD) 15
88	Parlophone RS 6198	Left To My Own Devices/The Sound Of The Atom Splitting (p/s, with inner sleeve) 5
88	Parlophone TCR 6198	Left To My Own Devices/Left To My Own Devices (The Disco Mix)/ The Sound Of The Atom Splitting (cassette with outer slip case) 7
88	Parlophone 12RS 6198	Left To My Own Devices (The Disco Mix)/Left To My Own Devices/ The Sound Of The Atom Splitting (12", p/s, with inner sleeve) 8
88	Parlophone CDR 6198	Left To My Own Devices/Left To My Own Devices (The Disco Mix)/ The Sound Of The Atom Splitting (CD, card p/s with inner) 10
89	Parlophone TCR 6220	It's Alright/One Of The Crowd/Your Funny Uncle (cassette) 4
89	Parlophone 10R 6220	It's Alright (Alternative Mix)/It's Alright (Extended Dance Mix) (10" with poster, different p/s) 10
89	Parlophone 12RX 6220	It's Alright (The Tyree Mix)/It's Alright (The Stetrling Void Mix) (2nd 12", different p/s) 7
89	Parlophone CDR 6220	It's Alright (7" version)/One Of The Crowd/Your Funny Uncle/It's Alright (Extended) (CD) 8
90	Parlophone 12RX 6269	So Hard (The KLF Versus Pet Shop Boys)/It Must Be Obvious (UFO Mix) (2nd 12" different p/s) 7
90	Parlophone 12RX 6275	Being Boring (Remix)/We All Feel Better In The Dark (After Hours Climax) We All Feel Better In The Dark (Ambient) (2nd 12", different p/s) 8
91	Parlophone CDR 6283	Jealousy (7" Version)//Losing My Mind (7" Version)/Losing My Mind (Disco Mix) (CD, withdrawn sleeve, last two tracks actually play "Losing My Mind [Disco Mix]", "Jealousy [Extended Mix") 7
91	Parlophone TCRX 6301	DJ Culturemix (Grid Remix)/Music For Boys Part 3/Overture To Performance (cassette) 5

91	Parlophone CDRX 6301	DJ Culturemix (Grid Remix)/Music For Boys Part 3/Overture To Performance (CD) 7
93	Parlophone 12R 6348	Can You Forgive Her? (MK Remix)/Can You Forgive Her? (MK Dub) (12", p/s) 8
87	Parlophone PCSDX 104	ACTUALLY (LP, with U.S. import "Always On My Mind" 12", stickered sl.) 12
87	Parlophone PCSDX 104	ACTUALLY (cassette, with U.S. import "Always On My Mind" cassette) 10
88	Parlophone PCSX 7325	INTROSPECTIVE (LP, 3 x 12" factory custom pressing, clear vinyl 12", with paper strip around sleeve, 10 copies only) 150
87	ParlophoneCDPCSDX 104	ACTUALLY (CD, with U.S. import "Always On My Mind" CD single) 18

(see also Eighth Wonder, Dusty Springfield)

NORMAN PETTY TRIO
| 54 | HMV 7M 274 | Mood Indigo/Petty's Little Polka .... 12 |

TOM PETTY & HEARTBREAKERS
77	Shelter WIP 6377	American Girl/Wild One Forever 5
77	Island WIP 6396	Anything That's Rock'n'Roll/Fooled Again 4
80	MCA/Backstreet MCA 596	Don't Do Me Like That/Century City//Something Else/Stories We Could Tell (double pack) 4
82	MCA MCAP 778	Refugee/Islander (picture disc) 4
76	Sire	OFFICIAL LIVE BOOTLEG (LP) 15

(see also Stevie Nicks)

PEYR
| 82 | Shout XW 1202 | THE FOURTH REICH (12" EP) .... 7 |

(see also Killing Joke)

PFM
| 73 | Manticore K 43502 | PHOTOS OF GHOSTS (LP, gatefold sleeve) .... 10 |

P-FUNK ALLSTARS
| 82 | Virgin VS 487 | Hydraulic Pump Pts 1 & 2 .... 4 |
| 82 | Virgin VS 487-12 | Hydraulic Pump Pts 1 & 2 (12") .... 8 |

(see also Parliament, Funkadelic)

PHANTOM
| 83 | Cool Ghoul COOL 1 | Lazy Fascist/Power Dub (no p/s) .... 5 |

(see also Tom Robinson, Blazing Sons)

PHANTOMS
| 61 | Palette PG 9014 | Phantom Guitar/Cachina .... 10 |
| 60s | Arc ARC | GREAT GUITAR HITS (LP) .... 25 |

PHAROAHS
| 58 | Decca DFE 6522 | PHAROAHS (EP) .... 250 |

PHASE 4
66	Decca F 12327	What Do You Say About That/Think I'll Sit Down And Cry 8
66	Fab FAB 1	What Do You Say About That/I'm Gonna Sit Down And Cry 8
67	Fab FAB 6	Man Am I Worried?/Listen To The Blues 30

(see also Mike Batt)

JAMES PHELPS
| 71 | Paramount PARA 3019 | Check Yourself/My Lover's Prayer .... 8 |

PHENOMENA
| 85 | Bronze BRO 193 | Dance With The Devil/Hell On Wings (p/s) .... 4 |
| 87 | Arista RIS 42 | Did It All For Love/Double 6, 55, 44... (box set with insert) .... 5 |

(see also Whitesnake, Cozy Powell, Black Sabbath, Thin Lizzy, A-Ha)

PHILADELPHIA SOCIETY
| 75 | Gull GULS 21 | 100 South Of Broadway Pts 1& 2 .... 4 |

PHILIP & HIS FOETUS VIBRATIONS
| 85 | Self Immol. WOMB KX 07 | Tell Me, What Is The Bane Of Your Life/Mother I've Killed The Cat (p/s) .... 25 |

(see also You've Got Foetus On Your Breath, Foetus Art Terrorism, Foetus Over Frisco, Foetus Under Glass)

PHILLIP'S LOUISVILLE JUG BANK
| 40s | Brunswick 01265 | Smackin' The Sax/That's Your Last (78) .... 25 |

ANTHONY PHILLIPS
77	Philips 6837 406	Collection/God If I Saw Her Now (p/s) 30
78	Arista ARIST 192	We're All As We Lie/Squirrel/Sitars And Nebulous 10
79	Arista ARIST 252	Um & Aargh/Souvenir (p/s) 8
81	RCA RCA 102	Preclude '84/Anthem 1984 8
84	Street Tunes JJ 102-12	Sally/Exocet/Women Were Watching (12", p/s) 10
88	PRT PYS 18	The Anthem From Tarka/The Rising Spring (p/s) 10
88	PRT PYD 18	The Anthem From Tarka (Single Mix)/The Rising Spring/Excerpt From Tarka (Movement 1)/(Movement 3)/The Anthem From Tarka (Extended Single Mix) (CD) 15
77	Hit & Run HIT 001	THE GEESE & THE GHOST (LP) 10
78	Arista SPART 1063	WISE AFTER THE EVENT (LP, gatefold sleeve) 10
79	AFL AFLP 1	PRIVATE PARTS & PIECES (LP, 500 only) 15
82	RCA INTS 5228	PRIVATE PARTS & PIECES III: ANTIQUES (LP) 10
84	Street Tunes STLP 013	INVISIBLE MEN (LP) 10
85	Cherry Red BRED 66	HARVEST OF THE HEART (LP) 10

(see also Genesis)

CONFREY PHILLIPS (TRIO)
55	Columbia DB 3622	You'll Always Be The One/It May Sound Silly (78) 5
55	Columbia DB 3664	Seventeen/Song Of The Dreamer (78) 5
56	Columbia SCM 5223	Love And Marriage/The Others I Like 4
56	Columbia DB 3716	Love And Marriage/The Others I Like (78) 5
56	Columbia DB 3751	Get Up! Get Up! (You Sleepy Head)/A Dangerous Age (78) 5

| 57 | Decca F 10835 | Am I Going Out Of My Mind?/Afterglow .... 4 |
| 57 | Decca F 10866 | Shotgun Rock 'n' Roll/Hokey-Kokey Rock 'n' Roll (as Confrey Phillips Trio) ....10 |

(LITTLE) ESTHER (PHILLIPS)

62	Stateside SS 140	Release Me/Don't Feel Rained On 6
63	Ember EMB S 174	Am I That Easy To Forget/I Really Don't Want To Know
		(as Little Esther Phillips) 6
65	Sue WI 395	The Chains/Feel Like I Wanna Cry (as Esther Philips) 12
65	Atlantic AT 4028	And I Love Him/Shangri-La 6
65	Atlantic AT 4048	Let Me Know When It's Over/I Saw Me 6
66	Atlantic AT 4077	I Could Have Told You/Just Say Goodbye 20
66	Ember EMBS 221	Release Me/Be Honest With Me (as Little Esther Phillips) 6
66	Atlantic 584 013	When A Woman Loves A Man/Ups And Downs 4
67	Atlantic 584 062	Someone Else Is Taking My Place/When Loves Comes To The Human Race ..4
67	Atlantic 584 103	And I Love Him/Shangri-La (reissue) 4
67	Atlantic 584 126	I'm Sorry/Cheater Man 4
68	Roulette RO 505	Too Late To Worry, Too Blue To Cry/I'm In The Mood For Love
		(Moody's Mood For Love) 4
68	Roulette RO 508	Tonight I'll Be Staying Here With You/Sweet Dreams 4
72	Atlantic K 10168	Catch Me I'm Falling/Release Me 5
73	Kudu KUS 4000	Home Is Where The Hatred Is/Till My Back Ain't Got No Bone 8
73	Kudu KUS 4002	I've Never Found A Man/Cherry Red 4
63	Ember CW 103	REFLECTIONS OF GREAT COUNTRY AND WESTERN STANDARDS (LP) 15
67	Atlantic 587/588 010	ESTHER PHILLIPS SINGS (LP) 12
73	Kudu KUL 2	FROM A WHISPER TO A SCREAM (LP) 20
75	Kudu KU 18	PERFORMANCE (LP) 10
76	Atlantic K 50521	CONFESSIN' THE BLUES (LP, gatefold sleeve) 10

GLENN PHILLIPS

| 75 | Caroline C 1519 | LOST AT SEA (LP) .... 10 |

GREGORY PHILLIPS

63	Pye 7N 15546	Angie/Please Believe Me 4
64	Pye 7N 15593	Everybody Knows/Closer To Me (with Remo Four) 4
64	Pye 7N 15633	Don't Bother Me/Make Sure That You're Mine 4
65	Immediate IM 004	Down In The Boondocks/That's The One 10
	(see also Remo Four)	

JOHN PHILLIPS

70	Stateside SS 8046	Mississippi/April Anne 4
70	Stateside SSL 5027	JOHN PHILLIPS: THE WOLFKING OF L.A. (LP) 12
	(see also Mamas & Papas)	

LESLIE PHILLIPS

| 59 | Parlophone R 4610 | The Navy Lark/The Disc .... 4 |

MICHELLE PHILLIPS

76	A&M AMS 7250	No Love Today/Aloha Louie 4
77	A&M AMLS 64651	VICTIM OF ROMANCE (LP) 10
	(see also Mamas & Papas)	

PHIL PHILLIPS & TWILIGHTS

59	Mercury AMT 1059	Sea Of Love/Juella 15
60	Mercury AMT 1072	Take This Heart/Verdi Mae 8
60	Mercury AMT 1093	Your True Love Once More/What Will I Tell My Heart 10
61	Mercury AMT 1139	I Love To Love You/No One Else But You 12

SHAWN PHILLIPS

65	Columbia DB 7611	Hey Nelly Nelly/Solitude 6
65	Columbia DB 7699	Doesn't Anybody Know My Name?/Nobody Listens 6
65	Columbia DB 7789	Little Tin Soldier/London Town 6
66	Columbia DB 7956	Summer Came/Storms 6
67	Parlophone R 5606	Woman Mine/Stargazer 20
65	Columbia 33SX 1748	I'M A LONER (LP) 90
66	Columbia SX 6006	SHAWN (LP) 75
70	A&M AMLS 978	CONTRIBUTION (LP) 10
71	A&M AMLS 2006	SECOND CONTRIBUTION (LP, with insert) 10

SID PHILLIPS BAND

56	HMV 7M 372	Bugle Call Rag/Memories Of You 5
56	HMV 7M 396	Rockin' Thru' The Rye/Everybody Step 5
56	HMV POP 204	Rockin' Thru' The Rye/Everybody Step (78) 5
56	HMV 7M 406	Juke Box Baby/My Honey's Lovin' Arms 5
56	HMV POP 214	Juke Box Baby/My Honey's Lovin' Arms (78) 5
56	HMV 7M 418	Mamma Don't Allow/Glad Rag Doll 5
56	HMV POP 269	Farewell Blues (Rock 'N' Roll Style)/It Goes Like This 4

STU PHILLIPS

58	London HL 8673	The Champlain And St. Lawrence Line/The Priest Who Slept 100 Years 8
60	Pye Intl. 7N 25062	Strangers When We Meet/BOB MERSEY ORCHESTRA: Song Of India 6
67	RCA RCA 1601	Angel Of Love/The Great El Tigre 4

TEDDY PHILLIPS' ORCHESTRA

54	London HL 8032	Ridin' To Tennessee/Alone Tonight 25
54	Parlophone CMSP 4	Down Boy/Meet Miss Pippin (export issue) 5
54	Parlophone CMSP 28	Life Is A Slice Of Cake/One Sided Love Affair (export issue) 5

WARREN PHILLIPS & ROCKETS

| 69 | Decca (S)PA 43 | WORLD OF ROCK 'N' ROLL (LP) .... 15 |
| | *(see also Savoy Brown)* | |

WOOLF PHILLIPS & HIS ORCHESTRA

| 54 | Melodisc M 1284 | Rock, Rock, Rock/Merci Beaucoup (78) .... 5 |

Woolf PHILLIPS & HIS ORCHESTRA

54	Decca F 10416	Count Your Blessings Instead Of .../Your Heart, My Heart (B-side w/Dennis Morley)	4

VINCE PHILPOTT & DRAGS
64	Decca F 11997	The Cramp/Eenie Meenie Miny Mo	15

PHILTHY PHIL & FAST EDDIE
89	Receiver RRLP 124	NAUGHTY OLD SANTA'S CHRISTMAS CLASSICS (LP)	10

(see also Motorhead)

PHILWIT & PEGASUS
70	Chapter One CH 131	And I Try/Pauper's Son	4
70	Chapter One CH 137	The Elephant Song/Pseudo Phoney Mixed Up Croney	4
70	Chapter One CHSR 805	PHILWIT & PEGASUS (LP)	30

(see also Mark Wirtz)

PHOENIX
76	CBS 81621	PHOENIX (LP)	10
80	Charisma CAS 1150	IN FULL VIEW (LP)	10

PAT PHOENIX
62	HMV POP 1030	The Rovers Chorus/Coronation Street Monologue	4

PHONES SPORTSMAN BAND
81	Rather GEAR 9	I REALLY LIKE YOU (EP)	5

(see also Swell Maps)

PHOTOGRAPHED BY LIGHTNING
86	Fierce FRIGHT 008	Sleeps Terminator/Winter Trees (foldaround p/s, hand-coloured labels)	30

PHOTOS
80	CBS 8785	Friends/Je T'Aime (p/s, withdrawn)	6
81	Epic PHOTO 5	THE PHOTOS (LP, with free LP "The Blackmail Tapes", inner & stickered sleeve)	10

(see also Satans Rats)

EDITH PIAF
60	Columbia DC 754	Milord/Je Sais Comment (export issue)	4
61	Columbia DB 4596	Non, Je Ne Regrette Rien/Les Amants D'Un Jour	4
61	Columbia DB 4642	Exodus/No Regrets	4
63	Columbia DB 7149	Polichinelle/Le Billiard Electrique	4
63	Columbia SEG 8220	GREAT PIAF (EP)	7
64	Columbia SEG 8308	NON, JE NE REGRETTE RIEN (EP)	7
65	Columbia SEG 8387	QU'IL ETAIT TRISTE (EP)	7
57	Columbia SCX 5	MEA CULPA (LP)	10
60	Columbia 33SX 1276	SINCERELY ... EDITH PIAF (LP)	10
61	Columbia 33SX 1330	PIAF AT THE PARIS OLYMPIA (LP)	10

PIANO RED
52	HMV B 10244	Rockin' With Red/Red's Boogie (78)	35
52	HMV B 10246	Just Right Bounce/Hey, Good Lookin' (78)	35
52	HMV B 10316	Count The Days I'm Gone/Bouncin' With Red (78)	35
52	HMV J 0276	Layin' The Boogie/Baby What's Wrong (78)	35
52	HMV J 0296	My Gal Jo/Let's Have A Good Time (78)	35
53	HMV 7M 108	Rockin' With Red/Red's Boogie	100
64	RCA RCX 7138	RHYTHM AND BLUES VOL. 2 (EP)	25

(see also Dr. Feelgood [U.S.])

PIBLOKTO
(see under Pete Brown & Piblokto)

PIC & BILL
67	Page One POF 024	All I Want Is You/It's Not You	8
67	Page One POF 037	This Is It/Nobody But My Baby	5
68	Page One POF 052	Sad World Without You/Just A Tear	10

PIC(C)ADILLY LINE
67	CBS 2785	At The Third Stroke/How Could You Say You're Leaving Me	8
67	CBS 2958	Emily Small (The Huge World Thereof)/Gone Gone Gone	8
68	CBS 3595	Yellow Rainbow/Evenings With Corrina (as Picadilly Line)	6
68	CBS 3743	Evenings With Corrina/My Best Friend	6
67	CBS (S)BPG 63129	THE HUGE WORLD OF EMILY SMALL (LP)	30

(see also Edward's Hand)

BUSTER PICKENS
60s	Heritage HLP 1008	TEXAS PIANO (LP)	40

BOBBY (BORIS) PICKETT & CRYPT-KICKERS
62	London HLU 9597	Monster Mash/Monsters' Mash Party	10
73	London ZGU 133	MONSTER MASH (LP)	10

DAN PICKETT
60s	XX MIN 710	DAN PICKETT (EP)	7

NICK PICKETT
72	Warner Bros K 44172	SILVERSLEEVES (LP)	20

(see also John Dummer Blues Band)

KENNY PICKETT
80	F-Beat PRO 2	Got A Gun (unreleased, promo only)	10

(see also Creation, Kennedy Express)

WILSON PICKETT
63	Liberty LIB 10115	It's Too Late/I'm Gonna Love You	15
65	Atlantic AT 4036	In The Midnight Hour/I'm Not Tired	6
65	MGM MGM 1286	Let Me Be Your Boy/My Heart Belongs To You	25

65	Atlantic AT 4052	Don't Fight It/It's All Over	6
66	Atlantic AT 4072	634-5789/That's A Man's Way	6
66	Atlantic 584 023	99 And A Half (Won't Do)/Danger Zone	6
66	Atlantic 584 039	Land Of 1000 Dances/You're So Fine	4
66	Atlantic 584 066	Mustang Sally/Three Time Loser	4
67	Atlantic 584 101	Everybody Needs Somebody To Love/Nothing You Can Do	4
67	Atlantic 584 107	New Orleans/Soul Dance III	4
67	London HLU 10146	Billy The Kid/I Don't Want No Part-Time Love (with Falcons)	6
67	Atlantic 584 130	Funky Broadway/I'm Sorry About That	4
67	Atlantic 584 142	Stag-O-Lee/I'm In Love	4
68	Atlantic 584 150	In The Midnight Hour/Danger Zone	4
68	Atlantic 584 173	That Kind Of Love/I've Come A Long Way	4
68	Atlantic 584 183	She's Looking Good/We've Got To Have Love	4
68	Atlantic 584 203	I'm A Midnight Mover/Deborah	4
68	Atlantic 584 221	I Found A True Love/For Better Or Worse	4
69	Atlantic 584 236	Hey Jude/Night Owl	4
69	Atlantic 584 261	Mini Skirt Minnie/Back In Your Arms	4
69	Atlantic 584 281	Hey Joe/Born To Be Wild	4
70	Atlantic 584 313	You Keep Me Hangin' On/Now You See Me, Now You Don't	4
70	Atlantic 2091 005	Sugar Sugar/Cole, Cooke And Redding	4
70	Atlantic 2091 032	Engine No. 9/International Playboy	5
72	President PT 319	If You Need Me/I'm Gonna Love You	5
73	President PT 322	I Can't Stop/Down To My Last Heartbreak	5
65	Atlantic ATL 5037	IN THE MIDNIGHT HOUR (LP)	18
66	Atlantic 587/588 029	THE EXCITING WILSON PICKETT (LP)	12
66	Atlantic 587 032	IN THE MIDNIGHT HOUR (LP, reissue)	12
67	Atlantic 587/588 057	THE WICKED PICKETT (LP)	12
67	Atlantic 587/588 080	THE SOUND OF WILSON PICKETT (LP)	12
68	Atlantic 587/588 092	THE BEST OF WILSON PICKETT (LP)	12
68	Atlantic 587/588 107	I'M IN LOVE (LP)	12
68	Atlantic 587/588 111	MIDNIGHT MOVER (LP)	12
69	Atlantic 588 170	HEY JUDE (LP)	12
70	Atlantic 2465 002	RIGHT ON (LP)	12
71	Atlantic 2400 026	ENGINE NO. 9 — IN PHILADELPHIA (LP)	15
71	Joy JOYS 181	IF YOU NEED ME (LP)	10
72	Atlantic K 40319	DON'T KNOCK MY LOVE (LP)	10

(see also Falcons)

GARY PICKFORD-HOPKINS & FRIENDS
| 83 | Spartan SP 143 | Why? (The Song)/Why? (The Story) (p/s) | 12 |
| 83 | Spartan SP 143T | Why? (The Song)/Why? (The Story) (12", p/s) | 15 |

(see also Deke Leonard, Man, Andy Fairweather-Low, Alan Ross)

PICKWICKS
64	Decca F 11901	Apple Blossom Time/I Don't Wanna Tell You Again	8
64	Decca F 11957	You're Old Enough/Hello Lady	8
65	Warner Bros WB 151	Little By Little/I Took My Baby Home	30

PIC-NIC
| 68 | Hispavox HXS 304 | Blamin's Not Hard To Do | 4 |

PICTURES FROM THE GREAT EXHIBITION
| 80s | Recommended RE/ARC | The Housewife's Nightmare (silkscreened, 1-sided, gatefold p/s) | 6 |

PIECES OF A DREAM
| 81 | Elektra K 12569 | Warm Weather/Body Magic | 4 |

PIED PIPERS
| 54 | Parlophone CMSP 21 | Kissin' Drive Rock/Please Understand (export issue) | 10 |
| 66 | Columbia DB 7883 | Ragamuffin/Fat Marie | 6 |

BILLY & DEDE PIERCE/JIM ROBINSON
| 64 | London HA-K/SH-K 8163 | JAZZ AT PRESERVATION HALL VOL. 2 (LP) | 10 |

JEFFREY LEE PIERCE
| 85 | Statik STAT LP 25 | WILDWEED (LP, with free 7": "Open The Door Osiris"/"The Fertility Goddess"/"Portrait Of the Artist In Hell"/"Chris And Maggie Meet Blind Willie McTell At The James Brown Concert" [no p/s]) | 12 |

(see also Gun Club)

WEBB PIERCE
56	Brunswick 05630	Teenage Boogie/Any Old Time	150
56	Brunswick 05630	Teenage Boogie/Any Old Time (78)	18
57	Brunswick 05682	Bye, Bye Love/Honky Tonk Song	25
57	Brunswick 05682	Bye, Bye Love/Honky Tonk Song (78)	15
59	Brunswick 05809	I Ain't Never/Shanghaied	10
59	Brunswick 05809	I Ain't Never/Shanghaied (78)	8
60	Brunswick 05820	No Love Have I/Whirlpool Of Love	8
60	Brunswick 05842	Drifting Texas Sand/All I Need Is You	8
56	Brunswick OE 9253	WEBB PIERCE PT. 1 (EP)	14
56	Brunswick OE 9254	WEBB PIERCE PT. 2 (EP)	14
56	Brunswick OE 9255	WEBB PIERCE PT. 3 (EP)	14
62	Ember EMB 4520	COUNTRY AND WESTERN FAVOURITES VOL. 1 (EP)	8
59	Parlophone GEP 8792	COUNTRY ROUND UP (EP)	20
55	Brunswick LA 8716	THE WONDERING BOY (10" LP)	30
60	Brunswick LAT 8324	WEBB! (LP)	20
65	Brunswick LAT 8540	HIDEAWAY HEART (LP)	20
65	Brunswick LAT 8551	CROSS COUNTRY (LP)	15
69	MCA MUPS 364	IN THE JAILHOUSE NOW (LP)	12

(see also Red Sovine & Webb Pierce)

CLIVE PIG & HOPEFUL CHINAMEN
88   Bam Caruso NRIC 020   THE WHALE ZOO (EP with free flexi) 5

PIGBAG
82   Masterbag BAG 001   Another Orangutango (33rpm flexidisc, free with 'Masterbag'
                              magazine) 5/4

PIGEON FLYERS
68   Columbia DB 8449   The Heaven We Shared Together/Keep On Sayin' 4

PIGGLESWICK FOLK
70s Acorn CF 256   PIG IN THE MIDDLE (LP) 20

PIGSTY HILL LIGHT ORCHESTRA
70   Village Thing VTS 1   PHLOP! (LP) 12
71   Village Thing VTS 8   PIGGERY JOKERY (LP) 12

DAVE PIKE
63   Starlite ST45 094   Melvalita/Ginha 4
66   Atlantic 584 052   Sunny/HERBIE MANN: Philly Dog 10

PiL
(see under Public Image Ltd)

RAY PILGRIM
60   Oriole CB 1557   Baby Doll/Gambler's Guitar 4
61   Oriole CB 1616   Little Miss Makebelieve/Granada 4

PILTDOWN MEN
60   Capitol CL 15149   McDonald's Cave/Brontosaurus Stomp 6
61   Capitol CL 15175   Piltdown Rides Again/Bubbles In The Tar 6
61   Capitol CL 15186   Goodnight Mrs Flintstone/The Great Imposter 6
61   Capitol CL 15211   Gargantua/Fossil Rock 8
62   Capitol CL 15245   A Pretty Girl Is Like A Melody/Big Lizard 7
61   Capitol EAP1 20155   GOODNIGHT MRS. FLINSTONE or PILTDOWN RIDES AGAIN (EP) 25

SIR HUBERT PIMM
55   London HL 8155   Goodnight And Cheerio/Honky Tonk Train Blues 30
(see also Duke & Duchess)

PINEAPPLE CHUNKS
65   Mercury MF 922   Drive My Car/Dream About 8

PINEWOOD TOM
59   Jazz Collector JEL 5   THE MALE BLUES (EP) 8

'PING PING' & AL VERLANE
60   Oriole CB 1589   Sucu Sucu/Maria Della Montagna 5

PINKERTON'S ('ASSORTED' COLOURS)
65   Decca F 12307   Mirror Mirror/She Don't Care (as Pinkerton's 'Assorted' Colours) 5
66   Decca F 12377   Don't Stop Loving Me Baby/Will Ya? (as Pinkerton's 'Assorted' Colours) 4
66   Decca F 12493   Magic Rocking Horse/It Ain't Right (as Pinkerton's Colours) 12
67   Pye 7N 17327   Mum And Dad/On A Street Car (as Pinkerton's Colours) 5
67   Pye 7N 17414   There's Nobody I'd Sooner Love/Look At Me (as Pinkerton's) 5
68   Pye 7N 17574   Kentucky Woman/Behind The Mirror (as Pinkerton's) 4
(see also Flying Machine, Liberators)

PINK FAIRIES
70   Polydor 2058 059   The Snake/Do It 18
72   Polydor 2059 302   Well Well Well/Hold On 10
76   Stiff BUY 2   Between The Lines/Spoiling For A Fight (p/s) 5
71   Polydor 2383 045   THE NEVER NEVER LAND (LP, printed PVC outer & gatefold card inner) 30
71   Polydor 2383 045   THE NEVER NEVER LAND (LP, black vinyl, standard sleeve) 10
71   Polydor 2383 045   THE NEVER NEVER LAND (LP, red vinyl, around 100 pressed) 200
72   Polydor 2383 132   WHAT A BUNCH OF SWEETIES (LP) 10
75   Polydor 2383 212   KINGS OF OBLIVION (LP, most with poster) 20/10
(see also Twink, Larry Wallis)

PINK FLOYD
67   Columbia DB 8156   Arnold Layne/Candy And A Currant Bun (promo-only in p/s) 250
67   Columbia DB 8156   Arnold Layne/Candy And A Currant Bun 18
67   Columbia DB 8214   See Emily Play/Scarecrow (promo-only in p/s) 250
67   Columbia DB 8214   See Emily Play/Scarecrow 20
67   Columbia DB 8310   Apples And Oranges/Paintbox (promo-only in p/s) 250
67   Columbia DB 8310   Apples And Oranges/Paintbox 25
68   Columbia DB 8401   It Would Be So Nice/Julia Dream 25
68   Columbia DB 8511   Point Me At The Sky/Careful With That Axe, Eugene 30
81   Harvest HAR 5217   Money (Edited Version)/Let There Be More Light (withdrawn, pink vinyl,
                              plain black sleeve) 15
82   Harvest HAR 5222   When The Tigers Broke Free/Bring The Boys Back Home 6
87   EMI EMP 26   Learning To Fly/One Slip (pink vinyl) 7
87   EMI EMP 34   On The Turning Away/Run Like Hell (live) (pink vinyl) 5
67   Columbia S(C)X 6157   THE PIPER AT THE GATES OF DAWN (LP, blue & black label, m/s) 30/20
68   Columbia S(C)X 6258   A SAUCERFUL OF SECRETS (LP, blue & black label, mono/stereo) 35/25
69   Columbia SCX 6157   THE PIPER AT THE GATES OF DAWN (LP, re-pressing, white &
                              black label) 10
68   Columbia SCX 6258   A SAUCERFUL OF SECRETS (LP, re-pressing, white & black label) 10
69   Columbia SCX 6346   MORE (LP) 12
73   Harvest SHVL 804   DARK SIDE OF THE MOON (LP, with 2 posters & 2 stickers) 10
73   Harvest Q4 SHVL 781   ATOM HEART MOTHER (LP, quadrophonic) 20
73   Harvest Q4 SHVL 804   DARK SIDE OF THE MOON (LP, quadrophonic) 20
76   Harvest Q4 SHVL 814   WISH YOU WERE HERE (LP, quadrophonic) 20

| 79 | Harvest PF 11 | THE FIRST XI (11-LP set, original sleeves, plus "Dark Side Of The Moon" & "Wish You Were Here" picture discs, 1,000 only) | 100 |

(see also Syd Barrett, Roger Waters, Dave Gilmour, Rick Wright, Nick Mason, Joker's Wild)

PINK INDUSTRY
82	Zulu ZULU 1	Is This The End?/47/Don't Let Go/Final Cry (12", p/s)	8
83	Zulu ZULU 2	LOW TECHNOLOGY (LP)	10
83	Zulu ZULU 4	WHO TOLD YOU — YOU WERE NAKED (LP)	10

(see also Pink Military, Big In Japan)

PINK MILITARY
79	Last Trumpet LT 001	BUDDHA WALKING DISNEY SLEEPING (EP, foldout sleeve)	8
79	Eric's 002	Spellbound/Blood And Lipstick/Clowntown/I Cry (12", p/s)	8
80	Eric's 005	Did You See Her/Everyday (p/s)	4
80	Virgin/Eric's ERIC'S 004	DO ANIMALS BELIEVE IN GOD? (LP)	10

(see also Pink Industry, Big In Japan, Ambrose Reynolds)

PINK PEOPLE
| 64 | Philips BF 1355 | Psychologically Unsound/Cow Catcher | 25 |
| 64 | Philips BF 1356 | Indian Hate Call/I Dreamt I Dwelt In | 15 |

PINKY (& FELLAS)
65	Polydor BM 56009	All Cried Out/Back Where I Belong	8
68	Decca F 12748	Manchester And Liverpool/Come Back Again (as Pinky & Fellas)	4
69	Polydor BM 56338	Let The Musisc Start/Oh, A Beautiful Day (as Pinky & Fellas)	4

PINKY & PERKY
| 58 | Decca F 11095 | Tom Dooley/The Velvet Glove (Pinky & Perky Theme) (p/s) | 4 |

PINNACLE
| 74 | Stag HP 125 | ASSASSIN (LP) | 80 |

PIN POINT
| 79 | Albion DEL 8 | Richmond/Love Substitute (p/s) | 4 |

PIONEERS
66	Rio R 102	Good Nannie/Doreen Girl	10
66	Rio R 106	Too Late/Give Up	10
68	Amalgamated AMG 811	Give Me A Little Loving/This Is Soul (B-side actually by Lyn Tait & Jets)	10
68	Amalgamated AMG 814	Long Shot/Dip And Fall Back	10
68	Amalgamated AMG 821	Jackpot/CREATORS: Kimble (B-side actually by Lee Perry)	10
68	Amalgamated AMG 823	No Dope Me Pony/LORD SALMONS: Great — Great In '68	10
68	Amalgamated AMG 826	Tickle Me For Days/VERSATILES: The Time Has Come	8
68	Amalgamated AMG 828	Catch The Beat/SIR GIBB'S ALLSTARS: Jana (B-side actually Immortals' "Jane Anne")	8
68	Amalgamated AMG 830	Sweet Dreams/DON DRUMMOND JUNIOR: Caterpillar Rock	8
68	Amalgamated AMG 833	Don't You Know/Me Naw Go A Believe	8
69	Amalgamated AMG 835	Mama Look Deh/BLENDERS: Decimal Currency	7
69	Amalgamated AMG 840	Who The Cap Fits/I'm Moving On	7
69	Amalgamated AMG 850	Alli Button/HIPPY BOYS: Death Rides	7
68	Blue Cat BS 100	Shake It Up/Rudies Are The Greastest	10
68	Blue Cat BS 103	Give It To Me/LEADERS: Someday Someway	10
68	Blue Cat BS 105	Whip Them/Having A Bawl	10
68	Blue Cat BS 139	Reggae Beat/Miss Eva	8
68	Caltone TONE 119	I Love No Other Girl/MILTON BOOTHE: I Used To Be A Fool	8
68	Pyramid PYR 6062	Easy Come, Easy Go/BEVERLEY'S ALLSTARS: Only A Smile (B-side actually by Lyn Tait & Jets)	8
69	Pyramid PYR 6065	Pee Pee Cluck Cluck/BEVERLEY'S ALLSTARS: Exclusively	8
69	Trojan TR 672	Long Shot Kick De Bucket/RECO: Jumping The Gun	5
69	Trojan TR 685	Black Bud/Too Late	5
69	Trojan TR 698	Poor Rameses/BEVERLEY'S ALLSTARS: In Orbit	5
69	Trojan TR 7710	Samfie Man/Mother Rittie	4
69	Trojan TR 7723	Boss Festival/Lucky Side	4
70	Trojan TR 7739	Driven Back/Trouble Deh A Bush	4
70	Trojan TR 7746	Simmer Down Quashie/Caranapo	4
70	Trojan TR 7760	Battle Of The Giants/Message To Maria	4
70	Summit SUM 8511	Starvation/BEVERLEY'S ALLSTARS: Version	4
68	Amalgam. AMGLP 2003	GREETINGS FROM THE PIONEERS (LP)	45
69	Trojan TBL 103	LONGSHOT (LP)	15
70	Trojan TBL 139	BATTLE OF THE GIANTS (LP)	15
71	Trojan TRL 24	YEAH! (LP)	10

(see also Sir Gibbs)

PIPES OF PAN
| 67 | Page One POF 038 | Monday Morning Rain/Monday Morning Rain (Instrumental Mix) | 4 |

PIPES OF PAN
| 71 | Rolling Stones COC 49100 | BRIAN JONES PRESENTS THE PIPES OF PAN AT JOUJOUKA (LP, gatefold & inner fold-out sleeve) | 40 |

(see also Rolling Stones)

PIPKINS
(see under Sweet)

PIPS
| 61 | Top Rank JAR 574 | Every Beat Of My Heart/Room In Your Heart | 15 |

(see also Gladys Knight & Pips)

PIRATES
| 64 | HMV POP 1250 | My Babe/Casting My Spell | 15 |
| 66 | Polydor BM 56712 | Shades Of Blue/Can't Understand | 20 |

(see also Johnny Kidd & Pirates, [Billy J. Kramer &] Dakotas)

PISCES
71	Trailer LER 2025	PISCES (LP)	25

PITCH PIKES
57	Mercury MT 171	Come Back To Me/How Will I Know (78)	5

GENE PITNEY
61	London HL 9270	(I Wanna) Love My Life Away/I Laughed So Hard I Cried	10
61	HMV POP 933	Every Breath I Take/Mr Moon, Mr Cupid & I	12
61	HMV POP 952	Town Without Pity/Air Mail Special	10
62	HMV POP 1018	The Man Who Shot Liberty Valance/Take It Like A Man	10
62	United Artists UP 1005	If I Didn't Have A Dime/Only Love Can Break A Heart	5
63	United Artists UP 1012	Half Heaven, Half Heartache/Tower Tall	5
63	United Artists UP 1021	Mecca/Teardrop By Teardrop	5
63	United Artists UP 1030	True Love Never Runs Smooth/Donna Means Heartbreak	4
63	United Artists UP 1035	24 Hours From Tulsa/Lonely Night Dreams	4
64	United Artists UP 1045	That Girl Belongs To Yesterday/Who Needs It?	4
64	United Artists UP 1055	I'm Gonna Find Myself A Girl/Lips Are Redder On You	4
64	United Artists UP 1063	It Hurts To Be In Love/Hawaii	5
64	Stateside SS 358	I'm Gonna Be Strong/Aladdin's Lamp	4
64	Stateside SS 365	It Hurts To Be In Love/Hawaii (reissue)	4
65	Stateside SS 390	I Must Be Seeing Things/Save Your Love	4
65	Stateside SS 420	Lookin' Thru The Eyes Of Love/Last Chance To Turn Around	4
65	Stateside SS 471	Princess In Rags/Amore Mio	4
66	Stateside SS 490	Backstage/In Love Again	4
66	Stateside SS 518	Nobody Needs Your Love/Dream World	4
66	Stateside SS 558	Just One Smile/The Boss's Daughter	4
67	Stateside SS 597	(In The) Cold Light Of Day/Flower Girl	4
68	Stateside SS 2118	Love Grows/Conquistador	4
68	Stateside SS 2131	Yours Until Tomorrow/She's A Heartbreaker	4
70	Stateside SS 2177	Shady Lady/Billy, You're My Friend	4
63	HMV 7EG 8832	TOWN WITHOUT PITY (EP)	15
64	United Artists UEP 1001	TWENTY FOUR HOURS FROM TULSA (EP)	8
64	United Artists UEP 1002	THAT GIRL BELONGS TO YESTERDAY (EP)	8
65	Stateside SE 1027	TWENTY FOUR HOURS FROM TULSA (EP, reissue)	12
65	Stateside SE 1030	I MUST BE SEEING THINGS (EP)	8
65	Stateside SE 1032	GENE ITALIANO (EP)	10
66	Stateside SE 1036	GENE PITNEY SINGS JUST FOR YOU (EP)	8
66	Stateside SE 1040	BACKSTAGE (EP)	8
67	Stateside SE 1045	THERE'S NO LIVING WITHOUT YOUR LOVING (EP)	8
62	HMV CLP 1566	THE MANY SIDES OF GENE PITNEY (LP)	25
63	United Artists (S)ULP 1028	ONLY LOVE CAN BREAK A HEART (LP, mono/stereo)	15/20
63	United Artists ULP 1043	GENE PITNEY SINGS JUST FOR YOU (LP)	15
64	United Artists ULP 1061	BLUE GENE (LP)	15
64	United Artists ULP 1064	GENE PITNEY MEETS THE FAIR YOUNG LADIES OF FOLKLAND (LP)	15
64	United Artists ULP 1073	GENE PITNEY'S BIG SIXTEEN (LP)	20
65	Stateside SL 10118	GENE PITNEY'S BIG SIXTEEN (LP, reissue)	10
65	Stateside SL 10119	BLUE GENE (LP, reissue)	10
65	Stateside SL 10120	I'M GONNA BE STRONG (LP)	12
65	Stateside SL 10132	GENE PITNEY'S MORE BIG SIXTEEN (VOL. 2) (LP)	12
65	Stateside SL 10147	GEORGE JONES AND GENE PITNEY (LP, with George Jones)	12
65	Stateside SL 10148	LOOKING THRU THE EYES OF LOVE (LP)	12
65	Stateside SL 10156	SINGS THE GREAT SONGS OF OUR TIME (LP)	12
66	Stateside SL 10173	IT'S COUNTRY TIME AGAIN (LP, with George Jones)	12
66	Stateside S(S)L 10181	BEING TOGETHER (LP, with Melba Montgomery)	12
66	Stateside S(S)L 10183	NOBODY NEEDS YOUR LOVE (LP)	12
67	Stateside S(S)L 10194	YOUNG, WARM AND WONDERFUL (LP)	12
67	Stateside S(S)L 10199	GENE PITNEY'S BIG SIXTEEN (VOL. 3) (LP)	12
67	Stateside S(S)L 10212	JUST ONE SMILE (LP)	12
67	Stateside S(S)L 10216	GOLDEN GREATS (LP)	10
68	Stateside S(S)L 10242	PITNEY TODAY (LP)	12
69	Stateside S(S)L 10286	THE BEST OF GENE PITNEY (LP)	12
72	Pye Int. NSPL 28165	THE NEW SOUNDS OF GENE PITNEY (LP)	10

(see also Marc Almond & Gene Pitney, George Jones)

RICHIE PITTS
73	Contempo C 3	Every Couple's Not A Pair/I Refuse To Know Your Name	4
75	Bus Stop BUS 1029	S'cuse Me Ma'am/Don't Take The Name Of Love In Vain	4

PIXIES
88	4AD BAD 805CD	Gigantic/River Euphrates/Vamos (live)/In Heaven (Lady In The Radiator Song) (live) (CD)	7
90	4AD 0009	Velouria/Make Believe (p/s, 2,000 only)	4
90	4AD C 0009	Velouria/Make Believe (cassette)	5
89	4AD CAD 905	DOOLITTLE (LP, with lyric booklet & postcard, some in carrier bag)	15/12

PIXIES THREE
63	Mercury AMT 1214	Birthday Party/Our Love	4

P.J. HARVEY
(see under H)

PLAGUE
68	Decca F 12730	Looking For The Sun/Here Today, Gone Tomorrow	60

PLAIN CHARACTERS
(see also Gadgets)

PLAINSONG
72	Elektra K 42120	IN SEARCH OF AMELIA EARHART (LP)	12

73	Elektra	PLAINSONG II (LP, white label, promo only)	100

(see also Andy Roberts, Ian Matthews)

PLANETS

60	Palette PG 9008	Like Party/Ippy Yippy Beatnik (some in p/s)	15/10
60	HMV POP 818	Chunky/Screwball	6
61	HMV POP 832	Jam Roll/Delaney's Theme	8
61	HMV POP 895	Jungle Street/The Grasshopper	10

ROBERT PLANT

66	CBS 202656	Our Song/Laughin', Cryin', Laughin'	120
66	CBS 202858	Long Time Coming/I've Got A Secret	120
85	Es Paranza B 9621 F	Little By Little (Remix)/Doo Doo A Do Do//Easily Led (live)/Rockin' At Midnight (live) (double pack)	4
88	Es Paranza A 9373 TB	Heaven Knows (Extended Remix)/Walking Towards Paradise/Heaven Knows (Astral Mix) (12", stickered sealed box set with colour poster & 2 prints)	7

(see also Led Zeppelin, Listen)

PLANXTY

73	Polydor 2383 186	PLANXTY (LP)	12
73	Polydor 2383 232	WELL BELOW THE VALLEY (LP)	12
74	Polydor 2383 301	COLD BLOW AND RAINY NIGHT (LP)	12
76	Polydor 2389 387	THE PLANXTY COLLECTION (LP)	12

PLASMATICS

80	Stiff BUY 76	Butcher Baby/Tight Black Pants (Alternate Version) (p/s, white & pink vinyl)	4
80	Stiff BUY 91	Monkey Suit/Squirm (live) (p/s, yellow & red vinyl)	4

(see also Motherhead with Wendy O'Williams)

PLASTIC GANGSTERS

80s	Secret SHH 144	Plastic Gangsters/Sretsgnag Citsalp (no p/s, DJ copies only)	15

(see also 4 Skins)

PLASTIC ONO BAND

(see under John Lennon & Plastic Ono Band, Yoko Ono & Plastic Ono Band)

PLASTIC PENNY

67	Page One POF 051	Everything I Am/No Pleasure Without Pain My Love	4
68	Page One POF 062	Nobody Knows It/Just Happy To Be With You	5
68	Page One POF 079	Your Way To Tell Me Go/Baby You're Not To Blame	4
69	Page One POF 107	Hound Dog/Currency	4
69	Page One POF 146	She Does/Genevieve	4
68	Page One POL(S) 005	TWO SIDES OF THE PENNY (LP)	40
69	Page One POLS 014	CURRENCY (LP)	40
70	Page One POS 611	HEADS YOU WIN, TAILS I LOSE (LP)	30

(see also Universals)

PLATFORM SIX

65	Piccadilly 7N 35255	Girl Down Town/Money Will Not Mean A Thing	15

PLATTERS

56	Mercury MT 107	(You've Got) The Magic Touch/Winner Takes All (78)	15
56	Mercury MT 117	The Great Pretender/Only You (And You Alone) (78)	7
56	Mercury MT 117	The Great Pretender/Only You (And You Alone) (export issue)	25
56	Mercury MT 120	My Prayer/Heaven On Earth (78)	7
57	Mercury MT 130	You'll Never Never Know/It Isn't Right (78)	5
57	Mercury MT 143	On My Word Of Honor/One In A Million (78)	6
57	Mercury MT 145	I'm Sorry/She's Mine (78)	5
57	Mercury MT 156	My Dream/I Wanna (78)	6
58	Mercury 7MT 197	Helpless/Indiff'rent	30
58	Mercury MT 197	Helpless/Indiff'rent (78)	5
58	Mercury 7MT 205	Are You Sincere?/Don't Let Go	20
58	Mercury MT 205	Are You Sincere?/Don't Let Go (78)	5
58	Mercury 7MT 214	Twilight Time/Out Of My Mind	12
58	Mercury MT 214	Twilight Time/Out Of My Mind (78)	5
58	Mercury 7MT 227	My Old Flame/You're Making A Mistake (B-side featuring Tony Williams)	15
58	Mercury MT 227	My Old Flame/You're Making A Mistake (B-side featuring Tony Williams) (78)	8
58	Mercury AMT 1001	I Wish/It's Raining Outside	12
58	Mercury AMT 1001	I Wish/It's Raining Outside (78)	10
58	Mercury AMT 1016	Smoke Gets In Your Eyes/No Matter What You Are	8
58	Mercury AMT 1016	Smoke Gets In Your Eyes/No Matter What You Are (78)	12
59	Mercury AMT 1039	Enchanted/The Sound And The Fury	6
59	Mercury AMT 1039	Enchanted/The Sound And The Fury (78)	15
59	Mercury AMT 1053	Remember When/Love Of A Lifetime (featuring Tony Williams)	5
59	Mercury AMT 1053	Remember When/Love Of A Lifetime (featuring Tony Williams) (78)	20
59	Mercury AMT 1066	My Blue Heaven/Wish It Were Me	7
60	Mercury AMT 1076	My Secret/What Does It Matter	6
60	Mercury AMT 1081	Harbour Lights/(By The) Sleepy Lagoon	6
60	Mercury AMT 1081	Harbour Lights/(By The) Sleepy Lagoon (78)	40
60	Mercury AMT 1098	Ebb Tide/(I'll Be With You In) Apple Blossom Time (featuring Tony Williams)	6
60	Mercury AMT 1106	Red Sails In The Sunset/Sad River (featuring Tony Williams)	6
60	Mercury AMT 1118	To Each His Own/Down The River Of Golden Dreams	6
61	Mercury AMT 1128	If I Didn't Care/True Lover	6
61	Mercury AMT 1154	I'll Never Smile Again/You Don't Say	6
62	Ember JBS 701	Only You/Tell The World	150
66	Stateside SS 511	I Love You 1000 Times/Hear No Evil, Speak No Evil, See No Evil	15
66	Stateside SS 568	I'll Be Home/(You've Got) The Magic Tough	7
67	Stateside SS 2007	With This Ring/If I Had A Love	8
67	Stateside SS 2042	Washed Ashore/What Name Shall I Give You My Love	8
67	Stateside SS 2067	Sweet Sweet Lovin'/Sonata	10

MINT VALUE £

69	Stateside SS 2150	With This Ring/If I Had A Love (reissue)	5
56	Mercury MEP 9504	THE FABULOUS PLATTERS (EP)	12
57	Mercury MEP 9514	THE FABULOUS PLATTERS VOL. II (EP)	14
57	Mercury MEP 9524	THE FABULOUS PLATTERS VOL. III (EP)	14
58	Mercury MEP 9526	THE FLYING PLATTERS VOL. I (EP)	15
58	Mercury MEP 9528	THE FLYING PLATTERS VOL. II (EP)	15
58	Mercury MEP 9537	THE PLATTERS (EP)	15
59	Mercury ZEP 10000	PICK OF THE PLATTERS NO. 1 (EP)	15
59	Mercury ZEP 10008	PICK OF THE PLATTERS NO. 2 (EP)	15
59	Mercury ZEP 10025	PICK OF THE PLATTERS NO. 3 (EP)	15
59	Mercury ZEP 10031	PICK OF THE PLATTERS NO. 4 (EP)	15
59	Mercury ZEP 10042	PICK OF THE PLATTERS NO. 5 (EP)	15
60	Mercury ZEP 10056	PICK OF THE PLATTERS NO. 6 (EP)	18
60	Mercury ZEP 10070	PICK OF THE PLATTERS NO. 7 (EP)	18
61	Mercury ZEP 10112	HARBOUR LIGHTS (EP)	15
62	Mercury ZEP 10126	THE PLATTERS ON A PLATTER (EP)	20
57	Mercury MPL 6504	THE PLATTERS (LP)	35
57	Mercury MPL 6511	THE PLATTERS VOL. 2 (LP)	35
58	Mercury MPL 6528	THE FLYING PLATTERS (LP)	30
58	Parlophone PMD 1058	THE PLATTERS (10" LP)	150
59	Mercury MMC 14009	AROUND THE WORLD WITH THE FLYING PLATTERS (LP)	30
59	Mercury MMC 14010	THE PLATTERS ON PARADE (LP)	30
59	Mercury MMC 14014	REMEMBER WHEN? (LP)	25
60	Mercury MMC 14045	REFLECTIONS (LP)	22
61	Mercury MMC 14072	LIFE IS JUST A BOWL OF CHERRIES (LP)	18
62	Ember EMB 3339	THE BEST OF THE PLATTERS (LP)	10
62	Mercury MMC 14091	GOLDEN HITS (LP)	12
64	Mercury MCL 20000	THE PLATTERS SING LATINO (LP)	12
66	Wing WL 1044	REFLECTIONS (LP, reissue)	10
67	Stateside S(S)L 10208	GOING BACK TO DETROIT (LP)	12
67	Wing WL 1174	TENTH ANNIVERSARY ALBUM (LP)	12
68	Stateside S(S)L 10227	THE NEW GOLDEN HITS OF THE PLATTERS (LP)	10
68	Stateside S(S)L 10245	SWEET, SWEET LOVIN' (LP)	10
68	Polydor Special 236 223	ONLY YOU (LP)	10
68	Fontana SFL 13040	THE PLATTERS SING LATINO (LP, reissue)	10

(see also Buck Ram's Ramrocks, Linda Hayes)

PLAYBOY CLUB BUNNIES
| 68 | Decca F 12832 | Keep The Ball Rollin'/I Only Want To Be with You | 4 |

PLAYBOYS
| 58 | London HLU 8681 | Over The Weekend/Double Talk | 30 |
| 58 | London HLU 8681 | Over The Weekend/Double Talk (78) | 15 |

PLAYBOYS
| 69 | Capitol CL 15621 | Let's Get Back To Rock And Roll/Homemade Cookin' | 4 |

PLAY DEAD
81	Fresh FRESH 29	Poison Takes A Hold/Introduction (p/s)	7
81	Fresh FRESH 38	T.V. Eye/Final Epitaph (p/s)	7
83	Jungle JUNG 002	Propaganda/Propaganda (Mix) (p/s)	5
83	Situation 2 SIT 28	Shine/Promise (p/s)	5
83	Situation 2 SIT 28T	Shine/Promise/Gaze (12", p/s)	8
84	Clay CLAY 31	Break/Blood Stains (p/s)	4
84	Clay 12CLAY 31	Break/Blood Stains/Pleasure (12", p/s)	7
84	Clay CLAY 35	Isabel/Solace (p/s)	4
84	Clay 12CLAY 35	Isabel/Solace (12", p/s)	7
85	Tanz TANZ 1	This Side Of Heaven (unissued, white label promos only)	8

PLAYER
| 78 | RSO 2394 193 | PLAYER (LP) | 10 |

PLAYERS
| 63 | Oriole CB 1861 | Mockingbird/Bizet As It May | 8 |

PLAYGIRLS (U.S.)
| 59 | RCA RCA 1133 | Hey Sport/Young Love Swings The World | 10 |
| 59 | RCA RCA 1133 | Hey Sport/Young Love Swings The World (78) | 12 |

PLAYGIRLS (Jamaica)
| 65 | Black Swan WI 456 | Looks Are Deceiving/BABA BROOKS BAND: Dreadnaught | 10 |

PLAYGROUND
| 67 | MGM MGM 1351 | At The Zoo/Yellow Balloon | 6 |

PLAYMATES
57	Columbia DB 3941	Pretty Woman/Barefoot Girl	6
57	Columbia DB 4033	Island Girl/Darling, It's Wonderful	6
58	Columbia DB 4084	Jo-Ann/You Can't Stop Me From Dreaming	6
58	Columbia DB 4127	Let's Be Lovers/Give Me Another Chance	6
58	Columbia DB 4151	Can't You Get It Through Your Head/Don't Go Home	6
58	Columbia DB 4207	While The Record Goes Around/The Day I Died	6
58	Columbia DB 4224	Beep Beep/Your Love	6
58	Columbia DB 4224	Beep Beep/Your Love (78)	5
59	Columbia DB 4288	Star Love/The Thing-A-Ma-Jig	5
59	Columbia DB 4338	What Is Love?/I Am	8
59	Columbia DB 4389	On The Beach/First Love	4
60	Columbia DB 4468	Parade Of Pretty Girls/Jubilation T. Cornpone	4
60	Columbia DB 4551	Wait For Me/Eyes Of An Angel	4
61	Columbia DB 4628	Little Miss Stuck Up/Real Life	4
60	Columbia 33SX 1215	BROADWAY SHOW STOPPERS (LP, also stereo SCX 3300)	10/12

PLAYN JAYN
84	A&M AM 215DJ	In Your Eyes (live)/Mezcal (p/s, DJ promos only)	5

PLAYTHINGS
70	Pye 7N 45212	Stop What You're Doing To Me/Sad Songs	5
74	Pye 7N 45399	Surrounded By A Ray Of Sunshine/Dance The Night Away	4

BOBBY PLEASE
57	London HLB 8507	Your Driver's License, Please/Heartache Street (unreleased, 2 x 1-sided demos only)	200

PLEASERS
77	Solid Gold SGR 104	You Know What I'm Thinking/Hello Little Girl (no p/s)	6
78	Arista ARIST 21	Girl I Know/Don't Go Breaking My Heart (p/s)	4
77	Arista ARIST 152	You Keep Tellin' Lies/I'm In Love/Who Are You (p/s)	4
78	Arista ARIST 180	The Kids Are Alright/Stay With Me (p/s)	5

PLEASURE
75	Fantasy FTC 115	Dust Yourself Off/Midnight At The Oasis	5
78	Fantasy FT 543	GET TO THE FEELIN' (LP)	12

PLEASURE FAIR
68	Uni UN 500	Morning Glory Blues/Fade Out Fade In	4
67	Uni UNL(S) 100	PLEASURE FAIR (LP)	10

PLEASURES
65	Sue WI 357	Music City/If I Had A Little Money	12

PLEBS
64	Decca F 12006	Bad Blood/Babe I'm Gonna Leave You	25

JACK PLEIS & HIS ORCHESTRA
56	Brunswick 05534	The Trouble With Harry (with Bonnie Lake & Her Beaux)/Pauline	4
57	Brunswick 05634	Giant (with Ralph Young)/Lonesome Without You	4
59	Brunswick 05795	Theme From "Compulsion"/Romantico	4
61	Brunswick 05846	Pepe/Theme From "The Sundowners"	4

(see also Ralph Young)

PLEXUS
78	Look LKLP 6175	PLEXUS (LP)	20

PLUGS
79	Cathedral CATH 1	Too Late/UFO/Sally (gatefold p/s)	4

JEAN PLUM
76	London HLU 10514	Look At The Boy/Back At You	5

PLUMMERS
64	Blue Beat BB 260	Joanie/Little Stars (actually by Plamers)	10

PLUS
70	Probe SPB 1009	SEVEN DEADLY SINS (LP)	20

PLUTO
71	Dawn DNS 1017	Rag A Bone Joe/Stealing My Thunder	15
72	Dawn DNS 1026	I Really Want It/Something That You Loved	15
73	Warner Bros K 16311	Mockingbird Hill/Pluto's Theme	4
72	Dawn DNLS 3030	PLUTO (LP)	80

NICK PLYTAS & ANN PIGALLE
82	Illuminated ILL 1210	HOT SAGAS (10" EP)	6

PNEUMONIA
79	Plastic PLAS 001	Exhibition/Coming Attack/U.K. DECAY: U.K. Decay/Carcrash (folded p/s)	18

(see also U.K. Decay)

POCO
71	Epic EQ 30209	DELIVERIN' (LP, quadrophonic)	12

(see also Buffalo Springfield)

POEMS
81	Polka DOT 1	ACHIEVING UNITY (EP)	6

(see also Strawberry Switchblade)

POET & ONE MAN BAND
69	Verve SVLP 6012	THE POET AND THE ONE MAN BAND (LP)	30

(see also Tony Colton, Nicky Hopkins, Heads, Hands & Feet)

POETS (U.K.)
64	Decca F 11995	Now We're Thru/There Are Some	6
65	Decca F 12074	That's The Way It's Got To Be/I'll Cry With The Moon	40
65	Decca F 12195	I Am So Blue/I Love Her Still	20
65	Immediate IM 006	Call Again/Some Things I Can't Forget	50
66	Immediate IM 024	Baby Don't You Do It/I'll Come Home	50
67	Decca F 12569	Wooden Spoon/In Your Tower	80
68	Pye 7N 17668	Locked In A Room/Alone Am I	80
71	Strike Cola SC 1	Heyla Hola/Fun Buggy	25

(see also Pathfinders, [White] Trash)

POETS (U.S.)
(see under American Poets)

POGUE MAHONE
84	Pogue Mahone PM 1	Dark Streets Of London/The Band Played Waltzing Mathilda (no p/s)	8
84	Pogue Mahone PM 1	Dark Streets Of London/The Band Played Waltzing Mathilda (white label tour copy with 'harp' sticker, 237 only)	50

POGUE MAHONE

84	Pogue Mahone PM 1	Dark Streets Of London/The Band Played Waltzing Mathilda (white label tour copy with printed hand-drawn 'harp' image on label) 4

(see also Pogues)

POGUES

84	Stiff BUY 207	Dark Streets Of London/The Band Played Waltzing Mathilda (reissue, no p/s) . . .12
84	Stiff BUY 212	Boys From The County Hell/Repealing Of The Licensing Laws (p/s, green-tinted p/s; A-label promos in blue-tinted p/s £18) 12
84	Stiff BUY 207/212	Dark Streets Of London/The Band Played Waltzing Mathilda//Boys From The County Hell/Repealing Of The Licensing Laws (sealed double pack) 25
85	Stiff BUY 220	A Pair Of Brown Eyes/Whiskey You're The Devil (p/s) 6
85	Stiff DBUY 220	A Pair Of Brown Eyes/Whiskey You're The Devil (picture disc) 15
85	Stiff BUYIT 220	A Pair Of Brown Eyes/Whiskey You're The Devil/Muirshin Durkin (12", p/s) 15
85	Stiff BUY 212/BUY 220	Boys From The County Hell/Repealing Of The Licensing Laws//A Pair Of Brown Eyes/Whiskey You're The Devil (sealed double pack) 20
85	Stiff BUY 224	Sally MacLennane/Wild Rover (wraparound poster p/s, some green vinyl) 5/10
85	Stiff BUY 224	Sally MacLennane/Wild Rover (p/s) 15
85	Stiff PBUY 224	Sally MacLennane/Wild Rover (shaped picture disc) 12
85	Stiff BUYIT 224	Sally MacLennane/Wild Rover/The Leaving Of Liverpool (12", p/s) 12
85	Stiff BUYC 224	Sally MacLennane/Wild Rover/The Leaving Of Liverpool/ Wild Cats Of Kilkenny (cassette) 20
85	Stiff BUY 229	Dirty Old Town/A Pistol For Paddy Garcia (p/s) 4
85	Stiff PBUY 229	Dirty Old Town/A Pistol For Paddy Garcia (picture disc) .8
85	Stiff BUYIT 229	Dirty Old Town/A Pistol For Paddy Garcia/The Pasting Glass (12", some with poster & stickered p/s) 20/15
85	Stiff MAIL 3	Dirty Old Town (live)/Sally MacLennane (live)/(interview) (12", mail-order only) 15
86	Stiff BUY 243	POGUETRY IN MOTION (EP) 4
86	Stiff PBUY 243	POGUETRY IN MOTION (EP, picture disc) 6
86	Stiff BUYIT 243	POGUETRY IN MOTION (12" EP) 7
86	Stiff BUYC 243	POGUETRY IN MOTION (EP, cassette) 4
86	MCA MCAT 1084	Haunted/Junk Theme/Hot Dogs With Everything (12", p/s, some with poster) 10/7
87	Stiff/Hell BLOOD 1	The Good, The Bad & The Ugly/Rake At The Gates Of Hell (unreleased)
87	Stiff/Hell BLOODY 1	The Good, The Bad & The Ugly/Rake At The Gates Of Hell (12", unreleased)
88	Pogue Mahone SGG 1-12	ST. PATRICK'S NIGHT EP (12" EP) 7
89	WEA YZ 409C	White City/Every Man Is A King (cassette) 4
89	WEA YZ 409TX	White City/Maggie May (live)/Every Man Is A King (12", p/s, with sticker sheet) . . .7
89	WEA YZ 409CD	White City/Every Man Is A King/The Star Of The County Down (3" CD) 7
89	WEA YZ 407C	Misty Morning Albert Bridge/Cotton Fields (cassette) 4
89	WEA SAM 553	Misty Morning Albert Bridge/(same) (12" promo, green vinyl, no p/s) 8

(see also Pogue Mahone, Nips, Nipple Erectors)

POGUES featuring KIRSTY MacCOLL

87	Pogue Mahone NYG 7	A Fairytale Of New York/Battle March Medley (open-up p/s) 4

POINTER SISTERS

75	ABC 4048	Live Your Life Before You Die/Shakey Flat Blues 4
75	ABC 4069	How Long/Easy Days 4
76	ABC 4089	Going Down Slowly/Sleeping Alone 4

POISON

87	M. F. Nations P12 KUT 125	Talk Dirty To Me/We Want Some Need Some/Interview (12", picture disc) 7
87	Music For Nations P12 KUT 127	Cry Tough/Cry Tough (U.S. Mix)/Look What The Cat Dragged In (12", picture disc) 7
88	Capitol CLP 486	Nothin' But A Good Time/Look But You Can't Touch (poster p/s) 4
88	Capitol CLP 486	Nothin' But A Good Time/Look But You Can't Touch (picture disc) 4
89	Capitol CLP 520	Every Rose Has Its Thorn/Back To The Rocking Horse (shaped picture disc) 4
89	Capitol CLS 523	Your Mama Don't Dance/Tearin' Down The Walls (p/s, green vinyl) 4

POISON GIRLS

80	Crass/Xntrix 421984	Persons Unknown/CRASS: Bloody Revolutions (folded 21" x 14" poster p/s) 4
80	Crass 421984/2	CHAPPAQUIDICK (LP, with flexidisc [421984/7]) 10

(see also Crass)

POLECATS

81	Nervous NER 1	Rockabilly Guy/Chicken Shack (p/s) 5
81	Mercury POLE 10	John I'm Only Dancing/All Night Long/Big Green Car (10", p/s, pink vinyl) 7
81	Lyntone LYN 10138/9	We Say Yeah/GRAHAM BONNET: Night Games/THIN LIZZY: Song For Jimmy/WAY OF THE WEST: Monkey Love (orange flexidisc with "Flexipop" issue 10) 5/4

ROLO POLEY

69	Jackpot JP 704	Zapatoo The Tiger/Music House (both sides actually by Lester Sterling) 5

POLICE

77	Illegal IL 001	Fall Out/Nothing Achieving (black & white p/s, red & black label) 15
78	A&M AMS 7348	Roxanne/Peanuts (2.52) ('telephone' p/s, typed matrix no., 'All Rights ...' on top half of label) 7
78	A&M AMS 7348	Roxanne/Peanuts (12", 'telephone' p/s) 7
78	A&M AMS 7381	Can't Stand Losing You/Dead End Job (glossy p/s, original issue, label credited to 'Police', some on mid-blue vinyl) .each 7
78	A&M AMS 7402	So Lonely/Time This Time (p/s, miscredited flip, label credited to 'Police') 5
79	A&M AMS 7348	Roxanne/Peanuts (3.54) (reissue, 'group' p/s, handwritten matrix number, blue or black vinyl) 6/4
79	A&M AMS 7348	Roxanne/Peanuts (2.52) (reissue, 'group' p/s, typed matrix number, blue or black vinyl) 6/4
79	A&M AMSP 7348	Roxanne/Peanuts (12", reissue, 'group' p/s) 8
79	A&M AMS 7381	Can't Stand Losing You/Dead End Job (reissue, label credited to 'The Police'; dark blue or light blue vinyl) . . . . .each 6

79	A&M AMS 7381	Can't Stand Losing You/Dead End Job (p/s, reissue, red, yellow, green or white vinyl) 10-12
79	A&M AMS 7381	Can't Stand Losing You/Dead End Job (p/s, mispressed B-side, plays "No Time This Time") ....20+
79	A&M AMS 7474	Message In A Bottle/Landlord (p/s, green vinyl) 4
79	A&M AMSP 7494	Walking On The Moon/Visions Of The Night (12", p/s) 7
79	Illegal IL 001	Fall Out/Nothing Achieving (reissue, green/black or purple/blue p/s, various label designs) 8
79	Illegal IL 001	Fall Out/Nothing Achieving (reissue, black & orange p/s, various label designs) 9
80	A&M AMPP 6001	POLICE PACK (6 x 7" PVC pack [AMS 7348, 7381, 7402, 7474 & 7494] & "Truth Hits Everybody"/"The Bed's Too Big Without You"; all on blue vinyl) 18
80	A&M SAMP 5	SIX-TRACK RADIO SAMPLER (custom p/s, promo radio sampler) 20
80	A&M AMS 7564	Don't Stand So Close To Me/Friends (poster p/s) 4
81	A&M AMS 8164	Invisible Sun/Shamelle (p/s with 'clear' sun instead of 'blurred' sun) 4
81	A&M AMS 8194	Spirits (In The Material World)/Low Life (poster p/s, some with badge) 8/4
83	A&M AM 117	Every Breath You Take/Murder By Numbers (p/s, with free badge) 4
83	A&M AM 117/AM 01	Every Breath You Take/Murder By Numbers//Truth Hits Everybody/Man In A Suitcase (double pack, gatefold p/s) 20
83	A&M AMSP 117	Every Breath You Take/Murder By Numbers (picture disc) 8
83	A&M AMP 127	Wrapped Around Your Finger/Someone To Talk To (Sting picture disc) 6
83	A&M AMP 127	Wrapped Around Your Finger/Someone To Talk To (Andy Summers or Stewart Copeland picture disc, 1000 each only) ....each 10
78	A&M AMLN 68502	OUTLANDOS D'AMOUR (LP, blue vinyl) 18
79	A&M AMLH 64792	REGATTA DE BLANC (LP, as 2 x 10" with poster) 15

(see also Sting, Klark Kent, Radio Actors, Zoot Money's Big Roll Band, Last Exit)

POLIPHONY
| 73 | Zella (no cat. no.) | POLIPHONY (LP, private press) ....160 |

POLITICIANS
| 72 | Hot Wax HWX 114 | Love Machine/Free Your Mind ....5 |
| 72 | Hot Wax SHW 5007 | THE POLITICIANS (LP) ....15 |

FRANK POLK
| 65 | Capitol CL 15389 | Trying To Keep Up With The Joneses/Welcome Home, Baby ....20 |

POLKA DOTS
58	Pye 7N 15144	Don't Make Small Talk Baby/There Will Never Be Another 4
59	Pye 7N 15194	Hey Liley, Liley Lo/Go Chase A Moonbeam 4
59	Pye 7N 15211	Girls In Arms/You've Done Something To My Heart (with Laurie Johnson Orchestra) 4

(see also Teddy Johnson)

RAY POLLARD
| 65 | United Artists UP 1111 | The Drifter/Let Him Go (And Let Me Love You) ....100 |
| 66 | United Artists UP 1133 | It's A Sad Thing/All The Things You Are ....60 |
(see also Wanderers)

MICHAEL POLNAREFF
66	Vogue VRS 7012	La Poupee Qui Fait Non/Beatnik 5
66	Vogue VRS 7013	No No No No No No/Beatnik 5
66	Vogue VRS 7019	Love Me Please Love Me/L'Amour Avec Toi 6

PONI-TAILS
58	HMV POP 516	Born Too Late/Come On Joey, Dance With Me (as Pony-Tails) 8
58	HMV POP 516	Born Too Late/Come On Joey, Dance With Me (as Pony-Tails) (78) 5
58	HMV POP 558	Close Friends/Seven Minutes In Heaven 7
58	HMV POP 558	Close Friends/Seven Minutes In Heaven (78) 5
59	HMV POP 596	Early To Bed/Father Time 8
59	HMV POP 596	Early To Bed/Father Time (78) 8
59	HMV POP 644	Moody/Oom Pah Polka 7
59	HMV POP 663	I'll Be Seeing You/I'll Keep Tryin' 7
57	HMV 7EG 8427	PONI TAILS (EP) 30

JEAN-LUC PONTY
| 69 | Liberty LBL/LBS 83262 | ELECTRIC CONNECTION (LP) ....10 |
| 70 | Liberty LBL/LBS 83375 | KING KONG (LP) ....10 |

POOGY
| 74 | EMI EMI 2136 | She Looked Me In The Eye (I Gave Her My Life)/Morris And His Turtle ....15 |

POOH STICKS
88	Fierce FRIGHT 011	On Tape (p/s, 1-sided, etched B-side) 50
88	Fierce FRIGHT 021	1-2-3 Red Light (p/s, 1-sided) 18
88	Fierce FRIGHT 021-025	FIERCE BOX SET (5 x 1-sided etched discs, hand coloured labels, with insert) 60
88	Fierce FRIGHT 026	ALAN McGEE (CD EP, with FRIGHT 021-025 tracks plus "On Tape"/"Please Hue, Please", some in 7" box with booklet) 25/20
89	Fierce FRIGHT 034	Dying For It (p/s, 300 only, some signed, sold at U.L.U. gig) 20/15
89	Fierce FRIGHT 034	Dying For It (1-sided, different p/s) 10
89	Cheree CHEREE 3	Go Go Girl/Simon E (flexidisc with foldout fanzine) 7
89	Woosh WOOSH 007/WOOSH 6	Hard On Love (yellow flexidisc with Pooh Sticks fanzine)//GROOVE FARM: Heaven Is Blue/ESMERALDA'S KITE: Vampire Girl (red flexidisc) (both discs free with "Woosh" fanzine issue 3) 15
89	Anonymous ANON 2	ENCORES (EP, numbered box set, multi-coloured vinyl 1-sided 7" with sweet watch, badge, sticker & booklet) 6
91	Cheree CHEREE 17	Who Loves You/Good Times (die-cut company sleeve) 4
92	Fierce FRIGHT 42	Million Seller (1-sided, die-cut RCA sleeve) 20
89	53rd & 3rd AGAMC 5	ORGASM (LP, a few on pink vinyl with insert for export) 25/10
89	Fierce FRIGHT 025	THE POOH STICKS (mini-LP, black & white sleeve, 1-side etched, w/inner) 15

POOH STICKS

90	Fierce FRIGHT 035	TRADE MARK OF QUALITY (LP, plain stickered sleeve with insert, numbered)	30

(see also Dumb Angels)

BRIAN POOLE & TREMELOES

62	Decca F 11455	Twist Little Sister/Lost Love	7
62	Decca F 11515	That Ain't Right/Blue	5
63	Decca F 11567	Meet Me Where We Used Meet/A Very Good Year For Girls	5
63	Decca F 11616	Keep On Dancing/Run Back Home	5
63	Decca F 11694	Twist And Shout/We Know	4
63	Decca F 11739	Do You Love Me?/Why Can't You Love Me?	4
63	Decca F 11771	I Can Dance/Are You Loving Me At All	4
64	Decca F 11823	Candy Man/I Wish I Could Dance	4
64	Decca F 11893	Someone, Someone/Till The End Of Time	4
64	Decca F 11951	Twelve Steps To Love/Don't Cry	4
64	Decca F 12037	Three Bells/Tell Me How To Care	4
65	Decca F 12124	After A While/You Know	4
65	Decca F 12197	I Want Candy/Love Me Baby	4
65	Decca F 12274	Good Lovin'/Could It Be You	4
64	Decca DFE 8566	BRIAN POOLE AND THE TREMELOES (EP)	20
65	Decca DFE 8610	BRIAN POOLE AND THE TREMELOES (EP)	20
63	Ace of Clubs ACL 1146	BIG BIG HITS OF '62 (LP)	22
63	Decca LK 4550	TWIST AND SHOUT WITH BRIAN POOLE AND THE TREMELOES (LP)	25
65	Decca LK 4685	IT'S ABOUT TIME (LP)	25

(see also Tremeloes)

BRIAN POOLE

66	Decca F 12402	Hey Girl/Please Be Mine	4
66	CBS 202349	Everything I Touch Turns To Tears/I Need Her Tonight	8
67	CBS 202661	That Reminds Me Baby/Tomorrow Never Comes	4
67	CBS 3005	Just How Loud/The Other Side Of The Sky	4
69	President PT 239	Send Her To Me/Pretty In The City (as Brian Poole & Seychelles)	4
69	President PT 264	What Do Women Most Desire/Treat Her Like A Woman	4

LOU & LAURA POOLE

72	Jay Boy BOY 63	Only You And I Know/Look At Me	7

POOR SOULS

65	Decca F 12183	When My Baby Cries/My Baby She's Not There	12
66	Alp ALP 595 004	Love Me/Please Don't Change Your Mind	30

IGGY POP

77	RCA PB 9093	China Girl/Baby	4
77	RCA PB 9160	Success/The Passenger	5
77	RCA PB 9160	Some Weird Sin/The Passenger	4
78	RCA PB 9213	Sixteen/I Got A Right	4
78	Radar ADA 4	Kill City (with James Williamson)/I Got Nothin'	4
79	Arista ARISP 274	Five Foot One/Pretty Flamingo (picture disc)	6
80	Arista ARIST 327	Loco Mosquito/Take Care Of Me (p/s)	4
83	Chrysalis/Melody Maker	Extracts from "Zombie Birdhouse"/STIFF LITTLE FINGERS: Now Then (flexidisc, free with 'Melody Maker')	5/4
73	CBS 65586	RAW POWER (LP, as Iggy & Stooges)	12
78	Radar RAD 2	KILL CITY (LP, as Iggy Pop & James Williamson)	10

(see also Stooges)

POPCORNS

63	Columbia DB 4968	Zero Zero/Chinese Twist	4

TIM POPE

84	Fiction FICS 21	I Want To Be A Tree/The Double Crossing Of Two Faced Fred (p/s)	12
84	Fiction FICSX 21	I Want To Be A Tree/(Elephant) Song/The Double Crossing Of Two Faced Fred (12", p/s)	20

(see also Cure)

POP GROUP

79	Radar ADA 29	She Is Beyond Good And Evil/3.38 (p/s)	5
79	Radar ADA 1229	She Is Beyond Good And Evil/3.38 (12", p/s)	7
80	Rough Trade RT 023	We Are All Prostitutes/Amnesty International Report On British Army Torture Of Irish Prisoners (p/s)	4
80	Rough Trade RT 039/ Y Y1	Where There's A Will There's A Way/SLITS: In The Beginning There Was Rhythm (p/s)	4
79	Radar RAD 20	Y (LP, with foldout colour poster)	15
80	Rough Trade ROUGH 9	FOR HOW MUCH LONGER DO WE TOLERATE MASS MURDER (LP, with 4 posters)	10

(see also Slits)

POP GUNS

80s	La Di Da LA-DI-DA 001	Where Do You Go/HOW MANY BEANS MAKE FIVE: Another Friendly Face (flexidisc, 33rpm, p/s)	5
89	Medium Cool MC 019T	LANDSLIDE (12" EP)	8

(see also Wedding Present)

POPINJAYS

88	Big Cat BBA 02	Don't Go Back/So Close/Move To Perish (12", p/s)	7

POPPIES

66	Columbia DB 7879	Lullaby Of Love/I Wonder Why	15

POPPYHEADS

88	Sha La La Ba Ba Ba Ba 4	POSTCARD FOR FLOSSY (EP, 1-sided flexidisc, p/s in poly bag)	8

88	Sarah SARAH 006	Cremation Town/Pictures You Weave/Dreamboat (foldaround p/s with large poster in poly bag) 8

POP RIVETS
79	Hypocrite HEP 001	POP RIVITS (EP) 8
79	Hypocrite HEP 002	Pop Rivits/Sulphate 7
79	Hypocrite JIM 1	FUN IN THE U.K. (EP, double pack) 12
79	Hypocrite HIP-O	EMPTY SOUNDS FROM ANARCHY RANCH (LP, coloured back, stamped labels) 20
80	Hypocrite HIP 007	THE POP RIVETS GREATEST HITS (LP) 15

(see also Milkshakes)

POPSICLES
65	Vogue V 9243	I Don't Want To Be Your Baby/Baby I Miss You 4

POPULAR 5
68	Minit MLF 11011	I'm A Lovemaker/Little Bitty Pretty One 10

POP WILL EAT ITSELF
86	Desperate SRT 1	THE POPPIES SAY GRRR! (EP, stamped white labels in brown paper bag) ...20
86	Desperate DAN 1	THE POPPIES SAY GRRR! (EP, reissue, in orange sleeve) 7
86	Chapter 22 CHAP 9	POPPIECOCK (EP) 6
86	Chapter 22 12CHAP 9	POPPIECOCK (12" EP) 7
87	Chapter 22 CHAP 11	Sweet Sweet Pie/Devil Inside/Runaround (p/s) 6
87	Chapter 22 CHAP 13	Love Missile F1-11/Orgone Acumulator (p/s) 5
87	Chapter 22 LCHAP 13	Love Missile F1-11(Designer Grebo Mix)/(Original Poppies Mix)/Orgone Acumulator (Original Version)/Everything That Rises (New Version) (p/s) 12
87	Chapter 22 LCHAP 16	Beaver Patrol/Bubbles (numbered p/s, clear vinyl in stickered PVC sleeve) 8
87	Chapter 22 LCHAP 16	Beaver Patrol/Bubbles (no'd p/s, signed, pink vinyl in stickered PVC sleeve) 8
88	Chapter 22 LCHAP 20	There Is No Love Between Us Anymore/Picnic in The Sky (picture disc) 4
88	Chapter 22 L12CHAP 20	There Is No Love Between Us Anymore (12" version)/Picnic in The Sky/ There Is No Love Between Us Anymore (Speciality Extended High Mix)/ Hit The Hi-Tech Groove (The M & K Mix) (12", die-cut sleeve) 10
88	Chapter 22 CLUB CHAP 20	There Is No Love Between Us Anymore (Speciality Extended High Mix)/ Hit The Hi-Tech Groove (The M & K Mix) (12", die-cut sleeve) 12
88	Chapter 22 PWEI L001	Def Con One (Radio Edit)/(same) (stickered PVC sl., stamped white label) 6
88	Chapter 22 PWEI L12001	Def Con One (The Doomsday Power Mix)/(7" Mix)/InsideYou (live)/ She's Surreal (live) (12", p/s) 8
89	RCA PB 43021	Very Metal Noise PolLUTION (EP, gatefold p/s) 4
89	RCA PK 43024	VERY METAL NOISE POLLUTION (EP cassette, in 7" presentation box) 4
89	RCA PT 43022	VERY METAL NOISE POLLUTION (EP, shaped picture disc) 4

(see also Wild & Wandering)

POP WORKSHOP
68	Page One POF 091	Fairyland/When My Little Girl Is Happy 5
69	Page One POF 129	Punch And Judy Man/Love Is A One Way Highway 5

PORK DUKES
77	Wood WOOD 9	Bend And Flush/Throbbing Gristle 5
78	Wood BRANCH 9	Making Bacon/Tight Pussy (12", p/s, yellow vinyl) 7
78	Wood Standard WOOD 56	Telephone Maturbator/Melody Makers (p/s) 4
78	Wood PORK 001	THE PORK DUKES (LP, pink vinyl with warning sticker & postcard) 10
80	Wood PORK 2	PIG OUT OF HELL (LP) 10
82	Butt PORK 1	PIG IN A POKE (LP) 10

DAVID PORTER
71	Stax 2362 006	INTO A REAL THING (LP) 10

NOLAN PORTER
72	Probe PRO 580	If I Could Only Be Sure/Work It Out In The Morning 8

PORTION CONTROL
82	In Phaze POR CON 006	Surface And Be Seen/Spinola (Blotch)/Terror Leads To Better Days/Simple As ABC/Monstrous Bulk/He Is A Barbarian (12", p/s, w/ plastic outer sleeve) 15
84	Illuminated ILL 2612	Raise The Pulse/Collapse/Bite My Head (12", p/s) 10
84	Illuminated ILL 3212	Rough Justice/The Man Who Did Backwards Somersaults (12", p/s, with inner sleeve) 9
85	Illuminated ILL 4312	Go-Talk/Upside Down/Drag Down (12", p/s) 8
85	Rhythmic/Havoc 7RMIC 7	The Great Divide/Totall Recall 4
85	Rhythmic/Havoc 12RMIC 7	The Great Divide/Divided/Bolt It Down (12", p/s) 7
86	Dead Man's Curve DMC 1	PRESENT PURGE (12" EP) 8
83	In Phaze EZ 2	HIT THE PULSE (mini-LP, 45/33rpm) 15
84	Illuminated JAMS 44	STEP FORWARD (LP) 12
86	Dead Man's Curve DMC 8	PSYCHO-GOD SAVES THE WORLD (LP, with inner sleeve) 10

PORTOBELLO EXPLOSION
69	Carnaby CNS 4001	We Can Fly/Hot Smoke And Sasafrass 25

PORTRAIT
69	CBS 4520	Sh Sh Sheila/Hurt Bad By Love 4
70	Pye 7N 45043	Tokaido Links/Cuddle Me Closer 4

SANDY POSEY
66	MGM MGM 1321	Born A Woman/Caution To The Wind 4
66	MGM MGM 1330	Single Girl/Blue Is My Best Colour 4
67	MGM MGM 1335	What A Woman In Love Won't Do/Shattered 4
67	MGM MGM 1342	I Take It Back/The Boy I Love 4
67	MGM MGM 1364	Are You Never Coming Home/I Can Show You How To Live 4
67	MGM C(S) 8035	BORN A WOMAN (LP) 15
67	MGM C(S) 8042	SINGLE GIRL (LP) 12
68	MGM C(S) 8051	SANDY POSEY (LP) 12
68	MGM C 8060	THE BEST OF SANDY POSEY (LP, original with blue label) 10
68	MGM C(S) 8073	LOOKING AT YOU (LP) 12

POSITIVE FORCE
79	Sugarhill SH 102	We Got The Funk/Tell Me What You See (12")	8

ROBERT POSS
80s	Sonic Life 001/LYN 21552	O Five O (33rpm flexidisc, mail order only)	4

(see also Band Of Susans)

HOWIE POST & SWIFTIES
63	Fontana TF 421	Tom Swift/The Elephant	8

MIKE POST COALITION
72	MGM PPSP 11	The Rockford Files Pts 1 & 2	4
75	Warner Bros K 16588	Afternoon Of The Rhino/Bubble Gum Breakthrough	4

ADRIENNE POSTER
63	Decca F 11797	Only Fifteen/There's Nothing You Can Do	6
64	Decca F 11864	Shang A Doo Lang/When A Girl Really Loves You	8
65	Decca F 12079	He Doesn't Love Me/The Way You Do The Things You Do	12
65	Decca F 12181	The Winds That Blow/Back Street Girl	10
66	Decca F 12329	Something Beautiful/So Glad You're Mine	10

POTATOES
66	Fontana TF 756	The Bend/Bend Ahead	5

KEITH POTGER
69	Mercury MF 1073	The World Would Never Again/Santa Marie (some in p/s)	10/4

(see also Seekers, Judith Durham)

POTLIQUOR
71	Dawn DNLS 3016	FIRST TASTE (LP, withdrawn)	85
71	Janus 6310 202	LEVEE BLUES (LP)	10
72	Janus 6310 203	FIRST TASTE (LP, reissue)	10

PHIL POTTER
70s	Genesis GEN 10	MY SONG IS LOVE UNKNOWN (LP)	30
79	Dove DOVE 61	THE RESTORER (LP)	15

POUND HOUNDS
55	Brunswick 05484	Home Sweet Home/MELLOMEN: Lady	6

(see also Peggy Lee)

ALLEN POUND'S GET RICH
66	Parlophone R 5532	Searchin' In The Wilderness/Hey You	200

BOBBY POWELL
72	Mojo 2092 034	Peace Begins Within/Question	8

BUD POWELL (TRIO)
64	Blue Note 45-1712	Buster Rides Again/Dry Soul	5
55	Vogue EPV 1030	BUD POWELL TRIO (EP)	8
55	Vogue EPV 1033	BUD POWELL'S MODERNISTS (EP)	8
55	Vogue EPV 1036	BUD POWELL TRIO (EP)	8
55	Columbia Clef SEB 10013	BUD POWELL (EP)	7
57	Columbia Clef SEB 10074	GENIUS OF BUD POWELL (EP)	7
58	Columbia Clef SEB 10094	GENIUS OF BUD POWELL NO. 2 (EP)	7
52	Vogue LDE 010	THE BUD POWELL TRIO (10" LP)	16
54	Vogue LDE 053	JAZZ AT THE MASSEY HALL VOL. 2 (10" LP)	15
56	Columbia Clef 33C 9016	BUD POWELL TRIO (10" LP)	14
57	Columbia Clef 33CX 10069	JAZZ ORIGINAL (LP)	12
58	Columbia Clef 33CX 10123	BLUES FOR BUD (LP)	12
59	HMV CLP 1294	THE LONELY ONE (LP)	12
63	Blue Note (B)BLP 1503	THE AMAZING BUD POWELL VOL. 1 (LP)	12
63	Vogue LAE 558	THE BUD POWELL TRIO (LP)	10
63	Columbia 33SX 1575	THE BUD POWELL TRIO FEATURING MAX ROACH (LP)	12
64	Blue Note (B)BLP 1504	THE AMAZING BUD POWELL VOL. 2 (LP)	12
65	Columbia 33SX 1701	THE RETURN OF POWELL (LP)	10
65	XTRA 1011	BOUNCING WITH BUD (LP)	10
65	Verve VLP 9075	THE VINTAGE YEARS (LP)	10
68	Fontana SFJL 901	BLUES FOR BOUFFEMONT (LP)	10
69	Fontana SFJL 924	AT THE BLUE NOTE CAFE, PARIS 1961 (LP)	10

COZY POWELL
73	Rak RAK 164	Dance With The Devil/And Then There Was Skin	4
74	Rak RAK 173	The Man In Black/After Dark	4
74	Rak RAK 180	Na Na Na/Mistral	4
79	Ariola ARO 189	Theme One/Over The Top Part 1 (p/s, red vinyl)	6
79	Ariola ARO 205	The Loner/El Sid (p/s, blue vinyl)	5
80	Ariola ARO 222	Heidi Goes To Town/Over The Top Part 2 (p/s, clear vinyl)	5
81	Polydor POSP 328	Sooner Or Later/The Blister (p/s)	4
79	Ariola ARL 5038	OVER THE TOP (LP)	12
81	Polydor POLD 5047	TILT (LP)	10

(see also Rainbow, Young Blood, Big Bertha, Ace Kefford Stand, Bedlam, Bernie Marsden, Phenomena, Black Sabbath, Jeff Beck, Whitesnake, Michael Schenker Group, Donovan)

JANE POWELL
53	MGM SP 1061	Something Wonderful/I Whistle A Happy Tune	4
53	MGM SP 1062	Hello, Young Lovers/We Kiss In A Shadow	4
56	HMV POP 267	True Love/Mind If I Make Love To You	6
59	MGM MGM EP 701	JANE POWELL SINGS (EP)	12
54	Capitol LC 6665	THREE SAILORS AND A GIRL (10" LP)	15
57	HMV CLP 1131	JANE POWELL (LP)	15

JIMMY POWELL (& DIMENSIONS)
62	Decca F 11447	Sugar Babe Pts 1 & 2 (solo)	5

62	Decca F 11544	Tom Hark/Dance Her By Me (solo)	5
63	Decca F 11570	Remember Them/Everyone But You (solo)	5
64	Pye 7N 15663	That's Alright/I'm Looking For A Woman	35
64	Pye 7N 15735	Sugar Babe/I've Been Watching You	15
66	Strike JH 309	I Can Go Down/Love Me Right	8
67	Decca F 12664	Unexpected Mirrors/Time Mends Broken Hearts (with Dimensions)	7
68	Decca F 12751	I Just Can't Get Over You/Real Cool (with Dimensions)	7
68	Decca F 12793	Sugar Babe Pts 1 & 2	7

KEITH POWELL (& VALETS)

63	Columbia DB 7116	The Answer Is No!/Come On And Join The Party (with Valets)	8
64	Columbia DB 7229	Tore Up/You Better Let Him Go (with Valets)	10
64	Columbia DB 7366	I Should Know Better (But I Don't)/Too Much Monkey Business (with Valets)	20
65	Piccadilly 7N 35235	People Get Ready/Paradise	5
65	Piccadilly 7N 35249	Come Home Baby/Beyond The Hill	4
66	Piccadilly 7N 35275	Goodbye Girl/It Was Easier To Hurt Her	5
66	Piccadilly 7N 35300	Victory/Some People Only	4
66	Piccadilly 7N 35353	It Keeps Rainin'/Song of The Moon	6

(see also Move, Carl Wayne & Vikings)

KEITH (POWELL) & BILLIE (DAVIES)

66	Piccadilly 7N 35288	When You Move, You Lose /Tastes Sour, Don't It? (as Keith & Billie)	5
66	Piccadilly 7N 35321	You Don't Know Like I Know/Two Little People	8
66	Piccadilly 7N 35340	Swingin' Tight/That's Really Some Good	4

(see also Keith Powell, Billie Davis)

MARILYN POWELL

64	Fontana TF 448	All My Loving/After The Party	7
69	CBS 4440	Have Another Dream On Me/Afraid To Love You	4

DUFFY POWER

59	Fontana H 194	Dream Lover/That's My Little Suzie	10
59	Fontana H 194	Dream Lover/That's My Little Suzie (78)	10
59	Fontana H 214	Kissin' Time/Ain't She Sweet	8
59	Fontana H 214	Kissin' Time/Ain't She Sweet (78)	10
59	Fontana H 230	Starry-Eyed/Prettier Than You	6
59	Fontana H 230	Starry-Eyed/Prettier Than You (78)	10
60	Fontana H 279	Whole Lotta Shakin' Goin' On/If I Can Dream	10
61	Fontana H 302	I've Got Nobody/When We're Walking Close	5
61	Fontana H 344	No Other Love/What Now	4
63	Parlophone R 4992	If I Get Lucky Someday/It Ain't Necessarily So	12
63	Parlophone R 5024	I Saw Her Standing There (with Graham Bond Quartet)/Farewell Baby	25
63	Parlophone R 5059	Hey Girl/Woman Made Trouble	6
64	Parlophone R 5111	Parchman Farm/Tired, Broke And Busted	7
64	Parlophone R 5169	I Don't Care/Where Am i?	6
67	Parlophone R 5631	Davy O'Brien (Leave That Baby Alone)/July Tree	5
70	CBS 5176	Hell Hound/Humming Bird	4
71	Epic EPC 7139	Hummingbird/Hell Bound	4
73	GSF GSZ 6	River/Little Soldiers	4
73	GSF GSZ 8	Liberation/Song About Jesus	4
71	Transatlantic TRA 229	INNOVATIONS (LP)	15
73	GSF GS 502	DUFFY POWER (LP)	15
73	Spark SRLM 2005	DUFFY POWER (LP)	15
76	BUK BULP 2010	POWERHOUSE (LP)	10

(see also Alexis Korner, John McLaughlin, Jack Bruce, Graham Bond)

POWERHOUSE

66	Decca F 12471	Chain Gang/Can You Hear Me?	15
66	Decca F 12507	Raindrops/La Bamba	6

POWERPACK

66	CBS 202335	It Hurts Me So/What You Gonna Do	20
67	CBS 202551	I'll Be Anything For You/The Lost Summer	8
69	Polydor 56311	Hannibal Brooks/Juliet Simkins	5
70	Polydor 2001 077	Oh Calcutta/Soul Searchin'	6

(see also Procol Harum)

POWER STATION

85	Parlophone RP 6091	Some Like It Hot/The Heat Is On (picture disc)	5
85	Parlophone 12 RP 6091	Some Like It Hot (Full Length Version)/The Heat Is On/Some Like It Hot (12", picture disc)	7

(see also, Duran Duran, Robert Palmer)

JETT POWERS

69	Liberty LBS 83320	CALIFORNIA LICENCE (LP)	50

(see also P.J. Proby)

JOEY POWERS

63	Stateside SS 236	Midnight Mary/Where Do You Want World Delivered	4

PEREZ 'PREZ' PRADO & HIS ORCHESTRA

54	HMV 7M 255	Skokiaan/The High And The Mighty	5
55	HMV 7M 295	Cherry Pink And Apple Blossom White/Maria Elena	8
58	RCA RCA 1067	Patricia/Why Wait	6
58	RCA RCA 1067	Patricia/Why Wait (78)	5
58	RCA RCA 1082	Guaglione/Paris	4
59	RCA RCA 1129	Tic Toc Polly Woc/My Roberta	4
60	RCA RCA 1199	Rockambo Baby/Oh, Oh, Rosie	4

PRAG VEC

78	Spec SP 001	Wolf/Cigarettes/Existential/Bits! (p/s)	4
79	Spec SP 002	Expert/The Follower! (p/s)	4

81	Spec RESPECT 1	NO COWBOYS (LP, with insert)	12

ANDY PRATT
69	Polydor 2489 003	RECORDS ARE LIKE LIFE (LP)	10

PHIL PRATT
68	Jolly JY 008	Sweet Song/THRILLERS: I'm Restless	10

PRAYING MANTIS
80	Ripper	THE SOUNDHOUSE TAPES (EP)	12
80	Gem GEMS 36	Praying Mantis/High Roller (p/s)	6
80	Harvest HAR 201	Captured City/Johnny Cool (p/s, reissue)	6
80	Arista ARIST 378	Cheated/Thirty Pieces Of Silver (p/s)	4
80	Arista ARIST 378	Cheated/Thirty Pieces Of Silver (p/s, with free single)	6
81	Arista ARIST 397	All Day And All Of The Night/Beads Of Ebony (p/s)	8
82	Jet JET 7026	Tell Me The Nightmare's Wrong/Turn The Tables (p/s)	7
81	Arista SPART 1153	TIME TELLS NO LIES (LP)	18

PREACHERS
65	Columbia DB 7680	Hole In My Soul/Too Old In The Head	35

(see also Herd, Peter Frampton, Denny Mitchel & Soundsations, Moon's Train)

PRECIOUS FEW
68	Pye 7N 17510	Young Girl/Little Children Sleep	4

PRECISIONS
67	Track 604 014	If This Is Love/You'll Soon Be Gone	10
79	Grapevine GRP 129	Such Misery/A Lovers Plea	4

PREDATOR
78	Bust SOL 2	Punk Man/Paperbag Song (with insert, no p/s)	6

PREFAB SPROUT
82	Candle CANDLE 1	Lions In My Own Garden (Exit Someone)/Radio Love (no p/s)	25
83	Kitchenware SK 4	Lions In My Own Garden (Exit Someone)/Radio Love (p/s, reissue, black labels)	10
83	Rough Trade RT 141/SK 4	Lions In My Own Garden (Exit Someone)/Radio Love (p/s, 2nd reissue)	7
84	Kitchenware SK 7	The Devil Has All The Best Tunes/Walk On (p/s)	6
84	Kitchenware SK 8	Lions In My Own Garden (Exit Someone)/Radio Love/The Devil Has All The Best Tunes/Walk On (12", p/s)	7
84	Kitchenware SK 9	Don't Sing/Green Isaac II (p/s)	4
84	Kitchenware SK 912	Don't Sing/He'll Have To Go/Green Isaac II (12", p/s)	7
84	Kitchenware SK 10	Couldn't Bear To Be Special/Spinning Belinda (p/s)	4
84	Kitchenware SK 1012	Couldn't Bear To Be Special/Spinning Belinda/Donna Summer (12", p/s)	7
84	Kitchenware SKDP 19	When Love Breaks Down/Diana//The Yearning Loins/Donna Summer (double pack, gatefold p/s)	6
84	Kitchenware SKK 19	When Love Breaks Down/The Yearning Loins/Cruel/Diana/ Donna Summer (12", p/s)	8
85	Kitchenware SKDQ 21	When Love Breaks Down/The Yearning Loins//Lions In My Own Garden/ Radio Love (shrinkwrapped double pack)	5
85	Kitchenware SKDP 21	When Love Breaks Down/The Yearning Loins//The Devil Has All The Best Tunes/Walk On (shrinkwrapped double pack)	5
85	Kitchenware SK 21	When Love Breaks Down (reissue, green/blue p/s)	4
85	Kitchenware SK 2112	When Love Breaks Down/The Yearning Loins/Spinning Belinda/ Donna Summer (12", pale green/blue p/s)	4
85	Kitchenware SK 21	When Love Breaks Down (2nd reissue, different red/black p/s & labels)	5
85	Kitchenware SKDP 22	Faron Young (Edit)/Silhouettes (Edit)//When Love Breaks Down/The Yearning Lions (shrinkwrapped double pack)	4
85	Kitchenware SKX 22	Faron Young (Truckin' Mix)/Silhouettes (Full Version) (12", p/s)	7
85	Kitchenware SKXDP 23	Appetite/Heaven Can Wait/Oh, The Swiss!/Faron Young (Truckin' Mix)/ Silhouettes (Full Length Version) (12", shrinkwrapped double pack)	7
85	Kitchenware SKD 21	When Love Breaks Down/The Yearning Lions//Spinning Belinda/ He'll Have To Go/Donna Summer (shrinkwrapped double pack)	4
86	Kitchenware SKX 24	Johnny Johnny/Wigs (shaped picture disc)	4
88	Kitchenware CDDSK 35	Cars And Girls/Faron Young (Truckin' Mix)/Real Life (Just Around The Corner) (CD, picture disc)	7
88	Kitchenware SKQ 35	Cars And Girls/Real Life (Just Around The Corner)/Vendetta (10", no'd p/s)	7
88	Kitchenware SKQ 37	King Of Rock 'N' Roll/Moving River (p/s, with foldout trivia game)	4
88	Kitchenware SKB 37	King Of Rock 'N' Roll/Moving River (box set with badges & postcards)	4

PREGNANT INSOMNIA
67	Direction 58-3132	Wallpaper/You Intrigue Me	30

PRELUDE
70s	Crotchet	PRELUDE (LP, private pressing)	40

PRELUDE
73	Dawn DNLS 3052	HOW LONG IS FOREVER (LP)	10
74	Dawn DNLS 3061	DUTCH COURAGE (LP)	10
75	Dawn DNLH 3	OWL CREEK INCIDENT (LP)	10

PREMIERS
64	Warner Bros WB 134	Farmer John/Duffy's Blues	10

PREMO & HOPETON
67	Rio RIO 139	Your Safekeep/Loving And Kind	10

PRESENCE
76	NC SLCW 1031	PRESENCE (LP)	35

PRESENCE
91	Reality LOL 1	In Wonder/Soft (p/s, withdrawn)	4
91	Reality LOLX 1	In Wonder/Soft/In Wonder (Didgeribdub Mix) (12", p/s, withdrawn)	7
91	Reality LOLCD 1	In Wonder/Soft/In Wonder (Didgeribdub Mix)/In Wonder (Millies Mix) (CD)	7

(see also Cure)

PRESIDENTS
| 64 | Decca F 11826 | Candy Man/Let The Sunshine In .... 25 |

PRESIDENTS
| 70 | A&M AMS 856 | 5-10-15-20/Triangle Of Love .... 4 |

ELVIS PRESLEY
56	HMV 7M 385	Heartbreak Hotel/I Was The One 150/100
56	HMV POP 182	Heartbreak Hotel/I Was The One (78) 15
56	HMV 7M 405	Blue Suede Shoes/Tutti Frutti 150/100
56	HMV POP 213	Blue Suede Shoes/Tutti Frutti (78) 20
56	HMV 7M 424	I Want You, I Need You, I Love You/My Baby Left Me 125/100
56	HMV POP 235	I Want You, I Need You, I Love You/My Baby Left Me (78) 15
56	HMV POP 249	Hound Dog/Don't Be Cruel 75/100
56	HMV POP 249	Hound Dog/Don't Be Cruel (78) 15
56	HMV POP 253	Love Me Tender/Anyway You Want Me (That's How I Will Be) 90/100
56	HMV POP 253	Love Me Tender/Anyway You Want Me (That's How I Will Be) (78) 15
56	HMV POP 272	Blue Moon/I Don't Care If The Sun Don't Shine 100
56	HMV POP 272	Blue Moon/I Don't Care If The Sun Don't Shine (78) 15
57	HMV POP 295	Mystery Train/Love Me 150/100
57	HMV POP 295	Mystery Train/Love Me (78) 25
57	HMV POP 305	Rip It Up/Baby, Let's Play House 150/100
57	HMV POP 305	Rip It Up/Baby, Let's Play House (78) 30
57	HMV POP 330	Too Much/Playin' For Keeps 80/75
57	HMV POP 330	Too Much/Playin' For Keeps (78) 15
57	HMV POP 359	All Shook Up/That's When Your Heartaches Begin 75/25
57	HMV POP 359	All Shook Up/That's When Your Heartaches Begin (78) 15
57	HMV POP 378	Paralyzed/When My Blue Moon Turns To Gold Again 70/50
57	HMV POP 378	Paralyzed/When My Blue Moon Turns To Gold Again (78) 15

(where two prices are given for the above 45s, the first applies to gold lettering pressings, the second to silver re-pressings)

57	HMV POP 408	Tryin' To Get To You/Lawdy, Miss Clawdy (silver lettering) 40
57	HMV POP 408	Tryin' To Get To You/Lawdy, Miss Clawdy (78) 20
57	HMV POP 428	I'm Left, You're Right, She's Gone/How Do You Think I Feel? (silver lettering) . . 50
57	HMV POP 428	I'm Left, You're Right, She's Gone/How Do You Think I Feel? (78) 15

(the below HMV singles are known export issues)

57	HMV 7MC 42	Mystery Train/I Forgot To Remember To Forget (mauve/gold label) 200
57	HMV 7MC 45	I Want You, I Need You, I Love You/My Baby Left Me (mauve/gold label) 175
57	HMV 7MC 50	Hound Dog/Don't Be Cruel (mauve label, gold lettering) 175
57	HMV JO 465	Love Me Tender/Anyway You Want Me (That's How I'll Be) (mauve/gold) 175
57	HMV JO 466	Too Much/Playin' For Keeps (mauve label, gold lettering) 175
57	HMV JO 473	All Shook Up/That's When Your Heartaches Begin (mauve/gold label) 150
57	RCA RCA 1013	Loving You/(Let Me Be Your) Teddy Bear 15
57	RCA RCA 1013	Loving You/(Let Me Be Your) Teddy Bear (78) 15
57	RCA RCA 1020	Party/Got A Lot O' Livin' To Do 12
57	RCA RCA 1020	Party/Got A Lot O' Livin' To Do (78) 15
57	RCA RCA 1025	Santa Bring My Baby Back (To Me)/Santa Claus Is Back In Town 20
57	RCA RCA 1025	Santa Bring My Baby Back (To Me)/Santa Claus Is Back In Town (78) 15
58	RCA RCA 1028	Jailhouse Rock/Treat Me Nice 12
58	RCA RCA 1028	Jailhouse Rock/Treat Me Nice (78) 15
58	RCA RCA 1043	Don't/I Beg Of You 12
58	RCA RCA 1043	Don't/I Beg Of You (78) 15
58	RCA RCA 1058	Wear My Ring (Around Your Neck)/Doncha' Think It's Time 12
58	RCA RCA 1058	Wear My Ring (Around Your Neck)/Doncha' Think It's Time (78) 15
58	RCA RCA 1070	Hard Headed Woman/Don't Ask Me Why 12
58	RCA RCA 1070	Hard Headed Woman/Don't Ask Me Why (78) 18
58	RCA RCA 1081	King Creole/Dixieland Rock 15
58	RCA RCA 1081	King Creole/Dixieland Rock (78) 18
58	RCA RCA 1088	All Shook Up/Heartbreak Hotel 25
58	RCA RCA 1088	All Shook Up/Heartbreak Hotel (78) 45
58	RCA RCA 1095	Hound Dog/Blue Suede Shoes 30
58	RCA RCA 1095	Hound Dog/Blue Suede Shoes (78) 60
59	RCA RCA 1100	One Night/I Got Stung 8
59	RCA RCA 1100	One Night/I Got Stung (78) 20
59	RCA RCA 1113	(Now And Then There's) A Fool Such As I/I Need Your Love Tonight 12
59	RCA RCA 1113	(Now And Then There's) A Fool Such As I/I Need Your Love Tonight (78) 30
59	RCA RCA 1136	A Big Hunk O' Love/My Wish Came True 12
59	RCA RCA 1136	A Big Hunk O' Love/My Wish Came True (78) 40

(all the above RCA 45s had triangular centres, later round centre pressings are worth a half to two thirds the value)

60	RCA RCA 1187	Stuck On You/Fame And Fortune 7
60	RCA RCA 1187	Stuck On You/Fame And Fortune (78) 125
60	RCA RCA 1194	A Mess Of Blues/The Girl Of My Best Friend 7
60	RCA RCA 1194	A Mess Of Blues/The Girl Of My Best Friend (78) 350
60	RCA RCA 1207	It's Now Or Never (O Sole Mio)/Make Me Know It 4
60	RCA RCA 1207	It's Now Or Never (O Sole Mio)/Make Me Know It (78, probably unissued) 800
61	RCA RCA 1216	Are You Lonesome Tonight?/I Gotta Know 4
61	RCA RCA 1226	Wooden Heart/Tonight Is So Right For Love 4
61	RCA RCA 1227	Surrender (Torna A Surriento)/Lonely Man 4
61	RCA RCA 1244	Wild In The Country/I Feel So Bad 5
61	RCA RCA 1258	(Marie's The Name) His Latest Flame/Little Sister 4
62	RCA RCA 1270	Rock-A-Hula Baby/Can't Help Falling In Love 4
62	RCA RCA 1280	Good Luck Charm/Anything That's Part Of You 4
62	RCA RCA 1303	She's Not You/Just Tell Her Jim Said Hello 4
62	RCA RCA 1320	Return To Sender/Where Do You Come From 4

(later black label pressings of the above RCA 45s on RCA Victor are worth the same as original RCA pressings)

63	RCA Victor RCA 1337	One Broken Heart For Sale/They Remind Me Too Much Of You 6
63	RCA Victor RCA 1355	(You're The) Devil In Disguise/Please Don't Drag That String Around 4
63	RCA Victor RCA 1374	Bossa Nova Baby/Witchcraft 6

Elvis PRESLEY

63	RCA Victor RCA 1375	Kiss Me Quick/Something Blue	6
64	RCA Victor RCA 1390	Viva Las Vegas/What'd I Say	6
64	RCA Victor RCA 1404	Kissin' Cousins/It Hurts Me	5
64	RCA Victor RCA 1411	Such A Night/Never Ending	7
64	RCA Victor RCA 1422	Ain't That Loving You Baby/Ask Me	5
64	RCA Victor RCA 1430	Blue Christmas/White Christmas	5
65	RCA Victor RCA 1443	Do The Clam/You'll Be Gone	6
65	RCA Victor RCA 1455	Crying In The Chapel/I Believe In The Man In The Sky	4
65	RCA Victor RCA 1489	Tell Me Why/Puppet On A String	8
66	RCA Victor RCA 1504	Blue River/Do Not Disturb	6
66	RCA Victor RCA 1509	Frankie And Johnny/Please Don't Stop Loving Me	7
66	RCA Victor RCA 1526	Love Letters/Come What May	5
66	RCA Victor RCA 1545	All That I Am/Spinout	6
66	RCA Victor RCA 1557	If Every Day Was Like Christmas/How Would You Like To Be?	5
67	RCA Victor RCA 1565	Indescribably Blue/Fools Fall In Love	7
67	RCA Victor RCA 1593	The Love Machine/You Gotta Stop	8
67	RCA Victor RCA 1616	Long-Legged Girl (With The Short Dress On)/That's Someone You Never Forget	8
67	RCA Victor RCA 1628	There's Always Me/Judy	25
67	RCA Victor RCA 1642	Big Boss Man/You Don't Know Me	8
68	RCA Victor RCA 1663	Guitar Man/Hi-Heel Sneakers	5
68	RCA Victor RCA 1688	U.S. Male/Stay Away	5
68	RCA Victor RCA 1714	Your Time Hasn't Come Yet Baby/Let Yourself Go	6
68	RCA Victor RCA 1747	You'll Never Walk Alone/We Call On Him	8
68	RCA Victor RCA 1768	A Little Less Conversation/Almost In Love	8

(the above RCA singles originally came with black labels, orange label reissues are worth £3-£5)

69	RCA RCA 1795	If I Can Dream/Memories	7
69	RCA RCA 1831	In The Ghetto/Any Day Now	5
69	RCA RCA 1869	Clean Up Your Own Backyard/The Fair's Moving On	5
69	RCA RCA 1900	Suspicious Minds/You'll Think Of Me (p/s)	6
70	RCA RCA 1916	Don't Cry Daddy/Rubberneckin' (p/s)	6
70	RCA RCA 1949	Kentucky Rain/My Little Friend (p/s)	5
70	RCA RCA 1974	The Wonder Of You/Mama Liked The Roses	4
70	RCA RCA 1999	I've Lost You/The Next Step Is Love	5
71	RCA RCA 2046	You Don't Have To Say You Love Me/Patch It Up	4
71	RCA RCA 2060	There Goes My Everything/I Really Don't Want To Know (p/s)	6
71	RCA RCA 2084	Rags To Riches/Where Did They Go, Lord (p/s)	6
71	RCA MAXI 2104	Heartbreak Hotel/Hound Dog/Don't Be Cruel (reissue)	5
71	RCA RCA 2125	I'm Leavin'/Heart Of Rome	5
71	RCA MAXI 2153	Jailhouse Rock/Are You Lonesome Tonight?/(Let Me Be Your) Teddy Bear/ Steadfast, Loyal And True (reissue)	7
71	RCA RCA 2158	I Just Can't Help Believin'/How The Web Was Woven	4
72	RCA RCA 2188	Until It's Time For You To Go/We Can Make The Morning (p/s)	6
72	RCA RCA 2229	American Trilogy/First Time Ever I Saw Your Face	4
72	RCA RCA 2267	Burning Love/It's A Matter Of Time	4
72	RCA RCA 2304	Always On My Mind/Separate Ways	4
73	RCA RCA 2359	Polk Salad Annie/See See Rider	4
73	RCA RCA 2393	Fool/Steamroller Blues	4
73	RCA RCA 2435	Raised On Rock/For Ol' Times Sake	4
74	RCA APBO 0196	Take Good Care Of Her/I've Got A Thing About You (withdrawn)	150
74	RCA APBO 0280	If You Talk In Your Sleep/Help Me	5
74	RCA RCA 2458	My Boy/Loving Arms	4
74	RCA PB 10074	Promised Land/It's Midnight	4
75	RCA RCA 2562	T-R-O-U-B-L-E/Mr. Songman	4
75	RCA MAXI 2601	Blue Moon/You're A Heartbreaker/I'm Left, You're Right, She's Gone (reissue)	8
75	RCA RCA 2635	Green Green Grass Of Home/Thinking About You	4
76	RCA RCA 2674	Hurt/For The Heart	4
78	RCA RCA 9265	Don't Be Cruel/Hound Dog (p/s)	4
78	RCA PB 9334	Old Shep/Paralysed (p/s)	4
80	RCA RCA 4	It's Only Love/Beyond The Reef (p/s)	4
80	RCA RCA 16	Santa Claus Is Back In Town/I Believe (p/s)	4
82	RCA RCA 196	Are You Lonesome Tonight? (Laughing Version)/From A Jack To A King (p/s)	4
82	RCA RCAP 232	The Sound Of Your Cry/I'll Never Know (picture disc)	5
83	RCA RCAP 1028	Jailhouse Rock/The Elvis Medley (reissue, picture disc)	5
83	RCA RCAP 1028	Jailhouse Rock/The Elvis Medley (reissue, picture disc, with "Hound Dog" credit)	8
83	RCA RCAP 332	(You're So Square) Baby, I Don't Care/One-Sided Love Affair/Tutti Frutti (picture disc)	5
83	RCA RCA 369	I Can Help/The Lady Loves Me (p/s)	4
83	RCA RCAP 369	I Can Help/If Every Day Was Like Christmas/The Lady Loves Me (10", picture disc)	6
83	RCA RCA 369	I Can Help/If Every Day Was Like Christmas/The Lady Loves Me (10", p/s)	8
84	RCA RCA 405	Green Green Grass Of Home/Release Me (And Let Me Love Again)/ Solitaire (p/s with free poster)	4
84	RCA RCA 459	The Last Farewell/It's Easy for You (p/s)	4
85	RCA RCA 476	The Elvis Medley/Blue Suede Shoes (p/s)	4
85	RCA PB 49943	Always On My Mind (Alternate Version)/Tomorrow Night (p/s)	4
87	RCA ARON 1	Ain't That Loving You Baby/Bossa Nova Baby (p/s)	4
57	Weekend Mail	THE TRUTH ABOUT ME (6" 78, mail order only, some in envelope)	100/70
75	Reader's Digest/RCA RD ELV 785/65	BRIAN MATTHEW INTRODUCES EXCERPTS FROM ELVIS PRESLEY'S GREATEST HITS (6" flexidisc, some with newsletter & advertising leaflet)	7/5
79	RCA LB 1	The Wonder Of You/Noel Edmonds Introduces Record Year (Lever Brothers premium)	6
83	Buttons BUT 3	A.F.N. RADIO INTERVIEW (p/s, fan club interview flexidisc)	4
83	Buttons BUT 4	NEW YORK PRESS CONFERENCE (orange fan club interview flexidisc, free with 'Elvis Monthly Collector's Special' issue 2)	4
83	Buttons BUT 5	INTERVIEW BETWEEN ELVIS, PETER NOONE AND TOM MOFFETT (fan club interview flexidisc free with 'Elvis Monthly Collector's Special' issue 4)	4

84	Buttons BUT 6	GERMAN RADIO INTERVIEW (fan club interview flexidisc free with 'Elvis Monthly Collector's Special' issue 6)	4
84	Buttons BUT 7	ELVIS' 1964 GREETING TO HIS BRITISH FANS/THE TRUTH ABOUT ME (fan club interview flexi with 'Elvis Monthly Collector's Special' issue 8)	4
85	Buttons BUT 8	1956 NEW ORLEANS INTERVIEW (fan club interview flexidisc free with 'Elvis Monthly Collector's Special' issue 10)	4
85	Buttons BUT 9	JACKSON, FLORIDA 1955 INTERVIEW/MEMPHIS 1957 INTERVIEW (fan club interview flexidisc free with 'Elvis Monthly Collector's Special' issue 10)	5/4
77	RCA Victor 2694-2709	"GOLD 16" SERIES (16 x p/s 7" in foldout cardboard carrier)	35
81	Ace NS 71	Conference 1957/DEKE RIVERS: Elvis Medley (picture disc)	5
56	HMV 7EG 8199	LOVE ME TENDER (EP)	80
57	RCA RCX 101	PEACE IN THE VALLEY (EP)	25
57	HMV 7EG 8256	GOOD ROCKIN' TONIGHT (EP, title on sleeve only)	90
57	RCA RCX 104	ELVIS PRESLEY (EP)	20
58	RCA RCX 106	JAILHOUSE ROCK (EP)	14
58	RCA RCX 117	KING CREOLE VOL. 1 (EP, black label)	16
58	RCA RCX 117	KING CREOLE VOL. 1 (EP, orange label, with different take of "Lover Doll")	10
58	RCA RCX 118	KING CREOLE VOL. 2 (EP)	14
58	RCA RCX 121	ELVIS SINGS CHRISTMAS SONGS (EP, 1st issue, single sleeve)	25
58	RCA RCX 121	ELVIS SINGS CHRISTMAS SONGS (EP, 2nd issue, round centre, gatefold p/s)	70
58	RCA RCX 131	ELVIS SAILS (EP, interview record)	20
59	RCA RCX 135	ELVIS IN TENDER MOOD (EP)	20
59	RCA RCX 1045	A TOUCH OF GOLD (EP)	18
60	RCA RCX 175	STRICTLY ELVIS (EP)	15
60	RCA RCX 1048	A TOUCH OF GOLD VOL. 2 (EP)	30

(the above RCA EPs originally had triangular centres, later round centre pressings are worth around two thirds the value)

60	RCA RCX 190	SUCH A NIGHT (EP)	15
62	RCA RCX 211	FOLLOW THAT DREAM (EP)	10
62	RCA RCX 211	FOLLOW THAT DREAM (EP, mispressing, 2nd side features Jim Reeves)	100
62	RCA RCX 7109	KID GALAHAD (EP)	12

(later RCA Victor pressings of the above EPs are worth the same value as RCA round centre pressings)

64	RCA RCX 7141	LOVE IN LAS VEGAS (EP)	15
64	RCA RCX 7142	ELVIS FOR YOU VOL. 1 (EP)	30
64	RCA RCX 7143	ELVIS FOR YOU VOL. 2 (EP)	30
65	RCA RCX 7173	TICKLE ME (EP)	14
65	RCA RCX 7174	TICKLE ME VOL. 2 (EP)	15
67	RCA RCX 7187	EASY COME, EASY GO (EP)	30

(all the RCA EPs originally came with black labels, later orange label pressings are worth around half the value)

82	RCA EP 1	THE EP COLLECTION (11-EP box set, reissues, with booklet)	50
82	RCA RCX 1	G.I. BLUES: THE ALTERNATE TAKES (EP)	12
82	RCA RCX 2	G.I. BLUES: THE ALTERNATE TAKES VOLUME TWO (EP)	10
82	RCA RCX 7191	LOVE ME TENDER (mail order-only EP, silver-plated, framed 25th Anniversary edition, Fan Club issue)	50+
83	RCA EP 2	THE EP COLLECTION VOL. 2 (11-EP box set, reissues, with booklet)	50
83	RCA RCX 3	COLLECTORS' GOLD (EP)	10
56	HMV CLP 1093	ROCK 'N' ROLL (LP)	200
57	HMV CLP 1105	ROCK 'N' ROLL NO. 2 (LP)	200
57	RCA RC 24001	LOVING YOU (10" LP, 'silver spot' label, later issues credit RCA Victor)	50/35
57	HMV DLP 1159	THE BEST OF ELVIS (10" LP)	200
57	RCA RD 27052	ELVIS' CHRISTMAS ALBUM (LP, laminated front & back covers)	70
58	RCA RD 27088	KING CREOLE (LP)	35
58	RCA RD 16069	ELVIS' GOLDEN RECORDS (LP, 'red seal' label, gatefold sleeve with 4-page photo booklet; later pressings have 2 pages of photos)	60/40
59	RCA RD 27120	ELVIS (LP)	40
59	RCA RD 27128	A DATE WITH ELVIS (LP)	40
59	RCA RD 27159	ELVIS' GOLDEN RECORDS VOL. 2 (LP)	30
60	RCA RD 27171/SF 5060	ELVIS IS BACK! (LP, mono/stereo, gatefold sleeve)	22/35
60	RCA RD 27192/SF 5078	G.I. BLUES (LP, mono/stereo)	15/30
61	RCA RD 27211/SF 5094	HIS HAND IN MINE (LP, mono/stereo)	22/30
61	RCA RD 27224/SF 5106	SOMETHING FOR EVERYBODY (LP, mono/stereo)	16/35
61	RCA RD 27238/SF 5115	BLUE HAWAII (LP, mono/stereo)	15/25
62	RCA RD 27265/SF 5135	POT LUCK (LP, mono/stereo)	16/22

(later RCA Victor black/silver label pressings of the above LPs are worth two thirds to the same value as originals)

62	RCA Victor RD/SF 7528	ROCK 'N' ROLL NO. 2 (LP, reissue, mono/stereo)	16/22
63	RCA Victor RD/SF 7534	GIRLS! GIRLS! GIRLS! (LP, mono/stereo)	15/20
63	RCA Victor RD/SF 7565	IT HAPPENED AT THE WORLD'S FAIR (LP, mono/stereo)	15/20
63	RCA Victor RD/SF 7609	FUN IN ACAPULCO (LP, mono/stereo)	15/20

(all the above RCA LPs had black/silver labels, RCA Victor reissues with black/red dot labels are worth two thirds the value)

64	RCA Victor RD/SF 7630	ELVIS' GOLDEN RECORDS VOL. 3 (LP, mono/stereo)	15/20
64	RCA Victor RD/SF 7645	KISSIN' COUSINS (LP, mono/stereo)	15/20
64	RCA Victor RD/SF 7678	ROUSTABOUT (LP, mono/stereo)	15/20
65	RCA Victor RD/SF 7714	GIRL HAPPY (LP, mono/stereo)	15/20
65	RCA Victor RD 7723	FLAMING STAR AND SUMMER KISSES (LP, black or orange label)	50/60
65	RCA Victor RD/SF 7752	ELVIS FOR EVERYONE (LP, mono/stereo)	15/20
65	RCA Victor RD/SF 7767	HAREM HOLIDAY (LP, mono/stereo)	15/20
66	RCA Victor RD/SF 7793	FRANKIE AND JOHNNY (LP, mono/stereo)	15/20
66	RCA Victor RD/SF 7810	PARADISE, HAWAIIAN STYLE (LP, mono/stereo)	15/18
66	RCA Victor RD/SF 7820	CALIFORNIA HOLIDAY (LP, mono/stereo)	17/22
67	RCA Victor RD/SF 7867	HOW GREAT THOU ART (LP, mono/stereo)	20/22
67	RCA Victor RD/SF 7892	DOUBLE TROUBLE (LP, mono/stereo)	15/18
68	RCA Victor RD/SF 7917	CLAMBAKE (LP, mono/stereo)	15/18
68	RCA Victor RD/SF 7924	ELVIS' GOLD RECORDS VOLUME 4 (LP, with "Never Ending" listed on sleeve instead of "Love Letters"; mono/stereo)	22/25
68	RCA Victor RD/SF 7924	ELVIS' GOLD RECORDS VOLUME 4 (LP, mono/stereo)	18/20
68	RCA Victor RD/SF 7957	SPEEDWAY (LP, soundtrack with Nancy Sinatra, mono/stereo)	18/25

(the above RCA Victor LPs originally came with black/red dot labels, later orange label pressings are worth up to half the value)

MINT VALUE £

69	RCA Victor RD 8011	ELVIS (LP, "TV Special" Soundtrack) 12
69	RCA Intl. INTS 1012	ELVIS SINGS FLAMING STAR (LP) 10
69	RCA Victor RD/SF 8029	FROM ELVIS IN MEMPHIS (LP, mono/stereo) 15/12
70	RCA Victor SF 8080/1	FROM MEMPHIS TO VEGAS — FROM VEGAS TO MEMPHIS
		(2-LP, some with 2 10" x 8" photos) 20/15
70	RCA Intl. INTS 1103	LET'S BE FRIENDS (LP) 10
70	RCA SF 8128	ON STAGE, FEBRUARY 1970 (LP) 12
70	RCA LPM 6401	TOUCH OF GOLD — WORLDWIDE 50 GOLD AWARD HITS VOL. 1
		(4-LP box set with photo book) 30
71	RCA LPM 6402	OTHER SIDES — WORLDWIDE 50 GOLD AWARD HITS VOL. 2
		(4-LP box with material patch & colour portrait) 30
71	RCA Victor SF 8162	THAT'S THE WAY IT IS (LP) 10
71	RCA Victor SF 8202	LOVE LETTERS FROM ELVIS (LP) 12
71	RCA Victor SF 8221	ELVIS SINGS THE WONDERFUL WORLD OF CHRISTMAS (LP) 12
72	RCA Victor SF 8266	ELVIS NOW (LP) 12
72	RCA Victor SF 8275	HE TOUCHED ME (LP) 12
73	RCA Victor SF 8378	ELVIS (LP) 12
73	RCA DPS 2040	ALOHA FROM HAWAII VIA SATELLITE (2-LP) 14
73	RCA R4P 5035	ALOHA FROM HAWAII (2-LP, quadrophonic) 25
73	RCA APL1 0388	RAISED ON ROCK (LP, U.K. pressing in U.S. sleeve) 150
74	RCA APL1 0475	GOOD TIMES (LP) 12
74	RCA APL1 0606	ELVIS AS RECORDED ON STAGE IN MEMPHIS (LP) 10
74	RCA LPL1 7527	HITS OF THE 70s (LP) 10
75	RCA APM1 0818	HAVING FUN WITH ELVIS ON STAGE (LP) 14
75	RCA RS 1011	TODAY (LP) 10
75	R. Digest RDS 9001/6	ELVIS PRESLEY'S GREATEST HITS (7-LP, original box set in thick card) 35
76	RCA RS 1060	FROM ELVIS PRESLEY BOULEVARD, MEMPHIS, TENNESSEE (LP) 10
77	RCA PL 42691	40 GREATEST (2-LP, gatefold sleeve, pink vinyl with booklet) 15
78	RCA CPL1 3078	ELVIS — A LEGENDARY PERFORMER VOL. 2 (LP, picture disc) 10
78	Marks/Spencer IMP 113	ELVIS (LP) 30
78	Marks/Spencer IMPD 204	THE WONDERFUL WORLD OF ELVIS PRESLEY 2-LP) 45
79	Golden First KING 1	THE FIRST YEAR (LP) 10
79	Hammer HMR 6002	THE KING SPEAKS (LP) 10
80	RCA CPL8 3699	ELVIS ARON PRESLEY (8-LP box set) 40
83	RCA RCALPP 9020	JAILHOUSE ROCK/LOVE IN LAS VEGAS (LP, picture disc) 10
84	RCA PLP 89287	I CAN HELP (LP, picture disc) 10
84	Imperial Records DR 1124	AMERICAN TRIOLOGY (3-LP box set) 20
84	RCA PD 89061/2/3	THE LEGEND (3-CD, box set of 3 gold discs, 5,000 only,
		with booklet, numbered) 180
84	RCA PD 89061/2/3	THE LEGEND (3-CD, box set of 3 silver discs, 5,000 only,
		with booklet, numbered) 50
84	RCA PL 85172	A GOLDEN CELEBRATION (6-LP box set with inserts) 25
80s	RCA PL 42358	LOVING YOU (LP, mail-order only, gold-plated commemorative edition,
		500 only, framed, Fan Club issue) ....100+
80s	RCA NE 1062	LOVE SONGS (LP, mail-order only, gold-plated commemorative edition,
		200 only, framed and numbered, Fan Club issue) ....120+

(see also Jordanaires)

REG PRESLEY

| 69 | Page One POF 131 | Lucinda Lee/Wichita Lineman ....4 |
| 73 | CBS 1478 | 'S Down To You Marianne/Hey Little Girl ....4 |

(see also Troggs)

PRESSURE GROUP

| 80s | Kirple KIRP 1 | EDHEARING (cassette) ....10 |

BILLY PRESTON

66	Sue WI 4012	Billy's Bag/Don't Let The Sun Catch You Crying 10
66	Capitol CL 15458	In The Midnight Hour/Advice 6
66	Capitol CL 15471	Sunny/Let The Music Play 6
69	President PT 263	Billy's Bag/Don't Let The Sun Catch You Cyring 6
69	President PT 298	If I Had A Hammer 4
69	Apple APPLE 12	That's The Way God Planned It/What About You (p/s) 10
69	Apple APPLE 19	Everything's Alright/I Want To Thank You (company sleeve) 5
70	Soul City SC 107	Greazee Pts 1 & 2 10
70	Apple APPLE 21	All That I've Got/As I Get Older (some in p/s) 20/6
70	Apple APPLE 29	My Sweet Lord/Long As I Got My Baby (unreleased)
73	A&M AMS 7049	Will It Go Round In Circles/Blackbird 4
75	A&M AMS 7198	Fancy Lady/Song Of Joy 4
67	Capitol (S)T 2532	THE WILDEST ORGAN IN TOWN (LP) 12
67	Sue ILP 935	THE MOST EXCITING ORGAN EVER (LP) 30
69	Apple SAPCOR 9	THAT'S THE WAY GOD PLANNED IT (LP) 18
70	Apple SAPCOR 14	ENCOURAGING WORDS (LP) 25
70	Soul City SCM 002	GREAZEE SOUL (LP) 10

(see also Beatles with Billy Preston)

EARL PRESTON

| 63 | Fontana TF 406 | I Know Something/Watch Your Step (with T.T.'s) ....8 |
| 64 | Fontana TF 481 | Raindrops/That's For Sure (with Realms) ....7 |

(see also Realm)

JOHNNY PRESTON

60	Mercury AMT 1079	Running Bear/My Heart Knows 6
60	Mercury AMT 1079	Running Bear/My Heart Knows (78) 40
60	Mercury AMT 1092	Cradle Of Love/City Of Tears 6
60	Mercury AMT 1092	Cradle Of Love/City Of Tears (78) 50
60	Mercury AMT 1104	Feel So Fine/I'm Starting To Go Steady 8
60	Mercury AMT 1114	Charming Billy/Up In The Air 6
61	Mercury AMT 1129	Leave My Kitten Alone/Do What You Did 12

MINT VALUE £

61	Mercury AMT 1145	Big Chief Heartache/Madre De Dios (Mother Of God)	6
61	Mercury AMT 1164	New Baby For Christmas/Rock And Roll Guitar	8
61	Mercury AMT 1167	Free Me/Kissing Tree	6
60	Mercury ZEP 10078	RUNNING BEAR (EP)	30
60	Mercury ZEP 10098	RING TAIL TOOTER (EP)	45
61	Mercury ZEP 10116	TOKEN OF LOVE (EP)	50
60	Mercury MMC 14051	JOHNNY PRESTON — RUNNING BEAR (LP)	60

MIKE PRESTON

58	Decca F 11053	My Lucky Love/A House, A Car And A Wedding Ring	7
58	Decca F 11087	Why, Why, Why/Whispering Grass	6
59	Decca F 11120	In Surabaya/Dirty Old Town	6
59	Decca F 11167	Mr. Blue/Just Ask Your Heart	6
60	Decca F 11222	A Girl Like You/Too Old	6
60	Decca F 11255	I'd Do Anything/Where Is Love?	6
60	Decca F 11287	Togetherness/Farewell My Love	6
60	Decca DFE 6635	FOUR SONGS BY RAY NOBLE (EP)	10
61	Decca DFE 6679	MARRY ME (EP)	10

PRETENDERS

79	Real ARE 9	Kid/Tattooed Love Boys/Stop Your Sobbing (cassette)	4
80	Real ARE 12	Talk Of The Town/DETROIT SPINNERS track (mispress)	4
80	Real ARE 12	Talk Of The Town/Cuban Slide (cassette)	4
83	Real ARE 20F	2000 Miles/Fast Or Slow (Christmas card fold-out sleeve)	4
81	Lyntone LYN 9650	Whatcha Gonna Do About It/Stop Your Sobbin' (orange flexidisc with 'Flexipop' issue 6)	5/4

PRETTY BOY FLOYD & GEMS

| 79 | Rip Off RIP OFF 1 | Spread The Word/Hold Tight (p/s) | 4 |

(BERNARD) PRETTY PURDIE

68	Direction 58-3301	Funky Donkey/Caravan	5
68	Direction 58-3628	Soul Clappin'/Blow Your Lid	5
71	Philips 6073 708	Good Livin' Good Lovin'/Day Dreaming	4
68	Direction 8-63290	SOUL DRUMS (LP)	35
71	Philips 6369 421	SOUL IS ... (LP)	10

PRETTY THINGS

64	Fontana TF 469	Rosalyn/Big Boss Man	10
64	Fontana TF 503	Don't Bring Me Down/We'll Be Together	6
65	Fontana TF 537	Honey I Need/I Can Never Say	6
65	Fontana TF 585	Cry To Me/Get A Buzz	6
65	Fontana TF 647	Midnight To Six Man/Can't Stand The Pain	8
66	Fontana TF 688	Come See Me/£.s.d.	8
66	Fontana TF 722	A House In The Country/Me Needing You	8
66	Fontana TF 773	Progress/Buzz The Jerk	8
67	Fontana TF 829	Children/My Time	10
67	Columbia DB 8300	Defecting Grey/Mr. Evasion	15
68	Columbia DB 8353	Talkin' About The Good Times/Walking Through My Dreams	20
68	Columbia DB 8494	Private Sorrow/Balloon Burning	15
69	Fontana TF 1024	Rosalyn/Don't Bring Me Down	4
70	Harvest HAR 5016	The Good Mr Square/Blue Serge Blues	7
70	Harvest HAR 5031	October 26/Cold Stone	6
71	Harvest HAR 5037	Stone-Hearted Mama/Summertime/Circus Mind	6
64	Fontana TE 17434	THE PRETTY THINGS (EP)	20
65	Fontana TE 17442	RAININ' IN MY HEART (EP)	20
66	Fontana TE 17472	ON FILM (EP)	70
65	Fontana TL 5239	THE PRETTY THINGS (LP)	35
65	Fontana TL 5280	GET THE PICTURE (LP)	40
67	Wing WL 1164	BEST OF THE PRETTY THINGS (LP)	20
67	Fontana (S)TL 5425	EMOTIONS (LP)	25
67	Wing WL 1167	THE PRETTY THINGS (LP, stereo reissue)	15
68	Columbia SCX 6306	S.F. SORROW (LP, gatefold sleeve; blue/black, later white/black label)	25/10
70	Harvest SHVL 774	PARACHUTE (LP, gatefold sleeve)	18
72	Warner Bros K 46190	FREEWAY MADNESS (LP)	10
74	Swan Song SSK 59400	SILK TORPEDO (LP, gatefold sleeve with inner)	10
75	Harvest SHDW 406	S.F. SORROW/PARACHUTE (2-LP)	14
75	Swan Song SSL 59401	SAVAGE EYE (LP, gatefold sleeve with inner)	10
77	Harvest SHSM 2022	THE SINGLES A's & B's (LP)	10
82	GI WAX 6	PARACHUTE (LP, reissue, 1,000 only)	10

(see also Electric Banana, Twink, Viv Prince)

EDDIE PREVOST BAND

| 78 | Matchless MR 1 | LIVE VOLUME 1 (LP, private pressing) | 15 |

(see also Amm)

JOEL PREVOST

| 78 | CBS SCBS 6300 | Somewhere Sometime/Il Y Aura Toujours Des Violins | 10 |

ALAN PRICE (SET)

65	Decca F 12217	Any Day Now (My Wild Beautiful Baby)/Never Be Sick On Sunday	4
66	Decca F 12367	I Put A Spell On You/Iechyd-Da	4
66	Decca F 12442	Hi-Lili, Hi-Lo/Take Me Home	4
66	Decca F 12518	Willow Weep For Me/Yours Until Tomorrow	4
67	Decca F 12570	Simon Smith And His Amazing Dancing Bear/Tickle Me	4
67	Decca F 12641	The House That Jack Built/Who Cares	4
67	Decca F 12691	Shame/Don't Do That Again	4
68	Decca F 12731	Don't Stop The Carnival/The Time Has Come	4
68	Decca F 12774	When I Was A Cowboy/Tappy Turquoise (export issue)	6
68	Decca F 12808	Love Story/My Old Kentucky Home	4

Alan PRICE (SET)

70	Decca F 13017	Sunshine And Rain/Is There Anybody Out There? (solo)	4
78	Jet UP 36358	Just For You/I'm A Gambler (heart-shaped red vinyl, p/s)	4
67	Decca DFE 8677	THE AMAZING ALAN PRICE (EP)	12
66	Decca LK 4839	THE PRICE TO PLAY (LP)	18
67	Decca LK/SKL 4907	A PRICE ON HIS HEAD (LP)	10

(see also Animals, Paul Williams Set)

KENNY PRICE

| 66 | Stateside SS 554 | Walking On New Grass/Wasting My Time | 4 |

LLOYD PRICE (ORCHESTRA)

57	London HL 8438	Just Because/Why	60
57	London HL 8438	Just Because/Why (78)	18
59	HMV POP 580	Stagger Lee/You Need Love	8
59	HMV POP 580	Stagger Lee/You Need Love (78)	25
59	HMV POP 598	Where Were You (On Our Wedding Day)?/Is It Really Love?	6
59	HMV POP 598	Where Were You (On Our Wedding Day)?/Is It Really Love? (78)	25
59	HMV POP 626	Personality/Have You Ever Had The Blues?	6
59	HMV POP 626	Personality/Have You Ever Had The Blues? (78)	25
59	HMV POP 650	I'm Gonna Get Married/Three Little Pigs	6
59	HMV POP 650	I'm Gonna Get Married/Three Little Pigs (78)	25
59	HMV POP 672	Won'tcha Come Home/Come Into My Heart	6
59	HMV POP 672	Won'tcha Come Home/Come Into My Heart (78)	30
60	HMV POP 712	Lady Luck/Never Let Me Go	6
60	HMV POP 712	Lady Luck/Never Let Me Go (78)	35
60	HMV POP 741	For Love/No If's — No And's	6
60	HMV POP 772	Question/If I Look A Little Blue (as Lloyd Price Orchestra)	7
60	HMV POP 772	Question/If I Look A Little Blue (as Lloyd Price Orchestra) (78)	50
60	HMV POP 799	Just Call Me (And I'll Understand)/Who Coulda' Told You (They Lied)	7
61	HMV POP 826	Know What You're Doin'/That's Why Tears Come And Go (as Lloyd Price Orchestra)	7
61	HMV POP 926	Boo Hoo/I Made You Cry	7
62	HMV POP 983	Be A Leader/'Nother Fairy Tale	6
62	HMV POP 1100	Under Your Spell, Again/Happy Birthday Mama	6
73	GSF GSZ 5	Love Music/Just For Baby	6
73	GSF GSZ 11	Trying To Slip Away/They Get Down	4
59	HMV 7EG 8538/GES 5784	THE EXCITING LLOYD PRICE (EP, mono/stereo)	30/40
59	HMV CLP 1285	THE EXCITING LLOYD PRICE (LP)	30
59	HMV CLP 1314	MR. PERSONALITY (LP)	30
60	London HA-U 2213	LLOYD PRICE (LP)	35
60	HMV CLP 1361	MR. PERSONALITY SINGS THE BLUES (LP)	25
60	HMV CLP 1393	THE FANTASTIC LLOYD PRICE (LP, also stereo CSD 1323)	20/30
62	HMV CLP 1519	COOKIN' (LP, also stereo CSD 1413)	20/35
63	Encore ENC 2004	PRICE SINGS THE MILLION DOLLAR SELLERS (LP)	15
69	Major Minor SMLP 57	LLOYD PRICE NOW (LP)	15
71	Joy JOYS 202	STAGGER LEE (LP)	10

MALCOLM PRICE (TRIO)

60s	Oak RGJ 106	PICKIN' ON THE COUNTRY STRINGS! (EP)	20
64	Decca LK 4627	COUNTRY SESSION (LP, as Malcolm Price Trio)	10
65	Decca LK 4665	WAY DOWN TOWN (LP)	10
60s	Saga	HIS SONGS, HIS GUITARS (LP)	10
75	Sweet Folk & C. SFA 017	THEN WE ALL GOT UP AND WALKED AWAY (LP)	10

RAY PRICE

| 57 | Philips BBE 12137 | RAY PRICE (EP) | 12 |

(ROCKIN') RED PRICE

56	Decca F 10822	Rocky Mountain Gal/Rock O' The North (as Red Price & His Rockin' Rhythm)	6
58	Pye 7N 15169	Weekend/The Sneeze	6
60	Pye 7N 15262	Wow!/My Baby's Door	6
61	Parlophone R 4789	Theme From "Danger Man"/Blackjack (as Red Price Combo)	10

(see also Cherry Wainer)

RED PRICE & BLUE BEATS

| 64 | Blue Beat BB 209 | Blue Beats Over/Kiss The Baby | 7 |

RICK PRICE

70	Gemini GMS 012	Davey Has No Dad/Bitter Sweet	4
70	Gemini GME 1002	THIS IS TO CERTIFY THAT (LP, as Rick Price & Gemini)	15
71	Gemini GME 1017	TALKING TO THE FLOWERS (LP)	12

(see also Move, Sheridan-Price)

RIKKI PRICE

58	Fontana H 162	Tom Dooley/(It Looks Like Rain In) Cherry Blossom Lane	4
59	Fontana H 171	Honey, Honey/The Very Thought Of You	4
59	Fontana H 217	Mr. Blue/Man On My Trail	4
62	Fontana H 371	You're For Real/When You Pass By	4
58	Fontana TFE 17100	RIKKI PRICE (EP)	10

(see also Sheridan-Price)

SAMMY PRICE

60s	Storyville A45 068	Boogieing With Big Sid/133 Street Boogie	20
57	Columbia SEG 7679	ORIGINAL SAMMY BLUES (EP)	10
58	Vogue EPV 1146	SAMMY PRICE (EP)	30
58	Vogue EPV 1151	SAMMY PRICE'S BLUESICIANS (EP)	30
50s	Vogue LAE 12027	SWINGIN' PARIS STYLE (LP)	20
62	London Jazz LTZ-R 15240	THE BLUES AIN'T NOTHIN' (LP, also stereo SAH-R 6234)	20/25

VINCENT PRICE

| 59 | Columbia 33SX 1141 | VINCENT PRICE (LP) | 10 |

CHARLEY PRIDE
69	RCA RCA 1796	The Little Folks/Kaw Liga	4
68	RCA RD 7966	MAKE MINE COUNTRY (LP)	10

DICKIE PRIDE
59	Columbia DB 4283	Slippin' 'N' Slidin'/Don't Make Me Love You	25
59	Columbia DB 4296	Midnight Oil/Fabulous Cure	12
59	Columbia DB 4340	Frantic/Primrose Lane	18
60	Columbia DB 4403	Betty, Betty (Go Steady With Me)/No John	10
60	Columbia DB 4451	You're Singin' Our Love Song To Somebody Else/Bye Bye Blackbird	6
59	Columbia SEG 7937	SHEIK OF SHAKE (EP)	100
61	Columbia 33SX 1307	PRIDE WITHOUT PREJUDICE (LP, also stereo SCX 3369)	80/100

(see also Guvners)

LOUIS PRIMA (& HIS ORCHESTRA)
54	Brunswick 05314	The Happy Wanderer/LOUIS PRIMA & KEELY SMITH: Until Sunrise (78)	5
56	Capitol CL 14669	5 Months, 2 Weeks, 2 Days/Banana Split For My Baby	25
56	Capitol CL 14669	5 Months, 2 Weeks, 2 Days/Banana Split For My Baby (78)	5
58	Capitol CL 14821	Buona Sera/Beep! Beep!	12
58	Capitol CL 14821	Buona Sera/Beep! Beep! (78)	8
60	London HLD 9230	Ol' Man Moses (with Sam Butera's Witnesses)/Wonderland By Night	8
60	London HLD 9230	Ol' Man Moses (with Sam Butera's Witnesses)/Wonderland By Night (78)	5
64	Prima PR 1001	Fee Fie Fo O Pts 1 & 2	4
64	Prima PR 1006	Spoonful Of Sugar/Stay Awake	4
64	Prima PR 1009	Robin Hood/Angelina	4
59	Capitol EAP1 1132	STRICTLY PRIMA (EP)	8
57	Capitol T 755	THE WILDEST (LP)	20
58	Capitol T 836	THE CALL OF THE WILDWEST (LP)	15
58	Capitol T 1010	LAS VEGAS PRIMA STYLE (LP)	15
62	Ember EMB 3348	LOUIS PRIMA SWINGS (LP)	12
60s	Dot GTL 0287	HIS GREATEST HITS (LP)	10

(see also Sam Butera's Witnesses)

LOUIS PRIMA & KEELY SMITH
50	Polygon P 1001	Oh Babe!/LOUIS PRIMA: Piccolina Lena (78)	10
54	Columbia SCM 5092	Take A Little Walk Around The Block/LOUIS PRIMA: Oh! Cumari	12
58	Capitol CL 14862	The Lip/KEELY SMITH: Foggy Day	5
58	Capitol CL 14948	That Old Black Magic/KEELY SMITH: You Are My Love	6
59	Capitol CL 14994	I've Got You Under My Skin/KEELY SMITH: Don't Take Your Love From Me	5
59	London HLD 8923	Bei Mir Bist Du Schon/I Don't Know Why	6
60	London HLD 9084	I'm Confessin' (That I Love You)/Night And Day	6
60	London HA-D 2243	LOUIS AND KEELY (LP)	10
61	London HA-D 2350	ON STAGE (LP, also stereo SAH-G 6149)	10/12
62	Capitol T 1531	THE HITS OF LOUIS & KEELY (LP)	12

(see also Keely Smith)

PRIMAL SCREAM
85	Creation CRE 017	All Fall Down/It Happens (foldaround sleeve in poly bag)	20
86	Creation CRE 026	Crystal Crescent/Velocity Girl (p/s)	12
87	Elevation ACID 3	Gentle Tuesday/Back Star Carnival (p/s)	5
87	Elevation ACID 3T	Gentle Tuesday/Back Star Carnival/I'm Gonna Make You Mine (12", p/s)	8
87	Elevation ACID 5	Imperial/Star Fruit Surf Rider	5
87	Elevation ACID 5T	Imperial/Star Fruit Surf Rider/So Sad About Us/Imperial (demo) (12", some in poster p/s)	10/8
89	Creation CRELP 054	PRIMAL SCREAM (LP, with free 45 "Split Wide Open [demo]"/ "Lone Star Girl [demo]")	15

(see also Jesus & Mary Chain, Revolving Paint Dream)

PRIMETTES
68	Ember EMBS 3398	LOOKING BACK WITH THE PRIMETTES AND EDDIE FLOYD (LP)	35
70s	Windmill WMD 192	LOOKING BACK WITH THE PRIMETTES AND EDDIE FLOYD (LP, reissue)	12

(see also Supremes, Eddie Floyd)

PRIME-MATES
69	Action ACT 4530	Hot Tamalas Versions 1 & 2	5

PRIMITIVES
64	Pye 7N 15721	Help Me/Let Them Tell	150
65	Pye 7N 15755	You Said/How Do You Feel	200

(see also Mal & Primitives)

PRIMITIVES
86	Head HEAD 010	Thru The Flowers/Across My Shoulder/Lazy/She Don't Need You (12", unreleased, white label test pressings only)	35
86	Lazy LAZY 01	Thru The Flowers/Across My Shoulder/She Don't Need You/Lazy (12", p/s)	15
86	Lazy LAZY 02	Really Stupid/We Found A Way To The Sun (p/s)	7
86	Lazy LAZY 02T	Really Stupid/We Found A Way To The Sun/Where The Wind Blows (12", p/s)	12
86	Lazy LAZY 03	Stop Killing Me/Buzz Buzz Buzz (p/s, initial copies with postcard, some sleeves printed back-to-front; also a very few with badge)	6/8
86	Lazy LAZY 03T	Stop Killing Me/Buzz Buzz Buzz/Laughing Up My Sleeve (12", p/s)	10
87	Lazy LAZY 05	Ocean Blue/Shadow (2,000 only, given free at London Astoria gig, no p/s)	10
87	Lazy LAZY 06	Thru The Flowers/Thru The Flowers (New Version)/ Everything Shining Bright (p/s)	4
87	Lazy LAZY 06L	Thru The Flowers (New Version)/Thru The Flowers (Original Version)/ Everything Shining Bright (p/s, numbered, 5,000 only)	5
87	Lazy LAZY 06T	Thru The Flowers (New Version)/Everything Shining Bright/ Across My Shoulder (Original Version) (12", p/s)	7
88	RCA PB 41761E	Crash (Again And Again)/Crash (Short)/Crash/I'll Stick With You (listed as PB 41761X on die-cut p/s)	6

88	RCA PB 41761X	Crash/I'll Stick With You/Crash (Live In Studio) (10", 4,000 only [1,500 signed], gatefold p/s)	6/5
88	RCA PB 42209E	Way Behind Me/All The Way Down (no'd [3,000 each in red, blue, green & yellow], foldover p/s in poly bag, postcard & badge, some with bubble bath)	4
89	RCA PB 43211	SECRETS (EP, in gatefold sleeve)	4

PRIMO & HOPETON
67	Rio R 139	Your Safekeep/Loving And Kind	10

PRIMROSE CIRCUS
70	President PT 314	P.S. Call Me Lulu	5

PRINCE (& REVOLUTION)
79	WEA K 17537	I Wanna Be Your Lover/Just As Long As We're Together (no p/s)	12
79	WEA K 17537T	I Wanna Be Your Lover/Just As Long As We're Together (12", die-cut co. sl.)	25
80	WEA K 17590	Sexy Dancer/Bambi (die-cut company sleeve)	20
80	WEA K 17590T	Sexy Dancer (Remix)/Bambi (12", die-cut company sleeve)	50
81	WEA K 17768	Do It All Night/Head (die-cut company sleeve)	25
81	WEA K 17768T	Do It All Night/Head (12", die-cut company sleeve)	50
81	WEA K 17819	Gotta Stop (Messin' About)/Uptown (p/s)	80
81	WEA K 17819	Gotta Stop (Messin' About)/I Wanna Be Your Lover (p/s)	80
81	WEA LV 47	Gotta Stop (Messin' About)/Uptown/Head (12", stickered p/s)	160
81	WEA LV 47	Gotta Stop (Messin' About)/I Wanna Be Your Lover/Head (12", stickered p/s)	160
81	WEA K 17866	Controversy/When You Were Mine (p/s)	30
81	WEA K 17866T	Controversy/When You Were MIne (12", p/s)	45
82	WEA K 17922	Let's Work/Ronnie Talk To Russia (p/s)	35
82	WEA K 17922T	Let's Work (Extended)/Ronnie Talk To Russia (12", p/s)	125
83	WEA W 9896	1999/How Come U Don't Call Me Anymore (p/s, some with free cassette)	25/16
83	WEA W 9896T	1999/How Come U Don't Call/D.M.S.R. (12", p/s)	25
83	WEA W 9688	Little Red Corvette/Lady Cab Driver (p/s)	10
83	WEA W 9688T	Little Red Corvette (Full Length Version)/Automatic/International Lover (12", stickered p/s, some with poster insert)	50/30
83	WEA W 9436	Little Red Corvette/Horny Toad (poster calendar p/s)	35
83	WEA W 9436T	Little Red Corvette (Full Length Version)/Horny Toad/D.M.S.R. (12"; p/s, with poster or spiral-bound calendar or without either)	60/100/40
84	WEA W 9296	When Doves Cry/17 Days (p/s)	4
84	WEA W 9296C	When Doves Cry/17 Days/1999/D.M.S.R. (cassette)	5
84	WEA W 9296T	When Doves Cry/17 Days (12", p/s)	10
84	WEA W 9296T	When Doves Cry/17 Days//1999/D.M.S.R. (12", shrinkwrapped double pack)	30
84	WEA W 9174	Purple Rain (short version)/God (vocal) (p/s)	4
84	WEA W 9174P	Purple Rain/God (motorbike-shaped picture disc)	35
84	WEA W 9174T	Purple Rain (instrumental)/God (12", p/s, initially with poster)	16/10
84	WEA W 9121T	I Would Die 4 U/Another Lonely Christmas (12", p/s)	8
84	WEA W 9121TE	I Would Die 4 U (U.S. Remix)/Another Lonely Christmas (Remix) (12", p/s)	35
85	WEA W 2000T	Let's Go Crazy (Extended)/Take Me With U/Erotic City (12", stickered p/s)	10
85	WEA W 9052P	Paisley Park/She's Always In My Hair (shaped picture disc)	50
85	WEA W 9052T	Paisley Park/She's Always In My Hair/Paisley Park (Remix) (12", p/s, some with poster & stickered p/s)	15/10
85	WEA W 9052T	Paisley Park/She's Always In My Hair/Paisley Park (Remix) (12", stickered p/s, mispressed with 4th track)	25
85	WEA W 8929	Raspberry Beret/Hello (p/s)	5
85	WEA W 8929T	Raspberry Beret (Extended Remix)/Hello (Extended Remix) (12", p/s)	10
85	WEA W 8858	Pop Life/Girl (p/s)	5
85	WEA W 8858T	Pop Life (Extended)/Girl (12", p/s)	12
86	WEA W 8751	Kiss/Love Or Money (p/s)	5
86	WEA W 8751P	Kiss/Love Or Money (shaped picture disc with stand)	20
86	WEA W 8751T	Kiss (Extended)/Love Or Money (12", p/s, some with poster)	15/8
86	WEA W 8711	Mountains/Alexa De Paris (p/s)	4
86	WEA W 8711W	Mountains (Ext.)/Alexa De Paris (Extended) (10" white vinyl in special bag)	30
86	WEA W 8711T	Mountains (Extended)/Alexa De Paris (12", p/s, some with poster)	15/7
86	WEA W 8586	Girls And Boys (Edit)/Under The Cherry Moon (p/s)	4
86	WEA W 8586F	Girls And Boys (Edit)/Under The Cherry Moon//She's Always In My Hair/17 Days (double pack, gatefold sleeve)	12
86	WEA W 8586P	Girls And Boys (Edit)/Under The Cherry Moon (shaped picture disc)	40
86	WEA W 8586T	Girls And Boys/Under The Cherry Moon/Erotic City (12", p/s, some with poster advertising London gigs)	15/7
86	WEA W 8521W	Anotherloverholenyohead/I Wanna Be Your Lover (poster p/s)	8
86	WEA W 8521F	Anotherloverholenyohead/I Wanna Be Your Lover//Mountains/Alexa De Paris (double-pack)	12
86	WEA W 8521T	Anotherloverholenyohead (Extended)/I Wanna Be Your Lover (12", double-sided poster p/s)	15
87	WEA W 8399TP	Sign O' The Times (Extended)/La La La He He Hee (extended) (12", picture disc)	30
87	WEA W 8334W	If I Was Your Girlfriend/Shockadelica (poster sleeve)	8
87	WEA W 8334E	If I Was Your Girlfriend/Shockadelica (peach vinyl, PVC cover, with postcards & stickers)	12
87	WEA K 8334TP	If I Was Your Girlfriend/Shockadelica (Extended) (12" picture disc)	18
87	WEA W 8289TP	U Got The Look (Long Look)/Housequake (7 min MoQuake)/U Got The Look (Single Cut) (12", picture disc)	18
87	WEA W 8288TP	I Could Never Take The Place Of Your Man/Hot Thing (Remixed Edit)/Hot Thing (Extended) (12" picture disc)	15
88	WEA W 7900CD	Alphabet Street (LP Version)/This Is Not Music, This Is A Trip (extended) (CD)	12
88	WEA W 7806CD	Glam Slam (Remix)/Escape Free Yo Mind/Glam Slam (Single Cut) (CD)	12
88	WEA W 7745	I Wish U Heaven (Edit)/Scarlet Pussy (Edit) (poster sleeve)	8
88	WEA W 7745TW	I Wish U Heaven (Parts 1/2/3)/CAMILLE: Scarlet Pussy (Edit) (12", p/s,w/poster)	15
88	WEA W 7745CD	I Wish U Heaven (Parts 1/2/3)/CAMILLE: Scarlet Pussy (Edit) (CD)	12
89	WEA W 8751	Kiss/Love Or Money ('re-promoted' Edition with plain black reverse of p/s)	4

89	WEA W 8751TP	Kiss/Love Or Money (shaped picture disc, 're-promoted' Edition with longer, Extended version of B-side, without plinth) 15
89	WEA W 8751T	Kiss (Extended)/Love Or Money (12", 're-promoted' Edition with plain black reverse of p/s & longer, Extended version of B-side) 7
89	WEA W 2924TX	Batdance (Batmix)/Batdance (Vicki Vale mix)/200 Balloons (12", p/s) 8
89	WEA W 2924TP	Batdance (LP version)/200 Balloons (12" picture disc) 8
89	WEA W 2924CDX	Batdance (LP version)/200 Balloons (3" CD in 'Batpack' box) 12
89	WEA W 2814TX	Partyman (The Purple Party Mix)/(Partyman Music Mix)/(The Video Mix)/ Feel U Up (Short Stroke) (12", p/s, with shorter version of 'The Video Mix') 7
89	WEA W 2814TP	Partyman (Video Mix)/Feel U Up (Long Stroke) (12" picture disc) 12
89	WEA W 2814CDT	Partyman (3" Remixes CD) 5
89	WEA W 2814CDX	Partyman (Video Mix)/Feel U Up (CD 'Partypack', hexagonal fold-out sleeve with film stills) 8
89	WEA W 2757CDX	The Arms Of Orion (Extended)/I Love U In Me/The Arms Of Orion (with Sheena Easton) (CD in tri-fold stickered sleeve, w/sticker insert) 10
92	Paisley Park W 0091TP	Money Don't Matter 2 Night (12", picture disc with insert) 7
83	WEA 923 809-1	1999 (LP) 15
84	WEA 925 110-1	PURPLE RAIN — MUSIC FROM THE MOTION PICTURE (LP, purple vinyl with poster) 30
86	WEA 925 395-1	PARADE — MUSIC FROM "UNDER A CHERRY MOON" (LP, picture disc with die cut cover) 35
89	WEA 925 978 2	BATMAN (LP, picture disc) 12

(Revolution credited on all records from "Purple Rain" to "Anotherloverholenyohead"; some releases are on Paisley Park label; see also Sheila E, Sheena Easton)

VIV PRINCE
| 66 | Columbia DB 7960 | Light Of The Charge Brigade/Minuet For Ringo .... 20 |

(see also Pretty Things, Kate)

PRINCE & PRINCESS
| 65 | Aladdin WI 609 | Take Me Serious/Ready Steady Go .... 12 |

PRINCE BUSTER (& ALLSTARS)
61	Starlite ST45 052	Buster's Shack (as Buster's Group)/ERIC MORRIS: Search The World 15
62	Blue Beat BB 101	My Sound That Goes Around/They Got To Go (as Prince Buster & Torchlighters) 10
62	Blue Beat BB 133	Time Longer Than Rope/Fake King (as Prince Buster & Voice Of The People) 10
62	Blue Beat BB 138	One Hand Washes The Other/Cowboy Comes To Town 10
63	Blue Beat BB 150	Run Man Run/Danny, Dane And Lorraine 10
63	Blue Beat BB 158	Open Up, Bartender/Enjoy It (B-side actually "Enjoy Yourself") 10
63	Blue Beat BB 162	Money/SCHOOL BOYS: Little Boy's Blues 10
63	Blue Beat BB 163	King, Duke, Sir/I See Them In My Sight (with Allstars) 10
63	Blue Beat BB 167	The Ten Commandments (with Allstars)/Buster's Welcome 10
63	Blue Beat BB 170	Madness/PRINCE BUSTER ALLSTARS: Toothache 10
63	Blue Beat BB 173	Burning Creation/PRINCE BUSTER ALLSTARS: Boop 10
63	Blue Beat BB 180	Three More Rivers To Cross/RAYMOND HARPER & PRINCE BUSTER ALLSTARS: African Blood 10
63	Blue Beat BB 185	Fowl Thief/Remember Me 10
63	Blue Beat BB 189	Watch It Blackhead/Hello My Dear 10
63	Blue Beat BB 192	Rolling Stones (with Charmers)/RICO & HIS BLUES BAND: This Day 8
63	Blue Beat BB 197	Window Shopping/Sodom And Gommorah 10
63	Blue Beat BB 199	Spider And Fly/Three Blind Mice 10
63	Blue Beat BB 200	Wash All Your Troubles Away/RICO & BLUE BEATS: Soul Of Africa 10
63	Dice CC 6	They Come (actually called "They Got To Come")/These Are The Times (as Prince Buster & Voice Of The People) 10
63	Dice CC 11	Blackhead Chinaman/You Ask (I Had A Girl) 10
63	Dice CC 18	World Peace/The Lion Roars 10
64	Stateside SS 335	30 Pieces Of Silver/Everybody Ska 10
64	Blue Beat BB 210	Wash All Your Troubles Away/RICO & BLUE BEATS: Soul Of Africa (reissue) ... 10
64	Blue Beat BB 211	Bluebeat Spirit/Beggars Have No Choice 10
64	Blue Beat BB 216	You're Mine/Tongue Will Tell 10
64	Blue Beat BB 225	Three Blind Mice/I Know 10
64	Blue Beat BB 232	Sheep On Top (misspelt, actually "She Pon Top")/Midnight 10
64	Blue Beat BB 234	She Loves You/Healing 10
64	Blue Beat BB 243	Jealous/Buster's Ska 10
64	Blue Beat BB 248	Thirty Pieces Of Silver/The National Dance 10
64	Blue Beat BB 254	Wings Of A Dove/MAYTALLS: Sweet Love 10
64	Blue Beat BB 262	Old Lady/Dayo Ska 10
64	Blue Beat BB 271	No Knowledge In College/In The Middle Of The Night 10
64	Blue Beat BB 274	I May Never Love You Again/Hey Little Girl 10
65	Blue Beat BB 278	Blood Pressure/Islam 10
65	Blue Beat BB 282	Big Fight/Red Dress 10
65	Blue Beat BB 293	Aguar Fumar/Long Winter (with Charmers) 8
65	Blue Beat BB 294	Eye For Eye/PRINCE BUSTER'S ALLSTARS: South Virginia 10
65	Blue Beat BB 302	Ling Ting Tong/Walk Along 10
65	Blue Beat BB 307	Bonanza/Wonderful Life 10
65	Blue Beat BB 309	Here Comes The Bride/Burkes' Law (with Princess Buster) 10
65	Blue Beat BB 313	Everybody Yeh Yeh (as Prince & Jamaica's Greatest)/BUSTER'S ALLSTARS: Gun The Man Down 10
65	Blue Beat BB 314	Like A Butterfly/Haunted Room 10
65	Blue Beat BB 316	Sugar Pop/Feel Up (as Prince & Jamaica's Greatest) 10
65	Blue Beat BB 317	Come Home/I Thank You 10
65	Blue Beat BB 321	My Girl/BUSTER'S ALLSTARS: The Fugitive 10
65	Blue Beat BB 324	Al Capone/One Step Beyond (both sides by Prince Buster's Allstars) 10
65	Blue Beat BB 328	Ambition/IVANHOE MARTIN: Rygin 10
65	Blue Beat BB 330	Rum And Coca Cola/(And) I Love Her 10

65	Blue Beat BB 334	The Ten Commandments/PRINCE BUSTER'S ALLSTARS: Sting Like A Bee (reissue) 8
66	Blue Beat BB 335	Respect/PRINCE BUSTER'S ALLSTARS: Virginia (B-side actually Val Bennett & Prince Buster's All Stars' "Dance Jamaica") 10
66	Blue Beat BB 338	Big Fight (as Prince Buster Vs Duke Reid)/Adios, Senorita 10
66	Blue Beat BB 339	Under Arrest/PRINCE BUSTER'S ALLSTARS: Say Boss Man 10
66	Blue Beat BB 343	Don't Throw Stones/Prince Of Peace 10
66	Blue Beat BB 352	Day Of Light/It's Too Late 10
66	Blue Beat BB 355	(Sunshine With) My Girl/Girl Answer Your Name 10
66	Blue Beat BB 357	I Won't Let You Cry/Hard Man Fe Dead 10
66	Blue Beat BB 359	The Prophet (actually with Slim Smith)/BUSTER'S ALLSTARS: Lion Of Judah 10
66	Blue Beat BB 362	To Be Loved/BUSTER'S ALLSTARS: Set Me Free 10
66	Rainbow RAI 107	Your Turn (Sad Song)/If You Leave Me (with Allstars) 8
67	Blue Beat BB 370	Shanty Town (Get Scanty)/BUSTER'S ALLSTARS: Duppy 10
67	Blue Beat BB 373	Knock On Wood/And I Love Her 10
67	Blue Beat BB 377	Dark End Of The Street/Love Oh Love 10
67	Blue Beat BB 378	Drunkard's Psalm/PRINCE BUSTER ALLSTARS: Seven Wonders Of The World 10
67	Blue Beat BB 382	Sit And Wonder (with Allstars)/ROLAND ALPHONSO: Sunrise In Kingston 10
67	Blue Beat BB 383	Sharing You/You'll Be Lonely On The Blue Train (as Prince Buster's Allstars; A-side actually by Prince Buster, B-side actually by Rico's Band) 10
67	Blue Beat BB 387	Judge Dread (Judge Four Hundred Years)/FITZROY CAMPBALL: Waiting For My Rude Girl 10
67	Blue Beat BB 388	Dance Cleopatra/All In My Mind 10
67	Blue Beat BB 390	Soul Serenade/Too Hot 10
67	Blue Beat BB 391	Land Of Imagination/APPEAL: The Barrister (B-side actually by Prince Buster) .10
67	Blue Beat BB 393	Johnny Dollar/Rude Boys Rule 10
67	Blue Beat BB 395	This Gun's For Hire/Yes, Daddy 10
67	Blue Beat BB 400	All In my Mind/Judge Dread Dance (The Pardon) 10
67	Blue Beat BB 402	Vagabond/PRINCE BUSTER ALLSTARS: Come Get Me 10
67	Philips BF 1552	The Ten Commandments/Don't Make Me Cry 15
67	Fab FAB 10	Shakin' Up Orange Street/Black Girl (with Allstars) 10
67	Fab FAB 11	Johnny Cool Pts 1 & 2 (with Allstars) 10
67	Fab FAB 16	Bye Bye Baby/Human (with Allstars) 10
67	Fab FAB 25	Train To Girls Town/Give Love A Try (with Allstars) 8
67	Fab FAB 26	Going To The River (with Allstars)/PRINCE BUSTER'S ALLSTARS: Julie On My Mind 8
68	Fab FAB 31	Kings Of Old (My Ancestors)/Sweet Inspiration (with Allstars) 8
68	Fab FAB 35	Try A Little Tenderness/All My Loving (with Allstars) 8
68	Fab FAB 36	Another Sad Night/The Glory Of Love (with Allstars) 8
68	Fab FAB 37	This Is A Hold Up/Julie On My Mind (with Allstars) 8
68	Fab FAB 38	Free Love (with Allstars)/DALTONS: All Over The World 8
68	Fab FAB 40	Rough Rider (with Allstars)/PRINCE BUSTER: 127 Orange Street (B-side actually by Prince Buster Allstars) 8
68	Fab FAB 47	Going To Ethiopia (with Allstars)/PRINCE BUSTER ALLSTARS: Shakin' Up Orange Street 8
68	Fab FAB 56	Intensified Dirt/Don't You Know I Love You (with Allstars) 7
68	Fab FAB 57	Green Green Grass Of Home (as Prince Buster's Allstars; actually by Prince Buster & Allstars)/SOUL MAKERS: Girls Like You 7
68	Fab FAB 58	We Shall Overcome/Keep The Faith (as Prince Buster's Allstars; actually Prince Buster & Allstars) 7
68	Fab FAB 64	Cool Stroker/It's You I Love (B-side actually by Little Roy) 7
68	Fab FAB 80	Hypocrite/New Dance (B-side actually by Little Roy) 7
68	Fab FAB 81	Wine And Grind/The Scorcher (with Allstars) 7
69	Unity UN 522	30 Pieces Of Silver/Everybody Ska (reissue) 10
69	Fab FAB 82	Dr. Rodney (Black Power)/Taxation 7
69	Fab FAB 92	Pharoah House Crash/Ob-La-Di, Ob-La-Da 7
69	Fab FAB 93	Ob-La-Di, Ob-La-Da/Wreck A Pum Pum 7
69	Fab FAB 94	Hey Jude/Django Fever 7
69	Fab FAB 102	Black Soul/CALEDONIANS: Oh Baby (B-side actually by Claredonians) 7
69	Fab FAB 108	Wine And Grind/The Scorcher (with Allstars) (reissue) 7
69	Fab FAB 118	Bull Buck/ROLAND ALPHONSO: One Heart 7
69	Fab FAB 119	Let Her Go/Tie The Donkey's Tail 7
69	Fab FAB 122	Stand Up/Happy Reggae (with Allstars) 6
70	Fab FAB 127	Young Gifted And Black/PRINCE BUSTER'S ALLSTARS: The Rebel 5
70	Fab FAB 131	That's All/The Preaching (B-side actually "The Preacher") 6
70	Fab FAB 132	Ganja Plant/Creation 5
70	Fab FAB 140	Hit Me Back/Give Peace A Chance 5
70	Fab FAB 150	Big Five/Musical College 5
70	Prince Buster PB 1	Big Five/Musical College (reissue) 5
70	Prince Buster PB 2	Rat Trap/Musical Organ (B-side actually by Ansell Collins & Prince Buster's Allstars) 5
71	Fab FAB 176	Police Trim Rasta (with Allstars)/Smooth (B-side actually by Ansell Collins & Prince Buster Allstars) 5
71	Prince Buster PB 4	Fishey/More Fishey 5
71	Prince Buster PB 7	I Wish Your Picture Was You/PRINCE BUSTER ALLSTARS: It Mash Up Version (B-side actually by Dennis Alcapone) 5
71	Prince Buster PB 8	Sons Of Zion (actually by Dennis Alcapone)/ANSELL COLLINS:Short Circuit 5
71	Prince Buster PB 9	My Happiness/Human (with Allstars) 5
72	Prince Buster PB 14	Big Sister Stuff/Satta Massagana (with Allstars) 5
72	Prince Buster PB 15	Protection/Cool Operator (with Allstars) 5
72	Prince Buster PB 16	My Heart is Gone/I Stand Accused (with Allstars) 5
72	Prince Buster PB 19	Four In One Medley/Drums Drums (as Prince Buster & Allstars, B-side actually by Prince Buster Allstars) 5
72	Prince Buster PB 32	Still/Sister Big Stuff (with Allstars) 5

72	Prince Buster PB 36	South Of The Border/South Of The Border (Version) (with Allstars) 5
72	Prince Buster PB 47	Baldhead Pum Pum/Giver Her (with Allstars) 5
79	Blue Beat DDBB 324	Al Capone/One Step Beyond (12", p/s) 7
79	Blue Beat DDBB 334	THREE OF THE BEST (12" EP, p/s) 8
79	Blue Beat DDPB 1	Big Five/FOLK BROTHERS: Carolina/PRINCE BUSTER: Shaking Up
		Orange Street (12", p/s) 8
79	Blue Beat DDPB 2	PICK OF THE PUNCH (12" EP, p/s, 2 tracks each by Tennors & Prince Buster) . . .8
79	Blue Beat DDPB 3	NAUGHTY BUT NICE (12" EP, p/s) 8
79	Blue Beat DDPB 4	BEHIND BARS (12" EP, p/s) 8
63	Blue Beat BBLP 802	I FEEL THE SPIRIT (LP) 70
65	Blue Beat BBLP 805	SKA-LYP-SOUL (LP) 70
65	Blue Beat BBLP 806	IT'S BURKE'S LAW/JAMAICA SKA EXPLOSION! (LP) 70
67	Blue Beat BBLP 807	WHAT A HARD MAN FE DEAD (LP, with Baba Brooks) 70
67	Blue Beat BBLP 808	ON TOUR (LP) 60
67	Blue Beat BBLP 809	JUDGE DREAD (LP) 60
67	Blue Beat/Fab BBLP 820	SHE WAS A ROUGH RIDER (LP) 40
68	Fab BBLP 821	WRECK A PUM PUM (LP) 20
69	Fab BBLP 822	THE OUTLAW (LP) 35
70	Fab MS 1	FABULOUS GREATEST HITS (LP) 12
70	Fab MS 2	I FEEL THE SPIRIT (LP) 15
70	Fab MS 6	TUTTI FRUTTI (LP) 18
72	Melodisc MLP 12-156	SISTER BIG STUFF (LP) 18
72	Melodisc MLP 12-157	BIG FIVE (LP) 15
73	Prince Buster PB 9	ORIGINAL GOLDEN OLDIES VOLUME 1 (LP) 15

(see also Buster's Allstars, Buster's Group)

PRINCE CHARLIE
| 69 | Coxsone CS 7101 | Hit And Run/Darling, There I Stand . . . . .10 |

PRINCE HAROLD
| 66 | Mercury MF 952 | Forget About Me/Baby You've Got Me . . . . .10 |

PRINCE OF DARKNESS
69	Downtown DT 441	Burial Of Long Shot/MUSIC DOCTORS: Burial Of Long Shot 5
69	Downtown DT 448	Meeting Over Yonder/MUSIC DOCTORS: Ghost Rider .4
70	Downtown DT 467	Sound Of Today/MUSIC DOCTORS: Red Red Wine Version 4

PRINCE PATO EXPEDITION
| 70s | Beacon BEAS 18 | FIREBIRD (LP) . . . . .25 |

PRINCESS & SWINEHERD
| 68 | Oak RGJ 633 | PRINCESS AND THE SWINEHERD (LP, plain black sleeve) . . . . .30 |

PRINCIPAL EDWARDS MAGIC THEATRE
70	Dandelion S 4405	Ballad Of The Big Girl Now/Lament For Earth 5
73	Deram DM 391	Captain Lifeboy/Nothing 4
73	Deram DM 398	Weekdaze/Whizzmore Kid 4
69	Dandelion 63752	SOUNDTRACK (LP) 15
71	Dandelion DAN 8002	THE ASOMOTO RUNNING BAND (LP, gatefold sleeve) 12
74	Deram SML 1108	ROUND ONE (LP) 15

JOHN PRINE
72	Atlantic K 40357	JOHN PRINE (LP) 10
73	Atlantic K 40427	DIAMONDS IN THE ROUGH (LP) 10
74	Atlantic K 40524	SWEET REVENGE (LP) 10
75	Atlantic K 50137	COMMON SENSE (LP) 10

MADDY PRIOR
(see under Tim Hart & Maddy Prior)

PRISM
78	EMI Intl. INS 3014	PRISM (LP) 10
78	Ariola ARL 5014	SEE FOREVER EYES (LP) 10
80	Capitol E-ST 12051	ARMAGEDDON (LP) 10
80	Capitol E-ST 12072	YOUNG AND RESTLESS (LP) 10

PRISONERS
83	Big Beat NS 90	Hurricane/Tomorrow (She Said) (p/s) 6
84	Big Beat SW 98	ELECTRIC FIT (EP) 5
82	Own Up OWN UP U2	A TASTE OF PINK (LP) 10
85	Own Up OWN UP U2	A TASTE OF PINK (LP, reissue in pink sleeve on pink vinyl) 12
85	Own Up OWN UP U3	THE LAST FOURFATHERS (LP) 10
86	Countdown DOWN 2	IN FROM THE COLD (LP) 10
89	Hangman HANG 23 UP	RARE AND UNISSUED (LP) 10

(see also James Taylor Quartet)

PRISONERS/MILKSHAKES
| 86 | Empire MIC 001 | THE LAST NIGHT AT THE MIC CLUB (LP, 1 side each) . . . . .10 |
| 87 | Media Burn MB 017 | MILKSHAKES V PRISONERS LIVE (LP, 1 side each) .10 |

(see also Milkshakes, Thee Mighty Caesars)

PRIVATE DICKS
| 79 | Heartbeat PULSE 6 | She Said So/Private Dicks (p/s) . . . . .4 |

PRIVATE SECTOR
| 78 | TJM TJM 8 | Just Just (Wanna) Stay Free/Things Get Worse (p/s) . . . . .6 |

P.J. PROBY
62	Liberty LIB 55367	Try To Forget Her/There Stands The One 8
64	Decca F 11904	Hold Me/The Tips Of My Fingers 4
64	Decca F 11967	Together/Sweet And Tender Romance 4
64	Liberty LIB 10182	Somewhere/Just Like Him 4
65	Liberty LIB 10188	I Apologise/What's On Your Mind 4

P.J. PROBY

65	Liberty LIB 10206	Let The Water Run Down/I Don't Want To Hear It Anymore	6
65	Liberty LIB 10215	That Means A Lot/My Prayer	8
65	Liberty LIB 10218	Maria/She Cried	4
66	Liberty LIB 10222	Per Questa Veslio Te/Quando Tornera	4
66	Liberty LIB 10223	You've Come Back/It Ain't Necessarily So	4
66	Liberty LIB 10236	To Make A Big Man Cry/Wicked Woman	4
66	Melodisc Fab FAB 2	You've Got Me Cryin'/I Need Love (some in p/s)	10/5
66	Liberty LIB 10250	I Can't Make It Alone/Sweet Summer Wine	5
67	Liberty LIB 55936	Nicki Hoeky/Good Things Are Coming My Way	6
67	Liberty LIB 55974	You Can't Come Home Again/Work With Me Annie	8
68	Liberty LIB 15046	It's Your Day Today/I Apologise Baby	5
68	Liberty LBF 15085	What's Wrong With My World/Why Baby Why	6
68	Liberty LBF 15152	The Day That Lorraine Came Down/Mery Hoppkins Never Had Days	
		Like These (B-side featuring Led Zeppelin)	10
69	Liberty LBF 15245	Hanging From Your Loving Tree/Empty Bottles	10
70	Liberty LBF 15280	Today I Killed A Man/It's Too Good To Last	10
70	Liberty LBF 15386	It's Goodbye/It's Too Good To Last	10
72	Columbia DB 8874	We'll Meet Again/Clown Shoes	5
73	Ember EMB S 328	Put Your Head On My Shoulder/Momma Married A Preacher	4
74	Seven Sun SSUN 13	The Champ Pts 1 & 2	6
81	Rooster RONS 101	You've Got It All/Starting All Over Again (with Polly Brown)	4
64	Liberty LEP 2192	P. J. PROBY (EP)	10
65	Liberty LEP 2229	SOMEWHERE (EP)	10
65	Liberty LEP 2239	CHRISTMAS WITH P. J. (EP)	15
66	Liberty LEP 2251	P. J.'s HITS (EP)	18
67	Liberty LEP 2267	PROBY AGAIN (EP)	20
65	Liberty LBY 1235	I AM P. J. PROBY (LP)	20
65	Liberty LBY 1264	P. J. PROBY (LP)	20
66	Liberty LBY 1291	P. J. PROBY IN TOWN (LP)	15
67	Liberty LBY 1361	ENIGMA (LP)	18
67	Liberty LBL/LBS 83018	P. J. PROBY IN TOWN (LP, blue label reissue)	10
67	Liberty LBL/LBS 83032	ENIGMA (LP, blue label reissue)	12
67	Liberty LBL/LBS 83045	PHENOMENON (LP)	16
68	Liberty LBL/LBS 83087	BELIEVE IT OR NOT (LP)	20
69	Liberty LBS 83219E	THREE WEEK HERO (LP, featuring Led Zeppelin on "Jim's Blues")	40
70	Ember NR 5069	I'M YOURS (LP)	12
81	Palm 7007	THE HERO (LP)	40

(see also Jett Powers)

PROCESSION

68	Mercury MF 1053	Every American Citizen/Essentially Susan (p/s)	6
69	Mercury SMCL 20132	PROCESSION (LP)	10

PROCOL HARUM

67	Deram DM 126	A Whiter Shade Of Pale/Lime Street Blues (1st issue with darker labels)	4
67	Regal Zonophone RZ 3003	Homburg/Good Captain Clack	4
68	Regal Zonophone RZ 3007	Quite Rightly So/In The Wee Small Hours Of Sixpence	4
69	Regal Zonophone RZ 3019	A Salty Dog/Long Gone Geek	4
72	Fly Magni Fly ECHO 101	A Whiter Shade Of Pale/A Salty Dog/Homburg (p/s)	6
70s	RCA LB 6	A Whiter Shade Of Pale/Noel Edmonds Introduces Record Year	
		(Lever Brothers premium)	4
67	Regal Zono. LRZ 1001	PROCOL HARUM (LP)	14
69	Regal Zono. (S)LRZ 1004	SHINE ON BRIGHTLY (LP, mono/stereo)	14/12
69	Regal Zono. SLRZ 1009	A SALTY DOG (LP)	12
70	Regal Zono. SLRZ 1014	HOME (LP, with lyric sheet)	12
71	Chrysalis ILPS 9158	BROKEN BARRICADES (LP, gatefold sleeve)	10

(see also Paramounts, Legend)

JUDD PROCTOR

61	Parlophone R 4769	Rio Grande/Plainsman	6
61	Parlophone R 4809	Palamino/Nola	6
61	Parlophone R 4841	Speakeasy/Clearway	6
62	Parlophone R 4885	The Turk/Mad	6
62	Parlophone R 4920	Backfire/It's Bluesy	6
64	Parlophone R 5126	Better Late/Boots	6
60s	Morgan MR 103P	GUITARS GALORE (LP)	15
70s	Gemini GMX 5004	GUITARS GALORE (LP, reissue)	10

MIKE PROCTOR

67	Columbia DB 8254	Mr. Commuter/Sunday, Sunday, Sunday	35

PROFESSIONALS

80	Virgin VS 376	1-2-3/White Light White Heat/Baby I Don't Care (p/s w/ giant foldout poster)	4
81	Sounds FREEBIE No. 2	Little Boys In Blue (extract)/GILLAN: I'll Rip Your Spine Out (extract)	
		(33rpm 1-sided flexi, printed die-cut sleeve, free with 'Sounds' magazine)	5/4

(see also Sex Pistols, Greedies)

PROFESSOR LONGHAIR

65	Sue WI 397	Baby Let Me Hold Your Hand/Looka No Hair	18
78	Harvest HAR 5154	Messaround/Tipitina	5
60s	XX MIN 708	PROFESSOR LONGHAIR (EP)	8
72	Speakeasy 10-78	NEW ORLEANS 88 (10" LP)	40
72	Atlantic K 40402	NEW ORLEANS PIANO (LP)	20
78	Harvest SHSP 4086	LIVE ON THE QUEEN MARY (LP)	10

PROFIL

80	CBS S CBS 8574	Hey Music Man/Jour De Chance (p/s)	10

PROFILE

65	Mercury MF 875	Haven't They Got Better Things To Do/Touch Of Your Hand	6

65	Mercury MF 981	Got To Fnd A Way/Don't Say Goodbye 6

(see also Karl Stuart & Profiles, Voice)

PROLES
78	Can't Play	THE PROLES GO TO THE SEASIDE (EP, 250 only) 20

PROLES
70s	Proles Wreck Chords	And The Beat Goes On (possibly unreleased)
79	Rock Against Racism	Stereo Love/Thought Crime/CONDEMNED: Soldier Boys/
	RAR 1	Endless Revolution (p/s, also listed as S/79/CUS 273) 5

PROPAGANDA
85	ZTT ZTAS 2	Dr. Mabuse/Dr. Mabuse Der Spieler (white glove p/s) 5
85	ZTT ZTAS 2	Dr. Mabuse (Instrumental Mix)/Dr. Mabuse Der Spieler (dark p/s, matrix: 2A X1) 7
85	ZTT 12 ZTAS 2	Das Testaments Des Mabuse/Femme Fatale (The Woman With The Orchid)/The 9th Life (Of Dr. Mabuse) (12", white p/s) 12
85	ZTT 12 ZTAS 2	Das Testaments Des Mabuse/Femme Fatale/The 9th Life (Of Dr. Mabuse) (12", white p/s, title sticker reads "13th Life New Mix", matrix: 2A 2U) 18
85	ZTT 12 ZTAS 2	Das Testaments Des Mabuse (The Third Side)/Femme Fatale (The Woman With The Orchid) The Fourth Side (12", black photo p/s) 12
85	ZTT CTIS 101	Das Testaments Des Mabuse/The Last Word/Dr. Mabuse (cassette, "Femme Fatale" is listed but does not appear) 12
85	ZTT P ZTAS 8	Duel/Jewel (Rough Cut) (ZTT logo-shaped picture disc) 8
85	ZTT DUAL 1	Duel/Jewel/Lied/The Lesson (double pack, gatefold ZTT sleeve) 12
85	ZTT 12 ZTAS 8	Duel (Bittersweet)/Jewel (Cut Rough) (12", p/s shrinkwrapped with "Dr. Mabuse" 12" in ZTT sleeve) 10
85	ZTT CTIS 108	DO WELL: The First Cut/Duel (7")/Jewel (Cut Rough)/Wonder/Bejewelled (cassette) 15
85	ZTT ZTAS 12	P-Machinery/Frozen Faces (p/s) 4
85	ZTT PZTAS 12	P-Machinery/Frozen Faces (clear vinyl, PVC sleeve) 6
85	ZTT 12P ZTAS 12	P-Machinery (Polish)/P Machinery (Passive)/Frozen Faces (12", p/s, clear vinyl) 10
85	ZTT 12X ZTAS 12	P-Machinery (Beta)/Complete Machinery/Frozen Faces (12", 'sofa' p/s) 15
85	ZTT 12X ZTAST 12	P-Machinery (Beta)//Complete Machinery/Frozen Faces (12", with "P Machinery", clear vinyl, PVC sleeve with poster) 18
85	ZTT ZTAS 21	P-Machinery (Beta Wraparound)/Frozen Faces (purple die cut p/s) 4
85	ZTT 12 ZTAS 21	P-Machinery (Polish)/P Machinery (Passive)/Frozen Faces (12", p/s, shrinkwrapped with "Duel" 12") 10
85	ZTT CTIS 12	COMPLETE MACHINERY: Introduction/P Machinery (Connected)/ P Machinery (Seperation)/Frozen Faces (cassette) 16
90	Virgin VSCDX 1245	Heaven Give Me Words (7" version)/Heaven Give Me Words (Honey In Heaven Mix)/Heaven Give Me Words (Doppleganger Mix) (CD, in box) 8
90	Virgin VSAX 1271	Only One Word/Only One Word (demo)/Open Spaces (10", box set with 3 prints) 6
85	ZTT ZCD 20	WISHFUL THINKING (CD, export issue) 40

(see also Act, Ralph Dorper)

ORVAL PROPHET
63	London HLL 9729	Run Run Run/My Lois And Me 8

REX PROPHET
55	Brunswick OE 9144	CANADIAN PLOWBOY (EP) 10

PROPHETS
69	Mercury MF 1097	I Got The Fever/Soul Control 15

(see also Creation [U.S.])

PROS & CONS
66	CBS 202341	Bend It/No Time 4

PROTEX
78	Good Vibrations GOT 6	Don't Ring Me Up/(Just Want) Your Attention/Listening In (wraparound p/s) 4

PROTOS
82	Airship AP 391	ONE DAY A NEW HORIZON (LP) 250

PROVIDENCE
73	Threshold TH 14	Fantasy Fugue/Island Of Light 4
72	Threshold THS 9	EVER SINCE THE DAWN (LP, gatefold sleeve with insert) 15

PRUDES
89	Yo Yo PRU 1	P.S. I'm Leaving/Lighthouse Keeper's Daughter (p/s, white vinyl) 6
90	Imaginary RED TWO	Never Penetrate (p/s, 1-sided) 4

SNOOKY PRYOR
70	Flyright LP 100	SNOOKY PRYOR (LP) 12

ARTHUR PRYSOCK
65	CBS 201820	It's Too Late Baby, Too Late 8
66	CBS EP 6076	AGAIN (EP) 12
78	Polydor 2383 481	DOES IT AGAIN (LP) 10

RED PRYSOCK
54	Mercury MB 3158	Blow Your Horn/Happy Feet (78) 25
57	Mercury MT 154	Teen-Age Rock/Paquino Walk (78) 18
59	Mercury AMT 1028	Chop Suey/Margie 10
59	Mercury AMT 1028	Chop Suey/Margie (78) 10
57	Mercury MPT 7512	FIRST ROCK 'N' ROLL PARTY (10" LP) 45
57	Mercury MPT 7517	JUMP RED, JUMP (10" LP) 45
58	Mercury MPL 6535	THE BEAT (LP) 40
58	Mercury MPL 6550	FRUIT BOOTS (LP) 35

PSEUDO EXISTORS

80	Dead Good DEAD 2	Pseudo Existence/Coming Up For Air/New Modern Warfare (folded p/s with stamped pink/white vinyl) 4

PSYCHEDELIC FURS

79	Epic EPC 8005	We Love You/Pulse (green, pink or orange p/s) 4-5
80	CBS 8179	Sister Europe/(untitled) (p/s) 4
80	CBS 9059	Mr. Jones/Susan's Strange (p/s) 4
81	CBS A 1166	Dumb Waiters/Dash (1st 5,000 with playable p/s) 5
81	CBS A 1327	Pretty In Pink/Mack The Knife (p/s) 4
81	CBS WA 1327	Pretty In Pink/Mack The Knife (picture disc) 5
81	CBS A 13 1327	Pretty In Pink/Mack The Knife/Soap Commercial (12", no p/s, shrinkwrapped with free T-shirt) 8
82	CBS A 2549	Love My Way/Aeroplane (5,000 in gatefold p/s) 5
84	CBS A 4300	Heaven Pts 1& 2 (with poster in plastic wrap) 4
84	CBS WA 4470	The Ghost In You/Another Edge (picture disc) 4
84	CBS TA 4300	Heaven/Heartbeat (12", p/s, with poster) 7
84	CBS DA 4654	Heartbeat/My Time//Heaven (U.S. Remix)/Here Come The Cowboys (U.S. Remix) (double pack) 4
86	CBS WA 7242	Pretty In Pink/Love My Way (picture disc) 4
86	CBS DA 7242	Pretty In Pink/Love My Way//Heaven/Heartbeat (double pack) 4
86	CBS 6501830	Heartbreak Beat/New Dream (shrinkwrapped with free cassette: "Sister Europe"/"Into You Like A Train"/"President Gas") 6
87	CBS FURS C3	Angels Don't Cry/No Release (with cassette "We Love You"/"Pretty In Pink"/ "Love My Way") 6
88	CBS FURS EP 4	All That Money Wants/Birdland/No Easy Street (live)/Heaven (Live) (EP) 4
90	CBS FURS QT 5	House/House (Flashback Mix)/Badman/Torch (Electric) (10", p/s) 5

PSYCHIC TV

82	Some Bizzare PTV 1	Just Drifting/Breakthrough (p/s) 10
82	Some Bizzare PTV 1T	Just Drifting/Breakthrough (12", p/s) 20
84	Temple TOPY 001	Unclean/Mirrors (12", p/s) 12
86	Temple TOPY 009	Godstar/Discopravity (p/s) 4
86	86 Temple TOPYS 009	Godstar/(B J Mix)//Discopravity (Fish Mix)/Yes It's The B Side (with Angels Of Light) (double pack) 5
86	Temple TOPYH 009	Godstar (Hyperdelic Mix)/(California Mix) (with Angels Of Light) (12", p/s) 7
86	Temple TOPIC 009	Godstar (Hyperdelic Mix)/(California Mix) (with Angels Of Light) (12" picture disc) 10
87	Temple TOPY 022	Magick Defends Itself: Papal Breakdance/Magick Defends Itself (12", p/s) 10
87	Temple TOPYT 023	Good Vibrations/Interzone/Roman P./Hex Sex (12", p/s) 10
87	Temple TOPYD 023	MAGICKAL MYSTERY D. TOUR (EP, double pack) 5
88	Temple TOPY 037	TUNE IN (TURN ON TO THEE ACIDE HOUSE) (12", p/s, Psychic TV/Jack The Tab) 10
89	Temple TOPY 048	Love War Riot/Eve Of Destruction (12", p/s) 8
89	Temple TOPY 048T	Love War Riot (Vocoder Mixes) (10", p/s) 10
90	Temple TOPY 058	I.C. Water (p/s, 1-sided, etched) 5
90	Temple TOPY 058T	I.C. Water (Radio Version)/I.C. Water (CD Version)/Alien Be-In (12", p/s) 8
82	WEA/Some Bizarre PSY 1	FORCE THE HAND OF CHANCE (LP, with bonus LP & double-sided poster) 20
83	CBS 25737	DREAMS LESS SWEET (LP, with free 12") 15
84	Temple TOPY 002	NEW YORK SCUM HATERS (LP, 5,000 only) 10
84	Temple TOPY 003	A PAGAN DAY (LP, picture disc, 999 only) 20
85	Temple TOPY 004	PSYCHICK TV VOL. 2 (LP) 15
85	Temple TOPY 008	PSYCHICK TV THEMES VOL. 3 (LP) 15
85	Temple TOPY 010	MOUTH OF THE NIGHT (LP, picture disc, 2300 only) 12
87	Temple TOPY 014	LIVE IN PARIS (LP, 5000 only) 10
87	Temple TOPY 015	LIVE IN TOKYO 1986 (LP, 5,000 only) 10
87	Temple TOPY 016	LIVE IN GLASGOW (LP, 5,000 only) 10
87	Temple TOPY 017	A PAGAN DAY (LP) 10
87	Temple TOPY 018	LIVE IN HEAVEN (LP, 3,000 only) 10
87	Temple TOPY 026	LIVE IN REYKJAVIK (LP, 5,000 only) 10
87	Temple TOPY 027	LIVE EN SUISSE (LP, 5,000 only) 10
87	Temple TOPY 028	LIVE IN TORONTO (LP, 5,000 only) 10
87	Temple TOPY 029	LIVE IN GOTTINGEN (LP, 5,000 only) 10
88	Temple TOPY 031	PSYCHIC TV (LP, picture disc) 10
88	Temple TOPY 032	ALBUM TEN (LP, picture disc, free with tokens from 9 previous LPs, 1,000 only) 20
88	Temple TOPY 036	LIVE AT THEE MARDI GRAS (LP) 10
88	Temple TOPY 038	ALLEGORY & SELF (LP) 10
88	Temple TOPY 038	ALLEGORY & SELF (LP, picture disc) 15
88	Temple TOPY 039	TECHNO ACID BEAT (LP, with friends) 12
88	Temple TOPY 042	LIVE AT THEE CIRCUS (LP) 10
89	Temple TOPY 045	LIVE AT THEE RITZ (LP) 10
89	Temple TOPY 047	LIVE AT THEE PYRAMID N.Y.C. 1988 (LP, picture disc) 15
89	Temple TOPY 047	LIVE AT THEE PYRAMID N.Y.C. 1988 (LP) 10
90	Temple TOPY 051	BEYOND THE INFINITE BEAT (LP, 2 x 12" remixes) 15

(see also Throbbing Gristle, Coil)

PSYCHO SURGEONS

86	Flexible Response FR 003	Give A Man A Badge/Diagnosis (p/s) 4

PSYCHO'S MUM

89	Woronzow W 011	A SIBILANT SIN (LP, with insert) 10

PUBLIC ENEMY

87	Def Jam 6512458	Rebel Without A Pause (Vocal Mix)/(Instrumental)/Bring The Noise (Noise Version)/Sophisticated Bitch (12", no p/s) 7
87	Def Jam 6512450	Rebel Without A Pause (Vocal Mix)/(Instrumental) (picture disc) 8
87	Def Jam 6513356	Bring The Noise (No Noise Version)/(No Noise Instrumental A Cappella)/ Sophisticated Bitch/(Instrumental) (12", p/s) 7

87	Def Jam 6513358	Bring The Noise/Bring The Noise (No Noise Version)/(No Noise Instrumental A Cappella)/Sophisticated Bitch/(Instrumental) (12", p/s, with sticker) 7
88	Def Jam 6528330	Don't Believe The Hype/Prophets Of Rage (p/s, with patch) 4
88	Def Jam 6530897	Night Of The Living Baseheads/Terminator X To The Edge Of Panic (p/s, badge pack) 4

PUBLIC FOOT THE ROMAN

73	Sovereign SVNA 7259	PUBLIC FOOT THE ROMAN (LP) 35

(see also Movies)

PUBLIC IMAGE LTD

78	Virgin VS 228	Public Image/The Cowboy Song (newspaper p/s) 5
79	Virgin VS 274	Death Disco/And No Bird Do Sing (p/s) 4
79	Virgin VS 274 12	Death Disco/And No Bird Do Sing (1/2 mix)/Death Disco Megamix (12", p/s) 8
79	Virgin VS 299	Memories/Another (p/s) 4
79	Virgin VS 299 12	Memories/Another (12", p/s) 8
81	Virgin VS 397	Flowers Of Romance/Home Is Where The Heart Is (p/s) 4
86	Virgin VS 855	Home/Round//Rise/Rise (Instrumental) (double pack) 4
87	Virgin VS 988	Seattle/Selfish Rubbish (box set with 7", badge, postcard & sew-on patch) 5
79	Virgin METAL 1	METAL BOX (LP, 3 x 12" with paper circles & inner sheet in circular tin box) 20

(see also Sex Pistols, Jah Wobble, Don Letts & Jah Wobble)

GARY PUCKETT & UNION GAP

68	CBS 3365	Young Girl/I'm Losing You (as Union Gap featuring Gary Puckett) 4
68	CBS 3551	Lady Willpower/Daylight Stranger 4
68	CBS 3713	Over You/If The Day Would Come 4
69	CBS 4505	This Girl Is A Woman Now/His Other Woman 4
69	CBS 4122	Don't Give In To Him/Could I 4
68	CBS (S) 63342	YOUNG GIRL (LP) 10
68	CBS (S) 63429	INCREDIBLE (LP) 10
70	CBS (S) 63794	THE NEW GARY PUCKETT AND THE UNION GAP ALBUM (LP) 10

PUDDING

67	Decca F 12603	The Magic Bus/It's Too Late 25

LEROY PULLINS

66	London HLR 10056	I'm A Nut/Knee Deep 10

PULP

79	Pulp Music PB 1	Low Flying Aircraft/Something Just Behind My Back/So Lo (p/s, 2,000 only, some numbered & signed) 10/8
83	Red Rhino RED 32	My Lighthouse/Looking For Love (p/s) 5
92	Caff CAFF 17	My Legendary Girlfriend/Sickly Grin/Back In L.A. (foldover p/s with insert in poly bag, 500 only) 10

PULSAR

76	Decca SKL-R 5228	POLLEN (LP) 18
76	Decca TXS 119	STRANDS OF THE FUTURE (LP) 15

PULSE

70	Major Minor SMLP 64	PULSE (LP) 45

PUNCHIN' JUDY

73	Transatlantic TRA 272	PUNCHIN' JUDY (LP) 15

PUNCTURE

77	Small Wonder SMALL 1	Mucky Pup/Can't Rock'n'Roll (p/s) 4

PUNKETTES

77	Response SR 511	Going Out Wiv A Punk/Polythene (no p/s) 6

PUPILS

66	Wing WL 1150	A TRIBUTE TO THE ROLLING STONES (LP) 70
69	Fontana SFL 13087	A TRIBUTE TO THE ROLLING STONES (LP, reissue) 25

(see also Eyes)

PUPPETS

63	Pye 7N 15556	Poison Ivy/Everybody's Talking 15
64	Pye 7N 15634	Baby Don't Cry/Shake With Me 15
64	Pye 7N 15625	Shake With Me/Three Boys Looking For Love 10

DANNY PURCHES

55	Columbia SCM 5183	Mama/Just One More Time 4

PURGE

69	Corn CP 101	The Mayor Of Simpleton Hall/The Knave (p/s) 75

JAMES & BOBBY PURIFY

66	Stateside SS 547	I'm Your Puppet/So Many Reasons 6
67	Stateside SS 595	Wish You Didn't Have To Go/You Can't Keep A Good Man Down 5
67	Stateside SS 2016	Shake A Tail Feather/Goodness Gracious 8
67	Stateside SS 2039	I Take What I Want/Sixteen Tons 5
67	Stateside SS 2049	Let Love Come Between Us/I Don't Want To Have To Wait 7
68	Stateside SS 2093	Do Unto Me/Everybody Needs Somebody 7
68	Bell BLL 1008	I Can't Remember/I Was Born To Lose Out 6
68	Bell BLL 1024	Help Yourself To All My Lovin'/Last Piece Of Love 6
69	Bell BLL 1043	Untie Me/We're Finally Gonna Make It 4
69	Bell BLL 1043	Let Love Come Between Us/Shake A Tail Feather 6
69	Bell BLL 1067	Do Unto Me/Wish You Didn't Have To Go 4
72	Mojo 2092 056	I'm Your Puppet/Wish You Didn't Have To Go 4
67	Stateside SL 10206	JAMES AND BOBBY PURIFY (LP) 15
67	Bell MBLL/SBLL 101	THE PURE SOUND OF THE PURIFYS (LP) 12
78	Casablanca CAL 2025	YOU AND ME TOGETHER, FOREVER (LP) 10

PURPLE FOX
71   Gold Award MER 340   TRIBUTE TO JIMI HENDRIX (LP) 15

PURPLE GANG
67   Big T BIG 101   Granny Takes A Trip/Bootleg Whisky 6
68   Big T BIG 111   Kiss Me Goodnight Sally Green/Auntie Monica 5
68   Transatlantic   THE PURPLE GANG STRIKES (LP) 25

PURPLE HEARTS
79   Fiction FICS 003   Millions Like Us/Beat That! (p/s) 5
79   Fiction FICS 007   Frustration/Extraordinary Sensations (p/s) 5
80   Fiction FICS 9   Jimmy/What Am I Gonna Do (p/s) 5
80   Safari SAFE 30   My Life's A Jigsaw/The Guy Who Made Her A Star/Just To Please You
         (initially in foldout jigsaw p/s) 6/4
80s   Road Runner RR 1   Plane Crash/Scooby Doo/Gun Of Life (p/s) 5
80   Fiction FIX 002/2383 568   BEAT THAT! (LP) 10
       (see also Bob Manton)

JIMMY PURSEY
81   Epic EPCA 1336   Animals Have More Fun/Sus (p/s) 5
       (see also Sham 69)

PUSSY
72   Deram DM 368   Feline Woman/Ska Child 15
       (see also Jerusalem)

PUSSY
69   Morgan Bluetown BT 5002   PUSSY PLAYS (LP) 300

PUSSYFOOT
66   Decca F 12474   Freeloader/Things That Still Remind Me 10
67   Decca F 12561   Mr Hyde/Hasty Words 10
68   Pye 7N 17520   Good Times/Till You Don't Want Me Anymore 10
       (see also Rare Breed)

ASHA PUTHLI
73   CBS 65804   ASHA PUTHLI (LP) 25
75   CBS 80978   SHE LOVES TO HEAR THE MUSIC (LP) 20
76   CBS 81443   THE DEVIL IS LOOSE (LP) 25

PUZZLE
69   Stateside SS 2146   Hey Medusa/Make The Children Happy 4
69   Stateside SSL 10285   PUZZLE (LP) 10

PVC 2
77   Zoom ZUM 2   Gonna Put You In The Picture/Pain/Deranged, Demented and Free (p/s) 5
       (see also Midge Ure, Slik, Zones)

PYLON
81   Armageddon AEP 12004   Cool Dub/Driving School Danger (10", p/s) 5

PYRAMID
67   Deram DM 111   Summer Of Last Year/Summer Evening 15
       (see also Fairport Convention)

PYRAMIDS (U.S.)
64   London HLU 9847   Penetration/Here Comes Marsha 15

PYRAMIDS (U.K.)
65   Polydor BM 56028   Baby's Gone Away/Kiss And Dance With You 4

PYRAMIDS (Jamaica)
69   Doctor Bird DB 1307   Stay With Him/Chicken Mary 8

PYRAMIDS (Jamaica)
67   President PT 161   Train Tour To Rainbow City/John Chewey 4
68   President PT 177   Wedding In Peyton Place/Girls Girls Girls 4
68   President PT 195   All Change On The Bakerloo Line/Playing Games 4
68   President PT 206   Mexican Moonlight/Mule 4
68   President PTL 1021   THE PYRAMIDS (LP) 18
       (see also Symarip, Equals, Little Grants & Eddie)

PYTHAGORAS THEOREM
70   Pye 7N 17990   Our House/Free Like Me 4

PYTHON LEE JACKSON
69   Young Blood YB 1002   In A Broken Dream/Doing Fine 4
72   Young Blood YB 1017   In A Broken Dream/Doing Fine (reissue) 4
76   Young Blood YB 1077   The Blues/Cloud Nine 4
80   Young Blood YB 0089   In A Broken Dream/The Blues 6
85   Young Blood YEP 89   In A Broken Dream (mono)/In A Broken Dream (stereo)/The Blues/
         Cloud Nine (EP, promo for "Kelly Girl" Employment Agency) 10
74   Young Blood YB 3001   IN A BROKEN DREAM (LP) 10
       (see also Rod Stewart)

ELVIS PRESLEY

MINT VALUE £

Q-TIPS
80	Shotgun SHOT 1	S.Y.S.L.J.F.M. (The Letter Song)/The Dance (p/s) 4
(see also Paul Young)		

QUADROPHONICS
75	Contempo CS 2054	Betcha If You Check It Out/Prove My Love To You 4

CHRISTINE QUAITE
62	Oriole CB 1739	Oh My!/Guilty Eyes 5
62	Oriole CB 1772	Your Nose Is Gonna Grow/It's Bad 5
63	Oriole CB 1845	Mister Heartache/Whisper Wonderful Words 5
63	Oriole CB 1876	In The Middle Of The Floor/Tell Me Mama 5
63	Oriole CB 1921	I Believe In Love/Here She Comes 5
64	Oriole CB 1945	Mister Stuck Up/Will You Be The Same Tomorrow 5
65	Stateside SS 435	If You've Got A Heart/So Near So Far 5
66	Stateside SS 482	Long After Tonight Is All Over/I'm Hoping 20

QUAKER CITY BOYS
59	London HLU 8796	Teasin'/Won't Y' Come Out, Mary Ann 8

QUAKERS
65	Oriole CB 1992	I'm Ready/Down The Road A Piece 60
65	Studio 36 KSP 109/110	She's Alright/Talk To Me 100

JOE QUARTERMAN & FREE SOUL
73	GSF GSZ 3	So Much Trouble In My Mind Pts 1 & 2 6
74	GSF GSZ 12	Thanks Dad Pts 1 & 2 5
73	GSF GS 504	JOE QUARTERMAN & FREE SOUL (LP) 50

QUARTER NOTES
57	Parlophone R 4365	Ten Minutes To Midnight/My Fantasy 6

QUARTET
69	Decca F 12974	Now/Will My Lady Come 4
70	Decca F 13072	Joseph/Mama Where Did You Fall 4

QUARTZ
77	Jet UP 36317	Street Fighting Lady 6
80	Reddingtons R.R. DAN 1	Nantucket Sleighride/Wildfire (p/s, white vinyl) 8
80	Jet JET 189	Street Fighting Lady (p/s, reissue) 4
80	Logo GO 387	Satan's Serenade/Bloody Fool (p/s) 4
80	Logo GOT 387	Satan's Serenade/Bloody Fool/Roll Over Beethoven (live) (12", p/s, blue or red vinyl) 8
80	MCA MCA 642	Stoking The Fires Of Hell/Circles (p/s) 6
81	MCA MCA 661	Stand Up And Fight/Charlie Snow (p/s) 5
83	Heavy Metal HEAVY 17	Tell Me Why/Streetwalker (p/s) 4
77	Jet UAG 30081	QUARTZ (LP, with inner sleeve) 12
79	Jet JETLP 233	DELETED (LP, in brown paper bag) 10
80	Reddingtons 001	QUARTZ LIVE COUNT DRACULA (LP) 12
80	MCA MCF 3080	STAND UP AND FIGHT (LP) 10
83	Heavy Metal HMRLP 9	AGAINST ALL ODDS (LP) 10
83	Heavy Metal HMRPD 9	AGAINST ALL ODDS (LP, picture disc) 12
(see also Black Sabbath)		

QUATERMASS
70	Harvest SVHL 775	QUATERMASS (LP, gatefold sleeve) 40
75	Harvest SHSM 2002	QUATERMASS (LP, reissue) 10
(see also Ian Gillan Band, Episode Six, Strapps)		

QUATRAIN
69	Polydor 583 743	QUATRAIN (LP) 10

SUZI QUATRO
72	Rak RAK 134	Rolling Stone/Brain Confusion 4
78	Rak RAK 285	Stumblin' In/Stranger With You (with Chris Norman) (clear vinyl) 4

QUAZAR
78	Arista ARIST 224	Funk 'N' Roll/Savin' My Love For A Rainy Day 4
83	Tabitha QUAZ 1	Silver Stallion/Dated And Signed 4

IKE QUEBEC
64	Blue Note 45-1749	Buzzard Lope/Blue Friday 8
63	Blue Note (B)BLP 4098	BLUE AND SENTIMENTAL (LP) 15
64	Blue Note (B)BLP 4114	BOSSA NOVA — SOUL SAMBA (LP) 15
65	Blue Note BLP 4105	IT MIGHT AS WELL BE STRING (LP) 15

QUEEN
73	EMI EMI 2036	Keep Yourself Alive/Son And Daughter 30
74	EMI EMI 2121	Seven Seas Of Rhye/See What A Fool I've Been 10
74	EMI EMI 2229	Killer Queen/Flick Of The Wrist 6
75	EMI EMI 2256	Now I'm Here/Lily Of The Valley 6
75	EMI EMI 2375	Bohemian Rhapsody/I'm In Love With My Car (initially in p/s) 25/4
76	EMI EMI 2494	You're My Best Friend/39 (no p/s) 6
76	EMI EMI 2565	Somebody To Love/White Man (p/s) 12

77	EMI EMI 2593	Tie Your Mother Down/You And I (no p/s)	4
77	EMI EMI 2623	QUEEN'S FIRST EP (p/s)	12
77	EMI EMI 2708	We Are The Champions/We Will Rock You (p/s)	8
78	EMI EMI 2575	Spread Your Wings/Sheer Heart Attack (p/s)	8
78	EMI EMI 2375	Bohemian Rhapsody/I'm In Love With My Car (EMI in-house edition, royal blue vinyl, Queen crest label, hand numbered, purple p/s, 200 only)	1000
78	EMI EMI 2375	Bohemian Rhapsody/I'm In Love With My Car (as above, with outer 'EMI International' card carrying envelope)	1200
78	EMI EMI 2375	Bohemian Rhapsody/I'm In Love With My Car (as above, with invites, outer card sleeve, commemorative scarf & EMI goblets)	1500
78	EMI EMI 2375	Bohemian Rhapsody/I'm In Love With My Car (EMI in-house edition, royal blue vinyl, Queen crest label, without p/s)	200
78	EMI EMI 2870	Bicycle Race/Fat Bottomed Girls (p/s)	7
79	EMI EMI 2910	Don't Stop Me Now/In Only Seven Days (p/s)	8
79	EMI EMI 2959	Love Of My Life (live)/Now I'm Here (live) (no p/s)	20
79	EMI EMI 5001	Crazy Little Thing Called Love/We Will Rock You (live) (p/s)	6
80	EMI EMI 5022	Save Me/Let Me Entertain You (live) (p/s)	7
80	EMI EMI 5076	Play The Game/A Human Body (p/s)	7
80	EMI EMI 5102	Another One Bites The Dust/Dragon Attack (p/s)	6
80	EMI EMI 5126	Flash/Football Fight (p/s)	5
81	EMI EMI 5250	Under Pressure (as Queen & David Bowie)/Soul Brother (p/s)	4
82	EMI EMI 5293	Body Language/Life Is Real (Song For Lennon) (p/s)	5
82	EMI EMI 5316	Las Palabras De Amour/Cool Cat (p/s)	10
82	EMI EMI 5325	Backchat (Remix)/Staying Power (p/s)	8
82	EMI 12EMI 5325	Backchat (Extended Remix)/Staying Power (12", p/s)	25
84	Flexi Ltd.	THE WORKS (flexidisc sampler, p/s)	15
84	EMI QUEEN 1	Radio Ga Ga (Edit)/I Go Crazy (p/s)	4
84	EMI 12QUEEN 1	Radio Ga Ga (Ext. Version)/Radio Ga Ga (Instrumental)/I Go Crazy (12", p/s)	8
84	EMI QUEEN 2	I Want To Break Free (Remix)/Machines (Back To Humans) (gold lettering p/s, 4 different solo designs; white lettering 2nd issues)	12/8
84	EMI 12QUEEN 2	I Want To Break Free (Extended Remix)/Machines (Back To Humans) (12", p/s with red or white background)	12
84	EMI QUEEN 3	It's A Hard Life/Is This The World We Created...? (p/s)	6
84	EMI QUEEN 3	It's A Hard Life/Is This The World We Created...? (with alternate photo p/s)	10
84	EMI 12QUEEN 3	It's A Hard Life (Extended Remix)/It's A Hard Life/Is This The World We Created...? (12", no p/s)	15
84	EMI 12QUEEN P3	It's A Hard Life/Is This The World We Created? (12", picture disc)	40
84	EMI QUEEN 4	Hammer To Fall (Edit)/Tear It Up (live p/s, withdrawn)	100
84	EMI QUEEN 4	Hammer To Fall (Edit)/Tear It Up (red p/s)	5
84	EMI 12 QUEEN 4	Hammer To Fall (The Headbangers Mix)/Tear It Up (12", live p/s, withdrawn)	125
84	EMI 12 QUEEN 4	Hammer To Fall (The Headbangers Mix)/Tear It Up (12", red p/s)	12
84	EMI QUEEN 5	Thank God It's Christmas/Man On The Prowl/Keep Passing The Open Windows (p/s)	8
84	EMI 12QUEEN 5	Thank God It's Christmas/Man On The Prowl (Extended Version)/Keep Passing The Open Windows (Extended Version) (12", p/s)	20
85	EMI QUEEN 6	One Vision (7" Mix)/Blurred Vision (p/s, initially with red lyric inner sleeve)	7/4
85	EMI 12QUEEN 6	One Vision (Extended Vision)/Blurred Vision (12", p/s, some with red inner sleeve)	12/8
85	EMI 12QUEEN 6	One Vision (Extended Vision)/Blurred Vision (12", printed PVC sleeve with red inner)	30
86	EMI QUEEN 7	A Kind Of Magic/A Dozen Red Roses For My Darling (p/s)	5
86	EMI 12QUEEN 7	A Kind Of Magic (Extended Version)/A Dozen Red Roses For My Darling (12", p/s)	12
86	EMI 12QUEENP7	A Kind Of Magic (Extended Version)/Don't Lose Your Head (Instrumental Version) (12", picture disc)	40
86	EMI QUEEN 8	Friends Will Be Friends/Seven Seas Of Rhye (p/s)	6
86	EMI QUEEN P8	Friends Will Be Friends/Seven Seas Of Rhye (picture disc)	25
86	EMI 12QUEEN 8	Friends Will Be Friends (Extended Version)/Friends Will Be Friends (7" version)/Seven Seas Of Rhye (12" p/s)	10
86	EMI QUEEN 9	Who Wants To Live Forever/Killer Queen (p/s)	8
86	EMI 12QUEEN 9	Who Wants To Live Forever (7" version)/Who Wants To Live Forever (Album Version)/Killer Queen/Forever (Piano Version) (12", p/s)	15
88	Parlophone QUECD 1	Seven Seas Of Rhye/See What A Fool I've Been/Funny How Love Is (3" CD)	10
88	Parlophone QUECD 2	Killer Queen/Flick Of The Wrist/Brighton Rock (3" CD)	10
88	Parlophone QUECD 3	Bohemian Rhapsody/I'm In Love With My Car/You're My Best Friend (3" CD)	10
88	Parlophone QUECD 4	Somebody To Love/White Man/Tie Your Mother Down (3" CD)	10
88	Parlophone QUECD 5	QUEEN'S FIRST EP (3" CD)	10
88	Parlophone QUECD 6	We Are The Champions/We Will Rock You (3" CD)	10
88	Parlophone QUECD 7	Crazy Little Thing Called Love/Spread Your Wings/Flash (3" CD)	10
88	Parlophone QUECD 8	Another One Bites The Dust/Dragon Attack/Las Parabras De Amour (3" CD)	10
88	Parlophone QUECD 9	Under Pressure/Soul Brother/Body Language (3" CD)	10
88	Parlophone QUECD 10	Radio Ga Ga/I Go Crazy/Hammer To Fall (3" CD)	10
88	Parlophone QUECD 11	I Want To Break Free/Machines (Back To Humans) (3" CD)	10
88	Parlophone QUECD 12	A Kind Of Magic/A Dozen Red Roses For My Darling/One Vision (3" CD)	10
89	Parlophone QUEEN 10	I Want It All/Hang On In There (p/s)	4
89	Parlophone QUEEN C10	I Want It All/Hang On In There (cassette)	5
89	Parlophone 12QUEEN 10	I Want It All (Single Version)/Hang On In There/I Want It All (Album Version) (12", p/s)	8
89	Parlophone CDQUEEN 10	I Want It All (Album Version)/Hang On In There/I Want It All (Single Version) (CD, picture disc)	20
89	Parlophone QUEEN 11	Breakthru (7" Mix)/Stealin' (p/s)	5
89	Parlophone QUEEN PD 11	Breakthru (7" Mix)/Stealin' (shaped picture disc, 12" PVC sleeve with insert)	18
89	Parlophone QUEEN C11	Breakthru (7" Mix)/Stealin' (cassette)	5
89	Parlophone 12QUEEN 11	Breakthru' (12" Version)/Breakthru' (Single Version)/Stealin' (12", p/s)	8
89	Parlophone CD QUEEN 11	Breakthru (7" Mix)/Stealin'/Breakthru (12" Mix) (CD)	8
89	Parlophone QUEEN 12	The Invisible Man/Hijack My Heart (black vinyl, p/s)	4

QUEEN

89	Parlophone QUEEN X12	The Invisible Man/Hijack My Heart (clear vinyl, p/s)	10
89	Parlophone QUEEN C12	The Invisible Man/Hijack My Heart (cassette)	5
89	Parlophone 12QUEEN 12	The Invisible Man (12" Version)/The Invisible Man (7" Version)/ Hijack My Heart (12", p/s)	8
89	Parlophone 12QUEENX12	The Invisible Man (12" Version)/The Invisible Man (7" Version)/ Hijack My Heart (12", clear vinyl, PVC sleeve with 12" insert)	18
89	Parlophone CD QUEEN 12	The Invisible Man (Ext.)/Hijack My Heart/Invisible Man (single version) (CD)	15
89	Parlophone QUEEN 14	Scandal/My Life Has Been Saved (p/s)	4
89	Parlophone QUEEN P14	Scandal/My Life Has Been Saved (poster p/s)	10
89	Parlophone QUEEN C14	Scandal/My Life Has Been Saved (cassette)	5
89	Parlophone 12QUEEN 14	Scandal (12" Version)/Scandal (7" Version)/My Life Has Been Saved (12", p/s)	8
89	Parlophone 12QUEENS 14	Scandal (12" Version)/My Life Has Been Saved/Scandal (7" Version)/ (12", p/s, one-sided, B-side laser-etched with group's signatures)	20
89	Parlophone CD QUEEN 14	Scandal/My Life Has Been Saved/Scandal (CD)	15
89	Parlophone QUEEN 15	The Miracle/Stone Cold Crazy (live) (p/s)	5
89	Parlophone QUEEN H15	The Miracle/Stone Cold Crazy (live) (hologram p/s)	10
89	Parlophone QUEEN C15	The Miracle/Stone Cold Crazy (live) (cassette)	5
89	Parlophone 12QUEEN 15	The Miracle/Stone Cold Crazy (live)/My Melancholy Blues (live) (12", yellow p/s)	10
89	Parlophone 12QUEENP 15	The Miracle/Stone Cold Crazy (live)/My Melancholy Blues (live) (12", turquoise p/s with print insert)	15
89	Parlophone QUEENCD 15	The Miracle/Stone Cold Crazy (live)/My Melancholy Blues (live) (CD)	15
91	Parlophone QUEEN16	Innuendo/Bijou (p/s)	4
91	Parlophone QUEEN C16	Innuendo/Bijou (cassette)	5
91	Parlophone 12QUEEN 16	Innuendo (Explosive Version)/Under Pressure/Bijou (12", p/s)	7
91	Parl. 12QUEEN PD16	Innuendo (Explosive Version)/Under Pressure/Bijou (12", picture disc, PVC sleeve with insert)	18
91	Parl. CD QUEEN PD16	Innuendo (Explosive Version)/Under Pressure/Bijou (CD)	7
91	Parlophone QUEEN 17	I'm Going Slightly Mad/The Hitman (p/s)	4
91	Parlophone QUEEN PD 17	I'm Going Slightly Mad/The Hitman (shaped picture disc)	18
91	Parlophone QUEEN C17	I'm Going Slightly Mad/The Hitman (cassette)	4
91	Parlophone 12QUEENG 17	I'm Going Slightly Mad/The Hitman/Lost Opportunity (12", gatefold p/s)	10
91	Parlophone CDQUEEN 17	I'm Going Slightly Mad/The Hitman/Lost Opportunity (CD)	7
91	Parlophone QUEEN 18	Headlong/All God's People (p/s)	4
91	Parlophone QUEEN C18	Headlong/All God's People (cassette)	4
91	Parlophone 12QUEEN 18	Headlong/All God's People/Mad The Swine (12", p/s)	7
91	Parl. 12QUEEN PD18	Headlong/All God's People/Mad The Swine (12", clear vinyl picture disc, with 12" insert in PVC sleeve)	14
91	Parlophone CD QUEEN 18	Headlong/All God's People/Mad The Swine (CD)	7
91	Parlophone QUEEN C19	The Show Must Go On/Keep Yourself Alive (cassette)	4
91	Parlophone 12QUEEN 19	The Show Must Go On/Keep Yourself Alive/Queen Talks (12", p/s)	7
91	Parl. 12QUEENSG 19	The Show Must Go On/Keep Yourself Alive/Queen Talks (12", B-side laser etched with group's signatures, gatefold p/s)	15
91	Parl. CD QUEENG 19	The Show Must Go On/Now I'm Here/Fat Bottomed Girls/Las Palabras De Amour (The Words Of Love) (CD in box, foldout poster, 1000 only)	20
75	EMI EMI 2378	Bohemian Rhapsody/I'm In Love With My Car (2nd issue, misprinted with wrong catalogue number, EMI 2378 instead of EMI 2375)	12
78	EMI EMI 2870	Bicycle Race/Fat Bottomed Girls (p/s, mispress, B-side plays Crystal Gayle's "3 O'Clock In The Morning" or Dollar track)	10
79	EMI EMI 2975	CLIFF RICHARD: We Don't Talk Anymore (mispressed, A-side plays "Bohemian Rhapsody")	12
79	EMI EMI 5001	Crazy Little Thing Called Love/We Will Rock You (live) (p/s, mispress, both sides play "We Will Rock You")	15
80	EMI EMI 5076	Play The Game/A Human Body (p/s, mispress, both sides play "A Human Body")	12
86	Parlophone RP 5452	BEATLES: Paperback Writer/Rain (mispressed picture disc, A-side plays "Friends Will Be Friends")	40
74	EMI EMA 767	QUEEN II (LP, gatefold sleeve with lyrics)	12
74	EMI EMC 3061	SHEER HEART ATTACK (LP, with lyrics on inner sleeve)	10
81	EMI EMTV 30	GREATEST HITS (LP, mispress, Side 2 plays "Anne Murray's Greatest Hits")	15
85	EMI QB 1	THE COMPLETE WORKS (13-LP, box set including "Complete Vision" LP of non-album tracks, 2 booklets & map, numbered; 600 autographed)	350/80

(see also Larry Lurex, Freddie Mercury, Brian May, Roger Taylor, Cross, Starfleet, Immortals, Hilary Hilary, Minako Honda)

QUEENSRYCHE

83	EMI America 12EA 162	Queens Of The Ryche/Nightrider/Blinded/Lady Wore Black (12", p/s)	15
84	EMI America EA 183	Take Hold Of The Flame/Nightrider (p/s)	12
86	EMI America EA 22	Gonna Get Close To You/Prophecy (p/s)	8
86	EMI America EAD 22	Gonna Get Close To You/Prophecy//Queen Of The Reich (live)/ Deliverance (live) (double pack)	15
86	EMI America EAD 22	Gonna Get Close To You/Prophecy/Queen Of The Reich (12", p/s)	15
88	EMI Manhattan 10QR 1	OVERSEEING THE OPERATION (10" EP)	12
89	EMI USA MT 65	Eyes Of A Stranger/Queen Of The Reich (gatefold p/s)	4
89	EMI USA 12MTG 65	Eyes Of A Stranger/Queen Of The Reich/Walk In The Shadows/ Take Hold Of The Flame (12", gatefold p/s)	12
89	EMI USA CDMT 65	Eyes Of A Stranger/Queen Of The Reich/Take Hold Of The Flame/Prophecy (CD)	8
90	EMI USA MTPD 90	Empire/Scarborough Fair Canticle (shaped picture disc)	6
90	EMI USA CDMT 90	Empire/Scarborough Fair Canticle/Prophecy (CD)	7
91	EMI USA MTS 94	Silent Lucidity/Mission (live) (box set with portraits & stencils)	5
91	EMI USA MTP 94	Silent Lucidity/Mission (live) (12", picture disc)	7
91	EMI USA 10MT 97	Best I Can/I Dream In Infrared (1991 Acoustic Remix)/Prophecy (10", box set with poster & badge)	6
91	EMI USA MTPD 98B	Jet City Woman/Empire (live) (shaped picture disc)	5
91	EMI 12MTS 98	Jet City Woman/Walk In The Shadows (live)/Empire (live) (12", box set with tour laminate & poster)	7
84	EMI America EJ 2402201	THE WARNING (LP, with inner sleeve)	10
88	EMI Manhattan MTL 1023	OPERATION MINDCRIME (LP, picture disc)	10

? & MYSTERIANS

66	Cameo Parkway C 428	96 Tears/Midnight Hour	18
66	Cameo Parkway C 441	I Need Somebody/'8' Teen	15
67	Cameo Parkway C 467	Can't Get Enough Of You, Baby/Smokes	7
67	Cameo Parkway C 479	Girl (You Captivate Me)/Got To	7
67	Cameo Parkway C 496	Do Something To Me/Love Me Baby	7
76	London HLU 10534	96 Tears/'8' Teen	6

QUESTIONS

68	Decca F 22740	We Got Love/Something Wonderful	15

QUESTIONS

78	Zoom ZUM 6	Some Other Guy/Rock 'n' Roll Ain't Dead (p/s)	4
79	Zoom ZUM 8	Can't Get Over You/Answers (p/s)	4

TOMMY QUICKLY (& REMO FOUR)

63	Piccadilly 7N 35137	Tip Of My Tongue/Heaven Only Knows (solo)	30
63	Piccadilly 7N 35151	Kiss Me Now/No Other Love	5
64	Piccadilly 7N 35167	Prove It/Haven't You Noticed	4
64	Piccadilly 7N 35183	You Might As Well Forget Him/It's As Simple As That	4
64	Pye 7N 15708	The Wild Side Of Life/Forget The Other Guy	4
64	Pye 7N 15748	Humpty Dumpty/I'll Go Crazy	12
	(see also Remo Four)		

QUICKSAND

70	Carnaby CNS 4015	Passing By/Cobblestones	6
73	Dawn DNS 1046	Time To Live/Empty Street, Empty Heart	6
74	Dawn DNLS 3056	HOME IS WHERE I BELONG (LP)	40

QUICKSILVER MESSENGER SERVICE

76	Capitol CL 15859	Gypsy Lights/Witches' Moon	4
68	Capitol (S)T 2904	QUICKSILVER MESSENGER SERVICE (LP)	18
69	Capitol E-(S)T 120	HAPPY TRAILS (LP)	15
69	Capitol E-ST 391	SHADY GROVE (LP)	12
70	Capitol EA-ST 498	JUST FOR LOVE (LP)	12
71	Capitol EA-ST 630	WHAT ABOUT ME? (LP)	12
72	Capitol E-SW 819	QUICKSILVER (LP)	10
72	Capitol EA-ST 11002	COMIN' THRU (LP)	10
75	Capitol E-ST 11462	SOLID SILVER (LP)	10
83	Psycho PSYCHO 10	MAIDEN OF THE CANCER MOON (2-LP)	30
	(see also Dino Valenti, Nicky Hopkins)		

QUIET FIVE

65	Parlophone R 5273	When The Morning Sun Dries The Dew/Tomorrow I'll Be Gone	5
65	Parlophone R 5302	Honeysuckle Rose/Let's Talk It Over	5
66	Parlophone R 5421	Homeward Bound/Ain't It Funny What Some Lovin' Can Do	5
66	Parlophone R 5470	I Am Waiting/What About The Time For Me	5
67	CBS 202586	Goodnight Sleep Tight/Just For Tonight	5

QUIET RIOT

83	Epic EPCA 3968	Metal Health/Love's A Bitch/Cum On Feel The Noise (double pack)	4
87	Epic EPC 25322	METAL HEALTH (LP, picture disc)	10

QUIET SUN

75	Island HELP 19	MAINSTREAM (LP)	10
	(see also Phil Manzanera, Roxy Music)		

QUIET WORLD

70	Pye 7N 45005	Rest Comfortably/Gemima	12
70	Dawn DNS 1005	Love Is Walking/Children Of The World	15
70	Dawn DNLS 3007	THE ROAD (LP)	60
	(see also Steve Hackett, Genesis)		

QUIK

67	Deram DM 121	Love Is A Beautiful Thing/Bert's Apple Crumble	30
67	Deram DM 139	King Of The World/My Girl	15
67	Deram DM 155	I Can't Sleep/Soul Full Of Sorrow	30

QUINCICASM

70s	Saydisc SDL 249	QUINCICASM (LP)	15

MIKE QUINN

66	Fontana TF 761	Someone's Slipping Into My Mind/I Know What You Know	4
69	CBS 4506	Apple Pie/There's A Time	4

PAUL QUINN & EDWYN COLLINS

84	Swamplands SWX-1	Pale Blue Eyes/Pale Blues Eyes (Western)/Burro (12", banded 'film' p/s w/ inner)	7
	(see also Edwyn Collins, Orange Juice)		

QUINTESSENCE

70	Island WIP 6075	Notting Hill Gate/Move Into The Light	6
71	Neon NE 1003	Sweet Jesus/You Never Stay The Same (some in p/s)	15/6
69	Island ILPS 9110	IN BLISSFUL COMPANY (LP, pink label)	20
70	Island ILPS 9128	QUINTESSENCE (LP, pink label)	20
70	Island ILPS 9143	DIVE DEEP (LP)	12
71	RCA SF 8273	SELF (LP)	10
72	RCA SF 8317	INDWELLER (LP)	10
	(see also Kala)		

QUINTET OF HOT CLUB OF FRANCE

53	Decca LF 1139	SWING FROM PARIS (10" LP)	15
	(see also Django Reinhardt)		

QUIREBOYS

DARYL QUIST

QUIVER

(see also Bridget St. John, Natural Gas, Village)

QUOTATIONS (U.S.)

QUOTATIONS (U.K.)

(see also Fleur De Lys, Johnny B. Great, Johnny Gustafson, Merseybeats)

QUODLING'S DELIGHT

QUO VARDIS

(see under Vardis)

QUEEN

RABBIT
73	Island WIP 6161	Broken Arrows/Blues My Guitar	4
73	Island ILPS 9238	BROKEN ARROWS (LP)	10
74	Island ILPS 9289	DARK SALOON (LP)	10
76	Jet JETLP 17	BOYS WILL BE BOYS (LP)	10

(see also Free, Kossoff Kirke Tetsu & Rabbit)

MIKE RABIN (& DEMONS)
64	Columbia DB 7350	Head Over Heels/Leaving You (as Mike Rabin & Demons)	30
65	Polydor BM 56007	If I Were You/What Do You Do	15

OSCAR RABIN & HIS BAND
53	Polygon P 1086	Crazy Man Crazy/Forgive Me (B-side with Mel Gaynor) (78)	5

TREVOR RABIN
79	Chrysalis CHS 2282	Painted Picture/Stay With Me (p/s)	4
79	Chrysalis CHS 2362	Don't You Ever Lose/Stay With Me/Getting To Know You Better (p/s)	4
81	Chrysalis CHS 2508	Take Me To A Party/Looking For A Lady (p/s, coloured vinyl)	4
78	Chrysalis CHR 1196	TREVOR RABIN (LP)	10
79	Chrysalis CHR 1221	FACE TO FACE (LP)	10

JOSEPH RACAILLE
80s	Recommended RRA 16.5	6 PETITES CHANSONS (EP, clear vinyl, foldaround sleeve)	6

STEVE RACE
62	Parlophone R 4894	Nicola/Ring Ding	4
63	Parlophone R 4981	The Pied Piper/Here And Now	4

RACE DANS
68	Trojan TR 610	Bookie Man/UNIQUES: More Love	8

COO-COO RACHAS
59	Capitol CL 15024	Chili Beans/Track Down	4

YANK RACHELL TENNESSE JUG BUSTERS
64	'77' LA 12-23	MANDOLIN BLUES (LP)	20

JIMMY RADCLIFFE
65	Stateside SS 374	Long After Tonight Is Over/What I Want I Can Never Have	20
73	Pye Intl. 7N 25614	Long After Tonight Is Over/What I Want I Can Never Have (reissue)	5
77	DJM DJS 10772	Long After Tonight Is Over/What I Want I Can Never Have (2nd reissue)	4

RADHA KRISHNA TEMPLE (LONDON)
69	Apple APPLE 15	Hare Krishna Mantra/Prayer To The Spiritual Masters (p/s, some with insert, as Radha Krishna Temple London)	18/10
70	Apple APPLE 25	Govinda/Govinda Jai Jai (p/s)	15
71	Apple SAPCOR 18	THE RADHA KRSNA TEMPLE (LP, gatefold sleeve)	35

RADIANTS
64	Chess CRS 8002	Voice Of Your Choice/If I Only Had You	6
68	Chess CRS 8073	Hold On/I'm Glad I'm The Loser	8

RADIATORS (FROM SPACE)
77	Chiswick S 10	Television Screen/Love Detective (p/s, original issue)	5
77	Chiswick NS 10	Television Screen/Love Detective (p/s, later pressings)	4
77	Chiswick NS 19	Enemies/Psychotic Reaction (p/s)	4
78	Chiswick NS 24	Prison Bars/(Why Can't I Be A) Teenager In Love (unreleased, white label in stamped white sleeve & loose printed labels)	25
78	Chiswick NS 29	Million Dollar Hero (In A Five And Ten Cents Store)/Blitzin' At The Ritz (as Radiators) (p/s)	4
79	Chiswick NS 45	Walkin' Home Alone Again/Try And Stop Me/The Hucklebuck (unreleased; white label test pressings exist with loose labels)	20
79	Chiswick CHIS 144	Song Of The Faithful Departed/They're Looting In The Town (Irish-only)	8
77	CBS 5572	Sunday World/(Why Can't I Be A) Teenager In Love (p/s, Irish-only issue)	25
77	Chiswick WIK 4	TV TUBE HEART (LP)	10

(see also Pogues)

MARK RADICE
72	Paramount PARA 3024	Hey My Love/Your Love Is Like Fire	7
72	Paramount PARA 3025	New Day/Take Me To The Park	7
72	Paramount SPFA 7004	MARK RADICE (LP)	10

RADIO ACTORS
78	Virgin NO NUKE 235	Nuclear Waste/Digital Love (as Fast Breeders & Radio Actors, with insert, a few with p/s)	20/10
79	Charly CYS 1058	Nuclear Waste/Digital Love (p/s, reissue, 2 slightly label designs)	7
79	DB DBS 5	Nuclear Waste/Digital Love (different p/s, 2nd reissue)	8

(see also Sting, Newcastle Big Band, Police, Gilli Smyth, Nik Turner [or Inner City Unit], Steve Hillage, Sphynx)

RADIO BIRDMAN
78	Sire 6078 617	What Gives/Anglo Girl Desire (no p/s)	10
78	Sire 9103 332	RADIOS APPEAR (LP, with inner sleeve)	15
78	Sire SRK 6050	RADIOS APPEAR (LP, reissue)	10

RADIO GHOSTS
82	Gramaphone GRAMP 02	SAY HELLO TO THE WORLD OF LOVE (EP)	4

MINT VALUE £

RADIO HEART

87	GFM GFM 109	Radio Heart/Radio Heart (Instrumental) (black or blue p/s) 4
87	GFM GFMP 109	Radio Heart/Radio Heart (Instrumental) (picture disc) 5
87	GFM GFMG 109	Radio Heart/Radio Heart (Instrumental) (radio-shaped picture disc) 8
87	GFM GFMT 109	Radio Heart (Extended Mix)/Radio Heart (Instrumental) (12", black p/s) 7
87	GFM GFMR 109	Radio Heart (Extended Mix)/Radio Heart (Instrumental)/Radio Heart
		(Mistasax Version 2) (12", blue p/s) 8
87	GFM GFMX 109	Radio Heart (Extended Mix)/Radio Heart (Instrumental) (12", picture disc) 8
87	GFM GFM 112	London Times/Rumour (p/s, with GFM sampler flexidisc) 4
87	GFM GFMP 112	London Times/Rumour (picture disc) 5
87	GFM GFMX 112	London Times/Rumour (oblong picture disc) 8
87	GFM GFMT 112	London Times (Extended Mix)/Rumour (12", with GFM sampler flexidisc) 7
87	NBR NBRX 1	All Across The Nation (Remix)/River/All Across The Nation (Instrumental)
		(12", blue p/s) 8
87	NBR CDNBR 1	All Across The Nation (Extended Remix)/All Across The Nation (Radio Mix)/
		River/All Across The Nation (Instrumental) (CD) 10
87	NBR NBRL 1	RADIO HEART (LP, withdrawn) 15
87	NBR NBRLPX 1	RADIO HEART (LP, picture disc, unreleased)

(see also Gary Numan)

RADIO MOSCOW

| 87 | Status | RADIO MOSCOW (mini-LP) .... 7 |

RADIO STARS

77	Chiswick (N)S 9	Dirty Pictures/Sail Away (p/s) 4
77	Chiswick SW 17	STOP IT! (EP) 4
77	Chiswick NS 23	Nervous Wreck/Horrible Breath (p/s) 4
77	Chiswick NST 23	Nervous Wreck/Horrible Breath (12", p/s, numbered) 7
78	Chiswick NS 36	From A Rabbit/The Beast No. 2 (p/s, 2 different mixes of B-side:
		matrix numbers 5288-1T & 5288-2T) 4
78	Chiswick NS 36	From A Rabbit/To A Beast (6" 'hip pocket' issue, p/s) 6
82	Snap ECG 001	My Mother Said/2 Minutes Mr. Smith (p/s) 5
82	Moonlight MNS 001	Good Personality/Talking 'Bout You (p/s) 4
77	Chiswick WIK 5	SONGS FOR SWINGING LOVERS (LP, shrinkwrapped with free single:
		"No Russians In Russia"/"Dirty Pictures" [PROMO 2, no p/s]) 12
78	Chiswick CWK 3001	THE HOLIDAY ALBUM (LP) 10
82	Moonlight MNA 001	TWO MINUTES MR SMITH (LP) 10

(see also John's Children, Andy Ellison, Gull)

JACKIE RAE

58	Fontana H 155	More Than Ever/Hello Ma Baby 4
58	Fontana H 170	Day By Day/Take A Deep Breath 4
60	Fontana H 242	Summer Place/The Moon Got In My Eyes 4
60	Fontana H 275	Dreamy/Close 4
67	Coral Q 72495	Believe In Love/Lonely One 4

RAELETS

| 67 | HMV POP 1591 | One Hurt Deserves Another/One Room Paradise .... 6 |

(see also Ray Charles, Clydie King, Merry Clayton)

R.A.F.

| 80 | A&M AMLH 64816 | R.A.F. (LP) .... 10 |
| 81 | A&M AMLH 68525 | THE HEAT IS ON (LP) .... 10 |

GERRY RAFFERTY

| 71 | Transatlantic TRA 241 | CAN I HAVE MY MONEY BACK? (LP) .... 10 |

(see also Humblebums)

RAG DOLLS

64	Cameo Parkway P 921	Society Girl/Ragen (with Caliente Combo) 4
65	Stateside SS 398	Dusty/Hey Hoagy 4
67	Columbia DB 8289	Never Had So Much Loving/Any Little Bit 4
68	Columbia DB 8378	My Old Man's A Groovy Old Man/They Didn't Believe Me 4

(see also Marionettes)

RAGE

86	Diamond RAGE 1	Looking For You/Come On Now (p/s) 4
86	Diamond RAGE 1	Looking For You/Come On Now/Great Balls Of Fire/
		Hallelujah I Love Her So (12", p/s) 7

RAGE

80	Carrere CAR 159	Money/Thank That Woman (p/s) 4
81	Carrere CAR 182	Out Of Control/Double Dealer (p/s) 4
81	Carrere CAR 199	Bootliggers (1981) (Live In Paris) (p/s) 4
81	Carrere CAR 199	Bootliggers (1981) (Live In Paris) (picture disc) 4
81	Carrere CAL 124	OUT OF CONTROL (LP) 10

RAGGAMUFFINS

| 67 | London HLU 10134 | Four Days Of Rain/It Wasn't Happening At All .... 4 |

RAGING STORMS

| 62 | London HLU 9556 | The Dribble/Hound Dog .... 12 |

LOU RAGLAND

| 73 | Warner Bros K 16312 | Since You Said You'd Be Mine/I Didn't Mean To Love You .... 8 |

RAGPICKERS

| 59 | Saga SAG 45-2906 | Fifi/Cat On A Cool Tin Roof .... 4 |

RAIDERS

70	CBS 5016	Gone Movin' On/Interlude 4
71	CBS 7474	Birds Of A Feather/The Turkey 4
72	CBS 7808	Country Wine/It's So Hard Gettin' Up Today 4

72	CBS 8129	Powder Blue Mercedes Queen/Golden Girls Sometimes	4
70	CBS 63973	COLLAGE (LP)	10
71	CBS 64471	INDIAN RESERVATION (LP)	10

(see also Paul Revere & Raiders)

RAIL
84	EMI	RAIL (LP)	10

RAILWAY CHILDREN
90	Virgin VSTX 1289	So Right (Laylow Mix)/So Right (Laylow Dub)/So Right (Emotional Dub) (cassette in autographed box)	4

RAIN
85	Jive Alive JA 002	Once/Tom Paine (with insert)	7
88	Medium Cool MC 012	First Of May	4
88	Medium Cool MC 012T	First Of May (12")	7

RAINBEAUS
60	Vogue V 9161	That's All I'm Asking Of You/Maybe It's Wrong	10

RAINBOW (U.S.)
72	Polydor 2058 226	Old Log Cabin/Who Would Be A Soldier	4

(RITCHIE BLACKMORE'S) RAINBOW (U.K.)
74	Oyster OYR 103	Man On The Silver Mountain/Snake Charmer (as Ritchie Blackmore's Rainbow)	5
77	Polydor 2066 845	Kill The King/Man On The Silver Mountain (live)/Mistreated (live) (p/s)	5
78	Polydor 2066 913	Long Live Rock'n'Roll/Sensitive To Light (art sleeve)	5
78	Polydor 2066 968	L.A. Connection/Lady Of The Lake (red vinyl, art sleeve)	8
79	Polydor POSP 70	Since You've Been Gone/Bad Girl (art sleeve)	4
79	Polydor POSP 70	Since You've Been Gone/Bad Girl (reissue, p/s)	4
80	Polydor POSP 104	All Night Long/Weiss Heim (p/s)	4
81	Polydor POSP 251	Can't Happen Here/Jealous Lover (p/s)	4
82	Polydor POSPX 421	Stone Cold (Long Version)/Rock Fever (12", blue vinyl, p/s)	7
83	Polydor POSPP 631	Street Of Dreams/Anybody There? (picture disc)	8
83	Polydor POSPX 631	Street Of Dreams/Anybody There?/Power (live) (12", p/s)	7
83	Polydor POSPP 654	Can't Let You Go/All Night Long (live) (guitar shaped picture disc)	5
75	Oyster OYA 2001	RITCHIE BLACKMORE'S RAINBOW (LP, gatefold sleeve, as Ritchie Blackmore's Rainbow)	12
79	Polydor POLD 5023	DOWN TO EARTH (LP, clear vinyl)	10

(see also Deep Purple, Elf, Dio, Graham Bonnett, Cozy Powell, Roger Glover, Ritchie Blackmore, David Kubinec)

RAINBOW FFOLLY
68	Parlophone R 5701	Go Girl/Drive My Car	20
67	Parlophone PMC/PCS 7050	SALLIES FFORTH (LP)	120

(see also Love Affair, Mott The Hoople)

RAINBOW PEOPLE
68	Pye 7N 17582	Walk'll Do You Good/Dream Time	10
68	Pye 7N 17624	The Sailing Song/Rainbows	4
69	Pye 7N 17759	Living In A Dream World/Happy To See You Again	6

RAINBOWS
69	CBS 3995	Rainbows/Nobody But You	4
69	CBS 4568	New Day Dawning/Days And Nights	4

RAINCOATS
79	Rough Trade RT 013	Fairytale In The Supermarket/In Love/Adventures Close To Home (p/s)	4
82	Rough Trade RT 093	N-One's Little Girl/Running Away (p/s)	4
79	Rough Trade ROUGH 3	THE RAINCOATS (LP)	10
81	Rough Trade ROUGH 13	ODYSHAPE (LP)	10

(see also Slits)

RAINCHECKS
64	Solar SRP 104	Something About You/You're My Angel	4
65	R&B MRB 5002	How Are You Boy/Bye Bye Baby	25

RAINDROPS (U.K.)
59	Parlophone R 4559	Italian Style/Along Came Jones	6
60	Oriole CB 1544	Let's Make A Foursome/If I Had My Life To Live Over	5
60	Oriole CB 1555	Banjo Boy/Crazy Rhythm	4
61	Oriole CB 1595	Will You Love Me Tomorrow/Raindrops	5
64	Fontana TF 463	The Book Of Love/I Won't Cry	6
67	CBS 202669	Foolman/Got To Find A Reason	4

(see also Jackie [Lee] & Raindrops, Jacky, Vince Hill)

RAINDROPS (U.S.)
63	London HL 9718	What A Guy/It's So Wonderful	15
63	London HL 9769	The Kind Of Boy You Can't Forget/Even Though You Can't Dance	12
64	London HL 9825	That Boy John/Hanky Panky	12
64	London RE 1415	WHAT A GUY (EP)	25
64	London HA 8140	THE RAINDROPS (LP)	40

LORRY RAINE
54	London HL 8043	You Broke My Broken Heart/I'm In Love With A Guy	25
55	London HL 8132	Love Me Tonight/What Would I Do	25

MA RAINEY
50s	Poydras 78	Bo Weavil Blues/Last Minute Blues (78)	8
50s	Poydras 88	Army Camp Harmony Blues/Explaining The Blues (78)	8
50s	Jazz Collector L 1	Travelling Blues/Deep Moaning Blues (78)	5
50s	Jazz Collector L 10	Jelly Bean Blues/Countin' The Blues (78)	5
50s	Jazz Collector L 16	Don't Fish My Sea/Soon This Morning (78)	5
50s	Jazz Collector L 20	Jealous Hearted Blues/See See Rider Blues (78)	5

MINT VALUE £

50s	Jazz Collector L 35	Blues The World Forgot Pts 1 & 2 (78)	5
50s	Jazz Collector L 42	New Bo-Weavil Blues/Moonshine Blues (78)	5
50s	Jazz Collector L 48	Barrel House Blues/Walking Blues (78)	5
50s	Jazz Collector L 52	Misery Blues/Dead Drunk Blues (78)	5
50s	Jazz Collector L 57	Morning Hour Blues/Weepin' Woman Blues (78)	5
50s	Jazz Collector L 66	Moonshine Blues/Southern Blues (78)	5
50s	Jazz Collector L 73	Stack O'Lee Blues/Yonder Come The Blues (78)	5
50s	Jazz Collector L 78	Those Dogs Of Mine/Lucky Rock Blues (78)	5
50s	Jazz Collector L 82	Honey Where Have You Been So Long/Ma Rainey's Mystery Record (78)	8
50s	Jazz Collector L 87	Slave To The Blues/Oh My Babe Blues (78)	5
50s	Jazz Collector L 98	Blues Oh Blues/Oh Papa Blues (78)	5
50s	Jazz Collector L 107	Lawd Send Me A Man Blues/South Bound Blues (78)	5
50s	Jazz Collector L 120	Gone Daddy Blues/Slow Driving Moan (78)	5
50s	Signature 908	Yonder Come The Blues/Stack O'Lee Blues (78)	8
50s	Poydras 62	Hear me Talking To You/Prove It On Me Blues (78)	8
53	London AL 3502	MA RAINEY VOLUME 1 (10" LP)	25
55	London AL 3538	MA RAINEY VOLUME 2 (10" LP)	25
56	London AL 3558	MA RAINEY VOLUME 3 (10" LP)	25
50s	Ristic LP 13	MA RAINEY (10" EP)	30
50s	Ristic LP 19	MA RAINEY (10" LP)	30
62	Riverside RL 12-108	MA RAINEY SINGS THE BLUES (LP)	20
75	Milestone M 47021	MA RAINEY (2-LP)	15

MA RAINEY & IDA COX

| 60 | Collector JEL 12 | THE FEMALE BLUES VOL. 1 (EP) | 12 |
| 64 | Collector JEL 22 | THE FEMALE BLUES VOL. 2 (EP, with Trixie Smith) | 12 |

(see also Ida Cox, Tommy Ladnier)

MA RAINEY & PAPA CHARLIE JACKSON

| 50s | Poydras 11 | Ma And Papa Poorhouse Blues/Big Feeling Blues (78) | 8 |

RAINMAKERS

| 87 | Mercury MERD 238 | Let My People Go-Go/Nobody Knows//Government Cheese/Kissin' (double pack box set) | 4 |

RAIN PARADE

| 83 | Enigma BOB 4/ LYN 15263 | Sad Eyes Kill (3.16) (1-sided flexidisc with 'Bucketfull Of Brains' magazine issue 10) | 6/4 |

MARVIN RAINWATER

55	MGM SP 1150	Tennessee Houn' Dog Yodel/Albino (Pink-Eyed) Stallion	35
55	MGM MGM 876	Tennessee Houn' Dog Yodel/Albino (Pink-Eyed) Stallion (78)	6
56	MGM MGM 929	What Am I Supposed To Do/Why Did You Have To Go And Leave Me	20
56	MGM MGM 929	What Am I Supposed To Do/Why Did You Have To Go And Leave Me (78)	5
57	MGM MGM 961	Gonna Find Me A Bluebird/So You Think You've Got	15
57	MGM MGM 961	Gonna Find Me A Bluebird/So You Think You've Got (78)	5
58	MGM MGM 974	Whole Lotta Woman/Baby, Don't Go	8
58	MGM MGM 974	Whole Lotta Woman/Baby, Don't Go (78)	5
58	MGM MGM 980	I Dig You Baby/Two Fools In Love (B-side with Sister Patty)	8
58	MGM MGM 980	I Dig You Baby/Two Fools In Love (B-side with Sister Patty) (78)	5
58	MGM MGM 988	Dance Me Daddy/Because I'm A Dreamer (B-side with Sister Patty)	10
58	MGM MGM 988	Dance Me Daddy/Because I'm A Dreamer (B-side with Sister Patty) (78)	5
59	MGM MGM 1030	Half-Breed/A Song Of New Love	8
59	MGM MGM 1030	Half-Breed/A Song Of New Love (78)	5
60	MGM MGM 1052	Nothin' Needs Nothin' (Like I Need You)/The Valley Of The Moon	10
61	London HLU 9447	Boo Hoo/I Can't Forget	90
58	MGM MGM-EP 647	MEET MARVIN RAINWATER (EP)	30
58	MGM MGM-EP 662	WHOLE LOTTA MARVIN (EP)	35
59	MGM MGM-EP 685	MARVIN RAINWATER (EP)	35
63	Ember EMB 4521	COUNTRY AND WESTERN FAVOURITES VOL. 2 (EP)	15
58	MGM MGM-D 152	SONGS BY MARVIN RAINWATER (10" LP)	75
72	Philips 6414 110	GETS COUNTRY FEVER (LP)	10

(see also Connie Francis & Marvin Rainwater)

RAINY DAY

| 84 | EMI EMI 5472 | Painting Pictures/Welche Farbe Hat Der Sonnenschein (p/s) | 12 |

RAINY DAZE

67	CBS 3200	Autumn Leaves/What Do You Think	10
68	Polydor BM 56737	Blood Of Oblivion/Stop Sign	12
68	CBS 56731	THAT ACAPULCO GOLD (LP)	10

RAISINS

68	Major Major MM 540	Ain't That Lovin' You Baby/Stranger Things Have Happened	5
69	Major Minor MM 602	I Thank You/Don't Leave Me Like This	5
68	Major Minor MMLP 20	THE RAISINS (LP, also stereo SMLP 20)	10

BONNIE RAITT

| 72 | Warner Bros K 16226 | Too Long At The Fair/Under The Falling Sky | 4 |

RAJAH

| 73 | Philips 6006 284 | The Godfather Theme/The Deadeye Dick | 4 |

DON RALKE ORCHESTRA

| 59 | Vogue V 9152 | Maverick/Travellin' West | 5 |
| 69 | Warner Bros WB 2 | 77 Sunset Strip (as Big Sound Of Don Ralke)/PETE CANDOLI & HIS ORCHESTRA: 77 Sunset Strip Cha-Cha | 5 |

TOMMY RALL, ANN MILLER, BOBBY VAN & BOB FOSSE

| 54 | MGM SP 1079 | From This Moment On/So Kiss Me Kate (by Kathryn Grayson & Howard Keel)/Brush Up Your Shakespeare (by Keenan Wynn & James Whitmore) | 5 |

RALLY ROUNDERS
60s	Lyntone LYN 574	Bike Beat/Bike Beat Part 2 (p/s, flexidisc) 40

(perhaps see also Outlaws, Ritchie Blackmore)

BUCK RAM'S RAMRODS
63	London HLU 9677	Benfica/Odd Man Theme 8

(see also Platters)

RAMASES
71	Vertigo 6360 046	SPACE HYMNS (LP, foldout sleeve, spiral label, later 'spaceship' label) 35/20
75	Vertigo 6360 115	GLASS TOP COFFIN (LP, gatefold sleeve, spiral label) 18

(see also 10cc)

RAMASES & SELKET
68	CBS 3717	Crazy One/Mind's Eye 70

RAMATAM
72	Atlantic K 40415	RAMATAM (LP) 10

(see also Iron Butterfly)

EDDIE RAMBEAU
62	Stateside SS 116	Summertime Guy/Last Night Was My Last Night 4
64	Stateside SS 301	Come Closer/She's Smilin' At Me 4
65	Stateside SS 448	My Name Is Mud/I Just Need Your Love 4
66	Stateside SS 486	The Train/Yesterday's Newspapers 4
66	Stateside SS 501	I'm The Sky/I Just Need Your Love 4
66	Stateside SS 561	The Clock/If I Were You 4

RAMBLER
66	Pye 7N 17164	Love Minus Zero No Limit/An Bonnan Bui 4

RAMBLERS
63	Decca F 11775	Dodge City/Just For Chicks 15

RAMBLERS TWO
65	Pye 7N 15989	Today Is The Highway/The Mountains And The Sea 4

RAMBLETTES
65	Brunswick 05932	Thinking Of You/On Back Street 4

CARLOS RAMIREZ
54	MGM SP 1072	I Had To Kiss You/Little More Of Your Armour 4

RAM JAM
76	Epic EPC 82215	RAM JAM (LP) 10
77	Epic EPC 82628	PORTRAIT OF THE ARTIST (LP) 10

RAM JAM BAND
65	Columbia DB 7621	Shake Shake Senora/Akinla 8

(see also Geno Washington & Ram Jam Band)

RAM RAM KINO
84	Temple TOPY 006	Advantage — Tantric Routines 1-4 (12", p/s) 7

(see also Crispy Ambulance)

RAMONES
76	Sire 6078 601	Blitzkrieg Bop/Havana Affair (some with p/s) 50/4
77	Sire 6078 603	I Remember You/California Sun (live)/I Don't Wanna Walk Around With You (live) (p/s) 15
77	Sire RAM 001 (6078 606)	Sheena Is A Punk Rocker/Commando/I Don't Care (p/s) 8
77	Sire RAM 001 (6078 606)	Sheena Is A Punk Rocker/Commando/I Don't Care (12", p/s, 10,000 only) 12
77	Sire 6078 607	Swallow My Pride/Pinhead/Let's Dance (live) (p/s) 8
77	Sire 6078 611	Rockaway Beach/Teenage Lobotomy/Beat On The Brat (p/s) 5
77	Sire 6078 611	Rockaway Beach/Teenage Lobotomy/Beat On The Brat (12", p/s, some possibly with poster) 15/7
78	Sire 6078 615	Do You Wanna Dance?/It's A Long Way Back To Germany/Cretin Hop (p/s) 5
78	Sire SRE 1031	Don't Come Close/I Don't Want You (p/s) 4
78	Sire SRE 1031	Don't Come Close/I Don't Want You (12", p/s yellow vinyl or no p/s red vinyl) 8
79	Sire SIR 4009	She's The One/I Wanna Be Sedated (p/s) 8
79	Sire SIR 4021	Rock'n'Roll High School/Rockaway Beach (live)/Sheena Is A Punk Rocker (live) (p/s) 4
80	Sire SIR 4031	Baby, I Love You/High Risk Insurance (cassette) 4
80	Sire SREP 1	MELTDOWN WITH THE RAMONES (EP) 8
81	RSO RSO 070	I Wanna Be Sedated/The Return Of Jackie And Judy (p/s) 8
81	Sire SIR 4052	She's A Sensation/All Quiet On The Eastern Front (p/s) 4
83	Sire W 9606	Time Has Come Today/Psycho Therapy (p/s) 12
83	Sire W 9606T	Time Has Come Today/Psycho Therapy/Baby I Love You/ Don't Come Close And Here And There (12", p/s) 15
85	Beggars Banquet BEG 128D	Chasing The Night/Howling At The Moon//Smash You/Street Fighting Man (double pack) 4
85	Beggars Banquet BEGTP 128	Chasing The Night/Howling At The Moon//Smash You/Street Fighting Man (12", picture disc) 7
76	Sire 9103 253	THE RAMONES (LP, with insert) 10
76	Sire 9103 254	THE RAMONES LEAVE HOME (LP, with "Carbona Not Glue") 15
77	Sire 9103 255	ROCKET TO RUSSIA (LP, with inner sleeve) 10
78	Sire SRK 6063	ROAD TO RUIN (LP, yellow vinyl) 10

(see also Paley Brothers & Ramones)

RAM RAM KINO
85	Temple TOPY 006	Advantage (3.23)/(Basket Mix) (4.00)/Into The Bush (3.26)/ Special (3.56) (12", p/s) 7

RAMRODS (U.S.)
61	London HLU 9282	Riders In The Sky/Zig Zag 6

| 61 | London HLU 9355 | Loch Lomond Rock/Take Me Back To My ....8 |
| 61 | London RE-U 1292 | RIDERS IN THE SKY (EP) ....40 |

RAMRODS (U.K.)
| 65 | United Artists UP 1113 | Overdrive/Stalker ....8 |

BILL RAMSEY
| 62 | Polydor NH 66812 | Go Man Go/Rocking Mountain ....8 |

RANCHERS
| 65 | Cavern Sound IMSTL 2 | An American Sailor At The Cavern/Sidetracked ....8 |

ELLIOTT RANDALL
| 70 | Polydor 2489 004 | RANDALL'S ISLAND (LP) ....10 |

FREDDY RANDALL & HIS BAND
53	Parlophone MSP 6007	Clarinet Marmalade/Original Dixieland One-step 4
53	Parlophone MSP 6030	At The Jazz Band Ball/Way Down Yonder In New Orleans 4
53	Parlophone MSP 6043	Twelve For Six/Copenhagen 4
54	Parlophone MSP 6087	Carolina In The Morning/Tin Roof Blues 4
54	Parlophone MSP 6098	Muskrat Ramble/Shine 4
54	Parlophone MSP 6137	Someday Sweetheart/Hotter Than That 4

TEDDY RANDAZZO
59	HMV POP 578	It's Magic/Richer Than I 5
59	HMV POP 578	It's Magic/Richer Than I (78) 5
60	HMV POP 806	Journey To Love/Misery 4
61	HMV POP 866	Happy Ending/But You Broke My Heart 4
61	HMV POP 925	Let The Sunshine In/Broken Bell 5
62	HMV POP 1062	Dance To The Locomotion/Cottonfields 6
63	HMV POP 1119	Echoes/It Wasn't A Dream 4
63	Pye Intl. 7N 25181	Big Wide World/Be Sure, My Love 4
62	HMV CLP 1527	JOURNEY TO LOVE (LP, also stereo CSD 1421) 15
63	HMV CLP 1601	TEDDY RANDAZZO TWISTS (LP, with Dazzlers) 40

LYNNE RANDELL
| 67 | CBS 2847 | Ciao Baby/Stranger In My Arms ....125 |
| 67 | CBS 2927 | That's A Hoe Down/I Need You Boy ....10 |

RANDELLS
| 63 | London HLU 9760 | The Martian Hop/Forgive Me Darling ....20 |

DON RANDI
| 65 | London HLU 9963 | Mexican Pearls/I Don't Wanna Be Kissed ....4 |

BARBARA RANDOLPH
| 67 | Tamla Motown TMG 628 | I Got A Feelin'/You Got Me Hurtin' All Over ....30 |
| 71 | Tamla Motown TMG 788 | I Got A Feelin'/You Got Me Hurtin' All Over (reissue) ....8 |

BOOTS RANDOLPH
62	London HLU 9567	Bluebird Of Happiness/Keep A Light In Your Window Tonight 5
63	London HLU 9685	Yakety Sax/I Really Don't Want To Know 8
63	London HLU 9798	Windy And Warm/Lonely Street 5
64	London HLU 9891	Hey, Mr. Sax Man/Baby Go To Sleep 6
66	London HLU 10017	Theme From A Dream/King Of The Road 4
66	London HLU 10028	These Boots Are Made For Walking/Honey In Your Heart 4
67	Monument MON 1001	The Shadow Of Your Smile/I'll Just Walk Away 4
67	Monument MON 1011	Big Daddy/Love Letters 4
68	Monument MON 1028	Games People Play/By The Time I Get To Phoenix 4
63	London RE-U 1365	YAKETY SAX OF BOOTS RANDOLPH (EP) 15
63	London HA-U 8106	YAKETY SAX (LP) 15
66	London HA-U 8280	MORE YAKETY SAX (LP, as Boots Randolph	
		& His Combo) 15
67	Monument LMO/SMO 5002	HIP BOOTS (LP) 10
67	Monument LMO/SMO 5003	BOOTS WITH STRINGS (LP) 10
68	Monument LMO/SMO 5012	FANTASTIC BOOTS RANDOLPH (LP) 10
69	Monument LMO/SMO 5022	SAXSATIONAL (LP) 10

CHARLES RANDOLPH GREEN SOUND
| 69 | London HLD 10283 | Quintin's Theme/Number One At The Blue Whale ....4 |
| 76 | UK USA 15 | Star Trek/The Hustle ....4 |

RANDY & RAINBOWS
| 63 | Stateside SS 214 | Denise/Come Back ....25 |

RANEE & RAJ
| 68 | Fontana TF 920 | Feel Like A Clown/Rainbow Land ....8 |
| 68 | Fontana TF 941 | Don't Tell Me I Must Go/Razor Edge ....6 |

SUE RANEY
57	Capitol CL 14757	The Careless Years/What's The Good Word, Mr. Bluebird 4
57	Capitol CL 14792	Please Hurry Home/Don't Take My Happiness 4
58	Capitol CL 14923	My, My, How The Time Goes By/Periwinkle Blue 4
59	Capitol CL 14980	Ever/The Restless Sea 4
59	Capitol CL 15045	Swingin' In A Hammock/I Don't Look Right Without You 4
60	Capitol CL 15132	Biology/I Stayed Too Long At The Fair 4
58	Capitol T 964	WHEN YOUR LOVER HAS GONE (LP) 10

WAYNE RANEY
| 54 | Parlophone CSMP 20 | Adam/The Roosters Are Crowing (export issue) ....15 |
| 58 | Parlophone GEP 8746 | COUNTRY AND WESTERN (EP) ....25 |

RANGLERS
| 68 | Trend TRE 1007 | You Never Said Goodbye/Step Down ....8 |

ERNEST RANGLIN

62	Island WI 015	Harmonica Twist/Mitty Gritty (as Ernest Ranglin Orchestra)	10
63	Island WI 128	Exodus/ROBERT MARLEY: One Cup Of Coffee	50
66	Black Swan IEP 704	SOHO (EP, as Ernest Ranglin & G.B.'s)	18
64	Island ILP 909	WRANGLIN' (LP)	30
64	Island ILP 915	REFLECTIONS (LP)	35

MASSIMO RANIERI

71	CBS S 7207	Goodbye My Love/The Sun Shining Down On Me	12

BILLY RANKIN

83	A&M AM 172	Baby Come Back/Part Of The Scenery (p/s)	5

KENNY RANKIN

60	Brunswick 05845	As Sure As You're Born/Teasin' Heart	5

PETER RANSOME

72	York FYK 402	PETER RANSOME (LP)	10

RAPED

78	Parole KNIT 1	PRETTY PAEDOPHILES (EP)	6
78	Parole PURL 1	Cheap Night Out/Foreplay Playground (p/s, with ad sheet)	5
84	Iguana PILLAGED 1	FINALLY ... HE RAPED (LP, official bootleg, with booklet)	15
	(see also Cuddly Toys)		

RAPEMAN

88	Fierce FRIGHT 031	Hated Chinee/Marmoset (p/s)	8
	(see also Big Black)		

RAPHAEL

66	Hispavox HXS 303	Please Speak To Me Of Love/Hablemos Del Amor	15

JOHNNY RAPHAEL

58	Vogue V 9104	We're Only Young Once/The Lonely Road To Nowhere	30
58	Vogue V 9104	We're Only Young Once/The Lonely Road To Nowhere (78)	5

RAPIERS

83	Red Door RA 001	THE RAPIERS VOL. 1 (EP)	10
84	Twang RA 002	THE RAPIERS VOL. 2 (EP)	8
85	Twang RA 003	THE RAPIERS VOL. 3 (EP)	7

BRIAN RAPKIN & KELVIN JONES

70s	MSR	DREAMS OF THE BEAST (LP)	20

RARE AMBER

69	Polydor BM 56309	Malfunction Of The Engine/Blind Love	10
69	Polydor 583 046	RARE AMBER (LP)	100

RARE BIRD

70	Charisma CB 120	Sympathy/Devil's High Concern	4
71	Charisma CB 138	What You Want To Know/Hammerhead	6
72	Charisma CB 179	Sympathy/Devil's High Concern/What Do You Want To Know/Hammerhead (p/s)	7
73	Polydor 2058 402	Virgina/Lonely Street	4
74	Polydor 2058 471	Body And Soul/Redman	4
75	Polydor 2058 591	Don't Be Afraid/Passin' Through	4
75	Charisma CB 262	Sympathy/Beautiful Scarlet	4
69	Charisma CAS 1005	RARE BIRD (LP)	15
70	Charisma CAS 1011	AS YOUR MIND FLIES BY (LP)	15
72	Polydor 2442 101	EPIC FOREST (LP, some with free p/s EP "Roadside Welcome"/ "Four Grey Walls"/"You're Lost" [2814 011] & poster)	25/15
73	Polydor 2383 211	SOMEBODY'S WATCHING (LP)	10
74	Polydor 2383 274	BORN AGAIN (LP)	10
	(see also Fields)		

RARE BREED

66	Strike JH 316	Beg, Borrow And Steal/Jeri's Theme	10
	(see also Pussyfoot)		

RARE EARTH

70	Tamla Motown TMG 742	Get Ready/Magic Key	6
70	T. Motown STML 11165	GET READY (LP)	12
71	T. Motown STML 11180	ECOLOGY (LP)	12
71	Rare Earth SREA 4001	ONE WORLD (LP)	10
72	Rare Earth SRESP 301	IN CONCERT (LP)	10
73	Rare Earth SRE 3008	WILLIE REMEMBERS (LP)	10
73	Rare Earth SRE 3010	MA (LP)	10

RASCALS

68	Atlantic 584 182	A Beautiful Morning/Rainy Day	6
68	Atlantic 584 210	People Got To Be Free/My World	4
69	Atlantic 584 255	Heaven/Baby I'm Blue	4
68	Atlantic 587/588 098	ONCE UPON A DREAM (LP)	12
68	Atlantic 587/588 120	TIME PEACE — RASCALS' GREATEST HITS (LP)	12
69	Atlantic 588 183	FREEDOM SUITE (2-LP)	14
70	Atlantic 588 210	SEE (LP)	10
71	Atlantic 2400 113	SEARCH AND NEARNESS (LP)	12
72	CBS 64756	THE ISLAND OF REAL (LP)	10
	(see also Young Rascals)		

RENATO RASCEI

60	RCA RCA 1177	Romantica/Dimmelo Con Un Fiore	10

RASPBERRIES

72	Capitol CL 15718	I Don't Want To Say Goodbye/Rock And Roll Mama	4

RASPBERRIES

72	Capitol CL 15730	Go All The Way/With You In My Life	4
73	Capitol CL 15740	I Wanna Be With You/Goin' Nowhere Tonight	4
74	Capitol CL 15801	Overnight Sensation/Hands On You	4
72	Capitol E-ST 11036	RASPBERRIES (LP)	10
72	Capitol E-ST 11123	FRESH RASPBERRIES (LP)	10
73	Capitol E-ST 11220	SIDE THREE (LP)	10
74	Capitol E-ST 11329	STARTING OVER (LP)	10

(see also Choir)

RASPUTIN'S STASH
71	Atlantic 2091 152	Your Love Is Certified/What's On Your Mind	4

RAT & WHALE
80	Rewind REWIND 5	Wheels On Fire/Wheels On Fire (long version)	4

(see also Alternative TV)

ARMAN RATIP
73	Regal Zono. SLRZ 1038	THE SPY FROM ISTANBUL (LP)	25

RATS
64	Oriole CB 1967	Parchman Farm/Every Day I Have The Blues	50
64	Oak RGJ 145	Spoonfull (1-sided)	150
65	Columbia DB 7483	Spoonful/I've Got My Eyes On You Baby	70
65	Columbia DB 7607	I Gotta See My Baby Everyday/Headin' Back (To New Orleans)	40

(see also Mark Peters; these records do NOT feature Mick Ronson)

RATS
65	CBS 201740	Sack Of Woe/Gimme That Wine	40

RATT
85	Atlantic A 9546P	Lay It Down/Got Me On The Line (shaped picture disc)	6
86	Atlantic A 9502P	You're In Love/Between The Eyes (shaped picture disc)	8

RATTLES
63	Philips BF 1277	The Stomp/Zip A Dee Doo Dah	8
64	Decca F 11873	Bye Bye Johnny/Roll Over Beethoven	12
64	Decca F 11936	Tell Me What I Can Do/Sunbeam At The Sky	8
65	Fontana TF 618	Come On And Sing/Candy To Me	8
66	Fontana TF 724	Say All Right/Love Of My Life	8
70	Decca F 23058	The Witch/Geraldine	4
71	Decca F 13243	Devil's On The Loose/I Know You Don't Know	4
64	Decca DFE 8568	TEENBEAT FROM THE STAR CLUB HAMBURG (EP)	50
71	Decca SKL-R 5088	THE RATTLES (LP)	15
64	Philips BL 7614	TWIST AT THE STAR CLUB HAMBURG (LP)	60
67	Mercury MG 1127	GREATEST HITS (LP)	20

(see also Achim Reichel, Wonderland Band, Propeller)

CARL RAVAZZA
51	HMV B 10202	Rock, Rock, Rock/Like A Dream (78)	5

CHRIS RAVEL & RAVERS
63	Decca F 11696	I Do/Don't You Dig This Kind Of Beat	10

RAVEN
70	CBS 5043	Children At Our Feet/Here Comes A Truck	5

RAVEN
80	Neat NEAT 06	Don't Need Your Money/Wiped Out (p/s)	5
81	Neat NEAT 11	Hard Ride/Crazy World (p/s)	4
82	Neat NEAT 15	CRASH BANG WALLOP (12" EP, mauve vinyl)	8
83	Neat NEAT 28	Break The Chain/Ballad Of Marshall (p/s)	4
83	Neat NEAT 29P	Born To Be Wild/Inquisitor (with Udo) (picture disc)	4
81	Neat NEATP 1001	ROCK TILL YOU DROP (LP, picture disc)	10
83	Neat NEAT 1011	ALL FOR ONE (LP)	10

JON RAVEN
70s	Broadside	HARVEST (LP, with book)	15
71	Argo ZFB 29	KATE OF COAL-BROOKDALE (LP, as Jon & Mike Raven with Jean Ward)	25
73	Trailer LER 2083	SONGS OF CHANGING WORLD (LP, with Nic Jones & Tony Rose)	10

MIKE RAVEN
69	Transatlantic TRASAM 5	MIKE RAVEN BLUES SAMPLER (LP)	15
66	Transatlantic XTRA 1047	MIKE RAVEN BLUES SHOW (LP)	12

PAUL RAVEN
60	Decca F 11202	Alone In The Night/Too Proud	25
61	Parlophone R 4812	Walk On Boy/All Grown Up	15
61	Parlophone R 4842	Tower Of Strength/Livin' The Blues	15
68	MCA MU 1024	Musical Man/Wait For Me	10
68	MCA MU 1035	Soul Thing/We'll Go Where The World Can't Find Us	10
70	MCA MKS 5053	Stand/Soul Thing	8
78	EMI NUT 2855	Tower Of Strength/Livin' The Blues/Walk On Boy/All Grown Up (p/s)	4

(see also Paul Monday, Rubber Bucket, Gary Glitter)

SIMON RAVEN
66	Piccadilly 7N 35301	I Wonder If She Remembers Me/Sea Of Love	25

RAVENS
53	Oriole CB 1148	Rock Me All Night Long/Write Me One Sweet Letter (78)	20
53	Oriole CB 1149	Begin The Beguine/Looking For My Baby (78)	20
53	Oriole CB 1258	Who'll Be The Fool?/Rough Ridin' (with Jimmy Ricks) (78)	20
54	Mercury MB 3008	Rock Me All Night Long/Write Me One Sweet Letter (78, reissue)	35
54	Mercury MB 3009	Begin The Beguine/Looking For My Baby (78, reissue)	35
54	Mercury MB 3093	Who'll Be The Fool/Rough Ridin' (with Jimmy Ricks) (78, reissue)	35

| 63 | Oriole CB 1910 | I Just Wanna Hear You Say/Send Me A Letter | 7 |

RAVENS ROCK GROUP

| 61 | Pye Intl. 7N 25077 | The Ghoul Friend/Career Girl | 6 |

RAVERS

| 69 | Upsetter US 312 | Badam Bam/UPSETTERS: Medical Operation | 5 |

RAVING SAVAGES

| 63 | Decca DFE 8546 | EVERYBODY SURF (EP) | 40 |

RAW DEAL

| 81 | Neat NEAT 12 | Lonewolf/Take The Sky (p/s) | 4 |

RAW HERBS

86	Medium Cool MC 002	Old Joe/That's How It Is (1-sided flexidisc in card sleeve with stuck-on prints, 2 different colour sleeves, 33rpm)	7
87	Medium Cool MC 003	She's A Nurse But She's Alright/So Wired! (p/s)	5
87	Medium Cool MC 006	Don't Bury Me Yet (p/s)	4
87	Medium Cool MC 006T	Don't Bury Me Yet (12", p/s)	7

RAW MATERIAL

69	Evolution E 2441	Time And Illusion/Bob's Party	20
70	Evolution E 2445	Hi There Hallelujah/Days Of The Fighting Cock	18
70	Evolution Z 1006	THE RAW MATERIAL ALBUM (LP)	180
71	RCA Neon NE 8	TIME IS (LP)	150

(see also Shoot)

LOU RAWLS

65	Capitol CL 15398	Three O'Clock In The Morning/Nothing Really Feels The Same	4
66	Capitol CL 15465	Love Is A Hurtin' Thing/Memory Lane	6
67	Capitol CL 15488	You Can Bring Me All Your Heartaches/A Woman Who's A Woman	5
67	Capitol CL 15499	Dead End Street/Yes It Hurts Doesn't It	6
67	Capitol CL 15507	Show Business/When Loves Goes Wrong	4
67	Capitol CL 15515	Hard To Get Thing Called Love/I Don't Love You Anymore	6
67	Capitol CL 15522	Little Drummer Boy/Child With A Toy	4
68	Capitol CL 15533	My Ancestors/Evil Woman	4
68	Capitol CL 15548	You're Good For Me/Soul Serenade	6
68	Capitol CL 15560	Down Here On The Ground/I'm Satisfied	4
69	Capitol CL 15583	It's You/Sweet Charity	4
69	Capitol CL 15611	Your Good Thing/Season Of The Witch	4
70	Capitol CL 15630	You've Made Me So Happy/Let's Burn The Cornfield	4
74	Bell BLL 1390	She's Gone/Hourglass	4
65	Capitol T 1824	BLACK AND BLUE (LP)	10
66	Capitol (S)T 2459	LIVE (LP)	10
67	Capitol (S)T 2566	SOULIN' (LP)	10
67	Capitol (S)T 2632	CARRYIN' ON! (LP)	10
68	Capitol (S)T 2864	FEELIN' GOOD (LP)	10

CLYDE RAY

57	Columbia DB 3875	Follow Me/Steady As A Rock	4
57	Columbia DB 3875	Follow Me/Steady As A Rock (78)	5
58	Columbia DB 4106	Locked In The Arms Of Love/I'm Not Afraid Anymore	4

JAMES RAY

| 62 | Pye Intl. 7N 25126 | If You Gotta Make A Fool Of Somebody/It's Been A Drag | 10 |
| 62 | Pye Intl. 7N 25147 | Itty Bitty Pieces/You Remember The Face | 8 |

JAMES RAY & PERFORMANCE

87	Merciful Release MRAY 38	Texas/Mountain Voices (p/s)	4
87	Merciful Rel. MRAY 38/T	Texas/Mountain Voices/Johnny Goodbye (12", p/s)	7
86	Merciful Rel. MRAY 52R	Mexico Sundown Blues (edit)/Mexico Sundown Blues (Instrumental) (p/s)	10
86	Merciful Release MRAY 52	Mexico Sundown Blues/Edie Sedgwick (12", p/s)	10
80s	Merciful Release	Live In Leeds (flexidisc)	5

JOHNNIE RAY

52	Columbia DB 2995	Cry (with Four Lads)/The Little White Cloud That Cried (78)	5
53	Columbia SCM 5015	Walkin' My Baby Back Home/The Lady Drinks Champagne (B-side with Four Lads)	25
53	Columbia SCM 5041	Whiskey And Gin/Tell The Lady I Said Goodbye	20
53	Columbia SCM 5074	Please Don't Talk About Me When I'm Gone/Coffee And Cigarettes (B-side with Four Lads)	20
54	Columbia SCM 5111	Nobody's Sweetheart/I Can't Escape From You	20
54	Columbia SCM 5122	She Didn't Say Nothin' At All/I'm Just A Shadow Of Myself	20
55	Philips PB 449	Flip Flop And Fly/Thine Eyes Are As The Eyes Of A Dove (78)	5
57	Philips JK 1004	You Don't Owe Me A Thing/Look Homeward, Angel (jukebox issue)	25
57	Philips JK 1011	So Long/I Miss You So (jukebox issue)	20
57	Philips JK 1016	Yes Tonight, Josephine/No Wedding Today (jukebox issue)	20
57	Philips JK 1025	Build Your Love (On A Strong Foundation)/Street Of Memories (jukebox issue)	18
57	Philips JK 1033	Pink Sweater Angel/Texas Tambourine (jukebox issue)	22
58	Philips PB 785	Miss Me Just A Little/Soliloquy Of A Fool	7
58	Philips PB 808	Strollin' Girl/Plant A Little Seed	7
58	Philips PB 829	Endlessly/Lonely For A Letter	6
58	Philips PB 849	Up Until Now/No Regrets	6
58	Philips PB 884	What More Can I Say/You're The One Who Knows	6
59	Philips PB 901	When's Your Birthday, Baby/One Man's Love Song Is Another Man's Blues	6
59	Philips PB 918	Call Me Yours/Here And Now	6
59	Philips PB 952	I'll Never Fall In Love Again/You're All That I Live For	5
60	Philips PB 990	Wagon Wheels/When It's Springtime In The Rockies	5
60	Philips PB 1025	Before You/I'll Make You Mine	5
60	Philips PB 1047	Tell Me/Don't Leave Me Now	5

Johnnie RAY

60	London HLA 9216	In The Heart Of A Fool/Let's Forget It Now	6
61	Philips PB 1126	An Ordinary Couple/Cool Water	5
61	HMV POP 902	How Many Nights How Many Days/I'll Bring Along My Banjo	8
62	London HLG 9484	I Believe/TIMI YURO: Smile	8
63	Brunswick 05884	Lookout Chatanooga/After My Laughter Came Tears	5
69	Pye 7N 17691	Wise To The Ways Of The World/Since I Lost You Baby	4
69	Pye 7N 17760	Long And Lonely Nights/Brokenhearted Me, Evilhearted You	4
54	Columbia SEG 7511	JOHNNIE RAY (EP)	15
55	Philips BBE 12006	JOHNNIE RAY (EP)	12
57	Philips BBE 12115	WALKING AND CRYING (EP)	12
57	Philips BBE 12153	FRANKIE AND JOHNNIE (EP)	12
58	Philips BBE 12192	YES TONIGHT (EP)	12
58	Philips BBE 12217	T.V. SERIES (EP)	10
61	Philips BBE 12460	ON THE TRAIL (EP)	12
54	Philips BBR 8001	AT THE LONDON PALLADIUM (10" LP, red or blue sleeve)	30/25
55	Philips BBR 8062	THE VOICE OF YOUR CHOICE (10" LP)	30
57	Philips BBL 7148	THE BIG BEAT (LP)	30
58	Philips BBL 7254	AT THE DESERT INN — LAS VEGAS (LP)	30
58	Philips BBL 7264	SHOWCASE OF HITS (LP)	20
59	Philips BBL 7285	TILL MORNING (LP, also stereo SBBL 555)	20/25
59	Philips BBL 7348	A SINNER AM I (LP)	25
60	Philips BBL 7363	ON THE TRAIL (LP)	20
61	Ace Of Clubs ACL 1059	TALES FROM THE VIENNA WOODS (LP)	12
62	Liberty LBY 1020	JOHNNIE RAY (LP)	15
66	CBS Realm 52317	THE BEST OF JOHNNIE RAY (LP)	12

(see also Four Lads, Frankie Laine & Johnnie Ray, Doris Day & Johnnie Ray)

RICARDO RAY
68	Roulette RO 501	Nitty Gritty/Mony Mony	10

WADE RAY
63	London HL 9700	Burning Desire/Two Red Red Lips	10

CHRIS RAYBURN
63	Parlophone R 5098	Slow Loving Woman/Same Old Places	5
64	Parlophone R 5144	I've Cried My Last Tear/You Forgot To Say When	5
66	Parlophone R 5422	I Wanna Be In Love Again/Another Night Alone	4
60s	Music Factory CUB 2	One Way Ticket/Photograph Of Love	4

CHRISTINE RAYBURN
69	Pye 7N 17679	Skip A Rope/Starlight	4

MARGIE RAYBURN
56	Capitol CL 14532	Wedding Song/That's The Chance I've Got To Take	6
57	London HLU 8515	I'm Available/If You Were	12
57	London HLU 8515	I'm Available/If You Were (78)	5
58	London HLU 8648	I Would/Alright, But It Won't Be Easy	12
58	London HLU 8648	I Would/Alright, But It Won't Be Easy (78)	5

ANTHONY RAYE
80	Grapevine GRP 147	Give Me One More Chance/Hold On To What You've Got	4

SOL RAYE
63	Oriole CB 1855	I Love You Because/Dear Michelle	4
67	Deram DM 154	While I'm Here/To Be With You	4

RAYMONDE'S MAGIC ORGAN
69	Deram SML 1032	SIXTIES HITS (LP)	10

BILLY RAYMOND
58	HMV POP 503	Making Love/I Would	4
58	HMV POP 526	One In Particular/Seven Daughters	4
59	HMV POP 614	Charlie Is Their Darling/Loch Lomond	4

LEE RAYMOND with COSTELLO SISTERS
55	Brunswick 05438	Foolishly Yours/Baby Darling	4

MARK RAYMOND & CROWD
64	Columbia DB 7308	Girls/Remember Me To Julie	5

TONY RAYMOND
59	Fontana H 213	Broken-Hearted Melody/This Earth Is Mine	5
62	Oriole CB 1777	The Infant King/Because Of You	6

JULIE RAYNE
59	HMV POP 665	Waltz Me Around/Love Where Can You Be?	5
60	HMV POP 785	Bim Bam Bom/One More Time	5
61	HMV POP 868	Green With Envy Purple With Passion/My First Romance	5
60s	Windsor WPS 123	Faithfully/Free To Love	5
60s	Windsor WPS 128	Yolu Can't Come Back/Straight To Your Arms	5

LISA RAYNE
65	Fontana TF 563	Don't Ever Change/It Had To Be You	4

MARTIN RAYNOR & SECRETS
65	Columbia DB 7563	Candy To Me/You're A Wonderful One	10

(see also Secrets, Simon's Secrets, Clifford T. Ward)

MIKE RAYNOR & CONDORS
67	Decca F 12605	Turn Your Head/Lazy Day	5
67	Decca F 22690	Is She A Woman Now?/My Shy Serenade	4
68	Decca F 22790	Wonderful Day/On Top Of The World	4
69	Decca F 22864	Ob-La-Di, Ob-La-Da/I'm Goin' Down (as Mike Raynor & Sky)	4

RAYS
| 57 | London HLU 8505 | Silhouettes/Daddy Cool | 30 |
| 57 | London HLU 8505 | Silhouettes/Daddy Cool (78) | 12 |

RAY'S PEOPLE
| 70 | Philips 6006 044 | Run To The Park/I Spy | 4 |

RAZORCUTS
86	Subway Org. SUBWAY 5	Big Pink Cake/I'll Still Be There (foldover p/s with insert, poly bag, 2,000 only)	10
86	Subway Org. SUBWAY 8	Sorry To Embarrass You/Summer In Your Heart (p/s, with insert, 2,000 only)	4
86	Subway Organisation SUBWAY 8T	Sorry To Embarrass You/Summer In Your Heart/Snowbirds Don't Fly/Mary Day (12", p/s, 2000 only)	7
87	Sha La La Ba Ba Ba-Ba Ba 02	Sad Kaleidoscope/TALULAH GOSH: I Told You So (flexidisc p/s, 2,500 only)	6
87	Legend LEG 100/ LYN 18042	Sad Kaleidoscope/WOLFHOUNDS: Rats On A Raft (flexidisc, free with "The Legend" & other fanzines, 500 only)	6
80s	Caff CAFF 10	Sometimes I Worry About You/For Always/Sorry To Embarrass You/Music From The Big Pink (foldaround p/s with insert, 500 only)	12

(see also Climactics, Red Chair Fadeaway)

RAZOR'S EDGE
| 66 | Stateside SS 532 | Let's Call It A Day Girl/April | 5 |

RAZZY
| 74 | MGM 2006 437 | I Hate Hate/Singing Other People's Songs | 6 |

CHRIS REA
74	Magnet MAG 10	So Much Love/Born To Lose (no p/s)	25
78	Magnet MAG 111	Fool (If You Think It's Over)/Midnight Love	4
78	Magnet MAG 121	Whatever Happened To Benny Santini?/Three Angels (some on red vinyl)	6/4
79	Magnet MAG 144	Diamonds/Cleveland Calling	4
79	Magnet 12 MAG 144	Diamonds/Cleveland Calling (12")	7
79	Magnet MAG 151	A Raincoat And A Rose/No Qualifications (p/s)	4
80	Magnet MAG 163	Tennis/If You Really Love Me (p/s)	4
80	Magnet MAG 176	Dancing Girls/Friends Across The Water (p/s)	4
82	Magnet MAG 215	Loving You/Let Me Be The One (p/s)	4
82	Magnet MAG 225	Every Beat Of My Heart/Don't Look Back (p/s)	4
82	Magnet MAG 233	Let It Loose/Sierra Sierra (p/s)	4
82	Magnet 12 MAG 233	Let It Loose/Sierra Sierra/Urban Samurai (12", p/s, with 7", [CHRIS 1]: "Fool (If You Think It's Over)"/"The Closer You Get"/"Diamonds"/"Guitar Street")	12
82	Magnet 12 MAG 233	Let It Loose/Sierra Sierra/Urban Samurai (12", p/s)	8
84	Magnet MAG 244	I Can Hear Your Heartbeat/From Love To Love (p/s)	4
83	Magnet MAG 245	Love's Strange Ways/Smile (p/s)	4
84	Magnet MAG 255	I Don't Know What It Is But I Love It/Mystery Man (p/s)	6
84	Magnet MAGT 255	I Don't Know What It Is But I Love It/Mystery Man (12", p/s)	10
84	Magnet MAG 259	Bombolini/True Love (p/s)	5
84	Magnet MAGT 259	Bombolini/Excerpts From Bombolini/True Love (12", p/s)	10
84	Magnet MAG 260	Touché D'Amour/Touché D'Amour (instrumental) (p/s)	4
84	Magnet MAGT 260	Touché D'Amour (extended)/Touché D'Amour (7" remix) Touché D'Amour (instrumental) (12", p/s)	8
84	Magnet MAGT 260	Touché D'Amour/Let It Loose/I Can Hear Your Heartbeat/I Don't Know What It Is But I Love It (Special 12" medley) (12", p/s)	7
84	Magnet MAGX 269/ (matrix: CHRIS 2)	Ace Of Hearts (Special Mix)/I Can Hear Your Heartbeat//Bittersweet/Auf Immer Und Ewig (shrinkwrapped, double pack, 2nd 45 with white labels)	6
84	Magnet ZC MAG 269	Ace Of Hearts (Special Mix)/I Can Hear Your Heartbeat (live excerpt) (cassette)	4
84	Magnet MAGT 269	Ace Of Hearts (Special Mix)/I Can Hear Your Heartbeat (live excerpt)/From Love To Love/True Love/Smile (12", p/s)	7
85	Magnet MAGX 276 (matrix: CHRIS 2)	Stainsby Girls (Sax Mix)/And When She Smiles//Bittersweet/Auf Immer Und Ewig (shrinkwrapped double pack, 2nd 45 with white labels)	6
85	Magnet ZC MAG 276	Stainsby Girls (Sax Mix)/And When She Smiles/Sunrise/Dancing Shoes/September Blue (cassette)	5
85	Magnet MAGT 276	Stainsby Girls (Sax Mix)/And When She Smiles/Sunrise/Dancing Shoes/September Blue (12", p/s)	7
85	Magnet MAG 280	Josephine (Remix)/Dancing Shoes (p/s)	5
85	Magnet MAGT 280	Josephine (Remix)/Dancing Shoes/Every Time It Rains (12", p/s)	10
86	Magnet ZC MAG 283	It's All Gone/Bless Them All/Crack That Mould/Look Out For Me/Let's Dance (cassette)	6
86	Magnet MAGT 283	It's All Gone/Bless Them All/Crack That Mould/Look Out For Me/Let's Dance (12", p/s)	7
86	Magnet MAG 294	On The Beach (Special Remix)/If Anybody Asks You (gatefold p/s)	4
86	Magnet MAG 294D	On The Beach (Special Remix)/If Anybody Asks You//One Golden Rule (live)/Midnight Blue (live) (double pack)	4
86	Magnet MAG 298D	Hello Friend/Driving Home For Christmas//It's All Gone (live)/Steel River (live) (double pack)	4
87	Magnet ZC MAG 299	Let's Dance/I Don't Care Anymore (cassette)	4
87	Magnet MAGT 299R	Let's Dance (Rea Mix)/Let's Dance/Josephine (Extended French Re-record)/I Don't Care Anymore (12", p/s)	10
87	Magnet CD MAG 299	Let's Dance/Let's Dance (12" Special Remix)/Josephine (Extended French Re-record)/I Don't Care Anymore (CD)	7
79	Magnet MAGL 5028	DELTICS (LP, blue vinyl, stickered sleeve)	10

REACTA
| 79 | Battery Operated WAC 1 | Stop The World/SUS (p/s) | 30 |

(see also Television Personalities)

REACTION
| 70 | Colombia Blue Beat DB 119 | Oh Me, Oh My/RECO: It's Love | 6 |

(see also Ezo Reco)

REACTION
68	President PT 208	That Man/Falling In Love With You	4

REACTION
78	Island WIP 6437	I Can't Resist/I Am A Case (p/s)	8

(see also Talk Talk)

AL READ
56	HMV POP 278	Though We Haven't Got The Money/What Is A Home? (A Shanty In Old ...)	4
59	HMV POP 575	That's Life/Our Maggie's Going To Get Married	4

MIKE READ
78	Satril SAT 131	Are You Ready/London Town (p/s)	4

(see also Just Plain Smith, Just Plain Jones, Micky Manchester, Trainspotters)

PAT READER
60	Triumph RGM 1024	Ricky/Dear Daddy	15
62	Piccadilly 7N 35077	May Your Heart Stay Young/Cha Cha On The Moon	20
63	Oriole CB 1903	Helpless/Lover's Lane	6

BERTICE READING
55	Parlophone R 4045	My One Sin (In Life)/Frankie And Johnnie (78)	8
55	Parlophone R 4064	Bessie Smith Blues/Everybody's Somebody's Fool (78)	6
57	Decca F 10965	No Flowers By Request/September In The Rain	12
58	Parlophone R 4462	Rock Baby Rock/It's A Boy	20
58	Parlophone R 4462	Rock Baby Rock/It's A Boy (78)	10
58	Parlophone R 4487	My Big Best Shoes/No More In Life	12
58	Parlophone R 4487	My Big Best Shoes/No More In Life (78)	5

WILMA READING
74	Pye 7N 45380	Two Can Have A Party/Play It Again	5

REAL McCOY
67	Fontana TF 794	Show Me How You Milk A Cow/I Paid For My Laughs	5
68	Pye 7N 17618	I Get So Excited/Somebody's Taken Maria Away	4
69	Pye 7N 17669	Quick Joey Small/Happiness Is Love	4
69	Pye 7N 17704	Round The Gum Tree/I Will	4
69	Pye 7N 17772	Gitarzan/Anytime You Need Me	4
69	Pye 7N 17850	Many The Memories/She's Different, She's Beautiful	4
70	Marble Arch MAL 1251	THIS IS THE REAL McCOY (LP)	30

REAL KIDS
78	Bronze BRO 54	All Kindsa Girls/Common At Noon (p/s)	6

REAL THING
72	Bell BLL 1232	Vicious Circles Pts 1 & 2	4

(see also Chants)

REALM
66	CBS 202044	Hard Time Loving You/Certain Kind Of Girl	10

(see also Earl Preston & Realms)

REBEL
81	Bridge House BHS 2	Arock A Shocka/Drift Away (p/s)	4
86	Flying Pig REBS 1	Valentino/Lonely Traveller (p/s, with free single)	4

REBEL ROUSERS
68	Fontana TF 973	Should I?/As I Look	15

(see also Cliff Bennett & Rebel Rousers, Soul Sounds)

REBELS
67	Page One POF 017	Hard To Love You/Call Me	20

REBOUNDS
64	Fontana TF 461	Help Me/The World Is Mine	15

REBS
58	Capitol CL 14932	Bunky/Renegade	8

(EZZ) RECO
62	Island WI 022	Reco's Farewell (as Reco & Happy Orchestra)/BUNNY & SKITTER: A Little Mashin'	10
64	Columbia DB 7217	King Of Kings/Blue Beat Dance (as Ezo Reco & Launchers)	7
64	Columbia DB 7222	Little Girl/The Bluest Beat (as Ezo Reco & Launchers)	6
64	Columbia DB 7290	Please Come Back/At A Party (as Ezz Reco & Launchers)	8
69	Downtown DT 417	Quando Quando/Reg 'A' Jeg (se Reco & Rudies)	5
69	Treasure Isle TI 7052	The Lion Speaks (as Reco)/ANDY CAPP: Pop A Top	6
64	Columbia SEG 8326	JAMAICAN BLUE BEAT (EP, as Ezz Reco & Launchers)	12
69	Pama ECO 14	RECO IN REGGAE LAND (LP)	12

(see also Reaction, Rico Rodriguez)

RECORD PLAYERS
78	Wreckord WRECK 001	DOUBLE C SIDE (EP, label also listed as Aerco AERO 1104)	5
80	Wreckord WRECK 002	Give An Inch/Squirming In The Vermin By The Bonny Banks Of Clyde/67/Parasite (p/s)	4

RECORDS
79	Virgin V 2122	SHADES IN BED (LP, with free single "High Heels")	10

RED
83	Jigsaw	RED (LP, private pressing)	18

TAMPA RED
65	RCA Victor RCX 7160	RHYTHM AND BLUES VOL. 3 (EP)	18

TAMPA RED & GEORGIA TOM
| 59 | Collector JE 13 | MALE BLUES NO. 2 (EP) | 12 |

RED ALERT
82	No Future OI 5	In Britain/Screaming At The Nation/Murder Missile (p/s)	4
82	No Future OI 13	Take No Prisoners/Empire Of Crime/Sell Out (p/s)	4
70s		Border Guards	6

RED BEANS & RICE
| 80 | Chiswick CHIS 124 | The Driving Beat/Throw It In The Grass | 4 |

REDBEAT
| 80 | Malicious Damage MD 440 | Machines In Motion/More Or Less Cut (12", no p/s, PVC bag) | 7 |

REDBONE
| 70 | CBS 64069 | REDBONE (LP) | 10 |
| 71 | CBS 64198 | POTLATCH (LP) | 10 |

REDCAPS
63	Decca F 11716	Shout/Little Things You Do	7
63	Decca F 11789	Talking 'Bout You/Come On Girl	10
64	Decca F 11903	Mighty Fine Girl/Funny Things	7

RED CHAIR FADEAWAY
89	Cosmic Eng. M. CTA 103	Let It Happen/Myra/Dragonfly/Grasshopper (12", p/s, 400 only)	8
89	Cosmic Eng. M. CTA 105	Mr. Jones/Chimney Pots/Faraway Lights/Out Of The Grey (12", p/s)	7
91	Tangerine	CURIOUSER AND CURIOUSER (LP, foldaround sleeve with booklet, no'd)	15

RED CRAYOLA
78	Radar ADA 22	Wives In Orbit/Yik Yak (p/s, red vinyl)	5
78	Radar/Sound For	Hurricane Fighter Plane/13TH FLOOR ELEVATORS: Reverberation	
	Industry SFI 347	(flexidisc free with 'Zig Zag' magazine No. 88)	8/6
(see also Art & Language)			

GENE REDD & GLOBETROTTERS
| 59 | Parlophone R 4584 | Red River Valley Rock/Kentucky Home Rock | 10 |

DEXTER REDDING
| 74 | Macon 2089 003 | Love Is Bigger Than A Baseball/God Bless | 4 |

GENE REDDING
| 74 | Capitol CL 15792 | Blood Brothers/Once A Fool | 4 |

NOEL REDDING BAND
76	RCA RCA 2662	Roller Coaster Kids/Snowstorm	4
77	RCA PB 9026	Take It Easy/Back On The Road Again	4
75	RCA RS 1030	CLONAKILTY COWBOYS (LP)	10
76	RCA RS 1084	BLOWIN' (LP)	10
(see also Loving Kind, Jimi Hendrix, Lord Sutch & Heavy Friends, Fat Mattress)			

OTIS REDDING
64	London HLK 9833	Pain In My Heart/Something Is Worrying Me	15
64	London HLK 9876	Come To Me/Don't Leave Me This Way	15
65	Atlantic AT 4024	Mr Pitiful/That's How Strong My Love Is	10
65	Sue WI 362	Shout Bamalama/Fat Girl	15
65	Atlantic AT 4029	I've Been Loving You Too Long/Winter Wonderland (unissued, demos only)	30
65	Atlantic AT 4039	Respect/I've Been Loving You Too Long	8
65	Atlantic AT 4050	My Girl/Down In The Valley	7
66	Atlantic AT 4080	(I Can't Get No) Satisfaction/Any Ole Way	5
66	Atlantic 584 019	My Lover's Prayer/Don't Mess With Cupid	5
66	Atlantic 584 030	I Can't Turn You Loose/Just One More Day	5
66	Atlantic 584 049	Fa-Fa-Fa-Fa-Fa (Sad Song)/Good To Me	5
67	Atlantic 584 070	Try A Little Tenderness/I'm Sick Y'all	5
67	Atlantic 584 091	Respect/These Arms Of Mine	4
67	Atlantic 584 092	My Girl/Mr Pitiful	5
67	Stax 601 005	Day Tripper/Shake (dark blue labels, later copies with light blue labels)	7/4
67	Stax 601 007	Let Me Come On Home/I Love You More Than Words Can Say	
		(dark blue labels, later copies with light blue labels)	7/4
67	Stax 601 011	Shake (live)/634-5789 (live)	6
67	Stax 601 017	The Glory Of Love/I'm Coming Home	5
67	Stax 601 027	(I Can't Get No) Satisfaction/I've Been Loving You Too Long	6
68	Stax 601 031	(Sittin' On) The Dock Of The Bay/My Sweet Lorene	5
68	Stax 601 040	The Happy Song/Open The Door	4
68	Pye Intl. 7N 25463	She's All Right/Gama Lama	8
68	Atlantic 584 199	Hard To Handle/Amen	4
68	Atlantic 584 220	Champagne And Wine/I've Got Dreams To Remember	5
68	Atlantic 584 234	Papa's Got A Brand New Bag/Direct Me	5
69	Atlantic 584 249	A Lover's Question/You Made A Man Out Of Me	4
69	Atco 226 001	Love Man/That's How Strong My Love Is	5
69	Atco 226 002	Free Me/Higher And Higher	5
69	Evolution E 2442	She's Alright/Tuff Enuff	8
70	Atco 226 012	Look At That Girl/That's A Good Idea	4
70	Atlantic 2091 020	Wonderful World/Security	4
71	Atlantic 2091 062	I've Been Loving You Too Long/Try A Little Tenderness	4
71	Atlantic 2091 112	(Sittin' On) The Dock Of The Bay/Respect/Mr Pitiful (reissue)	4
71	Atlantic K 10206	White Christmas/Merry Christmas Baby	5
66	Sue IEP 710	EARLY OTIS REDDING (EP)	20
65	Atlantic ATL 5029	THE GREAT OTIS REDDING SINGS SOUL BALLADS (LP)	18
66	Atlantic ATL 5041	OTIS BLUE: OTIS REDDING SINGS SOUL (LP)	18
66	Atlantic 587 011	THE SOUL ALBUM (LP)	16
66	Atlantic 587 035	THE GREAT OTIS REDDING SINGS SOUL BALLADS (LP, reissue)	12
66	Atlantic 587/588 036	OTIS BLUE: OTIS REDDING SINGS SOUL (LP, reissue, mono/stereo)	12/14

MINT VALUE £

67	Atlantic 587/588 050	THE OTIS REDDING DICTIONARY OF SOUL (LP)	20
67	Atlantic 587 042	PAIN IN MY HEART (LP)	15
67	Stax VOLT 418	THE HISTORY OF OTIS REDDING (LP)	15
68	Stax 589 016	OTIS REDDING IN EUROPE (LP)	15
68	Stax 230 001/231 001	DOCK OF THE BAY (LP)	12
68	Atlantic 587/588 113	THE IMMORTAL OTIS REDDING (LP)	12
68	Atlantic 587/588 148	OTIS REDDING AT THE WHISKEY A GO GO, LOS ANGELES (LP)	12
69	Atco 228 001	THE HISTORY OF OTIS REDDING (LP, reissue)	10
69	Atco 228 022	THE DOCK OF THE BAY (LP, reissue)	10
69	Atco 228 017	OTIS REDDING LIVE IN EUROPE (LP, reissue)	10
69	Atco 228 025	LOVE MAN (LP)	12
71	Atco 2400 018	TELL THE TRUTH (LP)	12

OTIS REDDING & CARLA THOMAS

67	Stax 601 012	Tramp/Oooh Carla, Oooh Otis (with Carla Thomas)	5
67	Stax 601 021	Knock On Wood/Let Me Be Good To You	4
68	Stax 601 033	Lovey Dovey/OTIS REDDING: New Year's Resolution	4
67	Stax 589 007	THE KING AND QUEEN OF SOUL (LP)	15

(see also Carla Thomas)

RED DIRT

| 70 | Fontana STL 5540 | RED DIRT (LP) | 300 |

HELEN REDDY

| 78 | Capitol CL 16007 | Poor Little Fool/We'll Sing In The Sunshine | 5 |

EMMA REDE

| 67 | Columbia DB 8136 | Just Like A Man/I Gotta Be With You | 12 |

TEDDY REDELL

| 60 | London HLK 9140 | Judy/Can't You See | 40 |

VANESSA REDGRAVE

| 64 | Topic STOP 111 | Hanging On A Tree/Where Have All The Flowers Gone | 4 |

RED HERRING

| 73 | GMS GMS 007 | I'm A Gambler/Working Class Man | 4 |

(see Pete Dello, Lace, Leah)

RED HOT CHILI PEPPERS

85	EMI America EA 205	Hollywood (Africa)/Never Mind (p/s)	8
85	EMI America 12EA 205	Hollywood (Africa) (Remix)/Hollywood (Africa) (Dub Mix)/Never Mind (12", p/s)	12
88	EMI America EA 241	Fight Like A Brave (LP Version)/Fire (p/s)	4
88	EMI America 12EA 241	Fight Like A Brave (LP Version)/(Mofo Mix)/(Knucklehead Mix)/Fire (12", p/s)	8
88	EMI America 12EAP 241	Fight Like A Brave (LP Version)/(Mofo Mix)/(Knucklehead Mix)/Fire (12", picture disc)	12
88	EMI Manhattan MT 41	ABBEY ROAD (EP)	4
88	EMI Manhattan 12MT 41	ABBEY ROAD (12" EP)	7
88	EMI Manhattan 12MTPD 41	ABBEY ROAD (12" EP, picture disc)	12
89	EMI Manhattan MT 70	Knock Me Down/Punk Rock Classic/Pretty Little Ditty (p/s)	4
89	EMI Manhattan MTPD 70	Knock Me Down/Punk Rock Classic/Pretty Little Ditty (shaped picture disc)	10
89	EMI Manhattan 12MTPD 70	Knock Me Down/Punk Rock Classic/Pretty Little Ditty (12", picture disc with insert)	7
89	EMI Manhattan 12MTX 75	Higher Ground/Higher Ground (Munchkin Mix)/Higher Ground (Dub Mix) Politician (Mini Rap) (12", pop-out sleeve)	7
90	EMI Manhattan 10MT 85	Taste The Pain (LP version)/Show Me Your Soul/Castles Made Of Sand (live) (8³/₄" square picture disc)	5

RED LIGHTS

| 78 | Free Range PF 5 | Never Wanna Leave/Seventeen (p/s) | 8 |

RED LORRY YELLOW LORRY

82	Red Rhino RED 20	Beating My Head/I'm Still Waiting (p/s)	12
83	Red Rhino RED 28	Take It All/Happy (p/s)	10
83	Red Rhino RED 39	He's Read/See The Fire (p/s)	8
84	Red Rhino RED 48	THIS TODAY (12" EP)	7
84	Red Rhino RED 49	Monkeys On Juice/Push (p/s)	5
84	Red Rhino REDT 49	Monkeys On Juice/Push/Silence (12", p/s)	7

(see also Mission)

ROY REDMOND

| 67 | Warner Bros WB 2075 | Good Day Sunshine/That Old Time Feeling | 6 |

RED NELSON

| 40s | Brunswick 03508 | Crying Mother Blues/Streamline Blues (78) | 20 |

RED ONION JAZZ BABIES

| 60 | Collector JE 19 | RED ONION JAZZ BABIES (EP) | 7 |

(see also Louis Armstrong)

REDSKINS

82	CNT CNT 007	Lev Bronstein/The Peasant Army (p/s)	18
83	CNT CNT 016	Lean On Me!/Unionize! (p/s)	8
83	CNT CNTX 016	Lean On Me! (Northern Mix)/Unionize! (Break Mix) (12", p/s)	8
84	Decca F 1	Keep On Keepin' On!/Reds Strike The Blues! (p/s)	4
84	Decca FX 1	Keep On Keepin' On! (Die On Your Feet Mix)!/16 Tons (Coal Not Dole)/Reds Strike The Blues! (12", with inner, some shrinkwrapped with free 7")	10/7
85	Decca FDP 2	Bring It Down! (This Insane Thing)/You Want It They've Got It/Turnin' Loose (The Furious Flames)/Take No Heroes (live)/Go Get Organized (live) (double pack, stickered gatefold p/s)	7

85	The Hit HOT 001	Kick Over The Statues (The Ramsey McKinnock Mix)/JESUS & MARY CHAIN: Just Like Cindy/STYLE COUNCIL: Walls Come Tumbling Down (live)/ SIMPLY RED: Every Bit Of Me (p/s, freebie EP with 'The Hit' mag issue 1)	6/4
86	Decca FXT 3	THE POWER IS YOURS ... THE BOOTLEG EXCERPTS PROPOGANDA EP (10", 33rpm, stickered plain black die-cut sleeve)	7
86	Decca FXT 4	It Can Be Done/Let's Make It Work! (live)/K.O.! K.O.! (live)/A Plateful Of Hateful (10" 'Russian Import', no'd stickered plain white die-cut sleeve)	7
86	Jamming!/London J 1	You Want It They've Got It (Red Soul & Fury Unleased Mix)/THEN JERICO: The Big Sweep/DAINTEES: Watch The Running Water/COMMUNARDS: Breadline Britain (free with 'Jamming!' magazine)	8/6

RED SQUARES
67	Columbia DB 8160	Mountain's High/Pity Me	5
67	Columbia DB 8257	True Love Story/Lollipop	5

RED TELEVISION
71	Brecht Times	RED TELEVISION (LP, private pressing with insert)	180

REDUCERS
78	Vibes XP 1/VR 001	Things Go Wrong/We Are Normal (p/s)	6

MIKE REDWAY
63	Embassy WB 5579	Just Like Eddie/Bad To Me	4
64	Oriole CB 1948	Many People/It's So Funny I Could Cry	5
67	Deram DM 124	Have No Fear, Bond Is Here (Casino Royale)/My Poem For You	8
67	Deram DM 157	Don't Speak Of Me/Sometimes I Remember	4

REDWOODS
62	Columbia DB 4859	Please Mr Scientist/Where You Used To Be	10

DIZZY REECE QUINTET
56	Tempo A 140	Chorous/Basie Line	4
55	Tempo LAP 3	A NEW STAR ... (10" LP)	10

CHUCK REED
57	Brunswick 05646	Whispering Heart/Another Love Has Ended	8
57	Brunswick 05646	Whispering Heart/Another Love Has Ended (78)	5
58	Columbia DB 4113	No School Tomorrow/Let's Put Our Hearts Together	12
58	Columbia DB 4113	No School Tomorrow/Let's Put Our Hearts Together (78)	8
62	Stateside SS 108	Just Plain Hurt/Talking No Trash	5

DEAN REED
59	Capitol CL 14986	The Search/Annabelle	5
59	Capitol CL 15030	I Kissed A Queen/A Pair Of Scissors (And A Pot Of Glue)	5

DENNY REED
61	London HLK 9274	A Teenager Feels It Too/Hot Water	5

JERRY REED
58	Capitol CL 14851	Bessie Baby/Too Young To Be Blue	100

JIMMY REED
60	Top Rank JAR 333	Baby What You Want Me To Do/Caress Me Baby	12
60	Top Rank JAR 394	Found Love/Where Can You Be	10
60	Top Rank JAR 533	Hush-Hush/Going By The River	10
63	Stateside SS 205	Shame Shame Shame/Let's Get Together	8
64	Stateside SS 330	Shame Shame Shame/Let's Get Together (reissue)	5
66	Sue WI 4004	Odds And Ends/Going By The River Part 2	16
67	HMV POP 1579	Two Ways To Skin A Cat/Got Nowhere To Go	8
64	Stateside SE 1016	BLUES OF JIMMY REED (EP)	15
64	Stateside SE 1026	I'M JIMMY REED (EP)	15
62	Stateside SL 10012	JIMMY REED AT CARNEGIE HALL (LP)	25
64	Stateside SL 10055	JUST JIMMY REED (LP)	25
64	Stateside SL 10069	SINGS THE BEST OF THE BLUES (LP)	18
64	Stateside SL 10086	PLAYS 12-STRING GUITAR BLUES (LP)	18
64	Stateside SL 10091	THE BOSS MAN OF THE BLUES (LP)	18
65	Fontana 688 514 ZL	THINGS AIN'T WHAT THEY USED TO BE (LP)	15
67	HMV CLP/CSD 3611	THE NEW JIMMY REED (LP)	12
68	Stateside S(S)L 10221	SOULIN' (LP)	15
69	Action ACLP 6011	DOWN IN VIRGINIA (LP)	12
69	Joy JOY(S) 111	THE LEGEND — THE MAN (LP)	10
69	Joy JOY(S) 120	AT CARNEGIE HALL (LP, reissue)	10
69	Joy JOYS 127	AT SOUL CITY (LP)	10
69	Joy JOYS 132	PLAYS THE 12-STRING GUITAR BLUES (LP, reissue)	10
69	Joy JOYS 141	ROCKIN' WITH REED (LP)	10
69	Joy JOYS 146	JUST JIMMY REED (LP, reissue)	10
69	Joy JOYS 151	JIMMY REED SINGS THE BEST OF THE BLUES (LP)	10
69	Joy JOYS 155	THE BEST OF JIMMY REED (LP)	10
76	DJM DJD 28033	BIG BOSS MAN (MEMORIAL ALBUM NO. 1) (2-LP, gatefold sleeve)	14

JIMMY REED & EDDIE TAYLOR
60s	XX MIN 704	JIMMY REED & EDDIE TAYLOR (EP)	7

LOU REED
72	RCA RCA 2240	Walk And Talk It/Wild Child	4
73	MGM 2006 283	Candy Says/I'm Waiting For The Man/Run Run Run (as Lou Reed & Velvet Underground)	8
74	RCA APBO 0221	Caroline Says Pts 1 & 2	4
74	RCA APBO 0238	Sweet Jane/Lady Day	4
74	RCA RCA 2467	Sally Can't Dance/Ennui	4
76	RCA RCA 2666	Charley's Girl/Nowhere At All	4
72	RCA SF 8281	LOU REED (LP, orange label)	10

Lou REED

73	RCA RS 1002	BERLIN (LP, orange label with insert)	10
75	RCA CPL 2 1101	METAL MACHINE MUSIC (2-LP, U.S. import with U.K. sticker)	30

(see also Velvet Underground)

LULU REED
55	Parlophone CMSP 34	Troubles On Your Mind/Bump On A Log (export issue)	15

LULU REED & SYL JOHNSON
63	Ember EMB 4535	LULU REED AND SYL JOHNSON (EP)	30

LULU REED & FREDDIE KING
63	Ember EMB 4536	LULU REED AND FREDDIE KING (EP)	25

(see also Freddie King)

NEHMIAH REED
68	Island WI 3102	Family War/Give Me That Love	10

(see also Leyroy Reid)

OLIVER REED
61	Decca F 11390	The Wild One/Lonely For A Girl	6

TAWNY REED
65	Pye 7N 15935	Needle In A Haystack/I've Got A Feeling	10
66	Pye 7N 17078	You Can't Take It Away/My Heart Cries	8

VIVIEN REED
68	Direction 58-3574	I Wanna Be Free/Yours Until Tomorrow	4
77	Epic S EPC 5422	Lean On Me/Missing You	4

VALA REEGAN & VALARONS
66	Atlantic 584 009	Fireman/Living In The Past	110

REEGS
89	Imaginary MIRAGE 006	See My Friends/Is There A Mother-In-Law In The Club/The Savage Garden (12", blue or green p/s)	7

(see also Chameleons)

DELLA REESE
57	London HL 7024	I Cried For You (Now It's Your Turn To Cry Over Me)/And That Reminds Me (export issue)	7
58	London HLJ 8687	You Gotta Love Everybody/I Wish	6
58	London HLJ 8687	You Gotta Love Everybody/I Wish (78)	5
59	London HLJ 8814	Sermonette/Dreams End At Dawn	6
59	London HLJ 8814	Sermonette/Dreams End At Dawn (78)	5
59	RCA RCA 1160	Not One Minute More/Soldier Won't You Marry Me	4
59	RCA RCA 1160	Not One Minute More/Soldier Won't You Marry Me (78)	8
60	RCA RCA 1185	Someday/Let's Get Away From It All	4
60	RCA RCA 1192	Everyday/There's No Two Ways About It	4
60	RCA RCA 1204	And Now/There's Nothing Like A Boy	4
66	HMV POP 1504	Home/Her Little Heart Went To Loveland	5
66	HMV POP 1553	It Wasn't A Very Good Year/Solitary Woman	5
68	Stateside SS 2128	It Was A Very Good Year/I Had To Know My Way Around	4
72	Avco 6105 010	If It Feels Good, Do It/Good Lovin'	4
74	People PEO 106	Who Is She And What Is She To You/If Loving You Is Wrong	5
60	RCA RD 27167/SF 5057	DELLA (LP)	12
61	RCA RD 27208/SF 5091	DELLA DELLA CHA-CHA-CHA (LP)	12
62	RCA RD 27234/SF 5112	SPECIAL DELIVERY (LP)	12
63	RCA Victor RD/SF 7508	ON STAGE (LP)	12
63	RCA Victor RD/SF 7584	WALTZ WITH ME, DELLA (LP)	10
64	RCA RD/SF 7628	AT BASIN STREET EAST (LP)	10
65	RCA RD 7695	MOODY (LP)	10
65	HMV CLP 1923	C'MON AND HEAR (LP, also stereo CSD 1636)	10
66	HMV CLP/CSD 3540	I LIKE IT LIKE DAT! (LP)	10
66	HMV CLP/CSD 3573	LIVE (LP, with Bill Doggett & others)	10
67	HMV CLP/CSD 3605	ONE MORE TIME! (LP)	10
68	Stateside S(S)L 10230	THE BEST OF DELLA REESE (LP)	10
68	Stateside S(S)L 10261	I GOTTA BE ME ... THIS TRIP OUT (LP)	10

TONY REESE
59	London HLJ 8987	Just About This Time Tomorrow/Lesson In Love	5
59	London HLJ 8987	Just About This Time Tomorrow/Lesson In Love (78)	5

DEL REEVES
65	United Artists UP 1092	Girl On The Billboard/Eyes Don't Come Crying To Me	4
66	United Artists UP 1122	Women Do Funny Things To Me/My Half Of Our Past	4
66	United Artists UP 1145	Gettin' Any Feed For Your Chickens/Plain As The Tears On My Face	4

EDDIE REEVES
62	London HL 9548	Talk Talk/Cry Baby	10

JIM REEVES
54	London HL 8014	Bimbo/Gipsy Heart	100
54	London HL 8014	Bimbo/Gipsy Heart (78)	10
54	London HL 8030	Mexican Joe/I Could Cry (with Circle O Ranch Boys)	100
54	London HL 8030	Mexican Joe/I Could Cry (with Circle O Ranch Boys) (78)	10
54	London HL 8055	Butterfly Love/It's Hard To Love Just One (with String Band)	100
54	London HL 8055	Butterfly Love/It's Hard To Love Just One (with String Band) (78)	10
54	London HL 8064	Echo Bonita/Then I'll Stop Loving You (with Louisiana Hayride Band)	100
54	London HL 8064	Echo Bonita/Then I'll Stop Loving You (with Louisiana Hayride Band) (78)	10
54	London HL 8105	Padre Of Old San Antone/Mother Went A-Walkin'	80
54	London HL 8105	Padre Of Old San Antone/Mother Went A-Walkin' (78)	10
55	London HL 8118	Penny Candy/I'll Follow You (with Louisiana Hayride Band)	90
55	London HL 8118	Penny Candy/I'll Follow You (with Louisiana Hayride Band) (78)	10

55	London HL 8159	Drinking Tequila/Red-Eyed And Rowdy	140
55	London HL 8159	Drinking Tequila/Red-Eyed And Rowdy (78)	20
55	London HLU 8185	Tahiti/Give Me One More Kiss	80
55	London HLU 8185	Tahiti/Give Me One More Kiss (78)	10
56	London HLU 8351	The Wilder Your Heart Beats, The Sweeter You Love/ Where Does A Broken Heart Go	75
56	London HLU 8351	The Wilder Your Heart Beats, The Sweeter You Love/ Where Does A Broken Heart Go (78)	10
57	RCA RCA 1005	Four Walls/I Know And You Know	25
57	RCA RCA 1005	Four Walls/I Know And You Know (78)	15
58	RCA RCA 1074	Blue Boy/Theme Of Love	15
58	RCA RCA 1074	Blue Boy/Theme Of Love (78)	5
59	RCA RCA 1144	Partners/I'm Beginning To Forget You	8
59	RCA RCA 1144	Partners/I'm Beginning To Forget You (78)	5
60	RCA RCA 1168	He'll Have To Go/In A Mansion Stands My Love	6
60	RCA RCA 1168	He'll Have To Go/In A Mansion Stands My Love (78)	10
60	RCA RCA 1197	I'm Getting Better/I Know One	5
60	RCA RCA 1214	Am I Losing You/I Missed Me	5
61	RCA RCA 1223	Whispering Hope/I'd Like To Be	4
61	RCA RCA 1233	Danny Boy/The Blizzard	4
61	RCA RCA 1261	You're The Only Good Thing (That's Happened To Me)/ Oh, How I Miss You Tonight	4
62	RCA RCA 1293	Adios Amigo/Letter To My Heart	4
62	RCA RCA 1317	I'm Gonna Change Everything/Pride Goes Before A Fall	4
63	RCA RCA 1330	Missing Angel/Is This Is Me?	5
63	RCA RCA 1342	Welcome To My World/Juanita	4
63	RCA RCA 1364	Guilty/Little Ole You	4
65	RCA RCA 1448	Don't Let Me Cross Over/The World You Left Behind	5
54	London RE-P 1015	THE BIMBO BOY (EP)	50
55	London RE-P 1033	THE BIMBO VOL. 2 (EP)	45
60	RCA RD 27176	HE'LL HAVE TO GO (LP)	15
61	RCA RD 27193	THE INTIMATE JIM REEVES (LP, also stereo SF 5079)	14
62	Camden CDN/SDN 5100	THE COUNTRY SIDE OF JIM REEVES (LP)	10
62	London HA-U 8015	BIMBO (LP)	25
62	RCA RD 7521	A TOUCH OF VELVET (LP)	12
62	RCA RD 7541	GENTLEMAN JIM (LP)	12
62	RCA RD 7577	THE INTERNATIONAL JIM REEVES (LP)	12
64	Camden CDN 5114	GOOD 'N' COUNTRY (LP)	10
64	RCA RD 7636	GOD BE WITH YOU (LP)	10
64	RCA RD 7637	WE THANK THEE (LP)	10
65	RCA RD/SF 7639	MOONLIGHT AND ROSES (LP)	10
65	RCA RD 7663	TWELVE SONGS OF CHRISTMAS (LP)	14
66	RCA RD 7666	THE BEST OF JIM REEVES (LP)	10
66	Camden CDN 5122	HAVE I TOLD YOU LATELY THAT I LOVE YOU (LP)	10
66	RCA RD/SF 7694	THE JIM REEVES WAY (LP)	10
66	RCA RD 7781	KIMBERLEY JIM (LP)	12
66	RCA RD 7814	DISTANT DRUMS (LP)	10
67	RCA RD/SF 7906	YOURS SINCERELY, JIM REEVES (LP)	10

(all the above LPs originally came with black labels, later orange label reissues are worth around £5)

69	RCA RD/SF 7978	A TOUCH OF SADNESS (LP)	10
69	RCA RD/SF 8022	JIM REEVES AND SOME FRIENDS (LP)	10
69	RCA RD/SF 8047	JIM REEVES 'ON STAGE' (LP)	10
71	RCA SF 8146	MY CATHEDRAL (LP)	10
71	RCA SF 8176	JIM REEVES WRITES YOU A RECORD (LP)	10
72	RCA SF 8258	MY FRIEND (LP)	10

MARTHA REEVES & VANDELLAS
(see under Martha & Vandellas)

REFLECTION
| 68 | Reflection RL 3015 | THE PRESENT TENSE: SONGS OF SYDNEY CARTER (LP) | 22 |

REFLECTIONS (U.S.)
64	Stateside SS 294	(Just Like) Romeo & Juliet/Can't You Tell By The Look In My Eyes	15
65	Stateside SS 406	Poor Man's Son/Comin' At You	8
74	Tamla TMG 907	(Just Like) Romeo & Juliet/Can't You Tell By The Look In My Eyes (reissue)	6
65	Stateside SE 1034	POOR MAN'S SON (EP)	25

REFLECTIONS (U.K.)
| 82 | Cherry Red BRED 22 | SLUGS AND TOADS (LP) | 10 |

(see also Alternative TV)

REFUGEE
| 74 | Charisma CAS 1087 | REFUGEE (LP) | 12 |

(see also Nice, Yes)

JOAN REGAN
54	Decca F 10362	Wait For Me, Darling (with Johnston Brothers)/Two Kinds Of Tears	12
54	Decca F 10373	If I Give My Heart To You/Faded Flowers	12
54	Decca F 10397	This Ole House/Can This Be Love?	15
55	Decca F 10432	Prize Of Gold/When You're In Love	12
55	Decca F 10474	Open Up Your Heart And Let The Love In (with Rusty Regan)/If You Learn To Love Each Other	12
55	Decca F 10505	Danger! Heartbreak Ahead/Don't Be Afraid Of Love	8
55	Decca F 10521	Just Say You Love Her/Nobody Danced With Me	8
55	Decca F 10598	The Shepherd Boy/The Rose And The Flame	8
56	Decca F 10659	Love And Marriage/Cross Of Gold (Croce Di Oro)	12
56	Decca F 10710	Don't Take Me For Granted/The Boy With The Magic Guitar	6
56	Decca F 10742	Honestly/I'd Never Leave You Baby (B-side with Johnston Brothers)	6

Joan REGAN

56	Decca F 10757	Sweet Heartaches/Second Fiddle (with Ted Heath)	6
56	Decca F 10801	Gone/Make Me A Child Again	6
57	Decca F 10871	Nearer To Me/Cross My Ever-Loving Heart	5
57	Decca F 10911	Wonderful! Wonderful!/Speak For Yourself John	5
57	Decca F 10934	7/.Cents/Good Evening Friends (with Max Bygraves)	5
57	Decca F 10942	Soft Sands/Love Me To Pieces	5
58	Decca F 11009	I May Never Pass This Way Again/Breezing Along With The Breeze	5
58	HMV POP 555	Love Like Ours/Take Me In Your Arms	5
59	HMV POP 593	May You Always/Have You Ever Been Lonely?	4
59	Pye 7N 15238	Happy Anniversary/So Close To My Heart	4
60	Pye 7N 15259	If Only You'd Be Mine/O Dio Mio	4
60	Pye 7N 15278	Papa Loves Mama/When You Know Someone Loves You	4
60	Pye 7N 15310	One Of The Lucky Ones/My Thanks To You	4
60	Pye 7N 15303	Must Be Santa/Will Santa Come To Shanty Town	4
61	Pye 7N 15400	Surprisin'/In The Arms Of My Love (p/s)	6
66	CBS 202100	Don't Talk To Me About Love/I'm No Toy	35
67	CBS 2657	No One Beside You/A Love So Fine	15
55	Decca DFE 6235	JOAN REGAN SUCCESSES (EP)	10
56	Decca DFE 6278	JOAN REGAN SUCCESSES VOL. 2 (EP)	15
54	Decca LF 1182	THE GIRL NEXT DOOR (10" LP)	25
56	Decca LK 4153	JUST JOAN (LP)	15
60s	Pye	LPs	10

RUS REGAN
| 59 | Capitol CL 15084 | Adults Only/Just The Two Of Us | 4 |

REGENTS (U.S.)
| 61 | Columbia DB 4666 | Barbara Ann/I'm So Lonely | 10 |
| 61 | Columbia DB 4694 | Runaround/Laura My Darling | 12 |

REGENTS (U.K.)
| 63 | Oriole CB 1912 | Bye Bye Johnny/Come Along (p/s) | 15 |

(see also Buddy Britten)

REGENTS (U.K.)
| 66 | CBS 202247 | Words/Worryin' Kind | 15 |

REGENTS
| 79 | Rialto TREB 111 | 7 Teen (Uncensored Version)/Hole In The Heart (p/s) | 8 |

REGGAE BOYS
69	Amalgamated AMG 841	Me No Born Ya/The Wicked Must Survive	6
69	Amalgamated AMG 843	The Reggae Train/Dolly House On Fire	6
69	Unity UN 530	What You Gonna Do/HEDLEY BENNETT: Hot Coffee	5
70	Pressure Beat PB 5503	Walk By Day, Fly By Night/JOE GIBBS & DESTROYERS: Unknown Tongue	5

AL REID
| 69 | Blue Cat BS 161 | Vietcong/MAX ROMEO: Me Want Man | 5 |

BERYL REID
| 65 | HMV POP 1489 | Love Makes The World Go Round/When The Circus Comes To Town | 8 |

CARLTON REID
| 66 | Ska Beat JB 254 | Funny/Turn On The Lights | 8 |
| 69 | Blue Cat BS 162 | Leave Me To Cry/Warning | 5 |

CLARENCE REID
| 69 | Atlantic 584 290 | Nobody But You Babe/Send Me Back My Money | 4 |
| 69 | Atlantic 584 301 | I'm Gonna Tear You A New Heart/I'm A Man Of My Word | 4 |

DANNY REID
| 61 | London HLK 9274 | Teenager Feels It Too/Hot Water | 5 |

DUKE REID (& HIS GROUP)
60	Blue Beat BB 24	Duke's Cookies (with His Group)/JIVING JUNIORS: I Wanna Love	10
62	Blue Beat BB 119	Twelve Minutes To Go (actually by Don Drummond)/HORTENSE ELLIS: Midnight Train	10
63	Blue Beat BB 165	Mood I Am In/STRANGER COLE: Rough And Tough	8
67	Trojan TR 001	Judge Sympathy (actually by Freedom Singers & Duke Reid All Stars)/ROLAND ALPHONSO: Never To Be Mine	15
60s	Duke DK 1002	Pink Lane Shuffle (as Duke Reid & His Group)/LAUREL AITKEN: Low Down Dirty Girl	8
71	Duke Reid DR 2522	Hurt Pts 1 & 2	5

LEYROY REID
| 68 | Blue Cat BS 125 | The Fiddler/LOVELETTES: Shook | 7 |
| 68 | Blue Cat BS 127 | Great Surprise/UNTOUCHABLES: Khaki | 5 |

(see also Nehemiah Reed)

MARC REID
66	CBS 202244	For No One/Lonely City Blues	4
67	CBS 202581	Magic Book/My World Turns Around	4
67	CBS 2950	We Should Live Together/Sale By Auction	4

NEHEMIAH REID
68	Island WI 3102	Family War/Give Me That Love	10
70s	Hot Shot HS 03	Hot Pepper/Seawave (as Nehemiah Reid's All Stars)	4
70s	Torpedo TOR 23	Mafia/H.E.L.L 5 (as Nehemiah Reid's All Stars)	4

P. REID
| 65 | Ska Beat JB 197 | Redeemed/Goodbye World | 8 |

TERRY REID (& JAYWALKERS)
| 67 | Columbia DB 8166 | The Hand Don't Fit The Glove/This Time (as Terry Reid & Jaywalkers) | 10 |
| 68 | Columbia DB 8409 | Better By Far/Fires Alive | 12 |

69	Columbia SCX 6370	TERRY REID (LP)	15
71	M. For Pleasure MFP 5220	THE MOST OF TERRY REID (LP)	10
73	Atlantic K 40340	RIVER (LP)	10

(see also Peter Jay & Jaywalkers)

REIGN
70	Regal Zono. RZ 3028	Line Of Least Resistance/Natural Lovin' Man	50

(see also Yardbirds, Keith Relf, Jim McCarty, Renaissance)

DJANGO REINHARDT
53	Decca F 10219	Le Soir/Deccaphonie (78)	5
50s	Collector JEN 6	SWING GUITARS (EP)	8
50s	Collector JEN 8	IMPROVISATION (EP)	8
55	HMV 7EG 8132	DJANGO REINHARDT (EP)	8
50s	Oriole/Mercury MG 10019	DJANGO (10" LP)	15
54	Vogue LDE 049	DJANGO REINHARDT VOL. 1 (10" LP)	15
54	Vogue LDE 084	DJANGO REINHARDT VOL. 2 (10" LP)	15
54	Vogue LDE 106	DJANGO REINHARDT VOL. 3 (10" LP, as Django Reinhardt Quintet)	15
54	HMV DLP 1045	DJANGO REINHARDT (10" LP)	15
54	Felsted EDL 87005	NUAGES (10" LP, as Django Reinhardt & His Rhythm)	15
59	HMV CLP 1249	DJANGO (LP)	12
60	HMV CLP 1340	THE ART OF DJANGO (LP)	12
60	HMV CLP 1389	DJANGO — THE UNFORGETTABLE (LP)	10
60s	Ember CJS 810	REQUIEM FOR A JAZZMAN (LP)	10

(see also Hot Club Quintet)

JOE REISMAN ORCHESTRA
55	HMV B 10891	Bo Diddley/Bubble Boogie (78)	7
56	HMV 7M 364	Robin Hood/His Name Was Judas	4
60	Columbia DB 4553	The World Of Suzi Wong (Theme)/Melodie D'Amour	4
61	Pye Intl. 7N 25087	The Guns Of Navarone/Yassu	4

REJOICE!
69	Stateside SS 8010	November Snow/Quick Draw Man	4
69	Stateside S(S)L 5009	REJOICE! (LP)	10

RELIGIOUS OVERDOSE
80	Glass GLASS 004	Control Addicts/25 Minutes (p/s, initially with green labels)	6/5
81	Glass GLASS 009	I Said Go/Alien To You (p/s)	4
82	Glass GLASS 018	In This Century/The Girl With The Disappearing Head (I've Got To Adjust It) (12", p/s)	7

BOB RELF
75	Black Magic BM 101	Blowin' My Mind To Pieces/PAULA RUSSELL: Blowin' My Mind To Pieces	5

(see also Bob & Earl)

JANE RELF
71	Decca F 13231	Without A Song From You/Make My Time Pass By	15

(see also Stairway, Renaissance)

KEITH RELF
66	Columbia DB 7920	Mr. Zero/Knowing	20
66	Columbia DB 8084	Shapes In My Mind/Blue Sands	30

(see also Yardbirds, Jim McCarty, Renaissance, Reign, Together)

RELUCTANT STEREOTYPES
76	Oval OVAL 1013	The Lull/The Rounds/Fetch Mr. Clifford, The Political Boys Are On Us (p/s)	4

(see also King)

R.E..M.
83	IRS PFD 1017	Radio Free Europe/There She Goes Again (p/s)	30
83	IRS PFB 1026	Talk About The Passion/Shaking Through (promo only, plain sleeve)	12
83	IRS PFSX 1026	Talk About The Passion/Shaking Through/Carnival Of Sorts (Box Cars)/1,000,000 (12", p/s)	25
84	IRS IRS 105	S. Central Rain (I'm Sorry)/King Of The Road (p/s)	20
84	IRS IRSX 105	S. Central Rain (I'm Sorry)/Voice Of Harold/Pale Blue Eyes (12", p/s)	20
84	IRS IRS 107	(Don't Go Back To) Rockville/Wolves (p/s)	20
84	IRS IRSX 107	(Don't Go Back To) Rockville/Wolves/9 Minus 9 (live)/Gardening At Night (live) (12", p/s)	20
85	Bucketfull of Brains BOB 5	Tighten Up (flexidisc with 'Bucketfull of Brains' magazine)	10
85	Bucketfull of Brains BOB 5	Tighten Up (hard vinyl test pressing)	20
85	IRS IRM 102	Can't Get There From Here/Bandwagon (p/s)	6
85	IRS IRT 102	Can't Get There From Here (Extended Mix)/Bandwagon/Burning Hell (12", p/s)	12
85	IRS IRM 105	Wendell Gee/Crazy (p/s)	5
85	IRS IRMD 105	Wendell Gee/Crazy//Ages Of You/Burning Down (double pack)	15
85	IRS IRT 105	Wendell Gee/Crazy/Driver 8 (live) (12", p/s)	10
86	IRS IRM 121	Fall On Me/Rotary Ten (p/s)	5
86	IRS IRMT 121	Fall On Me/Rotary Ten/Toys In The Attic (12", p/s)	10
86	IRS IRM 128	Superman/White Tornado (p/s)	4
86	IRS IRMT 128	Superman/White Tornado/Femme Fatale (12", p/s)	8
87	IRS IRM 145	It's The End Of The World As We Know It (And I Feel Fine)/This One Goes Out To The One I Love (live) (p/s)	4
87	IRS IRMT 145	It's The End Of The World As We Know It (And I Feel Fine)/This One Goes Out To The One I Love (live)/Maps And Legends (live) (12", p/s)	7
87	IRS IRM 146	The One I Love/Last Date (live) (p/s)	4
87	IRS IRMT 146	The One I Love/Last Date (live)/Disturbance At The Heron House (12", p/s)	7
87	IRS DIRM 146	The One I Love/Last Date (live)/Finest Worksong/It's The End Of The World As We Know It (And I Feel Fine) (CD)	7
87	IRS DIRMX 180	It's The End Of The World As We Know It (And I Feel Fine)/Radio Free Europe (Hibtone Version)/Last Date (Live Version)/White Tornado (CD, withdrawn)	15
88	IRS IRM 161	Finest Worksong (LP Version)/Time After Time Medley (p/s, with poster)	4

R.E.M.

88	IRS IRMT 161	Finest Worksong (Lengthy Club Mix)/Time After Time Medley [Time After Time/Red Rain/S. Central Rain] (12", p/s, with poster) 7
88	IRS DIRM 161	Finest Worksong (Lengthy Club Mix)/Time After Time Medley/It's The End Of The World As We Know It (And I Feel Fine) (CD in box) 8
89	Warner Bros W 7577 CD	Stand/Memphis Train Blues/(The Eleventh Untitled Song) (3" CD, 'maple-leaf' pack) 8
89	Warner Bros W 2833W	Stand/Pop Song '89 (Acoustic Version) (reissue, stencil die-cut p/s) 4
89	Warner Bros W 2960B	Orange Crush/Ghost Riders (box set with poster) 5
91	Warner Bros W 0015CDX	Losing My Religion/Rotary Eleven/After Hours (live) (CD) 10

(see also Full Time Men)

REMA-REMA
| 86 | 4AD BAD 5 | WHEEL IN THE ROSES (12" EP, with blue labels) ....8 |

REMAINS
| 80s | Lyntone LYN 14086 | Talkin' 'Bout You (U.K. flexi, originally with Swedish 'Larm' mag, issue 17) ......4 |

REMAYNS
| 85 | Bam Caruso NRIC 029 | FIRST (EP, coloured vinyl) ....5 |

REMO FOUR
64	Piccadilly 7N 35175	I Wish I Could Shimmy Like My Sister Kate/Peter Gunn 12
64	Piccadilly 7N 35186	Sally Go Round The Roses/I Know A Girl 12
67	Fontana TF 787	Live Like A Lady/Sing Hallelujah 40

(see also Tommy Quickly, Johnny Sandon, Gregory Phillips, Ashton, Gardner & Dyke, Mike Hurst, George Harrison)

RENAISSANCE
68	Polydor BM 56736	Mary Jane (Get Off The Devil's Merry-Go-Round)/Daytime Lovers 5
70	Island WIP 6079	The Sea/Islands 6
78	Sire SRE 1022	Northern Lights/Opening Out (picture disc, export issue) 15
79	Sire SIR 4019	Jekyll And Hyde/Forever Changing (withdrawn) 15
69	Island ILPS 9114	RENAISSANCE (LP, pink label) 18
71	Island HELP 27	ILLUSION (LP, unreleased, test pressings only) ....40+
73	Sovereign SVNA 7253	PROLOGUE (LP) 12
73	Sovereign SVNA 7261	ASHES ARE BURNING (LP) 12
79	Sovereign CAPACK 3	PROLOGUE/ASHES ARE BURNING (2-LP, shrinkwrapped) 15
75	BTM BTM 1000	TURN OF THE CARDS (LP) 10
75	BTM BTM 1006	SCHEHERAZADE AND OTHER STORIES (LP) 10
76	BTM BTM 2001	LIVE AT CARNEGIE HALL (2-LP) 14

(see also Jim McCarty, Keith Relf, Jane Relf, Yardbirds, Rupert's People)

RENALDO & LOAF
| 80 | Take It! | Honest Joe's Indian Gets The Goat On The Way To The Cowboy Conga/ YELLO: Bimbo (33rpm square blue flexidisc with 'Take It!' magazine) ....8/6 |

DIANE RENAY
64	Stateside SS 270	Unbelievable Guy/Navy Blue 6
64	MGM MGM 1262	Watch Out Sally/Billy Blue Eyes 4
65	MGM MGM 1274	I Had A Dream/Troublemaker 4

LINE RENAUD
53	Columbia SCM 5055	April In Portugal/The Song From Moulin Rouge 5
55	Capitol CL 14230	If I Love You /Pam-Pou-De (Pam-Poo-Day) (triangular centre) 12
56	Columbia SCM 5268	Flamenco Love/To You, My Love 5
56	Columbia DB 3824	Strange/You Can't Keep Running 5
58	Columbia DB 4193	Irma La Douce/Disc-Donc, Disc-Donc 4
60	Columbia DB 4485	Mon Coeur Au Portugal/Jeremy 4

LINE RENAUD & DEAN MARTIN
| 61 | Capitol EAP1 20060 | LINE AND DINO (EP) ....8 |

(see also Dean Martin)

RENAULTS
| 60 | Warner Bros WB 11 | Meloncolie/Stella ....4 |

JOHN RENBOURN
66	Transatlantic TRA 135	JOHN RENBOURN (LP) 15
67	Transatlantic TRA 149	ANOTHER MONDAY (LP) 15
68	Transatlantic TRA 167	SIR JOHN ALOT OF MERRY ENGLANDES MUSYK THYNG (LP) 15
70	Transatlantic TRA 224	THE LADY AND THE UNICORN (LP) 15
71	Transatlantic TRA 247	FARO ANNIE (LP) 15
74	Transatlantic TRASAM 18	HEADS AND TAILS (LP, with Stefan Grossman) 12

(see also Pentangle, Stefan Grossman, Bert Jansch & John Renbourn)

DON RENDELL
55	Tempo EXA 11	DON RENDELL QUARTET (EP) 7
55	Tempo EXA 12	DON RENDELL SEXTET (EP) 7
55	Tempo EXA 16	DON RENDELL SEXTET/DAMIAN ROBINSON TRIO (EP, 2 tracks each) 7
56	Tempo EXA 20	DON RENDELL QUINTET (EP) 7
57	Pye Jazz NJE 1044	DON RENDELL JAZZ SIX (EP) 10
58	Decca DFE 6501	PACKET OF BLUES (EP, as Don Rendell Jazz Six) 7
55	Vogue LDE 144	DON RENDELL IN PARIS (10" LP, with Bobby Jaspa) 30
55	Tempo LAP 1	MEET DON RENDELL (10" LP) 30
57	Nixa Jazz Today NJL 7	DON RENDELL PRESENTS THE JAZZ SIX (LP) 25
58	Decca LK 4265	PLAYTIME (LP, as Don Rendell Jazz 6) 15
62	Jazzland JLP 51	ROARIN' (LP, as Don Rendell New Jazz Quintet [featuring Graham Bond]) 75
71	Columbia SCX 6491	SPACEWALK (LP) 35

DON RENDELL & IAN CARR QUINTET
65	Columbia 33SX 1733	SHADES OF BLUE (LP) 40
68	Columbia S(C)X 6214	PHASE III (LP) 35
69	Columbia S(C)X 6316	LIVE (LP) 35
69	Columbia SCX 6368	CHANGE IS 1 (LP) 40

70	Columbia SX 6404	DUSK FIRE (LP)	40

(see also Neil Ardley, Ian Carr)

DON RENDELL QUARTET/JOE HARRIOT QUARTET

57	MGM MGM-EP 615	JAZZ BRITANNIA (EP, 2 tracks each)	10

(see also Joe Harriott)

GOOGIE RENE COMBO

60	London HLY 9056	Forever/Ez-zee	12
66	Atlantic AT 4076	Smokey Joe's La La/Needing You	20
66	Atlantic 584 015	Chica-Boo/Mercy Mercy (Too Much For The Soul)	7

HENRI RENE

59	London HLP 8960	La Shabla (The Shovel)/Destiny (with His Orchestra & Chorus)	4
55	HMV 7M 308	Enchantment/Crystal Chandelier (with Hugo Winterhalter Orchestra)	4

RENE & HIS ALLIGATORS

66	Decca F 22324	She Broke My Heart/I Can Wait	6

RENE & RENE

65	HMV POP 1468	Chantilly Lace/I'm Not The Only One	4
67	Island WIP 6001	Loving You Could Hurt Me So Much/Little Diamonds	4

RENEGADES

67	Parlophone R 5592	Take A Message/Second Thoughts	15
68	President PT 106	Thirteen Women/Walking Down The Street	40
68	Columbia DB 8383	No Man's Land/Sugar Loaf Mountain	15
70	Polydor BM 56508	Cadillac/Every Minute Of The Day	20

RENEGADE SOUNDWAVE

87	Rhythm King LEFT 8(T)	Kray Twins/Renegade Theme/Terror Drum Mix/7" Easy Mix/Dragonbass Sound System Mix (12", p/s, original issue)	12
88	Rhythm King LEFT 20(T)	Cocaine Sex (12", stamped white labels, giant stickered 'cocaine' wrap)	25
80s	Catalogue/Mute CAT 078	Pocket Porn (Dub Mix) (33rpm 1-sided square flexidisc with 'The Catalogue' mag)	4

(see also Jackal)

RENIA

73	Transatlantic TRA 261	FIRST OFFENDERS (LP)	16

DON RENNIE

56	Parlophone MSP 6218	To Love, To Love Is Wonderful/One Girl — One Boy	4
56	Parlophone MSP 6237	Who Are We?/Can You Find It In Your Heart?	4

DON RENO & RED SMILEY

58	Parlophone GEP 8777	COUNTRY AND WESTERN (EP)	20

GERRY RENO

62	Decca F 11477	Don't Ever Change/What Would You Do	4
62	Decca F 11516	Who's Fooling You/Three Deadly Sins	4
63	Decca F 11774	It Only Happens In The Movies/One Lonely Guy	4

PAUL RENO

63	Oriole CB 1872	Lonely Little Girl/Angela	5

ROBERT RENTAL

78	Regular ER 102	Paralysis/A.C.C. (photocopied foldover p/s)	8
78	Company/Regular RECO 2	Paralysis/A.C.C. (reissue, different p/s)	4
79	Industrial IR 0007	THE BRIDGE (LP, with Thomas Leer)	14
80	Rough Trade ROUGH 17	ROBERT RENTAL AND THE NORMAL (LP, 1-sided, plain red sleeve)	12

(see also Thomas Leer, Normal)

REPARATA & DELRONS

65	Stateside SS 382	Whenever A Teenager Cries/He's My Guy	6
65	Stateside SS 414	Tommy/Momma Don't Allow It	8
68	Bell BLL 1002	Captain Of Your Ship/Toom Toom Is A Little Boy	6
68	RCA Victor RCA 1691	I Can Hear The Rain/Always Waitin'	5
68	Bell BLL 1014	Saturday Night Didn't Happen/Panic	20
68	Bell BLL 1021	Weather Forecast/You Can't Change A Young Boy's Mind	4
72	Bell BLL 1252	Captain Of Your Ship/Toom Toom Is A Little Boy (reissue)	4

RESERVE

88	Sha La La Ba Ba Ba-Ba Ba 006	Wherever You Go/SIDDELEYS: The Sun Slid Down/Behind The Tower (flexidisc, foldover p/s)	6

RESIDENTS

80	Pre PRE 009	THE COMMERCIAL SINGLE (p/s)	15
84	Korova KOW 36	It's A Man's Man's Man's World/I'll Go Crazy (p/s, 5,000 only)	6
83	London RALPH 1	INTERMISSION (12" EP)	10
79	Virgin VR 3	NIBBLES (LP, 5000 only)	10
80	Pre PRE X2	PICNIC BOY - THE COMMERCIAL ALBUM (LP, 5,000 only, with incorrect song order)	15
84	Korova CODE 9	GEORGE AND JAMES (cassette with extra track)	10
80s	Doublevision DV 9	THE MOLE SHOW/WHATEVER HAPPENED TO VILENESS FATS (cassette)	20
85	Doublevision DVR 17	THE PAL TV LP (LP, red vinyl, 5000 only)	10

JOHNNY RESTIVO

59	RCA RCA 1143	The Shape I'm In/Ya Ya (initially with triangular centre, later round)	20/12
59	RCA RCA 1143	The Shape I'm In/Ya Ya (78)	50
59	RCA RCA 1159	Dear Someone/I Like Girls	12
59	RCA RCA 1159	Dear Someone/I Like Girls (78)	30

RESTRICTED HOURS

79	Stevenage	Getting Things Done/Still Living Out The Car Crash/SYNDICATE: One Way Or Another/I Want To Be Somebody (white label, foldover p/s)	6

RETREADS
80	Eddi Cosmo	Would You Listen Girl (p/s)	20

RETURN TO FOREVER
74	Polydor 2310 283	HYMN OF GALAXY (LP)	10
74	Polydor 2310 354	WHERE HAVE I KNOWN YOU BEFORE (LP)	10
75	Polydor 2310 378	NO MYSTERY (LP)	10

(see also Chick Corea, Stanley Clarke)

REVELLERS
66	Columbia DB 8093	Believe, Believe/Love Is The Greatest Thing	4

REVELS
59	Top Rank JAR 235	Midnight Stroll/Talking To My Heart	15

REVELLS
71	CBS 7050	Mind Party/Indian Ropeman	8

DIGGER REVELL'S DENVERMEN
63	Decca F 11657	Surfside/Lisa Marie	7

REVENGE
76	Normal QS 000	Go Away/Game	6
70s	Blood CUS 614	Don't Tell Me Lies/Gimmie The Good Times	5

REVENGE
78	Loony LOO 1	Our Generation	6
78	Loony LOO 2	We're Not Gonna Take It/Pornography	6

PAUL REVERE & RAIDERS (featuring Mark Lindsay)
61	Top Rank JAR 557	Like Long Hair/Sharon	12
65	CBS 202003	Steppin' Out/Blue Fox	7
66	Sue WI 344	Like Long Hair/Sharon (reissue)	10
66	CBS 202027	Just Like Me/B F D R F Blues	6
66	CBS 202205	Kicks/Shake It Up	8
66	CBS 202253	Hungry/There She Goes	6
66	CBS 202411	The Great Airplane Strike/In My Community	8
67	CBS 202502	Good Thing/Undecided Man	8
67	CBS 202610	Ups And Downs/Leslie	7
67	CBS 2737	Him Or Me — Who's It Gonna Be?/The Legend Of Paul Revere	8
67	CBS 2919	I Had A Dream/Upon Your Leaving	5
67	CBS 3186	Mo'reen/Oh! To Be A Man	5
68	CBS 3310	Too Much Talk/Happening '68 (featuring Mark Lindsay)	4
68	CBS 3586	Don't Take It So Hard/Observation From Flight 285 (featuring Mark Lindsay)	6
68	CBS 3757	Cinderella Sunshine/Theme From It's Happening (featuring Mark Lindsay)	5
69	CBS 4025	Mr. Sun, Mr. Moon/With You (featuring Mark Lindsay)	4
69	CBS 4260	Let Me/I Don't Know (featuring Mark Lindsay)	6
69	CBS 4504	We Gotta All Get Up Together/Frankfurt Side Street (featuring Mark Lindsay)	4
66	CBS (S)BPG 62406	JUST LIKE US (LP)	12
66	CBS (S)BPG 62797	MIDNIGHT RIDE (LP)	12
67	CBS (S)BPG 62963	GOOD THING (LP)	12
68	CBS (S)BPG 63095	REVOLUTION (LP)	12
69	CBS 63265	GOIN' TO MEMPHIS (LP, mono/stereo)	12
69	CBS 63649	HARD 'N' HEAVY (LP)	12

(see also Raiders, Mark Lindsay)

REVILLOS
79	Snatzo/Dindisc DIN 1	Where's The Boy For Me/The Fiend (p/s)	4
79	Snatzo/Dindisc DIN 5	Motor Bike Beat/No Such Luck (p/s)	4
80	Snatzo/Dindisc DINZ 16	Scuba Scuba/Scuba Boy Bop (p/s)	4
80	Snatzo/Dindisc DINZ 20	Hungry For Love/Voodoo 2 (p/s, label also lists SP 703)	4
82	Superville SV 1001	She's Fallen In Love With A Monster Man/Mind Bending Cutie Doll (p/s)	4
82	Superville SV 2001	Bongo Brain/Hip City — You Were Meant For Me (p/s)	4
82	Aura AUS 135	Tell Him/Graveyard Groove (p/s)	6
83	EMI RVL 1	Bitten By A Love Bug/Cat Call	4
83	EMI 12 RVL 1	Bitten By A Love Bug (Extended Version)/Cat Call (12", p/s)	7
84	EMI RVL 2	Midnight/Z-X-7 (p/s)	4
84	EMI 12 RVL 2	Midnight (Extended Version)/Midnight (7" Version)/Z-X-7 (12", p/s)	7
80	Snatzo/Dindisc DID X 3	REV UP (LP, green or pink titles)	10
82	Superville SV 4001	ATTACK! (LP, withdrawn)	35

(see also Rezillos)

REVOLUTION
66	Piccadilly 7N 35289	Hallelujah/Shades Of Blue	25

(see also Hellions, Luther Grosvenor, Family, Traffic)

REVOLUTIONARY BLUES BAND
70	MCA MUP(S) 402	REVOLUTIONARY BLUES BAND (LP)	12

REVOLVING PAINT DREAM
84	Creation CRE 002	Flowers In The Sky/In The Afternoon (foldaround p/s in poly bag)	22

KIMBERLEY REW
80	Armageddon AS 004	Stomping All Over The World/Nothing's Going To Change In Your Life/ Fighting Someone's War (p/s)	4
81	Armageddon AS 012	My Baby Does Her Hairdo Long/Fishing (p/s)	4

(see also Soft Boys, dB's, Waves)

ROBERTA REX
68	Fontana TF 967	Joey/I Can Feel It	4

REX (Morris) & MINORS
60	Triumph RGM 1023	Chicken Sax/Snake Eyes	20

ALVINO REY

| 61 | London HLD 9431 | Original Mama Blues/Steel Guitar Rag | 7 |
| 62 | London HA-D 2414 | ALVINO REY'S GREATEST HITS (LP) | 10 |

LITTLE BOBBY REY & HIS BAND

| 60 | Top Rank JAR 525 | Rockin' "J" Bells/Dance Of The New Year | 6 |

REYNARD

| 76 | Pilgrim/Grapevine GRA 102 | FRESH FROM THE EARTH (LP) | 50 |

AMBROSE REYNOLDS

82	New Hormones CAT 4	WORLD'S GREATEST HITS (cassette with Assassination Calendar)	10
83	Zulu ZULU 3	GREATEST HITS (LP)	12
	(see also Pink Military)		

DEBBIE REYNOLDS

51	MGM MGM 350	Aba Dada Honeymoon/Row, Row, Row (with Carleton Carpenter) (78)	5
55	MGM SP 1127	Carolina In The Morning/Never Mind The Noise In The Market (B-side as Debbie Reynolds' Naturals)	8
56	MGM SP 1155	Love Is The Tender Trap/Canoodlin' Rag	6
57	Vogue Coral Q 72274	Tammy/French Heels	8
58	MGM MGM 968	All Grown Up/Wall Flower	4
58	Coral Q 72297	A Very Special Love/I Saw A Country Boy	4
58	Coral Q 72324	This Happy Feeling/Hillside In Scotland	6
58	Coral Q 72345	Hungry Eyes/Faces There Are Fairer	5
59	MGM MGM 1019	The Mating Game/Right Away	4
59	MGM MGM 1043	It Started With A Kiss/Love Is A Gamble	4
60	London HLD 9028	Am I That Easy To Forget?/Ask Me To Go Steady	4
60	London HLD 9128	City Lights/Just For A Touch Of Your Love	4
61	London HLD 9351	Lonely People/Just A Little Girl	4
58	MGM MGM-EP 670	DEBBIE REYNOLDS (EP)	10
58	MGM MGM-EP 671	SINGING IN THE RAIN (EP, with Gene Kelly & Donald O'Connor)	10
59	MGM MGM-EP 694	DELIGHTFUL DEBBIE REYNOLDS (EP)	10
60	MGM MGM-EP 725	FROM DEBBIE WITH LOVE (EP)	10
59	London HA-D 2200	DEBBIE (LP, also stereo SAH-D 6051)	15/18
60	London HA-D 2294	AM I THAT EASY TO FORGET? (LP, also stereo SAH-D 6106)	15/18
61	London HA-D 2326	FINE AND DANDY (LP)	15
63	London HA-D/SH-D 8075	GREAT FOLK HITS (LP, mono/stereo)	14/16

DONN REYNOLDS

57	HMV POP 314	Hasta Luego/Lorelei	4
58	MGM MGM 971	Rose Of Ol' Pawnee/All Alone (With No One By My Side)	4
58	MGM MGM 996	Blue Eyes Crying In The Rain/Bella Belinda	4
58	Pye 7N 15122	Swing Low Sweet Chariot/Ramona	4

JODY REYNOLDS

| 58 | London HL 8651 | Endless Sleep/Tight Capris | 18 |
| 58 | London HL 8651 | Endless Sleep/Tight Capris (78) | 15 |

L.J. REYNOLDS & CHOCOLATE SYRUP

| 72 | Avco/Embassy 6105 014 | The Penguin Breakdown/YOUNGHEARTS: Ooh La Wee | 4 |

TIMMY REYNOLDS

| 62 | Ember EMB S 133 | Lullaby Of Love/JEFF MILLS: Daddy's Home | 7 |

REZILLOS

77	Sensible FAB 1	Can't Stand My Baby/I Wanna Be Your Man (p/s, 15,000 only, 5,000 individually numbered)	10/7
77	Sensible FAB 2	Flying Saucer Attack /(My Baby Does) Good Sculptures (p/s, withdrawn, copies may exist)	25+
77	Sire 6078 612	Flying Saucer Attack/(My Baby Does) Good Sculptures (p/s, reissue)	7
78	Sire 6198 215	Cold Wars/William Mysterious Overture (unissued)	
78	Sire SIR 4001	Top Of The Pops/20,000 Rezillos Under The Sea (p/s)	7
78	Sire SIR 4008	Destination Venus/Mystery Action (p/s)	6
79	Sire SIR 4014	Cold Wars (live)/Flying Saucer Attack (live)/Twist & Shout (live) (p/s)	7
79	Sensible FAB 1 (Mark 2)	Can't Stand My Baby/I Wanna Be Your Man (reissue, new p/s, run out groove reads "Come Back John Lennon")	4
79	Sensible FAB 1 (Mark 2)	Can't Stand My Baby/I Wanna Be Your Man (reissue, p/s, mispress, B-side plays "(My Baby Does) Good Sculptures (live)", run-off groove reads "De-sire-able product?", 4,000 only)	6
81	Sire SPC 3	Top Of The Pops/Destination Venus (cassette, flip-up box)	5
78	Sire K 56530	CAN'T STAND THE REZILLOS (LP, with inner sleeve & postcard insert)	12
78	Sire SRK 6069	MISSION ACCOMPLISHED ... BUT THE BEAT GOES ON (LP, live)	10
	(see also Revillos, Shake, Jo Callis, William Mysterious)		

RHABSTALLION

| 81 | Rhab | Day To Day (p/s) | 15 |

RHINOCEROS

68	Elektra EKSN 45051	Apricot Brandy/You're My Girl	4
69	Elektra EKSN 45058	I Will Serenade You/Belbuekul	5
69	Elektra EKSN 45080	Back Door/In A Little Room	5
71	Elektra 2101 009	Old Age/Let's Party	4
69	Elektra EKL 4030	RHINOCEROS (LP, also stereo EKS 74030)	12
69	Elektra EKL 4056	SATIN CHICKENS (LP, also stereo EKS 74056)	10
70	Elektra 2469 006	BETTER TIMES ARE COMING (LP)	10

RHODA with SPECIAL A.K.A.

82	2-Tone CHS TT 18	The Boiler/Theme From The Boiler (p/s)	4
82	2-Tone CHS TT 1218	The Boiler/Theme From The Boiler (12", p/s)	7
	(see also Special A.K.A.)		

PAT RHODEN
68	Trojan TR 606	Woman Is Greedy/Endlessy	6

(see also Pat Riden, Pat & Marie)

WINSTON RHODEN
66	Blue Beat BB 360	Send Your Love/Make Believe	7

EMITT RHODES
71	Probe SPBA 6256	EMITT RHODES (LP)	10
71	A&M AMLS 64254	AMERICAN DREAM (LP)	12
71	Probe SPBA 6262	MIRROR (LP)	10
72	Probe SPBA 6266	FAREWELL TO PARADISE (LP)	10

TODD RHODES ORCHESTRA
54	Parlophone R 4029	Specks/Silver Sunset (78)	12
55	Parlophone MSP 6171	Specks/Silver Sunset	15

RHUBARB RHUBARB
68	President PT 229	Rainmaker/Moneylender	20

RHYTHM ACES
61	Starlite ST45 061	A Thousand Teardrops/Wherever You May Go	15
61	Starlite ST45 066	Please Don't Go Away/Oh My Darling	12
62	Island WI 032	C-H-R-I-S-T-M-A-S/TOP GRANT: A Christmas Drink	8
62	Blue Beat BB 134	I'll Be There/DON DRUMMOND: Dewdrops	8

RHYTHM & BLUES INC.
65	Fontana TF 524	Louie Louie/Honey Don't	30

(see also Pete Kelley's Solution)

RHYTHM MAKERS
76	Polydor 2001 651	Zone/Prime Cut	6

RHYTHMETTES
59	Coral Q 72358	Page From The Future/I'll Be With You In Apple Blossom Time	6

RHYTHM KINGS
63	Vogue V 9212	Blue Soul/Exotic	12

RHYTHM OF LIFE
82	Rational RATE 6	Soon/Summertime (p/s; label also lists Rhythm RHYTHM 1)	7
82	Rational RATE 7	Uncle Sam/Portarit Of The Heart (p/s; label also lists Rhythm RHYTHM 2)	6

(see also Josef K, Paul Haig)

MANDY RICE-DAVIES
64	Ember EMB 4537	MANDY (EP)	20

TIM RICE & WEBBER GROUP
69	RCA RCA 1895	Come Back Richard/Roll On Over The Atlantic	4

BUDDY RICH
67	Fontana TF 836	Norwegian Wood/Monitor Theme	4
50s	Columbia Clef SEB 10024	BUDDY RICH (EP)	7
57	Columbia Clef SEB 10071	SWINGING BUDDY RICH (EP)	7
56	HMV CLP 1092	BUDDY RICH SINGS JOHNNY MERCER (LP)	10
56	Columbia Clef 33CX 10052	THE WAILING BUDDY RICH (LP)	10
57	Columbia Clef 33CX 10071	THIS ONE'S FOR BASIE (LP)	10
57	Columbia Clef 33CX 10080	BUDDY AND SWEETS (LP, with Harry 'Sweets' Edison)	10
58	HMV CLP 1185	BUDDY RICH JUST SINGS (LP)	10
59	Columbia Clef 33CX 10138	BUDDY RICH AT MIAMI (LP)	10

BUDDY RICH & MAX ROACH
60	Mercury MMC 14031	RICH VERSUS ROACH (LP, also stereo CMS 18021)	10

(see also Max Roach)

CHARLIE RICH
60	London HLU 9107	Lonely Weekends/Everything I Do Is Wrong	18
62	London HLS 9482	Just A Little Bit Sweet/It's Too Late	12
65	RCA RCA 1433	Too Many Teardrops/It's All Over Now	6
65	Philips BF 1432	Mohair Sam/I Washed My Hands In Muddy Water	7
67	London HLU 10104	Love Is After Me/Pass On By (silver top label, later box logo label)	15/5
69	Mercury MF 1109	Mohair Sam/I Washed My Hands In Muddy Water (p/s, reissue)	4
65	RCA RD 7719	THAT'S RICH (LP)	30
66	Philips BL 7695	THE MANY NEW SIDES OF CHARLIE RICH (LP)	18
73	CBS Q 65716	BEHIND CLOSED DOORS (LP, quadrophonic)	10

DAVE RICH
58	RCA RCA 1092	Burn On Love Fire/City Lights	8
58	RCA RCA 1092	Burn On Love Fire/City Lights (78)	12
66	Polydor BM 56113	Last Two People On Earth/I Just Wanna Dance	4

JOHNNY RICH
64	Mercury MF 836	Dream On/Together	4

LEWIS RICH
66	Parlophone R 5434	I Don't Want To Hear It Anymore/Shedding Tears	8

PAUL RICH (& BEATMEN)
59	Embassy WB 345	Battle Of New Orleans/BUD ASHTON: Peter Gunn	4
59	Embassy WB 363	Makin' Love/GORDON FRANKS SEXTET: Red River Rock	4
60	Embassy WB 374	Heartaches By The Number/BUD ASHTON: Some Kinda Earthquake	4
62	Embassy WB 548	Don't You Think It's Time/Little Town Flirt	4

62	Embassy WB 567	Young Lovers (as Paul Rich & Kay Barry)/JOAN BAXTER: I Will Follow Him 4
64	Embassy WB 637	No Particular Place To Go (as Paul Rich & Beatmen)/TERRY BRANDON & BEATMEN: I Love You Baby 4
65	Embassy WB 678	Keep Searchin' (as Paul Rich & Beatmen)/BURT SHANE: The Special Years 4

TONY RICH

| 66 | Piccadilly 7N 35291 | Save Your Love/Don't Mention Your Name ....4 |
| 66 | Piccadilly 7N 35323 | It's All Up To You Now/See Saw ....4 |

(see also Tony Sheveton)

RICHARD & YOUNG LIONS

| 66 | Philips BF 1520 | Open Up Your Door/Once Upon Your Smile ....35 |

CLIFF RICHARD (& DRIFTERS/SHADOWS)

58	Columbia DB 4178	Move It!/Schoolboy Crush (green label , later black) 12/25
58	Columbia DB 4178	Move It!/Schoolboy Crush (78) 20
58	Columbia DB 4203	High Class Baby/My Feet Hit The Ground (green label, later black) 10/25
58	Columbia DB 4203	High Class Baby/My Feet Hit The Ground (78) 20
59	Columbia DB 4249	Livin' Lovin' Doll/Steady With You (green label, later black) 20/30
59	Columbia DB 4249	Livin' Lovin' Doll/Steady With You (78) 40
59	Columbia DB 4290	Mean Streak/Never Mind (green label, later black) 10/25
59	Columbia DB 4290	Mean Streak/Never Mind (78) 40
59	Columbia DB 4306	Living Doll/Apron Strings (green label, later black) 5/20
59	Columbia DB 4306	Living Doll/Apron Strings (78) 30

(the above singles were credited to Cliff Richard & Drifters)

59	Columbia DB 4351	Travellin' Light/Dynamite 6
59	Columbia DB 4351	Travellin' Light/Dynamite (78) 45
60	Columbia DB 4398	A Voice In The Wilderness/Don't Be Mad At Me 6
60	Columbia DB 4398	A Voice In The Wilderness/Don't Be Mad At Me (78) 45
60	Columbia DB 4431	Fall In Love With You/Willie And The Hand Jive 6
60	Columbia DB 4431	Fall In Love With You/Willie And The Hand Jive (78, probably unissued) .....100+
60	Columbia DB 4479	Please Don't Tease/Where Is My Heart 6
60	Columbia DB 4506	Nine Times Out Of Ten/Thinking Of Our Love 7
60	Columbia DB 4547	I Love You/"D" In Love 6
61	Columbia DB 4593	Theme For A Dream/Mumblin' Mosie 6
61	Columbia DB 4667	A Girl Like You/Now's The Time To Fall In Love 5
61	Columbia DB 4716	When The Girl In Your Arms Is The Girl In Your Heart/Got A Funny Feeling (solo) 5
62	Columbia DB 4761	The Young Ones/We Say Yeah (green label, later black) 5/4
62	Columbia DB 4828	I'm Lookin' Out The Window/Do You Want To Dance? 5
62	Columbia DB 4886	It'll Be Me/Since I Lost You 5

(the above singles originally came with green labels, later black label copies are worth at least twice the value unless stated)

62	Columbia DB 4950	The Next Time/Bachelor Boy 4
63	Columbia DB 4977	Summer Holiday/Dancing Shoes 4
63	Columbia DB 7034	Lucky Lips/I Wonder 4
63	Columbia DB 7089	It's All In The Game/Your Eyes Tell On You (solo) 4
63	Columbia DB 7150	Don't Talk To Him/Say You're Mine 4
64	Columbia DB 7203	I'm The Lonely One/Watch What You Do With My Baby 4
64	Columbia DB 7272	Constantly/True True Lovin' (solo) 4
64	Columbia DB 7305	On The Beach/A Matter Of Moments 4
64	Columbia DB 7372	The Twelfth Of Never/I'm Afraid To Go Home (solo) 4
64	Columbia DB 7420	I Could Easily Fall (In Love With You)/I'm In Love With You 4

(the above singles were credited to Cliff Richard & Shadows unless stated.)

64	Columbia DB 7435	This Was My Special Day/I'm Feeling Oh So Lovely (withdrawn, credited to Cliff Richard, Audrey Bayley, Joan Palethorpe & Faye Fisher) 20
65	Columbia DB 7496	The Minute You're Gone/Just Another Guy 4
65	Columbia DB 7596	On My Word/Just A Little Bit Too Late 4
65	Columbia DB 7660	The Time In Between/Look Before You Love (as Cliff Richard & Shadows) 5
65	Columbia DB 7745	Wind Me Up (Let Me Go)/The Night 4
66	Columbia DB 7866	Blue Turns To Grey/Somebody Loses (as Cliff Richard & Shadows) 5
66	Columbia DB 7968	Visions/What Would I Do (For The Love Of A Girl?) 4
66	Columbia DB 8017	Time Drags By/La La La Song (as Cliff Richard & Shadows) 5
66	Columbia DB 8094	In The Country/Finders Keepers (as Cliff Richard & Shadows) 4
67	Columbia DB 8150	It's All Over/Why Wasn't I Born Rich? 5
67	Columbia DB 8210	I'll Come Runnin'/I Get The Feelin' 4
67	Columbia DB 8245	The Day I Met Marie/Our Story Book 4
67	Columbia DB 8293	All My Love/Sweet Little Jesus Boy 5
68	Columbia DB 8376	Congratulations/High 'N' Dry 4
68	Columbia DB 8437	I'll Love You Forever Today/Girl, You'll Be A Woman Soon 8
68	Columbia DB 8476	Marianne/Mr Nice 6
68	Columbia DB 8503	Don't Forget To Catch Me/What's More (I Don't Need Her) 6
69	Columbia DB 8548	Good Times (Better Times)/Occasional Rain 5
69	Columbia DB 8581	Big Ship/She's Leaving You 6
69	Columbia DB 8615	Throw Down A Line (as Cliff & Hank)/Reflections 5
69	Columbia DB 8641	With The Eyes Of A Child/So Long 5
70	Columbia DB 8657	Leave My Woman Alone/Boogitoo (as Cliff & Hank)/HANK MARVIN: Joy Of Living 6
70	Columbia DB 8685	Goodbye Sam, Hello Samantha/You Never Can Tell 4
70	Columbia DB 8708	I Ain't Got Time Anymore/Monday Comes Too Soon 5
71	Columbia DB 8747	Sunny Honey Girl/Don't Move Away (with Olivia Newton-John)/ I Was Only Fooling Myself 7
71	Columbia DB 8774	Silvery Rain/Annabella Umbrella/Time Flies 8
71	Columbia DB 8797	Flying Machine/Pigeon 7
71	Columbia DB 8836	Sing A Song Of Freedom/A Thousand Conversations 5
72	Columbia DB 8864	Jesus/Mister Cloud 8
72	Columbia DB 8917	Living In Harmony/Empty Chairs 4
72	Columbia DB 8957	Brand New Song/The Old Accordion 6

(the below Columbia singles were export issues)

Cliff RICHARD

61	Columbia DC 756	Gee Whiz It's You/I Cannot Find A True Love 8
63	Columbia DC 758	What'd I Say/Blue Moon 200
65	Columbia DC 762	Angel/Razzle Dazzle 50
73	EMI EMI 2012	Power To All Our Friends/Come Back Billie Joe 4
73	EMI EMI 2022	Help It Along/Tomorrow Rising/The Days Of Love/Ashes To Ashes (p/s) 10/5
73	EMI EMI 2088	Take Me High/Celestial Houses 5
74	EMI EMI 2150	(You Keep Me) Hangin' On/Love Is Here 5
75	EMI EMI 2279	It's Only Me You've Left Behind/You're The One 12
75	EMI EMI 2344	Honky Tonk Angel/(Wouldn't You Know It) Got Myself A Girl 12
76	EMI EMI 2376	Miss You Nights/Love Is Enough (later available with p/s in box set) ...4
76	EMI EMI 2458	Devil Woman/Love On 4
76	EMI EMI 2499	I Can't Ask For Anything More Than You/Junior Cowboy 5
76	EMI EMI 2559	Hey Mr Dream Maker/No One Waits 4
77	EMI EMI 2584	My Kinda Life/Nothing Left For Me To Say 5
77	EMI EMI 2633	When Two Worlds Drift Apart/That's Why I Love You 5
78	EMI EMI 2730	Yes! He Lives/Good On The Sally Army 8
78	EMI EMI 2832	Please Remember Me/Please Don't Tease 5
78	EMI EMI 2885	Can't Take The Hurt Anymore/Needing A Friend (p/s) 6
79	EMI EMI 2920	Green Light/Imagine Love (some in p/s) 30/5
79	EMI EMI 2975	We Don't Talk Anymore/Count Me Out (p/s) 4
79	EMI EMI 2975	We Don't Talk Anymore/Count Me Out (p/s, mispress, A-side plays Queen's "Bohemian Rhapsody") 12
79	EMI EMI 5003	Hot Shot/Walking In The Light (p/s) 4
80	EMI EMI 5006	Carrie/Moving In (p/s) 4
82	EMI EMI 5341	Where Do We Go From Here/Discovering (p/s) 4
82	EMI EMIP 5348	Little Town/Love And A Helping Hand/You Me And Jesus (picture disc) ...6
83	EMI 12EMI 5415	Never Say Die (Give A Little Bit More)/Lucille (12", p/s) 8
84	EMI EMI 5457	Ocean Deep/Baby You're Dynamite (different version) (p/s, A & B-sides reversed) 6
84	EMI 12EMI 5457	Baby You're Dynamite (Extended Mix)/Ocean Deep (12", p/s) 8
84	EMI RICHP 1	Shooting From The Heart/Small World (heart-shaped picture disc) 10
85	EMI RICHP 2/RICHP 1	Heart User/I Will Follow You//Shooting From The Heart/Small World (shrinkwrapped double pack, 2nd single as shaped picture disc) 12
85	EMI 12 RICH 2	Heart User (Extended)/I Will Follow You (12", poster p/s) 10
86	WEA YZ 65P	Living Doll (with Young Ones)/YOUNG ONES: (All The Little Flowers Are) Happy (picture disc) 5
85	EMI EMI 5531	She's So Beautiful/(Special Mix) (p/s, some with 'Time' inner sleeve) 6/4
85	EMI EMI 5537	It's In Every One Of Us/Alone (p/s, some with 'Time' inner sleeve) ...6/4
86	EMI EMI 5545	Born To Rock And Roll/Law Of The Universe (p/s, some with 'Time' inner) 6/4
86	EMI 12EMI 5545	Born To Rock And Roll/Law Of The Universe (12", p/s) 8
87	EMI EMG 4	My Pretty One/Love Ya (gatefold p/s) 5
87	EMI 12EMP 4	My Pretty One/Love Ya/Under The Gun (12", p/s, with poster) 7
87	EMI EMG 18	Some People/One Time Lover Man (gatefold p/s) 5
87	EMI EMP 18	Some People/One Time Lover Man (Cliff-shaped picture disc) 7
87	EMI EM 31	Remember Me/Another Christmas Day (gold embossed p/s) 4
87	EMI 12EMP 31	Remember Me/Another Christmas Day/Brave New World (12", gold embossed p/s) 7
87	EMI 12EMT 31	Remember Me/Another Christmas Day/Brave New World (12", poster p/s) ...7
87	EMI CDEM 31	Remember Me/Lindsay Jane/Move It/High Class Baby (CD) 7
87	EMI EMP 42	Two Hearts/Yesterday, Today, Forever (double heart-shaped picture disc) ...6
87	EMI EMG 42	Two Hearts/Yesterday, Today, Forever (gatefold p/s) 4
87	EMI 12EMG 42	Two Hearts/Yesterday, Today, Forever/Wild Geese (12", gatefold p/s) ...7
88	EMI CDEMG 42	Two Hearts/Yesterday, Today, Forever/Wild Geese (CD) 7
88	EMI EMS 78	Mistletoe And Wine/Marmaduke/True Love Ways (p/s) 4
88	EMI EMP 78	Mistletoe And Wine/Marmaduke (poster/calendar p/s) 5
88	EMI 12EMX 78	Mistletoe And Wine/Marmaduke/Little Town (12", p/s, with Advent calendar) 10
88	EMI CDEM 78	Mistletoe And Wine/Ganave (CD, with Christmas card) 7
89	EMI EM 101	I Just Don't Have The Heart/Wide Open Space (p/s, white s) 4
89	EMI 12EM 101	I Just Don't Have The Heart/I Just Don't Have The Heart (Instrumental)/ Wide Open Space (12", p/s, white s) 7
89	EMI 12EMP 101	I Just Don't Have The Heart/I Just Don't Have The Heart (Instrumental)/ Wide Open Space (12", picture disc) 7
89	EMI 12EMX 101	I Just Don't Have The Heart (Remix)/Wide Open Space/I Just Don't Have The Heart (Instrumental) (12", plain black sleeve) 8
89	EMI EMS 152	Silhouettes/The Winner ('photoframe' p/s with stand) 5
90	EMI EMPD 155	From A Distance/I Could Easily Fall (picture disc, PVC sleeve) 4
90	EMI XMAS P90	Saviour's Day/Oh! Boy Medley ('Xmas' pack, envelope p/s with 5 photos) ...5
91	EMI XMAS G91/XMAS 91	We Should Be Together/Miss You Nights (live)//We Should Be Together/ Twelve Days Of Christmas/Mistletoe And Wine/The Holly And The Ivy (Acapella Version) (double pack, gatefold p/s, discs sold separately) 5
60	Serenade Magazine/	Serenade Presents Cliff Richard's Personal Message To You
60s	Rainbow (no cat. no.)	(turquoise flexidisc free with magazine) 25/20
60s	Serenade Magazine	Cliff's Rock Party (flexidisc with magazine) 25/20
60s	Boyfriend Magazine	flexidisc 25/20
60s	Rainbow Magazine	Music From America (flexidisc) 25/20
60s	New Spotlight	Star Souvenir Greetings (208 Radio Luxembourg flexidisc) 15
73	Lyntone LYN SF 1218	The Cliff Richard Story (World Record Club flexidisc) 6
73	Spree (no cat. no.)	Good News (plain black flexidisc with spoken/sung introduction from Cliff, other side by Johnny Cash) 20
70s	Lyntone LYN 14745	The Best Of Cliff Richard And The Shadows (preview flexidisc) 10
59	Columbia SEG 7895	SERIOUS CHARGE (EP, soundtrack) 20
59	Columbia SEG 7903	CLIFF NO. 1 (EP, also stereo ESG 7754) 25/50
59	Columbia SEG 7910	CLIFF NO. 2 (EP, also stereo ESG 7769) 25/50
59	Columbia SEG 7971	EXPRESSO BONGO (EP, soundtrack, also stereo ESG 7783) 15/35
60	Columbia SEG 7979	CLIFF SINGS NO. 1 (EP, also stereo ESG 7788) 22/50
60	Columbia SEG 7987	CLIFF SINGS NO. 2 (EP, also stereo ESG 7794) 22/50
60	Columbia SEG 8005	CLIFF SINGS NO. 3 (EP, also stereo ESG 7808) 22/50

MINT VALUE £

60	Columbia SEG 8021	CLIFF SINGS NO. 4 (EP, also stereo ESG 7816) 25/50
60	Columbia SEG 8050	CLIFF'S SILVER DISCS (EP) 12
60	Columbia SEG 8065	ME AND MY SHADOWS NO. 1 (EP, also stereo ESG 7837) 20/35
61	Columbia SEG 8071	ME AND MY SHADOWS NO. 2 (EP, also stereo ESG 7481) 18/35
61	Columbia SEG 8078	ME AND MY SHADOWS NO. 3 (EP, also stereo ESG 7843) 20/35
61	Columbia SEG 8105	LISTEN TO CLIFF NO. 1 (EP, also stereo ESG 7858) 18/35
61	Columbia SEG 8119	DREAM (EP, also stereo ESG 7867) 15/35
61	Columbia SEG 8126	LISTEN TO CLIFF NO. 2 (EP, also stereo ESG 7870) 18/35
62	Columbia SEG 8133	CLIFF'S HIT PARADE (EP) 15
62	Columbia SEG 8151	CLIFF RICHARD (EP) 20
62	Columbia SEG 8159	HITS FROM 'THE YOUNG ONES' (EP) 12
62	Columbia SEG 8168	CLIFF RICHARD NO. 2 (EP) 20

(the above EPs originally came with turquoise s, later blue/black copies are worth two thirds to the same value)

62	Columbia SEG 8203	CLIFF'S HITS (EP) 15
63	Columbia SEG 8228	TIME FOR CLIFF AND THE SHADOWS (EP, mono) 18
63	Columbia ESG 7887	TIME FOR CLIFF AND THE SHADOWS (EP, stereo, turquoise or blue/black) ..45/40
63	Columbia SEG 8246	HOLIDAY CARNIVAL (EP, also stereo ESG 7892) 15/35
63	Columbia SEG 8250	HITS FROM 'SUMMER HOLIDAY' (EP, also stereo ESG 7896) 12/35
63	Columbia SEG 8263	MORE HITS FROM 'SUMMER HOLIDAY' (EP, also stereo ESG 7898) 20/35
63	Columbia SEG 8269	CLIFF'S LUCKY LIPS (EP) 15
63	Columbia SEG 8272	LOVE SONGS (EP, also stereo ESG 7900) 15/45
64	Columbia SEG 8290	WHEN IN FRANCE (EP) 18
64	Columbia SEG 8299	CLIFF SINGS 'DON'T TALK TO HIM' (EP) 18
64	Columbia SEG 8320	CLIFF'S PALLADIUM SUCCESSES (EP) 22
64	Columbia SEG 8338	WONDERFUL LIFE (EP, also stereo ESG 7902) 15/35
64	Columbia SEG 8347	A FOREVER KIND OF LOVE (EP) 20
64	Columbia SEG 8354	WONDERFUL LIFE NO. 2 (EP, also stereo ESG 7903) 15/35
64	Columbia SEG 8376	HITS FROM 'WONDERFUL LIFE' (EP, also stereo ESG 7906) 15/40
65	Columbia SEG 8384	WHY DON'T THEY UNDERSTAND? (EP) 20
65	Columbia SEG 8395	CLIFF'S HITS FROM 'ALADDIN AND HIS WONDERFUL LAMP' (EP) 15
65	Columbia SEG 8405	LOOK IN MY EYES, MARIA (EP) 22
65	Columbia SEG 8444	ANGEL (EP) 22
65	Columbia SEG 8450	TAKE FOUR (EP) 20
66	Columbia SEG 8474	WIND ME UP (EP) 18
66	Columbia SEG 8478	HITS FROM 'WHEN IN ROME' (EP) 45
66	Columbia SEG 8488	LOVE IS FOREVER (EP) 25
66	Columbia SEG 8510	THUNDERBIRDS ARE GO! (EP, 3 tracks by Cliff & Shadows, 1 solo) 45
66	Columbia SEG 8517	LA LA LA LA LA (EP, 1 track by Bruce Welch & Hank Marvin) 25
67	Columbia SEG 8527	CINDERELLA (EP) 75
67	Columbia SEG 8533	CAROL SINGERS (EP) 30
68	Columbia SEG 8540	CONGRATULATIONS (EP) 25
59	Columbia 33SX 1147	CLIFF (LP, green s, later blue/black s) 35/25
59	Columbia 33SX 1192	CLIFF SINGS (LP, green s, later blue/black s) 35/25
60	Columbia 33SX 1261	ME AND MY SHADOWS (LP, also stereo SCX 3330) 25/50
60	EMI Regal SREG 1120	ME AND MY SHADOWS (LP, export issue) 60
61	Columbia 33SX 1320	LISTEN TO CLIFF! (LP, also stereo SCX 3375) 25/50
61	Columbia 33SX 1368	21 TODAY (LP, also stereo SCX 3409) 25/50
61	Columbia 33SX 1384	THE YOUNG ONES (LP, soundtrack with inner, also stereo SCX 3397) 18/35
62	Columbia 33SX 1431	32 MINUTES AND 17 SECONDS WITH ... (LP, also stereo SCX 3436) 25/50

(the above LPs originally came with green s, later blue/black copies are worth nearly two thirds the value unless stated)

63	Columbia 33SX 1472	SUMMER HOLIDAY (LP, soundtrack with inner sleeve, mono) 15
63	Columbia SCX 3462	SUMMER HOLIDAY (LP, stereo, initially green s, later blue/black) 30/20
63	Columbia SX 1512	CLIFF'S HIT ALBUM (LP) 15
63	Columbia SX 1541	WHEN IN SPAIN (LP, also stereo SCX 3488) 20/30
64	Columbia SX 1628	WONDERFUL LIFE (LP, g/fold sleeve with inner, also stereo SCX 3515) 15/25
64	Columbia SX 1676/	ALADDIN AND HIS WONDERFUL LAMP (LP, with stage cast,
	SCX 3522	gatefold sleeve, mono/stereo) 15/18
64	World Record C. (S)T 643	HOW WONDERFUL TO KNOW (LP) 18/22
65	Columbia SX 1709	CLIFF RICHARD (LP, also stereo SCX 3546) 35/40
65	Columbia SX 1737	MORE HITS BY CLIFF (LP, also stereo SCX 3555) 14/18
65	Columbia SX 1762	WHEN IN ROME (LP) 30
65	Columbia SX 1769	LOVE IS FOREVER (LP, also stereo SCX 3569) 25
66	Columbia S(C)X 6039	KINDA LATIN (LP, mono/stereo) 30/35
66	Columbia S(C)X 6079	FINDERS KEEPERS (LP, soundtrack with inner sleeve, mono/stereo) 15/20
67	Columbia S(C)X 6103	CINDERELLA (LP, with stage cast) 25
67	Columbia S(C)X 6133	DON'T STOP ME NOW (LP) 25
67	Columbia S(C)X 6167	GOOD NEWS (LP) 18
67	Columbia JSX 6167	GOOD NEWS (LP, export issue) 35
68	Columbia S(C)X 6244	CLIFF IN JAPAN (LP, blue/black s, later white/black s) 30/20
68	Columbia S(C)X 6262	TWO A PENNY (LP, blue/black s, later white/black s) 25/18
68	Columbia S(C)X 6282	ESTABLISHED 1958 (LP, gatefold sleeve, half tracks by Shadows, m/s) 18/15

(the above Columbia LPs had blue/black s, later white/black copies are worth half the value unless stated)

69	Columbia S(C)X 6343	THE BEST OF CLIFF (LP) 12
69	Columbia S(C)X 6357	SINCERELY CLIFF RICHARD (LP, mono/stereo) 25/20
69	Regal Starline SRS 5011	IT'LL BE ME (LP, reissue of "32 Minutes And 17 Seconds
		With Cliff Richard") 10
70	Regal Starline SRS 5031	CLIFF 'LIVE' AT THE TALK OF THE TOWN (LP) 12
70	MFP MFP 1420	ALL MY LOVE (LP) 10
70	Columbia SCX 6408	ABOUT THAT MAN (LP, 4 songs plus narration) 100
70	Columbia SCX 6435	TRACKS 'N' GROOVES (LP) 25
70	Columbia SCX 6443	HIS LAND (LP, documentary soundtrack, with Cliff Barrows) 60
71	Columbia SCX 1512	CLIFF'S HIT ALBUM (LP, stereo reissue) 10
72	WRC SM 255-260	THE CLIFF RICHARD STORY (6-LP box set with booklet) 35
72	WRC CSM 255-260	THE CLIFF RICHARD STORY (6-cassette box set with booklet) 30
72	World Record C. STP 1051	CLIFF RICHARD (LP) 45
72	Columbia SCX 6519	THE BEST OF CLIFF VOLUME 2 (LP) 10
73	Sounds Superb SPR90018	IT'LL BE ME (LP, 2nd reissue, different cover) 10

Cliff RICHARD

73	EMI EMC 3016	TAKE ME HIGH (LP, soundtrack, some with poster)	25/15
74	EMI EMA 768	HELP IT ALONG (LP)	20
74	EMI EMC 3048	THE 31ST OF FEBRUARY STREET (LP)	20
74	EMI TC EXSP 1601	THE MUSIC AND LIFE OF CLIFF RICHARD (6-cassette box set)	25
75	Sounds Superb SPR90070	EVERYONE NEEDS SOMEONE TO LOVE (LP)	10
70s	Readers Digest	THE BEST OF CLIFF RICHARD AND THE SHADOWS (8-LP box set)	50
80	WRC ALBUM 26	THE CLIFF RICHARD SONGBOOK (6-LP box set)	35
80	WRC CASSETTE 26	THE CLIFF RICHARD SONGBOOK (6-cassette box set)	25
83	EMI EDP 1546303	WHEN IN ROME/WHEN IN SPAIN (2-LP, reissue)	14
85	Myrrh MYR 1176	WALKING IN THE LIGHT (LP)	30
85	Myrrh MYRC 1176	WALKING IN THE LIGHT (cassette)	12
85	Myrrh MYRCD 1176	WALKING IN THE LIGHT (CD)	20
86	Word WRD R 3017	HYMNS AND INSPIRATIONAL SONGS (LP)	30
86	Word WRD C 3017	HYMNS AND INSPIRATIONAL SONGS (cassette)	12
88	Myrrh MYR R 1209	IT'S A SMALL WORLD (LP)	40
88	Myrrh MYR C 1209	IT'S A SMALL WORLD (cassette)	12
88	Word WRD R 3034	CAROLS (LP)	30
88	Word WRD C 3034	CAROLS (cassette)	10
88	Word WRD R 3036	SMALL CORNERS (LP, reissue)	30
88	Word WRD C 3036	SMALL CORNERS (cassette, reissue)	10
89	EMI EMDB 1004	ALWAYS GUARANTEED (LP, box set, some in embossed sleeve)	10

(see also Drifters [U.K.], Shadows, Olivia Newton-John, Sheila Walsh, Janet Jackson, Elton John)

WENDY RICHARD & DIANA BERRY

63	Decca F 11680	We Had A Dream/Keep 'Em Looking Around	4

(see also Mike Sarne)

CYNTHIA RICHARDS

70	Trojan TBL 123	FOOLISH FOOL (LP, actually a Clancy Eccles productions compilation)	15

JOHN RICHARDS

57	HMV POP 401	Let Me Be Loved/By The Fireside	4
65	Oriole CB 312	Folks Get Married In The Spring/Then I'll Be There	4
66	Polydor BM 56705	I Will Go Again To Ireland/Midnight Sky	4

KEITH RICHARDS

79	Rolling Stones RSR 102	Run Rudolph Run/(The Harder They Come) (p/s)	10

(see also Rolling Stones, Aranbee Pop Symphony, Dirty Strangers, Screamin' Jay Hawkins)

LISA RICHARDS

65	Vocalion VP 9244	Mean Old World/Take A Chance	20

LLOYD RICHARDS

64	Port-O-Jam PJ 4004	Be Good/I Need You	8

ROY RICHARDS

66	Doctor Bird DB 1012	Contact/Maureen	12
66	Island WI 283	Double Trouble/FITZY & FREDDY: Why Did You You Do It	10
66	Island WI 299	Western Standard Time/(JA) EAGLES: What A Agony	10
66	Island WI 3000	South Vietnam/You Must Be Sorry (Vocal)	8
67	Island WI 3027	Rub-A-Dub/SHARKS: Baby Come Home	8
67	Island WI 3037	Hopeful Village Ska/DELROY WILSON: Ungrateful Baby	8
67	Studio One SO 2020	Hanky Panky/ALTON ELLIS: I Am Still In Love	15

RUSTY RICHARDS

60	Top Rank JAR 297	Middle Hand Road/Golden Moon (China Night)	5

TRUDY RICHARDS

57	Capitol CL 14728	Wishbone/Hangin' Around	6
57	Capitol CL 14744	Weaker Than Wise/I Want A Big Butter And Egg Man	4
58	Capitol CL 14857	Somebody Just Like You/The Night When Love Was Born	5
57	Capitol T 838	CRAZY IN LOVE (LP)	10

WINSTON RICHARDS

66	Island WI 297	Green Coolie (actually "Green Collie")/MARCIA GRIFFITHS: You No Good	8
67	Rio R 124	Studio Blitz/Don't Up	8

MARK RICHARDSON

65	Stateside SS 440	Baby, I'm Sorry/Blanket Fair	4
65	Stateside SS 467	See It My Way/Think	4

RICHENEL

86	4AD BAD 601	L'Esclave Endormi/L'Esclave Endormi (12", p/s)	7

LIONEL RICHIE

86	Motown LIO D1	Dancing On The Ceiling/Love Will Find A Way//Truly/ Just Put Some Love In Your Heart (double pack)	4

(see also Commodores)

RICH KIDS

78	EMI EMI 2738	Rich Kids/Empty Words (p/s, red vinyl)	4
78	EMI EMI 2803	Marching Men/Here Comes The Nice (p/s)	4
78	EMI EMI 2848	Ghosts Of Princes In Towers/Only Arsenic (no p/s)	4
78	EMI EMC 3263	GHOSTS OF PRINCES IN TOWERS (LP)	10

(see also Sex Pistols, Ultravox, Slik, Midge Ure)

JONATHAN RICHMAN & MODERN LOVERS

75	United Artists UP 36006	Road Runner/It Will Stand	6
77	Beserkley BZZ 1	Road Runner (Once)/Road Runner (Twice) (p/s)	4

RICHMOND

71	Dart ART 2008	Candy Dora/Willow Farm	4
73	Dart ART 2025	Frightened/Breakfast	4

MINT VALUE £

73	Dart ART 2031	Raise Your Heads To The Wind	4
74	Dart ART 2044	Peaches/Work For My Baby	4
73	Dart ARTS 65371	FRIGHTENED (LP)	30

BEN RICHMOND
63	Piccadilly 7N 35132	You Gotta Have Love/I Don't Care	4

JANET RICHMOND
60	Top Rank JAR 288	You Got What It Takes/Not One Minute More	5
60	Top Rank JAR 378	June Bride/My One And Only Love	4
61	Top Rank JAR 536	Senora/I Need You	4

MIKE RICHMOND
68	President PT 191	One More Chance/Come-A-Running	4

RICH MOUNTAIN TOWER
72	London HLO 10359	Thank You, Maggie/Uncle Bob White	4
72	London SH-O 8427	RICH MOUNTAIN TOWER (LP)	15

RICK & KEENS
61	Mercury AMT 1150	Peanuts/I'll Be Home	20

BERESFORD RICKETTS
60	Starlite ST45 025	Cherry Baby/I Want To Know	10
60	Starlite ST45 029	Baby Baby/When I Woke Up	10
61	Starlite ST45 048	Hold Me Tight/Dream Girl (as Ricketts & Rowe)	10
62	Starlite ST45 079	I'm Going To Cry/Waiting For Me	10
62	Blue Beat BB 107	You Better Be Going/I've Been Walking (as Beresford Ricketts & Blue Beats)	7
63	Dice CC 12	Oh Jean/Rivers Of Tears (with Laurel Aitken's Group)	7
65	Blue Beat BB 350	Jailer Bring Me Water/Careless Love	7

RICO (RODRIGUEZ)
61	Blue Beat BB 56	Luke Lane Shuffle (as Reco Rodriguez & Buster's Allstars)/ PRINCE BUSTER: Little Honey	10
67	Fab FAB 12	Jingle Bells/Silent Night (with His Boys)	7
68	Pama PM 706	Soul Man/It's Not Unusual (as Reco Rodriguez)	6
68	Pama PM 715	Tender Foot Ska/Memories (as Reco Rodriguez)	6
69	Blue Cat BS 160	The Bullet/Rhythm In (as Reco Rodriguez & His Rhythm Aces)	6
69	Doctor Bird DB 1302	Baby Face (as Reco & Rudies)/RUDIES: News	6
69	Bullet BU 407	Tribute To Don Drummond/Japanese Invasion (as Rico Rodriguez)	4
70s	Planetone RC 4	Planet Rock/You Win	6
70s	Planetone RC 5	Youth Boogie/Western Serenade (as Rico's Combo)	6
80	2-Tone CHS TT 15	Sea Cruise/Carolina (p/s, paper)	4
82	2-Tone CHS TT 19	Jungle Music/Rasta Call (p/s, paper , with Special A.K.A.)	4
82	2-Tone CHS TT 1219	Jungle Music/Rasta Call/You/Easter Island (12", p/s, with Special A.K.A.)	7
69	Trojan TTL 12	BLOW YOUR HORN (LP, as Reco & Rudies)	15
70s	Island ILPS 9485	MAN FROM WARREIKA (LP)	10
70s	Ghetto Rockers PRE 1	WARREIKA DUB (LP)	10

(see also [Ezz] Reco, Special A.K.A.)

RICOTTI & ALBUQUERQUE
71	Pegasus PEG 2	FIRST WIND (LP)	12

(see also Frank Ricotti)

FRANK RICOTTI
69	CBS 52668	OUR POINT OF VIEW (LP)	15

(see also Ricotti & Albuquerque)

DON RIDDELL FOUR
63	Decca F 11651	Casablanca/The Four Corners Of The Earth	4

NELSON RIDDLE ORCHESTRA
55	Capitol CL 14241	Vera Cruz/You Won't Forget Me	6
55	Capitol CL 14262	The Pendulum Song/Brother John	6
55	Capitol CL 14305	Run For Cover (with Bob Graham)/Make Believe That You're In Love With Me (with Pat Auld)	6
63	Capitol CL 15309	Supercar/The Dick Van Dyke Theme	10
61	Capitol EAP4 1771	ROUTE SIXTY SIX AND OTHER T.V. THEMES (EP)	7

RIDDLERS
66	Polydor BM 56716	Batman Theme/Weegie Walk	10

PAT RIDEN & BROTHER LLOYD'S ALL STARS
69	Mercury MF 1072	I Need Help/Let The Red Wine Flow (actually by Pat Rhoden)	4

(see also Pat Rhoden)

NICOLE RIEU
75	Barclay BAR 31	Live For Love/Et Bonjour A Toi L'Artiste	12

EDDIE RIFF
80	Fleetville FV 301	My Babie's Gone Away/Ain't That Loving You Baby	5

RIFF
63	Blue Beat BB 242	Oh What A Feeling/Primitive Man	8

RIFF RAFF
73	RCA RCA 2396	Copper Kettle/You Must Be Joking	4
73	RCA SF 8351	RIFF RAFF (LP)	15
74	RCA LPL1 5023	ORIGINAL MAN (LP)	15

RIFF RAFF
78	Chiswick SW 34	I WANNA BE A COSMONAUT (EP)	4
70s	Geezer GZ 1	Every Girl/You Shared House	4
70s	Geezer GZ 2	Kitten/Fantocide	4
70s	Geezer GZ 3	Little Girls Know/She Don't Matter	4

70s	Geezer GZ 4	New Home Town/Richard	4
79	Albion DEL 6	Barking Park	4

(see also Billy Bragg)

RIFKIN

68	Page One POF 071	Continental Hesitation/We're Not Those People Any More	40

ELEANOR RIGBY

85	Waterloo Sunset RUSS 101	I Want To Sleep With You/Till The End Of The Day (p/s, some with Durex & sticker, 1,000 only)	12/4
85	Waterloo Sunset RUSS 102	Take Another Shot Of My Heart/1995 (p/s, with signed story)	10/5
87	Waterloo Sunset RUSS 103	Over And Over/Last Night In Soho/See My Friends (p/s)	4
87	Waterloo Sunset RUSS 104	Kiss Me Quickly, It's Christmas/Mad Xmas (p/s)	4

BRAM RIGG SET

67	Stateside SS 2020	Take The Time Be Yourself/I Can Only Give You Everything	50

DIANA RIGG

72	RCA RCA 2178	Sentimental Journey/Forget Yourself	4

JACKIE RIGGS

56	London HLF 8244	The Great Pretender/His Gold Will Melt	25

RIGHTEOUS BROTHERS

63	London HL 9743	Little Latin Lupe Lu/I'm So Lonely	6
63	London HL 9814	My Babe/Fee-Fi-Fidily-I-Oh	5
65	London HL 9943	You've Lost That Lovin' Feelin'/There's A Woman	5
65	Pye Intl. 7N 25297	Bring Your Love To Me/Try To Find Another Man	5
65	Pye Intl. 7N 25304	Something's Got A Hold On Me/Night Owl	5
65	London HL 9962	Just Once In My Life/The Blues (withdrawn)	60
65	London HL 9975	Hung On You/Unchained Melody	6
65	Pye Intl. 7N 25323	Let The Good Times Roll/B Flat Blues	5
65	Pye Intl. 7N 25334	For Your Love/My Tears Will Go Away	5
65	London HL 10011	Ebb Tide/(I Love You) For Sentimental Reasons	5
66	Pye Intl. 7N 25358	Georgia On My Mind/My Tears Will Go Away	5
66	Verve VS 535	(You're My) Soul And Inspiration/B Side-Blues	6
66	Verve VS 537	He/He Will Break Your Heart	5
66	Sue WI 4018	You Can Have Her/Justine	10
66	London HL 10066	Just Once In My Life/The Blues (reissue)	5
66	Verve VS 542	Go Ahead And Cry/Things Didn't Go Your Way	4
66	London HL 10086	The White Cliffs Of Dover/Baby She's Mine	5
66	Verve VS 547	Island In The Sun/What Now My Love	4
67	Verve VS 554	Melancholy Music Man/Don't Give Up On Me	4
67	Verve VS 560	Stranded in The Middle Of No Place/Been So Nice	4
77	Phil Spector International 2010 022	You've Lost That Lovin' Feelin'/RIGHTEOUS BROTHERS BAND: Rat Race (instrumental)	4
65	Pye Intl. NEP 44043	THE RIGHTEOUS BROTHERS (EP)	12
66	Verve VEP 5024	SOUL AND INSPIRATION (EP)	10
66	Verve VEP 5025	THE RIGHTEOUS BROTHERS (EP, reissue)	7
65	Pye Intl. NPL 28056	SOME BLUE-EYED SOUL (LP)	20
65	London HA-U 8226	YOU'VE LOST THAT LOVIN' FEELIN' (LP)	25
65	Pye Intl. NPL 28059	RIGHT NOW! (LP)	18
65	London HA 8245	JUST ONCE IN MY LIFE (LP)	25
66	London HA 8278	BACK TO BACK (LP)	20
66	Verve (S)VLP 9131	SOUL AND INSPIRATION (LP)	18
66	Sue ILP 937	IN ACTION (LP)	30
66	Verve (S)VLP 9140	GO AHEAD AND CRY (LP)	10
67	Verve (S)VLP 9168	SAYIN' SOMETHIN' (LP)	10
67	Verve (S)VLP 9183	THE RIGHTEOUS BROTHERS GREATEST HITS (LP)	10
68	Verve (S)VLP 9190	SOULED OUT (LP)	12
68	Verve (S)VLP 9204	THE RIGHTEOUS BROTHERS STANDARDS (LP)	10
68	Verve (S)VLP 9228	ONE FOR THE ROAD (LP)	12
69	Verve (S)VLP 9240	GREATEST HITS VOLUME 2 (LP)	10
70	Verve (S)VLP 9249	RE-BIRTH (LP)	10

(see also Bill Medley, Bobby Hatfield)

RIGHTEOUS FLAMES

67	Fab FAB 30	When A Girl Loves A Boy	5
68	Coxsone CS 7061	You Don't Know/ROY RICHARDS & SOUL VENDORS: Summertime	12

RIGHTEOUS HOMES (FLAMES)

68	Coxsone CS 7049	I Was Born To Be Loved/NORMA FRAZER: Heartaches	12
68	Blue Cat BS 112	Seven Letters (actually by Winston Jarrett)/SOUL VENDORS: To Sir With Love	8

RIGHTEOUS TWINS

69	Blue Cat BS 174	If I Could Hear My Master/Satan Can't Prevail	6

RIGOR MORTIS

73	Track 2094 107	Made In Japan/Hound Dog	4
73	Track 2406 106	RIGOR MORTIS SETS IN (LP)	15

(see John Entwistle, Who)

RIKKI & CUFFLINKS

79	Different HAVE 17	Nervous Breakdown/Steamin' On (no p/s)	5

RIKKI & LAST DAYS OF EARTH

77	(own label)	single	20
77	DJM DJS 10814	City Of The Damned/Victimized	8
70s	DJM DJF 20526	RIKKI & THE LAST DAYS OF EARTH (LP)	10

RIKKI & NUMBERS

77	Rainbow RAIS 1001	The Heartbreak Kid/Headlines	4

BILLY LEE RILEY
65	King KG 1015	I've Been Searchin'/Everybody's Twistin'	8
69	Stax STAX 120	Going Back To Memphis/Family Portrait	4
72	CBS 8182	I Got A Thing About You Baby/You Don't Love Me	4

(see also Megatons)

BOB RILEY
58	MGM MGM 977	The Midnight Line/Wanda Jean	35
58	MGM MGM 977	The Midnight Line/Wanda Jean (78)	15

DESMOND RILEY
69	Downtown DT 432	Tear Them/GEORGE LEE & RUDIES: Chaka Ground	4
69	Downtown DT 435	tears On My Pillow/RUDIES: Man Pon Spot	4
69	Downtown DT 436	If I Had Wings	4
69	Downtown DT 438	Out Your Fire/No Return	4
69	Downtown DT 450	Skinhead, A Message To You/MUSIC DOCTORS: Going Strong	8
69	Downtown DT 454	If I Had Wings (reissue)	4

HOWARD RILEY (TRIO)
60s	Opportunity CP 2499	DISCUSSIONS (LP with insert, as Howard Riley Trio)	200
69	CBS 52669	ANGLE (LP)	20
70	CBS 64077	THE DAY WILL COME (LP)	10
71	Turtle TUR 301	FLIGHT (LP, gatefold sleeve)	50
76	Incus INCUS 13	SYNOPSIS (LP, as Howard Riley Trio with Tony Oxley & Barry Guy)	10

(see also Colosseum, Karyobin)

JEANNIE C. RILEY
68	Polydor 583 716	HARPER VALLEY P.T.A. (LP)	10
69	Polydor 583 733	YEARBOOKS AND YESTERDAYS (LP)	10
70	Polydor 583 753	THINGS GO BETTER WITH LOVE (LP)	10

TERRY RILEY
71	CBS 64259	CHURCH OF ANTHRAX (LP, with John Cale)	15
71	CBS 64564	A RAINBOW IN CURVED AIR (LP)	10
71	CBS 64565	IN "C" (LP)	12
72	Shandar 83501/2	PERSIAN SURGERY DERVISHES (LP)	10

(see also John Cale)

RILEY'S ALLSTARS
71	Banana BA 343	Glory Of Love (actually "Mystic Blue" by Hugh Hendricks & Buccaneers)/We'll Cry Together Version	5

SHANE RIMMER
59	Columbia DB 4293	(Roll Along) Wagon Train/A Touch Of Pink	5
59	Columbia DB 4343	The Three Bells (Jimmy Brown Song) (as Shane Rimmer & Spinners)/I Want To Walk You Home	6

RINGING
84	Pink PINKY 3	Caprice/Doctor (p/s)	4

RINGS
77	Chiswick S 14	Automobile/I Wanna Be Free (p/s)	4

(see also Maniacs, Twink)

RINGS & THINGS
68	Fontana TF 987	Strange Things Are Happening/To Me To Me To Me	50

RINKY DINKS
58	London HLE 8679	Early In The Morning/Now We're One (as Rinky Dinks featuring Bobby Darin)	45
58	London HLE 8679	Early In The Morning/Now We're One (78)	25
59	London HLE 8793	Mighty Mighty Man/You're Mine (as Bobby Darin with Rinky Dinks)	30
59	London HLE 8793	Mighty Mighty Man/You're Mine (78)	25
59	Capitol CL 14999	Catch A Little Moonbeam/Choo Choo Cha Cha	8

(see also Bobby Darin)

BOBBY RIO (& REVELLES)
63	Stateside SS 211	Don Diddley/I Got You (as Bobby Rio)	5
65	Pye 7N 15790	Boy Meets Girl/Don't Break My Heart And Run Away	20
65	Pye 7N 15897	Everything In The Garden/When Love Was Young	20
65	Pye 7N 15958	Value For Love/I'm Not Made Of Clay	20
66	Piccadilly 7N 35303	Ask The Lonely/Be Lonely Little Girl (as Bobby Rio)	5
66	Piccadilly 7N 35337	Angelica/Lovin' You (as Bobby Rio)	5

RIO GRANDES
66	Pyramid PYR 6001	Soldiers Take Over/Moses	8

RIOT
81	Elektra K 12565	Outlaw (Remix)/Rock City (p/s)	5
81	Elektra K 12565T	Outlaw (Remix)/Rock City (12", p/s)	8
77	Ariola ARL 5007	ROCK CITY (LP)	10
78	Capitol E-ST 12081	NARITA (LP)	10

RIOTS
65	Island WI 176	Heart Of Stone/Let Me Go	10
65	Island WI 195	You Don't Know/DON DRUMMOND & DRUMBAGO: Treasure Island	8
65	Island WI 197	I Am In Love/When You're Wrong	8
65	Island WI 247	Yeah Yeah/BABA BROOKS: Virginia Ska	8

(see also Techniques)

RIOT SQUAD
65	Pye 7N 15752	Any Time/Jump	20
65	Pye 7N 15817	I Wanna Talk About My Baby/Gonna Make You Mine	25
65	Pye 7N 15869	Nevertheless/Not A Great Talker	20

RIOT SQUAD

66	Pye 7N 17041	Cry Cry Cry/How Is It Done	20
66	Pye 7N 17092	I Take It We're Through/Working Man	25
66	Pye 7N 17130	It's Never Too Late To Forgive/Try To Realise	20
67	Pye 7N 17237	Gotta Be A First Time/Bitter Sweet Love	20

(see also Graham Bonney, Jimi Hendrix Experience, Blue Aces)

RIOT SQUAD

82	The THE 001	Total Onslaught (p/s)	5
82	Rondelet ROUND 23	Fuck The Tories/Civil Destruction (p/s)	5
82	Rondelet ROUND 25	Riot In The City/Religion (p/s)	4

RIPCHORDS

63	CBS AAG 143	Here I Stand/Karen	8
63	CBS AAG 162	Gone/She Thinks I Still Care	8
64	CBS AAG 181	Hey Little Cobra/The Queen	12
64	CBS AAG 202	Three Window Coupe/Hot Rod USA	18
64	CBS BPG 62228	HEY LITTLE COBRA (LP)	25

MINNIE RIPERTON

74	Epic EPC 80426	PERFECT ANGEL (LP)	10
75	Epic EPC 69142	ADVENTURES IN PARADISE (LP)	10

RIPPERS

68	Saga	HONESTLY (LP)	10

RISING MOON

74	Theatre Projects	RISING MOON (LP)	30

RISING SONS

65	Stateside SS 426	You're My Girl/Try To Be A Man	10

RISING SONS

68	Pye 7N 17554	Hold Me Just A Little While Longer/Fountain Of Love	4

RITA

69	Major Minor MM 653	Erotica/Sexologie	8

RITA & TIARAS

79	Destiny DS 1002	Gone With The Wind Is My Love/Wild Times	5

JEAN RITCHIE

53	Argo ARS 1009	SONGS FROM KENTUCKY (10" LP)	15

TEX RITTER

52	Capitol CL 13778	High Noon/Boogie Woogie Cowboy (78)	7
54	Capitol CL 14175	Is There A Santa Claus?/Old Tex Kringle	8
55	Capitol CL 14277	A Whale Of A Tale/High On A Mountain Top	8
55	Capitol CL 14335	Marshal Of Whichita/September Song	8
56	Capitol CL 14536	The Last Frontier/These Hands	6
56	Capitol CL 14581	The Wayward Wind/Gunsmoke	12
56	Capitol CL 14605	The Searchers (Ride Away)/Remember The Alamo	6
56	Capitol CL 14660	The Last Wagon/Paul Bunyan Love	6
57	Capitol CL 14684	Green Grow The Lilacs/The Touch Of The Master's Hand	5
57	Capitol CL 14715	Children And Fools/I Leaned On A Man	5
57	Capitol CL 14805	Here Was A Man/It Came Upon The Midnight Clear	5
58	Capitol CL 14900	Jealous Heart/Burning Sand	5
58	Capitol CL 14933	I Look For A Love/The History Song	4
59	Capitol CL 15041	Rye Whisky/Conversation With A Gun	4
52	Capitol LC 6552	COWBOY FAVOURITES (10" LP)	15
59	Capitol T 1100	PSALMS (LP)	10
60	Capitol (S)T 1292	BLOOD ON THE SADDLE (LP)	10

BOB RITTERBUSH

59	Top Rank JAR 118	I Wish That You Were Mine/Darling Corey	4

BOYD RIVERS & CLIFF AUNGIER

65	Decca LK 4696	WANDERIN' (LP)	15

(see also Cliff Aungier)

CLIFF RIVERS

63	London HLU 9739	True Lips/Marsha	15

(pseudonym for Joey Castle)

DANNY RIVERS

60	Top Rank JAR 408	Hawk/I Got	8
60	Decca F 11294	Can't You Hear My Heart/I'm Waiting For Tomorrow	8
61	Decca F 11357	My Baby's Gone Away/Once Upon A Time (with Alexander Combo)	10
64	Decca F 11865	There Will Never Be Anyone/I Don't Think ...	6
62	HMV POP 1000	We're Gonna Dance/Movin' In (as Danny Rivers & River Men)	20

DEKE RIVERS

62	Oriole CB 1735	One Kiss/Outsider	8
81	Chiswick NS 71	Elvis Presley Medley/ELVIS PRESLEY: Press Conference Vancouver 1957 (picture disc)	4

JOHNNY RIVERS

62	Pye Intl. 7N 25118	Blue Skies/That Someone Should Be Me	5
64	Liberty LIB 66032	Memphis/It Wouldn't Happen With Me	5
64	Liberty LIB 66056	Maybellene/Walk Myself On Home	5
64	Liberty LIB 66075	Mountain Of Love/Moody Love	4
64	Liberty LIB 66087	Midnight Special/Cupid	5
65	Liberty LIB 66112	Seventh Son/Un-Square Dance	4
65	Liberty LIB 12021	He Don't Love You Like I Love You/Where Have All The Flowers Gone	4
66	Liberty LIB 66144	Under Your Spell Again/Long Time Man	4
66	Liberty LIB 12023	Secret Agent Man/Tom Dooley	4

66	Liberty LIB 66175	I Washed My Hands In Muddy Water/Roogalator	4
66	Liberty LIB 66205	The Poor Side Of Town/Baby She's Mine	4
67	Liberty LIB 66227	Baby I Need Your Lovin'/Getting Ready For Tomorrow	4
67	Liberty LIB 66244	The Tracks Of My Tears/Rosecrans Blvd.	6
66	Liberty LEP 4049	MORE JOHNNY RIVERS (EP)	7
64	Liberty LBY 3031	AT THE WHISKY A GO-GO (LP)	15
65	Liberty LBY 3036	HERE WE A GO-GO AGAIN (LP)	12
65	Liberty LBY 3056	MEANWHILE BACK AT THE WHISKY A GO-GO (LP)	12
66	Liberty LBY 3064	RIVERS ROCKS THE FOLK (LP)	12
67	Liberty (S)LBY 3087	CHANGES (LP)	12
67	Liberty LBL/LBS 83040	REWIND (LP)	10
68	Liberty LBL/LBS 83118	REALIZATION (LP)	10
69	Liberty LBS 83141	A TOUCH OF GOLD (LP)	10

MAVIS RIVERS

60	Capitol CL 15120	So Rare/Longing, Longing, Longing	4
63	Reprise RS 20115	Slightly Out Of Tune/Footsteps Of A Fool	4

TONY RIVERS & CASTAWAYS

63	Columbia DB 7135	Shake Shake Shake/Row Row Row	10
64	Columbia DB 7224	I Love The Way You Walk/I Love You	7
64	Columbia DB 7336	Life's Too Short/Tell On Me	6
65	Columbia DB 7448	She/Till We Get Home	5
65	Columbia DB 7536	Come Back/What To Do	5
66	Columbia DB 7971	God Only Knows/Charade	5
66	Parlophone R 5400	Nowhere Man/The Girl From New York City	6
66	Immediate IM 027	Girl Don't Tell Me/The Girl From Salt Lake City	12
68	Polydor 56245	I Can Guarantee Your Love/Pantomime	6

(see also Grapefruit, Harmony Grass, Capability Brown)

RIVIERAS

60	HMV POP 773	Blessing Of Love/Moonlight Cocktails	10

RIVIERAS

64	Pye Intl. 7N 25237	California Sun/H B Goose Step	12

RIVINGTONS

62	Liberty LIB 55427	Papa Oom Mow Mow/Deep Water	20
63	Liberty LIB 55553	The Bird's The Word/I'm Losing My Grip	20
66	CBS 202088	Rose Growing In The Ruins/Tend To Business	15

MAX ROACH (& CLIFFORD BROWN GROUP)

50s	Vogue EPV 1074	MAX ROACH AND CLIFFORD BROWN (EP)	7
50s	Vogue EPV 1083	MAX ROACH AND CLIFFORD BROWN (EP)	7
50s	Vogue EPV 1091	MAX ROACH AND CLIFFORD BROWN (EP)	7
58	Emarcy ERE 1572	MAX ROACH AND CLIFFORD BROWN (EP, withdrawn)	15
55	Vogue LDE 117	MAX ROACH & CLIFFORD BROWN IN CONCERT VOL. 1 (10" LP)	15
55	Vogue LDE 128	MAX ROACH & CLIFFORD BROWN IN CONCERT VOL. 2 (10" LP)	15
58	Emarcy EJL 1282	JAZZ IN THREE-QUARTER TIME (LP)	15
59	Emarcy MMB 12005	MAX ROACH, NEWPORT (LP, by Max Roach)	12
59	Emarcy MMB 12009	THE MAX ROACH FOUR PLUS FOUR (LP, by Max Roach)	12
60	Mercury MMC 14041	I REMEMBER CLIFFORD (LP)	10

(see also Clifford Brown, Buddy Rich)

ROAD

73	Rare Earth SRE 3006	ROAD (LP)	15

ROADRUNNERS

65	Cavern Sound 2BSNL 7	PANTOMANIA (EP, with tracks by Chris Edwards & Clive Wood)	35

ROADSTERS

64	Stateside SS 293	Joy Ride/Drag	12

ROARING SIXTIES

66	Marmalade 598 001	We Love The Pirates/I'm Leaving Town	30

(see also Family)

ROBAN'S SKIFFLE GROUP

62	Storyville A45 062	Careless Love/Frankie And Johnny	12
50s	Storyville SEP 507	ROBAN'S SKIFFLE GROUP (EP)	20
50s	Storyville SEP 509	ROBAN'S SKIFFLE GROUP (EP)	20
50s	Storyville SEP 511	ROBAN'S SKIFFLE GROUP (EP)	20

E.G. ROBB

63	Columbia DB 7100	Stage To Cimarron/Jezebel	5

ROBBIE & RAY

66	Decca F 12452	This Little Bird/You Better Move On	4

KATE ROBBINS

78	Anchor ANC 1054	Tomorrow/Crowds Of You	5
78	Bright BULB 6	That First Love/That First Love (Instrumental Mix)/When You Go	4

MARTY ROBBINS

56	Philips PB 590	Long Tall Sally/Mr. Teardrop (78)	10
57	Philips JK 1019	A White Sport Coat (And A Pink Carnation)/Grown-Up Tears (jukebox issue)	20
57	Philips PB 741	Please Don't Blame Me/Teen-Age Dream (78)	5
58	Fontana H 102	The Story Of My Life/Once-A-Week Date (78)	8
58	Fontana H 128	Stairway Of Love/Just Married	15
58	Fontana H 128	Stairway Of Love/Just Married (78)	8
58	Fontana H 150	She Was Only Seventeen/Sittin' In A Tree House	10
58	Fontana H 150	She Was Only Seventeen/Sittin' In A Tree House (78)	10
59	Fontana H 184	The Hanging Tree/The Blues Country Style	7
59	Fontana H 184	The Hanging Tree/The Blues Country Style (78)	10

Marty ROBBINS

59	Fontana H 212	Cap And Gown/Last Night About This Time	6
59	Fontana H 212	Cap And Gown/Last Night About This Time (78)	12
59	Fontana H 229	Big Iron/Cool Water	6
59	Fontana H 229	Big Iron/Cool Water (78)	15
60	Fontana H 233	El Paso/Running Gun	6
60	Fontana H 233	El Paso/Running Gun (78)	15
60	Fontana H 263	I Told My Heart/Is There Any Chance	4
60	Fontana H 270	Ballad Of The Alamo/Five Brothers (some in p/s)	7/4
61	Fontana H 301	Don't Worry/Like All Other Times	4
61	Fontana H 324	Ghost Train/Jimmy Martinez	4
61	Fontana H 342	It's Your World/You Told Me So	4
62	CBS AAG 114	Devil Woman/April Fool's Day	5
63	CBS AAG 128	Ruby Ann/Won't You Forgive	4
63	CBS AAG 141	Cigarette And Coffee Blues/Teenagers Dad	5
63	CBS AAG 151	No Signs Of Loneliness Here/I'm Not Ready Yet	5
63	CBS AAG 164	Not So Long Ago/I Hope You Learn A Lot	4
65	CBS 201729	Whole Lot Easier/I Eish Tay Mah Su	4
65	CBS 201789	Ribbon Of Darkness/Little Robin	4
65	CBS 202012	While You're Dancing/Lonely Too	4
67	CBS 2955	Tonight Carmen/No Tears Milady	4
68	CBS 3585	Love Is In The Air/I've Been Leaving Every Day	4
68	CBS 3828	I Walk Alone/Lily Of The Valley	4
59	Fontana TFE 17161	MARTY'S BIG HITS (EP)	20
59	Fontana TFE 17168	WEDDING BELLS (EP)	8
60	Fontana TFE 17167	SONG OF THE ISLANDS (EP)	8
61	Fontana TFE 17224	GUNFIGHTER (EP)	8
62	CBS AGG 20004	JUST A LITTLE SENTIMENTAL (EP)	8
62	CBS AGG 20013	JUST A LITTLE SENTIMENTAL VOL. 2 (EP)	8
66	CBS AGG 20049	MARTY ROBBINS (EP)	8
59	Fontana TFL 5063	GUNFIGHTER BALLADS AND TRAIL SONGS (LP)	20
60	Fontana TFL 5086	MARTY'S GREATEST HITS (LP)	16
61	Font. TFL 5113/STFL 541	MORE GUNFIGHTER BALLADS AND TRAIL SONGS (LP, mono/stereo)	20/25
61	Font. TFL 5145/STFL 565	MORE GREATEST HITS (LP, mono/stereo)	16/20
61	Font. TFL 5162/STFL 579	JUST A LITTLE SENTIMENTAL (LP, with Jordanaires, mono/stereo)	20/25
62	CBS (S)BPG 62041	MARTY AFTER MIDNIGHT (LP)	15
63	CBS (S)BPG 62113	DEVIL WOMAN (LP, mono/stereo)	14/16
63	CBS BPG 62131	PORTRAIT OF MARTY (LP, mono/stereo)	12/14
63	CBS (S)BPG 62169	HAWAII'S CALLING ME (LP, mono/stereo)	14/16
64	CBS (S)BPG 62190	THE RETURN OF THE GUNFIGHTER (LP, mono/stereo)	10/12
64	CBS (S)BPG 62297	ISLAND WOMAN (LP, mono/stereo)	14/16
65	CBS (S)BPG 62437	R.F.D. (LP, mono/stereo)	14/16
65	CBS (S)BPG 62499	TURN THE LIGHTS DOWN LOW (LP)	16
65	CBS (S)BPG 62359	GUNFIGHTER BALLADS AND TRAIL SONGS (LP, reissue, mono/stereo)	10/12
66	CBS (S)BPG 62070	MORE GUNFIGHTER BALLADS AND TRAIL SONGS (LP, reissue, m/s)	10/12
66	CBS (S)BPG 62075	MORE GREATEST HITS (LP, reissue)	10
66	CBS (S)BPG 62689	WHAT GOD HAS DONE (LP)	12
66	CBS (S)BPG 62782	THE DRIFTER (LP)	15
67	CBS (S)BPG 62962	MY KIND OF COUNTRY (LP)	12
67	CBS (S)BPG 63116	TONIGHT CARMEN (LP)	12
68	CBS 63295	BY THE TIME I GET TO PHOENIX (LP, mono/stereo)	10
68	CBS 66211	A PORTRAIT OF MARTY (2-LP)	14
68	CBS 63354	CHRISTMAS WITH MARTY ROBBINS (LP, mono/stereo)	15
69	CBS 63431	I WALK ALONE (LP, mono/stereo)	10
70	CBS 64066	MY WOMAN, MY WOMAN, MY WIFE (LP)	10
72	CBS 64810	TODAY (LP)	10

MEL ROBBINS

59	London HLM 8966	Save It/To Know You (initially triangular centre, later round centre)	250/175
59	London HLM 8966	Save It/To Know You (78)	60

SYLVIA ROBBINS

60	London HLJ 9118	Frankie And Johnny/Come Home	12

(see also Mickey & Sylvia)

ROBBS

60s	Mercury MF 983	Rapid Transit/Cynthia Loves	4

ANDY ROBERTS

71	Pegasus PEG 5	NINA AND THE DREAM TREE (LP)	15
71	B&C CAS 1034	HOME GROWN (LP)	15
71	RCA SF 8086	HOME GROWN (LP, reissue)	12
73	Elektra K 42139	URBAN COWBOY (LP)	12
73	Elektra K 42151	. . . AND THE GREAT STAMPEDE (LP)	12

(see also Liverpool Scene, Everyone, Plainsong)

J. ROBERTS

70	Bamboo BAM 30	Someday We'll Be Together/SOUND DIMENSION: Everyday People	5

JOHN ROBERTS

67	Sue WI 4042	Sockin' 1, 2, 3, 4/Sophisticated Funk	12
68	Action ACT 4511	I'll Forget About You/Be My Baby	10
68	A&M AMS 835	When The Party's Over/Raindrops Love And Sunshine	5

KEITH ROBERTS

72	Trailer LER 3031	PIER OF THE REALM (LP)	15

KENNY ROBERTS

57	Brunswick 05638	I'm Looking For The Bully Of The Town/Broken Teenage Heart	4

KENNY ROBERTS

65	Pye 7N 15882	Say, Do You Mean It/Since My Love Has Gone	4

| 66 | Pye 7N 17054 | Run Like The Devil/Where Goes My Heart | 20 |

(see also Kenny Damon)

KIM ROBERTS
| 64 | Decca F 11813 | I'll Prove It/For Loving Me This Way | 40 |

PADDY ROBERTS
59	Decca LF 1322	STRICTLY FOR GROWN-UPS (10" LP)	12
60	Decca LK 4358	PADDY ROBERTS TRIES AGAIN (LP)	10
61	Decca LK 4410	PADDY ROBERTS AT THE BLUE ANGEL (LP)	10

RENE ROBERTS
| 62 | Oriole CB 1731 | I Want To Love You/Aching Heart | 5 |

RICK ROBERTS
| 72 | A&M AMLH 64372 | WINDMILLS (LP) | 10 |

(see also Flying Burrito Brothers)

DALE ROBERTSON
| 60 | RCA SF 5064 | PRESENTS HIS ALBUM OF WESTERN CLASSICS (LP) | 12 |

DON ROBERTSON
56	Capitol CL 14575	The Happy Whistler/You're Free To Go (B-side with Lou Dinning)	8
56	Capitol CL 14629	Every Day That I Live (with Lou Dinning)/You	4
59	Capitol CL 15088	Fine Day/The Merry Men	4

JEANNIE ROBERTSON
60	Collector JFS 4001	LORD DONALD (LP)	12
60	Topic 10T 52	I KEN WHERE I'M GOING (10" LP)	15
60s	Topic 12T 96	JEANNIE ROBERTSON (LP)	12

PAUL ROBESON
52	HMV 7P 113	Ol' Man River/I Suits Me	4
57	HMV DLP 1155	THE INCOMPARABLE VOICE OF PAUL ROBESON (10" LP)	10
57	HMV DLP 1165	EMPEROR SONG (10" LP)	10

IVO ROBIC
| 60 | Polydor NH 23923 | Morgen/Ay, Ay, Ay Paloma | 6 |
| 60 | Fontana H 239 | The Happy Muleteer/Rhondaly | 4 |

ROBIN HOODS
| 65 | Mercury MF 865 | Wait For The Dawn/Love You So | 4 |

RICHIE ROBIN
| 60 | Top Rank JAR 262 | Strange Dream/GERRY GRANAHAN: It Hurts | 12 |

TINA ROBIN
57	Vogue Coral Q 72284	Over Somebody Else's Shoulder/Lady Fair	12
57	Vogue Coral Q 72284	Over Somebody Else's Shoulder/Lady Fair (78)	10
57	Vogue Coral Q 72294	Never In A Million Years/Ca C'est L'Amour	8
58	Coral Q 72309	Everyday/Believe Me	8
58	Coral Q 72309	Everyday/Believe Me (78)	8
58	Coral Q 72323	No School Tomorrow/Sugar Blues	10
58	Coral Q 72323	No School Tomorrow/Sugar Blues (78)	8
62	Mercury AMT 1199	Get Out Of My Life/Why Did You Go	6

ROBINS
| 60 | Vogue V 9168 | Cherry Lips/Out Of The Picture | 70 |
| 60 | Vogue V 9173 | Just Like That/Whole Lot Imagination | 50 |

(see also Coasters)

JIMMY ROBINS
| 68 | President PT 118 | I Can't Please You/I Made It Over | 25 |

ALVIN ROBINSON
64	Pye Intl. 7N 25248	Something You Got/Searchin'	10
64	Red Bird RB10 010	Down Home Girl/Fever	12
66	Strike JH 307	You Bought My Heart Right Down To My Knees/Whatever You Had	12

BROTHER CLEOPHUS ROBINSON
| 57 | Vogue EPV 1196 | BROTHER CLEOPHUS ROBINSON (EP) | 20 |

ELZADIE ROBINSON
50s	Tempo R 33	The Santa Claus Crave/St. Louis Cyclone Blues (78)	8
50s	Tempo R 36	Arkansas Mill Blues/Gold Mansion Blues (78)	8
50s	Tempo R 37	Rowdy Man Blues/Going South Blues (78)	8

FLOYD ROBINSON
59	RCA RCA 1146	Makin' Love/My Girl	6
59	RCA RCA 1146	Makin' Love/My Girl (78)	25
60	RCA RCA 1179	I Believe In Love/Tattletale	4
60	RCA RD 27166	FLOYD ROBINSON (LP)	35

FREDDY ROBINSON
| 71 | Stax 2325 085 | AT THE DRIVE-IN (LP) | 10 |

HARRY ROBINSON
| 60 | Top Rank JAR 325 | The Skirl/Wimoweh (as Harry Robinson "String Sound") | 4 |
| 61 | Decca F 11319 | Heavy Date/Sentimental Journey (as Harry Robinson's XV) | 4 |

(see also Lord Rockingham's XI)

J.P. ROBINSON
| 72 | Atlantic K 10149 | George Jackson/Wall To Love | 5 |
| 72 | Atlantic K 10209 | What Can I Tell Her/Please Accept My Call | 4 |

JACKIE ROBINSON
68	Amalgamated AMG 819	Over And Over/Woman Of Samaria	8
68	Amalgamated AMG 824	Let The Little Girl Dance/DERRICK MORGAN: I Want To Go Home	8

JIM ROBINSON NEW ORLEANS BAND
61	Riverside RLP 369	NEW ORLEANS: THE LIVING LEGENDS (LP)	12
64	Riverside RLP 393	PLAYS SPIRITUAL AND BLUES (LP)	12

LLOYD ROBINSON
62	Blue Beat BB 122	Give Me A Chance/When You Walk	10
62	Blue Beat BB 159	You Told Me/I Told Your Love	10
68	Duke DU 5	Cuss Cuss/Lavender Blue	6

M. ROBINSON
64	Port-O-Jam PJ 4114	Who Are You/Follow You	7

ROSCO ROBINSON
66	Pye Intl. 7N 25385	That's Enough/One More Time	18
72	Wand WN 27	That's Enough/One More Time (reissue)	6
73	Contempo C 16	We're Losing It Baby/We Got A Good Thing Going	4

SMOKEY ROBINSON
86	Tamla Motown ZT 40553	Hold On To Your Love/Train Of Thought (cassette)	4

(see also [Smokey Robinson &] Miracles)

SUGAR CHILE ROBINSON
50	Capitol CL 13393	Christmas Boogie/Rudolf The Red Nosed Reindeer (78)	10
51	Capitol CL 13562	Numbers Boogie/Bouncing Ball Boogie (78)	10
51	Capitol CL 13589	After School Blues/Caldonia (78)	10
51	Capitol CL 13636	Green Grass/Baby Blues (78)	10
52	Capitol CL 13796	Lazy Boy's Boogie (78)	10
53	Capitol LC 6586	CAPITOL PRESENTS SUGAR CHILE ROBINSON (10" LP)	40

TOM ROBINSON (BAND)
75	Chebel SRT/CUS 015	GOOD TO BE GAY (EP, as Bradford Gay Liberation Front)	20
78	EMI EMI 2749	Don't Take No For An Answer/Glad To Be Gay (2-track jukebox issue)	4
79	EMI EMI 2946	All Right All Night/Black Angel (withdrawn, demos only)	10
79	Deviant DEVIANT 1	Stand Together/A Dyke's Gotta Do (with Gay Pride)	6
82	Panic PROMO 2	Now Martin's Gone (live)/Atmospherics (live) (flexidisc)	5

(see also Cafe Society, Phantom)

VICKI SUE ROBINSON
75	RCA RCA 2579	Baby, Now That I've Found You/Thanks A Million	4
76	RCA RCA 2651	Never Gonna Let You Go Pts 1 & 2	4
76	RCA RCA 2673	Turn The Beat Around/Common Thief	5
76	RCA RCA 2756	Daylight/Never Gonna Let You Go	4

ROBINSON CREW
63	Decca F 11706	Taxi (Theme From TV Series)/Stormalong	4

CARSON ROBISON (& HIS PLEASANT VALLEY BOYS)
53	MGM SP 1004	Lady Round The Lady/Pokeberry Promenade	8
53	MGM SP 1024	Square Dance Jitterbug/Keep On Circlin' 'Round	12
58	MGM MGM-EP 669	LIFE GETS TEEJUS (EP)	8
61	MGM MGM-EP 755	SQUARE DANCE — WITH CALLS (EP)	7
52	MGM MGM-D 101	EIGHT SQUARE DANCES (10" LP)	15

RALPH ROBLES
69	London HA/SH 8385	TAKING OVER (LP)	10

ROBOTNIK
81	Neutron NT 004	SPACE RACE (EP)	5

NICKY ROBSON
80	Scratch SCR 006	Stars/Eye To Eye (p/s)	20
80	Scratch SCRT 006	Stars (Extended)/Eye To Eye (12", no p/s)	35

(see also Gary Numan)

ROCAMARS
65	King KG 1031	All In Black Woman/Give Me Time	15

TONY ROCCO
62	Parlophone R 4886	Keep A Walking/Stalemate	10
62	Parlophone R 4946	Torture/Competition	4

HARRY ROCHE CONSTELLATION
67	CBS 202653	Casino Royale/In The Pad Of The Mountain King	4

JACKIE ROCHELLE
68	Olga OLE 011	Till The End/Grown Up Games	4

DICKIE ROCK & MIAMI SHOWBAND
63	Piccadilly 7N 35154	Boys/There's Always Me	4
64	Piccadilly 7N 35202	Twenty Flight Rock/From The Candy Store	4
65	Pye 7N 15750	Round And Around/Little Baby	4
65	Pye 7N 17063	Come Back To Stay/Can't Make Up My Mind (p/s)	12
65	Pye NEP 24251	COME BACK TO STAY (EP)	7

ROCK-A-TEENS
59	Columbia DB 4361	Woo-Hoo/Untrue	20

ROCK BROTHERS
56	Parlophone MSP 6201	Dungaree Doll/Livin' It Up	30
56	Parlophone R 4119	Dungaree Doll/Livin' It Up (78)	8

ROCKERS
59	Oriole CB 1501	Get Cracking/Counter Melody	7
59	Oriole CB 1501	Get Cracking/Counter Melody (78)	10

ROCKERS
83	CBS A 3929	We Are The Boys (Who Make All The Noise)/Rockin' On Stage (p/s)	4
83	CBS TA 3929	We Are The Boys (Who Make All The Noise) (Extended Version)/ Rockin' On Stage (12", p/s)	7

(see also Phil Lynott, Roy Wood, Status Quo)

ROCKETS
60	Philips PB 982	Gibralter Rock/Walkin' Home	12
60	Philips PB 982	Gibralter Rock/Walkin' Home (78)	20
60s	Zodiac ZR 0010	Warrior/Countdown	12

ROCK FOLLIES
76	Island WIP 6293	Glenn Miller Is Missing/Talkin' Pictures	4
76	Island WIP 6310	Sugar Mountain/War Brides	4
77	Polydor 2001 714	O.K./B-Side	4

(see also Andy McKay, Julie Covington)

ROCK GODDESS
82	A&M AMS 8263	Heavy Metal Rock 'N' Roll Revival/Satisfied Then Crucified (picture disc)	5
83	A&M AMS 8311	My Angel/In The Heat Of The Night (p/s)	4
83	A&M AMSX 8311	My Angel/In The Heat Of The Night (12", p/s)	7
84	A&M AMP 185	I Didn't Know I Loved You (Till I Saw You Rock'n'Roll)/Hell Hath No Fury (picture disc)	5
84	A&M AM 185	I Didn't Know I Loved You (Till I Saw You Rock'n'Roll)/Hell Hath No Fury (p/s)	4
84	A&M AMX 185	I Didn't Know I Loved You (Till I Saw You Rock'n'Roll)/Hell Hath No Fury/ In The Night (12", p/s)	7

ROCKIN' BERRIES
63	Decca F 11698	Wah Wah Woo/Rockin' Berry Stomp	12
63	Decca F 11760	Itty Bitty Pieces/The Twitch	12
64	Piccadilly 7N 35197	I Didn't Mean To Hurt You/You'd Better Come Home	5
64	Piccadilly 7N 35203	He's In Town/Flashback	4
64	Piccadilly 7N 35217	What In The World's Come Over You/You Don't Know What To Do	4
65	Piccadilly 7N 35236	Poor Man's Son/Follow Me	4
65	Piccadilly 7N 35254	You're My Girl/Brother Bill	4
65	Piccadilly 7N 35270	The Water Is Over My Head/Doesn't Time Fly	6
66	Piccadilly 7N 35304	I Could Make You Fall In Love/Land Of Love	5
66	Piccadilly 7N 35327	Midnight Mary/Money Grows On Trees	7
67	Piccadilly 7N 35373	Sometimes/Needs To Be	5
67	Piccadilly 7N 35400	Smiles/Breakfast At Sam's	6
67	Pye 7N 17411	Dawn (Go Away)/She's Not Like Any Girl	6
68	Pye 7N 17519	When I Reach The Top/Pain	5
68	Pye 7N 17589	Mr. Blue/Land Of Love	5
65	Piccadilly NEP 34039	I DIDN'T MEAN TO HURT YOU (EP)	15
65	Piccadilly NEP 34043	NEW FROM THE BERRIES (EP)	15
65	Piccadilly NEP 34045	HAPPY TO BE BLUE (EP)	18
64	Piccadilly NPL 38013	IN TOWN (LP)	60
64	Piccadilly NPL 38022	LIFE IS JUST A BOWL OF BERRIES (LP)	60
76	Satril SATL 4002	BLACK GOLD (LP)	10

ROCKIN' DUPSEE
70s	Flyright FLY 592	ROCKIN' WITH DUPSEE (LP)	10

ROCKIN' FOO
70	Stateside SS 2168	Rochester River/Stranger In The Attic	4
70	Stateside SSL 10303	ROCKIN' FOO (LP)	15

ROCKING VICKERS
64	Decca F 11993	I Go Ape/Someone Like You	15
66	CBS 202051	It's Alright/Stay By Me	40
66	CBS 202241	Dandy/I Don't Need Your Kind	25

(see also Sam Gopal, Motorhead)

ROCKIN' HENRI & HAYSEEDS
63	Decca F 11700	Sally/Sweet Adeline	4

ROCKIN' HORSE (U.K.)
71	Philips 6006 156	Biggest Gossip In Town/You Say	5
72	Philips 6006 200	Julian The Hooligan/Stayed Out Late Last Night	5
73	Randy's RAN 535	I'm So Fed Up Pts 1 & 2	4
70	Philips 6308 075	YES IT IS (LP)	50

(see also Jimmy Campbell, 23rd Turnoff, Kirbys, Merseys)

ROCKIN' HORSE (Jamaica)
74	Pyramid PYR 7009	New Situation/New Version	4

ROCKIN' R's
59	London HL 8872	The Beat/Crazy Baby	30
59	London HL 8872	The Beat/Crazy Baby (78)	35

ROCKIN' RAMRODS
70	Polydor BM 56512	Don't Fool With Fu Manchu/Tears Melt The Stone	15

ROCKIN' REBELS
63	Stateside SS 162	Wild Weekend/Wild Weekend Cha Cha	6
63	Stateside SS 187	Rockin' Crickets/Hully Gully Rock	6

ROCKIN' SAINTS
60	Brunswick 05843	Cheat On Me, Baby/Half And Half	50

ROCKIN' STRINGS
59   Columbia DB 4349   Red Sails In The Sunset/Autumn Leaves 5
(see also Eric Jupp)

ROCK'N'ROLL REVIVAL SHOW
68   Decca F 12752   Midnight Train/Oh Boy (both sides featuring Tommy Bishop) 6

ROCK-OLGA
60   Ember EMS S 105   Red Sails In The Sunset/My Dixieland Doll 4

ROCKPILE
80   F-Beat XX9C   Wrong Way/Now And Always (p/s, yellow vinyl) 4
80   F-Beat XXLP7   SECONDS OF PLEASURE (LP, with free EP "Nick Lowe & Dave
                                      Edmunds Sing The Everly Brothers" [BEV 1]) 10
(see also Dave Edmunds & Rockpile, Nick Lowe)

ROCKSTEADYS
67   Giant GN 2   Squeeze And Freeze/JUNIOR SMITH: I'm A Good Boy 7

ROCKSTONES
70   Trojan TR 7762   A.B.C. Reggae/BEVERLEY'S ALLSTARS: Be Yours 4
70   Summit SUM 8501   Everything Is Beautiful/BEVERLEY'S ALLSTARS: Give Up 4
(see also Gaylads)

ROCK WORKSHOP
70   CBS 5046   You To Lose/Born In The City 4
70   CBS 64075   ROCK WORKSHOP (LP) 15
71   CBS 64394   THE VERY LAST TIME (LP) 15
(see also Alex Harvey)

ROCKY FELLERS
63   Stateside SS 175   Killer Joe/Lonely Treardrops 6
63   Stateside SS 212   Great Big World/Like The Big Guys 6
63   Pye Intl. 7N 25225   Ching A Ling Baby/Hey Little Donkey 6

ROCKY HORROR SHOW
73   Ode ODS 66305   Science Fiction Double Feature/Time Warp 4
(see also Original Soundtracks)

RODD, KEN & CAVALIERS
60   Triumph RGM 1001   Magic Wheel/Happy Valley 25

GENE RODDENBERRY
76   CBS 4692   Star Trek Theme/Star Trek Philosophy 8

CLODAGH RODGERS
62   Decca F 11534   Believe Me I'm No Fool/End Of The Line 4
63   Decca F 11607   Sometime Kind Of Love/I See More Of Him 4
63   Decca F 11667   To Give My Love To You/I Only Live To Love You 4
64   Decca F 11812   Mister Heartache/Time 4
65   Columbia DB 7468   Wanting You/Johnny Come Home 4
66   Columbia DB 7926   Every Day Is Just The Same/You'll Come A Running 4
66   Columbia DB 8038   Stormy Weather/Lonely Room 4

EILEEN RODGERS
58   Fontana H 136   Careful, Careful/I'm Alone Because I Love You 7
58   Fontana H 156   Treasure Of Your Love/Little Bit Bluer 7
61   London HLR 9271   Sailor/Wait Till Tomorrow 10

JEAN RODGERS
65   Columbia DB 7637   Take What I Have/Baby What You Gonna Do? 4

JIMMIE RODGERS
58   HMV 7EG 8163   JIMMIE RODGERS (EP) 15
60   RCA RCX 1058   LEGENDARY JIMMIE RODGERS (EP) 12
59   RCA RD 27110   TRAIN WHISTLE BLUES (LP) 15
59   RCA RD 27138   NEVER NO MO' BLUES (JIMMIE RODGERS MEMORIAL ALBUM) (LP) 15
61   RCA RD 27203   MY ROUGH AND ROWDY WAYS (LP) 15
61   RCA RD 27241   JIMMIE THE KID (LP) 15
62   RCA RD 7505   COUNTRY MUSIC HALL OF FAME (LP) 15
63   RCA RD 7562   THE SHORT BUT BRILLIANT LIFE OF JIMMIE RODGERS (LP) 15
64   RCA RD 7644   MY TIME AIN'T LONG (LP) 15

JIMMIE RODGERS
57   Columbia DB 3986   Honeycomb/Their Hearts Were Full Of Spring 15
57   Columbia DB 3986   Honeycomb/Their Hearts Were Full Of Spring (78) 5
57   Columbia DB 4052   Kisses Sweeter Than Wine/Better Loved You'll Never Be 8
57   Columbia DB 4052   Kisses Sweeter Than Wine/Better Loved You'll Never Be (78) 5
58   Columbia DB 4078   Oh-Oh, I'm Falling In Love Again/The Long Hot Summer 8
58   Columbia DB 4078   Oh-Oh, I'm Falling In Love Again/The Long Hot Summer (78) 5
58   Columbia DB 4130   Secretly/Make Me A Miracle 6
58   Columbia DB 4175   Are You Really Mine/The Wizard 6
58   Columbia DB 4206   Women From Liberia/Girl In The Wood 6
59   Columbia DB 4235   Bimbombey/You Understand Me 5
59   Columbia DB 4281   Because You're Young/I'm Never Gonna Tell 5
59   Columbia DB 4327   Soldier, Won't You Marry Me?/Ring-A-Ling-A-Lario 4
59   Columbia DB 4362   Tucumcari/The Night You Became Seventeen 4
60   Columbia DB 4401   Waltzing Matilda/T.L.C. — Tender Loving Care 4
60   Columbia DB 4447   Joshua Fit The Battle Of Jericho/Just A Closer Walk With Thee 4
61   Columbia DB 4617   Little Shepherd Of Kingdom Come/When Love Is Young 4
62   Columbia DB 4847   English Country Garden/Little Dog Cried 4
62   Columbia DB 4904   The Fox And The Goose/Soldier, Won't You Marry Me 4
62   London HLD 9582   No One Will Ever Know/Because 5

63	London HLD 9654	Rhumba Boogie/Rainbow At Midnight	4
63	London HLD 9697	Face In A Crowd/Lonely Tears	4
63	London HLD 9752	I'm Gonna Be The Winner/Poor Little Raggedy Ann	5
64	London HLD 9904	I Forgot More Than You'll Ever Know/The World I Used To Know (unissued)	
64	Pye Intl. 7N 25253	I Forgot More Than You'll Ever Know/The World I Used To Know	4
58	Columbia SEG 7770	JIMMIE RODGERS (EP)	15
58	Columbia SEG 7811	JIMMIE RODGERS SINGS (EP)	12
59	Columbia SEG 7911	JIMMIE RODGERS NO. 2 (EP)	12
63	Columbia SEG 8253	ENGLISH COUNTRY GARDEN (EP)	7
65	Dot DEP 20007	JIMMIE RODGERS FAVOURITES (EP)	7
58	Columbia 33SX 1082	JIMMIE RODGERS (LP)	20
58	Columbia 33SX 1097	THE NUMBER ONE BALLADS (LP)	15
59	Columbia 33SX 1144	SINGS FOLK SONGS (LP)	12
59	Columbia 33SX 1176	JIMMIE RODGERS FAVOURITES (LP)	12
59	Columbia 33SX 1206	IT'S CHRISTMAS ONCE AGAIN (LP)	10
60	Columbia 33SX 1217	TWILIGHT ON THE TRAIL (LP, also stereo SCX 3302)	12/14
60	Columbia 33SX 1236	WHEN THE SPIRIT MOVES YOU (LP, also stereo SCX 3313)	10/12
61	Columbia 33SX 1292	AT HOME WITH JIMMIE RODGERS (LP, also stereo SCX 3355)	10/12
61	Columbia 33SX 1393	THE FOLK SONG WORLD OF . . . (LP, also stereo SCX 3425)	10/12
63	London HA-D 8040	NO ONE WILL EVER KNOW (LP)	10
65	London HA-D/SH-D 8116	HONEYCOMB (LP)	10
66	Dot DLP 3710	COUNTRY MUSIC 1966 (LP)	10

RICO RODRIGUEZ
(see under Rico)

RODS (U.K.)

77	Island WIP 12 6401	Do Anything You Wanna Do/Schoolgirl Love (12", stickered plain sleeve)	7

(see also Eddie & Hot Rods)

RODS (U.S.)

82	Arista ARIPD 467	You Keep Me Hangin' On/Wings Of Fire (picture disc)	5

TOMMY ROE (& ROEMANS)

62	HMV POP 1060	Sheila/Save Your Kisses	5
62	HMV POP 1092	Susie Darlin'/Piddle De Pat	5
63	HMV POP 1117	Gonna Take A Chance/Don't Cry Donna	4
63	HMV POP 1138	The Folk Singer/Count On Me	5
63	HMV POP 1174	What Makes The Blues/Kiss And Run	4
63	HMV POP 1207	Everybody/There's A Day A Coming	4
64	HMV POP 1290	Be A Good Little Girl/Carol	4
63	HMV POP 1259	Come On/There Will Be Better Years	4
64	HMV POP 1364	Little Miss Heartbreak/You Might As Well Forget Him (with Roemans)	4
65	HMV POP 1386	Diane From Manchester Square/Party Girl (as Tommy Roe & Roemans)	4
65	HMV POP 1469	Doesn't Anybody Know My Name/I'm A Rambler, I'm A Gambler	4
66	HMV POP 1539	Sweet Pea/Much More Love	4
66	HMV POP 1556	Hooray For Hazel/Need For Love	4
67	HMV POP 1574	It's Now Winter's Day/Kick Me Charlie	4
67	HMV POP 1611	Melancholy Mood/Paisley Dreams	5
69	Stateside SS 2143	Dizzy/The You I Need	4
69	Stateside SS 2152	Heather Honey/Money Is My Pay	4
69	Stateside SS 2156	Jam Up Jelly Tight/Moontalk	4
70	Stateside SS 2165	Stir It Up And Serve It/Firefly	4
70	Stateside SS 2174	Pearl/Dollar's Worth Of Pennies	4
63	HMV 7EG 8806	THE FOLK SINGER (EP)	15
63	HMV CLP 1614	SHEILA (LP)	25
64	HMV CLP 1704	EVERYBODY LIKES TOMMY ROE (LP)	25
65	HMV CLP 1860	BALLADS AND BEAT (LP)	20
69	Stateside S(S)L 10282	DIZZY (LP)	15
70	Stateside SSL 10296	TOMMY ROE'S GREATEST HITS (LP)	10
70	Probe SPB 1021	WE CAN MAKE MUSIC (LP)	10
71	Probe SPB 1046	BEGINNINGS (LP)	10

DANE ROGERS & NU BEATS

64	Pye 7N 15621	Mary Jane/Jeanette	4

DEAN ROGERS

60	Parlophone R 4732	End Of Time/Keep The Miracle Going	6
61	Parlophone R 4835	Timber/High In A Misty Sky	6

IKE ROGERS

50s	Jazz Collector L 55	It Hurts So Good/Screenin' The Blues (78)	6

JULIE ROGERS

64	Mercury MF 809	It's Magic/Without Your Love	4
64	Mercury MF 820	The Wedding (La Novia)/The Love Of A Boy	4
65	Mercury MF 838	Like A Child/Our Day Will Come	4
65	Mercury MF 849	Hawaiian Wedding Song/Turn Around, Look At Me	4
65	Mercury MF 858	Sudden Love/Play The Music	4
65	Mercury MF 868	Day By Day/I'm Walking Behind You	4
65	Mercury MF 901	In My Room/Three Unspoken Words	4
65	Mercury MF 917	I Love Him/Lullaby For Lovers	4
65	Mercury MF 950	While The Angels Was Ringing/Climb Every Mountain	4
66	Mercury MF 980	These Gentle Hands/When Two Worlds Collide	4
66	Mercury MF 993	Bless You/Go On Home	4
68	Mercury MF 1015	Let Me Belong To You/You Never Told Me	4
69	Ember EMB S 267	Almost Close To You (O Mio Angelo)/This Is Me (C'est Ton Nom) (p/s)	4
69	Ember EMB S 273	Which Way To Nowhere/Love Theme From The Motion Picture "Michael And Helga" (p/s)	4
70	Ember EMB S 287	Children Of My Mind/Once More With Feeling (p/s)	4

Julie ROGERS

70	Ember EMB S 300	Baby Don't You Leave Me/Where Do You Go (p/s)	4
64	Mercury 10023 MCE	JULIE ROGERS (EP)	7
65	Mercury 10028 MCE	THE SOUND OF JULIE (EP)	7
65	Mercury (S)MCL 20048	THE SOUND OF JULIE (LP)	12
66	Mercury 20086 (S)MCL	CONTRASTS (LP)	12
67	Mercury 20100 (S)MCL	SONGS OF INSPIRATION (LP)	12

KENNY ROGERS (& FIRST EDITION)

69	Reprise RS 20829	Ruby Don't Take Your Love To Town/Girl Get Ahold Of Yourself	4
70	Reprise RS 20888	Something's Burning/Moma's Waiting	4
70	Reprise RS 20923	Tell It All Brother/Just Remember You Are My Sunshine	4
70	Reprise RS 20953	Heed the Call/Stranger In My Place	4
70	Reprise RS 20999	Someone Who Cares/Mission Of San Nohero	4
72	Reprise K 14009	Ruby Don't Take Your Love To Town/Girl Get Ahold Of Yourself (p/s)	4
72	Reprise K 14206	Ruby Don't Take Your Love To Town/Me And Bobby McGee/Rueben James/Something's Burning (maxi-single)	4

(see also First Edition)

LINCOLN ROGERS

| 73 | Phoenix NIX 137 | Let Love Come Between Us/She Looked At Me With Love | 8 |

MARK ROGERS & MARKSMEN

| 63 | Parlophone R 5045 | Hold It!/Bubble Pop | 10 |

(see also Marksmen)

PAUL ROGERS

| 61 | HMV POP 872 | Four An' Twenty Thousand Kisses/Free To Love | 4 |
| 63 | HMV POP 1121 | Always/Joanie Don't Be Angry | 4 |

PAULINE ROGERS

| 54 | Columbia SCM 5106 | Spinnin' The Blues/But Good | 6 |

PIERCE ROGERS & OVERLANDERS

| 61 | Parlophone R 4838 | Do You Still Love Me?/That Someone | 6 |

ROY ROGERS

| 50s | HMV 7EG 8145 | ROY ROGERS (EP) | 10 |
| 50s | HMV 7EG 8182 | HAPPY TRAILS (EP) | 12 |

SHORTY ROGERS & HIS ORCHESTRA

54	HMV 7M 267	Tale Of An African Lobster/Sweetheart Of Sigmund Freud	4
50s	HMV 7EG 8044	SHORTY ROGERS AND HIS ORCHESTRA (EP)	7
52	Capitol LC 6549	MODERN SOUNDS (10" LP, as Shorty Rogers & His Giants)	10
54	HMV DLP 1030	COOL AND CRAZY (10" LP)	10
54	HMV DLP 1058	EIGHT SHORTY ROGERS' NUMBERS (10" LP)	10

(see also Bud Shank)

TIMMIE ROGERS

57	London HLU 8510	Back To School Again/I've Got A Dog Who Loves Me	35
57	London HLU 8510	Back To School Again/I've Got A Dog Who Loves Me (78)	10
58	London HLU 8601	Take Me To Your Leader/Fla-Ga-La-Pa	45
58	London HLU 8601	Take Me To Your Leader/Fla-Ga-La-Pa (78)	15

VERN ROGERS & HI-FI'S

62	Oriole CB 1785	That Ain't Right/Be Everything	6
63	Oriole CB 1826	He's New To You/Can't Complain	5
63	Oriole CB 1885	I Will/One Way Love Affair	6
63	Oriole CB 1923	Anna/Pride	5

ROGUES

| 65 | CBS 201 731 | Rogers Reef/Everyday | 7 |
| 67 | Decca F 12718 | Memories Of Missy/And You Let Her Pass By | 6 |

JAN ROHDE

| 60 | Qualiton PSP 7128 | Come Back Baby/So Shy | 6 |

ROKES

67	RCA RCA 1587	Let's Live For Today/Ride On	15
67	RCA RCA 1646	Hold My Hand/Regency Sue	20
68	RCA RCA 1694	When The Wind Arises/The Works Of Bartholemew	35

CHERRY ROLAND

63	Decca F 11579	Handy Sandy/Stay As I Am	4
63	Decca F 11648	What A Guy/Just For Fun	4
63	Fontana H 420	Boys/Nobody But Me	4

PAUL ROLAND

82	Aristocrat ARC 1398	Doctor Strange/Madeline (p/s)	6
82	Scoff DT 020	Doctor Strange/Madeline (p/s, Irish only)	6
83	Aftermath AEP 12011	Blades Of Battenburg (Remix)/Captain Blood/Puppet Master/Cavalier (12", p/s)	10
86	Aftermath AEP 12012	Death Or Glory (Revamped Version)/The Great Edwardian Air Raid/Beau Brummel/The Curios Case Of Richard Fielding (12", p/s)	8
86	Imaginary MIRAGE 002	Demon In A Glass Case/In The Opium Den (p/s)	7
87	Bam Caruso OPRA 081	Madam Guillotine/UNITED STATES OF EXISTENCE: Gone (radio jukebox promo, company sleeve)	5
87	Bucketfull Of Brains 14	Madhouse (Demo)/GIANT SAND: Wishing Well (flexidisc free with 'Bucketfull Of Brains' magazine)	4
87	Nineteen NIT 19005	Captain Blood/CORONADOS: Life I Live (flexidisc)	4
80	Ace ACE 013	THE WEREWOLF OF LONDON (LP)	10
81	Armageddon ARM 9	THE WEREWOLF OF LONDON (Revamped Version) (LP)	10

(see also Weird Strings, Midnight Rags, Beau Brummel)

WALTER ROLAND/GEORGIA SLIM
59	Jazz Collector JEL 2	THE MALE BLUES VOL. 1 (EP)	10

BARRY ROLFE
73	Philips 6006 384	Beam Me Aboard Mr. Spock/Boadecia	4

ROLLERS
61	London HLG 9340	Continental Walk/I Want You So	10

ROLLING STONES
63	Decca F 11675	Come On/I Want To Be Loved	8
63	Decca F 11742	Poison Ivy/Fortune Teller (release cancelled, copies exist with solid centre but possibly export issue)	200
63	Decca F 11764	I Wanna Be Your Man/Stoned	10
63	Decca F 11764	I Wanna Be Your Man/Stones (B-side mis-spelt)	10
64	Decca F 11845	Not Fade Away/Little By Little	5
64	Decca F 11934	It's All Over Now/Good Times, Bad Times	4
64	Decca F 12014	Little Red Rooster/Off The Hook	4

(original pressings of the above singles had 'Recording First Published ...' printed on left of label & 'fat' lettering)

65	Decca F 12104	The Last Time/Play With Fire	4
65	Decca F 12220	(I Can't Get No) Satisfaction/The Spider And The Fly	5
65	Decca F 12263	Get Off My Cloud/The Singer Not The Song	5
66	Decca F 12331	19th Nervous Breakdown/As Tears Go By	5
66	Decca F 12395	Paint It Black/Long Long While	5

(original pressings of the above singles all had round Decca logo, later pressings with rectangular box logos are worth £3-£4)

66	Decca F 12497	Have You Seen Your Mother, Baby, Standing In The Shadows/Who's Driving Your Plane	6
67	Decca F 12546	Let's Spend The Night Together/Ruby Tuesday	5
67	Decca F 12654	We Love You/Dandelion	5
69	Decca F 12952	Honky Tonk Women/You Can't Always Get What You Want	5
71	Rolling Stones RS 19100	Brown Sugar/Bitch/Let It Rock (some in p/s)	15/4
71	Decca F 13195	Street Fighting Man/Surprise Surprise/Everybody Needs Somebody To Love (33rpm maxi-single)	5
71	Decca F 13203	Street Fighting Man/Surprise Surprise (jukebox edition)	15
72	Rolling Stones RS 19103	Tumbling Dice/Sweet Black Angel	5
72	Sound For Industry 107	Mick Jagger Introduces 'Exile On Main Street' (flexidisc free with 'NME')	8/5
73	Decca F 13404	Sad Day/You Can't Always Get What You Want	6
73	Rolling Stones RS 19105	Angie/Silver Train	4
74	Decca F 13517	It's All Over Now/Paint It Black (release cancelled)	100
74	Atlantic K 19107	Brown Sugar/Happy/Rocks Off	18
74	Rolling Stones RS 19114	It's Only Rock 'N' Roll/Through The Lonely Nights	4
75	Decca F 13584	I Don't Know Why (A-side credited to 'Jagger/Richard/Taylor' or 'Stevie Wonder')/Try A Little Harder	12/8
75	Decca F 13597	Out Of Time/Jiving Sister Fanny	4
76	Rolling Stones RS 19121	Fool To Cry/Crazy Mama	4
78	Rolling Stones EMI 2802	Miss You/Faraway Eyes (p/s)	4
78	R. Stones 12EMI 2802	Miss You (8.26)/Faraway Eyes (12", p/s, some on pink vinyl)	10/8
78	Rolling Stones EMI 2861	Respectable/When The Whip Comes Down (p/s)	5
80	Decca STONE 1-12	SINGLE STONES (12-single box set)	45
80	Decca BROWSE 1	SINGLE STONES (in-store, 3 x 12-single box set, [STONE 1-12], with poster & badge, also available by mail-order)	150
80	Rolling Stones RSR 106	She's So Cold/Send It To Me (p/s)	4
81	Rolling Stones RSR 109	Waiting On A Friend/Little T & A (p/s)	4
81	Rolling Stones	Beast Of Burden/Everything Is Turning Gold (withdrawn, any pressed?)	30+
82	Rolling Stones RSR 111	Time Is On My Side (live)/Twenty Flight Rock (live) (p/s)	4
82	Rolling Stones 12RSR 111	Time Is On My Side (live)/Twenty Flight Rock (live)/Under My Thumb (live) (12", p/s)	7
83	Rolling Stones RS 83 70/1	Fan Club interview single	6
84	Rolling Stones RSR 114	She Was Hot/I Think I'm Going Mad (p/s)	4
84	Rolling Stones RSRP 114	She Was Hot/I Think I'm Going Mad (shaped picture disc)	12
84	Rolling Stones RSRP 114	She Was Hot/I Think I'm Going Mad (12", picture disc)	7
84	Rolling Stones SUGAR 1	Brown Sugar/Bitch (p/s, reissue)	4
84	Rolling Stones SUGARP 1	Brown Sugar/Bitch (shaped picture disc)	12
86	CBS A 6864	Harlem Shuffle/Had It With You (poster p/s)	4
86	CBS QTA 6864	Harlem Shuffle (N.Y. Mix)/(London Mix)/Had It With You (12", p/s)	7
86	CBS A 7160	One Hit (To The Body)/Fight (p/s)	4
86	CBS TA 7160	One Hit (To The Body) (London Mix)/Fight (12", p/s)	7
89	CBS 655214-2	Mixed Emotions/Waiting On A Friend/Miss You/Shattered (5" CD in tin with 'tongue' logo sticker)	7
89	R. Stones RSR 655448-2	Rock And A Hard Place/Cook Cook Blues (CD box set, with poster)	25
89	R. Stones RSR 655448-5	Rock And A Hard Place/Cook Cook Blues (CD, tongue-shaped p/s)	25
90	R. Stones RSR 655122-5	Terrifying (CD in tin, unreleased)	25

(all the below singles are export issues, manufactured in the U.K.)

65	Decca F 12104	The Last Time/Play With Fire (with Dutch p/s)	35
65	Decca F 22180	Heart Of Stone/What A Shame (some in p/s)	50/25
65	Decca F 12220	(I Can't Get No) Satisfaction/Under Assistant West Coast Promotional Man (some with p/s)	30/15
65	Decca F 22265	Get Off My Cloud/I'm Free (some in p/s)	40/20
66	Decca F 12331	19th Nervous Breakdown/As Tears Go By (with Dutch p/s)	35
67	Decca F 12546	Let's Spend The Night Together/Ruby Tuesday (p/s)	35
67	Decca F 12654	We Love You/Dandelion (p/s)	35
67	Decca F 22706	2000 Light Years From Home/She's A Rainbow	35
68	Decca F 22825	Street Fighting Man (remix)/No Expectations (some in p/s)	50/25
69	Decca F 12952	Honky Tonk Women/You Can't Always Get What You Want (p/s)	30
71	Decca F 13126	Little Queenie/Love In Vain (some in p/s)	30/15
71	Decca F 13195	Street Fighting Man/Surprise Surprise/Everybody Needs Somebody To Love (33rpm maxi-single, p/s)	25

ROLLING STONES

71	Decca F 13204	Street Fighting Man/Everybody Needs Somebody To Love (some in p/s) 30/15
63	Decca AT 15005	I Wanna Be Your Man/Stoned 25
64	Decca AT 15006	Not Fade Away/Little By Little 25
64	Decca AT 15032	Come On/Tell Me (You're Coming Back) 100
64	Decca AT 15035	Empty Heart/Around And Around 100
65	Decca AT 15039	Time Is On My Side/Congratulations 100
65	Decca AT 15040	Little Red Rooster/Off The Hook 100
65	Decca AT 15043	(I Can't Get No) Satisfaction/Under Assistant West Coast Promotional Man (p/s) 100
64	Decca DFE 8560	THE ROLLING STONES (EP) 8
64	Decca DFE 8590	FIVE BY FIVE (EP) 8
65	Decca DFE 8620	GOT LIVE IF YOU WANT IT! (EP) 8

(all below EPs are export issues, manufactured in the U.K.)

64	Decca SDE 7260	ROLLING STONES (EP, possibly unissued) 50
64	Decca SDE 7501	THE ROLLING STONES VOLUME 2 (EP) 50
65	Decca SDE 7502	GOT LIVE IF YOU WANT IT! (EP) 55
65	Decca DFE 8620	GOT LIVE IF YOU WANT IT! (EP, with red label, yellow titled on p/s) 60
66	Decca SDE 7503	ROLLING STONES (EP, with "Out Of Our Heads [U.K. version]" sleeve) 100
64	Decca LK 4605	ROLLING STONES (LP, flipback sleeve, with 2.52 version of "Tell Me") 40
64	Decca LK 4605	ROLLING STONES (LP, flipback sleeve, some sleeves say "Mona", others "I Need You, Baby") 20
64	Decca LK 4605	ROLLING STONES (LP, repressing, original red label, non-flipback) 15
65	Decca LK 4661	ROLLING STONES NO. 2 (LP, flipback/non-flipback sleeve) 20/15
65	Decca LK/SKL 4733	OUT OF OUR HEADS (LP, mono/stereo) 18/20
65	Decca SKL 4733	OUT OF OUR HEADS (LP, light green sleeve, boxed Decca logo) 15
66	Decca LK/SKL 4786	AFTERMATH (LP, mono/stereo) 18/20
66	Decca TXL/TXS 101	BIG HITS (HIGH TIDE AND GREEN GRASS) (LP, gatefold sleeve with stapled 12" x 12" picture booklet, mono/stereo) 16/18
66	Decca TXL/TXS 101	BIG HITS (HIGH TIDE AND GREEN GRASS) (LP, mono/stereo, gatefold sleeve, without booklet) 10/12
67	Decca LK/SKL 4852	BETWEEN THE BUTTONS (LP) 18
67	Decca TXL/TXS 103	THEIR SATANIC MAJESTIES REQUEST (LP, 3D gatefold sleeve with red inner, mono/stereo) 35/25
67	Decca TXL/TXS 103	THEIR SATANIC MAJESTIES REQUEST (LP, gatefold sleeve, mono/stereo) ..15/12
67	Decca TXL/TXS 103	THEIR SATANIC MAJESTIES REQUEST (LP, padded silk sleeve, promo only) ....300+
68	Decca LK/SKL 4955	BEGGARS BANQUET (LP, gatefold sleeve, some with Stones Decca label insert, mono/stereo) 30/25
68	Decca LK/SKL 4955	BEGGARS BANQUET (LP, gatefold sleeve, no insert, mono/stereo) 20/15
69	Decca LK/SKL 5019	THROUGH THE PAST, DARKLY (BIG HITS VOL. 2) (LP, octagonal gatefold sleeve, mono/stereo) 22/18
69	Decca LK 5025	LET IT BLEED (LP, mono, red inner, some with stickered sleeve & poster) ...35/25
69	Decca SLK 5025	LET IT BLEED (LP, stereo, blue inner, some with stickered sleeve/poster) 25/15

(the above LPs originally had labels with the Decca logo in large print without a box surrounding it, later pressings with smaller print & a boxed logo are worth between half the value for earlier LPs to two-thirds the value for later LPs)

69	Decca RSM 1	THE PROMOTIONAL ALBUM (LP, promo only, U.S. sleeve) 600
70	Decca SKL 5065	GET YER YA-YA'S OUT! (LP) 15
71	Decca SKL 5084	STONE AGE (LP) 10
71	Rolling Stones COC 59100	STICKY FINGERS (LP, zip sleeve with insert) 10
72	Decca SKL 5101	GIMME SHELTER (LP) 10
72	Decca SKL 5098	MILESTONES (LP) 10
72	Rolling Stones COC 69100	EXILE ON MAIN STREET (2-LP, with inners, some with postcard inserts) 20/15
72	Decca SKL 5149	ROCK 'N' ROLLING STONES (LP) 12
73	Decca SKL 5166	GOLDEN B-SIDES (LP, unreleased, test pressings only) 200
73	Decca SKL 5173	NO STONE UNTURNED (LP) 10

(the above Decca LPs originally had dark blue labels & laminated sleeves)

75	Decca SKL 5212	METAMORPHOSIS (LP, dark blue label, matt sleeve) 10
78	Rolling Stones CUN 39108	SOME GIRLS (LP, with uncensored inner sleeve) 10
80	Rolling Stones CUN 39111	EMOTIONAL RESCUE (LP, with wraparound sleeve & inner) 12
82	Rolling Stones CUNP 39115	STILL LIFE (AMERICAN CONCERT 1981) (LP, picture disc, a few mispressed with wrong tracks) 150/10
83	Readers's Digest	THE GREAT YEARS (5-LP box set) 15
83	Decca ROLL 1	THE FIRST EIGHT STUDIO ALBUMS (8-LP set with 192-page book) 100

(all the below LPs are export issues, manufactured in the U.K.)

65	Decca 4495	HITS LIVE (LP, promo-only) 150
65	Decca LK/SKL 4725	OUT OF OUR HEADS (LP, export, cover & tracks as U.S. issue) 70
66	Decca LK/SKL 4838	HAVE YOU SEEN YOUR MOTHER, LIVE (LP, original label) 70
66	Decca LK/SKL 4838	HAVE YOU SEEN YOUR MOTHER, LIVE (LP, boxed logo, later pressing) 35
67	Decca LK/SKL 4888	FLOWERS (LP, laminated sleeve, original label) 70
67	Decca LK/SKL 4888	FLOWERS (LP, boxed Decca label, later pressing) 35

(see also Mick Jagger, Brian Jones, Bill Wyman, Keith Richards, Charlie Watts, Andrew Oldham Orchestra, Bobbie Miller)

SONNY ROLLINS

50s	Esquire EP 94	SONNY ROLLINS AND THE MODERN JAZZ QUARTET (EP) 8
57	Esquire EP 148	SONNY ROLLINS WITH THELONIUS MONK (EP) 8
58	Esquire EP 198	WAILING MISTER ROLLINS (EP) 7
60	Esquire EP 228	VALSE HOT (EP, as Sonny Rollins Plus Four) 7
61	Esquire EP 238	ROLLINS AND BROWNIE (EP, with Clifford Brown) 7
62	Esquire EP 248	SAINT THOMAS (LP) 7
50s	Esquire 20-050	SONNY ROLLINS QUARTET (10" LP) 18
57	Esquire 20-080	SONNY ROLLINS QUINTET (10" LP) 18
57	Esquire 32-025	SONNY ROLLINS PLUS FOUR (LP) 15
57	Esquire 32-035	PERSPECTIVES (LP, with Modern Jazz Quartet) 15
58	Esquire 32-038	SONNY ROLLINS QUARTET (LP) 15
58	Esquire 32-045	SAXOPHONE COLOSSUS (LP, as Sonny Rollins Four) 15
58	Contemporary LAC 12118	WAY OUT WEST (LP) 15
58	Esquire 32-058	TENOR MADNESS (LP) 15

59	Esquire 32-075	SONNY ROLLINS QUINTET (LP) 15
59	Esquire 32-085	TOUR-DE-FORCE (LP) 15
59	MGM MGM-C 776	SONNY ROLLINS AND THE BIG BRASS (LP) 15
60	Contemporary SCA 5013	SONNY ROLLINS AND THE CONTEMPORARY LEADERS (LP, stereo only) 20
61	Riverside RLP 12-241	THE SOUND OF SONNY (LP) 12
61	Blue Note BLP 1558	SONNY ROLLINS VOL. 2 (LP) 15
62	Riverside RLP 12-258	FREEDOM SUITE (LP) 12
62	Esquire 32-155	MOVIN' OUT (LP) 12
62	RCA RD/SF 7504	THE BRIDGE (LP, mono/stereo) 12/15
63	Esquire 32-175	SONNY BOY (LP) 12
63	RCA RD/SF 7524	WHAT'S NEW (LP, mono/stereo) 12/15
63	RCA RD/SF 7546	OUR MAN IN JAZ (LP, mono/stereo) 12/15
64	RCA RD/SF 7593	SONNY MEETS HAWK (LP, with Coleman Hawkins, mono/stereo) 12/15
64	Blue Note (B)BLP 4001	NEWK'S TIME (LP) 15
64	RCA RD/SF 7626	SONNY ROLLINS & CO. (LP) 12
64	Blue Note (B)BLP 1581	A NIGHT AT THE VILLAGE VANGUARD (LP) 15
65	RCA RD 7670	NOW'S THE TIME (LP) 12
65	Blue Note (B)BLP 1542	THE SONNY ROLLINS QUARTET (LP) 15
65	Fontana FJL 124	BLOW! (LP) 12
66	HMV CLP 1915	ROLLINS ON IMPULSE (LP) 12
66	Stateside SL 10164	SAXOPHONE COLOSSUS (LP, reissue) 10
67	RCA RD/SF 7736	STANDARD SONNY ROLLINS (LP) 10
67	HMV CLP/CSD 3529	SONNY PLAYS ALFIE (LP) 10
67	HMV CLP/CSD 3610	EAST BROADWAY RUNDOWN (LP) 10

(see also Modern Jazz Quartet, Thelonious Monk, Clifford Brown, Coleman Hawkins)

ROLL MOVEMENT
67	Go AJ 11410	I'm Out On My Own/Just One Thing 10

ROLL-UPS
79	Bridgehouse BHLP 004	LOW DIVES FOR HIGBALLS (LP) 15

DICK ROMAN
59	MGM MGM 1004	Party Girl/My Greatest Mistake 4
59	MGM MGM 1004	Party Girl/My Greatest Mistake (78) 5
65	London HLU 10007	The Truth Hurts/What Good Does It Do Me 5
66	Coral Q 72485	Green Years/Ivy 4
63	Stateside SL 10023	TOUCH OF LOVE (LP) 10

LYN ROMAN
74	Brunswick BR 11	Stop, I Don't Need No Sympathy/Where Do You Go 5

MARK ROMAN
68	Columbia DB 8360	Gonna Get Along Without Ya Now/Cuddly Toy 4

MURRAY ROMAN
69	Track 613 007	YOU CAN'T BEAT PEOPLE UP AND HAVE THEM SAY I LOVE YOU (LP) 18
69	Track 613 015	A BLIND MAN'S MOVIE (LP) 15
70	Track 2407 013	YOU CAN'T BEAT PEOPLE UP AND HAVE THEM SAY I LOVE YOU (LP, 'Backtrack' reissue) 10

SANDY ROMAN
66	Columbia DB 7931	Dale Anne/Home Is Where The Heart Is 4

TONY ROMAN
67	Stateside SS 2022	Shadows Of A Foggy Day/Maggie 4

MAX ROMEO
67	Caltone TONE 106	Don't Want To Let You Go/I Can't Do No More (as Romeo & Emotions) 8
68	Island WI 3104	Put Me In The Mood/My One Girl 10
68	Island WI 3111	Walk Into The Room/DAWN PENN: I'll Get You 8
68	Island WI 3124	Twelfth Of Never (actually Pat Kelly)/VAL BENNETT: Caledonia 10
69	Blue Cat BS 163	It's Not The Way/AL REID: Darling 8
69	Nu Beat NB 022	Blowing In The Wind/LARRY MARSHALL: Money Girl 6
69	Trojan TR 656	Sweet Chariot/Far Far Away (with Hippy Boys) 5
68	Unity UN 503	Wet Dream/She's But A Little Girl 4
69	Unity UN 507	Belly Woman (actually by Derrick Morgan/PAULETT & LOVERS: Please Stay 5
69	Unity UN 511	Twelfth Of Never (actually by Pat Kelly)/TARTONS: Solid As A Rock (actually by Tartans) 5
69	Unity UN 516	Wine Her Goosie/KING CANNON: Fire Ball 5
70	Unity UN 545	Clap Clap/Death Rides A Horse 4
71	Pama Supreme PS 328	Ginal Ship/UPSETTERS: Version 2 4
72	Camel CA 85	Rasta Bandwagon/When Jah Speaks 4
72	Camel CA 86	Public Enemy Number One/How Long Must We Wait 4
72	Prince Buster PB 11	River Jordan/Words Sound And Power 4
74	Ackee ACK 529	Sixpence/Eating Competition 4
74	Dragon DRA 1028	No Joshua No/No Joshua No (Version) 4
69	Pama PMLP 11	A DREAM (LP) 20
71	Pama PMP 2010	LET THE POWER FALL (LP) 18

(see also Max & Elaine)

CHAN ROMERO
59	Columbia DB 4341	The Hippy Hippy Shake/If I Had A Way 50
60	Columbia DB 4405	My Little Ruby/I Don't Care Now 60

RONALD & RUBY
58	RCA RCA 1053	Lollipop/Fickle Baby 15
58	RCA RCA 1053	Lollipop/Fickle Baby (78) 8

RONNIE RONALDE
53	Columbia SCM 5006	Song Of The Mountains/If I Were A Blackbird 10
53	Columbia SCM 5007	In A Monastery Garden/Bells Across The Meadow 10

Ronnie RONALDE

54	Columbia SCM 5101	We'll Always Remember/On The Quarter Deck	7
54	Columbia SCM 5116	My Starlight Lullaby/Safe In The Harbour	7
54	Columbia SCM 5141	Ave Maria/Angels Sing	7
55	Columbia SCM 5205	"Christmastide With Ronnie Ronalde" Pts 1 & 2	6
56	Columbia SCM 5214	Ballad Of Davy Crockett/Hair Of Gold	10
56	Columbia SCM 5241	Robin Hood/Happy Trails	10
56	Columbia SCM 5262	The Yarmouth Song/Macnamara's Band	6
56	Columbia SCM 5275	The Happy Whistler/The Lady from Luxembourg	6
57	Columbia DB 3892	The Buccaneers/The Mountain Climber	4
57	Columbia DB 4003	A Bird Sings/The Alpine Polka	4
57	Columbia DB 4020	"Christmas At Home" Medley (both sides)	4
57	Columbia DB 4036	"Party Rhymes" Pts 1 & 2	4
58	Columbia DB 4092	Innocent Sinners/Sweetwater Mountains	4
59	Columbia DB 4320	When It's Springtime In The Rockies/The Pleasant Peasant	4
59	Columbia DB 4367	Christmas Lullaby/Morning Star	4
55	Columbia SEG 7512	RONNIE RONALDE (EP)	7
56	Columbia SEG 7651	YODELLING, WHISTLING AND SINGING (EP)	7
57	Columbia SEG 7678	BEAUTIFUL DREAMER (EP)	7
58	Columbia SEG 7784	T.V. TOP FOUR (EP)	7
58	Columbia SEG 7838	STORY OF CHRISTMAS (EP)	7
59	Columbia SEG 7945	RONNIE (EP)	7
60	Columbia SEG 7990	LITTLE BOY BLEW (EP, also stereo ESG 7797)	7/9
61	Columbia SEG 8087	YODELLING (EP, also stereo ESG 7850)	7/9
63	Golden Guinea GGL 0193	THE INIMITABLE RONNIE RONALDE (LP)	10

RONDELLS

58	London HLU 8716	Good Good/Dreamy (with Ned Jr.)	40
58	London HLU 8716	Good Good/Dreamy (with Ned Jr.) (78)	25

RONDELS

61	London HLU 9404	Back Beat No. 1/Shades Of Green	15

DON RONDO

56	Columbia DB 3854	Two Different Worlds/He Made You Mine	4
57	Columbia DB 3909	The Love I Never Had/Don't	4
57	London HLJ 8466	White Silver Sands/Stars Fell On Alabama	6
58	London HLJ 8567	What A Shame/Made For Each Other	6
58	London HLJ 8610	I've Got Bells On My Heart/School Dance	6
58	London HLJ 8610	I've Got Bells On My Heart/School Dance (78)	5
58	London HLJ 8641	Blonde Bombshell/Her Hair Was Yellow	6
58	London HLJ 8641	Blonde Bombshell/Her Hair Was Yellow (78)	5
58	London HLJ 8695	Dormi, Dormi, Dormi (Sleep, Sleep, Sleep)/In Chi Chi Chihuahua	4
58	London HLJ 8749	City Lights/I Could Be A Mountain	4
59	London HLJ 8808	Song From "The Geisha Boy"/Gretna Green	4
60	London HLL 9217	The King Of Holiday Island/Wanderlust	4
59	London REJ 1154	RONDO PT. 1 (EP)	10
59	London REJ 1155	RONDO PT. 2 (EP)	10

GENE RONDO

68	Giant GN 39	Ben Nevis/Grey Lies	5
69	Downtown DT 422	A Lover's Question/HERBIE GRAY & RUDIES: Blue Moon	4
69	Downtown DT 431	Sentimental Reasons/Then You Can Tell Me Goodbye	4
70	Downtown DT 459	Spreading Peace/MUSIC DOCTORS: Guitar Riff	4

RONETTES

63	London HLU 9793	Be My Baby/Tedesco And Pitman	5
64	London HLU 9826	Baby I Love You/Miss Joan And Mr Sam	7
64	London HLU 9905	(The Best Part Of) Breakin' Up/Big Red	8
64	London HLU 9922	Do I Love You?/When I Saw You	8
64	London HLU 9931	(Walking) In The Rain/How Does It Feel?	8
65	London HLU 9952	Born To Be Together/Blues For Baby	10
65	London HLU 9976	Is This What I Get For Loving You?/You Baby	10
66	London HLU 10087	I Can Hear Music/When I Saw You (withdrawn)	35
69	London HLU 10240	Be My Baby/Baby I Love You	4
69	A&M AMS 748	You Came, You Saw, You Conquered/I Can Hear Music	6
75	PSI 2010 009	I'm A Woman In Love/When I Saw You	4
64	London HA-U 8212	PRESENTING THE FABULOUS RONETTES FEATURING VERONICA (LP, originally on plum label, later on black label)	75/35
65	Colpix PXL 486	THE RONETTES (LP)	60
75	Phil Spector Intl. 2307 003	SING THEIR GREATEST HITS (LP)	10
	(see also Ronnie Spector)		

RONNIE & DEL AIRES

64	Coral Q 72473	Drag/Wigglin' 'N' Wobblin'	8

RONNIE & HI-LITES

62	Pye Intl. 7N 25140	I Wish That We Were Married/Twistin' And Kissin'	10

RONNIE & RAINBOWS

61	London HL 9345	Loose Ends/Sombrero	8

RONNIE & ROY

59	Capitol CL 15028	Big Fat Sally/Here I Am	70

RONNO

70	Vertigo 6059 029	Fourth Hour Of My Sleep/Powers Of Darkness	25
	(see also Mick Ronson)		

RONNY

64	Decca F 21908	Oh! My Darling Caroline/Lu La Lu	4

RONNY & DAYTONAS
64	Stateside SS 333	G.T.O./Hot Rod Baby	10
64	Stateside SS 367	California Bound/Hey Little Girl	7
65	Stateside SS 391	Bucket T/Little Rail Job	8
65	Stateside SS 432	Beach Boy/No Wheels	10
66	Stateside SS 484	Sandy/Sandy (Instrumental)	10

MICK RONSON
74	RCA APBO 212	Love Me Tender/Only After Dark	4
74	RCA	Love Me Tender (1-sided red or black flexidisc, included in press kits)	10
74	RCA LPBO 5022	Slaughter On 10th Avenue/Leave My Heart Alone	4
75	RCA RCA 2482	Billy Porter/Seven Days	4
74	RCA APL1 0353	SLAUGHTER ON 10TH AVE (LP)	10
75	RCA APL1 0681	PLAY, DON'T WORRY (LP)	10

(see also Ronno, Mott The Hoople, David Bowie, Slaughter & Dogs)

ROOFTOP SINGERS
63	Fontana 271 700 TF	Walk Right In/Cool Water	4
63	Fontana 271 702 TF	Tom Cat/Hey Boys	4
63	Fontana TF 411	Mama Don't Allow/It Don't Mean A Thing	4
63	Fontana 680 999 TL	WALK RIGHT IN (LP)	12
66	Fontana TFL 6065	RAINY RIVER (LP)	10

ROOGALATOR
76	Stiff BUY 3	All Aboard/Cinncinnati Fatback (p/s, 33rpm)	4
77	Do It RIDE 1	PLAY IT BY EAR (LP)	10

(see also Danny Adler)

ROOM
70	Deram SML 1073	PRE-FLIGHT (LP)	180

ROOM
80	Box BOX 001	Motion/Waiting Room (p/s)	6
80	Box BOX 002	BITTER REACTION (cassette)	8
81	Box BOX 003	In Sickness And Health/Bated Breath (p/s)	5

(see also Benny Profane)

ROOM 10
65	Decca F 12249	I Love My Love/Going Back	4

ROOM 13
82	Woronzow W 002	Murder Mystery/Need Some Dub (12", p/s)	30

(see also Bevis Frond)

MICKEY ROONEY
57	RCA RD 27038	MICKEY ROONEY SINGS GEORGE M. COHAN (LP)	10

MARY ROOS
72	CBS 7959	Wake Me Early In The Morning/When You're Singing (Don't Forget)	6

ROOT BOYS
70	Columbia Blue Beat DB 115	Please Don't Stop The Wedding/Your Love, Your Love	6

RO RO
70	Parlophone R 5920	Here I Go Again/What You Gonna Do	8
72	Regal Zonophone RZ 3056	Goin' Round My Head/Down On The Road	8
73	Regal Zonophone RZ 3076	Blackbird/Feel It Coming	8
72	Regal Zono. SRZA 8510	MEET AT THE WATER (LP)	140

EDMUNDO ROS (& HIS ORCHESTRA)
53	Decca F 10214	Blowin' Wind/Istanbul (B-side as Edmundo Ros & Johnston Brothers)	6
54	Decca F 10263	Somebody Bad Stole De Wedding Bell/Chili Sauce	6
55	Decca F 10480	Cherry Pink And Apple Blossom White/Ole Mambo	6
55	Decca F 10610	Grey Clouds/Les Claves	4
55	Decca F 10669	Sixteen Tons/Robin Hood	6
56	Decca F 10716	Mister Cuckoo/Don't Ringa Da Bell	4
57	Decca F 10834	I Saw Esau/Jamaica Farewell (Kingston Town)	4

(see also Johnston Brothers, Annette Klooger, Annie Ross)

ROSITA ROSANO
50s	Melodisc M 1308	Down In The Indies/Admiral's Daughters (78)	5
57	Melodisc M 1436	Queer Things/Little Boy	6

ANDY ROSE
58	London HLU 8761	Just Young/Lov-A Lov-A Love	20
58	London HLU 8761	Just Young/Lov-A Lov-A Love (78)	5

DAVID ROSE ORCHESTRA
53	MGM SP 1009	Harlem Nocturne (with Woody Herman)/Vanessa	4
53	MGM SP 1019	Beautiful Music To Love By (with Beryl Davis)/Satan And The Polar Bear	4
54	MGM SP 1083	I Live For You (with Rush Adams)/Migraine Melody	4
56	MGM SP 1181	Forbidden Planet/The Portuguese Washerwomen	4
56	MGM MGM 913	Forbidden Planet/The Portuguese Washerwomen (78)	5
56	MGM MGM 1158	The Stripper/Ebb Tide	4

(see also Woody Herman, Rush Adams)

DUSTY ROSE
55	London HLU 8162	The Birds And The Bees/It Makes Me So Mad	35
57	London RE-U 1078	COUNTRY SONGS (EP)	50

JOHNNY ROSE
60	Capitol CL 15166	Linda Lee/The Last One To Know	6

TIM ROSE
67	CBS 202631	Morning Dew/You're Slipping Away From Me	5

Tim ROSE

68	CBS 3277	I Got A Loneliness/Long Time Man	4
68	CBS 3478	I Guess It's Over/Hello Sunshine	4
68	CBS 3598	Long-Haired Boy/Looking At A Baby	4
69	CBS 4209	Roanoke/Baby You Turn Me On	4
67	CBS (S)BPG 63168	TIM ROSE (LP)	18
69	CBS 63636	THROUGH ROSE COLOURED GLASSES (LP)	12
70	Capitol ST 22673	LOVE — A KIND OF HATE STORY (LP)	10
74	Dawn DNLS 3062	TIM ROSE (LP)	12
75	Atlantic K 50183	MUSICIAN (LP)	10

ROSEHIPS

87	Subway Organisation SUBWAY 10	Room In Your Heart/Thrilled To Bits/Dead End (foldaround p/s with insert in poly bag)	5
87	Subway Organisation SUBWAY 10T	Room In Your Heart/Middle Of Next Week/Thrilled To Bits/So Naive/ Just Another Girl/Dead End (12", p/s)	8
87	Subway Organisation SUBWAY 16	I Shouldn't Have To Say/Loophole/Wastin' My Time/All Mine/ Sad As Sunday (p/s, with insert)	4
87	Subway Organisation SUBWAY 16T	I Shouldn't Have To Say/Loophole/Wastin' My Time/All Mine/ Sad As Sunday (12", p/s, with insert)	7
80s	Sweet William BILLY 001	Ask Johnny Dee/FAT TULIPS: You Opened My Eyes (33rpm flexidisc, p/s)	4

ROSE GARDEN

68	Atlantic 584 163	Next Plane To London/Flower Town	7

LEONARD ROSENMAN ORCHESTRA

57	London HA-P 2040	A TRIBUTE TO JAMES DEAN (LP)	10

ROSE OF AVALANCHE

85	L.I.L. 12 LIL 1	L.A. Rain/Rise To The Groove/Conceal Me (12", p/s)	10
85	L.I.L. 12 LIL 2	Goddess/A Thousand Landscapes/Gimme Some Lovin' (12", p/s)	8
87	Fire BLAZE 18T	Always There/Waiting For The Sun/Majesty (p/s)	4
87	Fire BLAZE 18TR	Always There (The Mainline Mix)/Waiting For The Sun/Majesty/ The Mainline Man (12", textured p/s)	7

JIMMY ROSELLI

62	Pye Intl. 7N 25156	I'm Gonna Sit Right Down And Write You A Letter/I Love You	5

ROSE TATTOO

81	Carrere CAR 200P	Rock 'N' Roll Outlaw/Remedy (picture disc)	4
81	Carrere CAR 220	Assault And Battery/Astra Wally//One Of The Boys/Manzil Madness (double pack, gatefold p/s)	4
83	Carrere CARP 263	It's Gonna Work Itself Out/Fightin' Sons (picture disc)	4

ROSIE (& ORIGINALS)

61	London HLU 9266	Angel Baby/Give Me Love (as Rosie & Originals)	20
61	Coral Q 72426	Lonely Blue Nights/We'll Have A Chance	10

EMPEROR ROSKO

69	Polydor BM 56316	Opposite Lock Pts 1 & 2	4

FRANK ROSOLINO SEXTET

54	Capitol KC 65001	That Old Black Magic/Yo Yo	6

(ALAN) ROSS

74	RSO 2090 125	Alright By Me/Carolina	4
74	RSO 2394 127	ROSS (LP)	10
75	RSO 2394 144	THE PIT AND THE PENDULUM (LP)	10
77	Ebony EBY 1000	ARE YOU FREE ON A SATURDAY (LP, as Alan Ross)	10
78	Ebony EBY 1003	RESTLESS NIGHTS (LP, as Alan Ross)	10

(see also Indian Summer, Gary Pickford-Hopkins)

ANNIE ROSS

55	Decca F 10514	Mama (He Treats Your Daughter Mean)/The Fish	10
55	Decca F 10637	I Want You To Be My Baby (with Tony Crombie)/TONY CROMBIE & HIS ORCHESTRA: Three Little Words	10
56	Decca F 10680	Cry Me A River/Only You	8
50s	Esquire EP 1	WITH THE TEACHO WILTSHIRE GROUP (EP)	7
50s	Pieces Of Eight PEP 604	WITH THE TONY CROMBIE FOURTET (EP)	7
57	Pye Jazz NJE 1035	NOCTURNE FOR VOCALIST (EP)	7
64	Transatlantic TRAEP 112	GO TO THE WALL (EP)	7
57	Nixa Jazz NJT 504	ANNIE BY CANDLELIGHT (10" LP)	12
59	Vogue LAE 12203	ANNIE ROSS (LP, with Gerry Mulligan Quintet)	10
60	Vogue LAE 12233	A GASSER (LP, with Zoot Sims)	10
66	Xtra XTRA 1049	ANNIE ROSS WITH THE TONY KINSEY QUINTET (LP)	10

(see also Tony Crombie, Dave Lambert, Gerry Mulligan, Zoot Sims, Jack Parnell)

DAVE ROSS

58	Oriole CB 1416	Everybody's Got A Girl But Tino/Pit-A-Patter Boom Boom	5

DIANA ROSS

70	Tamla Motown TMG 743	Reach Out And Touch (Somebody's Hand)/Dark Side Of The World	4
81	Tamla Motown TMG 1248	Tenderness/Supremes Medley (picture disc)	4
82	Capitol CLP 247	Work That Body/Two Can Make It (picture disc)	4
84	Capitol CLP 337	Touch By Touch/Fight For It (picture disc)	4

(see also [Diana Ross &] Supremes)

DOCTOR (Isiah) ROSS

66	Blue Horizon LP 1	THE FLYING EAGLE (LP)	700
66	Xtra XTRA 1038	DOCTOR ROSS (LP, reissue of "The Flying Eagle")	25
70s	Bounty BY 6020	CALL THE DOCTOR (LP)	15
72	Polydor 2460 169	LIVE AT MONTREUX (LP)	12
75	Big Bear BEAR 2	THE HARMONICA BOSS (LP)	10

GENE ROSS
| 58 | Parlophone R 4434 | Endless Sleep/The Only One | 20 |
| 58 | Parlophone R 4434 | Endless Sleep/The Only One (78) | 5 |

JACK ROSS
| 62 | London HLD 9534 | Cindarella/Margarita | 4 |
| 62 | London HLD 9485 | Happy Jose/Sweet Georgia Brown | 4 |

JACKIE ROSS
| 64 | Pye Intl. 7N 25259 | Selfish One/Everything But Love | 25 |
| 64 | Chess CRS 8003 | Jerk And Twine/New Lover | 12 |

SONNY ROSS
| 73 | Mojo 2093 001 | Alakazam/Piper Must Be Paid | 4 |

SPENCER ROSS
| 60 | Philips PB 992 | Tracy's Theme/Thanksgiving Day Parade | 4 |
| 60 | London HLX 9141 | Theme Of A Lonely Evening/Bobby's Blues | 4 |

LEON ROSSELSON
| 70s | Acorn CF 249 | PALACES OF GOLD (LP) | 20 |

NITA ROSSI
65	Piccadilly 7N 35258	Every Little Day Now/Untrue Unfaithful	10
66	Piccadilly 7N 35307	Here I Go Again/Something To Give	15
66	Piccadilly 7N 35354	The Daddy Christmas Song/Our Love Was Meant To Be	6
67	Piccadilly 7N 35384	Misty Blue	10

(Francis) ROSSI & (Bernard) SCOTT
85	Vertigo VER 17/FROS 1	Modern Romance (I Want To Fall In Love Again)/I Wonder Why (p/s)	6
85	Vertigo VERX 17/FROSX 1	Modern Romance (I Want To Fall In Love Again) (Extended Remix)/	
		I Wonder Why (Extended Remix) (12", p/s)	12
85	Vertigo VER 24	Jealousy/Where Are You Now? (p/s)	5
85	Vertigo VERX 24	Jealousy/Where Are You Now?/That's Alright (12", p/s)	10

(see also Status Quo)

LEONARD ROSSITER & RIGSBYETTES
| 80 | Chip CHI 101 | Rising Damp/Damp Disco (p/s) | 4 |

JOHN HENRY ROSTILL
| 71 | Columbia DB 8794 | Funny Old World/Green Apples | 50 |

(see also Shadows)

ROTARY CONNECTION
68	Chess CRS 8072	Soul Man/Ruby Tuesday	4
70	Chess CRS 8103	The Weight/Respect	4
70	Chess CRS 8106	Want To Know/Memory Band	5
68	Chess CRL 4538	ROTARY CONNECTION (LP)	12
69	Chess CRL 4547	ALADDIN (LP)	15
69	Chess CRLS 4551	SONGS (LP)	12

DAVID LEE ROTH
86	Warner Bros W 8656P	Yankee Rose/Shy Boy (pin-up shaped picture disc)	15
88	Warner Bros W 8119TP	Just Like Paradise/Bottom Line/Yankee Rose (12", picture disc)	7
88	Warner Bros W 7753W	Damn Good (Edit)/Stand Up (7" in 12" x 12" card p/s with poster)	6
91	Warner Bros W 0016P	Sensible Shoes/California Girls (5" backstage tour pass-shaped picture disc)	10

(see also Van Halen)

ROTHCHILDS
| 66 | Decca F 12411 | You've Made Your Choice/It's Love | 8 |
| 66 | Decca F 12488 | Artificial City/I Let Her Go | 10 |

ROULETTES
62	Pye 7N 15467	Hully Gully Slip 'n' Slide/La Bamba	8
63	Parlophone R 5072	Soon You'll Be Leaving Me/Tell Tale Tit	7
64	Parlophone R 5110	Bad Time/Can You Go	6
64	Parlophone R 5148	I'll Remember Tonight/You Don't Love Me	6
64	Parlophone R 5218	Stubborn Kind Of Fellow/Melody	6
65	Parlophone R 5278	I Hope He Breaks Your Heart/Find Out The Truth	8
65	Parlophone R 5382	Junk/The Long Cigarette	7
66	Parlophone R 5419	The Tracks Of My Tears/Jackpot	7
66	Oak RGJ 205	I Can't Stop (1-sided)	50
66	Parlophone R 5461	I Can't Stop/Yesterday, Today And Tomorrow	8
67	Fontana TF 822	Rhyme Boy, Rhyme/Airport People	10
67	Fontana TF 876	Help Me To Help Myself/To A Taxi Driver	10
65	Parlophone PMC 1257	STAKES AND CHIPS (LP)	300

(see also Adam Faith, Unit Four Plus Two)

ROUND ROBIN
| 64 | London HLU 9908 | Kick That Little Foot Sally Ann/Slauson Party | 20 |

ROUNDTABLE
| 69 | Jay Boy JSL 2 | SPINNING WHEEL (LP) | 10 |

ROUTERS
62	Warner Bros WB 77	Let's Go/Mashy	5
63	Warner Bros WB 91	Make It Snappy/Half Time	5
63	Warner Bros WB 97	Stingray/Snap Happy	7
63	Warner Bros WB 108	Big Band/A Ooga	5
64	Warner Bros WB 139	Stamp And Shake/Ah Ya	5
63	Warner Bros WM/WS 8126	LET'S GO! WITH THE ROUTERS (LP)	20
64	Warner Bros WM/WS 8144	PLAY 1963'S GREAT INSTRUMENTALS (LP)	18
65	Warner Bros WM/WS 8162	CHARGE! (LP)	15

(see also Scott Walker)

MINT VALUE £

JONATHAN ROUTH
57 Nixa NPT 19016   CANDID MIKE (10" LP) 10

ROVERS
55 Capitol CL 14283   Ichi-Bon Tami, Dachi/Why Oh-h (Why Do You Lie To Me?) 25
55 Capitol CL 14283   Ichi-Bon Tami, Dachi/Why Oh-h (Why Do You Lie To Me?) (78) 10

ROVING KIND
65 Decca F 12264   Ain't It True/Don't Tell Me The Time 4
66 Decca F 12381   Lies A Million/How Many Times 4

ROWAN BROS
73 CBS 1125   All Together/Lady Of Laughter 4
(see also Earth Opera)

ROWDIES
78 Birds Nest BN 109   A.C.A.B. (All Coppers Are Bastards)/Negative Malfunction/Freeze Out 6
79 Teenage Depression TD 1/2   She's No Angel/Had Me A Real Good Time (p/s) 8
(see also Cockney & Westerns)

NORMIE ROWE
66 Polydor BM 56144   Ain't Nobody Home/Ooh La La 4
67 Polydor BM 56159   Goin' Home/I Don't Care 4

MAJOR ROWELY
65 Stateside SS 438   There's A Riot Going On/Do It The Right Way 6

JEFF ROWENA GROUP
61 Pye 7N 15328   Peanut Vendoe/Bullfight 4
61 Pye 7N 15365   Ambush/John Peel 4
62 Pye 7N 15423   La Cucuracha/Ten Ton Caroline 4
63 Oriole CB 1787   Dance Baby Dance/Diddle De Dum (as Jeff Rowena) 5
63 Oriole CB 1797   Dance Baby Dance/Love Me Once Again 5
63 Oriole CB 1810   Diddle De Dum/Lovely Water Melon 5
67 CBS 202460   Eleanor/Short Skirts (as Jeff Rowena) 4

STEVE ROWLAND
67 Fontana TF 844   So Sad/I See Red 8

JOHN ROWLES
68 MCA MU 1000   If I Only Had Time/Now Is The Hour 4
69 MCA MKPS 2001   THAT LOVIN' FEELING (LP) 10

ROX
82 Teentees ROX 100   HOT LOVE IN THE CITY (EP) 5
83 M. For Nations 12 KUT 103   KRAZY KUTZ (12" EP) 7
83 Music For Nations MFN 11   VIOLENT BREED (LP) 10

ROXETTE
89 EMI EM 87   The Look/Silver Blue (Demo Version) (p/s) 5
89 EMI 12EM 87   The Look (Head Drum Mix)/Silver Blue (Demo Version)/The Look
     (7" Version) (12", p/s) 10
89 EMI CDEM 87   The Look (Head Drum Mix)//The Look (7" Version)/Silver Blue
     (Demo Version)/Sleeping Single (Demo Version) (CD) 12
89 EMI EM 96   Dressed For Success/The Look (p/s) 4
89 EMI 12EM 96   Dressed For Success (The Mark McGuire Mix)/The Look
     (Big Red Mix)/Dressed For Success (7" Version) (12", p/s) 10
89 EMI CDEM 96   Dressed For Success (The Mark McGuire Mix)/The Look
     (Big Red Mix)/Dressed For Success (7" Version) (CD) 15
90 EMI EM 108   Listen To Your Heart/(I Could Never) Give You Up (p/s) 4
90 EMI 12EM 108   Listen To Your Heart/(I Could Never) Give You Up/Dressed For Success
     (Success Mix) (12", p/s) 10
90 EMI CDEM 108   Listen To Your Heart/(I Could Never) Give You Up/Dressed For Success
     (Success Mix) (CD) 12
90 EMI EM 141   It Must Have Been Love/Paint (p/s) 6
90 EMI 12EM 141   It Must Have Been Love/Paint/Cry (live) (12", p/s) 8
90 EMI CDEM 141   It Must Have Been Love/Paint/Cry (live)/Surrender (live) (CD) 10
90 EMI 12EM 149   Listen To Your Heart (Swedish Single Mix)/Listen To Your Heart (U.S. Club
     Edit Mix)/Listen To Your Heart (Dangerous LP Mix) (12", p/s, reissue) 7
90 EMI CDEM 149   Listen To Your Heart (Swedish Single Mix)/Listen To Your Heart (U.S. Club
     Edit Mix)/Listen To Your Heart (Dangerous LP Mix) (CD, reissue) 10
91 EMI CDEM 177   Joyride (U.S. Remix)/Come Back Before You Leave (CD, 4-track) 7
91 EMI CDEM 190   Fading Like A Flower (Everytime You Leave) (Gatica Remix)/The Look/
     Physical Fascination (Guitar Solo Version)/I Remember You (CD) 7
91 EMI EM 215   Spending My Time/Listen To Your Heart (poster p/s) 6
92 EMI EMS 241   How Do You Do/Fading Like A Flower (Every Time You Leave) (live)
     (postcard pack) 5

ROXY
70 Elektra EKSN 45084   Rock And Roll Circus/Somebody Told You 4
70 Elektra EKS 74063   ROXY (LP) 10

ROXY MUSIC
72 Island WIP 6144   Virginia Plain/The Numberer (initially pink labels, later orange labels) ......each 4
73 Island WIP 6159   Pyjamarama/The Pride And The Pain 4
74 Island WIP 6173   Street Life/Hula Kula 4
74 Island WIP 6208   All I Want Is You/Your Application's Failed 4
75 Island WIP 6248   Love Is The Drug/Sultanesque 4
76 Island WIP 6262   Both Ends Burning/For Your Pleasure 4
76 Island WIP 6306   Do The Strand/Editions Of You (unissued)
77 Polydor/EG 2001 739   Virginia Plain/Pyjamarama (reissue, p/s) 4
78 Polydor/EG 2001 756   Do The Strand/Editions Of You (no p/s) 4

78	Polydor/EG 2001 756	Do The Strand/Editions Of You (12", p/s)	7
79	Polydor/EG POSP 32	Trash/Trash 2 (p/s)	4
79	Polydor/EGPOSPX 67	Angel Eyes (Extended 6.39)/My Little Girl (12", p/s)	7
82	EG ROXYX 3	More Than This/India (12", p/s)	8
86	EG EGOX 26	Love Is The Drug/Let's Stick Together (12", p/s, promo only)	15
72	Island ILPS 9200	ROXY MUSIC (LP, with different inside photo, gatefold sleeve)	10
76	Island ILPS 9400	VIVA! ROXY MUSIC (LP)	10
79	Polydor/EG EGPD 001	MANIFESTO (LP, picture disc)	10
79	Polydor/EG EGPD 001	MANIFESTO (LP, picture disc, mispress, 1 side plays Gordon Giltrap's "Fear Of The Dark" LP)	12
79	Polydor/EG EG 001	MANIFESTO (LP, with normal versions of "Angel Eyes" & "Dance Away", different inner sleeve to later issue)	10
81	Polydor/EG EGBS 001	THE FIRST SEVEN ALBUMS (7-LP box set)	45
81	Polydor/EG EGBS 001	THE FIRST SEVEN ALBUMS (7-cassette box set)	40
83	EG 815 849-2	THE ATLANTIC YEARS 1973-1980 (CD)	15

(see also Brian Eno, Bryan Ferry, Andy McKay, Phil Manzanera, Dumbelles)

ROY & ANNETTE

| 63 | R&B JB 107 | My Baby/Go Your Ways | 10 |

ROY & DUKE ALL STARS

| 68 | Blue Cat BS 113 | Pretty Blue Eyes Pts 1 & 2 | 8 |
| 68 | Blue Cat BS 117 | The Train Pts 1 & 2 | 8 |

(see also Roy Panton)

ROY & ENID

68	Coxsone CS 7063	Rocking Time/RALPH BLAKE: High Blood Pressure	12
68	Coxsone CS 7069	He'll Have To Go/CARLTON & SHOES: Love Is A Treasure	12
69	Coxsone CS 7088	Reggae For Days/SOUND DIMENSION: Holy Moses	12

ROY & MILLIE

62	Island WI 005	We'll Meet/ROLAND ALPHONSO: Blackbeat	10
63	Island WI 050	This World/Never Say Goodbye	10
63	Island WI 090	There'll Come A Day/I Don't Want You	10
64	Black Swan WI 409	Cherry I Love You/You're The Only One	10
64	Black Swan WI 410	Oh Merna/DON DRUMMOND: Dog War Bossanova	10
64	Black Swan WI 427	Oh Shirley/Marie	10

(see also Roy Panton, Millie [Small])

ROY & PATSY

| 62 | Blue Beat BB 118 | In Your Arms Dear/My Happy Home | 8 |

(see also Roy Panton)

ROY (Richards) & PAULETTE

| 63 | Island WI 067 | Have You Seen My Baby/Since You're Gone | 10 |

ROY (Panton) & YVONNE (Harrison)

| 64 | Blue Beat BB 258 | Little Girl/No More | 8 |
| 64 | Black Swan WI 436 | Two Roads/Join Together | 8 |

(see also Roy Panton)

DEREK ROY

| 57 | Oriole CB 1415 | "Derek Roy's All-Star Party" (with Bob Monkhouse, Richard Murdoch, Jon Pertwee, Ted Ray & others) | 4 |

LEE ROY

| 65 | Island WI 251 | Oh Ee Baby/My Loving Baby Come Back | 8 |

HUGH ROY

70	Duke DU 105	Love I Tender/JOYA LANDIS: When The Lights Are Low	5
70	Duke Reid DR 2509	Wake The Town/Big Boy And Teacher	5
70	Duke Reid DR 2510	Rule The Nation/NORA DEAN: Ay Ay Ay Ay	5
70	Duke Reid DR 2513	Wear You To The Ball (with John Holt)/EARL LINDO: The Ball	5
70	Duke Reid DR 2514	You'll Never Get Away/TOMMY McCOOK QUINTET: Rock Away	5
70	Duke Reid DR 2515	Version Galore/TOMMY McCOOK: Nehru	5
70	Supreme SUP 211	Double Attack/Puzzle	4
70	Explosion EX 2040	Whisper A Little Prayer (act. by Delroy Wilson)/Rain A Fall (actually by Melanie)	4
70	Punch PH 34	Scandal/Son Of The Wise	4
70	Smash SMA 2313	Wake The Nation (with Jeff Barnes)/JEFF BARNES: 1,000 Tons Of Version	4
71	Duke Reid DR 2517	Tom Drunk (with Hopeton Lewis)/TOMMY McCOOK: Wailing	5
71	Duke Reid DR 2518	True True/On The Beach	5
71	Duke Reid DR 2519	Flashing My Whip/Do I Right	5
71	Treasure Isle TI 7059	Drive Her Home Pts 1 & 2 (with Hopeton Lewis)	5
71	Treasure Isle TI 7062	Behold/Way Back Home	5
71	Treasure Isle TI 7064	Everybody Bawlin'/Ain't That Loving You	5
71	Upsetter US 375	Earthquake/Suspicious Minds	5
71	Pama Supreme PS 328	Ginal Ship/UPSETTERS: Version 2	5
72	Banana BA 367	Keep On Running/LARRY'S ALLSTARS: Version	5
72	Camel CA 85	Rasta Bandwagon/When Jah Speaks	4
72	Camel CA 86	Public Enemy Number One/How Long Must We Wait	4
72	Prince Buster PB 11	River Jordan/Words Sound And Power	4
72	Grape GR 3026	On Top The Peak/TYPHOON ALLSTARS: Race Attack	4
72	Punch PH 104	Nannyscrank (title actually "Nanny Skank")/PITTS BURG ALLSTARS: Scank Version	4
72	Green Door GD 4034	Hudson Affair/KEITH HUDSON: Hot Stick Version	5
73	Green Door GD 4052	King Tubby's Special/Here Come The Heartaches	4
73	Gayfeet GS 210	Hard Feeling/Regular Style	4
73	Duke DU 157	Higher The Mountain/OLD BOYS INC.: Version	4
73	Harry J HJ 6651	Treasure Isle Skank/Words Of Wisdom	4

(see also U Roy)

I ROY

MINT VALUE £

I ROY

71	Moodisc MU 3509	Musical Pleasure/JO JO BENNETT: Hot Pop	4
71	Moodisc MU 3510	Heart Don't Leap (with Dennis Walks)/DENNIS WALKS & MUDIES ALLSTARS: Snowbird	5
71	Moodisc MU 3512	Let Me Tell You Boy (with Ebony Sisters)/MUDIES ALLSTARS: Version	5
71	Moodisc HM 104	The Drifter (with Dennis Walks)/JO JO BENNETT: Snowbird	5
72	Green Door GD 4030	Hot Bomb (with Jumpers)/JUMPERS: The Bomb	5
72	Green Door GD 4044	Make Love/STAGE: Tic Toc Bill	4
73	Pyramid PYR 7001	Tip From The Prince/Fat Beef Skank	5
73	Attack ATT 8050	Space Flight/JERRY LEWIS: Burning Wire	5
73	Downtown DT 503	Blackman's Time/High Jacking	5
73	Downtown DT 519	Clapper's Tail/Live And Learn	5
73	Duke DU 156	Buck And The Preacher/PETE WESTON ALLSTARS: Version	4
73	Smash SMA 2337	The Magnificent Seven/Leggo Beast	5
73	Smash SMA 2338	Rose Of Sharon/Slip Out	5
73	Techniques TE 926	Pauper And The King/GREGORY ISAACS: Loving Pauper	5
73	Techniques TE 930	Monkey Fashion/Medley Mood	4
73	Ackee ACK 503	Great Great Great (with Ken Parker)/RUPIE EDWARDS ALLSTARS: Version	4
73	Ackee ACK 510	Sound Education/AUGUSTUS PABLO: Cinderella In Black	4
74	Ashanti ASH 412	Mood For Love Pts 1 & 2	5
74	Trojan TRLS 63	PRESENTING I ROY (LP)	10
74	Trojan TRLS 71	HELL AND SORROW (LP)	10

MAD ROY

70	Banana BA 324	Nanny Version (actually by Dennis Alcapone)/BIGGER D: Freedom Version	6
71	Banana BA 326	Home Version (actually by Dennis Alcapone)/SOUND DIMENSION: One Time	6
71	Banana BA 327	Universal Love/ROLAND ALPHONSO: Shelly Belly	6

(pseudonym for Leroy Wallace; see also Dennis Alcapone)

U ROY

72	Duke Reid DR 2520	Rock To The Beat/Love Is Not A Gamble (both actually by Dennis Alcapone)	5
71	Trojan TBL 161	VERSION GALORE (LP)	15
73	Attack ATLP 1006	U ROY (LP)	10

(see also Hugh Roy, Dennis Alcapone)

BILLY JOE ROYAL

62	Oriole CB 1751	Never In A Hundred Years/We Haven't A Moment To Lose	10
65	CBS 201802	Down In The Boondocks/Oh! What A Night	6
65	CBS 201983	You Make Me Feel Like A Man/I've Got To Be Somebody	4
65	CBS 202009	I Knew You When/Steal Away	4
66	CBS 202052	It's A Good Time/Don't Wait Up For Me Mama	4
66	CBS 202087	Heart's Desire/Everybody's Gotta Cry	35
66	Atlantic 584 002	Never In A Hundred Years/We Haven't A Moment To Lose (reissue)	4
66	CBS 202400	High On A Hilltop/I'm Gonna Get Right Tonight	4
67	CBS 202548	Yo Yo/We Tried	7
67	CBS 2861	The Greatest Love/These Are Not My People	4
67	CBS 3044	Hush/Watching From The Bandstand	4
68	CBS 3402	Don't You Be Ashamed/Don't You Think It's Time	4
68	CBS 3644	Storybook Children/Just Between You And Me	4
69	CBS 4470	Cherry Hill Park/Helping Hand	4
66	CBS BPG 62590	INTRODUCING BILLY JOE ROYAL (LP)	12

BOBBY ROYAL

63	HMV POP 1253	Big Big Star/Little Word Of Love	4

JAMES ROYAL (& HAWKS)

65	Parlophone R 5290	She's About A Mover/Black Cloud (as James Royal & Hawks)	10
65	Parlophone R 5383	Work Song/I Can't Stand It	12
67	CBS 202525	Call My Name/When It Comes To My Baby	5
67	CBS 2739	It's All In The Game/Green Days	5
68	CBS 3232	I Can't Stand It/Little Bit Of Rain	5
68	CBS 2959	Take Me Like I Am/Sitting In The Station	4
68	CBS 3450	Hey Little Boy/Thru' The Love	15
68	CBS 3624	A Woman Called Sorrow/Fire	10
69	CBS 3797	Time Hangs On My Mind/Anna-Lee	5
69	CBS 3915	House Of Jack/Which Way To Nowhere	4
69	CBS 4139	I've Got Something Bad On My Mind/She's Independent	5
69	CBS 4463	Send Out Love/I've Lost You	10
70	CBS 5032	And Soon Darkness/I'm Going Home	4
71	Carnaby CNS 4021	Carolina/Big Heat On The Loose	4
67	CBS 63780	CALL MY NAME (LP)	15
71	Carnaby CNLS 6008	THE LIGHT AND SHADE OF JAMES ROYAL (LP)	12

ROBBIE ROYAL

65	Mercury MF 923	Only Me/I Don't Need You	8
65	Decca F 12097	Within My Lonely Heart/When I Found You	4

ROYAL AIR FORCE CENTRAL BAND

56	HMV B 10957	"Reach For The Sky" Theme/The Jolly Airman	4
57	Decca F 10932	High Flight/Out Of The Blue	4
61	HMV 7P 287	The Dambusters March/Lilliburlero	4
57	HMV 7EG 8265	R.A.F. CENTRAL BAND (EP)	7

ROYAL BLUES

68	Pye 7N 17670	Mountain Of Love	4
69	Pye 7N 17732	Mendocino/Hi-Lili Hi-Lo	4
69	Pye 7N 17769	Proud Mary/Sunny Girl Friend	4

ROYALETTES

65	MGM MGM 1272	Poor Boy/Watch What Happens	10

65	MGM MGM 1279	It's Gonna Take A Miracle/Out Of Sight Out Of Mind	20
65	MGM MGM 1292	I Want To Meet Him/Never Again	10
66	MGM MGM 1302	You Bring Me Down/Only When You're Lonely	15
66	MGM MGM 1324	It's A Big Mistake/I Want To Meet Him	10
68	Big T BIG 106	River Of Tears/Something Wonderful	7
66	MGM MGM-C 8028	THE ELEGANT SOUND OF THE ROYALETTES (LP)	25

ROYAL GUARDSMEN

67	Stateside SS 574	Snoopy Vs The Red Baron/I Needed You	5
67	Stateside SS 2010	The Return Of The Red Baron/Sweetmeats Slide	4
67	Stateside SS 2035	Airplane Song/OM	4
67	Stateside SS 2051	Wednesday/So Right (To Be In Love)	6
67	London HLP 10171	Snoopy's Christmas/It Kinda Looks Like Christmas	4
68	London HLP 10211	Snoopy For President/Down Behind The Lines	4
68	London HLP 10235	Baby Let's Wait/So Right	4
68	London HLP 10182	I Say Love/I'm Not Gonna Stay	4
67	Stateside S(S)L 10202	SNOOPY VS. THE RED BARON (LP)	12
68	London HA-P/SHP 8351	THE RETURN OF THE RED BARON (LP)	12

ROYAL HOLIDAYS

58	London HLU 8722	Margaret/I'm Sorry (I Did You Wrong)	45
58	London HLU 8722	Margaret/I'm Sorry (I Did You Wrong) (78)	15

ROYAL ROCKERS

60	Top Rank JAR 326	Jet II/Swinging Mambo	8

ROYALS

68	Amalgamated AMG 831	Never See Come See/CANNONBALL BRYAN TRIO: Jumping Jack	8
64	Blue Beat BB 259	Save Mama/Out De Fire	8
69	Trojan TR 662	Pick Out Me Eye/Think You Too Bad	7
69	Duke DU 29	Never Gonna Give You Up/Don't Mix Up	6

ROYAL TEENS

58	HMV POP 454	Short Shorts/Planet Rock	25
58	HMV POP 454	Short Shorts/Planet Rock (78)	18
59	Capitol CL 15068	Little Cricket/Believe Me	15

ROYALTONES

58	London HLJ 8744	Poor Boy/Wail!	12
58	London HLJ 8744	Poor Boy/Wail! (78)	18
61	London HLU 9296	Flamingo Express/Tacos	10
64	Stateside SS 309	Our Faded Love/Holy Smokes	10

ROYALTY

69	CBS 4181	That Kind Of Girl/Will You Be Staying After Sunday	4

EARL ROYCE & OLYMPICS

64	Columbia DB 7433	Que Sera Sera/I Really Do	10
65	Parlophone R 5261	Guess Things Happen That Way/Sure To Fall	10

ROY'S BOYS

64	Columbia DB 7425	Do Wah Diddy Diddy/Oh! Pretty Woman	4

LITA ROZA

52	Decca F 9955	Oakie Boogie/Raminay (78)	8
53	Decca F 10070	(How Much Is) That Doggie In The Window/Tell Me We'll Meet Again (78)	5
53	Decca F 10144	Crazy Man, Crazy/Oo! What You Do To Me (78)	6
54	Decca F 10363	Skinnie ˉinnie (Fishtail)/My Kid Brother (78)	6
54	Decca F 10240	Changing Partners/Just A Dream Or Two Ago (B-side with Stargazers)	8
54	Decca F 10269	Bell Bottom Blues (with Johnston Brothers)/Make Love To Me (both with Ted Heath Orchestra)	10
54	Decca F 10277	Young At Heart/Secret Love	8
54	Decca F 10393	Call Off The Wedding/The "Mama-Doll" Song	6
55	Decca F 10427	Heartbeat/Leave Me Alone	8
55	Decca F 10431	Let Me Go, Lover!/Make Yourself Comfortable	8
55	Decca F 10479	Tomorrow/Foolishly	8
55	Decca F 10536	Two Hearts, Two Kisses (Make One Love)/Keep Me In Mind	8
55	Decca F 10541	The Man In The Raincoat/Today And Ev'ry Day	6
55	Decca F 10611	Hey There/Hernando's Hideaway	12
56	Decca F 10679	Jimmy Unknown/The Rose Tattoo	12
56	Decca F 10728	Too Young To Go Steady/You're Not Alone	6
56	Decca F 10761	No Time For Tears/But Love Me (Love But Me)	6
56	Decca F 10792	Innismore/The Last Waltz	6
56	Decca F 10830	Hey! Jealous Lover/Julie	6
57	Decca F 10861	Lucky Lips/Tears Don't Care Who Cries Them	8
57	Decca F 10884	Tonight My Heart She Is Crying/Five Oranges, Four Apples	6
57	Decca F 10921	I Need You/You've Changed	5
58	Pye 7N 15119	Pretend You Don't See Him/Ha-Ha-Ha!	4
58	Pye 7N 15133	I Need Somebody/You're The Greatest	4
58	Pye 7N 15139	I Could Have Danced All Night/The Wonderful Season Of Love	4
58	Pye 7N 15149	Sorry, Sorry, Sorry/Hillside In Scotland	4
58	Pye 7N 15155	Nel Blu Dipinto Di Blu (Volare)/It's A Boy	4
59	Pye 7N 15190	This Is My Town/Oh Dear What Can The Matter Be	4
59	Pye 7N 15204	Allentown Jail/Once In A While	4
59	Pye 7N 15241	Let It Rain, Let It Rain/Maybe You'll Be There	4
63	Ember EMB S 168	Mama (He Treats Your Daughter Mean)/(He's My) Dreamboat (as Lisa Rosa)	7
57	Decca DFE 6386	LITA ROZA SELECTION (EP)	12
57	Decca DFE 6399	LITA ROZA (EP)	12
58	Decca DFE 6443	BETWEEN THE DEVIL AND THE DEEP BLUE SEA NO. 1 (EP)	12
54	Decca LF 1187	PRESENTING LITA ROZA (10" LP)	25
56	Decca LF 1243	LISTENING IN THE AFTER HOURS (10" LP)	25

Lita ROZA

57	Decca LK 4171	LOVE IS THE ANSWER (LP)	18
57	Decca LK 4218	BETWEEN THE DEVIL AND THE DEEP BLUE SEA (LP)	18
57	Decca LK 4219	THE NIGHT IS YOUNG (LP)	18
58	Pye Nixa NPL 18020	ME ON A CAROUSEL (LP, also stereo NSPL 83003)	12/15
60	Pye NPL 18047	DRINKA LITA ROZA DAY (LP)	10
64	Ember NR 5009	LOVE SONGS FOR NIGHT PEOPLE (LP)	10

(see also Stargazers, Johnston Brothers)

RUB-A-DUBS
64	Blue Beat BB 304	Without Love/I Know	8

(see also Dandy)

RUBBER BAND
73	Youngblood YB 1052	Moonwalker/Wichita	4
69	Major Minor SMCP 5045	CREAM SONGBOOK (LP)	12
69	Major Minor SMCP 5048	HENDRIX SONGBOOK (LP)	12

RUBBER BOOTZ
67	Deram DM 134	Joy Ride/Chicano	8

RUBBER BUCKET
69	MCA MK 5006	We Are Living In One Place/Take Me Away	12

(see also Gary Glitter)

RUBELLA BALLET
82	Xntrix XN 2005	The Ballet Dance/Something To Give/Unemployed/Krak Trak (p/s)	4
82	Xntrix	BALLET DOG (C-30 cassette)	6

RUBIN
75	MCA MU 196	You've Been Away/Baby, You're My Everything	5

RUBIAYATS
68	Action ACT 4516	Omar Khayam/Tomorrow	5

RUBY
77	PBR Int. PBRL 5001	RUBY (LP)	10
78	PBR Int. PBRL 5003	ROCK'N'ROLL MADNESS (LP)	10

(see also Tom Fogerty)

RUBY & ROMANTICS
63	London HLR 9679	Our Day Will Come/Moonlight And Music	6
63	London HLR 9734	My Summer Love/Sweet Love And Sweet Forgiveness	7
63	London HLR 9771	Hey There Lonely Boy/Not A Moment Too Soon	7
63	London HLR 9801	Young Wings Can Fly/Day Dreaming	6
64	London HLR 9881	Our Everlasting Love/Much Better Off Than I've Ever Been	6
64	London HLR 9916	Baby Come Home/Every Day's A Holiday	6
64	London HLR 9935	When You're Young And In Love/I Cry Alone	7
65	London HLR 9972	Your Baby Doesn't Love Me Anymore/We'll Meet Again	7
63	London RER 1389	OUR DAY WILL COME (EP)	20
64	London RER 1427	HEY THERE LONELY BOY (EP)	20
63	London HA-R 8078	OUR DAY WILL COME (LP)	35
66	London HA-R 8282	GREATEST HITS (LP)	25

RUDE BOYS
67	Island WI 3088	Rock Steady Massachusetts/Going Home	8

RUDI
78	Good Vibrations GOT 1	Big Time/Number 1 (folded p/s, 3000 only)	4
79	Good Vibrations GOT 12	I Spy/Genuine Reply/Sometimes/Ripped In Two (p/s)	5

RUDIES (FANATICS)
68	Blue Cat BS 107	The 7-11 Go To The Go Go Club Pts 1 & 2	10
68	Blue Cat BS 109	Cupid/RECO'S ALLSTARS: Wise Message	10
68	Nu Beat NB 001	Train To Vietnam/Skaville To Rainbow City	6
68	Nu Beat NB 005	Engine 59/My Girl	5
68	Fab FAB 46	I Wanna Go Home/La Mer	7
68	Fab FAB 70	Give Me The Rights/I Do Love You (as Rudies Fanatics)	5
68	Fab FAB 71	Mighty Meaty/Go (as Rudies Fanatics)	5
69	Doctor Bird DB 1302	Boss Sound/RECO & RUDIES: Peace	6
69	Fab FAB 104	Brixton Market/Rudie's Joy	5
71	Spinning Wheel SW 106	My Sweet Lord/Devil's Lead Soup	4

(see also Freddie Notes, Sonny, Binns & Rudies)

RUDIMENTARY PENI
81	Outer Himalayan OH 003	FARCE (EP, A4 foldout p/s with booklet, later 14" x 7")	8/7

(see also Magits)

RUDY (Grant) & SKETTO (Rich)
62	Dice CC 5	Summer Is Just Around The Corner/Nothing Like Time (as Rudy & Sketto with Reco's Group)	6
62	Dice CC 7	Little Schoolgirl/Hush Baby (as Rudy & Sketto with Reco's Group)	6
62	Dice CC 10	Mr Postman/Christmas Blues (as Rudy & Sketto with Laurel's Group)	6
63	Dice CC 16	Hold The Fire/Good Morning Mr Jones	6
63	Dice CC 19	Never Set You Free/Brothers And Sisters	6
64	Blue Beat BB 230	Ten Thousand Miles Away/I Need Someone	6
64	Blue Beat BB 252	Minna I LoveYou So/If Only Tomorrow	6
65	Blue Beat BB 297	See What You Done/Heart's Desire	6

RUEFREX
80	Good Vibrations GOT 8	One By One/Cross The Line/Don't Panic (2 different foldover sleeves)	6
83	Kabuki KAR 7	Capital Letters/April Fool (p/s)	4

RAY RUFF & CHECKMATES
64	London HLU 9889	I Took A Liking To You/A Fool Again	15

RUFFIANS
71	Banana BA 359	Room Full Of Tears (actually by Sensations)/Black Soul (actually "Black And White Version" by Riley's Allstars)	5

BRUCE RUFFIN
69	Songbird SB 1002	Long About Now/Come See About Me (as Bruce Ruffin & Temptations)	5
69	Trojan TR 7704	Dry Up Your Tears/BEVERLEY'S ALLSTARS: One Way Street	5
70	Trojan TR 7737	I'm The One/Who's Gonna Be Your Man?	4
71	Trojan TR TRL 23	RAIN (LP)	10

(see also Temptations)

DAVID RUFFIN
69	Tamla Motown TMG 689	My Whole World Ended (The Moment You Left Me)/I Gotta Find Myself A Brand New Baby	4
69	Tamla Motown TMG 711	I've Lost Everything I've Ever Loved/We'll Have A Good Thing Going On	4
76	Tamla Motown TMG 1022	Heavy Love/Me And Rock And Roll Are Here To Stay	5
69	T. Motown (S)TML 11108	MY WHOLE WORLD ENDED (LP)	15
70	T. Motown (S)TML 11139	FEELIN' GOOD (LP)	12

(see also Temptations)

JIMMY RUFFIN
66	Tamla Motown TMG 577	What Becomes Of The Broken-Hearted?/Baby I've Got It	6
67	Tamla Motown TMG 593	I've Passed This Way Before/Tomorrow's Tears	6
67	Tamla Motown TMG 603	Gonna Give Her All The Love I Got/World So Wide, Nowhere To Hide	6
67	Tamla Motown TMG 617	Don't You Miss Me A Little Bit Baby/I Want Her Love	6
68	Tamla Motown TMG 649	I'll Say Forever My Love/Everybody Needs Love	5
68	Tamla Motown TMG 664	Don't Let Him Take Your Love From Me/Lonely Lonely Man Am I	6
70	Tamla Motown TMG 726	Farewell Is A Lonely Sound/If You Let Me, I Know I Can	4
71	Tamla Motown TMG 767	Let's Say Goodbye Tomorrow/Living In A World I Created For Myself	4
74	Polydor 2058 433	Tell Me What You Want/Going Home (p/s)	4
67	T. Motown (S)TML 11048	THE JIMMY RUFFIN WAY (LP)	18
69	T. Motown (S)TML 11106	RUFF 'N' READY (LP)	15
70	T. Motown STML 11161	JIMMY RUFFIN — FOREVER (LP)	10
74	Polydor 2383 240	JIMMY RUFFIN (LP)	10

JIMMY & DAVID RUFFIN
70	Tamla Motown STML 11176	I AM MY BROTHER'S KEEPER (LP)	12

(see also Temptations, David Ruffin)

RUFUS
74	ABC 4022	You Got The Love/Rags To Rufus	4
75	ABC 4038	Stop On By/Rufusized	5
75	ABC 4055	Once You Get Started/Right Is Right (p/s)	5
75	ABC ABCL 5151	RUFUS WITH CHAKA KHAN (LP)	12

(see also Chaka Khan)

PETE RUGOLO (& DIAMONDS)
61	Mercury AMT 1147	Marie/Moonglow And Theme From Picnic (as Pete Rugolo & His Perfect Presence Sound Orchestra)	5
58	Emarcy ERE 1577	MUSIC FOR HI-FI BUGS VOL. 1 (EP)	7
58	Emarcy ERE 1578	MUSIC FOR HI-FI BUGS VOL. 2 (EP)	7
59	Mercury ZEP 10020	THE DIAMONDS MEET PETE RUGOLO (EP)	20
60	Mercury ZEP 10084	RUGOLO PLAYS KENTON (EP, also stereo SEZ 19000)	7/8
61	Mercury ZEP 10097	PETE RUGOLO LEADS DIAMONDS (EP, also stereo SEZ 19012)	20/25
61	Mercury ZEP 10099	THE MASTERPIECES OF KENTON (EP, also stereo SEZ 19015)	7/8
54	Philips BBR 8024	PETE RUGOLO AND HIS ORCHESTRA (10" LP)	12
57	Mercury MPL 6517	BRASS IN HI-FI (LP)	10
57	Emarcy EJL 1254	FOR HI-FI BUGS (LP)	10
58	Emarcy EJL 1274	OUT ON A LIMB (LP)	10
59	Mercury MMC 14012	ADVENTURES IN SOUND — REEDS IN HI-FI (LP)	10
60	Mercury MMC 14034	"RICHARD DIAMOND" MUSIC (LP, also stereo CMS 18025)	10/12
60	Warner Bros WM 4001	BEHIND BRIGITTE BARDOT — COOL SOUNDS FROM HER HOT SCENES (LP, also stereo WS 8001)	10

(see also Diamonds)

BARBARA RUICK
52	MGM MGM 550	Tick Tock Boogie/Serenade To A Lemonade (78)	5
53	MGM SP 1044	Delishious/The Price I Paid For Loving	4

RULERS
66	Rio R 105	Don't Be A Rude Boy/Be Good	10
66	Rio R 107	Copasetic/Too Late	10
67	Rio R 132	Wrong Embryo/Why Don't You Change	10
67	Rio R 135	Well Covered/CARL DAWKINS: Help Time	10
67	Rio R 138	Be Mine/CARL DAWKINS: Hot And Sticky	8
69	Trojan TR 696	Got To Be Free/Situation	5

RUMBLEFISH
87	Pink PINKY 16	Tug Boat Line/Dum-Dum/Rave (p/s)	4
87	Pink PINKY 16T	Tug Boat Line/Dum-Dum/Everything Electrical/Theatre King/Rave (12", p/s)	7

RUMBLERS
63	London HLD 9684	Boss/I Don't Need You No More	15
65	King KG 1021	Soulful Jerk/Hey Did A Da Da	30
63	London RED 1396	BOSSOUNDS (EP)	30
63	London HA-D/SH-D 8081	BOSSOUNDS (LP, mono/stereo)	40/50

RUMOUR
79	Stiff BUY 45	Emotional Traffic/Hard Enough To Show (p/s, red, amber or green vinyl)	4

(see also Graham Parker & Rumour, Brinsley Schwarz)

Rambling Syd RUMPO

RAMBLING SYD RUMPO
67	Parlophone R 5638	The Ballad Of The Wogglers Moulie/Green Grow My Nadgers Oh!	4

(see also Kenneth Williams)

RUMPLESTILTSKIN
70	Bell BLL 1101	Squadron Leader Johnson/Rumplestiltskin	4
69	Bell SBLL 130	RUMPLESTILTSKIN (LP, gatefold sleeve)	25

RUNAWAYS
76	Mercury 6167 392	Cherry Bomb/Blackmail	5
77	Mercury 6167 493	Queens Of Noise/Born To Be Bad	4
77	Mercury 6167 587	School Days/Wasted	4
76	Mercury 9100 029	THE RUNAWAYS (LP, orange vinyl)	12
79	Cherry Red ARED 38	AND NOW ... THE RUNAWAYS (LP, blue vinyl)	12

(see also Joan Jett)

RUN DMC
86	London LON 118	You Be Illin'/Hit It Run (p/s, with 'Dictionary Of Rap' booklet)	4
87	London LONG 163	Christmas In Hollis/Peter Piper (gatefold p/s)	4
85	4th + Broadway PBRLP504	KING OF ROCK (LP, picture disc)	10

TODD RUNDGREN
72	Bearsville K 15502	I Saw The Light/Marlene	4
82	Avatar AVAB 1	TIME HEALS (EP, picture disc)	4
74	Bearsville K 85501	TODD (2-LP, with giant poster)	14
81	Island ILPS 9567	HEALING (LP with free 7": "Time Heals"/"Tiny Diamonds" [PSR 455])	10

(see also Nazz, Utopia, Runt)

RUNNING MAN
72	RCA Neon NE 11	RUNNING MAN (LP)	120

RUNRIG
82	Ridge RRS 103	Loch Lomond/Tuireadh Lain Ruaida (p/s)	12
84	Simple SIM 4	Dance Called America/Na H Uaina's T Earrach (p/s)	6
84	Simple 12 SIM 4	Dance Called America/Na H Uaina's T Earrach (12", p/s)	8
84	Simple SIM 8	Skye/Hey Mandu (p/s)	7
84	Neptune NA 105	PLAY GAELIC (LP)	20

RUNT
71	Bearsville K 44505	RUNT (LP)	15
71	Bearsville K 44506	RUNT — THE BALLAD OF TODD RUNDGREN (LP)	15

(see also Todd Rundgren, Utopia, Nazz)

RUN 229
80	MM JR 7040S	Soho/Dance/In This Day And Age (p/s)	12

R.U.1.2.
78	SRTS/78/CUS 131	She's Gone/Purely Physical/Teenage Girl (p/s)	5

RUPERT'S PEOPLE
67	Columbia DB 8226	Reflections Of Charles Brown/Hold On	20
67	Columbia DB 8278	A Prologue To A Magic World/Dream In My Mind	30
68	Columbia DB 8362	I Can Show You/I've Got The Love	30

(see also Renaissance, Fleur De Lys, Gun)

RUSH (Australia)
67	Decca F 12614	Happy/Once Again	6
67	Decca F 12635	Make Mine Music/Enjoy It	7

RUSH (Canada)
77	Mercury RUSH 7	Closer To The Heart/Bastille Day/Temples Of Syrinx (no p/s)	4
78	Mercury RUSH 12	Closer To The Heart/Anthem/Bastille Day/The Temples Of Syrinx (12", p/s)	8
80	Mercury RADIO 7	Spirit Of Radio/The Trees (p/s)	4
80	Mercury RADIO 12	Spirit Of Radio/The Trees/Working Man (12", p/s)	7
81	Mercury VITAL 7	Vital Signs/In The Mood (p/s)	4
81	Mercury VITAL 12	Vital Signs/In The Mood/A Passage To Bangkok/Circumstances (12", p/s)	7
81	Mercury EXIT 7	Tom Sawyer (live)/A Passage To Bangkok (live) (p/s)	4
81	Mercury EXIT 12	Tom Sawyer (live)/A Passage To Bangkok/Red Barchetta (live) (12", p/s)	7
81	Mercury RUSH 1	Closer To The Heart (live)/The Trees (live) (p/s)	4
82	Mercury RUSH 8	New World Man/Vital Signs (live) (p/s)	4
82	Mercury RUSH 812	New World Man/Vital Signs (live)/Freewill (live) (12", p/s)	7
82	Mercury RUSH 9	Subdivisions/Red Barchetta (live) (p/s)	4
82	Mercury RUSH P9	Subdivisions/Red Barchetta (live) (picture disc)	7
82	Mercury RUSH 912	Subdivisions/Red Barchetta (live)/Jacob's Ladder (live) (12", p/s)	7
82	Mercury RUSH 10	Countdown/New World Man (p/s)	4
82	Mercury RUSH 10 PD	Countdown/New World Man (shaped picture disc)	20
82	Mercury RUSH 1012	Countdown/New World Man/Spirit Of Radio (live)/Interview Excerpts (12", p/s)	7
84	Vertigo RUSH 11	The Body Electric/The Analog Kid (p/s)	4
84	Vertigo RUSH 1110	Body Electric/The Analog Kid/Distant Early Warning (10", p/s, red vinyl)	12
84	Vertigo RUSH 1112	(The) Body Electric/The Analog Kid/Distant Early Warning (12", p/s)	25
85	Vertigo RUSH D12	The Big Money/Territories//Closer To The Heart/Spirit Of Radio (double pack)	5
85	Vertigo RUSH 1212	The Big Money/Territories/Red Sector A (live) (12", p/s)	7
85	Vertigo RUSH G1212	The Big Money/Middletown Dreams/The Grand Design (12", gatefold p/s, maybe unissued)	20+
87	Vertigo RUSH 13	Time Stand Still/Force Ten (cut-out p/s)	4
87	Vertigo RUSH P1312	Time Stand Still/Force Ten/The Enemy Within (live) (12", picture disc)	7
87	Vertigo RUSH CD 13	Time Stand Still/Force Ten/The Enemy Within (live)/Witch Hunt (live) (CD)	8
88	Vertigo RUSH R14	Prime Mover/Distant Early Warning (live) (p/s, white vinyl)	4
88	Vertigo RUSH R1412	Prime Mover/Tai Shan/Distant Early Warning (live)/New World Man (live) (12", 3-D p/s)	7
88	Vertigo RUSH CD 14	Prime Mover/Tai Shan/Distant Early Warning (live)/New World Man (live) (CD, numbered)	10

91	Atlantic A 7524TE	Roll The Bones/The Pass/It's A Rap Part 1 (square picture disc) 5
77	Mercury 6672 015	ALL THE WORLD'S A STAGE (2-LP, with photo page in gatefold sleeve) 20
85	Vertigo VERHP 31	POWER WINDOWS (LP, picture disc, with sleeve) 16

(see also McKenzie Doug & Bob)

MERRILEE RUSH & TURNABOUTS
68	Bell BLL 1013	Angel Of The Morning/Reap What You Sow 4
68	Bell BLL 1026	That Kind Of Woman/Sunshine And Roses 4
69	Bell BLL 1041	Reach Out I'll Be There/Love Street 4
68	Bell SBLL 109	MERRILEE RUSH (LP) 10

OTIS RUSH
66	Vocalion V-P 9260	Homework/I Have To Laugh 15
69	Blue Horizon 57-3159	All Your Love/Double Trouble 12
68	Blue Horizon 7-63222	THIS ONE'S A GOOD UN (LP) 40
69	Atlantic 588 188	MOURNING IN THE MORNING (LP) 25
69	Atlantic K 40495	MOURNING IN THE MORNING (LP, reissue) 10
70	Python KM 3	GROANING THE BLUES (LP) 25
76	Delmark DS 63?	COLD DAY IN HELL (LP) 10
78	Sonet SNTF756	TROUBLES, TROUBLES (LP) 12

TOM RUSH
67	Elektra EKSN 45005	Who Do You Love/On The Road Again 5
67	Elektra EKSN 45015	On The Road Again/Love's Made A Fool Of You 5
68	Elektra EKSN 45025	No Regrets/Shadow Dream Song 4
68	Elektra EKSN 45032	Something In The Way She Moves Me/Who Do You Love 4
66	Xtra XTRA 5024	BLUES, SONGS & BALLADS (LP) 12
66	Xtra XTRA 5053	I GOT A MIND TO RAMBLE (LP) 12
67	Elektra EKL 308	TAKE A LITTLE WALK WITH ME (LP, also stereo EKS 7308) 15
68	Elektra EKL 4018	THE CIRCLE GAME (LP, red label, also stereo EKS 74018) 15
69	Elektra EKL 4062	CLASSIC RUSH (LP, red label, also stereo EKS 74062) 15
70	CBS 63940	TOM RUSH (LP) 10
70	CBS 64268	WRONG END OF A RAINBOW (LP) 10
72	CBS 64887	MERRIMACK COUNTRY (LP) 10

PATRICE RUSHEN
| 77 | Prestige PR 10101 | SHOUT IT OUT (LP) . . . . .10 |

MARTIN RUSHENT
| 79 | Albion DEL 1 | Give It All You've Got/Why Bother To Fight (p/s) . . . . .4 |

JIMMY RUSHING (& ADA MOORE)
50s	Philips BBE 12150	CAT MEETS CHICK (EP, as Jimmy Rushing & Ada Moore) 12
57	Vanguard EPP 14003	LITTLE JIMMY ALL STAR BAND (EP) 10
57	Parlophone GEP 8597	JIMMY RUSHING (EP) 10
58	Parlophone GEP 8695	THE WAY I FEEL (EP) 10
63	Ember EMB 4523	JIMMY RUSHING (EP) 8
55	Vanguard PPT 12002	SINGS THE BLUES (10" LP) 30
57	Vanguard PPT 12016	SHOWCASE (LP) 15
57	Philips BBL 7105	CAT MEETS CHICK (LP, with Ada Moore & Buck Clayton) 20
57	Philips BBL 7166	THE JAZZ ODYSSEY OF JAMES RUSHING ESQ (LP, with Buck Clayton) 20
58	Vanguard PPL 11008	IF THIS AIN'T THE BLUES (LP) 15
58	Philips BBL 7252	LITTLE JIMMY RUSHING AND THE BIG BRASS (LP, also
		stereo SBBL 524) 20
60	Philips BBL 7360	RUSHING LULLABIES (LP) 20
61	Philips BBL 7484	THE SMITH GIRLS — BESSIE, CLARA (LP, also
		stereo SBBL 631) 20/25
66	Ace Of Hearts AH 119	BLUES I LOVE TO SING (LP) 15
67	Golden Guinea GGL 0384	FIVE FEET OF SOUL (LP) 12
67	Fontana FJL 405	LISTEN TO THE BLUES (LP) 15
67	HMV CLP/CSD 3632	EVERYDAY I HAVE THE BLUES (LP) 15
71	Vanguard VRS 8513	IF THIS AIN'T THE BLUES (LP, reissue) 10

(see also Count Basie)

JIMMY RUSHING/CHAMPION JACK DUPREE
| 62 | Ember CJS 800 | TWO SHADES OF BLUE (LP, 1 side each) . . . . .15 |

(see also Champion Jack Dupree, Dave Brubeck)

BARBARA RUSKIN
65	Piccadilly 7N 35224	Halfway To Paradise/I Can't Believe In Miracles 4
65	Piccadilly 7N 35246	You Can't Blame A Girl For Trying/No More To Fall 4
66	Piccadilly 7N 35274	Well How Does It Feel/Wishing Your Life Away 4
66	Piccadilly 7N 35289	Song Without End/Love Came Too Late 4
66	Piccadilly 7N 35328	Light Of Love/At Times Like These Mama 4

ROGER RUSKIN SPEAR
| 72 | United Artists UAG 29381 | ELECTRIC SHOCKS (LP) . . . . .15 |

(see also Bonzo Dog Band)

LONNIE RUSS
| 62 | Fontana 267263 TF | Something Old Something New/My Wife Can't Cook . . . . .5 |

THANE RUSSAL (& THREE)
| 66 | CBS 202049 | Security/Your Love Is Burning Me (some with p/s) . . . . .100/50 |
| 66 | CBS 202403 | Drop Everything And Run/I Need You (solo) . . . . .40 |

BOBBY RUSSELL
68	Bell BLL 1019	Dusty/I Made You This Way 4
68	Bell BLL 1034	1432 Franklin Pike Circle Hero/Let's Talk About It 4
69	Bell BLL 1050	Carlie/Ain't Society Great? 4

BRENDA RUSSELL
| 79 | A&M AMLJ 739 | BRENDA RUSSELL (LP) . . . . .10 |

CONNIE RUSSELL
54	Capitol CL 14171	No One But You/One Arabian Night	10
54	Capitol CL 14197	Love Me/Papa's Puttin' The Pressure On	8
55	Capitol CL 14214	Foggy Night In San Francisco/This Is My Love	8
55	Capitol CL 14236	Ayuh, Ayuh/I'm Making Believe	10
55	Capitol CL 14246	Snow Dreams/Green Fire	7
55	Capitol CL 14268	Farewell, Farewell/The Magnificent Matador	6
57	Capitol CL 14676	All Of You/This Is My Love	5

DOROTHY RUSSELL
71	Duke Reid DR 2524	You're The One I Love/Version	4

JANE RUSSELL
51	London L 969	Five Little Miles From San Berdoo/You'll Know (78)	5
53	Columbia SCM 5043	Please Do It Again/Two Sleepy People (B-side with Bob Lowery)	8
53	Columbia DB 3293	Please Do It Again/Two Sleepy People (B-side with Bob Lowery) (78)	5
53	MGM MGM 662	A Little Girl From Little Rock/When Love Goes Wrong (78)	7
56	Capitol CL 14590	If You Wanna See Mamie Tonight/Keep Your Eyes On The Hands	6
59	MGM MGM-EP 702	JANE RUSSELL (EP)	15

JOHNNY RUSSELL
60	MGM MGM 1074	Lonesome Boy/Baby Won't You Tell Me So	7

KEITH RUSSELL
65	Piccadilly 7N 35235	People Get Ready/Paradise	4

LEON RUSSELL
65	Dot DS 16771	Everybody's Talkin' 'Bout The Young/It's Alright With Me	10
70	A&M AMLS 982	LEON RUSSELL (LP, with Shelter People)	12
71	A&M AMLS 65003	LEON RUSSELL AND THE SHELTER PEOPLE (LP)	10
71	A&M AMLS 68089	ASYLUM CHOIR II (LP, as Leon Russell & Asylum Choir, with Marc Benno)	10
72	A&M AMLS 68911	CARNEY (LP)	10
	(see also Asylum Choir)		

PAULA RUSSELL
75	Black Magic BM 101	Blowin' My Mind To Pieces/BOB RELF: Blowin' My Mind To Pieces	5

PEE WEE RUSSELL & RUBY BRAFF
57	London Jazz LTZ-C 15061	JAZZ AT STORYVILLE VOL. 2 (LP)	10

RAY RUSSELL QUARTET
68	CBS Realm 52586	TURN CIRCLE (LP)	15
69	CBS Realm 52663	DRAGON HILL (LP)	15
71	RCA SF 8214	JUNE 11th 1971 (LP)	12
71	CBS 64271	RITES AND RITUALS (LP)	15
73	Black Lion BLP 12100	SECRET ASYLUM (LP)	12

ROLAND RUSSELL
68	Nu Beat NB 019	Rhythm Hips/RHYTHM FLAMES: Deltone Special	5

ROSALIND RUSSELL & EDITH ADAMS
55	Brunswick 05406	Ohio/Little Bit Of Love	4

CHARLES RUSSO
63	Stateside SS 165	Preacherman/Teresa	4

RUSTIKS
64	Decca F 11960	What A Memory Can Do/Hello Anne	6
65	Decca F 12059	I'm Not The Loving Kind/Can't You See	5

RUSTLERS
61	Pye 7N 15398	High Strung/Matter Of Who	4

RUSTY & DOUG (Kershaw)
59	Oriole CB 1510	Hey Mae!/Why Don't You Love Me	100
59	Oriole CB 1510	Hey Mae!/Why Don't You Love Me (78)	75
59	London HL 8972	I Like You (Like This)/Dancing Shoes	20
59	London HL 8972	I Like You (Like This)/Dancing Shoes (78)	8
62	Polydor NH 66970	Hey Mae!/Sweet Thing	25
62	Fontana 267 238 TF	Cajun Joe (The Ballad Of The Bayou)/Sweet Sweet Girl To Me	12
	(see also Doug Kershaw)		

RUSTY HARNESS
70	Ember EMB S 283	Ain't Gonna Get Married/Goodbye (some in p/s)	5/10

RUTH
67	Columbia DB 8216	Leaf In The Wind/Society's Child	4
68	Columbia DB 8386	Cherish/Until It's Time For You To Go	4

RUTLES
78	Warner Bros K 17125	I Must Be In Love/Cheese And Onions/With A Girl Like You (p/s)	4
78	Warner Bros K 17180	Let's Be Natural/Piggy In The Middle	5
	(see also Dirk & Stig, Neil Innes, Monty Python, Beach Boys, Patto)		

MIKE RUTHERFORD
80	Charisma CB 353	Working In Line/Compression (no p/s)	4
80	Charisma CB 364	Time And Time Again/At The End Of The Day (p/s, mispressed, B-side plays "Overnight Job", 6,500 only)	5
80	Charisma CB 364	Time And Time Again/Overnight Job (p/s, new label on B-side)	7
80	Charisma CB 364	Time And Time Again/At The End Of The Day (p/s, correct B-side & label)	10
	(see also Genesis, Mike & Mechanics)		

PAUL RUTHERFORD
88	4th & Broadway BRCDP 113	Get Real (Happy House Mix)/Get Real (Radio)/Happy Face (CD, picture disc)	7
	(see also Frankie Goes To Hollywood)		

RUTS (D.C.)

79	People Unite RUT 1	In A Rut/H-Eyes (no p/s, original supposedly with black ringed label)	8/5
80	Virgin VS 327	Staring At The Rude Boys/Love In Vain (gatefold p/s)	4
80	RSO RSO 71	Babylon's Burning/XTC: Take This Town	6
83	Bohemian 12 BO 3	Weak Heart/Accusation/Militant (12", die-cut p/s, as Ruts DC)	7
83	Bohemian BO 4	Stepping Bondage/Lobotomy/Rich Bitch (p/s)	10
87	Strange Fruit SFPSC 011	PEEL SESSION (EP, cassette)	5

(see also Typhoons, Pete Zear)

BARRY RYAN (& MAJORITY)

68	MGM MGM 1423	Goodbye/I'm So Sad	4
68	MGM MGM 1442	Eloise/Love I Almost Found You (as Barry Ryan & Majority)	4
68	MGM MGM 1464	Love Is Love/I'll Be On My Way Dear	5
69	Polydor 56348	The Hunt/Oh, For The Love Of Me	5
68	MGM CS 8106	SINGS PAUL RYAN (LP)	15
69	Polydor 583 067	BARRY RYAN (LP)	12

(see also Paul & Barry Ryan)

CATHY RYAN

53	MGM SP 1051	Show Me The Way To Go Home/If I Had You	5

(see also Art Mooney)

KRIS RYAN (& QUESTIONS)

64	Mercury MF 818	Miss Ann/She Told Me Lies (as Kris Ryan & Questions)	5
64	Mercury MF 852	Marie Marie/I've Had Enough Of You Baby	5
65	Mercury MF 877	Tell Me Now/She Belongs To Me	5
65	Mercury 10024 MCE	ON THE RIGHT TRACK (EP, as Kris Ryan & Questions)	20

MARION RYAN

56	Pye Nixa N 15058	Hot Diggity (Dog Ziggity Boom)/Why Do Fools Fall In Love? (78)	5
57	Pye N 15105	Ding Dong Rock-A-Billy Wedding/That's Happiness (78)	5
58	Pye 7N 15121	Love Me Forever/Make The Man Love Me	5
58	Pye 7N 15130	Oh Oh, I'm Falling In Love Again/Always And Forever	6
58	Pye 7N 15138	Stairway Of Love/I Need You	6
58	Pye 7N 15157	The World Goes Around And Around/Please Don't Say Goodnight	4
58	Pye 7NSR 15157	The World Goes Around And Around/Please Don't Say Goodnight (stereo)	7
59	Pye 7N 15184	Wait For Me/Jeepers Creepers	4
59	Pye 7N 15206	Jo-Jo The Dog-Faced Boy/Doin' What Comes Natur'lly	6
59	Pye 7N 15216	Too Much/Promise Me	4
60	Columbia DB 4448	Sixteen Reasons/Mangos	4
60	Columbia DB 4550	It's You That I Love/Somebody	4
68	Philips BF 1721	Better Use Your Head/The Seasons Change	10
58	Pye NEP 24079	MARION RYAN HIT PARADE (EP)	15
59	Pye N(S)PL 18030	A LADY LOVES! (LP, mono/stereo)	25/30

(see also Ray Ellington)

PAUL & BARRY RYAN

65	Decca F 12260	Don't Bring Me Your Heartaches/To Remind Me Of Your Love	5
66	Decca F 12319	Have Pity On The Boy/There You Go	5
66	Decca F 12391	I Love Her/Gotta Go Out To Work	5
66	Decca F 12445	I Love How You Love Me/Baby I'm Sorry	5
66	Decca F 12494	Have You Ever Loved Somebody?/I'll Tell You Later	5
66	Decca F 12520	Missy, Missy/Rainbow Weather	5
67	Decca F 12567	Keep It Out Of Sight/Who Told You?	5
67	Decca F 12633	Claire/I'll Make It Worth Your While	6
67	MGM MGM 1354	Heartbreaker/Night Time	5
68	MGM MGM 1385	Pictures Of Today/Madrigal	5
67	Decca LK 4878	THE RYANS — TWO OF A KIND (LP)	20
68	MGM C(S) 8081	PAUL AND BARRY RYAN (LP)	15

(see also Barry Ryan)

PHIL RYAN & CRESCENTS

64	Columbia DB 7406	Mary Don't You Weep/Yes I Will	6
65	Columbia DB 7574	Gypsy Woman/Be Honest With Yourself	12

BOBBY RYDELL

59	Top Rank JAR 181	Kissin' Time/You'll Never Tame Me	8
59	Top Rank JAR 181	Kissin' Time/You'll Never Tame Me (78)	25
59	Top Rank JAR 227	We Got Love/I Dig Girls	8
60	Columbia DB 4429	Wild One/Little Bitty Girl	6
60	Columbia DB 4471	Swingin' School/Ding-A-Ling	6
60	Columbia DB 4495	Volare/I'd Do It Again	6
60	Columbia DB 4545	Sway/Groovy Tonight	4
61	Columbia DB 4600	Good Time Baby/Cherie	4
61	Columbia DB 4651	Don't Be Afraid/That Old Black Magic	4
61	Columbia DB 4690	The Fish/The Third House	5
61	Columbia DB 4731	I Wanna Thank You/The Door To Paradise	5
62	Columbia DB 4785	I've Got Bonnie/Lose Her	5
62	Columbia DB 4858	I'll Never Dance Again/Gee, It's Wonderful	4
63	Cameo Parkway C 108	Forget Him/Hey Ev'rybody (some in p/s)	8/4
62	Cameo Parkway C 129	It's Time We Parted/Too Much Too Soon	4
62	Cameo Parkway C 228	Cha Cha Cha/The Best Man Cried	4
63	Cameo Parkway C 242	Butterfly Baby/Love Is Blind	4
63	Cameo Parkway C 272	Since We Fell In Love/Childhood Sweetheart	4
64	Cameo Parkway C 309	Make Me Forget/Darling Jennie	4
65	Capitol CL 15371	I Can't Say Goodbye/Two Is The Loneliest Number	4
65	Capitol CL 15424	When I See That Girl Of Mine/It Takes Two	7
66	Cameo Parkway CP 601	Until I Met You/New Love	4
60	Top Rank JKP 2059	LOVINGEST (EP)	25

Bobby RYDELL

63	Cameo Parkway CPE 551	SWAY WITH BOBBY RYDELL (EP)	15
63	Cameo Parkway CPE 553	BOBBY RYDELL (EP)	15
63	Summit LSE 2036	BEST OF BOBBY RYDELL (EP)	10
60	Columbia 33SX 1243	WILD ONE (LP)	30
61	Columbia 33SX 1308	SINGS AND SWINGS (LP)	18
61	Columbia 33SX 1352	SALUTES "THE GREAT ONES" (LP)	15
62	Columbia 33SX 1425	RYDELL AT THE COPA (LP)	15
62	Cameo Parkway C 1019	ALL THE HITS (LP)	15
63	Cameo Parkway C 1040	ALL THE HITS VOL. 2 (LP)	15
63	Cameo Parkway C 1043	BYE BYE BIRDIE (LP)	12
63	Cameo Parkway C 1055	WILD (WOOD) DAYS (LP)	15
65	Capitol T 2281	SOMEBODY LOVES YOU (LP)	12

(see also Chubby Checker & Bobby Rydell)

FREDDIE RYDER

65	Mercury MF 864	To Get Your Love Back/A Little Thing Called Love	4
65	Mercury MF 879	Some Kind Of Wonderful/Slow Down	4
65	Mercury MF 935	Man Of The Moment/My Block	4
68	Columbia DB 8335	Shadows (I Can't See You)/Airport	4
68	Columbia DB 8427	Worst That Could Happen/World Of My Own	4

(see also Freddie Self, Trends)

MAL RYDER (& SPIRITS)

63	Decca F 11669	Cry Baby/Take Over (as Mal Ryder & Spirits)	12
64	Vocalion V 9219	See The Funny Little Clown/Slow Down	50
64	Piccadilly 7N 35209	Your Friend/Forget It (as Mal Ryder & Spirits)	20
65	Piccadilly 7N 35234	Lonely Room/Tell Your Friend	15

(see also Mal & Primitives)

MITCH RYDER (& DETROIT WHEELS)

66	Stateside SS 481	Jenny Take A Ride/Baby Jane	5
66	Stateside SS 498	Little Latin Lupe Lu/I Hope	6
66	Stateside SS 521	Breakout/I Need Help	15
66	Stateside SS 549	Devil With A Blue Dress On (Medley)/I Had It Made	6
67	Stateside SS 596	Sock It To Me Baby/I Never Had It Better	6
67	Stateside SS 2023	Too Many Fish In The Sea — Three Little Fishes/One Grain Of Sand	8
67	Stateside SS 2037	Joy/I'd Rather Go To Jail (solo)	5
67	Stateside SS 2063	What Now My Love/Blessing In Disguise (solo)	15
68	Stateside SS 2075	You Are My Sunshine/Wild Child (solo)	4
68	Stateside SS 2096	Personality/Chantilly Lace/I Make A Fool Of Myself (solo)	6
72	Paramount PARA 3022	It Ain't Easy/Long Neck Goose	4
75	Pye Disco Demand DDS 113	You Get Your Kicks/Breakout	4
66	Stateside SE 1039	RIDIN' (EP)	18
66	Stateside S(S)L 10178	TAKE A RIDE ... (LP)	16
67	Stateside S(S)L 10189	BREAKOUT... !! (LP)	20
67	Stateside S(S)L 10204	SOCK IT TO ME (LP)	18
68	Stateside S(S)L 10229	WHAT NOW MY LOVE (LP, solo)	10
68	Bell MBLL/SBLL 114	ALL MITCH RYDER HITS (LP)	10

(see also Detroit)

RYE & QUARTERBOYS

82	Replay REPLAY 001	Fantasy/Private Number (p/s)	12

RYE CATCHERS

87	Greedo GREED 001	It's All Over (Bar The Shouting)/Are You Gonna Be There (At The Love-In) (p/s, gig freebie some with "Bull & Gate" video)	18/12

TONY RYMOND

62	Oriole CB 1708	Handful Of Songs/She'll Have To Go	4

THE ROLLING STONES

R.E.M.

MINT VALUE £

PARK SABLE & JUNGLE 'N' BEATS
64   Fontana TF 457   Rave On/Never Be Blue 25

JEAN SABLON
55   HMV 7M 109   The Cab/Paris You Have Not Changed 4
54   HMV 7M 272   C'est Magnifique/Sur Les Pavements Of Paris 4

SABRE
83   Neat NEAT 23   Miracle Man/On The Loose (p/s) 7

SABRES
66   Decca F 12528   Roly Poly/Will You Always Love Me? 10
      (see also Peeps)

JIMMY SACCA
54   London L 8028   You're All That I Need/Alone 8
      (see also Hilltoppers)

SACRED ALIEN/VIRGIN
80s   Greenwood GW 1   Spiritual Planet/Energy (p/s) 25
83   Heighway SAD 001   Legends/Sittin' In Front Row (gatefold p/s) 12

SAD AMONG STRANGERS
80   Brave Tales NOW 1981   Sparks Fly Upwards/A Better View Of Baxtor/The Gongs (p/s) 5
81   Brave Tales NOW 1983   My Kind Of Loser/It's So Good It's Incest (p/s) 5

SAD CAFE
79   RCA PB 5180   Every Day Hurts/I Wish That This Night Would Never End (picture disc) 4
80   RCA PB 5202   Strange Little Girl/Time Is So Hard To Find (p/s, mispress, B-side plays
                                Jefferson Starship's "Jane") 4

S. SGT. BARRY SADLER
66   RCA RCA 1506   Ballad Of The Green Berets/I'm A Lucky One 4
66   RCA RCA 1520   The A Team/An Empty Glass 4

SAD LOVERS & GIANTS
81   Last Movements LM 003   CLE (EP) 12
81   Last Movements LM 005   Colourless Dream/Things We Never Did (p/s) 10
82   Midnight Music DING 1   Lost In A Moment/The Tightrope Touch (p/s) 7
83   Midnight Music DING 5   Man Of Straw/Cowboys (p/s) 5
83   Midnight Music DONG 5   Man Of Straw/Cowboys (Version)/Close To The Sea (12", p/s) 7

SAFARIS (& PHANTOM BAND)
60   Top Rank JAR 424   Image Of A Girl/Four Steps To Love 20
60   Top Rank JAR 528   The Girl With The Story In Her Eyes/Summer Nights (with Phantom Band) 6

SAFFRON SUMMERFIELD
74   Mother Earth MUM 1001   SALISBURY PLAIN (LP) 35
76   Mother Earth MUM 1202   FANCY MEETING YOU HERE (LP) 40

SAGA SATELLITES
59   Saga SAG 45-2901   Regimental Rock (with ex-R.S.M. Brittan)/Swingin' Sporrans 5

MIKE SAGAR (& CRESTERS)
60   HMV POP 819   Deep Feeling/You Know (as Mike Sagar & Cresters) 6
61   HMV POP 988   The Three Brothers/Set Me Free 5

SAGITTARIUS
67   CBS 2867   My World Fell Down/Libra 5
68   CBS 3276   Another Time/Virgo 4
      (see also Bruce Johnston, Glen Campbell)

SAGRAM
72   Windmill WMD 118   POP EXPLOSION SITAR STYLE (LP) 25
      (see also Clem Alford, Magic Carpet)

SAHARA
73   Dawn DNLS 3068   SUNRISE (LP) 15

MORT SAHL
59   HMV CLP 1252   THE FUTURE LIES AHEAD (LP) 10

DOUG SAHM
73   Atlantic K 40466   DOUG SAHM AND BAND (LP) 10
      (see also Sir Douglas Quintet, Bob Dylan)

OLIVER SAIN (& SHIRLEY BROWN)
72   Mojo 2092 031   St. Louis Breakdown/I Ain't Gonna Tell (with Shirley Brown) 6
74   Contempo CS 2026   Bus Stop/Nightime (solo) 4
75   Contempo CS 2057   London Express/Blowing For Love (solo) 4
      (see also Shirley Brown)

ST. CHRISTOPHER
84   Bluegrass GM 001   Crystal Clear/My Fond Farewell (p/s) 12
86   Bluegrass GM 003   Go Ahead Cry/Charmelle (p/s) 10
87   Veston VOD 001   Forevermore Stars Here/Remember Me To Her/Sinking Ships (flexidisc, p/s) 7
88   Clarity CLARITY 1   Josephine Why?/I Wish I Hadn't Hurt Her/Tell The World (flexidisc,
                                foldaround p/s, 33rpm) 5

CHERYL ST. CLAIR
| 66 | CBS 202041 | My Heart Is Not In It/We Want Love | 8 |
| 66 | Columbia DB 8077 | What About Me/I'll Forget You Tonight | 4 |

SAINT ETIENNE
90	The Catalogue CAT 084	Only Love Can Break Your Heart (remixed by Flowered Up)/FLOWERED UP: It's On (The Posh Facker Mix) (square flexidisc with 'The Catalogue' mag)	6/4
90	Heavenly HVN 2	Only Love Can Break Your Heart/Only Love Can Break Your Heart (Original Version) (p/s)	5
90	Heavenly HVN 212	Only Love Can Break Your Heart/Only Love Can Break Your Heart (Original Version) (12", p/s)	8
90	Heavenly HVN 212R	Only Love Can Break Your Heart (A Mix Of Two Halves)/The Official World Cup Theme (12", die-cut p/s)	10
90	Heavenly HVN 4	Kiss And Make Up/Sky's Dead (p/s)	4
90	Heavenly HVN 412R	Kiss And Make Up (Midsummer Madness Remix)/Sky's Dead (12" p/s)	7
90	Heavenly HVN 4CD	Kiss And Make Up (Midsummer Madness Remix)/Sky's Dead (CD)	7

BARRY ST. JOHN
64	Decca F 11933	A Little Bit Of Soap/Thing Of The Past	6
64	Decca F 11975	Bread And Butter/Cry To Me	6
65	Decca F 12111	Mind How You Go/Don't You Feel Proud	5
65	Decca F 12145	Hey Boy/I've Been Crying	5
65	Columbia DB 7783	Come Away Melinda/Gotta Brand New Man	6
66	Columbia DB 7868	Everything I Touch Turns To Tears/Sounds Like My Baby	40
68	Major Minor MM 587	Cry Like A Baby/Long And Lonely Night	6
69	Major Minor MM 604	By The Time I Get To Phoenix/Turn On Your Light	4
69	Major Minor MMLP 43	ACCORDING TO ST. JOHN (LP)	10

BRIDGET ST. JOHN
70	Dandelion K 4404	To B Without A Hitch/Autumn Lullaby	4
70	Warner Bros WB 8019	If You've Got Money/Yep	6
72	Polydor 2001 280	Fly High/There's A Place/Suzanne (p/s)	6
72	Polydor 2001 361	Nice/Goodbye Baby Goodbye	4
69	Dandelion 63750	ASK ME NO QUESTIONS (LP, gatefold sleeve)	25
71	Dandelion DAN 8007	SONGS FOR THE GENTLE MAN (LP, gatefold sleeve, also listed as K 49007)	30
72	Dandelion 2310 193	THANK YOU FOR ... (LP, gatefold sleeve)	25
74	Chrysalis CHR 1062	JUMBLE QUEEN (LP)	15

TAMMY ST. JOHN
64	Pye 7N 15682	Boys/Hey Hey Hey Hey	4
65	Pye 7N 15762	He's The One For Me/I'm Tired Of Just Looking At You	4
65	Pye 7N 15948	Dark Shadows And Empty Hallways/I Mustn't Cry	6
66	Pye 7N 17042	Nobody Knows What's Goin' On (In My Mind But Me)/Stay Together Young Lovers	20

(see also Trends)

ST. LOUIS UNION
66	Decca F 12318	Girl/Respect	6
66	Decca F 12386	Behind The Door/English Tea	18
66	Decca F 12508	East Side Story/Think About Me	20

ST. LOUIS JIMMY
| 53 | Esquire 10-319 | Harlem Bound/MEMPHIS SLIM: Holiday For Boogie (78) | 25 |

OLIVER ST. PATRICK & DIAMONDS
| 67 | Trojan TR 005 | I Want To Be Loved By You/Tulips | 12 |

CRISPIAN ST. PETERS
65	Decca F 12080	At This Moment/Goodbye, You'll Forget Me	4
65	Decca F 12207	No No No/Three Goodbyes	4
65	Decca F 12287	You Were On My Mind/What I'm Gonna Be	4
66	Decca F 12359	The Pied Piper/Sweet Dawn My True Love	4
66	Decca F 12480	Changes/My Little Brown Eyes	4
66	Decca F 12525	But She's Untrue/Your Ever Changin' Mind	4
67	Decca F 12596	Almost Persuaded/You Have Gone	4
67	Decca F 12677	Free Spirit/I'm Always Crying	4
68	Decca F 12761	That's The Time/The Silent Times	4
68	Decca F 12860	Carolina/That's Why We Are Through	4
69	Mencap MEN 002	Monumental Queen/Soft As A Rose	5
70	Decca F 13055	So Long/My Little Brown Eyes (withdrawn)	12
70	Square SQ 2	Wandering Hobo/Love Love Love	4
66	Decca LK 4805	FOLLOW ME (LP)	20
67	Decca DFE 8678	ALMOST PERSUADED (EP)	15
70	Square SQA 102	SIMPLY ... CRISPIAN ST. PETERS (LP)	15

KIRBY ST. ROMAIN
| 63 | Stateside SS 199 | Summer's Comin'/Miss You So | 4 |

ST. VALENTINE'S DAY MASSACRE
| 67 | Fontana TF 883 | Brother Can You Spare A Dime/Al's Party (some with p/s) | 75/30 |

(see also Artwoods)

ST. VITUS DANCE
| 80s | Lyntone LYN 17627 | Meet Mohammed/BLAH BLAH BLAH: Heavenly View (1-sided 33rpm | |
| | Good Vibes H 002 | flexidisc with 'Helden' fanzine) | 4 |

BUFFY SAINTE-MARIE
65	Fontana TF 574	Until It's Time For You To Go/The Flower And The Apple Tree	4
65	Fontana TF 614	The Universal Soldier/Cripple Creek	4
66	Fontana TF 695	Timeless Love/Lady Margret	4
65	Fontana TFL 6040	IT'S MY WAY! (LP)	12
65	Fontana TFL 6047	MANY A MILE (LP)	12

Buffy SAINTE-MARIE

66	Fontana (S)TFL 6071	LITTLE WHEEL SPIN AND SPIN (LP)	12
71	Vanguard VSD 79311	SHE USED TO WANNA BE A BALLERINA (LP)	10
71	Vanguard VSD 79300	ILLUMINATIONS (LP)	10
71	Vanguard VSD 79250	FIRE & FEET & CANDLELIGHT (LP)	10
71	Vanguard VSD 79280	I'M GONNA BE A COUNTRY GIRL AGAIN (LP)	10
72	Vanguard VSD 79312	MOONSHOT (LP)	10
73	Vanguard VSD 3/4	THE BEST OF BUFFY SAINTE-MARIE (2-LP)	15
73	Vanguard VSD 79330	QUIET PLACES (LP)	10
74	Vanguard VSD 79340	NATIVE NORTH AMERICAN CHILD (LP)	10
74	Vanguard VSD 33/44	THE BEST OF BUFFY SAINTE-MARIE VOL. 2 (2-LP)	15
74	MCA MCG 3517	BUFFY (LP)	10
75	MCA MCF 2594	CHANGING WOMAN (LP)	10
76	ABC ABCL 5168	SWEET AMERICA (LP)	15

SAINTS (U.K.)

63	Pye 7N 15548	Wipe Out/Midgets	12
63	Pye 7N 15582	Husky Team/Pigtails	12
	(see also Tornadoes, Heinz)		

SAINTS (U.K.)

60s	MJB BEV 73/4	SAINTS (10" LP)	250
64	MJB BEVLP 127/8	SAINTS ALIVE! (LP, private pressing)	250

SAINTS (Jamaica)

66	Doctor Bird DB 1009	Brown Eyes/BABA BROOKS & HIS BAND: King Size	10

SAINTS (Australia)

76	Power Exchange PX 242	I'm Stranded/No Time (p/s)	7
77	Power Exchange PXE 101	I'm Stranded/(STANLEY FRANK: 2 tracks) (p/s)	5
77	Harvest HAR 5123	Erotic Neurotic/One Way Street (no p/s)	5
77	Harvest HAR 5130	This Perfect Day/L-I-E-S (no p/s)	5
77	Harvest 12 HAR 5130	This Perfect Day/L-I-E-S/Do The Robot (12", with 'disclaimer' stickered p/s)	8
77	Harvest HAR 5137	1, 2, 3, 4 (EP, p/s)	4
77	Harvest HAR 5137	1, 2, 3, 4 (EP, double pack, gatefold p/s)	4
78	Harvest HAR 5148	Know Your Product/Run Down (no p/s)	4
78	Harvest HAR 5166	Security/All Times Through Paradise (p/s)	4
90	Bucketfull Of Brains BOB 26	I Dreamed Of Marie Antoinette/MOCK TURTLES: Croppies Lie Down (free with 'Bucketfull Of Brains' magazine, issue 32)	6/4
77	Harvest SHSP 4065	I'M STRANDED (LP)	12
78	Harvest SHSP 4078	ETERNALLY YOURS (LP, with inner sleeve)	12
78	Harvest SHSP 4094	PREHISTORIC SOUNDS (LP)	10

SAINTS JAZZ BAND

51	Parlophone R 3427	I Want A Girl Just Like The .../CRANE RIVER JAZZ BAND: I'm Travelling (78)	7
53	Parlophone MSP 6042	Hey Lawdy Papa/Who Walks In When I Walk Out?	5
56	Parlophone R 4240	Mahogany Hall Stomp/Stack O' Lee Blues	4
57	Parlophone R 4260	Blue Turning Grey Over You/'Till We Meet Again	4
57	Parlophone R 4304	How Come You Do Me Like You Do/Willie The Weeper	4
58	Parlophone R 4417	Swingin' The Blues/I've Found A New Baby	4

RUSS SAINTY (& NU NOTES)

60	Top Rank JAR 381	Happy-Go-Lucky-Me/Standing Around	6
60	Decca F 11270	Race With The Devil/Too Shy (solo)	6
61	Decca F 11325	Don't Believe Him, Donna/Your Other Love (solo)	5
62	HMV POP 1055	Keep You Love Locked/I've Got A Girl (as Russ Sainty & Nu Notes)	5
62	HMV POP 1069	Send Me The Pillow That You Dream On/What Do You Know About That (solo)	4
63	HMV POP 1181	Unforgettable Love/The Twinkle In Your Eye (solo)	4
64	Parlophone R 5168	That's How I'm Gonna Love You/Lonesome Town	
64	Columbia DB 7394	This Is My Lovely Day/Bless You, Girl (as Russ Sainty & Nu-Notes)	4
65	Columbia DB 7521	It Ain't That Easy/And Then (solo)	5
65	Columbia DB 7708	Saving My Tears (For A Rainy Day)/She (solo)	4
		(as Russ Sainty & Nu-Notes)	4
60s	Society SOC 1035	THE GENIUS OF LENNON AND McCARTNEY (LP)	10
	(see also Nu Notes)		

SALEM

82	Hilton	Cold As Steel/Reach To... (no p/s)	10

SIR SIDNEY SAITHESWAITE & GARBAGE COLLECTORS

67	Parlophone R 5591	Tea Lovely Tea/I Like Knees	4
67	Parlophone R 5636	Our Mabel/Chase Me Round The Garden	4

KYU SAKAMOTO

63	HMV POP 1171	Sukiyaki/Anoko No Namae Wa Nantenkana	4
63	HMV POP 1211	China Nights/Benkyo No Cha Cha Cha	4
64	HMV POP 1342	Rose Rose I Love You/Sayonara Tokyo	4

RUICHI SAKAMOTO

81	Island IPR 2048	Riot In Lagos/Iconic Storage (12", p/s)	8
	(see also David Sylvian, Yellow Magic Orchestra)		

(BOB) SAKER

68	Polydor BM 56231	Still Got You/Imagination (as Bob Saker)	4
68	Parlophone R 5740	Foggy Tuesday/Ooh Nana Na (as Bob Saker)	8
69	Parlophone R 5752	Hey Joe!/Christianity (as Saker)	8
71	CBS 7010	What A Beautiful World/City Of Angels (as Saker)	4
71	CBS 7399	Even Though We Ain't Got Money/Wild Winds Are Blowing (as Saker)	4

SALAMANDER

70	CBS 5102	Crystal Ball/Billy	12
70	Youngblood SSYB 14	TEN COMMANDMENTS (LP)	120

SOUPY SALES
65	HMV POP 1432	The Mouse/Pachalfaka 6

SALLY & ALLEY CATS
64	Parlophone R 5740	Is It Something I Said/You Forgot To Remember 6

SALLY ANGIE
69	Big T BIG 126	Two Ships/Colours Of The World 15
72	Philips 6006 259	Child Of Allah/Lady Go Lightly 15
68	Transatlantic TRA 176	CHILDREN OF THE SUN (LP, gatefold sleeve) 40
73	Transatlantic TRA 176	CHILDREN OF THE SUN (LP, reissue, different single sleeve) 15
	(see also Mike Oldfield)	

SALMONTAILS
85	Oblivion OBL 001	SALMONTAILS (LP) 25

SALOME
69	Page One POF 137	Vivo Cantando/Amigos Amigos 6

SALT & PEPPER
61	London HLU 9338	High Noon/Come Softly To Me 6

SALVATION
69	United Artists UP 35048	Cinderella/The Village Shuck 4
69	United Artists UAS 29062	SALVATION (LP) 15

SALVATION
83	Merciful Release MR 025	Girlsoul/Evelyn (p/s) 10
83	Merciful Release MRX 025	Girlsoul/Evelyn/Dust Up (12", p/s) 12
86	Batfish Inc. BF 103	Jessica's Crime/The Shining (p/s) 6
86	Batfish Inc. USS 104	Jessica's Crime (Extended Mix)/The Shining/Shattered Sky (12", p/s) 10
86	Ediesta CALC 4	Seek: Strange Fruit/Lady Faith (p/s) 5
86	Ediesta CALCT 4	Seek: Strange Fruit/Lady Faith/Angel Pain/The Answer (12", p/s) 7
88	Karbon KAR 609	Sunshine Superman/Payola (plain sleeve) 5
88	Karbon KAR 609T	Sunshine Superman/Payola/Pearl Necklace (12", p/s) 7
89	Karbon KAR 612T	All And More/The Happening/She's An Island (12", p/s) 7

SAMMY SALVO
58	RCA RCA 1032	Oh Julie/Say Yeah 15
58	RCA RCA 1032	Oh Julie/Say Yeah (78) 25
59	London HLP 8997	Afraid/Marble Heart 7
59	London HLP 8997	Afraid/Marble Heart (78) 12
62	Polydor NH 66974	Billy Blue/French Poodle 8

SAM & BILL
67	Brunswick 05973	I Feel Like Cryin'/I'll Try 20
66	Pye Intl. 7N 25355	Fly Me To The Moon/Treat Me Right 15

SAM & DAVE
66	King KG 1041	No More Pain/You Ain't No Big Thing Baby 8
66	Atlantic AT 4066	You Don't Know Like I Know/Blame Me, Don't Blame My Heart 7
66	Atlantic 584 003	Hold On I'm A Comin'/I Got Everything I Need 6
66	Atlantic 584 047	If You Got The Loving (I Got The Time)/Said I Wasn't Gonna Tell Nobody 5
67	Atlantic 584 064	You Got Me Hummin'/Sleep Good Tonight 6
67	Atlantic 584 086	You Don't Know Like I Know/Blame Me, Don't Blame My Heart (reissue) 5
67	Stax 601 004	Soothe Me/Sweet Pains (initially dark blue label, later light blue) 7/4
67	Stax 601 006	When Something Is Wrong With My Baby/A Small Portion Of Your Love
		(initially with dark blue labels, later light blue) 7/4
67	Stax 601 023	Soul Man/May I Baby 4
68	Stax 601 030	I Thank You/Wrap It Up 4
68	Atlantic 584 192	You Don't Know What You Mean To Me/This Is Your World 6
68	Atlantic 584 211	Can't You Find Another Way/Still Is The Night 6
68	Atlantic 584 228	Everybody's Got To Believe In Somebody/If I Didn't Have A
		Girl Like You 5
69	Atlantic 584 237	Soul Sister, Brown Sugar/Come On In 4
69	Atlantic 584 247	You Don't Know Like I Know/Hold On I'm A Comin' 4
69	Atlantic 584 303	Ooh Ooh Ooh/Holdin' On 5
70	Atlantic 584 324	Baby Baby Don't Stop Now/I'm Not An Indian Giver 5
66	Atlantic 587/588 045	HOLD ON, I'M A COMIN' (LP) 15
67	Stax 589 003	DOUBLE DYNAMITE (LP) 15
68	Stax 589 015	SOUL MEN (LP) 18
68	Major Minor MCP 5000	SAM AND DAVE (LP) 12
69	Atlantic 588 154	I THANK YOU (LP) 12
69	Atlantic 588 155	THE BEST OF SAM AND DAVE (LP) 10
69	Atlantic 587 181	DOUBLE TROUBLE (LP) 15
69	Atlantic 588 185	SOUL MEN (LP, reissue) 10

SAM & KITTY
80	Grapevine GRP 132	I've Got Something Good/Love Is The Greatest 4

SAM APPLE PIE
69	Decca F 22932	Tiger Man (King Of The Jungle)/Sometime Girl 10
73	DJM DJS 274	Call Me Boss/Old Tom 4
69	Decca LK-R/SKL-R 5005	SAM APPLE PIE (LP) 80
73	DJM DJLPS 429	EAST 17 (LP) 20

SAME
79	Wessex WEX 267	Wild About You/Movements (no p/s) 7
80	Blue Print BLU 2008	Wild About You/Movements (p/s, reissue) 5

SAM, ERV & TOM
68	Direction 58-3339	Soul Teacher/Hard To Get 4
	(see also Diplomats)	

SAM GOPAL
69	Stable STA 5602	Horse/Back Door Man	20
69	Stable SLE 8001	Escalator/Gold Embrace/Sky Is Burning/Angry Faces	
		(LP sampler)	35
69	Stable SLE 8001	ESCALATOR (LP, gatefold sleeve)	70

(see also Hawkwind, Motorhead, Vamp)

MIKE SAMMES & HIS SINGERS
62	Oriole CB 1738	Oh My Twisted Bach/Al Of A Twist	4

SAMMY
72	Philips 6006 227	Goo Ger Woogie/Big Lovin' Woman	4
72	Philips 6006 249	Sioux Eyed Lady/70 Days	4
72	Philips 6308 136	SAMMY (LP)	25

SAMPLES
80	Sample	VENDETTA (EP)	6
84	No Future OI 14	Dead Hero/Fire Around Round/Suspicion (p/s)	5

DAVE SAMPSON & HUNTERS
60	Columbia DB 4449	Sweet Dreams/It's Lonesome	12
60	Columbia DB 4502	If You Need Me/See You Around	12
61	Columbia DB 4597	Why The Chicken?/1999	8
61	Columbia DB 4625	Easy To Dream/That's All	10
62	Fontana H 361	Wide Wide, World/Since Sandy Moved Away (solo)	7
61	Columbia SEG 8095	DAVE (EP, also stereo ESG 7853)	60/90

TOMMY SAMPSON
58	Melodisc MEL 1411	Rockin'/Rock 'n' Roll Those Big Brown Eyes (with His Strongmen)	8
58	Melodisc MEL 1411	Rockin'/Rock 'n' Roll Those Big Brown Eyes (with His Strongmen) (78)	15
58	Parlophone R 4458	Lazy Train/Smooth Mood (as Tommy Sampson Orchestra)	4

SAMSON
69	Instant INSP 004	ARE YOU SAMSON (LP)	30

SAMSON
70	Parlophone R 5867	Venus/Wool & Water	6

SAMSON
78	Lightning GIL 547	Telephone/Leavin' You	20
79	Lightning GIL 553	Mr. Rock & Roll/Drivin' Music	5
79	Laser LAS 6	Mr. Rock & Roll/Primrose Shuffle (no p/s)	5
80	EMI EMI 5061	Vice Versa/Hammerhead (p/s)	10
80	Gem GEMS 34	Vice Versa/Hammerhead (p/s)	4
80	Gem GEMS 38	Hard Times/Angel With A Gun (p/s)	4
81	RCA RCA 67	Riding With The Angels/Little Big Man (picture disc)	7
82	Polydor POSPP 471	Losing My Grip/Pyramid To The Stars (picture disc)	6
82	Polydor POSP 471	Losing My Grip/Pyramid To The Stars (EP)	7
82	Polydor POSPG 519	Life On The Run/Drivin' With ZZ!/Walkin' Out On You/Bright Lights	
		(double pack)	6
83	Polydor POSPP 554	Red Skies/Livin' Lovin' Lyin' (picture disc)	7
83	Polydor POSPX 554	Red Skies/Livin' Lovin' Lyin' (12")	7
84	Polydor POSPP 670	Are You Ready/Front Page News (picture disc)	5
84	Polydor POSPG 670	Are You Ready/Front Page News (12")	7
84	Thunderbolt THBE 1.003	Mr Rock 'n' Roll/Primrose Shuffle/Telephone/Leavin' You (12")	7
79	Laser LAP 1	SURVIVORS (LP)	12
80	Gem GEMLP 108	HEAD ON (LP, with insert)	10
81	Gem GEMLP 113	SAMSON (LP)	12
81	RCA LP 5031	SHOCK TACTICS (LP, with insert)	10
84	Polydor POLD 5132	DON'T GET MAD GET EVEN (LP)	10

(see also Trapeze, Bruce Dickinson, Iron Maiden, John McCoy, Tiger, Strider)

SAM THE SHAM & PHARAOHS
65	MGM MGM 1269	Woolly Bully/Ain't Gonna Move	7
65	MGM MGM 1278	Ju Ju Hand/Big City Lights	6
65	MGM MGM 1285	Ring Dang Doo/Don't Try It	6
66	MGM MGM 1298	Red Hot/Long Long Way	6
66	MGM MGM 1315	Li'l Red Riding Hood/Love Me Like Before	6
66	MGM MGM 1326	The Hair On My Chinny Chin Chin/The Out Crowd	5
66	MGM MGM 1331	How Do You Catch A Girl/The Love You Left Behind	5
67	MGM MGM 1337	Oh That's Bad No That's Good/Take What You Can Get	5
67	MGM MGM 1343	Black Sheep/My Day's Gonna Come	5
68	MGM MGM 1379	Yakety Yak/Let Our Lovelight Shine	6
66	MGM MGM-EP 794	RED HOT (EP)	20
65	MGM MGM-C 1007	WOOLY BULLY (LP)	20
66	MGM MGM-C(S) 8032	LI'L RED RIDING HOOD (LP)	20
71	Atco 2400 146	SAM HARD AND HEAVY (LP, as Sam Samudio)	10

JERRY SAMUELS
56	HMV 7M 411	Puppy Love/The Chosen Few	6

(see also Napoleon XIV)

WINSTON SAMUELS
64	Columbia DB 7405	You Are The One/Angela	10
64	Rio R 26	Follow/I'm So Glad	10
64	Black Swan WI 419	Luck Will Come My Way/LLOYD BREVITT: One More Time	10
64	Black Swan WI 426	You Are The One/Gloria Love (B-side actually by Beltones)	10
65	Ska Beat JB 196	Be Prepared/Jericho Wall	10
65	Ska Beat JB 213	My Bride To Be/LLOYD PREVITT: Wayward Ska	10
65	Ska Beat JB 214	Never Again/My Angel	10
66	Ska Beat JB 238	What Have I Done/Broken Hearted	10

66	Ska Beat JB 241	Ups And Downs/Come What May	10
66	Ska Beat JB 244	Time Will Tell/I'm Sorry	10
67	Island WI 3051	The Greatest/FREDDIE & FITZY: Truth Hurts	10
67	Island WI 3053	I Won't Be Discouraged/FREDDIE & FITZIE: Why Did My Little Girl Cry	10

SAMURAI
| 71 | Greenwich GSLP 1003 | SAMURAI (LP) | 70 |

(see also Greenslade, Web)

SAMURAI
| 84 | Ebony EBON 24 | SACRED BLADE (LP) | 10 |

ALEX SANDERS
| 70 | A&M AMLS 984 | A WITCH IS BORN (LP, foldout sleeve with warning sticker, withdrawn) | 40 |

GARY SANDERS
| 66 | Warner Bros WB 5676 | Ain't No Beatle/Ain't I Good To You | 8 |

PHAROAH SANDERS
73	Impulse AS 9199	DEAF, DUMB, BLIND (LP)	12
73	Impulse AS 9219	BLACK UNITY (LP)	12
73	Impulse AS 9227	LIVE AT THE EAST (LP)	12
73	Impulse AS 9229-2	THE BEST OF PHAROAH SANDERS (LP, original issue)	12
76	Impulse IMPL 8023	WISDOM THROUGH MUSIC (LP)	12
77	Impulse AS 9138	TAUHID (LP)	12
77	Impulse AS 9181	KARMA (LP)	12
77	Impulse AS 9190	JEWELS OF THOUGHT (LP)	12
77	Impulse AS 9206	THEMBI (LP)	12

RAY SANDERS
| 60 | London HLG 7106 | A World So Full Of Love/A Little Bitty Tear (export issue) | 10 |

TOMMY SANDERSON & SANDMEN
| 61 | Ember EMB 131 | Deadline/Candelglow | 4 |
| 62 | Ember EMB 152 | Ding Dong Rag/Piano A Go Go | 4 |

CHRIS SANDFORD (& CORONETS)
63	Decca F 11778	Not Too Little — Not Too Much/I'm Lookin'	4
64	Decca F 11842	You're Gonna Be My Girl/Don't Leave Me Now (with Coronets)	4
65	Fontana TF 633	I Wish They Wouldn't Always Say I Sound Like The Guy From The U.S.A. Blues/Little Man, Nobody Cares	4

SANDKINGS
88	Long Beach BEACH 1	Rain/One Of These Days (p/s)	4
88	Long Beach BEACH 1T	Rain/One Of These Days/Spiral Steps (12", p/s)	7
89	House Of Dolls HOD 011	Colourblind/WONDER STUFF: Who Wants To Be The Disco King? (King Of Disco Mega Mix)/PRUDES: Christmas (no p/s, free with 'House Of Dolls' mag)	6/4

JOHNNY SANDON (& REMO FOUR)
63	Pye 7N 15542	Lies/On The Horizon (as Johnny Sandon & Remo Four)	7
63	Pye 7N 15559	Magic Potion/Yes (as Johnny Sandon & Remo Four)	7
64	Pye 7N 15602	Sixteen Tons/The Blizzard	6
64	Pye 7N 15665	Donna Means Heartbreak/Some Kinda Wonderful	6
64	Pye 7N 15717	The Blizzard/Legend In My Time	6

(see also Remo Four)

SANDPEBBLES
67	Track 604 015	Love Power/Because Of Love	8
68	Toast TT 505	If You Didn't Hear Me The First Time/Flower Power	5
69	Track 604 028	Love Power/Because Of Love (reissue)	4

SANDRA
86	10 TEN 78	I'll Never Be Maria Magdalena/Party Games/Little Girl (p/s)	4
86	10 TEN 78-12	I'll Never Be Maria Magdalena/Party Games/Little Girl (12", p/s)	7
86	10 TENY 78-12	I'll Never Be Maria Magdalena/Party Games/Little Girl (12", picture disc)	12
86	10 TEN 113	In The Heat Of The Night/Heatwave (p/s)	4
86	10 TEN 113-12	In The Heat Of The Night/Heatwave (12", p/s)	7
88	10 TEN 149	Everlasting Love (p/s)	5
88	10 TENT 149	Everlasting Love (Extended Mix) (12", p/s)	8

SANDROSE
| 72 | Polydor 2480 137 | SANDROSE (LP) | 125 |

SANDS
| 67 | Reaction 591 017 | Mrs. Gillespie's Refrigerator/Listen To The Sky | 90 |
| 70 | Major Minor MM 681 | Venus/Cara Mia | 12 |

(see also Others, Sundragon)

SANDS
| 70s | Tribune TRS 122 | Dance Dance Dance/The Cheater | 8 |
| 70s | Tribune | SAND DOIN'S (LP) | 40 |

SANDS
| 72 | RCA RCA 2210 | Salvation Sally/She Is Me | 5 |

CLIVE SANDS
69	CBS 3955	Lo Muchco Que Te Quiro/Picture On The Wall	4
69	SNB 55-4058	Hooked On A Feeling/Marie	5
69	SNB 55-4431	Whitchi Tai Yo/In A Dream	10
70	CBS 4672	A Very Lonely Man/You Made Me What I Am	4

(see also Brothers Kane, Sarstedt Brothers, Wes Sands)

DAVEY SANDS & ESSEX
| 65 | Decca F 12170 | Please Me Mine/All The Time | 12 |
| 67 | CBS 202620 | Advertising Girl/Without You I'm Nothing | 10 |

EVIE SANDS

65	Blue Cat BC 118	Take Me For A Little While/Run Home To Mama	20
66	Cameo Parkway C 413	Picture Me Gone/It Makes Me Laugh	50
67	A&M AMS 760	Anyway That You Want Me	5
75	Capitol CL 15818	You Brought The Woman Out In Me/Early Morning Sunshine	6

JODI(E) SANDS

57	London HL 8456	With All My Heart/More Than Only Friends (as Jodi Sands)	6
57	London HL 8530	Please Don't Tell Me (Sayonara)/If You're Not Completely Satisfied	6
58	Starlite ST45 005	All I Ask Of You/The Way I Love You	6
58	HMV POP 533	Someday (You'll Want Me To Want You)/Always In My Heart	5
58	HMV POP 533	Someday (You'll Want Me To Want You)/Always In My Heart (78)	5

TOMMY SANDS

57	Capitol CL 14695	Teen-age Crush/Hep Dee Hootie (Cutie Wootie)	12
57	Capitol CL 14695	Teen-age Crush/Hep Dee Hootie (Cutie Wootie) (78)	5
57	Capitol CL 14724	Ring-A-Ding-A-Ding/My Love Song	8
57	Capitol CL 14724	Ring-A-Ding-A-Ding/My Love Song (78)	5
57	Capitol CL 14745	Goin' Steady/Ring My 'Phone	8
57	Capitol CL 14745	Goin' Steady/Ring My 'Phone (78)	8
57	Capitol CL 14781	Let Me Be Loved/Fantastically Foolish	6
57	Capitol CL 14781	Let Me Be Loved/Fantastically Foolish (78)	5
57	Capitol CL 14811	Man, Like Wow!/A Swingin' Romance	10
57	Capitol CL 14811	Man, Like Wow!/A Swingin' Romance (78)	5
58	Capitol CL 14834	Sing, Boy, Sing/Crazy 'Cause I Love You	8
58	Capitol CL 14834	Sing, Boy, Sing/Crazy 'Cause I Love You (78)	8
58	Capitol CL 14872	Hawaiian Rock/Teen-Age Doll	12
58	Capitol CL 14889	After The Senior Prom/Big Date	6
58	Capitol CL 14925	Blue Ribbon Baby/I Love You Because (as Tommy Sands & Raiders)	12
59	Capitol CL 14971	Bigger Than Texas/The Worryin' Kind	18
59	Capitol CL 15013	Is It Ever Gonna Happen/I Ain't Gittin' Rid Of You	12
59	Capitol CL 15047	Sinner Man/Bring Me Your Love	6
59	Capitol CL 15071	That's The Way I Am/I'll Be Seeing You	6
60	Capitol CL 15109	I Gotta Have You/You Hold The Future	6
60	Capitol CL 15143	The Old Oaken Bucket/These Are The Things You Are	6
61	Capitol CL 15219	Love In A Gold Fish Bowl/I Love My Baby	5
63	HMV POP 1193	Connie/Young Man's Fancy	6
63	HMV POP 1247	Only 'Cause I'm Lonely/Cinderella	6
66	Liberty LIB 55842	The Statue/Little Rosita	20
57	Capitol EAP1 848	STEADY DATE WITH TOMMY SANDS PT. 1 (EP)	25
57	Capitol EAP2 848	STEADY DATE WITH TOMMY SANDS PT. 2 (EP)	25
57	Capitol EAP3 848	STEADY DATE WITH TOMMY SANDS PT. 3 (EP)	25
57	Capitol EAP1 851	TEENAGE CRUSH (EP)	25
59	Capitol EAP1 1081	SANDS STORM PART 1 (EP)	25
59	Capitol EAP2 1081	SANDS STORM PART 2 (EP)	30
59	Capitol EAP3 1081	SANDS STORM PART 3 (EP)	30
59	Capitol EAP1 1123	THIS THING CALLED LOVE (EP)	15
57	Capitol T 848	STEADY DATE WITH TOMMY SANDS (LP)	35
58	Capitol T 929	SING, BOY, SING (LP, soundtrack)	35
59	Capitol T 1081	SANDS STORM! (LP)	25
59	Capitol T 1123	THIS THING CALLED LOVE (LP)	20
60	Capitol (S)T 1239	WHEN I'M THINKING OF YOU (LP, mono/stereo)	20/25
61	Capitol T 1426	A DREAM WITH TOMMY SANDS (LP)	25

WES SANDS

63	Columbia DB 4996	There's Lots More Where This Came From/Three Cups	20

(see also Brothers Kane, Sarstedt Brothers, Clive Sands)

SANDS OF TIME

66	Pye 7N 17140	Where Did We Go Wrong/When I Look Back	4
67	Pye 7N 17236	One Day/Eve'ry Time We Say Goodbye	4

SANDY & TEACHERS

64	Columbia DB 7244	Listen With Mammy/Real Sweet	4

(see also Sandy Brown)

SANDY COAST

73	Polydor 2001 457	Blackboard Jungle Lady/Don't Get Me Wrong	18
69	Page One POLS 020	FROM THE STEREO WORKSHOP (LP)	150
69	Page One MORS 201	SHIPWRECK (LP)	150

SAN FRANCISCO EARTHQUAKE

68	Mercury MF 1036	Fairy Tales Can Come True/Su Su	8

SAMANTHA SANG

69	Parlophone R 5799	The Love Of A Woman/Don't Let It Happen Again	4

SAN REMO STRINGS

71	Tamla Motown TMG 795	Festival Time/All Turned On	4
72	Tamla Motown TMG 807	Reach Out, And I'll Be There/Hungry For Love	4
73	Tamla Motown STML 11216	SAN REMO STRINGS SWING (LP)	10

BOBBY SANSOM (& GIANTS)

63	Oriole CB 1837	There's A Place/Lucille (as Bobby Sansom & Giants)	8
63	Oriole CB 1888	Where Have You Been/Do You Promise (as Bobby Sansom & Giants)	6
70	Decca F 13104	Lady One And Only/Handbags And Gladrags	4
71	Decca F 13151	I Believe In Music/The Valley Of The Shadows Of Tears	4

MONGO SANTAMARIA

63	Riverside RIF 106909	Watermelon Man/Don't Bother Me No More	5
65	CBS 201766	El Pussycat/Black Eyed Peas And Rice	4

69	Direction 58-4086	Cloud Nine/Son Of A Preacher Man	4
69	Direction 58-4430	Twenty Five Miles/El Tres	6
71	CBS 63904	WORKING ON A GROOVY THING (LP)	10
73	Atlantic K 40210	MONGO'S WAY (LP)	10

SANTANA

69	CBS 4593	Persuasion/Savor	5
70	CBS 4940	Evil Ways/Jin-Go-Lo-Ba	5
70	CBS 5325	Black Magic Woman/Hope You're Feeling Better	5
71	CBS 7046	Oye Como Va/Samba Pa Ti	4
71	CBS 7546	Everybody's Everything/Guajira	4
70	CBS 63815	SANTANA (LP, laminated sleeve original)	12
74	CBS 64087	ABRAXAS (LP, gatefold sleeve)	10
74	CBS CQ 30130/Q 64087	ABRAXAS (LP, gatefold sleeve, quadrophonic)	15
74	CBS 69015	SANTANA III (LP, gatefold sleeve)	10
74	CBS CQ 30595/Q 69015	SANTANA III (LP, gatefold sleeve, quadrophonic)	15
74	CBS CQ 31610	CARAVANSERAI (LP, gatefold sleeve, quadrophonic)	15
74	CBS CQ 32445/Q 69040	WELCOME (LP, quadrophonic)	15
74	CBS Q 69081	GREATEST HITS (LP, quadrophonic)	15
74	CBS Q 69084	BORBOLETTA (LP, quadrophonic)	15
75	CBS Q 86005	AMIGOS (LP, quadrophonic)	15

CARLOS SANTANA & BUDDY MILES

72	CBS 8338	Evil Ways/Them Changes	4
83	CBS A 3359	They All Went To Mexico (with Willie Nelson)/BUDDY MILES: Mudbone (p/s)	4
72	CBS 65142	CARLOS SANTANA & BUDDY MILES (LP, gatefold sleeve)	10
73	CBS CQ 31308	CARLOS SANTANA & BUDDY MILES (LP, quadrophonic)	15

(see also Santana, Buddy Miles, Mahavishnu John McLaughlin & Carlos Santana)

SANTELLS

| 66 | Sue WI 4020 | So Fine/These Are Love | 15 |

DAVID SANTO

| 68 | London HLK 10219 | Jingle Down A Hill/Rising Of Scorpio | 4 |

SANTO & JOHNNY

59	Pye Intl. 7N 25037	Sleep Walk/All Night Diner	7
59	Pye Intl. N 25037	Sleep Walk/All Night Diner (78)	20
60	Parlophone R 4619	Tear Drop/The Long Walk Home	7
60	Parlophone R 4644	Caravan/Summertime	6
61	Pye Intl. 7N 25111	Theme From Come September/Hopscotch	6
61	Parlophone R 4844	Bullseye!/Twistin' Bells	7
62	Parlophone R 4865	Birmingham/The Mouse	6
62	Stateside SS 110	Spanish Harlem/Stage To Cimarron	6
64	Stateside SS 253	Three Cabelleros/Manhattan Spiritual	5
64	Stateside SS 292	In The Still Of The Night/Song For Rosemary	5
60	Parlophone GEP 8806	SANTO AND JOHNNY NO. 1 (EP)	16
60	Parlophone GEP 8813	SANTO AND JOHNNY NO. 2 (EP)	16
59	Parlophone	SANTO AND JOHNNY (LP)	30
64	Stateside S(S)L 1008	HAWAII (LP)	18
67	Philips (S)BL 7759	PULCINELLA (LP)	12
67	Philips (S)BL 7760	MONA LISA (LP)	12

LARRY SANTOS

| 76 | Casablanca CBX 515 | We Can't Hide It Anymore/Can't Get It Off My Mind | 4 |

SAPPHIRES

63	Stateside SS 223	Where Is Johnny Now/Your True Love	25
64	Stateside SS 267	Who Do You Love/Oh So Soon	25
65	HMV POP 1441	Gotta Have Your Love/Gee Baby I'm Sorry	100
65	HMV POP 1461	Evil One/How Could I Say Goodbye	85
72	Probe PRO 556	Gotta Have Your Love/Gee Baby I'm Sorry (reissue)	4
74	Probe PRO 609	Slow Fizz/Our Love Is Everywhere	4

SARABAND

| 73 | Folk Heritage FHR 050 | CLOSE TO IT ALL (LP) | 30 |

SARACEN

82	Nucleus SAR 1	No More Lonely Nights/Rock Of Ages (p/s)	8
83	Nucleus NEAT 30	We Have Arrived/Face In The Crowd (p/s)	8
82	Nucleus NEAT 492	HEROES, SAINTS AND FOOLS (LP)	18
84	Nucleus NEAT	CHANGE OF HEART (LP)	10

DON SARGENT

| 60 | Vogue Pop V 9160 | St. James' Infirmary/Gypsy Boots | 100 |

SARI & SHALIMARS

| 68 | United Artists UP 2235 | It's So Lonely Being Together/You Walked Out On Me Before | 12 |

DEREK SARJEANT

60s	Oak RGJ 101	FOLK SONGS SUNG BY DEREK SARJEANT (EP)	25
60s	Oak RGJ 103	SONGS WE LIKE TO SING (EP, with tracks by Lisa Turner & Mick Wells)	20
60s	Oak RGJ 105	FOLK SONGS SUNG BY DEREK SARJEANT VOL. 2 (EP)	25
63	Oak RGJ 117	MAN OF KENT (EP)	25

MIKE SARNE

62	Parlophone R 4902	Come Outside (with Wendy Richard)/Fountain Of Love	4
62	Parlophone R 4932	Will I What (with Billie Davis)/Bird Ya Know I Love Ya	4
62	Parlophone R 4974	Just For Kicks/Don't You Phone, Me I'll Phone You	4
63	Parlophone R 5010	Code Of Love/Are You Satisfied	4
63	Parlophone R 5060	Please Don't Say/Now You've Moved	4
63	Parlophone R 5090	Hello Lover Boy/Baby I'm On My Way	4
64	Parlophone R 5129	A Place To Go/Out And About	4

Mike SARNE

64	Parlophone R 5170	Love Me Please/You've Got Something (as Mike Sarne & Le Roys) 4
60s	Parlophone	Just Like Eddie (export issue) 50
63	Parlophone GEP 8879	MIKE SARNE HIT PARADE (EP, as Mike Sarne & Innocents) 18
62	Parlophone PMC 1187	COME OUTSIDE (LP) 25

(see also Wendy Richard, Innocents, Le Roys, Billie Davis)

SAROFEEN & SMOKE

71	Pye Intl. 7N 25556	Susan Jane/Tomorrow 4
71	Pye Intl. NSPL 28153	DO IT (LP) 12

SAROLTA

68	Island WIP 6035	Open Your Heart/L.O.V.E. 4

SARSTEDT BROTHERS

73	Regal Zono. SRZA 8516	WORLDS APART TOGETHER (LP) 10

(see also Brothers Kane, Peter Sarstedt, Eden Kane, Clive Sands, Wes Sands)

PETER SARSTEDT

69	United Artists (S) ULP 1219	PETER SARSTEDT (LP) 10

(see also Sarstedt Brothers, Brothers Kane, Peter Lincoln)

SASPARELLA

69	Decca F 12892	Spooky/Come Inside 5

SASSAFRAS

73	Polydor 2383 245	EXPECTING COMPANY (LP) 12

SASSENACHS

64	Fontana TF 518	That Don't Worry Me/All Over You 12

SATAN

85	Neat NEAT 1012	COURT IN THE ACT (LP) 12

SATANIC RITES

81	Heavy Metal HEAVY 8	Live To Ride/Hit And Run (p/s) 12
85	Chub CHUB 001	WHICH WAY THE WIND BLOWS (LP) 10
87	Chub CHUB 002	NO USE CRYING (LP) 10

SATAN'S RATS

77	DJM DJS 10819	In My Love For You (p/s) 12
78	DJM DJS 10821	Year Of The Rats/Louise (p/s) 12
78	DJM DJS 10840	You Make Me Sick/Louise (p/s) 12
90s	Overground	test pressing (white label, gold vinyl) 5

(see also Photos)

GIRL SATCHMO

61	Blue Beat BB 73	Twist Around Town/My New Honey (with Karl Rowe & Bluebeats) 7
62	Blue Beat BB 156	Don't Be Sad/Brother Joe & LES DAWSON COMBO (with Les Dawson Combo) ..7
64	Blue Beat BB 227	Blue Beat Chariot/Rhythm Of New Beat 7
69	Fab FAB 111	Take You For A Ride/I'm Coming Home 5

(see also Pat Satchmo)

PAT SATCHMO

69	Upsetter US 316	Hello Dolly/King Of The Trombone 5

(see also Girl Satchmo)

SATIN BELLES

68	Pye 7N 17531	Baby You're So Right For Me/When You're Ready 4

SATISFACTION

71	Decca SKL 5075	SATISFACTION (LP) 18

(see also Mike Cotton Sound)

SATISFIERS

57	Vogue Coral Q 72247	Where'll I Be Tomorrow Night?/Come Away, Love 12
57	Vogue Coral LVA 9068	THE SATISFIERS (LP) 10

LONNIE SATTIN

56	Capitol CL 14552	Trapped (In The Web Of Love)/Your Home Can Be A Castle 6
56	Capitol CL 14638	High Steel/What Time Does The Sun Go Down? 5
57	Capitol CL 14771	I'll Never Stop Loving You/Whoo-Pie Shoo-Pie 5
58	Capitol CL 14831	Ring Around The Moon/My Heart's Your Home 5
60	Warner Bros WB 15	I'll Fly Away/Any More Than I 5

LON SATTON

74	CBS 2016	The Love I See In Your Eyes/Do You Need My Love 5

SATURNALIA

69	Matrix TRIX 1	MAGICAL LOVE (LP, picture disc, with booklet & ticket) 25
69	Matrix TRIX 1	MAGICAL LOVE (LP, test pressing on black vinyl) 75
70s	Matrix TRIX 1	MAGICAL LOVE (LP, picture disc, reissue) 10

(see also Horse)

LARRY SAUNDERS

74	London HLU 10469	On The Real Side/Let Me Be The Special One 8

MAHALIA SAUNDERS

71	Upsetter US 374	Pieces Of My Heart/UPSETTERS: Version 5

MERL SAUNDERS

73	Fantasy FT 514	FIRE UP (LP) 10

LES SAUTERELLES

68	Decca F 22824	Heavenly Club/Dream Machine 35

SAVAGE

83	Ebony EBON 12	LOOSE 'N' LETHAL (LP) 10

85	Zebra ZEB 4	HYPERACTIVE (LP)	10

EDNA SAVAGE

55	Parlophone MSP 6175	Stars In Your Eyes/A Star Is Born	10
55	Parlophone MSP 6181	Candlelight/In The Wee Small Hours Of The Morning	10
55	Parlophone MSP 6189	Arrivederci Darling/Bella Notte	12
56	Parlophone MSP 6217	Tell Me, Tell Me, Tell Me That You Love Me/Please Hurry Home	8
56	Parlophone R 4226	My Prayer/Me 'n' You 'n' The Moon	8
56	Parlophone R 4253	Never Leave Me/Don't Ever Go (I Need You)	6
57	Parlophone R 4301	Me Head's In De Barrel/Five Oranges, Four Apples	6
57	Parlophone R 4360	Let Me Loved/Diano Marina	6
58	Parlophone R 4420	My Shining Star/Once	4
58	Parlophone R 4489	Why, Why, Why/Near You	4
59	Parlophone R 4572	Maybe This Year/Beautiful Love	4
60	Parlophone R 4648	All I Need/Everyday	4

JOAN SAVAGE

57	Columbia DB 3929	Five Oranges, Four Apples/Bamboozled	6
57	Columbia DB 3968	With All My Heart/Love Letters In The Sand	6
57	Columbia DB 4039	Shake Me, I Rattle/Lula Rock-A-Hula	12
58	Columbia DB 4159	Hello Happiness, Goodbye Blues/Left Right Out Of My Heart	6

SAVAGE RESURRECTION

68	Mercury MF 1027	Thing In E/Fox Is Sick	15
68	Mercury SMCL 20123	SAVAGE RESURRECTION (LP)	35

SAVAGE ROSE

68	Polydor 184 144	SAVAGE ROSE (LP)	10
68	Polydor 184 206	IN THE PLAIN (LP)	10
69	Polydor 184 316	TRAVELLIN' (LP)	10

SAVAGES

63	Decca DFE 8546	EVERYBODY SURF WITH THE SAVAGES! (EP)	70

(see also Soul Sounds, Screaming Lord Sutch)

JULIAN JAY SAVARIN

70s	Lyntone LYN 3426	I Am You/Kizeesh (Corgi Books sampler)	10
71	Birth RAB 2	WAITERS ON THE DANCE (LP, with insert)	150
87	Five Hours Back TOCK 002	WAITERS ON THE DANCE (LP, reissue)	10

(see also Julian's Treatment)

JIMMY SAVILLE

62	Decca F 11493	Ahab The Arab/Very Unlikely	4
63	Decca F 11576	The Bossa Nova/Don't Do Anything I LIke	4

(see also Vernons Girls)

RONNIE SAVOY

61	MGM MGM 1122	And The Heavens Cried/Big Chain	4
61	MGM MGM 1131	Bewitched/It's Gotta Be Love	4

SAVOY BROWN (BLUES BAND)

66	Purdah 45-3503	I Tried/Can't Quit You Baby (as Savoy Brown's Blues Band)	70
67	Decca F 12702	Taste And Try, Before You Buy/Someday People (as Savoy Brown Blues Band)	10
68	Decca F 12797	Walking By Myself/Vicksburg Blues	6
69	Decca F 12843	Train To Nowhere/Tolling Bells	6
69	Decca F 12978	I'm Tired/Stay With Me Baby	6
70	Decca F 13019	A Hard Way To Go/Waiting In The Bamboo Grove	5
70	Decca F 13098	Poor Girl/Master Hare	5
71	Decca F 13247	Tell Mama/Let It Rock	5
73	Decca F 13372	So Tired/The Saddest Feeling	4
73	Decca F 13431	Coming Down Your Way/I Can't Find You	4
67	Decca LK/SKL 4883	SHAKE DOWN (LP)	25
68	Decca LK/SKL 4925	GETTING TO THE POINT (LP)	20
68	Decca LK/SKL 4994	BLUE MATTER (LP, mono/stereo)	20/18
69	Decca LK/SKL 5013	A STEP FURTHER (LP, mono/stereo)	20/18
70	Decca LK/SKL 5030	RAW SIENNA (LP, mono/stereo, gatefold sleeve)	18/15
70	Decca SKL 5066	LOOKING IN (LP)	15
71	Decca TXS 104	STREET CORNER TALKING (LP)	12
72	Decca TXS 107	HELLBOUND TRAIN (LP)	12
73	Decca SKL 5152	LION'S SHARE (LP)	12
73	Decca TXS 112	JACK THE TOAD (LP)	12
74	Decca SKL 5186	BOOGIE BROTHERS (LP)	12

(see also Warren Philips & Rockets, Stone's Masonry, Jackie Lynton, Foghat)

TOM SAWYER

69	CBS 4243	Cookbook/Gates	4

(see Unit 4 Plus 2)

'ACE' DINNING SAX

59	Top Rank JAR 184	Mulholland Drive/My Love	4

MIKE SAX & IDOLS

65	Mercury MF 886	My Little One/Come Back To Me	4

(see also Idols)

SAXON

79	Carrere CAR 118	Big Teaser/Stallions Of The Highway (p/s)	6
79	Carrere CAR 129	Backs To The Wall/Militia Guard (p/s)	6
80	Carrere CAR 151	747 (Strangers In The Night)/See The Light Shining (12", p/s)	7
80	Carrere HM 6	Backs To The Wall/Militia Guard (p/s, reissue)	4
80	Carrere CAR 165	Suzie Hold On/Judgement Day (live) (p/s)	4

MINT VALUE £

81	Carrere CAR 180P	And The Bands Played On/Hungry Years/Heavy Metal Thunder (picture disc) 7
81	Carrere CAR 204/	Never Surrender/20,000 Ft (Remix)//Bap-shoo-ap! (live)/
	SAM 134	Street Fighting Gang (double pack) 4
83	Carrere CARP 284P	Nightmare/Midas Touch (picture disc) 4
83	Carrere SAXON P 1	The Power And The Glory/See The Light Shining (live)
		(picture disc, 600 signed) 6/4
83	Carrere RCXK 013	FLIPHITS (cassette EP) 4
84	Carrere CAR 323	Do It All For You/Just Let Me Rock (p/s) 4
84	Carrere CART 323	Do It All For You/Just Let Me Rock (12", p/s) 7
85	Parlophone RP 6103	Back On The Streets/Live Fast Die Young (shaped picture disc) 7
85	Parlophone 12RA 6103	Back On The Streets (Extended Version)/Back On The Streets/
		Live Fast Die Young (12", p/s, with poster & sticker) 7
86	Parlophone R 6112	Rock 'n' Roll Gypsy/Krakatoa (poster p/s) 4
86	Parlophone RP 6112	Rock 'n' Roll Gypsy/Krakatoa (picture disc) 4
86	EMI EMIP 5587	Rock The Nations/747/And The Bands Played On (shaped picture disc) 6
86	EMI 12EMI 5587	Rock The Nations/747/And The Bands Played On (12", clear vinyl, stkrd p/s) 7
88	EMI EMP 43	Ride Like The Wind/Red Alert (shaped picture disc) 5
88	EMI EMP 54	I Can't Wait Anymore/Broken Heroes (live)
		(pouch pack, with discography & poster) 5
80s	Din Disc DINSY 105	We Will Remember/Altar Of The Gods (shaped picture disc) 5
82	Carrere CAL 137	THE EAGLE HAS LANDED (LP, picture disc) 10
83	Carrere CAL 147	THE POWER AND THE GLORY (LP, picture disc) 10
84	Carrere CALP 200	CRUSADER (LP, picture disc) 10
85	Parlophone SAXONP 2	INNOCENCE IS NO EXCUSE (LP, picture disc) 10
87	EMI EMS 1163	DENIM AND LEATHER (LP, blue vinyl) 10

AL SAXON

58	Fontana H 138	Where The Black-Eyed Susans Grow/She Screamed 5
58	Fontana H 164	You're The Top-Cha/The Day The Rains Came (Le Jour Ou La Pluie Viendra) 6
59	Fontana H 188	Chattanooga Choo-Choo/Chip Off The Old Block 4
59	Fontana H 205	Only Sixteen/I'm All Right, Jack 6
59	Fontana H 205	Only Sixteen/I'm All Right, Jack (78) 5
59	Fontana H 222	Linda Lu/Heart Of Stone 5
59	Fontana H 222	Linda Lu/Heart Of Stone (78) 5
59	Fontana H 231	Marina/Me Without You 4
60	Fontana H 244	The Piper Of Love/Believe Me 4
60	Fontana H 261	I've Heard That Song Before/Someone Like You 4
60	Fontana H 278	Blue-Eyed Boy/Don't Push Your Luck 4
58	Fontana TFE 17014	THOSE YOU'VE NEVER HEARD (EP) 12
59	Fontana TFE 17202	BIG DEAL (EP) 12
60	Fontana TFE 17271	THE BATTLE OF THE SEXES (EP) 12

(see also Lana Sisters, Ella Stone & Moss)

SKY 'SUNLIGHT' SAXON

| 87 | Fierce FRIGHT 009 | Dog=God (p/s, with badges, T-shirt & sugar 'skycubes') ....12 |
| 84 | Psycho PSYCHO 29 | STARRY RIDE (LP) ....10 |

(see also Seeds)

SAXONS

| 65 | Decca F 12179 | Saxon War Cry/Click-Ete-Clack ....30 |

SAXONS

| 63 | Ace Of Clubs ACL 1173 | MEET THE SAXONS (LP) ....80 |

ALEXEI SAYLE

| 84 | Springtime IST 162 | 'Ullo John, Got A New Motor Pts 1 & 2 (shaped picture disc) ....4 |

JOHNNY SAYLES

| 66 | Liberty LIB 12042 | Deep Down In Your Heart/Anything For You ....10 |
| 60s | North NORW 103 | I Can't Get Enough/Hold My Own Baby ....4 |

RAT SCABIES

| 84 | Paradiddle Music HIT 1 | Let There Be Rats/Wiped Out/Drums Drums Drums (mail-order only, no p/s) .....6 |

(see also Damned)

SUE SCADDING

| 82 | Speed FIRED 5 | Simple Love/Poland (p/s) ....4 |

(see also Slade)

SCAFFOLD

66	Parlophone R 5443	2 Day's Monday/3 Blind Jellyfish 4
66	Parlophone R 5548	Goodbat Nightman/A Long Strong Black Pudding 6
68	Parlophone R 5679	Do You Remember?/Carry On Krow 4
68	Parlophone R 5703	1-2-3/Today 4
69	Parlophone R 5784	Charity Bubbles/Goose 4
69	Parlophone R 5812	Gin Gan Goolie/Liver Birds 4
70	Parlophone R 5847	All The Way Up/Please Sorry 4
70	Parlophone R 5866	Busdreams/If I Could Start All Over Again 4
71	Parlophone R 5922	Do The Albert/Commercial Break 4
74	Warner Bros K 16400	Liverpool Lou/Ten Years On After Strawberry Jam 4
68	Parlophone PMC/PCS 7051	AN EVENING WITH ... — LIVE AT QUEEN ELIZABETH HALL (LP) 12
69	Parlophone PMC/PCS 7077	L THE P (LP) 10
73	Island ILPS 9234	FRESH LIVER (LP) 10

(see also McGough-McGear, Roger McGough, Mike McGear, Liverpool Scene, Grimms, John Gorman)

BOZ SCAGGS

| 71 | CBS 7219 | We Were Always Sweethearts/Painted Bells ....4 |
| 74 | Atlantic 588 205 | BOZ SCAGGS (LP) ....12 |

(see also Steve Miller Band)

HARVEY SCALES & 7 SOUND

| 67 | Atlantic 584 146 | Get Down/Love It Is ....6 |

SCAMPS
59	London HLW 8827	Petite Fleur/Naomi	7
62	Ace Of Clubs ACL 1116	TEEN DANCE AND SING ALONG PARTY (LP)	10

SCARECROW
78	Spilt Milk SMFM 11278	SCARECROW LIVE (LP, numbered with inserts; beware of watermarked unnumbered copies)	70

SCARLET FANTASTIC
88	Artista 109 693B	Plug Me In (To The Central Love Line) Pts 1& 2 (p/s, scarlet vinyl with 6 postcards, numbered)	4
87	Arista RIST 36	No Memory (Extra Sensory Mix)/No Memory (Ecstacy Mix)/No Memory (No Technology) (12", p/s, red vinyl)	8

SCARLETS
64	Philips BF 1376	Let's Go/Tambourine Shake	4

CHARLES FRANCIS SCARRATT III
59	Felsted AF 113	Two Innocent Lovers/Lovemobile	4

SCARS
79	Fast Product FAST 8	Horrorshow/Adult-ery (p/s)	6
80s	ID ID-1	Your Attention Please (gold vinyl flexidisc with 'ID' magazine)	6/4
81	Pre PREX 5	AUTHOR! AUTHOR! (mini-LP with booklet)	8

SCENE
80	Inferno BEAT 2	I've Had Enough/Show 'Em Now (p/s)	6

SCENE
80	Hole In The Wall HS 1	Hey Girl/Reach The Top (p/s)	7

SCENE
83	Diamond DIA 001	Looking For A Love/Let Me Know (p/s)	6
85	Diamond DIA 003	Something That You Said/Stop Go (p/s)	4

SCHADEL
66	Parlophone R 5509	Stop Where You Are/One Touch Of Your Hand	4
67	Parlophone R 5584	Flower Shop Girl/Man In The Making	4
68	Pye 7N 17528	With The Sun In My Eyes/Goodbye Thimble Mill Lane	4
71	United Artists UAS 29114	SCHADEL NUMBER 1 (LP)	10

HAL SCHAEFER ORCHESTRA & CHORUS
58	London HLT 8692	March Of The Vikings/March Of The Parisian Bakers	6

MICHAEL SCHENKER GROUP
80	Chrysalis CHS 2455	Bijou Pleasurette/Armed And Ready (p/s, coloured vinyl)	4
80	Chrysalis CHS 2471	Cry For The Nations/Into The Arena (live) (p/s, clear vinyl)	4
81	Chrysalis CHS 2541	Ready To Rock/Attack Of The Mad Axeman (p/s, clear vinyl)	4
82	Chrysalis CHS 2636	Dancer/Girl From Uptown (picture disc)	5
82	Chrysalis CHS 2636	Dancer/Girl From Uptown (p/s, clear vinyl)	4
82	Chysalis PCHR 1393	ASSAULT ATTACK (LP, picture disc)	10
83	Chysalis CHRP 1441	BUILT TO DESTROY (LP, picture disc)	10
	(see also Scorpions, Macauley Schenker Group, Nazareth, UFO, Cozy Powell, Graham Bonnet, Alex Harvey Band)		

LALO SCHIFRIN
63	MGM MGM 1203	The Good Life/Broken Date	4
66	MGM MGM 1329	Our Venetian Affair/Venice After Dark	4
68	Dot DOT 103	Mission Impossible/Jim On The Move	8
75	20th Century BTC 2150	Escape From Tomorrow/Ape Shuffle	4
76	CTI CTSP 5	Jaws Theme/Quiet Village	5
68	Dot (S)LPD 503	MUSIC FROM 'MISSION: IMPOSSIBLE' TV SERIES (LP)	18

SCHMETTERLINGE
77	Pye Intl. 7N 25743	Boom Boom Boomerang/Mr Moneymaker's Music Show	10

ZAPPATA SCHMIDT
71	President PTLS 1041	IT'S GONNA GET YOU (LP)	15

OLIVER LINDSEY SCHMITT
72	private pressing	GRAFFENSTADDEN (LP)	50

VIC SCHOEN ORCHESTRA
55	Brunswick 05391	I Cover The Waterfront/La Vie En Rose	4

EBERHARD SCHOENER
79	Harvest HAR 5196	Video Magic/Code World Elvis (p/s)	4
79	Harvest SHSM 2030	VIDEO FLASHBACK (LP)	10
	(see also Police)		

SCHOLARS
70s	Unicorn 254	VERSATILITY OF THE SCHOLARS (LP)	10

SCHOOL BOYS
63	Blue Beat BB 162	Little Boy Blues/PRINCE BUSTER: Money	10
63	Blue Beat BB 174	Little Dilly/PRINCE BUSTER'S ALLSTARS: The Joker	10
64	Port-O-Jam PJ 4000	Dream Lover/I Want To Know	10

SCHOOLERS
69	Doctor Bird DB 1170	Ugly Man (actually by Scorchers)/Whip Cracker (actually by Vincent Gordon)	8

SCHOOLGIRL BITCH
80	Garage! AERS 102	Abusing The Rules/Think For Yourself (no p/s, with insert)	6

SCHOOL GIRLS
63	Blue Beat BB 168	Love Another Love/Little Keithie	8
63	Blue Beat BB 185	Live Up To Justice/Keith My Darling	8

MINT VALUE £

| 63 | Blue Beat BB 214 | Last Time/Sing And Shout | 10 |
| 64 | Blue Beat BB 263 | Never Let You Go/SKATALITES: Supercharge | 10 |

JOHN SCHROEDER ORCHESTRA

65	Piccadilly 7N 35240	The Fugitive Theme/Don't Break The Heart Of Kimble (some in p/s)	7/4
65	Piccadilly 7N 35253	You've Lost That Lovin' Feeling/Funny How Love Can Be	6
66	Piccadilly 7N 35280	Ave Maria No Morro/Peter Popgunn	4
66	Piccadilly 7N 35285	Hungry For Love/Soul Destoyer	8
65	Piccadilly 7N 35271	Agent 00 Soul/Night Rider	10
66	Piccadilly 7N 35319	On The Ball/The Britannia March	4
67	Piccadilly 7N 35362	Soul For Sale/Loving You Girl	12
69	Pye 7N 17862	The Virgin Soldiers' March/Sweet Soul Talk	6
66	Piccadilly N(S)PL 38025	JOHN SCHROEDER'S WORKING IN THE SOULMINE (LP)	15
67	Piccadilly N(S)PL 38036	THE DOLLY CATCHER! (LP)	10
68	Marble Arch MAL 839	WORKING IN THE SOULMINE (LP, reissue)	10
60s	Polydor 2460 149	TV VIBRATIONS (LP)	10

IVY SCHULMAN & BOWTIES

| 57 | London HLN 8372 | Rock, Pretty Baby/BOWTIES: Ever Since I Can Remember | 75 |
| 57 | London HLN 8372 | Rock, Pretty Baby/BOWTIES: Ever Since I Can Remember (78) | 15 |

KLAUS SCHULZE

| 75 | Caroline CA 2003 | BLACK DANCE (LP) | 10 |

(see also Tangerine Dream)

(Voices Of) WALTER SCHUMANN

| 54 | HMV 7M 229 | Haunted House/I Only Have Eyes For You | 6 |
| 55 | HMV 7M 323 | The Man From Laramie/Let Me Hear You Whisper | 6 |

SCHUNGE

72	Regal Zonophone RZ 3066	Misty/Joseph Demanio	6
73	Regal Zonophone RZ 3077	Ballad Of A Simple Love/Enter The Violins	6
72	Regal Zono. SLRZ 1033	BALLAD OF A SIMPLE LOVE (LP)	20

SCIENCE POPTION

| 67 | Columbia DB 8106 | You've Got Me High/Back In Town | 40 |

SCIENTIST

| 69 | Amalgamated AMG 848 | Professor In Action/SUPERSONICS: Reflections Of Don D | 5 |

SCI-FI SEX STARS

| 86 | Sputnikco WMI 001 | Rock It Miss U.S.A./Teenage Thunder (p/s) | 5 |
| 86 | Sputnikco WMI 1001 | Rock It Miss U.S.A. (Death Wish IV)/Commercial Break/Teenage Thunder (Spitstyle)/Suicide (12", p/s) | 10 |

(see also Sigue Sigue Sputnik)

SCISSOR FITS

| 79 | Dubious DUB 1/SJP 793 | TAUT? TENSE? ANGULAR? AND OTHER BRITISH RAIL SANDWICHES (EP, gatefold sleeve) | 6 |
| 80 | Tortch TOR 005 | SOON AFTER DARK (EP) | 5 |

SCORCHED EARTH

| 85 | Carrere CAR 342 | Tomorrow Never Comes/Questions (p/s) | 12 |
| 85 | Carrere CART 342 | Tomorrow Never Comes/Questions/So Long/Where Do We Go From Here (12", p/s) | 30 |

SCORE

| 66 | Decca F 12527 | Please Please Me/Beg Me | 70 |

SCORPIONS

| 61 | Parlophone R 4740 | (Ghost) Riders In The Sky/Torquay | 7 |
| 61 | Parlophone R 4768 | Rockin' At The Phil/Scorpio | 8 |

SCORPIONS

82	Harvest HARP 5219	No One Like You/Now! (picture disc)	5
84	Harvest 12HARP 5231	Big City Nights/Bad Boys Running Wild (12", picture disc)	7
88	Harvest HARX 5240	Rhythm Of Love/We Let It Rock (box set with postcards)	4
88	Harvest HARP 5240	Rhythm Of Love/We Let It Rock (picture disc)	4
82	H.M. Worldwide MHIPD 2	LONESOME CROW (LP, clear vinyl or picture disc)	12
88	Harvest SHSPP 4125	SAVAGE AMUSEMENT (LP, picture disc, with lyric sheet)	10

(see also Michael Schenker Group)

SCORPIO RISING

| 92 | Imaginary FREE 004 | Watermelon/BOO RADLEYS: Smile Fades Fast (12" promo, free with "Seconds Out Round One" LP [ILLUSION 34]) | 7 |

COLIN SCOT

71	United Artists UP 35216	Hey Sandy/Nite People	4
71	United Artists UAG 29154	COLIN SCOT WITH FRIENDS (LP, gatefold sleeve, with Peter Hammill & Peter Gabriel)	12
73	Warner Bros K 46236	JUST ANOTHER CLOWN (LP)	10

(see also Peter Hammill, Peter Gabriel)

SCOTIA FOLK

| 70 | Fontana 6438 021 | SCOTIA FOLK (LP) | 12 |

WINSTON SCOTLAND

| 72 | Green Door GD 4027 | My (Girl) Littl Filly/BUNNY BROWN: My Girl | 4 |

SCOTS OF ST. JAMES

| 66 | Go AJ 111404 | Gypsy/Tic Toc | 70 |
| 67 | Spot JW 1 | Timothy/Eiderdown Clown | 60 |

(see also Five Day Rain, Hopscotch)

ANDY SCOTT

| 75 | RCA RCA 2629 | Lady Starlight/Where D'Ya Go | 10 |

83	Static TAK 10	Krugerrands/Face (p/s)	6
84	Static TAK 24	Let Her Dance/Suck It And See (p/s)	10
84	Static TAK 24-12	Let Her Dance (Full Version)/(Instrumental)/Suck It And See (12", p/s)	10
84	Static TAK 31	Invisible/Never Too Young (p/s, clear vinyl)	5
84	Statik TAK 31-12	Invisible (Single Version)/(Instrumental)/Invisible (Extended Version)/Never Too Young (12", p/s, clear vinyl)	10

(see also Sweet, Elastic Band, Mayfield's Mule, G.O.S.H.)

ARTIE SCOTT ORCHESTRA
| 70 | Major Minor MM 670 | March Of The Skinheads/Love At First Sight | 5 |

BILLY SCOTT
| 58 | London HLU 8565 | You're The Greatest/That's Why I Was Born | 12 |
| 60 | Top Rank JAR 270 | Carole/Stairway To The Stairs | 5 |

BOBBY SCOTT
| 56 | London HL 8254 | Chain Gang/Shadrack | 25 |
| 55 | London Jazz LZ-N 14001 | BOBBY SCOTT TRIO (10" LP) | 15 |

DEREK SCOTT ORCHESTRA
| 63 | Pye 7N 15500 | Hancock's Tune/Spying Tonight | 4 |

FREDDY SCOTT
63	Colpix PX 692	Hey Girl/The Slide	15
63	Colpix PX 709	I Got A Woman/Brand New World	15
67	London HLZ 10103	Are You Lonely For Me/Where Were You	12
67	London HLZ 10123	Cry To Me/No One Could Ever Love You	10
67	London HLZ 10139	Am I Grooving You?/Never You Mind	10
67	London HLZ 10172	He Ain't Give You None/Run Joe	8
69	Roulette RO 509	Sugar Sunday/Johnny's Hill	8
71	Jay Boy JAY 34	Just Like A Flower/Spannish Harlem	4
72	Jay Boy JAY 59	Are You Lonely For Me Baby/The Woman Of My Love	4
70s	Upfront UP 1	The Great If/Deep In The Night	4

GERRY SCOTT
| 62 | Parlophone R 4908 | Stay With Me/Summer Love | 4 |

GLORIA SCOTT
| 75 | Casablanca CBX 512 | Just As Long As We're Together/There Will Never Be Another | 4 |

HAZEL SCOTT
| 53 | Capitol LC 6607 | LATE SHOW (10" LP) | 20 |

JACK SCOTT (& CHANTONES)
58	London HLU 8626	My True Love/Leroy	15
58	London HLU 8626	My True Love/Leroy (78)	10
58	London HLU 8765	With Your Love/Geraldine (as Jack Scott with Chantones)	18
58	London HLU 8765	With Your Love/Geraldine (as Jack Scott with Chantones) (78)	15
59	London HLL 8804	Goodbye Baby/Save My Soul (as Jack Scott with Chantones)	15
59	London HLL 8804	Goodbye Baby/Save My Soul (as Jack Scott with Chantones) (78)	18
59	London HL 7069	Goodbye Baby/Save My Soul (export issue)	8
59	London HLL 8851	I Never Felt Like This/Bella	15
59	London HLL 8851	I Never Felt Like This/Bella (78)	20
59	London HLL 8912	The Way I Walk/Midgie	18
59	London HLL 8912	The Way I Walk/Midgie (78)	25
59	London HLL 8970	There Comes A Time/Baby Marie	12
59	London HLL 8970	There Comes A Time/Baby Marie (78)	30
60	Top Rank JAR 280	What In The World's Come Over You/Baby, Baby	6
60	Top Rank JAR 375	Burning Bridges/Oh, Little One	6
60	Top Rank JAR 419	Cool Water/It Only Happened Yesterday	10
60	Top Rank JAR 524	Patsy/Old Time Religion	8
61	Top Rank JAR 547	Found A Woman/Is There Something On Your Mind	8
61	Capitol CL 15200	A Little Feeling/Now That I	8
61	Capitol CL 15216	Strange Desire/My Dream Come True	10
62	Capitol CL 15236	Steps 1 And 2/One Of These Days	10
62	Capitol CL 15261	I Can't Hold Your Letters In My Arms/Sad Story	12
63	Capitol CL 15302	All I See Is Blue/Meo Myo	12
59	London REI 1205	MY TRUE LOVE (EP, initially triangular centre, later round centre)	60/45
61	Top Rank JKP 3002	WHAT IN THE WORLD'S COME OVER YOU (EP)	30
61	Top Rank JKP 3011	I REMEMBER HANK WILLIAMS (EP)	25
64	Capitol EAP 20035	BURNING BRIDGES (EP, unreleased)	
58	London HA-L 2156	JACK SCOTT (LP)	90
60	Top Rank BUY 034	I REMEMBER HANK WILLIAMS (LP)	35
60	Top Rank 25-024	WHAT IN THE WORLD'S COME OVER YOU (LP)	50
61	Top Rank 35-109	THE SPIRIT MOVES ME (LP)	50
64	Capitol (S)T 2035	BURNING BRIDGES (LP)	40/50

JOHN SCOTT
| 60 | Parlophone R 4697 | Hi-Flutin' Boogie/Peace Pipe | 4 |

JOHN(NY) SCOTT
| 60 | Oriole CB 1542 | Darlin'/Why Don't You Write Me? (as Johnny Scott) | 5 |
| 60 | Philips PB 1056 | They Say/How About That (as John Scott) | 4 |

JOHNNY SCOTT QUINTET
| 67 | Columbia S(C)X 6149 | COMMUNICATION (LP) | 10 |
| 70 | Fontana 6383 002 | PURCELL VARIATIONS FOR FIVE (LP) | 10 |

JUDI SCOTT
| 68 | Page One POF 066 | Billy Sunshine/Happy Song | 10 |

JUDY SCOTT
| 57 | Brunswick 05687 | The Game Of Love (A-One And A-Two)/With All My Heart | 4 |

Judy SCOTT

57	Brunswick 05704	Parlour Piano Theme/A Tender Word	5

JULIAN SCOTT
61	Columbia DB 4571	My Steady Date/So Tired	4

KEVIN SCOTT
59	Parlophone R 4540	Ciao Ciao Bambina (Piove)/Broken-Hearted Clown	4
60	HMV POP 731	You Are Beautiful/Love Look Away	4

LINDA SCOTT
60	Columbia DB 4638	I've Told Every Little Star/Three Guesses	5
61	Columbia DB 4692	Don't Bet Money, Honey/Starlight Starbright	5
61	Columbia DB 4748	I Don't Know Why/It's All Because	6
61	Columbia DB 4829	Count Every Star/Land Of Stars	5
62	Pye Intl. 7N 25146	Never In A Million Years/Through The Summer	5
63	London HLR 9802	Let's Fall In Love/I Know It, You Know It	5
69	CBS 4528	The Composer/You Made A Fool Out Of Me	4
69	CBS 4246	First Of All/The Answer's In My Eyes	4
61	Columbia	GREAT SCOTT (LP)	50

MIKE SCOTT
65	Mercury MF 906	I Am A Rock/I'm Gonna Be Somebody Someday	6

NEIL SCOTT
61	Pye Intl. 7N 25096	Bobby/I Haven't Found It With Another	4

NICKY SCOTT
67	Immediate IM 044	Big City/Everything's Gonna Be Alright	20
67	Immediate IM 045	Backstreet Girl/Chain Reaction	12
68	Pye 7N 17688	Honey Pie/No More Tomorrow	4

PEGGY SCOTT
69	Polydor 56722	Every Little Bit Hurts/You Can Never Get Something	6
79	Pinnacle PIN 73	You've Got It All/Let Me Unite You (p/s)	4

(see also Peggy Scott & Jo Jo Benson)

PEGGY SCOTT & JO JO BENSON
68	Polydor 56745	Lover's Holiday/Here With Me	5
69	Polydor 56750	Pickin' Wild Mountain Berries/Pure Love And Pleasure	4
69	Polydor 56761	Soulshake/We Were Made For Each Other	4
69	Polydor 56773	We Got Our Own Bag/I Want To Love You Babe	4
69	Polydor 583 731	SOULSHAKE (LP)	10
70	Polydor 583 756	LOVER'S HEAVEN (LP)	10

(see also Peggy Scott)

RAMBLIN' TOMMY SCOTT
54	Parlophone CMSP 15	Ain't Love Grand/What Do You Know — I Love Her (export issue)	8

ROBIN SCOTT
69	Head HDS 4003	The Sailor/Sound Of The Rain	12
69	Head	WOMAN FROM THE WARM GRASS (LP, with insert)	125

(see also Mighty Baby)

RONNIE SCOTT
56	Decca FJ 10712	Basie Talks/Flying Home (as Ronnie Scott Orchestra)	4
57	Tempo A 153	I'll Take Romance/Speak Low (as Ronnie Scott New Quintet)	5
50s	Esquire 20-006	RONNIE SCOTT QUARTET (10" LP)	15
54	Esquire 32-001	THE RONNIE SCOTT JAZZ CLUB VOLUME 1 (LP)	12
54	Esquire 32-002	THE RONNIE SCOTT JAZZ CLUB VOLUME 2 (LP)	12
54	Esquire 32-003	THE RONNIE SCOTT JAZZ CLUB VOLUME 3 (LP)	12
54	Esquire 32-006	THE RONNIE SCOTT JAZZ CLUB VOLUME 4 (LP)	12
56	Decca LF 1261	AT THE ROYAL FESTIVAL HALL (10" LP)	12
57	Philips BBL 7153	PRESENTING THE RONNIE SCOTT SEXTET (LP)	10
66	Fontana TL 5332	THE NIGHT IS SCOTT AND YOU'RE SO SWINGABLE (LP)	10

(see also Jazz Couriers, Tubby Hayes)

SIMON SCOTT (& LE ROYS)
64	Parlophone R 5164	Move It Baby/What Kind Of Woman	7
64	Parlophone R 5207	My Baby's Got Soul/Midnight (with Le Roys)	6
65	Parlophone R 5298	Tell Him I'm Not Home/Heart Cry	6

(see also Le Roys)

TERRY SCOTT
62	Parlophone R 4967	My Brother/Don't Light The Fire 'Til After	10
66	Pye 7N 17093	Juanita Banana/I Like Birds	4

TOMMY SCOTT
64	Decca F 11839	Who Will It Be?/If It's Me That You Want	4
64	Decca F 11942	Wrap Your Troubles In Dreams/Blueberry Hill	4

SCOTT BROTHERS
61	Fontana H 317	Travellin' Home/Susie Black	4
63	Decca F 11539	Yuggi Duggi/Our Time	4

GIL SCOTT-HERON (& BRIAN JACKSON)
71	Philips 6073 705	Lady Day And John Coltrane/When You Are Who You Are	6
75	Arista ARIST 23	(What's The Word) Johannesburg/Fell Together	5
78	Arista ARIST 169	The Bottle (live)/Hello Sunday, Hello Road	6
79	Inferno HEAT 23	The Bottle (Drunken Mix)/The Bottle (with Brian Jackson)	5
79	Inferno HEAT 23-12	The Bottle (Drunken Mix)/The Bottle (Sober Mix) (12", with Brian Jackson)	8
81	Champagne VAT 302	The Bottle (Drunken Mix)/The Bottle (Sober Mix) (reissue)	5
81	Champagne VATS 302	The Bottle (Drunken Mix)/The Bottle (Sober Mix) (12", reissue)	7
73	Philips 6369 415	PIECES OF A MAN (LP)	25
74	RCA SF 8428	THE REVOLUTION WILL NOT BE TELEVISED (LP)	15

75	Arista ARTY 106	FIRST MINUTES OF A NEW DAY (LP)	12
76	Arista ARTY 121	FROM SOUTH AFRICA TO SOUTH CAROLINA (LP, with Brian Jackson)	10
76	Arista DARTY 1	IT'S YOUR WORLD (LP, with Brian Jackson)	35
77	Arista SPARTY 1031	BRIDGES (LP, with Brian Jackson)	10
78	Arista SPARTY 1073	SECRETS (LP, with Brian Jackson)	10

SCOTT'S WASHBOARD BAND

60	Columbia 33SX 1232	HARLEM WASHBOARD (LP)	10

SCOTTY (David Scott)

70	Songbird SB 1044	Sesame Street/CRYSTALITES: Version	4
71	Duke DU 106	Donkey Skank (with Tennors)/MURPHY'S ALLSTARS: Version	4
71	Songbird SB 1049	Riddle I This/Musical Chariot	4
71	Songbird SB 1051	Jam Rock Style/Jam Rock Style Version	4
71	Songbird SB 1056	Penny For Your Song/CRYSTALITES: Version	4
72	Songbird SB 1080	Clean Race/CRYSTALITES: Version Train	4
71	Trojan TRL 33	SCHOOLDAYS (LP)	20

SCRAPING FOETUS OFF THE WHEEL

82	Womb WOMB-OYBL-2	HOLE (LP, gatefold sleeve with lyrics, also listed as FDL3)	60

(see also Foetus, You've Got Foetus On Your Breath, Philip & His Foetus Vibrations)

SCREAMING BLUE MESSIAHS

87	Strange Fruit SFPSC 003	PEEL SESSION 27.7.84 (EP, cassette)	6
87	WEA YZ 176P	I Wanna Be A Flintstone/All Shook Down (shaped picture disc)	4

(see also Motor Boys Motor)

SCRITTI POLITTI

78	St. Pancras SCRIT 1	Skank Bloc Bologna/Is And Ought The Western World/28.8.78 (photocopied stapled foldout p/s, hand-stamped white labels)	8
79	Rough Trade RT 027T	4 A SIDES (12" EP)	7
79	St. Pancras SCRIT 2/RT 034	PEEL SESSIONS (EP, photcopied inserts in plastic wallet)	7
82	Rough Trade RT 111P	Asylums In Jerusalem/Jacques Derrida (picture disc, PVC sleeve)	4
84	Virgin VSY 657	Wood Beez Pts 1 & 2 (picture disc)	4
84	Virgin VSY 680	Absolute Pts 1 & 2 (picture disc)	4
84	Virgin VSY 725	Hypnotise Pts 1 & 2 (picture disc)	4
85	Virgin VSY 747	The Word Girl/Flesh And Blood (shaped picture disc)	5

SCROTUM POLES

80	Scrotum Poles ERECT 1	Revelation: Why Don't You Come Out Tonight?/Night Train/Pick The Cat's Eyes Out/Helicopter Honeymoon/Radio Tay (handwritten labels, 2 different sleeve designs)	8

SCRUGG

68	Pye 7N 17451	I Wish I Was Five/Everyone Can See	25
68	Pye 7N 17551	Lavender Popcorn/Sandwichboard Man	25
69	Pye 7N 17656	Will The Real Geraldine Please Stand Up/Only George	20

(see also John Kongos)

EARL SCRUGGS

72	CBS 64777	EARL SCRUGGS, HIS FAMILY AND FRIENDS (LP)	10

(see also Byrds)

IRENE SCRUGGS

50s	Poydras 80	You've Got What I Want/My Back To The Wall (78)	8

SEA-DERS

67	Decca F 22576	Thanks A Lot/Undecidedly	30

(see also Cedars)

MILT SEALEY TRIO

60s	Thompson DEP 95017	MILTON SEALEY AND KANSAS FIELDS (EP)	7

PHIL SEAMAN

68	Verve (S)VLP 9220	PHIL SEAMAN NOW ... LIVE (LP)	25
60s	Decibel BSN 103	PHIL SEAMAN STORY (LP)	15
60s	Saga OPP 102	MEETS EDDIE GOMEZ (LP)	10

SEARCHERS

63	Pye 7N 15533	Sweets For My Sweet/It's All Been A Dream	4
63	Philips BF 1274	Sweet Nuthins/What'd I Say	4
63	Pye 7N 15566	Sugar And Spice/Saints And Searchers (dark maroon or lighter pink label)	8/4
64	Pye 7N 15594	Needles And Pins/Saturday Night Out	4
64	Pye 7N 15630	Don't Throw Your Love Away/I Pretend I'm With You	4
64	Pye 7N 15670	Someday We're Gonna Love Again/No One Else Could Love You	4
64	Pye 7N 15694	When You Walk In The Room/I'll Be Missing You	4
64	Pye 7N 15739	What Have They Done To The Rain/This Feeling Inside	4
65	Pye 7N 15794	Goodbye My Love/Till I Met You	4
65	Pye 7N 15878	He's Got No Love/So Far Away	5
65	Pye 7N 15950	When I Get Home/I'm Never Coming Back	4
65	Pye 7N 15992	Take Me For What I'm Worth/Too Many Miles (a few in export p/s)	25/4
66	Pye 7N 17094	Take It Or Leave It/Don't Hide It Away	5
66	Pye 7N 17170	Have You Ever Loved Somebody/It's Just The Way	4
67	Pye 7N 17225	Popcorn, Double Feature/Lovers	8
67	Pye 7N 17308	Western Union/I'll Cry Tomorrow	10
67	Pye 7N 17424	Secondhand Dealer/Crazy Dreams	12
68	Liberty LBF 15159	Umbrella Man/Over The Weekend	15
69	Liberty LBF 15340	Kinky Kathy Abernathy/Suzanna	15
71	RCA RCA 2057	Desdemona/The World Is Waiting For Tomorrow	15
71	RCA RCA 2139	Love Is Everywhere/And A Button	8
72	RCA RCA 2231	Sing Singer Sing/Come On Back To Me	8
72	RCA RCA 2248	Needles And Pins/When You Walk In The Room/Come On Back To Me	4
72	RCA RCA 2288	Vahevala/Madman	4

73	RCA RCA 2330	Solitaire/Spicks And Specks	4
80	Sire SIR 4036	It's Too Late/This Kind Of Love Affair (p/s)	7
81	Sire SIR 4049	Another Night/Back To The War (p/s)	5
80s	private pressing	Don't Make Promises	10
80s	private pressing	Four Strong Winds	10
63	Pye NEP 24177	AIN'T GONNA KISS YOU (EP)	8
63	Pye NEP 24183	SWEETS FOR MY SWEET (EP)	7
64	Pye NEP 24184	HUNGRY FOR LOVE (EP)	8
64	Pye NEP 24201	THE SEARCHERS PLAY THE SYSTEM (EP)	10
64	Pye NEP 24204	WHEN YOU WALK IN THE ROOM (EP)	15
65	Pye NEP 24218	BUMBLE BEE (EP)	7
65	Pye NEP 24222	SEARCHERS '65 (EP)	8
65	Pye NEP 24228	FOUR BY FOUR (EP)	12
66	Pye NEP 24263	TAKE ME FOR WHAT I'M WORTH (EP)	70
62	private pressing	THE SEARCHERS (LP)	125
63	Pye NPL 18086	MEET THE SEARCHERS (LP)	15
63	Pye NPL 18089	SUGAR AND SPICE (LP)	15
64	Pye NPL 18092	IT'S FAB! IT'S GEAR! IT'S THE SEARCHERS (LP)	15
65	Pye NPL 18111	SOUNDS LIKE SEARCHERS (LP)	15
66	Pye NPL 18120	TAKE ME FOR WHAT I'M WORTH (LP)	15
67	Marble Arch MAL(S) 673	SMASH HITS VOL. 2 (LP, mono/stereo)	10/12
72	RCA SF 8289	SECOND TAKE (LP)	10
70s	Readers Digest	THE SEARCHERS (LP)	12

(see also Tony Jackson & Vibrations, Chris Curtis, Pasha, John McNally)

AL SEARS ORCHESTRA

69	Vogue V 2142	Berry Wells/Steady Eddie	4

SEA STONE

78	Plankton PKN 101	MIRRORED DREAMS (LP, with insert)	75

SEATHROUGH

70s	private pressing	LALA LAPLA (LP)	45

B.B. SEATON

73	Trojan TRLS 59	THIN LINE BETWEEN LOVE AND HATE (LP)	10

(see also Bibby)

HORACE SEATON

63	Island WI 123	I'm So Glad/Tell Me	10
64	R&B JB 143	Hold On/LESTER STERLING: Peace And Love	10

(see also Bibby, B.B. Seaton)

SEA TRAIN

69	A&M AMLS 941	SEA TRAIN (LP)	10
71	Capitol EA-ST 659	SEA TRAIN (LP)	10
72	Capitol EA-ST 829	MARBLEHEAD MESSENGER (LP, gatefold sleeve)	10

(see also Blues Project)

SEA URCHINS

87	Sha La La Ba Ba Ba 5	Summershine/ORCHIDS: From This Day (flexidisc, p/s, 2,500 only)	8
87	Sarah SARAH 001	Pristine Christine/Sullen Eyes/Everglades (foldaround p/s with	
		14" x 10" poster in poly bag, 1600 only)	30
88	Sarah SARAH 008	Solace/Please Rain Fall (foldaround p/s in poly bag)	15
88	Kvatch KVATCH 001	Clingfilm/GROOVE FARM: Baby Blue Marine	
		(flexidisc,1,000 only, 500 in p/s)	16/10
89	Fierce FRIGHT 032	30.10.88 (live) (p/s)	10
91	Cheree CHEREE 15	Please Don't Cry/Time Is All I've Seen (die-cut company sleeve)	4

SEAWIND

78	CT1 CTSP 13	One Sweet Night/Countin' The Days	12

JOHN SEBASTIAN

54	London HL 8029	Inca Dance/Foolish Waltz	20
55	London HL 8131	Stranger In Paradise/Autumn Leaves	20

JOHN (B.) SEBASTIAN

69	Kama Sutra 618 026	She's A Lady/The Room Nobody Lives In	4
70	Reprise RS 20902	Magical Connection/Fa-Fana-Fa	4
70	Reprise RSLP 6379	JOHN B. SEBASTIAN (LP)	10
70	Buddah 2361 003	JOHN SEBASTIAN SONGBOOK VOLUME ONE (LP)	10

(see also Lovin' Spoonful, Even Dozen Jug Band)

SECOND COMING

70	Mercury 6338 030	SECOND COMING (LP)	12

SECONDHAND

68	Polydor 583 045	REALITY (LP)	60
72	Mushroom MR 2006	DEATH MAY BE YOUR SANTA CLAUS (LP, some copies without "Funeral")	90

(see also Andreas Thomopoulos)

SECOND LAYER

79	Tortch-r TOR 001	FLESH AS PROPERTY (EP, white p/s, black printed labels)	12
79	Tortch/Fresh FRESH 5	FLESH AS PROPERTY (EP, reissue, yellow p/s & white labels)	10
80	Cherry Red CHERRY 21	FLESH AS PROPERTY (EP, 2nd reissue, unreleased)	
80	Tortch TOR 006	State Of Emergency/I Need Noise/The Cutting Motion (p/s)	8
82	Cherry Red BRED 14	WORLD OF RUBBER (LP, with inner)	12

(see also Sound)

SECRET AFFAIR

79	I Spy SEE 1	Time For Action/Soho Strut (brown p/s, black print)	4
79	I Spy SEE 3	Let Your Heart Dance/Sorry Wrong Number (p/s)	4
80	I Spy SEE 5	My World/So Cool (with badge) (p/s)	5

80	I Spy SEE 8	Sound Of Confusion/Take It Or Leave It (p/s)	4
81	I Spy SEE 10	Do You Know?/Dance Master (p/s)	4
82	I Spy SEE 11	Lost In The Night (Mack The Knife)/The Big Beat (p/s)	5

(see also New Hearts)

SECRET GOLDFISH
| 81 | Postcard 81-11 | Hey Mister/Poorest Boy In Town (unreleased) | |

SECRET OYSTER
| 74 | CBS 80489 | SEA SON (LP) | 10 |

SECRETS
| 64 | Philips BF 1298 | The Boy Next Door/Learnin' To Forget | 4 |
| 64 | Philips BF 1318 | Other Side Of Town/Hey Big Boy | 4 |

SECRETS
67	CBS 202466	Such A Pity/I Suppose	6
67	CBS 202585	Infatuation/She's Dangerous	6
67	CBS 2818	I Intend To Please/I Think I Need The Cash	6

(see also Simon's Secrets, Clifford T. Ward, Martin Raynor & Secrets)

SECT
| 81 | Shoestring SHOE 1 | This is Your Life/Private Eye (p/s) | 4 |

NEIL SEDAKA
59	RCA RCA 1099	The Diary/No Vacancy	15
59	RCA RCA 1099	The Diary/No Vacancy (78)	40
59	RCA RCA 1115	I Go Ape/Moon Of Gold	8
59	RCA RCA 1115	I Go Ape/Moon Of Gold (78)	40
59	RCA RCA 1130	You've Got To Learn Your Rhythm And Blues/Crying My Heart Out For You	15
59	RCA RCA 1130	You've Got To Learn Your Rhythm And Blues/Crying My Heart Out For You (78)	45
59	London HLW 8961	Ring A Rockin'/Fly Don't Fly On Me	30
59	London HLW 8961	Ring A Rockin'/Fly Don't Fly On Me (78)	45
59	RCA RCA 1152	Oh! Carol/One Way Ticket (triangular centre or round centre)	10/5
59	RCA RCA 1152	Oh! Carol/One Way Ticket (78)	50

(all the above 45s originally had triangular centres, round centre re-pressings are worth two thirds the value unless stated)

60	RCA RCA 1178	Stairway To Heaven/Forty Winks Away	5
60	RCA RCA 1178	Stairway To Heaven/Forty Winks Away (78)	70
60	RCA RCA 1198	You Mean Everything To Me/Run Samson Run	5
60	RCA RCA 1198	You Mean Everything To Me/Run Samson Run (78)	90
61	RCA RCA 1220	Calendar Girl/The Same Old Fool	4
61	RCA RCA 1236	Little Devil/I Must Be Dreaming	4
61	RCA RCA 1250	Sweet Little You/I Found My World In You	5
61	RCA RCA 1266	Happy Birthday, Sweet Sixteen/Don't Lead Me On	4
62	RCA RCA 1282	King Of Clowns/Walk With Me	5
62	Stateside SS 105	Oh Delilah/MARVELS: Neil's Twist	10
62	RCA RCA 1298	Breaking Up Is Hard To Do/As Long As I Live	5
62	RCA RCA 1319	Next Door To An Angel/I Belong To You	5
63	RCA RCA 1331	Circulate/Alice In Wonderland	5
63	RCA RCA 1343	Let's Go Steady Again/Waiting For Never	5
63	RCA RCA 1359	The Dreamer/Look Inside Your Heart	5
63	RCA RCA 1368	Bad Girl/Wait 'Til You See My Baby	5
65	RCA RCA 1475	World Through A Tear/High On A Mountain	7
74	Polydor 2058 532	Bad Blood/Hey Mister Sunshine (with Elton John)	4
59	RCA RCX 166	NEIL SEDAKA (EP)	22
60	RCA RCX 186	NEIL SEDAKA VOL. 2 (EP)	18
62	RCA RCX 212	NEIL SEDAKA VOL. 3 (EP)	18
59	RCA RD 27140	NEIL SEDAKA (LP)	50
60	RCA RD 27207/SF 5090	CIRCULATE (LP, mono/stereo)	25/30
64	RCA RD/SF 7608	THE THREE GREAT GUYS (LP, with Sam Cooke & Paul Anka)	15

(see also Sam Cooke, Paul Anka, 10cc)

MIKE SEDGEWICK
| 68 | Parlophone R 5694 | The Good Guys In The White Hats Never Lose/Woman (She's Got To Be Treated Right) | 4 |

(see also Adam, Mike & Tim)

TOMMY SEEBACH
| 79 | EMI EMI 2934 | Disco Tango (English)/Disco Tango (Danish) | 4 |

RUDY SEEDORF
| 65 | Island WI 189 | One Million Stars/Mr. Blue | 8 |

SEEDS
66	Vocalion VN 9277	Pushin' Too Hard/Try To Understand	20
67	Vocalion VN 9287	Can't Seem To Make You Mine/Daisy Mae	20
66	Vocalion VAN 8062	A WEB OF SOUND (LP)	30
67	Vocalion VAN/SAVN 8070	FUTURE (LP)	30
78	Sonet SNTF 746	THE SEEDS (LP)	10
89	Bam Caruso STRANGEP 1	THE BEST OF THE SEEDS (LP, picture disc)	10

(see also Sky Saxon)

MIKE SEEGER
| 65 | Fontana TFL 6039 | MIKE SEEGER (LP) | 10 |

(see also Peggy & Mike Seeger)

PEGGY SEEGER
57	Topic TRC 107	Freight Train/Cumberland Gap (78)	5
65	Decca F 12282	Pretty Little Baby/My Love And I Are One	4
57	Pye Jazz NJE 1043	ORIGINS OF SKIFFLE (EP, with Isla Cameron & Guy Carawan)	12
62	Topic TOP 73	EARLY IN THE SPRING (EP)	7

Peggy SEEGER

63	Topic TOP 72	TROUBLED LOVE (EP)	7
61	PRE 13005	THE BEST OF PEGGY SEEGER (LP)	12
69	Argo (Z)DA 63	PEGGY ALONE (LP)	12
70s	Topic 12T 133	WHO'S GOING TO SHOE (LP, with Tom Paley)	10

(see also Al Lloyd)

PEGGY SEEGER & GUY CARAWAN
58	HMV CLP 1174	AMERICA AT PLAY (LP)	15

(see also Guy Carawan)

PEGGY & MIKE SEEGER
68	Argo (Z)DA 80	PEGGY 'N' MIKE (LP)	15
70s	Argo ZFB 62	PEGGY 'N' MIKE (LP, reissue)	10

(see also Ewan MacColl & Peggy Seeger, Mike Seeger)

PETE SEEGER
60	Top Rank TR 5020	Careless Love/LEON BIBB: Times Are Getting Hard	6
63	CBS AAG 187	Little Boxes/Mail Myself To You	4
58	Melodisc EPM7 78	TRIBUTE TO LEADBELLY (EP)	10
58	Topic TOP 33	PETE AND FIVE STRINGS (EP)	10
59	Topic TOP 37	HOOTENANNY NEW YORK CITY (EP, with Sonny Terry)	12
64	CBS AGG 20055	IN CONCERT (EP)	7
65	CBS EP 6065	HEALING RIVER (EP)	7
66	Ember EP 4560	D DAY DODGERS (EP)	7
61	Philips BBL 7507	PETE SEEGER STORY SONGS (LP)	10
63	Folklore F-LAUT 1	PETE SEEGER IN CONCERT (LP)	12
63	Folklore F-LAUT 2	PETE SEEGER IN CONCERT VOL. 2 (LP)	12
64	CBS (S)BPG 62209	WE SHALL OVERCOME (LP)	15
65	Xtra XTRA 1005	SING WITH SEEGER (LP)	10
65	CBS (S)BPG 62462	I CAN SEE A NEW DAY (LP)	10
65	CBS (S)BPG 62528	STRANGERS AND COUSINS (LP)	10
66	Xtra XTRA 1016	BROADSIDES (LP)	10
66	Xtra XTRA 1034	FOLK SINGER'S GUITAR GUIDE (LP, with 16-page booklet)	10
66	Verve (S)VLP 5004	IN PERSON (LP)	10
68	Ember CW 130	PETE SEEGER (LP)	10
68	Xtra XTRA 1066	ABIYOYO AND OTHER SONGS (LP)	10

(see also Big Bill Broonzy, Sonny Terry [& Brownie McGhee])

PETE SEEGER & BIG BILL BROONZY
64	Xtra XTRA 1006	IN CONCERT — PETE SEEGER & BIG BILL BROONZY (LP)	20
66	Verve Folkways VLP 5006	IN CONCERT (LP, reissue)	15

SEEKERS
65	Oriole CB 1935	With A Swag On My Shoulder/Myra	7
65	Decca F 22167	Chilly Winds/Kumbaya	6
66	Columbia DB 7867	Someday, One Day/Nobody Knows The Trouble I've Seen	4
66	Columbia DB 8000	Walk With Me/We're Moving On	4
67	Columbia DB 8134	Georgy Girl/The Last Thing On My Mind	4
67	Columbia DB 8273	When Will The Good Apples Fall/Myra	4
67	Columbia DB 8313	Music Of The World A Turnin'/Emerald City	4
68	Columbia DB 8407	Days Of My Life/Study War No More (as Seekers with Judith Durham)	4
68	Columbia DB 8460	Love Is Kind, Love Is Wine/All I Can Remember	4
68	Columbia DB 8509	Island Of Dreams/Red Rubber Ball	4
69	Columbia DB 8609	Colours Of My Life/Rattler	4
60s	Columbia	other 45s (1964-1965)	3
81	Lyntone LYN 2359	A World Of Their Own (flexidisc sampler for World Record Club box set)	4
65	Columbia SEG 8425	THE SEEKERS (EP)	7
65	Columbia SEG 8465	THE SEEKERS (EP)	7
66	Columbia SEG 8496	HITS FROM THE SEEKERS (EP)	7
67	Columbia SEG 8522	MORNINGTOWN RIDE (EP)	7
65	Decca LK 4694	THE SEEKERS (LP)	12
65	Columbia 33SX 1722	A WORLD OF OUR OWN (LP)	10
66	Columbia S(C)X 6093	COME THE DAY (LP, mono/stereo)	10/12
67	Columbia S(C)X 6193	SEEN IN GREEN (LP, gatefold sleeve)	10
68	Columbia S(C)X 6278	LIVE AT THE TALK OF THE TOWN (LP)	10

(see also Judith Durham)

JEANNIE SEELY
66	London HLU 10052	Don't Touch Me/You Tied Tin Cans To My Heart	4
68	Monument MON 1023	How Is He?/Little Unfair	4

SEERS
88	Rough Trade RT 182	Lightning Strikes/Graveyard Of Love (p/s)	5
88	Rough Trade RTT 182	Lightning Strikes/Graveyard Of Love/Don't Get Hit (12", p/s)	7
90	Cherry Red BRED 86	PSYCH OUT (LP, with free single "Magic Potion"/"Lightning Strikes" [CHERRY 107])	10

SEFTONES
66	CBS 202491	I Can See Through You/Here Today	12

(see also Perishers)

VIVIENNE SEGAL & HAROLD LANG
54	Columbia SCM 5114	Den Of Iniquity/BARBARA ASHLEY: That Terrific Rainbow	4

BOB SEGER (SYSTEM)
68	Capitol CL 15574	Ramblin' Gamblin' Man/Tales Of Lucy Blue (as Bob Seger System)	6
70	Capitol CL 15642	Lucifer/Big River (as Bob Seger System)	8
73	Reprise K 14243	Rosalie/Back In '72	4
74	Reprise K 14364	Get Out Of Denver/Long Song Comin'	4
78	Capitol CL 16004	Hollywood Nights/Brave Strangers (silver vinyl, special sleeve, 20,000 only)	4
83	Capitol CLD 284	Even Now/Little Victories//We've Got Tonight/Brave Strangers (double pack)	4

83	Capitol TC-CL 284	Even Now/We've Got Tonight (cassette) 4
86	Capitol CLD 396	American Storm/Fortunate Son//Hollywood Nights/Hollywood Nights (live) (double pack) 4
72	Reprise K 44214	SMOKIN' OP'S (LP) 15
73	Reprise K 44227	BACK IN '72 (LP) 10
77	Capitol CAPS 1010	MONGREL (LP, gatefold sleeve) 12

SELECTED FOUR
| 71 | Banana BA 351 | Selection Train/SOUND DIMENSION: Version Train ....5 |

SELECTER
| 79 | 2-Tone CHS TT 4 | On My Radio/Too Much Pressure (paper label, company sleeve) ....4 |
| 82 | Flexipop 001/SFI 566 | Ready Mix Radio (1-sided clear flexidisc with 'Flexipop', No. 17) ....5/4 |

(see also Special A.K.A)

FREDDIE SELF
| 64 | Mercury MF 839 | Don't Cry/Why Should I? ....4 |

(see also Freddie Ryder, Trends)

RONNIE SELF
| 58 | Philips PB 810 | Bop-A-Lena/Ain't I'm A Dog (78) ....40 |

BROTHER JOHN SELLERS
56	Vanguard EPP 14002	BLUES AND SPIRITUALS (EP) 8
57	Columbia SEG 7740	BLUES AND SPIRITUALS (EP) 8
57	Decca DFE 6457	BROTHER JOHN SELLERS IN LONDON (EP) 7
56	Vanguard PPT 12008	BROTHER JOHN SELLERS SINGS BLUES AND FOLK SONGS (10" LP) 15
57	Vanguard PPT 12017	JACK OF DIAMONDS AND OTHER FOLK SONGS AND BLUES (10" LP) 15

PETER SELLERS (& SOPHIA LOREN)
57	Parlophone R 4337	Any Old Iron/Boiled Bananas And Carrots 6
58	Parlophone R 4491	I'm So Ashamed/A Drop Of The Hard Stuff 6
59	Parlophone R 4605	Puttin' On The Smile/My Old Dutch 6
60	Parlophone R 4702	Goodness Gracious Me! (with Sophia Loren)/Grandpa's Grave 5
61	Parlophone R 4724	Bangers And Mash (with Sophia Loren)/200 Be 200 Be 200 4
65	Parlophone R 5393	A Hard Day's Night/Help! 4
66	United Artists UP 1152	After The Fox (as Peter Sellers & Hollies)/BURT BACHARACH: The Fox-Trot ...25
60	Parlophone SGE 2013	SONGS FOR SWINGIN' SELLERS (EP, stereo) 7
60	Parlophone SGE 2016	SONGS FOR SWINGIN' SELLERS NO. 2 (EP, stereo) 7
61	Parlophone SGE 2019	SONGS FOR SWINGIN' SELLERS NO. 3 (EP, stereo) 7
61	Parlophone SGE 2020	SONGS FOR SWINGIN' SELLERS NO. 4 (EP, stereo) 7
61	Parlophone SGE 2021	PETER AND SOPHIA NO. 1 (EP, with Sophia Loren, stereo) 7
61	Parlophone SGE 2022	PETER AND SOPHIA NO. 2 (EP, with Sophia Loren, stereo) 7
61	Parlophone SGE 2023	PETER AND SOPHIA NO. 3 (EP, with Sophia Loren, stereo) 7
58	Parlophone PMD 1069	THE BEST OF SELLERS (10" LP) 12
59	Parlophone PMC 1111	SONGS FOR SWINGIN' SELLERS (LP, also stereo PCS 3003) 10/12
60	Parlophone PMC 1131	PETER AND SOPHIA (LP, with Sophia Loren, also stereo PCS 3012) 12/14
60s	United Artists UAG 30266	SELLERS' MARKET (LP) 10
60s	Guild 62002	THE VOICE BEHIND THE MASK (LP) 15

PETER SELLERS, SPIKE MILLIGAN & HARRY SECOMBE
| 64 | Philips AL 3464 | HOW TO WIN AN ELECTION (LP) ....10 |

(see also Goons, Spike Milligan, Sophia Loren, Hollies)

SELOFANE
| 68 | CBS 3413 | Girl Called Fantasy/Happiness Is Love ....4 |
| 68 | CBS 3700 | Shingle I.A.O./Chase The Face ....4 |

SEMA 4
| 79 | Pollen PBM 022 | 4 FROM SEMA 4 (EP, 2 different coloured sleeves, 500 only, numbered) ....8 |
| 79 | Pollen PBM 024 | UP AND DOWN (EP, 1,000 only) ....10 |

SEMPRINI
53	HMV 7M 104	Variations On Boogie/Kitten On The Keys 4
54	HMV 7M 169	Selection From "Bangwagon" (both sides) 4
54	HMV 7M 225	Dancing To The Piano, No. 23 (medley, both sides) 4

SENATE
| 67 | Columbia DB 8110 | I Can't Stop/Ain't As Sweet As You ....8 |
| 68 | United Artists (S)ULP 1180 | THE SENATE SOCK IT TO YOU ONE MORE TIME (LP) ....10 |

(see also Garnet Mimms)

SENATE
84	Burning Rome BRR 7	The Original Sin/Do You Believe In The Westworld? (p/s) 5
84	W.A.R. WAR 1	The Original Sin/Do You Believe In The Westworld? (live) (p/s) 5
84	W.A.R. 12WAR 1	The Original Sin (Extended)/The Original Sin (Version)/
		Do You Believe In The Westworld? (live) (12", p/s) 7

(see also Theatre Of Hate)

SENATOR BOBBY
| 62 | Cameo Parkway P 127 | Wild Thing/SENATOR EVERETT McKINLAY: Wild Thing ....6 |

SENATORS
64	Dial DSP 7001	She's A Mod/I Know A Lot About You 25
64	Oriole CB 1957	When Day Is Done/Breakdown 15
65	CBS 201768	The Tables Are Turning/Stop Wasting Time 15

(see also Tony Rivers & Castaways)

RAY SENDIT & HIS ROCKEY TEAM
| 57 | Felsted SD 80052 | Rocket 0869/Spike's Rock ....6 |

SENSATIONAL ALEX HARVEY BAND
(see under Alex Harvey)

SENSATIONAL CREED
| 84 | Beggars Banquet BEG 125 | Nocturnal Operations/Down Periscopes (p/s) ....8 |

84	Beggars Banquet BEG125T	Nocturnal Operations/Down Periscopes/Voyage Of The Titanic (12", p/s)	10

(see also Associates, Orbidöig)

SENSATIONS (U.K.)

66	Decca F 12392	Look At My Baby/What A Wonderful Feeling	7

SENSATIONS (featuring Yvonne) (U.S.)

61	Pye Intl. 7N 25110	Music, Music, Music/A Part Of Me (as Sensations featuring Yvonne)	10
62	Pye Intl. 7N 25128	Let Me In/Oh Yes I'll Be True	10

SENSATIONS (Jamaica)

67	Doctor Bird DB 1074	A Thing Called Soul/BOBBY LEE & SENSATIONS: I Was Born A Loser	10
67	Doctor Bird DB 1100	Right On Time/Lonely Lover	8
67	Doctor Bird DB 1102	Born To Love You/Your Sweet Love	8
68	Duke DU 2	Those Guys/I'll Never Fall In Love	8
68	Island WI 3110	Long Time Me No See You/ROY SHIRLEY: Million Dollar Baby	10
69	Camel CA 31	The Warrior (actually by Johnny Osbourne & Sensations)/ JOHNNY ORGAN: Don Juan	5
70	Techniques TI 902	War Boats/Mr Blue	4
71	Duke DU 120	Remember/LARRY'S ALLSTARS: Madhouse	4
71	Duke DU 121	What Are You Doing Sunday/RUFFIANS: Sweet Dream	4

(see also Bobby Davis & Sensations, Roy Shirley)

SENSELESS THINGS

88	Yo Jo Jo 3	I'm Moving/Low Time/(All You've Got To Do Is) Stay Together (flexidisc, p/s)	12
88	Sniffin' Rock SR 003	All Over You/CRAZYHEAD: So Amazing Baby/(BIRDHOUSE track) (no p/s, with 'Sniffin' Rock' magazine, issue 6)	7/5
88	Red RED 001T	UP AND COMING (12" EP, with insert)	30
89	Way Cool WC 001	Girlfriend/Standing In The Rain (p/s, pink/blue or pink/purple rear sleeve)	4
89	Way Cool WC 003	Too Much Kissing/Trevor (p/s)	4
91	Way Cool WC 006	UP AND COMING (12" EP, reissue in pink p/s, export issue, with extra tracks "Girlfriend" & "Standing In The Rain")	12
91	Way Cool WC 006CD	UP AND COMING (CD, reissue in pink sleeve, export issue, with extra tracks "Girlfriend" & "Standing In The Rain")	15
90	What Goes On GOESON 37	ANDI IN A KARMANN (12" EP, white label, unreleased)	25

SERENADES

59	Top Rank JAR 111	Sudden Holiday/Tango Madeira	4

SERENDIPITY

68	CBS 3733	Through With You/I'm Flying	80
69	CBS 4428	If I Could/Castles	40

WILL SERGEANT

82	WEA K 19238	Favourite Branches (p/s)	4
83	92 Happy Cust. HAPLP 1	THEMES FOR "GRIND" (LP)	10

(see also Echo & Bunnymen)

SERGIO & ESTIBALIZ

75	EPic S EPC 3187	Love Come Home/Tu Volveras	12

JOAN MANUEL SERRAT

68	Philips BF 1664	She Gives Me Love/La La La	4

SERVANTS

86	Head HEAD FIRST	She's Always Hiding/Transparent (p/s)	8
86	Head HEAD 3	The Sun, A Small Star/Meredith/It Takes No Gentlemen/ Funny Business (12", p/s)	8

SETTERS

70	Duke DU 65	Paint Your Wagon/Organ Man (both sides actually by Hot Rod All Stars)	5
70	Trojan TR 7738	Virgin Soldier/Brixton Reggae Festival (both sides actually by Hot Rod All Stars)	4

SET THE TONE

83	Island ILPS 9736-DJ	Prove It/Start The Bus/All Tied Up (12", unreleased, DJ copies only)	7

SETTLERS

64	Decca F 11938	Settle Down/Sassafras	5
65	Decca F 12123	When's It Gonna Be My Turn?/Good News	5
65	Pye 7N 15965	A Woman Called Freedom/I Know I'm Right	4
66	Pye 7N 17065	Nowhere Man/Call Again	4
66	Pye 7N 17104	Early Morning Rain/Without You	4
66	Pye 7N 17171	'Til Winter Follows Spring/Do You Want To Know The Reason Why	4
66	Pye 7N 17213	On The Other Side/Can't Stop Following You	4
67	Pye 7N 17375	Major To Minor/I Love 'Oo Kazoo	4
68	Columbia DB 8424	As Long As There's Love/Penny To My Name	4
71	Columbia DB 8750	Keep Movin' On/Love Is More Than Words	4
64	Decca LK 4645	SING OUT (LP)	10
67	Island ILP 947	EARLY SETTLERS (LP)	18

SEVEN AGES OF MAN

72	Rediffusion ZS 115	SEVEN AGES OF MAN (LP)	25

(see also Madeline Bell, Gordon Beck)

SEVEN GALLON JUG BAND

40s	Parlophone R 2329	Wipe 'Em Off/BESSIE SMITH: In The House Blues (78)	15

7 SECONDS

82	Alt. Tentacles VIRUS 15	SKIN, BRAINS AND GUTS (EP, with insert)	8

SEVEN LETTERS/SYMARIP

69	Treasure Isle TI 7050	Skinhead Moonstomp/Must Catch A Train (as Symarip)	8

MINT VALUE £

69	Treasure Isle TI 7054	Parson's Corner/Redeem (as Symarip) 8
69	Treasure Isle TI 7055	La Bella Jig/Holidays By The Sea (as Symarip) 8
69	Doctor Bird DB 1189	People Get Ready/The Fit (as Seven Letters) 8
69	Doctor Bird DB 1194	Please Stay/Special Beat (as Seven Letters) 8
69	Doctor Bird DB 1195	Flour Dumpling/Equality (as Seven Letters [Symarip]) 8
69	Doctor Bird DB 1206	Mama Me Want Girl/Sentry (as Seven Letters) 8
69	Doctor Bird DB 1207	Soul Crash/Throw Me Things (as Seven Letters) 6
69	Doctor Bird DB 1208	There Goes My Heart/Wish (as Seven Letters) 6
69	Doctor Bird DB 1209	Bam Bam Baji/Hold Him Joe (as Seven Letters [Symarip]) 6
69	Doctor Bird DB 1306	Fung Sure/Tomorrow At Sundown (as Symarip) 6
68	Trojan TBL 102	SKINHEAD MOON STOMP (LP, as Symarip) 15
	(see also Pyramids, Equals)	

SEVENTEEN

80	Vendetta VD 001	Don't Let Go/Bank Holiday Weekend (p/s) 40
	(see also Alarm)	

SEVENTH WAVE

74	Gull GULP 1001	THINGS TO COME (LP) 10
75	Gull GULP 1010	PSI-FI (LP) 10
	(see also Second Hand)	

SEVENTH WONDER

79	Grapevine GRP 130	Captain Of My Ship/Pharaoh 4

SEVERED HEADS

83	Plastic Canvas PC 002	Heavy Metal/Killin' The Kidz (p/s) 4

SEVERED HEADS

84	Ink INK 122	Dead Eyes Opened/Bullet/Mount (12", p/s) 8
85	Ink INK 129	Goodbye Tonsils/The Ant Can See Legs/I Stand On My Head/Acme Instant
		Dehydrated Boulder Kit (12", p/s) 7

SEVERIN

71	CBS S 7280	Chance In Time/Nothing Bad Can Be This Good 8

DAVID SEVILLE & HIS ORCHESTRA (& CHIPMUNKS)

57	London HLU 8359	Armen's Theme/Carousel In Rome (initially with gold lettering on label,
		later pressings with silver lettering) 15/8
57	London HLU 8411	The Gift/The Donkey And The Schoolboy 7
57	London HLU 8485	Gotta Get To Your House/Camel Rock 8
57	London HLU 8485	Gotta Get To Your House/Camel Rock (78) 5
58	London HLU 8582	Bonjour Tristesse/Dance From "Bonjour Tristesse" 6
58	London HLU 8619	Witch Doctor/Don't Whistle At Me Baby 6
58	London HLU 8659	The Bird On My Head/Hey There Moon 6
58	London HLU 8736	Little Brass Band/Take Five 5
58	London HLG 8762	Almost Good/CHIPMUNKS: The Chipmunk Song 5
58	London HLG 8762	Almost Good/CHIPMUNKS: The Chipmunk Song (78) 5
59	London HLG 8823	Alvin's Harmonica (with Chipmunks)/Mediocre 4
59	London HLU 8893	Judy/Maria From Madrid 5
59	London HLU 7083	Alvin's Harmonica/Ragtime Cowboy Joe 4
59	London HLU 8916	Ragtime Cowboy Joe (with Chipmunks)/Flip Side 4
60	London HLG 9061	Alvin's Orchestra (with Chipmunks)/Copyright 1960
		(B-side as Music Of David Seville) 4
60	London HLG 9061	Alvin's Orchestra (with Chipmunks)/Copyright 1960 (78) 5
60	London HLG 9125	Coming 'Round The Mountain/Sing A Goofy Tune (with Chipmunks) ...4
60	London HLG 9193	Alvin For President (with Chipmunks)/Sack Time 4
61	London HLU 9329	Oh Judge, Your Honour, Dear Sir/Freddy, Freddy 4
57	London RE-U 1085	ARMEN'S THEME (EP) 12
59	London RE-U 1219	WITCH DOCTOR AND FRIENDS (EP) 12
63	Liberty LEP 2057	SING ALONG WITH THE CHIPMUNKS (EP) 7
63	Liberty LEP 2117	SING AGAIN WITH THE CHIPMUNKS (EP) 7
59	Liberty HA-U 2153	THE WITCH DOCTOR PRESENTS DAVID SEVILLE AND HIS FRIENDS (LP) 15
	(see also Chipmunks, Alfi & Harry)	

ALEC SEWARD

56	Vogue LDE 165	CITY BLUES (10" LP) 25

SEX BEATLES

79	Charly CYS 1061	Well You Never/Fatal Fascination (p/s) 4

SEX GANG CHILDREN

82	Illuminated ILL 15	Into The Abyss/Deiche (p/s) 4
83	Illuminated ILL 20	Song And Legend/Sebastiane (p/s) 5
85	Illuminated ILL 1112	Beasts/Cannibal Queen/Times Of Our Lives/Sense Of Elation
		(12", withdrawn p/s) 7
83	Illuminated JAMS 666	SONG AND LEGEND (LP, with insert) 10

SEX PISTOLS

76	EMI EMI 2566	Anarchy In The U.K./I Wanna Be Me (black p/s, with Chris
		Thomas production credit on B-side) 18
76	EMI EMI 2566	Anarchy In The U.K./I Wanna Be Me (no p/s, Dave Goodman production
		credit on B-side) 12
77	A&M AMS 7284	God Save The Queen/No Feelings (withdrawn, no p/s) 800
77	Virgin VS 181	God Save The Queen/Did You No Wrong (p/s) 5
77	Virgin VS 184	Pretty Vacant/No Fun (p/s) 5
77	Virgin VS 191	Holidays In The Sun/Satellite (withdrawn p/s) 6
77	Virgin	Lentilmas (flexidisc, Xmas freebie to journalists) 100
78	Virgin VS 220	No One Is Innocent (A Punk Prayer By Ronald Biggs)/My Way (p/s) ...4
78	Virgin VS 220	No One Is Innocent (misspress, plays Motors track)/My Way (p/s) ...15
78	Virgin VS 220-12	The Biggest Blow (A Punk Prayer By Ronald Biggs)/(Interview)/My Way
		(12", with interview [matrix: VS 22012A3] or without [VS 22012 A1] 10/7

SEX PISTOLS

79	Virgin VS 240	Something Else/Friggin' In The Riggin' (p/s)	4
79	Virgin VS 240	Something Else/Friggin' In The Riggin' (p/s, mispress, A-side plays "Silly Thing")	15
79	Virgin VS 290	The Great Rock 'n' Roll Swindle/Rock Around The Clock (vocals by Tenpole Tudor) (withdrawn 'American Express' p/s)	8
79	Virgin VS 290	The Great Rock 'n' Roll Swindle (mispress with 'lawyers' telephone conversation' track)/Rock Around The Clock ('American Express' p/s)	10
80	Virgin VS 339	(I'm Not Your) Stepping Stone/Pistols Propaganda (p/s, mispress, B-side plays "Substitute")	6
80	Virgin VS 339	(I'm Not Your) Stepping Stone/Pistols Propaganda (p/s, mispress, plays Gillan track)	12
80	Virgin SEX 1	PISTOLS PACK (6 x 7" in p/s; all in plastic wallet)	18
85	Chaos DICK 1	Submission/No Feelings (p/s, blue, pink or yellow vinyl, 5,000 only)	7/6/5
85	Chaos EXPORT 1	Submission/Anarchy In The U.K. (12", p/s, on 6 different coloured vinyls)	7
85	Chaos	Pretty Vacant (unreleased, 20 copies only)	40+
89	Spiral Scratch SCRATCH 4	Pretty Vacant/I Wanna Be Me (with 'Spiral Scratch' magazine issue 4, B-side actually plays "Lazy Sod")	6/4
78	Virgin V 2086/SPOTS 001	NEVER MIND THE BOLLOCKS, HERE'S THE SEX PISTOLS (LP, with poster & 1-sided single, "Submission" [VDJ 24], shrinkwrapped with sticker)	20
78	Virgin V 2086	NEVER MIND THE BOLLOCKS, HERE'S THE SEX PISTOLS (LP, white or pink rear sleeve with no track listing)	15
78	Virgin VP 2086	NEVER MIND THE BOLLOCKS, HERE'S THE SEX PISTOLS (LP, picture disc)	20
78	Virgin CDV 2086	NEVER MIND THE BOLLOCKS, HERE'S THE SEX PISTOLS (CD, mispressing, plays country music titles)	30
79	Virgin VD 2510	THE GREAT ROCK 'N' ROLL SWINDLE (2-LP, including "Watcha Gonna Do About It", with card insert)	14
79	Virgin VD 2510	THE GREAT ROCK 'N' ROLL SWINDLE (2-LP, with spoken overdubs on "God Save The Queen Symphony")	20
80	Factory FACT 30	THE HEYDAY (interview cassette in satin pouch with Xmas card)	12
86	Chaos AMPL 37	MINI ALBUM (LP, picture disc)	7

(see also Public Image Ltd, Professionals, Rich Kids, Sid Vicious)

SEXY GIRLS

| 69 | Dice CC 100 | Pom-Pom Song/LITTLE JOE & BUSTER'S ALLSTARS: Hy There (B-side actually by Melltones) | 5 |
| 69 | Fab FAB 100 | Pom-Pom Song/LITTLE JOE & BUSTER'S ALLSTARS: Hy There (B-side actually by Melltones) (reissue) | 5 |

DENNY SEYTON & SABRES

64	Mercury MF 800	Tricky Dicky/Baby What You Want Me To Do	10
64	Mercury MF 814	Short Fat Fanny/Give Me Back My Heart	12
64	Mercury MF 824	The Way You Look Tonight/Hands Off	25
64	Parlophone R 5363	Just A Kiss/In The Flowers By The Trees (as Denny Seyton Group)	15
65	Wing WL 1032	IT'S THE GEAR (14 HITS) (LP)	20

SHA-BOOM

| 89 | WEA 244 970-1 | DANCING IN THE FIRE — THE RE-MIX ALBUM (LP) | 10 |

SHADE JOEY & NIGHTOWLS

| 64 | Parlophone R 5180 | Bluebirds Over The Mountain/That's When I Need You Baby | 25 |

SHADES (U.S.)

| 58 | London HLX 8713 | Sun Glasses (with Knott Sisters)/KNOTT SISTERS: Undivided Attention | 25 |
| 58 | London HLX 8713 | Sun Glasses (with Knott Sisters)/KNOTT SISTERS: Undivided Attention (78) | 12 |

SHADES

| 62 | Starlite ST45 074 | Weird Walk/Joe's Shuffle | 15 |

SHADES (Jamaica)

| 69 | Gas GAS 119 | Never Gonna Give You Up/Let Me Remind You (both actually by Techniques) | 4 |

(see also Techniques)

SHADES OF BLUE (U.K.)

| 65 | Parlophone R 5270 | Voodoo Blues/Luceanne | 20 |
| 65 | Pye 7N 15988 | Where Did All The Good Times Go/I Ain't No Use | 10 |

(see also Toby Twirl)

SHADES OF BLUE (U.S.)

| 66 | Sue WI 4022 | Oh How Happy/Little Orphan Boy | 12 |

SHADES OF GREEN

| 70s | Windmill | ROCKIN' POPPIN' RAVIN' (LP) | 10 |

SHADES OF JOY

| 69 | Fontana STL 5498 | SHADES OF JOY (LP) | 10 |

SHADES OF MORLEY BROWN

| 68 | Mercury MF 1054 | Silly Girl/Pretty Blue Bird | 4 |

(see also Help Yourself)

JOHNNY SHADOW (& DANNY GAVIN)

63	Pye 7N 15506	Golli Golli/I'm Coming Home To You (with Danny Gavin)	4
63	Pye 7N 15529	Golli Guitar/Week (with Danny Gavin)	4
65	Parlophone R 5286	What A Colour Is The Wind/Kiss Me Now	4
65	Parlophone R 5308	Atom Bomb Song Part 3/Talented Man	4

SHADOWS (U.S.)

| 58 | HMV POP 563 | Jungle Fever/Under Stars Of Love | 35 |
| 58 | HMV POP 563 | Jungle Fever/Under Stars Of Love (78) | 45 |

SHADOWS (U.K.)

| 59 | Columbia DB 4387 | Lonesome Fella/Saturday Dance (green label, later black label) | 30/15 |
| 60 | Columbia DB 4484 | Apache/The Quartermasster's Stores (green label, later black label) | 6/12 |

60	Columbia DB 4530	(Theme From) Man Of Mystery/The Stranger	6
61	Columbia DB 4580	F.B.I./Midnight	4
61	Columbia DB 4637	The Frightened City/Back Home	4
61	Columbia DB 4698	Kon-Tiki/36-24-36	4
61	Columbia DB 4726	The Savage/Peace Pipe	4
62	Columbia DB 4790	Wonderful Land/Stars Fell On Stockton	4
62	Columbia DB 4870	Guitar Tango/What A Lovely Tune	6

(the above singles originally came with green labels, later black label reissues are worth £8-£12, unless stated)

62	Columbia DB 4948	Dance On!/All Day	4
63	Columbia DB 4984	Foot Tapper/The Breeze And I	4
63	Columbia DB 7047	Atlantis/I Want You To Want Me	4
63	Columbia DB 7106	Shindig/It's Been A Blue Day	5
63	Columbia DB 7163	Geronimo/Shazam	4
64	Columbia DB 7231	Theme For Young Lovers/This Hammer	4
64	Columbia DB 7261	The Rise And Fall Of Flingel Bunt/It's A Man's World	4
64	Columbia DB 7261	The Rise And Fall Of Flingel Bunt/It's A Man's World (mispress with A-side on both sides)	10
64	Columbia DB 7342	Rhythm 'n' Greens/The Miracle	4
64	Columbia DB 7416	Genie With The Light Brown Lamp/Little Princess	4
65	Columbia DB 7476	Mary Anne/Chu-Chi	5
65	Columbia DB 7588	Stingray/Alice In Sunderland	6
65	Columbia DB 7650	Don't Make My Baby Blue/My Grandfather's Clock	5
65	Columbia DB 7769	The War Lord/I Wish I Could Shimmy Like My Sister Arthur	5
66	Columbia DB 7853	I Met A Girl/Late Night Set	7
66	Columbia DB 7952	A Place In The Sun/Will You Be There	7
66	Columbia DB 8034	The Dreams I Dream/Scotch On The Socks	7
67	Columbia PRS 305	Thunderbirds Are Go (1-sided advance promo)	35
67	Columbia DB 8170	Maroc 7/Bombay Duck	6
67	Columbia DB 8264	Tomorrow's Cancelled/Somewhere	10
68	Columbia DB 8326	Running Out Of World/HANK MARVIN: London's Not Too Far	8
68	Columbia DB 8372	Dear Old Mrs. Bell/Trying To Forget The One You Love	7
69	Columbia DB 8628	Slaughter On Tenth Avenue/HANK MARVIN: Midnight Cowboy	10
72	Columbia DB 8959	Apache/Wonderful Land/F.B.I.	4
72	Lyntone LYN 10099	The Shadows (flexidisc sampler from World Record Club box set)	5
73	EMI EMI 2081	Turn Around And Touch Me/Jungle Jam	4
75	EMI EMI 2269	Let Me Be The One/Stand Up Like A Man	4
75	EMI EMI 2310	Run Billy Run/Honourable Puff-Puff	5
76	EMI EMI 2461	It'll Be Me Babe/Like Strangers	6
77	EMI EMI 2573	Apache/Wonderful Land/F.B.I. (reissue)	4
77	EMI EMI 2660	Another Night/Cricket Bat Boogie	5
78	EMI EMI 2838	Love Deluxe/Sweet Saturday Night	5
78	EMI 12EMI 2890	Don't Cry For Me Argentina/Cavatina (dble groove)/Montezuma's Revenge (12")	10
79	EMI EMI 2939	Theme From "The Deer Hunter"/Bermuda Triangle (p/s)	4
79	EMI EMI 5004	Rodrigo's Guitar Concerto/Song For Duke (p/s)	4
80	EMI EMI 5083	Heart Of Glass/Return To The Alamo (p/s)	4
80	Polydor POSP 148	Equinoxe (Part V)/Fender Bender (p/s)	4
80	Polydor POSP 187	Mozart Forte/Midnight Creepin' (no p/s)	4
81	Polydor POSP 255	The Third Man/The Fourth Man (no p/s)	4
81	Polydor POSP 316	Telstar/Summer Love '59 (no p/s)	4
81	Polydor POSP 376	Imagine — Woman (Medley)/Hats Off To Wally (no p/s)	4
82	Polydor POSP 439	Treat Me Nice/Spot The Ball (p/s)	4
82	Polydor POSP 485	The Theme From "Missing"/The Shady Lady (p/s)	4
83	Polydor POSP 629	Diamonds/Elevenis (p/s)	5
83	Polydor POSP 657	Goin' Home/Cat 'N' Mouse (p/s)	4
61	Columbia SEG 8061	THE SHADOWS (EP, also stereo ESG 7834)	10/20
61	Columbia SEG 8094	THE SHADOWS TO THE FORE (EP)	10
62	Columbia SEG 8135	SPOTLIGHT ON THE SHADOWS (EP)	10
62	Columbia SEG 8148	THE SHADOWS NO. 2 (EP, only some sleeves list "No. 2")	12
62	Columbia SEG 8166	THE SHADOWS NO. 3 (EP)	12
62	Columbia SEG 8171	THE WONDERFUL LAND OF THE SHADOWS (EP)	10

(the above EPs originally came with turquoise labels, later blue/black label copies are worth two-thirds the value)

62	Columbia SEG 8193	THE BOYS (EP, mono)	10
62	Columbia ESG 7881	THE BOYS (EP, stereo, turquoise labels, later black/blue labels)	25/20
63	Columbia SEG 8218	OUT OF THE SHADOWS (EP, mono)	12
63	Columbia ESG 7883	OUT OF THE SHADOWS (EP, stereo, turquoise or black/blue labels)	25/20
63	Columbia SEG 8233	DANCE ON WITH THE SHADOWS (EP)	12
63	Columbia SEG 8249	OUT OF THE SHADOWS NO. 2 (EP, also stereo ESG 7895)	12/25
63	Columbia SEG 8268	FOOT TAPPING WITH THE SHADOWS (EP)	12
63	Columbia SEG 8278	LOS SHADOWS (EP, 2 different sleeves)	12
63	Columbia SEG 8286	SHINDIG WITH THE SHADOWS (EP)	12
64	Columbia SEG 8321	THOSE BRILLIANT SHADOWS (EP)	12
64	Columbia SEG 8342	DANCE WITH THE SHADOWS (EP)	14
64	Columbia SEG 8362	RHYTHM AND GREENS (EP, also stereo ESG 7904)	12/25
64	Columbia SEG 8375	DANCE WITH THE SHADOWS NO. 2 (EP)	15
65	Columbia SEG 8396	THEMES FROM "ALADDIN AND HIS WONDERFUL LAMP" (EP)	14
65	Columbia SEG 8408	DANCE WITH THE SHADOWS NO. 3 (EP)	16
65	Columbia SEG 8445	ALICE IN SUNDERLAND (EP)	18
65	Columbia SEG 8459	THE SOUND OF THE SHADOWS (EP)	15
66	Columbia SEG 8473	THE SOUND OF THE SHADOWS NO. 2 (EP)	15
66	Columbia SEG 8494	THE SOUND OF THE SHADOWS NO. 3 (EP)	15
66	Columbia SEG 8500	THOSE TALENTED SHADOWS (EP)	15
66	Columbia SEG 8510	THUNDERBIRDS ARE GO! (EP, with Cliff Richard)	40
67	Columbia SEG 8528	THE SHADOWS ON STAGE AND SCREEN (EP)	22
61	Columbia 33SX 1374	THE SHADOWS (LP, also stereo SCX 3414)	12/30
62	Columbia 33SX 1458	OUT OF THE SHADOWS (LP, also stereo SCX 3449)	15/20

(the above LPs originally came with green labels, later blue/black label copies are worth two-thirds the value)

63	Columbia 33SX 1522	GREATEST HITS (LP)	10
64	Columbia 33SX 1619	DANCE WITH THE SHADOWS (LP, also stereo SCX 3511)	14/17
65	Columbia 33SX 1736	THE SOUND OF THE SHADOWS (LP, also stereo SCX 3554)	15/18
65	Columbia 33SX 1791	MORE HITS! (LP, also stereo SCX 3578)	12
66	Columbia 33SX/SCX 6041	SHADOW MUSIC (LP)	12
67	Columbia S(C)X 6148	JIGSAW (LP)	15
67	Columbia S(C)X 6199	FROM HANK, BRUCE, BRIAN AND JOHN (LP)	14
68	Columbia S(C)X 6282	ESTABLISHED 1958 (LP, half by Cliff Richard, mono/stereo)	18/15

(the above LPs originally came with blue/black labels, later white/black label copies are worth half the value)

70	M. For Pleasure MFP 1388	WALKIN' WITH THE SHADOWS (LP, royal blue sleeve & red lettering)	10
70	Columbia SCX 6420	SHADES OF ROCK (LP)	10
72	World Records ALBUM 72	THE SHADOWS (6-LP box set)	30
73	EMI EMA 762	ROCKIN' WITH CURLY LEADS (LP)	15
77	EMI EMTV 3	TWENTY GOLDEN GREATS (LP, mispressing, side 2 plays Pink Floyd's "Animals")	12

(see also Cliff Richard, Drifters, Five Chesternuts, Hank Marvin, Marvin Welch & Farrar, Bruce Welch, John Henry Rostill, Brian Bennett, Jet Harris, Tony Meehan, Vipers Skiffle Group, Marty Wilde & Wildcats, Krewcats, Interns, Strangers, Wasp)

SHADOWS OF KNIGHT
66	Atlantic AT 4085	Gloria/Dark Side	15
66	Atlantic 584 021	Oh Yeah/Light Bulb Blues	15
66	Atlantic 584 045	Bad Little Woman/Gospel Zone	15
67	Atlantic 584 136	Someone Like Me/Three For Love	15
68	Buddah 201 024	Shake/From Way Out To Way Under	10
79	Radar ADA 11	GLORIA (LP)	10

SHADROCKS
67	Island WI 3061	Go Go Special/Count Down	10

SHAFTESBURY
80	OK OKA 001	THE LULL BEFORE THE STORM (LP, with insert)	35
81	OK OKA 002	WE ARE THE BOYS (LP)	20

BOBBY SHAFTO
62	Parlophone R 4870	Over And Over/I Want My Bed	6
62	Parlophone R 4958	Feel So Blue/I Haven't Got A Girl	5
64	Parlophone R 5130	She's My Girl/Wonderful You	4
64	Parlophone R 5167	Love, Love, Love (Don't Let Me Down)/I Don't Love You Anymore	4
64	Parlophone R 5184	Who Wouldn't Love A Girl Like That/I Remember	4
65	Parlophone R 5252	How Could You Do A Thing Like That To Me/Baby Then	4
66	Parlophone R 5403	Lonely Is As Lonely Does/The Same Old Room	4
66	Parlophone R 5481	A Little Like You/See Me Cry	4

SHAG NASTY
79	Shag Nasty SN 1	No Bullshit Just Rock 'n' Roll/Looking For A Love? (p/s)	5

SHAGRAT
90	Shagrat ORC 001	Amanda/Peppermint Flickstick (p/s)	4

(see also Tyrannosaurus Rex)

SHAKE
79	Sire SIR 4016	Culture Shock/Dream On (p/s)	4
79	Sire SIR 4016-10	Culture Shock/Glass House/Dream On/(But) Not Mine (10", p/s)	7
80	Sire SIR 4035	Invasion Of The Gamma Men/Night By Night (p/s)	4

(see also Rezillos, Jo Callis, TV 21)

SHAKEOUTS
65	Columbia DB 7613	Every Little Once In A While/Well Who's That	18

SHAKERS (U.K.)
63	Polydor NH 52158	Money/Memphis Tennessee	12
63	Polydor NH 52213	Hippy Hippy Shake/Dr. Feelgood	12
63	Polydor NH 52258	Money/Hippy Hippy Shake	12
64	Polydor NH 52272	Whole Lotta Lovin'/I Can Tell	12
63	Polydor 237 139	LET'S DO THE SLOP, TWIST, MADISON, HULLY GULLY WITH ... (LP)	25

(see also Kingsize Taylor & Dominoes)

SHAKERS (U.S.)
73	Probe PRO 582	One Wonderful Moment/Love, Love, Love	5
74	ABC ABC 4018	One Wonderful Moment/Love, Love, Love (reissue)	4

CHRIS SHAKESPEARE GLOBE SHOW
69	Page One POF 113	Ob La Di, Ob la Da/Tin Soldier	15

SHAKESPEAR'S SISTER
89	ffrr FPD 112	You're History/Dirty Mind (picture disc in p/s)	4

(see also Bananarama)

SHAKEY JAKE
69	Liberty LBL 83217E	FURTHER ON UP THE ROAD (LP)	15

SHAKEY VICK
69	Pye NSPL 18276	LITTLE WOMAN, YOU'RE SO SWEET (LP)	40

SHAKIN' PYRAMIDS
81	Cuban Libre DRINK 2	Reeferbilly Boogie/Wake Up Little Suzie/Harmonica Lisa (p/s)	5
81	Virgin VS 404	Take A Trip/Hellbent On Rockin'//Reeferbilly Boogie/I & Others (double pack)	4

SAM SHAM
69	Blue Cat BS 157	Drumbago's Dead/SPARTERS: Song Of The Year	7

SHAME
67	MGM MGM 1349	Don't Go Away Little Girl/Dreams Don't Bother Me	40

(see also Shy Limbs, King Crimson, Gods, Emerson Lake & Palmer)

SHAME

85	Fierce FRIGHT 003	Real Tears (1-sided, possibly unissued)	50+

SHAMEN

86	One Big Guitar OBG 003T	THEY MAY BE RIGHT ... BUT THEY'RE CERTAINLY WRONG (12" EP)	12
86	Skipping Kitten	WAYWARD WEDNESDAY IN MAY AFFAIR ("Four Letter Girl"/"Stay In Bed") (33rpm 1-sided flexidisc, with insert, free with 'Skipping Kitten' fanzine)	15/10
86	Moksha SOMA 1	Young Till Yesterday/World Theatre/Golden Hair (p/s)	7
86	Moksha SOMA 1T	Young Till Yesterday/It's All Around/World Theatre/ Strange Days Dream (12", p/s)	10
87	Moksha SOMA 2	Something About You/Do What You Will (p/s)	6
87	Moksha SOMA 2T	Something About You/Do What You Will/Grim Reaper Of Love (12", p/s)	8
87	Moksha SOMA 3	Christopher Mayhew Says/Shitting On Britain (p/s)	6
87	Moksha SOMA 3T	Christopher Mayhew Says/Fire Engine/Shitting On Britain/ Christopher Mayhew Says A Lot (12", p/s)	8
88	Moksha SOMA 4	Knature Of A Girl/Happy Days (p/s)	4
88	Moksha SOMA 4T	Knature Of A Girl/What's Going Down/Happy Days/ Sub Knature Of A Girl (12", p/s)	7
88	Ediesta CALC 069	Jesus Loves Amerika/Darkness In Zion/Do What You Will/ Sub Knature Dub (12", p/s)	7
88	Ediesta CALC CD 069	Jesus Loves Amerika/Darkness In Zion/Do What You Will/ Sub Knature Dub (CD)	7
88	Demon D 1063	Synergy/Misinformation/Adam Strange (LP sampler, white labels)	10
89	The Catalogue CAT 074	Purple Haze/SLEEPING DOGS WAKE: This Little Piggy/SUGARCUBES: Cindy/KITCHENS OF DISTINCTION: Margaret's Injection/HAM: Voulez Vous (square flexidisc with 'The Catalogue' magazine)	5/4
89	One Little Indian 30 TP 12	Ω Amigo/Ω A/Ω Pre-Mix/PH 1 (12", p/s)	7
90	One Little Indian 36 TP 7	Pro>gen (Beatmasters Mix)/(Dub Edit) (p/s)	4
90	One Little Indian 36 TP 12	Pro>gen (Paul Oakenfold 'Land Of Oz' Mix)/Lightspan (Ben Chapman Mix) (12", p/s)	7
90	One Little Indian 36 TP7CD	Pro>gen (Paul Oakenfold 'Land Of Oz' Mix)/Lightspan (Ben Chapman Mix)/Pro>gen (Steve Osborne Mix) (CD)	8
90	One Little Indian 36 TP 7C	Pro>gen (C-Mix F+)/(Paul Oakenfold 'Land Of Oz' Mix)/Lightspan (Ben Chapman Mix)/(Beatmasters Mix) (cassette)	5
90	One Little Indian 36 TP12L	Pro>gen (C-Mix F+)/Pro>gen 7b/Lightspan Soundwave (12", p/s)	12
87	Moksha SOMALP 1	DROP (LP, with free promotional poster)	10
89	Moksha SOMALP 3	PHORWARD (10" mini-LP with white card inner sleeve, some with free white label 7", "The S&N Sessions" [SOMA 7])	12/7
90	One L. Indian TPLP 22SP	EN-TACT (LP, 2 x 12", 45rpm, with inserts)	10

(see also Alone Again Or)

SHAMES

66	CBS 202344	Sugar And Spice/Ben Franklin's Almanac	20
66	CBS 202450	I Wanna Meet You/We Could Be Happy	6
67	CBS 2704	Mr Unreliable/Georgia	7
67	CBS 2929	It Could Be We're In Love/It Was Lonely When	4
68	CBS 3820	Greenburg Glickstein Charles David Smith And Jones/Warm	7

(see also Cryan' Shames)

SHAM 69

77	Step Forward SF 4	I Don't Wanna/Ulster/Red London (black & white photo p/s)	8
77	Step Forward SF 412	I Don't Wanna/Ulster/Red London (12", black & white photo p/s)	10
77	no label credit	Song Of The Streets/Fanx (1-sided concert freebie)	8
78	Polydor (no cat. no.)	What Have We Got? (1-sided freebie, red label)	10
78	Polydor 2058 966	Borstal Breakout/Hey Little Rich Boy (p/s)	4
78	Polydor 2059 023	Angels With Dirty Faces/The Cockney Kids Are Innocent (p/s)	4
78	Polydor 2059 050	If The Kids Are United/Sunday Morning Nightmare (p/s)	4
78	Polydor POSP 7	Hurry Up Harry/No Entry (p/s)	4
79	Step Forward SF 4	I Don't Wanna/Red London/Ulster (reissue, yellow p/s)	4
79	Step Forward SF 412	I Don't Wanna/Red London/Ulster (12" reissue, yellow p/s)	7
79	Polydor POSP 27	Questions And Answers/I Gotta Survive/With A Little Help From My Friends (p/s)	4
79	Polydor POSP 64	Hersham Boys/I Don't Wanna (live)/Tell Us The Truth (live) (p/s)	4
79	Polydor POSPX 64	Hersham Boys/I Don't Wanna (live)/Rip Off (live)/I'm A Man, I'm A Boy (live)/ Tell Us The Truth (live) (12", p/s)	7
79	Polydor POSP 82	You're A Better Man Than I/Give A Dog A Bone (p/s)	4
80	Polydor POSP 136	Tell The Children/Jack (p/s)	4
80	Polydor 2059 259	Unite And Win/I'm A Man (p/s)	4
79	Polydor POLD 5025	THE ADVENTURES OF THE HERSHAM BOYS (LP, with 12" EP [2812 045])	10
80	Polydor 2383 596	THE FIRST, THE BEST AND THE LAST (LP, with live EP [RIOT 1/2816 028])	10

(see also Jimmy Pursey)

SHA NA NA

70	Buddah 2361 001	ROCK AND ROLL IS HERE TO STAY (LP)	10
71	Buddah 2319 007	SHA NA NA (LP)	10
72	Buddah 2319 019	THE NIGHT IS STILL YOUNG (LP)	10

SHA NA NETTES

75	Disco Demand DDS 114	Romeo And Juliet/Flint Nit Rock	5

WINSTON SHAN(D)

69	Bullet BU 399	Throw Me Corn/Darling Remember (B-side actually by Pat Edwards)	4
69	Bullet BU 411	Matilda (as Wilston Shan)/HARMONIANS: Come To Me	4
70	Moodisc MU 3505	I'll Run Away/Time Is The Master	4

DAVE SHAND & HIS ROCKIN' RHYTHM

56	Oriole CB 1321	You Can't Chop Your ... (Lizzie Borden)/Rockin' The Boat (78)	5

SHANE & SHANE GANG
64	Pye 7N 15662	Whistle Stop/Who Wrote That Song 10

JOHN SHANE
77	Full Moon	CROSS MY PALM WITH SILVER (LP) 12

VALERIE SHANE
58	Philips PB 833	When The Boys Talk About The Girls/Careful, Careful 4
58	Philips PB 879	One Billion Seven Million Thirty-Three/Meet Me Tonight In Dreamland 8
59	Philips PB 929	Make Love To Me/Baisez Moi (Kiss Me) 4

SHANES
65	Columbia DB 7601	I Don't Want Your Love/New Orleans 40

SHANGRI-LAS
64	Red Bird RB 10008	Remember (Walking In The Sand)/It's Easier To Cry 4
64	Red Bird RB 10014	Leader Of The Pack/What Is Love? 5
65	Red Bird RB 10018	Give Him A Great Big Kiss/Twist And Shout 6
65	Red Bird RB 10019	Maybe/Shout 10
65	Red Bird RB 10025	Out In The Streets/The Boy 6
65	Red Bird RB 10030	Give Us Your Blessings/Heaven Only Knows 8
65	Red Bird RB 10036	Right Now And Not Later/Train From Kansas City 15
66	Red Bird RB 10043	I Can Never Go Home Anymore/Bulldog 7
66	Red Bird RB 10048	Long Live Our Love/Sophisticated Boom Boom 8
66	Red Bird RB 10053	He Cried/Dressed In Black 8
66	Red Bird RB 10068	Past, Present, And Future/Paradise 10
67	Mercury MF 962	The Sweet Sound Of Summer/I'll Never Learn 4
67	Mercury MF 979	Take Your Time/Footsteps On The Roof 7
65	Red Bird RB 40 002	THE SHANGRI-LAS (EP) 30
66	Red Bird RB 40 004	I CAN NEVER GO HOME ANYMORE (EP, unreleased)
65	Red Bird RB 20 101	THE SHANGRI-LAS — LEADER OF THE PACK (LP) 40
66	Mercury MCL 20096	GOLDEN HITS OF THE SHANGRI-LAS (LP) 12

BUD SHANK
56	Vogue V 2376	Royal Garden Blues/It Had To Be You (with Bill Perkins Quintet) 4
56	Vogue V 2383	When Your Lover Has Gone/There's A Small Hotel (with Bob Brookmeyer) 4
56	Vogue V 2385	Shank's Pranks/Left Bank (with Shorty Rogers Quintet) 4

(see also Shorty Rogers)

RAVI SHANKAR
66	Fontana TF 712	Song From The Hills/Dhun 8
71	Apple APPLE 37	Joi Bangla/Oh Bhaugowan/Raga Mishri-Jhinjhoti (p/s) 15
74	Dark Horse AMS 7133	I Am Missing You/Lust (as Shankar Family & Friends) 4
59	Vogue VA 160156	INDIA'S MASTER MUSICIAN (LP, 2nd reissue) 20
62	HMV ASD 463	MUSIC OF INDIA (LP, reissue) 15
65	Fontana TF 5253	INDIA'S MASTER MUSICIAN (LP, reissue) 15
66	Fontana TL 5285	PORTRAIT OF GENIUS (LP) 15
66	Fontana TL 5357	SOUND OF THE SITAR (LP) 15
67	Fontana TL 5424	IN NEW YORK (LP) 15
67	HMV ASD 2304	DUETS: RAVI SHANKAR & ALI AKBAR KHAN (LP) 10
67	HMV ASD 2341	MUSIC OF INDIA NO. 4 (LP) 10
68	HMV ASD 2418	MUSIC OF INDIA NO. 8 (LP) 10
68	Liberty LBL/LBS 83076	IMPROVISATIONS (LP) 10
68	Liberty LBL/LBS 83077	IN CONCERT (LP) 10
68	Liberty LBL/LBS 83078	INDIA'S MASTER MUSICIAN (LP, 2nd reissue) 10
68	Liberty LBL/LBS 83079	PORTRAIT OF GENIUS (LP, reissue) 10
68	Liberty LBL/LBS 83080	SOUND OF THE SITAR (LP, reissue) 10
68	Liberty LBL/LBS 83081	IN NEW YORK (LP, reissue) 10
68	Columbia S(C)X 6273	LIVE AT THE MONTEREY POP FESTIVAL (LP) 12
69	Transatlantic TRA 182	A SITAR RECITAL (LP) 10
69	Transatlantic TRA 183	DHUN PALAS KAFI (LP, with Ali Akbar Khan) 10
71	Melodisc	FOUR RAGA MOODS (2-LP) 18
70	Columbia SCX 6382	RAVI SHANKAR IN SAN FRANCISCO (LP) 12
70	United Artists UAG 29379	AT THE WOODSTOCK FESTIVAL (LP) 10
71	Mushroom 300 MR 8	FOUR RAGA MOODS (2-LP, reissue) 45
73	Apple SAPDO 1002	IN CONCERT — 1972 (2-LP, with Ali Akbar Khan) 100
74	Dark Horse AMLH 22002	SHANKAR FAMILY & FRIENDS (LP) 10
76	Dark Horse AMLH 22007	RAVI SHANKAR'S MUSIC FESTIVAL FROM INDIA (LP) 10

(see also Ali Akbar Khan)

JOHNNY SHANLY
60	Columbia DB 4425	This Day I Promise/Makin' Love To You 4
60	Columbia DB 4526	I Wonder/It Happens That Way 4

DEAN SHANNON
60	HMV POP 820	Jezebel/Blinded With Love 10
62	HMV POP 1103	Ubangi Stomp/Blowing Wild 15

DEL SHANNON
61	London HLX 9317	Runaway/Jody 5
61	London HLX 9317	Runaway/Jody (mispressed B-side, plays MAXIMILIAN: "The Snake") 15
61	London HLX 9402	Hats Off To Larry/Don't Gild The Lily, Lily 5
61	London HLX 9462	So Long Baby/The Answer To Everything 4
62	London HLX 9515	Hey! Little Girl/You Never Talked About Me 4
62	London HLX 9587	Cry Myself To Sleep/I'm Gonna Move On 6
62	London HLX 9609	The Swiss Maid/Ginny In The Mirror 4
63	London HLX 9653	Little Town Flirt/The Wamboo 4
63	London HLX 9710	Two Kinds Of Teardrops/Kelly 4
63	London HLX 9761	Two Silhouettes/My Wild One 5
63	London HLU 9800	Sue's Gonna Be Mine/Since She's Gone 5

64	London HLU 9858	That's The Way Love Is/Time Of The Day	6
64	Stateside SS 269	Mary Jane/Stains On My Letter	5
64	Stateside SS 317	Handy Man/Give Her Lots Of Lovin'	5
64	Stateside SS 349	Do You Want To Dance/This Is All I Have To Give	5
65	Stateside SS 368	Keep Searchin' (We'll Follow The Sun)/Broken Promises	4
65	Stateside SS 395	Stranger In Town/Over You	5
65	Stateside SS 430	Break Up/Why Don't You Tell Him	6
65	Stateside SS 452	Move It On Over/She Still Remembers Tony	10
66	Stateside SS 494	I Can't Believe My Ears/I Wish I Wasn't Me Tonight	8
66	Liberty LIB 55866	The Big Hurt/I Got It Bad	8
66	Liberty LIB 55889	For A Little While/Hey Little Star	8
67	Liberty LIB 55939	She/What Makes You Run	8
67	Liberty LIB 10277	Mind Over Matter/Led Along	7
67	Liberty LBF 15020	Runaway '67/Show Me	7
68	Liberty LBF 15061	Thinkin' It Over/Runnin' On Back	8
68	Liberty LBF 15079	Gemini/Magical Musical Box	8
69	Stateside SS 8025	Comin' Back To Me/Sweet Mary Lou	8
70	Stateside SS 8040	Sister Isabelle/Colorado Rain	8
72	United Artists UP 35460	What's A Matter, Baby/Early In The Morning	7
75	United Artists UP 35535	Kelly (live)/Coppersville Yodel	5
74	United Artists UP 35740	And The Music Plays On/In My Arms Again	5
83	Demon D 1017	Cheap Love/Distant Ghost (p/s)	5
83	Demon D 1019	Sea Of Love/Help Me (p/s)	5
62	London RE-X 1332	DEL SHANNON (EP)	16
63	London RE-X 1346	DEL SHANNON NO. 2 (EP)	16
63	London RE-X 1383	DEL'S OWN FAVOURITES (EP)	16
63	London RE-X 1387	FROM DEL TO YOU (EP)	18
65	Stateside SE 1029	DEL SHANNON'S HITS (EP)	15
67	Liberty LEP 2272	THE NEW DEL SHANNON (EP)	30
61	London HA-X 2402	RUNAWAY WITH DEL DHANNON (LP)	30
63	London HA-X 8071	HATS OFF TO DEL SHANNON (LP)	25
63	London HA-X 8091	LITTLE TOWN FLIRT (LP)	25
65	Stateside SL 10115	HANDY MAN (LP)	22
65	Stateside SL 10130	DEL SHANNON SINGS HANK WILLIAMS (LP)	22
65	Stateside SL 10140	ONE THOUSAND SIX HUNDRED AND SIXTY-ONE SECONDS WITH DEL SHANNON (LP)	22
66	Liberty (S)LBY 1320	THIS IS MY BAG (LP, mono/stereo)	18/25
66	Liberty (S)LBY 1335	TOTAL COMMITMENT (LP, mono/stereo)	18/25
68	Liberty LBL/LBS 83114E	THE FURTHER ADVENTURES OF CHARLES WESTOVER (LP)	20
73	United Artists UAS 29474	LIVE IN ENGLAND (LP)	12

MIKE SHANNON & STRANGERS
(see under Strangers)

SHAPE OF THE RAIN

| 71 | RCA Neon NE 7 | RILEY RILEY WOOD & WAGGET (LP) | 25 |

SHAPES & SIZES

| 66 | Decca F 12441 | A Little Lovin' Somethin'/Rain On My Face | 4 |

HELEN SHAPIRO

61	Columbia DB 4589	Don't Treat Me Like A Child/When I'm With You	5
61	Columbia DB 4670	You Don't Know/Marvellous Lie	4
61	Columbia DB 4715	Walkin' Back To Happiness/Kiss 'N' Run	4
62	Columbia DB 4782	Tell Me What He Said/I Apologise	4
62	Columbia DB 4824	Let's Talk About Love/Sometime Yesterday	4
62	Columbia DB 4869	I Don't Care/Little Miss Lonely	4
62	Columbia DB 4908	Keep Away From Other Girls/Cry My Heart Out	4
63	Columbia DB 4966	Queen For Tonight/Daddy Couldn't Get Me One Of Those	4
63	Columbia DB 7026	Woe Is Me/I Walked Right In	4
63	Columbia DB 7072	Not Responsible/No Trespassing	4
63	Columbia DB 7130	Look Who It Is/Walking In My Dreams	4
64	Columbia DB 7190	Fever/Ole Father Time	6
64	Columbia DB 7266	Look Over Your Shoulder/You Won't Come Home	5
64	Columbia DB 7340	Shop Around/He Knows How To Love Me	7
64	Columbia DB 7395	I Wish I'd Never Loved You/I Was Only Kidding	5
65	Columbia DB 7517	Tomorrow Is Another Day/It's So Funny I Could Cry	5
65	Columbia DB 7587	Here In Your Arms/Only Once	5
66	Columbia DB 7810	Forget About The Bad Things/Wait A Little Longer	5
66	Columbia DB 8073	In My Calendar/Empty House	5
67	Columbia DB 8148	Make Me Belong To You/The Way Of The World	5
67	Columbia DB 8256	Stop And You Will Become Aware/She Needs Company	50
68	Pye 7N 17600	You'll Get Me Loving You/Silly Boy (I Love You)	6
69	Pye 7N 17714	Today Has Been Cancelled/Face The Music	6
69	Pye 7N 17785	You've Guessed/Take Me For Awhile	6
70	Pye 7N 17893	Take Down A Note Miss Smith/Couldn't You See	6
70	Pye 7N 17975	Waiting On The Shores Of Nowhere/A Glass Of Wine	6
84	Oval OVAL 26	Brickyard Blues/Just Another Weekend	
61	Columbia SEG 8128	HELEN (EP, 2 different sleeves for mono issue, also stereo ESG 7872)	8/12
61	Columbia SEG 8136	HELEN'S HIT PARADE (EP)	8
62	Columbia SEG 8170	A TEENAGER SINGS THE BLUES (EP, also stereo ESG 7880)	10/15
62	Columbia SEG 8174	MORE HITS FROM HELEN (EP)	8
62	Columbia SEG 8209	EVEN MORE HITS FROM HELEN (EP)	8
63	Columbia SEG 8229	'TOPS' WITH ME NO. 1 (EP, also stereo ESG 7888)	15/30
63	Columbia SEG 8243	'TOPS' WITH ME NO. 2 (EP, also stereo ESG 7891)	15/30
63	Columbia SEG 8268	HELEN'S HIT PARADE VOL. 2 (EP)	8
62	Columbia 33SX 1397	'TOPS' WITH ME (LP, also stereo SCX 3428)	14/25
63	Columbia 33SX 1494	HELEN'S SIXTEEN (LP, also stereo SCX 3470)	18/30

MINT VALUE £

63	Columbia 33SX 1561	HELEN IN NASHVILLE (LP)	20
64	Columbia 33SX 1661	HELEN HITS OUT (LP, also stereo SCX 3533)	20/30
65	EMI Encore! ENC 209	12 HITS AND A MISS HELEN SHAPIRO (LP)	15

(see also Ella Stone & Moss)

SHARADES
| 64 | Decca F 11811 | Dumb Head/Boy Trouble .... | 40 |

(see also Breakaways)

BILLY SHA RAE
| 71 | Action ACT 4602 | Do It/Crying Clown .... | 7 |

(BILLY) SHARI
| 58 | Decca F 11069 | Going Home For Christmas/Count Every Star (as Shari) .... | 4 |
| 68 | United Artists UP 2235 | It's So Lonely Being Together/You Walked Out On Me Before .... | 4 |

SHARKEY & HIS KINGS OF DIXIELAND
57	Capitol CL 14767	Look Sharp, Be Sharp/Sharkey Strut	4
51	Capitol LC 6531	SHARKEY'S SOUTHERN COMFORT (10" LP)	10
53	Capitol LC 6600	MIDNIGHT ON BOURBON STREET (10" LP)	10
54	Melodisc MLP 503	SHARKEY'S KINGS OF DIXIELAND (10" LP)	10

SHARKS
| 68 | RCA RCA 1776 | Goodbye Lorene/Funkology .... | 7 |

SHARKS
| 73 | Island ILPS 9233 | FIRST WATER (LP, 'palm tree' label) .... | 10 |
| 74 | Island ILPS 9271 | JAB IT IN YOUR EYE (LP, with inner sleeve, 'palm tree' label) .... | 10 |

(see also Chris Spedding, Andy Fraser Band)

SHARK TABOO
| 82 | Risque SRTS 82CUS1374 | Crossfire/Dream Crumble (no p/s) .... | 4 |

SHARK VEGAS
| 85 | Factory FAC 111D | You Hurt Me But Now Your Flesh Lays Rotting In Hell (cassette EP, with insert) . . | 4 |

SHARONETTES
| 75 | Black Magic BM 102 | Papa Ooh Mow Mow/Papa Ooh Mow Mow (Instrumental Version) .... | 4 |
| 75 | Black Magic BM 104 | Going To A Go Go/Going To A Go Go (Instrumental Version) .... | 4 |

RALPH SHARON
53	Decca LF 1107	SPRING FEVER (10" LP)	10
53	Decca LF 1138	AUTUMN LEAVES (10" LP)	10
53	Lyragon AF 1	COCKTAIL TIME (10" LP)	15

SHARONS
| 70 | Emblem JDR 325 | SOMEONE TO TURN TO (LP) .... | 75 |

BOBBY SHARP & OTHERS
| 65 | Stateside SS 404 | Blues For Mr. Charlie Pts 1 & 2 (with Paul Sindap, Joe Lee Wilson & Little Butler) | 4 |

DEE DEE SHARP
62	Columbia DB 4818	Mashed Potato Time/Set My Heart At Ease	8
62	Columbia DB 4874	Gravy (For My Mashed Potatoes)/Baby Cakes	8
62	Cameo Parkway C 230	Ride/Night	6
63	Cameo Parkway C 244	Do The Bird/Lover Boy	10
63	Cameo Parkway C 260	Rock Me In The Cradle Of Love/You'll Never Be Mine	8
63	Cameo Parkway C 274	Wild/Why Doncha Ask Me	6
65	Cameo Parkway C 375	Standing In The Need Of Love/I Really Love You	35
65	Cameo Parkway C 382	It's A Funny Situation/There Ain't Nothing I Wouldn't Do (demo only)	35
66	Atlantic 584 056	My Best Friend's Man/Bye Bye Baby	10
69	Action ACT 4522	What Kind Of Lady/You're Gonna Miss Me	20

STEVIE SHARP & CLEANCUTS
| 80 | Happy Face MM 122 | We Are The Mods/He Wants To Be A Mod (no p/s) .... | 40 |

BILL SHARPE
| 85 | Polydor 825497-2 | FAMOUS PEOPLE (CD) .... | 16 |

(see also Sharpe & Numan)

RAY SHARPE
59	London HLW 8932	Linda Lu/Red Sails In The Sunset	25
59	London HLW 8932	Linda Lu/Red Sails In The Sunset (78)	25
63	United Artists UP 1032	Hey Little Girl/Day You Left Me	15

SHARPE & NUMAN
85	Polydor POSPP 722	Change Your Mind/Remix, Remake, Remodel (picture disc)	8
85	Polydor POSPX 722	Change Your Mind (Extended Mix)/Remix, Remake, Remodel/Fools In A World Of Fire (12", picture disc)	12
86	Numa NUP 19	New Thing From London Town/Time To Die (picture disc)	5
86	Numa NUMP 19	New Thing From London Town (Extended Mix)/Time To Die (12", picture disc) . .	10
88	Polydor POSP B/W/T 894	No More Lies/Voices (p/s, blue, white or clear vinyl)	6
88	Polydor POSPP 894	No More Lies/Voices (picture disc)	5
88	Polydor POPX 894	No More Lies (Extended Mix)/Voices (12", picture disc)	8
88	Polydor POCD 894	No More Lies (Extended Mix)/Voices/Change Your Mind/No More Lies (CD, some autographed)	8
89	Polydor POPB 43	I'm On Automatic/No More Lies ('89 Remix) (poster p/s)	6
89	Polydor PO 43	I'm On Automatic/Love Like A Ghost (p/s)	4
89	Polydor POPD 43	I'm On Automatic/Love Like A Ghost (picture disc)	6
89	Polydor PZ 43	I'm On Automatic (Extended Mix)/Love Like A Ghost (12", picture disc)	8
89	Polydor PVCD 43	I'm On Automatic (12" mix)/Love Like A Ghost/Voices ('89 Remix) (CD)	7

(see also Gary Numan, Bill Sharpe)

SHARPEES
| 66 | Stateside SS 495 | Tired Of Being Lonely/Just To Please You .... | 45 |

| 74 | President PT 389 | Do The 45/Make Up Your Mind | 5 |
| 74 | President PT 399 | Tired Of Being Lonely/Just To Please You (reissue) | 5 |

BOB SHARPLES & HIS (DANCE) MUSIC/ORCHESTRA

55	Decca F 10450	Capitano/Time Remembered	4
56	Decca F 10707	Hurricane Boogie/Concetta	6
56	Decca F 10748	The Portugese Washerwoman/Sadie's Shawl	4

SHARPS

57	Vogue V 9086	Lock My Heart/Love Is Here To Stay	150
57	Vogue V 9086	Lock My Heart/Love Is Here To Stay (78)	30
58	Vogue V 9096	Shufflin'/What Will I Gain	125
58	Vogue V 9096	Shufflin'/What Will I Gain (78)	30
	see also Thurston Harris)		

S-HATERS

| 81 | Outer Himmilayan OHR 02 | Death Of A Vampire/Research (p/s) | 5 |
| 81 | Outer Himmilayan OHR 05 | STORIES AS COLD AS THE IRISH SEA (EP, foldover p/s) | 4 |

SHAVED FISH

| 87 | Antar ANTAR 4501 | Two Minutes Silence/Two Minutes Silence (Demo Version) (p/s) | 4 |

ARTIE SHAW

54	Brunswick LA 8677	SPEAK TO ME OF LOVE (10" LP)	12
55	Columbia Clef 33C 9006	ARTIE SHAW AND HIS GRAMERCY FIVE (10" LP)	12
58	RCA RD 27065	ANY OLD TIME (LP)	10

GEORGIE SHAW

55	Brunswick 05356	Give Me The Right/Yearning (Just For You)	4
55	Brunswick 05362	Unsuspecting Heart/Let Me Go, Devil	4
55	Brunswick 05426	I'll Step Aside/The Water Tumbler Tune	4
55	Brunswick 05476	Banjo Woogie/I Can Tell	6
	(see also Kitty Kallen)		

MARLENA SHAW

67	Chess CRS 8054	Mercy Mercy Mercy/Go Away Little Boy	8
76	United Artists UP 36125	It's Better Than Walking Out/Be For Real	4
76	United Artists UP 36163	Love Has Gone Away/No Hiding Place	5
77	CBS 5550	Go Away Little Boy/Look At Me Look At You	5

NINA SHAW

68	CBS 3239	Woven In My Soul/Love So Fine	6
68	CBS 3556	From Now Till Then/Window Of My Mind	4
69	CBS 4227	One Fine Day/Somewhere In The World	4

RICKY SHAW

| 62 | London HLU 9606 | No Love But Your Love/Be Still, Be Still, My Own | 6 |

ROLAND SHAW ORCHESTRA

54	Decca F 10407	No One But You (with Kim Bennett)/The High And The Mighty	4
55	Decca F 10449	Softly, Softly (with Kim Bennett)/A Trumpeter's Lullaby	4
67	Decca F 12595	The Look Of Love/Have No Fear, Mr Bond Is Here	4
66	Decca DFE 8670	I SPY (EP)	15
65	Decca LK 4730	JAMES BOND IN ACTION (LP)	15

SANDIE SHAW

64	Pye 7N 15671	As Long As You're Happy Baby/Ya-Ya-Da-Da	20
66	Pye 7N 17212	Think Sometimes About Me/Hide All Emotion	4
68	Pye 7N 17564	Show Me/One More Life	4
68	Pye 7N 17587	Together/Turn On The Sunshine	4
60s	Pye 7N series	other 45s	3
84	Rough Trade RT 130	Hand In Glove/I Don't Owe You Anything (p/s, with Smiths)	6
84	Rough Trade RTT 130	Hand In Glove/I Don't Owe You Anything/Jeanne (12", p/s, with Smiths)	10
64	Pye NEP 24208	(THERE'S) ALWAYS SOMETHING THERE TO REMIND ME (EP)	8
65	Pye NEP 24220	LONG LIVE LOVE (EP)	8
65	Pye NEP 24232	TALK ABOUT LOVE (EP)	8
65	Pye NEP 24234	SANDIE (EP)	8
66	Pye NEP 24236	MESSAGE UNDERSTOOD (EP)	8
66	Pye NEP 24237	TOMORROW (EP)	15
66	Pye NEP 24264	RUN WITH SANDIE SHAW (EP)	15
67	Pye NEP 24271	SANDIE SHAW IN FRENCH (EP)	20
67	Pye NEP 24273	SANDIE SHAW IN ITALIAN (EP)	20
67	Pye NEP 24281	TELL THE BOYS (EP)	15
65	Pye NPL 18110	SANDIE SHAW (LP)	12
65	Pye NPL 18122	ME (LP)	12
67	Pye N(S)PL 18110	PUPPET ON A STRING (LP)	12
67	Pye N(S)PL 18205	LOVE ME, PLEASE LOVE ME (LP)	12
68	Pye N(S)PL 18232	THE SANDIE SHAW SUPPLEMENT (LP)	10
70	Pye N(S)PL 18323	REVIEWING THE SITUATION (LP)	10

SANDY SHAW

| 58 | Starlite ST45 007 | Hello, Goodbye/TERRY TAYLOR: The Only Way | 5 |

THOMAS SHAW

| 72 | Xtra XTRA 1132 | THOMAS SHAW (LP) | 12 |

TIMMY SHAW & STERNPHONES

| 64 | Pye Intl. 7N 25239 | Gonna Send You Back To Georgia/I'm A Lonely Guy | 10 |

DOROTHY SHAY

| 53 | Capitol LC 6618 | THE PARK AVENUE HILLBILLIE (10" LP) | 10 |

GEORGE BEVERLY SHEA

| 54 | HMV 7M 184 | Robe Of Calvary/I Found A Friend | 4 |

MINT VALUE £

54	HMV 7M 204	I'd Rather Have Jesus/Tenderly He Watches	4
54	HMV 7M 205	If You Know The Lord/The King Of All Kings	4
54	HMV 7M 218	He Bought My Soul At Calvary/Each Step Of The Way	4

GEORGE SHEARING (QUINTET)

53	MGM SP 1006	I'll Remember April/Jumping With Symphony Sid	4
53	MGM SP 1017	There's A Lull In My Life/Bassic English	4
53	MGM SP 1031	Night Flight/Love (Your Magic Spell Is Everywhere) (B-side with Teddi King)	4
53	MGM SP 1035	How High The Moon/So This Is Cuba	4
53	MGM SP 1046	Body And Soul/The Lady Is A Tramp	4
53	MGM SP 1047	Love Is Just Around The Corner/Point And Counterpoint	4
54	MGM SP 1066	Tiempo De Cencerro (both sides)	4
54	MGM SP 1080	Rap Your Troubles In Drums/Love Is Here To Stay	4
54	MGM SP 1090	Spring Is Here/Easy To Love	4
54	MGM SP 1103	Mambo Inn/I've Never Been In Love Before	4
56	MGM SP 1113	Lullaby Of Birdland/Get Off My Bach	4
56	MGM SP 1161	I'll Never Smile Again/If You Were The Only Girl In The World	4
56	MGM SP 1171	I Wished On The Moon/It's Easy To Remember (with Teddi King)	4
51	Decca LF 1036	THE NEARNESS OF YOU (10" LP, as George Shearing Trio)	10
52	MGM MGM-D 103	YOU'RE HEARING GEORGE SHEARING (10" LP)	10
53	MGM MGM-D 118	I HEAR MUSIC (10" LP)	10
54	MGM MGM-D 129	TOUCH OF GENIUS (10" LP)	10
56	Vogue LDE 188	THE VERY FIRST SESSION (10" LP)	10
56	Capitol LC 6803	THE SHEARING SPELL (10" LP)	10

(see also Peggy Lee)

HENRY SHED

| 71 | Stateside SS 2198 | Save The Last Dance For Me/Bend Me Shape Me | 5 |

SHEDS

| 80s | John Wayne's S'bags 1 | BIMBO EP (cassette, shrinkwrapped with free packet of tomato seeds) | 18 |

SHEEBA

| 81 | Ritz RITZ 6 | Horoscopes/You Came Through Love With Me (p/s) | 4 |

BOBBY SHEEN

| 66 | Capitol CL 15455 | Dr. Love/Sweet, Sweet Love | 50 |
| 72 | Capitol CL 15713 | Dr. Love/Sweet, Sweet Love (reissue) | 6 |

SHEEP (U.S.)

| 66 | Stateside SS 493 | Hide And Seek/Twelve Months Later | 12 |
| 69 | Stateside SS 2147 | Hide And Seek/HAWKS: The Grissle | 6 |

SHEEP (U.K.)

| 73 | Myrrh MYR 1000 | SHEEP (LP) | 40 |

(see also Lonesome Stone)

IREEN SHEER

| 74 | Polydor 2041 533 | Bye Bye I Love You/Roseberry Avenue | 6 |

SHEFFIELDS

64	Pye 7N 15600	It Must Be Love/Say Girl	40
64	Pye 7N 15627	I Got My Mojo Working/Hey Hey Lover Boy	50
65	Pye 7N 15767	Bag's Groove (Skat Walking)/Plenty Of Love	60

SHEIKS (U.S.)

| 59 | London HLW 9012 | Tres Chic/Little French Doll | 6 |

SHEIKS (U.K.)

| 66 | Parlophone R 5500 | Missing You/Tell Me Bird | 7 |

ERNIE SHELBY

| 74 | Mojo 2093 026 | Bend Over Backwards/Punish Me | 4 |

DOUG SHELDON

61	Decca F 11368	The Book Of Love/Play Me The Blues	5
61	Decca F 11398	Runaround Sue/Come With Me	4
61	Decca F 11416	Your Ma Said You Cried In Your Sleep/You're Only Fooling Yourself	4
62	Decca F 11433	My Kingdom For A Girl/You Never Had It So Good	4
62	Decca F 11463	A Big Big Baby/If You'd Be Mine	4
62	Decca F 11514	Lollipops And Roses/One Way To Say Goodbye	4
62	Decca F 11529	Live Now Pay Later/Me	4
63	Decca F 11564	I Saw Linda Yesterday/My Billy	4
63	Decca F 11654	Let's Make A Habit Of This/I Was Alone	5
63	Decca F 11790	Mickey's Monkey/Falling In Love With Love	6
65	Sue WI 332	Take It Like A Man/Lonely Boy	8
65	Pye 7N 17011	It's Because Of You/How Can I Tell Her?	4
63	Decca DFE 8527	HERE I STAND (EP)	30

SANDI SHELDON

| 76 | Epic EPC 4186 | You're Gonna Make Me Love You/Baby You're Mine | 5 |

SHELL

| 66 | Columbia DB 8082 | Goodbye Little Girl/Little Bit Of Lovin' | 8 |

SHELLEY

64	Pye 7N 15711	I Will Be Wishing/Why Don't You Say You Love Me	8
65	Pye 7N 15773	Stairway To A Star/I Heard A Whisper	4
65	Pye 7N 15913	Where Has Your Smile Gone/Paradise	4

LIZ SHELLEY

| 65 | Brunswick 05940 | Make Me Your Baby/You Made Me Hurt | 7 |
| 66 | Brunswick 05953 | No More Love/I Can't Find You | 4 |

PETE SHELLEY

80	Groovy STP 2	SKY YEN (12", maxi single, p/s)	15
81	Island WID 6740	I Don't Know What It Is/Witness The Change//In Love With Someone Else/Maxine (double pack)	5
82	Lyntone 10952/53	Qu'est-Ce Que C'est, Qu'est Que Ça (Dub)/ANIMAL MAGNET: More (clear vinyl flexidisc with 'New Sounds, New Styles' magazine, issue 9)	5/4
82	Lyntone 10952/53	Qu'est-Ce Que C'est, Qu'est Que Ça (Dub)/ANIMAL MAGNET: More (hard vinyl test pressing)	10

(see also Buzzcocks, Free Agents, Tiller Boys)

SHELLS

61	London HLU 9288	Baby, Oh Baby/Angel Eyes	25
62	London HLU 9644	It's A Happy Holiday/Deep In My Heart	15

ALAN SHELLY & MANU DIBANGO'S BROTHERS

69	Philips BF 1709	Lady Black Wife/Give Me Time	12

ANNE SHELTON

53	HMV 7M 164	Answer Me (Mutterlein)/The Bridge Of Sighs	8
54	HMV 7M 186	The Book/Why Does It Have To Be Me	8
54	HMV 7M 197	Cross Over The Bridge/(O Baby Mine) I Get So Lonely	8
54	HMV 7M 240	Goodnight, Well It's Time To Go/If I Give My Heart To You	8
54	HMV 7M 279	My Gypsy Heart/Teach Me Tonight	8
57	Philips JK 1012	Absent Friends/Seven Ages Of Man (jukebox issue)	8
58	Philips PB 779	Until They Sail/Ha! Ha! Ha!	5
58	Philips PB 815	The Girl He Left Behind/Sail Along, Silv'ry Moon	5
58	Philips PB 852	Volare/Do You Love Me Like You Kiss Me?	5
58	Philips PB 878	Hurry Home/I.T.A.L.Y. (I Trust And Love You)	5
59	Philips PB 920	Just Love Me/Could I Love You More	4
59	Philips PB 956	Now Hear This!/To Love And Be Loved	4
59	Philips PB 969	The Village Of St. Bernadette/You're Not Living In Vain	4
60	Philips PB 994	The Angels' Lullaby/Where Can I Go	4
60	Philips PB 1042	Papa Loves Mama/Come Back Again	4
61	Philips PB 1096	Sailor/Souvenir Of Ireland (p/s)	5
56	Decca DFE 6321	FOUR STANDARDS (EP)	8
56	Philips BBE 12090	ANNE SHELTON (EP)	15
58	Philips BBE 12169	THE SHELTON SOUND (EP)	7
58	Philips BBE 12205	ITALIAN TOUCH (EP)	7
58	Philips BBE 12218	ANNE SHELTON (EP)	7
59	Philips BBE 12292	JUST LOVE ME (EP)	7
60	Philips BBE 12344	SONGS OF FAITH (EP)	7
60	Philips BBE 12347	MY YIDDISHE MOMMA (EP, also stereo SBBE 9003)	7/8
61	Philips BBE 12430	FAVOURITES (EP)	7
62	Philips BBE 12526	SPRING FEVER (EP)	7
52	Decca LF 1023	FAVOURITES (10" LP)	20
53	Decca LF 1106	FAVOURITES VOL. 2 (10" LP)	20
57	Philips BBL 7188	THE SHELTON SOUND (LP)	15
59	Philips BBL 7291	SONGS FROM THE HEART (LP)	12
60	Philips BBL 7393	ANNE SHELTON SHOWCASE (LP)	10
62	Philips BBL 7541	A SOUVENIR OF IRELAND (LP, also stereo SBBL 664)	10/12
62	Ace Of Clubs ACL 1101	ANNE (LP)	10

JO SHELTON

59	Top Rank JAR 124	Tread Softly (You're Stepping On My Heart)/More, More, More Romancing	4
59	Top Rank JAR 245	If There Are Stars In My Eyes/I Need Your Arms Around Me	4

ROSCOE SHELTON

65	Sue WI 354	Strain On My Heart/Question	12

DEANNA SHENDERY

65	Decca F 12090	Comin' Home Baby/I've Got That Feeling	10

SHENLEY (Duffas) & ANNETTE

61	Blue Beat BB 72	Million Dollar Baby/The First Time I Met You	10

SHENLEY (Duffas) & HYACINTH (Brown)

66	Rio R 80	The World Is On A Wheel/ROY & CORNELL: Salvation	10

SHENLEY (Duffas) & (Little) LUNAN

65	Rio R 52	Something On Your Mind/The Rain Came Tumbling Down	10

SHEP & LIMELITES

61	Pye Intl. 7N 25090	Daddy's Home/This I Know	50
61	Pye Intl. 7N 25112	Ready For Your Love/You'll Be Sorry	35

JEAN SHEPARD

59	Capitol CL 15031	Jeopardy/Better Love Next Time	4
56	Capitol EAP 1030	SONGS OF A LOVE AFFAIR NO. 1 (EP)	7
56	Capitol EAP2 728	SONGS OF A LOVE AFFAIR NO. 2 (EP)	7
60	Capitol T 1253	THIS IS JEAN SHEPARD (LP)	10

BILL SHEPHERD ORCHESTRA

58	Pye 7N 15137	Big Guitar/Tequila	6
59	Pye 7N 15180	Inn Of The 6th Station/DR. BARNARDO'S CHILDREN: This Old Man	4

PAULINE SHEPHERD

57	Columbia DB 4010	Love Me To Pieces/Just Between You And Me	5

SHEPHERD BOYS (& GIRLS)

56	Columbia SCM 5282	Little Girls And Little Boys/Teenage Love (as Shepherd Boys & Girls)	6
56	Columbia DB 3816	Summer Sweetheart/Song For A Summer Night	4

SHEPHERD/SHEPPARD SISTERS

57	HMV POP 411	Alone (Why Must I Be Alone)/Congratulations To Someone	8
58	Mercury 7MT 196	Gettin' Ready For Freddy/Best Thing There Is (Is ...) (as Sheppard Sisters)	10
56	Mercury 7MT 218	Eating Pizza/A Boy And A Girl (as Sheppard Sisters)	6
58	Mercury AMT 1005	Dancing Baby/Is It A Crime?	6
63	London HLK 9681	Don't Mention My Name/What Makes Little Girls Cry	8
63	London HLK 9758	Talk Is Cheap/Greatest Lover	6

ARCHIE SHEPP

66	HMV CLP/CSD 3524	FOUR FOR TRANE (LP)	12
66	HMV CLP/CSD 3561	ON THIS NIGHT (LP)	12
67	HMV CLP/CSD 3600	LIVE IN SAN FRANCISCO (LP)	12
67	Polydor 623 235	ARCHIE SHEPP AND THE NEW YORK CONTEMPORARY FIVE (LP)	12
67	Fontana 681 014 ZL	RUFUS (LP, with John Tchicai)	12
68	Impulse MIPL/SIPL 508	MAMA TOO TIGHT (LP)	10
68	Polydor 623 267	NEW YORK CONTEMPORARY FIVE VOL. 2 (LP)	10
69	Impulse MILP/SIPL 512	THE MAGIC OF JU-JU (LP)	10
69	Impulse MIPL/SIPL 516	THE WAY AHEAD (LP)	10
69	Atlantic 583 732	ONE FOR THE TRANE (LP)	12
69	Impulse SIPL 520	THREE FOR A QUARTER, ONE FOR A DIME (LP)	10

(see also John Coltrane)

SHEPPARDS

70	Jay Boy BOY 30	Stubborn Heart/How Do You Feel	6

SHEPPERTON FLAMES

69	Deram DM 257	Take Me For What I Am/Goodbye	10

DANI SHERIDAN

66	Planet PLF 106	Guess I'm Dumb/Songs Of Love	12

MIKE SHERIDAN & NIGHT RIDERS

63	Columbia DB 7141	Tell Me What'cha Gonna Do/No Other Guy	20
63	Columbia DB 7183	Please Mr. Postman/In Love	15
64	Columbia DB 7302	What A Sweet Thing That Was/Fabulous	15
65	Columbia DB 7462	Here I Stand/Lonely Weekends	15

(see also Roy Wood, Idle Race, Mike Sheridan's Lot, Nightriders, Sheridan-Price)

MIKE SHERIDAN'S LOT

65	Columbia DB 7677	Take My Hand/Make Them Understand	20
66	Columbia DB 7798	Don't Turn Your Back On Me, Babe/Stop, Look, Listen	20

(see also Roy Wood, Idle Race, Mike Sheridan & Night Riders, Nightriders, Sheridan-Price)

TONY SHERIDAN (& BEAT BROTHERS)

64	Polydor NH 52315	Jambalaya/Will You Still Love Me Tomorrow (with Beat Brothers)	12
64	Polydor NH 52927	Skinnie Minnie/You'd Better Move On (with Beat Brothers)	12
75	Buk BU 3026	Lonely/I Should Have Stayed	4

(see also Bobby Patrick Big Six, Beat Brothers)

TONY SHERIDAN (& BEATLES)

62	Polydor NH 66833	My Bonnie (as Tony Sheridan & Beatles)/The Saints (orange label)	40
64	Polydor NH 52906	Sweet Georgia Brown/Nobody's Child (orange or red label label)	80/25
64	Polydor NH 52275	Cry For A Shadow/Why	40
64	Polydor NH 52317	Ain't She Sweet (A-side by Beatles)/If You Love Me Baby	35
64	Polydor NH 66833	My Bonnie (with Beatles)/The Saints (red label, 2 separate reissues)	12
63	Polydor EPH 21 610	MY BONNIE (EP, with Beatles, German pressing in British p/s, "Why" credited to 'Sheridan' or 'Sheridan-Crompton')	40
64	Polydor Special 236 201	THE BEATLES' FIRST (LP, as Tony Sheridan & Beatles, rough red label)	50
67	Polydor Special 236 201	THE BEATLES' FIRST (LP, reissue, smooth red label)	35
71	Contour 2870-111	THE EARLY YEARS (LP, as the Beatles featuring Tony Sheridan, 2nd reissue of "The Beatles' First", different sleeve)	12
80s	Polydor POLD 666	THE BEATLES' FIRST (LP, 3rd reissue, withdrawn)	40

(see also Beatles)

SHERIDAN-PRICE

70	Gemini GMS 009	Sometimes I Wonder (as Sheridan & Rick Price)/SHERIDAN: Lightning Never Strikes Twice	8
70	Gemini GME 1002	THIS IS TO CERTIFY THAT ... (LP)	18

(see also Rick Price, Mike Sheridan & Nightriders, Mike Sheridan's Lot, Idle Race)

ALLAN SHERMAN

63	Warner Bros WB 106	Hello Muddah! Hello Fadduh!/Rat Fink	4

BOBBY SHERMAN

69	Pye Intl. 7N 25498	Little Woman/One Too Many Mornings	4

GARRY SHERMAN ORCHESTRA

69	United Artists UP 35055	Alice's Restaurant Massacre/The Let Down	4

JOE SHERMAN

58	Fontana H 129	Miraculous Music Box/Make Me Laugh	4
58	Fontana H 147	Buttermilk/Please Don't Say Goodnight	4

BILLY SHERRILL

61	Mercury AMT 1131	Like Making Love/Rules Of The Game	5

SHERRYS

62	London HLW 9625	Pop Pop Pop-Pie/Your Hand In Mine	6
63	London HL 9686	Let's Stomp Again/Slop Time	8
63	London RE 1363	DO THE POPEYE (EP)	30

BOBBY SHERWOOD

55	Vogue Coral Q 72097	The Kentuckian Song/Far Away Places	4

ROBERTA SHERWOOD

56	Brunswick 05572	Lazy River/This Train	5
57	Brunswick 05654	Tears Don't Care Who Cries Them/You're Nobody Till Somebody Loves You	5
57	Brunswick 05670	Mary Lou/What Does It Matter	5
63	Stateside SS154	You Always Hurt The One You Love/In San Francisco	4
63	Stateside SL 10039	ON STAGE (LP)	10

TONY SHERWOOD TRIO

| 60s | Zodiac ZR 010 | Piano Boogie Twist/Tom Dooley | 8 |

SHERWOODS

| 61 | Pye Intl. 7N 25097 | El Scorpion/Nanette | 6 |
| 64 | Solar SRP 105 | Memories/Some Other Time | 4 |

SHE TRINITY

66	Columbia DB 7874	He Fought The Law/The Union Station Blues	5
66	Columbia DB 7943	Have I Sinned/Wild Flower	5
66	Columbia DB 7959	Wild Flower/The Man Who Took The Valise Off The Floor Of Grand Central Station At Noon	5
66	Columbia DB 7992	Yellow Submarine/Promise Me You'll Never Cry	7
67	CBS 2819	Across The Street/Over And Over Again	5
69	President PT 283	Hair/Climb That Tree	4

(see also Shotgun Express, Beryl Marsden)

SHEVELLES

| 63 | Oriole CB 1915 | Ooh Poo Pa Doo/Like I Love You | 6 |

SHEVELLS

64	United Artists UP 1059	I Could Conquer The World/How Would You Like Me To Love You	12
65	United Artists UP 1076	Walking On The Edge Of The World/Not So Close	12
65	United Artists UP 1081	Watermelon Man/Taking Over Your Life	12
66	United Artists UP 1125	Come On Home/I Gotta Travel All Over	30
68	Polydor 56239	Big City Lights/Coffee Song	10

(see also Mike Stevens & Shevells)

TONY SHEVETON

62	Oriole CB 1705	Lullaby Of Love/I Have A Feeling	6
62	Oriole CB 1726	Lonely Heart/Foolish Doubts	6
62	Oriole CB 1766	Hey Little Girl/Kissing Date	6
63	Oriole CB 1788	Runaround Sue Is Getting Married/I Love The Girl Next Door	6
63	Oriole CB 1895	Million Drums/Dance With Me	5
64	Oriole CB 1975	Excuses/Is It Me, Is It You?	6

(see also Tony Rich)

SHIDE & ACORN

| 73 | private pressing | UNDER THE TREE (LP) | 400 |

TREVOR SHIELD

| 69 | Trojan TR 644 | The Moon Is Playing A Trick/KING CANNON: Soul Special | 6 |

SHIELDS

| 58 | London HLD 8706 | You Cheated/That's The Way It's Gonna Be | 25 |
| 58 | London HLD 8706 | You Cheated/That's The Way It's Gonna Be (78) | 20 |

KEITH SHIELDS

67	Decca F 12572	Hey Gyp (Dig The Slowness)/Deep Inside Your Mind	40
67	Decca F 12609	The Wonder Of You/Run, Run, Run	10
67	Decca F 12666	So Hard Livin' Without You/Baby Do You Love Me	12

(see also Marty Wilde [& Wildcats])

SHILLELAGH SISTERS

| 84 | CBS WA 217 | Give Me My Freedom/Cheatin' Teasin' Man (picture disc) | 4 |

SHINDIGS

| 65 | Parlophone R 5316 | One Little Letter/What You Gonna Do | 25 |
| 65 | Parlophone R 5377 | A Little While Back/Why Say Goodbye | 25 |

SHINDOGS

| 67 | Fontana TF 790 | Who Do You Think You Are/Yes, I'm Going Home | 8 |

(see also Delaney & Bonnie, James Burton)

JOHNNY SHINES

| 69 | Blue Horizon 7-63212 | LAST NIGHT'S DREAM (LP) | 45 |
| 74 | Xtra XTRA 1142 | COUNTRY BLUES (LP) | 16 |

DON SHINN

| 69 | Columbia S(C)X 6319 | TEMPLES WITH PROPHETS (LP) | 22 |
| 69 | Columbia SCX 6355 | DEPARTURES (LP) | 18 |

(see also Soul Agents)

SHIP

| 72 | Elektra K 42122 | THE SHIP (LP) | 10 |

SHIRALEE

| 67 | Fontana TF 855 | I'll Stay By Your Side/Penny Wren | 10 |

SHIRELLES

58	Brunswick 05746	I Met Him On A Sunday/I Want You To Be My Boyfriend	30
58	Brunswick 05746	I Met Him On A Sunday/I Want You To Be My Boyfriend (78)	25
60	London HL 9233	Tonight's The Night/The Dance Is Over	12
60	Top Rank JAR 540	Will You Love Me Tomorrow/Boys	6
61	Top Rank JAR 549	Dedicated To The One I Love/Look-A-Here Baby	6
61	Top Rank JAR 567	Mama Said/Blue Holiday	6
61	Top Rank JAR 578	What A Sweet Thing That Was/A Thing Of The Past	5
61	Top Rank JAR 590	Big John/Twenty One	7

MINT VALUE £

Year	Label	Title	Value
62	Top Rank JAR 601	Baby It's You/The Things I Want To Hear	7
62	HMV POP 1019	Soldier Boy/Love Is A Swingin' Thing	7
62	Stateside SS 119	Welcome Home Baby/Mama Here Comes The Bride	8
62	Stateside SS 129	Stop The Music/It's Love That Really Counts	8
63	Stateside SS 152	Everybody Loves A Lover/I Don't Think So	6
63	Stateside SS 181	Foolish Little Girl/Not For All The Money In The World	6
63	Stateside SS 213	Don't Say Goodnight And Mean Goodbye/I Didn't Mean To Hurt You	6
63	Stateside SS 232	What Does A Girl Do/Don't Let It Happen To Us	6
63	Pye Intl. 7N 25229	It's A Mad, Mad, Mad, Mad World/31 Flavours	5
64	Pye Intl. 7N 25233	Tonight You're Gonna Fall In Love With Me/20th Century Rock And Roll	6
64	Pye Intl. 7N 25240	Sha La La/His Lips Get In The Way	7
64	Pye Intl. 7N 25279	Maybe Tonight/Lost Love	12
65	Pye Intl. 7N 25288	Are You Still My Baby/I Saw A Tear	6
66	Pye Intl. 7N 25386	Shades Of Blue/When The Boys Talk About The Girls	6
67	Pye Intl. 7N 25425	Too Much Of A Good Thing/Bright Shiny Colours	10
69	Mercury AMT 1093	There's A Storm Going On In My Heart/Call Me (If You Want Me)	12
71	United Artists UP 31592	Take Me/Dedicated To The One I Love	5
75	Pye Disco Demand DDS 115	Last Minute Miracle/March	4
61	Top Rank JKP 3012	THE SHIRELLES' SOUND (EP)	40
61	Top Rank 35-115	THE SHIRELLES SING — TO TRUMPET AND STRINGS (LP)	80
62	Stateside SL 10006	BABY IT'S YOU (LP)	50
63	Stateside SL 10041	THE SHIRELLES' HITS (LP)	35
70	Wand WNS 4	ETERNALLY SOUL (LP, with King Curtis)	10

(see also Shirley & Shirelles)

DON SHIRLEY

Year	Label	Title	Value
61	London HLA 9391	Water Boy/Freedom, I'm On My Way	4
62	London HLA 9503	I'll Drown My Tears/Lonesome Road	4
56	London HA-A 2003	PIANO PERSPECTIVES (LP)	10
56	London HA-A 2004	TONAL EXPRESSIONS (LP)	10

ROY SHIRLEY

Year	Label	Title	Value
66	Ska Beat JB 253	Paradise/Calling	10
66	Doctor Bird DB 1068	Hold Them/Be Good	10
67	Doctor Bird DB 1079	I'm A Winner/Sleeping Beauty	10
67	Doctor Bird DB 1088	Prophet/What To Do	10
67	Doctor Bird DB 1093	Musical Field/LEE PERRY & DYNAMITES: Trial And Crosses	10
67	Doctor Bird DB 1108	Thank You/Touch Them	10
68	Doctor Bird DB 1165	Hush A Bye/Musical Dinner	10
68	Doctor Bird DB 1168	Dance The Reggae/The Agreement	10
68	Giant GN 32	Dance Hall Arena/The Musical Train	10
68	Giant GN 33	Warming Up The Scene/GLEN ADAMS: Lonely Girl	10
67	Caltone CAL 101	Get On The Ball/JOHNNY MOORE: Sound And Soul	10
67	Island WI 3071	Musical War/Soul Voice	8
68	Island WI 3098	Thank You/Touch Them	8
68	Island WI 3108	Move All Day/Rollin' Rollin'	8
68	Island WI 3110	Million Dollar Baby/SENSATIONS: Long Time No See You Girl	8
68	Island WI 3118	Good Is Better Than Bad/Fantastic Lover	8
68	Island WI 3119	Facts Of Life/Leads Us Not Into Temptation (as Roy Shirley & Uniques)	10
68	Island WI 3125	If I Did Know/Good Ambition	8
68	Amalgamated AMG 815	The World Needs Love/Dance The A Ups	8
68	Fab FAB 54	Think About The Future/Golden Festival	10
69	Duke DU 18	Life/I Like Your Smile	5

(see also Val Bennett, Glen Adams)

SUSAN SHIRLEY

Year	Label	Title	Value
68	Mercury MF 1038	Sun Shines Out Of Your Shoes/Tomorrow Today	4
69	Mercury MF 1087	Too Many Tears/Boy From Boston	4
70	Philips 6006 037	Really Into Somethin'/My Friend The Clown	15

SHIRLEY & JOHNNY

Year	Label	Title	Value
64	Parlophone R 5149	It Must Me Love/I Don't Want To Know	4
65	Parlophone R 5246	Only Once/Make Me An Offer	4
65	Parlophone R 5319	Day Dreamin' Of You/Till You Say You'll Be Mine	4
66	Parlophone R 5411	I'm Sorry/Breakaway	4
67	Parlophone R 5630	And I Don't Want Your Love/There Go The Heartaches	4

SHIRLEY & LEE

Year	Label	Title	Value
56	Vogue V 9059	Let The Good Times Roll/Do You Mean To Hurt Me So	55
56	Vogue V 9059	Let The Good Times Roll/Do You Mean To Hurt Me So (78)	25
57	Vogue V 9063	I Feel Good/Now That It's Over	45
57	Vogue V 9063	I Feel Good/Now That It's Over (78)	20
57	Vogue V 9067	That's What I Wanna Do/When I Saw You	40
57	Vogue V 9067	That's What I Wanna Do/When I Saw You (78)	20
57	Vogue V 9072	Rock All Nite/Don't You Know I Love You	60
57	Vogue V 9072	Rock All Nite/Don't You Know I Love You (78)	25
57	Vogue V 9084	Rockin' With The Clock/The Flirt	60
57	Vogue V 9084	Rockin' With The Clock/The Flirt (78)	25
57	Vogue V 9088	I Want To Dance/Marry Me	35
57	Vogue V 9088	I Want To Dance/Marry Me (78)	20
57	Vogue V 9094	Feel So Good/You'd Be Thinking Of Me	45
57	Vogue V 9094	Feel So Good/You'd Be Thinking Of Me (78)	20
58	Vogue V 9103	I'll Thrill You/Love No One But You	35
58	Vogue V 9103	I'll Thrill You/Love No One But You (78)	20
58	Vogue V 9118	Everybody's Rockin'/Don't Leave Me Here To Cry	50
58	Vogue V 9118	Everybody's Rockin'/Don't Leave Me Here To Cry (78)	35
59	Vogue V 9129	All I Want To Do Is Cry/Come On And Have Your Fun	35
59	Vogue V 9129	All I Want To Do Is Cry/Come On And Have Your Fun (78)	25
59	Vogue V 9135	A Little Word/That's What I'll Do	35

59	Vogue V 9135	A Little Word/That's What I'll Do (78)	20
59	Vogue V 9137	I'll Do It/Lee's Dream	30
59	Vogue V 9137	I'll Do It/Lee's Dream (78)	20
59	Vogue V 9156	True Love/When Day Is Done	30
59	Vogue V 9156	True Love/When Day Is Done (78)	30
60	London HLI 9186	I've Been Loved Before/Like You Used To Do	20
60	London HLI 9209	Let The Good Times Roll/Keep Loving Me	15
65	Island WI 257	Let The Good Times Roll/I'm Gone	15
57	Vogue VE 1-70101	ROCK 'N' ROLL (EP)	150
60	Vogue VE 1-70145	SHIRLEY AND LEE (EP)	125

SHIRLEY & RUDE BOYS

| 65 | Blue Beat BB 375 | Gently Set Me Free/BUSTER'S ALL STARS: Rock Steady | 10 |

SHIRLEY & SHIRELLES

69	Bell BLL 1049	Look What You've Done To My Heart/A Most Unusual Boy	6
69	Bell BLL 1065	Plaything/Looking Glass	5
72	Bell BLL 1251	Look What You've Done To My Heart/A Most Unusual Boy (reissue)	4

(see also Shirelles)

SHIVA

82	Heavy Metal HEAVY 13	Rock Lives On/Sympathy For The Devil (p/s)	6
82	Heavy Metal HEAVY 11/13	THREE-PACK (3 x 7")	12
82	Heavy Metal HEAVY 16	Angel Of Mons (p/s)	6
82	Heavy Metal HMRLP 6	FIREDANCE (LP)	10

BUNNY SHIVEL

| 67 | Capitol CL 15487 | You'll Never Find Another Love Like Mine/The Slide | 10 |

JOYCE SHOCK

58	Philips PB 824	Take Your Foot From The Door!/I've Got Bells On My Heart	5
58	Philips PB 872	Hoopa Hoola/You're Not Losing A Daughter, Mama	6
59	Philips PB 934	Personality/I Can't Love You Anymore	4
59	Philips PB 934	Personality/I Can't Love You Anymore (78)	5
59	Philips PB 957	Cry, Baby, Cry/Dear Diary	4
59	Philips PB 957	Cry, Baby, Cry/Dear Diary (78)	5

SHOCK HEADED PETERS

84	él EL 1	I, Blood Brother Be/Truth Has Come (p/s)	6
84	él ONET	I, Blood Brother Be/Truth Has Come/Hate On Sight (12", p/s)	8
85	él Benelux ELT 3	The Kissing Of Gods/Heartbreak Hotel/Always Be Waiting/Mr. Very Big (12", p/s)	7
86	Beach Culture 3BC	LIFE EXTINGUISHER (12" EP)	7
85	él Benelux FIN 1	NOT BORN BEAUTIFUL (LP, with inner sleeve)	10
87	Produkt Korps PKLP 0020	FEAR ENGINE (LP)	10

(see also Lemon Kittens, Underneath, Karl Blake)

SHOCKING BLUE

69	Penny Farthing PEN 702	Venus/Hot Sand	4
70	Penny Farthing PEN 713	Mighty Joe/Wild Wind	4
70	Penny Farthing PEN 721	Never Marry A Railroad Man/Roll Engine Roll	4
70	Penny Farthing PEN 744	Sally Was A Good Old Girl/Long And Lonesome Road	4
71	Penny Farthing PEN 758	Shocking You/Waterloo	4
69	Penny Farthing PELS 500	SHOCKING BLUE AT HOME (LP)	15
70	Penny Farthing PELS 510	SCORPIO'S DANCE (LP)	15

SHOES (U.K.)

| 68 | Polydor BM 56739 | Farewell In The Rain/What In The World Is Love | 4 |

SHOES (U.S.)

| 79 | Sire SRK 6075 | BLACK VINYL SHOES (LP) | 10 |

TROY SHONDELL

61	London HLG 9432	This Time/Girl After Girl	8
62	Liberty LIB 55398	Island In The Sky/Tears From An Angel	6
63	London HL 9668	I Got A Woman/Some People Never Learn	8
64	London HAY 8128	MANY SIDES OF TROY SHONDELL (LP)	50

SHONDELLS

| 64 | Ember EMB S 191 | Don't Cry My Soldier Boy/My Love | 6 |

SHOOT

| 73 | EMI EMI 2026 | On The Frontier/Ships And Sails | 4 |
| 72 | EMI EMA 73 | ON THE FRONTIER (LP) | 12 |

(see also Raw Material)

SHOOTING STAR

| 79 | Virgin V 2130 | SHOOTING STAR (LP) | 10 |
| 81 | Virgin V 2221 | HANG ON TO YOUR LIFE (LP) | 10 |

SHOP ASSISTANTS

85	Subway Organisation SUBWAY 1	All Day Long/All That Ever Mattered/It's Up To You/Switzerland (red foldaround, hand coloured p/s in poly bag, later blue)	12/6
85	Subway Organisation GVP 007	Home Again/CHESTERFIELDS: Nose Out Of Joint (33rpm flexidisc, with 'The Underground' issue 4, 'Screed' & 'The Legend!' fanzines)	8/6
86	53rd & 3rd AGAAR 1	Safety Net/Somewhere In China/Almost Made It (p/s)	5
86	53rd & 3rd AGAAR 112	Safety Net/Somewhere In China/Almost Made It (12", p/s)	7
90	Avalanche AGAP 001C	Here It Comes/I'd Rather Be With You//You Trip Me Up/The Other One (with 33rpm Flexi Records flexidisc)	4
90	Avalanche AGAP 001B	Here It Comes/Look Out/I'd Rather Be With You/Adrenalin (box set with flexidisc, badge, postcard & lyric sheet, 1st 200 numbered)	6/4

(see also Buba & Shop Assistants)

MINT VALUE £

DINAH SHORE

53	HMV 7M 119	Keep It A Secret/Bella Musica	12
53	HMV 7M 139	Sweet Thing/Three-Cornered Tune	8
54	HMV 7M 183	Changing Partners/Think	8
54	HMV 7M 221	This Must Be The Place/Come Back To My Arms	8
54	HMV 7M 236	Three Coins In The Fountain/Pakistan	10
54	HMV 7M 250	If I Give My Heart To You/Let Me Know	10
56	HMV 7M 352	Love And Marriage/Compare	7
57	RCA RCA 1003	The Cattle Call/Promises, Promises (Skip Redwine)	5
58	RCA RCA 1054	Thirteen Men/I'll Never Say "Never Again" Again	4
58	RCA RCA 1060	The Secret Of Happiness/I've Never Left Your Arms	4
58	RCA RD 27072	HOLDING HANDS AT MIDNIGHT (LP)	12
59	Capitol (S)T 1247	DINA, YES INDEED! (LP)	10
60	Fontana Fortune Z 4026	BUTTONS AND BOWS (LP)	10
60	Capitol (S)T 1296	SOMEBODY LOVES ME (LP)	10
60	Capitol (S)T 1354	DINA SINGS SOME BLUES WITH RED (LP, with Red Norvo)	10

BRIAN SHORT

| 72 | Transatlantic TRA 245 | ANYTHING FOR A LAUGH (LP) | 15 |

(see also Black Cat Bones)

SHORT KUTS with EDDIE HARRISON

| 68 | United Artists UP 2233 | Your Eyes May Shine/Letting The Tears Tumbling Down | 12 |

SHORTWAVE BANDS

| 70s | Crescent ARS 111 | GREATEST HATS (LP) | 20 |

SHORTY & THEM

| 64 | Fontana TF 460 | Pills Or Love's Labours Lost/Live Laugh And Love | 20 |

SHOTGUN EXPRESS

| 66 | Columbia DB 8025 | I Could Feel The Whole World Turn Round/Curtains | 25 |
| 67 | Columbia DB 8178 | Funny 'Cos Neither Could I/Indian Thing | 25 |

(see also Rod Stewart, Peter Bardens, Spencer Davis, Brian Auger, She Trinity, Beryl Marsden, Fleetwood Mac)

SHOTS

| 65 | Columbia DB 7713 | She's A Liar/Keep A Hold Of What You've Got | 25 |

(see also Smoke)

SHOUTS

| 64 | React EA 001 | She Was My Baby/That's The Way It's Gonna Be | 10 |

SHOWBIZ KIDS

| 80s | Top Secret CON 1 | She Goes To Finos/I Don't Want To Discuss That (p/s) | 15 |

(see also Toy Dolls)

SHOWMEN

62	London HLP 9481	It Will Stand/Country Fool	30
62	London HLP 9571	The Wrong Girl/I Love You Can't You See	50
69	Pama PM 767	Action/What Would It Take	5

(see also Norman Johnson, General Johnson, Chairmen Of The Board)

SHOW OF HANDS

| 70 | Elektra EKS 74084 | FORMERLY ANTHRAX (LP, gatefold sleeve) | 10 |

SHOWSTOPPERS

68	Beacon 3-100	Ain't Nothing But A House Party/What Can A Man Do (red swirly label)	8
68	Beacon 3-106	Shake Your Mini/Heartbreaker	5
68	MGM MGM 1436	Eeny Meeny/How Easy Your Heart Forgets Me	4
69	Beacon BEA 100	Ain't Nothing But A House Party/What Can A Man Do (reissue, yellow label)	4
69	Beacon BEA 110	Don't Leave Me Standing In The Rain/Do You Need My Love	5
69	Beacon BEA 130	Just A Little Bit Of Lovin'/School Prom	4
71	Beacon BEA 177	Reach In The Goody Bag/How Do You Feel	4
71	Beacon BEA 182	Action Speaks Louder Than Words/Pick Up Your Smile	4

SHOWTIMERS

| 64 | HMV POP 1328 | You Must Be Joking/Don't Say Goodbye | 4 |

SHOX

| 80 | Axis AXIS 4 | No Turning Back/Lying Here (p/s) | 12 |
| 80 | Beggars Banquet BEG 33 | No Turning Back/Lying Here (p/s, reissue) | 8 |

SHRIEKBACK

| 84 | Arista SHRSD 1 | Hand On My Heart/Nerve (shaped picture disc) | 4 |
| 85 | Arista FSHRK 4 | Fish Below The Ice/Coelacanth//All Lined Up/My Spine Is The Bass Line (double pack) | 4 |

(see also Barry Andrews)

SHUBERT

| 68 | Fontana TF 942 | Until The Rains Come/Let Your Love Go | 12 |

MORT SHUMAN

59	Decca F 11184	I'm A Man/Turn Me Loose (initially triangular centre, later round centre)	40/20
66	Fontana TF 685	Cry A Little/She Ain't Nothing But A Little Child	4
67	Immediate IM 048	Monday Monday/Little Children	12

SHUSHA

74	United Artists UP 35699	Barun Baruneh/Wild Flowers	4
74	United Artists UP 35759	Ev'ry Time We Say Goodbye/Siren's Call	4
70	Tangent TGS 108	PERSIAN LOVE SONGS AND MYSTIC CHANTS (LP)	15
72	Tangent TGS 114	SONGS OF LONG TIME LOVERS (LP)	15
74	United Artists UAS 29575	SHUSHA (LP)	12
74	United Artists UAS 29684	THIS IS THE DAY (LP)	10
75	United Artists UAS 29879	BEFORE THE DELUGE (LP)	10

78	Tangent TGS 138	FROM EAST TO WEST (LP)	15

SHUTDOWNS
63	Colpix PX 11016	Four In The Floor/Beach Buggy	12

SHY
83	Ebony EBON 15	ONCE BITTEN TWICE SHY (LP)	20

SHY LIMBS
69	CBS 4190	Reputation/Love	40
69	CBS 4624	Lady In Black/Trick Or Two	40
(see also Shame)

SHY ONES
63	Oriole CB 1848	Nightcap/Carry Me Back	10
64	Oriole CB 1924	Le Route/Susanna	8
(see also Spotnicks)

SHYSTER
68	Polydor 56202	Tick Tock/That's A Hoe Down	80

LEROY SIBBLES & ROCKY ELLIS
68	Studio One SO 2042	Love Me Girl/WRIGGLERS: Reel Up	12

DUDLEY SIBLEY
67	Coxsone CS 7010	Run Boy Run/Message Of Old (B-side actually by Joe Higgs & Ken Boothe)	15
67	Island WI 3034	Gun Man/The Monkey Speaks His Mind (B-side actually by Denzil Thorpe)	10

SICKIDZ
84	Big Beat SWT 97	I COULD GO TO HELL FOR YOU (EP)	4

SICK THINGS
83	Chaos CH 3	THE LEGENDARY SICK THINGS (EP)	4

SIDDELEYS
80s	Sha La La Ba Ba Ba 006	Wherever You Go/RESERVE: The Sun Slid Down (flexidisc with fanzines, p/s)	8/6
87	Medium Cool MC 005	What Went Wrong This Time? (p/s)	5
88	Sombrero THREE	Sunshine Thuggery/Are You Still Evil When You're Sleeping/Falling Off My Feet Again (12", p/s)	7

FRANK SIDEBOTTOM
87	In Tape IT 048	TIMPERLEY SUNSET (EP)	5
87	Go! Discs	THE BEASTIE PUPPETS (p/s, unreleased, demos only)	10+
(see also Chris Sievey, Freshies)

SIDEKICKS
66	RCA RCA 1538	Suspicions/Up On The Roof	10

ANN SIDNEY
65	HMV POP 1411	The Boy In The Woolly Sweater/Lonely Doll	4

SID PRESLEY EXPERIENCE
84	I.D. EYE 4	Hup 2-3-4/Public Enemy No. 1 (p/s)	8
84	I.D. EYET 4	Hup 2-3-4/Public Enemy No. 1 (12", p/s)	8
84	Sid Presley Exp. SPE 41	Cold Turkey/'F' For Fake/Firewater (12", stickered p/s)	10
(see also Godfathers)

PAUL SIEBEL
70	Elektra EKSN 45085	Bride 1945/Miss Cherry Lane	4
70	Elektra EKS 74064	WOODSMOKE & ORANGES (LP)	10
71	Elektra EKS 74081	JACK KNIFE GYPSY (LP)	10

SIEGEL-SCHWALL BAND
68	Vanguard SVRL 19044	SHAKE (LP)	12
71	RCA SF 8246	THE SIEGEL-SCHWALL BAND (LP)	12

CHRIS SIEVEY
79	Rabid TOSH 109	Baiser/Last (p/s)	4
79	Razz RAZZXEP 1	BAISER (33rpm EP, 2 tracks each by Sievey & Freshies, handwritten labels)	10
80	Razz RAZZ 4	My Tape's Gone/Moon Midsummer (some with fanzine, "True Life Revealing Confessions Of Romance And Love")	6/4
81	Razz RAZZ 5	Hey/FRESHIES: We're Like You (p/s)	4
82	Razz RAZZ 8	RED INDIAN MUSIC (EP)	5
82	Razz RAZZ 9	Skip The Flight/Jim Baiser ("Baiser"/"Last" with new labels & sleeve)	5
83	Random RND 1	Camouflage/(ZX 81 Programme "Camouflage")/Flying Train/F.T. (p/s, 'computer' single, B-side at 33rpm, 2,000 only)	5
80s	CV CVS 1	If You Really Love Me, Buy Me A Shirt/I Am The Walrus (with Freshies)	4
75	Hey Boss (no. cat. no.)	GIRL IN MY BLUE JEANS (16-track cassette, 250 only)	20
76	Razz CS-1	ALL SLEEPS SECRETS (cassette, 1,000 only)	12
80	Razz (no cat. no.)	NO GO DEMOS (cassette, with "Complete Book Of Rejection Slips" booklet, 400 only)	12
82	Razz RAZZ 4	DENIGRATION NOW (cassette, with booklet, 500 only)	10
85	11.37 ETS-S	DENIGRATION NOW (cassette, reissue with 2 extra tracks, 250 only)	10
86	Cordelia ERICAT 015	CHRIS SIEVEY'S BIG RECORD (LP, with free 7" "Baiser"/"Last" [TOSH 109])	10
(see also Freshies, Frank Sidebottom)

SIGHT & SOUND
68	Fontana TF 927	Ebenezer/Our Love (Is In The Pocket)	12
68	Fontana TF 982	Alley Alley/Little Jack Monday	12

BUNNY SIGLER
62	Cameo Parkway P 153	Let The Good Times Roll/There's No Love Left	12
73	Epic S EPC 1177	Tossin' And Turnin'/Picture Us	6
76	London HLU 10518	Let The Good Times Roll/Girl Don't Make Me Wait	4

SIGNS
66   Decca F 12522   Ain't You Got A Heart/My Baby Comes To Me 10

SIGUE SIGUE SPUTNIK
88   Parlophone 12SSSW 3   Success (Extended)/Frankenstein Cha Cha Cha (Extended)/Nightmare Of
                                            Neal X/Success Sputnik Style (12", picture disc) 7
(see also Sci Fi Sex Stars, Generation X, Sisters Of Mercy.)

SILENT MAJORITY
71   Hot Wax HWX 110   Frightened Girl/Colours Of My Love 4

SILHOUETTES (U.S.)
58   Parlophone R 4407   Get A Job/I Am Lonely 30
58   Parlophone R 4407   Get A Job/I Am Lonely (78) 25
58   Parlophone R 4425   Headin' For The Poorhouse/Miss Thing 40
58   Parlophone R 4425   Headin' For The Poorhouse/Miss Thing (78) 25

SILHOUETTES (Jamaica)
69   Sound System SSR 103   In Times Like These (actually by Lloyd Jackson & Groovers)/
                                            In Times Like These 4

SILKIE
65   Fontana TF 556   Blood Red River/Close The Door Gently 4
65   Fontana TF 603   You've Got To Hide Your Love Away/City Winds 5
66   Fontana TF 659   Keys To My Soul/Leave Me To Cry 4
66   Fontana TF 709   Born To Be With You/So Sorry Now 4
65   Fontana TL 5256   THE SILKIE SING THE SONGS OF BOB DYLAN (LP) 15

JUDEE SILL
71   Asylum SYLA 8751   JUDEE SILL (LP) 12
73   Asylum SYL 9006   HEART FOOD (LP) 12

SILVER
68   Jolly JY 012   Things/Sweet Lovin' (as Silver) 6
70   Columbia Blue Beat DB 117 Love Me Forever/Sugar, Sugar (B-side as Silver & Noreen) 6
71   Fab FAB 163   Change Has Got To Come/Magnet Stomp (as Silver & Magnets) 6

ANDEE SILVER
64   HMV POP 1297   Too Young To Go Steady/Sleeping Beauty 5
64   HMV POP 1344   The Boy I Used To Know/What Do You Do 5
66   Fontana TF 666   Only Your Love Can Save Me/Window Shopping 5
69   Decca F 22872   Go Now/You're Just What I'm Looking For 4
69   Decca F 22953   With A Little Love/Te Quiero (unreleased)

EDDIE SILVER
58   Parlophone R 4439   Seven Steps To Love/Put A Ring On Her Finger 12
58   Parlophone R 4439   Seven Steps To Love/Put A Ring On Her Finger (78) 5
58   Parlophone R 4483   Rockin' Robin/The Ways Of A Woman In Love 8
58   Parlophone R 4483   Rockin' Robin/The Ways Of A Woman In Love (78) 5

HORACE SILVER QUINTET/TRIO
61   Blue Note 45-1750   Sister Sadie/Break City 8
63   Blue Note 45-1873   Too Much Sake Pts 1 & 2 8
63   Blue Note 45-1902   Let's Get To The Nitty Gritty/Silver's Serenade 8
64   Blue Note 45-1903   Sweet Sweetie Dee/Dragon Lady 8
54   Vogue LDE 065   THE HORACE SILVER TRIO (10" LP) 15

LORRAINE SILVER
65   Pye 7N 15922   Lost Summer Love/I'll Know You'll Be There 50
66   Pye 7N 17055   The Happy Faces/When The Light Starts Shining Thru Your Eyes 30

SILVER BULLITT
70s Philips 6073 808   Willpower Weak, Temptation Strong/Hittin' 5

SILVER BYKE
68   London HLZ 10200   Who Needs Tomorrow/I've Got Time 4

SILVER EAGLE
67   MGM MGM 1345   Theodore/True As A Brand New Lie 15

SILVERHEAD
73   Purple TPSA 7506   SILVERHEAD (LP) 10
73   Purple TPSA 7511   SIXTEEN AND SAVAGED (LP) 10

SILVER SISTERS
60   Parlophone R 4669   Waiting For The Stars To Shine/When A Boy Meets A Girl 5

SILVERS
66   Polydor BM 56094   What A Way To Start A Day/Blue Blue Eyes 5

PHIL SILVERS
60   Fontana Fortune Z 4040   BUGLE CALLS FOR BIG BAND (LP) 10

SILVER STARS STEEL BAND
63   Island ILP 904   THE SILVER STARS STEEL BAND (LP) 25

DOOLEY SILVERSPOON
76   Seville SEV 1022   Game Players/Believe In Me 5

SILVERSTARS
68   Trojan TR 646   Old Man Say/Promises 6

SILVERTONES
66   Doctor Bird DB 1028   True Confession (with Duke Reid)/TOMMY McCOOK & SUPERSONICS:
                                            More Love 10
66   Doctor Bird DB 1041   It's Real (with Lynn Tait & Boys)/LYNN TAIT & BOYS: Storm Warning 10
67   Treasure Isle TI 7020   Cool Down/TOMMY McCOOK & SUPERSONICS: Shadow Of Your Smile 10

68	Treasure Isle TI 7027	In The Midnight Hour/TOMMY McCOOK & SUPERSONICS: Soul For Sale	10
69	Trojan TR 7705	Intensified Change/Marie	6
73	Techniques TE 924	That's When It Hurts/I'll Take You Home	6
71	Trojan TRLS 69	SILVER BULLETS (LP)	12

(see also Valentines)

SILVERWING

80	Mayhem SILVER 1	Rock'n'Roll Are Four-Letter Words/High Class Woman (p/s)	6
82	Mayhem SILV 00212	Sittin' Pretty/Teenage Love/Flashbomb Fever/Rock'n'Roll Mayhem (12")	7
82	Mayhem SILV 3	That's Entertainment/Flashbomb Fever (poster p/s)	7
83	Bullet BULP 1	ALIVE & KICKING (LP)	10

(see also Pet Hate)

VICTOR SILVESTER & HIS ROCK 'N' ROLL RHYTHM

57	Columbia DB 3888	Rockin' Rhythm Roll/Society Rock	8
57	Columbia DB 3888	Rockin' Rhythm Roll/Society Rock (78)	5
57	Columbia DB 3907	Alligator Roll/Off Beat Rock	8
57	Columbia DB 3907	Alligator Roll/Off Beat Rock (78)	5

BEVERLEY SIMMONS

68	Pama PM 716	Mr. Pitiful/That's How Strong My Love Is	6
69	Pama PMLP/PMSP 9	REMEMBER OTIS (LP)	12

(JUMPIN') GENE SIMMONS

64	London HLU 9913	Haunted House/Hey, Hey Little Girl	10
64	London HLU 9933	The Jump/The Dodo	12

GENE SIMMONS

79	Casablanca CAN 134	Radioactive/When You Wish Upon A Star (p/s, red vinyl, with mask, picture label)	20
79	Casablanca CAN 134	Radioactive/When You Wish Upon A Star (p/s, black vinyl)	12

(see also Kiss)

JEFF SIMMONS

69	Straight STS 1057	LUCILLE HAS MESSED UP MY MIND (LP)	45

(see also Frank Zappa)

LITTLE MAC SIMMONS

66	Outasite OSEP 1	BLUES FROM CHICAGO (EP)	70

SIMTEC SIMMONS

75	Contempo CS 2053	Some Other Time/Classified Crazy Man	4

ZOOT SIMMS

62	Blue Beat BB 133	Press Along/PRINCE BUSTER ALL STARS: 100 Ton Megaton	10
62	Blue Beat BB 143	Searching/White Christmas (as Simms & [Lloyd] Robinson)	10
64	Port-O-Jam PJ 4007	Please Don't Do It/Don't Do It (as Simms & [Lloyd] Robinson)	10
68	Blue Cat BS 118	Bye Bye Baby/AL & THRILLERS: Heart For Sale	10
69	Coxsone CS 7095	Tit For Tat/We Can Talk It Over (as Simms & Elmond)	12

SEIJA SIMOLA

78	Sonet SON 2145	Give Love A Chance/Little Smile (p/s)	12

JOE SIMON

75	Polydor 2006 551	Get Down Get Down/In My Baby's Arms	4
66	London HLU 10057	A Teenager's Prayer/Long Hot Summer	12
67	Monument MON 1004	My Special Prayer/Travelin' Man	6
68	Monument MON 1010	Nine Pound Steel/The Girl's Alright With Me	6
68	Monument MON 1014	No Sad Songs/Come On And Get It	5
68	Monument MON 1019	You Keep Me Hangin' On/What Makes A Man Feel Good	5
68	Monument MON 1025	Message From Maria/I Worry About You	5
69	Monument MON 1029	Looking Back/Standing In The Safety Zone	5
69	Monument MON 1032	The Chokin' Kind/Come On And Get It	5
69	Monument MON 1038	San Francisco Is A Lonely Town/It's Hard To Get Along	4
70	Monument MON 1042	Moon Walk Pts 1 & 2	4
70	Monument MON 1044	Further Down The Road/Wounded Man	4
70	Monument MON 1049	I Gotta Whole Lot Of Lovin'/Your Love	4
70	Monument MON 1051	That's The Way I Want Our Love/When	8
67	Monument LMO 5006	SIMON PURE SOUL (LP, also stereo SMO 5006)	10
68	Monument LMO 5017	NO SAD SONGS (LP, also stereo SMO 5017)	10
69	Monument LMO 5026	SIMON SINGS (LP, also stereo SMO 5026)	10
70	Monument LMO 5030	THE CHOKIN' KIND (LP, also stereo SMO 5030)	10
70	Monument LMO 5033	BETTER THAN EVER (LP, also stereo SMO 5033)	10
73	Mojo 2918 001	THE SOUNDS OF SIMON (LP)	10
74	Mojo 2918 003	DROWNING IN THE SEA OF LOVE (LP)	10

PAUL SIMON

65	CBS 201797	I Am A Rock/Leaves That Are Green	15
73	CBS 1545	Kodachrome (withdrawn, any pressed?)	10+
65	CBS 62579	THE PAUL SIMON SONGBOOK (LP, mono/stereo)	15
72	CBS CQ 30750/Q 69007	PAUL SIMON (LP, quadrophonic)	12
73	CBS CQ 32280/Q 69035	THERE GOES RHYMIN' SIMON (LP, quadrophonic)	12
75	CBS Q 86001	STILL CRAZY AFTER ALL THESE YEARS (LP, quadrophonic)	12

(see also Simon & Garfunkel, Jerry Landis, Tom & Jerry)

TONY SIMON

67	Track 604 012	Gimme A Little Sign/Never Too Much To Love	8

SIMON & GARFUNKEL

65	CBS 201977	The Sound Of Silence/We've Got A Groovy Thing Goin'	6
66	CBS 202045	Homeward Bound/Leaves That Are Green	6
66	CBS 202303	I Am A Rock/Flowers Never Bend With The Rainfall	6
66	CBS 202285	The Dangling Conversation/The Big Bright Green Pleasure Machine	12

SIMON & GARFUNKEL

66	CBS 202378	A Hazy Shade Of Winter/For Emily, Whenever I May Find Her	6
67	CBS 202608	The 59th Street Bridge Song (Feelin' Groovy)/At The Zoo	8
67	CBS 2911	Fakin' It/You Don't Know Where Your Interest Lies	8
68	CBS Special Products WB 728	The 59th Street Bridge Song (Feelin' Groovy)/TREMELOES: Here Comes My Baby (p/s, mail-order only with Pepsi Cola tokens)	5
65	CBS EP 6053	SIMON AND GARFUNKEL (EP)	8
66	CBS EP 6074	I AM A ROCK (EP)	7
67	CBS EP 6360	FEELING GROOVY (EP)	7
68	CBS EP 6400	MRS ROBINSON (EP)	10
66	CBS (S)BPG 62690	THE SOUNDS OF SILENCE (LP)	10
66	CBS (S)BPG 62860	PARSLEY, SAGE, ROSEMARY AND THYME (LP)	10
67	Allegro ALL 836	SIMON AND GARFUNKEL (LP)	20
68	CBS 70042	THE GRADUATE (LP, soundtrack, mono/stereo)	10
68	CBS 63370	WEDNESDAY MORNING 3AM (LP, mono/stereo)	10
73	CBS CQ 30995/Q 63699	BRIDGE OVER TROUBLED WATER (LP, quadrophonic)	12

(see also Paul Simon, Art Garfunkel, Tom & Jerry)

NINA SIMONE

59	Parlophone R 4583	I Loves You Porgy/Love Me Or Leave Me	6
59	Pye Intl. 7N 25029	Solitaire/Chilly Winds Don't Blow	6
63	Colpix PX 200	You Can Have Him/Return Home	5
64	Colpix PX 799	Exactly Like You/The Other Woman	5
65	Philips BF 1388	Don't Let Me Be Misunderstood/Monster	5
65	Philips BF 1415	I Put A Spell On You/Gimme Some	7
66	Philips BF 1465	Either Way I Lose/Break Down And Let It Out	8
67	RCA Victor RCA 1583	Do I Move You?/Day And Night	4
68	Philips BF 1736	I Put A Spell On You/Don't Let Me Be Misunderstood	4
68	Pye Intl. 7N 25466	The Other Woman/Exactly Like You	4
70	RCA Victor RCA 1697	Why? (The King Of Love Is Dead) Pts 1 & 2	4
61	Parlophone GEP 8844	MY BABY JUST CARES FOR ME (EP)	12
62	Parlophone GEP 8864	INTIMATE NINA SIMONE (EP)	10
64	Colpix PXE 303	FINE AND MELLOW (EP)	7
66	Colpix PXE 306	JUST SAY I LOVE HIM (EP)	7
66	Colpix PXE 307	I LOVE TO LOVE (EP)	7
65	Philips BE 12585	DON'T LET ME BE MISUNDERSTOOD (EP)	7
65	Philips BE 12589	STRANGE FRUIT (EP)	7
61	Pye Intl. NPL 28014	AT THE TOWN HALL (LP)	15
61	Pye Jazz NJL 36	FORBIDDEN FRUIT (LP)	15
64	Colpix PXL 465	FOLKSY NINA (LP)	12
65	Philips BL 7662	BROADWAY . . . BLUES . . . BALLADS (LP)	10
65	Philips BL 7671	I PUT A SPELL ON YOU (LP)	10
65	Colpix PXL 419	FORBIDDEN FRUIT (LP, reissue)	10
65	Philips BL 7678	IN CONCERT (LP)	10
65	Colpix PXL 421	NINA AT THE VILLAGE GATE (LP)	12
66	Philips BL 7683	PASTEL BLUES (LP)	10
66	Philips (S)BL 7722	LET IT ALL OUT (LP)	10
66	Philips BL 7726	WILD IS THE WIND (LP)	10
67	Philips BL 7764	HIGH PRIESTESS OF SOUL (LP)	10
67	RCA RD/SF 7883	SINGS THE BLUES (LP)	10
68	RCA RD/SF 7967	SILK AND SOUL (LP)	10

SUGAR SIMONE

66	Rainbow RAI 103	Is It Because/I Want To Know	5
67	Rainbow RAI 114	I Love My Baby/I'll Keep You Satisfied	5
67	Sue WI 4029	Suddenly/King Without A Throne	15
67	Go AJ 11409	It's Alright/Take It Easy	10
68	CBS 3250	The Vow/Spinning Wheel	6
69	Doctor Bird DB 1192	Black Is Gold/The Invitation	5
69	Doctor Bird DB 1193	The Squeeze Is On/Tell Me	5
69	Doctor Bird DB 1201	Come And Try/Don't Listen To What They Say	5
69	Fab FAB 106	Boom Biddy Boom/RUDIES: What Can I Do	5
69	Fab FAB 107	I Need A Witness/Johnny Dollar	5
69	Beacon BEA 156	Keep On Trying/Only The Lonely	4

(see also Sugar & Dandy)

SIMON PLUG & GRIMES

70	Deram DM 296	Is This A Dream?/I'm Going Home	8

SIMON'S SECRETS

67	CBS 3056	I Know What Her Name Is/Keeping My Head Above Water	12
68	CBS 3406	Naughty Boy/Sympathy	12

(see also Secrets, Clifford T. Ward, Martin Raynor & Secrets)

SIMON SISTERS

64	London HLR 9893	So Glad I'm Here/Winkin', Blinkin' And Nod	8
65	London HLR 9984	Cuddlebug/No One To Talk My Trouble To	6

SIMPLE IMAGE

70	Carnaby CNS 4013	Spinning Spinning Spinning/Shy Boy	4

SIMPLE MINDS

79	Zoom ZUM 10	Life In A Day/Special View (p/s)	8
79	Zoom ZUM 11	Chelsea Girl/Garden Of Hate (p/s)	7
80	Arista ARIST 325	Changeling/Premonition (live) (p/s)	12
80	Arista ARIST 372	I Travel/New Warm Skin (p/s, some with blue vinyl flexidisc: "Kaleidoscope"/"Film Theme Dub")	15/4
80	Arista ARIST 12372	I Travel (Mix)/Film Theme (12", p/s)	12
81	Arista ARIST 394	Celebrate/Changeling (p/s)	10
81	Arista ARIST 12394	Celebrate (Mix)/Changeling/I Travel (12", stickered p/s)	12
81	Virgin VS 410	The American/League Of Nations (p/s)	4

81	Virgin VS 410-12	The American/League Of Nations (12", p/s) 7
81	Virgin VS 434	Love Song/This Earth That You Walk Upon (p/s) 4
81	Virgin VS 434-12	Love Song/This Earth That You Walk Upon (12", p/s) 7
81	Virgin VS 451	Sweat In Bullet/20th Century Promised Land (p/s) 4
81	Virgin VS 451	Sweat In Bullet/20th Century Promised Land//Premonition (live)/League Of Nations (live) (double pack) 6
81	Virgin VS 451-12	Sweat In Bullet/20th Century Promised Land/LeagueOf Nations (live)/In Trance As Mission (live) (12", p/s) 7
82	Arista ARIST 448	I Travel/30 Frames A Second (live) (p/s, reissue) 5
82	Arista ARIST 12-448	I Travel (Mix)/30 Frames A Second (live)/I Travel (live) (12", p/s, reissue) 10
82	Virgin VS 538	Someone, Somewhere (In Summertime)/King Is White And In The Crowd (poster p/s) 8
82	Virgin VSY 538	Someone, Somewhere (In Summertime)/King Is White And In The Crowd (picture disc) 10
83	Virgin VS 578-12	I Travel (6.14)/Film Theme (12", p/s, 2nd reissue) 7
84	Virgin VSY 649	Speed Your Love To Me/Bass Line (picture disc) 10
84	Virgin VSY 661	Up On The Catwalk/A Brass Band In Africa (picture disc) 10
84	Virgin VS 661-12	Up On The Catwalk/A Brass Band In African Chimes (12", p/s) 8
85	Virgin VSS 749	Don't You (Forget About Me)/A Brass Band In Africa (shaped picture disc) 20
85	Virgin VS 749-12	Don't You (Forget About Me)/A Brass Band In African Chimes (12", p/s) 7
85	Virgin VS 817-13	Alive And Kicking/(Instrumental)/Up On The Catwalk (live) (12", gold p/s) 7
86	Virgin SMP 1	Sanctify Yourself/Sanctify Yourself (Instrumental)//Street Hassle (live)/Love Song (live) (double pack, gatefold p/s) 6
86	Virgin VS 860-12	All Things She Said/Don't You (Forget About Me) (live)/Promised You A Miracle (U.S. Remix) (12", p/s) 7
86	Virgin MIKE 907-12	Ghostdancing (Mix)/(Instrumental)/Jungleland (Mix)/(Instrumental) (CD) 10
87	Virgin SM 2-10	Promised You A Miracle (live)/Book Of Brilliant Things (live) (10", p/s with poster) 6
87	Virgin SMC 2-12	Promised You A Miracle (live)/Book Of Brilliant Things (live)/Glittering Prize (live)/Celebrate (live) (cassette) 5
89	Virgin SMX B3	BALLAD OF THE STREETS (12" box set, with 4 black & white photos) 8
89	Virgin SMX CD 3	BALLAD OF THE STREETS (CD) 7
89	Virgin SMXTG 4	This Is Your Land/Saturday Girl/Year Of The Dragon (12", gatefold p/s) 7
89	Virgin SMXC 5	Kick It In/Waterfront (Mix 89) (cassette) 4
89	Virgin SMXTG 5	Kick It In/Waterfront (Mix 89)/Kick It In (Mix) (12", gatefold p/s with 2-sided poster) 7
89	Virgin SMXTR 6	THE AMSTERDAM EP (12", gatefold p/s with fold-out poster) 7
79	Zoom ZULP 1	LIFE IN A SIMPLE DAY (LP, original issue) 10
80	Arista SPART 1109	REAL TO REAL (CACOPHONY) (LP, original issue) 10
80	Arista SPART 1140	EMPIRES AND DANCE (LP, original issue) 10
81	Virgin V 2207	SONS AND FASCINATION/SISTER FEELINGS CALL (2-LP, stickered & shrinkwrapped) 18
84	Virgin V 2300	SPARKLE IN THE RAIN (LP, white vinyl, stickered sleeve) 16
85	Virgin V2364	ONCE UPON A TIME (LP, picture disc in gatefold sleeve) 14
87	Virgin SMDL 1	LIVE IN THE CITY OF LIGHT (2-LP, with booklet & gold embossed sleeve) 14
89	Virgin SMBXC 1	STREET FIGHTING YEARS (box set, with interview cassettes, & songbook, no'd) 18

SIMPLY RED

85	Lyntone LYN 15914	Something's Burning/10,000 MANIACS: Grey Victory (33rpm 1-sided clear flexidisc free with 'Jamming' magazine, issue 29) 9/7
85	The Hit HOT 001	Every Bit Of Me/STYLE COUNCIL: Walls Come Tumbling Down (live)/REDSKINS: Kick Over The Statues (The Ramsey McKinnock Mix)/JESUS & MARY CHAIN: Taste Of Cindy (p/s, free with 'The Hit' mag, issue 1) 6/4
85	Elektra EKR 9P	Money's Too Tight To Mention/Open Up The Red Box (picture disc) 8
85	Elektra EKR 9TX	Money's Too Tight To Mention (Cutback Remix)/Open Up The Red Box/Money's Too Tight To Mention (Dub Version) (12", p/s) 8
85	Elektra EKR 19TX	Come To My Aid (Survival Mix)/Granma's Hand/Come To My Aid (Heavy Dub Mix)/Valentine (12", p/s) 7
85	Elektra EKR 29F	Holding Back The Years/I Won't Feel Bad (gatefold p/s, with poster) 5
85	Elektra EKR 29P	Holding Back The Years/I Won't Feel Bad (shaped picture disc) 20
86	WEA YZ 75B	Open Up The Red Box/Look At You Now (foldout box sleeve) 8
86	WEA YZ 75F	Open Up The Red Box/Look At You Now//Holding Back The Years/I Won't Feel Bad (double pack) 8
86	WEA YZ 75T	Open Up The Red Box (Remix)/Look At You Now (live)/Heaven The Musical (live) (12", p/s) 7
86	WEA YZ 75TF	Open Up The Red Box (Remix)/Look At You Now (live)/Heaven The Musical (live)//Money's Too Tight To Mention/Open Up The Red Box (12"/7" picture disc) 15
87	WEA YZ 103V	The Right Thing/There's A Light (foldout p/s) 4
87	WEA YZ 103P	The Right Thing/There's A Light (picture disc) 4
87	WEA YZ 103DP	The Right Thing/There's A Light//Holding Back The Years/Drowning In My Own Tears (double pack) 5
87	WEA YZ 103TP	The Right Thing/There's A Light/Everytime We Say Goodbye (12", clear vinyl picture disc) 10
87	WEA YZ 114TP	Infidelity (Stretch Mix)/Love Fire (Massive Red Mix)/Lady Godiva's Room (12", picture disc) 12
87	WEA YZ 161TE	Ev'ry Time We Say Goodbye/Love For Sale (live in the studio)/Sad Old Red/Broken Man (10", p/s) 8
87	WEA YZ 161TW	Ev'ry Time We Say Goodbye/Love For Sale (live in the studio)/Sad Old Red/Broken Man (12", white envelope pack with sheet music & 4 postcards) 12
89	WEA YZ 349TE	IT'S ONLY LOVE (10" EP) 7
89	WEA YZ 349 CDX	It's Only Love (Valentine Mix)/Turn It Up/I'm Gonna Lose You (3" CD, in flip top box) 7
89	WEA YZ 404TE	A NEW FLAME (10" EP) 7
89	WEA YZ 404CD	A NEW FLAME (CD EP) 7
89	WEA YZ 377TE	IF YOU DON'T KNOW ME BY NOW (10" EP) 7
89	WEA YZ 377CDX	IF YOU DON'T KNOW ME BY NOW (3" CD) 7
89	WEA YZ 424TE	YOU'VE GOT IT (10" EP) 7
89	WEA YZ 424CD	YOU'VE GOT IT (CD) 7

(see also Frantic Elevators)

BILL SIMPSON
64	Piccadilly 7N 35179	I Love You For Sentimental Reasons/My Love Is Like A Red Red Rose (p/s)	5

DANNY SIMPSON
69	Trojan TR 653	Outa Sight/JOHN HOLT: I Want You Closer	6

HOKE SIMPSON
58	HMV POP 442	I Finally Found You/Gi-Gi	6

JEANETTE SIMPSON
67	Giant GN 16	Rain/Whatcha Gonna Do About It	6
68	Giant GN 29	My Baby Just Cares For Me/Don't Let Me Cry No More (with Superboys)	8
68	Giant GN 35	Through Loving You/Send Me Some Lovin' (with Missions)	8

LEO SIMPSON
65	Blue Beat BB 351	I Love Her So/Good To Be Seen	6
73	Pyramid PYR 7004	Waxy Doodle/Go Away	8

(see also Lionel Simpson)

LIONEL SIMPSON
65	Ska Beat JB 205	Tell Me What You Want/Love Is A Game	6
65	Ska Beat JB 221	Red River Valley/Eight People	8
66	Ska Beat JB 233	Give Over/Never Before	8

(see also Leo Simpson)

MARTIN SIMPSON
76	Trailer LER 2099	GOLDEN VANITY (LP)	20

CHUCK SIMS
58	London HLR 8577	Little Pigeon/Life Isn't Long Enough	120
58	London HLR 8577	Little Pigeon/Life Isn't Long Enough (78)	40

FRANKIE LEE SIMS
71	Speciality SPE 5009	Married Woman Blues/Lucy Mae Blues	5
71	Speciality SNTF 5004	LUCY MAE BLUES (LP)	12

JASON SIMS & MUSIC THROUGH SIX
68	Domain D 5	It's Got To Be Mellow/Floppy Ears	4

(see also Music Through Six)

KELLY SIMS
60	Top Rank JAR 321	Betrayed By Love/A Girl In Love	4

ZOOT SIMS
52	Esquire 20-002	ZOOT SIMS QUARTET/QUINTET (10" LP)	15
53	Esquire 20-010	ZOOT SIMS ALLSTARS (10" LP)	15
53	Esquire 20-018	ZOOT SIMS QUARTET/QUINTET (10" LP)	15
54	Vogue LDE 056	ZOOT SIMS GOES TO TOWN (10" LP)	15
55	Esquire 20-040	ZOOT SIMS QUARTET/QUINTET (10" LP)	15
50s	Esquire 32-040	ZOOT SIMS SEPTET (LP)	12
58	HMV CLP 1165	GEORGE HANDY COMPOSITIONS (LP)	12
58	HMV CLP 1188	PLAYS FOUR ALTOS (LP)	12
61	Vogue LAE 12309	CHOICE (LP)	15
60s	Xtra XTRA 5001	TROTTING! (LP)	12
65	Fontana FJL 123	COOKIN'! (LP)	10

(see also Sims-Wheeler Vintage Jazz Band)

SIMS-WHEELER VINTAGE JAZZ BAND
60	Polydor NH 66638	Never On A Sunday/Ma Curly Headed Baby	4

(see also Zoot Sims)

FRANK SINATRA
40	HMV BD 5601	Shake Down The Stars/TOMMY DORSEY ORCHESTRA: Starlit Hour (78)	6
40	HMV BD 5611	April Played The Fiddle/I Haven't Got Time To Be A Millionaire (78)	6
40	HMV BD 9102	I'll Never Smile Again/Whispering (78)	6
40	HMV BD 5645	Trade Winds/TOMMY DORSEY ORCHESTRA: And So I Do (78)	6
41	HMV BD 5650	Our Love Affair/TOMMY DORSEY ORCHESTRA: That's For Me (78)	6
41	HMV BD 5655	We Three/TOMMY DORSEY ORCHESTRA: Two Dreams Met (78)	6
41	HMV BD 5656	All This And Heaven Too/TOMMY DORSEY ORCHESTRA: All Those In Favour Of Swing Say Aye (78)	6
41	HMV BD 5665	East Of The Sun/The One I Love (78)	6
41	HMV BD 5679	Stardust/TOMMY DORSEY ORCHESTRA: Swanee River (78)	6
41	HMV BD 5688	Dolores/TOMMY DORSEY ORCHESTRA: You're Dangerous (78)	6
41	HMV BD 5712	I'll Never Let A Day Pass By/TOMMY DORSEY ORCHESTRA: Kiss The Boys Good-bye (78)	6
41	HMV C 3262	Without A Song/TOMMY DORSEY ORCHESTRA: Deep River (12" 78)	10
41	HMV BD 5719	Do I Worry?/I Guess I'll Have To Dream The Rest (78)	6
42	HMV BD 5739	Two In Love/A Sinner Kissed An Angel (78)	6
44	HMV BD 5864	Blue Skies/TOMMY DORSEY ORCHESTRA: I Never Knew (78)	5
44	Columbia DB 2141	A Lovely Way To Spend An Evening/I Couldn't Sleep A Wink Last Night (78)	5
45	Columbia DB 2145	All Or Nothing At All/Ciribiribin (78)	5
45	Columbia DB 2149	You'll Never Know/Sunday Monday Or Always (78)	5
45	Columbia DB 2150	From The Bottom Of My Heart/Here Comes The Night (78)	5
45	Columbia DB 2176	Saturday Night (Is The Loneliest Night In The Week)/Embraceable You (78)	5
45	Columbia DB 2181	If You Are But A Dream/Kiss Me Again (78)	5
45	Columbia DB 2186	When Your Lover Is Gone/She's Funny That Way (78)	5
45	Columbia DB 2190	There's No You/Cradle Song (78)	5
45	Columbia DB 2197	I Begged Her/I Fall In Love You Easily (78)	5
45	Columbia DX 1216	Ol' Man River/Stormy Weather (12" 78)	10
46	Columbia DB 2200	What Makes The Sunset?/The Charm Of You (78)	5
46	Columbia DB 2202	Nancy (With The Laughing Face)/A Friend Of Yours (78)	5
46	Columbia DB 2209	These Foolish Things (Remind Me Of You)/You Go To My Head (78)	5

46	Columbia DB 2214	I Dream Of You (More Than You Dream I Do)/Someone To Watch Over Me (78) 5
46	Columbia DB 2216	Homesick — That's All/Oh What It Seemed To Be (78) 5
46	Columbia DB 2224	You Are Too Beautiful/Day By Day (78) 5
46	Columbia DB 2226	I Only Have Eyes For You/I Don't Know Why (78) 5
46	Columbia DB 2227	Begin The Beguine/All Through The Day (78) 5
46	Columbia DB 2238	I Fall In Love With You Ev'ry Day/Paradise (78) 5
46	Columbia DB 2237	Silent Night, Holy Night/White Christmas (78) 5
46	Columbia DC 385	How Deep Is The Ocean /Home On The Range (78) (export issue) 8
47	Columbia DB 2275	Five Minutes More/Try A Little Tenderness (78) 5
47	Columbia DB 2283	The Things We Did Last Summer/Somewhere In The Night (78) 5
47	Columbia DB 2286	September Song/Souvenirs (In My Souvenirs) (78) 5
47	Columbia DB 2296	Time After Time/It's The Same Old Dream (78) 5
47	Columbia DB 2313	Oh What A Beautiful Mornin'/The Girl That I Marry (78) 5
47	Columbia DB 2307	People Will Say We're In Live/They Say It's Wonderful (78) 5
47	Columbia DB 2321	There's No Business Like Show Business/Mam'selle (78) 5
47	Columbia DB 2330	All Of Me/I'm Sorry I Made You Cry (78) 5
47	Columbia DB 2339	Always/The Moon Was Yellow And The Night Was Young (78) 5
47	Columbia DB 2346	I Love You (Ich Liebe Dich)/Stella By Starlight (78) 5
47	Columbia DB 2355	Sweet Lorraine (with Metronome All-Stars)/NAT COLE & JUNE CHRISTY: Nat Meets Jane (78) 5
47	Columbia DB 2357	One Love/Poinciana (Song Of The Tree) (78) 5
47	Columbia DB 2365	Christmas Dreaming (A Little Early This Year)/ I'll Make Up For Everything (78) 5
47	HMV BD 1166	Hear My Song Violetta/TOMMY DORSEY ORCHESTRA: Gotta Get Me Somebody To Love (78) 5
48	HMV BD 1230	The Sunshine Of Your Smile/TOMMY DORSEY ORCHESTRA: Until (78) 5
48	Columbia DC 428	That Old Feeling/Nature Boy (78) (export issue) 8
48	Columbia DC 431	Adeste Fideles/Jingle Bells (78) (export issue) 8
48	Columbia DB 2376	Stars Will Remember (So Will I)/Coffee Song (They've Got An Awful Lot Of Coffee In Brazil) (78) 5
48	Columbia DB 2381	It All Came True/Mean To Me (78) 5
48	Columbia DB 2388	Falling In Live With Love/Love For You (78) 5
48	Columbia DB 2403	S'posin'/How Deep Is The Ocean (78) 5
48	Columbia DB 2423	But Beautiful/My Cousin Louella (78) 5
48	Columbia DB 2431	We Just Couldn't Say Goodbye/If I Only Had A Match (78) 5
48	Columbia DB 2459	Everybody Loves Somebody/What'll I Do (78) 5
48	Columbia DB 2471	It Only Happens When I Dance With You/A Fella With An Umbrella (78) 5
49	Columbia DB 2507	While The Angelus Was Ringing/When Is Sometime (78) 5
49	Columbia DB 2531	No Orchids For My Lady/Almost Like Being In Love (78) 5
49	Columbia DB 2567	A Little Learnin' Is A Dangerous Thing Pts 1 & 2 (78, with Pearl Bailey) 5
40s	HMV JO 27	Stardust/TOMMY DORSEY ORCHESTRA: Song Of India (78) (export issue) 10
50	Columbia DB 2630	That Lucky Old Sun/Let Her Go Let Her Go Let Her Go (78) 5
50	Columbia DB 2664	Chattanoogie Shoe Shine Boy/The Old Master Painter (78) 5
50	Columbia DX 1666	Soliloquy Pts 1 & 2 (12" 78) 10
50	Columbia DB 2737	Goodnight Irene/My Blue Heaven (78) 5
51	Columbia LB 104	If She'd Only Look My Way/London By Night (78) 8
53	Columbia SCM 5052	Birth Of The Blues/Why Try To Change Me Now? 16
53	Columbia DB 3257	Birth Of The Blues/Why Try To Change Me Now (78) 5
53	Columbia SCM 5060	You Do Something To Me/Lover 16
53	Columbia SCM 5076	Santa Claus Is Comin' To Town/My Girl 16
53	Capitol CL 13924	Lean Baby/I'm Walking Behind You (78) 8
53	Capitol CL 13980	I Love You/Don't You Worry 'Bout Me (78) 8
53	Capitol CL 14023	From Here To Eternity/My One And Only Love (78) 8
54	Capitol CL 14031	South Of The Border/I've Got The World On A String (78) 8
54	Capitol CL 14174	The Christmas Waltz/White Christmas (78) 6
54	Capitol CL 14064	Young-At-Heart/Take A Chance 18
54	Capitol CL 14120	Three Coins In The Fountain/I Could Have Told You 16
54	Capitol CL 14174	The Christmas Waltz/White Christmas 16
54	Capitol CL 14188	When I Stop Loving You/It Worries Me 12
55	Capitol CL 14221	Someone To Watch Over Me/The Gal That Got Away 12
55	Capitol CL 14238	Melody Of Love/I'm Gonna Live Till I Die 12
55	Columbia SCM 5167	S'posin'/How Deep Is The Ocean 16
55	Capitol CL 14240	You, My Love/Just One Of Those Things 12
55	Capitol CL 14270	Don't Change Your Mind About Me/Why Should I Cry Over You 12
55	Capitol CL 14292	Two Hearts, Two Kisses (Make One Love)/From The Bottom To The Top 12
55	Capitol CL 14296	Learnin' The Blues/If I Had Three Wishes 12
55	Capitol CL 14326	Not As A Stranger/How Could You Do A Thing Like That To Me 12
55	Capitol CL 14352	My Funny Valentine/I Get A Kick Out Of You 10
55	Capitol CL 14360	It Never Entered My Mind/In The Wee Small Hours Of The Morning 10
55	Capitol CL 14373	Fairy Tale/Same Old Saturday Night 10

(all the above Capitol 45s originally came with triangular centres, round centre reissues are worth around half these prices)

56	Capitol CL 14503	Love And Marriage/Look To Your Heart 8
56	Capitol CL 14511	(Love Is) A Tender Trap/Weep They Will 8
56	Capitol CL 14564	You'll Get Yours/Flowers Mean Forgiveness 6
56	Capitol CL 14584	Five Hundred Guys/(How Little It Matters) How Little We Know 4
56	Capitol CL 14607	"Johnny Concho" Theme (Wait For Me)/Hey! Jealous Lover 4
56	Capitol CL 14620	The Impatient Years/Our Town 4
56	Capitol CL 14644	Who Wants To Be A Millionaire? (with Celeste Holm)/Mind If I Make Love To You 6
56	Capitol CL 14646	You're Sensational/You Forgot All The Words 4
57	Capitol CL 14696	Can I Steal A Little Love?/Your Love For Me 4
57	Capitol CL 14719	So Long, My Love/Crazy Love 4
57	Capitol CL 14750	Something Wonderful Happens In Summer/You're Cheatin' 4
57	Capitol CL 14800	All The Way/Chicago 4
57	Capitol CL 14804	Mistletoe And Holy/Jingle Bells 4

Frank SINATRA

58	Fontana H 109	I Could Write A Book/Nevertheless (I'm In Love With You) (78)	5
58	Capitol CL 14819	Witchcraft/Tell Her You Love Her	4
58	Fontana H 140	If I Forget You/I'm A Fool To Want You	7
50s	Capitol	other 45s	3-4
62	Reprise RS 20063	Ev'rybody's Twistin'/Nothing But The Best	4
66	Reprise RS 20531	That's Life/I've Got You Under My Skin	4
54	HMV 7EG 8004	TOMMY DORSEY AND HIS ORCHESTRA (EP, plain sleeve, 2 tracks with Sinatra)	10
54	HMV 7EG 8070	FRANK SINATRA (EP, plain sleeve)	8
54	Capitol EAP1-488	SONGS FOR YOUNG LOVERS No. 1 (EP)	7
55	HMV 7EG 8128	MOONLIGHT SINATRA (EP, plain sleeve)	10
55	Columbia SEG 7565	FRANK SINATRA (EP, plain sleeve)	10
55	Columbia SEG 7582	SINATRA SERENADE (EP, plain sleeve)	10
55	Columbia SEG 7597	FRANKIE'S FAVOURITES (EP, plain sleeve)	10
55	Capitol EAP 2-488	SONGS FOR YOUNG LOVERS No. 2 (EP)	7
55	Capitol EAP 1-571	SONGS FROM "YOUNG AT HEART" (EP)	8
56	Capitol EAP 1-590	MELODY OF LOVE (EP)	7
56	Capitol EAP 1-629	SESSION WITH SINATRA (EP)	8
56	Capitol EAP 1025	OUR TOWN (EP)	8
56	Capitol EAP 2-488	YOUNG AT HEART (EP)	7
60	Fontana TFE 17273	'BYE BABY (EP)	12
61	Capitol SEP1-221	NO ONE CARES (EP, stereo)	12
61	Capitol SEP2-1221	NO ONE CARES No. 2 (EP, stereo)	12
61	Capitol SEP3-1221	NO ONE CARES No. 3 (EP, stereo)	12
54	Capitol LC 6654	SONGS FOR YOUNG LOVERS (10" LP)	20
54	Capitol LC 6689	SWING EASY (10" LP)	20
54	Philips BBR 8003	SING AND DANCE WITH FRANK SINATRA (10" LP)	25
55	Capitol LC 6702	IN THE WEE SMALL HOURS VOL. 1 (10" LP)	16
55	Capitol LC 6705	IN THE WEE SMALL HOURS VOL. 2 (10" LP)	16
55	Philips BBR 8038	FABULOUS FRANK (10" LP)	20
55	Philips BBR 8040	YOUNG AT HEART (10" LP, with Doris Day)	20
56	Capitol LCT 6106	SONGS FOR SWINGIN' LOVERS (LP)	10
56	Capitol LCT 6111	FRANK SINATRA CONDUCTS TONE POEMS OF COLOUR (LP)	15
56	HMV DLP 1123	IT'S D-LOVELY (LP, with Tommy Dorsey Orchestra)	25
57	Capitol LCT 6123	THIS IS SINATRA (LP)	10
57	Capitol LCT 6130	CLOSE TO YOU (LP)	14
57	Capitol LCT 6135	A SWINGIN' AFFAIR (LP)	12
57	Capitol LCT 6144	A JOLLY CHRISTMAS FROM FRANK SINATRA (LP)	14
57	Philips BBR 8114	CHRISTMAS DREAMING (10" LP)	25
57	Philips BBL 7137	DORIS AND FRANK (LP, 6 tracks each by Doris Day & Frank Sinatra)	15
57	Philips BBL 7168	FRANKIE (LP)	18
57	Philips BBL 7180	THAT OLD FEELING (LP)	18
58	Capitol (S)LCT 6152	WHERE ARE YOU? (LP, mono/stereo)	12/15
58	Capitol LCT 6155	THIS IS SINATRA VOL. 2 (LP)	14
58	Capitol (S)LCT 6168	FRANK SINATRA SINGS FOR ONLY THE LONELY (LP)	14
58	RCA RD 27069	FRANKIE AND TOMMY (LP, with Tommy Dorsey Orchestra)	20
58	Fontana TFL 5000	THE VOICE (LP)	20
58	Fontana TFL 5006	ADVENTURES OF THE HEART (LP)	18
58	Fontana TFL 5030	THE FRANK SINATRA STORY (LP)	17
59	Capitol (S)LCT 6179	COME DANCE WITH ME (LP)	14
59	Capitol LCT 6181	LOOK TO YOUR HEART (LP)	15
59	Capitol (S)LCT 6185	NO ONE CARES (LP)	12
59	Fontana TFL 5048	PUT YOUR DREAMS AWAY (LP)	25
59	Fontana TFL 5054	THE BROADWAY KICK (LP)	18
60	Capitol W 587	SWING EASY (LP)	12
60	Fontana TFL 5074	LOVE IS A KICK (LP)	16
60	Fontana TFL 5082	COME BACK TO SORRENTO (LP)	15
60	Fontana TFL 5107	REFLECTIONS (LP)	14
61	Fontana TFL 5138	SINATRA SOUVENIR (LP)	16
61	Capitol W(S) 1417	NICE'N'EASY (LP)	12
61	Capitol W(S) 1491	SINATRA'S SWINGIN' SESSION! (LP)	12
61	Reprise R 1001	RING-A-DING-DING! (LP)	12
61	Reprise R/R9 1002	SINATRA SWINGS (LP, mono/stereo)	10
61	Fontana SET 303	SINATRA PLUS (2-LP)	14
61	Encore ENC 101	WHEN YOUR LOVER HAS GONE (LP)	10
61	World Record Club TP 81	LOOK OVER YOUR SHOULDER (LP)	10
62	Capitol W(S) 1594	COME SWING WITH ME! (LP)	12
62	Capitol W(S) 1676	POINT OF NO RETURN (LP)	14
62	Capitol T 20389	LONDON BY NIGHT (LP)	15
62	Capitol W(S) 1538	ALL THE WAY (LP)	12
62	Reprise R/R9 1003	I REMEMBER TOMMY! (LP)	10
62	Reprise R/R9 1004	SINATRA AND STRINGS (LP)	12
62	Reprise R/R9 1005	SINATRA AND SWINGIN' BRASS (LP)	10
62	Reprise R/R9 1006	SINATRA SINGS GREAT SONGS FROM GREAT BRITAIN (LP, mono/stereo)	40/25
63	Capitol W(S) 1729	SINATRA SINGS ... OF LOVE AND THINGS! (LP)	12
63	Capitol W 1/2/3-1762	THE GREAT YEARS (3-LP)	20
63	Capitol W 1825	FRANK SINATRA SINGS RODGERS AND HART (LP)	12
63	Reprise R 1007	ALL ALONE (LP)	10
63	Reprise R/R9 1008	SINATRA-BASIE (LP)	10
63	Reprise R/R9 1009	THE CONCERT SINATRA (LP)	10
63	Reprise R 1010	SINATRA'S SINATRA (LP)	10
64	Capitol T 20577	MY FUNNY VALENTINE (LP)	14
64	Reprise R/R9 1011	FRANK SINATRA SINGS "DAYS OF WINE AND ROSES" & OTHER ACADEMY AWARD WINNERS (LP)	10
64	Reprise R/R9 1012	IT MIGHT AS WELL BE SWING (LP, with Count Basie)	10
64	Reprise R 2022	TWELVE SONGS OF CHRISTMAS (LP, with Bing Crosby, Fred Waring, etc)	12
65	Capitol W 20652	SINGING AND SWINGING (LP)	10

65	Capitol (S)T 1919	TELL HER YOU LOVE HER (LP)	10
65	Capitol T 20734	THE CONNOISSEUR'S SINATRA (LP)	10
65	Reprise R/R9 1012	SOFTLY AS I LOVE YOU (LP)	10
65	Reprise R/R9 1014	SEPTEMBER OF MY YEARS (LP)	10
65	Reprise R/R9 6167	SINATRA '65 (LP)	12
66	Capitol T 20757	SINATRA FOR THE SOPHISTICATED (LP)	10
66	Reprise R/R9 1015	MY KIND OF BROADWAY (LP)	10
66	Reprise R/R9 1016	SINATRA: A MAN AND HIS MUSIC (2-LP)	15
66	Reprise R/R9 1018	MOONLIGHT SINATRA (LP)	15
66	Reprise R/R9 1017	STRANGERS IN THE NIGHT (LP)	10
66	Reprise R(S)LP 1019	IN CONCERT: SINATRA AT 'THE SANDS' (2-LP, with Count Basie)	15
67	World Record C. (S)T 635	SEPTEMBER SONG (LP)	10
67	Capitol (S)T 2700	THE MOVIE SONGS (LP)	12
67	Reprise R(S)LP 1020	THAT'S LIFE (LP)	10
67	Reprise R(S)LP 1021	FRANCIS ALBERT SINATRA — ANTONIO CARLOS JOBIM (LP)	10
67	Reprise R(S)LP 1022	FRANK SINATRA (LP)	12
68	CBS 63172	THE ESSENTIAL FRANK SINATRA VOL. 1 (LP)	10
68	CBS 63173	THE ESSENTIAL FRANK SINATRA VOL. 2 (LP)	10
68	CBS 63174	THE ESSENTIAL FRANK SINATRA VOL. 3 (LP)	10
68	Reprise R(S)LP 1024	FRANCIS A. EDWARD K. (LP, with Duke Ellington)	12
69	Reprise R(S)LP 1026	THE SINATRA FAMILY WISH YOU A HAPPY CHRISTMAS (LP, with Nancy Sinatra)	16
69	Reprise R(S)LP 1027	CYCLES (LP)	10
69	Reprise R(S)LP 1030	A MAN ALONE — THE WORDS AND MUSIC OF ROD McKUEN (LP)	10
69	World Records SM137-142	THE SINATRA TOUCH (6-LP)	35
70	Valiant VS 144	FRANK SINATRA WITH COUNT BASIE (LP, reissue)	10
70	Reprise R(S)LP 1031	WATERTOWN (LP)	12
71	Reprise RSLP 1033	SINATRA AND COMPANY (LP)	12
77	Reprise K 94003	SINATRA — THE REPRISE YEARS (4-LP)	18
81	World Records ALBUM 47	THE SINATRA TOUCH (4-LP)	20
85	Capitol SINATRA 20	FRANK SINATRA: THE CAPITOL YEARS (20-LP box set)	80
90	Capitol C1-94777	THE CAPITOL YEARS (5-LP box set)	30

(see also Nancy Sinatra, Count Basie, Tommy Dorsey)

NANCY SINATRA

61	Reprise RS 20017	Cuff Links And Tie Clips/Not Just Your Friend	4
62	Reprise RS 20045	To Know Him Is To Love Him/Like I Do	4
63	Reprise RS 20144	I See The Moon/Put Your Head On My Shoulder	4
64	Reprise RS 20335	True Love/The Answer To Everything	4
65	Reprise RS 20407	So Long Babe/If He'd Loved Me	4
66	Reprise RS 20432	These Boots Are Made For Walkin'/The City Never Sleeps At Night	4
67	Reprise RS 20595	You Only Live Twice/Jackson	3-4
60s	Reprise RS series	other 45s	3-4
66	Reprise REP 30069	RUN FOR YOUR LIFE (EP)	8
66	Reprise REP 30072	I MOVE AROUND (EP)	8
67	Reprise REP 30080	SORRY 'BOUT THAT (EP)	8
67	Reprise REP 30082	SOMETHING STUPID (EP)	7
67	Reprise REP 30086	NASHVILLE NANCY (EP)	8
66	Reprise R 6207	HOW DOES THAT GRAB YOU? (LP)	10
66	Reprise RLP 6202	BOOTS (LP)	10
66	Reprise R(S)LP 6221	NANCY IN LONDON (LP)	12
67	Reprise RLP 6239	SUGAR (LP)	10
67	Reprise R(S)LP 6251	COUNTRY, MY WAY (LP)	10
68	Reprise R(S)LP 6277	MOVIN' WITH NANCY (LP)	10
69	Reprise RSLP 6333	NANCY (LP)	10
72	RCA SF 8331	WOMAN (LP)	12

(see also Lee Hazelwood, Elvis Presley)

NANCY SINATRA & LEE HAZLEWOOD

67	Reprise RS 23215	Some Velvet Morning/Tony Rome	4
67	Reprise REP 30083	JACKSON (EP)	7
68	Reprise R(S)LP 6273	NANCY & LEE (LP)	10
72	RCA Victor SF 8240	DID YOU EVER? (LP)	10

(see also Nancy Sinatra, Lee Hazlewood)

JIMMY SINCLAIR & RENTON SPENCE ORCHESTRA

| 61 | Blue Beat BB 47 | Verona/To Prove My Love | 10 |

STEPHEN SINCLAIR

| 62 | HMV POP 1066 | Mister Sandman/Part Lights | 5 |

WINSTON SINCLAIR

| 69 | Nu Beat NB 026 | Another Heartache/Come On Little Girl | 4 |

SINDELFINGEN

| 73 | Medway | ODGIPIG (LP, private pressing, with insert) | 600 |
| 90 | Cenotaph CEN 111 | ODGIPIG-TRIANGLE (2-LP, reissue with live album, 300 only) | 30 |

TONY SINDEN, ALAN BAKER & INSECTS

| 79 | Piano SING 001 | Magnificent Cactus Trees/Cast Shadows | 4 |

PETE SINFIELD

| 73 | Manticore K 43501 | STILL (LP, textured gatefold sleeve) | 12 |

(see also King Crimson)

SINGAROUND

| 69 | Golden Guinea | SINGAROUND (LP) | 10 |

RAY SINGER

| 64 | Ember EMB S 187 | Tell Me Now/I'm Comin' Home | 4 |
| 64 | Ember EMB S 199 | It's Gotta Be/Hey, Who? | 4 |

65	Ember EMB S 215	I'm The Richest Man Alive/Pretty Little Rambling Rose 4
65	Fontana TF 621	You'll Come Crying To Me/Who Can I Talk To About You 4
67	Ember EMB S 231	What's Been Done/Won't It Be Fine 12

(see also Nirvana [U.K.])

SUSAN SINGER

62	Oriole CB 1703	Gee It's Great To Be Young/Hello First Love 6
62	Oriole CB 1741	Baby's Loving Touch/Johnny Summertime 6
62	Oriole CB 1778	Love Me With All Your Heart/Autumn Leaves 6
63	Oriole CB 1802	Lock Your Heart Away/Answer To A Prayer 6
63	Oriole CB 1882	I Know/That Old Feeling 6

(see also Susan Holiday)

SINGING BELLES

| 60 | Top Rank JAR 350 | The Empty Mailbox/Someone Loves You, Joe ....6 |

SINGING DOGS

55	Pye Nixa N 15009	Medley Pts 1 & 2 (78) 5
56	Pye Nixa N 15065	Barking Dog Boogie/Rock Around The Dogs (78) 7
57	Pye NEP 24029	SINGING DOGS (EP) 12

SINGING REINDEER

| 60 | Capitol CL 15124 | The Happy Birthday Song/I Wanna Be An Easter Bunny ....4 |

MARGIE SINGLETON

| 60 | Melodisc 45-1544 | Angel Hands/The Eyes Of Love ....6 |
| 62 | Mercury AMT 1197 | Magic Star/Only Your Shadow Knows ....8 |

SINISTER DUCKS

| 83 | Situation 2 SIT 25 | Suicide: March Of The Sinister Ducks/Homiside: Old Gangsters Never (foldout p/s) ....15 |

(see also Bauhaus)

EARL SINKS

61	Warner Bros WB 38	Supermarket Super Market/Look For Me, I'll Be There 7
61	Warner Bros WB 51	Superstitious/Little Suzie Parker 7
63	Capitol CL 15310	Looking For Love/Raining On My Side Of Town 8

(see also Crickets)

SINNERS

| 63 | Columbia DB 7158 | I Can't Stand It/If You Leave Me Now ....7 |
| 64 | Columbia DB 7295 | It's So Exciting/Leave Him ....8 |

(see also Linda Laine & Sinners)

SIOUXSIE & BANSHEES

78	Polydor 2059 052	Hong Kong Garden/Voices (10,000 only in gatefold p/s; beige plastic, silver plastic, red plastic or red paper label) 12-16
78	Polydor 2059 052	Hong Kong Garden/Voices (p/s) 5
79	Polydor POSP 9	The Staircase (Mystery)/20th Century Boy (p/s) 6
79	Polydor POSP 59	Playground Twist/Pull To Bits (p/s, some with red paper label) 7/5
79	Polydor 2059 151	Mittageisen (Metal Postcard)/Love In A Void (p/s) 8
80	Polydor POSP 117	Happy House/Drop Dead/Celebration (p/s) 4
80	Polydor 2059 249	Christine/Eve White, Eve Black (p/s) 5
80	Polydor 2059 249	Christine/Eve White, Eve Black (with Nigel Gray credit on B-side, p/s) 6
80	Polydor POSP 205	Israel/Red Over White (p/s) 5
80	Polydor POSPX 205	Israel (Extended)/Red Over White (Extended) (12", no p/s) 15
81	Polydor POSP 273	Spellbound/Follow The Sun (p/s) 4
81	Polydor POSPX 273	Spellbound/Follow The Sun/Slap Dash Snap (12", p/s) 7
81	Polydor POSP 309	Arabian Knights/Supernatural Thing (p/s) 4
81	Polydor POSPX 309	Arabian Knights/Supernatural Thing/Congo Conga (12", p/s) 7
82	Polydor POSPG 450	Fireworks/Coal Mind (gatefold p/s) 5
82	Polydor POSP 510	Slowdive/Cannibal Roses (p/s, red paper label) 8
83	Wonderland SHEG 4	Dear Prudence/Tattoo (foldout p/s) 6
85	Wonderland SHE 9	Cities In Dust/An Execution (poster p/s) 4
86	Wonderland SHEDP 10	Candyman/Lullaby (with free 2nd single, gatefold p/s, 2,000 only) 8
87	Wonderland SHEG 11	This Wheel's On Fire/Shooting Sun/Sleepwalking (On The High Wire)/ She's Cracked (numbered double pack, gatefold p/s) 8
87	Wonderland SHEG 12	The Passenger/She's Cuckoo (poster p/s) 4
87	Wonderland SHEP 13	Song From The Edge Of The World/The Whole Price Of Blood (picture disc) 4
87	Wonderland SHEC 13	Song From The Edge Of The World/The Whole Price Of Blood/Song From The Edge Of The World (Columbus Mix)/Mechanical Eyes (cassette) 4
88	Wonderland SHEG 14	Peek-A-Boo/False Face (gatefold p/s, numbered) 4
88	Wonderland SHECS 14	Peek-A-Boo/False Face/Catwalk/Peek-A-Boo (Big Spender Mix) (cassette) 4
88	Wonderland SHEG 15	The Killing Jar/Something Wicked (This Way Comes) (clear vinyl, stickered gatefold p/s, numbered) 4
88	Wonderland SHEP 15	The Killing Jar/Something Wicked (This Way Comes) (picture disc) 4
88	Wonderland SHEG 16	The Last Beat Of My Heart/El Dia De Los Muertos (stickered gilded p/s, numbered) 4
83	Fan Club FILE 1	Head Cut/Running Town (freebie, p/s) 40
80s	SIOUX 1	Interview (picture disc) 5
80s	Spiral Scratch SCRATCH 2	AN INTERVIEW WITH (free with 'Spiral Scratch' magazine, 5,000 only, no p/s) 5/4
87	Strange Fruit SFPSC 012	PEEL SESSION 5.12.77 (cassette EP) 5
87	Wonderland SHELP 4	THROUGH THE LOOKING GLASS (LP, mispressing, 1 side plays Jimi Hendrix's "War Heroes") 15

(see also Creatures, Cure, Glove)

SIR ALEC & HIS BOYS

| 67 | Deram DM 116 | I'm A Believer/Green Green Grass Of Home ....5 |

SIR ALICK & PHRASER

82	Recommended/Black Noise 7 NO 5	In Search Of The Perfect Baby/PROLIFIKURDS: Nursery Crymes (printed p/s & plastic sleeve; also in normal p/s) 4/5

(see also Homosexuals)

SIR (Clancy) COLLINS BAND

68	Collins Downbeat CR 0011	Collins And The Boys/Bob Stackie In Soho (both with Bob Stackie) 7
68	Collins Downbeat CR 0017	Soul Feelings/SIR COLLINS: Hello Stella 7

(see also Bob Stackie)

SIR DOUGLAS QUINTET

65	London HLU 9964	She's About A Mover/We'll Take Our Last Walk Tonight 6
65	London HLU 9982	The Tracker/Blue Norther 7
65	London HLU 10001	The Story Of John Hardy/In Time 6
66	London HLU 10019	The Rains Came/Bacon Fat 6
69	Mercury MF 1079	Mendocino/I Wanna Be Your Mama Again 6
69	Mercury MF 1129	Dynamite Woman/Too Many Dociled Minds 6
65	London HA-U 8311	THE SIR DOUGLAS QUINTET (LP) 60
69	Mercury SMCL 20160	MENDOCINO (LP) 15
69	Mercury SMCL 20186	TOGETHER AFTER FIVE (LP) 15

(see also Doug Sahm)

SIR HENRY & HIS BUTLERS

68	Columbia DB 8497	The Rolo Sensation (Camp)/Pretty Style 12

SIR HORATIO

82	Rock Steady Mix 1T	Abracadubra/Sommadub (12") 8

(see also A Certain Ratio)

SIR LORD COMIC

67	Doctor Bird DB 1070	The Great Wuga Wuga (with Cowboys)/THREE TOPS: Feel So Lonesome 12
69	Pressure Beat PB 5506	Jack Of My Trade/CYNTHIA RICHARDS: United We Stand 5

SIR WASHINGTON

69	Star ST 1	Apollo 12/When You Kiss Me 4

SIR WILLIAM

67	Stateside SS 583	Shakespeare's Shrew/Patsy 4

SIREN

71	Dandelion DAN 7002	Strange Locomotion/I'm All Aching (label also lists K 19004) 5
69	Dandelion 63755	SIREN (LP) 18
71	Dandelion DAN 8001	STRANGE LOCOMOTION (LP, gatefold sleeve, label also lists K 49001) 15

(see also Kevin Coyne, Clague)

SISTERHOOD

86	Merciful Release SIS 001	Giving Ground (RSV)/Giving Ground (AV) (p/s) 4

(see also Sisters Of Mercy)

SISTER SLEDGE

73	Atlantic K 10375	Mama Never Told Me/Neither One Of Us 5
75	Atlantic K 10551	Love Don't You Go Through No Changes On Me/Don't You Miss Me 5
75	Atlantic K 10683	Love Has Found Me/Love Ain't Easy 5
77	Cotillion K 10876	Cream Of The Crop/Love Ain't Easy 4

SISTERS LOVE

70	A&M AMS 772	Forget It, I've Got It/Eye To Eye 6
70	A&M AMS 808	The Bigger Your Love/Piece Of My Heart 4
72	Tamla Motown TMG 858	Mr. Fix It Man/You've Got To Make Your Choice 4
73	Mowest MW 3009	I'm Learning To Trust My Man/Try It You'll Like It 6
75	Tamla Motown TMG 1002	I'm Learning To Trust My Man/Try It You'll Like It (reissue) 4

SISTERS OF MERCY

80	Merciful Release MR 007	The Damage Done/Watch/Home Of The Hitmen (p/s, 1,000 only; beware of counterfeits without 'MR 7' matrix number) 100
82	CNT CNT 002	Body Electric/Adrenochrome (p/s) 50
82	Merciful Release MR 015	Alice/Floorshow (p/s with white background, later black) 15/5
83	Merciful Release MR 019	Anaconda/Phantom (p/s) 4
83	Merciful Release MR 021	Alice/Floorshow/1969/Phantom (12", p/s) 7
83	Merciful Release MR 023	THE REPTILE HOUSE (12" EP, some with lyric sheet) 10/7
83	Merciful Release MR 027	Temple Of Love/Heartland (p/s) 4
83	Merciful Release MRX 027	Temple Of Love (Extended)/Heartland/Gimme Shelter (12", p/s) 7
84	Merciful Release MR 029	Body And Soul/Train (p/s) 8
84	Merciful Release MR 029T	Body And Soul/Body Electric/Train/Afterhours (12", p/s) 8
84	Merciful Release/WEA	ALICE/TEMPLE OF LOVE/REPTILE HOUSE/BODY AND SOUL (4 x 12" box set, promo-only) 60
84	Merciful Release MR 033	Walk Away/Poison Door (p/s, some with flexidisc "Long Train" [SAM 218]) ...15/8
84	Merciful Release MR 033T	Walk Away/Poison Door/On The Wire (12", p/s, with flexi "Long Train") 15/8
85	Merciful Release MR 035	No Time To Cry/Blood Money (p/s) 8
85	Merciful Release MR 035T	No Time To Cry/Blood Money/Bury Me Deep (12", p/s) 10
87	Merciful Release MR 039	This Corrosion/Torch (p/s) 4
87	Merciful Release MR 039	This Corrosion/Torch (box set, with 3 postcards, 5,000 only) 10
87	Merciful Release MR 039C	This Corrosion/Torch/Colours (cassette) 4
87	Merciful Release MR 039T	This Corrosion (Extended)/Torch/Colours (12", p/s, some in card spined sl.) ...8/7
87	Merciful Release MR 039CD	This Corrosion (Extended)/Torch/Colours (CD, 1st issue without 'WEA' logo on back sleeve) 20
88	Merciful Release MR 043	Dominion/Untitled/Sandstorm (p/s) 4
88	Merciful Release MR 043C	Dominion/Untitled/Sandstorm/Ozymandias (cassette) 7
88	Merciful Release MR 043T	Dominion (Extended)/Untitled/Sandstorm/Emma (12", p/s, black label) 7
88	Merciful Release MR 043T	Dominion (Extended)/Untitled/Sandstorm/Emma (12", box set with poster) 7
88	Merciful Release MR 043CD	Dominion (Extended)/Untitled/Sandstorm/Ozymandias (CD) 7
88	Merciful Release MR 044	Lucretia My Reflection/Long Train (p/s) 4

88	Merciful Rel. MR 044T	Lucretia My Reflection (extended)/Long Train (12", p/s)	8
88	Merciful Rel. MR 044CD	Lucretia My Reflection (extended)/Long Train (CD)	7
90	Merciful Rel. MR 47	More/You Could Be The One (p/s)	4
90	Merciful Rel. MR 47	More (extended)/You Could Be The One (p/s)	7
90	Merciful Rel. MR 47C	More/More (extended)/You Could Be The One (cassette)	4
90	Merciful Rel. MR 47CD	More/More (extended)/You Could Be The One (CD)	7
90	Merciful Rel. MR 47CDX	More/More (extended)/You Could Be The One (CD, 12" foldout sleeve)	10
90	Merciful Rel. MR 51	Doctor Jeep/Knocking On Heaven's Door (live) (p/s)	4
90	Merciful Rel. MR 51T	Doctor Jeep (extended)/Knocking On Heaven's Door (live) (12", p/s)	7
90	Merciful Rel. MR 51TX	Doctor Jeep (extended)/Burn (live)/Amphetamine Logic (live) (12", p/s, 6,000 only)	10
90	Merciful Rel. MR 51CD	Doctor Jeep (radio edit)/Doctor Jeep (extended version)/Knocking On Heaven's Door (live) (CD)	7
92	Merciful Rel. MR 53CD	Temple Of Love (1992) (CD, box set)	7
80s	(no label credit)	An Interview With Andrew Eldritch (1,000 only, red vinyl, p/s)	5
80s	(no label credit)	Sisters Of Mercy (4 Interview picture discs in plastic hanging case)	12
88	Spiral Scratch SCRATCH 1	An Interview With ... (black or clear vinyl, free with 'Spiral Scratch' magazine issue 1, 10,000 only)	5/4
85	Merciful Rel. MR 337L	FIRST AND LAST AND ALWAYS (LP, gatefold sleeve, beware of copies with faked autographs!)	18
87	Merciful Rel. MR 441L	FLOODLAND (LP, numbered sleeve with lyric sheet)	10

(see also Mission, Sisterhood, James Ray & Performance, Ghost Dance)

SITUATION
| 66 | CBS 202392 | Situation Now/Time | 8 |

SITZ & COOLERS
| 68 | Nu Beat NB 003 | Cover Me/Darling | 5 |

SIXPENCE
| 67 | London HLJ 10124 | You're The Love/What To Do | 4 |

SIX TEENS
| 56 | London HLU 8345 | A Casual Look/Teen Age Promise | 250 |
| 56 | London HLU 8345 | A Casual Look/Teen Age Promise (78) | 50 |

SIZE SEVEN GROUP
65	Mercury MF 845	Where Do We Go From Here/Till I Die	4
65	Mercury MF 854	In Time/Walking Proud	4
65	Mercury MF 896	It's Got To Be Love/I Met Her In The Rain	4

SKA CHAMPIONS
| 64 | Blue Beat BB 305 | My Tears/Yesterday's Dreams | 8 |

SKA CITY ROCKERS
| 80 | Inferno HEAT 1 | Time Is Tight/Roadrunner/You Don't Know Like I Know (p/s) | 5 |
| 80 | Inferno HEAT 1 | Time Is Tight/Roadrunner/You Don't Know Like I Know (12", p/s) | 7 |

SKA KINGS
| 64 | Atlantic AT 4003 | Jamaica Ska (actually by Keith Lynn & Ken Lazarus & Byron Lee & Dragonaires)/Oil In My Lamp (actually by Eric Morris with Byron Lee & Dragonaires) | 6 |
| 65 | Parlophone R 5338 | Bimbo/Ska'ville | 6 |

RICKY SKAGGS
| 85 | Epic DA 6447 | Waitin' For The Sun To Shine/Uncle Pen//Honey/Highway 40 Blues (double pack) | 4 |

SKATALITES
65	Island WI 161	Trip To Mars/DOTTIE & BONNIE: Bunch Of Roses	10
65	Island WI 164	Good News/OWEN & LEON: Fits Is On Me	10
65	Island WI 165	Around The World/OWEN & LEON: Running Round	10
65	Island WI 168	Guns Of Navarone/Marcus Garvey	6
65	Island WI 175	Dragon Weapon/DESMOND DEKKAR & ACES: It Was Only A Dream	12
65	Island WI 191	Dr. Kildare/Sucu Sucu	10
65	Island WI 207	Ball O' Fire/LINVAL SPARKER: Can't Go On	10
65	Island WI 226	Dick Tracy/SOULETTES: One More Chance	10
65	Island WI 228	Beardman Ska/BONNIE & RITA: Bless You	10
65	Island WI 244	Lucky Seven/JUSTIN HINDS & DOMINOES: Never Too Young	10
65	Island WI 236	Skalarama/JUSTIN HINDS: Peace And Love	10
66	Island WI 260	Independent Anniversary Ska/WAILERS: Jumbie Jamboree	30
65	Ska Beat JB 177	Latin Goes Ska/LORD TANAM: Night Food Ska	10
65	Ska Beat JB 178	Silver Dollar/My Business	10
65	Ska Beat JB 182	Street Corner/DREAMLETS: Really Now	10
65	Ska Beat JB 206	Timothy/KING SCRATCH & DYNAMITES: Gumma	10
68	Decca F 12743	Don't Knock It/I Know	6
71	Spark SRL 1034	'Cos You're The One I Love	8
66	Doctor Bird DLM 5000	SKA-BOO-BA-DO (LP)	80
67	Studio One SOL 9006	SKA AUTHENTIC (LP)	70

SK'BOO
| 70s | Cuecumber CUE 1001 | It's A Hard Road/Music Is Life/Talking Pictures/God's Peace In Mind | 4 |

(see also Them)

SKELETAL FAMILY
83	Luggage RRP 00724	Trees/Just A Friend (foldout p/s)	12
83	Red Rhino RED 36	The Night/Waiting Here (p/s)	8
84	Red Rhino RED 41	She Cries Alone/The Wind Blows (p/s)	6
84	Red Rhino REDT 41	She Cries Alone/The Wind Blows/Eternal (12", p/s)	9
84	Red Rhino REDT 42	RECOLLECT (12" EP)	8
84	Red Rhino RED 43	So Sure/Batman (p/s)	5
84	Red Rhino REDT 43	So Sure/Batman/Trees/Lies (12", p/s)	7
85	Red Rhino RED 54	Promised Land/Stand By Me (p/s)	5

85   Red Rhino REDT 54   Promised Land/Stand By Me/Just A Friend (12", p/s) 7
(see also Ghost Dance)

PETER SKELLERN
74   Decca SKL 5178   NOT WITHOUT A FRIEND (LP) 10

SKID ROW (U.K.)
70   CBS 4893   Sandie's Gone Pts 1 & 2 5
71   CBS 7181   Night Of The Warm Witch/Mr. Deluxe 5
70   CBS 63965   SKID (LP, orange label, red & blue sleeve) 12
71   CBS 64411   34 HOURS (LP) 12
(see also Gary Moore, Thin Lizzy)

SKID ROW (U.S.)
90   Atlantic A 8883P   18 And Life/Midnight Tornado (shaped picture disc) 7

ALAN SKIDMORE (QUINTET)
69   Deram Nova SDN 11   ONCE UPON A TIME (LP) 30
70   Philips 6308 041   T.C.B. (LP) 35
(see also John Mayall's Blues Breakers, Brian Bennett)

SKIDS
78   No Bad NB 1   Charles/Reasons/Test Tube Babies (p/s) 6
78   Virgin VS 227   Sweet Suburbia/Open Sound (p/s, white vinyl) 5
78   Virgin VS 232   The Saints Are Coming/Of One Skin (p/s) 4
78   Virgin VS 232-12   WIDE OPEN (12" EP, red vinyl) 7
79   Virgin VS 241   Into The Valley/TV Stars (p/s, white vinyl) 4
79   Virgin VS 262   Masquerade/Out Of Town//Another Emotion/Aftermath Dub (double pack) 5
79   Virgin VS 306   Working For The Yankee Dollar/Vanguard's Crusade//All The Young Dudes/
Hymns From A Haunted Ballroom (double pack) 5
80   Virgin VS 373   Goodbye Civilian/Monkey McGuire Meets Specky Potter Behind The Lochore
Institute (poster p/s in poly bag) 4
80   Virgin VSP 373   Goodbye Civilian/Monkey McGuire Meets Specky Potter Behind The Lochore
Institute (picture disc) 4
81   Virgin VSK 101   Woman In Winter/Working For The Yankee Dollar (p/s, with comic booklet) 4
79   Smash Hits HIT 002   The Olympian/XTC: Ten Feet Tall (33rpm red flexidisc with 'Smash Hits' mag) . .5/4
80   Virgin V 2174   THE ABSOLUTE GAME (LP, with free LP "Strength Through Joy" [VDJ 33]) 10
(see also Big Country)

BJORN SKIFS
78   EMI EMI 2785   When The Night Comes/Don't Stop Now 6
81   EMI EMI 5172   Haunted By A Dream/Fangad I En Drom 8

SKIN ALLEY
72   Transatlantic BIG 506   You Got Me Danglin'/Skin Valley Serenade 4
72   Transatlantic BIG 511   In The Midnight Hour/Broken Eggs 4
69   CBS 63847   SKIN ALLEY (LP) 50
70   CBS 64140   TO PAGHAM AND BEYOND (LP) 20
72   Transatlantic TRA 260   TWO QUID DEAL (LP) 15
73   Transatlantic TRA 273   SKIN TIGHT (LP) 15

SKIN, FLESH & BONES
74   Pyramid PYR 7014   Butter Te Fish/Bammie And Fish 4

JIMMIE SKINNER
59   Mercury AMT 1030   Walkin' My Blues Away/Dark Hollow 6
59   Mercury AMT 1062   John Wesley Hardin/Misery Loves Company 6
60   Mercury AMT 1088   Riverboat Gambler/Married To A Friend 5
60   Mercury AMT 1117   Reasons To Live/I'm A Lot More Lonesome Now 5
59   Mercury ZEP 10012   COUNTRY AND WESTERN (EP, 2 tracks by George Jones) 25
64   London REB 1421   KENTUCKY COLONEL VOL. 1 (EP) 10
64   London REB 1422   KENTUCKY COLONEL VOL. 2 (EP) 10
64   London REB 1423   KENTUCKY COLONEL VOL. 3 (EP) 10

J. SCOTT SKINNER
60s   Topic 12T 280   THE STRATHSPEY KING (LP) 10

SKI PATROL
80   Clever Metal VIN 1   Everything Is Temporary/Silent Screams (p/s) 4
80   Malicious Damage MD 2   Agent Orange/Driving (p/s, with insert) 8
81   Malicious Damage MD 3   Cut/Faith In Transistion (p/s) 4

SKIP & FLIP
59   Top Rank JAR 156   It Was I/Lunch Hour 8
59   Top Rank JAR 156   It Was I/Lunch Hour (78) 12
59   Top Rank JAR 248   Fancy Nancy/It Could Be 7
60   Top Rank JAR 358   Cherry Pie/(I'll Quit) Cryin' Over You 8
(see also Gary Paxton, Skip Battin)

SKIP BIFFERTY
67   RCA Victor RCA 1621   On Love/Cover Girl 15
67   RCA Victor RCA 1648   Happy Land/Reason To Live 10
68   RCA Victor RCA 1720   Man In Black/Mr. Money Man 10
67   RCA Victor RD/SF 7941   SKIP BIFFERTY (LP, black label, later orange) 75/50
(see also Heavy Jelly, Griffin, Graham Bell, Arc, Bell & Arc)

ANITA SKORGEN
79   CBS S CBS 7259   Oliver/Together 4
82   Epic EPC A 2370   Tell Me (Adieu)/Adieu 4

SKREWDRIVER
77   Chiswick S 11   You're So Dumb/Better Off Crazy (p/s, orange or green p/s) 8
77   Chiswick NS 18   Anti-Social/19th Nervous Breakdown (p/s) 8
78   Chiswick NS 28   Streetfight/Unbeliever (unissued, test pressings only) . . . . .50+

MINT VALUE £

80	TJM TJM 4	Built Up, Knocked Down/A Case Of Pride/Breakout (p/s)	20
82	Skrewdriver SKREW 1T	BACK WITH A BANG (12", p/s)	15
83	White Noise WN 1	White Power/Smash The I.R.A./Shove The Dove (p/s, label also lists as S83/CUS/1796)	25
83	White Noise WN 2	Voice Of Britain/Sick Society (p/s, label also lists S83/CUS/2041)	20
83	White Noise WN 3	Hards/Brutal Attack (p/s)	20
77	Chiswick CH 3	ALL SKREWED UP (mini-LP, 12-track, 45rpm)	15
77	Chiswick WIK 3	ALL SKREWED UP (LP, 15-track, 33rpm, unissued in UK; Germany only)	

SKULLFLOWER

89	Broken Flag BFV 9	Birth, Death/Grub Song/Time Bomb/Blood Harvest (12", p/s)	7
89	Shock SX 001	(I Live) In The Bottomless Pit/Bo Diddley's Shitpump (foldaround p/s in poly bag, 500 only)	15
89	Shock SX 008	Xaman (p/s)	10
90	Toe Jam	Rotten Sun/Spook Rise (p/s, numbered, 500 only)	7
89	Broken Flag BFV 10	FORM DESTROYER (LP)	10

SKULLS

80s	Snakeskin SS 001	Graveyard Signal/Idols And Dolls (p/s, numbered, 300 only)	6

SKULLSNAPS

73	GSF GSZ 7	My Hang Up Is You/It's A New Day	10

SKUNKS

78	Eel Pie EPS 001	Good From The Bad/Back Street Fightin' (2,000 only, die-cut 'swirl' sleeve)	6

(see also Craze, Hard Corps)

SKY

71	RCA SF 8168	DON'T HOLD BACK (LP)	12

(see also Knack)

PATRICK SKY

65	Vanguard VSD 79179	PRIVATE SKY (LP)	15
70	Vanguard SVRL 19054	A HARVEST OF GENTLE CLANG (LP)	15

SKYBIRD

74	Holyground HGS 118	SUMMER OF '73 (LP, 250 copies only)	45

SKYLARK

73	Capitol CL 15764	Wildflower/Writing On the Wall	5

SKYLINERS

59	London HLB 8829	Since I Don't Have You/One Night, One Night	125
59	London HLB 8829	Since I Don't Have You/One Night, One Night (78)	30
59	London HLU 8924	This I Swear/Tomorrow	60
59	London HLU 8924	This I Swear/Tomorrow (78)	35
59	London HLU 8971	It Happened Today/Lonely Way	30
59	London HLU 8971	It Happened Today/Lonely Way (78)	35
60	Polydor NH 66951	Pennies From Heaven/I'll Be Seeing You	12
61	Pye Intl. 7N 25091	The Door Is Still Open/I'll Close My Eyes	12

FREDDIE SLACK

51	Capitol LC 6529	FREDDIE SLACK'S BOOGIE WOOGIE (10" LP)	30

SLACK ALICE

74	Philips 6308 214	SLACK ALICE (LP)	12

SLADE

69	Fontana TF 1056	Wild Winds Are Blowing/One Way Hotel	50
70	Fontana TF 1079	Shape Of Things To Come/C'mon C'mon	50
70	Polydor 2058 054	Know Who You Are/Dapple Rose	60
71	Polydor 2058 112	Get Down And Get With It/Do You Want Me/The Gospel According To Rasputin (some copies titled "Get Down With It")	8
73	Polydor 2058 422	Merry Xmas Everybody/Don't Blame Me (p/s, green background, 4 individual photos)	25
74	Polydor 2058 492	The Bangin' Man/She Did It To Me (p/s)	25
74	Polydor 2058 522	Far Far Away/O.K. Yesterday Was Yesterday (p/s)	4
75	Polydor 2058 547	How Does It Feel?/So Far So Good (p/s)	4
75	Polydor 2058 585	Thanks For The Memory/Raining In My Champagne	4
75	Polydor 2058 585	Thanks For The Memory (with altered lyrics)/Raining In My Champagne	25
75	Polydor 2058 663	In For A Penny/Can You Just Imagine (p/s)	8
76	Polydor 2058 690	Let's Call It Quits/When The Chips Are Down	4
76	Polydor 2058 716	Nobody's Fool/L.A. Jinx	6
77	Barn 2014 105	Gypsy Roadhog/Forest Full Of Needles	5
77	Barn 2014 106	Burning In The Heat Of Love/Ready Steady Kids	15
77	Barn 2014 114	My Baby Left Me; That's Alright/O.H.M.S. (p/s)	10
78	Barn 2014 121	Give Us A Goal/Daddio	6
78	Barn 2014 127	Rock'n'roll Bolero/It's Alright By Me	12
79	Barn BARN 002	Ginny Ginny/Dizzy Mama (no p/s, with sticker, yellow vinyl only)	12
79	Barn BARN 010	Sign Of The Times/Not Tonight Josephine (no p/s)	15
79	Barn BARN 011	Okey Cokey/My Baby's Got It (no p/s)	10
80	RSO RSO 051	Okey Cokey/My Baby's Got It (unissued)	6
80	S.O.T.B. SUPER 3	Night Starvation/When I'm Dancing I Ain't Fightin' (demo only)	25
80	S.O.T.B. SUPER 45 3	SIX OF THE BEST — NIGHT STARVATION (12" EP, die-cut sleeve)	12
80	Cheapskate CHEAP 5	SLADE ALIVE AT READING '80 (EP, die-cut sleeve)	7
80	Cheapskate CHEAP 11	Merry Xmas Everybody/Okey Cokey/Get Down And Get With It (as Slade & Reading Choir, some in die-cut p/s)	8/4
80	Polydor 2058 422	Merry Xmas Everybody/Don't Blame Me (reissue, green background, 'holly leaf' design, colour group photo p/s)	4
81	Cheapskate CHEAP 16	We'll Bring The House Down/Holding On To Your Hats (p/s)	7/4
81	Cheapskate CHEAP 21	Wheels Ain't Comin' Down/Not Tonight Josephine (p/s)	8/4
81	Cheapskate CHEAP 24	Knuckle Sandwich Nancy/I'm Mad (p/s)	7/4

81	RCA RCA 124	Lock Up Your Daughters/Sign Of The Times (no p/s) 4
81	Polydor POSP 399	CUM ON FEEL THE NOIZE (EP) 6
81	Polydor POSPX 399	CUM ON FEEL THE NOIZE (12" EP) 9
82	RCA RCA 191	Ruby Red/Funk Punk And Junk (p/s) 10
82	RCA RCAD 191	Ruby Red/Funk Punk And Junk//Rock And Roll Preacher (live)/Take Me Bak 'Ome (live) (double pack, gatefold p/s) 6
82	RCA RCA 291	(And Now The Waltz) C'est La Vie/Merry Xmas Everybody (p/s) 4
82	Speed SPEED 201	Okey Cokey/Get Down And Get With It (p/s) 10
82	Speed SPEEDP 201	Okey Cokey/Get Down And Get With It (picture disc) 7
83	RCA RCA 373	My Oh My/Merry Xmas Everybody (live)/Keep Your Hands Off My Power Supply (p/s) 4
83	RCA RCAT 373	My Oh My/Keep Your Hands Off My Power Supply/Don't Tame A Hurricane (12", p/s) 7
84	RCA RCAT 455	All Join Hands/My Oh My/Here's To... (The New Year)/Merry Xmas (Live & Kickin') (12", stickered p/s) 15
85	RCA RCA 475	Seven Year Bitch/Leave Them Girls Alone (p/s) 4
85	RCA RCAT 475	Seven Year Bitch/Leave Them Girls Alone/We'll Bring The House Down (live) (12", p/s) 7
85	RCA PB 40027	Myzterious Mizster Jones/Mama Nature Is A Rocker (p/s) 4
85	RCA PB 40027	Myzterious Mizster Jones/Mama Nature Is A Rocker (picture disc, PVC sleeve) ...7
85	RCA PT 40028	Myzterious Mizster Jones (Extended Version)/Mama Nature Is A Rocker/ My Oh My (Piano And Vocal Version) (12", p/s) 8
85	RCA PB 40449/PB 40549	Do You Believe In Miracles/My Oh My (Swing Version)//Santa Claus Is Coming To Town/Auld Lang Syne/You'll Never Walk Alone (double pack, in gatefold PVC cover) 12
85	RCA PT 40450D (PT 40450/PT 40550)	Do You Believe In Miracles/My Oh My (Swing Version)/Time To Rock//Santa Claus Is Coming To Town/Auld Lang Syne/You'll Never Walk Alone (12", 'Slade Xmas' double pack, separate sleeves in gatefold PVC cover) 15
85	Polydor POSP 780	Merry Xmas Everybody/Don't Blame Me (p/s, 3rd reissue) 4
85	Polydor POSPX 780	Merry Xmas Everybody/Don't Blame Me (12", p/s, 3rd reissue) 7
87	RCA PB 41137	Still The Same/Gotta Go Home (p/s) 4
87	RCA PB 41147D	Still The Same/Gotta Go Home//The Roaring Silence/Don't Talk To Me About Love (21st anniversary double pack, gatefold p/s) 8
87	RCA PT 41138	Still The Same/Gotta Go Home (12", p/s) 7
87	Cheapskate BOYZ 1	You Boyz Make Big Noize/Boyz Instrumental (p/s, B-side plays U.S.A. Mix) ...5
87	Cheapskate BOYZ 1	You Boyz Make Big Noize (Noize Remix)/(The Instrumental Mix)/ (The USA Mix) (T Boyz 1) 8
88	Cheapskate BOYZCD 3	Let's Dance (1988 Remix)/Far Far Away/How Does It Feel/Standing On The Corner (3" CD with adaptor) 7
88	Counterpoint CDEP 12 C	How Does It Feel/Far Far Away//(WIZZARD: 2 tracks) (CD) 7
89	Receiver CD BOYZ 4	Merry Xmas Everybody/Don't Blame Me/Far Far Away (CD) 7
72	Polydor/Sound For Industry SFI 122	The Whole World's Going Crazy/MIKE HUGG: Bonnie Charlie (33rpm flexidisc free with 'Music Scene' magazine) 12/8
73	Lyntone LYN 2645	Slade Talk To 'Melanie' Readers (flexidisc with 'Melanie' magazine) 12/8
73	Lyntone LYN 2797	Slade Talk To '19' Readers (flexidisc with '19' magazine) 12/8
75	Fan Club LYN 2645/2797	Slade Talk To 'Melanie' Readers/Slade Talk To '19' Readers (flexidisc) 12
70s	Lyntone LYN 3156/7	Far Far Away/Thanks For The Memory (flexidisc with Smith's Crisps offer) 10
80s	SLADE 1	An Interview With Slade (picture disc, 2,000 only, PVC sleeve) 15
70	Polydor 2383 026	PLAY IT LOUD (LP) 12
72	Polydor 2383 101	SLADE ALIVE (LP, gatefold sleeve) 10
73	Polydor 2442 119	SLADEST 10
73	Polydor 2383 261	OLD NEW BORROWED AND BLUE (LP, gatefold sleeve) 10
74	Polydor 2442 126	SLADE IN FLAME (LP, soundtrack, gatefold sleeve) 10
76	Polydor 2383 377	NOBODY'S FOOLS (LP, with lyric inner sleeve) 12
77	Barn 2314 103	WHATEVER HAPPENED TO SLADE (LP, with lyric sheet) 20
78	Barn 2314 106	ALIVE VOLUME 2 (LP) 20
79	Barn NARB 003	RETURN TO BASE (LP) 35

(see also Ambrose Slade, Steve Brett & Mavericks, In-Be-Tweens, Dummies, Gary Holton, China Dolls, Sue Scadding)

PRENTIS SLADE

| 61 | Parlophone R 4850 | I Can Tell/Looking For A Friend .... 7 |

SLAM CREEPERS

| 68 | Olga OLE 009 | Saturday/Hold It Baby .... 15 |
| 73 | Sonet SON 2003 | We Are Happy People/Yansbro Memories .... 4 |

SLANES

| 65 | Blue Beat BB 300 | It Takes Time/LIGES: Have Mercy Baby .... 8 |

IVOR SLANEY ORCHESTRA

53	Philips PB 156	Silhouette D'Amour/Biscuits In Bed 4
61	HMV POP 943	The Sir Francis Drake Theme/Midsummer Madness 4
64	HMV POP 1347	High Wire/Sacremento 5
66	Columbia DB 8020	Long Weekend/Eleven Up (as Slaney Strings) 4

SLAPP HAPPY

74	Virgin VS 105	Casablanca Moon/Slow Moon's Rose 4
75	Virgin VS 124	Johnny's Dead/Mr. Rainbow 4
83	Half Cat HC 001	Everybody's Slimmin' (Even Men And Women!)/Blue-Eyed Vallain (p/s) 5
72	Polydor 2310 204	SORT OF (LP, with insert) 60
74	Virgin V 2014	SLAPP HAPPY (LP) 10
74	Virgin V 2024	DESPERATE STRAIGHTS (LP, with Henry Cow) 10
86	Recommended RRS 5	SORT OF (LP, reissue) 15

(see also Henry Cow, Peter Blegvad, Anthony Moore, Art Bears)

FELIX SLATKIN ORCHESTRA

| 61 | London HLG 9256 | Sundowners (Theme)/Gaythers Gone .... 4 |

SLAUGHTER (& DOGS)

| 77 | Rabid TOSH 101 | Cranked Up Really High/The Bitch (p/s, blue, later cream plastic labels) ....6/5 |

SLAUGHTER (& DOGS)

77	Rabid TOSH 101	Cranked Up Really High/The Bitch (p/s, repressings with b&w paper label)	4
77	Decca FR 13723	Where Have All The Boot Boys Gone/You're A Bore (p/s, paper or plastic label)	5/4
77	Decca LF 13723	Where Have All The Boot Boys Gone/You're A Bore (12", p/s, 10,000 only)	7
77	Decca FR 13743	Dame To Blame/Johnny T (no p/s)	4
78	Decca FR 13758	Quick Joey Small/Come On Back (no p/s, with Mick Ronson)	4
79	TJM TJM 3	It's Alright/Edgar Allen Poe/Twist & Turn/UFO (12", p/s)	7
79	DJM DJS 10927	You're Ready Now/Runaway (p/s)	4
80	DJM DJS 10936	East Side Of Town/One By One (p/s, as Slaughter)	4
80	DJM DJS 10945	I'm The One/What's Wrong Boy? (live)/Hell In New York (p/s, as Slaughter)	4
81	Damaged Goods FNARR 1	Where Have All The Boot Boys Gone/You're A Bore/Johnny T. (p/s 1,000 only: 500 on green vinyl, 500 on red vinyl)	4
78	Decca SKL 5292	DO IT DOG STYLE (LP)	20
78	Rabid HAT 23	LIVE SLAUGHTER RABID DOGS (LP, plain white sleeve with large sticker)	12
80	DJM DJF 20566	BITE BACK (LP, as Slaughter)	10
80	Thrush THRUSH 1	LIVE AT THE FACTORY (LP)	10
81	Damaged Goods FNARRLP 2	DO IT DOG STYLE (LP, reissue, 1,000 only multi-coloured vinyl, numbered, with 2 multi-coloured stickers)	10

(see also Studio Sweethearts, Ed Banger)

SLAUGHTER JOE

85	Creation CRE 019	I'll Follow You Down/Napalm Girl (foldaround p/s in poly bag)	10
85	Creation CRE 019T	I'll Follow You Down/Napalm Girl/Surely Some Of Slaughter's Blues/ Fall Apart (12", p/s)	10
86	Creation CRE 035	She's Out Of Touch/I Know You Rider (p/s)	5
86	Creation CRE 035T	She's Out Of Touch/I Know You Rider/The Lonesome Death Of Thurston Moore (12", p/s)	7

(see also Television Personalities, Missing Scientists)

SLAVE

77	Cotillion K 50358	SLAVE (LP)	10

MARTIN SLAVIN & HIS GANG

60	Oriole CB 1587	Rock-A-Charleston/The Charleston's Gonna Rock The Hop	5

(see also Martinas & His Music)

FRANK SLAY

62	Top Rank JAR 599	Cincinatti/Flying Circle	5

SLAYER

87	London LON 133	Criminally Insane (Remix)/Aggressive Perfector (red vinyl, 'cross' p/s)	15
87	Enigma 720151	LIVE UNDEAD (LP, picture disc)	10
87	London LONPP 34	REIGN IN BLOOD (LP, picture disc)	12

F. SLEDGE

65	Blue Beat BB 386	Red Eye Girl/Try To Love Again	8

PERCY SLEDGE

66	Atlantic 584 001	When A Man Loves A Woman/Love Me Like You Mean It	4
66	Atlantic 584 034	Warm And Tender Love/Sugar Puddin'	5
66	Atlantic 584 055	Heart Of A Child/My Adorable One	5
67	Atlantic 584 071	It Tears Me Up/Oh, How Happy	4
67	Atlantic 584 080	Baby, Help Me/You've Lost That Something Wonderful	6
67	Atlantic 584 108	Out Of Left Field/It Can't Be Stopped	4
67	Atlantic 584 140	Pledging My Love/You Don't Miss Your Water	4
68	Atlantic 584 177	Take Time To Know Her/It's All Wrong But It's Alright	4
68	Atlantic 584 225	Come Softly To Me/You're All Around Me	4
69	Atlantic 584 264	Any Day Now/The Angels Listened In	4
69	Atlantic 584 286	Kind Woman/Woman Of The Night	4
69	Atlantic 584 300	True Love Travels On A Gravel Road/Faithful And True	4
72	Atlantic K 10165	Baby, Help Me/Warm And Tender Love/Take Time To Know Her	4
74	Capricorn 2089 009	I'll Be Your Everything/Walkin' In The Sun	4
67	Atlantic 587/588 048	WARM AND TENDER SOUL (LP)	12
67	Atlantic 587/588 081	THE PERCY SLEDGE WAY (LP)	12
68	Atlantic 587/588 105	WHEN A MAN LOVES A WOMAN (LP)	10
69	Atlantic 587/588 153	THE BEST OF PERCY SLEDGE (LP)	10

SLEDGEHAMMER

79	Slammer SRTS 79 CUS 395	Sledgehammer/Feelgood (p/s)	8
80	Slammer CELL 2	Living In Dreams/Fantasia (p/s)	4
80	Valiant STRONG 1	Sledgehammer/Feelgood (p/s, reissue)	5
80	Valiant ROUND 2	Sledgehammer/Feelgood (p/s, 2nd reissue)	4
85	Illuminated ILL 33	In The Queue/Oxford City (shaped picture disc)	15

SLEEPWALKERS

59	Parlophone R 4580	Sleep Walk/Golden Mile	6

SLEEPY

68	CBS 3592	Love's Immortal Fire/Is It Really The Same	15
68	CBS 3838	Rosie Can't Fly/Mrs. Bailey's Barbecue And Grill	15

SLENDER PLENTY

67	Polydor BM 56189	Silver Tree Top School For Boys/I've Lost A Friend And Found A Lover	20

JIMI SLEVIN

82	Claddagh CCF 7	FREEFLIGHT (LP)	50

(see also Peggy's Leg)

GRACE SLICK

74	Grunt BFL1 0347	MANHOLE (LP, with booklet)	10

(see also Jefferson Airplane, Jefferson Starship, Paul Kantner, Great Society)

RICKY SLICK

72	Dynamic DYN 449	Family Man/Version	4

SLICKERS

68	Blue Cat BS 133	Wala Wala/LESTER STERLING: Super Special	10
68	Blue Cat BS 134	Nana (actually by George Dekker)/MARTIN RILEY: I May Never See	
		My Baby Anymore	8
69	Blue Cat BS 154	Frying Pan/RARFIELD WILLIAMS: Code It	7
69	Amalgamated AMG 852	Man Beware/Matty Matty	6
69	Amalgamated AMG 866	Money Reaper/Man Beware	6
70	Dynamic DYN 406	Johnny Too Bad/ROLAND ALPHONSO: Saucy Horde	5
72	Dynamic DYN 419	You Can't Win/Don't Fight The Law	4
69	Trojan TR 7719	Run Fattie/Hoola Bulla	6
71	Punch PH 59	Johnny Too Bad/Johnny Too Bad Version	4

SLIM & SLAM

| 40s | Parlophone R 2634 | Dopey Joe/Buck Dance Rhythm (78) | 10 |

(see also Slim Gaillard)

GEORGIA SLIM

| 50s | Collector JEL 2 | THE MALE BLUES VOL. 1 (EP) | 12 |

TARHEEL SLIM & LITTLE ANN

| 65 | Sue WI 390 | You Make Me Feel So Good/Got To Keep On Lovin' You | 12 |

TENDER SLIM

| 60s | XX MIN 702 | TENDER SLIM AND COUSIN LEROY (EP) | 7 |

SLIM & FREEDOM SINGERS

| 70 | Banana BA 304 | Do Dang Do (actually by Leroy Sibbles)/JACKIE MITTOO & SOUND | |
| | | DIMENSION: Hot Milk | 5 |

SLIK

75	Bell BELL 1414	The Boogiest Band In Town/Hatche	4
75	Bell BELL 1464	Forever And Ever/Again My Love (p/s)	4
76	Arista ARIST 83	Don't Take Your Love Away/This Side Up	4

(see also PVC 2, Zones, Rich Kids, Midge Ure)

SLIME

| 78 | Toadstool GOOD 1 | Controversial/Loony (p/s) | 5 |

(see also Johnny Moped)

SLITS

79	Island WIP 6505	Typical Girls/I Heard It Through The Grapevine (p/s)	4
79	Island 12 WIP 6505	Typical Girls (Brink Style)/I Heard It Through The Grapevine/Liebe And	
		Romanze (12", p/s)	7
80	Rough Trade RT 039/Y 1	In The Beginning There Was Rhythm/POP GROUP: Where There's A Will	
		There's A Way (p/s)	4
79	Island ILPS 9573	CUT (LP, with inner sleeve)	10
80	Rough Trade/Y Y 3	BOOTLEG RETROSPECTIVE (LP, plain sleeve)	10
81	CBS 85269	THE RETURN OF THE GIANT SLITS (LP, some with free 45 "American Radio	
		Interview"/"Face Dub" [XPS 125])	15/10

P.F. SLOAN

65	RCA RCA 1482	Sins Of The Family/This Mornin'	4
67	RCA RCA 1623	Sunflower Sunflower/The Man Behind The Red Balloon	4
72	Epic EPC 65179	RAISED ON RECORDS (LP)	10

(see also Grass Roots)

SAMMI SLOAN

| 68 | Columbia DB 8480 | Yes I Would/Be His Girl | 8 |

SLOW DOG

| 72 | Parlophone R 5942 | Ain't Never Going Home/Walking Through The Blue Grass | 4 |

SLOWBURNER

| 89 | Burn | AN EMOTIONAL BUSINESS (LP) | 10 |

SLY & FAMILY STONE

(see under Sly [& Family] Stone)

JOAN SMALL

56	Parlophone MSP 6219	Change Of Heart/Come Next Spring	4
56	Parlophone R 4211	Love Is A Stranger/Autumn Concerto	4
57	Parlophone R 4269	Gonna Get Along Without You Now/You Can't Say I Love You To A R&R Tune	8
58	Parlophone R 4431	Afraid/How Many Times (Can I Fall In Love)	4
60	Parlophone R 4622	The Big Hurt/Ask Me To Go Steady	4

KAREN SMALL

| 66 | Vocalion V 9281 | To Get You Back Again/That's Why I Cry | 7 |

MARY SMALL

| 56 | Vogue Coral Q 72196 | None Of That Now/Dino | 4 |

MILLIE SMALL

(see under Millie)

SMALL FACES

65	Decca F 12208	Whatcha Gonna Do About It?/What's A Matter, Baby?	5
65	Decca F 12276	I've Got Mine/It's Too Late	7
66	Decca F 12317	Sha-La-La-La-Lee/Grow Your Own	5
66	Decca F 12393	Hey Girl/Almost Grown	5
66	Decca F 12470	All Or Nothing/Understanding (curved or boxed Decca logo)	5/4
66	Decca F 12500	My Mind's Eye/I Can't Dance With You	5
67	Decca F 12565	I Can't Make It/Just Passing	7
67	Decca F 12619	Patterns/E Too D	12
67	Immediate IM 050	Here Comes The Nice/Talk To You	5
67	Immediate IM 052	Itchycoo Park/I'm Only Dreaming	5

67	Immediate IM 062	Tin Soldier/I Feel Much Better (some in p/s)	12/4
68	Immediate IM 064	Lazy Sunday/Rollin' Over	4
68	Immediate IM 069	The Universal/Donkey Rides, A Penny A Glass	4
69	Immediate IM 077	Afterglow (Of Your Love)/Wham Bam, Thank You Mam	4
70s	Immediate IM 064	Lazy Sunday/Rollin' Over (p/s, reissue with white label)	6
66	Decca LK 4790	SMALL FACES (LP, original red label)	25
67	Decca LK 4879	FROM THE BEGINNING (LP, original red label)	30
67	Immediate IMLP/IMSP 008	SMALL FACES (LP)	35
68	Immediate IMLP/IMSP 012	OGDENS' NUT GONE FLAKE (LP, pink label, circular foldout sleeve)	20
69	Immediate IMLP/IMSP 022	IN MEMORIAM (LP, export issue)	35
69	Immediate IMAL 01/02	THE AUTUMN STONE (2-LP, gatefold sleeve)	25

(see also Faces, Steve Marriott, Humble Pie, Jimmy Winston & His Reflections, Winston's Fumbs)

SMALL HOURS
80	Automatic K 17708	The Kid/Business In Town/Midnight To Six/End Of The Night (p/s)	30
80	Automatic K 17708X	The Kid/Business In Town/Midnight To Six/End Of The Night (10", p/s)	20

SMALL WORLD
82	Whaam! WHAAM 003	Love Is Dead/Liberty (p/s)	20

SMILIN' JOE
54	London HL 8106	A.B.C.'s Pts 1 & 2 (78)	80

(see also Cousin Joe)

SMITH
69	Stateside SS 8028	Baby It's You/I Don't Believe	4
69	Stateside SSL 5016	A GROUP CALLED SMITH (LP)	10
70	Stateside SSL 5031	MINUS-PLUS (LP)	10

ADAM (Eric) SMITH
62	Island WI 057	I Wonder Why/My Prayer	10

A.S.A.P. (Adrian Smith & Project)
89	EMI 12 EMPD 107	Silver And Gold/Blood Brothers (12", no p/s, silver & gold vinyl)	7
90	EMI EMPD 131	Down The Wire (Crossed Line Mix)/When She's Gone (shaped picture disc)	4

(see also Iron Maiden, Urchin)

ARTHUR 'GUITAR BOOGIE' SMITH (& HIS CRACKERJACKS)
49	MGM MGM 191	Careless Hands/Lady Of Spain (78, with Crackerjacks)	6
49	MGM MGM 220	Boomerang/Cracker Boogie (78, with Crackerjacks)	6
50	MGM MGM 254	Mule Train/ROY LEAR & BETTY SMITH: Dime A Dozen (78)	6
50	MGM MGM 329	Guitar Boogie/Be Bop Rag (78)	5
51	MGM MGM 363	Mandolin Boogie/The Memphis Blues (78)	6
52	MGM MGM 484	Alabama Jubilee/Fiddle-Faddle (78, with Crackerjacks)	5
52	MGM MGM 518	Guitar And Piano Boogie/Banjo Buster (78)	5
52	MGM MGM 555	Express Train Boogie/River Rag (78)	5
53	MGM SP 1008	Guitar Boogie/Be Bop Rag	25
53	MGM SP 1021	Five String Banjo Boogie/South	18
53	MGM MGM 599	Five String Banjo Boogie/South (78)	5
53	MGM SP 1039	Express Train Boogie/River Rag	18
53	MGM MGM 630	Recitation Sonny Smith: In Memory Of Hank Williams/HANK WILLIAMS & HIS DRIFTING COWBOYS: I Saw The Light (78)	15
53	MGM MGM 660	Big Mountain Shuffle/KEN CURTIS: The Call Of The Faraway Hills (78)	5
53	MGM MGM 695	Three D Boogie/He Went That-A-Way (78)	6
54	MGM SP 1096	Oh, Baby Mine, I Get So Lonely/Outboard	18
54	MGM MGM 755	Oh, Baby Mine, I Get So Lonely/Outboard (78)	5
54	MGM SP 1110	Redheaded Stranger/Texas Hop	18
54	MGM MGM 779	Redheaded Stranger/Texas Hop (78)	5
55	MGM SP 1122	Hi Lo Boogie/Truck Stop Grill	18
55	MGM MGM 805	Hi Lo Boogie/Truck Stop Grill (78)	5
54	MGM MGM-EP 510	ARTHUR 'GUITAR BOOGIE' SMITH AND HIS CRACKERJACKS (EP)	15
59	MGM MGM-EP 695	ARTHUR 'GUITAR BOOGIE' SMITH AND HIS CRACKERJACKS (EP)	18
63	Stateside SE 1005	MISTER GUITAR (EP)	12
53	MGM MGM-D 111	FINGERS ON FIRE (10" LP)	30
54	MGM MGM-D 131	FOOLISH QUESTIONS (10" LP)	30

BARRY SMITH
74	People PEO 114	Hold On To It Pts 1 & 2	15

BEASLEY SMITH & HIS ORCHESTRA
56	London HLD 8235	Goodnight, Sweet Dreams/Parisian Rag	25
56	London HLD 8273	My Foolish Heart/Old Spinning Wheel	25

BESSIE SMITH
30s	Parlophone R 1793	Do Your Duty/I'm Down In The Dumps (78)	25
30s	Parlophone R 2146	Gimme A Pigfoot/Take Me For A Buggy Ride (78)	20
40s	Parlophone R 2329	In The House Blues/SEVEN GALLON JUG BAND: Wipe 'Em Off (78)	15
40s	Parlophone R 2344	The St. Louis Blues/Cold In Hand Blues (78)	12
40s	Parlophone R 2476	Reckless Blues/St. Louis Blues (78)	12
40s	Parlophone R 2477	Alexander's Ragtime Band/There'll Be A Hot Time In The Old Town Tonight (78)	12
40s	Parlophone R 2478	Money Blues/Muddy Water (A Mississippi Moan) (78)	12
40s	Parlophone R 2479	Weeping Willow Blue/Careless Love Blues (78)	12
40s	Parlophone R 2480	The Yellow Dog Blues/Trombone Cholly (78)	12
40s	Parlophone R 2481	Backwater Blues/Nobody Knows You When You're Down And Out (78)	12
40s	Parlophone R 2482	Soft Pedal Blues/I Used To Be Your Sweet Man (78)	12
40s	Parlophone R 2483	Preachin' The Blues/Thinking Blues (78)	12
51	Columbia DB 2796	Empty Bed Blues Parts 1 And 2 (78)	20
58	Philips BBE 12202	EMPRESS OF THE BLUES (EP)	12
59	Philips BBE 12231	EMPRESS OF THE BLUES NO. 2 (EP)	12
59	Philips BBE 12233	EMPRESS OF THE BLUES NO. 3 (EP)	12
60	Philips BBE 12360	BESSIE SMITH (EP)	8

55	Philips BBL 7019	THE BESSIE SMITH STORY VOLUME 1 (LP, with Louis Armstrong)	25
55	Philips BBL 7020	THE BESSIE SMITH STORY VOLUME 2 (LP)	25
55	Philips BBL 7042	THE BESSIE SMITH STORY VOLUME 3 (LP)	25
55	Philips BBL 7049	THE BESSIE SMITH STORY VOLUME 4 (LP)	25
62	Philips BBL 7513	BESSIE'S BLUES 1923-1924 (LP)	30
66	CBS BPG 62377	THE BESSIE SMITH STORY VOLUME 1 (LP)	10
66	CBS BPG 62378	THE BESSIE SMITH STORY VOLUME 2 (LP)	10
66	CBS BPG 62379	THE BESSIE SMITH STORY VOLUME 3 (LP)	10
66	CBS BPG 62380	THE BESSIE SMITH STORY VOLUME 4 (LP)	10
71	CBS 66258	THE WORLD'S GREATES BLUES SINGER (2-LP, some with booklet)	20/15
71	CBS 66262	ANY WOMAN'S BLUES (2-LP)	15
71	CBS 66273	EMPTY BED BLUES (2-LP)	15
72	CBS 66264	THE EMPRESS (2-LP)	15
73	CBS 67232	NOBODY'S BLUES BUT MINE (2-LP)	15
70s	Empress 10006	THE COMPLETE ST. LOUIS BLUES SOUNDTRACK (10" LP)	10

BETTY SMITH SKIFFLE GROUP

| 57 | Tempo A 162 | There's A Blue Ridge Round My Heart, .../Double Shuffle | 10 |
| 57 | Tempo A 163 | Sweet Georgia Brown/Little White Lies | 10 |

(see also Betty Smith Quintet)

BETTY SMITH QUINTET

58	Decca F 10986	Hand Jive/Bewitched	8
58	Decca F 11031	Will The Angels Play Their Harps For Me/Betty's Blues	8
58	Decca F 11071	Begin The Beguine/Song Of The Boulevards	6
59	Decca F 11124	Song Of India/Stormy Weather	6
57	Decca DFE 6446	BETTY SMITH QUINTET (EP)	12

(see also Betty Smith Skiffle Group)

BUSTER SMITH

| 61 | London Jazz LTZ-K 15206 | THE LEGENDARY BUSTER SMITH (LP) | 12 |

CARL SMITH

| 59 | Philips PB 943 | Ten Thousand Drums/The Tall, Tall Gentlemen | 8 |
| 60 | Philips BBL 7437 | THE CARL SMITH TOUCH (LP) | 15 |

CLARA SMITH

69	VJM VLP 15	CLARA SMITH VOLUME 1 (LP)	15
69	VJM VLP 16	CLARA SMITH VOLUME 2 (LP)	15
69	VJM VLP 17	CLARA SMITH VOLUME 3 (LP)	15

CLARA SMITH & FLETCHER HENDERSON

| 61 | Philips BBE 12491 | BLUES BY CLARA SMITH 1926-1928 (EP) | 12 |

COUNTY SMITH

| 68 | Decca F 12818 | Low Bad Hurting/No Longer Mine | 4 |

D. SMITH

| 70 | Smash SMA 2311 | Ball Of Confusion (actually Dennis Alcapone)/KEITH HUDSON: Don't Get Me Confused | 4 |

(see also Dennis Alcapone)

DAVE SMITH & ASTRONAUTS

| 67 | Col. Blue Beat DB 104 | A Lover Like You/Cup Of Love | 7 |

EDDIE SMITH

| 55 | Parlophone MSP 6186 | Silver Star Stomp/Stumbling (as Eddie Smith & Chiefs) | 12 |
| 60 | Top Rank JAR 285 | Upturn/Border Beat (as Eddie Smith & Hornets) | 8 |

EDGEWOOD SMITH (& FABULOUS TAILFEATHERS)

| 67 | Sue WI 4037 | Yeah/Ain't That Lovin' You | 12 |

EFFIE SMITH

| 66 | Sue WI 4010 | Dial That Telephone Pts 1 & 2 | 12 |

ELSON SMITH

| 61 | Fontana H 291 | Flip Flop/Are You Ready For That | 10 |

ETHEL SMITH

| 55 | Brunswick 05470 | Hernando's Hideaway/Lemon Merengue | 4 |

(LITTLE) GEORGE (HARMONICA) SMITH

65	Blue Horizon 45-1002	Blues In The Dark/Telephone Blues (as Little George Smith)	40
70	Blue Horizon 57-3170	Someday You're Gonna Learn/Before You Do Your Thing	10
69	Liberty LBL 83218	A TRIBUTE TO LITTLE WALTER (LP)	15
70	Blue Horizon 7-63856	NO TIME TO JIVE (LP)	65
71	Deram SML 1082	ARKANSAS TRAP (LP)	40

(see also Bacon Fat)

GLORIA SMITH

| 59 | London HLU 8903 | Playmates/Don't Take Your Love From Me | 8 |
| 59 | London HLU 8903 | Playmates/Don't Take Your Love From Me (78) | 5 |

GORDON SMITH

| 69 | Blue Horizon 57-3156 | Too Long/Funk Pedal | 10 |
| 68 | Blue Horizon 7-63211 | LONG OVERDUE (LP) | 30 |

(see also Kevin Coyne)

HAROL SMITH & MAJESTIC CHOIR

| 69 | Chess CRS 8100 | We Can Walk A Little Prouder/Why Am I Treated So Bad | 4 |

HUEY 'PIANO' SMITH & CLOWNS

58	Columbia DB 4138	Don't You Just Know It/High Blood Pressure	50
58	Columbia DB 4138	Don't You Just Know It/High Blood Pressure (78)	30
60	Top Rank JAR 282	Don't You Just Know Yokomo/FRANKIE FORD: Cheatin' Woman	20
62	Top Rank JAR 614	Pop-Eye/Scald-Dog (as Huey Smith)	15

MINT VALUE £

65	Sue WI 364	If It Ain't One Thing It's Another/Tu Ber Cu Lucas & The Sinus Blues	15
65	Sue WI 380	Rockin' Pneumonia And The Boogie Woogie Flu Pts 1 & 2	15
78	Chiswick NS 43	Rockin' Pneumonia And The Boogie Woogie Flu (unissued)	
65	Sue ILP 917	ROCKIN' PNEUMONIA AND THE BOOGIE WOOGIE FLU (LP)	40
80s	Chiswick/Ace CH 9	ROCKIN' PNEUMONIA AND THE BOOGIE WOOGIE FLU (LP, reissue)	10

(see also Frankie Ford)

HURRICANE SMITH
| 71 | Columbia DB 8785 | Don't Let It Die/The Writer Sings His Songs | 4 |

JENNIE SMITH
| 59 | Philips PB 924 | Huggin' My Pillow (Sweet Side)/Huggin' My Pillow (Sweet Beat Side) | 4 |

JIMMY SMITH
62	HMV POP 1025	Walk On The Wild Side Pts 1 & 2	5
63	Blue Note 45-1904	When My Dreamboat Comes Home Pts 1 & 2	5
64	Blue Note 45-1879	The Sermon Pts 1 & 2	10
64	Blue Note 45-1905	Can Heat/Matilda	10
65	Verve VS 509	Hobo Flats Pts 1 & 2	4
65	Verve VS 521	Who's Afraid Of Virginia Woolf Pts 1 & 2	5
65	Verve VS 523	The Cat/Basin Street Blues	5
65	Verve VS 531	The Organ Grinder's Swing/I'll Close My Eyes	5
66	Verve VS 534	Slow Theme From "Where The Spies Are" Pts 1 & 2	5
66	Verve VS 536	Got My Mojo Working Pts 1 & 2	4
66	Verve VS 540	I'm Your Hoochie-Coochie Man Pts 1 & 2	6
67	Verve VS 551	Cat In A Tree Pts 1 & 2	5
67	Verve VS 562	Mickey Mouse Pts 1 & 2	4
64	Verve VEP 5008	WALKING ON THE WILD SIDE (EP)	7
65	Verve VEP 5021	CREEPER (EP)	7
65	Verve VEP 5016	PLAYS THE BLUES (EP)	7
65	Verve VEP 5022	SWINGING WITH THE INCREDIBLE JIMMY SMITH (EP)	7
61	Blue Note (B)BLP 4030	CRAZY BABY (LP)	15
61	Blue Note (B)BLP 4050	HOME COOKIN' (LP)	15
62	Blue Note (B)BLP 4078	MIDNIGHT SPECIAL (LP)	15
62	Verve CLP 1596/CSD 1462	BASHIN' THE UNPREDICTABLE (LP, Verve label with HMV number)	10
63	Verve (S)VLP 9039	HOBO FLATS (LP)	12
64	Verve VLP 9057	ANY NUMBER CAN WIN (LP)	10
64	Blue Note (B)BLP 4100	SMITH PLAYS FATS WALLER (LP)	15
64	Blue Note (B)BLP 4117	BACK AT THE CHICKEN SNACK (LP, as Jimmy Smith Big Band)	15
64	Blue Note (B)BLP 4141	ROCKIN' THE BOAT (LP, as Jimmy Smith Big Band)	15
64	Verve VLP 9068	WHO'S AFRAID OF VIRGINIA WOOLF (LP)	10
64	Verve (S)VLP 9079	THE CAT (LP)	12
64	Blue Note (B)BLP 1551	THE INCREDIBLE SMITH VOL. 1 (LP)	15
64	Blue Note (B)BLP 4146	PRAYER MEETIN' (LP)	15
64	Blue Note (B)BLP 4002	HOUSEPARTY (LP)	15
65	Verve (S)VLP 9093	MONSTER (LP)	10
65	Blue Note (B)BLP 1552	THE INCREDIBLE SMITH VOL. 2 (LP)	15
66	Blue Note (B)BLP 4011	THE SERMON (LP)	15
66	Verve (S)VLP 9108	ORGAN GRINDER SWING (LP)	10
66	Blue Note (B)BLP 1528	AT CLUB 'BABY GRAND' WILMINGTON, DELAWARE VOL. 1 (LP)	15
66	Blue Note (B)BLP 1529	AT CLUB 'BABY GRAND' WILMINGTON, DELAWARE VOL. 2 (LP)	15
66	Blue Note (B)BLP 4200	SOFTLY AS IN A SUMMER BREEZE (LP)	15
66	Verve (S)VLP 9123	GOT MY MOJO WORKING (LP)	12
66	Verve (S)VLP 9142	HOOCHIE COOCHIE MAN (LP)	12
67	Verve (S)VLP 9159	PETER & THE WOLF (LP)	10
67	Verve (S)VLP 9160	THE DYNAMIC DUO (LP, with Wes Montgomery)	10
67	Blue Note BLP 4255	I'M MOVIN' ON (LP, also stereo BST 84255)	15
67	Verve (S)VLP 9182	RESPECT (LP)	10
68	Verve (S)VLP 9218	STAY LOOSE (LP)	10
68	Verve (S)VLP 9227	LIVIN' IT UP (LP)	10
68	Verve (S)VLP 9231	CHRISTMAS COOKIN' (LP)	10
69	Verve (S)VLP 9241	FURTHER ADVENTURES OF JIMMY AND WES (LP, with Wes Montgomery)	10
70	Blue Note BST 84296	PLAIN TALK (LP)	15
70s	Blue Note BST 81512	A NEW STAR — A NEW SOUND — 1 (LP)	10
70s	Blue Note BST 81514	A NEW STAR — A NEW SOUND — 2 (LP)	10
70s	Blue Note BST 81525	AT THE ORGAN (LP)	10
70s	Blue Note BST 81547	A DATE WITH JIMMY SMITH VOL. 1 (LP)	10
70s	Blue Note BST 81551	AT THE ORGAN VOL. 1 (LP)	10
70s	Blue Note BST 81552	AT THE ORGAN VOL. 2 (LP)	10
70s	Blue Note BST 81556	THE SOUND OF JIMMY SMITH (LP)	10
70s	Blue Note BST 81585	GROOVIN' AT SMALLS PARADISE 1 (LP)	10
70s	Blue Note BST 81586	GROOVIN' AT SMALLS PARADISE 2 (LP)	10
70s	Blue Note BST 84235	BUCKET (LP)	10
70s	Blue Note BST 84269	OPEN HOUSE (LP)	10
70s	Blue Note BST 84296	PLAIN TALK (LP)	10
70s	Blue Note BST 81563	PLAYS PRETTY JUST FOR YOU (LP)	10
70s	Blue Note BST 89901	GREATEST HITS (LP)	10
70s	Polydor 2304 020	I'M GON GIT MYSELF TOGETHER (LP)	10
74	Verve 2304 167	PORTUGUESE SOUL (LP)	10
75	DJM DJLPS 451	BLACK SMITH (LP)	10

(see also Kenny Burrell)

JOEY SMITH & BABA BROOKS BAND
| 64 | R&B JB 131 | Maybe Once/Tell Me You're Mine | 10 |

JUDI SMITH
| 65 | Decca F 12132 | Leaves Come Tumbling Down/Come My Way | 10 |

JUNIOR SMITH
| 67 | Giant GN 1 | Cool Down Your Temper/I'm Groovin' | 8 |

| 68 | Giant GN 18 | I'm Gonna Leave You Girl/I Love You, I Love You | 8 |
| 68 | Giant GN 25 | Come Cure Me/I Want Your Lovin' | 8 |

KEELY SMITH (& LOUIS PRIMA)

57	Capitol CL 14717	Hurt Me/High School Affair	4
57	Capitol CL 14739	Young And In Love/You Better Go Now	4
57	Capitol CL 14754	Good Behaviour/You'll Never Know	4
57	Capitol CL 14803	Autumn Leaves/I Keep Forgetting	4
58	Capitol CL 14862	Foggy Day/The Lip (B-side with Louis Prima)	5
58	Capitol CL 14885	The Whippoorwill/Sometimes	4
58	Capitol CL 14948	That Old Black Magic (with Louis Prima)/You Are My Love	6
59	Capitol CL 14994	I've Got You Under My Skin (with Louis Prima)/Don't Take Your Love From Me	6
59	London HLD 8984	If I Knew I'd Find You (I'd Climb The Highest Mountain)/Don't Let The Stars Get In Your Eyes	6
59	London HLD 8984	If I Knew I'd Find You (I'd Climb The Highest Mountain)/Don't Let The Stars Get In Your Eyes (78)	10
60	London HLD 9240	Here In My Heart/Close	4
58	Capitol (S)T 914	I WISH YOU LOVE (LP, mono/stereo)	10/12
59	Capitol T 1073	POLITELY (LP)	10
59	Capitol T 1145	SWINGIN' PRETTY (LP)	10
59	Capitol T 1160	HEY BOY! HEY GIRL! (LP, soundtrack, with Louis Prima)	10

(see also Louis Prima, Frank Sinatra)

KELLY SMITH

| 64 | Reprise RS 20482 | If I Fell/Do You Want To Know A Secret | 5 |
| 64 | Reprise RS 20536 | If I Fell/Do You Want To Know A Secret (reissue) | 4 |

KENNY SMITH & NITELITERS

| 73 | President PT 390 | Night Beat/Let's Try Again | 4 |

LONNIE LISTON SMITH (& COSMIC ECHOES)

75	RCA RCA 2568	Expansions Pts 1 & 2 (& Cosmic Echoes)	6
76	RCA RCA 2668	Chance For Peace/Sunset	6
76	RCA RCA 2727	Get Down Everybody/Inner Beauty	6
79	RCA PB 9450	Expansions/A Chance For Peace	5
79	RCA PC 9450	Expansions/A Chance For Peace (12", reissue)	12
75	RCA SF 8434	EXPANSIONS (LP, with Cosmic Echoes)	15
76	RCA SF 8461	VISIONS OF A NEW WORLD (LP)	10
76	RCA RS 1053	REFLECTIONS OF A GOLDEN DREAM (LP, with Cosmic Echoes)	10
77	RCA PL 11822	RENAISSANCE (LP, with Cosmic Echoes)	15

LONNIE SMITH

70s	Blue Note BST 84290	THINK (LP)	20
70s	Blue Note BST 84313	TURNING POINT (LP)	10
70s	Blue Note BST 84326	MOVE YOUR HAND (LP)	25
70s	Blue Note BST 84351	DRIVES (LP)	10

LORENZO SMITH

| 66 | Outasite 45-503 | (Too Much) Firewater/Count Down | 30 |

LOU SMITH

| 60 | Top Rank JAR 520 | Cruel Love/Close To My Heart | 5 |

MAMIE SMITH

| 30s | Parlophone R 1195 | Jenny's Ball/LONNIE JOHNSON & BLIND WILLIE DUNN: Two Tone Stomp (78) | 30 |

MARVIN SMITH

| 66 | Coral Q 72486 | Time Stopped/Have More Time | 20 |
| 74 | Contempo CS 2034 | Let The Good Times Roll/Ain't That A Shame | 4 |

MURIEL SMITH

| 55 | Brunswick 05370 | Dat's Love/JUNE HAWKINS: Beat Out Dat Rhythm On A Drum | 4 |

O.C. (OCIE) SMITH

57	London HLA 8480	Lighthouse/Too Many (as Ocie Smith)	50
57	London HLA 8480	Lighthouse/Too Many (as Ocie Smith)	8
68	CBS 3343	The Son Of Hickory Holler's Tramp/On A Clear Day You Can See Forever	4
68	CBS (S) 63147	THE DYNAMIC O.C. SMITH (LP)	10
68	CBS (S) 63362	HICKORY HOLLER REVISITED (LP)	10

(see also Art Mooney)

OTELLO SMITH & TOBAGO BAD BOYS

| 67 | Direction 58-3082 | My Home Town/Trouble | 4 |
| 68 | Direction 8-63242 | THE BIG ONES GO SKA (LP) | 10 |

PATTI SMITH (GROUP)

76	Arista ARIST 47	Gloria (In Excelsis Deo) (Edit)/My Generation	4
76	Arista ARIST 47	Gloria (In Excelsis Deo)/My Generation (12", in brown paper bag)	7
78	Sire 6078 614	Hey Joe (version)/Piss Factory (p/s)	6
78	Arista ARIST 181	Because The Night/Godspeed (p/s)	6
78	Arista ARIST 197	Privilege (Set Me Free)/Ask The Angels (p/s)	4
78	Arista ARIST 12197 EP	Privilege (Set Me Free)/Ask The Angels/25th Floor (live)/Poem (12", p/s)	7
79	Arista ARIST 264	Frederick/Fire Of Unknown Origin (p/s)	4
79	Arista ARIST 281	Dancing Barefoot/5-4-3-2-1 (live) (p/s)	4
79	Arista ARIST 291	So You Wanna Be A Rock'n'Roll Star/Frederick (live) (p/s)	4
88	Fierce FRIGHT 017	Brian Jones/Stockinged Feet/Jesus Christ (1-sided, white label)	15
76	Arista SPARTY 1001	RADIO ETHIOPIA (LP, as Patti Smith Group, with 4-sided lyric insert)	10

PAUL SMITH

| 65 | Columbia DB 7636 | Piccadilly Paper Boy/Yakety Yak | 4 |

PINE TOP SMITH

| 46 | Brunswick 03600 | Pine Top Blues/Pine Top's Boogie Woogie (78) | 12 |

Pine Top SMITH

50	Brunswick 04426	I'm Sober Now/Jump Steady Blues (78)	15

RAY SMITH
60	London HL 9051	Rockin' Little Angel/That's All Right	40

ROY SMITH (& STARGAZERS) (U.K.)
55	Decca F 10529	Red Roses (For My Lady Fair)/The Devil's In Your Eyes	4
55	Decca F 10644	He/Glengarry (solo)	4

(see also Stargazers)

ROY SMITH (Jamaica)
69	Grape GR 3013	See Through Craze/I'm The One	4

SIMON SMITH
67	Columbia DB 8213	And This Is My Beloved/I Just Can't Live Without You	4

SLIM SMITH (& UNIQUES)
66	Island WI 3023	I've Got Your Number/The New Boss	10
67	Coxsone CS 7016	Hip Hug/FREEDOM SINGERS: I Want Money	12
67	Coxsone CS 7034	Rougher Yet/I'll Never Let Go	12
67	Coxsone CS 7009	Mercy Mercy/JACKIE MITTOO: Baba Boom	12
68	Trojan TR 619	Watch This Sound/Out Of Love (as Slim Smith & Uniques)	5
69	Unity UN 504	Everybody Needs Love/JUNIOR SMITH: Come Back Girl	5
69	Unity UN 508	For Once In My Life/Burning Desire	4
69	Unity UN 510	Zip A Dee Doo Dah/On Broadway	4
69	Unity UN 513	Let It Be Me/Love Makes Me Do Foolish Things (both with Paulette)	4
69	Unity UN 515	Somebody To Love/Confusion	4
69	Unity UN 520	Slip Away/Spanish Harlem	4
69	Unity UN 524	Sunny Side Of The Sea/A Place In The Sun	4
69	Unity UN 537	Keep That Light Shining On Me/Build My World Around You	4
69	Unity UN 539	Love Me Tender/This Feeling	4
69	Unity UN 542	Honey/There's A Light	4
69	Jackpot JP 703	If It Don't Work Out/Love Power	4
70	Gas GAS 150	What Kind Of Life/MARTIN RILEY: It's All In The Game	4
70	Unity UN 570	Jenny/The Race	4
71	Supreme SUP 219	Stay/You're My Everything	4
71	Pama Supreme PS 334	Send Me Some Loving/I'm Lost	4
71	Camel CA 81	Spanish Harlem/Slip Away	4
71	Escort ERT 851	My Love Come True/This Feeling	4
71	Escort ERT 852	Life Keeps Turning/My Girl	4
71	Jackpot JP 779	Keep Walking/Will You Still Love Me Tomorrow	4
72	Jackpot JP 786	I Need Your Loving/You've Got What It Takes	4
72	Jackpot JP 788	Take Me Back/Where Do I Turn	4
72	Jackpot JP 789	Rain From The Skies/You're No Good	4
72	Pama Supreme PS 373	A Place In The Sun/Stranger On The Shore	4
72	Camel CA 89	Take Me Back/Where Do I Turn	4
72	Dynamic DYN 428	Just A Dream/Send Me Some Loving	4
72	Explosion EX 2074	The Time Has Come/Blessed Is The Man	4
73	Explosion EX 2078	Stand Up And Fight/The Sunny Side Of The Sea	4
73	Green Door GD 4058	Let Me Love You/If It Don't Work Out	4
73	Bullet BU 523	A Place In The Sun/Burning Fire	4
69	Pama ECO 9	EVERYBODY NEEDS LOVE (LP)	30
72	Trojan TBL 186	JUST A DREAM (LP)	15
73	Trojan TBL 198	GREATEST HITS (LP)	10
70s	Lord Koos KLP 1	SLIM SMITH (LP)	20

(see also Wonder Boy)

SOMETHIN' SMITH & REDHEADS
58	Fontana H 154	I Don't Want To Set The World On Fire/You Made Me Love You	6
58	Fontana TFR 6005	PUT THE BLAME ON ME (10" LP)	10

STUART SMITH
68	Polydor 56271	She's A Woman Now/Where Did Holly Go	4
69	Polydor 56336	My Head Goes Round/Where You Are	7

TAB SMITH & HIS ORCHESTRA
53	Vogue V 2172	Ace High/Deejay Special (78)	6
54	Vogue V 2203	Down Beat/Boogie Joogie (78)	6
54	Vogue V 2282	Cuban Boogie/Red Hot And Blue (78)	6
55	Vogue V 2299	All My Life/Seven Up (78)	5
56	Vogue V 2410	Jump Time/Rock City	12
57	Vogue V 2410	Jump Time/Rock City (78)	15
59	London HLM 8801	My Happiness Cha-Cha/Smoke Gets In Your Eyes	6
60	Vogue V 2416	My Mother's Eyes/These Foolish Things	5
62	Vogue V 2299	All My Life/Seven Up	5

TERRY SMITH
69	Philips SBL 7871	FALL OUT (LP)	10
77	Lambert LAM 002	TERRY SMITH AND TONY LEE TRIO (LP)	22

(see also If)

TRIXIE SMITH
40s	Vocalion S 217	Freight Train Blues/Trixie's Blues (78)	25
40s	Vocalion S 229	He May Be Your Man But He Comes To See Me Some Times/Jack I'm Mellow (78)	25
40s	Vocalion S 235	My Daddy Rocks Me Pts 1 & 2 (78)	25
51	Tempo R 42	Black Botton Stomp/He Likes It Slow (78)	10
52	Vocalion V 1006	Freight Train Blues/Trixie's Blues (78)	15
52	Vocalion V 1017	My Daddy Rocks Me Pts 1 & 2 (78)	15
50s	Jazz Collector L 102	The World's Jazz Crazy And So Am I/Railroad Blues (78)	5
50s	Poydras 101	TRIXIE SMITH (10" EP, 45 rpm)	12

50s	Ristic 12	TRIXIE SMITH (10" EP, 45 rpm)	12
50s	Audubon AAE	TRIXIE SMITH (10" LP)	25

TRIXIE SMITH/MA RAINEY
60s	Collector JEL 22	FEMALE BLUES VOL. 3 (EP, 2 tracks each)	12

TRULY SMITH
66	Decca F 12373	My Smile Is Just A Frown Turned Upside Down/Love Is Me, Love Is You	20
66	Decca F 12415	I Love Him/Buttermilk Hill	4
66	Decca F 12489	You Are The Love Of My Life/The Merry Go Round Is Slowing	4
67	Decca F 12554	Windows And Doors/Take A Broken Heart	4
67	Decca F 12645	I Wanna Go Back There Again/Window Cleaner	4
67	Decca F 12700	The Boy From Chelsea/Little Man With A Stick	5
68	MGM MGM 1431	This Is The First Time/Taking Time Off	8

T.V. SMITH'S EXPLORERS
81	Kaleidoscope KRLA 1359	Have Fun/Imagination (p/s, miscredited to 'T.V. Smith' only)	5
81	Kaleid. KRLA 40-1162	The Servant/Looking Down On London (unreleased cassette)	30
81	Kaleidoscope KRLA 1590	Perfect Life/Imagination (p/s)	5
81	Kaleidoscope KRL 85087	LAST WORDS OF THE GREAT EXPLORER (LP, with free single "Walk In A Straight Line"/"World Of My Own" [SXPS 119])	10

(see also Adverts)

VERDELLE SMITH
66	Capitol CL 15234	In My Room/Like A Man	5
66	Capitol CL 15456	Tar And Cement/A Piece Of The Sky	6
66	Capitol CL 15481	I Don't Need Anything/If You Can't Say Anything Nice	10
67	Capitol CL 15516	There's So Much Love Around Me/Baby Baby	6

WARREN SMITH
60	London HL 7101	I Don't Belive I'll Fall In Love/Cave In (export issue)	25
61	London HLG 7110	Odds And Ends/A Whole Lot Of Nothin'	25
64	Liberty LIB 55699	Judge And Jury/Blue Smoke	10

WHISPERING SMITH
71	Blue Horizon 2431 015	OVER EASY (LP)	40

WHISTLING JACK SMITH
67	Deram DM 112	I Was Kaiser Bill's Batman/The British Grin And Bear	4
67	Deram DML 1009	AROUND THE WORLD WITH WHISTLING JACK SMITH (LP)	12

(see also Rudi Bennett)

SMITH & D'ABO
76	CBS 81583	SMITH & D'ABO (LP)	10

(see also Manfred Mann, Dave Clark Five, Band Of Angels)

SMITH & JONES
89	Alias ALE 02	Pete And Ben/Amnesty/Duel To The End (p/s, with postcard insert)	8

SMITH BROTHERS (U.K.)
56	Decca F 10759	Smith (What A Name To Be Stuck With)/Bacon Barbecue	4

(see also Five Smith Brothers)

SMITH BROTHERS (U.S.)
78	Grapevine GRP 109	There Can Be A Better Way/Payback's A Drag	4

SMITHEREENS
87	Enigma ENIG 1	In A Lonely Place/Beauty And Sadness (p/s, red vinyl)	6

SMITHFIELD MARKET
73	Gloucester GLS 0435	LONDON IN 1665 (LP, private pressing, gatefold sleeve)	200

SMITH, PERKINS & SMITH
72	Island ILPS 9198	SMITH, PERKINS & SMITH (LP)	10

SMITHS
83	Rough Trade RT 131	Hand In Glove/Handsome Devil (p/s, original pressing)	10
83	Rough Trade RT 131	Hand In Glove/Handsome Devil (repressing, misprinted blue negative p/s)	70
83	Rough Trade RT 136	Reel Around The Fountain (unissued white label test pressings only)	100
83	Rough Trade RT 136	This Charming Man/Jeane (p/s, 2 different pressings)	15
83	Rough Trade RTT 136	This Charming Man (Manchester)/This Charming Man (London)/Accept Yourself/Wonderful Woman (12", p/s)	20
83	Rough Trade/RTT 136NY	This Charming Man (New York Mix)/This Charming Man (London Mix)/ Accept Yourself/Wonderful Woman (12", p/s)	25
84	Rough Trade RT 61 DJ	Still Ill/You've Got Everything Now (promo only)	15
84	Rough Trade RT 146	What Difference Does It Make?/Back To The Old House (Terence Stamp or Morrissey p/s)	6/4
84	Rough Trade RTT 146	What Difference Does It Make?/Back To The Old House (12", T. Stamp p/s)	12
84	Rough Trade RT 166	Wiliam, It Was Really Nothing/Please Please Let Me Get What I Want (original p/s)	12
84	Rough Trade RTT 166	Wiliam, It Was Really Nothing/How Soon Is Now?/Please Please Let Me Get What I Want (12", original p/s)	15
85	Rough Trade RT 186	MEAT IS MURDER (EP, test pressing)	40
85	Rough Trade RTT 186	MEAT IS MURDER (12" EP, test pressing)	50
86	Rough Trade RT 193	Panic/Vicar In A Tutu (p/s, with 'Hang The DJ' stickers)	10
86	Rough Trade RTT 193	Panic/Vicar In A Tutu/The Draize Train (12", p/s, with 'Hang The DJ' stickers)	12
86	Rough Trade RT 194C	Ask/Cemetry Gates/Golden Lights (cassette with picture inlay)	12
87	Rough Trade RTT 195	Shoplifters Of The World Unite/Half A Person (12", p/s, mispressing, A-side plays "You Haven't Earned It Yet Baby")	50
87	Rough Trade RTT 195	Shoplifters Of The World Unite/Half A Person/London (12", p/s, with carrier bag)	10
87	Rough Trade RTT 197C	Girlfriend In A Coma/Work Is A Four Letter Word/I Keep Mine Hidden (cassette with picture inlay)	12

87	Rough Trade RTT 198C	I Started Something I Couldn't Finish/Pretty Girls Make Graves/ Some Girls Are Bigger Than Others/What's The World (live) (cassette) 5
88	Spiral Scratch SCRATCH 3	An Interview With The Smiths (with issue 3 of 'Spiral Scratch' magazine) 6/4
88	R/Trade ROUGH CD 76	HATFUL OF HOLLOW (CD, original sleeve) 18
88	Rough Trade ROUGH 126D	RANK (DAT) 20

(see also Morrissey, The The, Electronic, Sandie Shaw)

SALLY SMITT & HER MUSICIANS

70s	Groovy STP 3	SOUNDTRACK OF THE FILM HANGAHAIR (LP) 10

SMOKE

67	Columbia DB 8115	My Friend Jack/We Can Take It 15
67	Columbia DB 8252	If The Weather's Sunny/I Would If I Could, But I Can't 12
67	Island WIP 6023	It Could Be Wonderful/Have Some More Tea 30
68	Island WIP 6031	Utterly Simple/Sydney Gill (unreleased, would be worth £200+)
70	Revolution Pop REVP 1002	Dreams Of Dreams/My Birth 12
71	Pageant SAM 101	Ride Ride Ride/Guy Fawkes 8
72	Regal Zonophone RZ 3071	Sugar Man/That's What I Want 15
74	Decca FR 13484	Shagalagalu/Gimme Good Loving 4
74	Decca FR 13514	My Lullaby/Looking High 4

(see also Shots, Chords Five)

SMOKESTACK LIGHTNIN'

69	Bell BLL 1046	Light In My Window/Long Stemmed Eyes 6
69	Bell MBLL/SBLL 116	OFF THE WALL (LP) 20

SMOKEY & FABULOUS BLADES

75	Route RT 10	Jerk Baby Jerk/Charlie's Theme 4

SMOKEY BABE

62	'77' LA 12-12	SMOKEY BABE AND HIS FRIENDS (LP) 20

SMOKEY CIRCLES

70	Carnaby CNLS 6006	THE SMOKEY CIRCLES ALBUM (LP) 50

SMOKIE & HIS SISTER

67	CBS 202605	Creators Of Rain/In Dreams Of Silent Seas 4

SMOKEY SMOTHERS

69	Polydor 623 239	THE DRIVING BLUES (LP) 20

DES SMYTH & COLLEGEMEN

65	Pye 7N 15867	The Pillow That Whispers/Lonely Streets 4
65	Pye 7N 15996	Wedding Bells/All For The Love Of A Girl 4

GLORIA SMYTHE

60	Vogue V 9159	I'll Be Over After While/Gee Baby Ain't I Good To You 5

SNAFU

74	WWA WWS 007	Dixie Queen/Monday Morning 4
74	WWA WWA 003	SNAFU (LP) 12
74	WWA WWA 013	SITUATION NORMAL (LP) 12

SNAIL'S PACE

77	Brian MR 76575	I Left My Trail In San Francisco/Shell Out Slug (foldout p/s) 25

SNAKEFINGER

79	Virgin VS 312	Kill The Great Raven/What Wilbur (p/s) 5
79	Virgin V 2140	CHEWING HIDES THE SOUND (LP) 10

(see also Residents)

SNAPE

73	Transatlantic TRA 269	ACCIDENTALLY BORN IN NEW ORLEANS (LP) 10

(see also Alexis Korner)

SNAPPERS

59	Top Rank JAR 167	Big Bill/If There Were 10
59	Top Rank JAR 167	Big Bill/If There Were (78) 25

SNAPPERS

67	CBS 2719	Upside Down Inside Out/Memories 10

SNATCH

78	Lightning LIG 502	Stanley/I.R.T. (p/s) 4
78	Lightning LIG 505	All I Want/When I'm Bored ('foil' p/s) 5
80	Fetish FET 004	Shopping For Clothes/Joey/Red Army (12", die-cut p/s) 8

(see also Johnny Thunders & Patty Palladin, Judy Nylon)

SNEAKY PETES

60	Decca F 11199	Savage Pts 1 & 2 6

SNEEKERS

64	Columbia DB 7385	I Just Can't Get To Sleep/Bald Headed Woman 50

LEN SNIDER

63	London HLU 9790	Everyone Knows/I'll Be Coming Home Tonight 4

SNIVELLING SHITS

77	Ghetto Rockers PRE 2	Terminal Stupid/I Can't Come (p/s) 15
89	Damaged Goods FNARR 4	Isgodaman?/Terminal Stupid/I Can't Come (p/s) 4
89	Damaged Goods FNARR4B	Isgodaman?/Terminal Stupid/I Can't Come (box set with badge & inserts, pink vinyl in stamped plain white sleeve) 7

(see also Doctor Dark)

SNOBS

64	Decca F 11867	Buckle Shoe Stomp/Stand And Deliver 20

THE SMITHS

THE STRANGLERS

SNOOKY & MOODY

MINT VALUE £

SNOOKY & MOODY
66 Blue Horizon 45-1003 Snooky And Moody's Blues/Telephone Blues 35

HANK SNOW (& RAINBOW RANCH BOYS)
52 HMV B 10284 My Two Timin' Woman/The Rhumba Boogie (78) 7
54 HMV 7MC 7 Why Do You Punish Me (For Loving You)/When Mexican Joe Meets Jole Blon
(with Rainbow Ranch Boys) (export issue) 8
54 HMV 7MC 15 Spanish Fire Ball/Between Fire And Water (with Rainbow Ranch Boys)
(export issue) 8
54 HMV 7MC 24 My Arabian Baby/I Don't Hurt Anymore (with Rainbow Ranch Boys)
(export issue) 8
54 HMV 7MC 25 My Religion's Not Old-Fashioned (But It's Real Genuine)/The Alphabet
(with Rainbow Ranch Boys) (export issue) 8
54 HMV 7MC 31 Yellow Roses/Would You Mind (with Rainbow Ranch Boys) (export issue) 8
59 RCA RCA 1151 Old Shep/The Last Ride 4
59 RCA RCA 1151 Old Shep/The Last Ride (78) 8
58 RCA RCX 116 COUNTRY GUITAR NO. 4 (EP) 10
59 RCA RCX 142 COUNTRY GUITAR NO. 7 (EP) 12
63 RCA RCX 7125 WHEN TRAGEDY STRUCK (EP) 7
64 RCA RCX 7154 THAT COUNTRY GENTLEMAN (EP) 12
59 RCA RD 27115 WHEN TRAGEDY STRUCK (LP) 15
62 RCA Camden CDN 164 SOUTHERN CANNONBALL (LP) 10
63 RCA Camden CDN 5102 THE ONE AND ONLY HANK SNOW (LP) 12
63 RCA RD/SF 7579 RAILROAD MAN (LP) 12
64 RCA RD/SF 7607 I'VE BEEN EVERYWHERE (LP) 12
64 RCA Victor RD 7658 SONGS OF TRAGEDY (LP) 12
65 RCA Camden CDN 5124 THE OLD AND GREAT SONGS (LP) 10
66 RCA Victor RD 7741 SINGS YOUR FAVOURITE COUNTRY HITS (LP) 12
67 RCA Victor RD 7831 GOSPEL TRAIN (LP) 10
68 RCA RD/SF 7945 HANK IN HAWAII (LP) 10
(see also Chet Atkins)

BILL SNYDER & HIS (MAGIC PIANO &) ORCHESTRA
53 Parlophone MSP 6005 Bewitched/Drifting Sands (B-side with Ralph Sterling) 4
56 Brunswick 05578 The March Hare/The Eleventh Hour 4
54 London REP 1011 BEWITCHED (EP) 7
51 London H-APB 1004 BEWITCHED (10" LP) 12
54 Brunswick LA 8667 THE STARLIT HOUR (10" LP) 10
57 Brunswick LAT 8200 CAFE RENDEZVOUS (LP) 10
58 Brunswick LAT 8254 SWEET AND LOVELY (LP) 10

ERROL SOBERS
71 Beacon BEA 159 Sugar Shaker/You're In Love 6
(see also Bobby Bridger)

SOCIALITES
64 Warner Bros WB 148 Jive Jimmy/You're Losing Your Touch 15

SOCIETIE
67 Deram DM 162 Bird Has Flown/Breaking Down 15

SOCRATES
72 Deram DM 362 Eating Momma's Cookin'/Dearest Agnes 4

SODS
70s Tap TAP 1 Mobey Grape/Negative Positive (p/s) 5
79 Stortbeat SB 5 No Pictures Of Us/Plaything (p/s) 4

SOFT BOYS
77 Raw RAW 5 GIVE IT TO THE SOFT BOYS (EP) 18
78 Radar ADA 8 (I Want To Be An) Angelpoise Lamp/Fat Man's Son (p/s) 12
79 Raw RAW 37 GIVE IT TO THE SOFT BOYS (EP, unreleased reissue)
79 Raw RAW 41 Where Are The Prawns (unreleased)
80 Armageddon AEP 002 NEAR THE SOFT BOYS (EP) 12
80 Armageddon AS 005 I Wanna Destroy You/I'm An Old Pervert (Disco) (p/s) 10
81 Armageddon AS 029 Only The Stones Remain/The Asking Tree (p/s) 8
82 Bucketfull Of Brains Love Poisoning/When I Was A Kid (flexidisc with
BOB 1 'Bucketfull Of Brains' magazine) 10/7
82 Bucketfull Of Brains Love Poisoning/When I Was A Kid (hard vinyl test pressing, some with p/s) .. 18/12
83 Midnight Music DING 4 He's A Reptile/Song No. 4 (p/s) 7
87 Bucketfull Of Brains Deck Of Cards/ROBYN HITCHCOCK & PETER BUCK: Flesh No. 1
BOB 17 (flexidisc with issue 23 of 'Bucketfull Of Brains' magazine) 6/4
79 Two Crabs CLAW 1001 A CAN OF BEES (LP, original issue) 20
80 Aura AUL 709 A CAN OF BEES (LP, reissue) 10
80 Armageddon ARM 1 UNDERWATER MOONLIGHT (LP) 10
82 Armageddon BYE 1 TWO HALVES FOR THE PRICE OF ONE (LP) 10
84 Two Crabs CLAW 1001 A CAN OF BEES (LP, 2nd reissue) 10
85 Delorean SOFT 1P WADING THROUGH THE VENTILATOR (12" EP, some as picture disc) 10/7
(see also Robyn Hitchcock, Kimberley Rew, Knox)

SOFT CELL
80 Big Frock ABF 1 MUTANT MOMENTS (EP, with insert, beware of counterfeits!) 70
81 Some Bizzare HARD 1 A Man Can Get Lost/Memorabilia (p/s, 10,000 only) 12
81 Some Bizzare HARD 12 Memorabilia (Extended)/Persuasion (Extended) (12", p/s) 15
81 Some Bizzare BZS 212 Tainted Love/Where Did Our Love Go/Tainted Dub (12", p/s) 8
81 Lyntone LYN 10410 Metro Mr. X/B-MOVIE: Remembrance Day//WEAPON OF PEACE: West Park
Baby, When I've Gone (2 flexidiscs, various colours, free with 'Flexipop'
magazine issue 12) 8/6
82 Some Bizzare BZS 912 Torch (Extended)/Insecure Me (Extended) (12", p/s) 7
82 Some Bizzare BZS 1112 What! (Extended)/... So (Remix) (12", p/s) 7

82	Some Bizzare BZS 1612	Where The Heart Is (Extended)/It's A Mug's Game (Extended) (12", p/s) 7
82	Some Bizzare CELBX 1	THE 12" SINGLES (5 x 12" box set, with booklet) 60
83	Some Bizzare BZS 1712	Numbers (Extended)/Barriers (Extended) (12", p/s) 7
83	Some Bizzare BZS 2020	Soul Inside/Loving You, Hating Me (Extended Remix)//You Only Live Twice/ 007 Theme (double pack) 8
83	Some Bizzare BZS 2012	Soul Inside/You Only Live Twice/007 Theme/Loving You, Hating Me (Extended Remix) (12", p/s) 7
84	Some Bizzare BZS 22	Down In The Subway/Disease And Desire (p/s) 4
84	Some Bizzare BZS 2212	Down In The Subway (Extended)/Disease And Desire/Born To Lose (12", p/s) 8
84	Some Bizzare BZSR 2212	Down In The Subway (Remix)/Disease And Desire/Born To Lose (12", gold & red p/s) 18
83	Lyntone	Say Hello, Wave Goodbye (live) (flexidisc, blue vinyl, fan club issue) 15
84	Lyntone	Ghostrider (live '83) (flexidisc, blue, black or green vinyl, fan club issue) 12
83	Some Bizzare BIZL 3	THE ART OF FALLING APART (LP, with free 12" Martin/Hendrix Medley: "Hey Joe"/"Purple Haze"/"Voodoo Chile" [APART 12]) 10
80s	Some Bizzare	BOX SET (6-LP) 80

(see also Marc Almond, Marc & Mambas, Bronski Beat with Marc Almond, Dave Ball, Annie Hogan)

SOFTIES
| 78 | Charly CYS 1036 | Suicide Pilot/C.I.Angel (p/s) .... 5 |

MICK SOFTLEY
65	Immediate IM 014	I'm So Confused/She's My Girl 10
67	CBS 202469	Am I The Red One/That's Not My Kind Of Love 30
70	CBS 5130	Can You Hear Me Now/Time Machine 4
72	CBS 8269	Lady Willow/From The Land Of The Crab 4
65	Columbia 33SX 1781	SONGS FOR SWINGIN' SURVIVORS (LP) 100
70	CBS 64098	SUNRISE (LP) 20
71	CBS 64395	STREET SINGER (LP) 18
72	CBS 64841	ANY MOTHER DOESN'T GRUMBLE (LP) 20

SOFT MACHINE
67	Polydor 56151	Love Makes Sweet Music/Reelin' Feelin' Squealin' 70
78	Harvest HAR 5155	Soft Space Pts 1 & 2 4
69	Probe SPB 1002	VOLUME TWO (LP) 15
70	CBS 66246	THIRD (2-LP) 15
71	CBS 64280	FOURTH (LP) 10
72	CBS 64806	FIFTH (LP) 10
73	CBS 68214	SIX (2-LP) 14
73	CBS 65799	SEVEN (LP, gatefold sleeve) 10
75	Harvest SHSP 404	BUNDLES (LP) 10
76	Harvest SHSP 4056	SOFTS (LP) 10
77	Harvest SHTW 800	TRIPLE ECHO (3-LP, box set, with colour booklet) 30
78	Harvest SHSP 4083	ALIVE & WELL (LP) 10

(see also Robert Wyatt, Kevin Ayers, Hugh Hopper, Elton Dean, Daevid Allen, Matching Mole)

SOFT PEDALLING
| 70 | Decca F 23034 | It's So Nice/Rolling On Home .... 4 |

SOFT SHOE
| 78 | Aardvark AARD 1 | FOR THOSE ALONE (LP, with insert) .... 125 |

SOHO SKIFFLE GROUP
57	Melodisc 1403	Give Me A Big Fat Woman/The Midnight Special (78) 5
57	Melodisc 1421	Frankie And Johnny/Streamline Train (78) 5
57	Melodisc EMP 7 72	SOHO SKIFFLE GROUP (EP) 20

SOLAR PLEXUS
| 73 | Polydor 2383 222 | SOLAR PLEXUS (LP) .... 12 |

SOLDIER
| 82 | Heavy Metal HEAVY 12 | Sheralee/Force .... 8 |

SOLID GOLD CADILLAC
| 72 | RCA SF 8311 | SOLID GOLD CADILLAC (LP) .... 15 |
| 73 | RCA SF 8365 | BRAIN DAMAGE (LP) .... 15 |

(see also Chris Spedding, Mike Westbrook)

SOLID SENDERS
(see under Wilko Johnson)

SOL INVICTUS
80s	Cerne 004	Abbatoirs Of Love/CURRENT 93: This Ain't The Summer Of Love (live in Japan, gig freebie, 93 only with insert & gig ticket [200 without insert]) 20/10
91	Shock SX 016	See The Dove Fall/Somewhere In Europe (numbered foldover p/s in poly bag, 1,000 only) 8
91	World Serpent WS7 002	Looking For Europe (1-sided, etched B-side, foldover sleeve in poly bag) 8
89	SVL SVL 009	IN THE JAWS OF THE SERPENT (LP, with insert) 10

(see also Current 93, Death In June, Nurse With Wound, Karl Blake, Shock Headed Peters)

SOLITAIRES
| 58 | London HLM 8745 | Walking Along/Please Kiss This Letter .... 125 |
| 58 | London HLM 8745 | Walking Along/Please Kiss This Letter (78) .... 25 |

BOBBY SOLO
| 64 | Fontana TF 456 | Una Lacrima Sul Viso/Ora Che Se I Già Una Donna (some in p/s) .... 8/4 |
| 65 | Fontana TF 573 | Se Piangi Se Ridi/Saro Un Illuso .... 4 |

SAL SOLO
| 84 | MCA MCAD 1012 | Forever Be/Just A Feeling//San Damiano (Heart & Soul)/San Damiano
(Hymn) (double pack, gatefold p/s) .... 4 |

(see also Classix Nouveaux)

SOLSTICE
83	Roke RO 001C	New Life/Peace For The New Age (cassette)	6
84	Equinox EQRLP 001	SILENT DANCE (LP, gatefold sleeve)	25

(see also Nigel Mazlyn Jones)

SOLUTION
72	Decca SKL-R 5124	SOLUTION (LP)	10

SOME CHICKEN
77	Raw RAW 7	New Religion/Blood On The Wall (p/s)	7
78	Raw RAW 13	Arabian Daze/No. 7 (p/s)	8
78	Raw RAWT 13	Arabian Daze/No. 7 (12", p/s)	8
78	Raw RAWT 17	Arabian Daze/No. 7 (12", no p/s, reissue)	10

SOMEONE'S BAND
70	Deram DM 313	Story/Give It To You	10
70	Deram SML 1068	SOMEONE'S BAND (LP)	100

GORDON SOMERS & HIS GROUP
64	Top Ten TPSX 101	THE SOUND OF THE BEATLES (EP)	7

VIRGINIA SOMERS
54	Decca F 10301	Lovin' Spree/Cross Over The Bridge	7

SOMETHING HAPPENS!
86	Cooking Vinyl WILD 001	TWO CHANCES (EP, 2 different label designs)	12

ELKE SOMMER
61	Columbia DB 4688	Be Not Notty/The Faithfull Hussar	5

JOANIE SOMMERS
60	Warner Bros WB 23	Be My Love/Why Don't You Do Right?	4
61	Warner Bros WB 31	Ruby Duby Du/Bob White	4
61	Warner Bros WB 44	One Boy/I'll Never Be Free	4
62	Warner Bros WB 71	Johnny Get Angry/Summer Place	6
63	Warner Bros WB 85	Goodbye Joey/Bobby's Hobbies	4
63	Warner Bros WB 105	Little Girl Bad/Wishing Well	4
60	Warner Bros WEP 6010	KOOKIE (EP)	12
60	Warner Bros WEP 6013	POSITIVELY THE MOST (EP, also stereo WSEP 2013)	10/18
61	Warner Bros WEP 6047	THE VOICE OF THE SIXTIES (EP, also stereo WSEP 2047)	10/18
64	Warner Bros W(S)EP 6121	JOHNNY GET ANGRY No. 1 (EP, mono/stereo)	12/20
64	Warner Bros W(S)EP 6123	JOHNNY GET ANGRY No. 2 (EP, mono/stereo)	12/20
61	Warner Bros WM 4045	THE VOICE OF THE 60s (LP, also stereo WS 8045)	18/20
62	Warner Bros WM 4062	FOR THOSE WHO THINK YOUNG (LP, also stereo WS 8062)	16/18
63	Warner Bros WM 8107	JOHNY GET ANGRY (LP, also stereo WS 8107)	20/22
64	Warner Bros WM 8119	LET'S TALK ABOUT LOVE (LP, also stereo WS 8119)	15/17

SONGSTERS
54	London HL 8100	Bahama Buggy Ride/It Isn't Right	25

SON HOUSE
60s	Saydisc Roots SL 504	THE VOCAL INTENSITY OF SON HOUSE (LP)	12
66	CBS (S)BPG 62604	LEGENDARY FATHER OF FOLK BLUES (LP)	12
70	Liberty LBS 83391	JOHN THE REVELATOR (LP)	15

SON HOUSE/J.D. SHORT
69	Xtra XTRA 1080	DELTA BLUES (LP)	20

SONIC BOOM
90	Silvertone SONIC 1	Octaves/Tremeloes (10", orange vinyl PVC sleeve, mail-order only)	12
91	Silvertone SONIC 2	(I Love You) To The Moon And Back/Capo Waltz (live) (gig freebie in black die cut sleeve, promo only, 33rpm, p/s later available separately)	12/8
90	Silvertone ORE ZLP 506	SPECTRUM (LP, gatefold rotating plastic disc sleeve with inner)	10

(see also Spacemen 3)

SONIC YOUTH
86	Blast First BFFP 3	Flower/Halloween (12", p/s, some on yellow vinyl)	15/12
86	Blast First BFFP 3	Flower/Rewolf (12", p/s, censored version)	20
86	Blast First BFFP 3(B)	(Savage Pencil etch)/Halloween II (12", p/s, A-side engraved, 1st 100 signed)	40/15
86	Blast First BFFP 3X	Flower/Halloween/Satan Supermix (12", unreleased)	
86	Blast First BFFP 7	Starpower (edit)/Bubblegum (p/s, some with badge & poster)	12/4
88	Fierce FRIGHT 015/016	Stick Me Donna Magick Momma/Making The Nature Scene (live) (p/s, 2 x 1-sided 7"s with etched B-sides)	25
88	Fierce FRIGHT 015/016	Stick Me Donna Magick Momma/Making The Nature Scene (live) (p/s, single disc reissue)	15
88	Catalogue CAT 064	Teenage Riot (square flexidisc sewn into 'The Catalogue' magazine)	5/4
89	Blast First BFFP 48	Providence (stereo)/Providence (mono) (p/s)	5
87	Blast First CHAT 1	SISTER INTERVIEW DISC (LP)	10
88	Blast First BFFP 34	DAYDREAM NATION (2-LP, 1st 1,000 with signed poster)	14

(see also Thurston Moore Kim Gordon & Epic Soundtracks)

SONNY
71	Ackee ACK 127	Love And Peace/LARRY & ALVIN: Throw Me Corn	5

SONNY (& SONNY'S GROUP)
65	Atlantic AT 4038	Laugh At Me/Tony (as Sonny & Sonny's Group)	4
65	Atlantic AT 4060	The Revolution Kind/Georgia And John Quetzal (as Sonny & Sonny's Group)	4
67	Atlantic 584 131	I Told My Love To Go Away/Misty Roses (solo)	4

(see also Sonny & Cher)

SONNY (Burke) & YVONNE
64	Island WI 134	Life Without Fun/SONNY BURKE GROUP: Mount Vesuvius	6

SONNY & CHER

64	Reprise R 20309	Baby Don't Go/Walkin' The Quetzal	5
65	Atlantic AT 4035	I Got You Babe/It's Gonna Rain	4
65	Atlantic AT 4047	But You're Mine/Hello	4
65	Vocalion VL 9247	The Letter/SONNY BONO: Spring Fever	5
66	Atlantic AT 4069	What Now My Love/I Look For You	4
66	Atlantic 584 018	Have I Stayed Too Long/Leave Me Be	4
66	Atlantic 584 040	Little Man/Monday	4
66	Atlantic 584 057	Living For You/Turn Around	4
67	Atlantic 584 078	The Beat Goes On/Love Don't Come	4
67	Atlantic 584 110	Podunk/Beautiful Story	4
67	Atlantic 584 129	It's The Little Things/Plastic Man	4
68	Atlantic 584 162	Good Combination/You And Me	4
68	Atlantic 584 168	Circus/SONNY BONO: I Would Marry You Today	4
68	Atlantic 584 215	You Gotta Have A Thing Of Your Own/I Got You Babe	4
65	Reprise R 30056	CAESAR AND CLEO (EP, 2 tracks each by Sonny & Cher, Caesar & Cleo)	10
64	Atlantic ATL/STL 5036	LOOK AT US (LP, mono/stereo)	12/14
66	Atlantic 587 006	THE WONDROUS WORLD OF SONNY AND CHER (LP)	12
67	Atlantic 587/588 052	IN CASE YOU'RE IN LOVE (LP)	10

(see also Caesar & Cleo, Cher, Sonny)

SONNY & DAFFODILS

63	Ember EMB EP 4538	SONNY & DAFFODILS (EP)	25

SONS & LOVERS

67	Camp 602 002	Matters/Peaceful Is The River	6
68	Beacon 3-101	Help Me (I'm On Top Of The World)/Feel Alright	4
68	Beacon 3-107	Happiness Is Love/Things You Do	4

SONS OF CHAMPLIN

73	CBS 65663	WELCOME TO THE DANCE (LP)	10

SONS OF FRED

65	Columbia DB 7605	Sweet Love/I'll Be There	70
65	Parlophone R 5391	I, I, I (Want Your Lovin')/She Only Wants A Friend	40
66	Parlophone R 5415	Baby What Do You Want Me To Do/You Told Me	50

(see also Odyssey)

SONS OF MAN

67	Oak RGJ 612	SONS OF MAN (EP, no p/s)	250

SONS OF MOSES

75	MCA MCA 169	Soul Symphony/Fatback	4

SONS OF PILTDOWN MEN

63	Pye Intl. 7N 25206	Mad Goose/Be A Party	10

SONS OF PIONEERS

54	HMV 7EG 8069	SONS OF THE PIONEERS (EP)	10
57	RCA RD 27016	FAVOURITE COWBOY SONGS (LP)	10

SONS OF ROBIN STONE

74	Atlantic K 10441	Got To Get You Back/Love Is Just Around The Corner	5

SONS OF SOUL

66	Doctor Bird DB 1037	Yeah Yeah Baby/So Ashamed	8

SOPWITH CAMEL

66	Kama Sutra KAS 205	Hello Hello/Treadin'	5
73	Reprise K 44251	THE MIRACULOUS HUMP RETURNS FROM THE MOON (LP)	12

SORROWS

65	Piccadilly 7N 35219	I Don't Wanna Be Free/Come With Me	25
65	Piccadilly 7N 35230	Baby/Teenage Letter	20
65	Piccadilly 7N 35260	Take A Heart/We Should Get Along Fine	6
66	Piccadilly 7N 35277	You've Got What I Want/No, No, No, No (a few with export p/s)	20/10
66	Piccadilly 7N 35309	Let The Live Live/Don't Sing No Sad Songs For Me	20
66	Piccadilly 7N 35336	Let Me In/How Love Used To Be	20
67	Piccadilly 7N 35385	Pink, Purple, Yellow And Red/My Gal	50
65	Piccadilly NPL 38023	TAKE A HEART (LP)	100

(see also Don Fardon)

SORT SOL

81	4AD AD 101	Marble Station/Misguided (p/s)	10

S.O.S. BAND

84	Tabu TA 4621	Just The Way I Like It/Body Relax//Just Be Good To Me/Just Be Good To Me (Instrumental) (double pack)	4

HORATIO SOUL

68	Island WI 3132	Ten White Horses/Angela	8

JIMMY SOUL

62	Stateside SS 103	Twistin' Matilda/I Can't Hold Out Any Longer	8
63	Stateside SS 178	If You Want To Be Happy/Don't Release Me	8
64	Stateside SS 274	I Hate You Baby/Change Partners	8
64	Stateside SE 1010	IF YOU WANNA BE HAPPY (EP)	15

JUNIOR SOUL (Murvin)

68	Doctor Bird DB 1112	Miss Cushie/LYNN TAITT & JETS: Dr. Paul	10
68	Big Shot BI 503	Chattie Chattie/The Magic Touch	6
69	Big Shot BI 527	The Hustler/The Magic Touch	5

SHARON SOUL

65	Stateside SS 411	How Can I Get To You/Don't Say Goodbye Love	45

SOUL AGENTS (U.K.)

64	Pye 7N 15660	I Just Wanna Make Love To You/Mean Woman Blues	30
64	Pye 7N 15707	Seventh Son/Let's Make It Pretty Baby	30
65	Pye 7N 15768	Don't Break It Up/Gospel Train	30

(see also Loot, Don Shinn, Hookfoot)

SOUL AGENTS (Jamaica)

67	Coxsone CS 7007	Get Ready It's Rocksteady/BOB & BELTONES: Smile Like An Angel	
		(B-side actually by Bop & Beltones)	15
67	Coxsone CS 7018	For Your Education/SUMMERTAIRES: Tell Me	15
67	Coxsone CS 7027	Lecture/SOUL BOYS: Blood Pressure	15

SOUL BOYS

67	Island WL 3052	Bood Pressure/RITA MARLEY: Come To Me	10

SOUL BROTHERS (U.K.)

65	Mercury MF 916	Good Lovin' Never Hurt/I Love Him	5
65	Decca F 12116	I Keep Ringing My Baby/I Can't Take It	8
65	Parlophone R 5321	I Can't Believe It/You Don't Want To Know	12

SOUL BROTHERS (Jamaica)

65	Ska Beat JB 226	Train To Skaville/WAILERS: I Made A Mistake	30
66	Rio R 118	Crawfish/RITA MARLEY: You Lied	10
66	Rio R 121	Mr T.N.T./MARCIA GRIFFITHS: Mr Everything	10
66	Island WI 282	Green Moon/E Gal OK	10
66	Island WI 294	Ska Bostello/DON DRUMMOND: Looking Through The Window	10
66	Island WI 296	Sound One/EMILLO STRAKER & MERRYMEN: Grandfather's Clock	10
66	Island WI 3016	Mr Flint/Too Young To Love (B-side actually by Freddie McGregor)	10
67	Island WI 3036	Sound Pressure/ETHIOPIANS: For You	10
67	Island WI 3039	Hi Life/DELROY WILSON: Close To Me	10
67	Island WI 3052	Blood Pressure/RITA MARLEY: Come To Me	12
67	Coxsone CS 7001	Take Ten/HUGH GODFREY: Deh Pon Dem	12
67	Coxsone CS 7020	Hey Windell/KEN BOOTHE: Home Home Home	12
67	Coxsone CS 7024	One Stop/TENNORS: Pressure And Slide	12
67	Studio One SO 2006	Hot And Cold/TERMITES: Mercy Mr. Percy	12
67	Studio One SO 2016	Honeypot/VICEROYS: Lose And Gain	12
67	Coxsone CSL 8001	HOT SHOT SKA (LP)	70
67	Coxsone CSL 8002	CARIB SOUL (LP)	50

(see also Earl Van Dyke & Soul Brothers)

SOUL BROTHERS SIX

67	Atlantic 584 118	Some Kind Of Wonderful/I'll Be Loving You	18
69	Atlantic 584 256	Some Kind Of Wonderful/Somebody Else Is Loving My Baby	5
74	Atlantic K 10471	Thank You For Loving Me/Somebody Else Is Loving My Baby	4

SOUL CATS

69	Camel CA 23	Keep It Moving/Your Sweet Love	4
71	Hillcrest HCT 2	Reggay Got Soul (actually by Carl Bryan)/Land Of Love	5
70s	Junior JR 103	Reggay Got Soul (actually by Carl Bryan)/Land Of Love (reissue)	5

SOUL CHILDREN

69	Stax STAX 137	The Sweeter He Is Pts 1 & 2	4
74	Stax STXS 2006	Love Makes It Right/Love Makes It Right (mono)	4
72	Stax 2325 076	GENESIS (LP)	12
74	Stax STX 1005	FRICTION (LP)	15

SOUL CITY

62	Cameo Parkway P 103	Everybody Dance Now/Who Knows	25

SOUL CITY EXECUTIVES

69	Soul City SC 109	Happy Chatter/Falling In Love	6

SOUL CLAN

68	Atlantic 584 202	Soul Meeting/That's How It Feels (some in p/s)	10/5

(see also Solomon Burke, Arthur Conley, Don Covay, Ben E. King, Joe Tex)

SOUL DEFENDERS

71	Banana BA 354	Way Back Home/SOUL REBELS: Stand For Your Rights	6
72	Ackee ACK 147	Sound Almighty/COUNT OSSIS: Meditation	5

GEORGE SOULE

75	United Artists UP 35771	Get Involved/Everybody's Got A Song To Sing	10

SOULETTES

65	Ska Beat JB 204	Opportunity/DIZZY JOHNNY & STUDIO 1 ORCHESTRA:	
		Sudden Destruction	10
71	Jackpot JP 766	My Desire/Bring It Up	8

SOUL EXPLOSION

69	Downtown DT 455	Let's Try It Again/Gumpton Rock	4

SOUL FLAMES

68	Nu Beat NB 020	Mini Really Fit Dem/Soul Train	5

SOULFUL STRINGS

67	Chess CRS 8068	Burning Spear/Within You, Without You	15
69	Chess CRS 8094	I Wish It Would Rain/Listen Here	5
69	Chess CRLS 4534	GROOVIN' WITH THE SOULFUL STRINGS (LP)	15

SOUL GENERATION

79	Grapevine GRP 131	Hold On/The Lonely Sea	4

SOUL KINGS

69	Blue Cat BS 169	The Magnificent Seven/RUPIE EDWARDS: Long Lost Love	6

SOUL LEADERS
| 67 | Rio R 134 | Pour On The Sauce/Beauty Is Only Skin Deep ....6 |

SOULMATES (U.K.)
65	Parlophone R 5334	Too Late To Say You're Sorry/Your Love 8
66	Parlophone R 5407	Bring Your Love Back Home/When Love Is Gone 8
66	Parlophone R 5506	Mood Melancholy/Sayin' Something 7
67	Parlophone R 5601	Is That You?/Time's Run Out 6

SOULMATES (Jamaica)
69	Amalgamated AMG 836	Them A Laugh And A Ki Ki/The Hippys Are Here (B-side actually by Hippy Boys) 5
69	Amalgamated AMG 842	On The Move/Jump It Up (B-side actually by Viceroys) 5
69	Camel CA 33	Beware Of Bad Dogs/Short Cut (actually by Glen Adams) 4

SOUL MERCHANTS
| 67 | President PT 166 | Whole Lot Of Lovin'/Stormy Weather ....4 |

SOUL PEOPLE
| 68 | Island WIP 6040 | Hummin'/Soul Drink ....8 |

SOUL REBELS
| 72 | Banana BA 374 | Listen And Observe/What's Love ....5 |

SOUL RHYTHMS
| 69 | High Note HS 013 | National Lottery/Round Seven ....5 |
| 69 | Gas GAS 113 | Soul Call/Musical Gate ....5 |

SOUL RUNNERS
| 67 | Polydor 56732 | Grits 'n' Cornbread/Spreading Honey ....8 |

SOUL SEARCHERS
| 74 | Sussex SXX 2 | Blow Your Whistle Pts 1 & 2 ....4 |
| 74 | Sussex LPSX 4 | SALT OF THE EARTH (LP) ....20 |

SOUL SISTERS (U.S.)
64	Sue WI 312	I Can't Stand It/Blueberry Hill 20
64	Sue WI 336	Loop De Loop/Long Gone 25
65	London HLC 9970	Good Time Tonight/Foolish Dreamer 20
72	United Artists UP 35388	Good Time Tonight/Some Soul Food 5
64	Sue ILP 913	THE SOUL SISTERS (LP) 40

SOUL SISTERS (Jamaica)
| 69 | Amalgamated AMG 839 | Wreck A Buddy/VERSATILES: Push It In ....5 |

SOUL SOUNDS
| 67 | Columbia SX 6158 | SOUL SURVIVAL (LP) ....12 |
| | *(see also Savages, Rebel Rousers)* | |

SOUL STIRRERS
(see under Sam Cooke)

SOUL SURVIVORS
67	Stateside SS 2057	Expressway To Your Heart/Hey Gyp 12
68	Stateside SS 2094	Explosion (In Your Soul)/Dathon's Theme 6
69	Atlantic 584 275	Mama Soul/Tell Daddy 4

SOUL TWINS
| 77 | Grapevine GRP 101 | Quick Change Artist/Give The Man A Chance ....4 |

SOUL VENDORS
67	Coxsone CS 7028	You Troubled Me/BOP & BELTONES: Love 15
67	Coxsone CS 7029	Fat Fish/MARCIA GRIFFITHS: Call To Me 15
67	Studio One SO 2018	Rocking Sweet Pea/JOE HIGGS: Change Of Plans 15
67	Studio One SO 2022	Cool Shade/RICHARD ACE: I Need You 15
67	Studio One SO 2031	Take Me/DELROY WILSON: I'm Not A King 15
67	Studio One SO 2032	Pe Da Pa/ERNEST WILSON: Money Worries 15
67	Studio One SO 2034	Hot Rod/GAYLADS: Africa (We Want To Go) 15
67	Studio One SO 2035	Pupa Lick/ETHIOPIANS: Leave My Business Alone 15
68	Studio One SO 2038	Psychedelic Rock/GAYLADS: I'm Free 15
68	Studio One SO 2043	Chinese Chicken/JACKIE MITTOO: Put It On 15
68	Studio One SO 2044	Happy Organ/INVADORS: Soulful Music 15
68	Studio One SO 2048	Evening Time/RIGHTEOUS FLAMES: Ease Up 15
68	Studio One SO 2058	Frozen Soul/ERNEST WILSON: If I Were A Carpenter 15
68	Studio One SO 2066	Soul Joint/Soul Limbo 15
68	Studio One SO 2070	Captain Cojoe/JACKIE MITTOO: Drum Song 15
68	Coxsone CS 7037	Grooving Steady/ROY RICHARDS: Warm And Tender Ska 15
68	Coxsone CS 7038	Whipping The Prince (actually by Ed Hangle & Alton Ellis)/HEPTONES: If You Knew 15
68	Coxsone CS 7048	Last Waltz/HAMLINS: Sentimental Reasons 15
68	Coxsone CS 7057	Real Rock/AL CAMPBELL: Don't Run Away 15
68	Coxsone CS 7071	West Of The Sun/ALTON ELLIS: A Fool 15
69	Coxsone CS 7084	Sixth Figure/DENZIL LAING: Man Payaba 15
67	Coxsone CSL 8010	ON TOUR (LP) 70

SOUND
80	Korova KOW 10	Heyday/Brute Force (p/s) 4
81	Korova KOW 21	Sense Of Purpose/Point Of No Return (p/s) 4
79	Tortch TOR 003	PHYSICAL WORLD (EP) 18
79	Tortch TOR 008	SOUND (LP, possibly unissued) ....20+
80	Korova KODE 2	JEOPARDY (LP) 10
	(see also Outsiders, Second Layer)	

SOUND BARRIER
68	Beacon BEA 109	She Always Comes Back To Me/Groovin' Slow 4

SOUND DIMENSION
69	Coxsone CS 7083	Scorcia/CECIL & JACKIE: Breaking Up (B-side actually "Hold Me Baby" by Basil Daley) 12
69	Coxsone CS 7085	Soul Trombone (Suffering Stink)/LARRY & ALVIN: Your Cheating Heart 12
69	Coxsone CS 7090	Soulful Strut/Breaking Up 12
69	Coxsone CS 7093	More Scorcha/LENNIE HIBBERT: Village Soul 12
69	Coxsone CS 7097	Time Is Tight/BARRY LLEWELLYN: Sad Song 12
69	Bamboo BAM 5	Doctor Sappa Too/Soul Eruption (B-side actually by Roy Richards & Sound Dimension) 6
69	Bamboo BAM 7	Baby Face/GLADIATORS: Anywhere 6
69	Bamboo BAM 9	Jamaica Rag/C. MARSHALL: I Need Your Loving 6
69	Bamboo BAM 13	Whoopee/NORMA FRAZER: Working (B-side actually by Marcia Griffiths) 6
69	Bamboo BAM 14	Black Onion/Bitter Blood 6
70	Bamboo BAM 18	Poison Ivy/Botheration Version 6
70	Banana BA 313	In The Summertime/In The Summertime Version 5
70	Banana BA 338	My Sweet Lord (Instrumental)/DENNIS BROWN: Silky (B-side actually by Monty Alexander & Cyclones) 5

(see also Brentford Road Allstars, Jackie Mittoo)

SOUNDGARDEN
89	A&M AM 574	Louder Than Love (p/s) 5
89	A&M AMY 574	Louder Than Love (12", p/s, etched one side) 10
90	A&M AMX 560	HANDS ALL OVER (10" EP, foldout pack) 10
90	A&M AMCD 560	Hands All Over/Come Together/Heretic/Big Dumb Sex (CD) 10
91	A&M AM 691	Jesus Christ Pose (picture disc) 4
91	A&M AM 691	Jesus Christ Pose (poster pack) 6
91	A&M AM 691	Jesus Christ Pose/Stray Cat Blues/Into The Void (Sealth)/Somewhere (12", 1 side etched, die-cut p/s with inner) 7
91	A&M AMCD 691	Jesus Christ Post (4-track digi-pak CD with black inner, 5,000 only, numbered) .. 7
92	A&M AM723	Rusty Cage (p/s, etched vinyl) 4
92	A&M AMY 723	Rusty Cage /Touch Me/Show Me(12", poster p/s, etched vinyl) (Edit) 7
92	A&M AMCD 723	Rusty Cage (CD, digipak) 7

SOUND NETWORK
65	Mercury MF 944	Watching/How About Now 12

SOUNDS AROUND
66	Piccadilly 7N 35345	What Does She Do?/Sad Subject 10
67	Piccadilly 7N 35396	Red White And You/One Of Two 5

SOUNDS INCORPORATED
61	Parlophone R 4815	Mogambo/Emily 6
62	Decca F 11540	Sounds Like Locomotion/Taboo 5
63	Decca F 11590	Stop/Go 6
63	Decca F 11723	Order Of The Keys/Keep Moving 12
64	Columbia DB 7239	The Spartans/Detroit 5
64	Columbia DB 7321	Spanish Harlem/Rinky Dink 5
64	Columbia DB 7404	William Tell/Bullets 5
65	Columbia DB 7545	Time For You/Hall Of The Mountain King 5
65	Columbia DB 7676	My Little Red Book/Justice Neddi 5
65	Columbia DB 7737	On The Brink/I'm Comin' Thru 10
67	Polydor 56209	How Do You Feel/Dead As You Go 4
64	Columbia SEG 8360	TOP GEAR (EP) 12
64	Columbia S(C)X 3531	SOUNDS INCORPORATED (LP, mono/stereo) 12/10
65	Regal SREG 1071	RINKY DINK (LP, EXPORT ISSUE) 12
66	Studio Two TWO 144	SOUNDS INCORPORATED (LP) 10

SOUNDS NICE
69	Parlophone R 5797	Love At First Sight/Love You Too 5
69	Parlophone R 5821	Sleepless Night/Continental Exchange (as Sounds Nice featuring Tim Mycott) 5
69	Parlophone PMC/PCS 7089	LOVE AT FIRST SIGHT (LP) 25

(see also Third Ear Band, Chris Spedding, Flowers, Clem Cattini)

SOUNDS OF ZION
60s	Tabernacle TEP 1	HOME TO GLORY (EP) 7

SOUND SIXTY-SIX
66	Decca F 12323	Flight 4864/The Bouncer 5

SOUNDS SENSATIONAL
67	HMV POP 1584	Love In The Open Air/Night Cry 8

SOUND SYSTEM
65	Island WI 258	You Don't Know Like I Know/Take Me Serious 8

EPIC SOUNDTRACKS
81	Rough Trade RT 084	Popular, Classical: Jelly Babies/A 3-Acre Floor/Pop In Packets (p/s) 4
82	Rough Trade RT 104	Rain Rain Rain/Ghost Train (12", p/s with Jowe Head, featuring Carmel) 7

(see also Swell Maps, Thurston Moore Kim Gordon & Epic Soundtracks)

SOUP DRAGONS
86	Popshop 001/ Lyntone LYN 16674	If You Were The Only Girl In The World/LEGEND: Talk Open (33rpm flexidisc free with 'Pure Popcorn' fanzine, later with 'The Legend' fanzine) 10/8/6
86	Subway Organisation SUBWAY 2	THE SUN IS IN THE SKY (EP, unreleased, 1,000 only, foldaround p/s in poly bag) 18
86	Subway Organisation SUBWAY 4	Whole Wide World/I Know Everything (with insert in poly bag, orange or blue foldaround p/s) 6/5
86	Subway Org. SUBWAY 4T	Whole Wide World/I Know Everything/Pleasantly Surprised (12", p/s) 7

86	Raw TV Products RTV 1	Hang Ten!/Slow Things Down (p/s, blue or red vinyl, later black) 6/4
86	Raw TV Products RTV 121	Hang Ten!/Just Mind Your Step/Slow Things Down/Man About Town
		With Chairs (12", p/s) 8
86	Raw TV Products RTV 2	Head Gone Astray/Girl In The World (p/s, with sew-on patch) 4
87	Raw TV ProductsRTVP 122	Head Gone Astray/Girl In The World/So Sad I Feel (12", poster pack in
		black PVC sleeve, with insert) 7
87	Raw TV Products RTVL 123	Can't Take No More/Hang Ten!/Whitewash/Purple Haze (12", p/s, numbered) 7
87	Raw TV Products	Soft As Your Face or Can't Take No More (Vocal Squad Version)/
	RTV 124D	It's Always Autumn or Whole Wide World (live) (12", p/s, double grooved) 7
88	Raw TV Products	The Majestic Head/4-Way Brain/Corporation Headlock (12", picture disc,
	RTV 125P	stickered PVC sleeve) 7
88	Sire W 7820TE	Kingdom Chairs/White Cruising/Family Way/King Of The Castle (10", p/s) 6
89	Raw TV Products	DEEP TRASH (cassette, withdrawn) 15
90	Raw TV Products SOUPLP 2	LOVEGOD (LP, with foiled sleeve & lyric sheet) 10

(see also BMX Bandits)

SOUP GREENS
| 65 | Stateside SS 457 | That's Too Bad/Like A Rolling Stone ....25 |

GLEN SOUTH
| 69 | Decca F 22888 | Too Late For Tears/Pasadena ....4 |

HARRY SOUTH ORCHESTRA
| 75 | EMI EMI 2252 | The Sweeney (TV Theme) Pts 1 & 2 ....4 |

JOE SOUTH
62	Oriole CB 1752	Masquerade/I'm Sorry For You 6
65	HMV POP 1474	I Want To Be Somebody/Deep Inside Me 5
65	MGM MGM 1267	Concrete Jungle/Last One To Know 5
68	Capitol CL 15535	Birds Of A Feather/It Got Away 4
70	Capitol CL 15363	Clock Up On The Wall/What Makes Lovers Hurt One Another 4
69	Capitol CL 15568	Don't It Make You Wanna Go Home/Heart's Desire 5
69	Capitol CL 15579	Games People Play/Mirror Of Your Mind 4
69	Capitol CL 15594	Leanin' On You/Don't Be Ashamed 4
69	Capitol CL 15602	Birds Of A Feather/These Are Not My People 4
70	Capitol CL 15625	Walk A Mile In My Shoes/Shelter 4
70	Capitol CL 15666	Hush/Party People 5
69	Capitol E-(S)T 108	INTROSPECT (LP) 10

SOUTH COAST SKA STARS
| 80 | Safari SAFE 27 | South Coast Rumble/Head On (p/s) ....8 |

JERI SOUTHERN
51	London L 1070	I'm In Love Again/You're The Cause Of It All (78) 5
54	Brunswick 05343	Remind Me/Little Boy Grown Tall 8
55	Brunswick 05367	The Man That Got Away/Speak Softly To Me 8
55	Brunswick 05490	An Occasional Man/It's D'Lovely 8
56	Brunswick 05529	Where Walks My True Love?/Don't Explain 6
57	Brunswick 05665	Fire Down Below/Smoke Gets In Your Eyes 6
57	Brunswick 05709	Scarlet Ribbons (For Her Hair)/Would I 5
57	Brunswick 05722	Bells Are Ringing/Just In Time 5
58	Brunswick 05737	I Waited So Long/The Mystery Of Love 5
58	Brunswick 05737	I Waited So Long/The Mystery Of Love (78) 5
59	Capitol CL 14993	Senor Blues/Take Me Back Again 4
59	Capitol CL 15054	Run/Don't Look At Me That Way 5
59	Brunswick OE 9438	CARESSES (EP) 10
59	Columbia SEG 7935	RIDIN' HIGH (EP) 10
55	Brunswick LA 8699	WARM (10" LP) 25
56	Brunswick LAT 8100	THE SOUTHERN STYLE (LP) 20
57	Brunswick LAT 8209	JERI GENTLY JUMPS (LP) 20
58	Columbia 33SX 1110	SOUTHERN BREEZE (LP) 15
58	Columbia 33SX 1134	COFFEE, CIGARETTES AND MEMORIES (LP) 15
59	Columbia 33SX 1155	JERI SOUTHERN MEETS JOHNNY SMITH (LP) 12
59	Capitol (S)T 1173	JERI SOUTHERN MEETS COLE PORTER (LP, mono/stereo) 10/12
60	Capitol (S)T 1278	AT THE CRESCENDO (LP, mono/stereo) 10/12

JOHNNY SOUTHERN & HIS WESTERN RHYTHM KINGS
| 57 | Melodisc MEL 1434 | She's Long, She's Tall/Lonesome Whistle ....7 |
| 58 | Melodisc MEL 1413 | We Will Make Love/Crazy Heart ....6 |

SOUTHERN COMFORT
| 71 | Harvest SHSP 799 | SOUTHERN COMFORT (LP) ....10 |

(see also Matthews Southern Comfort)

SOUTHERN DEATH CULT
| 82 | Situation 2 SIT 19 | Moya/Fatman (poster p/s) ....7 |

(see also Cult, Death Cult, Into A Circle)

SOUTHERN SOUND
| 66 | Columbia DB 7982 | Just The Same As You/I Don't Wanna Go ....150 |

SOUTHERN TONES
| 58 | Jazz Collector JEN 10 | WAITING FOR THE LORD (EP) ....8 |

SOUTHLANDERS
55	Parlophone R 4025	The Crazy Otto Rag/Earth Angel (Will You Be Mine?) (78) 5
55	Parlophone MSP 6182	Ain't That A Shame/Have You Ever Been Lonely 18
55	Parlophone R 4069	Ain't That A Shame/Have You Ever Been Lonely (78) 5
56	Parlophone MSP 6236	Hush-A-Bye Rock/The Wedding Of The Lucky Black Cat 12
56	Parlophone R 4171	Hush-A-Bye Rock/The Wedding Of The Lucky Black Cat (78) 5
57	Decca F 10946	Alone/Swedish Polka 6
57	Decca F 10958	Peanuts/I Never Dreamed 7

MINT VALUE £

58	Decca F 10982	Put A Light In The Window/Penny Loafers And Bobby Socks	15
58	Decca F 11014	Down Deep/Wishing For Your Love	6
58	Decca F 11032	I Wanna Jive Tonight/Torero	12
58	Decca F 11067	The Mole In A Hole/Choo-Choo-Choo-Choo Cha-Cha-Cha	7
60	Top Rank JAR 403	Imitation Of Love/Charlie	5
58	Decca DFE 6508	THE SOUTHLANDERS NUMBER ONE (EP)	25

SOUTHSIDE JOHNNY & ASBURY DUKES
| 77 | Epic EPC 5230 | Little Girl So Fine/I Ain't Got The Fever (withdrawn) | 20 |

SOUTH SIDE MOVEMENT
| 73 | Pye Intl. 7N 25615 | I Been Watchin' You/Have A Little Mercy | 5 |

SOUTHWEST F.O.B.
| 68 | Stax STAX 107 | Smell Of Incense/Green Skies | 6 |

SOUTHWIND
| 70 | Harvest HAR 5019 | Boogie Woogie Country Girl/Honky Tonk | 4 |

SOVEREIGNS
| 66 | King KG 1050 | Bring Me Home Love/That's The Way Love Is | 6 |

SOVIET-FRANCE
| 82 | Red Rhino RED 12 | SOVIET FRANCE (12" EP, printed hessian sleeve) | 15 |

RED SOVINE
56	Brunswick 05513	Why Baby Why? (with Webb Pierce)/Sixteen Tons	40
56	Brunswick 05513	Why Baby Why? (with Webb Pierce)/Sixteen Tons (78)	8
62	Top Rank JKP 3015	COUNTRY MUSIC (EP)	12
66	London HA-B 8288	GIDDY-UP GO (LP)	12
67	London HA-R 8343	I DIDN'T JUMP THE FENCE (LP)	12
69	London HA-B 8379	TELL MAUDE I SLIPPED (LP)	10

(see also Webb Pierce)

BOB B. SOXX & BLUE JEANS
63	London HLU 9646	Zip-A-Dee-Doo-Dah/Flip And Nitty	10
63	London HLU 9694	Why Do Lovers Break Each Other's Heart?/Dr Kaplin's Office	12
63	London HLU 9754	Not Too Young To Get Married/Annette	10
63	London HA-U 8121	ZIP-A-DEE-DOO-DAH (LP)	70

(see also Darlene Love)

SPACE
| 79 | Pye NSPH 28725 | JUST BLUE (LP, picture disc) | 20 |

(see also Madeline Bell)

SPACE
| 90 | Space LP 1 | SPACE (LP) | 25 |
| 90 | Space CD 1 | SPACE (CD) | 30 |

(see also J.A.M.S., KLF, Timelords, Disco 2000)

SPACEMEN
| 59 | Top Rank JAR 228 | The Lonely Jet Pilot/The Clouds | 8 |

SPACEMEN 3
86	Glass GLAEP 105	Walkin' With Jesus (Sound Of Confusion)/Rollercoaster/Feel So Good (12" maxi-single, p/s, some with numbered insert)	35/30
87	Glass GLAEP 108	Transparent Radiation/Ecstacy Symphony/Transparent Radiation (Flashback)/Things'll Never Be The Same/Starship (12" maxi-single, p/s)	30
88	Glass GLASS 12054	Take Me To The Other Side (remix)/Soul 1/That's Just Fine (12", p/s)	15
89	Fire THREEBIE 3	Revolution/Suicide/Repeater/Love Intro Theme (Xtacy) (12", mail-order only, numbered p/s)	20
89	Cheree CHEREE 5	Extract From A Contemporary Sitar Evening (p/s, flexidisc with 'Cheree' fanzine)	8
86	Glass GLALP 018	SOUND OF CONFUSION (LP)	15
87	Glass GLALP 026	THE PERFECT PRESCRIPTION (LP, gold/silver or bronze/silver sleeve)	15
87	Glass GLAMC 026	THE PERFECT PRESCRIPTION (cassette)	10
88	Glass GLALP 030	PERFORMANCE (LP)	15
88	Glass GLACD 030	PERFORMANCE (CD)	18
90	Fierce FRIGHT 042	DREAMWEAPON/ECSTASY IN SLOW MOTION (LP)	15
90	Fierce FRIGHT 042CD	DREAMWEAPON/ECSTASY IN SLOW MOTION (CD)	18

(see also Sonic Boom, Spiritualized, Darkside)

SPAGHETTI JUNCTION
| 72 | Columbia DB 8935 | Work's Nice — If You Can Get It/Step Right Up | 10 |

(see also Hank Marvin)

CHARLIE SPAND
| 50s | Jazz Collector L 18 | She's Got Good Stuff/Big Fat Mama Blues (78) | 5 |

SPANDAU BALLET
80	Reformation ZCHL 2509	To Cut A Long Story Short/Freeze/Glow (cassette)	4
82	Chrysalis CHSP 2602	Instinction/Gently (picture disc)	4
82	Chrysalis CHSP 2642	Lifeline/Live And Let Live (picture disc)	4
83	Chrysalis CHSP 2668	Communication Pts 1 & 2 (picture disc)	4
83	Reformation SPANP 1	True/Lifeline (picture disc)	4
83	Reformation SPANP 2	Gold Pts 1 & 2 (picture disc)	4
84	Reformation SPANP 3	Only When You Leave/Paint Me Down (picture disc)	4
84	Reformation SPANP 4	I'll Fly For You/To Cut A Long Story Short (live) (5 different picture discs)	each 4
84	Reformation SPAN 5	Highly Strung Pts 1 & 2 (p/s, silver vinyl)	4
84	Reformation SPAN 6	Round And Round/True (gatefold p/s, with booklet)	7
84	Reformation SPANX 6	Round And Round/True/Gold (12", p/s, gold vinyl)	7
84	Reformation SPANX 6	Round And Round/True/Gold (12", p/s, with poster, sticker, postcard & 5 photos)	8
89	CBS SPANS 4	Be Free With Your Love/Be Free With Your Love (Dance Mix Edit) (with 5 postcards in presentation pack)	4

89	CBS SPANSP 4	Be Free With Your Love (Extended 12" Mix)/Be Free With Your Love (Dance Mix Edit)/Through The Barricades (CD, picture disc) 7
82	Chrysalis/Lyntone	Smash Hits (flexidisc free with 'Smash Hits' magazine) 5/4
82	Chrysalis C BOX 1353	DIAMOND (LP, box set as 4 x 12" singles, with posters & lyric sheet) 12

SPANIELS
| 60 | Joy JOYS 197 | THE SPANIELS (LP) ....12 |

MUGGSY SPANIER & DIXIELAND/RAGTIME BAND
56	Tempo A 36	Tin Roof Blues/Muskrat Rumble 4
53	Vogue LDE 015	MUGGSY SPANIER BROADCASTS "THIS IS JAZZ" (10" LP) 15
54	London AL 3528	MUGGSY SPANIER AND THE BUCKTOWN FIVE (10" LP) 15
54	HMV DLP 1031	MUGGSY SPANIER AND HIS RAGTIME BAND (10" LP) 15
55	Brunswick LA 8722	MUGGSY SPANIER AND HIS BAND (10" LP) 15
57	Mercury MPL 6516	MUGGSY SPANIER AND HIS DIXIELAND BAND (LP) 12
63	MGM MGM-C 936	THE GEM OF THE OCEAN (LP) 10
	(see also Sidney Bechet)	

SPANISH BOYS
| 65 | Blue Beat BB 331 | I Am Alone/PRINCE BUSTER'S ALLSTARS: Vera Cruz ....10 |

SPANISHTOWN SKABEATS
| 65 | Blue Beat BB 315 | Oh My Baby/Stop That Train ....8 |

SPANISHTOWN SKABOYS
| 65 | Blue Beat BB 320 | King Solomon/PRINCE BUSTER'S ALLSTARS: Devil's Daffodil ....10 |

SPANKY & OUR GANG
67	Mercury MF 982	Sunday Will Never Be The Same/Distance 4
67	Mercury MF 1010	Lazy Day/It Ain't Necessarily Byrd Avenue 4
68	Mercury MF 1018	Sunday Mornin'/Echoes 4
68	Mercury MF 1023	Like To Get To Know You Well/Three Ways From Tomorrow 4
67	Mercury 20114 (S)MCL	SPANKY AND OUR GANG (LP) 12
68	Mercury SCML 20121	LIKE TO GET TO KNOW YOU (LP) 10
69	Mercury SCML 20150	ANYTHING YOU CHOSE B/W WITHOUT RHYME OR REASON (LP) 10
	(see also Mama & Papas)	

OTIS SPANN
64	Decca F 11972	Stirs Me Up/Keep Your Hand Out Of My Pocket 10
68	Blue Horizon 57-3142	Bloody Murder/Can't Do Me No Good 6
69	Blue Horizon 57-3155	Walkin'/Temperature Is Rising (with Fleetwood Mac) 12
64	Decca LK 4615	THE BLUES OF OTIS SPANN (LP) 18
64	Storyville SLP 157	GOOD MORNING MR. BLUES (LP) 15
64	Storyville SLP 168	PIANO BLUES (LP, with Memphis Slim) 15
65	Decca LK 4661	BLUES NOW (LP) 15
66	Stateside SL 10169	THE BLUES NEVER DIE (LP) 18
67	HMV CLP/CSD 3609	BLUES ARE WHERE IT'S AT (LP) 20
67	Storyville 670 157	PORTRAITS IN BLUES VOL. 3 (LP, reissue of SLP 157) 12
67	Polydor 545 030	NOBODY KNOWS MY TROUBLES (LP) 15
67	Bounty BY 6037	NOBODY KNOWS MY TROUBLES (LP) 15
68	Stateside (S)SL 10255	BOTTOM OF THE BLUES (LP) 18
69	Chess CRLS 4556	FATHERS AND SONS (LP) 15
69	Blue Horizon 7-63217	BIGGEST THING SINCE COLOSSUS (LP, with Fleetwood Mac) 60
69	Deram DML/SML 1036	CRACKED SPANNER HEAD (LP) 40
69	Python KM 4	RAISED IN MISSISSIPPI (LP, with Robert Jnr. Lockwood) 25
70	Vanguard VSD 6514	CRYIN' TIME (LP) 10
	(see also Fleetwood Mac, Memphis Slim)	

SPANNER THRU MA BEATBOX
| 87 | Earthly Delights EARTH 3 | SPANNER THRU MA BEATBOX (LP) ....15 |

SPARKERS
| 69 | Blue Cat BS 155 | Dig It Up/DELROY WILSON: This Life Makes Me Wonder ....10 |

SPARKS
72	Bearsville K 15505	Wonder Girl/(No More) Mr. Nice Guy 12
74	Bearsville K 15516	Girl From Germany/Beaver O'Lindy 5
74	Island WIP 6211	Never Turn You Back On Mother Earth/Alabamy Right (p/s) 5
76	Island WIP 6282	I Want To Hold Your Hand/England (withdrawn after 1 day!) 12
76	Island WIP 6377	I Like Girls/England 7
79	Virgin VS 244	Number One Song In Heaven Pts 1 & 2 (p/s, green vinyl) 4
86	Epic A 6671	Armies Of The Night/EVELYN KING: Give It Up (p/s) 4
73	Bearsville K 45510	A WOOFER IN TWEETER'S CLOTHING (LP) 10
74	Bearsville K 45511	SPARKS (LP) 10

RANDY SPARKS
| 59 | HMV POP 683 | Birmingham Train/A Girl Like You ....6 |

SPARROW (U.S.)
| 66 | CBS 202342 | Tomorrow's Ship/Isn't It Strange ....25 |
| | (see also Steppenwolf) | |

SPARROW (Jamaica)
60	Kalypso XX 10	Carnival Boycott/Gloria (with Lord Melody) 5
60	Kalypso XX 17	The Sack/Round And Around 5
60s	Melodisc CAL 15	Leading Calypsonians/Love Is Everywhere 5
60s	Melodisc CAL 17	Clara Honey Bunch/Family Sized Cokes 5
60s	Melodisc CAL 18	Goaty/I Confess 5
60	Kalypso XXEP1	THE SPARROW (EP) 7
60	Melodisc XXEP 3	A PARTY WITH THE SPARROW (EP) 7

JACK SPARROW
66	Doctor Bird DB 1005	Ice Water/ROLAND ALPHONSO: Ska-Culation	10
66	Doctor Bird DB 1027	More Ice Water/ROLAND ALPHONSO: Miss Ska-Culation	10

(see also Leonard Dillon)

SPARTANS
62	Stateside SS 117	Can You Waddle? Pts 1 & 2	4

ROGER RUSKIN SPEAR
74	United Artists UP 35683	On Her Doorstep Last Night	4
74	United Artists UP 35720	I Love To Bumpity Bump/When Yuba Plays The Rumba	4
71	United Artists UP 35221	REBEL TROUSER (EP)	4
72	United Artists UAG 29381	UNUSUAL (LP)	12
72	United Artists UAS 29508	ELECTRIC SHOCKS (LP)	12

(see also Bonzo Dog Doo Dah Band)

SPEAR OF DESTINY
83	Epic SPEAR 1	Flying Scotsman/The Man Who Tunes The Drums (p/s)	5
83	Epic SPEAR 13-1	Flying Scotsman (Extended)/Africa/The Man Who Tunes The Drums (12", p/s, 1st 5,000 with poster)	8
83	Epic A 3372	The Wheel/The Hop (p/s)	4
83	Epic WA 3372	The Wheel/The Hop (picture disc)	7
83	Epic DA 3372	The Wheel/The Hop//Grapes Of Wrath (live)/The Preacher (live) (double pack)	8
83	Epic TA 3372	The Wheel/The Hop/Solution (live)/Roof Of The World (live)/ Love Is A Ghost (live) (12", p/s)	7
84	Epic A 4068	Prisoner Of Love/Rosie (p/s)	4
84	Epic DA 4068	Prisoner Of Love/Rosie//Rainmaker (live)/Don't Turn Away (live) (double pack)	7
84	Epic TA 4068	Prisoner Of Love/Rosie/Grapes Of Wrath (1984 Version) (12", p/s)	7
84	Epic A 4310	Liberator/Forbidden Planet (p/s)	5
84	Epic TA 4310	Liberator (Extended Remix)/Liberator (Dub Mix)/Forbidden Planet (12", p/s)	7
85	Epic A 6333	All My Love (Ask Nothing)/Last Card (p/s)	4
85	Epic QTA 6333	All My Love (Ask Nothing) (Extended)/Last Card/The Wheel (live)/ Prisoner Of Love (live)/Liberator (live) (12", p/s)	7
85	Epic DTA 6445	Come Back (Dub Mix)/Cole Younger//Young Men (Return Of)/Come Back (WL Remix) (12", double pack)	7
87	10 TENX 148	Strangers In Our Town (Extended)/Somewhere Out There/Time Of Our Lives (Original Version)//Strangers In Our Town (Alternative Version)/ Time Of Our Lives (Dub Version) (12", double pack)	7
87	10 TENX 162	Never Take Me Alive (Extended)/Pumpkin Man//Land Of Shame (Extended)/ Embassy Song (12", double pack)	7
87	10 TENZ 162	Never Take Me Alive (Omar Santana Version)/The Man That Never Was// Land Of Shame (Omar Santana Version)/Jack Straw (12", double pack)	7
87	10 TENZ 173	Was That You Pts 1 & 2 (CD)	10
87	10 TEN 189/RAZOR 1	The Traveller/Late Night Psycho (box set, with lyric sheet, patch & sticker)	4
88	Virgin VSX 1123	So In Love With You/March Or Die (box set, with lyric sheet, poster & enamel badge)	4

(see also Theatre Of Hate, Pack)

SPECIALS (SPECIAL A.K.A.)
79	2-Tone TT 1/TT 2	Gangsters (as Special A.K.A.)/SELECTER: The Selecter (paper label, some in stamped plain white sleeve; matrix numbers TT1-3 & TT2-1)	8/6
79	2-Tone TT 1/TT 2	Gangsters (as Special A.K.A.)/SELECTER: The Selecter (paper label, die-cut 2-Tone sleeve, 2nd issue with Chrysalis CHS TT 1/2 matrix no.)	4
79	2-Tone CHS TT 5	Message To You Rudy/Nite Klub (paper label, company sleeve, as Specials featuring Rico)	5
80	2-Tone CHS TT 7	THE SPECIAL A.K.A. LIVE (EP, p/s, paper label)	4
80	2-Tone CHS TT 11	Rat Race/Rude Boys Outa Jail (p/s, paper label, as Specials)	4
80	2-Tone CHS TT 13	Stereotype/International Jet Set (p/s, paper label, as Specials)	4
80	2-Tone CHS TT 16	Do Nothing/Maggie's Farm (p/s, paper label, as Specials)	4
82	2-Tone CHS TT 1023	War Crimes (The Crime Is Still The Same)/War Crimes (The Crime Is Still The Same) (Version) (10", p/s, as Special A.K.A.)	6
83	2-Tone CHS TPTT 23	Racist Friend/Bright Lights (picture disc, as Special A.K.A.)	4
84	2-Tone CHS TT 27	What I Like Most About You Is Your Girlfriend/Can't Get A Break//War Crimes (The Crime Is Still The Same)/(Version) (double pack, as Special A.K.A.)	4
84	2-Tone CHS TPTT 27	What I Like Most About You Is Your Girlfriend/Can't Get A Break (picture disc)	6
84	2-Tone CHS TT 1227	What I Like Most About You Is Your Girlfriend/Can't Get A Break (12", poster p/s with free single)	7
87	Strange Fruit SFPSC 018	PEEL SESSION 23.5.79 (cassette EP)	5
80	2-Tone CDL TT 5001	MORE SPECIALS (LP, with poster & 7": Roddy Radiation & Specials' "Braggin' And Tryin' Not To Lie"/Judge Roughneck's "Rude Buoys Outa Jail" [TT 999])	10

(see also Fun Boy Three, Colour Field, Selecter, Rhoda, Rico)

SPECIMEN
83	London LON 24	Returning From A Journey/Kiss Kiss Bang Bang (bat-shaped disc)	6

(see also Diskord Datkord)

SPECKLED RED
60s	Storyville SEP 384	STORYVILLE BLUES ANTHOLOGY VOL. 4 (EP)	12
63	Esquire 32-190	THE DIRTY DOZENS (LP)	30
66	Storyville DL 601	THE DIRTY DOZENS (LP, reissue)	10
71	VJM LC 11	OH RED (LP)	15

PHIL SPECTOR
63	London HA-U 8141	A CHRISTMAS GIFT FOR YOU (LP, various artists, Spector as producer)	30
72	Apple APCOR 24	PHIL SPECTOR'S CHRISTMAS ALBUM (LP, reissue of London HA-U 8141)	15
74	Warner Bros K 59010	PHIL SPECTOR'S CHRISTMAS ALBUM (LP, 2nd reissue)	10
76	Phil Spector Intl. 2307 008	RARE MASTERS VOL. 1 (LP, various artists, Spector as producer)	10

76	Phil Spector Intl. 2307 009	RARE MASTERS VOL. 2 (LP, various artists, Spector as producer)	10
80	Phil Spector Intl. 2307 015	PHIL SPECTOR '74/'79 (LP, various artists, Spector as producer)	10
81	Phil Spector Intl. WOS 001	WALL OF SOUND (9-LP box set, various artists, Spector as producer)	40

(see also Ronettes, Crystals, Darlene Love, Bob B. Soxx & Blue Jeans, Teddy Bears)

RONNIE SPECTOR
71	Apple APPLE 33	Try Some Buy Some/Tandoori Chicken (initially with p/s)	12/5

(see also Ronettes)

SPECTRES (Ireland)
65	Lloyd Sound UED QU 1	The Facts Of Life/Whirlpool	100

SPECTRES (U.K.)
66	Piccadilly 7N 35339	I (Who Have Nothing)/Neighbour, Neighbour	150
66	Piccadilly 7N 35352	Hurdy Gurdy Man/Laticia	150
67	Piccadilly 7N 35368	We Ain't Got Nothin' Yet/I Want It	150

(see also Traffic Jam, Status Quo)

SPECTRES (U.K.)
80	Direct Hit DH 1	This Strange Effect/Getting Away With Murder (p/s)	5
81	Demon D 1002	Stones/Things (p/s)	4

(see also Rich Kids)

SPECTRUM
65	Columbia DB 7742	Little Girl/Asking You	4
67	RCA RCA 1589	Samantha's Mine/Saturday's Child	4
67	RCA RCA 1619	Portobello Road/Comes The Dawn	7
67	RCA RCA 1651	Headin' For A Heatwave/I Wanna Be Happy With You	4
68	RCA RCA 1700	London Bridge Is Coming Down/Tables And Chairs	5
68	RCA RCA 1753	Little Red Boat By The River/Forget Me Not	4
68	RCA RCA 1775	Ob-La-Di, Ob-La-Da/Music Soothes The Savage Beast	4
69	RCA RCA 1853	Free/The Tale Of Wally Toft	4
69	RCA RCA 1883	Gloria/Nodnol	4
70	RCA RCA 1976	Portobello Road/Comes The Dawn (reissue)	5
71	Parlophone R 5908	I'll Be Gone/Launching Place Pt II	6
74	RCA Intl. INTS 118	THE LIGHT IS DARK ENOUGH (LP)	70

CHRIS SPEDDING
70	Harvest HAR 5013	Rock 'n' Roll Band/BATTERED ORNAMENTS: Goodbye We Loved You (Madly)	10
70	Harvest SHSP 4004	BACKWOODS PROGRESSION (LP)	18
72	Harvest SHSP 4017	THE ONLY LICK I KNOW (LP)	18

(see also Sharks, Nucleus, Sounds Nice, Panhandle, Solid Gold Cadillac, Matthew Ellis, Vibrators, Battered Ornaments)

SPEED
78	It IT 1	Big City/All Day And All The Night (no p/s)	5

(see also Wish, Cobra, Tearjerkers)

SPEEDBALL(S)
80	No Pap/Dirty Dick DD 1/2	No Survivor/Is Somebody There? (miscredited as 'Speedballs', some in printed sleeve)	25/15

SPEEDOMETERS
78	Mascot NICE 1	Disgrace/Work (p/s)	4
78	Mascot NICE 2	Liverpool Ladies (p/s)	4

SPELLBINDERS
66	CBS 202453	Help Me (Get Myself Back Together)/Danny Boy	15
67	CBS 202622	Chain Reaction/For You	15
67	CBS 2776	Since I Don't Have You/I Believe	7
69	Direction 58-3970	Help Me/Chain Reaction	6

BENNY SPELLMAN
62	London HLP 9670	Fortune Teller/Lipstick Traces	25

JOHNNY SPENCE
62	Parlophone R 4872	Dr. Kildare Theme/Midnight Theme	4

DON SPENCER
62	HMV POP 1087	Fireball/I'm All Alone Again (blue or black labels)	12/8
63	HMV POP 1186	Busy Doing Nothing/The Joker	4
63	HMV POP 1205	Worried Mind/Give Give Give A Little	4
64	HMV POP 1306	Pride Is Such A Little Word/For Love (with Le Roys)	4
66	Page One POF 006	Why Don't They Understand/Marriage Is For Old Folks	4

(see also Le Roys)

DON SPENCER/XL5
63	HMV 7EG 8802	FIREBALL AND OTHER TITLES (EP, 2 tracks each)	25

JEREMY SPENCER
70	Reprise RS 27002	Linda/Teenage Darling	4
71	Reprise K 44105	JEREMY SPENCER (LP)	40
73	CBS 65387	JEREMY SPENCER AND THE CHILDREN OF GOD (LP)	10

(see also Fleetwood Mac)

JO SPENCER
71	Dynamic DYN 415	Bed Of Roses/Forgive Me	4

JOHN SPENCER'S LOUTS
78	Beggars Banquet BEGA 3	THE LAST LP (LP)	10

SONNY SPENCER
59	Parlophone R 4611	Oh Boy/Gilee	15

SPERM WAILS
80s	Spurt/Lyntone LYN 18751	GRIM/STROKE (EP, 33rpm flexidisc)	4

SPHERES
78 Sphere   FESTIVAL AND SUNS (LP, with insert) 25
SPHERICAL OBJECTS
78 Object Music OM 01   The Kill/The Knot (p/s) 5
78 Object Music OM 04   Seventies Romance/Sweet Tooth (p/s) 5
78 Object Music PBJ 001   PAST & PARCEL (LP) 10
79 Object Music OBJ 004   ELLIPTICAL OPTIMISM (LP) 10
80 Object Music OBJ 012   FURTHER ELLIPSES (LP) 10
81 Object Music OBJ 016   NO MAN'S LAND (LP) 10
    (see also Alter Nomen Unlimited)
SPHYNKTA
83 Sultanic SUL 666   In The Shade Of The Gods/Jesus Bless My Upside-Down Cross (p/s,
                              red vinyl, with 'devil' tattoo) 15
83 Sultanic SUL 999   Death And Violence/Ritual Slaughter (Of Your Daughter) (p/s, red vinyl) 10
SPHYNX
78 Charisma CDS 4011   XITINTODAY (LP, some with booklet) 25/12
    (see also Inner City Unit, Gong, Radio Actors)
SPICE
68 United Artists UP 2246   What About The Music/In Music 35
68 Olga OLE 013   Union Jack/Delicious 40
    (see also Uriah Heep)
SPIDELLS
66 Sue WI 4019   Find Out What's Happening/That Makes My Heart Break 18
SPIDER
66 Decca F 12430   The Comedown Song/Blow Ya Mind 15
SPIDER
80 Alien ALIEN 14   Children Of The Street/Down 'n' Out (p/s) 7
80 Alien ALIEN 16   College Luv/Born To Be Wild (p/s) 6
80 Dreamland 2090 441   New Romance/Cross Fire (p/s) 4
80 Dreamland DSLP 4   Everything Is Alright/Shady Lady (p/s) 4
81 Dreamland DSLP 11   Better Be Good To Me/I Love (p/s) 4
81 City NIK 7   All The Time/Feel Like A Man (p/s) 5
82 Creole CR 30   Talkin' 'Bout Rock'N'Roll/'Til I'm Certain (p/s) 4
82 RCA RCA 268   Rock 'N' Roll Will Forever Last/Did Ya Like It Baby?//Amazin' Grace Medley
                              Pts 1 & 2 (double pack, separate sleeves) 4
84 A&M AMP 180   Here We Go Rock 'N' Roll/Death Row (picture disc) 5
86 PRT 7PX 344   Gimme Gimme It All/Rock Tonite//Live Recording From Kerrang Corner
                              (double pack) 4
SPIDER-MAN
71 Buddah 2318 075   FROM BEYOND THE GRAVE (LP) 10
SPIDERS
54 London L 8086   I'm Slippin' In/I'm Searching (78) 60
SPIDERS FROM MARS
75 Pye 7N 45578   White Man Black Man/National Poll 4
76 Pye 7N 45578   I Don't Wanna Limbo/Can't Be Fair 4
76 Pye NSPL 18479   SPIDERS FROM MARS (LP) 10
    (see also David Bowie)
BERND SPIER
65 Oriole CB 1987   A Million And One Times/My Mistake 4
ARTHUR SPINK BAND
68 Beltona BL 2766   Beatles Och Aye/Harry Lauder Medley 4
SPINNERS (U.K.)
59 Columbia DB 4267   The "I Had A Dream, Dear" Rock/Pedro The Fisherman 4
64 Fontana TL 5201   THE SPINNERS (LP) 10
    (see also Shane Rimmer)
SPINNERS (U.S.)
61 Columbia DB 4693   That's What Girls Are Made Of/Heebie Jeebies 125
65 Tamla Motown TMG 514   Sweet Thing/How Can I (later pressings credit Detroit Spinners, £40) 100
    (see also Detroit Spinners)
SPINNING WIGHATS
85 Lyntone LYN 16928   Christmas In New Zealand (1-sided flexidisc with 'Bucketfull Of Brains' mag) 4
86 Bucketfull Of Brains BOB 12 Encore From Hell/10-5-60 (live) (flexidisc with 'Bucketfull Of Brains' mag) 4
    (see also Long Ryders)
SPIRALS
58 Capitol CL 14958   The Rockin' Cow/Everybody Knows 12
SPIRAL STAIRCASE
68 CBS 3507   Baby What I Mean/Makin' Your Mind Up 10
69 CBS 4187   More Today Than Yesterday/Broken Hearted Man 20
69 CBS 4524   No One For Me To Turn To/Sweet Little Thing 15
SPIRIT
68 CBS 3523   Uncle Jack/Mechanical World 6
69 CBS 3880   I Got A Line On You/She Smiles 6
69 CBS 4511   Dark Eyed Woman/Ice 5
69 CBS 4565   Dark Eyed Woman/New Dope In Town 4
70 CBS 4773   1984/Sweet Stella Baby 6
70 CBS 5149   Animal Zoo/Red Light Roll On 6
84 Mercury MER 1626   Fresh Garbage/Mr Skin (6", p/s) 4

78	Sound For Industry SFI 326	Midnight Train/Potatoland Theme (flexidisc free with 'Dark Star' magazine)	7/4
68	CBS 63278	SPIRIT (LP)	10
68	CBS 63523	THE FAMILY THAT PLAYS TOGETHER (LP)	10
69	CBS 63729	CLEAR (LP)	10
71	Epic EPC 64191	THE TWELVE DREAMS OF DR. SARDONICUS (LP, gatefold sleeve, yellow label)	10
72	Epic EPC 64507	FEEDBACK (LP)	10
81	Beggars Banquet BEGA 23	POTATOLAND (LP, with cartoon book)	15
88	Chord CHDAT 010	POTATOLAND (DAT)	15

(see also Kapt. Kopter & Fabulous Twirlybirds, Randy California)

DARIEN SPIRIT
73	Charisma CAS 1065	ELEGY TO MARILYN (LP)	10

SPIRIT OF JOHN MORGAN
69	Carnaby CNS 4005	Train For All Seasons/Ride On	8
69	Carnaby CNLS 6002	THE SPIRIT OF JOHN MORGAN (LP)	45
70	Carnaby CNLS 6007	AGE MACHINE (LP)	45
71	Carnaby 6437 503	THE SPIRIT OF JOHN MORGAN (LP, reissue)	20

(see also John Morgan)

SPIRIT OF MEMPHIS QUARTET
58	Parlophone PMD 1070	NEGRO SPIRITUALS (10" LP)	20
65	Vogue LAE 1033	NEGRO SPIRITUALS (LP, reissue)	15

SPIRITUALIZED
90	Dedicated ZB 43783	Anyway That You Want Me/Step Into The Breeze (p/s)	5
90	Dedicated ZT 43784	Anyway That You Want Me/Step Into The Breeze 1 & 2 (12", p/s)	8
90	Dedicated ZT 43784	Anyway That You Want Me (remix)/Step Into The Breeze 1 & 2 (12", p/s)	12
90	Dedicated ZD 43784	Anyway That You Want Me/Step Into The Breeze 1 & 2 (CD)	10
91	Fierce FRIGHT 053	Feel So Sad/I Want You (gig freebie, no p/s, stamped plain white sleeve with date & venue details)	20
90s	Dedicated SPIRT 004	LAZER GUIDED MELODIES SAMPLER (p/s, mail-order only)	6
90s	Dedicated SPIRT 004 CD	LAZER GUIDED MELODIES SAMPLER (CD, mail-order only)	8

(see also Spacemen 3)

SPIROGYRA
72	Pegasus PEGS 3	Dangerous Dave/Captain's Log	8
71	B&C CAS 1042	ST. RADIGUND'S (LP, with lyric inner)	60
72	Pegasus PEG 13	OLD BOOT WINE (LP)	55
73	Polydor 2310 246	BELLS, BOOTS AND SHAMBLES (LP)	150

SPITFIRE BOYS
77	RK RK 1001	British Refugee/Mein Kampf (punch-out centre, no p/s)	8
77	RK RK 1001	British Refugee/Mein Kampf (reissue, solid centre, p/s)	8

(see also Frankie Goes To Hollywood)

VICTORIA SPIVEY
3-	Parlophone R 2177	Funny Feathers/How Do You Do It That Way? (78)	40
3-	Parlophone R	Toothache Blues Parts 1 And 2 (78)	40
60	Fontana TFE 17264	TREASURES OF NORTH AMERICAN NEGRO MUSIC No. 5 (EP)	10
56	HMV 7EG 8190	VICTORIA SPIVEY (EP)	15
65	Xtra XTRA 1022	VICTORIA SPIVEY (LP)	25

SPIZZ (OIL/ENERGI)
79	Rough Trade RTSO 1	6000 Crazy/1989/Fibre (p/s)	4
79	Rough Trade RTSO 2	Cold City/Red And Black/Solarisation (shun)/Platform 3 (as Spizz Oil) (p/s)	4
79	Rough Trade RTSO 3	Soldier Soldier/Virgina Plain (as Spizz Energi) (p/s)	4
79	Rough Trade RTSO 4	Where's Captain Kirk?/Amnesia (as Spizz Energi) (p/s)	4

S.P.K. (SEPPUKU/SURGICAL PENIS CLINIC)
83	Side Effekts SER 003	DEKOMPOSITIONES (12", p/s, as Seppuku)	15
8-	Industrial IR 0011	MEAT PROCESSING SECTION (Mekano/Slogun) (p/s, labels list "Slogan"/ "Factory", with insert, as Surgical Penis Clinic)	15
84	WEA YZ 24	Junk Funk/High Tension (p/s, as S.P.K.)	4
85	Desire WANT 1	Metal Dance/Will To Power (p/s, as S.P.K.)	5
85	Desire WANTX 1	Metal Dance/Will To Power (12", p/s, as S.P.K.)	8
86	Side Effekts SFX 01	In Fragrante Delicto/Invocation (12", p/s, as S.P.K.)	8
80s	Side Effekts SER 002	LEICHENSCHREI (LP)	15
84	WEA WX 10	MACHINE AGE VOODOO (LP)	10
86	Sterile SRC 4	LIVE AT THE CRYPT (LP, cassette)	12

SPLAT!
83	Ron Johnson RON 1	Yeah...The Dum Dum/Book Face/Biggles Bloodbath (foldaround p/s & stamped white label)	5

SPLIT BEAVER
81	Heavy Metal HEAVY 7	Savage/Hound Of Hell (p/s)	4
82	Heavy Metal HMRLP 3	WHEN HELL WON'T HAVE YOU (LP)	10

SPLIT CROW
84	Guardian GRC 2167	ROCKSTORM (LP)	12

SPLIT ENZ
76	Chrysalis CHS 2120	Late Last Night/Walking Down The Road (p/s)	5
77	Chrysalis CHS 2131	Another Great Divide/Stranger Than Fiction (p/s)	5
77	Chrysalis CHS 2170	My Mistake/Crosswords (p/s)	5
77	Chrysalis CHS 2170-12	My Mistake/Crosswords/The Woman Who Loves You (12", p/s)	8
80	Illegal ILS 19	I See Red/Give It A Whirl/Hermit McDermitt (p/s)	5
81	A&M AMS 8128	History Never Repeats/Shark Attack/What's The Matter With You (p/s)	4
81	A&M AMS 8146	One Step Ahead/In The Wars (p/s, laser etched)	4
80	A&M AMLH 64822	TRUE COLOURS (LP, laser etched)	10

(see also Crowded House)

SPLIT KNEE LOONS
81	Avatar AAA 111	THE SPECIAL COLLECTORS EP (p/s, brown or black vinyl)	8/10

(see also Gillan, Bernie Torme, John McCoy)

SPLIT SCREENS
78	Rok ROK III/IV	Just Don't Try/JUST FRANK: You	5

SPLINTER
74	Dark Horse AMS 7135	Costafine Town/Elly May	4
76	Dark Horse AMS 5501	Drink All Day/Haven't Got Time	4
76	Dark Horse AMS 5503	Which Way Will I Get Home/Green Bus Line	4
74	Dark Horse AMLH 22001	THE PLACE I LOVE (LP)	10
75	Dark Horse AMLH 22006	HARDER TO LIVE (LP)	10

(see also Elastic Oz Band)

SPLINTERED
91	Fourth Dimension	Mouth Clamp/CINDYTALK: In Sunshine (numbered freebie with 'Grim Humour' magazine Vol. 2 No. 1)	7/5

SPOKESMEN
65	Brunswick 05941	The Dawn Of Correction/For You Babe	4
65	Brunswick 05948	It Ain't Fair/Have Courage Be Careful	4
66	Brunswick 05950	Michelle/Better Days Are Yet To Come	4
66	Brunswick 05958	Today's The Day/Enchanté	4

SPONTANEOUS COMBUSTION
71	Harvest HAR 5046	Lonely Singer/200 Lives/Leaving	6
72	Harvest HAR 5060	Gay Time Night/Spaceship	6
73	Harvest HAR 5066	Sabre Dance Pts 1 & 2	6
72	Harvest SHVL 801	SPONTANEOUS COMBUSTION (LP)	20
72	Harvest SHVL 805	TRIAD (LP)	35

SPONTANEOUS MUSIC ENSEMBLE
66	Eyemark EMP L1002	CHALLENGE (LP)	40
68	Island ILP 979	KARYOBIN ... ARE THE IMAGINARY BIRDS SAID TO LIVE IN PARADISE (LP, pink label)	50
69	Marmalade 608 008	SPONTANEOUS MUSIC ENSEMBLE (LP)	15
71	Tangent TNGS 107	SOURCE FROM AND TOWARDS (LP)	10
72	Marmalade 2384 009	SPONTANEOUS MUSIC ENSEMBLE (LP, reissue)	10
73	Tangent TNGS 118	SO WHAT DO YOU THINK (LP)	10

(see also John Stevens, Howard Riley Trio)

SPOOKY TOOTH
67	Island WIP 6022	Sunshine Help Me/Weird	7
68	Island WIP 6037	Love Really Changed Me/Luger's Grove	6
68	Island WIP 6046	The Weight/Do Right People	6
69	Island WIP 6060	Son Of Your Father/I've Got Enough Heartache	6
73	Island WIP 6168	All Sewn Up/As Long As The World Keeps Turning	4
68	Island ILP 980/ILPS 9080	IT'S ALL ABOUT A ROUNDABOUT (LP, pink label)	25
69	Island ILPS 9098	SPOOKY TWO (LP, pink label)	15
70	Island ILPS 9107	CEREMONY (LP, with Pierre Henry, pink label, gatefold sleeve)	15
70	Island ILPS 9117	THE LAST PUFF (LP, pink label)	15
73	Island ILPS 9227	YOU BROKE MY HEART SO I BUSTED YOUR JAW (LP)	10
73	Island ILPS 9255	WITNESS (LP)	10
74	Island ILPS 9292	THE MIRROR (LP, export issue)	15

(see also Gary Wright, V.I.P.s, Art, Luther Grosvenor, Hellions, Revolution, State Of Mickey & Tommy)

COOL SPOON
67	Coxsone CS 7031	Yakety Yak/SOUL VENDORS: Drum Song (both sides actually by Jeff Dixon & Alton Ellis)	12

SPOTLIGHTERS
59	Vogue Pop V 9130	Please Be My Girlfriend/Whisper (with Bob Thompson & His Band)	150
59	Vogue Pop V 9130	Please Be My Girlfriend/Whisper (with Bob Thompson & His Band) (78)	60

SPOTLIGHTS
66	Philips BF 1485	Batman And Robin/Day Flower	6

SPOTNICKS
62	Oriole CB 1724	Orange Blossom Special/The Spotnicks Theme	4
62	Oriole CB 1755	Galloping Guitars/The Rocket Man	4
63	Oriole CB 1790	Hava Nagila/High Flyin' Scotsman	4
63	Oriole CB 1819	Just Listen To My Heart/Pony Express	5
63	Oriole CB 1844	Valentina/Save The Last Dance For Me/No Yaga Daga Blues	6
63	Oriole CB 1886	Anna/The Sailor's Hornpipe	8
64	Oriole CB 1953	Lovesick Blues/The Space Creatures	8
64	Oriole CB 1981	Donner Wetter/Shamus O'Toole	8
63	Oriole EP 7075	ON THE AIR (EP)	8
64	Oriole EP 7078	SPOTNICKS IN PARIS (EP)	12
64	Oriole EP 7079	SPOTNICKS AT THE OLYMPIA PARIS (EP)	15
63	Oriole PS 40036/ SPS 40037	OUT-A SPACE: THE SPOTNICKS IN LONDON (LP, mono/stereo)	18/30
64	Oriole PS 40054	THE SPOTNICKS IN SPAIN (LP)	20
65	Oriole PS 40064	THE SPOTNICKS IN BERLIN (LP)	30
81	Air CHM 1171	THE VERY BEST OF THE SPOTNICKS (LP)	10

(see also Bob Lander & Spotnicks, Shy Ones, Stranglers)

JACK SPRATT & LEROY SIBBLES & HEPTONES
69	Coxsone CS 7100	Give Me Your Love/LARRY & ALVIN: Magic Moments	12

SPREADEAGLE
72	Charisma CB 183	How Can We Be Lost/Nightmare	4

| 72 | Charisma BCP 7 | Nightingale Lane (p/s) | 5 |
| 72 | Charisma CAS 1055 | THE PIECE OF PAPER (LP) | 10 |

SPRIGUNS (OF TOLGUS)

76	Decca F 13676	Nothing Else To Do/Lord Lovell	8
77	Decca F 13739	White Witch/Time Will Pass	8
74	private pressing	ROWDY DOWDY DAY (cassette, as Spriguns Of Tolgus)	25
75	Alida Star Cottage ASC7755	JACK WITH A FEATHER (LP, as Spriguns Of Tolgus)	700
76	Decca SKL 5262	REVEL WEIRD & WILD (LP, with insert)	80
77	Decca SKL 5286	TIME WILL PASS (LP, with insert)	80

(see also Mandy Morton Band)

SPRING

| 71 | RCA Neon NE 6 | SPRING (LP, foldout sleeve) | 90 |

SPRINGBOARD

| 69 | Polydor | SPRINGBOARD (LP) | 40 |

DUSTY SPRINGFIELD

63	Philips BF 1292	I Only Want To Be With You/Once Upon A Time	4
64	Philips BF 1313	Stay Awhile/Something Special	4
64	Philips BF 1348	I Just Don't Know What To Do With Myself/My Colouring Book	4
64	Philips BF 1369	Losing You/Summer Is Over	4
64	Philips BF 1381	Oh Holy Child/SPRINGFIELDS: Jingle Bells (some with p/s)	8/5
65	Philips BF 1396	Your Hurtin' Kind Of Love/Don't Say It Baby	4
65	Philips BF 1418	In The Middle Of Nowhere/Baby Don't You Know	4
65	Philips BF 1430	Some Of Your Lovin'/I'll Love You For A While	4
66	Philips BF 1466	Little By Little/If It Hadn't Been For You	4
66	Philips BF 1482	You Don't Have To Say You Love Me/Every Ounce Of Strength	4
66	Philips BF 1502	Goin' Back/I'm Gonna Leave You	4
66	Philips BF 1510	All I See Is You/Go Ahead On (some with p/s)	8/5
67	Philips BF 1553	I'll Try Anything/The Corrupt Ones	6
67	Philips BF 1577	Give Me Time/The Look Of Love	4
67	Philips BF 1608	What's It Gonna Be/Small Town Girl	12
68	Philips BF 1682	I Close My Eyes And Count To Ten/No Stranger Am I	4
68	Philips BF 1706	I Will Come To You/The Colour Of Your Eyes	5
68	Philips BF 1730	Son Of A Preacher Man/Just A Little Lovin'	4
69	Philips BF 1811	Am I The Same Girl/Earthbound Gypsy	4
69	Philips BF 1826	Brand New Me/Bad Case Of The Blues	4
70	Philips BF 1835	Morning Please Don't Come (with Tom Springfield)/TOM SPRINGFIELD: Charley	5
70	Philips 6006 045	How Can I Be Sure/Spooky	4
72	Philips 6006 214	Yesterday When I Was Young/I Start Counting	4
73	Philips 6006 295	Who Gets Your Love/Of All The Things	4
74	Philips 6006 325	Learn To Say Goodbye/Easy Evil	4
74	Philips 6006 350	What's It Gonna Be/Bring Him Back	4
64	Philips BE 12560	I ONLY WANT TO BE WITH YOU (EP)	8
64	Philips BE 12564	DUSTY (EP)	10
65	Philips BE 12572	DUSTY IN NEW YORK (EP)	12
65	Philips BE 12579	MADEMOISELLE DUSTY (EP)	15
68	Philips BE 12605	IF YOU GO AWAY (EP)	10
68	Philips 6850 751	STAR DUSTY (EP, Audio Club Of Great Britain release)	7
68	Philips MCP 1004	THE HITS OF THE WALKER BROTHERS AND DUSTY SPRINGFIELD (cassette EP)	10
71	Philips MCP 100	THE HITS OF DUSTY SPRINGFIELD (cassette EP)	10
64	Philips (S)BL 7594	A GIRL CALLED DUSTY (LP, mono/stereo)	12/15
65	Philips (S)RBL 1002	EVERYTHING'S COMING UP DUSTY (LP, gatefold sleeve with booklet, mono/stereo)	12/15
66	Philips (S)BL 7737	GOLDEN HITS (LP)	10
67	Philips (S)BL 7820	WHERE AM I GOING? (LP)	12
68	World Record Club ST 848	DUSTY SPRINGFIELD (LP)	12
68	Philips (S)BL 7864	DUSTY ... DEFINITELY (LP)	12
68	Wing WL 1211	STAY AWHILE (LP)	10
69	Philips SBL 7889	DUSTY IN MEMPHIS (LP)	12
70	Philips SBL 7927	FROM DUSTY ... WITH LOVE (LP)	12
71	Philips 6382 016	THIS IS DUSTY SPRINGFIELD (LP)	10
71	Audio Club Of G.B. 6850 002	STAR DUSTY (LP)	10
71	Audio Club Of G.B. 6856 020	SHEER MAGIC (LP)	12
72	Philips 6308 117	SEE ALL HER FACES (LP)	10
73	Philips 6382 063	THIS IS DUSTY SPRINGFIELD VOL. 2 — MAGIC GARDEN (LP)	10
73	Philips 6308 152	CAMEO (LP)	10
75	Philips 6382 105	SINGS BURT BACHARACH AND CAROLE KING (LP)	10

(see also Springfields, Tom Springfield, Lana Sisters)

RICK SPRINGFIELD

| 84 | RCA RICKP 2 | Jessie's Girl/Affair Of The Heart (10", picture disc) | 5 |

TOM SPRINGFIELD ORCHESTRA

63	Philips BF 1294	The Moon Behind The Clouds/The Londonderry Air	4
64	Philips BF 1331	Brazilian Shake/Brazilian Blues	4
65	Philips BF 1423	The Mogul Theme/Homage To Spewdley Parsons	4
69	Philips BF 1759	Theme From From The Troubleshooters/Homage To Spewdley Parsons	4
69	Decca LK/SKL 5003	LOVE'S PHILOSOPHY BY... (LP, featuring Dusty Springfield)	20

(see also Springfields, Dusty Springfield)

SPRINGFIELD PARK

| 68 | CBS 3775 | Never An Everyday Thing/I Can See The Sun Shine | 4 |

SPRINGFIELDS

| 61 | Philips BF 1145 | Dear John/I Done What They Told Me To | 5 |

SPRINGFIELDS

62	Philips 326 536 BF	Swahili Papa/Gotta Travel On	6
62	Philips 326 557 BF	Island Of Dreams/The Johnson Boys	4
63	Philips 326 577 BF	Say I Won't Be There/Little Boat	4
60s	Philips	other 45s	3
61	Philips BBE 12476	THE SPRINGFIELDS (EP, also stereo SBBE 9068)	7/15
62	Lyntone P125E	CHRISTMAS WITH THE SPRINGFIELDS (EP, mail-order via 'Woman's Own')	8
62	Philips 433 622 BE	KINDA FOLKSY (EP)	10
63	Philips 433 623 BE	KINDA FOLKSY No. 2 (EP)	10
63	Philips 433 624 BE	KINDA FOLKSY No. 3 (EP)	10
63	Philips BBE 12538	HIT SOUNDS (EP)	7
62	Philips BBL 7551/SBBL 674	KINDA FOLKSY (LP, mono/stereo)	10/12
63	Philips 632 304 BL	FOLK SONGS FROM THE HILLS (LP)	10
64	Philips BET 606	THE SPRINGFIELDS STORY (2-LP)	14
69	Fontana SFL 13098	THE SPRINGFIELDS SING AGAIN (LP)	10

(see also Dusty Springfield, Lana Sisters, Tom Springfield, Mike Hurst)

SPRINGFIELDS

88	Sarah SARAH 010	Sunflower/Clown/Are We Gonna Be Alright? (foldaround p/s & 14" x 10" poster in poly bag; yellow p/s with blue name, later orange p/s)	12/8

BRUCE SPRINGSTEEN

75	CBS A 3661	Born To Run/Meeting Across The River	8
76	CBS A 3940	Tenth Avenue Freeze-Out/She's The One	12
78	CBS A 6424	Prove It All Night/Factory	15
78	CBS A 6532	Badlands/Something In The Night	12
78	CBS A 6720	Promised Land/Streets Of Fire	10
80	CBS A 9309	Hungry Heart/Held Up Without A Gun (p/s, blue or black lettering)	18/12
80	CBS A 9309	Hungry Heart/Held Up Without A Gun (no p/s)	4
80	CBS A 9568	Sherry Darling/Be True (p/s)	12
81	CBS A 1179	The River/Independence Day (p/s)	12
81	CBS A13 1179	The River/Born To Run/Rosalita (12", some picture sleeves credit 'East Street Band')	20/12
81	CBS A 1557	Cadillac Ranch/Wreck On The Highway (p/s)	20
82	CBS A 2794	Atlantic City/Mansion On The Hill (p/s)	20
83	CBS A 2969	Open All Night/The Big Payback (p/s)	20
84	CBS A 4436	Dancing In The Dark/Pink Cadillac (p/s)	4
84	CBS WA 4436	Dancing In The Dark/Pink Cadillac (Cadillac-shaped picture disc)	25
84	CBS TA 4436	Dancing In The Dark (remix)/Pink Cadillac (12", p/s)	8
84	CBS A 4662	Cover Me/Jersey Girl (poster p/s)	10
84	CBS WA 4662	Cover Me/Jersey Girl (withdrawn Bruce-shaped picture disc with plinth)	18
84	CBS DA 4662/A 4436	Cover Me/Cover Me (Version)//Dancing In The Dark/Pink Cadillac (shrinkwrapped double pack, both 45s in p/s)	12
84	CBS DA 4662/A 7077	Cover Me/Cover Me (Version)//Born To Run/Meeting Across The River (shrinkwrapped double pack, no p/s on 2nd 45)	12
84	CBS QTA 4662	Cover Me (Undercover Mix)/Cover Me (Dub)/Shut Out The Light/ Dancing In The Dark (Dub)/Jersey Girl (12", p/s)	8
85	CBS A 7077	Born To Run/Meeting Across The River (reissue, blue p/s, withdrawn)	20
85	CBS A 6342	I'm On Fire/Born In The U.S.A. (p/s, with competition postcard)	7
85	CBS WA 6342	I'm On Fire/Born In The U.S.A. (p/s, flag-shaped picture disc)	12
85	CBS TA 6342	I'm On Fire/Rosalita/Born In The U.S.A (Freedom Mix)/ Johnny Bye Bye (12", p/s)	10
85	CBS A 6375	Glory Days/Stand On It (poster p/s)	6
85	CBS QTA 6375	Glory Days/Stand On It/Sherry Darling/Dancing In The Street (12", poster p/s)	8
85	CBS BRUCE 1	BORN IN THE U.S.A. — THE 12" COLLECTION (4 x 12" & 7", with poster)	20
86	CBS 650 193-7	War/Merry Xmas Baby//My Home Town/Santa Claus Is Coming To Town (shrinkwrapped double pack, both 45s in p/s)	8
87	CBS 650 383-7	Fire (live)/For You (live) (p/s)	6
87	CBS 650 383-6	Fire (live)/For You (live)/Born To Run/No Surrender/10th Avenue Freeze-Out (12", p/s)	8
87	CBS BRUCE 2	Born To Run/Johnny 99 (p/s)	4
87	CBS BRUCE B2	Born To Run/Spirit In The Night//Johnny 99/Because The Night (double pack box set)	12
87	CBS BRUCE BP 2	Born To Run/Johnny 99 (p/s, badge pack)	7
87	CBS BRUCE C2	Born To Run/Spirit In The Night/Johnny 99/Seeds (CD)	8
87	CBS 651 141-7	Brilliant Disguise/Lucky Man (p/s)	4
87	CBS 651 141-7	Brilliant Disguise/Lucky Man (gatefold p/s)	6
87	CBS 651 295-8	Tunnel Of Love/Two For The Road (p/s)	4
87	CBS 651 295-5	Tunnel Of Love/Two For The Road (postcard-shaped picture disc)	15
87	CBS 651 295-6	Tunnel Of Love/Two For The Road/Santa Claus Is Coming To Town (12", p/s, with poster)	10
87	CBS 651 295-2	Tunnel Of Love/Two For The Road/Santa Claus Is Coming To Town (CD)	25
88	CBS BRUCE 3	Tougher Than The Rest/Tougher Than The Rest (live) (p/s, with patch)	6
88	CBS BRUCE Q3	Tougher Than The Rest/Roulette/Tougher Than The Rest (live)/ Born To Run (live) (12", poster p/s)	8
88	CBS BRUCE C3	Tougher Than The Rest/Roulette/Be True/Born To Run (live) (CD)	8
88	CBS BRUCE T4	Spare Parts/Pink Cadillac/Spare Parts (live)/Chimes Of Freedom (12", p/s)	7
88	CBS BRUCE Q4	Spare Parts/Cover Me (live)/Spare Parts (live)/I'm On Fire (live) (12", different p/s)	8
88	CBS BRUCE C4	Spare Parts/Pink Cadillac/Spare Parts (live)/Chimes Of Freedom (CD)	7
88	CBS BRUCE B4	Spare Parts/Pink Cadillac/Spare Parts (live)/Chimes Of Freedom (CD in tin)	20
92	Sony 6581 38/5	57 Channels (And Nothin' On)/Stand On It/Janey, Don't You Lose Heart (CD, picture disc, digipak)	8
86		The Interviews (2 x 7" box set)	10
86		Bruce Springsteen Interview (12", box set, with 'Bruce' passport)	12
73	CBS 65480	GREETINGS FROM ASBURY PARK, N.J. (LP, gatefold sleeve, orange label)	15

73	CBS 65780	THE WILD, THE INNOCENT AND THE E STREET SHUFFLE (LP, orange label, yellow lettering on sleeve; some with "Ashbury" misspelt on label) 15/12
75	CBS 69170	BORN TO RUN (LP, with "*John* Landau" misprint on rear sleeve) 12
79	CBS 66353	BRUCE SPRINGSTEEN (3-LP boxed set) 30
84	CBS 86304	BORN IN THE U.S.A. (LP, picture disc) 35
87	CBS 460279-2	TUNNEL OF LOVE (LP, picture disc) 15
87	CBS CDCBS 460279-2	TUNNEL OF LOVE (CD, picture disc) 15
88	Music & Media BS 1012	BRUCE SPRINGSTEEN INTERVIEW (LP, picture disc, 5,000 only) 12
92	Sony 471423-0	HUMAN TOUCH (LP, picture disc) 10
92	Sony 471424-0	LUCKY TOWN (LP, picture disc) 10

(see also Nils Lofgren)

SPRINGTIME
78	Sonet SON 2143	Mrs Caroline Robinson/Honey Bye Bye (p/s) 6

SPRONG & NYAH SHUFFLE
69	Grape GR 3001	Moonwalk/Think 5

BILLY SPROUD & ROCK 'N' ROLL SIX
57	Columbia DB 3893	Rock Mr. Piper/If You're So Smart (How Come You Ain't ...) 30
57	Columbia DB 3893	Rock Mr. Piper/If You're So Smart (How Come You Ain't ...) (78) 15

SPROUTS
58	RCA RCA 1031	Teen Billy Baby/Goodbye, She's Gone 40
58	RCA RCA 1031	Teen Billy Baby/Goodbye, She's Gone (78) 20

SPUD
75	Philips 9108 002	A SILK PURSE (LP) 15
75	Philips 9108 003	A HAPPY HANDFUL (LP) 15
77	Sonet SNTF 742	SMOKING IN THE BOG (LP, with lyric sheet) 12

WILD JIMMY SPURRILL
60s	XX MIN 717	NOBLE 'THIN MAN' WATTS AND WILD JIMMY SPURRILL (EP) 10

(see also Noble 'Thin Man' Watts)

SPYS
79	No Bad NB 3	The Young Ones/Heavy Scene (p/s) 5

(perhaps see also XTC)

SQUADRONAIRES
54	Decca F 10248	Coach Call Boogie/Donegal Cradle Song 8
54	Decca F 10274	Wolf On The Prowl/Mudhopper 8
53	Decca LF 1141	CONTRASTS IN JAZZ (10" LP) 10

(see also Ronnie Aldrich)

SQUEEZE
77	BTM SBT 107	Take Me I'm Yours/No, Disco Kid, No (unreleased)
77	Deptford Fun City DFC 01	PACKET OF THREE (EP, red & blue photo p/s) 6
77	Deptford Fun City DFC 01	PACKET OF THREE (12" EP, plain pink die-cut sleeve, 500 only) 12
78	A&M AMS 7335	Take Me I'm Yours/Night Nurse (p/s) 4
78	A&M AMSP 7335	Take Me I'm Yours/Night Nurse (12", p/s) 7
78	A&M AMS 7360	Bang Bang/All Fed Up (p/s, green vinyl) 5
78	A&M AMS 7398	Goodbye Girl/Saints Alive (3-D p/s) 6
79	A&M AMS 7426	Cool For Cats/Model (p/s, pale pink vinyl) 4
79	A&M AMS 7426	Cool For Cats/Model (p/s, brilliant pink vinyl, 5,000 only) 8
79	A&M AMS 7426	Cool For Cats/Model (p/s, red vinyl, 1,000 only) 12
79	A&M AMSP 7426	Cool For Cats/Model (12", p/s, pale pink vinyl) 10
79	A&M AMS 7444	Up The Junction/It's So Dirty (p/s, lilac vinyl) 5
79	A&M AMS 7466	Slap And Tickle/All's Well (p/s, red vinyl) 5
79	A&M AMS 7495	Christmas Day/Going Crazy (p/s, white vinyl) 6
79	A&M AMS 7507	Another Nail In My Heart/Pretty Thing (p/s, clear vinyl) 5
80	A&M AMS 7523	Pulling Mussels (From A Shell)/What The Butler Saw (p/s, red vinyl) ... 5
80	Lyntone LYN 7010/1	Wrong Way (green flexidisc, free with 'Smash Hits' magazine) 5/4
81	A&M AMS 8147	Tempted/Yap Yap Yap (p/s, with free U.S. 5" single "Another Nail In My Heart"/"If I Didn't Love You", shrinkwrapped) 6
81	A&M AMS 8166	Labelled With Love/Squabs On Forty Five (withdrawn p/s) 10
82	A&M AMS 8219	Black Coffee In Bed/The Hunt (picture disc) 4
82	A&M AMS 8237	When The Hangover Strikes/Elephant Girl (picture disc) 5
85	A&M AMY 291	Heartbreaking World/Big Beng/Tempted/By Your Side (10", p/s) 6

(see also Jools Holland)

SQUIBBY & REFLECTIONS
68	Direction 58-3606	Loving You Has Made My Life Worthwhile/Better Off Without You 4

SQUIRE
79	Rok ROK I/II	Get Ready To Go/COMING SHORTLY: Doing The Flail (company sleeve) 7
80	Stage One STAGE 2	My Mind Goes Round In Circles/Does Stephanie Know? (p/s) 6
82	Hi-Lo HI 001	No Time Tomorrow/Don't Cry To Me (p/s) 4
82	Hi-Lo HI 002	Girl On A Train/Every Trick In The Book (p/s) 4
83	Hi-Lo HI 003	Every Trick In The Book/Every Trick In The Book (Instrumental) (p/s) ... 4
83	Hi-Lo HIT 003	Every Trick In The Book/Every Trick In The Book (Elastic Mix) (12", p/s) ... 7
83	Hi-Lo HI 004	Jesamine/When I Try, I Lie (p/s) 4
84	Hi-Lo HI 005/SFC2	The Young Idea/It's Getting Better (Squire Fan Club issue) 10
85	Hi-Lo LOX 1	Does Stephanie Know? (flexidisc) 8

BILLY SQUIRE
82	Capitol CL 231	Too Daze Gone/Whadda You Want From Me (p/s, coloured vinyl) 4
82	Capitol CL 261	Emotions In Motion/Catch 22 (p/s) 4
84	Capitol SQD 1	Rock Me Tonite/Can't Get Next To You//She's A Runner/Listen To The Heart (double pack) 4

(see also Freddie Mercury, Roger Taylor)

MINT VALUE £

CHRIS SQUIRE
75	Atlantic K 50203	FISH OUT OF WATER (LP, with inner sleeve & poster)	12

(see also Yes)

DOROTHY SQUIRES
57	Columbia DB 3895	Song Of The Valley/Our Song	4
58	Columbia DB 4070	Bewitched/A Secret That's Never Been Told	4
62	Columbia DB 4942	Are You/Moonlight And Roses	4
57	Pye NEP 24036	DOROTHY SQUIRES (EP)	12
58	Pye Nixa NPL 18015	SINGS BILLY REID (LP)	10

SRC
69	Capitol CL 15576	Black Sheep/Morning Mood	8
88	Bam Caruso OPRA 063	Black Sheep/BRAIN: Nightmares In Red (jukebox issue, die-cut co. sleeve)	4
68	Capitol (S)T 2991	SRC (LP)	30
69	Capitol E-(S)T 134	MILESTONES (LP)	30
70	Capitol E-(S)T 273	TRAVELLER'S TALE (LP)	30

STACCATOS (U.K.)
61	Parlophone R 4828	Main Line/Topaz	10

STACCATOS (U.S.)
66	Capitol CL 15478	Let's Run Away/Face To Face (With Love)	8
67	Capitol CL 15505	Half Past Midnight/Weatherman	8

STACCATOS (U.K.)
68	Fontana TF 966	Butchers And Bakers/Imitations Of Love	15

CLARENCE STACEY
59	Pye International 7N 25025	Just Your Love/Lonely Guy	8

BOB STACKIE
68	Collins Downbeat CR 009	Grab It Hold It Feel It (with Sir Collins Band)/DAN SIMMONDS: Way Out Sound	7

(see also Sir Collins [Band])

STACKRIDGE
71	MCA MDKS 8002	STACKRIDGE (LP)	12
72	MCA MKPS 2025	FRIENDLINESS (LP)	10
73	MCA MCS 3501	THE MAN IN THE BOWLER HAT (LP, gatefold sleeve)	10
76	MCA MCF 2747	DO THE STANLEY (LP)	10
76	Rocket ROLL 3	MR. MICK (LP)	10

STACKWADDY
70	Dandelion S 5119	Roadrunner/Kentucky	8
72	Pol./Dandelion 2001 331	You Really Got Me/Willie The Pimp	6
71	Dandelion DAN 8003	STACKWADDY (LP, gatefold sleeve; also listed as K 49003)	35
72	Dandelion 2310 231	BUGGER OFF (LP)	50

JO STAFFORD
53	Columbia SCM 5011	Star Of Hope/Somebody	10
53	Columbia SCM 5012	It Is No Secret/He Bought My Soul At Calvary	12
53	Columbia SCM 5013	You Belong To Me/Jambalaya (On The Bayou)	20
53	Columbia SCM 5026	Keep It Secret/Once To Every Heart	12
53	Columbia SCM 5046	Something To Remember You By/Blue Moon	10
53	Columbia SCM 5064	September In The Rain/JO STAFFORD & FRANKIE LAINE: Chow, Willy	15
57	Philips JK 1003	On London Bridge/Perfect Love (jukebox issue)	8
58	Philips PB 818	With A Little Bit Of Luck/Wouldn't It Be Loverly	6
58	Philips PB 876	Hibiscus/How Can We Say Goodbye	4
59	Philips PB 898	My Heart Is From Missouri/It Won't Be Easy	4
59	Philips PB 935	Pine Top's Boogie Woogie/All Yours	8
60	Philips PB 991	It Is No Secret/He Bought My Soul At Calvary (reissue)	5
60	Philips PB 1034	Candy/Indoor Sport	4
61	Capitol CL 15225	The Old Rugged Cross/In The Gloaming (with Gordon McRae)	4
62	Pye International 7N 25127	Adios My Love/Misty	4
62	Pye International 7N 25139	Symphony/If My Heart Had A Window	4
54	Columbia SEG 7516	WITH NELSON EDDY (EP, plain sleeve)	8
54	Columbia SEG 7548	SHOW SONGS (EP, plain sleeve)	8
55	Philips BBE 12014	JO STAFFORD No. 1 (EP)	15
57	Philips BBE 12138	JO STAFFORD No. 2 (EP)	8
57	Philips BBE 12141	JO STAFFORD WITH THE ART VAN DAMME QUINTET (EP)	8
57	Philips BBE 12147	JO STAFFORD SINGS SACRED SONGS (EP)	7
58	Philips BBE 12163	SINGS SONGS OF SCOTLAND (EP)	7
58	Philips BBE 12198	JO STAFFORD SINGS SACRED SONGS No. 2 (EP)	7
58	Philips BBE 12214	T.V. SERIES (EP)	10
60	Philips BBE 12378	JO STAFFORD SINGS SACRED SONGS No. 3 (EP)	7
60	Capitol EAP 20049	THE JO STAFFORD TOUCH (EP)	7
61	Capitol EAP 20154	SIMPLE MELODY (EP)	7
61	Philips BBE 12459	JO + JAZZ (EP)	8
50	Capitol LC 6500	AMERICAN FOLK SONGS (10" LP)	20
51	Capitol LC 6515	KISS ME KATE (10" LP, with Gordon MacRae)	16
53	Capitol LC 6575	CAPITOL PRESENTS JO STAFFORD (10" LP)	20
53	Capitol LC 6611	SUNDAY EVENING SONGS (10" LP, with Gordon MacRae)	18
54	Capitol LC 6635	CAPITOL PRESENTS JO STAFFORD, VOL. 2 (10" LP)	20
54	Columbia 33S 1024	AS YOU DESIRE ME (10" LP)	25
54	Philips BBR 8011	MY HEART'S IN THE HIGHLANDS (10" LP)	18
56	Philips BBR 8076	THE VOICE OF YOUR CHOICE (10" LP)	18
56	Philips BBL 7100	HAPPY HOLIDAY (LP, soundtrack)	15
57	Philips BBL 7169	ONCE OVER LIGHTLY (LP)	14
57	Philips BBL 7187	SKI TRAILS (LP)	15
58	Philips BBL 7243	SWINGIN' DOWN BROADWAY (LP)	12
59	Philips BBL 7290	I'LL BE SEEING YOU (LP)	12

59	Philips BBL 7327	BALLAD OF THE BLUES (LP)	12
60	Philips BBL 7395	JO STAFFORD SHOWCASE (LP)	16
61	Philips BBL 7428	JO + JAZZ (LP, also stereo SBBL 595)	12/14
62	Capitol (S)T 1653	AMERICAN FOLK SONGS (LP, reissue, mono/stereo)	10/12
62	Capitol (S)T 1696	WHISPERING HOPE (LP, with Gordon MacRae)	10
63	Encore ENC 144	JO STAFFORD'S SMOKE DREAMS (LP)	10
64	Capitol (S)T 1921	THE HITS OF JO STAFFORD (LP)	10

(see also Jonathan & Darlene Edwards, Gordon MacRae, Tommy Dorsey)

JO STAFFORD & FRANKIE LAINE

| 53 | Columbia SCM 5014 | Settin' The Woods On Fire/Piece A-Puddin' | 18 |
| 55 | Philips BBR 8075 | FLOATIN' DOWN TO COTTON TOWN (10" LP) | 25 |

(see also Frankie Laine)

TERRY STAFFORD

63	Stateside SS 225	Heartache On The Way/You Left Me Here To Cry	8
64	London HLU 9871	Suspicion/Judy	6
64	London HLU 9902	Playing With Fire/I'll Touch A Star	6
64	London HLU 9923	Follow The Rainbow/Are You A Fool Like Me	8
64	London RE-U 1436	SUSPICION (EP)	20
64	London HA-U 8200	SUSPICION (LP)	40

CHRIS STAINTON & GLEN TURNER

| 76 | Decca SKL-R 5259 | TUNDRA (LP) | 12 |

STAIRS

| 92 | Imaginary MIRAGE 029 | Weed Bus (12", unissued, test pressings may exist) | |

STAIRSTEPS

71	Buddah 2011 092	Stay Close To Me/I Made A Mistake	4
76	Dark Horse AMS 5505	From Us To You/Time	4
76	Dark Horse AMS 5507	Pasado/Throwin' Stones Atcha	4
71	Buddah 2359 021	STEP BY STEP BY STEP (LP)	10
71	Buddah 2365 015	STAY CLOSE TO ME (LP)	10
72	Buddah 2365 016	STAIRSTEPS (LP)	10
76	Dark Horse AMLH 22004	2ND RESURRECTION (LP)	10

(see also Five Stairsteps)

STAIRWAY

| 86 | New World NWCD 168 | MOONSTONE (CD) | 18 |
| 86 | New World NWC 168 | MOONSTONE (cassette) | 12 |

(see also Jane Relf, Yardbirds)

TERRY STAMP

| 75 | A&M AMLH 63329 | FAT STICKS (LP) | 15 |

(see also Third World War)

STAMPEDE

82	Polydor POSP 507	Days Of Wine And Roses/Photographs (p/s)	8
82	Polydor POSPX 507	Days Of Wine And Roses/Photographs (12", p/s)	10
83	Polydor POSP 592	The Other Side/The Runner (p/s)	6
82	Polydor ROCK 1	OFFICIAL BOOTLEG (LP)	10
83	Polydor POLS 1083	HURRICANE TOWN (LP)	10

STAMPEDERS

| 72 | Regal Zono. SLRZ 1032 | STAMPEDERS (LP) | 18 |
| 74 | Regal Zono. SLRZ 1039 | FROM THE FIRE (LP) | 18 |

JOE STAMPLEY

| 73 | Dot DOT 145 | Not Too Long Ago/Soul Song | 5 |

JEAN STANBACK

| 70 | Deep Soul DS 9101 | I Still Love You/If I Ever Needed Love | 12 |

STANDELLS

64	Liberty LIB 55722	I'll Go Crazy/Help Yourself	15
66	Capitol CL 15446	Dirty Water/Rari	15
65	Liberty LBY 1243	THE STANDELLS IN PERSON AT P.J.'S (LP)	30

ARNOLD STANG

| 59 | Fontana H 226 | Ivy Will Cling/Where Ya' Calling From, Charlie | 6 |
| 59 | Fontana H 226 | Ivy Will Cling/Where Ya' Calling From, Charlie (78) | 5 |

STANLEY

| 73 | Action ACT 4615 | I'll Go Down And Getcha Pts 1 & 2 | 4 |

PAUL STANLEY

| 79 | Casablanca CAN 140 | Hold Me Touch Me/Goodbye (p/s) | 12 |
| 79 | Casablanca CAN 140 | Hold Me Touch Me/Goodbye (p/s, purple vinyl with mask & picture label, some with mispressed B-side: "Love In Chains") | 20 |

(see also Kiss)

PETE STANLEY & WIZZ JONES

| 65 | Columbia DB 7776 | The Ballad Of Hollis Brown/Riff Minor | 10 |
| 66 | Columbia SX 6083 | SIXTEEN TONS OF BLUEGRASS (LP) | 100 |

(see also Wizz Jones)

STANLEY BROTHERS

| 61 | Melodisc MLP 12-118 | MOUNTAIN SONG FAVOURITES (LP) | 10 |
| 61 | Melodisc MLP 12-122 | SACRED SONGS FROM THE HILLS (LP) | 10 |

LISA STANSFIELD

81	Devil DEV 2	Your Alibis/Thought Police (p/s)	20
82	Polydor POSP 521	The Only Way/Only Love (p/s)	10
83	Polydor POSP 556	Listen To Your Heat (p/s)	8

MINT VALUE £

83	Polydor POSP 651	I Got A Feeling/Red Lights (p/s)	8

(see also Blue Zone)

VIV(IAN) STANSHALL

70	Fly BUG 4	Suspicion (with Gargantuan Chums)/Blind Date (with biG GRunt)	5
74	Warner Bros K 16424	Lakonga/Baba Tunde	4
76	Harvest HAR 5114	Young Ones/Are You Havin' Any Fun/Question	4
80	Charisma CB 373	Jerry Keeps His Clips On/King Cripple (p/s)	4
74	Warner Bros K 56052	MEN OPENING UMBRELLAS AHEAD (LP)	20
78	Charisma CAS 1139	SIR HENRY AT RAWLINSON END (LP, with insert)	10
81	Charisma CAS 1153	TEDDY BOYS DON'T KNIT (LP)	10

(see also Bonzo Dog Doo Dah Band, Grimms)

STAPLE SINGERS

64	Riverside 106902 RIF	Hammer And Nails/Glory Land	10
67	Columbia DB 8292	For What It's Worth/Are You Sure?	10
69	Soul City SC 117	For What It's Worth/Are You Sure? (reissue)	8
69	Stax STAX 118	I See It/The Ghetto	4
72	Stax 2025 068	Respect Yourself/You're Gonna Make Me Cry	4
62	Riverside REP 3220	THE SAVIOUR IS BORN (EP)	10
63	Stateside SL 10015	SWING LOW (LP)	25
63	Riverside RLP 3501	HAMMER AND NAILS (LP)	30
65	Fontana 688 515 ZL	UNCLOUDY DAY (LP)	20
66	Columbia SX 6023	FREEDOM HIGHWAY (LP)	25
69	Stax (S)XATS 1004	SOUL FOLK IN ACTION (LP)	10
69	Stax SXATS 1018	WE'LL GET OVER (LP)	10
70	Stax 2325 069	BEALTITUDE/RESPECT YOURSELF (LP)	10
72	Stax STX 1001	CITY IN THE SKY (LP)	10

CYRIL STAPLETON & HIS ORCHESTRA

52	Decca F 9901	Boogie Woogie March/What Might Have Been (B-side with Jean Campbell) (78)	5
54	Decca F 10293	Long Distance Love/There'll Be No Teardrops Tonight	4
55	Decca F 10456	Tango Mambo/Mexican Madness	4
55	Decca F 10470	Fanfare Boogie/Time After Time	6
55	Decca F 10488	Elephant Tango/Gabrielle	8
55	Decca F 10559	Blue Star (The "Medic" Theme) (with Julie Dawn)/Honey Babe (with Gordon Langhorn)	8
56	Decca F 10703	The Italian Theme/Come Next Spring	8
56	Decca F 10735	The Happy Whistler (with Desmond Lane)/Tiger Tango	8
56	Decca F 10793	Highway Patrol/Maids Of Madrid	4
57	Decca F 10883	Rock, Fiddle, Rock/Chantez, Chantez	4
57	Decca F 10912	Forgotten Dreams/It's Not For Me To Say	6
58	Decca F 10979	Monday Blues Pts 1 & 2	4
56	Decca DFE 6288	PRESENTING CYRIL STAPLETON (EP)	8
62	Ace Of Clubs ACL 1114	COME TWISTIN' (LP)	20

(see also Gordon Langhorn, Desmond Lane)

STA-PREST

81	Avatar AAA 103	Schooldays/Tomorrow (p/s)	15

BUDDY STARCHER

64	London REB 1424	BUDDY STARCHER AND HIS MOUNTAIN GUITAR VOL. 1 (EP)	10
64	London REB 1425	BUDDY STARCHER AND HIS MOUNTAIN GUITAR VOL. 2 (EP)	10
64	London REB 1426	BUDDY STARCHER AND HIS MOUNTAIN GUITAR VOL. 3 (EP)	10

ALVIN STARDUST

75	Magnet MAG 21	Good Love Can Never Die/The Danger Zone (p/s)	6
82	Stiff PBUY 152	I Want You Back In My Life Again/I Just Wanna Make Love To You (picture disc)	4
83	Chrysalis ALV 3	So Near To Christmas/Alright OK//Clock On The Wall/Show You The Way (double pack)	4
84	Chrysalis CHSP 2829	I Won't Run Away/Tigers Don't Climb Trees (picture disc)	4
86	Magnet DUST 1	Jailhouse Rock/Love Is Real (picture disc)	4

(see also Shane Fenton & Fentones)

STARFIGHTERS

80	Motor City	I'm Calling	10
81	Jive JIVET 6	Power Crazy/I Want You/Get Out While You Can (12", p/s)	7
82	Jive HOP 200	POWER CRAZY (LP)	10

STARGAZERS

53	Decca F 10047	Broken Wings/Make It Soon (78)	5
54	Decca F 10213	I See The Moon/Eh Cumpari	15
54	Decca F 10259	The Happy Wanderer/Till We Two Are One	12
54	Decca F 10379	365 Kisses/I Need You Now	6
54	Decca F 10412	Rose Of The Wildwood/Come The Morning	6
55	Decca F 10437	Somebody/(My Baby Don't Love Me) No More (& Sonny Farrar Banjo Band)	12
55	Decca F 10523	The Crazy Otto Rag/Hey, Mr. Banjo	12
55	Decca F 10569	At The Steamboat River Ball/I Love You A Mountain (with Sonny Farrar Banjo Band)	4
55	Decca F 10594	Close The Door/I've Got Four Big Brothers	12
55	Decca F 10626	Twenty Tiny Fingers/An Old Beer Bottle	12
55	Decca F 10668	(Love Is) The Tender Trap/When The Swallows Say Goodbye	6
56	Decca F 10696	Zambesi/When The Swallows Say Goodbye	6
56	Decca F 10731	Hot Diggity (Dog Ziggity Boom)/Rockin' And Rollin'	12
56	Decca F 10775	She Loves To Rock/John Jacob Jingleheimer Smith	12
57	Decca F 10867	You Won't Be Around/Mangos	6
57	Decca F 10898	Honky Tonk Song/Golly!	6
57	Decca F 10916	Who Is It? (It's The Milkman)/Sorry, You'll Have To Wait	6
57	Decca F 10969	The Skiffling Dogs/Out Of This World	6

58	Decca F 11034	Big Man/Lonely For A Letter 4
59	Decca F 11105	My Blue Heaven/How Ja Lika 4
60	Palette PG 9003	Manhattan Spiritual/Three Beautiful Words 4
56	Decca DFE 6341	THE STARGAZERS (EP) 15
56	Decca DFE 6362	ROCKIN' AND ROLLIN' (EP) 15
54	Decca LF 1186	PRESENTING THE STARGAZERS (10" LP) 30
59	Decca LK 4309	SOUTH OF THE BORDER (LP) 20

(see also Roy Smith & Stargazers, Lita Roza, Dickie Valentine)

STARLINGS
80s	Ruffin A-M 029	NEW BLOOD (EP) 4

CINDY STARR
68	Columbia Blue Beat DB 107	Pain Of Love/Hippy Ska (as Cindy Starr & Rude Boys) 6

(see also Mopeds)

EDWIN STARR
66	Polydor BM 56702	Stop Her On Sight (S.O.S.)/I Have Faith In You 8
66	Polydor BM 56717	Headline News/Harlem 8
67	Polydor BM 56726	It's My Turn Now/Girls Are Getting Prettier 15
68	Polydor BM 56753	Stop Her On Sight (S.O.S.)/Headline News (reissue) 5
67	Tamla Motown TMG 630	I Want My Baby Back/Gonna Keep On Tryin' Till I Win 15
68	Tamla Motown TMG 646	I Am The Man For You Baby/My Weakness Is You 10
68	Tamla Motown TMG 672	Twenty Five Miles/Mighty Good Lovin' 5
69	Tamla Motown TMG 692	Way Over There/If My Heart Could Tell The Story 7
70	Tamla Motown TMG 725	Time/Running Back And Forth 5
70	Tamla Motown TMG 754	War/He Who Picks A Rose 4
71	Tamla Motown TMG 764	Stop The War Now/Gonna Keep On Tryin' Till I Win 4
71	Tamla Motown TMG 790	Agent 00-Soul/Back Street 5
75	Bradleys BRAD 7520	Stay With Me/I'll Never Forget You 5
75	Bradleys BRAD 7531	Pain/Party 5
76	GTO GT 65	Accident/Eavesdropper 5
69	T. Motown (S)TML 11094	SOUL MASTER (LP) 20
69	T. Motown (S)TML 11115	25 MILES (LP) 15
70	Tamla Motown STML 11171	WAR AND PEACE (LP) 10

(see also Blinky & Edwin Starr)

FRANK STARR
62	London HLU 9545	Little Bitty Feeling/Lost In A Dream 12

FREDDIE STARR & MIDNIGHTERS
63	Decca F 11663	Who Told You?/Peter Gunn Locomotion 20
63	Decca F 11786	Baby Blue/It's Shaking Time 25
64	Decca F 12009	Never Cry On Someone's Shoulder/Just Keep On Dreaming 25

JIMMY STARR
58	London HL 8731	It's Only Make Believe/Ooh Crazy 30
58	London HL 8731	It's Only Make Believe/Ooh Crazy (78) 12

KAY STARR
51	Vogue V 9009	Ain't Misbehavin'/Good For Nothin' Joe (78) 6
51	Vogue V 9010	Them There Eyes/What Is This Thing Called Love? (78) 6
52	Capitol CL 13717	Wheel Of Fortune/Wabash Cannon Ball (78) 5
52	Capitol CL 13808	Comes A-Long A-Love/Three Letters (78) 5
53	Capitol CL 13871	Side By Side/Too Busy! (78) 5
54	Capitol CL 14050	Changing Partners/I'll Always Be In Love With You (78) 5
54	Capitol CL 14151	Am I A Toy Or A Treasure?/Fortune In Dreams 15
54	Capitol CL 14167	Fool, Fool, Fool/Allez-Vous-En 20
55	HMV 7M 300	If Anyone Finds This, I Love You/Turn Right 10
55	HMV 7M 307	Foolishly Yours/For Better Or Worse 10
55	HMV 7M 315	Where, What Or When?/Good And Lonesome 10
56	HMV 7M 371	Rock And Roll Waltz/I've Changed My Mind A 1,000 Times 20
56	HMV POP 168	Rock And Roll Waltz/I've Changed My Mind A 1,000 Times (78) 5
56	HMV POP 420	Second Fiddle/Love Ain't Right 12
57	HMV POP 345	A Little Loneliness/Touch And Go 7
57	HMV POP 357	Jamie Boy/The Things I Never Had 7
58	RCA RCA 1065	Stroll Me/Rockin' Chair 6
58	RCA RCA 1065	Stroll Me/Rockin' Chair (78) 5
60	Capitol CL 15105	Riders In The Sky/Night Train 5
60	Capitol CL 15137	Wheel Of Fortune/If You Love Me (Really Love Me) 6
60	Capitol CL 15154	Just For A Thrill/Out In The Cold Again 4
61	Capitol CL 15194	Foolin' Around/Kay's Lament 6
61	Capitol CL 15213	Nobody/I'll Never Be Free 4
63	Capitol CL 15293	Swingin' At The Hungry O/Bossa Nova Cassanova 4
63	Capitol CL 15308	No Regrets/Cherche La Rose 4
55	Vogue EPV 1014	KAY STARR (EP) 12
60	Top Rank JKP 2042	HEAVENLY KAY STARR (EP) 10
60	Capitol EAP1 1254	MOVING (EP) 7
60	Capitol EAP2 1254	MOVING PT. 2 (EP) 7
60	Capitol EAP3 1254	MOVING PT. 3 (EP) 15
61	Capitol EAP 1-20063	WHEEL OF FORTUNE (EP) 12
62	Capitol EAP 1-20210	WELL I ASK YOU (EP) 7
56	HMV 7EG 8165	WHAT A STAR IS KAY (EP) 7
56	HMV 7EG 8184	KAY STARR'S AGAIN (EP) 7
53	Capitol LC 6574	CAPITOL PRESENTS KAY STARR (10" LP) 20
54	Capitol LC 6630	THE KAY STARR STYLE (10" LP) 18
56	Capitol LC 6835	THE HITS OF KAY STARR (10" LP) 18
57	Capitol T 580	IN A BLUE MOOD (LP) 12
57	London HA-U 2039	SWINGING WITH THE STARR (LP) 25
58	RCA RD 27056	BLUE STARR (LP) 15

Kay STARR

60	Capitol (S)T 1254	MOVIN'! (LP)	10
60	Capitol (S)T 1303	LOSERS, WEEPERS (LP)	10
60	Capitol (S)T 1374	MOVIN' ON BROADWAY (LP)	10
61	Capitol T 1358	ONE MORE TIME (LP)	12
61	Capitol (S)T 1438	JAZZ SINGER (LP)	10
62	Capitol T 1468	ALL STARR HITS! (LP)	10
62	Capitol (S)T 1681	I CRY BY NIGHT (LP)	10
63	Capitol (S)T 1795	JUST PLAIN COUNTRY (LP)	10
64	Capitol (S)T 2106	THE FABULOUS FAVOURITES (LP)	10
5-	World Record Club T 100	WISH UPON A STARR (LP)	10

LUCILLE STARR
64	London HL 9900	The French Song/Sit Down And Write Me A Letter	4

LUCKY STARR
62	Parlophone R 4963	I've Been Everywhere/Wrong	4

MAXINE STARR
63	London HLU 9712	Wishing Star/Sailor Boy	5

RANDY STARR
57	London HL 8443	After School/Heaven High (Man So Low)	25
57	London HL 8443	After School/Heaven High (Man So Low) (78)	8
58	Felsted AF 106	Pink Lemonade/Count On Me	10
58	Felsted AF 106	Pink Lemonade/Count On Me (78)	10
60	Top Rank JAR 264	Workin' On The Santa Fe/You're Growing Up	6

RINGO STARR
71	Apple R 5898	It Don't Come Easy/Early 1970 (B-side 'produced by Ringo Starr' credit, p/s)	10
71	Apple R 5898	It Don't Come Easy/Early 1970 (B-side 'produced by George Harrison', p/s)	8
72	Apple R 5944	Back Off Boogaloo/Blindman (p/s, blue Apple label)	8
73	Apple R 5992	Photograph/Down And Out (p/s)	6
74	Apple R 5995	You're Sixteen/Devil Woman (p/s)	5
74	Apple R 6000	Only You/Call Me (p/s)	7
75	Apple R 6004	Snookeroo/Oo-wee	6
76	Apple R 6011	Oh My My/No No Song	12
76	Polydor 2001 694	A Dose Of Rock 'N' Roll/Cryin'	6
76	Polydor 2001 699	Hey Baby/Lady Gaye	6
77	Polydor 2001 734	Drowning In The Sea Of Love/Just A Dream	30
78	Polydor 2001 782	Lipstick Traces/Old Time Relovin' (release cancelled)	
78	Polydor 2001 795	Tonight/Heart On My Sleeve	20
81	RCA RCA 166	Wrack My Brain/Drumming Is My Madness (p/s)	5
84	Old Gold OG 4513	It Don't Come Easy/Back Off Boogaloo (p/s)	8
70	Apple PCS 7101	SENTIMENTAL JOURNEY (LP)	20
70	Apple PAS 10002	BEAUCOUPS OF BLUES (LP, gatefold sleeve)	20
73	Apple PCTC 252	RINGO (LP, gatefold sleeve with booklet)	10
74	Apple PCS 7168	GOODNIGHT VIENNA (LP, with inner sleeve)	10
76	Polydor 2302 040	RINGO'S ROTOGRAVURE (LP, gatefold sleeve with inner & magnifying glass)	10
78	Polydor 2480 429	SCOUSE THE MOUSE (LP, with Adam Faith, Donald Pleasance etc.; stickered sleeve with printed competition insert)	80
78	Polydor 3194 429	SCOUSE THE MOUSE (cassette)	25

(see also Beatles, Harry Nilsson, Billy Connolly & Chris Tummings)

STELLA STARR
67	Piccadilly 7N 35366	Bring Him Back/Say It	30

TONY STARR
64	Decca F 11847	I'll Take A Rocket To The Moon/Next Train Leaving	15

STARS OF HEAVEN
85	Hotwire HWS 853	Clothes Of Pride/All About You (beige or black label, some with p/s)	15/8

STATE OF MICKEY & TOMMY
67	Mercury MF 996	With Love From One To Five/I Know What I Will Do	50
67	Mercury MF 1009	Frisco Bay/Nobody Knows Where You've Been	50

(see also Spooky Tooth, Nero & Gladiators)

STATESMEN
63	Decca F 11687	Look Around/I'm Wondering	6
64	Fontana TF 432	I've Just Fallen In Love/It's All Happening	6

STATE STREET RAMBLERS/LOVELY AUSTIN BLUE SERENADERS
60s	Collector JE 123	SMALL JAZZ BAND VOL. 1 (EP, shared by State Street Ramblers & Lovey Austin Blue Serenaders)	7

STATE STREET SWINGERS/CHICAGO BLACK SWANS
73	Collectors Items 003	STATE STREET SWINGERS (LP)	12

STATIC
67	Page One POF 039	When You Went Away/Let Me Tell You	8

STATION SKIFFLE GROUP
57	Esquire 10-503	Don't You Rock Me Daddy-O/Hugged My Honey (78)	5
57	Esquire 10-516	Steamboat Bill/Titanic (78)	5
58	Esquire EP 161	STATION SKIFFLE GROUP (EP)	20

STATLER BROTHERS
65	CBS 201796	Flowers On The Wall/Bill Christian	4

CANDI STATON
69	Capitol CL 15620	Heart On A String/I'm Just A Prisoner	4
75	United Artists UP 35823	Love Chain/I'm Gonna Hold On	6
70	Capitol ST 21631	I'M JUST A PRISONER (LP)	10

DAKOTA STATON

55	Capitol CL 14314	Don't Leave Me Now/A Little You	10
55	Capitol CL 14339	I Never Dreamt/Abracadabra	7
58	Capitol CL 14828	Trust In Me/The Late, Late Show	4
58	Capitol CL 14870	The Party's Over/Invitation	6
59	Capitol CL 14917	Confessin' The Blues/(I'm Left With ...) Blues In My Heart (with George Shearing Quintet)	8
59	Capitol CL 14931	My Funny Valentine/A Foggy Day	5
59	Capitol EAP1 1054	THE DYNAMIC DAKOTA STATON (EP)	8
59	Capitol EAP2 1054	THE DYNAMIC DAKOTA STATON (EP)	8
59	Capitol EAP3 1054	THE DYNAMIC DAKOTA STATON (EP)	8
58	Capitol T 876	THE LATE, LATE SHOW (LP)	12
59	Capitol (S)T 1054	THE DYNAMIC DAKOTA STATON (LP)	12
59	Capitol T 1170	CRAZY HE CALLS ME (LP)	12
60	Capitol (S)T 1325	MORE THAN THE MOOD (LP)	12
60	Capitol (S)T 1387	BALLADS AND THE BLUES (LP)	12
61	Capitol (S)T 1241	TIME TO SWING (LP)	12
62	Capitol (S)T 1597	'ROUND MIDNIGHT (LP)	10
62	Capitol (S)T 1649	DAKOTA AT STORYVILLE (LP)	10

STATUES

60	London HLG 9192	Blue Velvet/Keep The Hall Burning	12

STATUS QUO

68	Pye 7N 17449	Pictures Of Matchstick Men/Gentleman Joe's Sidewalk Café (some with '75c Minimum' on B-side label credit)	7/4
68	Pye 7N 17497	Black Veils Of Melancholy/To Be Free	15
68	Pye 7N 17581	Ice In The Sun/When My Mind Is Not Live	4
68	Pye 7N 17650	Technicolor Dreams/Paradise Flat (withdrawn, demos more common £150)	400
69	Pye 7N 17665	Make Me Stay A Bit Longer/Auntie Nellie	18
69	Pye 7N 17728	Are You Growing Tired Of My Love/So Ends Another Life	15
69	Pye 7N 17825	The Price Of Love/Little Miss Nothing	18
70	Pye 7N 17907	Down The Dustpipe/Face Without A Soul	4
70	Pye 7N 17998	In My Chair/Gerdundula (a few with p/s)	60/4
71	Pye 7N 45077	Tune To The Music/Good Thinking	15
72	Phonogram DJ 005	Roadhouse Blues/BLACK SABBATH: Children Of The Grave (100 promo copies only)	150
72	Vertigo 6059 071	Paper Plane/Softer Ride (spiral label)	8
73	Pye 7N 45229	Mean Girl/Everything	4
73	Pye 7N 45253	Gerdundula/Lakky Lady	7
73	Vertigo 6059 085	Caroline/Joanne (with B-side miscredited to Lancaster)	6
75	Vertigo QUO 13	ROLL OVER LAY DOWN (EP)	4
76	Lyntone LYN 3154/5	Down Down/Break The Rules (Smiths Crisps flexidisc, a few with p/s)	10/6
77	Vertigo 6-59 184	Rockin' All Over The World/Ring Of A Change (p/s)	10
78	Vertigo QUO 2	Accident Prone/Let Me Fly (p/s, silver plastic label)	4
79	Pye Flashbacks FBS 2	Pictures Of Matchstick Men/Down The Dustpipe (reissue, yellow vinyl, p/s)	8
79	Pye 7P 103	In My Chair/Gerundula (p/s)	5
79	Vertigo 6059 242	Whatever You Want/Hard Ride (p/s)	4
79	Vertigo 6059 248	Livin' On A Island/Runaway (p/s)	4
79	Pye QUO 1/SFI 434	In My Chair (flexidisc, concert freebie, some with 'Record Mirror' Quo special)	10/6
81	Vertigo QUO 5	Something 'Bout You Baby I LIke/Enough Is Enough (red or blue p/s)	4
81	Vertigo QUO JB 6	Rock 'n' Roll/Hold You Back (no p/s, jukebox edition, B-side 45rpm)	8
82	Vertigo QUO 8	She Don't Fool Me/Never Too Late (p/s)	4
82	Vertigo QUO 9	Jealousy/Calling The Shots (Irish promos only; unreleased in U.K.)	60
82	Vertigo QUOP 10	Caroline (live)/Dirty Water (live) (picture disc)	8
82	Vertigo QUOP 1012	Caroline (live)/Dirty Water (live)/Down Down (live) (12", p/s)	10
83	Vertigo QUO B-11	Ol' Rag Blues/Stay The Night (blue vinyl, different rear p/s to black vinyl)	4
83	Vertigo QUO 1112	Ol' Rag Blues (Extended Remixed Edition)/Stay The Night/ Whatever You Want (live) (12", p/s)	10
83	Vertigo QUO 1212	A Mess Of Blues (Extended)/Big Man/Young Pretender (12", p/s)	12
83	Vertigo QUOP 14	Marguerita Time/Resurrection (picture disc)	15
83	Vertigo QUO 1414	Marguerita Time/Resurrection/Caroline/Joanne (Christmas double pack, gatefold p/s)	20
84	Vertigo QUO 15	Too Close To The Ground/I Wonder Why (release cancelled)	
84	Vertigo QUOP 16	The Wanderer/Can't Be Done (12" clear vinyl, picture labels)	20
85	Vertigo QUO 17	Naughty Girl (actually "Dreamin' ") (unreleased)	
86	Vertigo QUOPD 18	Rollin' Home/Lonely ('Q'-shaped picture disc)	15
86	Vertigo QUODP 19	Red Sky/Don't Give It Up/Rockin' All Over The World/Whatever You Want (double pack, gatefold p/s)	10
86	Vertigo QUOPB 191	Red Sky/Don't Give It Up/The Milton Keynes Medley (12", 'Wembley Souvenir Pack', poster p/s)	15
86	Vertigo QUO 20	In The Army Now/Heartburn (p/s, with sew-on patch, sealed)	6
86	Vertigo QUOPD 20	In The Army Now/Heartburn (picture disc)	25
86	Vertigo QUODP 20	In The Army Now/Heartburn//Marguerita Time/What You're Proposing (double pack, gatefold p/s)	10
86	Vertigo QUO 2012	In The Army Now/Heartburn/Late Last Night (12", shrinkwrapped with poster)	15
86	Vertigo QUOP 21	Dreamin'/Long-Legged Girls (with foldout poster/calender)	15
88	Vertigo QUOH 22	Ain't Complainin'/That's Alright ('History Pack' with family tree in envelope)	4
88	Vertigo QUOCD 22	Ain't Complainin' (Extended)/That's Alright/Lean Machine/ In The Army Now (Remix) (CD, card p/s)	8
88	Vertigo QUOH 23	Who Gets The Love?/Hallowe'en ('History Pack' with family tree part 2, in envelope p/s)	4
88	Vertigo QUOCD 23	Who Gets The Love? (Extended)/Hallowe'en/The Reason For Goodbye/ The Wanderer (Sharon The Nag Mix) (CD, card p/s)	8
88	Vertigo QUACD 1	Running All Over The World (Extended)/Magic/Whatever You Want (CD, card p/s)	7

STATUS QUO

88	Vertigo QUOCD 25	Burning Bridges (On And Off And On Again) (Extended)/Whatever You Want/Marguerite Time (CD, jewel case) 7
90	Vertigo QUOP 27	Little Dreamer/Rotten To The Bone (p/s, sew-on patch) 4
90	Vertofo QUODJ 28	Anniversary Waltz Pts 1 & 2 (p/s, promo only) 20
90	Vertigo QUOG 28	Anniversary Waltz Part 1/The Power Of Rock (p/s, silver vinyl, with booklet) 6
90	Vertigo QUO 2812	Anniversary Waltz/The Power Of Rock/Perfect Remedy (12", p/s, mispress, B-side plays "Little Lady" & "Paper Plane" re-recording) 20
91	Vertigo STATUS 30	Can't Give You More (Radio Edit)/Dead In The Water (no p/s, promo only) 18
91	Vertigo QUO 31	Fakin' The Blues/Heavy Daze (cancelled, about 25 copies exist) 100
91	Vertigo QUO 3112	Fakin' The Blues/Heavy Daze/Better Times (12", cancelled, about 25 copies exist) 120
92	Vertigo QUO 3212	Rock 'Til You Drop/Medley/Forty-Five Hundred Times (12", p/s, mispressing, omits 3rd track) 10
93	Vertigo QUOCD 31	Fakin' The Blues (Edit)/Fakin' The Blues (Album Version)/Heavy Daze/ Better Times (CD, no case, unreleased from 1991, fan club freebie) 15
80s	Lyntone QUO 1-4	Interview picture discs (4-single pack) 20
68	Pye N(S)PL 18220	PICTURESQUE MATCHSTICKABLE MESSAGES (LP) 50
68	Pye N(S)PL 18301	SPARE PARTS (LP) 50
69	Marble Arch MAL(S) 1193	STATUS QUO-TATIONS (LP) 40
70	Pye NSPL 18344	MA KELLY'S GREASY SPOON (LP, a few with poster) 20/10
71	Pye NSPL 18371	DOG OF TWO HEAD (LP, gatefold sleeve) 10
72	Vertigo 6360 082	PILEDRIVER (LP, spiral label, gatefold sleeve) 10
73	Vertigo 6360 098	HELLO! (LP, spaceship label, with inner sleeve & poster) 15
74	Vertigo 9102 001	QUO (LP, with poster/lyric sheet) 10
77	Pye FILD 005	THE FILE SERIES (2-LP, single sleeve, printed inner) 20
77	PRT FILD 005	THE STATUS QUO FILE SERIES (2-LP, different sleeve) 18
79	Pye NPSL 18607	JUST FOR THE RECORD (LP, red vinyl) 15
82	Phonogram PRO BX 1	FROM THE MAKERS OF ... (3-LP, in numbered round metal tin) 20
83	Vertigo 800 035-2	1+9+8+2 (CD) 15
83	Vertigo 800 053-2	NEVER TOO LATE (CD) 15
83	Vertigo 814 66-2	BACK TO BACK (CD) 16
88	PRT PYX 4007	FROM THE BEGINNING (LP, picture disc) 12

(see also Spectres, Traffic Jam, Rossi & Frost, Rockers, Young & Moody)

STAVELY MAKEPEACE

70	Concord CON 8	Edna/Tarzan Harvey 4
73	Spark SRL 1081	Slippery Rock 70's/Don't Ride A Paula Pillion 4
73	Deram DM 386	Cajun Band/Memories Of Your Love 4
74	Deram DM 423	Runaround Sue/There's A Wall Between Us 4

(see also Lieutenant Pigeon)

STAVERTON BRIDGE

70s	Saydisc SDL 266	STAVERTON BRIDGE (LP, with lyrics) 30

STEAM

69	Fontana TF 1058	Na Na Hey Hey Kiss Him Goodbye/It's The Magic In You Girl 4

STEAMHAMMER

69	CBS 4141	Junior's Wailing/Windmills 6
69	CBS 4496	Autumn Song/Blues For Passing People 6
68	CBS (S) 63611	STEAMHAMMER (LP) 30
69	CBS (S) 63694	STEAMHAMMER MK. II (LP) 25
70	B&C CAS 1024	MOUNTAINS (LP) 25
70	Reflection RELF 1	STEAMHAMMER (LP, reissue, different sleeve) 35

STEEL

81	Neat NEAT 14	Rock Out/All Systems Go (p/s) 10

BETTE ANNE STEELE

55	Capitol CL 14315	Barricade/Give Me A Little Kiss Will "Ya", Huh? 8

DORIS STEELE

59	Oriole CB 1468	Why Must I?/Never Again 4

JAN STEELE & JOHN CAGE

76	Obscure OBS 5	VOICES AND INSTRUMENTS (LP) 12

SONDRA & JON STEELE

55	Parlophone MSP 6166	I'm Crazy With Love/Fill My Heart With Happiness 6

TOMMY STEELE (& STEELMEN)

56	Decca F 10795	Rock With The Caveman/Rock Around The Town (with Steelmen) 30
56	Decca F 10808	Doomsday Rock/Elevator Rock 20
56	Decca F 10819	Singing The Blues/Rebel Rock (with Steelmen) 15
57	Decca F 10849	Knee Deep In The Blues/Teenage Party (with Steelmen) 12
57	Decca F 10877	Butterfingers/Cannibal Pot 8
57	Decca F 10896	Shiralee/Grandad's Rock 10
57	Decca F 10915	All Star Hit Parade No. 2 (with other artists) 5
57	Decca F 10923	Water Water/A Handful Of Songs 7
57	Decca F 10941	Hey You!/Plant A Kiss 8
58	Decca F 10976	Happy Guitar/Princess 6
58	Decca F 10991	Nairobi/Neon Sign 6
58	Decca F 11026	It's All Happening/What Do You Do 4
58	Decca F 11041	The Only Man On The Island/I Puts The Lightie On 6
58	Decca F 11072	Come On Let's Go/Put A Ring On Her Finger 6
58	Decca F 11089	A Lovely Night/Marriage Type Love 4
59	Decca F 11117	Hiawatha/The Trial 6
59	Decca F 11152	Tallahassee Lassie/Give! Give! Give! 8
59	Decca F 11162	You Were Mine/Young Ideas 4
59	Decca F 11177	Little White Bull/Singing Time (some in p/s) 8/4

(the above singles originally came with triangular centres; later round centre reissues are worth two-thirds the value)

MINT VALUE £

60	Decca F 11245	What A Mouth (What A North And South)/Kookaburra	4
60	Decca F 11258	Drunken Guitar/Light Up The Sky (unreleased)	
60	Decca F 11275	Happy Go Lucky Blues/(The Girl With The) Long Black Hair	4
60	Decca F 11299	Boys And Girls/Must Be Santa	4
61	Decca F 11361	My Big Best Shoes/The Dit Dit Song	4
61	Decca F 11372	Drunken Guitar/Writing On The Wall	4
62	Decca F 11479	Hit Record/What A Little Darling	4
62	Decca F 11551	He's Got Love/Green Eyes	4
63	Decca F 11532	Where Have All The Flowers Gone/Butter Wouldn't Melt in Your Mouth	4
63	Decca F 11615	Flash, Bang, Wallop!/She's So Far Above Me	4
63	Columbia DB 7070	Egg And Chips/The Dream Maker	4
56	Decca DFE 6388	YOUNG LOVE (EP)	15
56	Decca DFE 6389	SINGING THE BLUES (EP)	15
57	Decca DFE 6398	THE TOMMY STEELE STORY NO. 1 (EP)	12
57	Decca DFE 6424	THE TOMMY STEELE STORY NO. 2 (EP)	12
		(the above EPs originally came with triangular centres; later round centre reissues are worth two-thirds the value)	
58	Decca DFE 6472	THE DUKE WORE JEANS (EP)	12
58	Decca DFE 6551	C'MON LET'S GO (EP)	10
59	Decca DFE 6592	SWEET GEORGIA BROWN (EP)	10
59	Decca DFE 6607	TOMMY THE TOREADOR (EP)	7
60	Decca DFE 6660	WHAT A MOUTH (EP)	8
57	Decca LF 1287	THE TOMMY STEELE STAGE SHOW (10" LP)	25
57	Decca LF 1288	THE TOMMY STEELE STORY (10" LP)	20
58	Decca LF 1308	THE DUKE WORE JEANS (10" LP, soundtrack)	15
60	Decca LK 4351	GET HAPPY WITH TOMMY (LP)	10

STEELEYE SPAN

71	B&C CB 164	Rave On/Reels/Female Drummer (p/s)	6
72	Pegasus PGS 6	JIGS AND REELS (maxi-single)	5
74	Chrysalis CHS 2007	Gaudete/The Holly And The Ivy (p/s)	5
77	Chysalis CHS 2129	The Boar's Head Carol/Guadette/Some Rival (p/s)	5
70	RCA SF 8113	HARK! THE VILLAGE WAIT (LP, with insert)	18
71	B&C CAS 1029	PLEASE TO SEE THE KING (LP, initially in 'hessian' textured sleeve)	20/12
71	Pegasus PEG 9	TEN MAN MOP, OR MR. RESERVOIR BUTLER RIDES AGAIN (LP, gatefold sleeve with 8-page booklet)	15

(see also Tim Hart & Maddy Prior, Gay & Terry Woods, Ashley Hutchings, Fairport Convention, Martin Carthy)

STEEL MILL

71	Penny Farthing PEN 770	Green Eyed God/Zang Will	18
71	Penny Farthing PEN 783	Get On The Line/Summer's Child	18
75	Penny Farthing PEN 894	Green Eyed God/Zang Will (reissue)	6
75	Penny Farthing PELS 549	GREEN EYED GOD (LP)	120

STEEL PULSE

77	Anchor ANC 1046	Nyah Luv/Luv Nyah	4
70s	private pressing	Nyah Luv/Luv Nyah (12")	10

STEEL RIVER

70	Evolution Z 2018	WEIGHING HEAVY (LP)	12
71	Evolution Z 3006	BETTER ROAD (LP)	12

STEELY DAN

72	Probe PRO 562	Dallas/Sail The Waterway	5
73	Probe PRO 577	Do It Again/Fire In The Hole	4
73	Probe PRO 587	Reelin' In The Years/Only A Fool	4
73	Probe PRO 602	Show Biz Kids/Razor Boy	4
73	Probe PRO 606	My Old School/Pearl Of The Quarter	4
74	Probe PRO 622	Rikki Don't Lose That Number/Any Major Dude Will Tell You	4
79	ABC ABC 4241	Rikki Don't Lose That Number/Any Major Dude Will Tell You (p/s, reissue, yellow vinyl)	4
73	Probe SPB 1062	CAN'T BUY A THRILL (LP, original)	10
73	Probe SPD 1079	COUNTDOWN TO ECSTASY (LP, original)	10
80s	MCA 203 16009	GAUCHO (LP, audiophile pressing)	10
82	MCA MCF 3165	GOLD (LP, with free EP [MSAMT 21])	10
80s	MCA 203 16016	GOLD (LP, audiophile pressing)	10

WOUT STEENHUIS

66	Columbia DB 8027	Nivram/Bay Of Paradise	4
64	Columbia 33SX 1585	SURFIN' WITH STEENHUIS (LP)	12
66	Columbia SX 6024	PARADISE ISLAND (LP)	10
66	Studio Two TWO 116	PARADISE ISLAND (LP)	10

STEEPLECHASE

70	Polydor	LADY BRIGHT (LP)	12

BILL STEGMEYER & HIS ORCHESTRA

54	London HL 8078	On The Waterfront (From The Film)/We Just Couldn't Say Good-bye	22

LOU STEIN

57	London HLZ 8419	Almost Paradise/Soft Sands	12
58	Mercury 7MT 226	Who Slammed The Door/Got A Match?	7

JIM STEINMAN

81	Epic EPCA 13-1236	Rock And Roll Dreams Come True/Love And Death/The Storm (12", p/s, blue vinyl)	7
81	Epic EPC 84361	BAD FOR GOOD (LP, with free 45 "Storm"/"Rock And Roll Dreams Come True" [XPS 117])	10
81	Epic EPC 84361	BAD FOR GOOD (LP, picture disc)	10
		(see also Meatloaf)	

STELLA

82	President PT 504	Si Tu Aimes Ma Musique/If You Do Like My Music (p/s)	7

MINT VALUE £

EWAN STEPHENS
71	Decca F 13219	Queen Of The Good Times/We Can Give It A Try	4
72	Decca F 13299	Brother, Surely We Can Work It Out/Long, Long Summer	4

(see also Turquoise)

LEIGH STEPHENS
69	Philips SBL 7897	RED WEATHER (LP)	25
71	Charisma CAS 1040	AND A CAST OF THOUSANDS (LP)	15

(see also Blue Cheer)

STEPPENWOLF
68	RCA RCA 1679	Sookie Sookie/Take What You Need	7
68	RCA RCA 1735	Born To Be Wild/Everybody's Next One	6
68	Stateside SS 8003	Magic Carpet Ride/Sookie Sookie	6
69	Stateside SS 8013	Rock Me/Jupiter Child	5
69	Stateside SS 8017	Born To Be Wild/Everybody's Next One (reissue)	4
69	Stateside SS 8027	Magic Carpet Ride/Sookie Sookie (reissue)	4
70	Stateside SS 8035	Monster/Move Over	4
70	Stateside SS 8038	The Pusher/Your Wall's Too High	5
70	Stateside SS 8049	Hey Lawdy Mama/Twisted	5
70	Stateside SS 8056	Screaming Night Hog/Spiritual Fantasy	4
70	Probe PRO 510	Who Needs Ya/Earschplittenloudenboomer	4
70	Probe PRO 525	Snowblind Friend/Hippo Stomp	4
71	Probe PRO 534	Ride With Me/For Madmen Only	5
71	Probe PRO 544	For Ladies Only/Sparkle Eyes	4
68	RCA RD/SF 7974	STEPPENWOLF (LP, initially white sleeve, later silver sleeve)	15/12
68	Stateside (S)SL 5003	STEPPENWOLF THE SECOND (LP)	12
69	Stateside (S)SL 5011	AT YOUR BIRTHDAY PARTY (LP)	12
69	Stateside (S)SL 5015	EARLY STEPPENWOLF (LP)	12
69	Stateside (S)SL 10276	CANDY (LP, soundtrack, 1 track with Byrds)	12
70	Stateside SSL 5020	STEPPENWOLF (reissue)	10
70	Stateside SSL 5021	MONSTER (LP, gatefold sleeve)	12
70	Stateside SSL 5029	STEPPENWOLF LIVE (LP)	10
70	Probe SPBA 6254	STEPPENWOLF 7 (LP)	10
71	Probe SPBA 6260	FOR LADIES ONLY (LP)	10
72	Probe SPBA 1059	REST IN PEACE (LP)	10

(see also Sparrow, John Kay)

STEPPES
79	South Circular SGS 108	The Beat Drill/FIFTY FANTASTICS: God's Got Religion (p/s, white label)	10

(see also Fifty Fantastics, Disco Zombies)

STEPPING TALK
79	Eustone/Rough Trade TO1	Alice In Sunderland/Health And Safety/Common Problems/John Turtles (p/s)	4

STEPTOE & SON
(see under Harry H. Corbett & Wilfred Bramble)

STEREOLAB
91	Duophonic DS 45-01	SUPER 45 (THE LIGHT THAT WILL CEASE TO FAIL) (10", with insert, mail-order issue, 800 only; 40 with hand-painted p/s)	40/25
91	Duophonic DS 45-02	STUNNING DEBUT ALBUM (7", p/s, clear vinyl)	20

(see also McCarthy)

STEREOS
61	MGM MGM 1143	Please Come Back To Me/I Really Love You	20
61	MGM MGM 1149	The Big Knock/Sweet Water	20
66	MGM MGM 1328	The Big Knock/Sweet Water (reissue)	10

STEREOTYPES
80	Art Theft AT 001	Calling All The Shots/Lovers Of The Future (p/s)	4

DEAN STERLING & TEENBEATS
61	Pye 7N 15345	Send Me A Girl/Lost Love	4

LESTER STERLING (& HIS GROUP)
63	Island WI 121	Clean The City/Long Walk Home (B-side actually by Charmers)	10
63	R&B JB 111	Air Raid Shelter/ROY & ANNETTE: I Mean It	10
63	R&B JB 115	Gravy Cool/WINSTON & BIBBY: Lover Lover Man	10
64	R&B JB 143	Peace And Love/HORACE SEATON: Hold On	10
64	R&B JB 150	Hot Cargo/MAYLABS: Marching On	8
64	R&B JB 155	Baskin' Hop (as Lester Sterling & His Group)/MAYTALS: Shining Light	8
64	R&B JB 172	Indian Summer (as Lester Sterling & His Group)/STRANGER & PATSY: I'll Forgive You	8
66	Doctor Bird DB 1057	Inez (with Tommy McCook & Supersonics)/GLORIA CRAWFORD: Sad Movies	10
67	Doctor Bird DB 1107	Soul Voyage/ALVA LEWIS: Revelation	10
67	Collins Downbeat CR 001	Sir Collins Special/Lester Sterling '67	8
68	Coxsone CS 7080	Africkaan Beat/PARAGONS: My Satisfaction	12
68	Blue Cat BS 116	Zigaloo/Wiser Than Solomon	10
68	Big Shot	It Might As Well Be Spring/DERRICK MORGAN: Shower Of Rain	6
68	Big Shot B 507	Forest Gate Rock/Rock Rock And Cry	6
68	Unity UN 502	Bangarang (with Stranger Cole)/STRANGER COLE: If We Should Ever Meet	5
69	Unity UN 505	Reggae On Broadway/CLIQUE: Love Can Be Wonderful	5
69	Unity UN 509	Spoogy/TOMMY McCOOK: Monkey Fiddle	5
69	Unity UN 512	Regina/Bright As A Rose	5
69	Unity UN 517	1,000 Tons Of Megaton/KING CANNON: Five Card Stud	5
69	Unity UN 518	Man About Town/Man At The Door	5
69	Unity UN 531	Lonesome Feeling/Bright As A Rose	5
69	Gas GAS 103	Reggae In The Wind/SOUL SET: Try Me One More Time (B-side actually by Stranger & Gladdy)	5
70	Unity UN 562	Slip Up/DAVE BARKER: On Broadway	5

Rare Record Price Guide

| 69 | Pama SECO 15 | BANGARANG (LP) | 30 |

(see also Mister Versatile)

STEROIDS
| 78 | Radar ADA 11 | In The Colonies/Sha La La Loo Ley (p/s) | 6 |

STEVE & STEVIE
| 68 | Toast TLP 2 | STEVE AND STEVIE (LP) | 50 |

(see also Tin Tin)

APRIL STEVENS
53	Parlophone MSP 6060	C'est Si Bon/Soft Warm Lips	8
54	Parlophone MSP 6088	How Could Red Riding Hood (Have ...)/You Said You'd Do It	8
67	MGM MGM 1366	Falling In Love Again/Wanting You	50
76	MGM 2006 586	Wanting You/Falling In Love Again (reissue)	4

(see also Nino Tempo & April Stevens)

CAT STEVENS
66	Deram DM 102	I Love My Dog/Portobello Road	4
66	Deram DM 110	Matthew And Son/Granny	4
67	Deram DM 118	I'm Gonna Get Me A Gun/School Is Out	4
67	Deram DM 140	Bad Night/Laughing Apple	4
67	Deram DM 156	Kitty/Blackness Of The Night	4
68	Deram DM 178	Lovely City/Image Of Hell	4
68	Deram DM 211	Here Comes My Wife/It's A Super Duper Day	4
69	Deram DM 260	Where Are You/The View From The Top	4
70	Island WIP 6086	Lady D'Arbanville/Time/Fill My Eyes (p/s)	5
67	Deram DML/SML 1004	MATTHEW AND SON (LP)	10
67	Deram DML/SML 1018	NEW MASTERS (LP)	10
67	Deram	CATS AND DOGS (LP, unreleased, test pressings only)	30
75	Island ILPS 9310	GREATEST HITS (LP, with calendar & poster)	10

CHUCK STEVENS
| 57 | Columbia DB 3883 | Take A Walk/The Way I Do | 4 |
| 57 | Columbia DB 3938 | My London/Couldn't Care More | 4 |

CONNIE STEVENS
60	Warner Bros WB 3	Sixteen Reasons (with Don Ralke)/Little Sister (with Buddy Cole Trio)	6
60	Warner Bros WB 17	Too Young To Go Steady/A Little Kiss Is A Kiss, Is A Kiss	4
60	Warner Bros WB 25	Apollo/Why Do I Cry For Joey	4
61	Warner Bros WB 41	And This Is Mine/Make-Believe Lover	5
61	Warner Bros WB 47	The Greenwood Tree/If You Don't, Somebody Else Will	4
62	Warner Bros WB 63	Why's You Wanna Make Me Cry/Just One Kiss	4
62	Warner Bros WB 73	Mr. Songwriter/I Couldn't Say No	4
64	Warner Bros WB 128	They're Jealous Of Me/A Girl Never Knows	4
60	Warner Bros WEP 6007	CONNIE STEVENS AS CRICKET (EP, also stereo WSEP 2007)	8/12
63	Warners WEP/ WSE 6105	CONNIE STEVENS AS CRICKET No. 2 (EP, mono/stereo)	8/12
63	Warners WEP/WSE 6112	CONNIE STEVENS AS CRICKET No. 3 (EP, mono/stereo)	8/12
62	Warner Bros WM 4061	CONNIE (LP, also stereo WS 8061)	15/20
63	Warner Bros WM/WS 8111	THE HANK WILLIAMS SONG BOOK (LP)	12

(see also Edward Byrnes)

DODIE STEVENS
59	London HLD 8834	Pink Shoe Laces/Coming Of Age	12
59	London HLD 8834	Pink Shoe Laces/Coming Of Age (78)	10
60	London HLD 9174	No/A-Tisket A-Tasket	5
61	London HLD 9280	Yes, I'm Lonesome Tonight/Too Young	7
63	London HLP 9672	Don't Send Me Roses/Daddy Couldn't Get Me One Of Those	5
64	Liberty LIB 83	I Wore Out The Record/You Don't Have To Prove A Thing	4

JOHN STEVENS (AWAY)
| 76 | Vertigo 6059 140 | Annie Pts 1 & 2 | 4 |
| 76 | Vertigo 6059 154 | Can't Explain Pts 1 & 2 | 4 |

(see also Spontaneous Music Ensemble)

JOHNNY STEVENS & LES DAWSON SYNDICATE
| 50s | Melodisc M 1586 | Last Chicken In The Shop/Oh Yeah | 4 |

JOHNNY STEVENS & BLUE BEATS
| 64 | Blue Beat BB 229 | Ball And Chain/It's A Shame | 6 |

KIRK STEVENS
| 57 | Decca F 10863 | Once/This Silver Madonna | 6 |

MEIC STEVENS
70	Warner Bros	OUTLANDER (LP, with insert)	140
79	Tic Toc	CANERNON CYNNAR (LP, private press)	100
70s	Sain	LPs	10-20

(see also Gary Farr)

MIKE STEVENS (& SHEVELLS)
65	Decca F 12174	Did I Dream/I Saw A Field (solo)	4
66	Pye 7N 17243	Cathy's Clown/Go-Go Train (as Mike Stevens & Shevells)	4
68	Polydor 56269	Guaranteed To Drive You Wild/Hog-Tied (as Mike Stevens & Shevells)	4

(see also Shevells)

PAUL STEVENS
| 68 | Page One POF 080 | Sometimes You Love Me/Hey Mr. Love | 4 |

RAY STEVENS
| 58 | Capitol CL 14881 | Chickie-Chickie Wah Wah/Crying Goodbye | 6 |
| 61 | Mercury AMT 1158 | Jeremiah's Peabody's Polyunsaturated Quick Dissolving Fast Acting Pleasant Tasting Green And Purple Pills/Teen Years | 6 |

Ray STEVENS

MINT VALUE £

62	Mercury AMT 1184	Ahab The Arab/It's Been So Long	6
63	Mercury AMT 1207	Harry The Hairy Ape/Little Stone Statue	6
66	London HLU 10027	Devil May Care/Make A Few Memories	4

RICKY STEVENS

61	Columbia DB 4739	I Cried For You/I Am	4
62	Columbia DB 4778	Forever/Now, It's Over	4
63	Columbia DB 4981	My Mother's Eyes/I'll Get By	4
62	Columbia SEG 8172	I CRIED FOR YOU (EP)	30

ROY STEVENS

| 66 | London HLU 10016 | Party People/ABC | 4 |

SHAKIN' STEVENS (& SUNSETS)

70	Parlophone R 5860	Down On The Farm/Spirit Of Woodstock	30
72	Polydor 2058 213	Sweet Little Rock'n'Roller/White Lightning	22
74	Emerald MD 1176	Honey Honey/Holey Moley 2001	18
76	Mooncrest MOON 51	Jungle Rock/Girl In Red	15
77	Track 2094 134	Never/You Always Hurt The One You Love	12
77	Track 2094 136	Somebody Touched Me/Way Down Yonder In New Orleans (some in p/s)	15/8
78	Track 2094 141	Justine/Wait And See	12
78	Epic SEPC 6567	Treat Her Right/I Don't Want No Other Baby	12
79	Epic SEPC 6845	Endless Sleep/Fire	12
79	Epic SEPC 7235	Spooky/I Don't Want No Other Baby	12
80	Epic SEPC 8090	Hot Dog/Apron Strings (p/s)	15
80	Epic SEPC 8573	Hey Mae/I Guess I Was A Fool (some in p/s)	12/4
80	Epic SEPC 8725	Marie Marie/Baby If We Touch (p/s)	4
80	Epic SEPC 8778	Solid As A Rock/Generation X (p/s)	4
80	Epic SEPC 9064	Shooting Gallery/Make It Right Tonight (p/s)	12
81	Epic SEPC 9555	This Ole House/Let Me Show You How (p/s)	4
81	Battle Of The Bands BOB 2	Jungle Rock/Girl In Red (p/s, reissue, as Shakin' Stevens & Sunsets)	6
81	Mint CHEW 51	No Other Baby/Manhattan Melodrama (p/s)	4
81	Epic A 1643	It's Raining/You And I Were Meant To Be (picture disc)	7
81	Solid Gold SGR 107	Shaky Sings Elvis Pts 1 & 2 (medley) (p/s)	10
82	Epic EPCA 1742	Oh Julie/I'm Knocking (poster p/s)	5
82	Epic EPCA 40-2620	GREATEST ORIGINAL HITS (cassette EP)	6
82	Epic EPCA 2656	Give Me Your Heart Tonight/Thinkin' Of You (p/s, with poster)	5
82	Epic EPCA 2656	Give Me Your Heart Tonight/Thinkin' Of You (picture disc)	5
82	Everest/Premier RAY 1	Tiger/Give Me A Break (p/s)	7
82	Everest/Premier EV 10000	Tiger/Sweet Little Sixteen/Give Me A Break (picture disc)	7
83	Epic A 3565	It's Late/It's Good For You Baby (p/s)	4
83	Epic WA 3565	It's Late/It's Good For You Baby (feet-shaped picture disc)	10
83	Epic WA 3774	Cry Just A Little Bit/Love Me Tonight (picture disc)	7
83	Kelloggs KELL 1	Oh Julie/ABBA: I Have A Dream (free with Kelloggs 'Rice Krispies')	10
84	Epic A 4291	A Love Waiting For You/As Long As I Have You (live) (poster p/s)	10
84	Epic QA 4677	A Letter To You/Come Back And Love Me (p/s, with free post bag game)	5
84	Epic DA 4882	Teardrops/You Shake Me Up//Shakin' Stevens Party Mix Pts 1 & 2 (double pack)	10
85	Epic GA 6072	Breakin' Up My Heart/I'll Give You My Heart (gatefold pop-up p/s)	5
85	Epic TA 6072	Breakin' Up My Heart/I'll Give You My Heart (12", p/s)	7
85	Epic GTA 6769	Merry Christmas Everyone/With My Heart (12", advent calendar p/s)	7
86	Epic QA 6819	Turning Away/Diddle (poster p/s)	5
86	Epic SHAKY 2	Because I Love You/Tell Me One More Time (2 picture sleeves, sealed together on edge with sticker, with autograph)	8
86	Epic SHAKY G2	Because I Love You/Tell Me One More Time (gatefold p/s)	6
86	Epic GA 6769	Merry Christmas Everyone/Blue Christmas (reissue, gatefold p/s)	6
87	Epic SHAKY C3	A Little Boogie Woogie (In The Back Of My Mind)/If You're Gonna Cry (cassette)	4
87	Epic SHAKY Q4	Come See About Me/Boppity Bop (12", p/s, with patch, sealed)	7
87	Epic SHAKY 5	What Do You Want To Make Those Eyes At Me For/You're Evil (p/s, with competition entry form)	4
87	Epic SHAKY P5	What Do You Want To Make Those Eyes At Me For/You're Evil (picture disc)	5
87	Epic SHAKY G5	What Do You Want To Make Those Eyes At Me For/You're Evil + 2 (gatefold p/s)	5
88	Epic SHAKY Q6	Feel The Need In Me/If I Can't Have You (poster p/s)	4
88	Epic SHAKY 7	How Many Tears Can You Hide/If I Really Knew (p/s, with poster)	4
88	Epic SHAKY Q7	How Many Tears Can You Hide/If I Really Knew (p/s, shrinkwrapped with badge)	8
88	Epic SHAKY Q8	True Love/Come On Little Girl (poster p/s)	4
89	Epic SHAKY Q9	Jezebel/As Long As I Have You (p/s, with competition entry form)	4
89	Epic SHAKY P9	Jezebel/As Long As I Have You (poster p/s)	4
89	Epic SHAKY M10	Love Attack/As Long As I Have You (cassette)	4
81	Magnum Force MFEP 001	Memphis Earthquake/You Mostest Girl/Evil Hearted Ada/My Bucket's Got A Hole In It (EP, p/s)	7
82	Magnum Force MFEP 007	Frantic/Ready Teddy/Tear It Up/Monkey's Uncle (EP, p/s)	7
83	Magnum Force MFEP 010	Justine/Jungle Rock/Story Of The Rockers/My Baby Died (EP, p/s)	7
83	Epic 40-2620	GREATEST ORIGINAL HITS (cassette EP)	10
70	Parlophone PCS 7112	A LEGEND (LP)	40
71	CBS 52901	I'M NO J.D. (LP)	35
72	Contour 2870 152	ROCKIN' AND SHAKIN' (LP)	15
73	Emerald GES 1121	SHAKIN' STEVENS AND THE SUNSETS (LP)	12
78	Track 2406 011	SHAKIN' STEVENS (LP)	15
80	Epic EPC 83978	TAKE ONE (LP)	10
80	Epic EPC 84547	MARIE MARIE (LP, withdrawn)	15
81	Epic EPC 10027	SHAKY (LP, feet-shaped picture disc)	10
83	Epic BX 86301	THE BOP WON'T STOP (LP & cassette, box set, with Shaky autograph book)	18
85	CJS CJS 1	MANHATTAN MELODRAMA (LP)	10

SHAKIN' STEVENS & BONNIE TYLER

83	Epic WA 4071	A Rockin' Good Way/Why Do You Treat Me This Way (picture disc)	5

(see also Bonnie Tyler)

TERRI STEVENS

59	Felsted AF 112	My Wish Tonight/All Alone	5
59	Felsted AF 112	My Wish Tonight/All Alone (78)	5
59	Felsted AF 126	Adonis/Vieni, Vieni	4
59	Felsted AF 126	Adonis/Vieni, Vieni (78)	15

(Dave) STEWART & HARRISON

70	Multicord MULT SH 1	GIRL (EP)	15

(see also Longdancer, Tourists, Eurythmics)

AL STEWART

66	Decca F 12467	The Elf/Turn To Earth	70
67	CBS 3034	Bedsitter Images/Swiss Cottage Manoeuvres	5
70	CBS 4843	Electric Los Angeles Sunset/My Enemies Have Sweet Voices	4
71	CBS 5351	The News From Spain/Elvaston Place	4
72	CBS 7763	You Don't Even Know Me/I'm Falling	4
72	CBS 7992	Amsterdam/Songs Out Of Clay	4
67	CBS (S)BPG 63087	BEDSITTER IMAGES (LP)	60
69	CBS (S) 63460	LOVE CHRONICLES (LP, gatefold sleeve)	15
70	CBS 63848	ZERO SHE FLIES (LP, gatefold sleeve)	15
70	CBS 64023	FIRST ALBUM (BEDSITTER IMAGES) (LP, remixed reissue, different track selection)	15
72	CBS 64739	ORANGE (LP)	10
73	CBS 65726	PAST PRESENT AND FUTURE (LP)	10
75	CBS 80477	MODERN TIMES (LP)	10

(see also Jimmy Page)

AMII STEWART

79	Atlantic K 11278	Light My Fire/Bring It On Back To Me (picture disc)	4
85	Sedition EDITP 3307	You Really Touch My Heart Pts 1 & 2 (with free single)	4
86	Sedition EDITP 3310	My Guy, My Girl/Bring It On Back To Me (shaped picture disc)	4

ANDY STEWART

60	Top Rank JAR 427	Donald, Where's Your Troosers?/Dancing In The Kyle	6
60	Top Rank JAR 512	A Scottish Soldier/The Muckin' O' Geordie's Brye	4

BILLY STEWART

62	Pye Intl. 7N 25164	Reap What You Sow/Fat Boy	7
63	Pye Intl. 7N 25222	Strange Feeling/Sugar And Spice	6
65	Chess CRS 8009	I Do Love You/Keep Loving	8
65	Chess CRS 8017	Sitting In The Park/Once Again	8
66	Chess CRS 8028	Because I Love You/Mountains Of Love	12
66	Chess CRS 8038	Love Me/Why Am I Lonely	7
66	Chess CRS 8040	Summertime/To Love To Love	6
66	Chess CRS 8045	Secret Love/Look Back And Smile	8
66	Chess CRS 8050	Ole Man River/Every Day I Have The Blues	6
67	Chess CRS 8067	Cross My Heart/Why (Do I Love You So)	5
69	Chess CRS 8092	Summertime/I Do Love You	4
66	Chess CRE 6010	IN CROWD (EP)	15
67	Chess CRE 6024	I DO LOVE YOU (EP)	10
66	Chess CRL 4523	UNBELIEVABLE (LP)	15

BOB STEWART

55	MGM SP 1114	It's A Woman's World/I Went Out Of My Way	4

BOB STEWART

70s	Broadside	UP LIKE THE SWALLOWS (LP)	10

DELANO STEWART

68	Doctor Bird DB 1138	That's Life/Tell Me Baby	10
68	High Note HS 004	Let's Have Some Fun/Dance With Me	8
69	High Note HS 014	Rocking Sensation/GAYTONES: One Look	7
69	High Note HS 027	Got To Come Back/Don't Believe Him	6
69	High Note HS 034	Hallelujah/I Wish It Could Last	4
70	High Hote HS 039	Wherever I Lay My Hat/Don't Believe Him (B-side actually by Gladstone Anderson & Gaytones)	4
70	High Note HS 041	Stay A Little Bit Longer/Stay A Little Bit Longer (Version II) (B-side actually by Gladstone Anderson & Gaytones)	4
70	Trojan TBL 138	STAY A LITTLE BIT LONGER (LP)	12

(see also Winston Stewart, Gaylads)

JAMES STEWART

65	Brunswick 05938	The Legend Of Shenandoah/CHARLES 'BUD' DANT CHORUS: We're Ridin' Out Tonight	5

JAMES STEWART & HENRY FONDA

70	Stateside SS 2179	Rolling Stone/Theme From Cheyenne Social Club	4

JOHN STEWART

69	Capitol E-(S)T 203	CALIFORNIA BLOODLINES (LP)	10

PAUL STEWART (MOVEMENT)

66	Philips BF 1513	Queen Boadicea/Talkin'	4
67	Decca F 12577	Saturday Morning Man/Too Too Good (as Paul Stewart Movement)	4

(see also Hamilton & [Hamilton] Movement)

ROD STEWART (& FACES)

64	Decca F 11996	Good Morning Little Schoolgirl/I'm Gonna Move To The Outskirts Of Town	40
65	Columbia DB 7766	The Day Will Come/Why Does It Go On?	30

Rod STEWART

66	Columbia DB 7892	Shake/I Just Got Some 30
67	Immediate IM 060	Little Miss Understood/So Much To Say 30
70	Vertigo 6086 002	It's All Over Now/Jo's Lament 7
70s	Mercury BRAUN 3	MAGGIE MAY (EP, freebie) 6
74	Warner Bros K 16494	You Can Make Me Dance, Sing Or Anything/As Long As You Tell Him (as Rod Stewart & Faces, p/s) 5
76	Mercury 6160 007	Mandolin Wind/Girl From The North Country/Sweet Little Rock'N'Roller 4
76	Mercury 6167 327	It's All Over Now/Handbags And Gladrags 4
77	Riva RIVA 3	Tonight's The Night/The First Cut Is The Deepest (withdrawn B-side) 10
77	Riva RIVA 9	Sailing/Stone Cold Sober (HMS Ark Royal Commemorative issue, blue vinyl, p/s, 3,000 only) 15
79	Mercury 6160 006	Maggie May/You Wear It Well/Twistin' The Night Away (p/s) 5
80	Virgin VS 366	Little Miss Understood/So Much To Say (reissue) 4
81	Riva RIVA 29M	Oh God I Wish I Was Home Tonight/Somebody Special (cassette) 4
82	Riva RIVA 35	How Long/Jealous (p/s, with free sticker) 4
82	Decca F 11996	Good Morning Little Schoolgirl/I'm Gonna Move To The Outskirts Of Town (reissue) 5
82	Immediate IM 060	Little Miss Understood/So Much To Say (reissue, p/s) 4
83	Warner Bros W 9440P	Sweet Surrender/Ghetto Blaster (picture disc) 4
83	Warner Bros W 9440TP	Sweet Surrender/Ghetto Blaster (12", picture disc) 7
86	Warner Bros W 8668TP	Love Touch/Heart Is On The Line/Hard Lesson To Learn (12", picture disc) ..7
86	Warner Bros W 8625TE	Every Beat Of My Heart (Tartan Mix)/Trouble/Some Guys Have All The Luck (Live from Wembley Stadium 5.7.86) (12", p/s, with poster) 7
86	Warner Bros WX 8652 TP	Every Beat Of My Heart/Lost In You/Almost Illegal/Baby Jane (12", picture disc) ..7
88	Warner Bros WX 152TP	Lost In You (extended)/Almost Illegal (12", picture disc) 7
79	Riva	Excerpts from "Foolish Behaviour" (flexidisc) 4
69	Vertigo VO 4	AN OLD RAINCOAT WON'T EVER LET YOU DOWN (LP, gatefold sleeve, spiral label) 10
70	Vertigo 6360 500	GASOLINE ALLEY (LP, gatefold sleeve, spiral label) 10
75	Riva RVLP 4	ATLANTIC CROSSING (LP, gatefold sleeve, blue or orange vinyl) 15/10
78	Riva RVLP 8	BLONDES HAVE MORE FUN (LP, picture disc) 10
78	St. Michael 21020 102	REASON TO BELIEVE (LP, only available in Marks & Spencer) 20
84	Warner Bros 9250 951	CAMOUFLAGE (LP, with free 1-sided picture disc "Infatuation" in wallet with interview tape [SAM 194]) 20

(see also Jeff Beck, Shotgun Express, Faces, Python Lee Jackson, Long John Baldry)

SANDY STEWART
58	London HLE 8683	A Certain Smile/Kiss Me Richard 12
63	Pye Intl. 7N 25176	My Colouring Book/I Heard You Cried Last Night 5

SONNY STEWART & HIS SKIFFLE KINGS
57	Philips PB 719	The Northern Line/Black Jack (78) 7
57	Philips PB 773	Let Me Lie/Mama Don't Allow It (78) 5

TINGA STEWART
74	Dragon DRA 1025	The Message/Dub 4

WINSTON STEWART
64	R&B JB 147	But I Do/MAYTALS: Four Seasons 10
64	Port-O-Jam PJ 4002	All Of My Life/How Many Times 10

(see also Delano Stewart, Winston & Bobby, Winston & Tonettes)

WYNN STEWART
60	London HL 7087	Wishful Thinking/Uncle Tom Got Caught 25

COOL STICKY
68	Amalgamated AMG 825	Train To Soulsville/ERIC MONTY MORRIS: Cinderella 8

ARBEE STIDHAM
70s	Mainstream MSL 1011	A TIME FOR BLUES (LP) 12

STIFF LITTLE FINGERS
78	Rigid Digits SRD-1	Suspect Device/Wasted Life (500 only, hand-made p/s, red label with catalogue number on right-hand side) 15
78	Rigid Digits SRD-1	Suspect Device/Wasted Life (re-pressing, machine-cut p/s, with various colour labels/yellow labels) 6/10
78	Rough Trade RT 004	78 R.P.M./Alternative Ulster (p/s, A & B-sides reversed) 8
78	Rough Trade RT 004	Alternative Ulster/78 R.P.M. (p/s) 5
78	Rough Trade RT 006	Suspect Device/Wasted Life (reissue) 5
79	Rough Trade RT 015	Gotta Getaway/Bloody Sunday (p/s) 5
82	Chrysalis CHSDJ 2580	Listen/Two Guitars Clash (p/s, jukebox issue) 8
82	Melody Maker/Chrysalis	Excerpts From "Now Then"/IGGY POP: Zombie Birdhouse (flexidisc, free with 'Melody Maker') 5/4
87	Strange Fruit SFPSC 004	THE PEEL SESSION (EP, cassette) 5
89	Limited Edition LTD EDT 3LP	LIVE IN SWEDEN (LP, green vinyl) 10
92	Essential! EPDLP 171	FLAGS AND EMBLEMS (LP, picture disc) 10

STILL LIFE
68	Columbia DB 8345	What Did We Miss/My Kingdom Cannot Lose 25
71	Vertigo 6360 026	STILL LIFE (LP, gatefold sleeve, spiral label) 70

STEPHEN STILLS
70	Atlantic 2401 004	STEPHEN STILLS (LP) 10
71	Atlantic 2401 013	STEPHEN STILLS 2 (LP) 10

(see also Buffalo Springfield, Manassas, Crosby Stills & Nash, Al Kooper, Mike Bloomfield, Stills-Young Band)

STILLS-YOUNG BAND
76	Reprise K 14446	Long May You Run/12-8 Blues 4
76	Reprise K 54081	LONG MAY YOU RUN (LP) 10

(see also Stephen Stills, Manassas, Neil Young, Buffalo Springfield, Crosby Stills Nash & Young)

STING

82	A&M PARTY 1	Need Your Love So Bad (promo-only, no p/s)	6
82	A&M PARTY 2	Tutti Frutti (promo-only, no p/s)	6
85	A&M AMY 272	Love Is The Seventh Wave/Consider Me Gone (live) (12", p/s, with poster)	8
87	A&M AMCD 410	We'll Be Together (Extended Mix)/We'll Be Together/Conversation With A Dog/We'll Be Together (Instrumental) (3" CD, in box)	7
87	A&M AMCD 431	Englishman In New York/Ghost In The Strand (Instrumental)/Bring On The Night — When The World Is Running Down (live) (CD)	7
88	A&M AM 439	Fragile/Fragile (Portuguese Version) (p/s, with poster)	6
88	A&M AMCD 439	Fragile/Fragile (Portuguese Version)/Fragilidad/Mariposa Libre (CD)	7
88	A&M AMX 458	They Dance Alone/Ellas Damzon Solas/St. Estamos Juntos (10", promo, p/s)	10
88	A&M AMCDR 580	Englishman In New York/Englishman In New York (Ben Liebrand Mix)/If You Love Somebody Set Them Free (Jellybean Dance Mix) (CD, picture disc)	7
91	A&M AMCD 713	All This Time/I Miss You Kate (Instrumental)/King Of Pain (live) (CD, with 12" print)	7
85	A&M DREAMP 1	THE DREAM OF THE BLUE TURTLES (LP, picture disc)	12
91	A&M 397 171-2	ACOUSTIC LIVE IN NEWCASTLE (CD, box set with book)	30

(see also Police, Last Exit, [Fast Breeder &] Radio Actors, Newcastle Big Band)

STINGERS

72	Upsetter US 395	Preacher Man/UPSETTERS: Version	6

STINGRAY (TV series)

(see under Century 21)

STING-RAYS

83	Big Beat SW 82	Dinosaurs/Math Of Trend/Another Cup Of Coffee/ You're Gonna Miss Me (p/s)	6
84	Big Beat NS 95	Escalator/Loose Lip Synch Ship/Escalator (Instrumental) (p/s)	5
85	Big Beat NS 109	Don't Break Down/Don't Break Down (Version) (p/s)	4
85	Big Beat NST 109	Don't Break Down/Don't Break Down (Version) (12", p/s)	7
85	Media Burn MB 2/ Lyntone LYN 16436	Bonus Track/I Want My Woman/Flash On You (33 rpm, red vinyl flexidisc with 'The Sting-Rays Story' magazine)	5
86	ABC ABCS 009T	June Rhyme/Militant Tendency/Wedding Ring (12", p/s)	7
86	Kaleidoscope Sound KS 702	BEHIND THE BEYOND (EP)	5
86	Kaleidoscope Sound KS 102	BEHIND THE BEYOND (12" EP)	7

STINKY TOYS

77	Polydor 2056 630	Boozy Creed/Driver Blues (p/s)	4
77	Polydor 2393 174	STINKY TOYS (LP)	12

(PETER) LEE STIRLING (& BRUISERS)

63	Columbia DB 4992	My Heart Commands Me/Welcome Stranger (as Lee Stirling & Bruisers)	4
63	Parlophone R 5063	I Could If I Wanted To/Right From The Start (as Lee Stirling & Bruisers)	4
64	Parlophone R 5112	Now That I've Found You/I Believe (as Peter Lee Stirling & Bruisers)	4
64	Parlophone R 5158	Sad, Lonely And Blue/I'm Looking For Someone To Love (as Peter Lee Stirling & Bruisers)	4
64	Parlophone R 5198	Everything Will Be Alright/You'll Be Mine (as Peter Lee Stirling & Bruisers)	4
66	Decca F 12433	The Sweet And Tender Hold Of Your Love/Everybody Needs A Someone	4
66	Decca F 12535	Oh What A Fool/I'm Sportin' A New Baby	4
67	Decca F 12628	You Don't Live Twice/8.35 On The Dot	6
67	Decca F 12674	Goodbye Thimblemill Lane/Hey Conductor	4
69	MCA MU 1093	Big Sam/Mr. Average Man	4

(see also Bruisers)

STITCHED-BACK FOOT AIRMAN

87	Very Mouth EAT 10	Wouldn't You Like To Know/Sinking Ship/Neverbend Manchester/ Some People (p/s)	4
86	Very Mouth EAT 9	SEVEN EGG-TIMING GREATS (mini-LP with insert)	8

GARY STITES

59	London HLL 8881	Lonely For You/Shine That Ring	12
59	London HLL 8881	Lonely For You/Shine That Ring (78)	20
59	London HLL 9003	Starry Eyed/Without Your Love	8
59	London HLL 9003	Starry Eyed/Without Your Love (78)	20
60	London HLL 9082	Lawdy, Miss Clawdy/Don't Wanna Say Goodbye	12

KING STITT

66	Clandisc CLA 200	Who Yea/DYNAMITES: Mr. Midnight	5
66	Clandisc CLA 202	Vigerton Two/On The Street	5
66	Clandisc CLA 203	On The Street/CYNTHIA RICHARDS: Foolish Fool	5
66	Clandisc CLA 206	The Ugly One/CLANCY ECCLES: Dance Beat	5
66	Clandisc CLA 207	Herbsman Shuffle (with Andy [Capp])/(Joe) HIGGS & (Ron) WILSON: Don't Mind Me	5
70	Clandisc CLA 223	King Of Kings/DYNAMITES: Reggaedelic	5
71	Banana BA 332	Back Out Version/VEGETABLES: Holly Rhythm	6
71	Banana BA 334	Rhyming Time/Reality	6

SONNY STITT

53	Esquire 20-013	SONNY STITT-BUD POWELL QUARTET (10" LP)	15
58	Esquire 32-049	S.P.J. JAZZ (LP, with Bud Powell & J.J. Johnson)	12
58	Columbia Clef 33CX 10114	NEW YORK JAZZ (LP)	12
59	Esquire 32-078	STITT'S BITS (LP)	12
59	HMV CLP 1280	ONLY THE BLUES (LP)	10
60	HMV CLP 1363	PERSONAL APPEARANCE (LP)	10
60	HMV CLP 1384	SONNY STITT WITH THE OSCAR PETERSON TRIO (LP)	10
61	HMV CLP 1420/CSD 1341	BLOWS THE BLUES (LP, mono/stereo)	10/12

(see also Oscar Peterson)

ALAN STIVELL
74	Philips 6325 304	FROM CELTIC ROOTS (LP)	12

STOCKER, GREENWOOD & FRIENDS
79	Changes	BILL + NINE (LP)	50

STOCKING TOPS
68	Toast TT 500	You're Never Gonna Get My Lovin'/You Don't Know What Love Is All About	4

STOICS
68	RCA RCA 1745	Earth, Fire, Air And Water/Search Of The Sea	4

STOKES
65	London HLU 9955	Whipped Cream/Pie Crust	6

RHET STOLLER (& HIS ECHOES)
60	Decca F 11271	Walk Don't Run/All Rhet	10
60	Decca F 11302	Chariot/Night Theme	8
63	Decca F 11738	Countdown/Over The Steppes (as Rhet Stoller & His Echoes)	8
64	Melodisc MEL 1595	Beat That/Treble Gold + One	12
64	Windsor PS 118	Bandit/Tonight (unissued)	
64	Windsor PS 119	Caravan/Short Cut	12
64	Windsor PS 130	Ricochet/Knockout	12
66	Columbia DB 8013	Uncrowned King/Surf Ride (unissued, demos only)	20
60s	Mosaic MOSAIC 1	SUNSHINE ANYTIME (EP)	7

JACKIE STOLLINGS
60s	Starlite ST45 092	Footsteps Of A Fool/And Then I Knew	4

MORRIS STOLOFF & COLUMBIA PICTURES ORCHESTRA
56	Brunswick 05553	Theme From "Picnic"/Moonglow	6
56	Brunswick 05597	Theme From "The Solid Gold Cadillac"/Sweet Sue Just You	4
57	Brunswick 05666	Theme From "Fire Down Below"/Theme From "Full Of Life"	4

STOMPERS
62	Fontana H 385	Quarter To Four Stomp/Foolish One	8

CLIFFIE STONE & HIS ORCHESTRA
55	Capitol CL 14330	Barracuda/The Popcorn Song (with Billy Strange & Speedy West)	50
55	Capitol CL 14330	Barracuda/The Popcorn Song (with Billy Strange & Speedy West) (78)	15
56	Capitol CL 14666	Jingle Bells/Rudolph The Red Nosed Reindeer	4
58	Capitol CL 14928	Near You/Nobody's Darlin' But Mine	5
59	Capitol CL 14982	Maybe/I Don't Want To Walk Without You	4
59	Capitol CL 14996	Blood On The Saddle/Cool Water	5
59	Capitol T 1080	THE PARTY'S ON ME (LP)	10

(see also Billy Strange)

ELLA STONE & MOSS
70s	Phoenix SNIX 128	The Prophet/Now Or Never	6

(see also Helen Shapiro, Al Saxon)

GEORGE STONE
65	Stateside SS 479	Hole In The Wall/My Beat	7

KIRBY STONE QUARTET/FOUR
56	Vogue Coral Q 72129	Honey Hush/Lassus Trombone	10
56	Vogue Coral Q 72129	Honey Hush/Lassus Trombone (78)	7
59	Philips PB 903	That "I Had A Dream, Dear" Rock/Sweet Nothings	4
63	Warner Bros WB 102	The Great Escape (March)/Fancy Dan	4
63	Warner Bros WB 118	Washington Guitar/Blue Guitar	4
56	Vogue Coral Q 72129	Honey Hush/Lassus Trombone	4
59	London HA-A 2164	MAN, I FLIPPED WHEN I HEARD THE KIRBY STONE FOUR (LP)	10

MARK STONE
58	London HLR 8543	Ever Since I Met Lucy/The Stroll	75
58	London HLR 8543	Ever Since I Met Lucy/The Stroll (78)	20

SLY (& FAMILY) STONE
68	Columbia DB 8369	Dance To The Music/Let Me Hear It From You	25
68	Direction 58-3568	Dance To The Music/Let Me Hear It From You (reissue)	4
68	Direction 58-3707	M'Lady/Life	4
69	Direction 58-3938	Everyday People/Sing A Simple Song	4
69	Direction 58-4279	Stand/I Want To Take You Higher	4
69	Direction 58-4471	Hot Fun In The Summertime/Fun	4
70	Direction 58-4782	Thank You (For Lettin Me Be Myself Again)/Everybody Is A Star	4
70	CBS 5054	I Want To Take You Higher/You Can Make It If You Try	4
71	Epic EPC 7632	Family Affair/Luv n' Haight	4
72	Epic EPC 7810	Running Away/Brave And Strong	4
73	Epic EPC 1148	Family Affair/Dance To The Music (p/s)	5
74	Epic EPC 2530	Time For Livin'/Small Talk (as Sly Stone)	4
75	Epic EPC 2882	Loose Booty/Can't Strain My Brain (as Sly Stone)	4
68	Direction 8-63412	DANCE TO THE MUSIC (LP)	18
68	Direction 8-63461	M'LADY (LP)	18
69	Direction 8-63655	STAND! (LP, CBS sleeve with Direction label)	18
70	Epic EPC 69002	GREATEST HITS (LP, gatefold sleeve)	10
71	Epic EPC 64613	THERE'S A RIOT GOING ON (LP, gatefold sleeve, with free EP/newspaper)	15
73	CBS Q 69002	GREATEST HITS (LP, quadrophonic, gatefold sleeve)	15
73	Epic EPC 69039	FRESH (LP, gatefold sleeve)	10
74	Epic EPC 69070	SMALL TALK (LP)	10
75	Epic EPC 22004	HIGH ENERGY (2-LP, gatefold sleeve)	20
75	Epic EPC 69165	HIGH ON YOU (LP, as Sly Stone)	10
76	Epic EPC 81641	HEARD YA MISSED ME, WELL I'M BACK (LP)	10

(see also Rosie Banks)

STONE ANGEL
75	SSLP 04	STONE ANGEL (LP, private pressing)	200

(see also Ken Saul)

STONED AID
80s	Hit STONE 1	Are You Going To Stonehenge/Magical Carpet Ride (p/s)	5

(see also Cannibals)

STONEFIELD TRAMP
74	Acorn/Tramp CF 247	DREAMING AGAIN (LP, private pressing)	150

(see also Terry Friend, Rob Van Spyk)

STONEGROUND
71	Warner Bros K 16126	You Must Be One Of Us/It Takes A Lot To Laugh	4
71	Warner Bros K 46087	STONEGROUND (LP)	10
71	Warner Bros K 53999	FAMILY ALBUM (LP)	10

STONEGROUND BAND
70s	Nut	SUNSTRUCK!! (LP, stickered sleeve)	30

STONEHENGE MEN
62	HMV POP 981	Big Feet/Pinto	25

STONEHOUSE
71	RCA SF 8197	STONEHOUSE CREEK (LP)	90

STONEPILLOW
69	Decca PFS 4163	ELEAZAR'S CIRCUS (LP)	10

STONE PONEYS
67	Capitol CL 15523	A Different Drum/I've Got To Know	7

(see also Linda Ronstadt)

STONE ROSES
85	Thin Line THIN 001	So Young/Tell Me (12", p/s, 1,200 only; beware of counterfeits!)	40
87	Black/Revolver 12 REV 36	Sally Cinnamon/Here It Comes/All Across The Sand (12", with 'Printed In England' on rear p/s & no bar code; later reissued with different mixes)	15
88	Silvertone ORE 1	Elephant Stone/The Hardest Thing In The World (catalogue number in black print on rear of p/s; later reissued with red print)	6
88	Silvertone ORE 1T	Elephant Stone (12" Mix)/Elephant Stone (7" Mix)/The Hardest Thing In The World/Full Fathom Five (12", catalogue number in black print on rear of p/s; later reissued with red print)	10
89	Silvertone ORE 2	Made Of Stone/Going Down (p/s, catalogue number in black print on rear of p/s; later reissued with blue print)	4
89	Silvertone ORE 2T	Made Of Stone/Going Down/Guernica (12", p/s, catalogue number in black print on rear of p/s; later reissued with blue print)	7
89	Silvertone OREX 6	She Bangs The Drums (Remix)/Standing Here (p/s, 1st 3,000 with postcard)	4
89	Silvertone OREZ 6	She Bangs The Drums (Remix)/Mersey Paradise/Standing Here (12", p/s, with colour print, 5,000 only)	7
89	Silvertone ORE 13	What The World Is Waiting For/Fools Gold 4.15 (p/s, with postcard & sticker, paper label)	4
89	Silvertone ORET 13	What The World Is Waiting For/Fools Gold 9.23 (12", p/s, with print & sticker)	7

STONE'S MASONRY
66	Purdah 45-3504	Flapjacks/Hot Rock	70

(see also Action, Mighty Baby, Savoy Brown)

STONE THE CROWS
70	Polydor 2425 017	STONE THE CROWS (LP)	15
70	Polydor 2425 042	ODE TO JOHN LAW (LP)	15
71	Polydor 2425 701	TEENAGE LICKS (LP)	15
72	Polydor 2391 043	CONTINUOUS PERFORMANCE (LP)	12

(see also White Trash)

STONEY & MEATLOAF
71	Rare Earth RES 103	The Way You Do The Things You Do/What You See Is What You Get	8
71	Rare Earth SRE 3005	STONEY AND MEATLOAF (LP)	15

(see also Meatloaf)

STOOGES
69	Elektra EKS 74051	THE STOOGES (LP, red label)	35
70	Elektra EKS 74071	FUN HOUSE (LP, red label)	30
70	Elektra 2410 009	FUN HOUSE (LP, reissue, 'butterfly' label)	12
73	CBS 65586	RAW POWER (LP, initially with inner sleeve)	15/10

(see also Iggy Pop)

STOREY SISTERS
58	London HLU 8571	Bad Motorcycle/Sweet Daddy	50
58	London HLU 8571	Bad Motorcycle/Sweet Daddy (78)	8

STORM BUGS
70s	Storm Bugs	STORM BUGS (EP, white label, foldout insert, plain white sleeve)	5

STORMER
78	Ring O' 2017 113	My Home Town/Shake It Baby (p/s)	4

STORMTROOPER
78	Solent SS 047	I'm A Mess/It's Not Me (stamped plain sleeve with insert)	8
80	Heartbeat BEAT 1	Pride Before A Fall/Still Comin' Home (p/s)	5

BILLY STORM
59	Philips PB 916	I've Come Of Age/This Is Always	4
60	London HLK 9236	Sure As You're Born/In The Chapel In The Moonlight	8

MINT VALUE £

DANNY STORM (& STROLLERS)

62	Piccadilly 7N 35025	Honest I Do/Sad But True (some in p/s)	8/4
62	Piccadilly 7N 35053	Just You/I Told You So	8
62	Piccadilly 7N 35091	I Just Can't Fool My Heart/Thinking Of You	10
63	Piccadilly 7N 35143	Say You Do/Let The Sunshine In (as Danny Storm & Strollers)	10

GALE STORM

56	London HLD 8222	I Hear You Knocking/Never Leave Me	30
56	London HLD 8222	I Hear You Knocking/Never Leave Me (78)	5
56	London HLD 8232	Memories Are Made Of This/A Teen-Age Prayer	25
56	London HLD 8232	Memories Are Made Of This/A Teen-Age Prayer (78)	5
56	London HLD 8283	Ivory Tower/I Ain't Gonna Worry	30
56	London HLD 8283	Ivory Tower/I Ain't Gonna Worry (78)	5
56	London HLD 8286	Why Do Fools Fall In Love/I Walk Alone	25
56	London HLD 8286	Why Do Fools Fall In Love/I Walk Alone (78)	5
56	London HL 7008	Why Do Fools Fall In Love/I Walk Alone (export issue)	10
56	London HLD 8311	Don't Be That Way (Please Listen To Me)/Tell Me Why	25
56	London HLD 8311	Don't Be That Way (Please Listen To Me)/Tell Me Why (78)	5
56	London HLD 8329	A Heart Without A Sweetheart/Now Is The Hour	20
56	London HLD 8329	A Heart Without A Sweetheart/Now Is The Hour (78)	5
57	London HLD 8393	Lucky Lips/On Treasure Island	25
57	London HLD 8393	Lucky Lips/On Treasure Island (78)	5
57	London HLD 8413	Orange Blossoms/My Heart Belongs To You	15
57	London HLD 8413	Orange Blossoms/My Heart Belongs To You (78)	5
57	London HLD 8424	Dark Moon/A Little Too Late	12
58	London HLD 8570	Love Theme From "Farewell To Arms"/I Get That Feeling	12
58	London HLD 8632	You/Angry	10
56	London HB-D 1056	PRESENTING GALE STORM (10" LP)	30
58	London HA-D 2104	SENTIMENTAL ME (LP)	25

RORY STORM & HURRICANES

| 63 | Oriole CB 1858 | Dr. Feelgood/I Can Tell | 25 |
| 64 | Parlophone R 5197 | America/Since You Broke My Heart | 15 |

(see also Keef Hartley, Paddy Klaus & Gibson)

ROBB STORME (& WHISPERS)

60	Decca F 11282	1000, 900 And When/I Don't Need Your Love Anymore	5
61	Decca F 11313	Music/Five Minutes More (as Robb Storme & Whispers)	4
61	Decca F 11364	Near You/Lonely Town (as Robb Storme & Whispers)	4
61	Decca F 11388	Transistor Sister/Earth Angel	4
62	Decca F 11432	Pretty Hair And Angel Eyes/A Mile Of Broken Hearts	4
63	Pye 7N 15515	Sixteen Years Ago Tonight/Surprise Surprise	4
63	Piccadilly 7N 35133	Happens Ev'ryday/Surprise Surprise	4
63	Piccadilly 7N 35160	Bu Bop A Lu Bop A Lie/To Know Her Is To Love Her	4
65	Pye 7N 15819	Love Is Strange/Shy Guy	4
65	Columbia DB 7756	Where Is My Girl?/Double Oh Seven (as Robb Storme & Whispers)	6
66	Columbia DB 7993	Here Today/Don't Cry (as Robb Storme Group)	62
62	Decca DFE 6700	WHEELS (EP)	30

STORYTELLER

71	CBS 7182	Remarkable/Laugh That Came Too Soon	5
70	Transatlantic TRA 220	STORYTELLER (LP)	25
71	Transatlantic TRA 232	MORE PAGES (LP)	18

(see also Johnny Neal & Starliners)

WALLY STOTT ORCHESTRA

58	Philips BBE 12225	BEST WISHES FOR CHRISTMAS (EP)	7
54	Philips BBR 8004	EMBRACEABLE YOU (10" LP)	10
54	Philips BBR 8015	A MERRY CHRISTMAS (10" LP)	10
55	Philips BBR 8053	WALLY STOTT AND HIS ORCHESTRA (10" LP)	10

BABE STOVALL

| 76 | Southern Sound SD 203 | THE BABE STOVALL STORY (LP) | 12 |

STRAIGHT EIGHT

| 80 | Logo LOGO 1032 | STRAIGHT TO THE HEART (LP) | 10 |

STRAIGHT UP

| 80 | Rok XX/XIX | One Out All Out/JUSTIN CASE: T.V. (die-cut company sleeve) | 5 |

STRAITJACKET FITS

| 90 | Rough Trade G5SFI | Hail/GALAXIE 500: Blue Thunder/Victory Garden (promo-only, stickered sleeve) | 8 |

EMILLE STRAKER & HIS MERRYMEN

(see under Merrymen)

PETER STRAKER

| 69 | Polydor BM 56345 | Breakfast In Bed/The Right To Cry | 4 |
| 69 | Polydor BM 56362 | I Never Thought I'd Fall In Love/Birdie Told Me | 4 |

BILLY STRANGE (& CHALLENGERS)

61	London HLG 9321	Where Your Arms Used To Be/Sadness Done Come	5
64	Vocalion V-N 9228	The James Bond Theme/007 Theme	5
64	Vocalion V-N 9231	Goldfinger/"Munsters" Theme	5
66	Vocalion V-N 9257	Thunderball/"Ninth Man" Theme	5
66	Vocalion V-N 9259	Get Smart/Run Spy, Run	4
67	Vocalion V-N 9289	"Few Dollars More" Theme/You Only Live Twice	4
70	London ZGL 104	GREAT WESTERN THEMES (LP)	15
63	Vocalion VA/SVN 8022	12-STRING GUITAR (LP)	10
64	Vocalion VAN 8026	MR GUITAR (LP)	10
64	Vocalion VAN/SAVN 8032	THE JAMES BOND THEME (LP)	10

65	Vocalion VAN/SAVN 8038	GOLDFINGER (LP)	10
65	Vocalion VAN/SAVN 8042	ENGLISH HITS OF '65 (LP)	10
65	Vocalion VAN/SAVN 8045	STRANGE PLAYS THE HITS (LP)	10
66	Vocalion VAN/SAVN 8050	FOLK-ROCK HITS (LP)	10
66	London HA-F/SH-F 8274	THE FUNKY 12 STRING GUITAR (LP, as Billy Strange & Transients)	10
66	Vocalion VAN/SAVN 8065	BILLY STRANGE & THE CHALLENGERS (LP)	10

(see also Cliffie Stone)

STEVE STRANGE

| 82 | Palace PALACE 1 | In The Year 2525/Strange Connexions (white label, unreleased) | 50 |
| 82 | Palace PALACE 1 | In The Year 2525/Strange Connexions (p/s, available separately!) | 35 |

(see also Visage)

STRANGE DAYS

| 75 | Retreat RTS 263 | Monday Morning/Joe Soap | 5 |
| 75 | Retreat RTL 6005 | NINE PARTS TO THE WIND (LP) | 25 |

STRANGE FRUIT

| 71 | Village Thing VTSX 1001 | Cut Across Shorty/Shake That Thing | 12 |

STRANGELOVES

66	London HLZ 10020	Night Time/Rhythm Of Love	15
66	London HLZ 10063	Hand Jive/I Gotta Dance	8
69	London HLZ 10238	Honey Do/I Wanna Do It	8
65	Stateside SS 446	I Want Candy/It's About My Baby	15
65	Immediate IM 007	Cara-Lin/Roll On Mississippi	8

STRANGER (Cole)

| 63 | Blue Beat BB 195 | Miss Reams/RICH & HIS BAND: Blues From The Hills | 8 |

(see also Stranger Cole)

STRANGER (Cole) & GLADYS (Gladstone Anderson)

| 67 | Island WI 3128 | Love Me Today/Over Again | 10 |
| 68 | Amalgamated AMG 806 | Seeing Is Knowing/ROY SHIRLEY: Music Is The Key | 8 |

(see also Stranger Cole, Gladdy & Followers)

STRANGER (Cole) & KEN (Boothe)

| 63 | R&B JB 120 | Thick In Love/All Your Friends | 10 |

(see also Stranger Cole, Ken Boothe)

STRANGER (Cole) & PATSY (Todd)

63	Blue Beat BB 171	Call My Name/Take My Heart	10
63	Island WI 113	Senor And Senorita/DON DRUMMOND: Snowboy	10
64	Island WI 141	Oh Oh I Need You/DON DRUMMOND: J.F.K.'s Memory	10
64	Island WI 144	Tom, Dick And Harry/We Two Happy People	10
64	Island WI 152	Yeah Yeah Baby/BABA BROOKS: Boatride	10
64	Island WI 160	Thing Come To Those Who Wait/Miss B	10
65	Black Swan WI 462	Hey Little Girl/CORNELL CAMBELL: Make Hay	10
66	Rio R 81	Give Me One More Chance/Fire In Cornfield	10
66	Doctor Bird DB 1050	Give Me The Right/Tonight	10
67	Doctor Bird DB 1084	Tell It To Me/Your Photograph	10
67	Doctor Bird DB 1087	Down The Trainlines/Sing And Pray	10

(see also Stranger Cole)

STRANGERS (with Mike Shannon)

| 64 | Philips BF 1335 | One And One Is Two/Time And The River (as Strangers with Mike Shannon) | 30 |
| 64 | Philips BF 1378 | Do You Or Don't You/What Can I Do | 4 |

(see also John Farrar, Shadows)

STRANGERS

67	Pye 7N 17240	Look Out (Here Comes Tomorrow)/Mary Mary	15
67	Pye 7N 17351	You Didn't Have To Be So Nice/Daytime Turns To Night	5
68	Pye 7N 17585	I'm On An Island/Step Inside	5

STRANGLERS

77	United Artists UP 36211	(Get A) Grip (On Yourself)/London Lady (paper p/s, later in card p/s)	5/4
77	United Artists UP 36248	Peaches/Go Buddy Go (withdrawn 'group' p/s, 'blackmail' punk lettering)	200
77	United Artists FREE 4	Peaches (Radioplay)/Go Buddy Go (promo only, plain sleeve)	60
77	United Artists UP 36248	Peaches/Go Buddy Go ('peach' p/s)	6
77	United Artists UP 36277	Something Better Change/Straighten Out (p/s)	6
77	United Artists UP 36300	No More Heroes/In The Shadows (p/s, some with wreath design label)	6/4
77	United Artists FREE 8	No More Heroes (1-sided radio edit, promo only)	25
78	United Artists UP 36350	5 Minutes/Rok It To The Moon (p/s)	4
78	United Artists UP 36379	Nice 'N' Sleazy/Shut Up (p/s)	4
78	United Artists UP 36429	Walk On By/Old Codger (with George Melly & Lew Lewis)/Tank (33rpm) (p/s)	4
79	United Artists BP 308	Duchess/Fools Rush Out (p/s)	4
79	United Artists BP 318	Nuclear Device (The Wizard Of Aus)/Yellowcake UF (p/s)	4
79	United Artists STR 1	DON'T BRING HARRY (EP, 33rpm)	4
80	United Artists BP 344	Bear Cage/Shah Shah A Go Go (p/s)	4
80	United Artists 12-BP 344	Bear Cage (Extended)/Shah Shah A Go Go (Extended) (12", some in p/s)	25/10
80	United Artists BP(X) 355	Who Wants The World?/The Meninblack (Waiting For 'Em) (p/s, initially as '79p budget issue' [BPX 355])	4/5
80	Stranglers Info Ser. 001	Tomorrow Was The Hereafter/Bring On The Nubiles (Cocktail Version) (fan club issue, originally without p/s; 2nd press, push-out centre & "Numbiles" on label)	5/4
80	Stranglers Info Ser. 001	Tomorrow Was The Hereafter/Bring On The Nubiles (Cocktail Version) (fan club issue, 3rd pressing, non-pushout centre, 1,000 with numbered p/s)	7
81	Liberty BP 383	Thrown Away/Top Secret (p/s)	5
81	Liberty BP 393	Just Like Nothing On Earth/Maninwhite (p/s)	6
81	Liberty BP 405	Let Me Introduce You To The Family/Vietnamerica (guns or hearts on rear of p/s)	4/6
83	Epic EPCA 11-2893	European Female/Savage Beast (picture disc)	7

MINT VALUE £

83	Epic A 4738	Skin Deep/Here And There (10,000 in 'skin-feel' p/s, some with free 'Skin Deep' tattoo)	6/4
83	Epic TA 4738	Skin Deep (Extended)/Here And There/Vladimir And The Beast (12", 5,000 in 'skin-feel' p/s)	7
84	Epic EPC GA 4921	No Mercy/In One Door//Hot Club (Riot Mix)/Head On The Line (double pack)	4
84	Epic WA 4921	No Mercy/In One Door (ear-shaped picture disc)	6
84	Epic GA 4921	No Mercy/In One Door/Hot Club (Riot Mix)/Head On The Line (12", gatefold p/s, 5,000 only)	7
85	Epic EPC QTA 6045	Let Me Down Easy (Extended)/Achilles Heel/Place De Victories (Instrumental)/Vladimir Goes To Havanna/The Aural Sculpture Manifesto (12", p/s, with poster)	7
86	Epic 650055-0	Nice In Nice/Since You Went Away (shaped picture disc)	6
86	Epic SOLAR P1	Always The Sun/Norman Normal (shaped picture disc)	5
86	Epic SOLAR D1	Always The Sun/Norman Normal//Nice In Nice/Since You Went Away (double pack, shrinkwrapped & stickered)	5
86	Epic HUGE P1	Big In America/Dry Day (shaped picture disc)	5
86	Epic HUGE D1	Big In America/Dry Day//Always The Sun/Norman Normal (double pack, shrinkwrapped & stickered)	4
87	Epic SHIEK P1	Shakin' Like A Leaf/Hit Man (shaped picture disc)	5
87	Epic SHIEK Q1	Shakin' Like A Leaf (Jelly Mix)/Hit Man/Was It You? (live) (12", p/s, with poster)	7
87	Epic SHIEK B1	Shakin' Like A Leaf (Live)/Hit Man/An Evening With Hugh Cornwell (12", p/s, 'official bootleg')	7
88	Epic VICE 1	All Day And All Of The Night/Viva Vlad! (withdrawn Monica Couglan p/s, sold via fan club)	12
88	Epic VICE P1	All Day And All Of The Night/Viva Vlad! (shaped picture disc)	5
88	Epic VICE QT1	All Day And All Of The Night (Jeff Remix)/Viva Vlad!/Who Wants The World (live) (12", p/s, with poster)	7
88	Epic CDVICE 1	All Day And All Of The Night (Jeff Remix)/Viva Vlad!/Who Wants The World (live)/Strange Little Girl (live) (CD, 5,000 only)	15
89	Liberty EMR 84	Grip '89 — (Get A) Grip (On Yourself)/Waltzinblack (p/s, red vinyl, with poster in gatefold PVC wallet, 5,000 only)	4
90	Epic TEARS Q1	96 Tears/Instead Of This (in stickered tin)	4
77	United Artists FREE 3	Choosy Susie/Peasant In The Big Shitty (S.I.S. fan club reissue, black p/s with "Ello 'Elen" in run-off groove, later pressed with Liberty label)	5/4
83	Epic/S.I.S. XPS 167	Aural Sculpture (reissue, 1-sided fan club issue with silent groove on flip)	4
80s	Stranglers Info Service SIS 004	New Day Today (flexidisc with 'Strangled' fan magazine issue 32)	4
78	United Artists UP 36248	Peaches/Go Buddy Go (p/s, mispress, B-side plays Buzzcocks' "Oh Shit")	15
78	United Artists UP 36379	Nice 'N' Sleazy/Shut Up (p/s, mispress, B-side plays tracks by other artist)	10
81	Liberty BP 393	Just Like Nothing On Earth/Maninwhite (p/s, mispress, plays A-side both sides)	8
77	United Artists UAG 30045	RATTUS NORVEGICUS (LP, 10,000 with 7" "Choosey Susie"/"Peasant In The Big Shitty" (live) [FREE 3, red p/s, "What Do You Expect ..." in run-off groove])	15
78	United Artists UAK 30222	BLACK AND WHITE (LP, 75,000 with white vinyl 7" "Walk On By"/"Tits"/ "Mean To Me" [FREE 9, black die-cut sleeve & card insert], a few freebies mispressed on blue vinyl)	25/10
79	United Artists UAG30262	THE RAVEN (LP, 20,000 with 3-D cover)	15
79	United Artists UAG	LIVE CERT X (LP)	10
82	Liberty LBG 30353	STRANGLERS SINGLES COLLECTION (LP, with dark sleeve)	12
83	Epic EPC 25237	FELINE (LP, with 1-sided 7" "Aural Sculpture" [XPS 167])	10
83	Epic 40 25237	FELINE (cassette, initial copies include "Midnight Summer Dream" instead of listed "Aural Sculpture")	10
86	Epic EPC 26648	DREAMTIME (LP, picture disc)	12

(see also Jean Jacques Burnel [& Dave Greenfield], Hugh Cornwell, Celia & Mutations, A Marriage Of Convenience)

STRAPPS
76	Harvest HAR 5108	In Your Ear/Rita B (p/s)	5
76	Harvest SHSP 4055	STRAPPS (LP)	10

(see also Gillan, Quatermass)

STRAPS
83	Cyclops CYC 2	THE STRAPS ALBUM (LP)	10

STRATUS
85	Steel Trax STEEL 31001	THROWING SHAPES (LP)	14

STRAWBERRY ALARM CLOCK
67	Pye International 7N 25436	Incense And Peppermints/The Birdman Of Alkatrash	15
68	Pye International 7N 25446	Tomorrow/Birds In My Tree	12
68	Pye International 7N 25456	Sit With The Guru/Pretty Song From Psych-Out	12
69	MCA MU 1080	Good Morning Starshine/Me & The Township	8
68	Pye Intl. N(S)PL 28106	INCENSE AND PEPPERMINTS (LP)	25

STRAWBERRY CHILDREN
67	Liberty LBF 15012	Love Years Coming/One Stands Here	10

STRAWBERRY JAM
69	Pye 7N 17711	Per-So-Nal-Ly/This Is To A Girl	6

STRAWBERRY SWITCHBLADE
83	92 Happy Cust. HAP 1	Trees And Flowers/Go Away (p/s)	6
83	92 Happy Cust. HAPT 1	Trees And Flowers/Go Away/Trees And Flowers (Just Music) (12", p/s)	8
85	Korova KOW 39	Let Her Go/Beautiful End (shaped picture disc)	4
85	Korova KOW 42	Jolene/Being Cold (strawberry-shaped picture disc)	4
85	Korova/Flexi FLX 388-1	Strawberry Switchblade LP sampler (clear vinyl square flexidisc sewn into gatefold booklet; cat. no. only visible in run-off groove)	6

(see also Poems, Rose McDowall)

STRAWBS

68	A&M AMS 725	Oh How She Changed/Or Am I Dreaming	7
68	A&M AMS 738	The Man Who Called Himself Jesus/Poor Jimmy Wilson	6
70	A&M AMS 791	Forever/Another Day	7
71	A&M AMS 837	Witchwood/Devil Outside — We'll Meet Again Sometime (live) (promo only)	8
71	A&M AMS 874	Benidictus/Keep The Devil Outside	5
70s	LO LO 1	The King/Ringing Down The Years (p/s)	8
69	A&M AMLS 936	STRAWBS (LP)	18
70	A&M AMLS 970	DRAGONFLY (LP)	20
70	A&M AMLS 994	JUST A COLLECTION OF ANTIQUES AND CURIOUS (LP)	15
71	A&M AMLH 64304	FROM THE WITCHWOOD (LP, gatefold sleeve)	12
72	A&M AMLH 68078	GRAVE NEW WORLD (LP, with booklet)	12
73	A&M AMLH 68144	BURSTING AT THE SEAMS (LP)	10
73	Hallmark SHM 813	ALL OUR OWN WORK (LP, with Sandy Denny)	15
74	A&M AMLS 63607	HERO AND HEROINE (LP, with inner sleeve)	10
74	A&M AMLH 68259	BY CHOICE (LP)	10
75	A&M AMLH 68277	GHOSTS (LP)	10
76	A&M AMLH 68331	NOMADNESS (LP)	10
76	Oyster 2391 234	DEEP CUTS (LP)	12
77	Oyster 2391 287	BURNING FOR YOU (LP)	10

(see also Fire, Dave Cousins, Sandy Denny, Foggy)

STRAWHEAD

| 70s | Tradition TSR 032 | FORTUNES OF WAR (LP) | 10 |

STRAY

70	Transatlantic TRA 216	STRAY (LP, die-cut sleeve)	15
71	Transatlantic TRA 233	SUICIDE (LP)	12
72	Transatlantic TRA 248	SATURDAY MORNING PICTURES (LP, gatefold sleeve)	12
73	Transatlantic TRA 268	MUDANZAS (LP, gatefold sleeve)	12
74	Transatlantic TRA 281	MOVE IT (LP, die-cut sleeve with inner)	10
75	Transatlantic TRA 3066	TRACKS (LP)	10
75	Dawn DNLS 3066	STAND UP AND BE COUNTED (LP)	12
76	Pye NSLP 18482	HOUDINI (LP)	10
76	Pye NSLP 18512	HEARTS OF FIRE (LP)	12

STRAY DOG

| 74 | Manticore K 43506 | STRAY DOG (LP) | 10 |

(see also Emerson, Lake & Palmer)

STREAMLINERS & JOANNE

| 61 | Columbia DB 4689 | Frankfurter Sandwiches/Pachalfaka | 5 |
| 62 | Columbia DB 4808 | Everybody's Doin' The Twist/Do Something | 5 |

STREET

| 69 | London HLU 10275 | Apollo...Amen/Why Concern Yourself | 4 |

DANNY STREET

| 65 | Philips BF 1387 | Don't Go To Him/As It's Meant To Be | 4 |
| 60s | Domino DO 114 | Melanie/Birds An' Bees An' Things | 4 |

GARY STREET & FAIRWAYS

| 68 | Domain D 2 | Flipperty Flop/Hold Me Closer | 4 |

HILLARD STREET

| 58 | Capitol CL 14960 | River Love/It Will Never Happen Again | 6 |

JOHN STREET & INMATES OF NO. 12

| 67 | Deram DM 147 | Keep A Little Love/My Kind Of Luck | 4 |

JUDY STREET

| 78 | Grapevine GRP 106 | What/You Turn Me On | 4 |

STREETWALKERS

74	Reprise K 54017	STREETWALKERS (LP, with lyric sheet)	10
75	Vertigo 6360 123	DOWNTOWN FLIER (LP)	10
76	Vertigo 9102 010	RED CARD (LP, red vinyl with poster & lyric sheet, numbered)	12
77	Vertigo 9102 012	VICIOUS BUT FAIR (LP)	10

(see also Roger Chapman, Family)

BARBRA STREISAND

68	CBS 3363	Our Corner Of The Night	6
64	CBS AGG 20042	LOVER COME BACK TO ME (EP)	7
64	CBS AGG 20054	BARBRA STREISAND (EP)	7
65	CBS EP 6048	EN FRANCAIS (EP)	12
66	CBS EP 6068	MY MAN (EP)	7
67	CBS EP 6150	SECOND HAND ROSE (EP)	7
73	CBS CQ 30378/Q 64269	STONEY END (LP, quadrophonic)	10
73	CBS CQ 30792	BARBRA JOAN STREISAND (LP, quadrophonic)	12
73	CBS SQ 30992/Q 70044	FUNNY GIRL (soundtrack LP, quadrophonic)	10
73	CBS CQ 31760/Q 65210	LIVE CONCERT AT THE FORUM (LP, quadrophonic)	10

'TEXAS' BILL STRENGTH

| 55 | Capitol CL 14357 | Cry, Cry, Cry/The Yellow Rose Of Texas | 20 |

STRETCH

75	Anchor ANC 1021	Why Did You Do It/Write Me A Note	5
75	Anchor ANC 1027	That's The Way The Wind Blows/Hold On	4
75	Anchor ANC 1034	Love's Got A Hold On Me/If The Cap Fits	4
78	Hot Wax WAX 2	Forget The Past/Fooling Me	4
75	Anchor ANCL 2014	ELASTIQUE (LP)	15
76	Anchor ANCL 2016	YOU CAN'T BEAT YOUR BRAIN FOR ENTERTAINMENT (LP)	12
77	Anchor ANCL 2023	LIFE BLOOD (LP)	12

MINT VALUE £

78   Hot Wax HW 1   FORGET THE PAST (LP) 30
     (see also Elmer Gantry, Kirby)

STRETCHHEADS
88   Moksha SOMA 5   BROS ARE PISH (EP, stamped brown sleeve with insert) .5

WILLIAM R. STRICKLAND
69   Deram DML/SML 1041   WILLIAM R. STRICKLAND IS ONLY THE NAME (LP) 15

PETE STRIDE & JOHN PLAIN
80   Beggars Banquet BEGA 17 NEW GUITARS IN TOWN (LP, with inner) 10
     (see also Lurkers)

STRIDER
73   GM GML 1002   EXPOSED (LP) 15
74   GM GML 1012   MISUNDERSTANDING (LP) 15
     (see also Samson)

STRIKE
77   Outlaw OUT 1   School/Go/Feel So Good (p/s) 4

LIZA STRIKE
68   Parlophone R 5725   All's Quiet On West 23rd/Mr Daddy-Man 4
     (see also Soulmates, Vice Versa)

STRING-A-LONGS
61   London HLU 9278   Wheels/Am I Asking Too Much 5
61   London HLU 9354   Panic Button/Brass Buttons 6
61   London HLU 9394   Should I/Take A Minute 5
61   London HLU 9452   Scottie/Ming Bird 8
62   London HLD 9535   Sunday/Twistwatch 8
62   London HLD 9588   Spinning My Wheels/My Blue Heaven 7
63   London HLD 9652   Mathilda/Replica 10
61   London REU 1322   THE STRING-A-LONGS (EP) 20
63   London REU 1350   THE STRING-A-LONGS (EP) 20
63   London REU 1398   STRINGALONG WITH THE STRING-A-LONGS (EP) 20
63   London HA-D/SH-D 8054   THE STRING-A-LONGS (LP, mono/stereo) 25/30
69   London HA/SH 8371   WIDE WORLD HITS (LP) 10

STRING CHEESE
71   RCA SF 8222   STRING CHEESE (LP) 25

STRING DRIVEN THING
70   Concord CON 7   Another Night/Say What You Like 15
70   Concord CON 1001   STRING DRIVEN THING (LP, private press, 100 only) 125
72   Charisma CAS 1062   STRING DRIVEN THING (LP, pink label) 12
73   Charisma CAS 1070   THE MACHINE THAT CRIED (LP, pink label, gatefold sleeve) 15
74   Charisma CAS 1097   PLEASE MIND YOUR HEAD (LP) 10
76   Charisma CAS 1112   KEEP YOUR 'AND ON IT (LP) 10

STRIPES OF GLORY
62   Vogue V 9194   The Denial/O' Send The Fire 15

SYLVIA STRIPLIN
80s Streetwave   Give Me Your Love/Give Me Your Love(Version) (12") 15

STROLLERS
58   Vogue V 9113   Jumping With Symphony Sid/Swinging Yellow Rose Of Texas 20
58   Vogue V 9113   Jumping With Symphony Sid/Swinging Yellow Rose Of Texas (78) 5
58   Vogue V 9124   Little Bitty Pretty One/Flute Cha-Lypso 20
58   Vogue V 9124   Little Bitty Pretty One/Flute Cha-Lypso (78) 10
61   London HLL 9336   Come On Over/There's No One But You 10

STROLLERS
65   Fontana TF 598   Cuckoo/Rich And Rambling Boy 4
     (see also David & Toni Arthur)

BARRETT STRONG
60   London HLU 9088   Money (That's What I Want)/Oh I Apologise 100
76   Capitol CL 15864   Man Up In The Sky/Gonna Make It Right 6

JOE STRUMMER
88   Epic TRASH P1   Trash City/Permanent Record (picture disc) 4
     (see also Clash, 101'ers)

STRUTT
76   Brunswick BR 35   Time Moves On/Front Row 4

STRYPER
88   Enigma ENCS 1   Always There For You/Always There For You
                             (shaped picture disc) 4
87   Music For Nations MFN 74 YELLOW AND BLACK ATTACK (LP, blue vinyl, round sleeve) 10

CHAD STUART & JEREMY CLYDE
     (see under Chad & Jeremy)

GLEN STUART & CLANSMEN
59   Pye 7N 15232   Weepy Willow/Della Darling 4

GLEN STUART
60s Honey Hit TB 126   Make Me An Angel/Walking To Heaven (p/s) 5

KARL STUART & PROFILES
65   Mercury MF 870   Love Of My Eyes/Not A Girl In A Million 4
65   Mercury MF 875   Haven't They Got Better Things To Do/The Touch Of Your Hand 4
     (see also Profiles, Voice)

MIKE STUART SPAN
66	Columbia DB 8066	Come On Over To Our Place/Still Nights	20
67	Columbia DB 8206	Dear/Invitation	20
68	Jewel JL 01	Children Of Tomorrow/Concerto Of Thoughts	80
68	Fontana TF 959	You Can Understand Me/Baubles And Bangles	10

(see also Leviathan)

NAT STUCKEY
67	Pye International 7N 25403	Sweet Thang/Paralyze My Mind	5
69	RCA RCA 1833	Loving You/Joe And Mabel's 12th Street Bar And Grill	4
69	RCA RCA 1890	Cut Across Shorty/Understand Little Man	4

STUD
| 71 | Deram SML-R 1084 | STUD (LP) | 35 |

(see also Taste, Family, Blossom Toes, Eric Burdon & Animals)

STUDIO ONE ALLSTARS
| 67 | Island WI 3038 | Sherry/Out Of My Mind | 10 |

STUDIO SIX
66	Polydor BM 56131	When I See My Baby/Don't Tell Lies	6
67	Polydor BM 56189	Times Were When/I Can't Sleep	6
67	Polydor BM 56219	Strawberry Window/Falling Leaves	15
69	Polydor BM 56361	Bless My Soul/People Say	4

STUDIO SWEETHEARTS
| 79 | DJM DJS 10915 | I Believe/It Isn't Me (p/s) | 10 |

(see also Slaughter & Dogs)

STUMP
| 86 | Ron Johnson ZRON 6 | MUD ON A COLON (12" EP) | 7 |

STUPIDS
| 85 | Children Of Rev. COR 3 | VIOLENT NUN (EP, mispresses exist) | 15 |

STYLE COUNCIL
83	Polydor TSC 2	Money Go Round Pts 1 & 2 (p/s, with insert)	4
83	Polydor TSCG 4	Solid Bond In Your Heart/It Just Came To Pieces In My Hands/Solid Bond In Your Heart (instrumental) (gatefold sleeve, different to standard p/s)	5
85	Polydor TSC DP 10	The Lodgers/You're The Best Thing (live)/The Big Boss Groove (live)//You're The Best Thing/Long Hot Summer (stickered, shrinkwrapped double pack)	4
86	Polydor CINE 1/CINEC 1	Have You Ever Had It Blue/Mr. Cool's Dream//Have You Ever Had It Blue Uncut Version/With Everything To Lose (live in London) (p/s, with free cassette & insert in printed PVC sleeve)	5
89	Polydor TSCB 17	Promised Land (Juan Atkins Mix)/Can You Still Love Me (stickered box set, with numbered 7" & poster)	4
84	Lyntone LYN 15344/45	It Just Came To Pieces In My Hands (Coventry)/Speak Like A Child (London) (33rpm fan club flexidisc)	10
85	The Hit HOT 001	Walls Come Tumbling Down (live in Manchester)/SIMPLY RED: Every Bit Of Me/REDSKINS: Kick Over The Statues (The Ramsey McKinnock Mix)/JESUS & MARY CHAIN: Taste Of Cindy (EP, p/s, free with 'The Hit' magazine)	6/4

(see also Jam, Merton Parkas)

STYLISTICS
| 72 | Avco/Embassy 6105 015 | I'm Stone In Love With You/The Point Of No Return | 4 |

STYLOS
| 64 | Liberty LBS 10173 | Head Over Heels/Bye Bye, Baby, Bye Bye | 70 |

POLY STYRENE
80	United Artists BP 370	Talk In Toytown/Sub Tropical (p/s)	5
86	Awesome AOR 7	Trick Of The Witch/Paramatma (p/s)	4
86	Awesome AOR 7T	GODS AND GODDESSES (12" EP)	7
80	United Artists UAG 30320	TRANSLUCENCE (LP)	10

(see also X-Ray Spex, Mari Elliott)

STYX
75	RCA RCA 2518	Lady/Children Of The Land	4
78	A&M AMS 7388	Blue Collar Man/Superstars (12", coloured vinyl)	7
79	A&M AMS 7446	Renegade/Sing For The Day (p/s, red vinyl)	4
81	A&M AMS 8102	The Best Of Times/Light (p/s, laser etched)	4
81	A&M AMS 8118	Too Much Time On My Hands/Queen Of Spades (p/s, coloured vinyl)	4
83	A&M AM 120	Don't Let It End/Rockin' The Paradise (shaped picture disc)	4
78	A&M AMLH 64724	PIECES OF EIGHT (LP, translucent vinyl)	10

SUBMARINES
| 87 | Head HEAD 4 | Grey Skies Blue/I Saw The Children (p/s) | 6 |

SUBSTITUTE
| 79 | Ignition IR 2 | The One/Look Sharp (some in p/s) | 15/10 |

SUBTERRANEANS
| 87 | Mother MUM 6 | Slum/Maxi Joy (p/s) | 4 |
| 87 | Mother 12MUM 6 | Slum/Maxi Joy/Head For The Light (12", p/s) | 7 |

SUBURBAN STUDS
77	Pogo POG 001/LYN 44845	No Faith/Questions (p/s)	4
78	Pogo POG 002	I Hate School/Young Power (p/s)	4
78	Pogo POW 001	SLAM (LP)	10

SUBWAY SECT
| 78 | Braik BRS 01 | Don't Split It/Nobody's Scared (p/s) | 6 |
| 79 | Rough Trade RT 007 | Ambition/A Different Story (initially in yellow p/s, later orange) | 5/4 |

(see Jo Boxers)

MINT VALUE £

NIKKI SUDDEN

81	Rather GEAR 11	Back To The Start/Running On My Train (p/s)	5
82	Abstract ABS 009	Channel Steamer/Chelsea Embankment (p/s)	4
80s	Rather RATHER 10	BEAU GESTE (cassette)	10
85	Hotwire HWLP 8504	THE LAST BANDITS IN THE WORLD (LP)	10

(see also Swell Maps, Last Bandits)

SUDDEN SWAY

80	Chant CHANT 1	Jane's Third Party/Don't Go (p/s)	12
80	own label	Jane's Third Party/Don't Go (cassette)	8
81	Chant CHANT 2/EJSP9692	TO YOU, WITH REGARD (12" EP, with insert)	8
84	Chant CHANT 3/ SRT/82/CUS 1592	THE TRAFFIC TAX SCHEME (12" with badge & inserts in folder)	12
86	WEA BYN 8B	SPACEMATE (2 x 12" box set with stickers, info sheets, 2 booklets & poster)	12
87	Strange Fruit SFPSC 005	PEEL SEESION 16.11.83 (EP, cassette)	5

(see also A Sudden Sway)

SUE & MARY

62	Decca F 11517	Traitor In Disguise/I Love You	4

SUE & SUNNY

65	Columbia DB 7748	Every Ounce Of Strength/So Remember	4
67	Columbia DB 8099	You Can't By-Pass Love/I Like Your Style	4
68	CBS 3874	Little Black Book/The Show Must Go On	7
68	Island WIP 6043	Set Me Free/NIRVANA ORCHESTRA: City Of The South	5
70	CBS 63740	SUE AND SUNNY (LP)	10
70s	Reflection	LP	20

(see also Sue & Sunshine, Myrtelles)

SUE & SUNSHINE

64	Columbia DB 7409	Little Love/If You See Me Crying	4
65	Columbia DB 7533	We're In Love/Don't Look Behind	4

(see also Sue & Sunny, Myrtelles)

SUEDE

90	RML RML 001	Be My God/Art (12", unreleased, white labels only, no sleeve)	120
92	Nude NUD 1S	The Drowners (Radio Edit)/To The Birds (p/s)	5
92	Nude NUD 1CD	The Drowners (Radio Edit)/To The Birds/My Insatiable One (CD, promo only)	15
93	Nude SUEDE 1	My Insatiable One (clear flexidisc, gig freebie)	10

SUGAR (Simone) & DANDY (Livingstone)

66	Blue Beat BB 367	Meditation/GIRL SATCHMO & JET LINERS: Nature Of Love	6
63	Carnival CV 7006	One Man Went To Mow/Cryin'	5
64	Carnival CV 7009	Oh Dear What Can The Matter Be/Tra La La	5
64	Carnival CV 7015	What A Life/Time And Tide	5
64	Carnival CV 7016	I'm Not Crying Now/Blues Got A Hold On Me	5
65	Carnival CV 7023	Let's Ska/Only Heaven Knows	5
65	Carnival CV 7024	I'm Into Something Good/Crazy For You	5
65	Carnival CV 7027	Think Of The Good Times/Girl Come See	5
65	Carnival CV 7029	I Want To Be Your Lover/I Don't Know What I'm Going To Do Now	5
67	Page One POF 044	Let's Ska/Only Heaven Knows	5
67	Page One FOR 006	THE SKA'S THE LIMIT (LP)	10

(see also Sugar Simone)

SUGAR & PEE WEE

58	Vogue Pop V 9112	One, Two, Let's Rock/Just A Few Little Words	200
58	Vogue Pop V 9112	One, Two, Let's Rock/Just A Few Little Words (78)	50

SUGAR & SPICE

69	London HLU 10259	Cruel War/Not To Return	5

SUGARBEATS

66	Polydor BM 56069	I Just Stand Here/Ballad Of Ole Betsy	6
66	Polydor BM 56120	Alice Designs/Sunny Day Girl	6

SUGARCUBES

87	One Little Indian 7 TP 7	Birthday/Birthday (Icelandic) (p/s)	4
87	One Little Indian 12 TP 7	Birthday/Birthday (Icelandic)/Cat (Icelandic) (12", p/s)	8
87	One Little Indian 7 TP 7CD	Birthday/Motorcrash/Cat (Icelandic)Birthday (Icelandic) (CD)	10
87	One Little Indian L12 TP 9	Cold Sweat (Remix)/Birthday (Original Demo Version)/Dragon (Icelandic)/ Traitor (Icelandic) (12", p/s, 5,000 only)	7
88	One Little Indian 10 TP 10	Deus (Remix)/Cowboy/Organic Prankster/Luftgitar (Icelandic) (p/s)	5
88	One Little Indian 12TP 11L	BIRTHDAY CHRISTMAS MIX (12" EP, double groove, with Jesus & Mary Chain)	7
88	One L. Indian12TP 11CD	BIRTHDAY CHRISTMAS MIX (CD EP, with Jesus & Mary Chain)	7
80s	Catalogue CAT 074	Cindy/SHAMEN: Purple Haze/SLEEPING DOGS WAKE: This Little Piggy/ KITCHENS OF DISTINCTION: Margaret's Injection/HAM: Voulez Vous (flexidisc free with 'The Catalogue' magazine)	6/4
90	One Little Indian TP BOX 2	7.8 (8 x single box set)	16
90	One Little Indian TP BOX 1	12.11 (11 x 12" box set)	25
90	One Little Indian TP BOX 3	CD.6 (6 x CD box set)	25
88	One Little Indian DTP LP 5	LIFE'S TOO GOOD (DAT issue)	18
89	One Little Indian TPLP 15SP	Here TODAY, TOMORROW, NEXT WEEK! (LP, gatefold sleeve, silver vinyl & inner)	10
89	One Little Indian TPLP 15L	SYKURMOLARNIR ILLUR ARFUR! (LP, gatefold sleeve)	10

(see also Kukl)

SUGAR SHOPPE

68	Capitol CL 15555	Skip-A-Long Sam/Let The Truth Come Out	6

SUGARLOAF

70	Liberty LBS 83415	SUGARLOAF (LP)	10

MINT VALUE £

74	United Artists UAS 29165	SPACESHIP EARTH (LP)	10
75	Polydor 2310 394	DON'T CALL US, WE'LL CALL YOU (LP, with Jerry Corbetto)	22

SUICIDAL TENDENCIES
87	Virgin VS 967-12	Possessed To Skate/Human Guinea Pig/Two Wrongs Don't Make A Right (12", picture disc)	10

SUICIDE
78	Red Star/Bronze BRO 57	Cheree/I Remember (12", p/s)	8
79	Island WIP 6543	Dream Baby Dream/Radiation (p/s)	4
79	Island 12 WIP 6543	Dream Baby Dream (Long Version)/Radiation (12", p/s)	8
77	R. Star/Bronze BRON 508	SUICIDE (LP)	12
78	R. Star/Bronze FRANKIE 1	24 MINUTES OVER BRUSSELS (LP, official bootleg, 1,000 only)	30

(see also Alan Vega, Martin Rev)

SUICIDE TWINS
86	Lick LICLP 9	SILVER MISSILES AND NIGHTINGALES (LP)	10

(see also Hanoi Rocks)

BIG JIM SULLIVAN
61	Decca F 11387	You Don't Know What You've Got/Hot Hiss Of Steam (as Big Jim Sullivan Combo)	6
65	Mercury MF 928	She Walks Through The Fair/Don't Know What I'm Doing (as Jim Sullivan Sound)	20
68	Mercury SML 30001	SITAR BEAT (LP)	12

(see also Maureeny Wishfull, Brian Bennett)

MAXINE SULLIVAN
54	Parlophone MSP 6086	Boogie Woogie Maxixe/Piper In The Glen	6

PHIL SULLIVAN with LONZO & OSCAR'S PEAPICKERS
50s	Melodisc M 1512	Love Never Dies/Luckiest Man In Town	4

HUBERT SUMLIN
65	Blue Horizon 45-1000	Across The Board/Sumlin Boogie	50

(see also Howlin' Wolf)

DONNA SUMMER
74	People PEO 115	The Hostage/Let's Work Together Now	6
79	Casablanca SANL 151	Hot Stuff/Journey To The Centre Of Your Heart (12", red vinyl)	15
87	WEA U 8237P	Dinner With Gershwin Pts 1 & 2 (12", picture disc)	8
89	WEA U 7780P	This Time I Know It's For Real/Whatever Your Heart Desires (shaped picture disc)	4

SAFFRON SUMMERFIELD
75	Mother Earth MUM 1001	SALISBURY PLAIN (LP)	25
76	Mother Earth MUM 1202	FANCY MEETING YOU HERE (LP)	30
76	Spectator	FANCY MEETING YOU HERE (LP, reissue)	20

SUMMERHILL
69	Polydor 583 746	SUMMERHILL (LP)	40

ANDY SUMMERS & ROBERT FRIPP
82	A&M (no cat. no.)	Hardy Country/Stultified/Yellow Leader/I Advance Masked (clear flexidisc)	6

(see also Police, King Crimson)

BOB(BY) SUMMERS
59	Capitol CL 15063	Rattle Rhythm/Excitement (as Bob Summers)	7
60	Capitol CL 15130	Little Brown Jug/Twelfth Street Rag (as Bobby Summers)	8

SUMMER SET
66	Columbia DB 8004	Farmer's Daughter/What Are You Gonna Do	10
67	Columbia DB 8215	It's A Dream/Overnight Changes	40

SUMMERTAIRES
66	Ska Beat JB 258	My Heart Cries Out/SOUL BROTHERS: James Bond Girl	10

SUN
78	Capitol EMC 3262	LIVE ON DREAM ON (LP)	10

SUN ALSO RISES
70	Village Thing VTS 2	THE SUN ALSO RISES (LP)	15

SUN & MOON
88	Geffen GEF 39	The Speed Of Life/Death Of Imagination (p/s)	4
88	Geffen GEF 39T	The Speed Of Life/Death Of Imagination/The Boy Who Sees Everything/ I Love You, You Bastard (12", p/s)	7

(see also Chameleons)

SUNDAE TIMES
68	President PT 203	Baby Don't Cry/Aba-Aba	4
68	President PT 219	Jack Boy/I Don't Want Nobody	4
69	President PT 285	Live Today/Take Me Higher Baby	4
70s	Joy JOYS 159	US COLORED KIDS (LP)	20

SUNDANCE
73	Decca TXS 111	RAIN STEAM SPEED (LP, with insert)	18
74	Decca SKL 5183	CHUFFER (LP)	15

SUNDAY AFTERNOONS
70s	Longman	SUNDAY AFTERNOONS (LP)	80

SUNDAYS
89	Rough Trade RTX 218	Can't Be Sure/I Kicked A Boy (export issue, brown p/s)	5
89	Rough Trade RTTX 218	Can't Be Sure/I Kicked A Boy (12", export issue, brown p/s)	10
90	Catalogue CAT 076	I Won (square flexidisc with 'The Catalogue' magazine)	4
90	Rough Trade ROUGH148P	READING, WRITING AND ARITHMETIC (LP, picture disc, stickered sleeve)	10

SUN DIAL

90	Bucketfull Of Brains BOB 30	Visitation/JEFF DAHL & AMERICAN RUSE: One Track Mind (flexidisc free with 'Bucketfull Of Brains' magazine issue 36)	5/4
91	Tangerine (no cat. no.)	Exploding In Your Mind (12", unreleased, 80 white label test pressings only)	50
91	UFO PF 2	Fireball/Only A Northern Song ('Pre-Flight' 7", promo only, no p/s)	5
90	Tangerine MM 07	OTHER WAY OUT (LP, with insert, some signed in silver pen)	35/30

(see also Modern Art)

SUNDOWNERS

63	Piccadilly 7N 35142	House Of The Rising Sun/Baby Baby	6
64	Piccadilly 7N 35162	Come On In/Shot Of Rhythm And Blues	6
65	Parlophone R 5243	Where Am I/Gonna Make The Future Bright	5
68	Columbia DB 8339	Dr. J. Wallace-Brown/Love Is In The Air	7
68	Spark SRL 1016	Gloria The Bosom Show/Don't Look Back	4

SUNDOWN PLAYBOYS

72	Apple APPLE 44	Saturday Nite Special/Valse De Soleil Couche (some in p/s)	25/7
72	Apple APPLE 44	Saturday Nite Special/Valse De Soleil Couche (10" 78rpm, pink-patterned die-cut sleeve)	175

SUNDRAGON

68	MGM MGM 1380	Green Tambourine/I Need All The Friends I Can Get	6
68	MGM MGM 1391	Blueberry Blue/Far Away Mountain	8
68	MGM C(S) 8090	GREEN TAMBOURINE (LP)	40

(see also Sands, Others)

SUNFOREST

69	Deram Nova SDN 7	SOUND OF SUNFOREST (LP)	35

SUNNYLAND SLIM

65	'77' LA 12-23	CHICAGO BLUES SESSION (LP, with Little Brother Montgomery)	20
65	Storyville SLP 169	I DONE YOU WRONG (LP)	15
68	Storyville 670 169	PORTRAITS IN BLUES (LP, reissue of SLP 169)	15
69	Liberty LBS 83237	SLIM'S GOT THIS THING GOIN' ON (LP)	20
69	Blue Horizon 7-63213	MIDNIGHT JUMP (LP)	40

SUNNY & HI-JUMPERS

65	Carnival CV 7022	Tarry Till You're Better/Dance Til You're Better	4
65	Carnival CV 7025	Going To Damascus/Sweet Potatoes	4

SUNNY & SUNGLOWS/SUNLINERS

63	London HL 9792	Talk To Me (as Sunny & Sunglows)/Every Week, Every Month, Every Year (as Sunny & Sunliners)	15

SUNNYSIDERS

55	London HL 8135	Hey! Mr. Banjo/Zoom, Zoom, Zoom	25
55	London HL 8160	Oh Me Oh My Oh/(Let's Gather Round) The Parlour Piano	25
55	London HLU 8180	Banjo Woogie/She Didn't Even Say Goodbye	25
55	London HLU 8202	I Love You Fair Dinkum/Stay On The Sunny Side	20
56	London HLU 8246	Doesn't He Love Me/Humdinger	22

SUN RA ARKESTRA

70s	Delmark DL 411	SUN SONG (LP)	10
70s	Delmark DL 414	SOUND OF JOY (LP)	10
70s	Polydor 2460 106	PICTURES OF INFINITY (LP)	12
78	Affinity AFF 10	S-M APPROACH (LP, with Solar-Myth Ark)	10
79	Cobra COB 37001	FATE IN A PLEASANT MOOD (LP)	10

SUNRAYS

65	Capitol CL 15416	I Live For The Sun/Bye, Baby, Bye	6
66	Capitol CL 15433	Andrea/You Don't Phase Me	6

SUNSET BOYS

79	Gimp GIM 1234	Wreck My Bed/Tutti Frutti/Copy Cat (Blues)/Wreck My Bed (Hippy Version) (p/s)	5

(see also Maxim's Trash)

SUN SET

67	Polydor BM 56193	East Baby/You Can Ride My Rainbow	4

SUNSETS

60	Ember EMB S 125	Cry Of The Wild Goose/Manhunt	8

SUNSHINE

72	Warner Bros K 46169	SUNSHINE (LP)	10

MONTY SUNSHINE

62	Pye Jazz 7NJ 2011	Hushabye/Whistling Rufus (with His Jazz Band)	4
62	London HL 9629	Gonna Build A Mountain/Hushabye (with His Band)	5
63	London HLR 9822	Carnival — From "Black Orpheus"/Charmaine (with His Orchestra)	5
63	London RER 1368	GONNA BUILD A MOUNTAIN (EP, with His Band)	10

MR. SUNSHINE

56	MGM SP 1160	Along The China Coast/MRS. SUNSHINE: Two Car Garage	4

SUNSHINE COMPANY

67	Liberty LBF 15008	Happy/Blue May	4
67	Liberty LBF 15034	Back On The Street Again/The Year Of Jaine Time	4
68	Liberty LBF 15060	Look Here Comes The Sun/It's Sunday	4
68	Liberty LBF 15149	On A Beautiful Day/To Put Up With You	4
68	Liberty LBL/LBS 83120	SUNSHINE COMPANY (LP)	12
69	Liberty LBL/LBS 83159	SUNSHINE AND SHADOWS (LP)	12

SUNSPOTS

63	Decca F 11672	Vancouver/Paella	4

SUNTREADER
73	Island HELP 13	ZIN ZIN (LP)	10

(see also Stomu Yamashta)

SUPERBOYS
68	Giant GN 22	Ain't That A Shame/Do It Right Now	5
68	Giant GN 31	You're Hurtin' Me/Funky Soul	5

(see also Dandy & Superboys, Little Sal)

SUPERSISTER
72	Polydor 2001 379	No Tree Will Grow/She Was Naked	4
71	Dandelion 2310 146	TO THE HIGHEST BIDDER (LP, gatefold sleeve)	25
71	Polydor 2419 030	SUPER STARSHINE 3 (LP)	10
72	Polydor 2419 058	PUDDING & GISTEREN (LP)	10
72	Polydor 2419 061	PRESENT FROM NANCY (LP)	10

SUPERSONICS
53	London L 1197	New Guitar Boogie Shuffle/The Sheik Of Araby (78)	7
54	London HL 8022	Cherokee/Linger Awhile (B-side with Arlene James) (78)	5

SUPERTONES
70	Banana BA 312	Freedom Blues/First Time I Met You	6

SUPERTRAMP
74	A&M AMS 7101	Land Ho/Summer Romance	4

(see also John Andrews & Lonely Ones)

(DIANA ROSS &) SUPREMES
64	Stateside SS 257	When The Lovelight Starts Shining Thru' His Eyes/Standing At The Crossroads Of Love	30
64	Stateside SS 327	Where Did Our Love Go/He Means The World To Me	5
64	Stateside SS 350	Baby Love/Ask Any Girl	5
65	Stateside SS 376	Come See About Me/(You're Gone But) Always In My Heart	12
65	Tamla Motown TMG 501	Stop! In The Name Of Love/I'm In Love Again	6
65	Tamla Motown TMG 516	Back In My Arms Again/Whisper You Love Me Boy	12
65	Tamla Motown TMG 527	Nothing But Heartaches/He Holds His Own	18
65	Tamla Motown TMG 543	I Hear A Symphony/Who Could Ever Doubt My Love	7
66	Tamla Motown TMG 548	My World Is Empty Without You/Everything Is Good About You	15
66	Tamla Motown TMG 560	Love Is Like An Itching In My Heart/He's All I Got	20
66	Tamla Motown TMG 575	You Can't Hurry Love/Put Yourself In My Place	5
66	Tamla Motown TMG 585	You Keep Me Hangin' On/Remove This Doubt	5
67	Tamla Motown TMG 597	Love Is Here And Now You're Gone/There's No Stopping Us Now	6
67	Tamla Motown TMG 607	The Happening/All I Know About You	5

(the above singles are credited to Supremes, the singles below to Diana Ross & Supremes unless stated)

67	Tamla Motown TMG 616	Reflections/Going Down For The Third Time (most are crackly at A-side start; push-out or solid centres)	6/5
67	Tamla Motown TMG 632	In And Out Of Love/I Guess I'll Always Love You	5
68	Tamla Motown TMG 650	Forever Came Today/Time Changes Things	5
68	Tamla Motown TMG 662	Some Things You Never Get Used To/You've Been So Wonderful To Me	5
68	Tamla Motown TMG 677	Love Child/Will This Be The Day?	4
69	Tamla Motown TMG 695	I'm Living In Shame/I'm So Glad I Got Somebody (Like You Around) ...	5
69	Tamla Motown TMG 704	No Matter What Sign You Are/The Young Folks	5
69	Tamla Motown TMG 721	Someday We'll Be Together/He's My Sunny Boy	4
70	Tamla Motown TMG 747	Everybody's Got The Right To Love/But I Love You More (as Supremes)	4
65	Tamla Motown TME 2008	THE SUPREMES (EP; originals with flipback sleeve/push-out centre)	14/12
66	Tamla Motown TME 2011	SHAKE (EP, as Supremes)	40
64	Stateside SL 10109	MEET THE SUPREMES (LP)	20
65	Tamla Motown TML 11002	WITH LOVE — FROM US TO YOU (LP)	35
65	Tamla Motown TML 11012	WE REMEMBER SAM COOKE (LP)	40
65	Tamla Motown TML 11018	THE SUPREMES SING COUNTRY, WESTERN AND POP (LP)	35
65	Tamla Motown TML 11020	MORE HITS BY THE SUPREMES (LP)	18
66	Tamla Motown TML 11026	THE SUPREMES AT THE COPA (LP)	18
66	Tamla Motown TML 11028	I HEAR A SYMPHONY (LP)	15
66	T. Motown (S)TML 11039	SUPREMES A' GO-GO (LP)	15
67	T. Motown (S)TML 11047	THE SUPREMES SING MOTOWN (LP)	15
67	T. Motown (S)TML 11054	THE SUPREMES SING RODGERS AND HART (LP)	12

(the above LPs are credited to Supremes, the LPs below to Diana Ross & Supremes unless stated)

68	T. Motown (S)TML 11063	GREATEST HITS (LP, original pressing)	10
68	T. Motown (S)TML 11070	'LIVE' AT LONDON'S TALK OF THE TOWN (LP)	12
68	T. Motown (S)TML 11073	REFLECTIONS (LP)	12
69	T. Motown (S)TML 11088	DIANA ROSS & THE SUPREMES SING & PERFORM FUNNY GIRL (LP)	12/10
69	T. Motown (S)TML 11095	LOVE CHILD (LP)	12/10
69	T. Motown (S)TML 11114	LET THE SUNSHINE IN (LP)	10
70	T. Motown (S)TML 11137	CREAM OF THE CROP (LP)	10
70	T. Motown STML 11157	RIGHT ON (LP, as Supremes)	10

(the above albums originally came with flipback sleeves, later pressings are worth two-thirds the value)

SUPREMES & FOUR TOPS
71	T. Motown STML 11179	THE SUPREMES AND THE FOUR TOPS (LP)	10

DIANA ROSS & SUPREMES & TEMPTATIONS
69	Tamla Motown TMG 685	I'm Gonna Make You Love Me/A Place In The Sun	4
69	Tamla Motown TMG 709	I Second That Emotion/The Way You Do The Things You Do	4
70	Tamla Motown TMG 730	Why (Must We Fall In Love)/Uptight (Everything Is Alright)	4
69	T. Motown (S)TML 11096	DIANA ROSS & THE SUPREMES JOIN THE TEMPTATIONS (LP)	10
69	T. Motown (S)TML 11110	THE ORIGINAL SOUNDTRACK FROM TCB (LP, gatefold laminated sleeve)	10
70	T. Motown STML 11122	TOGETHER (LP, flipback sleeve)	10

(see also Primettes, Diana Ross, Temptations, Four Tops)

SURFARIS

63	London HLD 9751	Wipe Out/Surfer Joe	6
63	Brunswick 05894	Waikiki Run/Point Panic	6
64	Brunswick 05902	Scatter Shield Run/Bat Man	7
66	Dot DS 26756	Wipe Out/Surfer Joe (reissue)	5
63	London RED 1405	WIPE OUT (EP)	25
63	London HA-D 8110	WIPE OUT (LP)	30
63	Brunswick LAT 8561	SURFARIS PLAY (LP)	25
64	Brunswick LAT 8567	HIT CITY '64 (LP)	25
64	Brunswick LAT 8582	FUN CITY (LP)	25
65	Brunswick LAT 8605	HIT CITY '65 (LP)	15
65	Brunswick HA-D 8631	IT AIN'T ME BABE (LP, also stereo STA 8631)	20
66	Dot DLP 3535	WIPE OUT (LP, reissue)	15

SURF DRUMS

85	Swordfish SWF 003	Take It With Me/Stone And Silver/These Seven Years/Everything (12", p/s)	8

(see also Korova Milk Bar)

SURFERS

59	Vogue V 9147	Mambo Jambo/ALAN KALANI: A Touch Of Pink	10

JOHN SURMAN

69	Deram DM 224	Obeah Wedding/Can't Stop The Carnival	6
68	Deram DML/SML 1030	JOHN SURMAN (LP)	40
69	Deram DMLR/SMLR 1045	HOW MANY CLOUDS CAN YOU SEE? (LP)	45
70	Futura GER 12	ALORS! (LP)	40
71	Deram SML 1094	TALES OF THE ALGONQUIN (LP, with John Warren)	40
71	Dawn DNLS 3022	CONFLAGRATION (LP)	25
72	Island HELP 10	WESTERING HOME (LP)	10
74	Dawn DNLS 3072	LIVE AT WOODSTOCK TOWN HALL (LP, with Stu Martin)	15

(see also Morning Glory, Trio, Mike Westbook)

SURPRISES

79	Dead Dog DEAD 01	Jeremy Thorpe Is Innocent/Flying Attack/Little Sir Echo (p/s)	6

SURVIVOR

82	Scotti Bros A 2411P	Eye Of The Tiger/Take You On A Sunday (picture disc)	4
84	Scotti Bros SCTA 2813	American Heartbeat/Silver Girl (shaped picture disc)	4
86	Scotti Bros DA 6708	Burning Heart/Feels Like Love//Eye Of The Tiger/Take You On A Sunday (double pack)	4
86	Scotti Bros A 6708 P	Burning Heart/Feels Like Love (shaped picture disc)	4

SURVIVORS

60s	Rio R 55	Take Charge/Ska-Ology	6
60s	Rio R 70	Rawhide Ska/OWEN GRAY: Girl I Want You	6

SUSSED

80	Graduate GRAD 7	I've Got Me A Parka/Myself, Myself And I Repeated (p/s, paper labels; later reissued with silver labels)	4
81	Shoestring LACE 002	I Like You/Tango/The Perv (p/s)	4

(SCREAMING) LORD SUTCH (& SAVAGES)

61	HMV POP 953	Till The Following Night/Good Golly Miss Molly	15
63	Decca F 11598	Jack The Ripper/Don't You Just Know It	12
63	Decca F 11747	I'm A Hog For You/Monster In Black Tights	12
64	Oriole CB 1944	She's Fallen In Love With A Monster Man/Bye Bye Baby	20
64	Oriole CB 1962	Dracula's Daughter/Come Back Baby	20
65	CBS 201767	Honey Hush/The Train Kept A-Rollin' (as Lord Sutch)	30
66	CBS 202080	The Cheat/Black And Hairy	20
70	Atlantic 584 321	'Cause I Love You/Thumping Beat	10
70	Atlantic 2091 006	'Cause I Love You/Thumping Beat (reissue)	8
70	Atlantic 2091 017	Election Fever/Rock The Election	8
72	Atlantic K 10221	Gotta Keep A-Rockin'/Flashing Lights/Hands Of Jack The Ripper	8
76	SRT SRTS 76361	Monster Ball/Rang-Tang-A-Lang	4
76	SRT SRTS 76375	I Drink To Your Health Marie Pts 1 & 2	4
63	Decca F 13697	Jack The Ripper/I'm A Hog For You	4
81	Ace SW 70	SCREAMING LORD SUTCH AND THE SAVAGES (EP)	6
70	Atlantic 2400 008	LORD SUTCH AND HEAVY FRIENDS (LP)	20
72	Atlantic K 40313	HANDS OF JACK THE RIPPER (LP)	20
81	Ace MAD 1	THE METEORS MEET SCREAMING LORD SUTCH (mini-LP, 1 side each, plain grey sleeve with cartoon print, 1,000 only)	30

(see also Savages, Meteors, Led Zeppelin)

RALPH SUTTON

53	Lyragon LF 2	STRIDE PIANO (10" LP)	10

SUZANNE

77	Ring O' 2017 108	Born On Hallowe'en/Like No One Else (company sleeve)	4
78	Ring O' 2017 111	You Really Got A Hold On Me/You Could Be Right This Time (company sleeve)	4

SUZI & BIG DEE IRWIN

66	Polydor BM 65715	Ain't That Lovin' You Baby/I Can't Get Over You	10

(see also Big Dee Irwin)

SUZY & RED STRIPES

77	A&M AMS 7461	Seaside Woman/B-side To The Seaside (yellow vinyl, die-cut p/s)	6
79	A&M AMSP 7461	Seaside Woman/B-side To The Seaside (yellow vinyl, die-cut p/s, in box set with badge & 10 'saucy' mini-postcards)	25
80	A&M AMS 7548	Seaside Woman/B-side To The Seaside (reissue, cartoon p/s, as Linda McCartney alias Suzy & Red Stripes)	4

Rare Record Price Guide

| 80 | A&M AMSP 7548 | Seaside Woman/B-side To The Seaside (12", as Linda McCartney alias Suzy & Red Stripes) .... 7 |

(see also Paul McCartney [& Wings])

PAT SUZUKI
| 58 | RCA RCA 1069 | Daddy/Just One Of Those Things .... 4 |
| 60 | RCA RCA 1171 | I Enjoy Being A Girl/Sunday .... 6 |

SVANTE
| 68 | United Artists UP 2224 | Baby I Need Your Lovin'/Just One Word From You .... 10 |

SVENSK
| 67 | Page One POF 036 | Dream Magazine/Getting Old .... 12 |
| 67 | Page One POF 050 | You/All I Have To Do Is Dream .... 12 |

SWALLOWS with SONNY THOMPSON
| 52 | Vogue V 2136 | Roll, Roll Pretty Baby/It Ain't The Meat (78) .... 25 |

SWALLOWS/DOMINOES
| 56 | Vogue EPV 1113 | RHYTHM AND BLUES (EP, 2 tracks each) .... 125 |

SWAN ARCADE
| 73 | Trailer LER 2032 | SWAN ARCADE (LP) .... 18 |

SWANEE RIVER BOYS
| 54 | Parlophone CMSP 7 | Do You Believe/Gloryland Boogie (export issue) .... 6 |

BETTYE SWANN
67	CBS 2942	Make Me Yours/I Will Not Cry (demos in p/s £45) 25
69	Capitol CL 15586	Don't Touch Me/My Heart Is Closed For The Season 15
72	Atlantic K 10174	Victim Of A Foolish Heart/Cold Day In Hell 10
72	Atlantic K 10273	Today I Started Loving You Again/I'd Rather Go Blind 8
75	Atlantic K 10622	Doing It For The One I Love/All The Way In Or All The Way Out 4
76	Atlantic K 10851	Heading In The Right Direction/Be Strong Enough To Hold On 10
73	Mojo 2092 059	Make Me Yours/I Will Not Cry (reissue) 5
75	Contempo CS 9019	Make Me Yours/I Will Not Cry (2nd reissue) 4

(see also Sam Dees & Bettye Swann)

SWANS
| 64 | Cameo Parkway C 302 | The Boy With The Beatle Hair/Please Hurry Home .... 10 |
| 63 | Stateside SS 224 | He's Mine/You Better Be A Good Girl Now .... 10 |

SWANS
| 88 | Product Inc. PROD 23B | Love Will Tear Us Apart (Red Version)/Trust Me/Love Will Tear Us Apart (Black Version)/New Mind (Purple Version) (12", black p/s, 750 only) .... 7 |

BERNICE SWANSON
| 65 | Chess CRS 8008 | Baby I'm Yours/Lying Awake .... 25 |

DAVE SWARBRICK
67	Polydor Special 236 514	RAGS, REELS AND AIRS (LP, with Martin Carthy & Diz Disley) 50
76	Transatlantic TRA 337	SWARBRICK (LP) 10
77	Transatlantic TRA 341	SWARBRICK 2 (LP) 10
78	Sonet SNTF 764	THE CEILIDH ALBUM (LP, as Dave Swarbrick & Friends) 10

(see also Martin Carthy & Dave Swarbrick, Fairport Convention, Young Tradition)

SWARBRIGGS (PLUS TWO)
| 75 | MCA MCA 179 | That's What Friends Are For/Love Is .... 7 |
| 77 | EMI EMI 2606 | It's Nice To Be In Love Again/Here We Are Again (as Swarbriggs Plus Two) .... 4 |

SWEAT/PRETTY BOY FLOYD & GEMS
| 79 | Rip Off RIP 101 | START ALL OVER AGAIN (EP) .... 4 |

ROSALYN SWEAT & PARAGONS
| 73 | Duke DU 160 | Blackbird Singing/Always .... 4 |
| 73 | Horse HRLP 703 | BLACKBIRD SINGING (LP) .... 12 |

(see also Paragons)

SWE-DANES
60	Warner Bros WB 7	Scandanavian Shuffle/Hot Toddy 4
60	Warner Bros WB 22	Swe-Dane Shuffle/At A Georgia Camp Meeting 4
61	Warner Bros WEP 6017	THE SWE-DANES (EP; also stereo SWEP 2017) 8/12

JIM SWEENY
| 58 | Philips PB 811 | The Midnight Hour/Till The Right One Comes Along .... 5 |

SWEENEY'S MEN
68	Pye 7N 17459	Waxies Dargle/Old Woman In Cotton 10
69	Transatlantic TRASP 19	Sullivan's John/Rattlin' Roarin' Willy 10
68	Transatlantic TRA 170	RATTLIN' AND ROARIN' WILLY (LP) 35
69	Transatlantic TRA 200	TRACKS OF SWEENEY (LP) 35
76	Transatlantic TRASAM 37	SWEENEY'S MEN (LP) 15
77	Transatlantic TRASAM 40	TRACKS OF SWEENEY (LP, reissue) 15

(see also Gay & Terry Woods, Dr. Strangely Strange)

SWEET
68	Fontana TF 958	Slow Motion/It's Lonely Out There 300
69	Parlophone R 5803	The Lollipop Man/Time 30
70	Parlophone R 5826	All You'll Ever Get From Me/The Juicer 25
70	Parlophone R 5848	Get On The Line/Mr. McGallagher 30
71	RCA RCA 2051	Funny Funny/You're Not Wrong For Me 4
71	Parlophone R 5902	All You'll Ever Get From Me/The Juicer (reissue) 15
71	RCA RCA 2087	Co-Co/Done Me Wrong Alright 4
71	RCA RCA 2121	Alexander Graham Bell/Spotlight 4
72	RCA RCA 2164	Poppa Joe/Jeanie 4
72	RCA RCA 2225	Little Willy/Man From Mecca 4

MINT VALUE £

73	RCA RCA 2403	Ballroom Blitz/Rock & Roll Disgrace	4
73	RCA RCA 2403	Ballroom Blitz/Rock & Roll Disgrace (mispressed at wrong speed, 49rpm; matrix RCA 2403-A-1E)	15
74	RCA LPBO 5037	The Sixteens/Burn On The Flame	4
74	RCA RCA 2480	Turn It Down/Someone Else Will	4
75	RCA RCA 2524	Fox On The Run/Miss Demeanour	4
75	RCA RCA 2578	Action/Sweet F.A.	4
76	RCA RCA 2641	The Lies In Your Eyes/Cockroach	4
76	RCA RCA 2748	Lost Angels/Funk It Up	5
77	RCA PB 5001	Fever Of Love/Distinct Lack Of Ancient	5
77	RCA PB 5046	Stairway To The Stars/Why Don't You Do It To Me	8
78	Polydor POSP 5	California Nights/Show Me The Way (unreleased)	
79	Polydor POSP 36	Call Me/Why Don't You	7
79	Polydor POSP 73	Big Apple Waltz/Why Don't You	20
80	RCA PE 5226	Fox On The Run/Hellraiser/Ballroom Blitz/Blockbuster (EP, p/s)	15
80	Polydor POSP 131	Give That Lady Some Respect/Tall Girls	7
80	Polydor POSP 160	Sixties Man/Oh Yeah (mispress, plays "Tall Girls")	20
80	Polydor POSP 160	Sixties Man/Oh Yeah	5
81	RCA GOLD 524	Blockbuster/Hellraiser (pink 'Golden Groove' p/s)	5
81	RCA GOLD 551	Ballroom Blitz/Wig Wam Bam (pink 'Golden Groove' p/s)	5
84	Anagram ANA 27	The Sixteens/Action (p/s)	5
84	Anagram ANA 28	It's It's The Sweetest Mix/Fox On The Run (p/s)	4
84	Anagram 12 ANA 28	It's It's The Sweetest Mix/Fox On The Run (12" p/s; matrix no. 12 ANA 28 AI)	8
84	Anagram 12 ANA 28	It's It's The Sweetest Mix/Fox On The Run (12" p/s; matrix no. 12 ANA 28.A)	10
85	Anagram ANA 29	Sweet 2th — The Wig Wam-Willy Mix/The Teen Action Mix (p/s)	5
85	Anagram ANA 29	Sweet 2th — The Wig Wam-Willy Mix/The Teen Action Mix (12" p/s)	8
89	RCA PB 43337	Wig Wam Bam/Litty Wally (p/s)	4
71	MFP MFP 5248	GIMME DAT DING (LP, Sweet on Side 1 only; Side 2 by Pipkins)	10
71	RCA SF 8288	FUNNY HOW SWEET CO-CO CAN BE (LP)	20
72	RCA SF 8316	SWEET'S BIGGEST HITS (LP)	10
74	RCA LPL1 5039	SWEET FANNY ADAMS (LP)	10
75	RCA LPL1 5080	DESOLATION BOULEVARD (LP, with insert)	10
75	RCA SPC 0001	STRUNG UP (2-LP, with inserts)	15
76	RCA RS 1936	GIVE US A WINK (LP)	10
77	RCA PL 25072	OFF THE RECORD (LP)	15
78	Polydor POLD 5001	LEVEL HEADED (LP)	10
78	RCA Camden CDS 1168	THE SWEET (LP)	10
79	Polydor POLD 5022	CUT ABOVE THE REST (LP)	15
80	Polydor POLS 1021	WATER'S EDGE (LP)	15
82	Polydor 2311 1179	IDENTITY CRISIS (LP)	25
84	Anagram P GRAM 16	SWEET SIXTEEN (LP, picture disc)	30

(see also Brian Connelly, Mayfield's Mule, Elastic Band, Andy Scott)

SWEET CHARIOT
72	De Wolfe	SWEET CHARIOT & FRIENDS (LP, promo only)	80

SWEET CHARLES
88	Urban URB 15	Yes It's You/LYN COLLINS: Rock Me Again And Again And Again (co. sleeve)	4
88	Urban URBX 15	Yes It's You/LYN COLLINS: Rock Me Again And Again And Again/ Think About It (12", company sleeve)	10
88	Urban URBLP 9	FOR SWEET PEOPLE FROM SWEET CHARLES (LP)	15

SWEET CORPORALS
59	Top Rank JAR 217	The Same Old Army/Warm And Willing	4

SWEET DREAMS
74	Bradleys BRADL 1008	WE'LL BE YOUR MUSIC (LP)	10

SWEET DREAMS
83	Ariola AROPD 333	I'm Never Giving Up/Two Way Mirror (picture disc)	5

SWEET FEELING
67	Columbia DB 8195	All So Long Ago/Charles Brown	40

SWEET INSPIRATIONS
67	Atlantic 584 117	Why (Am I Treated So Bad)/I Don't Want To Go On Without You	5
67	Atlantic 584 132	Let It Be Me/When Something Is Wrong With My Baby	5
68	Atlantic 584 167	Sweet Inspiration/I'm Blue	5
68	Atlantic 584 233	What The World Needs Now Is Love/You Really Didn't Mean It	5
69	Atlantic 584 279	Sweets For My Sweet/Get A Little Older	4
70	Atlantic 584 312	Brand New Lover Pts 1 & 2	4
68	Atlantic 587/588 090	THE SWEET INSPIRATIONS (LP)	10
69	Atlantic 588 137	WHAT THE WORLD NEEDS NOW IS LOVE (LP)	10

SWEET JESUS
90s	Chapter 22 CHAP 63	Cat Thing/Honey Loving Honey/Peach/Baby Blue (12" EP, unreleased, test pressings exist, 25 copies only)	10

SWEET PAIN
71	United Artists UP 35268	Timber Gibbs/Chain Up The Devil	4
69	Mercury SMCL 20146	SWEET PAIN (LP)	30

SWEET PLUM
69	Middle Earth MDS 103	Lazy Day/Let No Man Steal Your Thyme	10
69	Middle Earth MDS 105	Set The Wheels In Motion/Catch A Cloud	10

SWEET SAVAGE
81	Sweet Savage 1980	Take No Prisoners/Killing TIme	15
81	Park PRK 1001	Take No Prisoners/Killing TIme (reissue)	5
80s	private pressing	Straight Through The Heart/Teaser	10
80s	private pressing	The Raid/Prosecutors Of Greed	10

SWEETSHOP
68   Parlophone R 5707   Barefoot And Tiptoe/Lead The Way 4
(see also Mark Wirtz, Ross Hannahan)

SWEET SLAG
71   President PTLS 1042   TRACKING WITH CLOSE-UPS (LP) 20

SWEET THUNDER
78   Fantasy FTC 158   Everybody's Singin' Love Songs/Joyful Noise 4

SWEET THURSDAY
69   Polydor 2310 051   SWEET THURSDAY (LP) 20
(see also Nicky Hopkins, Mark-Almond)

RACHEL SWEET
79   Stiff SEEZP 12   FOOL AROUND (LP, picture disc) 10

SWEETHEARTS
65   Blue Beat BB 289   Sit Down And Cry/PRINCE BUSTER: Ghost Dance 10

SWEGAS
71   Trend 6480 002   CHILD OF LIGHT (LP) 15

SWELL MAPS
78   Rather GEAR ONE   Read About Seymour/Ripped And Torn/Black Velvet (p/s) 12
79   Rough Trade RT 010/   Read About Seymour/Ripped And Torn/Black Velvet (p/s, reissue, different
       Rather GEAR ONE MK. 2   back sleeve) 6
79   R. Trade RT 012/GEAR 3   Dresden Style/Mystery Track/Ammunition Train/Full Moon (Dub)
                         (p/s) 6
79   R. Trade RT 021/GEAR 6   Real Shocks/English Verse/Monlogues (p/s, 2 different colours) 6
79   R. Trade RT 036/GEAR 7   Let's Build A Car/Big Maz In The Country/...Then Poland 6
81   Rough Trade RT 012/   Dresden Style (new vocal)/Ammunition Train/Full Moon (Dub) (p/s, reissue,
       Rather GEAR 3   altered rear sleeve) 7
79   Rough Trade ROUGH 2/   A TRIP TO MARINEVILLE (LP, with inner sleeve, some with free EP in
       Rather TROY 1   die-cut sleeve [Rather GEAR FIVE]) 15/10
80   Rough Trade ROUGH 15   SWELL MAPS IN 'JANE FROM OCCUPIED EUROPE' (LP) 10
81   Rough Trade ROUGH 21   WHATEVER HAPPENS NEXT... (2-LP) 18
84   Rough Trade ROUGH 41   SWELL MAPS IN 'COLLISION TIME' (LP) 10
(see also Cult Figures, Nikki Sudden, Steve Treatment, Phones Sportsman Band, Epic Soundtracks, Metrophase)

SWERVEDRIVER
92   Imaginary FREE 002   Jesus/DYLANS: Who Loves The Sun (promo only) 5

ANTHONY SWETE
69   RCA RCA 1905   Backfield in Motion/Soul Deep 5

JONATHAN SWIFT
71   CBS 64412   INTROVERT (LP, nude cover) 10
72   CBS 64751   SONGS (LP) 10

STEVE SWINDELLS
74   RCA LPL1 5057   MESSAGES (LP) 10
(see also Hawkwind)

SWINGERS
60   Vogue V 9158   Love Makes The World Go Round/Jackie 8

SWINGERS
81   Magnet MAG 202   Be My Baby/Swinging (no p/s) 4
(see also Spectres, Rich Kids)

SWINGING BLUE JEANS
63   HMV POP 1170   It's Too Late Now/Think Of Me 4
63   HMV POP 1206   Do You Know/Angie 5
63   HMV POP 1242   Hippy Hippy Shake/Now I Must Go 4
64   HMV POP 1273   Good Golly Miss Molly/Shakin' Feelin' 4
64   HMV POP 1304   You're No Good/Don't You Worry About Me 4
64   HMV POP 1327   Promise You'll Tell Her/It's So Right 4
64   HMV POP 1375   It Isn't There/One Of These Days 4
65   HMV POP 1409   Make Me Know You're Mine/I've Got A Girl 4
65   HMV POP 1477   Crazy 'Bout My Baby/Good Lovin' 4
66   HMV POP 1501   Don't Make Me Over/What Can I Do Today 5
66   HMV POP 1533   Sandy/I'm Gonna Have You 5
66   HMV POP 1564   Rumours, Gossip, Words Untrue/Now The Summer's Gone 6
67   HMV POP 1596   Tremblin'/Something's Coming Along 5
67   HMV POP 1605   Don't Go Out Into The Rain/One Woman Man 5
64   HMV 7EG 8850   SHAKE WITH THE SWINGING BLUE JEANS (EP) 18
64   HMV 7EG 8868   YOU'RE NO GOOD MISS MOLLY (EP) 25
64   HMV CLP 1802   BLUE JEANS A' SWINGING (LP, also stereo CSD 1570) 40/50
64   Regal SREG 1073   TUTTI FRUTTI (LP, export issue) 30
67   MFP MFP 1163   SWINGING BLUE JEANS (LP, reissue of HMV CLP 1802) 10
74   Dart BULL 1001   BRAND NEW AND FADED (LP) 15
(see also Ray Ennis & Blue Jeans)

SWINGING CATS
80   Two Tone CHS TT 14   Away/Mantovani (p/s) 4

SWINGIN' MEDALLIONS
66   Phillips BF 1500   Double Shot Of My Baby's Love/Here it Comes Again 4
66   Phillips BF 1515   She Drives Me Out Of My Mind/You Gotta Have Faith 8

SWINGING SOUL MACHINE
69   Polydor 56760   Spooky's Day Off/Nobody Wants You 5
(see also Machine)

ERIC SYKES & HATTIE JACQUES
63	Decca LK 4507	ERIC, HATTIE AND THINGS (LP)	10

JOHN SYKES
82	MCA MCA 792	Please Don't Leave Me/Instrumental (with Phil Lynott) (p/s)	30

(see also Thin Lizzy, Phil Lynott)

ROOSEVELT SYKES & HIS HONEYDRIPPERS
56	Vogue V 2389	Fine And Brown/Too Hot To Hold	45
56	Vogue V 2393	Walkin' This Boogie/Security Blues	60
56	Vogue V 2393	Walkin' This Boogie/Security Blues (78)	25
50s	Jazz Collector L 40	Three-Six And Nine/We Can Sell That Thing (78)	6
66	Delmark DJB 2	BACK TO THE BLUES (EP)	20
59	Encore ENC 183	BIG MAN OF THE BLUES (LP)	15
67	'77' 77LEU 12-50	BLUES FROM BAR ROOMS (LP)	15
61	Columbia 33SX 1343	FACE TO FACE WITH THE BLUES (LP)	25
62	Columbia 33SX 1422	THE HONEYDRIPPER (LP)	25
67	Riverside RLP 8819	MR SYKES BLUES 1929-1932 (LP)	20
60s	Ember EMB 3391	SINGS THE BLUES (LP)	15
70s	Delmark DL 607	HARD DRIVIN' BLUES (LP, blue label)	12

SYKO & CARBIS
63	Blue Beat BB 213	Do The Dog/Jenny	6
63	Blue Beat BB 223	Sugar Baby/Big Boy	6

SYLSESTRA ABSURD
80s	Spangle SPANG 3	Dog-Faced Nun Living On The Edge/Heavy Whip Scene	6

SYLTE SISTERS
63	London HLU 9753	Summer Magic/Well It's Summertime	6

SYLVAIN SYLVAIN
80	RCA PB 9500	Every Boy And Every Girl/Emily	4

(see also New York Dolls)

FOSTER SYLVERS
73	MGM 2006 292	Misdemeanour/So Close	4

C. SYLVESTER & PLANETS
64	Blue Beat BB 206	Going South/LITTLE JOYCE: Oh Daddy	8

ROLAND SYLVESTER
64	Carnival CV 7018	Grandfather's Clock/SANDRA MURRAY: Nervous	5

TERRY SYLVESTER
74	Polydor 2383 394	I BELIEVE (LP, with insert)	10

(see also Escorts, Swinging Blue Jeans, Hollies)

SYLVIA
68	Fontana TF 932	Down Hill/A Few Sweet Moments Of Love	4
70	Soul City SC103	I Can't Help It/It's A Good Life	8

DAVID SYLVIAN
84	Virgin VSY 633	Red Guitar/Forbidden Colours (Version) (picture disc)	6
84	Virgin VS 700	The Ink In The Well (Remix)/Weathered Wall (Instrumental)	5
84	Virgin VS 700-12	The Ink In The Well (Remix)/Weathered Wall (Instrumental) (12", g/fold p/s)	7
84	Virgin VS 717	Pulling Punches (7" Mix)/Backwaters (Remix) (p/s with 3 postcards)	4
84	Virgin VS 717-12	Pulling Punches (Extended Mix)/Backwaters (Remix) (12", p/s, with 3 postcards)	7
85	Virgin VS 835-12	WORDS WITH THE SHAMAN (12", p/s)	7
86	Virgin VSS 815	Taking The Veil/Answered Prayers (rectangular picture disc, stickered PVC sleeve)	6
86	Virgin VS 895	Silver Moon/Gone To Earth (p/s)	4
86	Virgin VSP 895	Silver Moon/Gone To Earth (gatefold p/s)	6
89	Virgin DSCD 1	WEATHERBOX (5-CD box set, with poster & booklet)	45

DAVID SYLVIAN & RYUICHI SAKAMOTO
82	Virgin VS 510	Bamboo Houses (7" Mix)/Bamboo Music (7" Mix) (some with g/fold sleeve)	5/4
83	Virgin VSY 601	Forbidden Colours/RYUICHI SAKAMOTO: The Seed And The Sower (picture disc in stickered sleeve)	6

(see also Japan, Yellow Magic Orchestra, Virginia Astley)

SYMARIP
(see under Seven Letters/Symarip, see also Pyramids)

SYMBOLS
67	President PT 173	(The Best Part Of) Breaking Up/Again	4
68	President PT 190	Lovely Way To Say Goodnight/Pretty City	4
68	President PT 216	Do I Love You/Schoolgirl	4
68	President PTL 1018	THE BEST PART OF THE SYMBOLS (LP)	18

SYMON & PI
68	Parlophone R 5662	Baby Baby/Sha La La La Lee	8
68	Parlophone R 5719	Got To See The Sunrise/Love Is Happening To Me	8

SYMPHONICS
72	Polydor 2058 341	Heaven Must Have Sent You/Using Me	4

SYMPHONIC SLAM
76	A&M AMLH 69023	SYMPHONIC SLAM (LP)	12

PAT SYMS
64	Oriole CB 1971	It's Got To Be You Or No One/Lost	4

SYN
67	Deram DM 130	Created By Clive/Grounded	50

67	Deram DM 145	14-Hour Technicolour Dream/Flowerman	50

(see also Syndicats, Yes)

SYNCHROMESH
80s Rok ROK XI/XII — October Friday/E.F. BAND: Another Day Gone (die-cut company sleeve) 8

SYNCOPATORS
61 Decca F 11359 — Everything Stops For Tea/If I Had A Talking Picture Of You 4

RON SYNDER
63 Parlophone R 4993 — Oh My Twisted Bach/Narcissus 4

SYNDICATE
80s Rock Against Racism — Getting Things Done/RESTRICTED HOURS: Still Living Out The Car Crash 6

(see also Astronauts)

SYNDICATE
84 Supreme Intl. Ed.'s 85-9 — Golden Key/Bodyheat (p/s) 4

SYNDICATE OF SOUND
66 Stateside SS 523 — Little Girl/You 20
66 Stateside SS 538 — Rumours/The Upper Hand 12
66 Stateside S(S)L 10185 — LITTLE GIRL (LP) 30

SYNDICATS
64 Columbia DB 7238 — Maybellene/Try To Me 80
65 Columbia DB 7441 — Howlin' For My Baby/What To Do 80
65 Columbia DB 7686 — On The Horizon/Crawdaddy Simone 300

(see also Tomorrow, Syn, Yes)

SYNTHANESIA
69 RCA SF 8058 — SYNTHANESIA (LP) 80

SYSTEM
70s private pressing — THE OTHER SIDE OF TIME (LP) 60

SYSTEM 7
90 10 TENX 335 — Miracle/Sunburst (12", p/s, some on clear vinyl) 15/8

(see also Orb, Steve Hillage)

SLADE

TABLE
77	Virgin VS 176	Do The Standing Still/Magical Melon Of The Tropics (p/s)	5
78	Chiswick NS 31	Sex Cells/The Road Of Lyfe (p/s)	4

TABLE TOPPERS
62	Starlite ST45 069	Rocking Mountain Dew/My Wild Irish Rose Rock	12

CHARLIE TABOR
63	Island WI 061	Blue Atlantic/Red Lion Madison	6

JUNE TABOR
76	Topic 12TS 298	AIRS AND GRACES (LP)	10
77	Topic 12TS 360	ASHES AND DIAMONDS (LP)	10

TACKHEAD
87	4th + Broadway BRWP 65	The Game/The Game (picture disc)	4
87	World WR 012C	Ticking Time Bomb/Body To Burn (cassette)	4
87	On-U Sound ONUDP 13	What's My Mission Now?/Now What? (10", p/s)	6

TAD & SMALL FRY
62	London HLU 9542	Checkered Continental Pants/Pretty Blue Jean Baby	7

TAGES
66	Columbia DB 8019	Crazy 'Bout My Baby/In My Dreams	6
66	HMV POP 1515	So Many Girls/I'm Mad	25
67	Parlophone R 5640	Treat Me Like A Lady/Wanting	6
68	Parlophone R 5702	There's A Blind Man Playin' Fiddle In The Street/Like A Woman	5
68	MGM MGM 1443	Halcyon Days/I Read You Like An Open Book	5

TAGMEMICS
80	Index INDEX 003	Chimneys/(Do The) Big Baby/Take Your Brain Out For A Walk (p/s, with insert)	12

(see also Art Attacks)

BLIND JOE TAGGART
52	Tempo R 55	Religion Is Something Within You/Mother's Love (78)	10
50s	Jazz Collector L 129	Religion Is Something Within You/Mother's Love (78)	5

JACQUELINE TAIEB
68	Fontana TF 952	Tonight I'm Going Home/7 A.M.	40

LYN(N) TAIT(T) (& JETS)
66	Doctor Bird DB 1006	Vilma's Jump Up (as Lyn Taitt & Comets)/GLEN MILLER & HONEYBOY MARTIN: Dad Is Home	8
66	Doctor Bird DB 1047	Spanish Eyes (with Tommy McCook)/STRANGER & HORTENSE: Loving Wine	8
67	Island WI 3066	Something Stupid/Blue Tuesday (as Lyn Tait & Jets)	10
67	Island WI 3075	I Don't Want To Make You Cry/Nice Time (as Lyn Tait & Jets)	10
68	Island WI 3139	Napoleon Solo/Pressure And Slide (as Lyn Taitt & Jets)	10
68	Amalgamated AMG 810	El Casino Royale/Dee's Special (as Lynn Taitt & Jets)	8
68	Pama PM 723	Soul Food/Music Flames (as Lyn Taitt & Jets)	6
68	Island ILP 969	SOUNDS ROCK STEADY (LP, as Lyn Taitt & Jets)	70
68	Big Shot BBTL 4002	GLAD SOUNDS (LP, as Lynn Taitt & Jets)	30

TAKE IT
80s	Fresh Hold TRI	Man Made World/Taking Sides/How It Is (p/s)	4
80	Fresh Hold FHR 1	Twenty Lines/Armchairs/Friends And Relations (p/s)	4

'TAKERS
64	Pye 7N 15690	If You Don't Come Back/Think	10

(see also.Undertakers, Jackie Lomax)

TAKE THAT
91	Dance U.K. DUK 2	Do What You Like/Waiting Around (p/s)	15
91	Dance U.K. CADUK 2	Do What You Like/Waiting Around (cassette)	15
91	Dance U.K. 12DUK 2	Do What You Like (Club Mix)/Do What You Like (Radio Mix)/ Waiting Around (12", p/s)	12
91	RCA PB 45085	Promises/Do What U Like (p/s)	5
91	RCA PB 45085P	Promises/Do What U Like (poster p/s)	12
91	RCA PK 45085	Promises/Do What U Like (cassette)	8
91	RCA PT 45085	Promises (12" Mix)/Do What U Like (12" Mix) (12", p/s)	10
92	RCA PB 45257	Once You've Tasted Love/Guess Who Tasted Love (p/s)	5
92	RCA PB 45265	Once You've Tasted Love/Guess Who Tasted Love (hexagonal pop-up p/s)	12
92	RCA PK 45257	Once You've Tasted Love/Guess Who Tasted Love (cassette with stencil)	10
92	RCA PB 45257	Once You've Tasted Love (Aural Mix)/Guess Who Tasted Love (Guess Who Mix)/Once You've Tasted Love (Radio Version) (12" picture disc, with insert)	20
92	RCA 74321 10100 7	It Only Takes A Minute/Satisfied (p/s, with Mark & Robbie prints)	4
92	RCA 74321 10100 7	It Only Takes A Minute/It Only Takes A Minute (Royal Rave Mix) (different p/s, with Jason & Howard prints and paper frame)	5
92	RCA 74321 10813 7B	I Found Heaven (7" Radio Mix)/I'm Out (picture disc)	5
92	RCA 74321 11600 7	A Million Love Songs/A Million Love Songs (The Lovers Mix) (p/s, with tattoos)	6
92	RCA 74321 11630 7	THE LOVE SONGS (EP)	4
92	RCA 7432 110923-19	TAKE THAT AND PARTY (LP, with poster)	10

TALBOT BROTHERS
59	Melodisc MEL 1507	Bloodshot Eyes/She's Got Freckles	8

ZIGGY TALENT
55	Brunswick 05506	Cheek To Cheek (Cha Cha)/Bozooki Blues	6

TALES OF JUSTINE
67	HMV POP 1614	Albert/Monday Morning (some in p/s)	40/20

TALISKER
75	Caroline CA 1513	DREAMING OF GLENISLA (LP)	12

TALISMAN
72	Argo ZFB 33	PRIMROSE DREAMS (LP)	12
73	Argo ZDA 161	STEPPING STONES (LP)	12

TALISMEN
65	Stateside SS 408	Masters Of War/Casting My Spell	25

TALKING HEADS
77	Sire 6078 604	Love Goes To Building On Fire/New Feeling (p/s)	7
77	Sire 6078 610	Psycho Killer/I Wish You Wouldn't Say That (p/s)	5
77	Sire 6078 610	Psycho Killer/Psycho Killer (Acoustic)/I Wish You Wouldn't Say That (12", p/s)	12
78	Sire 6078 620	Pulled Up/Don't Worry About The Government (p/s)	8
79	Sire SIR 4004	Take Me To The River/Found A Job (p/s)	4
79	Sire SIR 4004/SAM 87	Take Me To The River/Found A Job//Love Goes To Building On Fire/ Psycho Killer (double pack, gatefold p/s)	10
79	Sire SIR 4027	Life During Wartime/Electric Guitar (p/s)	4
79	WEA SPC 9	Take Me To The River/Psycho Killer (cassette)	6
80	Sire SIR 4033	I Zimbra/Paper (p/s)	4
80	Sire SIR 4040	Cities/Cities (live) (p/s)	4
80	Sire SIR 4040T	Cities/Cities (live)/Artists Only (live) (12", p/s)	7
80	Sire SIR 4050	Houses In Motion (Special Re-Mixed Version)/Air (p/s)	4
84	Sire W 9451T/SAM 176	This Must Be The Place (Full Version)/Moon Rocks//Slippery People (Remix)/ Making Flippy Floppy (Remix) (12", p/s, double pack)	8
85	EMI 12EMID 5520	The Lady Don't Mind/Give Me Back My Name//Slippery People (live)/ This Must Be The Place (Naive Melody) (live) (12", p/s, double pack)	7
85	EMI EMIP 5530	Road To Nowhere/Television Man (picture disc)	7
85	EMI 12 EMID 5530	Road To Nowhere (12", double pack)	8
86	EMI 12 EMIP 5543	And She Was (Extended Mix)/And She Was/Perfect World (12", picture disc)	7
87	EMI EMD 1	Radio Head/Hey Now (Movie Version)//Radio Head (Movie Version)/ Radio Head (Extended Remix) (double pack, gatefold sleeve)	5
88	EMI 10EM 53	Nothing But Flowers/Facts Of Life/Ruby Dear/Mommy, Daddy, You And I (10", p/s, numbered)	5
79	Sire K 56707	FEAR OF MUSIC (LP, with free single "Psycho Killer [live]")	12
79	Sire SRK 6076	FEAR OF MUSIC (LP, re-pressing, with free single "Psycho Killer [live]")	10
83	EMI 9237711	SPEAKING IN TONGUES (LP, clear vinyl in special cover)	15

(see also David Byrne, Dinosaur, Tom Tom Club)

TALK TALK
82	EMI EMI 5265	Mirror Man/Strike Up The Band (p/s)	4
82	EMI EMIP 5352	Talk Talk (Remix)/Mirror Man (picture disc)	7
84	EMI EMID 5433	THE TALK TALK DEMOS (double pack, poster p/s [EMI 5433 & PSR 467])	12
86	EMI 12EMID 5540	Life Is What You Make It (Extended)/It's Getting Late In The Evening// It's My Life/Does Caroline Know? (12", p/s, double pack)	7
86	EMI 12EMIX 5540	Life Is What You Make It (Extended Dance Mix)/Life Is What You Make It (Early Mix)/It's Getting Late In The Evening (12", p/s)	8
86	EMI EMIP 5551	Living In Another World/For What It's Worth (shaped picture disc)	7

(see also Reaction)

TOM TALL
55	London HL 8150	Are You Mine/Boom Boom Boomerang (as Ginny Wright & Tom Tall)	20
55	London HL 8150	Are You Mine/Boom Boom Boomerang (as Ginny Wright & Tom Tall) (78)	5
55	London HLU 8216	Give Me A Chance/Remembering You	25
55	London HLU 8216	Give Me A Chance/Remembering You (78)	5
56	London HLU 8231	Underway/Goldie Jo Malone	25
56	London HLU 8231	Underway/Goldie Jo Malone (78)	5
57	London HLU 8429	Don't You Know/If You Know What I Know (with Ruckus Taylor)	20
57	London HLU 8429	Don't You Know/If You Know What I Know (with Ruckus Taylor) (78)	5
55	London REU 1035	COUNTRY SONGS VOL. 2 (EP, as Tom Tall & Ginny Wright)	30

(see also Ginny Wright)

TALL BOYS
82	Big Beat NS 79	Island Of Lost Souls/Another Half Hour Till Sunrise (p/s)	5
84	Big Beat NED 8	WEDNESDAY ADDAM'S BOYFRIEND (EP)	4

(see also Meteors)

TALMY/STONE BAND
62	Decca F 11543	Madison Time/Madison Time (B-side with Alan Freeman)	5
62	Ace Of Clubs ACL 1134	ROSES ARE RED & OTHER HITS OF 1962 (LP)	15

TALULAH GOSH
86	53rd & 3rd AGARR 4	Beatnik Boy/My Best Friend (p/s)	5
86	53rd & 3rd AGARR 5	Steaming Train/Just A Dream (p/s)	5
86	53rd & 3rd AGARR 4/5T	Beatnik Boy/My Best Friend/Steaming Train/Just A Dream (12", p/s)	7
86	Sha La La 002/LYN 18147	WHO NEEDS THE BLOODY CARTEL ANYWAY (EP, p/s flexidisc)	7
87	53rd & 3rd AGARR 8	Talulah Gosh/Don't Go Away (p/s)	5
87	53rd & 3rd AGARR 8T	Talulah Gosh/Don't Go Away (12", p/s)	7
88	53rd & 3rd AGARR 14	Bringing Up Baby/The Girl With The Strawberry Hair (p/s)	5
88	53rd & 3rd AGARR 14T	Bringing Up Baby/I Can't Get No Satisfaction, Thank God/The Girl With The Strawberry Hair/Do You Remember?/Sunny Inside (12", p/s)	
88	53rd & 3rd AGARR 16	Testcard Girl (p/s)	5
87	53rd & 3rd AGAS 004	ROCK LEGENDS VOL. 69 (LP, clear vinyl)	10

(see also Carousel)

MINT VALUE £

TAMANGOE'S
| 79 | Grapevine GRP 122 | I Really Love You/You've Been Gone So Long (withdrawn) | 6 |

JAMES TAMLIN
| 65 | Columbia DB 7438 | Is There Time/Main Line Central Station | 10 |
| 65 | Columbia DB 7577 | Yes I Have/Now There Are Two | 4 |

TAMPA RED
50s	Square M 2	Moot It Boy/She Rocks Me (With One Steady Roll) (78)	50
50s	HMV JO 301	Pretty Baby Blues/Since My Baby's Been Gone (78, export issue)	35
50s	Jazz Collector L 58	Easy Rider Blues/Come On Mama Do That Dance (78)	8
64	RCA RCX 7160	R & B VOL. 3 (EP)	20

TAMPA RED/GEORGIA TOM
| 59 | Jazz Collector JEL 3 | THE MALE BLUES VOLUME 2 (EP) | 8 |

TAMS
63	Stateside SS 146	Untie Me/Disillusioned	6
63	HMV POP 1254	What Kind Of Fool Do You Think I Am/Laugh It Off	10
64	HMV POP 1298	It's All Right, You're Just In Love/You Lied To Your Daddy	8
64	HMV POP 1331	Hey Girl Don't Bother Me/Take Away	25
65	HMV POP 1464	Concrete Jungle/Till The End Of Time	10
69	Stateside SS 2123	Be Young, Be Foolish, Be Happy/That Same Old Song	8
70	Capitol CL 15650	Too Much Foolin' Around/How Much Love	4
75	ABC ABC 4020	Hey Girl Don't Bother Me/Be Young, Be Foolish, Be Happy	4
68	Stateside (S)SL 10258	A LITTLE MORE SOUL (LP)	12
70	Stateside SSL 10304	BE YOUNG, BE FOOLISH, BE HAPPY (LP)	12
74	Probe ABCL 5118	THE BEST OF THE TAMS (LP)	10

TANAHILL WEAVERS
| 76 | Plant Life PLR 001 | ARE YE SLEEPING MAGGIE? (LP) | 10 |
| 78 | Plant Life PLR 010 | THE OLD WOMAN'S DANCE (LP) | 10 |

SHARON TANDY
65	Mercury MF 898	Love Makes The World Go Round/By My Side	6
65	Pye 7N 15806	Now That You've Gone/Hurtin' Me	6
65	Pye 7N 15939	I've Found Love/Perhaps Not Forever	6
67	Atlantic 584 098	Toe Hold/I Can't Let Go	7
67	Atlantic 584 124	Stay With Me/Hold On	12
67	Atlantic 584 137	Our Day Will Come And Find	8
68	Atlantic 584 166	Fool On The Hill/For No One	7
68	Atlantic 584 181	Love Is Not A Simple Affair/Hurry Hurry Choo-Choo	7
68	Atlantic 584 194	You've Gotta Believe It/Border Town	7
68	Atlantic 584 214	The Way She Looks At You/He'll Hurt Me	7
68	Atlantic 584 219	Hold On/Daughter Of The Sun	10
69	Atlantic 584 242	Gotta Get Enough Time/Somebody Speaks Your Name	7

(see also Fleur-De-Lys, Tony & Tandy)

TANDY-MORGAN BAND
| 86 | FM Revolver WKFMLP 68 | EARTHRISE (LP, with lyric sheet) | 10 |

(see also E.L.O.)

NORMA TANEGA
| 66 | Stateside SS 496 | Walkin' My Cat Named Dog/I'm In The Sky | 4 |
| 66 | Stateside S(S)L 10182 | WALKIN' MY CAT NAMED DOG (LP) | 12 |

TANGERINE DREAM
74	Virgin PR 214	Phaedra (Edit)/Mysterious Semblance At The Strand Of Nightmares (promo-only)	10
76	Virgin VDJ 17	Stratosfear/The Big Sleep In Search Of Hades (promo-only)	8
77	MCA PSR 413	Betrayal (Sorceror Theme)/Search (promo-only)	7
77	Virgin VS 199	Encore/Hobo March (no p/s)	4
84	Jive Electro P 74	Warsaw In The Sun/Polish Dance (map-shaped picture disc)	5
74	Polydor Super 2383 297	ATEM (LP)	10
75	Polydor Super 2383 314	ALPHA CENTAURI (LP)	10
79	Virgin V 2111	FORCE MAJEURE (LP, clear vinyl)	10
80	Virgin VBOX 2	TANGERINE DREAM '70-'80 (4-LP box set)	20
84	MCA MCF 3233	FIRESTARTER (LP, soundtrack)	10
84	Jive Electro HIPX 22	POLAND — THE WARSAW CONCERT (2-LP, picture disc)	18
85	Heavy Metal HM1 PD 29	FLASHPOINT (LP, soundtrack, picture disc)	10

TANGERINE PEEL
67	United Artists UP 1193	Every Christian Lion-Hearted Man Will Show You/Trapped	12
68	CBS 3402	Solid Gold Mountain/Light Across The River	4
68	CBS 3676	Talking To No One/Wishing Tree	5
70	RCA RCA 2036	What Am I To Do?/Don't Let Me Be Misunderstood	5

TANK
81	Kamaflage KAM 1	Don't Walk Away/The Snake	4
81	Kamaflage KAM 1	Don't Walk Away/The Snake (with camouflage p/s)	5
82	Kamaflage KAM 7	Crazy Horses/Filth Bitch Boogie	4
82	Kamaflage KAP 1	(He Fell In Love With A) Stormtrooper/Blood Guts And Beer (picture disc)	4
82	Kamaflage KAMLP 1	FILTH HOUNDS OF HADES (with bonus 7")	10
82	Kamaflage KAMLP 3	POWER OF THE HUNTER	10

HOLLY TANNEN & PETE COOPER
| 79 | Plant Life PLR 015 | FROSTY MORNING (LP) | 12 |

TANTONES
| 57 | Vogue V 9085 | So Afraid/Tell Me | 250 |
| 57 | Vogue V 9085 | So Afraid/Tell Me (78) | 50 |

TANTRUM
80	Ovation OV 1247	RATHER BE ROCKIN' (LP)	10

TANZ DER YOUTH
78	Radar ADA 19	I'm Sorry, I'm Sorry/Delay	4

(see also Brian James)

TAPESTRY
67	London HLZ 10138	Carnaby Street/Taming Of The Shrew	8
68	NEMS 56-3679	Like The Sun/Florence	4

DEMETRISS TAPP
64	Coral Q 72470	Lipstick Paint A Smile On Me/If You Find Love	4

TARA
78	Polydor 2066 009	Happy/El Amor De Una Mujer	8

TARANTULA
70	A&M AMLS 959	TARANTULA (LP)	12

JIMMY TARBUCK
65	Immediate IM 018	Someday/(We're) Wastin' Time	8

TARHEEL SLIM & LITTLE ANN
65	Sue WI 390	You Make Me Feel So Good/Got To Keep On Lovin' You	8

TARRIERS
57	Columbia DB 3891	The Banana Boat Song/No Hidin' Place	6
57	Columbia DB 3961	Tom Dooley/Everybody Loves Saturday Night	6
57	Columbia DB 4025	Dunya/Quinto (My Little Pony)	5
58	Columbia DB 4148	I Know Where I'm Going/Acres Of Clams	5
58	London HLU 8600	Lonesome Traveller/East Virginia	10
57	Columbia 33S 1115	THE TARRIERS (10" LP)	12

TARTAN HORDE
75	United Artists UP 35891	Bay City Rollers, We Love You/Rollers Theme	6

(see also Nick Lowe, Rat Scabies, Roogalator)

TARTANS
67	Island WI 3058	Dance All Night/What Can I Do	8
68	Caltone TONE 115	Awake The Town (with Lynn Taitt's Band)/LYNN TAITT & JETS: The Brush	8
68	Caltone TONE 117	Coming On Strong/It's Alright (with Tommy McCook's Band)	8

(see also Devon & Tartans)

TASAVALLAN PRESIDENTI
73	Sonet SNTF 636	LAMBERTLAND (LP)	10
74	Sonet SNTF 658	MILKY WAY MOSES (LP, with insert)	10

TASSELS
59	London HL 8885	To A Soldier Boy/The Boy For Me	60
59	London HL 8885	To A Soldier Boy/The Boy For Me (78)	15
59	Top Rank JAR 229	To A Young Lover/My Guy And I	18

TASTE
68	Major Minor MM 560	Blister On The Moon/Born On The Wrong Side Of Time	10
69	Polydor 583 042	TASTE (LP)	15
70	Polydor 583 083	ON THE BOARDS (LP)	12
71	Polydor 2310 082	LIVE TASTE (LP)	10
72	Polydor 2383 120	TASTE — LIVE AT THE ISLE OF WIGHT (LP)	10

(see also Rory Gallagher)

BUDDY TATE
58	Felsted FAJ 7004	SWINGING LIKE TATE (LP)	15

HOWARD TATE
66	Verve VS 541	Ain't Nobody Home/How Come My Bulldog Won't Bark	8
67	Verve VS 549	Look At Granny Run Run/Half A Man	10
67	Verve VS 552	Get It While You Can/Glad I Knew Better	6
67	Verve VS 555	Baby I Love You/How Blue Can You Get	7
67	Verve VS 556	I Learned It All The Hard Way/Part Time Love	6
68	Verve VS 565	Stop/Shoot 'Em All Down	6
68	Verve VS 571	Night Owl/Every Day I Have The Blues	8
70	Major Minor MM 696	My Soul's Got A Hole In It/It's Too Late	5
67	Verve (S)VLP 9179	GET IT WHILE YOU CAN (LP)	15

PHIL TATE ORCHESTRA
59	Oriole CB 1514	Countdown (Jive)/Green Turtle	5
63	Oriole CB 1832	Hi-Lili, Hi-Lo/Theme From 'Dr. Kildare'	5
63	Oriole CB 1878	Devils Horn (Twist)/Hitch Hike (Twist)	5
62	Oriole EP 7052	PARTY DANCES (EP)	7
62	Oriole EP 7060	TUNES FOR TWISTERS (EP)	10

TOMMY TATE
66	Columbia DB 8046	Big Blue Diamonds/A Lover's Reward	20

ART TATUM
54	Vogue EPV 1008	ART TATUM (EP)	8
55	Columbia SEG 7540	ART TATUM (EP)	8
50s	Melodisc EPM7 108	ART TATUM TRIO (EP)	7
55	Columbia Clef SEB 10003	ART TATUM (EP)	7
56	Columbia Clef SEB 10027	TATUM-CARTER-BELLSON TRIO (EP, with Benny Carter & Louis Bellson)	8
57	Columbia Clef SEB 10062	TATUM-CARTER-BELLSON TRIO (EP, with Benny Carter & Louis Bellson)	8
57	Philips BBE 12136	UNFORGETTABLE ART (EP)	8
58	Columbia Clef SEB 10084	ART TATUM AT HOLLYWOOD BOWL (EP)	7
58	Columbia Clef SEB 10101	ART TATUM — BUDDY DE FRANCO QUARTET (EP)	7

Art TATUM

59	Columbia Clef SEB 10116	DELICATE TOUCH OF ART TATUM (EP)	7
60	Fontana TFE 17235	ART TATUM NO. 1 (EP)	7
60	Fontana TFE 17236	ART TATUM NO. 2 (EP)	8
60	Fontana TFE 17237	ART TATUM NO. 3 (EP)	7
60	HMV 7EG 8604	THE GREATEST PIANO OF THEM ALL (EP)	7
60	HMV 7EG 8619	ART TATUM — BUDDY DE FRANCO QUARTET (EP)	7
61	HMV 7EG 8684	INCOMPARABLE MUSIC OF ART TATUM (EP)	7
62	Ember EMB 4502	MEMORIES OF ART TATUM (EP)	7
57	Vogue EPV 1212	ART TATUM (EP)	8
51	Capitol LC 6524	ART TATUM (10" LP)	18
53	Capitol LC 6625	OUT OF NOWHERE (10" LP)	16
54	Vogue LDE 081	ART TATUM "JUST JAZZ" (10" LP)	15
55	Vogue Coral LRA 10011	THE ART TATUM TRIO (10" LP)	15
55	Columbia Clef 33CX 10005	THE GENIUS OF ART TATUM (LP)	12
55	Capitol LC 6638	ART TATUM ENCORES (10" LP)	15
56	Columbia Clef 33CX 10053	THE GENIUS OF ART TATUM (NO. 2) (LP)	12
57	Columbia Clef 33C 9033	THE GENIUS OF ART TATUM (NO. 3) (10" LP)	15
57	Columbia Clef 33C 9039	PRESENTING THE ART TATUM TRIO (10" LP)	15
57	Vogue Coral LVA 9047	HERE'S ART TATUM (LP)	12
58	Columbia Clef 33CX 10115	ART TATUM (LP)	12
59	Columbia Clef 33CX 10137	ART TATUM-BEN WEBSTER QUARTET (LP)	12
60	Top Rank 35/067	ART TATUM DISCOVERIES (LP)	10
61	Brunswick LAT 8358	THE ART OF TATUM (LP)	10
61	Ember EMB 3314	MEMORIES OF ART TATUM (LP)	10
61	Ember EMB 3326	MEMORIES OF ART TATUM VOL. 2 (LP)	10
64	Xtra XTRA 1007	ART TATUM (LP)	10
67	Fontana FJL 904	ART (LP)	10

TAVARES

74	Capitol CL 15795	She's Gone/To Love You	5
75	Capitol CL 15809	Remember What I Told You To Forget/My Ship	5
76	Capitol CL 15848	Free Ride/In The Eyes Of Love	4
76	Capitol CL 15867	Love I Never Had/In The City	4
77	Capitol E-ST 11628	LOVE STORM (LP)	10

JOHN TAVENER

70	Apple SAPCOR 15	THE WHALE (LP, gatefold sleeve)	60
71	Apple SAPCOR 20	CELTIC REQUIEM (LP, gatefold sleeve, with insert)	120
77	Ring O' 2320 104	THE WHALE (LP, reissue)	25

TAVERNERS (Blackpool)

69	Saga EROS 8146	SELDOM SOBER (LP)	20
73	Trailer LER 2080	BLOWING SAND (LP)	15
74	Folk Heritage FHR 062	TIMES OF OLD ENGLAND (LP)	12

TAVERNERS (Brighton)

78	Folk Heritage FHR 101	SAME OLD FRIENDS (LP, with insert)	10

TAW FOLK

75	Sentinel SENS 1030	DEVONSHIRE CREAM AND CIDER (LP)	15

TAXI GIRL

80	Virgin VS 467	Cherchez Le Garçon/Jardin Chinois (p/s)	4

ALLAN TAYLOR

71	Liberty LBF 15447	Sometimes/Song For Kathy	4
71	Liberty LBS 83483	SOMETIMES (LP)	15

AUSTIN TAYLOR

60	Top Rank JAR 511	Push Push/A Heart That's True	6

BILLY TAYLOR (TRIO)

50s	Esquire EP 115	BILLY TAYLOR (EP)	7
50s	Esquire EP 169	BILLY TAYLOR TRIO (EP)	7
54	Felsted EDL 87009	JAZZ AT STORYVILLE (10" LP)	10

BOBBY TAYLOR

64	Columbia DB 7282	Temptation/Mod Bod	5

BOBBY TAYLOR (& VANCOUVERS)

68	Tamla Motown TMG 654	Does Your Mama Know About Me/Fading Away (with Vancouvers)	15
73	Epic EPC 1720	I Can't Quit Your Love/Queen Of The Ghetto (solo)	6
69	T. Motown (S)TML 11093	BOBBY TAYLOR AND THE VANCOUVERS (LP)	15
70	T. Motown (S)TML 11125	TAYLOR MADE SOUL (LP, as Bobby Taylor)	12

BRYAN TAYLOR

61	Piccadilly 7N 35018	The Donkey Smile/Let It Snow On Christmas Day	15

CECIL TAYLOR QUARTET

60	Contemporary LAC 12216	LOOKING AHEAD! (LP)	12

CHIP TAYLOR

62	Warner Bros WB 82	Here I Am/I Love You But I Know	5
72	Buddah 2011 151	Angel Of The Morning/Swear To God Your Honor	4
73	Buddah 2318 074	GASOLINE (LP)	10
74	Warner Bros K 56032	CHIP TAYLOR'S LAST CHANCE (LP)	10

DEBBIE TAYLOR

76	Arista ARIST 50	I Wanna Leave You/Just Don't Pay	5

EDDIE TAYLOR

65	Big Bear BEAR 6	READY FOR EDDIE (LP)	10

EDDIE TAYLOR & FLOYD JONES

60s	XX MIN 712	EDDIE TAYLOR & FLOYD JONES (EP)	10

EDDIE TAYLOR & JIMMY REED
60s	XX MIN 704	EDDIE TAYLOR & JIMMY REED (EP)	10

(see also Jimmy Reed)

ELIZABETH TAYLOR
63	Colpix PXL 459	ELIZABETH TAYLOR IN LONDON (LP, with music by John Barry)	25

(see also John Barry)

EVA TAYLOR
24	Parlophone E 521	Irresistable Blues/Jazzin' Babies Blues (78)	50
30s	Parlophone E 5670	Mandy Make Up Your Mind/I'm A Little Blackbird Looking For A Bluebird (78)	35
30s	Edison 14046	Have You Ever Felt That Way?/West End Blues (78)	50
30s	Edison 52646	Have You Ever Felt That Way?/West End Blues (78, reissue)	50
35	Parlophone R 1680	Shim Sham Shimmy Dance/ Chizzlin' Sam (78)	35
37	Regal Zono. MR 2539	Wanted/CLARENCE WILLIAMS & HIS WASHBOARD BAND: Turn Off (78)	40

FELICE TAYLOR
67	President PT 120	It May Be Winter Outside/BOB KEENE ORCHESTRA: Winter Again	5
67	President PT 133	I'm Under The Influence/BOB KEENE ORCHESTRA: Love Theme	5
67	President PT 155	I Feel Love Comin' On/BOB KEENE ORCHESTRA: Comin' On Again	4
68	President PT 193	I Can Feel Your Love/Captured By Your Love	6
68	President PT 220	Suree-Surrender/All I Want To Do Is Love You	4

GEOFF TAYLOR
50s	Esquire EP 55	GEOFF TAYLOR SEXTET (EP)	7
50s	Esquire EP 105	GEOFF TAYLOR ALL STARS (EP)	7

GLORIA TAYLOR
70	Polydor BM 56788	You Gotta Pay The Price/Loving You And Being Loved By You	6

HOUND DOG TAYLOR
66	Outasite 45-504	Christine/Alley Music	30

JAMES TAYLOR
70	Apple APPLE 32	Carolina In My Mind/Something's Wrong	8
68	Apple (S)APCOR 3	JAMES TAYLOR (LP, gatefold sleeve, black cover lettering, mono/stereo)	30/20
70	Apple SAPCOR 3	JAMES TAYLOR (LP, 2nd issue, gatefold sleeve, orange cover lettering)	15
70	Warner Bros WS 1843	SWEET BABY JAMES (LP, red label, later green label)	12/10
71	Warner Bros WS 2561	MUD SLIDE SLIM AND THE BLUE HORIZON (LP, g/fold sleeve, green label)	10
72	Warner Bros K 46185	ONE MAN DOG (LP, green label, with insert)	10

JAMES TAYLOR QUARTET
87	Re-Elect President FORD1	Blow Up/One Mint Julep (p/s)	7
92	Big Life JTQ 7 PROMO 1	Absolution (live) (gig freebie, plain black sleeve with postcard, 1 side etched)	5
87	Re-Elect Pres. REAGAN 2	MISSION IMPOSSIBLE (mini-LP, 45rpm)	8

(see also Prisoners, Daggermen)

JEREMY TAYLOR
62	Decca F 11502	Ag. Pleeze Daddy/Jo'burg Talking Blues	4
68	Fontana TF 962	Red Velvet Steering Wheel/Nasty Spider	4
64	Decca DFE 8581	"WAIT A MINIM" SONGS (EP)	10
66	Decca LK 4731	ALWAYS SOMETHING NEW (LP)	25
68	Fontana STL 5475	HIS SONGS (LP)	12
70	Fontana STL 5523	MORE OF HIS SONGS (LP)	12
72	Galliard GAL 4018	PIECE OF GROUND (LP)	18
73	Canon CPT 3982	JOBSWORTH (LP)	12
75	Spark SRLP 115	COME TO BLACKPOOL (LP)	10

JOHN TAYLOR
71	Turtle	PAUSE AND THINK AGAIN (LP)	40

JOHNNIE TAYLOR
67	Stax 601 003	Ain't That Lovin' You/Outside Love (dark blue label, later light blue)	7/4
68	Stax STX 2025	Friday Night/I Ain't Particular	7
68	Stax STX 106	Who's Makin' Love/I'm Trying	4
69	Stax STAX 114	Take Care Of Your Homework/Hold On This Time	4
69	Stax STAX 122	(I Wanna) Testify/I Had To Fight With Love	4
69	Stax STAX 129	I Could Never Be President/It's Amazing	4
70	Stax STAX 141	Love Bones/Separation Line	4
70	Stax STAX 150	Steal Away/Friday Night	6
70	Stax STAX 156	I Am Somebody Pts 1 & 2	4
71	Stax 2025 021	Jody's Got Your Girl And Gone/A Fool Like Me	4
73	Stax 2025 083	Standing In For Jody/Shackin' Up	4
73	Stax 2025 194	I Believe In Love/Love Depression	4
75	Stax STXS 2021	It's September/Just One Moment	4
70	CBS 4886	Disco Lady/Sombody's Gettin' It (blue vinyl)	4
67	Stax 589 008	WANTED, ONE SOUL SINGER (LP)	14
69	Stax (S)XATS 1006	WHO'S MAKING LOVE (LP)	14
69	Stax 228 008	LOOKING FOR JOHNNIE TAYLOR (LP)	12
70	Stax SXATS 1024	THE J.T. PHILOSOPHY CONTINUES (LP)	12
71	Stax 2363 009	WHO'S MAKING LOVE (LP, reissue)	10
74	Stax STXH 5003	SUPER TAYLOR (LP)	10
75	Stax STS 3014	TAYLORED IN SILK (LP)	10
78	CBS 82776	EVER READY (LP)	10

(LITTLE) JOHNNY TAYLOR
65	Vocalion V 9234	Part Time Love/Somewhere Down The Line	10
66	Vocalion VP 9264	One More Chance/Looking At The Future	10
72	Mojo 2092 033	Everybody Knows About My Good Thing Pts 1 & 2	4
73	Mojo 2092 044	It's My Fault Darling/There's Something On Your Mind	4
65	Vocalion VA-F 8031	LITTLE JOHNNY TAYLOR (LP)	25

Johnny TAYLOR

72	Polydor 2916 015	EVERYBODY KNOWS ABOUT MY GOOD THING (LP)	12
73	Contempo COLP 1003	OPEN HOUSE AT MY HOUSE (LP)	10
74	Contempo CLP 502	SUPER TAYLORS (LP, with Ted Taylor)	10

KINGSIZE TAYLOR (& DOMINOS)

63	Polydor NH 66990	Memphis Tennessee/Money	12
64	Decca F 11874	Stupidity/Bad Boy	12
64	Decca F 11935	Somebody's Always Trying/Looking For My Baby (solo)	12
65	Polydor BM 56152	Thinkin'/Let Me Love You	18
63	Polydor EPH21 628	TWIST AND SHAKE (EP)	40
64	Decca DFE 8569	TEENBEAT 2 — FROM THE STAR CLUB, HAMBURG (EP)	60

(see also Shakers, Paddy Klaus & Gibson)

KO KO TAYLOR

| 66 | Chess CRS 8035 | Wang Dang Doodle/Blues Heaven | 10 |
| 72 | Chess 6145 018 | Violent Love/The Egg Or The Hen/Wang Dang Doodle | 4 |

MICK TAYLOR

| 65 | CBS 201770 | London Town/Hoboin' | 15 |

(this is NOT the Rolling Stones' guitarist)

MIKE TAYLOR

| 65 | Columbia SX 6042 | PENDULUM (LP) | 50 |
| 66 | Columbia SX 6137 | TRIO (LP) | 60 |

(see also Jack Bruce)

MONTANA TAYLOR

| 50s | Vocalion V 1011 | Indiana Avenue Stomp/ROMEO NELSON: Head Rag Hop (78) | 5 |

NEVILLE TAYLOR (& CUTTERS)

58	Parlophone R 4447	House Of Bamboo/Mercy, Mercy, Percy (solo)	12
58	Parlophone R 4447	House Of Bamboo/Mercy Mercy Percy (solo) (78)	5
58	Parlophone R 4476	I Don't Want To Set The World On Fire/Tears On My Pillow (solo)	10
58	Parlophone R 4476	I Don't Want To Set The World On Fire/Tears On My Pillow (solo) (78)	5
58	Parlophone R 4493	A Baby Lay Sleeping/The Miracle Of Christmas (solo)	7
58	Parlophone R 4493	A Baby Lay Sleeping/The Miracle Of Christmas (solo) (78)	5
59	Parlophone R 4524	Crazy Little Daisy/The First Words Of Love (solo)	12
59	Parlophone R 4524	Crazy Little Daisy/The First Words Of Love (solo) (78)	20
60	Oriole CB 1546	Dance With A Dolly/Free Passes	7
60s	Honey Hit TB 127	Joshua Fit The Battle Of Jericho/It's Me, It's Me, It's Me, My Love (p/s)	6

(see also Hal Munro)

R. DEAN TAYLOR

68	Tamla Motown TMG 656	Gotta See Jane/Don't Fool Around	5
71	Rare Earth RES 101	Ain't It A Sad Thing/Backstreet	5
71	T. Motown STML 11185	INDIANA WANTS ME (LP)	20

ROGER TAYLOR

77	EMI EMI 2679	I Wanna Testify/Turn On The TV (no p/s)	35
81	EMI EMI 5157	Future Management/Laugh Or Cry (p/s)	8
81	EMI EMI 5200	My Country (Edit)/Fun In Space (p/s)	12
84	EMI EMI 5478	Man On Fire/Killing Time (p/s)	12
84	EMI 12 EMI 5478	Man On Fire (Extended)/Killing Time (12", p/s)	25
84	EMI EMI 5490	Strange Frontier/I Cry For You (Remix) (p/s)	18
84	EMI 12 EMI 5490	Strange Frontier (Extended)/I Cry For You (Extended Remix)/ Two Sharp Pencils (12", p/s)	25
81	EMI EMC 3369	FUN IN SPACE (LP)	15
84	EMI RTA 1	STRANGE FRONTIER (LP)	15

(see also Queen, Cross, Hilary Hilary, Ian Hunter, Fox, Kansas)

SAM ('THE MAN') TAYLOR

| 54 | MGM SP 1106 | Please Be Kind/This Can't Be Love (as Sam 'The Man' Taylor & Cat Men) | 20 |
| 56 | MGM MGM-EP 531 | SAM TAYLOR ORCHESTRA (EP) | 18 |

(see also Claude Cloud)

TED TAYLOR

| 73 | Contempo C 19 | I Want To Be Part Of You Girl/Going In The Hole | 4 |

TED TAYLOR FOUR

58	Oriole CB 1464	Son Of Honky Tonk/Farrago	6
60	Oriole CB 1573	M.1./You Are My Sunshine	6
61	Oriole CB 1574	Fried Onions/Yellow Rock Of Texas	6
61	Oriole CB 1628	Cat's Eyes/Canyon	6
61	Oriole CB 1630	Flyover/Haunted Pad	8
62	Oriole CB 1713	Jericho/Everytime We Say Goodbye	8
62	Oriole CB 1767	Surfrider/Talent Spot	12

VERNON TAYLOR

| 59 | London HLS 8905 | Today Is A Blue Day/Breeze (unreleased) | |
| 60 | London HLS 9025 | Mystery Train/Sweet And Easy To Love | 60 |

VIC TAYLOR

| 67 | Treasure Isle TI 7021 | Heartaches/When It Comes To Loving You I'm Alright (B-side actually "Loving Pauper" by Dobby Dobson) | 10 |
| 71 | Trojan TRLS 38 | DOES IT HIS WAY (LP) | 10 |

VINCE TAYLOR (& HIS PLAYBOYS)

58	Parlophone R 4505	Right Behind You Baby/I Like Love (solo)	20
58	Parlophone R 4505	Right Behind You Baby/I Like Love (solo) (78)	45
59	Parlophone R 4539	Brand New Cadillac/Pledging My Love	20
60	Palette PG 9001	I'll Be Your Hero/Jet Black Machine	15
61	Palette PG 9020	Move Over Tiger/What Cha Gonna Do	18
76	Chiswick (N)S 2	Brand New Cadillac/Pledging My Love (no p/s)	5

WALTER TAYLOR
50s   Poydras 2   Thirty-Eight And Plus/Diamond Ring Blues (78) 8

TAYLOR MAIDS
55   Capitol CL 14322   Po-Go Stick/Theme From "I Am A Camera" (Why Do I) 7

T-BONES
64   Columbia DB 7401   How Many More Times/I'm A Lover Not A Fighter 25
65   Columbia DB 7489   Won't You Give Him (One More Chance)/Hamish's Express Relief 20
(see also Gary Farr & T-Bones)

BRAM TCHAIKOVSKY
79   Radar ADA 28   Girl Of My Dreams/Come Back//Robber (live)/Whiskey & Wine (double pack) 5
79   Radar ADA 37   I'm The One That's Leaving/Amelia (picture disc) 5
79   Criminal SWAG 3   Sarah Smiles/Turn On The Light (no p/s) 4
79   Criminal DSWAG 3   Sarah Smiles/Turn On The Light/Bloodline (12", p/s) 7
79   Criminal DSWAG 8   Lullaby On Broadway/Rock 'n' Roll Cabaret/Who Wants To Be A Criminal (12") 7

(see also Motors, Heroes)

T. CONNECTION
77   TK XB 9109   Do What You Wanna Do/Got To See My Baby 4
77   TK XC 9109   Do What You Wanna Do/Got To See My Baby (12") 7

TEA
74   Vertigo 6147 006   Good Times/Judy 4
75   Philips 6305 238   TEA (LP) 10
75   Philips 9118 001   THE SHIP (LP) 10
(see also Krokus)

TEA & SYMPHONY
69   Harvest HAR 5005   Boredom/Armchair Theatre 10
69   Harvest SHVL 761   AN ASYLUM FOR THE MUSICALLY INSANE (LP) 45
70   Harvest SHVL 785   JO SAGO (LP) 70

TEACHO & HIS STUDENTS
58   Felsted AF 104   Rock-et/Stop 25
58   Felsted AF 104   Rock-et/Stop (78) 30

TEA COMPANY
68   Mercury SMCL 20127   COME AND HAVE SOME TEA WITH THE TEA COMPANY (LP) 25

TEARDROP EXPLODES
79   Zoo CAGE 003   Sleeping Gas/Camera Camera/Kirkby Workers' Dream Fades (red or blue p/s) 12/10
79   Zoo CAGE 005   Bouncing Babies/All I Am Is Loving You (p/s) 10
80   Zoo CAGE 008   Treason (It's Just A Story)/Read It In Books (p/s) 8
80   Mercury TEAR 1   When I Dream/Kilimanjaro (p/s) 4
81   Mercury TEAR 312   Treason (It's Just A Story) (Remix)/Traison (C'est Juste Une Histoire)/Use Me (12", p/s) 8
81   Mercury TEAR 4   Ha Ha I'm Drowning/Poppies In The Field (with withdrawn p/s, £30) 5
81   Mercury TEAR 44   Ha Ha I'm Drowning/Poppies In The Field/Bouncing Babies/Read In Books (double pack, gatefold p/s) 8
81   Mercury TEAR 44   Ha Ha I'm Drowning/Poppies In The Field/Bouncing Babies/Read In Books (double pack, withdrawn gatefold p/s) 40
81   Mercury TEAR 512   Passionate Friend/Christ Versus Warhol (12", no p/s) 8
81   Mercury TEAR 6   Colours Fly Away/Window Shopping For A New Crown Of Thorns (p/s, with insert) 5
81   Mercury TEAR 612   Colours Fly Away/East Of The Equator/Window Shopping (12", p/s) 7
82   Mercury TEAR 7   Tiny Children/Rachael Built A Steamboat (p/s) 5
82   Mercury TEAR 7G   Tiny Children/Rachael Built A Steamboat (gatefold p/s) 4
82   Mercury TEAR 712   Tiny Children/Rachael Built A Steamboat/Sleeping Gas (live) (12", p/s) ...7
83   Mercury TEAR 88   You Disappear From View/Suffocate//Ouch Monkey's/Soft Enough For You The In-Psychlopedia (double pack, gatefold p/s) 6
80   Mercury 6359 035   KILIMANJARO (LP, original issue with 'group photo' on cover) 10
(see also Julian Cope, Rabbi Joseph Gordon)

TEARDROPS
79   TJM TJM 9   Seeing Double/Teardrops And Heartaches (p/s) 4

TEAR GAS
70   Famous SFMA 5751   PIGGY GO GETTER (LP) 15
71   Regal Zono. SLRZ 1021   TEAR GAS (LP) 100
(see also Sensational Alex Harvey Band)

TEARJERKERS
80   Back Door DOOR 1   Murder Mystery/Heart On The Line (die cut p/s with insert) 4
81   Good Vibrations GOT 9   Love Affiar/Bus Stop (p/s) 5
80s   GRAY GRC 1   TEARJERKERS (Tape) 10

TEARS FOR FEARS
81   Mercury IDEA 1   Suffer The Children/Wind (original issue with light labels and p/s) 5
81   Mercury IDEA 12   Suffer The Children (Remix)/Wind/Suffer The Children (Instrumental) (12", p/s) 8
82   Mercury IDEA 2   Pale Shelter (You Don't Give Me Love)/The Prisoner (original issue with light labels and p/s) 4
82   Mercury IDEA 212   Pale Shelter (You Don't Give Me Love) (Extended)/Pale Shelter/The Prisoner (12", p/s) 7
82   Mercury IDEA 3   Mad World/Ideas As Opiates (p/s) 4
82   Mercury IDEA 33   Mad World/Mad World (World Remix)//Suffer The Children/Ideas As Opiates (double pack) 8

TEARS FOR FEARS

82	Mercury IDEA 4	Change/The Conflict (p/s)	4
82	Mercury IDEA 4	Change/The Conflict (poster p/s)	6
83	Mercury IDEA W/R/B/G 5	Pale Shelter (You Don't Give Me Love)/The Prisoner (p/s, white, red, blue or green vinyl)	each 5-7
83	Mercury IDEAP 5	Pale Shelter (You Don't Give Me Love)/We Are Broken (picture disc)	8
83	Mercury IDEA 6	(The) Way You Are/The Marauders (p/s, with poster)	5
83	Mercury IDEAS 6	(The) Way You Are/The Marauders//Change (Live)/Start Of The Breakdown (live) (shrinkwrapped double pack)	8
83	Mercury IDEA 612	(The) Way You Are (Extended)/The Marauders/Start Of The Breakdown (live) (12", p/s)	7
84	Mercury IDEA 7	Mother's Talk/Empire Building (clear vinyl picture disc)	8
84	Mercury IDEAP 7	Mother's Talk/Empire Building (p/s, green vinyl, with sticker)	4
84	Mercury IDEA 712	Mother's Talk (The Beat Of The Drum Mix)/Empire Building (12", p/s)	7
84	fan club	Mother's Talk/Interview	20
85	Mercury IDEC 8	Shout/The Big Chair (calendar pack with 6 cards)	5
84	Mercury IDEA 810	Shout/The Big Chair (10", p/s)	7
85	Mercury IDEA 910	Everybody Wants To Rule The World/Pharoahs (10", p/s)	7
85	Mercury IDEA 912	Everybody Wants To Rule The World (Urban Mix)/Everybody Wants To Rule The World (Instrumental)/Pharoahs (12", p/s)	7
85	Mercury IDEA 99	Everybody Wants To Rule The World/Pharoahs//Everybody Wants To Rule The World (Urban Mix)/Interview (double pack)	7
85	Mercury IDEAP 10	Head Over Heels (Remix)/When In Love With A Blind Man (poster p/s)	4
85	Mercury IDEP 10	Head Over Heels (Remix)/When In Love With A Blind Man (clover-shaped picture disc)	7
85	Mercury IDEA 1010	Head Over Heels (Remix)/When In Love With A Blind Man (10", p/s)	7
85	Mercury IDEA 1110	I Believe/Sea Song/I Believe (US Mix) (10", p/s)	7
85	Mercury IDEA 1111	I Believe (A Soulful Re-recording)/Sea Song//I Believe (Original Version)/Shout (Dub Version) (double pack, gatefold p/s)	5

(see also Graduate)

TEARS ON THE CONSOLE
75	Holyground HG 120	TEARS ON THE CONSOLE (LP, with booklet, 120 demo copies only)	200
90	Magic Mixture MM 3	TEARS ON THE CONSOLE (LP, reissue, 425 only, with insert)	15

(actually by Chick Shannon & Last Exit)

TEA SET
66	King KG 1048	Join The Tea Set/Ready Steady Go!	8

TEA SET
78	Waldo's Beat Series 003	CUPS AND SAUCERS (EP, with stapled lyric book sleeve)	5
79	Waldo's Beat PS 006	Parry Thomas/Tri-X Pan (gatefold p/s with poster 'mystery' envelope)	5
80	Demon D 1009	South Pacific/The Preacher (foldout sleeve with inserts)	4
80	Mainly Modern STP 3	Keep On Running (Big Noise From The Jungle)/Flaccid Pot (p/s)	4

TECHNIQUES (U.S.)
58	Columbia DB 4072	Hey! Little Girl/In A Round About Way	20
58	Columbia DB 4072	Hey! Little Girl/In A Round About Way (78)	10

TECHNIQUES (Jamaica)
65	Island WI 231	Little Did You Know/DON DRUMMOND: Cool Smoke	10
67	Treasure Isle TI 7001	You Don't Care/TOMMY McCOOK & SUPERSONICS BAND: Travelling On Bond Street	10
67	Treasure Isle TI 7019	Queen Majesty/Fighting For The Right	10
67	Treasure Isle TI 7026	Love Is Not A Gamble/Bad-Minded People	10
68	Treasure Isle TI 7031	My Girl/Drink Wine (with Tommy McCook & Supersonics)	10
68	Treasure Isle TI 7038	Devoted/Bless You (with Tommy McCook & Supersonics)	10
68	Treasure Isle TI 7040	It's You I Love/Travelling Man (with Tommy McCook & Supersonics)	10
68	Duke DU 1	I Wish It Would Rain/There Comes A Time	8
68	Duke DU 6	A Man Of My Word/The Time Has Come	8
69	Duke DU 22	What Am I To Do/You're My Everything	5
69	Duke DU 60	Where Were You/Just One Smile	5
69	Camel CA 10	Who You Gonna Run To/Hi There (B-side actually "Look Who's Back" by Carl Bryan)	5
69	Camel CA 19	Everywhere Everyone/Find Yourself Another Fool	4
70	Techniques TE 904	Lonely Man/I Feel Alive	5
70	Techniques TE 906	Feel A Little Better (actually by Techniques Allstars)/You'll Get Left	5
71	Banana BA 350	Since I Lost You/RILEY'S ALLSTARS: Version	5

(see also Riots, Tommy McCook)

TECHNO TWINS
82	PRT 7P 232	Can't Help Falling In Love/Kings And Queens Of Pleasure (picture disc)	4

TEDDIE & TIGERS
67	Spin SP 2004	Hold On I'm Comin'/First Love Never Dies	12

TEDDY & FRAT GIRLS
85	Alternative Tentacles VIRUS 19	I Wanna Be A Man/I Owe It All To The Girls/Clubnite/Alophen Baby/The Eggman Don't Cometh (p/s)	4

TEDDY & PEARL
58	Pye Nixa 7N 15123	Sweet Elizabeth/Never Let Me Go	5

(see also Teddy Johnson & Pearl Carr)

TEDDY & TWILIGHTS
63	Stateside SS 167	I'm Just Your Clown/Bikini Bimbo	10

TEDDY BEARS
58	London HL 8733	To Know Him Is To Love Him/Don't You Worry My Little Pet	10
58	London HL 8733	To Know Him Is To Love Him/Don't You Worry My Little Pet (78)	8
59	London HLP 8836	I Don't Need You Anymore/Oh Why	15
59	London HLP 8836	I Don't Need You Anymore/Oh Why (78)	12
59	London HLP 8889	You Said Goodbye/If You Only Knew	25

MINT VALUE £

| 59 | London HLP 8889 | You Said Goodbye/If You Only Knew (78) | 20 |
| 59 | London HA-P 2183 | THE TEDDY BEARS SING! (LP) | 125 |

(see also Phil Spector, Carol Connors)

WILLIE TEE
67	Atlantic 584 116	Thank You John/Walking Up A One-Way Street	15
71	Mojo 2092 025	Walking Up A One-Way Street/Thank You John/Teasin' You	6
78	Contempo CS 8002	Walking Up A One-Way Street/Thank You John (unissued)	

TEENAGE FANCLUB
90	Paperhouse PAPER 003	Everything Flows/Primary Education/Speeeder (1,500 only, die-cut p/s)	15
90	Paperhouse PAPER 005	The Ballad Of John And Yoko (p/s, 1-sided, 5,000 only, 2nd side engraved)	8
90	Paperhouse PAPER 007	God Knows It's True/So Far Gone (p/s)	4
91	Creation CRE 105L	Star Sign/Like A Virgin (p/s, with reversed colours)	4
91	Creation CRE LP 096	THE KING (LP, withdrawn, sprayed plain sleeve)	10
91	Creation CRE CD 096	THE KING (CD, withdrawn, sprayed plain sleeve)	15

(see also Boy Hairdressers)

TEENAGE FILMSTARS
79	Clockwork COR 002	(There's A) Cloud Over Liverpool/Sometimes Good Guys Don't Follow Trends (1st 150 with p/s)	50/15
80	Wessex WEX 275	The Odd Man Out/I Apologise (no p/s)	12
80s	Blueprint BLU 2013	The Odd Man Out/I Apologise (reissue, p/s)	10
80	Fab Listening FL 1	I Helped Patrick McGoohan Escape/We're Not Sorry (p/s)	10

(see also Television Personalities, Times, O Level)

TEENAGERS
| 57 | RCA RCX 102 | THE TEENAGERS (EP) | 20 |

TEEN BEATS (U.S.)
| 60 | Top Rank JAR 342 | The Slop Beat/Califf Boogie (featuring Don Rivers & Califfs) | 10 |

TEENBEATS (U.K.)
| 79 | Safari SAFE 17 | I Can't Control Myself/I Never Win (p/s) | 6 |
| 80 | Safari SAFE 19 | Strength Of The Nation/I'm Gone Tomorrow (p/s) | 5 |

TEEN QUEENS
| 65 | R&B MRB 5000 | Eddie My Love/Just Goofed | 25 |

TEE SET
| 70 | Columbia SCX 6419 | MA BELLE AMIE (LP) | 10 |

TEETH
| 79 | Soho | Say Hello To Suzy/Human Bondage (no p/s) | 5 |

JAHN TEIGEN
| 83 | Epic EPC A 3391 | Do Re Mi (English)/Do Re Mi (Norwegian) (unissued, promos only) | 7 |

TELESCOPES
87	private cassette	THE TREE 'ATES EP (demo cassette)	15
88	Cheree CHEREE 1	Forever Close Your Eyes/LOOP: Soundhead (33rpm flexi, p/s, 1,000 only)	10
89	Cheree CHEREE 2	Kick The Wall/This Is The Last Of What's Coming Now (p/s, with insert, 1,000 only, light grey/blue p/s)	15
89	Cheree CHEREE 2	Kick The Wall/This Is The Last Of What's Coming Now (numbered re-press, 500 only, red p/s)	15
89	Cheree CHEREET 4	7th #Disaster/Nothing/This Planet/Cold (12", p/s, with insert)	8
89	What Goes On WHAT 15T	The Perfect Needle/Sadness Pale/S.H.C. Burn/You Cannot Be Sure (12", p/s)	7
90	What Goes On WHAT 18	To Kill A Slow Girl Walking/Treasure (p/s)	4
90	What Goes On WHAT 18T	To Kill A Slow Girl Walking/Treasure/Forever Now/Pure Sweetest Ocean (12", p/s)	7
90	Fierce FRIGHT 039	TRADE MARK OF QUALITY (LP)	10
90	Fierce FRIGHTCD 039	TRADE MARK OF QUALITY (CD)	15

TELEVISION
77	Elektra K 12252	Marquee Moon Pts 1 & 2 (no p/s)	4
79	Ork/WEA NYC 1T	Little Johnny Jewel Pts 1 & 2/Little Johnny Jewel (live) (12", p/s)	12
78	Elektra K 52072	ADVENTURE (LP, red vinyl with lyric insert)	10

TELEVISION PERSONALITIES
78	Teen '78 SRTS/ CUS/77/089	14th Floor/Oxford Street W1 (p/s, various different sleeve designs)	35-45
78	Kings Road LYN 5976/7	WHERE'S BILL GRUNDY NOW? (EP, hand-stamped label, 2,000 only)	18
78	Kings Road LYN 5976/7	WHERE'S BILL GRUNDY NOW? (EP, white labels, various sleeves)	12-15
79	Rough Trade RT 033	WHERE'S BILL GRUNDY NOW? (EP, reissue, different p/s, printed labels)	10
80	Rough Trade RT 051	Smashing Time/King & Country (p/s)	16
81	Rough Trade RT 063	I Know Where Syd Barrett Lives/Arthur The Gardener (p/s)	18
82	Whaam! WHAAM 4	Three Wishes/Geoffrey Ingram/And Don't The Kids Just Love It (p/s, 2 different sleeve designs, 2,000 only)	12/16
82	Creation Artefact 002/ Lyntone LYN 13546	Biff Bang Pow!/A Picture Of Dorian Gray (1-sided flexidisc, some with 'Communication Blur' fanzine)	25/18
83	Rough Trade RT 109	A Sense Of Belonging/Paradise Estate (p/s)	12
86	Dreamworld DREAM 4	How I Learnt To Love The Bomb/Then God Snaps His Fingers/ Now You're Just Being Ridiculous (12", p/s, 3,700 only)	12
86	Dreamworld DREAM 10	How I Learnt To Love The Bomb/Grocer's Daughter/Girl Called Charity (7", reissue, p/s, 1,000 only)	15
87	Dreamworld DREAM 13(T)	Privilege/Me And My Desires (unreleased)	
89	Overground OVER 03	14th Floor/Oxford Street W1 (numbered p/s, yellow or white vinyl; also black)	6/4
89	Caff CAFF 5	I Still Believe In Magic/Respectable (p/s, in poly bag, 500 only)	25
81	Rough Trade ROUGH 24	AND DON'T THE KIDS JUST LOVE IT (LP, 1st 1,000 with insert)	30/25
82	Whaam! WHAAM 3	MUMMY YOUR NOT WATCHING ME (LP, 3,500 only, 1st 1,000 with insert)	30/25
82	Whaam! BIG 5	THEY COULD HAVE BEEN BIGGER THAN THE BEATLES (LP, 2,500 only, hand-painted sleeve)	30
83	Whaam! BIG 10	TURN ON … TUNE IN (LP, unreleased)	
85	Illuminated JAMS 37	THE PAINTED WORD (LP)	30

86	Dreamworld BIG DREAM 2	THEY COULD HAVE BEEN BIGGER THAN THE BEATLES (LP, reissue, with insert) 15
86	Dreamworld BIG DREAM 4	MUMMY YOUR NOT WATCHING ME (LP, reissue with insert) 15
87	Dreamworld BIG DREAM 6	PRIVILEGE (LP, unreleased)

(see also Teenage Filmstars, Times, O Level, Missing Scientists, Reacta, Dry Rib)

TELLERS
74	Pyramid PYR 7011	No Work, No Pay/Version 6
74	Dragon DRA 1031	Ta It Deh/Hit Dib 6

TELSTARS
62	Oriole CB 1754	I Went A' Walkin'/A Rose And A Thorn 5

TEMPERANCE SEVEN
61	Argo RG 11	THE TEMPERANCE SEVEN PLUS ONE (LP) 12
61	Parlophone PMC 1152	THE TEMPERANCE SEVEN 1961 (LP, also stereo PCS 3021) 10

TEMPEST
73	Bronze ILPS 9220	TEMPEST (LP, fold-over cover with lyric inner sleeve) 20
74	Bronze ILPS 9267	LIVING IN FEAR (LP, die-cut cover with inner sleeve) 20

(see also Colosseum)

TEMPEST
83	Glass GLASS 029	Lady Left This/Attic (p/s) 5
83	Anagram ANA 17	Montezuma/ABC (p/s) 4
83	Anagram 12 ANA 17	Montezuma/ABC (Extended Mix)/The Calm Before (12", p/s) 7

BOBBY TEMPEST
59	Decca F 11125	Love Or Leave/Don't Leave Me 8

BOB TEMPLE
57	Parlophone R 4264	Come Back, Come Back/Vim Vam Vamoose 7

GERRY TEMPLE
61	HMV POP 823	No More Tomorrows/So Nice To Walk You Home 15
61	HMV POP 939	Seventeen Come Sunday/Tell You What I'll Do 15
63	HMV POP 1114	Angel Face/Since You Went Away 15
68	RCA Victor RCA 1670	Lovin' Up A Storm/Everything I Do is Wrong 8

RICHARD TEMPLE
70	Jay Boy BOY 31	That Beatin' Rhythm/Could It Be 4

SHIRLEY TEMPLE
59	Top RankJAR 139	On The Good Shiop Lollipop/Animal Crackers In My Soup 5
59	Top Rank JKR 8003	I REMEMBER (EP) 12

TEMPLEAIRES
70	Vogue V 2421	He Spoke/What Will Heaven Have In Store For Me 8

NINO TEMPO
57	London HLU 8387	Tempo's Tempo/June's Blues (as Nino Tempo & His Band) 100
57	London HLU 8387	Tempo's Tempo/June's Blues (as Nino Tempo & His Band) (78) 18
75	A&M AMS 7190	Come See Me Round Midnight/High On Music (as Nino Tempo & 5th Avenue) 5
58	London HB-U 1075	ROCK 'N' ROLL BEACH PARTY (10" LP) 75

(see also Nino Tempo & April Stevens, April Stevens)

NINO TEMPO & APRIL STEVENS
62	London HLK 9580	Sweet And Lovely/TOP NOTES: Twist And Shout 8
63	London HLK 9782	Deep Purple/I've Been Carrying A Torch For You So Long That I Burned A Great Big Hole In My Heart 6
64	London HLK 9829	Whispering/Tweedle Dee 6
64	London HLK 9859	Stardust/1-45 6
64	London HLK 9890	Tea For Two/I'm Confessin' (That I Love You) 6
66	London HLU 10084	All Strung Out/I Can't Go On Living Baby Without You 5
67	Atlantic 584 048	The Habit Of Lovin' You Baby/You'll Be Needing Me Baby 5
68	Atlantic 584 151	Deep Purple/Sweet And Lovely 4
67	London HLU 10106	The Habit Of Lovin' You Baby/You'll Be Needing Me Baby (reissue) ...4
67	London HLU 10130	My Old Flame/Wings Of Love 4
68	London HLU 10209	Ooh Poo Pah Doo/Let It Be Me 4
73	A&M AMS 7075	Put It Where You Want It/I Can't Get Over You Baby 5
64	London REK 1412	DEEP PURPLE (EP) 12
64	London HA-K 8168	NINO TEMPO AND APRIL STEVENS — DEEP PURPLE (LP) 25
64	Atlantic (S)AL 5006	SING THE GREAT SONGS (LP, mono/stereo) 15/18
67	London HA-U/SHU 8314	ALL STRUNG OUT (LP) 20

(see also Nino Tempo, April Stevens)

TEMPOS
59	Pye International 7N 25026	See You In September/Bless You My Love 12

TEMPREES
74	Stax STS 2027	At Last/I'll Live Her Life 4
72	Stax 2325 083	LOVE MEN (LP) 15
74	Stax STX 1040	THREE (LP) 20

TEMPTATIONS
60	Top Rank JAR 384	Barbara/Someday 15

TEMPTATIONS
64	Stateside SS 278	The Way You Do The Things You Do/Just Let Me Know 35
64	Stateside SS 319	I'll Be In Trouble/The Girl's Alright With Me 35
64	Stateside SS 348	(Girl) Why You Wanna Make Me Blue/Baby Baby I Need You 45
65	Stateside SS 378	My Girl (Talking 'Bout)/Nobody But My Baby 22
65	Tamla Motown TMG 504	It's Growing/What Love Has Joined Together 18
65	Tamla Motown TMG 526	Since I Lost My Baby/You've Got To Earn It 15

65	Tamla Motown TMG 541	My Baby/Don't Look Back	15
66	Tamla Motown TMG 557	Get Ready/Fading Away	12
66	Tamla Motown TMG 565	Ain't Too Proud To Beg/You'll Lose A Precious Love	7
66	Tamla Motown TMG 578	Beauty Is Only Skin Deep/You're Not An Ordinary Girl	7
66	Tamla Motown TMG 587	(I Know) I'm Losing You/Little Miss Sweetness	6
67	Tamla Motown TMG 610	All I Need/Sorry Is A Sorry Word	8
67	Tamla Motown TMG 620	You're My Everything/I've Been Good To You	5
67	Tamla Motown TMG 633	(Loneliness Made Me Realise) It's You That I Need/ I Want A Love I Can See	15
68	Tamla Motown TMG 641	I Wish It Would Rain/I Truly, Truly Believe	5
68	Tamla Motown TMG 658	I Could Never Love Another (After Loving You)/Gonna Give Her All The Love I've Got	5
68	Tamla Motown TMG 671	Why Did You Leave Me Darling/How Can I Forget	5
69	Tamla Motown TMG 707	Cloud Nine/Why Did She Have To Leave Me (Why Did She Have To Go)	5
69	Tamla Motown TMG 716	Runaway Child, Running Wild/I Need Your Lovin'	4
70	Tamla Motown TMG 722	I Can't Get Next To You/Running Away (Ain't Gonna Help You)	4
70	Tamla Motown TMG 741	Psychedelic Shack/That's The Way Love Is	5
70	Tamla Motown TMG 749	Ball Of Confusion (That's What The World Is Today)/It's Summer	4
72	Tamla Motown TMG 808	Take A Look Around/Smooth Sailing (From Now On)	4
65	Tamla Motown TME 2004	THE TEMPTATIONS (EP)	20
66	Tamla Motown TME 2010	IT'S THE TEMPTATIONS (EP)	16
65	Tamla Motown TML 11009	MEET THE TEMPTATIONS (LP)	30
65	Tamla Motown TML 11016	SING SMOKEY (LP)	35
66	Tamla Motown TML 11023	THE TEMPTIN' TEMPTATIONS (LP)	25
66	Tamla Motown TML 11035	GETTIN' READY (LP)	35
67	T. Motown (S)TML 11042	GREATEST HITS (LP)	15
67	T. Motown (S)TML 11053	THE TEMPTATIONS LIVE! (LP)	15
67	T. Motown (S)TML 11057	WITH A LOT O'SOUL (LP)	15
68	T. Motown (S)TML 11068	IN A MELLOW MOOD (LP)	15
68	T. Motown (S)TML 11079	THE TEMPTATIONS WISH IT COULD RAIN (LP)	20
69	T. Motown (S)TML 11104	LIVE AT THE COPA (LP)	12
69	T. Motown (S)TML 11109	CLOUD NINE (LP)	15
70	T. Motown (S)TML 11133	PUZZLE PEOPLE (LP)	15
70	T. Motown (S)TML 11141	LIVE AT THE TALK OF THE TOWN (LP)	12
70	T. Motown (S)TML 11147	PSYCHEDELIC SHACK (LP)	18
70	T. Motown STML 11170	GREATEST HITS II (LP)	10
71	T. Motown STML 11184	THE SKY'S THE LIMIT (LP)	10
72	T. Motown STML 11202	SOLID ROCK (LP)	10
72	T. Motown STML 11218	ALL DIRECTIONS (LP)	10
73	T. Motown STML 11229	MASTERPIECE (LP)	10

(see also David Ruffin, Eddie Kendricks)

TEMPUS FUGIT
69	Philips BF 1802	Come Alive/Emphasis On Love	20

(see also Jensens)

10cc
72	UK UK 22	Johnny Don't Do It/4% Of Something	5
74	UK UK 57	The Worst Band In The World/18 Carat Man Of Means	5
75	UK UK 100	Waterfall/4% Of Something	4
77	Mercury 6008 028	People In Love/I'm So Laid Back I'm Laid Out	4
73	UK UKAL 1005	10cc (LP)	10
80s	Mercury HS 9102 500	THE ORIGINAL SOUNDTRACK (LP, half-speed master)	12
80s	Mercury HS 9102 504	GREATEST HITS (LP, half-speed master)	12

(see also Godley & Creme, Graham Gouldman, Mindbenders, Mockingbirds, Hotlegs, Whirlwinds, Tristar Airbus)

TEN FEET
66	RCA RCA 1544	Got Everything But Love/Factory Worker	20
66	CBS 3045	Shot On Sight/Losing Game	20

TEN FEET FIVE
65	Fontana TF 578	Baby's Back In Town/Send Me No More Lovin'	15

(see also Troggs)

TENNORS
68	Doctor Bird DB 1152	Massie Massa/CLIVE ALLSTARS: San Sebastian	10
68	Doctor Bird DB 1175	Sufferer (Make It)/Little Things	10
68	Island WI 3133	Ride Your Donkey/I've Got To Get You Off My Mind	8
68	Island WI 3140	Copy Me Donkey/ROMEO STEWART: The Stage	7
68	Island WI 3156	Grampa/ROMEO STEWART: While I Was Walking	10
68	Blue Cat BS 127	Khaki/LEROY REID: Great Surprise (Pound Get A Blow)	8
68	Big Shot BI 501	Reggae Girl/CLIVE ALLSTARS: Donkey Trot	8
68	Fab FAB 41	Ride Your Donkey/I've Got To Get You Off My Mind	7
68	Fab FAB 50	Let Go Yah Donkey/ROMEO STEWART: While I Was Walking	7
69	Big Shot BI 514	You're No Good/Do The Reggae	7
69	Big Shot BI 517	Another Scorcher/My Baby	7
69	Duke Reid DR 2502	Hopeful Village/TOMMY McCOOK: The Village	5
69	Bullet BU 406	Greatest Scorcher/Making Love	4
69	Crab CRAB 26	Baff Boom/Feel Bad	4
69	Crab CRAB 29	True Brothers/Sign Of The Time	4
69	Crab CRAB 36	I Want Everything/Cherry	4

(see also Jennors)

10,000 MANIACS
84	Reflex RE 1	My Mother The War (Remix)/Planned Obsolescence/National Education Week (12", p/s)	20
84	Press P 2010	HUMAN CONFLICT #5 (12" EP, gatefold p/s)	35
85	Elektra EKR 11	Can't Ignore The Train/Daktari (p/s)	6
85	Elektra EKR 11T	Can't Ignore The Train/Daktari/Grey Victory/The Colonial Wing (12", p/s)	12

10,000 MANIACS

85	Elektra EKR 19	Just As The Tide Was A-Flowin'/Among The Americans	10
86	Elektra EKR 28	Scorpio Rising/Arbor Day (no p/s)	6
87	Elektra EKR 61	Peace Train/The Painted Desert (booklet p/s)	4
87	Elektra EKR 64	Don't Talk/City Of Angels (7" with 12" p/s, with inserts)	4
89	Elektra EKR 93CDX	Trouble Me/The Lion's Share/Party Of God (3" CD in elephant-shaped pack)	7
89	Elektra EKR 100TE	Eat For Two/What's The Matter Here (Acoustic)/Eat For Two (Acoustic)/ From The Time You Say Goodbye (10", numbered p/s)	4
85	Lyntone LYN 15914	Grey Victory/SIMPLY RED: Something's Burning (33rpm 1-sided clear flexidisc free with 'Jamming!' magazine, issue 29)	9/7
84	Press P 3001 LP	SECRETS OF THE I-CHING (LP, with insert)	40
87	Elektra EKT 41	IN MY TRIBE (LP, with free 7" sampler: "What's The Matter Here?"/ X: See How We Are/CALL: In The River [SAM 390, gatefold p/s])	12

TEN WHEEL DRIVE

71	Polydor 2066 034	Morning Much Better/Stay With Me	4
69	Polydor 583 577	CONSTRUCTION NO. 1 (LP)	10
70	Polydor 2425 002	BRIEF REPLIES (LP)	10
71	Polydor 2425 065	PECULIAR FRIENDS (LP, as Ten Wheel Drive with Genya Raven)	10

(see also Genya Ravan)

TEN YEARS AFTER

68	Deram DM 176	Portable People/The Sounds	5
68	Deram DM 221	Hear Me Calling/I'm Going Home	5
70	Deram DM 299	Love Like A Man (studio)/Love Like A Man (live)	5
70	Deram DM 310	Love Like A Man (studio)/Love Like A Man (live) (reissue)	4
67	Deram DML/SML 1015	TEN YEARS AFTER (LP)	20
68	Deram DML/SML 1023	UNDEAD (LP, mono/stereo)	18/15
68	Deram DML/SML 1029	STONEDHENGE (LP, mono/stereo)	18/15
69	Deram SML 1052	SSSH! (LP)	12
70	Deram SML 1065	CRICKLEWOOD GREEN (LP)	12
70	Deram SML 1078	WATT (LP)	12
72	Chrysalis CHR 1001	A SPACE IN TIME (LP)	12

(see also Jaybirds, Chick Churchill)

TERESA DEL FUEGO

81	Satril HH 155	Don't Hang Up/Wonder Wonder (no p/s)	8

(see also Swing Out Sister)

TERMINAL CHEESECAKE

91	World Serpent WS7 001	Unhealing Wound (live) (1-sided, B-side etched, foldover sleeve in poly bag)	5

TERMITES (U.K.)

65	Oriole CB 1989	Tell Me/I Found My Place	15
65	CBS 201761	Every Day Every Day/No-One In The Whole Wide World	5

TERMITES (Jamaica)

67	Studio One SO 2006	Mercy Mr. Percy/SOUL BROTHERS: Hot And Cold	15
67	Studio One SO 2029	It Takes Two To Make Love/Beach Boy	15
67	Coxsone CS 7008	Sign Up/DELROY WILSON: Troubled Man	15
67	Coxsone CS 7025	Do It Right Now/SUMMERTAIRES: Stay (B-side actually by Gaylads)	15
68	Studio One SO 2040	Mr D.J. (actually by Delroy Wilson)/Tripe Girl (actually by Heptones)	15
68	Coxsone CS 7039	Mama Didn't Know/I Made A Mistake	15
68	Nu Beat NB 017	Push Push/Girls (actually by Hi Tones)	7
68	Pama PM 729	Push It Up/Two Of A Kind (B-side act. by Clancy Eccles & Cynthia Richards)	7
68	Pama PM 738	Show Me The Way/What Can I Do	7
67	Studio One SOL 9003	DO THE ROCK STEADY (LP)	80

PETE TERRACE

67	Pye International 7N 25427	At The Party/No! No! No!	8
67	Pye International 7N 25440	Shotgun Boo-Ga-Loo/I'm Gonna Make It	15
67	Pye International NPL 28102	BOOGALOO (LP)	20

TERRAPLANE

81	Strange Days S-DAYS-2	Evil Going On/It's Hip	5
83	City NIK 8	I Survive/Gimme The Money (p/s)	4
84	Epic TX 4936	I Can't Live Without Your Love/Beginning Of The End/Let The Wheels Go Round (12", p/s)	7
87	Epic TERRAP 1	if That's What It Takes/Living After Dark (shaped picture disc)	7
87	Epic TERRAD 1	If That's What It Takes/Living After Dark (p/s, with free single)	4
87	Epic TERRAG 3	Moving Target/When I Sleep Alone//I Survive (live)/I Can't Live Without Your Love (double pack, gatefold p/s)	4
80s	Flexi FLX 394/XPS 200	I'm The One (live)/When You're Hot (live) (p/s, flexidisc free with Meatloaf's 'Bad Attitude' tour programme)	7/4

(see also Thunder)

LLOYD TERRELL

68	Pama PM 710	Bang Bang Lulu/MRS MILLER: I Never Knew	6
68	Pama PM 740	How Come/MRS MILLER: Oh My Lover	6
68	Pama PM 752	Lulu Returns/MRS MILLER: I Feel The Music	6

(see also Lloyd Tyrell & Charmers)

TAMMI TERRELL

66	Tamla Motown TMG 561	Come On And See Me/Baby Don'tcha Worry	30
69	T. Motown (S)TML 11103	THE IRRESISTIBLE TAMMI TERRELL (LP)	25

(see also Marvin Gaye & Tammi Terrell)

CLARK TERRY (& BOB BROOKMEYER)

61	Riverside RLP 12-246	DUKE WITH A DIFFERENCE (LP)	10
65	Fontana TL 5265	TONIGHT (LP, with Bob Brookmeyer)	10
66	Fontana TL 5290	POWER OF POSITIVE SWINGING (LP, with Bob Brookmeyer)	10
66	Fontana TL 5373	MUMBLES (LP)	10
67	Fontana (S)TL 5394	GINGERBREAD MEN (LP, with Bob Brookmeyer)	10

68	Impulse MIPL/SIPL 507	IT'S WHAT HAPPENIN' (LP)	10

DEWEY TERRY

73	Tumbleweed TW 3502	CHIEF (LP)	15

(see also Don & Dewey, Don Harris)

GORDON TERRY

57	London REA 1098	COUNTRY CLAMBAKE (EP)	20

SONNY TERRY (TRIO)

53	Parlophone MSP 6017	Hootin' Blues/TOMMY REILLY: Bop! Goes The Weasel	25
53	Parlophone R 3598	Hootin' Blues/TOMMY REILLY: Bop! Goes The Weasel (78)	15
55	Vogue V 2326	Fox Chase/John Henry (78)	10
56	Vogue EPV 1095	SONNY TERRY (EP)	15
50s	Realm REP 4002	PAWN SHOP BLUES (EP)	10
50s	Melodisc EPM 7-83	WHOOPIN' THE BLUES (EP)	10
55	Vogue LDE 137	FOLK BLUES (10" LP)	15
55	Vogue LDE 165	CITY BLUES (10" LP)	15
58	Melodisc MLP 516	WHOOPIN' THE BLUES (10" LP)	15
50s	Topic 10T 30	HARMONICA BLUES (10" LP)	20
66	Xtra XTRA 5025	SONNY'S STORY (LP)	15
67	Capitol T 20906	WHOOPIN' THE BLUES (LP, reissue)	10
69	Ember CW 136	BLIND SONNY TERRY & WOODY GUTHRIE (LP)	10
69	Xtra XTRA 1064	SONNY TERRY (LP)	12
70	Xtra XTRA 1099	BLUES FROM EVERYWHERE (LP)	12
71	Xtra XTRA 1110	ON THE ROAD (LP, with J.C. Burris)	12

SONNY TERRY & BROWNIE McGHEE

60	Columbia DB 4433	Talking Harmonica Blues/Rockin' And Whoopin'	15
64	Oriole CB 1946	Goin' Down Slow/Dissatisfied Woman	12
50s	Melodisc EPM7 83	ME AND SONNY (EP)	10
58	Pye Jazz NJE 1060	THE BLUEST (EP)	8
59	Pye Jazz NJE 1073	SONNY TERRY AND BROWNIE McGHEE AND CHRIS BARBER'S JAZZ BAND (EP)	8
59	Pye Jazz NJE 1074	TERRY AND McGHEE IN LONDON PT. 1 (EP)	10
61	Top Rank JKP 3007	WORK-PLAY-FAITH-FUN-SONGS (EP)	10
61	Topic TOP 37	HOOTENANNY NEW YORK CITY (EP, with Pete Seeger)	15
64	Ember EP 4562	SONNY TERRY AND BROWNIE McGHEE (EP)	10
64	Topic TOP 121	R AND B FROM S AND B (EP)	12
64	Realm REP 4002	PAWNSHOP BLUES (EP)	12
64	Vocalion EPV 1274	SONNY TERRY AND BROWNIE McGHEE (EP)	12
65	Vocalion EPV 1279	I SHALL NOT BE MOVED (EP)	12
56	Topic 12T 29	BROWNIE McGHEE AND SONNY TERRY (LP)	20
58	Pye Nixa Jazz NJT 515	SONNY, BROWNIE AND CHRIS (10" LP, with Chris Barber)	25
58	Pye Nixa Jazz NJL 18	SONNY TERRY AND BROWNIE McGHEE IN LONDON (LP)	18
60	Columbia 33SX 1223	BLUES IS MY COMPANION (LP)	25
61	Vogue LAE 12247	BLUES IS A STORY (LP, also stereo SEA 5014)	20/30
63	Vogue LAE 12266	DOWN SOUTH SUMMIT MEETIN' (LP)	15
64	Vogue LAE 552	BROWNIE McGHEE AND SONNY TERRY (LP)	18
64	Realm RM 165	BACK COUNTRY BLUES (LP)	12
64	Stateside SL 10076	BLUES HOOT (LP, some tracks by Lightnin' Hopkins)	20
64	Fontana 688 006ZL	LIVIN' WITH THE BLUES (LP)	15
66	Philips BL 7675	AT THE BUNK HOUSE (LP)	12
66	Verve (S)VLP 5010	GUITAR HIGHWAY (LP, mono/stereo)	12/15
66	Fontana TL 5289	HOMETOWN BLUES (LP)	15
67	Ace Of Hearts (Z)AHT 182	HOMETOWN BLUES (LP, reissue)	10
69	Capitol T 20906	WHOOPIN' THE BLUES (LP)	14
69	Fontana SFJL 979	WHERE THE BLUES BEGAN (LP)	15
69	Stateside SSL 10291	LONG WAY FROM HOME (LP)	10
60s	World Record Club T 379	SONNY TERRY AND BROWNIE McGHEE (LP)	12

(see also Brownie McGhee, Chris Barber, Pete Seeger, Big Bill Broonzy, Lightnin' Hopkins)

TERRY & JERRY

65	R&B MRB 5009	People Are Doing It Every Day	8

TERRY, CARL & DERRICK

69	Grape GR 3012	True Love/ROY SMITH: Another Saturday Night	4

TERRY SISTERS

57	Parlophone R 4364	It's The Same Old Jazz/Broken Promise	10
58	Parlophone R 4509	Sweet Thing (Tell Me That You ...)/You Forgot To Remember	5

TERRY-THOMAS ESQUIRE

56	Decca F 10804	A Sweet Old Fashioned Boy (with Rock 'N' Roll Rotters)/Lay Down Your Arms	8
61	Decca LK 4398	STRICTLY T-T (LP)	10

TESCO BOMBERS

82	Y Y14	Hernandos Hideaway/Break The Ice At Parties/Girl From/Panema (p/s)	5

TEST DEPARTMENT

83	Some Bizzare TEST 112	Compulsion/Pulsations (12", p/s)	12
80s	Media City CMC 1	Godaddin (12" Welsh gig freebie with Brith Gof)	15
91	Jungle CAT 088	Pax Brittanica (Excerpt)/CREAMING JESUS: Charlie Jumps The Bandwagon/ MERCURY REV: Dripping/MUTTON GUN: Baby Born With Wooden Arm (flexidisc free with 1/91 issue of 'The Catalogue' magazine)	4
80s	Pleasantly Surprised PS 5	ECSTASY UNDER DURESS (cassette, in bag with inserts, 2 editions)	20/15
84	Test TEST 33	BEATING THE RETREAT (LP, boxed set)	15
86	Ministry Of Power MOP 2	THE UNACCEPTABLE FACE OF FREEDOM (LP)	10

JOE TEX

65	Atlantic AT 4015	Hold What You've Got/Fresh Out Of Tears	7
65	Atlantic AT 4021	You Better Get It/You Got What It Takes	10

MINT VALUE £

65	Sue WI 370	Yum Yum Yum/You Little Baby Faced Thing	15
65	Atlantic AT 4027	Women Can Change A Man/Don't Let Your Left Hand Know	6
65	Atlantic AT 4045	I Want To (Do Everything For You)/Funny Bone	7
65	Atlantic AT 4058	A Sweet Women Like You/Close Your Door	7
66	Atlantic AT 4081	The Love You Save/If Sugar Was As Sweet As You	5
66	Atlantic 584 016	S.Y.S.L.J.F.M. (Letter Song)/I'm A Man	4
66	Atlantic 584 035	You Better Believe It/I Believe I'm Gonna Make It	4
67	Atlantic 584 068	Papa Was Too/The Truest Woman In The World	4
67	Atlantic 584 096	Hold What You've Got/A Sweet Woman Like You	4
67	Atlantic 584 102	Show Me/Woman Sees A Hard Time (When Her Man Is Gone)	6
67	Atlantic 584 119	Woman Like That, Yeah/I'm Going And Get It	4
67	Atlantic 584 144	Skinny Legs And All/Watch The One (That Brings The Bad News)	4
68	Atlantic 584 171	Men Are Getting Scarce/You're Gonna Thank Me Woman	4
68	Atlantic 584 212	Go Home And Do It/Keep The One You Got	4
69	Atlantic 584 296	We Can't Sit Down Now/It Ain't Sanitary	4
70	Atlantic 584 318	You're Alright Ray Charles/Everything Happens On Time	4
71	Mercury 6052 067	I Knew Him/Bad Feet	4
72	Mercury 6052 111	Give The Baby Anything/Takin' A Chance	4
72	Mercury 6052 129	I Gotcha/Mother Prayer	4
72	Mercury 6052 156	You Said A Bad Word/It Ain't Gonna Work Baby	4
65	Atlantic ATL 5043	THE NEW BOSS (LP)	25
67	Atlantic 587 053	I'VE GOT TO DO A LITTLE BETTER (LP)	14
67	Atlantic 587/588 059	THE NEW BOSS (LP, reissue)	12
67	London HA-U 8334	THE BEST OF JOE TEX (LP)	25
67	Atlantic 587/588 079	GREATEST HITS (LP)	10
68	Atlantic 587/588 104	LIVE AND LIVELY (LP)	12
68	Atlantic 587/588 118	SOUL COUNTRY (LP)	12
69	Atlantic 588 130	YOU BETTER GET IT (LP)	10
69	Atlantic 588 193	BUYING A BOOK (LP)	10

(see also Soul Clan)

TEXANS
| 64 | Columbia DB 7242 | Being With You/Wondrous Look Of Love | 4 |

TEXAS RANGERS
| 57 | HMV 7EG 8387 | WAY OUT WEST (EP) | 8 |

TEXTOR SINGERS
| 54 | Capitol CL 14211 | Sobbin' Women/Remember Me | 6 |

RUDY THACKER & STRINGBEANS
| 62 | Starlite ST45 087 | The Ballad Of Johnny Horton/Tomorrow Is My Last Day | 12 |

THAMESIDERS/DAVY GRAHAM
| 63 | Decca DFE 8538 | FROM A LONDON HOOTENANNY (EP, 2 tracks each) | 12 |

THANES
| 87 | DDL DISP 008 | HEY GIRL (EP) (p/s) | 4 |
| 87 | DDL DISP 008 | HEY GIRL (EP) (12", p/s) | 7 |

SISTER ROSETTA THARPE
40s	Brunswick 02737	Rock Me/The Lonesome Road (78)	15
40s	Brunswick 02784	I Looked Down The Line (And I Wondered)/God Don't Like It (78)	15
52	Brunswick 04989	Can't No Grave Hold My Body Down/Ain't No Room In Church For Liars (78)	10
57	Mercury MT 126	When The Saints Go Marching In/Cain't No Grave Hold My ... (78)	6
57	Mercury MT 185	Up Above My Head There's Music In The Air/Jericho (78)	6
60	MGM MGM 1072	If I Can Help Somebody/Take My Hand, Precious Lord	6
57	Mercury MPL 6529	GOSPEL TRAIN (LP)	15
59	Brunswick LAT 8290	GOSPEL TRAIN (LP)	12
61	Mercury MMC 14057	THE GOSPEL TRUTH (LP)	12

SISTER ROSETTA THARPE & SISTER MARIE KNIGHT
4-	Decca F 48054	Didn't It Rain/Stretch Out (78)	10
48	Brunswick 04554	Journey To The Sky/Up Above My Head (78)	12
49	Brunswick 04632	Precious Memories/Beams Of Heaven (78)	10
51	Brunswick 04851	Didn't It Rain/Two Little Fishes And Five Loaves Of Bread (78)	10

(see also Marie Knight, Rev. Kelsey)

THAT PETROL EMOTION
85	Pink PINKY 4	Keen/A Great Depression On A Slum Night (p/s)	8
85	Noise A Noise NAN 1	V2/The Gonest Thing (p/s)	7
85	Noise A Noise NAN 1T	V2/The Gonest Thing/Happiness Drives Me Round The Bend (12", p/s)	10
86	Demon D 1042	It's A Good Thing/The Deadbeat (p/s)	5
86	Demon D 1042T	It's A Good Thing/The Deadbeat/Mine (12", p/s)	7
86	Demon D 1043	Natural Kind Of Joy/Can't Stop (p/s)	5
86	Demon D 1043T	Natural Kind Of Joy/Can't Stop/Non Alignment Pact/Jesus Said (12", p/s)	7
86	Pink PINKY 13T	Keen/A Great Depression On A Slum Night/Zig Zag Wanderer (12", p/s)	7
87	Polydor TPET 1	Big Decision (extended)/Split/Souldeep (10", p/s)	6
87	Polydor TPEE 2	Swamp/Dance Your Ass Off/Creeping To The Cross (live)/Me And Baby Brother (live) (EP, 33rpm)	4
89	Virgin VSA 1159	Groove Check (10")/Chemicrazy/Tension (live)/Under The Sky (live) (10", p/s)	6
91	Virgin VSAX 1261	Sensitize/Groove Check/Chemicrazy/Cinnamon Girl (10" box set with poster, numbered)	6
91	Virgin VSTX 1312	Tingle (The Christmas In Kreuzberg Mix)/Tingle (Jazz Tup Mix) (12", numbered p/s with poster)	7

(see also Undertones)

THEATRE OF HATE
| 87 | SS SS 3 | Original Sin/Legion (p/s) | 10 |
| 81 | Burning Rome BRR 1 | Rebel Without A Brain/My Own Invention (p/s) | 7 |

81	Burning Rome BRR 1	Rebel Without A Brain/My Own Invention (p/s, mispress with 2 B-side labels)	. . .12
81	Burning Rome BRR 1931	Nero/Incinerator (12", p/s)	8
82	Burning Rome BRR 2	Do You Believe In The West World?/Propaganda (p/s)	4
82	Burning Rome BRR T2/2T	Do You Believe In The West World?/The Version/Propaganda/Ministry Of Broadcast/Original Sin (Re-recording) (12", p/s)	7
82	Burning Rome BRR 3	The Hop/Conquistador (p/s)	4
82	Masterbag BAG 002	Ghost Of Love (live) (flexidisc, free with 'Masterbag' magazine)	8/6
82	Burning Rome BRR 4	Eastworld/Assegai (p/s)	5
82	Burning Rome BRR 4T	Eastworld (Russian Roulette)/Poppies/Assegai (Extended) (12", p/s)	7
85	Bliss TOH 1EP	The Wake/Love Is A Ghost/Poppies/Legion (EP, with T-shirt in 12" pack)	12
81	SS SSSSS 1P	HE WHO DARES WINS — LIVE AT THE WAREHOUSE, LEEDS (LP, white labels, some copies autographed)	18/12
81	Straight Music TOH 1	LIVE AT THE LYCEUM (cassette)	10

(see also Pack, Spear Of Destiny, Senate)

THEE

65	Decca F 12163	Each And Every Day/There You Go!	25

THEE MIGHTY CAESARS

80s	Swag SWG 001	She's Just Fifteen Years Old/The Swag (1-sided flexidisc)	4

(see also Milkshakes, Prisoners)

THEM

64	Decca F 11973	Don't Start Crying Now/One Two Brown Eyes	35
64	Decca F 12018	Baby Please Don't Go/Gloria	6
65	Decca F 12094	Here Comes The Night/All For Myself	5
65	Decca F 12175	One More Time/How Long Baby?	8
65	Decca F 12215	(It Won't Hurt) Half As Much/I'm Gonna Dress In Black	8
65	Decca F 12281	Mystic Eyes/If You And I Could Be As Two	8
66	Decca F 12355	Call My Name/Bring 'Em On In	8
66	Decca F 12403	Richard Cory/Don't You Know?	8
67	Major Minor MM 509	Gloria/Friday's Child	8
67	Major Minor MM 513	The Story Of Them Pts 1 & 2	10
65	Decca DFE 8612	THEM (EP)	40
65	Decca DFE 8612	THEM (EP, export p/s)	70
65	Decca LK 4700	(THE ANGRY YOUNG) THEM (LP, initially with flipback sleeve)	40/30
66	Decca LK 4751	THEM AGAIN (LP, initially with flipback sleeve)	40/30
69	Decca LK 4700	(THE ANGRY YOUNG) THEM (LP, re-pressing, red label, boxed Decca logo)	15
69	Decca LK 4751	THEM AGAIN (LP, re-pressing, red label, boxed Decca logo)	15
70	Decca (S)PA 86	THE WORLD OF THEM (LP, original issue)	10
78	Sonet SNTF 738	BELFAST GYPSIES (LP, features Them without Van Morrison)	10

(see also Van Morrison, Trader Horne, Taste, Sk'boo, Belfast Gypsies)

THEME MACHINE

81	BBC RESL 104	Themes Ain't What They Used To Be/Lost In A World Of Dreams	4

THEN JERICO

85	Immaculate 12 TJ 1	The Big Sweep/The Big Sweep (Club Mix)/The Rack (12", p/s)	20
85	London LON 63	Fault/The Big Sweep (Club Mix) (p/s)	5
85	London LONX 63	Fault (Club Mix)/The Fault/The Big Sweep (Club Mix) (12", p/s)	10
86	London LON 86	Muscledeep/Clank (Countdown To Oblivion) (p/s)	4
86	London LONX 86	Muscledeep/Clank (Countdown To Oblivion)/Distant Homes (12", p/s)	8
86	London LON 97	Let Her Fall/Searching (p/s)	4
86	London LONX 97	Let Her Fall (Absolute Version)/Blessed Days (Tokyo Mix)/Searching (12", p/s)	7
87	London LON 131	Prairie Rose/Electric (p/s)	4
87	London LONX 131	Prairie Rose/Prairie Rose (Original Version)/Electric/One Life/Fault (12", poster p/s)	8
87	London LONX 131	Prairie Rose/Prairie Rose (Original Version)/Electric/One Life/Fault (12", p/s)	7
87	London LONCD 131	Prairie Rose (Extended 7" Version)/Blessed Days (12" Version)/Electric/Muscledeep (CD)	8
87	London LONCS 145	The Motive (Extended)/Prairie Rose (7" Mix)/Let Her Fall (7" Mix)/The Word (cassette)	4
87	London LONT 145	The Motive/The Word/The Hitcher (live)/Let Her Fall (live) (10", p/s)	7
87	London LONX 145	The Motive (Extended)/The Word/The Motive (Midnight Mix) (12", poster p/s)	7
87	London LONB 186	Muscledeep/Fault (NYC Mix) (7" pack with postcards, badge & booklet)	4
87	London LONCS 186	Muscledeep/Fault (cassette)	4
87	London LONX 186	Muscledeep/Fault (NYC Mix)/Muscle Deep (7" version) (12", p/s)	4
89	London LONB 204	Big Area/The Big Sweep (Dance Mix) (box set with postcards & badge)	4
89	London LONI 223	What Does It Take?/Jungle (mirror p/s with 5 postcards)	4
89	London LONB 235	Sugar Box/The Happening (box set with postcards)	4
80s	Jamming!/London J 1	The Big Sweep/REDSKINS: You Want It They've Got It (Red Soul & Fury Unleashed Mix)/DAINTEES: Watch The Running Water/COMMUNARDS: Breadline Britain (free with 'Jamming!' magazine, no p/s)	8/6

THERAPY

73	Indigo IRS 5124	ONE NIGHT STAND (LP, private pressing)	30
76	CBS 69017	ALMANAC (LP)	10

THERAPY?

90	Multifuckingnational MFN1	Meat Abstract/Punishment Kiss (p/s, 1,000 only)	15

THERMOMETERS

80	Fokker FEP 100	20th Century Girl/Newtown Refugees/Stole Your Drugs (p/s)	6

THE THE

80	4AD AD 10	Controversial Subject/Black And White (p/s)	25
81	Some Bizzare BZS 4	Cold Spell Ahead/Hot Ice (p/s)	25
82	Epic EPC A 2787	Uncertain Smile/Three Orange Kisses From Kazan	

		(p/s, some with photo insert)	10/7
82	Epic EPC A 12 2787	Uncertain Smile/Three Orange Kisses From Kazan/Waiting For The Upturn (12", p/s, some with photo insert)	15/10
82	Epic EPC A 13 2787	Uncertain Smile/Three Orange Kisses From Kazan/Waiting For The Upturn (12", yellow vinyl, p/s, some with photo insert)	30/25
83	Epic EPC A 3119	Perfect/The Nature Of Virtue (p/s)	8
83	Epic EPC A 13 3119	Perfect/The Nature Of Virtue (12", p/s)	12
83	Epic A 3710	This Is The Day/Mental Healing Process (p/s)	7
83	Epic A 3710	This Is The Day/Mental Healing Process//Absolute Liberation/ Leap Into The Wind (double pack, gatefold p/s)	20
83	Epic TA 3710	This Is The Day/I've Been Waiting For Tomorrow (All Of My Life) (12", p/s)	12
83	Melody Maker	Dumb As Death's Head/SINES: Johnathon (flexi with 'Melody Maker')	7/5
83	Epic A 3588	Uncertain Smile/Dumb As Death's Head (p/s)	5
83	Epic TA 3588	Uncertain Smile/Soul Mining (12", p/s)	8
86	Epic TRUTH 1	Sweet Bird Of Truth/Harbour Lights/Sleeping Juice (12", p/s, 7,500 only)	10
86	Epic TRUTH C2	Heartland/Harbour Lights/Flesh And Bones//Born In The New S.A./ Sweet Bird Of Truth (cassette)	6
86	Epic TRUTH D2	Heartland/Born In the New S.A./Flesh And Bones//Perfect/ Fruit Of The Heart (12", double pack)	8
86	Epic TRUTH Q3	Infected/Infected (Energy Mix)/Disturbed (12", uncensored p/s)	18
86	Epic TRUTH C3	Infected (Skull Crusher Mix)/Disturbed/Soul Mining (12" Mix)/The Sinking Feeling (Original Version)/Infected (12") (cassette)	6
86	Epic TRUTH D3	Infected/Infected (Energy Mix)/Disturbed//Soul Mining (Remix)/ Sinking Feeling (12", double pack)	10
87	Epic TENSE 1	Slow Train To Dawn/Harbour Lights (p/s, with 2 car stickers)	4
89	Epic EMUQT 10	THE THE VS THE WORLD (10" EP)	6
82	private cassette	PORNOGRAPHY OF DESPAIR (LP, unreleased, cassettes exist)	
83	Epic EPC 25525	SOUL MINING (LP, with inner sleeve, initially with 12" single "Perfect"/"Soup Of Mixed Emotions"/"Fruit Of The Heart")	15
86	Epic EPC 26770	INFECTED (LP, 1st 25,000 with 'torture' sleeve, poster & inner)	12
	(see also Matt Johnson)		

LLANS THEWELL & HIS CELESTIALS

66	Island WI 262	Choo Choo Ska/BUSTY BROWN: Lonely Night	8

THEY MUST BE RUSSIANS
(see also Joe 9T & Thunderbirds)

THIEVES

79	Arista ARIGV 226	400 Dragons/Headlights (green vinyl)	4
	(see also Fairport Convention)		

THIN LIZZY

70	Parlophone DIP 513	The Farmer/I Need You (Ireland-only)	500
71	Decca F 13208	NEW DAY (EP, 33rpm)	100
72	Decca F 13355	Whiskey In The Jar/Black Boys On The Corner	4
73	Decca F 13402	Randolph's Tango/Broken Dreams (2 versions of A-side pressed, with matrices ZDR 53384 & ZCPDR 53312) .... each	15
73	Decca F 13467	The Rocker/Here I Go Again	8
74	Decca F 13507	Little Darlin'/Buffalo Gal	8
74	Vertigo 6059 111	Philomena/Sha La La	6
75	Vertigo 6059 124	Rosalie/Half Caste	6
75	Vertigo 6059 129	Wild One/For Those Who Love To Die	6
76	Vertigo 6059 150	Jailbreak/Running Back (p/s)	5
77	Vertigo 6059 177	Dancing In The Moonlight/Bad Reputation (p/s)	4
78	Decca F 13748	Whiskey In The Jar/Vagabond Of The Western World/Sitamoia (p/s)	4
79	Vertigo LIZZY 3	Waiting For An Alibi/With Love (p/s)	4
79	Vertigo LIZZY 4	Do Anything You Want To/Just The Two Of Us (p/s)	4
79	Decca THIN 1	Things Ain't Working Out Down At The Farm/The Rocker (10,000 with p/s)	4
79	Vertigo LIZZY 5	Sarah/Got To Give Up (5 different p/s designs) .... each	4
80	Vertigo LIZZY 6	Killer On The Loose/Don't Play Around (p/s)	4
80	Vertigo LIZZY 7 701	Killer On The Loose/Don't Play Around//Got To Give It Up (live)/ Chinatown (live) (double pack)	6
81	Vertigo LIZZY 8	LIVE KILLERS (EP)	4
81	Vertigo LIZZY 812	LIVE KILLERS (12" EP, with extra track)	7
81	Lyntone LYN 10138/9	Song For Jimmy/GRAHAM BONNET: Night Games/POLECATS: We Say Yeah/ WAY OF THE WEST: Monkey Love (orange flexi with 'Flexipop' No. 10)	5/4
81	Vertigo LIZZY 9	Trouble Boys/Memory Pain (p/s)	4
82	Vertigo LIZZY 10	Hollywood (Down On Your Luck)/Pressure Will Blow (p/s)	4
82	Vertigo LIZZY 10	Hollywood (Down On Your Luck) (10", 1-sided)	10
82	Vertigo LIZZY PD 10	Hollywood (Down On Your Luck)/Pressure Will Blow (picture disc)	6
83	Vertigo LIZZY 1111/22	Cold Sweat/Bad Habits//Angel Of Death (live)/Don't Believe A Word (live) (double pack)	5
83	Vertigo LIZZY 1112	Cold Sweat/Bad Habits/Angel Of Death (live)/Don't Believe A Word (live) (12", p/s)	7
83	Vertigo LIZZY 12	Thunder And Lightning/Still In Love With You (live) (p/s)	4
83	Vertigo LIZZY 1212	Thunder And Lightning/Still In Love With You (live) (12", p/s, some with poster)	15/7
83	Vertigo LIZZY 13	The Sun Goes Down/Baby Please Don't Go (p/s)	4
83	Vertigo LIZZY 1312	The Sun Goes Down (Remix)/The Sun Goes Down/Baby Please Don't Go (12", p/s)	7
71	Decca SKL 5082	THIN LIZZY (LP, dark blue label)	18
72	Decca TXS 108	SHADES OF A BLUE ORPHANAGE (LP, gatefold sleeve, dark blue label)	12
73	Decca SKL 5170	VAGABONDS OF THE WESTERN WORLD (LP, dark blue label, some with insert)	15/12

83 Vertigo VERL 3   THUNDER AND LIGHTNING (LP, with free 12") 12
(see also Phil Lynott, Wild Horses, Phenomena)

THIRD & FOURTH GENERATION
72 Punch PH 91   Rudies Medley (actually by Peter Tosh & Soulmates)/Rude Boy Version 5

THIRD EAR BAND
69 Harvest SHVL 756   ALCHEMY (LP) 20
70 Harvest SHSP 773   ELEMENTS (LP) 15
72 Harvest SHSP 4019   MUSIC FROM MACBETH (LP) 15
76 Harvest SHSM 2007   EXPERIENCES (LP) 10
(see also High Tide)

THIRD QUADRANT
82 Rock Cottage (no cat. no.) SEEING YOURSELF AS YOU REALLY ARE (LP, private press, wraparound
                               sleeve with handwritten insert, blank white label) 120
88 private label   LAYERED (private cassette, 500 only) 10

THIRD RAIL
67 Columbia DB 8274   Run, Run, Run/No Return 25

THIRD TIME AROUND
75 Contempo C 2076   Soon Everything Gonna Be Alright/(Vocal Version) 4

THIRD WORLD
85 Island ISP 219   Now That We've Found Love/Prisoner In The Street (picture disc) 4

THIRD WORLD WAR
71 Fly BUG 7   Ascension Day/Teddy Teeth Goes Sailing (p/s) 6
71 Fly BUG 11   A Little Bit Of Urban Rock/Working Class Man 4
71 Fly FLY 4   THIRD WORLD WAR (LP) 15
72 Track 2406 108   THIRD WORLD WAR II (LP) 35

13TH CHIME
81 Ellie Jay EJSP 9700   Cuts Of Love/Coffin Maker (poster p/s) 5
81 13th Chime THC 1   Cursed/Dug Up (p/s) 4
82 13th Chime THC 2   Fire/Hide And Seek/Sally Ditch (p/s) 4

THIRTEENTH FLOOR ELEVATORS
78 Radar/Sound For   Reverberation/RED CRAYOLA: Hurricane Fighter Plane
    Industry SFI 347   (flexidisc free with 'Zig Zag' magazine No. 88) 8/6
78 Radar ADA 13   You're Gonna Miss Me/Tried To Hide (green vinyl) 6
78 Radar RAD 13   THE PSYCHEDELIC SOUNDS OF ... (LP, reissue) 10
79 Radar RAD 15   EASTER EVERYWHERE (LP, reissue) 10
(see also Roky Erickson, Red Crayola)

31ST OF FEBRUARY
69 Vanguard (S)VRL 19045   THE 31st OF FEBRUARY (LP) 12

35mm DREAMS
81 More Than This ASA 100   More Than This/The Bearer (foldout p/s) 4
81 More Than This ASA 200   Fasten Your Safety Belts/Corstorphine/Instomatic Dance (p/s) 4

THIRTY-SECOND TURN-OFF
69 Jay Boy JSL 1   THIRTY-SECOND TURN OFF (LP) 40
(see also Equals)

THIS DRIFTIN'S GOTTA STOP
70s private pressing   THIS DRIFTIN'S GOTTA STOP (LP) 30

THIS HEAT
80 Piano THIS 1201·   Health And Efficiency/Graphic/Varispeed (12", p/s, with insert) 8
79 Piano THIS 1   THIS HEAT (LP) 12
81 Rough Trade ROUGH 26   DECEIT (LP, original) 10

THIS MORTAL COIL
83 4AD AD 310   Song To The Siren/16 Days (Reprise) (p/s) 4
83 4AD BAD 310   Song To The Siren/16 Days/Gathering Dust (12", p/s) 7
84 4AD AD 410   Kangaroo/It'll End In Tears (p/s, 2 different p/s & label colours) ... 4
86 4AD BAD 608   Come Here My Love/Drugs (10", p/s, with inner sleeve) 10
(see also Cocteau Twins, Modern English)

THIS 'N' THAT
66 Mercury MF 938   Someday/Loving You 15
67 Strike JH 310   Get Down With It/I Care About You 5
(see also Cleo)

THIS POISON!
87 Reception REC 004   Engine Failure/You;-Think!! (p/s) 6
87 Reception REC 008   Poised Over The Pause Button/I'm Not Asking (p/s) 5
87 Reception REC 008/12   THE FIERCE CRACK EP! (12", p/s) 7

B.J. THOMAS
66 Pye Intl. 7N 25374   Mama/Wendy 5
68 Pye Intl. 7N 25467   The Eyes Of A New York Woman/I May Never Get To Heaven 4
70 Wand WN 5   I Just Can't Help Believing/Send My Picture To Scranton, PA 4
72 Wand WN 24   Rock And Roll Lullaby/Are We Losing Touch? 4

CARLA THOMAS
61 London HLK 9310   Gee Whiz/For You 10
61 London HLK 9359   A Love Of My Own/Promises 8
62 London HLK 9618   I'll Bring It On Home To You/I Can't Take It 8
64 Atlantic AT 4005   I've Got No Time To Lose/A Boy Named Tom 7
66 Atlantic AT 4074   Comfort Me/I'm For You 6
66 Atlantic 584 011   Let Me Be Good To You/Another Night Without My Man 5
66 Atlantic 584 042   B-A-B-Y/What Have You Got To Offer Me 5

MINT VALUE £

67	Stax 601 002	Something Good (Is Going To Happen To You)/It's Starting To Grow (dark blue label, later light blue)	7/4
67	Stax 601 008	When Tomorrow Comes/Unchanging Love (dark blue label, later light blue)	7/4
68	Stax 601 032	Pick Up The Pieces/Separation	4
68	Stax STAX 103	Where Do I Go/I've Fallen In Love	4
69	Stax STAX 112	I Like What You're Doing To Me/Strung Out	4
69	Stax STAX 131	Unyielding/I've Fallen In Love	4
67	Stax 589 004	CARLA THOMAS (LP)	15
67	Stax 589 012	THE QUEEN ALONE (LP)	15
69	Stax SXATS 1019	MEMPHIS QUEEN (LP)	12
71	Stax 2362 023	LOVE MEANS ... (LP)	10

(see also Otis Redding & Carla Thomas)

CHARLIE THOMAS (& DRIFTERS)
| 74 | EMI International INT 502 | Midsummer Night In Harlem/Lonely Drifter Don't Cry (with Drifters) | 4 |
| 75 | EMI International INT 506 | I'm Gonna Take You Home/Run, Run, Roadrunner | 10 |

CLAUDETTE THOMAS
| 68 | Caltone TONE 116 | Roses Are Red My Love/YVONNE HARRISON: Near To You | 8 |

DAVID THOMAS & PEDESTRIANS
83	Recommended REDT 7	Didn't Have A (Very) Good Time (1-sided picture disc free with label's quarterly magazine)	6
84	Rough Trade ROUGH 30	THE SOUND OF THE SAND (LP)	10
85	Rough Trade ROUGH 80	MORE PLACES FOREVER (LP)	10

(see also Pere Ubu)

DON THOMAS
| 76 | DJM DJS 10670 | Come On Train Pts 1 & 2 | 4 |

EVELYN THOMAS
| 76 | 20th Century BTC 1027 | Love Is Not Just An Illusion/Chicago Hustle | 4 |

GENE THOMAS EDITION
| 64 | United Artists UP 1047 | Baby's Gone/Stand By Love | 12 |

HERSAL THOMAS
| 27 | Parlophone R 3261 | Suitcase Blues/Hersal Blues (78) | 50 |

IRMA THOMAS
64	Liberty LIB 66013	Wish Someone Would Care/Breakaway	15
64	Liberty LIB 66041	Time Is On My Side/Anyone Who Knows What Love Is	20
65	Liberty LIB 66080	He's My Guy/True True Love	10
65	Liberty LIB 66095	Some Things You Never Get Used To/You Don't Miss A Good Thing	15
65	Liberty LIB 66106	I'm Gonna Cry Till My Tears Run Dry/No-One Wants To Hear Troubles	18
66	Liberty LIB 66137	Take A Look/What Are You Trying To Do	15
66	Liberty LIB 66178	It's A Man's Woman's World Pts 1 & 2	8
65	Sue WI 372	Don't Mess With My Man/Set Me Free	12
65	Liberty LEP 4035	TIME IS ON MY SIDE (EP)	30
68	Minit MLL/MLS 400004E	TAKE A LOOK (LP)	25
76	Island HELP 29	LIVE (LP)	10

JAMO THOMAS & HIS PARTY BROTHERS ORCHESTRA
66	Polydor 56709	I Spy (For The F.B.I.)/Snake Hip Mama	7
69	Polydor 56755	I Spy (For The F.B.I.)/Snake Hip Mama (reissue)	5
69	Chess CRS 8098	I'll Be Your Fool/Jamo Soul	8
71	Mojo 2092 013	I Spy (For The F.B.I.)/Snake Hip Mama (2nd reissue)	4

JIMMY THOMAS
69	Parlophone R 5773	The Beautiful Night/Above A Whisper (withdrawn; demos more common, £75)	100
71	Spark SRL 1035	(We Ain't Looking) For No Trouble/Springtime	4
71	Spark SRL 1040	White Dove/You Don't Have To Say Goodbye	4

KID THOMAS
| 70s | JSP 4503 | Rockin' This Joint Tonight/Cozy Lounge Blues | 6 |

KID THOMAS/EMANUEL BAND
| 64 | 77 LA 12/26 | VICTORY WALK (LP, with Barry Martyn's Band) | 10 |

LEON THOMAS
| 73 | Philips 6369 417 | BLUES & SOULFUL TRUTH (LP) | 15 |

NICKY THOMAS
70	Amalgamated AMG 860	Let It Be/Turn Back The Hands Of Time	5
70	Amalgamated AMG 863	Danzella/JOE GIBBS ALLSTARS: Kingstonians Reggae	4
70	Trojan TBL 143	LOVE OF THE COMMON PEOPLE (LP)	10

RAMBLIN' THOMAS
| 52 | Tempo R 51 | Jig Head Blues/Hard Dallas Blues (78) | 8 |

RAY THOMAS
| 75 | Threshold THS 16 | FROM MIGHTY OAKS (LP) | 10 |
| 76 | Threshold THS 17 | HOPES, WISHES & DREAMS (LP) | 10 |

(see also Moody Blues)

RUFUS THOMAS
63	London HLK 9799	Walking The Dog/Fine And Mellow	12
64	London HLK 9850	Can Your Monkey Do The Dog/I Want To Get Married	8
64	London HLK 9884	Somebody Stole My Dog/I Want To Be Loved	8
64	Atlantic AT 4009	Jump Back/All Night Worker	6
66	Atlantic 584 029	Willy Nilly/Sho' Gonna Mess Him Up	6
67	Atlantic 584 089	Jump Back/Walking The Dog	5
67	Stax 601 013	Greasy Spoon/Sophisticated Sissy	6
68	Stax 601 028	Down Ta My House/Steady Holding On	6

68	Stax 601 037	The Memphis Train/I Think I Made A Boo-Boo	6
68	Stax STAX 105	Funky Mississippi/So Hard To Get Along With	4
70	Stax STAX 144	Do The Funky Chicken/Turn Your Damper Down	4
70	Stax STAX 149	Old McDonald Had A Farm/The Preacher & The Bear	4
71	Stax 2025 016	(Do The) Push & Pull Pts 1 & 2	4
72	Stax 2025 060	Breakdown Pts 1 & 2	4
73	Stax 2025 080	Do The Funky Penguin Pts 1 & 2	4
73	Stax 2025 187	Do The Funky Chicken/Happy/Hang 'Em High	4
75	Stax STXS 2029	Do The Double Bump Pts 1 & 2	4
64	Atlantic AET 6001	DO THE DOG (EP)	18
65	Atlantic AET 6011	JUMP BACK WITH RUFUS (EP)	18
64	London HA-K 8183	WALKING THE DOG (LP)	30
72	Stax 2362 028	DID YOU HEARD ME? (LP)	20
70	Stax SXATS 1033	FUNKY CHICKEN (LP)	12
71	Stax 2363 001	FUNKY CHICKEN (LP, reissue)	10
71	Stax 2362 010	DOING THE PUSH AND PULL LIVE AT P.J.'s (LP)	15
74	Stax STX 1004	CROWN PRINCE OF DANCE (LP)	10

TIMMY THOMAS
73	Mojo 2027 012	Why Can't We Live Together/Funky Me	4
77	TK XB 9052	The Magician/Don't Put It Down	4
75	Polydor 2956 002	WHY CAN'T WE LIVE TOGETHER (LP)	10

WAYNE THOMAS
| 67 | Coral Q 72491 | I've Never Known A Lady/My Life's Gonna Change | 5 |

ANDREAS THOMOPOULOS
70	Mushroom 100 MR 1	SONGS OF THE STREET (LP)	50
71	Mushroom 150 MR 4	BORN OUT OF THE TEARS OF THE SUN (LP)	60
	(see also Secondhand)		

BOBBY THOMPSON
| 69 | Col. Blue Beat DB 113 | That's How Strong My Love Is/Trouble In Town | 6 |

CHERYLE THOMPSON
| 64 | Stateside SS 291 | Teardrops/Black Night | 5 |

CHRIS THOMPSON
| 73 | Village Thing VTS 21 | CHRIS THOMPSON (LP) | 20 |

ERIC THOMPSON
| 68 | CBS EP 6398 | THE MAGIC ROUNDABOUT NO. 1 (EP) | 7 |
| 68 | CBS EP 6399 | THE MAGIC ROUNDABOUT NO. 2 (EP) | 7 |

HANK THOMPSON (& BRAZOS VALLEY BOYS)
56	Capitol CL 14517	Honey, Honey Bee Ball/Don't Take It Out On Me	12
56	Capitol CL 14517	Honey, Honey Bee Ball/Don't Take It Out On Me (78)	5
56	Capitol CL 14668	I'm Not Mad, Just Hurt/The Blackboard Of My Heart	12
56	Capitol CL 14668	I'm Not Mad, Just Hurt/The Blackboard Of My Heart (78)	5
58	Capitol CL 14869	Li'l Liza Jane/How Do You Hold A Memory	10
58	Capitol CL 14869	Li'l Liza Jane/How Do You Hold A Memory (78)	5
58	Capitol CL 14945	Gathering Flowers/Squaws Along The Yukon	8
58	Capitol CL 14961	I've Run Out Of Tomorrows/You're Going Back To Your Old Ways Again	7
59	Capitol CL 15014	Anybody's Girl/Total Strangers	6
59	Capitol CL 15074	I Guess I'm Getting Over You/I Didn't Mean To Fall In Love	6
60	Capitol CL 15114	A Six Pack To Go/What Made Her Change	12
60	Capitol CL 15156	She's Just A Whole Lot Like You/There My Future Goes (solo)	5
61	Capitol CL 15177	Will We Start It All Over Again/It Got To Be A Habit (solo)	5
62	Capitol CL 15247	The Wild Side Of Life (solo)/Give The World A Smile	5
76	Capitol CL 15877	Rockin' In The Congo/I Was The First One	4
56	Capitol EAP 1028	SONGS OF THE BRAZO VALLEY NO. 1 (EP)	12
57	Capitol EAP1 826	HANK (EP)	12
59	Capitol EAP1-1111	FAVOURITE WALTZES (EP)	8
57	Capitol T 729	HANK THOMPSON'S ALL-TIME HITS (LP)	20
58	Capitol T 975	DANCE RANCH (LP)	20
61	Capitol (S)T 1246	SONGS FOR ROUNDERS (LP)	15
61	Capitol (S)T 1469	THIS BROKEN HEART OF MINE (LP)	15
62	Capitol (S)T 1632	AT THE GOLDEN NUGGET (LP)	15
65	Capitol T 2089	GOLDEN COUNTRY HITS (LP)	12

KAY THOMPSON
| 56 | London HLA 8268 | Eloise/Just One Of Those Things | 18 |

LUCKY THOMPSON
| 56 | Vogue V 2388 | But Not For Me/East Of The Sun | 4 |

MIKE THOMPSON Jnr.
| 67 | Island WI 3090 | Rocksteady Wedding/Flowerpot Bloomers | 8 |

PAUL THOMPSON & NTH DEGREE
| 65 | Fontana TF 656 | For Me It's All Over/The Way You Used To Do | 4 |

RICHARD THOMPSON
72	Island ILPS 9197	HENRY THE HUMAN FLY (LP)	12
81	Elixir LP 1	STRICT TEMPO (LP)	10
	(see also Fairport Convention)		

RICHARD & LINDA THOMPSON
74	Island WIP 6186	I Want To See The Bright Lights Tonight/When I Get To The Border	4
75	Island WIP 6220	Hokey Pokey/I'll Regret It All In The Morning	4
74	Island ILPS 9305	HOKEY POKEY (LP)	10
75	Island ILPS 9348	POUR DOWN LIKE SILVER (LP, with lyrics)	10

Richard & Linda THOMPSON

75	Island	OFFICIAL LIVE TOUR 1975 (LP, unreleased, possibly test pressings only)	60

ROY THOMPSON
67	Columbia DB 8108	Sookie Sookie/Love You Say	8

SIR CHARLES THOMPSON
53	Vogue LDE 032	SIR CHARLES THOMPSON'S ALL STARS WITH CHARLIE PARKER (10" LP)	12
56	Vanguard PPT 12011	AND HIS BAND FEATURING COLEMAN HAWKINS (10" LP)	12

SONNY THOMPSON & HIS RHYTHM & BLUES BAND
52	Vogue V 2143	Real, Real Fine Pts 1 & 2 (78)	25
53	Esquire 10-320	House Full Of Blues/Creepin' (78)	25
53	Esquire 10-339	Screamin' Boogie/The Fish (78)	25
60	Starlite ST45 008	Screamin' Boogie/The Fish	125

(see also Claude Cloud & Thunderclaps)

SUE THOMPSON
61	Polydor NH 66967	Sad Movies/Throwing Kisses	8
62	Polydor NH 66973	Never Love Again/Norman	8
62	Polydor NH 66976	Two Of A Kind/It Has To Be Me	6
62	Polydor NH 66979	Have A Good Time/If The Boy Only Knew	6
63	Polydor NH 66987	What's Wrong Billy/I Need A Harbour	6
62	Fontana 267 244TF	James (Hold The Ladder Steady)/My Hero	8
63	Fontana 267 262TF	Willie Can/Too Much In Love	7
64	Hickory 45-1240	Big Daddy/I'd Like To Know You Better	6
64	Hickory 45-1255	Bad Boy/Toys	8
65	Hickory 45-1284	Paper Tiger/Mama Don't Cry Ata My Wedding	6
65	Hickory 45-1328	It's Break Up Time/Afraid	8
65	Hickory 45-1340	Just Kiss Me/Sweet Hunk Of Misery	5
65	Hickory 45-1359	I'm Looking For A World/Walkin' My Baby	6
65	Hickory 45-1381	What Should I Do/After The Heartache	5
67	London HLE 10142	Ferris Wheel/Don't Forget To Cry	4
64	Hickory LPE 1507	INTRODUCING KRIS JENSEN AND SUE THOMPSON (EP)	12
64	Hickory LPM 102	PAPER TIGER (LP)	18

SUE THOMPSON & BOB LUMAN
63	Polydor NH 66989	I Like Your Kind Of Love/Too Hot To Dance	8

(see also Bob Luman)

THOMPSON TWINS
80	Dirty Discs RANK 1	Squares And Triangles/Could Be Her ... Could Be You (p/s, different colours)	12
80	Latent LATE 1	She's In Love With Mystery/Fast Food/Food Style (p/s)	7
81	T TEE 1	The Perfect Game/Politics (p/s)	5
82	T TEE 2	Animal Laugh/Anything Is Good Enough/A Dab Product (p/s)	4
82	T TEE 122	Animal Laugh/A Dub Product/Anything Is Good Enough (12", p/s)	7
82	T RANK 2	Squares And Triangles/TOM BAILEY: Weather Station/ THE BLANKETS: Modern Plumbing (freebie)	7
82	T TEE 3	Make Believe (Let's Pretend)/Version (p/s)	4
82	T TEE 123	Make Believe (Let's Pretend)/Version (12", p/s)	7
82	T TEE 5/RANK 3	Runaway/Open Your Eyes (p/s, with free single)	5
83	Arista ARIST 504	Love On Your Side/Love On Your Back//In The Name Of Love/In The Beginning (double pack)	5
83	Arista TWISD 1	Watching/Dangerous (picture disc)	5
83	Arista TWISD 2	Hold Me Now/Let Loving Start (picture disc)	4
84	Arista TWISD 3	Doctor Doctor/Nurse Shark (shaped picture disc)	4
84	Arista TWISD 4	You Take Me Up/Passion Planet (3 different picture discs)	each 4
84	Arista TWISD 5	Sister Of Mercy/Out Of The Gap (picture disc)	4
84	Arista TWISD 6	Lay Your Hands On Me/The Lewis Carol (picture disc)	4
85	Arista TWISD 9	Don't Mess With Doctor Dream/Big Business (picture disc)	4
88	Arista FRETT 1	Here's Future Days: The Remixes (12", p/s)	7
88	Arista 208979	HERE'S TO FUTURE DAYS (LP, with free 12" [FRETT 1])	10
80s	Fan Club	fan club freebie LP	10

BILLY THORBURN & HIS STRICT TEMPO MUSIC
56	Parlophone MSP 6227	Jimmy Unknown/Ooh Bang Jiggilly Jang	4
57	Parlophone R 4276	True Love/Singing The Blues	4

GUNILLA THORN
63	HMV POP 1239	Merry-Go-Round/Go On Then	30

TRACEY THORN
82	Cherry Red CHERRY 53	Plain Sailing/Goodbye Joe (p/s)	4

(see also Marine Girls, Everything But The Girl, Grab Grab The Haddock)

DAVID THORNE
62	Stateside SS 141	The Alley Cat Song/The Moon Was Yellow	5
63	Stateside SS 190	One More Fool, One More Broken Heart/Don't Let It Get Away	5
63	Stateside SL 10036	THE ALLEY CAT SONGSTER (LP)	18

KEN THORNE ORCHESTRA
63	HMV POP 1176	"The Legion's Last Patrol" Film Theme/Kisses In The Night	4

WOODY THORNE
62	Vogue Pop V 9202	Sadie Lou/Teenagers In Love	125

CLAUDE THORNHILL & HIS ORCHESTRA
54	London HL 8042	Pussy-Footin'/Adios	25
54	London REP 1009	CLAUDE THORNHILL GOES MODERN (EP)	12
54	London H-ABP 1019	CLAUDE THORNHILL GOES MODERN (10" LP)	12
54	London H-ABP 1021	DREAM MUSIC (10" LP)	12

WILLIE MAE 'BIG MAMA' THORNTON
55	Vogue V 2284	Hound Dog/Mischievous Boogie (78)	35
69	Mercury SMCL 20176	STRONGER THAN DIRT (LP)	10
78	Vanguard VPC 40001	MAMA'S PRIDE (LP)	12

(see also Willie Mae Thornton)

EDDIE THORNTON OUTFIT
| 69 | Instant IN 003 | Baby Be My Gal/SONNY BURKE OUTFIT: All You | 8 |

WILLIE MAE THORNTON
| 64 | Sue WI 345 | Tom Cat/Monkey In The Barn | 40 |

(see also Big Mama Thornton)

GEORGE THOROGOOD & DESTROYERS
78	Sonet SON 2148	Can't Stop Lovin'/Homesick Boy	4
78	Sonet SON 2158	Madison Blues/Delaware Slide	4
78	Sonet SON 2169	Cocaine Blues/Move It On Over	4
78	Sonet SON 2171	It Wasn't Me/Who Do You Love	4
79	Sonet SON 2183	SO MUCH TROUBLE (EP)	4
80	Sonet SON 2220	Night Time/The Kids From Philly (p/s)	4
77	Sonet SNTF 760	GEORGE THOROGOOD AND THE DESTROYERS (LP)	10

BILLY THORPE
| 79 | Polydor 2391 424 | CHILDREN OF THE SUN (LP) | 10 |

BILLY THORPE & AZTECS
| 65 | Parlophone R 5381 | Twilight Time/Over The Rainbow | 4 |

THOR'S HAMMER
| 65 | Parlophone | THOR'S HAMMER (EP, w/drawn export issue, some with promo p/s) | 700/350 |

LINDA THORSON
| 68 | Ember EMB S 251 | Here I Am/Better Than Losing You | 4 |

THOSE HELICOPTERS
| 80 | State Of The Art STATE 1 | Shark/Eskimo (p/s) | 5 |
| 81 | Lavender LAVENDER 001 | Dr. Janov/Technical Smack | 4 |

THOSE NAUGHTY LUMPS
| 79 | Zoo CAGE 002 | Iggy Pop's Jacket/Pure And Innocent (foldout p/s) | 6 |
| 80 | Open Eye OP-EP 1002 | DOWN AT THE ZOO (EP) | 6 |

THOSE OBNOXIOUS TYPES
| 85 | Exoteric EX 2 | Love Is Dead/I'm Glad I'm Sick (p/s) | 4 |

THOUGHTS
| 66 | Planet PLF 118 | All Night Stand/Memory Of Your Love | 50 |

(see also Tiffany [& Thoughts], Paul Dean & Soul Savages)

THOUGHTS & WORDS
| 69 | Liberty LBL 83224 | THOUGHTS & WORDS (LP) | 10 |

THOUGHTS OF DES COX
| 69 | Morgan MR 4S | Isn't It Nice/It's All Very Strange | 4 |

THOUSAND YARD STARE
90	Stifled Aardvark AARD 003	WEATHERWATCHING (12" EP, 1st 1,000 with insert & no barcode on p/s)	12
90	Stifled Aardvark AARD 003	WEATHERWATCHING (12" EP, 2nd pressing, slightly altered sl., no insert)	10
91	Stifled Aardvark AARD 4	KEEPSAKE (10" EP, yellow vinyl, numbered white stickered sleeve)	6
91	Stifled Aardvark AARD5SP	SEASONSTREAM (10" EP, blue vinyl)	6
91	Stifled Aardvark AARD 6T	Strange/Twice Timing (12", plain sleeve, 1-sided, ULU gig freebie)	12
91	Stifled Aardvark AARD 8	HANDS ON (LP, with free bootleg EP & inner sleeve)	10

THREADBARE CONSORT
| 80s | private pressing | WEARING THIN (LP) | 15 |

THREADS OF LIFE
| 72 | Alco ALC 530 | THREADS OF LIFE (LP) | 600 |

(band's name is actually 'Alco')

THREE BARRY SISTERS
59	Decca F 11099	Little Boy Blue/My Sweetie's Coming To Call	4
59	Decca F 11118	Tall Paul/Till Then	5
59	Decca F 11141	Jo Jo — The Dog Faced Boy/I-Aye Ove-Lay Oo-Yay	5
60	Decca F 11201	Spoilsport/Bonnie Prince Charlie	4

THREE BELLS
60	Pye 7N 15252	Steady Date/In Between (Wishing I Was Sweet Sixteen)	4
64	Columbia DB 7399	Softly In The Night/He Doesn't Love Me	4
65	Columbia DB 7570	Someone To Love/Over And Over Again	4
66	Columbia DB 7980	Cry No More/He Doesn't Want You	6

THREE CAPS
66	Atlantic 584 043	I Got To Handle It/Zig-Zagging	5
69	Atlantic 584 251	Cool Jerk/Hello Stranger	5
66	Atlantic 587/588 019	DANCE THE COOL JERK (LP)	15

(see also Capitols)

THREE CHUCKLES
55	HMV 7M 292	Runaround/At Last You Understand	20
55	HMV B 10835	Runaround/At Last You Understand (78)	25
56	HMV 7M 333	Still Thinking Of You/Times Two I Love You	15
56	HMV POP 123	Still Thinking Of You/Times Two I Love You (78)	30
57	HMV POP 292	We're Gonna Rock Tonight/Want You Give Me A Chance	100
57	HMV POP 292	We're Gonna Rock Tonight/Want You Give Me A Chance (78)	30

THREE CITY FOUR
65	Decca LK 4705	THREE CITY FOUR (LP)	90
67	CBS 63039	SMOKE AND DUST WHERE THE HEART SHOULD HAVE BEEN (LP)	35

(see also Martin Carthy)

THREE CROWS
75	Junction Inn J NC 2	INN SONG (LP, private pressing)	10

THREE DEGREES
65	Stateside SS 413	Gee Baby I'm Sorry/Do What You're Supposed To Do	12
65	Stateside SS 459	Close Your Eyes/Gotta Draw The Line	30
71	Mojo 2092 001	Maybe/There's So Much Love	4
71	Mojo 2092 002	You're The One/Rose Garden	4
75	Pye Intl. 7N 25671	Sugar On Sunday/Maybe	6

THREE DOLLS
57	MGM MGM 958	The Living End/The Octopus Song	6

THREE GOOD REASONS
65	Mercury MF 883	Build Your Love/Don't Leave Me Now	4
65	Mercury MF 899	Nowhere Man/Wire Wheels	6
65	Mercury MF 929	The Moment Of Truth/Funny Kind Of Loving	4

THREE JOHNS
82	CNT CNT 003	English White Boy Engineer/Secret Agent (p/s)	8
83	CNT CNT 011	Pink Headed Bug/Lucy In The Rain (p/s)	7
83	CNT CNT 013	Men Like Monkeys/Two Minute Ape!/Windolene/Marx's Wife/ Paris 1941 (12", p/s)	7

THREE KAYES (SISTERS)
56	HMV 7M 401	Ivory Tower/Mister Cuckoo (Sing Your Song)	15
56	HMV POP 251	Lay Down Your Arms/First Row Balcony (as Three Kaye Sisters)	12

(see also Kaye Sisters, Frankie Vaughan)

THREE MAN ARMY
72	Pegasus PGS 1	What's Your Name/Travellin'	5
74	Reprise K 14292	Polecat Woman/Take Me Down From The Mountain	5
71	Pegasus PEG 3	A THIRD OF A LIFETIME (LP)	25
73	Reprise K 44254	THREE MAN ARMY (LP)	20
74	Reprise K 54015	THREE MAN ARMY TWO — POLECAT WOMAN (LP)	20

(see also Gun, Baker Gurvitz Army, Adrian Gurvitz)

THREE PROFESSORS
56	Columbia DB 3845	Yew Stept Owt Offa Dreme/Vulgar Boatman Rock	4

THREE QUARTERS
65	Columbia DB 7467	People Will Talk/Love Come A-Tricklin' Down	4
65	Columbia DB 7576	The Pleasure Girls/Little People	4

THREE'S A CROWD
66	Fontana TF 673	Look Around The Corner/Living In A Dream	4

THREE SUNS
55	HMV 7M 297	Perdido/For You	5
55	HMV 7M 346	Cha Cha Joe/Arrivederci Darling (Arriverderci Roma)	5

THREE TOPS
67	Doctor Bird DB 1101	Miserable Friday/This World Has A Feeling	10
67	Studio One SO 2023	Moving To Progress/Love And Inspiration	15
67	Trojan TR 003	It's Raining/Sound Of Music	10
67	Treasure Isle TI 7008	Do It Right/You Should Have Known	10
68	Coxsone CS 7033	A Man Of Chances/HORTENSE ELLIS: A Groovy Kind Of Love	15
68	Coxsone CS 7051	Great Train In '68/You Should Have Known	15
73	Bullet BU 527	Take Time Out/Just Like A Log	4

(see also Tree Tops, Dion Cameron & Three Tops)

THREE WISE MEN
83	Virgin VS 642	Thanks For Christmas/Countdown To Christmas Partytime (p/s)	8

(see also XTC)

THRILLED SKINNY
87	Hunchback HUNCH 001	PIECE OF PLASTIC (12" EP)	7
88	Hunchback HUNCH 002	White Grid/Pinless (flexidisc with stapled b&w sleeve with Wilderness Children flexidisc, free with 'Sowing Seeds' fanzine, issue 5)	7/5

(see also Wilderness Children)

THRILLERS
68	Blue Cat BS 128	The Last Dance/DELTA CATS: Unworthy Baby	10

PERCY 'THRILLS' THRILLINGTON
77	Regal Zono. EMI 2594	Uncle Albert; Admiral Halsey/Eat At Home	25
77	Regal Zono. EMC 3175	THRILLINGTON (LP, with inner sleeve)	75
77	Regal Zono. TC-EMC 3175	THRILLINGTON (cassette)	15

THRILLS
66	Capitol CL 15469	No One/What Can Go Wrong	25
79	Grapevine GRP 126	Show The World Where It's At/What Can Go Wrong	4

(see also Paul McCartney)

THROBBING GRISTLE
78	Industrial IR 0003	United/Zyklon B Zombie (p/s)	8
78	Industrial IR 0003/U	United/Zyklon B Zombie (p/s, white or clear vinyl, 1,000 only of each)	15
80	Industrial IR 0003	United/Zyklon B Zombie (longer version) (p/s, reissue, 'Memorial Issue' in matrix)	12
80	Industrial IR 0013	Subhuman/Something Came Over Me (in polythene camouflage bag)	10

80	Industrial IR 0015	Adrenalin/Distant Dreams (Part Two) (in polythene camouflage bag) 10
81	Fetish FET 006	Discipline (live)/Discipline (live) (12", p/s) 15
77	Industrial IR 0002	SECOND ANNUAL REPORT (LP, 785 only, white heavy duty sleeve, with questionnaire, xerox strip & 2 stickers) 70
78	Industrial IR 0004	D.O.A. THE THIRD AND FINAL REPORT (LP, 1st 1,000 with calendar & postcard) 20/15
78	Fetish FET 2001	SECOND ANNUAL REPORT (LP, 2,000 only, T.G. 'lightning flash' sleeve, with questionnaire & insert) 18
79	Fetish FET 2001	SECOND ANNUAL REPORT (LP, reissue, glossy sleeve with inserts) 12
79	Industrial IR 0004	D.O.A. THE THIRD AND FINAL REPORT (LP, 1,000 only, 16 equal length tracks) 15
79	Industrial IR 0008	20 JAZZ FUNK GREATS (LP, 5,000 only, 1st 2,000 with b&w poster) 20/12
80	Industrial IR 0009	HEATHEN EARTH (LP, gatefold sleeve, 785 on blue vinyl) 60/12
81	Fetish FET 2001	SECOND ANNUAL REPORT (LP, backwards version, 1st 2,000 in T.G. 'flash' sleeve, later b&w sleeve) 18/10
81	Fetish FX 1	A BOXED SET (5-LP box set with 28-page booklet & badge, 5,000 only) 80
82	Death 01	MUSIC FROM THE DEATH FACTORY, MAY '79 (LP, 50 only) ....50+
82	Power Focus 001	ASSUME POWER FOCUS (LP, 500 only, numbered) 20
82	POWER FOCUS 001 T.G. 33033	LIVE AT THE DEATH FACTORY, MAY '79 (LP, picture disc, 1,355 only) 20
80s	Walter Ulbricht 001	JOURNEY THROUGH THE BODY (LP, 1,000 only) 25
80s	Sprut 001	VERY FRIENDLY — THE FIRST ANNUAL REPORT OF T.G. (LP) 15
80s	Karnage/Illuminated KILL1	THEE PSYCHICK SACRIFICE (2-LP) 20
84	Casual Abandon CAS 1J	ONCE UPON A TIME (LP) 15
80s	Industrial IRC 1-IRC 24	24 HOURS (box set of cassettes) 150-200

(see also Psychic TV, Chris Carter, Chris & Cosey, Coil)

THROWING MUSES
86	4AD MUSE ONE	Counting Backwards/Say Goodbye/Hook In Her Head (12", p/s) 8
87	4AD BAD 701C	Chains Changed/Finished/Reel/Snail Head/Cry Baby Cry (cassette) 6
89	4AD BADD 903	Dizzy/Santa Claus/Mania (live)/Downtown (live) (10", p/s) 6

THUNDER
89	EMI EMS 11	She's So Fine/Girl's Going Out Of Her Head (p/s, with free patch) 5
89	EMI 12EMP 11	She's So Fine/Girl's Going Out Of Her Head/Another Shot Of Love (12", p/s, with poster) 7
90	EMI EMPD 126	Dirty Love/Fired Up (picture disc) 5
90	EMI EMS 137	Back Street Symphony/No Way Out Of The Wilderness (box set with badge & postcards) 4
90	EMI 10EMI 148	Gimme Some Lovin'/I Wanna Be Her Slave (10" red vinyl, gatefold booklet) 5
90	EMI 10EMI 158	She's So Fine (Full Length Version)/Backstreet Symphony (Live At Donnington '90) (10" blue vinyl, gatefold p/s) 5

(see also Terraplane)

JOHNNY THUNDER
63	Stateside SS 149	Loop De Loop/Don't Be Ashamed 5
63	Stateside SS 168	Rock-A-Bye My Darling/The Rosy Dance 4
63	Stateside SS 200	Jailer, Bring Me Water/Outlaw 5
63	Stateside SS 229	Hey Child/Everybody Likes To Dance With Johnny 5
64	Stateside SS 337	More, More, More Love, Love/Shout It To The World 5
65	Stateside SS 370	Send Her To Me/Everybody Likes To Dance With Johnny 4
65	Stateside SS 454	Dear John I'm Going To Leave You/Suzie-Q 5
65	Stateside SS 476	Everybody Do The Sloopy/Beautiful 5
66	Stateside SS 499	My Prayer/A Broken Heart 4
63	Stateside SL 10029	LOOP DE LOOP (LP) 18

JOHNNY THUNDER & RUBY WINTERS
| 67 | Stateside SS 2005 | Make Love To Me/Teach Me Tonight ....5 |

MARGO THUNDER
| 75 | Capitol CL 15808 | Expressway To Your Heart/Hush Up Your Mouth ....5 |

THUNDERBIRDS (U.S.)
| 55 | London HL 8146 | Ayuh, Ayuh/Blueberries ....35 |

(see also Bert Convy & Thunderbirds)

THUNDERBIRDS (Australia)
| 61 | Oriole CB 1610 | Wild Weekend/Rat Race ....10 |
| 61 | Oriole CB 1625 | New Orleans Beat/Delilah Jones ....10 |

THUNDERBIRDS (U.K.)
| 66 | Polydor 56710 | Your Ma Said You Cried In Your Sleep/Before It's Too Late ....30 |

(see also Chris Farlowe & Thunderbirds)

THUNDERBIRDS (TV)
(see under Barry Gray)

THUNDERBOLTS
| 62 | Decca F 11522 | Fugitive/Feelin' In A Mood ....7 |

THUNDERBOYS
| 80 | Recent EJSP 9339 | Fashion/Someone Like You (p/s) ....8 |

(see also Carmel)

THUNDERCLAP NEWMAN
69	Track 604 031	Something In The Air/Wilhelmina 4
70	Track 2094 001	Accidents/I See It All 4
70	Track 2094 002	Wild Country/Hollywood 4
70	Track 2094 003	The Reason/Stormy Petrel 4
79	Track 2095 002	Wild Country/Hollywood (p/s) 6
70	Track 2406 003	HOLLYWOOD DREAM (LP) 20

(see also Stone The Crows, One In A Million, Paul McCartney & Wings, Speedy Keen)

THUNDER COMPANY

70	Columbia DB 8706	Ridin' On The Gravy Train (5.03)/Bubble Drum	25
70	Columbia DB 8706	Ridin' On The Gravy Train (2.35 Edit)/Bubble Drum (demo only)	25

(see also Brian Bennett, Shadows)

THUNDERMUG

73	London HLZ 10411	Africa/Will They Ever	4
72	Axe AXS 502	STRIKES (LP)	10

JOHNNY THUNDERS (& HEARTBREAKERS)

78	Real ARE 1	Dead Or Alive/Downtown (p/s)	12
78	Real ARE 3	You Can't Put Your Arms Around A Memory (Edit)/Hurtin' (p/s)	10
78	Real ARE 3T	You Can't Put Your Arms Around A Memory (Edit)/Hurtin' (12", p/s, blue or pink vinyl, die-cut company sleeve)	7
83	Jungle JUNG 5	VINTAGE '77 (12" EP)	10
84	Jungle JUNG 14P	Get Off The Phone/All By Myself (picture disc)	5
85	Jungle JUNG 23P	Crawfish/Tie Me Up (with Patti Palladin, picture disc)	4
77	Real RAL 1	SO ALONE (LP, with inner sleeve)	10

(see also New York Dolls, Heartbreakers)

THUNDER THUMBS & TOETSENMAN

82	Polydor POSP 480	Freedom/Freedom A Go Go (p/s)	12
82	Polydor POSPX 480	Freedom/Freedom A Go Go (12", p/s)	18

(see also Level 42, Mark King)

THUNDERTRAIN

77	Jelly JPLP 1	TEENAGE SUICIDE (LP)	18

THURSDAY'S CHILDREN

66	Piccadilly 7N 35276	Just You/You Don't Believe Me	5
66	Piccadilly 7N 35306	Crawfish/Come Softly To Me	5

THYRDS

64	Oak RGJ 133	Hide 'N' Seek/I've Got My Mojo Working	125
64	Decca F 12010	Hide 'N' Seek/No Time Like The Present	25

TICH & QUACKERS

65	Oriole CB 1980	Santa Bring Me Ringo/Santa's Got Such A Terrible Cold	4

TICKAWINDA

75	Pennine PSS 153	ROSEMARY LANE (LP)	300

(see also Any Trouble)

TICKETS

79	Bridgehouse BHS 3	I'll Be Your Pin Up/Guess I Have To Sit Alone (p/s)	6

TICKLE

67	Regal Zonophone RZ 3004	Subway (Smokey Pokey World)/Good Evening	100

(see also Junior's Eyes)

TIDAL WAVE

69	Decca F 22973	With Tears In My Eyes/We Wanna Know	8

TIDBITS

71	Fly BUG 12	Jean Harlow/Vietnam/Six O'Clock Blues	4

PETER TIERNEY & NIGHTHAWKS

65	Fontana TF 547	Oh How I Need You/That's Too Bad	4

ROY TIERNEY

61	Philips BF 1159	Cupid/The Lonely One (some in p/s)	7/4
61	Philips BF 1194	Just Out Of Reach (Of My Two Empty Arms)/Casanova	4

TIERNEY'S FUGITIVES

65	Decca F 12247	Did You Want To Run Away?/Morning Mist	8

TIFFANIES

67	Chess CRS 8059	It's Got To Be A Great Song/He's Good For Me	35

TIFFANY

88	MCA TIFFP 2	Could've Been/The Heart Of Love (picture disc)	4
88	MCA TIFFP 3	I Saw Him Standing There/Mr Mambo (picture disc)	4
88	MCA TIFFP 4	Feelings Of Forever/Out Of My Heart (picture disc)	4
88	MCA TIFFTP 5	Radio Romance (12" picture disc)	7
89	MCA TIFFB 6	All This Time (numbered box set with postcards)	4

TIFFANY (& THOUGHTS)

65	Parlophone R 5311	I Know/Am I Dreaming	5
66	Parlophone R 5439	Find Out What's Happening/Baby Don't Look Down (as Tiffany & Thoughts)	20

(see also Thoughts)

TIFFANY SHADE

68	Fontana (S)TL 5469	TIFFANY SHADE (LP)	25

TIGER (U.K.)

75	United Artists UP 35848	I Am An Animal/Stop That Machine	4
76	Retreat RTL 6006	TIGER (LP)	12
76	EMI EMC 3153	GOIN' DOWN LAUGHING (LP)	10

(see also Hackensack, Samson, Brinsley Schwarz)

TIGER (Jamaica)

71	Camel CA 70	Guilty/United We Stand	5
70	New Beat NB 052	Soul Of Africa/Dallas Texas	4
70	New Beat NB 064	Musical Scorcher/Three Dogs Night	4
71	New Beat NB 075	African Beat/Black Man Land	4
71	New Beat NB 088	Have You Ever Been Hurt/Our Day Will Come	4

TIGER LILY
75	Gull GULS 12	Monkey Jive/Ain't Misbehavin' (some with p/s)	30/12
77	Gull GULS 54	Monkey Jive/Ain't Misbehavin' (reissue, different p/s)	12/5
80	Dead Good DEAD 11	Monkey Jive/Ain't Misbehavin' (2nd reissue)	6

(see also Ultravox)

TIGERS
69	Polydor 56339	Smile For Me/Rain Falls On The Lonely	4

TIGERTAILZ
88	M. For Nations MFN 78P	YOUNG AND CRAZY (LP, picture disc)	10
90	M. For Nations MFN 96P	BERSERKER (LP, picture disc)	10

JIMMY & LOUISE TIGG
70	Deep Soul DS 9105	Who Can I Turn To/Love That Never Grows Cold	10

TIGHT LIKE THAT
72	Village Thing VTS 12	HOKUM (LP)	20

TIGHTS
78	Cherry Red CHERRY 1	Bad Hearts/It/Cracked (p/s)	5
78	Cherry Red CHERRY 2	Howard Hughes/China's Eternal (p/s)	4
78	Ch. Red CSP-CHERRY 2	Howard Hughes/China's Eternal (cassette)	10

TIK & TOK
82	Survival SURP 007	Summer In The City/Crisis (picture disc)	5
82	Survival SUR 12 007	Long Hot Summer In The City/Crisis (12", p/s)	7
83	Survival SURP 016	Cool Running/Vile Bodies (picture disc)	5
83	Survival SUR 12 016	Cool Running (Gargantuan Mix)/Vile Bodies/Souless Synthetic Heartsteps Of Unconcerned Androids (12", p/s)	7
83	Survival SURP 020	Screen Me, I'm Yours/Dangerous And Unafraid (picture disc)	5
84	Survival SUR 12 020	Screen Me, I'm Yours/Dangerous And Unafraid/The Garden (12", p/s)	7
84	Survival SURP 024	Everything Will Change/Cracking Up (picture disc)	4
84	Survival SUR 12 024	Everything Will Change/Cracking Up/Theme From The Dome Brothers (12", p/s)	7
84	Survival SURP 027	Higher Ground/Down From The Sky (picture disc)	4
84	Survival SUR 12 027	Higher Ground (extended)/Down From The Sky/Psych-Out At The Dunheadin Masquerade Ball (12", p/s)	7
84	Survival SURLP 008	INTOLERANCE (LP, gatefold sleeve)	10
84	Survival SURPP 008	INTOLERANCE (LP, picture disc)	12

TANITA TIKARAM
88	WEA YZ 321TE	Twist In My Sobriety (Edit)/Friends/The Kill In Your Heart/For All These Years (10", autographed gatefold p/s)	5
88	WEA YZ 321TE	Twist In My Sobriety (Edit)/Friends/The Kill In Your Heart/For All These Years (10", gatefold p/s)	5
89	WEA YZ 331B	Cathedral Song/Sighing Innocents/Let's Make Everybody Smile Today (live)/Over You All (live) (boxed EP, with prints)	4
89	WEA YZ 363CDX	World Outside Your Window (Remix)/Good Tradition (live)/He Likes The Sun (live)/For All These Years (Instrumental) (boxed CD)	5
90	WEA YZ 459 CDP	Little Sister (Leaving Town)/I Love The Heaven's Solo/Hot Pork Sandwiches/Twist In My Sobriety (CD, picture disc)	7

TIKKI TAKI SUZI LIES
80s	UPC UPC 109	Ba Da Da Dim/Dreamstealer	12

TILLER BOYS
81	New Hormones ORG 3	Big Noise From The Jungle/Slaves And Pyramids/What Me Worry? (p/s)	6

(see also Buzzcocks, Pete Shelley)

MEL TILLIS
67	London HLR 10141	Life Turned Her That Way/If I Could Only Start Over	4
68	London HA-R 8345	MR. MEL (LP)	15

JOHNNY TILLOTSON
59	London HLA 8930	True True Happiness/Love Is Blind	40
59	London HLA 8930	True True Happiness/Love Is Blind (78)	40
60	London HLA 9048	Why Do I Love You So/Never Let Me Go	20
60	London HLA 9101	Earth Angel/Pledging My Love	20
60	London HLA 9231	Poetry In Motion/Princess, Princess	5
61	London HLA 9275	Jimmy's Girl/His True Love Said Goodbye	5
61	London HLA 9412	Without You/Cutie Pie	5
62	London HLA 9514	Dreamy Eyes/Much Beyond Compare	5
62	London HLA 9550	It Keeps Right On A-Hurtin'/She Gave Sweet Love To Me	5
62	London HLA 9598	Send Me The Pillow You Dream On/What'll I Do	5
62	London HLA 9642	I Can't Help It/I'm So Lonesome I Could Cry	5
63	London HLA 9695	Out Of My Mind/Judy, Judy, Judy	5
63	London HLA 9811	Funny How Time Slips Away/A Very Good Year For Girls	5
63	MGM MGM 1214	Talk Back Trembling Lips/Another You	5
63	MGM MGM 1225	Worried Guy/Please Don't Go Away	5
63	MGM MGM 1235	I'm Watching My Watch/I Rise, I Fall	5
64	MGM MGM 1247	Suffering From A Heartache/Worry	5
64	MGM MGM 1252	She Understands Me/Tomorrow	5
64	MGM MGM 1266	Angel/Little Boy	5
65	MGM MGM 1275	Then I'll Count Again/One's Yours, One's Mine	5
65	MGM MGM 1281	Heartaches By The Number/Your Memory Comes Along	5
65	MGM MGM 1290	Our World/My Gidget	5
66	MGM MGM 1300	Hello Enemy/I Never Loved You Anyway	5
66	MGM MGM 1311	Me Myself And I/Country Boy, Country Boy	5
68	MGM MGM 1393	Cabaret/If I Were A Rich Man	5
62	London RE-A 1345	JOHNNY TILLOTSON (EP)	20

Johnny TILLOTSON

63	London RE-A 1388	J.T. (EP)	20
63	MGM MGM-EP 788	JOHNNY TILLOTSON (EP)	18
64	MGM MGM-EP 790	JOHNNY TILLOTSON'S HIT PARADE (EP)	18
61	London HA-A 2431	JOHNNY TILLOTSON'S BEST (LP)	50
62	London HA-A 8019	IT KEEPS RIGHT ON A-HURTIN' (LP)	40
65	MGM C(S) 8005	JOHNNY TILLOTSON SINGS OUR WORLD (LP)	15
66	MGM C(S) 8025	NO LOVE AT ALL (LP)	15

TILSLEY ORCHESTRA

66	Fontana TF 783	"Thunderbirds" Theme/Theme From "The Power Game"	8
67	Fontana (S)TL 5411	TOP T.V. THEMES (LP)	15
69	Fontana SFL 13139	TOP T.V. THEMES (LP, reissue)	10

STEVE TILSTON

71	Village Thing VTS 5	AN ACOUSTIC CONFUSION (LP)	18
72	Transatlantic TRA 252	COLLECTION (LP)	10
77	Cornucopia CR 1	SONGS FROM THE DRESS REHEARSAL (LP)	20
83	TM PROP 4	IN FOR A PENNY IN FOR A POUND (LP)	10

TIMBER

| 72 | Elektra K 42093 | BRING AMERICA HOME (LP) | 10 |

TIME

| 65 | Pye 7N 17019 | Take A Bit Of Notice/Every Now And Then | 30 |
| 66 | Pye 7N 17146 | The First Time I Saw The Sunshine/Annabel | 15 |

TIME

| 75 | B.U.K. BULP 2005 | TIME (LP) | 60 |

(see also Spontaneous Combustion)

T.I.M.E.

| 69 | Liberty LBF 15082 | Take Me Along/Make It Alright | 6 |
| 69 | Liberty LBS 83232 | SMOOTH BALL (LP) | 20 |

TIMEBOX

67	Piccadilly 7N 35369	I'll Always Love You/Save Your Love	18
67	Piccadilly 7N 35379	Soul Sauce/I Wish I Could Jerk Like My Uncle Cyril	25
67	Deram DM 153	Walking Through The Streets Of My Mind/Don't Make Promises	10
68	Deram DM 194	Beggin'/A Woman That's Waiting	8
68	Deram DM 219	Girl Don't Make Me Wait/Gone Is The Sad Man	10
69	Deram DM 246	Baked Jam Roll In Your Eye/Poor Little Heartbreaker	10
69	Deram DM 271	Yellow Van/You've Got The Chance	10

(see also [Mike] Patto, Felder's Orioles)

TIMELORDS

88	KLF 003GG	Gary In The Tardis (Radio)/Gary In The Tardis (Minimal) (white label)	15
88	KLF 003P	Doctorin' The Tardis (Radio)/Doctorin' The Tardis (Minimal) (shaped picture disc)	4
88	KLF 003R	Doctorin' The Tardis (Radio)/Doctorin' The Tardis (Minimal)/Gary Glitter Joins The JAMs (12" p/s, Remix, 4,000 only)	7
88	KLFCD 003	Doctorin' The Tardis (Radio)/Doctorin' The Tardis (Minimal)/Doctorin' The Tardis (Club Mix)/Doctorin' The Tardis (Video) (CD video)	10

(see also KLF, Disco 2000, JAMs, Bill Drummond, Orb, Gary Glitter)

TIME MACHINE

| 80s | Rip Off RIP 6 | Never Met Suzie/Come Dancing/Let Me Tell You | 5 |

TIMES

65	EMI/Columbia 7ES 24	Ooh Wee/Shepherd Blues/Suzie/Running And Hiding (demo EP, no p/s)	50
66	Columbia DB 7804	Think About The Times/Tomorrow Night	15
66	Columbia DB 7904	(She Can't Replace) The Love We Knew/Reconciled	15

TIMES

81	Whaam! WHAAM 2	Red With Purple Flashes/Biff! Bang! Pow! (p/s)	30
82	Artpop POP 50	Here Come The Holidays/Three Cheers For The Sun (A-side as Joni Dee & Times, p/s, some with sticker)	15/12
83	Artpop POP 49	I Helped Patrick McGoohan Escape/The Theme From "Danger Man" (p/s)	12
84	Artpop POP 46	Boys Brigade/Power Is Forever (p/s)	7
84	Artpop POP 45	Blue Fire/Where The Blue Begins (p/s)	6
85	Unicorn PHZ 1	London Boys/(Where To Go) When The Sun Goes Down (p/s)	4
91	Caff CAFF 13	Extase/BIFF BANG POW!: Sleep (p/s, with insert)	20
85	Artpop 43DOZ	BOYS ABOUT TOWN (EP)	10
83	Artpop No. 1	I HELPED PATRICK McGOOHAN ESCAPE (mini-LP)	15
83	Artpop ART 17	HELLO EUROPE (LP)	12
83	Artpop ART 19	THIS IS LONDON (LP)	12
84	Artpop ART 20	POP GOES ART (LP, 'hand-painted' picture disc reissue, signed)	15

(see also Television Personalities, Teenage Filmstars, O Level, Biff Bang Pow!)

TIME U.K.

| 83 | Red Bus TIMS 123 | The Cabaret/Remember Days//Arcade Radio Present Time U.K.: The Beginning (The Radio Show) (double pack) | 4 |

(see also Jam, Jimmy Edwards)

SALLY TIMMS & DRIFTING COWGIRLS

86	T.I.M. MT 4	Long Black Veil/Butchers Boy (p/s)	4
87	T.I.M. MOT 6	This House Is A House Of Trouble!/Chained To The Anchor Of Love (with Marc Almond) (p/s)	5
87	T.I.M. 12 MOT 6	This House Is A House Of Trouble!/Chained To The Anchor Of Love/My Little Pony (12", p/s, with Marc Almond)	8

(see also Marc Almond, Mekons)

TIMON

| 68 | Pye 7N 17451 | Bitter Thoughts Of Little Jane/Ramblin' Boy | 25 |

70	Threshold TH 3	And Now She Says She's Young/I'm Just A Travelling Man	5

(see also Tymon Dogg)

TIMONEERS
76	WHM	ROASTED LIVE (LP)	25

AL TIMOTHY & HIS BAND
55	Decca F 10558	Gruntin' Blues/You Mad Man!	5

TIM TAM & TURN ONS
67	Island WI 6007	Wait A Minute/Ophelia	12

TINA
74	Polydor 2058 449	Cross Your Heart/What Would I Be	4

TINGA (Stewart) & ERNIE (Wilson)
69	Explosion EX 2009	She's Gone/Old Old Song	5

TINGHA & TUCKER
(see under Century 21)

TINKERBELL'S FAIRYDUST
67	Decca F 12705	Lazy Day/In My Magic Garden	20
68	Decca F 12778	Twenty Ten/Walking My Baby	20
69	Decca F 12865	Sheila's Back In Town/Follow Me Follow	30
69	Decca LK 5028	TINKERBELL'S FAIRYDUST (LP, unreleased, test pressings in sleeve)	800

TINKERS
69	Fontana SFJL 935	TIL THE WILD BIRDS (LP)	10
70	Argo ZFB 35	SPRING RAIN (LP)	15

TIN MACHINE
89	EMI Manhattan 10MT 68	Under The God/Sacrifice Yourself/The Interview (10", p/s)	5
89	EMI Manhattan MTPD 73	Tin Machine/Maggie's Farm (live) (shaped picture disc with card insert)	5
89	EMI M/hattan MT/MTG 73	Tin Machine/Maggie's Farm (live) (normal or numbered gatefold p/s)	4/5
89	EMI Manhattan MTS 76	Prisoner Of Love (Edit)/Baby Can Dance (live) (silver envelope w/4 cards)	6
89	EMI Manhattan MTPD 76	Prisoner Of Love (Edit)/Baby Can Dance (live) (heart-shaped picture disc with printed PVC sleeve & insert)	6

(see also David Bowie)

BABS TINO
62	London HLR 9589	Forgive Me/If I Didn't Love You So Much	12
63	London RER 1377	FORGIVE ME (EP)	40

TINTERN ABBEY
67	Deram DM 164	Beeside/Vacuum Cleaner	100

TIN TIN
69	Polydor 56332	Only Ladies Play Croquet/He Wants To Be A Star	5
70	Polydor 2058 023	Toast And Marmalade For Tea/Manhattan Woman	5
70	Polydor 2058 076	Come On Over Again/Back To Winona	4
71	Polydor 2058 114	Is That The Way/Swans On The Canal	4
69	Polydor 2384 011	TIN TIN (LP)	10
71	Polydor 2382 080	ASTRAL TAXI (LP)	10

(see also Steve & Stevie)

TIN TIN
83	WEA TIN 1T	Kiss Me (Dub Version)/Love's Duet (Dub) (12", p/s)	8
83	WEA X 9763T	Hold It (Extended)/Instrumental/Blowing Kisses//Kiss Me (US Remix)/Love's Duet/Kiss Me (Instrumental) (12" double pack)	8
84	WEA X 9823T	Kiss Me (U.S. Remix)/(Instrumental)/Love's Duet (12", p/s)	7

(see also Stephen 'Tin Tin' Duffy, Hawks, Lilac Time)

TINY ALICE
72	Kama Sutra 2013 043	Doctor Jazz/The Chocolate Dandies Of 1932/15c Hamburger Mama	4
72	Kama Sutra 2319 015	TINY ALICE (LP)	10

TINY LIGHTS
86	Temple TOPY 008T	FLOWERS IN THE AIR (12" EP)	7

TINY TIM
68	Reprise RS 20760	Bring Back Those Rockabye Baby Days	4
68	Reprise RS 23258	Tiptoe Through The Tulips/I Got You Babe	4
68	Reprise RS 20769	Hello Hello/The Other Side	4
68	Reprise RS 20802	Great Balls Of Fire/As Time Goes By	4
69	Reprise RS 20855	Mickey The Monkey/Neighbourhood Children	4
68	Reprise RSLP 6292	GOD BLESS TINY TIM (LP)	15
69	Reprise RSLP 6323	2ND ALBUM (LP)	15

JULIE TIPPETT
76	Utopia UTS 601	SUNSET GLOW (LP)	10

(see also Julie Discoll, Brian Auger)

KEITH TIPPETT
69	Polydor 2384 004	YOU ARE HERE, I AM THERE (LP)	25
71	Vertigo 6360 024	DEDICATED TO YOU BUT YOU WEREN'T LISTENING (LP, gatefold sleeve, spiral label)	30
72	RCA SF 8290	BLUEPRINT (LP)	30
76	Steam SJ 104	TNT (LP, with Stan Tracey)	12
77	Vinyl VS 101	WARM SPIRITS, COOL SPIRITS (LP)	10
78	Ogun OGD 003/4	FRAMES (2-LP)	14

(see also Centipede, Ovary Lodge)

TIPPIE & CLOVERS
63	Stateside SS 160	My Heart Said/Bossa Nova Baby	10

LESTER TIPTON
79   Grapevine GRP 136   This Won't Change/MASQUERADERS: How 8

TIP TOPS
63   Cameo Parkway P 868   He's Draggin'/Oo-Kook-A-Boo 15

TIR NA NOG
70   Chrysalis WIP 6090   I'm Happy To Be/Let My Love Grow 4
73   Chrysalis CHS 2016   Strong In The Sun/The Mountain & I 4
71   Chrysalis ILPS 9153   TIR NA NOG (LP) 12
72   Chrysalis CHR 1006   A TEAR AND A SMILE (LP) 12
73   Chrysalis CHR 1047   STRONG IN THE SUN (LP) 10

TITANS
58   London HLU 8609   Don't You Just Know It/Can It Be 55
58   London HLU 8609   Don't You Just Know It/Can It Be (78) 15

TITUS GROAN
70   Dawn DNLS 3012   TITUS GROAN (LP, gatefold sleeve) 55

CAL TJADER
65   Verve VS 529   Soul Sauce/Naked City Theme 35
68   Verve (S)VLP 9192   THE BEST OF CAL TJADER (LP) 10
68   Verve (S)VLP 9215   HIP VIBRATIONS (LP) 10
69   Fontana STL 5527   SOLAR HEAT (LP) 10

TNT
84   Neat NEAT 39   Back On The Road/Rockin' The Night (p/s) 4

TOAD
72   RCA SF 8241   TOAD (LP) 135

TOAD THE WET SPROCKET
79   Sprocket   Pete's Punk Song 15
80   Sprockets BRS 008   Reaching For The Sky/One Glass Of Whiskey (foldout stapled p/s) 10

TOBRUK
83   Neat NEAT 32   Wild On The Run/Must Go On 4

TOBY JUG
69   private press   GREASY QUIFF (LP, with insert) 600

TOBY JUG
71   Decca F 13173   Breakaway Man/Brotherhood 4

TOBY TWIRL
68   Decca F 12728   Harry Faversham/Back In Time 18
68   Decca F 12804   Toffee Apple Sunday/Romeo And Juliet 1968 25
69   Decca F 12867   Movin' In/Utopia Daydream 15
(see also Shades Of Blue)

ART & DOTTY TODD
52   HMV B 10399   Broken Wings/Heavenly — Heavenly (78) 5
58   London HLB 8620   Chanson D'Amour (Song Of Love)/Along The Trail With You 15
59   London HLN 8838   Straight As An Arrow/Stand There, Mountain 15

DIANE TODD
58   Decca F 10993   It's A Wonderful Thing To Be Loved/You Are My Favourite Dream 4

NICK TODD
57   London HLD 8500   Plaything/The Honey Song 30
57   London HLD 8500   Plaything/The Honey Song (78) 5
58   London HLD 8537   At The Hop/I Do 15
58   London HLD 8537   At The Hop/I Do (78) 5
59   London HLD 8902   Tiger/Twice As Nice 20
59   London HLD 8902   Tiger/Twice As Nice (78) 8

PATSY TODD
68   High Note HS 007   Fire In Your Wire/AL & VIBRATORS: Move Up Calypso 5
68   High Note HS 012   We Were Lovers/Give Me A Chance (B-side with Delano Stewart) 5
(see under Patsy, Stranger & Patsy, [Monty] Derrick & Patsy, Derrick Patsy & Basil)

SHARKEY TODD & MONSTERS
59   Parlophone R 4536   Cool Ghoul/The Horror Show 8
59   Parlophone R 4536   Cool Ghoul/The Horror Show (78) 10
(see also Wally Whyton)

WILF TODD COMBO
63   Blue Beat BB 240   He Took Her Away/Have You Ever Been Lonely 6

DAVE TODDERDELL
77   Cottage COT 711   WHITBY BELLS (LP) 10

TOE-FAT
70   Parlophone R 5829   Working Nights/Bad Side Of The Moon 6
72   Chapter One CH 175   Brand New Band/Can't Live Without You 5
70   Parlophone PCS 7097   TOE-FAT (LP) 30
71   Regal Zono. SLRZ 1015   TOE-FAT II (LP) 40
(see also Cliff Bennett, Uriah Heep, Glass Menagerie)

TOGETHER
68   Columbia DB 8491   Henry's Coming Home/Love Mum And Dad 40
(see also Keith Relf)

TOGGERY FIVE
64   Parlophone R 5175   Bye Bye Bird/I'm Gonna Jump 25
65   Parlophone R 5249   I'd Much Rather Be With The Boys/It's So Easy 30

TOKENS

61	Parlophone R 4790	Tonight I Fell In Love/I Love My Baby	6
61	RCA RCA 1263	The Lion Sleeps Tonight/Tina	4
62	RCA RCA 1279	B'wana Nina/Weeping River	4
62	RCA RCA 1313	I'll Do My Crying Tomorrow/Dream Angel Goodnight	4
62	RCA RCA 1322	Wishing/A Bird Flies Out Of Sight	4
64	Fontana TF 500	He's In Town/Oh Kathy	4
66	Fontana TF 683	I Hear Trumpets Blow/I Could See Me Dancing With You	4
62	RCA RD 27256/SF 5128	THE LION SLEEPS TONIGHT (LP, mono/stereo)	20/25
62	RCA RD 7535	WE THE TOKENS SING FOLK (LP)	12

TOKYO ROSE

80s	Guardian GRC 270	Dry Your Eyes (p/s)	4

HARRY TOLEDO & ROCKETS

77	Spy SPY 001	Busted Chevrolet/Yo Ho/Who Is That Saving Me/John Glenn (33rpm)	4

TOM & JERRIO

65	HMV POP 1435	Boo-Ga-Loo/Boomerang	15

TOM & JERRY (cartoon characters)

58	MGM MGM EP688	JOHANN MOUSE (EP)	12

TOM & JERRY

63	Pye International 7N 25202	Looking At You/I'm Lonesome	40

(see also Simon & Garfunkel)

TOM & MICK

68	Olga OLE 014	Somebody's Taken Maria Away/Pandemonium	5

TOM CATS

61	Starlite ST45 054	Tom Tom Cat/Big Brother	20

LEE TOMLIN

66	CBS 202455	Sweet Sweet Lovin'/Save Me	8

ALBERT TOMLINSON

68	Giant GN 28	Don't Wait For Me/LLOYD EVANS: Losing You	8

ROY TOMLINSON

68	Coxsone CS 7056	I Stand For I/MARTIN: I Second That Emotion	12

TOMMY (McCook) & UPSETTERS

69	Trojan TR 7717	Lock Jaw (actually by Dave Barker)/YARDBROOMS: My Desire	5

(see also Tommy McCook, Upsetters)

TOMORROW

67	Parlophone R 5597	My White Bicycle/Claramont Lake	20
67	Parlophone R 5627	Revolution/Three Jolly Little Dwarfs	20
69	Parlophone R 5813	My White Bicycle/Claramont Lake (reissue)	20
68	Parl. PMC/PCS 7042	TOMORROW (LP)	50
76	Harvest SHSP 2010	TOMORROW (LP, reissue)	10

(see also Keith West, Steve Howe, Twink, Four + One, In Crowd, Syndicats, Aquarian Age, Fairies, Yes)

TOMORROW COME SOME DAY

69	SNB 97	TOMORROW COME SOME DAY (LP)	650

(see also Ithaca, Agincourt, Alice Through The Looking Glass)

TOMORROW'S CHILDREN

67	Island WI 3073	Bang, Bang, Rock Steady/Rain Rock Steady	12

TONE DEAF & IDIOTS

80s	Lyntone BLI 1/Angel BL 12	Why Does Politics Turn Men Into Toads/Repatriate The National Front (flexi)	4

ELEANOR TONER

65	Decca F 12119	All Cried Out/A Hundred Guitars	7
65	Decca F 12192	Will You Still Love Me Tomorrow/Between The Window And The Phone	7

TONES ON TAIL

82	4AD BAD 203	A Bigger Splash/Means Of Escape/Copper/Instrumental (12", p/s)	12
82	Beggars Banquet BEG 85T	There's Only One/Now We Lustre (12", p/s)	10
83	Situation 2 SIT 21	Burning Skies/OK, This Is The Pops (p/s)	6
83	Situation 2 SIT 21T	Burning Skies/OK, This Is The Pops/When You're Smiling/You, The Night And The Music (12", p/s)	8
84	B. Banquet BEG 109T	Lions/Go! (Club Mix) (12", p/s, red or black vinyl)	10/7
84	Beggars Banquet BEG 121	Christian Says/Twist (p/s)	4
84	B. Banquet BEG 121T	Christian Says/Twist (12", p/s, blue vinyl)	8

(see also Bauhaus, Love & Rockets)

TONETTES

62	Island WI 064	Love That Is Real/Pretty Baby	10

OSCAR TONEY JR.

67	Stateside SS 2033	For Your Precious Love/Ain't That True Love	5
67	Stateside SS 2046	Turn On Your Love Light/Any Day Now	6
67	Stateside SS 2061	You Can Lead Your Woman To The Altar/Unlucky Guy	7
68	Bell BLL 1003	Without Love There Is Nothing/Love That Never Grows Cold	4
68	Bell BLL 1011	No Sad Songs/Never Get Enough Of Your Love	6
73	Capricorn K 17505	Thank You Honey Chile/I Do What You Wish	5
74	Contempo CS 2002	Is It Because I'm Black/Make It Easy On Yourself	4
75	Contempo CS 2043	I've Been Loving You Too Long/For Your Precious Love	4
67	Stateside (S)SL 10211	FOR YOUR PRECIOUS LOVE (LP)	15

TERY TONIK

80	Posh TOFF 1	Just A Little Mod/Smashed And Blocked (die-cut p/s)	25

MINT VALUE £

TONGUE & GROOVE
69 Fontana STL 5528   TONGUE & GROOVE (LP) 20
(see also Charlatans)

TONTO
74 Polydor 2383 308   IT'S ABOUT TIME (LP) 10
(see also Tonto's Expanding Head Band)

TONTON MACOUTE
71 RCA Neon NE 4   TONTON MACOUTE (LP) 50

TONTO'S EXPANDING HEAD BAND
71 Atlantic 2400 150   ZERO TIME (LP, gatefold sleeve) 15
(see also Tonto)

TONTRIX
80s Townton 1-TRICK/1-TON   Shell Shocked/Slipping Into Life (p/s, with 2 inserts) 4

TONY
69 Grape GR 3004   Casa Boo Boo/My Girl 4

TONY & DENNIS
67 Trojan TR 002   Folk Song/TOMMY McCOOK & SUPERSONICS: Starry Night 8

TONY & GRADUATES
60s Hit HIT 13   The Statue 40

TONY & HOWIE
72 Banana BA 371   Fun It Up/Fun Version 5

TONY & JOE
58 London HLN 8694   The Freeze/Gonna Get A Little Kissin' Tonight 35
58 London HLN 8694   The Freeze/Gonna Get A Little Kissin' Tonight (78) 30

TONY (Tomas) & LOUISE
62 Island WI 058   Ups And Downs/TONY TOMAS: Brixton Lewisham 6

TONY & TANDY
69 Atlantic 584 262   Two Can Make It Together/The Bitter And The Sweet (with Fleur De Lys) 12
71 Atlantic 2091 075   Two Can Make It Together/Look And Find 5
(see also Sharon Tandy, Fleur De Lys)

TONY & TYRONE
70 Ember EMB 290   Everyday Fun/Whip Your Loving On Me 4

TONY & VELVETS
63 Decca F 11637   Sunday/One More Once 5

TONY'S DEFENDERS
66 Columbia DB 7850   Yes I Do/It's Easy To Say Hello 20
66 Columbia DB 7996   Since I Lost You Baby/Waiting For A Call From You 15

TOOLS
81 Oily SLICK 2   Gotta Make Some Money Somehow/TV Eyes (p/s) 4

TOOLS YOU CAN TRUST
83 Red Energy Dynamo S1.01   Working And Shopping/The Work Ahead Of Us (plain white sleeve with insert) ...5
84 Red Energy Dynamo S301   Show Your Teeth/Messy Body Thrust (p/s, with insert) 4
84 Red Energy Dynamo S401   CUT A NEW SEAM (EP) 4
84 Red Energy Dynamo S501   SHARPEN THE TOOLS (12" EP) 7
85 Red Energy Dynamo T7.01   Say It Low/A Blaze Of Shame (12", p/s) 7

TOOMORROW
70 RCA RCA 1978   You're My Baby Now/Goin' Back 35
70 Decca F 13070   I Could Never Live Without Your Love/Roll Like A River 35
70 RCA LSA 3008   TOOMORROW (LP, with insert) 70
(see also Olivia Newton-John)

TOO MUCH TEXAS
86 Lyntone LYN 17555/DEB 1   Fried Link/SOIL: Front Room (flexidisc with 'Debris' magazine) 5/4
(see also Inspiral Carpets)

DAVID TOOP
78 Obscure OBS 48   NEW AND REDISCOVERED MUSICAL INSTRUMENTS (LP, with
                     Max Eastley & Brian Eno) 10
70s Quartz   WOUNDS (LP, with Paul Burwell) 10
(see also Brian Eno)

TOOTS
70 Upsetter US 327   Do You Like It/UPSETTERS: Touch Of Fire 5

TOOTS & MAYTALS
(see under Maytals)

TOP TOPHAM
69 Blue Horizon 57-3167   Christmas Cracker/Cracking Up Over Christmas 12
70 Blue Horizon 7-63857   ASCENSION HEIGHTS (LP) 80

TOP NOTES
(see under Nino Tempo & April Stevens)

TOPO GIGIO
(see under Century 21)

TINY TOPSY (& CHARMS)
58 Parlophone R 4397   Come On, Come On, Come On/A Ring Around My Finger (with Charms) 30
58 Parlophone R 4397   Come On, Come On, Come On/A Ring Around My Finger (with Charms) (78) 25
58 Parlophone R 4427   Waterproof Eyes/You Shocked Me (solo) 30

| 58 | Parlophone R 4427 | Waterproof Eyes/You Shocked Me (solo) (78) | 30 |
| 61 | Pye International 7N 25104 | After Marriage Blues/Working On Me Baby (solo) | 20 |

TORA TORA
| 80 | Mancinian Metal TT 5000 | Red Sun Setting/Highway (Shooting Like A Bullet) (p/s) | 10 |

STEVE TORCH
| 70s | Redball RR 005 | Live In Fear/Smoke Your Own (p/s) | 5 |

(BERNIE) TORMÉ (BAND)
78	Jet JET 126	I'm Not Ready/Free (orange or black vinyl, p/s, as Bernie Tormé Band)	8/4
79	Jet JET 137	Weekend/Secret Service/All Night/Instant Impact (as Bernie Tormé Band, p/s)	5
80	Island WIP 6586	The Beat/I Want/Bony Maronie (p/s, pink vinyl)	6
81	Fresh FRESH 7	All Day And All Of The Night/What's Next (p/s, also listed as Parole PURL 5)	6
82	Kamaflage KAM 8	Shoorah Shoorah/Star//Search And Destroy (live)/Possession (live) (double pack, as Bernie Tormé & Electric Gypsies)	5
82	Kamaflage KAMLP 2	TURN OUT THE LIGHTS (LP, white vinyl)	10
85	Zebra ZEB 6	BACK TO BABYLON (LP, red vinyl, as Tormé)	10
80s	Heavy Metal HMRLP 94	DIE PRETTY DIE YOUNG (LP, with 12" [12HM 95], gold stickered sleeve)	10

(see also Gillan, Split Knee Loons)

MEL TORME
56	Vogue Coral Q 72150	Mountain Greenery/Jeepers Creepers	8
56	Vogue Coral Q 72159	Blue Moon/That Old Black Magic	8
56	Vogue Coral Q 72185	Love Is Here To Stay/Goody Goody	6
56	London HLN 8305	Lulu's Back In Town/The Lady Is A Tramp	15
56	London HLN 8322	Lullaby Of Birdland/I Love To Watch The Moonlight	15
56	MGM MGM 922	I Can't Give You Anything But Love/There's No Business	6
56	Vogue Coral Q 72202	All Of You/It Don't Mean A Thing	6
56	Decca F 10800	Walkin' Shoes/The Cuckoo In The Clock (with Ted Heath & His Music)	6
56	Decca F 10809	Waltz For Young Lovers/I Don't Want To Walk Without You	5
57	Vogue Coral Q 72217	My Rosemarie/How	6
60	Philips PB 1045	The White Cliffs Of Dover/I've Got A Lovely Bunch Of Coconuts	4
61	HMV POP 859	Blue Moon/The Moon Song	4
61	MGM MGM 1144	The Christmas Song/Shine On Your Shoes	5
62	London HLK 9643	Comin' Home Baby/Right Now	8
64	Verve VS 505	Yes Indeed/Her Face	5
56	Decca DFE 6384	WALKIN' SHOES (EP)	8
56	MGM MGM EP 562	VOICE IN VELVET (EP)	10
57	MGM MGM EP 591	VOICE IN VELVET NO. 2 (EP)	10
58	London Jazz EZN 19027	MEL TORME SINGS FRED ASTAIRE PT. 1 (EP)	8
58	London Jazz EZN 19028	MEL TORME SINGS FRED ASTAIRE PT. 2 (EP)	8
58	London Jazz EZN 19029	MEL TORME SINGS FRED ASTAIRE PT. 3 (EP)	8
58	Philips BBE 12181	TORME MEETS THE BRITISH (EP)	10
59	Coral FEP 2026	MEL TORME SINGS AT THE CRESCENDO PT. 1 (EP)	8
59	Coral FEP 2027	MEL TORME SINGS AT THE CRESCENDO PT. 2 (EP)	8
59	Coral FEP 2028	MEL TORME SINGS AT THE CRESCENDO PT. 3 (EP)	8
63	London REK 1372	MAGIC OF MEL (EP)	10
55	Vogue Coral LVA 9004	MEL TORME AT THE CRESCENDO (LP)	20
56	Vogue Coral LVA 9032	MUSICAL SOUNDS ARE THE BEST SONGS (LP)	20
56	London Jazz LTZN 15009	AND THE MARTY PAICH "DEK-TETTE" (LP)	20
56	London HA-N 2016	IT'S A BLUE WORLD (LP)	18
57	London Jazz LTZ-N 15076	MEL TORME SINGS FRED ASTAIRE (LP)	15
57	Philips BBL 7205	TORME MEETS THE BRITISH (LP)	40
58	HMV CLP 1238	MEL TORME (LP)	12
59	Parlophone PMC 1096	GENE NORMAN PRESENTS MEL TORME AT THE CRESCENDO (LP)	15
60	Parlophone PMC 1114	SONGS FOR ANY TASTE (LP)	20
60	HMV CLP 1315	OLÉ TORME (LP, with Billy May)	12
60	HMV CLP 1382	BACK IN TOWN (LP, with Mel-Tones)	18
60	HMV CLP 1405/CSD 1330	SWINGS SCHUBERT ALLEY (LP, with Marty Paich Orchestra)	18
61	HMV CLP 1449/CSD 1349	SWINGIN' ON THE MOON (LP)	18
62	HMV CLP 1584/CSD 1442	MY KIND OF MUSIC (LP)	15
63	London HA-K/SH-K 8021	MEL TORME AT THE RED HILL (LP, with Jimmy Wisner Trio)	15
63	London HA-K 8065	COMIN' HOME BABY (LP)	15
63	Verve (S)VLP 9027	I DIG THE DUKE, I DIG THE COUNT (LP)	10
64	Atlantic ATL/SAL 5005	SUNDAY IN NEW YORK (LP)	10
65	CBS (S) BPG 62250	THAT'S ALL (LP)	10
67	Atlantic 590 008	RIGHT NOW! (LP)	10

TORNADOS
62	Decca F 11449	Love And Fury/Popeye Twist	10
62	Decca F 11494	Telstar/Jungle Fever	4
63	Decca F 11562	Globetrotter/Locomotion With Me	5
63	Decca F 11606	Robot/Life On Venus	6
63	Decca F 11662	The Ice Cream Man/Theme From "The Scales Of Justice"	6
63	Decca F 11745	Dragonfly/Hymn For Teenagers	6
63	Decca F 11838	Hot Pot/Joystick	6
64	Decca F 11889	Monte Carlo/Blue Blue Beat	10
64	Decca F 11946	Exodus/Blackpool Rock	10
65	Columbia DB 7455	Granada/Ragunboneman	12
65	Columbia DB 7589	Early Bird/Stompin' Through The Rye	12
65	Columbia DB 7687	Stingray/Aqua Marina	20
66	Columbia DB 7856	Pop-Art Goes Mozart/Too Much In Love To Hear	18
66	Columbia DB 7984	Is That A Ship I Hear/Do You Come Here Often	20
62	Decca DFE 8510	THE SOUNDS OF THE TORNADOS (EP)	12
62	Decca DFE 8511	TELSTAR (EP)	18
63	Decca DFE 8521	MORE SOUNDS FROM THE TORNADOS (EP)	15
63	Decca DFE 8533	TORNADO ROCK (EP)	20

MINT VALUE £

63	Decca LK 4552	AWAY FROM IT ALL (LP)	35
72	Decca SPA 253	THE WORLD OF THE TORNADOS (LP)	10
76	Decca REM 4	REMEMBERING (LP)	10

(see also Heinz, Billy Fury, Clem Cattini Ork, Saints, Fury's Tornados, Original Tornados)

MITCHELL TOROK

54	London HL 8004	Caribbean/Weep Away (with Louisiana Hayride Band)	25
54	London HL 8048	Hootchy Kootchy Henry (From Hawaii)/Gigolo	30
54	London HL 8083	The Haunting Waterfall/Dancerette (with Louisiana Hayride Band)	30
55	Brunswick 05423	The World Keeps Turning Around/A Peasant's Guitar	15
56	Brunswick 05586	When Mexico Gave Up The Rhumba/I Wish I Was A Little Bit Younger	15
56	Brunswick 05626	Red Light, Green Light (with Tulane Sisters)/Havana Huddle	20
56	Brunswick 05626	Red Light, Green Light (with Tulane Sisters)/Havana Huddle (78)	5
57	Brunswick 05642	Drink Up And Go Home/Take This Heart	12
57	Brunswick 05557	Pledge Of Love/What's Behind That Strange Door	10
57	Brunswick 05718	Two Words (True Love)/You're Tempting Me (with Anita Kerr Quartet)	10
60	London HLW 9130	Pink Chiffon/What You Don't Know (Won't Hurt You)	7
54	London RE-P 1014	LOUISIANA HAYRIDE (EP)	35
60	London HA-W 2279	CARIBBEAN (LP)	40

MICHELLE TORR

77	Sonet SON 2104	I'm Just A Simple Country Girl From France/Une Petite Francaise (some in p/s)	5/4

GEORGE TORRENCE & NATURALS

68	London HLZ 10181	Lickin' Stick/So Long Goodbye	10
71	Jay Boy BOY 48	Lickin' Stick/So Long Goodbye (reissue)	6

PETER TOSH

65	Island WI 211	Hoot Nanny Hoot (as Peter Touch)/BOB MARLEY: Do You Remember	30
65	Island WI 215	Shame And Scandal/The Jerk (as Peter Tosh & Wailers)	30
67	Island WI 3042	I Am The Toughest (as Peter Touch & Wailers)/MARCIA GRIFFITHS: No Faith	25
69	Jackpot JP 706	The Crimson Pirate/Moon Duck (as Peter Touch)	10
69	Unity UN 525	The Return Of Al Capone/LENNEX BROWN: O Club (B-side by Lennon Brown)	8
69	Unity UN 529	Sun Valley (as Peter Touch)/HE(A)DLEY BENNETT: Drums Of Fu Manchu	8
71	Bullet BU 486	Maga Dog/THIRD & FOURTH GENERATION: Bull Dog	12
72	Pressure Beat PB 5509	Them A Fe Get A Beatin' (as Peter Touch)/THIRD & FOURTH GENERATION: Version	12
79	Rolling Stones RSR 103	I'm The Toughest/Toughest Version	4
79	Rolling Stones RSR 104	Buck In Hamm Palace/The Day The Dollar Die	4
78	Rolling Stones COC 39109	BUSH DOCTOR (LP, with 'scratch & sniff' sticker)	10

(see also Bob Marley & Wailers)

TOTAL CHAOS

83	Volume VOL 1	There Are No Russians In Afghanistan/Primitive Feeling/Revolution Part 10 (p/s)	4
83	Volume VOL 2	Factory Man/Brixton Prison/She Don't Care/Die (p/s)	4

TOTALLY OUTTA HAND BAND

78	Kilgaron KIL 1	Teenage Revolution/Too Much Trouble By Far (p/s)	4

TOTNAMITES

61	Oriole CB 1615	Danny Boy/Spurs Song	5

TOTO

78	CBS S 116784	Hold The Line/Takin' It Back (picture disc)	6
82	CBS A 112079	Rosanna/It's A Feeling (picture disc)	6
82	CBS A 112510	Africa/We Made It (Africa-shaped picture disc)	6
83	CBS A 113392	I Won't Hold You Back/Afraid Of Love (picture disc)	6

TOUCH

69	Deram DM 243	Miss Teach/We Feel Fine	8
69	Deram DML/SML 1033	THIS IS TOUCH (LP, some with poster)	30/18

TOUCH

80	Ariola ARO 209	When The Spirit Moves You/My Life Depends On You (p/s)	8
80	Ariola ARO 243	Don't You Know What Love Is/My Life Depends On You (p/s)	10
80	Ariola ARO 250	Love Don't Fail Me Now (p/s)	6
88	Touch T7:45	Departing Platford 5/Touch Ritual (Radio Cut-up)	5
80	Ariola ARL 5036	TOUCH (LP)	15

PETER TOUCH

(see under Peter Tosh)

TOURISTS

79	Logo GO 350	Blind Among The Flowers/He Who Laughs Last (p/s)	5
79	Logo GO(D) 350	Blind Among The Flowers/He Who Laughs Last//The Golden Lamp/Wrecked (double pack, gatefold p/s)	7
79	Logo GO 360	The Loneliest Man In The World/Don't Get Left Behind (p/s)	5
79	Logo GO(P) 360	The Loneliest Man In The World/Don't Get Left Behind (picture disc)	8
79	Logo GO 370	I Only Want To Be With You/Summer Night (p/s)	4
80	Logo TOUR 1	So Good To Be Back Home/Circular Fever (p/s)	4
79	RCA TOUR 2	Don't Say I Told You So/Strange Sky (p/s)	4
79	Logo LOGO 1018	THE TOURISTS (LP)	10
80	RCA RCALP 5001	LUMINOUS BASEMENT (LP, with yellow vinyl single "From The Middle Room"/"Into The Future" [FREE 5001], no p/s)	12

(see also Catch, Longdancer, Eurythmics, David A.Stewart, Stewart-Harrison)

AL TOUSAN

61	London HLU 9291	Naomi/Indinna (some copies miscredited to 'Al Pousan')	8

(see also Allen Toussaint)

ALLEN TOUSSAINT
69	Soul City SC 119	We Are People/Tequila	10
75	Reprise K 54021	SOUTHERN NIGHTS (LP)	12

(see also Al Tousan)

CALINE & OLIVER TOUSSAINT
78	Epic SEPC 6334	The Gardens Of Monaco/Les Jardins De Monaco	12

TOWER OF POWER
72	Warner Bros K 16190	Down To The Night Club/You Got To Funkifize	4
73	Warner Bros K 46223	TOWER OF POWER (LP)	12
74	Warner Bros K 46282	BACK TO OAKLAND (LP)	10
75	Warner Bros K 56093	URBAN RENEWAL (LP)	10

TOWERS
58	Capitol CL 14944	To Know Him Is To Love Him (with Evelyn Kingsley)/Let Me Be The One (with Frank Perry)	6

TOWNSEL SISTERS
60	Polydor NH 66954	Will I Ever/I Know	8

ED TOWNSEND
58	Capitol CL 14867	For Your Love/Over And Over Again	5
58	Capitol CL 14927	When I Grow Too Old To Dream/You Are My Everything	5
59	Capitol CL 14976	Richer Than I/Getting By Without You	4
59	Capitol CL 15020	Don't Ever Leave Me/Lover Come Back To Me	4
59	Capitol CL 15072	This Little Love Of Mine/Hold On	4
60	Capitol CL 15141	Don't Get Around Much Anymore/Do Nothin' Till You Hear	4
60	Warner Bros WB 21	Stay With Me (A Little While Longer)/I Love Everything About You	5
59	Capitol EAP1 1091	ED TOWNSEND (EP)	7
59	Capitol T 1140	NEW IN TOWN (LP)	10

ED TOWNSEND
76	Curtom K 56180	NOW (LP)	12

PETE TOWNSHEND
80	Atco K 11486	Let My Love Open The Door/Classified/Greyhound Girl (p/s, with sticker)	4
82	Atco K 11751P	Uniforms/Dance It All Away (picture disc)	5
82	Atco K 11751PT	Uniforms/Dance It All Away (12" picture disc)	10
82	Eva-Tone 623827XS	My Generation/Pinball Wizard (U.S. flexidisc sewn into U.K. copies of Richard Barnes' 'Maximum R&B' book; with/without book)	12/5
72	Track 2408 201	WHO CAME FIRST (LP, gatefold sleeve, with poster)	15

(see also Who, Billy Nicholls)

PETE TOWNSHEND & RONNIE LANE
77	Polydor 2058 944	Street In The City/RONNIE LANE: Annie	4
77	Polydor 2058 944	Street In The City/RONNIE LANE: Annie (12")	7

(see also Who, Small Faces, Faces)

TOXIC REASONS
84	Skysaw HANG 1	God Bless America/Destroyer/Can't Get Away (p/s)	6

TOYAH
79	Safari SAFE 15	Victims Of The Riddle/Victims Of The Riddle (Vivisection) (p/s)	4
79	Safari SAP 1	SHEEP FARMING IN BARNET (EP)	5
81	Safari SAFE 28	Ieya/The Helium Song (p/s, white vinyl)	4
81	Safari SAFEP 28	Ieya/The Helium Song (picture disc)	4
81	Lyntone LYN 9899	Sphinx/For You (green vinyl flexidisc 'Flexipop' magazine No. 8)	5/4
81	Safari SAFEP 38	Thunder In The Mountains/Street Addict (picture disc)	4
81	Safari TOY 2	FOUR MORE FROM TOYAH (EP, with flexidisc "Stand Proud" [FLX 215])	5
81	Safari SAFEX 28	Ieya/The Helium Song (reissue picture disc)	4
82	Safari SAFEX 52	Be Loud Be Proud (Be Heard)/Laughing With The Fools (picture disc)	4
81	Safari VOOR 1	ANTHEM (LP, picture disc)	10

TOY DOLLS
81	GBH SSM 005	Tommy Kowie's Car/She Goes To Finos (no p/s)	20
81	GRC GRC 104	Tommy Kowie's Car/She's A Worky Ticket/Everybody Jitterbug/ Teenager In Love/I've Got Asthma (p/s)	15
82	Zonophone Z 31	Everybody Jitterbug/Worky Ticket (p/s)	10
83	Volume VOL 3	Nellie The Elephant/Dig That Groovy Baby (p/s)	8
83	Volume VOL 5	Cheerio And Toodle Pip/H.O. (p/s)	6
83	Volume VOL 7	Alfie From The Bronx/Hanky panky (p/s)	5
84	Volume VOL 10	We're Mad/Deirdre's A Slag (p/s)	4
84	Volume VOLT 10	We're Mad/Deirdre's A Slag/Rupert The Bear (12", p/s)	7

(see also Showbiz Kids)

TOYS
65	Stateside SS 460	A Lover's Concerto/This Night	6
66	Stateside SS 483	Attack/See How They Run	6
66	Stateside SS 502	May My Heart Be Cast Into Stone/On Backstreet	8
66	Stateside SS 519	Silver Spoon/Can't Get Enough Of You Baby	8
66	Stateside SS 539	Baby Toys/Happy Birthday Broken Heart	6
67	Philips BF 1563	Ciao Baby/I Got Carried Away	5
67	Philips BF 1581	My Love Sonata/I Close My Eyes	8
66	Stateside (S)SL 10175	TOYS SING "A LOVER'S CONCERTO" AND "ATTACK" (LP, mono/stereo)	20/25

TOYS
79	SRT SRTS/79/CUS 345	My Mind Wanders/The Girl On My Wall/Toytime/I'd Do Anything For You (p/s)	5
79	Toy TOYS 2	STILL DANCING (EP, hand-stamped white label, foldaround p/s)	5

T'PAU
87	Siren SRN 52	Intimate Strangers/No Sense Of Pride (p/s)	4
87	Siren SRN 52-12	Intimate Strangers/No Sense Of Pride (12", p/s)	7

T'PAU

87	Siren SRNCD 64	China In Your Hand/No Sense Of Pride/Heart And Soul/ Friends Like These (CD)	10
88	Siren SRNCD 69	Valentine/Giving My Love Away/A Believer (live)/ China In Your Hand (live) (CD)	7
88	Siren SRNCD 80	Sex Talk (live)/Monkey House (live)/You Give Up (live)/Heart And Soul (live) (CD, picture disc)	7
88	Siren SRNG 87	I Will Be With You/Still So In Love (gatefold sleeve)	4
88	Siren SRNCD 87	I Will Be With You/Still So In Love/Thank You For Goodbye/ Walk Away Renee (CD, picture disc)	7
88	Siren SRNCD 93	Secret Garden/This Girl/You'll Never Notice Me (live)/Crying (CD, picture disc, 4-track)	7
88	Siren SRNB 100	Road To Our Dream/Time Of Our Lives (with tour patch)	4
89	Siren SRNG 107	Only The Lonely/Between The Lines (with booklet)	4

TRACE

74	Vertigo 6360 852	TRACE (LP)	10
75	Vertigo 6413 080	BIRDS (LP)	10

(see also Curved Air)

AL TRACE & HIS LITTLE TRACERS

53	MGM MGM 693	Mocking Bird Boogie/You're Only A Part-Time Sweetheart (78)	5

MARK TRACEY

62	Parlophone R 4944	Caravan Of Lonely Men/Never Ending (with John Barry & His Orchestra)	6

STAN TRACEY

58	Vogue LA 160130	STAN TRACEY SHOWCASE (LP)	15
59	Vogue LA 160155	LITTLE KLUNK (LP, as Stan Tracey Trio)	15
65	Columbia 33SX 1774	JAZZ SUITE (LP, as Stan Tracey Quartet; also stereo SCX 3589)	15
66	Columbia SX/SCX 6051	ALICE IN JAZZLAND (LP, as Stan Tracey Big Band)	15
67	Columbia SX/SCX 6124	STAN TRACEY . . . IN PERSON (LP)	12
68	Columbia SX/SCX 6205	WITH LOVE FROM JAZZ (LP)	15
69	Ace Of Clubs ACL 1259	LITTLE KLUNK (LP, reissue)	10
69	Columbia SX/SCX 6320	WE LOVE YOU MADLY (LP, as Stan Tracey Big Brass)	12
69	Columbia SCX 6358	THE LATIN AMERICAN CAPER (LP, with Big Brass & Woodwind)	10
70	Columbia SCX 6385	FREE AN' ONE (LP, as Stan Tracey Quartet)	15
70	Columbia SCX 6413	SEVEN AGES OF MAN (LP, as Stan Tracey Big Band)	12
71	Columbia SCX 6485	PERSPECTIVES (LP as Stan Tracey Trio)	12
70s	Cadillac SAC 1002	ORIGINAL (LP, as Mike Osborne and Stan Tracey)	10

ZEN TRACEY

62	Decca F 11492	Two By Two/Shamrocker (Phil The Fluter's Ball)	5

TRACK

66	Columbia DB 7987	Why Do Fools Fall In Love?/Cry To Me	10

TRACTOR

72	Polydor 2001 282	Stone Glory/Marie/As You Say	10
75	UK UK 93	Roll The Dice/Vicious Circle	5
81	Cargo CRS 002	No More Rock & Roll/Northern City (p/s with insert)	10
81	Roach RR 2	Average Man's Hero/Big Big Boy (p/s)	5
72	Dandelion 2310 217	TRACTOR (LP)	60

(see also Way We Live, Jim Milne & Tractor)

GRANT TRACY & SUNSETS

61	Ember EMBS 126	Say When/Please Baby Please	12
61	Ember EMBS 130	Pretend/Love Me	10
62	Ember EMBS 148	The Great Matchmaker/Tears Came Rolling Down	10
62	Ember EMBS 155	Taming Tigers/The Painted Smile	10
63	Decca F 11741	Everybody Shake/Turn The Lights Down, Jenny	8
64	Ember EMB 3352	TEENBEAT (LP)	18

WENDALL TRACY

58	London HLM 8664	Who's To Know/Corrigidor Rock	20
58	London HLM 8664	Who's To Know/Corrigidor Rock (78)	5

TRADER HORNE

69	Pye 7N 17846	Sheena/Morning Way	8
70	Dawn DNS 1003	Here Comes The Rain/Goodbye Mercy Kelly	5
70	Dawn DNLS 3004	MORNING WAY (LP, with photo & insert)	50

(see also Them, Fairport Convention)

TRADEWINDS

59	RCA RCA 1141	Furry Murray/Crossroads	10
59	RCA RCA 1141	Furry Murray/Crossroads (78)	30

TRADE WINDS

65	Red Bird RB 10020	New York Is A Lonely Town/Club Seventeen	8
66	Kama Sutra KAS 202	Mind Excursion/Little Susan's Dreaming	7
69	Kama Sutra 2013 008	Mind Excursion/Little Susan's Dreaming (reissue)	4

TRAFFIC

67	Island WIP 6002	Paper Sun/Giving To You (some in p/s)	12/4
67	Island WIP 6017	Hole In My Shoe/Smiling Phases (some in p/s)	10/4
67	Island WIP 6025	Here We Go Round The Mulberry Bush/Coloured Rain (some in p/s)	8/4
68	Island WIP 6030	No Face, No Name, No Number/Roamin' In The Gloamin' With 40,000 Headmen	5
68	Island WIP 6041	Feelin' Alright/Withering Tree	5
68	Island WIP 6050	Medicated Goo/Shanghai Noodle Factory	5
74	Island WIP 6207	Walking In The Wind/Walking In The Wind (Instrumental)	5
78	Island IEP 7	HOLE IN MY SHOE (EP, picture disc)	
67	Island ILP 961/ILPS 9061	MR FANTASY (LP, pink label, mono/stereo)	15/12
68	Island ILP 981/ILPS 9081	TRAFFIC (LP, pink label, mono/stereo)	15/12

69	Island ILP 9097	LAST EXIT (LP, pink label)	15
74	Island ILP 9112	THE BEST OF TRAFFIC (LP, pink label)	10
70	Island ILP 9116	JOHN BARLEYCORN MUST DIE (LP)	12
71	Island ILPS 9142	LIVE (LP, unreleased, possibly exists on white label)	100+

(see also Spencer Davis Group, Stevie Winwood, Revolution, Hellions, Dave Mason)

TRAFFIC JAM
| 67 | Piccadilly 7N 35386 | Almost But Not Quite There/Wait Just A Minute | 150 |

(see also Status Quo, Spectres)

TRAINER
| 72 | BASF | TRAINER (LP) | 25 |

(see also Trees)

TRAGIC MULATTO
| 83 | Alt. Tentacles VIRUS 33 | The Suspect/No Juice (p/s) | 4 |

TRAINSPOTTERS
| 79 | Arista ARIST 290 | High Rise/Rock'n'Roll Hall Of Fame (p/s) | 5 |
| 79 | Arista ARIST 320 | Unfaithful/Hiring The Hall (no p/s) | 4 |

(see also Mike Read, Just Plain Smith, Just Plain Jones, Micky Manchester)

TRAITS
| 67 | Pye International 7N 25404 | Harlem Shuffle/Strange Lips (Start Ole Memories) | 10 |

ALAN TRAJAN
| 69 | MCA MKPS 2000 | FIRM ROOTS (LP) | 75 |

TRAMLINE
| 68 | Island ILPS 9088 | SOMEWHERE DOWN THE LINE (LP, pink label) | 40 |
| 69 | Island ILPS 9095 | MOVES OF VEGETABLE CENTURIES (LP, pink label) | 40 |

(see also Whitesnake)

BOBBY LEE TRAMMELL
| 64 | Sue WI 326 | New Dance In France/Carolyn | 15 |

TRAMMPS
72	Buddah 2011 140	Zing Went The Strings Of My Heart/Penguin At The Big Apple	4
75	Atlantic K 10664	Hooked For Life/It's Alright	4
76	Phil. Intl. PIR 80409	TRAMMPS (LP)	10

TRAMP
69	Youngblood SBY 4	Each Day	4
74	Spark SRL 1107	Put A Record On/You've Gotta Move	4
69	Music Man SMLS 603	TRAMP (LP)	90
73	Spark SRLM 2001	TRAMP (LP)	40
74	Spark SRLP 112	PUT A RECORD ON (LP)	30

(see also Dave Kelly, Jo-Ann Kelly, Brunning Hall Sunflower Blues Band, Danny Kirwan, Fleetwood Mac)

TRANSATLANTICS
65	Fontana TF 593	Many Things From Your Window/I Tried To Forget	8
65	Fontana TF 638	Stand Up And Fight Like A Man/But I Know	8
65	King KG 1033	Run For Your Life/It's All Over	8
65	Mercury MF 948	Don't Fight It/Look Before You Leap	20

TRANSMITTERS
70s	Ebony EBY 1002	24 HOURS (LP)	10
78	Ebony EYE 11	Party/0.5 Alive (p/s)	4
78	Ebony EYE 12	Nowhere Train/Uninvited Guest/Persons Unknown (die cut p/s)	4
79	Step Forward SF-1212	The Ugly Man/The One That Won The War/Free Trade/Curious (p/s)	7
78	Ebony EB-10002	24 HOURS (LP)	10
81	Heartbeat MB-4	AND WE CALL THIS LEISURE TIME (LP)	10
70s	Eccentric EX-2 C-50	I JAX DUB (tape)	10

TRANSPORTER
(see also Claire Hamill)

TRANSVISION VAMP
87	MCA TVV 1	Revolution Baby/Vid Kid Vamp (Remix) (p/s)	4
87	MCA TVVT 1	Revolution Baby (Remix)/Vid Kid Vamp (Remix)/No It U Lover (12", p/s)	8
87	MCA TVV 2	Psycho-Sonic Cindy/God Save The Royalties (unreleased, test pressings only)	15
87	MCA TVVT 2	Psycho-Sonic Cindy/God Save The Royalties/Psycho-Sonic Cindy (Extramental Mix) (12", unissued, test pressings only)	25
88	MCA TVV 2	Tell That Girl To Shut Up/God Save The Royalties (3-D p/s)	4
88	MCA TVVPR 2	Tell That Girl To Shut Up/God Save The Royalties (poster p/s)	4
88	MCA TVVT 2	Tell That Girl To Shut Up (Extended Mix)/(Knuckle Duster Mix)/God Save The Royalties (12", 3-D p/s)	7
88	MCA DVVT 2	Tell That Girl To Shut Up (Extended Mix)/God Save The Royalties/Tell That Girl To Shut Up (7" Mix)/(Knuckle Duster Mix) (CD, 3D picture disc)	10
88	MCA TVVTR 3	I Want Your Love (I Don't Want Your Money Mix)/Sweet Thing/Evolution Evie (Electric Version) (12", poster p/s)	7
88	MCA DTVV 3	I Want Your Love (I Don't Want Your Money Mix)/Sweet Thing/Evolution Evie (Electric Version)/Tell That Girl To Shut Up (3" CD)	7
88	MCA TVVPR 4	Revolution Baby (Remix)/Honey Honey/Long Lonely Weekend (p/s, 3,000 only with poster insert)	4
88	MCA TVVTP 4	Revolution Baby (Electra-Glide Mix)/Honey Honey/Long Lonely Weekend (12", picture disc)	7
88	MCA TVVTG 5	Sister Moon (Groove On)/Walk On By/Sex Kick (Ciao Portabello)/Oh Yeah (12", gatefold p/s)	7
88	MCA TVVP 5	Sister Moon/Oh Yeah/Walk On By (picture disc)	5
89	MCA TVVG 6	Baby, I Don't Care/Time For A Change/Strings Of My Heart (gatefold p/s with postcard)	4
89	MCA TVVP 8	Landslide Of Love/Hardtime/He's Only One For Me (picture disc)	4

MINT VALUE £

| 88 | MCA MCFP 3421 | POP ART (LP, picture disc) | 10 |
| 89 | MCA MCGP 6050 | VELVETEEN (picture disc) | 10 |

(see also Fan-Club)

TRAPEZE

69	Threshold TH 2	Send Me No More Letters/Another Day	5
72	Threshold TH 11	Coast To Coast/Your Love Is Alright	5
75	Warner Bros K 16606	Sunny Side Of The Street/Monkey	4
70	Threshold THS 2	TRAPEZE (LP)	20
70	Threshold THS 4	MEDUSA (LP)	25
72	Threshold THS 8	YOU ARE THE MUSIC (LP)	15
74	Warner Bros K 56064	HOT WIRE (LP)	10
75	Warner Bros K 56165	TRAPEZE (LP)	10

(see also Deep Purple, Judas Priest)

TRAPEZE

| 79 | Aura AUS 114 | Don't Ask Me How I Know/Take Good Care (p/s) | 8 |
| 80 | Aura AUS 116 | Running Away/Don't Break My Heart (p/s) | 8 |

(WHITE) TRASH

| 69 | Apple APPLE 6 | Road To Nowhere/Illusions (credited to White Trash or Trash) | 12/15 |
| 69 | Apple APPLE 17 | Golden Slumbers-Carry That Weight/Trash Can | 12 |

(see also Poets, Pathfinders)

TRASHMEN

| 64 | Stateside SS 255 | Surfin' Bird/King Of The Surf | 25 |
| 64 | Stateside SS 276 | Bird Dance Beat/A-Bone | 18 |

TRAVELING WILBURYS

88	Warner Bros W 7732	Handle With Care/Margarita (gatefold p/s with sticker)	7
88	Warner Bros W 7732 TE	Handle With Care (Extended)/Margarita (10", p/s)	8
91	Warner Bros W 0018 W	Wilbury Twist/New Blue Moon (Instrumental) (card p/s with postcards)	7

(see also George Harrison, Bob Dylan, Roy Orbison, Jeff Lynne, Tom Petty)

PAT TRAVERS

70s	Polydor	Makes No Difference (1-sided flexidisc, promo only, black-and-white p/s)	15
70s	Polydor	THE PT YOU MISSED (12" EP, LP sampler, promo only, plain red sleeve)	7
79	Polydor POLS 1011	GO FOR WHAT YOU KNOW (LP, red vinyl)	10

MERLE TRAVIS

56	Capitol EAP1 032	MERLE TRAVIS GUITAR (EP)	20
57	Capitol EAP2 650	MERLE TRAVIS GUITAR NO. 2 (EP)	12
59	Capitol EAP1 891	BACK HOME (EP)	12
63	Capitol EAP1 1391	WALKIN' THE STRINGS (EP)	12
57	Capitol T 891	BACK HOME (LP)	20
63	Capitol (S)T 1664	TRAVIS! (LP)	12
65	Capitol T 2102	MERLE TRAVIS & JOE MAPHIS (LP)	12

TRAVIS & BOB

| 59 | Pye International 7N 25018 | Tell Him No/We're Too Young | 6 |
| 61 | Mercury AMT 1142 | Baby Stay Close To Me/Give Your Love To Me | 4 |

JACK TRAYLOR & STEELWIND

| 73 | Grunt FTR 0194 | CHILD OF NATURE (LP) | 10 |

TREASURE BOY

| 67 | Trojan TR 010 | Love Is A Treasure (actually by Freddie McKay)/TOMMY McCOOK: Zazuka | 12 |

STEVE TREATMENT

| 78 | Rather GEAR 2 | 5-A-SIDED 45 (EP) | 6 |

(see also Swell Maps)

TREBLETONES

| 63 | Oriole CB 1838 | In Real Life/Dream Of A Lifetime | 5 |

TREDEGAR

| 86 | Aires CEP 0001 | Duma/The Jester (p/s) | 20 |
| 86 | Aires CEP LP 001 | TREDEGAR (LP) | 25 |

VIRGINIA TREE

| 75 | Minstrel 0001 | FRESH OUT (LP) | 30 |

(see also Ghost, Shirley Kent)

TREES

70	CBS 5078	Nothing Special/Epitaph	10
70	CBS 63837	THE GARDEN OF JANE DELAWNEY (LP)	70
70	CBS 64168	ON THE SHORE (LP)	60

TREETOPS (U.K.)

67	Parlophone R 5628	Don't Worry Baby/I Remember	5
68	Parlophone R 5669	California My Way/Carry On Living	5
71	Columbia DB 8799	Without The One You Love/So Here I Go Again	7

TREETOPS (Jamaica)

| 67 | Trojan TR 003 | It's Raining/The Sound Of Music | 10 |
| 67 | Studio One SO 2023 | Moving To Progress/Love And Inspiration | 10 |

(see also Three Tops)

TREKKAS

| 65 | Planet PLF 105 | Please Go/I Put A Spell On You | 30 |

TREMELOES

66	Decca F 12423	Blessed/The Right Time	5
66	CBS 202242	Good Day Sunshine/What A State I'm In	5
67	CBS 202519	Here Comes My Baby/Gentleman Of Pleasure	4

67	CBS 2723	Silence Is Golden/Let Your Hair Hang Down (p/s)	5
67	CBS 2930	Even The Bad Times Are Good/Jenny's Alright (p/s)	5
67	CBS 3043	Be Mine/Suddenly Winter	4
68	CBS Special Products	Here Comes My Baby/SIMON & GARFUNKEL: The 59th Street	
	WB 728	Bridge Song (p/s, mail order only with Pepsi Cola tokens)	5
60s	CBS	other singles	3
68	CBS EP 6402	MY LITTLE LADY (EP)	7
67	CBS (S)BPG 63017	HERE COME THE TREMELOES (LP)	12
68	CBS (S)BPG 63138	THE TREMELOES: CHIP, RICK, ALAN AND DAVE (LP)	10
69	CBS 63547	THE TREMELOES 'LIVE' IN CABARET (LP)	12
70	CBS 64242	MASTER (LP)	10

(see also Brian Poole & Tremeloes, Chip Hawkes)

TREMORS
| 80s | Redball RR 0002 | Modern World/Smashed Reality (p/s) | 4 |

TREND
| 67 | Page One POF 004 | Boyfriends And Girlfriends/Shot On Sight | 15 |

TRENDS
| 64 | Piccadilly 7N 35171 | All My Loving/Sweet Little Miss Love | 8 |
| 64 | Pye 7N 15644 | You're A Wonderful One/The Way You Do The Things You Do | 8 |

(see also Tammy St. John, Freddie Self, Freddie Ryder)

TRENDSETTERS
| 64 | Silver Phoenix 1001 | You Don't Care/My Heart Goes | 25 |

TRENDSETTERS
| 60s | Oak RGJ 999 | AT THE HOTEL DE FRANCE (EP) | 25 |

TRENDSETTERS LIMITED
64	Parlophone R 5118	In A Big Way/Lucky Date	8
64	Parlophone R 5161	Hello Josephine/Move On Over	10
64	Parlophone R 5191	Lollipops And Roses/Go Away	7
65	Parlophone R 5324	You Sure Got A Funny Way Of Showing Your Love/I'm Coming Home	6

(see also King Crimson, Giles Giles & Fripp, Brain)

TRENIERS
58	Coral Q 72319	Ooh-La-La/Pennies From Heaven	18
58	Coral Q 72319	Ooh-La-La/Pennies From Heaven (78)	5
58	Fontana H 137	Go! Go! Go!/Get Out Of The Car (featuring Don Hill, Alto Sax)	75
58	Fontana H 137	Go! Go! Go!/Get Out Of The Car (featuring Don Hill, Alto Sax) (78)	35
59	London HLD 8858	When Your Hair Has Turned To Silver/Never, Never	25
59	London HLD 8858	When Your Hair Has Turned To Silver/Never, Never (78)	5

JACKIE TRENT
65	Pye 7N 15776	Where Are You Now/On The Other Side Of The Tracks	4
66	Pye 7N 17047	You Baby/Send Her Away	8
65	Pye NEP 4225	WHERE ARE YOU NOW (EP)	7
65	Pye NPL 18125	THE MAGIC OF JACKIE TRENT (LP)	12
67	Pye NPL 18173	ONCE MORE WITH FEELING (LP)	10
67	Pye NPL 18201	STOP ME AND BUY ONE (LP)	10

(see also Family Affair)

TRESPASS
79	Trial CASE 1	One Of These Days/Bloody Moon (p/s)	15
80	Trial CASE 2	Jealousy/Live It Up! (p/s)	12
81	Trial CASE 3	Bright Lights/The Duel/Man And Machine (EP, p/s)	12

TREVOR (Shield)
64	Blue Beat BB 228	Down In Virginia/Hey Little Schoolgirl (with Caribs)	6
68	Blue Cat BS 129	Tender Arms (with Joe White & Glen Brown)/DERMOTT LYNCH:	
		Something Is Worrying Me	10
68	Blue Cat BS 130	Pretty Girl (with Joe White & Glen Brown)/DERMOTT LYNCH: You Went Away	8
69	Blue Cat BS 153	Everyday Is Like A Holiday/Have You Time (by Trevor & Maytones)	6

T. REX
(see under Marc Bolan & T. Rex; see also Tyrannosaurus Rex)

TRIBAN
| 72 | Cambrian | RAINMAKER (LP) | 15 |

TRIBE (U.K.)
| 66 | Planet PLF 108 | The Gamma Goochie/I'm Leavin' | 30 |
| 67 | RCA RCA 1592 | Love Is A Beautiful Thing/Steel Guitar | 12 |

TRIBE (U.S.)
| 70 | Polydor 56510 | Dancin' To The Beat Of My Heart/Woofin' | 15 |

TRIBE
| 73 | Probe PRO 597 | Koke Parts 1 & 2 | 5 |

TONY TRIBE
| 69 | Downtown DT 419 | Red Red Wine/RECO & RUDIES: Blues | 4 |
| 69 | Downtown DT 439 | Gonna Give You All The Love/HERBIE GREY: Why Wait | 4 |

TRIBUTE TO YOUTH PRAISE
| 69 | Key KL 003 | TRIBUTE TO YOUTH PRAISE (LP) | 15 |

TRIFFIDS (U.K.)
63	Columbia DB 7084	Lookin' Around/She's No Longer Your Girl	8
63	Columbia DB 7177	Over Again/Lonely Boy	6
64	Columbia DB 7251	So Shy/Enough Of Your Love	6

TRIFFIDS (U.K.)
| 65 | Fontana TL 5231 | THE TRIFFIDS ARE REALLY FOLK (LP) | 10 |

TRIFFIDS (Australia)

88	Island 10 IS 350	Trick Of The Light/Love The Fever/Bad News Always Reminds Me Of You (12", p/s) 5
89	Island 10 IS 420	Goodbye Little Boy/Go Home Eddie/Shell Of A Man/Me Minus You (10", numbered p/s) 5
89	Island CID 424	Bury Me Deep In Love/Rent/Into The Groove (3" CD, gatefold p/s) 7

TRIFLE

| 70 | Dawn DNS 1008 | Old-Fashioned Prayer Meeting/Dirty Old Town ....5 |
| 71 | Dawn DNLS 3017 | FIRST MEETING (LP) ....20 |

PANDIT KANWAR SAIN TRIKHA

| 71 | Mushroom 100 MR 7 | THREE SITAR PIECES (LP) ....35 |

TRILOGY

| 70 | Mercury 6338 034 | I'M BEGINNING TO FEEL IT (LP) ....15 |

TRINITY HOUSE

| 77 | Profile | FLASHBACK THROUGH HISTORY (LP, private pressing, with insert) ....30 |

TRIO

70	Dawn DNLS 3006	TRIO (2-LP, with poster) 30
71	Dawn DNLS 3022	CONFLAGRATION (LP) 20
76	Dawn DNLS 3072	LIVE AT WOODSTOCK TOWN HALL (LP) 10
	(see also John Surnam)	

TRIPPERS

| 66 | Pye International 7N 25388 | Dance With Me/Keep A-Knockin' ....10 |

TRISHA

| 65 | CBS 201800 | The Darkness Of My Night/Confusion ....4 |

TRISTAR AIRBUS

| 72 | RCA RCA 2170 | Travellin' Man/Willie Morgan On The Wing ....4 |
| | (see also Wimple Winch, 10cc, Hotlegs) | |

TRIUMPH

| 83 | RCA RCA 319 | World Of Fantasy/Too Much Thinking (picture disc) ....4 |

TRIUMVIRATE

| 74 | Harvest SHSP 4030 | ILLUSION ON A DOUBLE DIMPLE (LP) ....10 |
| 75 | Harvest SHSP 4048 | SPARTACUS (LP) ....10 |

TRIXIE'S BIG RED MOTORBIKE

82	Chew CH 9271	A Splash Of Red/Invisible Boyfriend (white label, stapled foldover p/s) ...10
83	Private pressing	TRIXIE'S BIG RED MOTORBIKE (EP, white label, plain sleeve with stapled strip) 8
84	Lobby Ludd L 100001	Norman And Narcissus/In Timbuktu (p/s) 10
84	Lobby Ludd L 100002	A Splash Of Red/Invisible Boyfriend (reissue, different p/s) 8
84	Lobby Ludd L 100003	TRIXIE'S BIG RED MOTORBIKE (EP, reissue, stapled p/s) 8
84	Nathan NAT 001	That's The End Of That/CLIVE PIG & LEE VALLEY: As Soon As She's Gone (33rpm flexi & sweet with 'Wally's Dog' fanzine) 8/6

MARCUS TRO

| 65 | Ember EMB S 203 | Tell Me/What's The Matter Little Girl ....8 |

TROGGS

66	CBS 202038	Lost Girl/The Yella In Me 20
66	Fontana TF 689	Wild Thing/From Home 5
66	Fontana TF 717	With A Girl Like You/I Want You 5
66	Page One POF 001	I Can't Control Myself/Gonna Make You 5
66	Page One POF 010	Any Way That You Want Me/66-5-4-3-2-1 5
67	Page One POF 015	Give It To Me/You're Lyin' 5
67	Page One POF 022	My Lady/Girl In Black (withdrawn) 30
67	Page One POF 022	Night Of The Long Grass/Girl In Black 5
67	Page One POF 030	Hi Hi Hazel/As I Ride By 4
67	Page One POF 040	Love Is All Around/When Will The Rain Come 4
68	Page One POF 056	Little Girl/Maybe The Madman? 5
68	Page One POF 064	Surprise Surprise/Marbles And Some Gum? 4
68	Page One POF 082	You Can Cry If You Want To/There's Something About You 5
68	Page One POF 092	Hip Hip Hooray/Say Darlin'! 4
69	Page One POF 114	Evil Woman/Sweet Madeline 5
70	Page One POF 164	Easy Lovin'/Give Me Something 4
70	Page One POF 171	Lover/Come Now 4
70	Page One POF 182	The Raver/You 4
71	DJM DJM 248	Lazy Weekend/Let's Pull Together 5
70	Pye 7N 45147	Everything's Funny/Feels Like A Woman 5
73	Pye 7N 45244	Listen To The Man/Queen Of Sorrow 5
73	Pye 7N 45295	Strange Movies/I'm On Fire 5
75	Penny Farthing PEN 861	Good Vibrations/Push It Up To Me 5
75	Penny Farthing PEN 884	Wild Thing (Reggae Version)/Jenny Come Down 5
75	Penny Farthing PEN 889	Summertime/Jenny Come Down 5
75	Penny Farthing PEN 901	(I Can't Get No) Satisfaction/Memphis, Tennessee 5
76	Penny Farthing PEN 919	I'll Buy You An Island/Supergirl 4
77	Penny Farthing PEN 929	Feeling For Love/Summertime 4
78	Raw RAW 25	Just A Little Too Much/The True Troggs Tapes (p/s) 5
81	DJM DJS 6	TROGGS TAPES (EP, double pack) 5
84	10 TENY 21	Every Little Thing/Blackjack And Poker/With A Girl Like You (picture disc) 4
67	Page One POE 001	TROGGS TOPS (EP) 8
67	Page One POE 002	TROGGS TOPS VOLUME TWO (EP) 20
67	Page One	TRACK A TROGG (EP, unreleased, demos may exist)
66	Fontana (S)TL 5355	FROM NOWHERE — THE TROGGS (LP, mono/stereo) 20/25

Rare Record Price Guide

66	Page One POL 001	TROGGLODYNAMITE (LP)	25
67	Page One FOR 001	THE BEST OF THE TROGGS (LP)	15
67	Page One POL 003	CELLOPHANE (LP)	35
68	Page One FOR 007	THE BEST OF THE TROGGS VOLUME TWO (LP)	15
68	Page One POLS 012	MIXED BAG (LP)	85
69	Page One POS 602	TROGGLOMANIA (LP)	20
70	DJMSilverline DJML 009	CONTRASTS (LP, original)	20

(see also Reg Presley, Chris Britton, Ronnie Bond, Ten Foot Five)

CHUCK TROIS & AMAZING MAZE
| 68 | Action ACT 4517 | Call On You/Woodsman | 8 |

TROJANS
| 58 | Decca F 11065 | Man I'm Gonna Be/Make It Up | 15 |

TROLL BROTHERS
| 70s | SRT SRT 73316 | You Turn Me On/Turn Out The Lights | 10 |

TRONICS
| 61 | Fontana H 348 | Cantina/Pickin' & Stompin' | 10 |

TRONICS
80s	Tronics T 001	Suzie/Favourite Girls (plain sleeve with inserts)	5
80s	Tronics T 002	Time Off/Goodbye (p/s)	5
81	Alien ALIEN 18	Shark Fucks/Time Off (p/s, with insert)	4
81	Alien BALIEN 3	LoVE BACKED BY FORCE (LP)	10

(see also Les Zarjaz)

TROOPERS
| 57 | Vogue V 9087 | Get Out/My Resolution | 175 |
| 57 | Vogue V 9087 | Get Out/My Resolution (78) | 50 |

TROOPS OF TOMORROW
| 82 | Troops TROOPS 1 | TROOPS OF TOMORROW (12" EP) | 7 |

(see also Vibrators)

ARCHIBALD TROTT
| 64 | Black Swan WI 407 | Get Together/Just Because | 8 |

TROUBADORS/TROUBADOUR SINGERS
57	London HLR 8469	Fascination/Midnight In Athens	10
58	London HLR 8541	The Lights Of Paris/The Flaming Rose	10
58	London HA-R 2095	THE TROUBADORS IN SPAIN (LP)	12
58	London HA-R 2106	THE TROUBADORS IN THE LAND OF THE GIPSIES (LP)	10
58	London HA-R 2114	THE TROUBADORS IN ROME (LP)	10
58	London HA-A 2121	THE TROUBADORS IN HAWAII (LP)	10
60	London HA-R 2249	THE TROUBADORS IN PARIS (LP)	10
66	London SH-F 8275	SING OUT BIG (LP, as Troubadour Singers)	10

(see also Jane Morgan)

BOBBY TROUP
| 54 | Capitol CL 14219 | Julie Is Her Name/Instead Of You | 6 |
| 54 | Capitol LC 6660 | BOBBY TROUP (10" LP) | 12 |

BOB TROW QUARTET
| 54 | London HL 8082 | Soft Squeeze Baby/I Went Along For The Ride | 25 |

ROBIN TROWER
78	Chrysalis CHS 2247	It's For You/My Love (p/s, red vinyl)	4
73	Chrysalis CHR 1039	TWICE REMOVED FROM YESTERDAY (LP)	10
74	Chrysalis CHR 1057	BRIDGE OF SIGHS (LP)	10
75	Charisma CHR 1073	FOR EARTH BELOW (LP)	10

(see also Procol Harum, Jack Bruce & Robin Trower)

TROY & T-BIRDS
| 61 | London HL 9476 | Twistle/Take Ten | 7 |

DORIS TROY
62	Cameo Parkway C 101	I'll Do Anything (Anything He Wants Me To)/Just Like That	50
63	London HLK 9749	Just One Look/Bossa Nova Blues	10
64	Atlantic AT 4011	What'cha Gonna Do About It/Tomorrow Is Another Day	8
65	Atlantic AT 4020	Please Little Angel/One More Chance	8
65	Atlantic AT 4032	Heartaches/You'd Better Stop	8
68	Atlantic 584 148	Just One Look/What'cha Gonna Do About It	6
68	Toast TT 507	I'll Do Anything (Anything He Wants Me To)/Heartaches	6
70	Apple APPLE 24	Ain't That Cute/Vaya Con Dios (some with p/s)	12/8
70	Apple APPLE 28	Jacob's Ladder/Get Back (company sleeve)	8
71	Mojo 2092 011	I'll Do Anything (Anything He Wants Me To)/But I Love Him	4
73	Mojo 2092 062	Baby I Love You/To My Father's House	4
74	People PEO 112	Stretchin' Out/Don't Tell Your Mama	5
65	Atlantic AET 6007	WATCHA GONNA DO ABOUT IT (EP)	25
70	Apple SAPCOR 13	DORIS TROY (LP)	25
72	Polydor 2956 001	THE RAINBOW TESTAMENT (LP)	12
74	Polydor 2464 001	JUST ONE LOOK (LP)	10
74	People PLEO 12	STRETCHING OUT (LP)	10

TRUDY
84	Torso TDY 045	The Invisible Man/Holiday Planet (foldout p/s)	6
87	Primitive TDY 049	Captain Scarlet/Lunar Love Affair (p/s)	4
89	Planet Miron TDY 051	Living On A Moon/Countdown To Love (box set with card, inserts & plastic figure)	6

TRUTH
| 65 | Pye 7N 15923 | Baby Don't You Know/Come On Home | 10 |

MINT VALUE £

65	Pye 7N 15998	Who's Wrong/She's A Roller	12
66	Pye 7N 17035	Girl/Jailer Bring Me Water	6
66	Pye 7N 17095	I Go To Sleep/Baby You've Got It	20
66	Deram DM 105	Jingle Jangle/Hey Gyp (Dig The Slowness)	25
67	Decca F 12582	Walk Away Renee/Fly Away Bird	5
68	Decca F 22764	Seuno/Old Ma Brown	10

TRUTH
80s	WEA/Formation TRUTH D1	Fried Link/SOIL: Front Room (flexidisc with 'Debris' magazine)	7/5
83	WEA/Formation TRUTH D2	Step In The Right Direction/Beat Generation//What You Want Me/	
		Second Time Lucky (double pack)	4

(see also 9 Below Zero)

TRUTH CLUB
70s	Le Ray LR 1 EJSP 9597	Sleight/FOTE: Lost Toy (p/s)	4

TRUTH OF TRUTHS
71	Oak OR 1001	TRUTH OF TRUTHS (LP)	20

TRYDAN
80	Sain SAIN 77S	Mods A Rocers/Di-Waith, Di-'Fynedd	4

TANIA TSANAKLIDOU
82	Alt. Tentacles VIRUS 10	WEATHERED STATUES (EP)	6

T.S.O.L.
78	EMI EMI 2797	Charlie Chaplin (English)/Charlie Chaplin (Greek)	12

T2
70	Decca SKL 5050	IT'S ALL WORK OUT IN BOOMLAND (LP)	60

(see also Cross & Ross)

ERNEST TUBB (& HIS TEXAS TROUBADORS)
56	Brunswick 05527	Thirty Days/Answer The Phone (triangular centre)	40
56	Brunswick 05527	So Doggone Lonesome/If I Never Have Anything Else	15
50s	Decca BM 31214	What Am I Living For/Goodbye Sunshine, Hello Blues (export issue)	10
55	Brunswick OE 9148	COUNTRY DOUBLE DATE (EP)	12
58	Brunswick OE 9372	THE DADDY OF 'EM ALL PT. 1 (EP)	12
58	Brunswick OE 9373	THE DADDY OF 'EM ALL PT. 2 (EP)	12
58	Brunswick OE 9374	THE DADDY OF 'EM ALL PT. 3 (EP)	12
56	Brunswick LA 8736	JIMMIE RODGERS SONGS (10" LP)	25
57	Brunswick LAT 8161	FAVOURITES (LP)	20
58	Brunswick LAT 8260	THE DADDY OF 'EM ALL (LP)	20
59	Brunswick LAT 8292	THE IMPORTANCE OF BEING ERNEST (LP)	20
60	Brunswick LAT 8313	THE ERNEST TUBB STORY VOLUME ONE (LP)	15
60	Brunswick LAT 8314	THE ERNEST TUBB STORY VOLUME TWO (LP)	15
60	Brunswick LAT 8349	THE ERNEST TUBB RECORD SHOP (LP)	20

(see also Red Foley & Ernest Tubb)

JUSTIN TUBB
67	RCA Victor RCA 1585	But Wait There's More/The Second Thing I'm Gonna Do	5
64	RCA RCX 7133	JUSTIN TUBB (EP)	20
63	Ember CW 100	STAR OF THE GRAND OLE OPRY (LP)	12

TUBES
79	A&M AMSP 7423	Prime Time/No Way Out (picture disc)	4
79	A&M AMS 7423	Prime Time/No Way Out (p/s, 7 different coloured vinyl editions)	each 4
79	A&M AMS 7423	Prime Time (box set of 7 different coloured vinyl editions)	30
79	A&M AMS 7462	TV Is King/Telecide (p/s, yellow vinyl)	4

TUBEWAY ARMY
78	Beggars Banquet BEG 5	That's Too Bad/Oh! I Didn't Say (p/s)	8
78	Beggars Banquet BEG 8	Bombers/O.D. Receiver/Blue Eyes (p/s)	8
79	Beggars Banquet BEG 17	Down In The Park/Do You Need The Service? (p/s)	4
79	Beggars Banquet BEG 17	Down In The Park/Do You Need The Service? (12", p/s)	20
79	Beggars Banquet BEG 18P	Are "Friends" Electric?/We Are So Fragile (picture disc, with insert)	8
79	Beggars Banquet BACK 2	That's Too Bad/Oh! Didn't I Say/Bombers/Blue Eyes/	
		OD Receiver (gatefold p/s)	5
79	Beggars Banquet BACK 2	That's Too Bad/Oh! Didn't I Say/Bombers/Blue Eyes/	
		OD Receiver (gatefold p/s, mispressed 2nd disc omits 'OD Receiver')	12
83	Beggars Banquet BEG 92E	TUBEWAY ARMY VOL. 1 (12" EP, with "That's Too Bad [Alternate Mix]",	
		yellow vinyl)	8
83	Beggars Banquet BEG 92E	TUBEWAY ARMY VOL. 1 (12" EP, with "That's Too Bad [Single Version]")	7
84	B. Banquet BEG 123E	TUBEWAY ARMY VOL. 2 (12" EP, red or black vinyl)	7/10
84	B. Banquet BEG 124E	TUBEWAY ARMY VOL. 3 (12" EP, blue or black vinyl)	7/10
78	Beggars Banquet BEGA 4	TUBEWAY ARMY (LP, blue vinyl, gatefold stickered sleeve, some with badge)	45/40
78	Beggars Banquet BEGA 4	TUBEWAY ARMY (LP, reissue, white stickered sleeve)	10
79	Beggars Banquet BEGA 7	REPLICAS (LP, with large black & white poster)	15

(see also Gary Numan, Paul Gardiner)

BESSIE TUCKER
55	HMV 7EG 8085	BLUES BY BESSIE (EP)	20

BILLY JOE TUCKER
61	London HLD 9455	Boogie Woogie Bill/Mail Train	50

COLIN LLOYD TUCKER
86	Rouge DJ 1	Head/Sex Slave (picture disc)	4

(see also Gadgets, Plain Characters)

CY TUCKER
63	Fontana TF 424	My Prayer/High School Dance (with Earl Preston & TTs)	6
64	Fontana TF 470	I Apologise/Let Me Call You Sweetheart	5

(see also Earl Preston & TTs)

SOPHIE TUCKER

23	Parlophone R 100	The Man I Love/My Pet (78)	10
24	Parlophone R 197	Oh! You Have No Idea/Cause I Feel Low Down (78)	7
54	Mercury MG 20035	MY DREAM (LP)	15
54	Mercury MG 20046	CABARET DAYS (LP)	15
54	Mercury MPL 6000	LATEST AND GREATEST SPICY SAUCY SONGS (LP)	12
56	Mercury MPL 6503	CABARET DAYS (LP, reissue)	10
57	Brunswick LAT 8144	THE GREAT SOPHIE TUCKER (LP)	12
57	Mercury MPL 6513	BIGGER AND BETTER THAN EVER (LP)	10

TOMMY TUCKER

64	Pye International 7N 25238	Hi-Heel Sneakers/I Don't Want 'Cha	10
64	Pye International 7N 25246	Long Tall Shorty/Mo' Shorty	10
64	London HLU 9932	Oh! What A Feeling/Wine Bottles	22
69	Chess CRS 8086	Hi-Heel Sneakers/I Don't Want 'Cha (reissue)	8
64	Pye International NEP 44027	HI HEEL SNEAKERS (EP)	15

TUCKY BUZZARD

71	Capitol CL 15687	She's A Striker/Heartbreaker	4
73	Purple PUR 113	Gold Medallions/Fast Bluesy Woman	4
77	Purple PUR 134	Gold Medallions/Superboy Rock'n'Roller	4
69	Capitol E-ST 864	WARM SLASH (LP)	20
73	Purple TPSA 7510	ALRIGHT ON THE NIGHT (LP)	12
73	Purple TPSA 7512	BUZZARD (LP)	12
	(see also End)		

TUDOR LODGE

71	Vertigo 6059 044	The Lady's Changing Home/The Good Times We Had	15
71	Vertigo 6360 043	TUDOR LODGE (LP, foldout textured sleeve, spiral label)	130

TUDOR MINSTRELS

66	Decca F 12536	Love In The Open Air/A Theme From "The Family Way"	12

TUESDAY BLUE

86	Mother MUM 3	Tunnel Vision/Tell The Boys (p/s)	4
86	Mother 12MUM 3	Tunnel Vision/Tell The Boys/Don't Go Away (12", p/s)	7

TUESDAY'S CHILDREN

66	Columbia DB 7978	When You Walk In The Sand/High And Drifting	8
66	Columbia DB 8018	High On A Hill/Summer Leaves Me With A Sigh	8
67	King KG 1051	A Strange Light From The East/That'll Be The Day	12
67	Pye 7N 17406	Baby's Gone/Guess I'm Losin' You	8
68	Pye 7N 17474	In The Valley Of The Shadow Of Love/Ain't You Got A Heart	6
68	Mercury MF 1063	She/Bright-Eyed Apples	4
	(see also Warm Sounds)		

LEE TULLY

57	London HL 8363	Around The World With Elwood Pretzel Pts 1 & 2 (gold or silver lettering)	50/35
57	London HL 8363	Around The World With Elwood Pretzel Pts 1 & 2 (78)	7

TUNE ROCKERS

58	London HLT 8717	The Green Mosquito/Warm Up	25
58	London HLT 8717	The Green Mosquito/Warm Up (78)	18

TUNEWEAVERS

57	London HL 8503	Happy Happy Birthday Baby/PAUL GAYTEN: Yo, Yo, Walk	75
57	London HL 8503	Happy Happy Birthday Baby/PAUL GAYTEN: Yo, Yo, Walk (78)	20

TUNNELVISION

81	Factory FAC 39	Watching THe Hydroplanes/Morbid Fear (clear vinyl, p/s)	5

DENNIS TURNER

62	London HL 9537	Lover Please/How Many Times	5

GORDON TURNER

70	Charisma CAS 1009	MEDITATION (LP)	25

IKE TURNER

72	United Artists UP 35411	Lawdy Miss Clawdy/Tacks In My Shoes/Soppin' Molasses	4
84	Fleetville FV 303	New Breed Part 1/New Breed Part 1	4
60s	Ember EMB 3395	IKE TURNER ROCKS THE BLUES (LP)	10
72	United Artists UAG 29362	BLUES ROOTS (LP)	10
	(see also Ike & Tina Turner)		

IKE & TINA TURNER

60	London HLU 9226	A Fool In Love/The Way You Love Me	10
61	London HLU 9451	It's Gonna Work Out Fine/Won't You Forgive Me	12
64	Sue WI 306	It's Gonna Work Out Fine/Won't You Forgive Me (reissue)	12
64	Sue WI 322	The Argument/Poor Fool	12
64	Sue WI 350	I Can't Believe What You Say/My Baby Now	12
65	Warner Bros WB 153	Finger Poppin'/Ooh Poo Pah Doo	8
65	Sue WI 376	Please Please Please/Am I A Fool In Love	12
66	London HLU 10046	River Deep Mountain High/I'll Keep You Happy	6
66	Warner Bros WB 5753	Tell Her I'm Not Home/Finger Poppin'	6
66	HMV POP 1544	Anything You Wasn't Born With/Beauty Is Just Skin Deep	15
66	London HLU 10083	A Love Like Yours (Don't Come Knockin' Every Day)/Hold On Baby	6
66	Stateside SS 551	Goodbye, So Long/Hurt Is All You Gave Me	7
66	Warner Bros WB 5766	Somebody (Somewhere) Needs You/(I'll Do Anything) Just To Be With You	8
67	HMV POP 1583	I'm Hooked/Dust My Broom	20
67	London HLU 10155	I'll Never Need More Than This/Save The Last Dance For Me	6
68	London HLU 10189	So Fine/So Blue Over You	6
68	London HLU 10217	We Need An Understanding/It Sho' Ain't Me	6
69	London HLU 10242	River Deep Mountain High/Save The Last Dance For Me	4

MINT VALUE £

69	Minit MLF 11016	I'm Gonna Do All I Can/You've Got Too Many Ties That Bind	10
69	London HLU 10267	I'll Never Need More Than This/A Love Like Yours	4
69	Liberty LBF 15223	Crazy 'Bout You Baby/I've Been Lovin' You Too Long	8
70	Liberty LBF 15303	Come Together/Honky Tonky Women	4
70	A&M AMS 783	Make 'Em Wait/Everyday I Have To Cry	10
70	Harvest HAR 5018	The Hunter/Bold Soul Sister	8
70	Liberty LBF 15367	I Want To Take You Higher/Contact High	4
70	Liberty LBF 15432	Proud Mary/Funkier Than Mosquito's Tweeter	4
71	A&M AMS 829	River Deep Mountain High/Oh Baby	7
64	Sue IEP 706	THE SOUL OF IKE AND TINA TURNER (EP)	100
65	Warner Bros WEP 619	THE IKE AND TINA TURNER SHOW (EP)	25
66	Warner Bros WEP 620	SOMEBODY NEEDS YOU (EP)	25
65	Warner Bros WM 8170	THE IKE AND TINA TURNER SHOW (LP)	20
65	London HA-C 8248	THE GREATEST HITS OF IKE & TINA TURNER (LP)	20
66	Ember EMB 3368	THE IKE AND TINA TURNER REVUE (LP)	12
66	Warner Bros W 1579	THE IKE AND TINA TURNER SHOW (LP)	12
66	London HA-U/SH-U 8298	RIVER DEEP MOUNTAIN HIGH (LP)	20
67	Warner Bros WB 5904	THE IKE AND TINA TURNER SHOW VOL. 2 (LP)	12
69	London HA-U/SH-U 8370	SO FINE (LP, with Fontella Bass)	12
69	Liberty LBS 83241	OUTTA SEASON (LP)	12
69	Minit MLS 40014	IN PERSON (LP)	12
70	Liberty LBS 83350	COME TOGETHER (LP)	10
70	Harvest SHSP 4001	THE HUNTER (LP)	30
71	Liberty LBS 83455	WORKIN' TOGETHER (LP)	10
71	Liberty LBS 83468/9	LIVE IN PARIS (LP)	10

(see also Ike Turner, Tina Turner, Ikettes)

JESSE LEE TURNER

59	London HLL 8785	The Little Space Girl/Shake, Baby, Shake	50
59	London HLL 8785	The Little Space Girl/Shake, Baby, Shake (78)	18
60	London HLP 9108	I'm The Little Space Girl's Father/Valley Of Lost Soldiers	20
60	Top Rank JAR 303	That's My Girl/Teenage Misery	15
60	Top Rank JAR 516	Do I Worry (Yes I Do)/All Right, Be That Way	12
62	Vogue V 9201	The Voice Changing Song/All You Gotta Do Is Ask	12

(BIG) JOE TURNER

40s	Parlophone R 2672	Goin' Away Blues/Roll 'Em Pete (78)	40
40s	Parlophone R 2773	Lowdown Dirty Shame Blues/I Can't Give You Anything But Love (as Joe Sullivan & Café Society Orchestra) (78)	30
40s	Brunswick 03430	Lucille/Lonesome Graveyard Blues (78)	35
40s	Brunswick 03462	Lonesome Graveyard Blues/SNUB MOSELEY: Blues At High Noon (78)	25
49	MGM MGM 253	Mardi Gras Boogie/My Heart Belongs To You (78)	20
56	London HLE 8301	Corrine Corrina/Morning, Noon And Night	225
56	London HLE 8301	Corrine Corrina/Morning, Noon And Night (78)	35
56	London HLE 8332	Boogie Woogie Country Girl/The Chicken And The Hawk	350
56	London HLE 8332	Boogie Woogie Country Girl/The Chicken And The Hawk (78)	40
57	London HLE 8357	Lipstick, Powder And Paint/Rock A While (gold lettering, later silver)	350/200
57	London HLE 8357	Lipstick, Powder And Paint/Rock A While (78)	25
60	London HLE 9055	Honey Hush/Tomorrow Night	40
60	London HLK 9119	My Little Honey Dripper/Chains Of Love	40
65	Atlantic AT 4026	Midnight Cannonball/Baby I Still Want You	12
57	London REE 1111	PRESENTING JOE TURNER (EP, initially tri-centre, later round centre)	65/50
57	London Jazz LTZK 15053	BOSS OF THE BLUES (LP, also stereo SAH-K 6019)	50/60
59	London HA-E 2173	ROCKIN' THE BLUES (LP)	75
60	London Jazz LTZK 15205	BIG JOE RIDES AGAIN (LP, also stereo SAH-K 6123)	50/60
60	London HA-E 2231	BIG JOE IS HERE (LP)	60
64	77 LEU 12/32	STRIDE BY STRIDE (2-LP)	15
65	Fontana 688 802 ZL	JUMPIN' THE BLUES (LP)	15
67	Atlantic 590 006	BOSS OF THE BLUES (LP)	12
68	Stateside (S)SL 10226	SINGING THE BLUES (LP)	15
70	Philips SBL 7911	THE REAL BOSS OF THE BLUES (LP)	10

(see also Pete Johnson, Meade Lux Lewis, Pete Johnson, Albert Ammons, Joe Sullivan & Café Society Orchestra)

JOE TURNER/RUTH BROWN

| 56 | London REE 1047 | KING AND QUEEN OF R & B (EP, 2 tracks each) | 120 |

(see also Ruth Brown, Big Joe Turner)

JOE TURNER & PETE JOHNSON GROUP

| 56 | Emarcy ERE 1500 | JOE TURNER & PETE JOHNSON GROUP (EP) | 30 |

(see also Pete Johnson, Big Joe Turner)

LAVINIA TURNER

| 23 | Actuelle 10134 | How Many Times?/Can't Get Lovin' Blues (78) | 50 |

MEL TURNER

62	Columbia DB 4791	Daddy Cool/Swing Low Sweet Chariot (with Bandits)	7
63	Columbia DB 4963	Don't Cry/I Need	5
63	Columbia DB 7076	I Can't Stand Up Alone/Doing The Ton (with Mohicans)	5
63	Carnival CV 7003	Mohican Crawl/White Christmas	4
66	Island WI 276	Welcome Home Little Darlin'/C'est L'Amour	7

NIK TURNER

(see under Inner City Unit, Sphynx, Hawkwind)

SAMMY TURNER

59	London HLX 8918	Lavender Blue (Dilly, Dilly)/Sweet Annie Laurie	12
59	London HLX 8918	Lavender Blue (Dilly, Dilly)/Sweet Annie Laurie (78)	8
59	London HLX 8963	Always/Symphony	8
59	London HLX 8963	Always/Symphony (78)	8
60	London HLX 9062	Paradise/I'd Be A Fool Again	8

MINT VALUE £

| 62 | London HLX 9488 | Raincoat In The River/Falling | 15 |
| 60 | London HA-X 2246 | LAVENDER BLUE MOODS (LP) | 45 |

SIMON TURNER

72	UK UK 20	Shoeshine Boy/17	4
73	UK UK 33	Baby/Love Around	4
73	UK UK 37	Baby/I Wanna Love My Life Away	4
73	UK UK 44	The Prettiest Star/Love Around	4
73	UK UK 52	California Revisited Pts 1 & 2	4
74	UK UK 60	She Was Just A Young Girl/I'll Take Your Hand	4
74	UK UK 74	Sex Appeal/Little Lady	4
73	UK UKAL 1003	SIMON TURNER (LP)	10

SPYDER TURNER

| 67 | MGM MGM 1332 | Stand By Me/You're Good Enough For Me | 15 |
| 74 | Kwanza 19502 | Since I Don't Have You/Happy Days | 5 |

TINA TURNER

82	Virgin VS 500	Ball Of Confusion/Ball Of Confusion (Instrumental) (with B.E.F.) (p/s)	4
83	Capitol 12CLP 316	Let's Stay Together/I Wrote A Letter (12", picture disc)	7
84	Capitol CLP 325	Help/Rock'n'Roll Widow (picture disc)	6
84	Capitol CLP 338	Better Be Good To Me/When I Was Young (picture disc)	6
84	Capitol CL 343	Private Dancer/Nutbush City Limits (p/s)	4
85	Capitol CLP 364	We Don't Need Another Hero/(Instrumental) (picture disc)	6
86	Capitol CLP 338	Break Every Rule/Girls (picture disc)	5
87	Capitol CLD 439	What You Get Is What You See/Tina Turner Montage (box set)	4
87	Capitol 7CLD 439	What You See Is What You Get/Take Me To The River//Tina Turner Montage Mix Pts 1 & 2 (double pack)	6
87	Capitol CLP 452	Break Every Rule/Girls (picture disc)	6
87	Capitol CLP 459	Paradise Is Here/The Midnight Hour (picture disc)	5
87	Capitol 12 CLP 459	Paradise Is Here/The Midnight Hour (12" picture disc)	7
89	Capitol CLS 543	The Best/Undercover Agent For The Blues (7" pack, with 6 postcards)	5
89	Capitol 12 CLP 553	I Don't Wanna Lose You/Not Enough Romance (12", picture disc)	7
90	Capitol CLPD 593	Be Tender With Me Baby/Be Tender With Me Baby (live) (picture disc)	5
85	Capitol TINAP 1	PRIVATE DANCER (LP, picture disc)	10
89	Capitol CDESTU 2103	FOREIGN AFFAIR (CD in deluxe passport package)	14

(see also Ike & Tina Turner)

TITUS TURNER

60	London HLU 9024	We Told You Not To Marry/Taking Care Of Business	18
61	Oriole CB 1611	Pony Train/Bla Bla Cha Cha Cha	15
61	Parlophone R 4746	Sound-Off/Me And My Lonely Telephone	20
61	Blue Beat BB 32	Miss Rubberneck Jones/Way Down Yonder	7

ZEB TURNER

| 51 | Vogue V 9002 | Chew Tobacco Rag/No More Nothin' (78) | 10 |

TURNING SHRINES

| 86 | Temple TOPY 7 | FACE OF ANOTHER (12" EP) | 7 |

TURNSTYLE

| 68 | Pye 7N 17653 | Riding A Wave/Trot | 60 |

TURQUOISE

| 68 | Decca F 12756 | 53 Summer Street/Tales Of Flossie Fillett | 25 |
| 68 | Decca F 12842 | Woodstock/Saynia | 25 |

(see also Ewan Stephens)

STANLEY TURRENTINE

64	Blue Note 45-1894	Never Let Me Go/Major's Minor	8
76	Fantasy FTC 131	Have You Ever Seen The Rain/Tommy's Tune	4
78	Fantasy FTC 149	Papa'T Pts 1 & 2	4
78	Fantasy FTC 162	Disco Dancing/Heritage	4
61	Blue Note BLP 4039	LOOK OUT! (LP)	15
62	Blue Note BLP 4069	UP AT MINTON'S (LP)	15
64	Blue Note (B)BLP 4070	UP AT MINTON'S PART 2 (LP)	15
64	Blue Note (B)BLP 4129	NEVER LET ME GO (LP)	15
64	Blue Note (B)BLP 4057	BLUE HOUR (LP)	15
64	Blue Note (B)BLP 4081	DEARLY BELOVED (LP)	15
65	Blue Note (B)BLP 4150	A CHIP OFF THE OLD BLOCK (LP)	15
65	Blue Note (B)BLP 4162	HUSTLIN' (LP)	15
66	Blue Note (B)BLP 4201	JOYRIDE (LP)	15
66	Fontana TL 5300	TIGER TAIL (LP)	12
69	Blue Note BST 84286	THE LOOK OF LOVE (LP)	12
69	Blue Note BST 84298	ALWAYS SOMETHING THERE (LP)	12
69	Blue Note BST 84315	THE COMMON TOUCH (LP)	12
70	Blue Note BST 84336	ANOTHER STORY (LP)	12
72	Polydor 2383 111	FLIPPED — FLIPPED OUT (LP)	10
73	CTI CTL 3	SUGAR (LP)	10
73	CTI CTL 8	CHERRY (LP, with Milt Jackson)	10
77	Fantasy FT 535	NIGHTWINGS (LP)	10
78	Fantasy FT 551	WHAT ABOUT YOU (LP)	10

(see also Milt Jackson & Stanley Turrentine)

TURTLES

65	Pye International 7N 25320	It Ain't Me Babe/Almost There	7
66	Pye International 7N 25341	Let Me Be/Your Ma Said You Cried (In Your Sleep Last Night)	7
66	Immediate IM 031	You Baby/Wanderin' Kind	10
66	London HLU 10095	Can I Get To Know You Better/Like The Seasons	5
67	London HLU 10115	Happy Together/We'll Meet Again	5
67	Pye International 7N 25421	Let Me Be/Almost There	5

MINT VALUE £

67	London HLU 10135	She'd Rather Be With Me/The Walking Song	5
67	London HLU 10153	You Know What I Mean/Rugs Of Woods And Flowers	5
67	London HLU 10168	She's My Girl/Chicken Little Was Right	5
68	London HLU 10184	Sound Asleep/Umbassa The Dragon	5
68	London HLU 10207	The Story Of Rock And Roll/Can't You Hear The Cows	5
68	London HLU 10223	Elenore/Surfer Dan	4
69	London HLU 10251	You Showed Me/Buzz-Saw	4
69	London HLU 10279	You Don't Have To Walk In The Rain/Come Over	4
69	London HLU 10291	Love In The City/Bachelor Mother	4
67	Pye Intl. NEP 44089	IT AIN'T ME BABE (EP)	15
67	London HA-U 8330	HAPPY TOGETHER (LP)	18
68	London HA-U/SH-U 8376	THE TURTLES PRESENT THE BATTLE OF THE BANDS (LP)	15

(see also Flo & Eddie)

RITA TUSHINGHAM & LYNN REDGRAVE
68	Stateside SS 2081	Smashing Time/Waiting For My Friend	6

TU-TONES
59	London HLW 8904	Still In Love With You/Saccharin Sally	75
59	London HLW 8904	Still In Love With You/Saccharin Sally (78)	18

WESLEY & MARILYN TUTTLE
55	Capitol CL 14291	Jim, Johnny And Jonas/Say You Do	6

T.V. PERSONALITIES
(see under Television Personalities)

T.V. PRODUCT
79	Limited Edition TAKE 3	Nowhere's Safe/Jumping Off Walls/PRAMS: Me/Modern Man (folded p/s)	8

(see also Mission)

T.V. & TRIBESMEN
66	Pye International 7N 25375	Barefootin'/Fat Man	15

TV 21
80	Powbeat AAARGH! 1	Playing With Fire/Shattered By It All (foldout p/s)	12
80	Powbeat AAARGH! 2	Ambition/Ticking Away/This Is Zero (foldout p/s)	15
81	Deram DM 442/DMF 442	Snakes And Ladders/Artistic Licence//Ambition/Playing With Fire (double pack)	5

(see also DNV, Shake)

TWANG
86	Ron Johnson ZRON 14	Sharp/Eight At A Time (p/s)	4
87	Ron Johnson ZRON 29	Snapback/Snapback (Defence Mix) (12", die-cut p/s)	7

TWELFTH NIGHT
80	Twelfth Night TN 001	THE FIRST 7" ALBUM (The Cunning Man/Für Helene)	10
80s	Revolution REV 009	Eleanor Rigby/East Of Eden (p/s)	5
86	Charisma CB 424-12	Shame (Full Mix)/Shame (7")/Blue Powder Monkey (12", p/s)	8
86	Charisma CB 424	Shame (picture disc)	8
86	Charisma CB 425	Take A Look/Blondon Fair (p/s)	4
80	private cassette TN 001	TWELFTH NIGHT (cassette)	15
81	Twelth Night TN 002	LIVE AT THE TARGET (LP)	12
82	Twelth Night TN 003	SMILING AT GRIEF (cassette)	10
83	Twelth Night TN 006	FACT AND FICTION (LP)	10
84	Music For Nations MFN 18	LIVE AND LET LIVE (LIVE AT THE MARQUEE) (LP)	10
84	Music For Nations MFN 36	ART & ILLUSION (mini-LP)	10
86	Charisma CASG 1174	X (LP, limited editon fold-out cover)	10

25TH OF MAY
80s	White Trash 25 MAY 1	Fuck The Right To Vote (Yeltsin Mix)/Made In The USA (Scud Mix) (12", available only by mail-order, 3,000 only, with insert)	7

25 RIFLES
79	25 Rifles TFR + 1	World War 3/Revolution Blues/Hey Little/Dance 'Bout Now (p/s)	10

23RD TURNOFF
67	Deram DM 150	Michael Angelo/Leave Me Here	30

(see also Kirkbys, Jimmy Campbell)

23 JEWELS
79	Temporary TEMP 1	You Don't Know Me/Playing Bogart (white label, plain sleeve with photocopied insert)	5
80	Temporary TEMP 2	WELTSCHMERZ A GO-GO! (EP, white label)	4

23 SKIDOO
81	Pineapple PULP 23	Ethics/Another Baby's Face (p/s)	8
81	Fetish FE 10	Last Words/Version (promo-only, no p/s)	8
81	Fetish FE 11	The Gospel Comes To New Guinea/Last Words (12", p/s)	8
82	Fetish FP 20	Tearing Up The Plans/Just Like Everybody/Gregouka (12", p/s)	7
85	Illuminated ILL 2812	Coup/Version (In The Palace) (12", p/s)	7
82	Fetish FM 2008	SEVEN SONGS (mini-LP)	8

TWICE AS MUCH
66	Immediate IM 033	Sittin' On The Fence/Baby I Want You	6
66	Immediate IM 036	Step Out Of Line/Simplified	6
66	Immediate IM 039	True Story/You're So Good	8
67	Immediate IM 042	Crystal Ball/Why Don't They All Go Away And Leave Me Alone	8
66	Immediate IMLP/IMSP 007	OWN UP (LP)	15
69	Immediate IMCP 013	THAT'S ALL (LP)	15

TWIGGY
66	Ember EMB S 239	Beautiful Dreams/I Need Your Hand In Mine (some in p/s)	15/10

| 66 | Ember EMB S 244 | When I Think Of You/Over And Over | 4 |

(see also Twiggy & Annie)

TWIGGY & ANNIE
| 66 | Columbia DB 7799 | Some Do, Some Don't/With Open Arms | 4 |

(see also Twiggy)

TWILIGHTS (U.S.)
| 65 | London HLU 9992 | Take What I Got/She's There | 12 |

TWILIGHTS (Australia)
66	Columbia DB 8065	Needle In A Haystack/I Don't Know Where The Wind Will Blow Me	10
67	Columbia DB 8125	What's Wrong With The Way I Live/It's Dark	10
68	Columbia DB 8396	Cathy, Come Home/The Way They Play	15

TWILIGHT ZONERZ
| 79 | ZIP/Dining Out ZEROZERO 1 | ZERO ZERO ONE (EP, various silk-screened in red & hand-coloured p/s, signed & numbered) | 10 |
| 80 | ZIP/Dining Out ZIP 002 | Brighton Rock/Diversion (p/s) | 4 |

TWINK (& FAIRIES)
78	Chiswick SWT 26	Do It '77/Psychedelic Punkeroo (12", p/s, with Fairies)	7
70	Polydor 2343 032	THINK PINK (LP, with insert)	70
70	Polydor 2343 032	THINK PINK (LP, red vinyl, with insert)	200

(see also Pretty Things, Pink Fairies, Fairies, Tomorrow, Aquarian Age, Rings)

TWINKLE
64	Decca F 12013	Terry/The Boy Of My Dreams	5
65	Decca F 12076	Golden Lights/Ain't Nobody Home But Me	5
65	Decca F 12139	Tommy/So Sad	5
65	Decca F 12219	Poor Old Johnny/I Need Your Hand In Mine	6
65	Decca F 12305	The End Of The World/Take Me To The Dance	6
66	Decca F 12464	What Am I Doing Here With You?/Now I Have You	6
69	Instant IN 005	Micky/Darby And Joan	7
74	Bradleys BRAD 7418	Days/Caroline	4
65	Decca DFE 8621	TWINKLE — A LONELY SINGING DOLL (EP)	20

TWINKLE BROTHERS
70	Jackpot JP 731	Shu Be Du/All My Enemies Beware	4
70	Jackpot JP 740	Miss World/Take What You've Got	4
70	Jackpot JP 741	Sweet Young Thing/Grandma	4
71	Jackpot JP 768	Do Your Own Thing/PAT KELLY: Talk About Love	4
71	Green Door GD 4007	Miss Labba Labba/The Best Is Yet To Come	4
71	Tropical AL 002	Love Sweet Love/HERON ATTAR: Poor Man's Life	4

TWINSET
| 67 | Decca F 12629 | Tremblin'/Sneakin' Up On You | 8 |

TWIN-TONES
| 58 | RCA RCA 1040 | Jo Ann/Before You Go | 30 |
| 58 | RCA RCA 1040 | Jo Ann/Before You Go (78) | 15 |

TWIN TUNES QUINTET
| 58 | RCA RCA 1046 | The Love Nest/Baby Lover | 8 |
| 58 | RCA RCA 1046 | The Love Nest/Baby Lover (78) | 8 |

TWIST
79	Polydor 20 59156	This Is Your Life/Life's A Commercial Break (p/s)	6
79	Polydor POSP 84	Ads/Rebound	6
79	Polydor 2383 552	THIS IS YOUR LIFE (LP)	20

TWISTED ACE
| 81 | Heavy Metal HEAVY 9 | Firebird/I Won't Surrender (p/s) | 12 |

TWISTED SISTER
82	Secret SHH 137-12	RUFF CUTS (12" EP, p/s)	10
83	Atlantic A 9827P	The Kids Are Back Shoot 'Em Down (shaped picture disc)	8
83	Atlantic A 9792	You Can't Stop Rock 'n' Roll/Let The Good Times Roll (live)/I Feel So Fine (poster p/s)	4
84	Atlantic A 9634T	I Wanna Rock/Burn In Hell (live)/SMF (live) (12", poster p/s)	7
86	Atlantic A 9478D	Leader Of The Pack/I Wanna Rock (p/s, with free single)	5
86	Atlantic A 9478F	Leader Of The Pack/I Wanna Rock (gatefold p/s with poster)	4
86	Atlantic A 9478P	Leader Of The Pack/I Wanna Rock (shaped picture disc)	6
85	Atlantic 781 275-1P	COME OUT AND PLAY (LP, picture disc)	12

TWISTERS
| 60 | Capitol CL 15167 | Turn The Page/Dancing Little Clown | 6 |
| 62 | Aral/Windsor PSA 106 | Peppermint Twist Time/Silly Chilli | 8 |

CONWAY TWITTY
57	Mercury MT 173	Shake It Up/Maybe Baby (78)	50
58	MGM MGM 992	It's Only Make Believe/I'll Try	5
58	MGM MGM 992	It's Only Make Believe/I'll Try (78)	6
59	MGM MGM 1003	The Story Of My Love/Make Me Know You're Mine	6
59	MGM MGM 1003	The Story Of My Love/Make Me Know You're Mine (78)	7
59	MGM MGM 1016	Hey Little Lucy! (Don't Cha Put ...)/When I'm Not With You	6
59	MGM MGM 1016	Hey Little Lucy! (Don't Cha Put ...)/When I'm Not With You (78)	12
59	MGM MGM 1029	Mona Lisa/Heavenly	5
59	MGM MGM 1029	Mona Lisa/Heavenly (78)	18
59	MGM MGM 1047	Rosaleena/Halfway To Heaven	6
59	MGM MGM 1047	Rosaleena/Halfway To Heaven (78)	20
60	MGM MGM 1056	Lonely Blue Boy/My One And Only You	7
60	MGM MGM 1066	What Am I Living For/The Hurt In My Heart	6
60	MGM MGM 1082	Is A Blue Bird Blue/She's Mine	6

Conway TWITTY

60	MGM MGM 1095	What A Dream/Tell Me One More Time	6
60	MGM MGM 1108	Whole Lotta Shakin' Goin' On/The Flame	8
61	MGM MGM 1118	C'est Si Bon/Don't You Dare Let Me Down	6
61	MGM MGM 1129	The Next Kiss/Man Alone	6
61	MGM MGM 1137	It's Drivin' Me Wild/Sweet Sorry	7
62	MGM MGM 1152	Tower Of Tears/Portrait Of A Fool	7
62	MGM MGM 1170	Comfy An' Cozy/Unchained Melody	7
62	MGM MGM 1187	I Hope I Think I Wish/The Pick Up	8
63	MGM MGM 1201	Handy Man/Little Piece Of My Heart	8
63	MGM MGM 1209	She Ain't No Angel/Got My Mojo Workin'	8
63	HMV POP 1258	Go On And Cry/She Loves Me	6
68	MGM MGM 1404	It's Only Make Believe/Mona Lisa	4
70	MCA MU 1120	That's When She Started To Stop Loving You/I'll Get Over Losing You	5
70	MCA MU 1132	I Can't Stop Loving You/Since Sue's Not With The One	4
72	MCA MU 1169	That's When She Started To Stop Loving You/I'll Get Over Losing You	5
73	MCA MMU 1149	Lead Me On/One's On The Way/You're Looking At Country (with Loretta Lynn)	4
73	MCA MMU 1150	I Can't See Me Without You/I Wonder What She'll Think About Me Leaving	4
73	MCA MU 1223	You've Never Been This Far Before/You Make It Hard	4
75	MCA MCA 180	As Soon As I Hang Up The Phone/A Lifetime Before (with Loretta Lynn)	4
75	MCA MCA 197	I See The Want-To In Your Eyes/The Girl From Tupelo	4
75	MCA MCA 211	Don't Cry Joni/Touch The Hand	4
58	MGM MGM EP 684	IT'S ONLY MAKE BELIEVE (EP)	40
59	MGM MGM EP 698	HEY LITTLE LUCY (EP)	40
60	MGM MGM EP 719	SATURDAY NIGHT WITH CONWAY TWITTY (EP)	30
60	Mercury ZEP 10069	I NEED YOUR LOVIN' (EP)	110
60	MGM MGM EP 738	IS A BLUEBIRD BLUE? (EP)	35
61	MGM MGM EP 752	THE ROCK 'N' ROLL STORY (EP)	40
59	MGM MGM-C 781	CONWAY TWITTY SINGS (LP)	40
60	MGM MGM-C 801	SATURDAY NIGHT WITH CONWAY TWITTY (LP)	45
60	MGM MGM-C 829	LONELY BLUE BOY (LP)	45
63	MGM MGM-C 950	R AND B '63 (LP)	30
68	MCA MUP(S) 342	HERE'S CONWAY TWITTY (AND HIS LONELY BLUE BOYS) (LP)	15
68	MGM C/CS 8100	THE ROCK AND ROLL STORY (LP)	30
69	MCA MUPS 363	NEXT IN LINE (LP)	15
69	MCA MUPS 386	DARLING, YOU KNOW I WOULDN'T LIE (LP)	12
70	MCA MUP(S) 404	I LOVE YOU MORE TODAY (LP)	12
70	MCA MUP(S) 412	TO SEE MY ANGEL CRY (LP)	12
71	MCA MUPS 426	FIFTEEN YEARS AGO (LP)	10
72	MCA MUPS 443	I WONDER WHAT SHE'LL THINK ABOUT ME LEAVING (LP)	10
73	MCA MUPS 429	WE ONLY MAKE BELIEVE (LP, with Loretta Lynn)	10
74	MCA MCF 2547	LOUISANA WOMAN/MISSISSIPPI MAN (LP, with Loretta Lynn)	10
74	MCA MCF 2557	YOU'VE NEVER BEEN THIS FAR BEFORE (LP)	10

(see also Loretta Lynn)

TWO & A HALF

66	CBS 202248	Midnight Swim/Faith	4
66	CBS 202404	Questions/In Harmony	4
67	Decca F 22672	Suburban Early Morning Station/Just Couldn't Believe My Ears	12
67	Decca F 22715	I Don't Need To Tell You/Christmas Will Be Round Again	10

TWO HELENS

88	Sharko TUFT-57	Silver And Gold/XV Rhythm/Gun (p/s, with sticker insert)	6
86	Sharko SHARKO 2 TUFT-4	REFLECTIONS IN RED (LP)	12

TWO KINGS

65	Island WI 240	Rolling Stone/SUFFERER: Tomorrow Morning	6
65	Island WI 249	Hit You Let You Feel It/Honey I Love You	6

TWO MUCH

67	Fontana TF 858	Wonderland Of Love/Mister Money	4
68	Fontana TF 900	It's A Hip Hip Hippy World/Stay In My World	4

TWO NINETEEN SKIFFLE GROUP

57	Esquire 10-497	Freight Train Blues/Railroad Bill (78)	5
57	Esquire 10-502	I'm A-Lookin' For A Home/When The Saints Go Marching In (78)	5
57	Esquire 10-509	In The Valley/Tom Dooley (78)	5
57	Esquire 10-512	Where Can I Go?/Roll The Union On (78)	5
57	Esquire 10-515	This Little Light Of Mine/Union Maid (78)	5
57	Esquire EP 126	TWO NINETEEN SKIFFLE GROUP (EP)	15
57	Esquire EP 146	TWO NINETEEN SKIFFLE GROUP (EP)	15
58	Esquire EP 176	TWO NINETEEN SKIFFLE GROUP (EP)	15
58	Esquire EP 196	TWO NINETEEN SKIFFLE GROUP (EP)	25

TWO OF CLUBS

64	Columbia DB 7371	The Angels Must Have Made You/True Love Is Here	4

TWO OF EACH

67	Decca F 12626	Every Single Day/I'm Glad I Got You	4
68	Pye 7N 17555	The Summer Of Our Love/Saturday Morning	4

TWO SPARKS

72	Moodisc HM 113	Run Away Girl/When We Were Young	4

TWO THIEVES & A LIAR

80s	Lyntone LYN 18236/DEB 5	Shackles And Chains/DUB SEX: Tripwire (flexidisc with 'Debris' magazine, issue 13)	8/6

2.3

78	Fast Products FAST 2	Where To Now?/All Time Low (p/s)	4

ARLYNE TYE
59	London HLL 8825	The Universe/Who Is The One	12
59	London HLL 8825	The Universe/Who Is The One (78)	6

TYGERS OF PANTANG
79	Neat NEAT 03	Don't Touch Me There/Burning Up/Bad Times (p/s)	6
80	MCA MCA 582	Don't Touch Me There/Burning Up/Bad Times (p/s, reissue)	4
80	MCA MCA 612	Rock'n'Roll Man/All Right on The Night/Wild Man (p/s)	5
80	MCA MCA 634	Suzie Smiled/Tush (p/s)	5
80	MCA MCA 644	Euthanasia/Straight As A Die (p/s)	5
81	MCA MCA 672	Hellbound/Bad Times//Bad Times/Don't Take Nothin' ('The Audition Tapes' double pack)	5
81	MCA MCA 692	The Story So Far/Silver And Gold/All Or Nothing (p/s)	5
81	MCA MCA 723	Don't Stop By/Slave To Freedom (p/s)	4
81	MCA MCA 769	Love Potion No. 9/The Stormlands (p/s)	4
81	MCA MCA 769	Love Potion No. 9/The Stormlands (picture disc)	5
82	MCA MCA 777	Rendezvous/Life Of Crime (p/s)	4
82	MCA MCA 790	Paris By Air/Love's A Lie (picture disc)	4
82	MCA MCA 790	Paris By Air/Love's A Lie (p/s, with earring)	4
82	MCA MCA 790	Paris By Air/Love's A Lie (poster p/s)	4
82	MCA MCA 798	Making Tracks/What You Saying (12", p/s)	7
82	MCA MCA 759	Do It Good/Slip Away (p/s)	4
83	MCA MCA 755	Love Don't Stay/Paradise Drive (p/s)	4
83	MCA MCA 777	Rendezvous/Life Of Crime (p/s)	4
83	MCA MCA 841	Lonely At The Top/You Always See What You Want To See (p/s)	4
81	MCA MCL 3123	CRAZY NIGHTS (LP, with bonus 12")	10

TYLA GANG
76	Stiff BUY 4	Styrofoam/Texas Chainsaw Massacre Boogie (die-cut printed sleeve)	5
78	Beserkley BSERK 16	MOONPROOF (LP, yellow vinyl)	10
	(see also Ducks Deluxe)		

TOBY TYLER
89	Archive Jive TOBY 1	The Road I'm On (Gloria) (1-sided, numbered p/s, 1000 only)	8
	(see also Marc Bolan/T.Rex)		

BIG 'T' TYLER
57	Vogue V 9079	King Kong/Sadie Green	100
57	Vogue V 9079	King Kong/Sadie Green (78)	30

BONNIE TYLER
83	CBS WA 3338	Gonna Get Better/Faster Than The Speed Of Night (picture disc)	4
86	CBS QA 6867	If You Were A Woman/Under Suspicion (poster p/s)	4
	(see also Shakin' Stevens & Bonnie Tyler)		

JIMMY TYLER & HIS ORCHESTRA
56	Parlophone MSP 6215	Fool 'Em Devil/Stardust	10

(Alvin) RED TYLER & GYROS
60	Top Rank JAR 306	Junk Village/Happy Sax	10

TERRY TYLER
61	Pye International 7N 25119	A Thousand Feet Below/Answer Me	5

TEXAS T. TYLER
59	Parlophone GEP 8788	COUNTRY ROUND UP (EP)	20
67	London HA-B 8322	MAN WITH A MILLION FRIENDS (LP, as T. Texas Tyler)	15

TYMES
63	Cameo Parkway P 871	So Much In Love/Roscoe James McClain	6
63	Cameo Parkway P 884	Wonderful Wonderful/Come With Me To The Sea (some in p/s)	15/7
64	Cameo Parkway P 891	Somewhere/View From My Window	7
64	Cameo Parkway P 908	To Each His Own/Wonderland Of Love	7
64	Cameo Parkway P 919	The Magic Of Our Summer Love/With All My Heart	6
64	Cameo Parkway P 924	Here She Comes/Malibu	40
64	Cameo Parkway P 933	The Twelfth Of Never/Here She Comes	10
63	Cameo Parkway P 7032	SO MUCH IN LOVE (LP)	25
69	Direction 8-63558	PEOPLE (LP, mono/stereo)	10

ROB TYNER & HOT RODS
77	Island WIP 6418	'Till The Night Is Gone (Let's Rock)/Flipside Rock (p/s)	4
	(see also MC 5, Eddie & Hot Rods)		

TYPHOONS
63	Embassy WB 577	Sweets For My Sweet/LES CARLE: You Can Never Stop Me Loving You	4

TYPHOONS
81	Bohemian BO 1	Telstar/In Fae A Brothin' (p/s)	5
	(see also Ruts)		

TYRANNOSAURUS REX
68	Regal Zonophone RZ 2008	Debora/Child Star (p/s with promos only)	200
68	Regal Zonophone RZ 2008	Debora/Child Star	20
68	Regal Zonophone RZ 3011	One Inch Rock/Salamanda Palaganda (p/s with promos only)	200
68	Regal Zonophone RZ 3011	One Inch Rock/Salamanda Palaganda	25
69	Regal Zonophone RZ 3016	Pewtor Suitor/Crocodiles	30
69	Regal Zonophone RZ 3022	King Of The Rumbling Spires/Do You Remember (p/s with promos only)	200
69	Regal Zonophone RZ 3022	King Of The Rumbling Spires/Do You Remember	30
70	Regal Zonophone RZ 3025	By The Light Of A Magical Moon/Find A Little Wood	30
72	Magni Fly ECHO 102	Debora/One Inch Rock/Woodland Bop/The Seal Of Seasons (p/s)	8
83	Old Gold OG 9234	Debora/Beltane Walk (mispress; B-side should play "One Inch Rock")	5
91	Tyrannosaurus Rex TYR 1	Sleepy Maurice/1968 Radio Promos (Fan Club issue, p/s, with card insert)	5

TYRANNOSAURUS REX

LLOYD TYRELL

TYSONDOG

TYTAN

TZUKE & PAXO

JUDIE TZUKE

IKE & TINA TURNER

UB40

84	DEP International DEPY 10	Cherry Oh Baby/Frilla (picture disc)	4
80	Graduate GRAD LP 2	SIGNING OFF (LP, with free 12", "Madame Medusa"/"Strange Fruit"/ "Instrumental")	10
81	DEP International DEP 1	PRESENT ARMS (LP, with free 12", "Don't Walk On The Grass"/"Dr. X")	10
82	DEP International DEP 3	UB44 (LP, hologram sleeve)	10
85	DEP International DEP 10	BAGARIDDIM (LP, with free 12", "Mi Spliff"/"I Got You Babe"/ "Don't Break My Heart")	10

UFFINGTON

83	Plant Life	CHRONICLES OF THE WHITE HORSE (LP)	10

U.F.O.

70	Beacon BEA 161	Shake It About/Evil	8
70	Beacon BEA 165	Come Away Melinda/Unidentified Flying Object	8
70	Beacon BEA 172	Boogie For George/Treacle People	8
71	Beacon BEA 181	Prince Kajuku/The Coming Of Prince Kajuku	8
74	Chrysalis CHS 2040	Doctor Doctor/Lipstick Traces	4
77	Chrysalis CHS 2146	Alone Again/Electric Phase	4
78	Chrysalis CHS 2241	Only You Can Rock Me/Rock Bottom/Cherry (red vinyl, p/s with frisbee offer)	4
79	Chrysalis CHS 2287	Doctor Doctor (live)/On With The Action (live)/Try Me (p/s, clear vinyl)	4
79	Chrysalis CHS 2318	Shoot Shoot (live)/Only You Can Rock Me (live)/I'm A Loser (live) (p/s, clear vinyl)	4
79	Chrysalis CHS 2399	Young Blood/Lights Out (p/s, red vinyl)	4
80	Chrysalis CHS 2454	Couldn't Get It Right/Hot 'n' Ready (p/s, coloured vinyl)	4
81	Chrysalis CHS 2482	Lonely Heart/Long Gone (p/s, clear vinyl, with patch)	4
81	Chrysalis CHS 2576	Let It Rain/Heel Of A Stranger/You'll Get Love (p/s, clear vinyl)	4
82	Chrysalis CHS 2607	Back Into My Life/The Writer (picture disc)	4
83	Chrysalis CHS 2672	When It's Time To Rock/Everybody Knows (picture disc)	4
85	Chrysalis UFOP 1	This Time/The Chase (shaped picture disc)	4
70	Beacon BEAS 12	UFO 1 (LP)	18
71	Beacon BEAS 19	UFO 2 FLYING (LP)	15
78	Chrysalis CDL 1182	OBSESSION (LP, with poster)	10
	(see also Michael Schenker Group)		

LESLIE UGGAMS

58	Columbia DB 4160	The Ice Cream Man/I'm Old Enough	5
59	Philips PB 954	One More Sunrise (Morgen)/The Eyes Of God	5
59	Philips PB 999	The Carefree Years/Lullaby Of The Leaves	5
60	Philips PB 1063	Inherit The Wind/Love Is Like A Violin	4
61	Philips PB 1124	Sixteen Going On Seventeen/My Favourite Things	4
60	Philips BBL 7370	THE EYES OF GOD (LP)	10

UGLY CUSTARD

70	Kaleidoscope KAL 100	UGLY CUSTARD (LP)	60
	(see also Hungry Wolf, Alan Parker)		

UGLYS

65	Pye 7N 15858	Wake Up My Mind/Ugly Blues	15
65	Pye 7N 15968	It's Alright/A Friend	15
66	Pye 7N 17027	A Good Idea/The Quiet Explosion	15
66	Pye 7N 17178	End Of The Season/Can't Recall Her Name	15
67	CBS 2933	Real Good Girl/And The Squire Blew His Horn	25
69	MGM MGM 1465	I See The Light/Mary Cilento	250
	(see also Steve Gibbons, Balls, Lemon Tree, Move, Trevor Burton)		

U.K. BONDS

65	Polydor BM 56061	The World Is Watching Us/I Said Goodbye To The Blues	5

U.K. DECAY

79	Plastic PLAS 001	U.K. Decay/Car Crash/PNEUMONIA: Exhibition/Coming Attack (folded p/s)	18
81	Plastic PLAS 002	BLACK EP (p/s, reissue with slightly different p/s)	6/5
81	Fresh FRESH 12	For My Country/Unwind Tonight (foldout card p/s)	4
81	Fresh FRESH 26	Unexpected Guest/Dresden (some with badge)	6/4
81	Fresh FRESH 33	Sexual/Twist In The Tale (poster p/s)	4
82	Corpus Christi CHRIST ITS 1	Rising From The Dread/Testament/Werewolf/Jerusalem Over (The White Cliffs Of Dover) (12", p/s, with insert)	8

U.K.s

64	HMV POP 1310	Ever Faithful, Ever True/Your Love Is All I Want	10
64	HMV POP 1357	I Will Never Let You Go/I Know	15

U.K. SUBS

78	City NIK 5	C.I.D./Live In A Car/B.I.C. (p/s, clear, red, blue, green or orange vinyl; also black vinyl)	7/5
79	City/Pinnacle NIK 5/PIN 22	C.I.D./Live In A Car (p/s, reissue, black vinyl)	4
79	Gem GEMS 5	Stranglehold/World War/Rockers (p/s, red vinyl)	5
79	Gem GEMS 10	Tomorrow's Girls/Scum Of The Earth/Telephone Numbers (p/s, blue vinyl)	6
79	Gem GEMS 14	She's Not There/Kicks/Victims/The Same Thing (p/s, green vinyl)	5
80	Gem GEMS 23	Warhead/The Harper/I'm Waiting For The Man (p/s, brown vinyl)	5
80	Gem GEMS 30	Teenage/Left For Dead/New York State Police (p/s, pink or orange vinyl)	4/5

MINT VALUE £

80	Gem GEMS 42	Party In Paris/Fall Of The Empire (p/s, yellow vinyl)	4
81	Gem GEMS 45	Keep Runnin' (Till You Burn)/Perfect Girl (p/s, blue vinyl)	4
81	Gem GEMEP 45	Keep Runnin' (Till You Burn)/Ice Age/Perfect Girl/Party In Paris (French Version) (EP)	5
82	Abstract ABS 012	SHAKE UP THE CITY (EP, red vinyl)	4
82	Ramkup CAC 2	Party In Paris (1-sided fan club single, no p/s, 500 only)	25
82	Chaos LIVE 009	LIVE AT GOSSIPS (EP, cassette)	6
82	Abstract ABS 012	SHAKE UP THE CITY (EP, red vinyl)	4
79	Gem GEM GEMLP 100	ANOTHER KIND OF BLUES (LP, blue vinyl)	10
80	Gem GEM GEMLP 106	BRAND NEW AGE (LP, clear vinyl)	10
80	Gem GEM GEMLP 111	CRASH COURSE LIVE (LP, purple vinyl, 15,000 with export 12" [GEMEP 1])	15/10
81	Gem GEM GEMLP 112	DIMINISHED RESPONSIBILITY (LP, red vinyl with inner sleeve)	10
82	Abstract AABT 300	RECORDED '79-'81 (LP, blue vinyl with free stencil)	10
86	RFB RFBLP 2	IN ACTION (LP, green vinyl, 5,000 only)	10
80s	Link Classics CLINK 4	ENDANGERED SPECIES (LP, red vinyl, 1,500 only)	10

(see also Charlie Harper)

U.K. TOUPEE

| 79 | Syrup Of Figs WIG 002 | Paul Daniels' Reject/Looks Real Enough To Me (foldout p/s) | 15 |

JAMES 'BLOOD' ULMER

| 81 | Rough Trade RT 045 | Are You Glad To Be In America?/T.V. Blues (p/s) | 4 |

PETER ULRICH

| 90 | Cornerstone PTD 001 | Taqaharu's Leaving/Evocation (p/s) | 4 |

ULTIMATE SPINACH

| 68 | MGM C 8071 | ULTIMATE SPINACH (LP) | 25 |
| 68 | MGM C 8094 | BEHOLD AND SEE (LP) | 25 |

ULTRAFUNK

74	Contempo CS 2001	Living In The City/Who Is He And What Is He To You	4
74	Contempo CS 2023	Freddy Mack/Kung Fu Man	4
75	Contempo CS 2020	Sweet F.A./Use Me	5
76	Contempo CX 14	Gotham City Boogie/Sunrise	5
77	Contempo CS 2071	Sting Your Jaws Parts 1 & 2	4
75	Contempo CLP 509	ULTRAFUNK (LP)	15
77	Contempo	(LP)	15

ULTRA HIGH FREQUENCY

| 74 | Pye Intl. 7N 25628 | We're On The Right Track Parts 1 & 2 | 4 |

ULTRA VIVID SCENE

89	4AD BAD 906	Mercy Seat/Codine/H Like In Heaven/Mercy Seat (LP Version) (12", uncut sleeve)	20
89	4AD AD 908	Something To Eat/H Like In Heaven (no p/s, freebie, 1,000 only)	8
90	4AD AD 0016	Special One/Kind Of Drag (no p/s)	6

(see also Crash)

ULTRAVOX

77	Island WIP 6375	Dangerous Rhythm/My Sex (later with p/s)	5
77	Island WIP 6392	Young Savage/Slip Away (p/s)	5
77	Island WIP 6404	Rockwrock/Hiroshima Mon Amour (p/s)	5
77	Island IEP 8	RETRO (EP, 33rpm)	4
78	Island WIP 6454	Slow Motion/Dislocation (p/s)	5
78	Island 12WIP 6454	Slow Motion/Dislocation (12", p/s, translucent vinyl)	8
78	Island WIP 6459	Quiet Men/Cross Fade (p/s)	7
78	Island 12WIP 6459	Quiet Men/Cross Fade (12", white vinyl) (p/s)	8
80	Chrysalis CHS 2441	Sleepwalk/Waiting (p/s, clear vinyl)	6
80	Chrysalis CHS 2481	Vienna/Passionate Reply (p/s, clear vinyl)	8
80	Chrysalis CHS 12 2481	Vienna/Passionate Reply/Herr X (12", p/s)	7
80	Chrysalis CHS 2457	Passing Strangers/Face To Face (p/s, clear vinyl)	5
80	Chrysalis CHS 12 2457	Passing Strangers/Face To Face/King's Lead Hat (12", p/s)	7
81	Island WIP 6691	Slow Motion/Quiet Men (p/s)	4
81	Island DWIP 6691	Slow Motion/Dislocation//Quiet Men/Hiroshima Mon Amour (Remix) (double pack)	5
81	Island WIP 6691	Slow Motion/Quiet Men (cassette)	6
81	Chrysalis CHS 2522	All Stood Still/Alles Klar (p/s, clear vinyl)	5
81	Chrysalis CHS 12 2522	All Stood Still/Alles Klar/Keep Talking (12", p/s)	7
81	Chrysalis CHS 2549	Thin Wall/I Never Wanted To Begin (p/s, clear vinyl)	4
81	Chrysalis CHS 12 2549	Thin Wall/I Never Wanted To Begin (12", p/s)	7
81	Chrysalis CHS 2559	The Voice/Paths And Angels (p/s, clear vinyl)	5
81	Chrysalis CHS 12 2559	The Voice/All Stood Still/Private Lives/Paths And Angels (12", p/s, clear vinyl)	7
81	Fan Club	The Voice (live)	8
82	Chrysalis CHS 12 2639	Reap The Wild Wind/Hosanna (12", p/s)	7
82	Chrysalis CHS 2557	Hymn/Monument (p/s, clear vinyl)	4
82	Chrysalis CHS 12 2557	Hymn/Monument (12", p/s, clear vinyl)	7
83	Chrysalis VOX 1	We Came To Dance/Overlook (picture disc)	4
84	Chrysalis UVX 1	Dancing With Tears In My Eyes/Building (12", clear vinyl, gatefold p/s with poster)	7
84	Chrysalis UV 3	Love's Great Adventure/White China (p/s, clear vinyl, with booklet)	4
84	Chrysalis UV 3	Love's Great Adventure/White China (picture disc)	4
86	Chrysalis UV 4	Same Old Story/3 (picture disc)	4
86	Chrysalis UV 5	All Fall Down/Dreams (p/s, with free single)	5
77	Island ILPS 9505	HA! HA! HA! (LP, with free 7" "Quirks"/"Modern Love" [WIP 6417] & inner sleeve)	12
82	Chrysalis PCDL 1394	QUARTET (LP, marbled picture disc)	10
84	Chrysalis CDL 1459	LAMENT (LP, screen-printed sleeve)	10

| 84 | Chrysalis PCDL 1459 | LAMENT (LP, picture disc) | 10 |
| 85 | Chrysalis UTV 1 | THE COLLECTION (LP, with free 12") | 10 |

(see also Tiger Lily, John Foxx, Midge Ure, Helden)

UNCLE DOG

| 72 | Signpost SGP 752 | River Road/First Night | 4 |
| 72 | Signpost SG 4253 | OLD HAT (LP) | 10 |

(see also Carol Grimes)

UNDER THE SUN

| 70s | Redball | UNDER THE SUN (LP) | 70 |

UNDERGRADS

| 66 | Decca F 12492 | Looks Like It's Gonna Be My Year/Calling You | 5 |

UNDERGROUND SET

| 70 | Pantonic PAN 6302 | UNDERGROUND SET (LP) | 25 |

UNDERGROUND SUNSHINE

| 69 | Fontana TF 1049 | Birthday/All I Want Is You | 6 |

UNDERNEATH

86	Acme ACME 9	Lunatic Dawn Of The Dismantler (p/s)	15
86	El GPO 17	THE IMP OF THE PERVERSE (EP)	8
86	El GPO 17T	THE IMP OF THE PERVERSE (12" EP)	10

UNDERNEATH WHAT?

| 88 | 11th Hour SRT-6KL 961 | A LAND FOR YOUR WORLD (EP) | 10 |
| 89 | One Big Guitar OBG 005T | Firebomb Telecom/Springtime In My Skull/2000 Light Years From Home (12", hand-printed p/s, numbered, 2,000 only) | 7 |

UNDERTAKERS

63	Pye 7N 15543	Everybody Loves A Lover/Mashed Potatoes	10
63	Pye 7N 15562	What About Us/Money	10
64	Pye 7N 15607	Just A Little Bit/Stupidity	10

(see also 'Takers, Jackie Lomax)

UNDERTONES

78	Good Vibrations GOT 4	TEENAGE KICKS (EP, poster p/s)	10
78	Sire SIR 4007	TEENAGE KICKS (EP, reissue)	5
79	Sire SIR 4010	Get Over You/Really Really/She Can Only Say No (p/s)	7
79	Sire SIR 4015	Jimmy Jimmy/Mars Bars (green vinyl, printed PVC slv & insert; also p/s)	5/4
79	Sire SIR 4022	Here Comes The Summer/One Way Love/Top Twenty (p/s)	4
79	Sire SIR 4024	You've Got My Number (Why Don't You Use It!)/Let's Talk About Girls (p/s)	4
80	Sire SIR 4038	My Perfect Cousin/Hard Luck (Again)/I Don't Wanna See You Again (double or single p/s)	5/4
80	Sire SIR 4042	Wednesday Week/Told You So (p/s)	4
81	Ardeck ARDS 8	It's Going To Happen!/Fairly In The Money Now (p/s)	4
81	Ardeck ARDS 9	Julie Ocean/Kiss In The Dark (p/s)	4
82	Ardeck ARDS 10	Beautiful Friend/Life's Too Easy (p/s)	4
83	Ardeck ARDS 11	The Love Parade/Like That (p/s)	4
83	Ardeck 12 ARDS 11	The Love Parade/Like That/You're Welcome/Crises Of Mine/Family Entertainment (12", p/s)	7
83	Ardeck ARDS 12	Got To Have You Back/Turning Blue (p/s)	4
83	Ardeck 12 ARDS 12	Got To Have You Back/Turning Blue/Bye Bye Baby Blue (12", p/s)	7
83	Ardeck ARDS 13	Chains Of Love/Window Shopping For New Clothes (p/s)	5
79	Sire SRK 6071	UNDERTONES (LP, without "Teenage Kicks" & "Get Over You" & with different version of "Teenage Kicks" to later issue, black & white cover)	10
80	Sire SRK 6088	HYPNOTISED (LP, with cardboard mobile)	10
83	Ardeck ARD 104	THE SIN OF PRIDE (LP, mispress with different tracks: "Bittersweet" & "Stand So Close")	40

(see also Feargal Sharkey, That Petrol Emotion)

UNDERWATER HAIRDRESSERS

| 79 | Sassoon VIDAL 1 | Swimmin' With The Wimmin/Underneath The Driers (p/s, with 'Henna' sachet) | 15 |

(see also Dodo Resurrection)

UNDISPUTED TRUTH

71	Tamla Motown TMG 776	Save My Love For A Rainy Day/Since I Lost You	4
71	Tamla Motown TMG 776	Save My Love For A Rainy Day/Since I Lost You (mispress on Parlophone)	10
71	Tamla Motown TMG 789	Smiling Face Sometimes/You Got The Love I Need	4
72	Tamla Motown TMG 818	Superstar/Ain't No Sun Since You've Been Gone	4
74	Tamla Motown TMG 897	Help Yourself/What It Is	4
76	Whitfield K 16804	You + Me = Love Parts 1 & 2	4
76	Whitfield K 16804	You + Me = Love Parts 1 & 2 (12")	7
72	T. Motown STMA 8004	FACE TO FACE (LP)	10
72	T. Motown STML 11197	THE UNDISPUTED TRUTH (LP)	12
73	T. Motown STML 11240	THE LAW OF THE LAND (LP)	12
75	T. Motown STML 11277	DOWN TO EARTH (LP)	10
75	T. Motown STMA 8023	COSMIC TRUTH (LP)	12
75	T. Motown STML 12009	HIGHER THAN HIGH (LP)	12
77	T. Motown STML 8029	BEST OF THE UNDISPUTED TRUTH (LP)	15
77	Whitfield K 56289	METHOD TO THE MADNESS (LP)	12

UNDIVIDED

| 74 | Decca F 13522 | Listen To The World/Harder They Come | 4 |
| 74 | Decca SKL 5168 | LISTEN TO THE WORLD (LP) | 10 |

UNFOLDING BOOK OF LIFE

| 69 | Island ILPS 9093 | UNFOLDING BOOK OF LIFE VOL. 1 (LP, pink label) | 20 |
| 69 | Island ILPS 9094 | UNFOLDING BOOK OF LIFE VOL. 2 (LP, pink label) | 20 |

UNICORN

60s	Hollick & Taylor HT 1258	Going Home/Another World	30
71	Big T BIG 138	P.F. Sloan/Going Back Home	4
72	Big T BIG 509	Cosmic Kid/All We Really Want To Do	4
71	Transatlantic TRA 238	UPHILL ALL THE WAY (LP)	10
74	Charisma CAS 1092	BLUE PINE TREES (LP)	10

UNIFICS

68	London HLR 10231	Court Of Love/Which One Should I Choose	6

UNION GAP

(see under Gary Puckett & Union Gap)

UNIQUE

83	Prelude TA 3707	What You Got Is What Is I Need/What You Got Is What Is I Need (Instr.) (12")	7

UNIQUES (featuring Joe Stampley)

65	Pye Intl. 7N 25303	Not Too Long Ago/Fast Way Of Living	40

UNIQUES

67	Collins Downbeat CR 002	Dry The Water/I'm A Fool For You	8
67	Island WI 3070	People Rock Steady/I'm Trying To Find A Home	12
67	Island WI 3084	Gypsy Woman/KEN ROSS: Wall Flower	12
67	Island WI 3086	Let Me Go Girl/SOULETTES: Dum Dum	12
68	Island WI 3087	Never Let Me Go/HENRY III: Won't Go Away	10
68	Island WI 3106	Speak No Evil/GLAN ADAMS: That New Girl	10
68	Island WI 3107	Lesson Of Love/DELROY WILSON: Til I Die	10
68	Island WI 3114	Build My World Around You/LLOYD CLARKE: I'll Never Change	10
68	Island WI 3117	Give Me Some More Of Your Loving/VAL BENNETT: Lovell's Special	10
68	Island WI 3122	My Conversation/SLIM SMITH: Love One Another	10
68	Island WI 3123	The Beatitude/KEITH BLAKE: Time On The River	10
68	Island WI 3145	Girl Of My Dreams/LESTER STERLING: Tribute To King Scratch	10
68	Blue Cat BS 126	Girls Like Dirt/GLEN ADAMS: She Is Leaving	8
68	Trojan TR 619	Watch This Sound/Out Of Love	8
68	Trojan TR 645	A-Yuh/Just A Mirage	8
69	Gas GAS 117	Too Proud To Beg/Love And Devotion	6
69	Nu Beat NB 034	Crimson And Clover/What A Situation	6
69	Nu Beat NB 037	I'll Make You Love Me/Lover's Prayer	6
69	Unity UN 527	The Beatitude/My Conversation	6
72	Trojan TR 7852	Mother And Child Reunion	4
72	Trojan TR 7866	Lonely For Your Love	4
69	Trojan TRL 15	ABSOLUTELY THE UNIQUES (LP)	50

UNITED SONS OF AMERICA

70	Mercury 6338 036	GREETINGS FROM THE U.S. OF A. (LP)	10

UNITED STATES DOUBLE QUARTET

67	Stateside SS 590	Life Is Groovy/Split	5

UNITED STATES OF AMERICA

68	CBS 3745	Garden Of Earthly Delights/Love Song For The Dead Che	8
68	CBS 63340	UNITED STATES OF AMERICA (LP)	20

UNITED STATES OF EXISTENCE

87	Bam Caruso OPRA 081	Gone/PAUL ROLAND: Madam Guillotine (radio jukebox issue, co. sleeve)	5

UNIT FOUR PLUS TWO

64	Decca F 11821	The Green Fields/Swing Down Chariot	10
64	Decca F 11994	Sorrow And Pain/The Lonely Valley	8
65	Decca F 12071	Concrete And Clay/When I Fall In Love	4
65	Decca F 12144	(You've) Never Been In Love Like This Before/Tell Somebody You Know	4
65	Decca F 12211	Hark/Stop Wasting Your Time	6
65	Decca F 12299	You've Got To Be Cruel To Be Kind/I Won't Let You Down	6
66	Decca F 12333	Baby Never Say Goodbye/Rainy Day	6
66	Decca F 12398	For A Moment/Fables	7
66	Decca F 12509	I Was Only Playing Games/I've Seen The Light	7
67	Fontana TF 834	Too Fast, Too Slow/Booby Trap	12
67	Fontana TF 840	Butterfly/A Place To Go	8
67	Fontana TF 891	Loving Takes A Little Understanding/Would You Believe What I Say?	5
68	Fontana TF 931	You Ain't Goin' Nowhere/So You Want To Be A Blues Player	10
69	Fontana TF 990	I Will/3.30	20
65	Decca DFE 8619	UNIT FOUR PLUS TWO (EP)	15
65	Decca LK 4697	UNIT FOUR PLUS TWO — FIRST ALBUM (LP)	45
69	Fontana SFL 13123	UNIT FOUR PLUS TWO — FIRST ALBUM (LP, reissue)	15

(see also Roulettes, Tom Sawyer, Capability Brown)

UNIVERSALS

67	Page One POF 032	I Can't Find You/Hey You	20
67	Page One POF 049	Green Veined Orchid/While The Cat's Away	12

(see also Chris Lamb & Universals, Gidian, Lace, Gary Walker & Rain, Plastic Penny)

UNKNOWNS

66	London HLU 10082	Melody For An Unknown Girl/Peith's Song	4

UNLIMITED TOUCH

83	Prelude PRL 25294	YES, WE'RE READY (LP)	10

UNREST

92	Guernica GU 1LP	IMPERIAL (LP, with free 7": "Yes She Is My Skinhead Girl"/ "Hydrofoil No. 3"/"Range Recording" [GU 1S, no p/s])	10

UNTAMED

64	Decca F 12045	So Long/Just Wait	25

65	Parlophone R 5258	Once Upon A Time/I'm Asking You	50
65	Stateside SS 431	I'll Go Crazy/My Baby Is Gone	40
66	Planet PLF 103	It's Not True/Gimme Gimme Some Shade	25

(see also Lindsay Muir's Untamed)

UNTAMED YOUTH
| 79 | HAR 001 | Untamed Youth/Runnin' Wild (p/s) | 5 |

UNTOUCHABLES (Jamaica)
68	Trojan TR 613	Tighten Up/ROY SHIRLEY: Good Ambition	5
68	Blue Cat BS 137	Prisoner In Love/EDWARD RAPHAEL: True Love	8
70	Upsetter US 345	Same Thing All Over/UPSETTERS: It's Over	5
70	Upsetter US 350	Knock On Wood/UPSETTERS: Tight Spot	5
71	Bullet BU 460	Can't Reach You/CARL DAWKINS: Natural Woman	4

UNTOUCHABLES (U.S.)
85	Stiff BUY 221	Free Yourself/Lebanon (shaped picture disc, various designs)	each 5
85	Stiff BUY 227	I Spy For The F.B.I./Whiplash (picture disc)	4
85	Stiff DBUY 240	What's Gone Wrong/The Lonely Bull//The General/Tropical Bird (double pack, p/s, shrinkwrapped with stickered white label 7" in plain black sleeve)	4

UNWANTED
77	Raw RAW 6	Withdrawal/1978/Bleak Outlook (p/s)	15
78	Raw RAW 15	Secret Police/These Boots Are Made For Walking (p/s)	8
77	Raw RAWT 6	Withdrawal/1978/Bleak Outlook (12", p/s, reissue)	12
78	Raw RAW 30	Memory Man/Guns Of Love (unissued)	

STANLEY UNWIN
| 61 | Pye NPL 18062 | ROTATEY DISKERS WITH UNWIN (LP) | 10 |

UPBEATS
58	London HLU 8688	Just Like In The Movies/My Foolish Heart	15
58	London HLU 8688	Just Like In The Movies/My Foolish Heart (78)	5
59	Pye Intl. 7N 25016	You're The One I Care For/Keep Cool Crazy Heart	8
59	Pye Intl. 7N 25016	You're The One I Care For/Keep Cool Crazy Heart (78)	5
59	Pye Intl. 7N 25028	Teenie Weenie Bikini/Satin Shoes	8
59	Pye Intl. 7N 25028	Teenie Weenie Bikini/Satin Shoes (78)	8

PHIL UPCHURCH COMBO
61	HMV POP 899	You Can't Sit Down Pts 1 & 2	20
66	Sue WI 4005	You Can't Sit Down Pts 1 & 2 (reissue)	12
66	Sue WI 4017	Nothing But Soul/Evad	12
72	Blue Thumb ILPS 9219	DARKNESS DARKNESS (LP)	12

ROBERT UPCHURCH
| 74 | Phil. Intl. PIR 2652 | The Devil Made Me Do It/Glad You're Mine | 6 |

UPCOMING WILLOWS
| 65 | Island WI 182 | Jonestown Special/SHENLEY DUFFAS: La La La | 10 |

UPP
| 76 | Epic EPC 80625 | THIS WAY UPP (LP) | 10 |

(see also Clark-Hutchinson)

UPROAR
| 82 | Beat The System RAW 1 | Rebel Youth/No More War/Fallen Angel/Victims (p/s) | 4 |
| 83 | Lightbeat RAW 2 | DIE FOR ME (EP) | 4 |

UPS & DOWNS
| 86 | What Goes On GOES ON 8 | In The Shadows/Trash (mirrored p/s with insert) | 4 |

UPSET
| 80 | Upset UPSET 1 | Hurt/Lift Off (p/s) | 5 |

(see also Innocents, Woodentops)

UPSETTERS
65	Island WI 223	Country Girl/Strange Country	8
65	Rio R 70	Walk Down The Isle/So Bad	10
66	Doctor Bird DB 1034	Wildcat/I Love You So	10
69	Duke DU 11	Eight For Eight/Stand By Me (B-side actually by Inspirations)	7
69	Camel CA 13	Taste Of Killing/My Mob	5
69	Punch PH 18	Return Of The Ugly/I've Caught You	5
69	Punch PH 19	Dry Acide/REGGAE BOYS: Selassie	5
69	Punch PH 21	Clint Eastwood/Lennox Mood	5
69	Upsetter US 300	Eight For Eight/You Know What I Mean (B-side actually by Inspirations)	6
69	Upsetter US 301	Return Of Django/Dollar In The Teeth	6
69	Upsetter US 303	Ten To Twelve/LEE PERRY: People Funny Fi True	6
69	Upsetter US 307	Night Doctor/TERMITES: I'll Be Waiting	5
69	Upsetter US 309	Kiddyo/Endlessly (both sides actually Silvertones)	5
69	Upsetter US 310	A Dangerous Man From MI5/WEST INDIANS: Oh Lord	5
69	Upsetter US 313	Live Injection/BLEECHERS: Everything For Fun	5
69	Upsetter US 315	Cold Sweat/Pound Get A Blow (B-side actually by Bleechers)	5
69	Upsetter US 317	Vampire/BLEECHERS: Check Him Out	5
69	Upsetter US 318	Soulful I/MILTON HENRY: Bread And Butter	5
69	Upsetter US 321	Drugs And Poison/Stranger On The Shore	5
70	Trojan TR 7748	Family Man/Mellow Mood	4
70	Trojan TR 7749	Capo/Mama Look	4
70	Upsetter US 325	Kill Them All/Soul Walk	5
70	Upsetter US 326	Bronco/One More	5
70	Upsetter US 332	Na Na Hey Hey/Pick Folk Kinkiest	5
70	Upsetter US 333	Granny Show/Version	5
70	Upsetter US 334	Fire Fire/Jumper	5
70	Upsetter US 335	The Pillow/Grooving	5

MINT VALUE £

70	Upsetter US 336	Self Control/The Pill	5
70	Upsetter US 338	Fresh Up/Toothache	5
70	Upsetter US 342	Dreamland/Version Of Cup	6
70	Upsetter US 343	Sipreano/Ferry Boat	5
70	Upsetter US 346	Bigger Joke/Return Of The Vampire	5
70	Upsetter US 352	Heart And Soul/Zig Zag	5
70	Upsetter US 353	Illusion/Big John Wayne (as Upsetters & King Teddy)	5
70	Punch PH 27	The Result/Feel The Spirit	5
70	Spinning Wheel SW 100	Haunted House/Double Wheel	5
70	Spinning Wheel SW 101	The Miser/CHUCK JUNIOR: Do It Madly	5
70	Spinning Wheel SW 102	The Chokin' Kind/CHUCK JUNIOR: Penny Wise	5
70	Spinning Wheel SW 103	Land Of Kinks/O'NEIL HALL: This Man	5
71	Bullet BU 461	All Combine Pts 1 & 2	5
71	Upsetter US 361	Copasetic/All Africans	5
71	Upsetter US 365	Earthquake/JUNIOR BYLES: Palace Called Africa	6
71	Upsetter US 370	Dark Moon/DAVID ISAACS: You'll Be Sorry	5
72	Upsetter US 385	French Connection/Version	5
72	Upsetter US 393	Crummy People/BIG YOUTH: Moving Version	6
72	Upsetter US 394	Water Pump Pts 1 & 2	5
73	Upsetter US 396	Puss Sea Hole/WINSTON GROOVY: Want To Be Loved	5
73	Upsetter US 397	Jungle Lion/Freak Out Skank	5
69	Pama PSP 1014	CLINT EASTWOOD (LP)	25
69	Trojan TTL 13	THE UPSETTER (LP)	15
69	Trojan TRL 19	THE RETURN OF DJANGO (LP)	20
70	Trojan TTL 28	SCRATCH THE UPSETTER AGAIN (LP)	20
70	Trojan TBL 119	THE GOOD THE BAD AND THE UPSETTERS (LP)	20
70	Trojan TBL 125	EASTWOOD RIDES AGAIN (LP)	20
70	Pama SECO 24	THE MANY MOODS OF THE UPSETTERS (LP)	30
71	Trojan TBL 166	AFRICA'S BLOOD (LP)	15
71	Trojan TBL 167	BATTLE AXE (LP)	15
74	Trojan TRLS 70	DOUBLE SEVEN (LP)	15

(see also Lee Perry, Ossie & Upsetters, Hippy Boys)

UPTOWNERS
64	London HLU 9877	If'n/Search Is Over	5

URBAN DISTURBANCE
79	Rok ROK V/VI	Wild Boys In Cortinas/V.I.Ps: Can't Let You Go (die-cut company sleeve)	5

URBAN DOGS
88	Fallout FALL LP 12	URBAN DOGS (LP)	10
88	Fallout FALL CLP 12	URBAN DOGS (cassette, with 2 extra tracks)	10

(see also Hanoi Rocks)

URCHIN
77	DJM DJS 10776	Black Leather Fantasy/Rock & Roll Woman	40
78	DJM DJS 10850	She's A Roller/Long Time No Woman	35

(see also A.S.A.P., Iron Maiden)

URCHINS
66	Polydor BM 56145	I Made Her That Way/Twas On A Night Like This	4

MIDGE URE
85	Chrysalis UREP 2	That Certain Smile/The Gift (picture disc)	4
85	Chrysalis UREX 2	That Certain Smile/The Gift//That Certain Smile (Instrumental)/ Fade To Grey (12" double pack)	7
86	Chrysalis URE 3	Wastelands/The Chieftain (gatefold p/s)	5
88	Chrysalis URECD 6	Dear God/Music 1 (CD, in tin box)	7

(see also Ultravox, Rich Kids, Slik, PVC 2)

URIAH HEEP
70	Vertigo 6059 037	Lady In Black/Simon The Bullet Freak	7
71	Bronze WIP 6111	Look At Yourself/Simon The Bullet Freak	5
72	Bronze WIP 6126	The Wizard/Gypsy	5
72	Bronze WIP 6140	Easy Livin'/Why	5
73	Bronze BRO 7	Stealin'/Sunshine	4
74	Bronze BRO 10	Something Or Nothing/What Can I Do	4
75	Bronze BRO 17	Prima Donna/Shout It Out	4
76	Bronze BRO 27	One Way Or Another/Misty Eyes	4
77	Bronze BRO 37	Wise Man/Crime Of Passion	4
77	Bronze BRO 47	Free Me/Masquerade (p/s)	5
78	Bronze BRO 62	Come Back To Me/Cheater	5
82	Bronze BRO 143	THE ABOMINOG JUNIOR (EP)	5
83	Bronze BROP 166	Lonely Nights/Weekend Warriors (picture disc)	4
83	Bronze BROG 168	Stay On Top/Playing For Time//Gypsy/Easy Livin'/Sweet Lorraine/ Stealin' (double pack, gatefold p/s)	4
85	Portrait WA 6103	Rockerama/Back Stage Girl (shaped picture disc)	6
85	Portrait WA 6309	Poor Little Girl/Bad Blood (picture disc)	4
70	Vertigo 6360 006	VERY 'EAVY ... VERY 'UMBLE (LP, gatefold sleeve, spiral label)	20
71	Vertigo 6360 028	SALISBURY (LP, gatefold sleeve, spiral label)	15
71	Bronze ILPS 9169	LOOK AT YOURSELF (LP, mirror sleeve)	12

(see also Gods, Head Machine, Natural Gas, Spice, King Crimson)

U.S. DOUBLE QUARTET
67	BT Puppy BTS 45524	Life Is Groovy/Split	4

USERS
77	Raw RAW 1	Sick Of You/(I'm) In Love With Today (p/s, some numbered on rear)	10/6
77	Raw RAWT 1	Sick Of You/(I'm) In Love With Today (12", no p/s)	10
78	Warped WARP 1	Warped 45: Kicks In Style/Dead On Arrival (p/s, 5,000 only, numbered)	5

U.S. T-BONES

65	Liberty LIB 55836	No Matter What Shape/Feelin' Fine 5
66	Liberty LIB 55867	Sippin'n'Chippin'/Moment Of Softness 6
66	Liberty LIB 55951	The Proper Thing To Do/Tee-Hee-Hee 6

PETER USTINOV

| 53 | Parlophone MSP 6012 | Mock Mozart/Phoney Folk-Lore ....4 |

US:UK

| 80s | Tackattack TACK 1 | US:UK/Sonic Beat City (no p/s) ....4 |

UT

| 80s | Catalogue CAT 075/3 | Griller/MEKONS: Amnesia (square flexidisc with 'The Catalogue' magazine) .....4 |

UTOPIA

| 73 | United Artists UAG 29438 | UTOPIA (LP) ....12 |

(see also Amon Duul II)

U2

79	CBS 7951	U2: THREE: Out Of Control/Stories For The Boys/Boy-Girl (p/s, black vinyl) 20
79	CBS 7951	U2: THREE: Out Of Control/Stories For The Boys/Boy-Girl (p/s, white vinyl) 70
79	CBS 7951	U2: THREE: Out Of Control/Stories For The Boys/Boy-Girl (p/s, orange vinyl) ...45
79	CBS 7951	U2: THREE: Out Of Control/Stories For The Boys/Boy-Girl (p/s, yellow vinyl) ...40
79	CBS 7951	U2: THREE: Out Of Control/Stories For The Boys/Boy-Girl (p/s, mispressing on brown vinyl) 100
79	CBS 12-7951	U2: THREE (12" EP, with sticker, orange CBS sleeve, 1,000 only, no'd) 125
79	CBS 12-7951	U2: THREE (12" EP, reissue, plain black sleeve, slightly different labels) 20
85	CBS 40-7951	U2: THREE (cassette, reissue) 15
80	CBS 8306	Another Day/Twilight (Demo Version) (p/s, yellow or orange vinyl) 45
80	CBS 8306	Another Day/Twilight (Demo Version) (p/s, white vinyl) 60
80	CBS 8306	Another Day/Twilight (Demo Version) (p/s, black vinyl) 30
82	CBS PAC 1	4 U2 PLAY (4 x 7", each in p/s, black vinyl) 50

(some copies of the above packs included 7"s on yellow, orange & a few on white vinyl ; these are generally sold separately)

| 80s | CBS PAC 2 | PAC 2 (4 x 7" with p/s in plastic wallet) ....25 |
| 80s | CBS PAC 3 | PAC 3 (4 x 7" with p/s in plastic wallet) ....20 |

(the above singles were only issued in the Republic Of Ireland)

80	Island WIP 6601	11 O'Clock Tick Tock/Touch (p/s) 10
80	Island WIP 6630	A Day Without Me/Things To Make And Do (p/s) 12
80	Island WIP 6656	I Will Follow/Boy-Girl (live) (p/s) 8
81	Island WIP 6679	Fire/J. Swallo (p/s) 7
81	Island UWIP 6679	Fire/J. Swallo//11 O'Clock Tick Tock (live)/The Ocean (live)/Cry (live)/ The Electric Co. (live) (double pack, gatefold p/s) 14
81	Island WIP 6733	Gloria/I Will Follow (live) (p/s) 8
82	Island WIP 6770	A Celebration/Trash, Trampoline And The Party Girl (p/s) 15
83	Island WIP 6848	New Year's Day/Treasure (p/s) 4
83	Island WIP 6848	New Year's Day/Treasure (p/s, mispress, B-side plays Martha Reeves, Motown label) 10
83	Island UWIP 6848	New Year's Day/Treasure (Whatever Happened To Pete The Chop)// Fire (live)/I Threw A Brick Through A Window (live)/A Day Without Me (live) (double pack, single p/s, black inners) 10
83	Island 12WIP 6848	New Year's Day/Treasure/Fire/I Threw A Brick/A Day Without Me (12", p/s) 7
83	Island IS 109	Two Hearts Beat As One/Endless Deep (p/s) 4
83	Island ISD 109	Two Hearts Beat As One/Endless Deep//New Year's Day (U.S.A. Remix)/ Two Hearts Beat As One (U.S.A. Remix) (double pack, gatefold p/s) 10
83	Island 12IS 109	Two Hearts Beat As One/New Year's Day/Two Hearts Beat As One/Two Hearts Beat As One (12", p/s) 7
84	Island IS 202	Pride (In The Name Of Love)/Boomerang II (p/s) 4
84	Island ISP 202	Pride (In The Name Of Love)/Boomerang II (picture disc) 20
84	Island CIS 202	Pride (In The Name Of Love)/Boomerang II/4th Of July/Boomerang II/ A Celebration (live) (cassette) 10
84	Island ISD 202	Pride (In The Name Of Love)/Boomerang II//4th Of July/Boomerang II (double pack, gatefold p/s) 8
84	Island ISX 202	Pride (In The Name Of Love)/Boomerang II/Boomerang II/11 O'Clock Tick Tock/Touch (12", blue p/s) 15
85	Island ISD 220	The Unforgettable Fire/Sort Of Homecoming (live)//Three Sunrises/Sixty Seconds In Kingdom Come/Love Comes Tumbling (double pack) 8
85	Island ISP 220	Unforgettable Fire/Sort Of Homecoming (live) (logo-shaped picture disc) 22
85	Island ISC 220	The Unforgettable Fire/Sort Of Homecoming (live)//Three Sunrises/ Bass Trap/Love Comes Tumbling (cassette) 6
87	Island ISC 319	With Or Without You/Luminous Times/Walk To The Water (cassette) 4
87	Island CID 319	With Or Without You/Luminous Times/Walk To The Water (CD, gatefold p/s) 8
87	Island ISC 328	I Still Haven't Found What I'm Looking For/Spanish Eyes/ Deep In The Heart (cassette) 4
87	Island CID 328	I Still Haven't Found What I'm Looking For/Spanish Eyes/ Deep In The Heart (CD) 12
87	Island ISC 340	Where The Streets Have No Name/Race Against Time/Silver And Gold/ Sweetest Thing (cassette) 4
87	Island CID 340	Where The Streets Have No Name/Race Against Time/Silver And Gold/ Sweetest Thing (CD, gatefold p/s) 8
88	Island IS 400	Desire/Hallelujah (non-gatefold p/s) 4
88	Island 12 CIDP 400	Desire/Hallelujah/Desire (remix) (CD, picture disc) 7
89	Island ISB 422	All I Want Is You/Unchained Melody (tin box, numbered) 6
89	Island 12 ISB 422	All I Want Is You/Unchained Melody/Everlasting Love (12" box set with photos) 7
88	U2-72S	1987 Press Conference (shaped picture disc, 2,000 only) 4
88	U2-72S	1987 Press Conference (green vinyl, shamrock-shaped) 4

MINT VALUE £

85	Island ISSP 22	WIDE AWAKE IN AMERICA (mini-LP, initially with picture labels) 10
83	Island PILPS 9733	WAR (LP, picture disc) 50
88	Island U 27	RATTLE AND HUM (2-LP, with studio versions of "Still Haven't Found What I'm Looking For" & "With You Or Without You") 100

(see Edge)

UV POP
82	Pax PAX 9	Just A Game/No Song Tomorrow (individually screen-printed p/s, at least 2 different designs/colours) 8
85	Flowmotion FM 007	Anyone For Me/Hands To Me (p/s) 5
85	Flowmotion FM 007	Anyone For Me/Hands To Me (12", p/s, with 4 extra tracks) 7

UZI
69	Beacon BEA 152	Morning Train/Where Were You Last Night 4

GENE VINCENT

VACELS
65   Pye International 7N 25330   Can You Please Crawl Out Of Your Window/I'm Just A Poor Boy 10

VAGABONDS
64   Decca LK 4617   SKA TIME (LP) 18
64   Island ILP 916   PRESENTING THE FABULOUS VAGABONDS (LP) 40

VAGINA DENTATA ORGAN
80s   WSNS 004   Cold Meat: Sex Star I/II (12", picture disc) 20
87   Temple TOPY 012   MUSIC FOR HASHASINS (LP) 30

VAGRANTS
66   Fontana TF 703   I Can't Make A Friend/Young Blues 40

VAL & V's
67   CBS 2780   Do It Again A Little Bit Slower/For A Rainy Day 4
67   CBS 2956   I Like The Way/With This Theme 4

VALADIERS
63   Oriole CBA 1809   I Found A Girl/You'll Be Sorry Someday 450

RICKY VALANCE
60   Columbia DB 4493   Tell Laura I Love Her/Once Upon A Time 5
60   Columbia DB 4543   Movin' Away/Lipstick On Your Lips 6
61   Columbia DB 4586   Jimmy's Girl/Only The Young 6
61   Columbia DB 4592   Why Can't We/Fisherboy 5
61   Columbia DB 4680   Bobby/I Want To Fall In Love 6
61   Columbia DB 4725   I Never Had A Chance/It's Not True 6
62   Columbia DB 4787   Try To Forget Her/At Times Like These 6
62   Columbia DB 4864   Don't Play No. 9/Till The Final Curtain Falls 6
65   Decca F 12129   Six Boys/Face The Crowd 5

RITCHIE VALENS
58   Pye International 7N 25000   Come On, Let's Go/Dooby Dooby Wah 70
58   Pye International 7N 25000   Come On, Let's Go/Dooby Dooby Wah (78) 50
59   London HL 8803   Donna/La Bamba 20
59   London HL 8803   Donna/La Bamba (78) 45
59   London HL 7068   Donna/La Bamba (export issue) 10
59   London HL 8886   That's My Little Suzie/Bluebirds Over The Mountains 20
59   London HL 8886   That's My Little Suzie/Bluebirds Over The Mountains (78) 50
62   London HL 9494   La Bamba/Ooh, My Head 15
66   Sue WI 4011   Donna/La Bamba (reissue, unreleased)
67   President PT 126   Donna/La Bamba (reissue) 6
59   London RE 1232   RITCHIE VALENS (EP, initially tri-centre, later round centre) 75/55
61   London HA 2390   RITCHIE (LP) 55
64   London HA 8196   RITCHIE VALENS' GREATEST HITS (LP) 35
67   President PTL 1001   I REMEMBER RITCHIE VALENS (LP) 15
79   London HA-R 8535   RITCHIE VALENS (LP) 15

CATERINA VALENTE
60   Polydor NH 66816   La Malaguena/Secret Love 10
60   Polydor NH 66953   The Breeze And I (Andalucia)/Side By Side 8
60   Decca F 11306   Till/Amour 5
61   Decca F 11321   Canto De Ossanha/The Breeze And I (Andalucia) 4
63   Decca F 11621   La Malaguena/Together 5
69   Decca F 22881   Hare Krishna/Canto De Ossanha 4
62   London Globe GEB 7001   FRENESI (EP) 7
63   Polydor EPH 20 282   CATERINA VALENTE (EP) 7
60   Decca LK 4350   RENDEZVOUS WITH CATERINA (LP) 20
60   Polydor LPHM 46.065   COSMOPOLITAN LADY (LP) 20
61   Polydor LPHM 46.310   CATERINA CHERIE (LP) 20
61   RCA RD 27216/SF 5099   SUPERFONICS (LP) 18
62   Decca LK/SKL 4508   GREAT CONTINENTAL HITS (LP) 15
63   Decca LK/SKL 4537   VALENTE IN SWINGTIME (LP) 15
64   Decca LK 4604   VALENTE ON TV (LP) 15
64   Decca LK/SKL 4630   I HAPPEN TO LIKE NEW YORK (LP) 20
65   Decca LK/SKL 4646   VALENTE & VIOLINS (LP) 18

DINO VALENTI
68   CBS 65715   DINO (LP) 12
     (see also Quicksilver Messenger Service)

JOHN VALENTI
76   Ariola AA 108   Anything You Want/That's The Way Life Goes 4

BILLY VALENTINE
55   Capitol CL 14320   It's A Sin/Your Love Has Got Me (Reelin' And Rockin') 12

DICKIE VALENTINE (& STARGAZERS)
54   Decca F 10346   Endless/I Could Have Told You 15
54   Decca F 10394   The Finger Of Suspicion Points At You (with Stargazers)/Who's Afraid (Not I, Not I, Not I) 20
54   Decca F 10415   Mister Sandman/Runaround 30
55   Decca F 10430   A Blossom Fell/I Want You All To Myself (Just You) 15

MINT VALUE £

55	Decca F 10484	Ma Cherie Amie/Lucky Waltz	12
55	Decca F 10493	I Wonder/You Too Can Be A Dreamer	12
55	Decca F 10517	Hello Mrs. Jones (Is Mary There?)/Lazy Gondolier	10
55	Decca F 10549	No Such Luck/The Engagement Waltz	10
55	Decca F 10628	Christmas Alphabet/Where Are You Tonight?	25
55	Decca F 10645	The Old Pi-Anna Rag/First Love	12
55	Decca F 10667	Dreams Can Tell A Lie/Song Of The Trees	8
56	Decca F 10714	The Voice/The Best Way To Hold A Girl	8
56	Decca F 10753	My Impossible Castle/When You Came Along	7
56	Decca F 10766	Day Dreams/Give Me A Carriage With Eight White Horses	8
56	Decca F 10798	Christmas Island/The Hand Of Friendship	12
56	Decca F 10820	Dickie Valentine's Rock 'N' Roll Party Medley Pts 1 & 2	8
57	Decca F 10874	Chapel Of The Roses/My Empty Arms	6
57	Decca F 10906	Puttin' On The Style/Three Sides To Every Story	7
57	Decca F 10949	Long Before I Knew You/Just In Time	6
57	Decca F 10950	Snowbound For Christmas/Convicted	8
58	Decca F 11005	Love Me Again/King Of Dixieland	6
58	Decca F 11020	In My Life/Come To My Arms	5
58	Decca F 11066	Take Me In Your Arms/An Old-Fashioned Song	5
59	Pye 7N 15192	Venus/Where? (In The Old Home Town)	6
59	Pye 7N 15202	A Teenager In Love/My Favourite Song	5
59	Pye 7N 15221	One More Sunrise (Morgen)/You Touch My Hand	4
60	Pye 7N 15255	Standing On The Corner/Roundabout	4
60	Pye 7N 15294	Once, Only Once/A Fool That I Am	4
61	Pye 7N 15336	How Unlucky Can You Be/Hold Me In Your Arms	4
61	Pye 7N 15366	Climb Ev'ry Mountain/Sometimes I'm Happy	4
61	Pye 7N 15381	Shalom/I'll Never Love Again	4
55	Decca DFE 6236	SWING ALONG WITH DICKIE VALENTINE (EP)	10
56	Decca DFE 6279	PRESENTING DICKIE VALENTINE (EP)	15
56	Decca DFE 6363	ONLY FOR YOU (EP)	10
57	Decca DFE 6408	MERRY CHRISTMAS (EP)	12
57	Decca DFE 6427	DICKIE GOES DIXIE (EP)	10
58	Decca DFE 6529	WITH VOCAL REFRAIN BY DICKIE VALENTINE (EP)	10
59	Decca DFE 6549	BELONGING TO SOMEONE (EP)	8
59	Pye NPL 24120	DICKIE VALENTINE HIT PARADE (EP)	8
54	Decca LF 1163	PRESENTING DICKIE VALENTINE (10" LP)	20
55	Decca LF 1211	HERE IS DICKIE VALENTINE (10" LP)	20
56	Decca LF 1257	OVER MY SHOULDER (10" LP)	18
58	Decca LK 4269	WITH VOCAL REFRAIN BY ... (LP)	12
61	Ace Of Clubs ACL 1082	DICKIE (LP)	10

VALENTINES
| 60 | Ember EMB S 123 | Hey Ruby/That's How I Feel .... | 25 |

VALENTINES
| 67 | Doctor Bird DB 1065 | Blam Blam Fever/BABA BROOKS: The Scratch .... | 10 |

VALENTINO
| 75 | Gaiee GAE 101 | I Was Born This Way/Liberation .... | 5 |

ANNA VALENTINO
| 57 | London HLD 8421 | Calypso Joe/You're Mine .... | 15 |

DANNY VALENTINO
59	MGM MGM 1049	Stampede/(You Gotta Be A) Music Man	20
60	MGM MGM 1067	Biology/A Million Tears	12
60	MGM MGM 1109	Pictures/'Till The End Of Forever	7

MARK VALENTINO
63	Stateside SS 148	The Push And Kick/Walking Alone	6
63	Stateside SS 186	Do It/Hey You're Looking Good	6
63	Stateside SS 233	Jivin' At The Drive In/Part Time Job	15

VALENTINOS
68	Stateside SS 2137	Tired Of Being Nobody/The Death Of Love	6
68	Soul City SC 106	It's All Over Now/Tired Of Livin' In The Country	8
70	Polydor 2058 090	Raise Up Your Hands In Anger/Stand Up And Be Counted	4
68	Soul City SCM 001	THE VALENTINOS/THE SIMS TWINS (LP, with Sims Twins)	12
	(see also Bobby Womack)		

VALERIE (THE ROCK 'N' ROLL YOUNGSTER)
| 56 | Columbia DB 3832 | Tonight You Belong To Me/The Man Who Owns The Sunshine .... | 12 |

VALHALLA
| 84 | Neat NEAT 36 | Still In Love With You/Jack (p/s) .... | 6 |

JOE VALINO (& GOSPELAIRES)
56	Columbia DB 3832	Hidden Persuasion/Back To Your Eyes (78)	5
57	HMV POP 283	The Garden Of Eden/Caravan	8
57	HMV POP 283	The Garden Of Eden/Caravan (78)	5
58	London HLT 8705	God's Little Acre/I'm Happy With What I've Got (with Gospelaires)	10
58	London HLT 8705	God's Little Acre/I'm Happy With What I've Got (78, with Gospelaires)	5
60	Columbia DB 4406	Hidden Persuasion/Back To Your Eyes	4

VALJEAN (At The Piano)
62	London HLL 9593	Till There Was You/The Eighteenth Variation	4
63	London HLL 9659	Mewsette (From "Gay Purr-Ee")/Mr Mozart's Mash	4
63	London REL 1366	MR MOZART'S MASH (EP)	7

VALKYRIES
| 64 | Parlophone R 5123 | What's Your Name?/Rip It Up .... | 12 |

DIORIS VALLADARES ORCHESTRA
64	Island ILP 910	LET'S GO LATIN (LP, possibly unreleased)	25+

JEAN VALLÉE
78	CBS SCBS 6257	Goodbye/L'Amour Ca Fait Chanter La Vie	4

RUDY VALLEE
54	HMV 7MC 8	The Whiffenpoof Song/Taps (export issue)	4

VALLEY OF ACHOR
75	Dovetail	A DOOR OF HOPE (LP, gatefold sleeve)	40

FRANKIE VALLI
66	Philips BF 1467	(You're Gonna) Hurt Yourself/VALLI BOYS: Night Hawk	4
66	Philips BF 1512	You're Ready Now/Cry For Me	10
66	Philips BF 1529	The Proud One/Ivy	4
67	Philips BF 1556	Beggin'/Dody	4
67	Philips BF 1580	Can't Take My Eyes Off You/The Trouble With Me	4
67	Philips BF 1603	I Make A Fool Of Myself/September Rain	4
68	Philips BF 1634	To Give (The Reason I Live)/Watch Where You Walk	4
69	Philips BF 1795	The Girl I'll Never Know/A Face Without A Name	4
62	Philips 320 226 BF	You're Ready Now/Cry For Me (reissue)	4
74	Private Stock PVT 1	My Eyes Adored You/Watch You Walk	4
67	Philips (S)BL 7814	SOLO (LP)	10
69	Philips SBL 7856	TIMELESS (LP)	10
77	Private Stock PVLP 1029	LADY PUT THE LIGHT OUT (LP)	10

FRANKIE VALLI & FOUR SEASONS
71	Warner Bros K 16107	Whatever You Say/Sleeping Man	10
72	Tamla Motown TMG 819	You're A Song/Sun Country	5
72	Mowest MW 3002	The Night/When The Morning Comes	8
73	Mowest MW 3003	Walk On, Don't Look Back/Touch The Rain Child	4
75	Mowest MW 3024	The Night/When The Morning Comes (reissue)	4
	(see also Four Seasons)		

JUNE VALLI
54	HMV 7M 245	I Understand (Just How You Feel)/Old Shoes And A Bag Of Rice	10
54	HMV 7M 259	Tell Me, Tell Me/Boy Wanted	10
55	HMV 7M 284	Wrong, Wrong, Wrong/Ole Pappy Time	8
56	HMV 7M 347	Por Favor (Please)/The Things They Say	8
59	Mercury AMT 1034	The Answer To A Maiden's Prayer/In His Arms	6
59	Mercury AMT 1048	An Anonymous Letter/Bygones	6
60	Mercury AMT 1091	Apple Green/Oh! Why	6
61	Mercury AMT 1130	I Guess Things Happen That Way/Tell Him For Me	5
62	HMV POP 1062	Hush Little Baby/Afraid	4

VALUES
66	Ember EMB S 211	Return To Me	10

VALVES
77	Zoom ZUM 1	Robot Love/For Adolfs Only (p/s)	5
77	Zoom ZUM 3	Tarzan Of The Kings Road/Ain't No Surf In Portobello (p/s)	4
79	Albion DEL 3	I Don't Mean Nothing At All/Linda Vindalco (p/s)	4

VAMP
68	Atlantic 584 213	Floatin'/Thinkin' Too Much	35
69	Atlantic 584 263	Green Pea/Wake Up And Tell Me (unissued)	
	(see also Sam Gopal)		

VAMPIRES
59	Parlophone R 4599	Swinging Ghosts/Clap Trap	10

VAMPIRES
68	Pye 7N 17553	Do You Wanna Dance/My Girl	7

ILA VAN
74	Pye Intl. DDS 108	Can't Help Loving Dat Man/I've Got The Feeling	4

PAUL VANCE
66	Pye International 7N 25387	Dommage, Dommage/Sexy	4

TOMMY VANCE
66	Columbia DB 7999	You Must Be The One/Why Treat Me This Way	5
66	Columbia DB 8062	Off The Hook/Summertime	7

HARRY VANDA
69	Polydor BM 56357	I Love Marie/Gonna Make It	4
	(see also Easybeats)		

VAN DER GRAAF GENERATOR
68	Polydor 56758	People You Were Going To/Firebrand	150
70	Charisma CB 122	Refugees/The Boat Of Millions Of Years	35
72	Charisma CB 175	Theme One/W (some with p/s)	25/5
76	Charisma CB 297	Wondering/Meurglys 111	8
69	Charisma CAS 1007	THE LEAST WE CAN DO IS WAVE TO EACH OTHER (LP, pink label, original mix, matrices read: CAS 1007 A/B, gatefold sleeve, some with poster)	45/30
69	Charisma CAS 1007	THE LEAST WE CAN DO IS WAVE TO EACH OTHER (LP, pink label, remix, matrices read: CAS 1007 A+G/B+G, gatefold sleeve; some with poster)	30/15
70	Charisma CAS 1027	H TO HE, WHO AM THE ONLY ONE (LP, pink label, gatefold sleeve)	15
71	Charisma CAS 1051	PAWN HEARTS (LP, gatefold sleeve, pink label, some with insert)	20/15
72	Charisma CS 2	1968-71 (LP, pink label)	10
75	Charisma CAS 1109	GODBLUFF (LP, with inner sleeve)	10
76	Charisma CAS 1116	STILL LIFE (LP)	10

VAN DER GRAAF GENERATOR

76	Charisma CAS 1120	WORLD RECORD (LP)	10

(see also Peter Hammill, Long Hello, Misunderstood, Koobas, Juicy Lucy)

MAMIE VAN DOREN
58	Capitol CL 14850	Something To Dream About/I Fell In Love	6

VAN DYKE PARKS
(see under P)

EARL VAN DYKE (& SOUL BROTHERS)
64	Stateside SS 357	Soul Stomp/Hot 'N' Tot	75
65	Tamla Motown TMG 506	All For You/Too Many Fish In The Sea (as Earl Van Dyke & Soul Brothers)	60
70	Tamla Motown TMG 759	Six By Six/All For You (original pressing, non-shiny black label)	6
72	Tamla Motown TMG 814	I Can't Help Myself/How Sweet It Is (To Be Loved By You) (& Soul Brothers)	4
65	T. Motown TML 11014	THAT MOTOWN SOUND (LP)	80

(see also Soul Brothers, Van Dykes)

GULLIVER VAN DYKE
68	Vogue VRS 7034	Set Me Free/The Day Has Gone	4

LEROY VAN DYKE
61	Mercury AMT 1166	Walk On By/My World Is Caving In	5
62	Mercury AMT 1173	A Big Man In A Big House/Faded Love	6
62	Mercury AMT 1183	A Broken Promise/I Sat Back And Let It Happen	6
65	Warner Bros WB 5650	It's All Over Now Baby Blue/Just A State Of Mind	6
66	Warner Bros WB 5807	You Couldn't Get My Love Back/Fool Such As I	5
67	Warner Bros WB 5777	Almost Persuaded/Less Of Me	5
62	Mercury MMC 14101	WALK ON BY (LP)	25
63	Mercury MMC 14118	MOVIN' VAN DYKE (LP)	25

VANDYKE & BAMBIS
64	Piccadilly 7N 35180	Doin' The Mod/All I Want Is You	6

VAN DYKES
66	Stateside SS 504	No Man Is An Island/I Won't Hold It Against You	7
66	Stateside SS 530	I've Gotta Go On Without You/What Will I Do	10

(see also Earl Van Dyke)

LON & DERREK VAN EATON
73	Apple APPLE 46	Warm Woman/More Than Words (some in p/s)	30/5
75	A&M AMS 7157	Wildfire/Music Lover	4
75	A&M AMS 7178	Dancing In The Dark/All You're Hungry For Is Love	4
73	Apple SAPCOR 25	BROTHER (LP, gatefold sleeve, some with insert)	25/20

NICK VAN EEDE
78	Barn 201 4128	Rock'n'Roll Fool/Ounce Of Sense	4
79	Barn BARN 003	All Or Nothing/Hold On To Your Heart	5
79	Barn BARN 008	I Only Want	5

(see also Cutting Crew)

VANGELIS
83	Polydor BOX 1	CHARIOTS OF FIRE (LP, box set)	10

VAN HALEN
78	Warner Bros K 17107	You Really Got Me/Atomic Punk	4
78	Warner Bros K 17162	Runnin' With The Devil/D.O.A.	4
79	Warner Bros K 17371	Dance The Night Away/Outta Love Again	7
79	Warner Bros K 17371P	Dance The Night Away/Outta Love Again (picture disc)	10
80	Atlantic HM 10	Runnin' With The Devil/D.O.A. (p/s)	4
80	Warner Bros K 17645	And The Cradle Will Rock/Everybody Wants Some (p/s)	4
85	Warner Bros W 9199T	Hot For Teacher/Little Dreamer/Hear About It Later (12")	8
86	Warner Bros W 8740P	Why Can't This Be Love/Get Up (shaped picture disc with plinth, stickered PVC sleeve)	8
86	Warner Bros W 8642P	Dreams/Inside (car-shaped picture disc with stand, stickered PVC sleeve)	10
88	Warner Bros W 7816TW	When It's Love/Apolitica Blues (12", silver foldout p/s)	8
88	Warner Bros W 7816TP	When It's Love/Apolitica Blues (12", picture disc)	8

(see also David Lee Roth, Sammy Hagar)

VANILLA FUDGE
67	Atlantic 584 123	You Keep Me Hanging On/Take Me For A Little While	4
67	Atlantic 584 139	(Illusions Of My Childhood) Eleanor Rigby Pts 1 & 2	5
68	Atlantic 584 179	Where Is My Mind?/The Look Of Love	6
69	Atlantic 584 257	Shotgun/Good Good Lovin'	5
69	Atlantic 584 276	Some Velvet Morning/Thoughts	4
67	Atlantic 587/588 086	VANILLA FUDGE (LP)	12
68	Atlantic 587/588 100	THE BEAT GOES ON (LP)	12
68	Atlantic 587/588 110	RENAISSANCE (LP)	12
69	Atco 228 020	NEAR THE BEGINNING (LP)	10
70	Atco 228 029	ROCK 'N' ROLL (LP)	10

(see also Pigeons, Beck Bogert Appice, Cactus)

VANITY FAIR
68	Page One POF 075	I Live For The Sun/On The Other Side Of Life	4
68	Page One POF 100	Summer Morning/Better Carter	4
69	Page One POF 117	Highway Of Dreams/Waiting For The Downfall	4
69	Page One POF 142	Early In The Morning/You Made Me Love You	4
68	Page One POLS 010	THE SUN, THE WIND AND OTHER THINGS (LP)	15

THIJS VAN LEER
72	CBS 65589	INTROSPECTION (LP)	10

(see also Focus)

TEDDY VANN
60	London HLU 9097	Cindy/I'm Waiting	12

DAVID VAN RUNK
65	Stateside SL 10153	INSIDE (LP)	10

ROB VAN SPYK
70s	private pressing	FOLLOW THE SUN (LP)	40

(see also Stonefield Tramp)

TOWNES VAN ZANDT
73	United Artists UAS 29442	THE LATE GREAT TOWNES VAN ZANDT (LP)	10

VAPORS
79	United Artists BP 321	Prisoners/Sunstroke (p/s)	4

PETER VARDAS
59	Top Rank JAR 173	He Threw A Stone/Checkerboard Love	6

VARDI & HIS ORCHESTRA
62	London HLR 9518	Ballad Of A Soldier Theme/Exodus Theme	4

(QUO) VARDIS
80	Castle C QUEL 2/100 MPH	Out Of The Way/If I Were King (plain brown sleeve)	10
80	Logo VARFREE 1	Guaranteed No Overdubs/Situation Negative/Jeepster// Too Many People/Steamin' (p/s)	6
80	Logo VAR 2/VARFREE 2	Too Many People/The Lion's Share//Blue Rock (I Miss You)/Dirty Money (double pack, with insert)	6
81	Logo VAR 3	Silver Machine/Come On (die-cut sleeve)	5
81	Logo VAR 4	All You'll Ever Need/If I Were King/Jumping Jack Flash (p/s)	4
80	Logo VAR 1/FREE 1	Let's Go/Situation Negative//100 MPH/Out Of The Way (double pack)	7
79	Redball RB 001	100 MPH (EP, as Quo Vardis)	15
80	Logo MOGO 4012	100 MPH (LP, with poster)	10
81	Logo LOGO 1034	QUO VARDIS (LP, with free 45 [VARFREE 1])	10
85	Big Beat NST 103	Standing In The Road/Freezing History (12")	7

(see also Quo Vardis)

VARIATIONS
65	Immediate IM 019	The Man With All The Toys/She'll Know I'm Sorry	10

VARICOSE VEINS
78	Warped WARP 1	INCREDIBLE (EP, mail-order only, no p/s, 200 only)	25

(see also Perfect Disaster, Orange Disaster, Architects Of Disaster)

REG VARNEY
68	CBS 3742	Jingling Rag/Reg's Rag Kitten On The Keys/Russian Rag/12th Street Rag	4

SYLVIE VARTAN
65	RCA RCA 1490	One More Day/I Made My Choice	4
65	RCA RCA 1495	Another Heart/Think About You	4

VARUKERS
81	Tempest/Inferno HELL 1	Protest And Survive/No Scapegoat (EP)	4
82	Tempest/Inferno HELL 4	DON'T WANNA BE A VICTIM (EP, as Verukas)	4

VASELINES
87	53rd & 3rd AGARR 10	Son Of A Gun/Rory Rides Away/You Think You're A Man (die-cut sleeve)	12
88	53rd & 3rd AGARR 17	Dying For It/Molly's Lips (p/s)	6
88	53rd & 3rd AGARR 17T	Dying For It/Molly's Lips/Teenage Superstars/Jesus Wants Me For A Sunbeam (12", p/s)	10
90	53rd & 3rd AGAS 7	DUM DUM (LP)	15

(see also Pastels)

VASHTI
65	Decca F 12157	Some Things Just Stick In Your Mind/I Want To Be Alone	15
66	Columbia DB 7917	Train Song/Love Song	8

(see also Vashti Bunyan)

RAY VASQUEZ
61	Starlite ST45-055	Nothing Ever Changes My Love For You/Easy To Love	4

FRANKIE VAUGHAN
53	HMV 7M 167	Istanbul (Not Constantinople)/Cloud Lucky Seven	14
54	HMV 7M 182	The Cuff Of My Skirt/Heartless	10
54	HMV 7M 252	My Son, My Son/Cinnamon Sinner (Selling Lollipop Lies)	10
54	HMV 7M 270	Happy Days And Lonely Nights/Danger Signs	10
55	HMV 7M 298	Too Many Heartaches/Unsuspecting Heart	10
55	Philips PB 423	Give Me The Moonlight, Give Me The Girl/Happy Go Lucky	10
57	Philips JK 1002	Garden Of Eden/Priscilla (jukebox issue)	12
57	Philips JK 1014	What's Behind That Strange Door/Cold, Cold Shower (jukebox issue)	10
57	Philips JK 1022	These Dangerous Years/Isn't This A Lovely Evening (jukebox issue)	10
57	Philips JK 1030	Got-ta Have Something In The Bank, Frank/Single (as Frankie Vaughan & Kaye Sisters, jukebox issue)	10
57	Philips JK 1035	Kisses Sweeter Than Wine/Rock-A-Chicka (jukebox issue)	12
58	Philips PB 793	We're Not Alone/Can't Get Along Without You	5
58	Philips PB 825	Kewpie Doll/So Many Women	5
58	Philips PB 834	Wonderful Things/Judy	4
58	Philips PB 865	Am I Wasting My Time On You/So Happy In Love	4
59	Philips PB 895	That's My Doll/Love Is The Sweetest Thing	4
59	Philips PB 896	Honey Bunny Baby/The Lady Is A Square	4
59	Philips PB 913	Come Softly To Me/Say Something Sweet To Your Sweetheart (as Frankie Vaughan & Kaye Sisters)	4
59	Philips PB 930	The Heart Of A Man/Sometime Somewhere	4
59	Philips PB 931	Walkin' Tall/I Ain't Gonna Lead This Life	4
60	Philips PB 985	What More Do You Want/The Very Very Young	4
60	Philips PB 1054	Kookie Little Paradise/Mary Lou	4

Frankie VAUGHAN

60	Philips PB 1066	Milord/Will You Still Love Me? (some in p/s)	6/4
61	Philips PB 1195	Tower Of Strength/Rachel	4
61	Philips BF 1215	Don't Stop, Twist!/Red Red Roses	4
62	Philips BF 1233	I'm Gonna Clip Your Wings/Travellin' Man	4
62	Philips 326 542BF	Hercules/Madeleine (Open The Door)	4
63	Philips 326 566BF	Loop De Loop/There'll Be No Teardrops Tonight	4
63	Philips BF 1280	You're The One For Me/I Told You So	4
64	Philips BF 1310	Alley Alley Oh/Gonna Be A Good Boy Now	4
64	Philips BF 1373	Susie Q/I'll Always Be In Love With You	4
65	Philips BF 1460	There Goes The Forgotten Man/Wait	7
56	Philips BBE 12022	FRANKIE VAUGHAN (EP)	7
57	HMV 7EG 8245	MISTER ELEGANT (EP)	8
57	Philips BBE 12111	FRANKIE VAUGHAN (EP)	7
59	Philips BBE 12299	HEART OF A MAN (EP)	7
61	Philips BBE 12484	LET ME SING AND I'M HAPPY (EP, also in stereo SBBE 9071)	7/10
61	Philips BBE 12485	LET ME SING AND I'M HAPPY NO. 2 (EP, also in stereo SBBE 9072)	7/10
61	Philips BBE 12486	LET ME SING AND I'M HAPPY NO. 3 (EP, also in stereo SBBE 9073)	7/10
57	Philips BBL 7198	HAPPY GO LUCKY (LP)	14
58	Philips BBL 7233	THE FRANKIE VAUGHAN SHOWCASE (LP)	15
59	Philips BBL 7330	AT THE LONDON PALLADIUM (LP, also on stereo SBBL 511)	12
61	Philips BBL 7482	LET ME SING — AND I'M HAPPY! (LP, also stereo SBL 629)	12/14
61	Philips BBL 7490	WARM FEELING (LP, also stereo SSBL 645)	10/12

(see also Kaye Sisters, Alma Cogan & Frankie Vaughan, Marilyn Monroe)

MALCOLM VAUGHAN

55	HMV 7M 317	More Than A Millionaire/Take Me Back Again	6
55	HMV 7M 338	With Your Love/Small Talk	8
56	HMV 7M 389	Only You (And You Alone)/I'll Be Near You	6
56	HMV POP 250	St. Therese Of The Roses/Love Me As Though There Were Tomorrow	6
57	HMV POP 303	The World Is Mine/Now	6
57	HMV POP 325	Chapel Of The Roses/Guardian Angel	6
57	HMV POP 381	What Is My Destiny/Oh! My Papa	4
58	HMV POP 419	My Special Angel/The Heart Of A Child	5
58	HMV POP 459	To Be Loved/My Loving Arms	4
58	HMV POP 502	Ev'ry Hour, Ev'ry Day Of My Life/Miss You	4
58	HMV POP 538	More Than Ever (Come Prima)/A Night To Remember	4
57	HMV 7EG 8272	SINCERITY IN SONG (EP)	10
58	HMV 7EG 8377	SINCERITY IN SONG VOL. 2 (EP)	7
59	HMV 7EG 8453	SINCERITY IN SONG VOL. 3 (EP)	7
60	HMV GES 5785	HELLO MALCOLM VAUGHAN NO. 1 (EP, stereo)	7
60	HMV GES 5793	HELLO MALCOLM VAUGHAN NO. 2 (EP, stereo)	7
60	HMV GES 5799	REQUESTS FOR MALCOLM VAUGHAN (EP, stereo)	7
59	HMV CLP 1284	HELLO, MALCOLM VAUGHAN (LP)	12

ROY VAUGHAN BOOGIE TRIO

51	Jazz Parade B 3	Oval Boogie/Rumble Boogie (78)	7

SARAH VAUGHAN

58	Mercury 7MT 198	My Darling, My Darling/Bewitched	5
58	Mercury 7MT 212	Padre/Spin Little Bottle	5
58	Mercury 7MT 222	Too Much, Too Soon/What's So Bad About It	5
59	Mercury AMT 1010	Everything I Do/I Ain't Hurtin'	4
59	Mercury AMT 1029	Cool Baby/Are You Certain?	5
59	Mercury AMT 1044	Careless/Separate Ways	5
59	Mercury AMT 1057	Broken-Hearted Melody/Misty	5
59	Mercury AMT 1057	Broken-Hearted Melody/Misty (78)	5
59	Mercury AMT 1080	You're My Baby/Eternally	4
59	Mercury AMT 1087	Don't Look At Me That Way/Sweet Affections	4
60	Columbia DB 4491	Ooh! What A Day/My Dear Little Sweetheart	4
60	Columbia DB 4511	If I Were A Bell/Teach Me Tonight (with Count Basie & Joe Williams)	4
60	Columbia DB 4542	Serenata/Let's	4
69	Mercury AMT 1107	The Boy From Ipanema/The Fever (p/s)	4
56	London RE-U 1065	SARAH VAUGHAN (EP)	10
57	Emarcy YEP 9507	SARAH VAUGHAN (EP)	7
57	Mercury MEP 9511	SARAH VAUGHAN HIT PARADE (EP)	7
57	Mercury MEP 9519	SARAH VAUGHAN HIT PARADE NO. 2 (EP)	7
59	Mercury ZEP 10011	SONGS FROM SARAH (EP)	7
59	Mercury ZEP 10030	AFTER HOURS AT THE LONDON HOUSE (EP)	7
59	Mercury ZEP 10041	SARAH WITH FEELING (EP)	7
60	Mercury ZEP 10054	SMOOTH SARAH (EP)	7
60	Mercury ZEP 10087	LIVE FOR LOVE (EP, also stereo SEZ 19006)	7/10
62	Mercury ZEP 10115	NO COUNT BLUES (EP, also stereo SEZ 19023)	7/10
55	Oriole/Mercury MG 26005	IMAGES (10" LP)	15
56	London HB-U 1049	SARAH VAUGHAN SINGS (10" LP, with John Kirby & His Orchestra)	15
56	Emarcy EJL 100	IN THE LAND OF HI FI (10" LP)	15
56	Philips BBL 7082	SARAH VAUGHAN (LP)	12
56	Mercury MPT 7503	MAKE YOURSELF COMFORTABLE (10" LP)	15
57	Mercury MPT 7518	IMAGES (10" LP, reissue)	12
57	Emarcy EJL 1258	SASSY (LP)	12
57	Mercury MPL 6522	SINGS GREAT SONGS FROM HIT SHOWS PART 1 (LP)	12
57	Philips BBL 7165	LINGER AWHILE (LP)	12
57	Mercury MPL 6523	SINGS GREAT SONGS FROM HIT SHOWS PART 2 (LP)	12
57	Mercury MPL 6525	SINGS GEORGE GERSHWIN VOL. 1 (LP)	12
57	Mercury MPL 6527	SINGS GEORGE GERSHWIN VOL. 2 (LP)	12
58	Mercury MPL 6532	WONDERFUL SARAH (LP)	12
58	Emarcy EJL 1273	SWINGIN' EASY (LP)	12
58	Mercury MPL 6540	IN ROMANTIC MOOD (LP)	12
58	Mercury MPL 6542	AT MISTER KELLY'S (LP)	12

59	Mercury CMS 18011	SINGS GEORGE GERSHWIN VOL. 1 (LP, stereo reissue of MPL 6525) 15
59	Mercury CMS 18012	SINGS GEORGE GERSHWIN VOL. 2 (LP, stereo reissue of MPL 6527) 15
59	Mercury MMC 14001	AFTER HOURS AT THE LONDON HOUSE (LP) 10
59	Mercury MMC 14011	VAUGHAN AND VIOLINS (LP, also stereo CMS 18003) 10/12
60	Mercury MMC 14021	NO COUNT SARAH (LP) 10
60	Mercury MMC 14024	GREAT SONGS FROM HIT SHOWS PART 1 (LP, also stereo CMS 18019; reissue of MPT 6522) 10/12
60	Mercury MMC 14026	GREAT SONGS FROM HIT SHOWS PART 2 (LP, also stereo CMS 18023; reissue of MPT 6523) 10/12
60	Columbia 33SX 1252	DREAMY (LP, also stereo SCX 3324) 10/12
61	Mercury MMC 14059	CLOSE TO YOU (LP, also stereo CMS 18040) 10/12
62	Columbia 33SX 1340	THE DIVINE ONE (LP, also stereo SCX 3390) 10/12
62	Columbia 33SX 1360	COUNT BASIE — SARAH VAUGHAN (LP, also stereo SCX 3403) 10/12
64	Mercury 20011 MCL	SASSY SWINGS THE TIVOLI (LP) 10
65	Mercury 20042 MCL	MY HEART SINGS (LP) 10
60s	Mercury MG 25188	THE DIVINE SARAH (LP) 10

SARAH VAUGHAN & BILLY ECKSTINE

59	Mercury AMT 1020	Alexander's Ragtime Band/No Limit 4
59	Mercury AMT 1071	Passing Strangers/SARAH VAUGHAN: Smooth Operator 6
69	Mercury MF 1082	Passing Strangers/Always 4
59	MGM MGM-EP 690	BILLY ECKSTINE AND SARAH VAUGHAN (EP) 7
59	Mercury 10025 MCE	PASSING STRANGERS (EP) 7
60	Mercury 10027 MCE	TOGETHER AGAIN (EP) 7
61	Mercury ZEP 10108	BEST OF BERLIN VOL. 1 (EP, also stereo SEZ 19016) 7/10
58	Mercury MPL 6530	THE BEST OF IRVING BERLIN (LP) 14
60	Mercury MMC 14035	THE BEST OF IRVING BERLIN (LP, reissue) 10

(see aslo Billy Eckstine)

BILLY VAUGHN (& HIS ORCHESTRA)

55	London HL 8112	Melody Of Love/Joy Ride (gold lettering labels) 25
55	London HLD 8205	The Shifting Whispering Sands Pts 1 & 2 (with Ken Nordine) (gold lettering) 15
56	London HLD 8238	Theme From "The Threepenny Opera"/I'd Give A Million Tomorrows (gold lettering labels, later with silver lettering labels) 15/8
56	London HLD 8319	When The Lilac Blooms Again/Autumn Concerto (gold lettering, later silver) 15/8
56	London HLD 8342	Petticoats From Portugal/La La Colette (gold lettering, later silver) 12/8
57	London HLD 8417	The Ship That Never Sailed/Little Boy Blue (with Ken Nordine) 6
57	London HLD 8511	Johnny Tremain/Naughty Annetta (as Billy Vaughn's Orchestra & Chorus) 6
57	London HLD 8522	Raunchy/Sail Along Silvery Moon 7
58	London HLD 8612	Tumbling Tumbleweeds/Trying 7
58	London HLD 8680	Sail Along Silvery Moon/The Singing Hills 4
58	London HLD 8703	La Paloma/Here Is My Love 4
58	London HLD 8772	Cimarron (Roll On)/You're My Baby Doll 4
59	London HLD 8797	Blue Hawaii/Tico Tico 4
59	London HLD 8859	Your Cheatin' Heart/Lights Out 4
59	London HLD 8920	All Nite Long/Blues Stay Away From Me 4
59	London HLD 8952	Morgen (One More Sunrise)/Sweet Leilani 4
59	London HLD 8996	(It's No) Sin/After Hours 4
60	London HLD 9152	Look For A Star/He'll Have To Go 4
61	London HLD 9259	Theme From "The Sundowners"/Old Cape Cod 4
61	London HLD 9279	Wheels/Orange Blossom Special 4
61	London HLD 9380	Blue Tomorrow/Red Wing 4
61	London HLD 9423	Berlin Melody/Theme From "Come September" 4
62	London HLD 9507	Everybody's Twisting Down In Mexico/Melody In The Night 4
62	London HLD 9541	Chapel By The Sea/A Lover's Guitar 4
62	London HLD 9578	A Swingin' Safari/Summertime 4
63	London HLD 9675	Meditation/Release Me 4
63	London HLD 9735	Happy Cowboy/Sukiyaki 4
64	London HLD 9865	Blue Tango/Boss 4

(the singles listed below are all export issues)

60	London HL 7093	Red Sails In The Sunset/Harbour Lights 6
60	London HL 7094	Brazil/Perfidia 6
60	London HLD 7107	La Paloma/Green Fields 6
57	London RED 1083	THE GOLDEN INSTRUMENTALS NO. 1 (EP) 8
57	London RED 1084	THE GOLDEN INSTRUMENTALS NO. 2 (EP) 8
59	London RED 1189	SAIL ALONG SILVERY MOON (EP) 8
60	London RED 1248	THEMES FROM BILLY VAUGHN (EP) 7
61	London RED 1285	BILLY VAUGHN (EP) 7
62	London RED 1329	BILLY VAUGHN PLAYS THE HITS NO. 1 (EP) 7
62	London RED 1330	BILLY VAUGHN PLAYS THE HITS NO. 2 (EP) 7
63	London RED 1352	SWINGIN' SAFARI (EP) 8
63	London RED 1380	HAPPY COWBOY (EP) 7
63	London RED 1395	SIXTY-TWO'S GREATEST HITS (EP) 7
65	Dot DEP 20004	THE GREAT BILLY VAUGHN (EP) 7
56	London HB-D 1048	MELODIES OF LOVE (10" LP) 15
57	London HA-D 2025	THE GOLDEN INSTRUMENTALS (LP, also stereo SAH-D 6018) 15/25
57	London HA-D 2045	SWEET MUSIC AND MEMORIES (LP) 10
58	London HA-D 2072	INSTRUMENTAL SOUVENIRS (LP) 10
58	London HA-D 2090	MELODIES IN GOLD (LP) 10
58	London HA-D 2120	SAIL ALONG SILVERY MOON (LP, also stereo SAH-D 6037) 12/18
58	London HA-D 2129	PLAYS THE MILLION SELLERS (LP, also stereo SAH-D 6003) 12/18
59	London HA-D 2151	LA PALOMA (LP, also stereo SAH-D 6009) 10/15
59	London HA-D 2178	BILLY VAUGHN PLAYS (LP) 10
59	London HA-D 2195	CHRISTMAS CAROLS (LP) 10
59	London HA-D 2201	BLUE HAWAII (LP) 10
60	London HA-D 2209	GOLDEN HITS (LP, also stereo SAH-D 6056) 10/15
60	London HA-D 2241	GOLDEN SAXOPHONES (LP, also stereo SAH-D 6070) 10/15

Billy VAUGHN

60	London HA-D 2251	MUSIC FOR THE GOLDEN HOURS (LP, also stereo SAH-D 6075)	10/15
60	London HA-D 2256	A SUMMER PLACE (LP, also stereo SAH-D 6080)	10/15
60	London HA-D 2278	LINGER AWHILE (LP, also stereo SAH-D 6096)	10/15
60	London HA-D 2292	LOOK FOR A STAR (LP, also stereo SAH-D 6104)	10/15
61	London HA-D 2304	GREAT GOLDEN HITS (LP, also stereo SAH-D 6114)	10/15
61	London HA-D 2324	HIT PARADE (LP, also stereo SAH-D 6127)	10/15
62	London SAH-D 6228	GREATEST STRING BAND HITS (LP, stereo)	10

CHUCK VEDDER

| 59 | London HL 8951 | Spanky Boy/Arriba | 20 |
| 59 | London HL 8951 | Spanky Boy/Arriba (78) | 8 |

BOBBY VEE

60	London HLG 9179	Devil Or Angel/Since I Met You, Baby	20
61	London HLG 9255	Rubber Ball/Everyday	8
61	London HLG 9316	More Than I Can Say/Stayin' In	6
61	London HLG 9389	How Many Tears/Baby Face	7
61	London HLG 9438	Take Good Care Of My Baby/Bashful Bob	6
61	London HLG 7111	Take Good Care Of My Baby/Bashful Bob (export issue)	8
61	London HLG 9459	Susie Q/Love's Made A Fool Of You	10
61	London HLG 9470	Run To Him/Walkin' With My Angel	5
62	Liberty LIB 55388	Run To Him/Walkin' With My Angel (reissue)	8
62	Liberty LIB 55419	Please Don't Ask About Barbara/I Can't Say Goodbye	6
62	Liberty LIB 55451	Sharing You/At A Time Like This	5
62	Liberty LIB 10046	Remember Me Huh/A Forever Kind Of Love	4
63	Liberty LIB 10069	The Night Has A Thousand Eyes/Tenderly Yours	5
63	Liberty LIB 55530	Bobby Tomorrow/Charms	5
63	Liberty LIB 10124	Stranger In Your Arms/Yesterday And You	5
63	Liberty LIB 10141	She's Sorry/Buddy's Song	8
64	Liberty LIB 55700	Hickory, Dick And Doc/I Wish You Were Mine Again	7
65	Liberty LIB 10197	Keep On Trying/Cross My Heart	7
65	Liberty LIB 10213	True Love Never Runs Smooth/Hey Little Girl	7
65	Liberty LIB 55828	Run Like The Devil/Take A Look Around Me	8
66	Liberty LIB 55877	Look At Me Girl/Save A Love	7
67	Liberty LIB 10272	Like You've Never Known It Before/Growing Pains	7
67	Liberty LIB 15016	Come Back When You Grow Up/Let The Four Winds Blow	5
67	Liberty LIB 15042	Beautiful People/I May Be Gone	5
68	Liberty LBF 15058	Maybe Just Today/You're A Big Girl Now	4
68	Liberty LBF 15096	My Girl, Hey Girl/Take Good Care Of My Baby	4
68	Liberty LBF 15134	Thank You/Do What You Gotta Do	4
69	Liberty LBF 15178	Someone To Love Me/Sunrise Highway	4
70	Liberty LBF 15370	Woman In My Life/No Objections	4
73	United Artists UP 35516	Take Good Care Of My Baby/Every Opportunity (as Robert Thomas Velline)	4
61	London REG 1278	BOBBY VEE NO. 1 (EP)	20
61	London REG 1299	BOBBY VEE NO. 2 (EP)	20
61	London REG 1308	BOBBY VEE NO. 3 (EP)	20
61	London REG 1323	BOBBY VEE NO. 4 (EP)	20
61	London REG 1324	HITS OF THE ROCKIN' FIFTIES (EP)	20
62	Liberty LEP 2053	SINCERELY (EP)	15
63	Liberty LEP 2084	JUST FOR FUN (EP, 2 tracks by Bobby Vee, 2 by Crickets)	15
63	Liberty LEP 2089	A FOREVER KIND OF LOVE (EP)	15
63	Liberty (S)LEP 2102	BOBBY VEE'S BIGGEST HITS (EP, mono/stereo)	15/22
63	Liberty (S)LEP 2116	BOBBY VEE MEETS THE CRICKETS (EP, mono/stereo)	18/25
64	Liberty LEP 2149	BOBBY VEE MEETS THE CRICKETS VOL. 2 (EP)	18
64	Liberty LEP 2181	NEW SOUNDS (EP)	20
65	Liberty LEP 2212	BOBBY VEE MEETS THE VENTURES (EP, with Ventures)	20
61	London HA-G 2320	BOBBY VEE SINGS YOUR FAVOURITES (LP)	35
61	London HA-G 2352	RUBBER BALL (LP)	35
61	London HA-G 2374	WITH STRINGS AND THINGS (LP, also stereo SAH-G 6174)	35/40
61	London HA-G 2406	SINGS HITS OF THE ROCKIN' 50s (LP, also stereo, SAH-G 6206)	35/40
61	London HA-G 2428	TAKE GOOD CARE OF MY BABY (LP, also stereo, SAH-G 6224)	30/35
61	Liberty (S)LBY 1004	TAKE GOOD CARE OF MY BABY (LP, reissue)	20/25
62	Liberty (S)LBY 1084	BOBBY VEE RECORDING SESSION (LP, mono/stereo)	25/30
62	Liberty (S)LBY 1086	BOBBY VEE MEETS THE CRICKETS (LP, mono/stereo)	15/18
62	Liberty (S)LBY 1112	BOBBY VEE'S GOLDEN GREATS (LP, mono/stereo)	25/30
63	Liberty (S)LBY 1139	THE NIGHT HAS A THOUSAND EYES (LP, mono/stereo)	25/30
63	Liberty (S)LBY 1147	BOBBY VEE MEETS THE VENTURES (LP, with Ventures)	25/30
63	Liberty (S)LBY 1188	I REMEMBER BUDDY HOLLY (LP, mono/stereo)	25/30
65	Liberty (S)LBY 1263	BOBBY VEE LIVE! ON TOUR (LP, mono/stereo)	20/25
67	Liberty (S)LBY 1341	LOOK AT ME GIRL (LP)	18
68	Liberty LBL/LBS 83112E	JUST TODAY (LP)	15
68	Sunset SLS 50022	BOBBY VEE (LP)	10
69	Liberty LBL/LBS 83130E	DO WHAT YOU GOTTA DO (LP)	15
69	Sunset SLS 50050	A FOREVER KIND OF LOVE (LP)	10

(see also Crickets, Ventures)

VAZZ

| 85 | CRV 5401 | Breath/Violent Silence (in folder and bag with postcards and inserts) | 6 |

VEE VV

85	Cathexis CRV 5455	Kindest Cut/Romance Is Over (p/s, with A4 folder in zip-lock bag)	6
80s	Debris DEB 4	Romance is Over/THAT TED: Long Expected One And Twenty (flexidisc, with 'Debris' magazine)	5/4
80s	Blam	Love Canal (flexidisc, foldout p/s, free with 'BLAM' fanzine)	5/4

SUZANNE VEGA

| 85 | A&M AM 275 | Marlene On The Wall/Small Blue Thing (p/s) | 4 |
| 85 | A&M AM 294 | Small Blue Thing/The Queen And The Soldier//Black Widow Station/ Some Journey (double pack) | 7 |

MINT VALUE £

86	A&M AMX 320	Left Of Centre/Undertow/Left Of Centre (live)/Freeze Tag (live) (10", p/s) 5
86	A&M AM 349	Gypsy Standing/Cracking (live) (gatefold p/s with booklet) 4
86	A&M CDQ 320	Left Of Centre/Undertow/Cracking (CD) 12
87	A&M VEGA 110	Luka/Straight Lines (live)/Neighbourhood Girls (Live)/Left Of Centre (live) (10", p/s) 5
87	A&M VEGA 210	Tom's Diner/Left Of Centre/Luka (live) (10", p/s) 5
87	A&M VEGA 310	Solitude Standing/Ironbound-Fancy Poultry/Marlene (live)/ Some Journey (live) (10", p/s) 5

JORGE VEIGA & MARIO AUGUSTO
| 61 | HMV POP 918 | Brigitte Bardot/Tenha Pena De Min .... 5 |

VEJTABLES
| 65 | Pye Intl. 7N 25339 | I Still Love You/Anything .... 8 |

JOSE VELEZ
| 78 | Decca FR 13774 | Bailemos Un Vals (Voulez-Vous Danser Avec Moi)/Si Tu Fueras Mia .... 4 |

MARTHA VELEZ
69	London HLK 10266	It Takes A Lot To Laugh/Come Here Sweet Man 5
69	London HLK 10280	Tell Mama/Swamp Man 5
72	Blue Horizon 2096 010	Boogie Kitchen/Two Bridges 10
69	London HA-K/SH-K 8395	FIENDS AND ANGELS (LP) 12
70	Blue Horizon 7-63867	FIENDS AND ANGELS AGAIN (LP) 30

VELICIA
| 74 | Tiffany 6121 507 | Stop The World Pts 1 & 2 .... 4 |

VELVELETTES
64	Stateside SS 361	Needle In A Haystack/Should I Tell Them 22
65	Stateside SS 387	He Was Really Sayin' Something/Throw A Farewell Kiss 35
65	Tamla Motown TMG 521	Lonely Lonely Girl Am I/I'm The Exception To The Rule 80
66	Tamla Motown TMG 580	These Things Will Keep Me Loving You/Since You've Been Loving Me 20
65	Tamla Motown TMG 595	He Was Really Sayin' Something/Needle In A Haystack (narrow label print) ... 12
67	Tamla Motown TMG 595	He Was Really Sayin' Something/Needle In A Haystack (later pressing) 6
71	Tamla Motown TMG 780	These Things Will Keep Me Loving You/Since You've Been Loving Me (reissue) 4
72	Tamla Motown TMG 806	Needle In A Haystack/I'm The Exception To The Rule 4

VELVET HUSH
| 68 | Oak RGJ 648 | Broken Heart/Lover Please .... 100 |

VELVET OPERA
69	CBS 4189	Anna Dance Square/Don't You Realize 5
70	CBS 4802	Black Jack Davy/Statesboro Blues 4
69	CBS 63692	RIDE A HUSTLER'S DREAM (LP) 40

(see also Elmer Gantry's Velvet Opera, Stretch)

VELVETS
61	London HLU 9328	That Lucky Old Sun/Time And Time Again 20
61	London HLU 9372	Tonight (Could Be The Night)/Spring Fever 20
61	London HLU 9444	Laugh/Lana 20
61	London REU 1297	VELVETS (EP) 50

VEL-VETS
| 74 | Disco Demand DDS 109 | I Got To Find Me Somebody/What Now My Love .... 5 |

VELVETTES
| 64 | Mercury MF 802 | He's The One I Want/That Little Boy Of Mine (some in p/s) .... 12/6 |

VELVETT FOGG
| 69 | Pye 7N 17673 | Telstar '69/Owed To The Dip .... 10 |
| 67 | Pye NSPL 18272 | VELVETT FOGG (LP, laminated sleeve; beware of non-laminated counterfeits) ..75 |

(see also Ghost)

VELVET UNDERGROUND
71	Atlantic 2091 008	Who Loves The Sun?/Sweet Jane 15
73	MGM 2006 283	Candy Says/I'm Waiting For The Man/Run Run Run (as Lou Reed & Velvet Underground) 8
73	Atlantic K 10339	Sweet Jane (live)/Rock And Roll (live) 8
67	Verve (S)VLP 9184	THE VELVET UNDERGROUND AND NICO (LP, single sleeve, mono/stereo) ..50/40
68	Verve (S)VLP 9201	WHITE LIGHT WHITE HEAT (LP, 'skull' sleeve, mono/stereo) 40/35
69	MGM CS 8108	THE VELVET UNDERGROUND (LP) 30
71	Atlantic 2400 111	LOADED (LP) 15
71	MGM 2315 056	THE VELVET UNDERGROUND AND NICO (LP, reissue, gatefold sleeve, a few housed in peelable U.S. sleeve) 50/15
71	MGM Select 2353 022	THE VELVET UNDERGROUND (LP, reissue, gatefold sleeve) 10
71	MGM Select 2353 024	WHITE LIGHT WHITE HEAT (LP, reissue) 10
72	Atlantic K 30022	LIVE AT MAX'S KANSAS CITY (LP) 10
73	Polydor 2383 180	SQUEEZE (LP) 10

(see also Lou Reed, Nico, John Cale)

VENDORS
| 64 | private pressing | Peace Pipe .... 150 |

(see also Slade)

VENEICE
| 72 | London HLU 10372 | Stepchild/18 Days .... 4 |

VENGERS
| 63 | Oriole CB 1879 | Shake And Clap/Shakedown .... 5 |

VENOM
| 81 | Neat NEAT 08 | In League With Satan/Live Like An Angel, Die Like An Devil (p/s) ...... 8 |
| 82 | Neat NEAT 13 | Blood Lust/In Nomine Satanas (p/s) .... 8 |

MINT VALUE £

83	Neat NEAT 27	Die Hard/Acid Queen (p/s, with poster) 5
83	Megaforce LOM1/NEAT 27	Die Hard/Acid Queen (picture disc, export issue, 1,000 only) 10
84	Neat NEAT 38	Warhead/Lady Lust (p/s) 4
84	Neat NEATP 38	Warhead/Lady Lust (p/s, mauve vinyl) 6
84	Neat NEAT 3812	Warhead/Lady Lust/Gates Of Hell (12", p/s) 7
85	Neat NEATP 43	Manitou/Woman (picture disc) 5
85	Neat NEATSHAPE 43	Manitou/Woman (shaped picture disc) 7
85	Neat NEATC 43	Manitou/Woman/Dead Of Night/Dutch Radio Interview (cassette) 5
85	Neat NEATSP 47	Nightmare/Satanarchist (shaped picture disc) 5
85	Neat NEATSC 47	Nightmare/Satanarchist/F.O.A.D./Radio Intro To Warhead/Warhead (live)/
		Venoms (cassette) 5
85	Neat NEATSP 4712	Nightmare/Satanarchist/F.O.A.D./Warhead (live) (12" picture disc, withdrawn) .. 10
85	Neat NEATP 1002	WELCOME TO HELL (LP, picture disc) 10
85	Neat NEATP 1015	AT WAR WITH SATAN (LP, picture disc) 10
85	Neat NEATP 1024	POSSESSED (LP, picture disc) 10
86	Demon APKPD 12	OBSCENE MATERIAL (LP, picture disc) 10
89	Under One Flag FLAG 36P	PRIME EVIL (LP, picture disc) 10

CAROL VENTURA

65	Stateside SS 466	Please Somebody Help Me/The Old Lady Of Threadneedle Street 4
65	Stateside SL 10146	CAROL! (LP) 10
66	Stateside SL/SSL10180	I LOVE TO SING (LP) 10

CHARLIE VENTURA

| 54 | Vogue Coral Q 2022 | I Love You/Intermezzo (unreleased) |
| 55 | Vogue Coral Q 72048 | I Love You/Intermezzo .... 4 |

DOLORES VENTURA (& HER SOUTHERNAIRES)

54	Decca F 10390	Two Parrots/Ringin' The Rag 4
56	Parlophone R 4160	Georgian Rumba/Song Of The Andes 4
56	Parlophone R 4243	The Seven Hills Of Lisbon/When The Dog Sits On The Tucker Bo
		(as Dolores Ventura & Her Southernaires) 4

TOBY VENTURA

| 63 | Decca F 11581 | If My Heart Were A Storybook/Vagabond .... 18 |

VENTURES

60	Top Rank JAR 417	Walk Don't Run/Home 6
60	London HLG 9232	Perfidia/No Trespassing 6
61	London HLG 9292	Ram-Bunk-Shush/Lonely Heart 6
61	London HLG 9344	Lulluby Of The Leaves/Ginchy 6
61	London HLG 9411	Theme From Silver City/Bluer Than Blue 7
61	London HLG 9465	Blue Moon/Wailin' 8
61	London HLG 7113	Lady Of Spain/Blue Moon (export issue) 20
64	Liberty LIB 60	Lolita Ya-Ya/Lucille 6
64	Liberty LIB 67	The 2000 Pound Bee Pts 1 & 2 8
64	Liberty LIB 68	El Cumbanchero/Skip To M'Limbo 6
64	Liberty LIB 78	Damaged Goods/The Ninth Wave 6
64	Liberty LIB 91	Walkin' With Pluto/Journey To The Stars 6
64	Liberty LIB 96	Walk Don't Run '64/The Cruel Sea 6
64	Liberty LIB 10142	Penetration/Solar Race 6
65	Liberty LIB 300	Slaughter On Tenth Avenue/Rap City 6
65	Liberty LIB 303	Diamond Head/Lonely Girl 6
65	Liberty LIB 306	The Swingin' Creeper/Pedal Pusher 6
65	Liberty LIB 308	The Stranger/Bird Rockers 6
65	Liberty LIB 10219	Sleigh Ride/White Christmas 6
66	Liberty LIB 316	Secret Agent Man/007-11 6
67	Liberty LIB 10266	Theme From The Wild Angels/High And Dry 6
67	Liberty LIB 55967	Strawberry Fields Forever/Endless Dream 5
68	Liberty LBF 15075	Flights Of Fantasy/Pandora's Box 6
69	Liberty LBF 15221	Hawaii Five-O/Higher Than Thou 6
72	United Artists UP 36316	Theme From Shaft/Tight Fit 4
72	United Artists UP 35326	Joy/Cherries Jubilee 4
77	United Artists UP 36223	Starsky And Hutch/Charlie's Angels 5
61	London REG 1279	THE VENTURES (EP) 15
61	London REG 1288	RAM-BUNK-SHUSH! (EP) 18
61	London REG 1326	ANOTHER SMASH (EP) 18
61	London REG 1328	COLOURFUL VENTURES (EP) 15
62	Liberty LEP 2058	TWIST WITH THE VENTURES (EP) 15
63	Liberty LEP 2104	THE VENTURES PLAY TELSTAR AND LONELY BULL (EP) 15
63	Liberty LEP 2131	SMASH HITS (EP) 15
64	Liberty LEP 2174	THE VENTURES PLAY COUNTRY GREATS (EP) 15
65	Liberty LEP 2212	BOBBY VEE MEETS THE VENTURES (EP, with Bobby Vee) 20
66	Liberty LEP 2250	SECRET AGENT MEN (EP) 18
61	London HA-G 2340	THE VENTURES (LP, also stereo SAH-G 6143) 30/40
61	London HA-G 2376	ANOTHER SMASH (LP, also stereo SAH-G 6176) 25/30
61	London HA-G 2409	THE COLOURFUL VENTURES (LP, also stereo, SAH-G 6209) 25/30
62	Liberty LBY 1002	WALK DON'T RUN (LP) 20
62	London HA-G 2429	TWIST WITH THE VENTURES (LP, also stereo, SAH-G 6225) 25/30
62	Liberty LBY 1072	TWIST PARTY (LP) 20
63	Liberty (S)LBY 1110	GOING TO THE VENTURES DANCE PARTY! (LP, mono/stereo) 22/25
63	Liberty (S)LBY 1147	BOBBY VEE MEETS THE VENTURES (LP, with Bobby Vee) 25/30
63	Liberty LBY 1150	SURFING (LP) 18
64	Liberty LBY 1169	LET'S GO! (LP) 14
64	Liberty (S)LBY 1189	THE VENTURES IN SPACE (LP, mono/stereo) 18/20
65	Liberty LBY 1228	WALK DON'T RUN — VOL. 2 (LP) 20
65	Liberty (S)LBY 1252	KNOCK ME OUT (LP, mono/stereo) 16/18
65	Liberty LBY 1270	ON STAGE (LP) 15
66	Liberty LBY 1274	VENTURES A GO-GO (LP) 12

66	Liberty LBY 1285	THE VENTURES' CHRISTMAS ALBUM (LP)	18
66	Liberty LBY 1297	WHERE THE ACTION IS! (LP)	15
66	Liberty LBY 1323	GO WITH THE VENTURES (LP)	15
67	Liberty LBY 1345	GUITAR FREAKOUT (LP)	15
67	Liberty LBY 1372	SUPER PSYCHEDELICS (LP)	12
67	Liberty (S)LBY 1375	THE BEST OF THE VENTURES (LP)	12
68	Liberty LBL/LBS 83015E	ON STAGE (LP, reissue)	10
68	Liberty LBL/LBS 83033E	SUPER PSYCHEDELICS (LP, reissue)	10
68	Liberty LBL/LBS 83046E	GOLDEN GREATS (LP)	10
68	Liberty LBL/LBS 83085E	GREAT PERFORMANCES VOL. 1 (LP)	10
68	Liberty LBL/LBS 83089E	GUITAR FREAKOUT (LP, reissue)	10
68	Liberty LBL/LBS 83092E	$1,000,000 WEEKEND (LP)	10
68	Liberty LBL/LBS 83116E	I LIKE IT LIKE THAT (LP)	10
68	Liberty LBL/LBS 83123E	WALK — DON'T RUN (LP)	10
68	Liberty LBL/LBS 83124E	LONELY BULL (LP)	10
68	Liberty LBL/LBS 83125E	LET'S GO! (LP)	10
68	Liberty LBL/LBS 83126E	OUT OF LIMITS (LP)	10
68	Liberty LBL/LBS 83127E	KNOCK ME OUT (LP)	10
69	Liberty LBL/LBS 83193E	UNDERGROUND FIRE (LP)	10

(see also Bobby Vee)

VENUS & RAZORBLADES

77	Spark SRL 1153	I Wanna Be Where Where The Boys Are/Dogfood (numbered p/s)	4
77	Spark SRL 1156	Punk-A-Rama/Alright You Guys	4
78	Spark SRL 1159	Workin' Girl/Midnight	4

VENUS IN FURS

84	Movement MOO 1	EXTENDED PLAY (EP, 500 only, 33rpm)	8
85	Backs PNCH 105	Momento Mori/Rogue Male/Playback (picture disc with inserts)	8

BILLY VERA

68	Atlantic 584 196	With Pen In Hand/Good Morning Blues	4

BILLY VERA & JUDY CLAY

68	Atlantic 584 164	Storybook Children/Really Together	5

(see also Judy Clay)

JOHN VERITY BAND

74	Probe SPB 1087	JOHN VERITY BAND (LP)	10

(see also Argent)

LARRY VERNE

60	London HLN 9194	Mr. Custer/Okeefenokee Two Step	6
61	London HLN 9263	Mr. Livingstone/Roller Coaster	7

LYN VERNON

60	Top Rank JAR 323	Woodchoppers Ball/Caravan	4

MIKE VERNON

71	Blue Horizon 2096 007	Let's Try It Again/Little Southern Country Girl	10
71	Blue Horizon 2931 003	BRING IT BACK HOME (LP, textured sleeve, with insert)	70

VERNON BURCH

75	United Artists UP 35838	Ain't Gonna Tell Nobody/Loving You Gets Better With Time	5

VERNONS GIRLS

58	Parlophone R 4497	Lost And Found/White Bucks And Saddle Shoes	12
58	Parlophone R 4497	Lost And Found/White Bucks And Saddle Shoes (78)	5
59	Parlophone R 4532	Jealous Heart/Now Is The Month Of Maying	7
59	Parlophone R 4596	Don't Look Now But/Who Are They To Say?	6
60	Parlophone R 4624	We Like Boys/Boy Meets Girl	6
60	Parlophone R 4654	Madison Time (with Jimmy Saville)/The Oo-We	5
61	Parlophone R 4734	Ten Little Lonely Boys/Anniversary Song	4
61	Parlophone R 4832	Let's Get Together/No Message	4
62	Decca F 11450	Lover Please/You Know What I Mean	4
62	Decca F 11495	The Loco-motion/Don't Wanna Go	4
62	Decca F 11549	Funny All Over/See For Yourself	4
63	Decca F 11629	Do The Bird/I'm Gonna Let My Hair Down	4
63	Decca F 11685	He'll Never Come Back/Stay-At-Home	4
63	Decca F 11781	Tomorrow Is Another Day/Why Why Why	4
64	Decca F 11807	We Love The Beatles/Hey Lover Boy	6
64	Decca F 11887	Only You Can Do It/Stupid Little Girl	4
64	Decca F 12021	It's A Sin To Tell A Lie/Don't Say Goodbye	4
62	Decca DFE 8506	THE VERNONS GIRLS (EP)	12
58	Parlophone PMC 1052	THE VERNONS GIRLS (LP)	50

(see also Wilde Three, Jimmy Saville)

VERSATILE NEWTS

80	Shanghai No. 2	Newtrition/Blimp (p/s, stamped white label)	25

(see also Felt)

VERSATILES

68	Island WI 3142	Teardrops Falling/Someone To Love	10
68	Amalgamated AMG 802	Just Can't Win/LEADERS: Sometimes I Sit Down Down And Cry	8
68	Crab CRAB 1	Children Get Ready/Someone To Love	5
69	Amalgamated AMG 854	Lu Lu Bell/Long Long Time	6
69	Big Shot BI 520	Worries A Yard/VAL BENNETT: Hound Dog Special	5
69	Crab CRAB 5	Spread Your Bed/Worries A Yard	5
70	New Beat NB 060	Pick My Pocket/FREEDOM SINGERS: Freedom	4

VERUKAS

(see under Varukers)

VERY THINGS

84	Reflex RE 5	The Bushes Scream While My Daddy Prunes/Shearing Machine (p/s)	5
80s	Corp. Christi CHRISTITS 2	The Gong Man/The Colours (Are Speaking To Me) (foldout p/s)	5

(see also Cravats)

VHF

80	Lion	Heart Of Stone	15

VIBES

84	Big Beat SW 99	Can You Feel … /The Underestimated Man/Double Decker Bus/Mini Skirt Blues/Stranger In The House (p/s)	5

VIBRATIONS

61	Pye Intl. 7N 25107	The Watusi/Wallflower	15
64	London HLK 9875	My Girl Sloopy/Daddy Woo Woo	12
66	Columbia DB 7895	Canadian Sunset/The Story Of A Starry Night	10
67	Columbia DB 8175	Pick Me/You Better Beware	15
67	Columbia DB 8318	Talkin' 'Bout Love/One Mint Julep	8
68	Direction 58-3511	Love In Them There Hills/Remember The Rain	8
67	Columbia SX 6106	NEW VIBRATIONS (LP)	20
69	Direction 8-63644	GREATEST HITS (LP)	20

VIBRATORS (U.K.)

76	RAK RAK 245	We Vibrate/Whips And Furs (no p/s)	5
76	RAK RAK 246	Pogo Dancing/The Pose (p/s, as Vibrators with Chris Spedding)	6
77	RAK RAK 253	Bad Times/No Heart (unreleased)	
77	Epic EPC 5302	Baby Baby/Into The Future (p/s)	5
77	Epic EPC 5565	London Girls/Stiff Little Fingers (live) (p/s)	4
78	Epic EPC 6137	Automatic Lover/Destroy (p/s)	4
78	Epic EPC 6393	Judy Says (Knock You On The Head)/Pure Mania (p/s)	4
86	Rat Race RAT 2	Gimme Some Lovin'/Power Cry (live) (in slightly different colour sleeves)	4
86	Rat Race RAT 4	Disco In Moscow/Take A Chance (p/s, with various coloured writing)	5
77	Epic EPC 82097	PURE MANIA (LP)	10
78	Epic EPC 82495	V2 (LP)	10

(see also John Ellis, Knox, Chris Spedding)

VIBRATORS (Jamaica)

66	Doctor Bird DB 1036	Sloop John B/Amour	10

(see also Al & Vibrators, Wilbert Francis & Vibrators)

VICE CREEMS

78	Tiger GRRRR 1	Won't You Be My Girl?/01-01-212 (gatefold p/s)	6
79	Zig Zag ZZ22 001	Danger Love/Like A Tiger (p/s)	5

VICEROYS

67	Island WI 3095	Lip And Tongue/DAWN PENN: When Am I Gonna Be Free	10
67	Coxsone CS 7031	Maga Down/RICHARD ACE: Don't Let The Sun Catch You Crying	15
67	Studio One SO 2016	Lose And Gain (as Voiceroys)/SOUL BROTHERS: Honey Pot	15
67	Studio One SO 2025	Shake Up/NORMA FRAZER: Telling Me Lies	15
68	Studio One SO 2064	Last Night/Ya Ho	15
68	Blue Cat BS 121	Fat Fish/OCTAVES: You're Gonna Lose	10
69	Studio One SO 2077	Things A Come To Bump/LYRICS: Old Man Say	12
69	Punch PH 3	Jump In A Fire/Give To Get (as Voiceroys)	5
69	Crab CRAB 12	Work It/You Mean So Much To Me (B-side actually by Paragons)	5
69	Crab CRAB 27	Death A Come (actually by Lloyd Robinson)/MATADOR ALLSTARS: The Sword	4
70	Bullet BU 441	Chariot Coming/SYDNEY ALLSTARS: Stackata	4
70	Bullet BU 444	Power Control/SLICKERS: Dip Dip	4
70	Bullet BU 450	Come On Over/SYDNEY ALLSTARS: Version	4
70	Bullet BU 453	Fancy Clothes/BIGGIE: Jack And Jill	4
71	Bullet BU 470	Rebel Nyah/Feel The Spirit	4
73	Harry J. HJ 6658	Chucky Pts 1 & 2	8
74	Harry J. HJ 6669	Wheel & Jig Pts 1 & 2	8

VICE SQUAD

80	Riot City RIOT 1	Last Rockers/Living On Dreams/Latex Love (p/s, with poster)	4
81	Riot City RIOT 2	Resurrection/Young Blood/Hurricane (p/s)	4
82	Zonophone Z 26	Out Of Reach/Sterile/Out Of Reach (p/s)	4
82	Zonophone Z 30	Rock 'n' Roll Massacre/Stand Strong And Proud/Tomorrow	4
80s	Vice Squad Fan Club	EVIL (EP, flexidisc)	6

VICE VERSA

80	Neutron NT 001/PX 1092	MUSIC 4 (EP, poster p/s)	8

(see also ABC)

VICIOUS PINK (PHENOMENA)

82	Mobile Suit Corp CORP 1	My Private Tokyo/Promises (p/s, with Soft Cell)	8
82	Mobile Suit Corp CORP 12	My Private Tokyo/Promises (12", p/s, with Soft Cell)	12
83	Warehouse WARE 1	Je T'aime (Moi Non Plus)/In The Swim (p/s)	4
83	Warehouse WARE 1T	Je T'aime (Moi Non Plus)/In The Swim (12", p/s)	8
85	EMI PINKP 1	Fetish/Spooky Situation (picture disc, as Vicious Pink)	4

(see also Soft Cell)

MIKE VICKERS (ORCHESTRA)

65	Columbia DB 7657	On The Brink/The Puff Adder (as Mike Vickers & Orchestra)	20
66	Columbia DB 7825	Eleventy One/The Inkling	6
66	Columbia DB 7906	Morgan — A Suitable Case For Treatment/Gorilla Of My Dreams (as Mike Vickers Orchestra)	6
67	Columbia DB 8171	Air On A String/Proper Charles (as Mike Vickers Orchestra)	5
67	Columbia DB 8281	Captain Scarlet And The Mysterons/Kettle Of Fish	12
68	Columbia S(C)X 6180	I WISH I WERE A GROUP AGAIN (LP)	15

(see also Manfred Mann)

MACK VICKERY
60   Top Rank JAR 420   Fantasy/Hawaiian Stroll 4

VICKY
67   Philips BF 1565   Colours Of Love (Love Is Blue)/Who Can Tell 10

VICKY & JERRY
60   HMV POP 715   Don't Cry/A Year Ago Tonight 10

VICTIM
78   Good Vibrations GOT 2   Strange Things By Night/Mixed Up World (wraparound p/s) 4
80   TJM TJM 13   THE VICTIM (EP, unreleased)
80   TJM TJM 14   Why Are Fire Engines Red/I Need You (p/s) 5
80   TJM TJM 15   The Teen Age/Junior Criminals/Hung On To Yourself (p/s) 6
80   Illuminated ILL 1   The Teen Age/Junior Criminals/Hung On To Yourself (p/s, reissue) 4

VICTIMIZE
79   I.M.E. IME 1   Baby Buyer/Hi Rising Failure (folded p/s) 5
80   I.M.E. IME 2   Wh?r Did Th? Mon?y Go (p/s) 4

VICTIMS OF CHANCE
70   Stable SLE 8004   VICTIMS OF CHANCE (LP) 30

VICTIMS OF PLEASURE
80   P.A.M. VOP 1   When We're Young/If I Was/Sporting Times (p/s) 7
     (see also Virginia Astley)

TONY VICTOR
62   Decca F 11459   Dear One/There Was A Time 12
63   Decca F 11626   Thinking Of You/Hokey Cokey 5
63   Decca F 11708   In The Still Of The Night/Money 5

VICTORIAN PARENTS
81   Vienna EJSP 9579   Dead Red Grass Of Home/Another Waste Of Time 5

VICTORS
65   Oriole CB 1984   Take This Old Hammer/Answer's No 4

VIDELS
60   London HLI 9153   Mister Lonely/I'll Forget You 25

VIEWERS
80   Fire Exit LOCK 1   Accident/Pen Friend (p/s) 4

VIGILANTES
61   Pye International 7N 25082   Man In Space/Eclipse 10

(PAUL) VIGRASS
68   RCA RCA 1755   New Man/Curly 5
69   RCA RCA 1800   Suzie/Funky Piano Joe (as Vigrass) 4
69   RCA RCA 1857   Free Lorry Ride/Flying 4
70   RCA RCA 1911   Stop/Like It Never Want 4

VIKINGS
63   Island WI 065   Hallelujah/Helping Ages Past 10
63   Island WI 075   Six And Seven Books Of Moses/Zaicons 10
63   Island WI 101   Never Grow Old/Irene 10
63   Island WI 107   Just Got To Be/You Make Me Do 10
63   Island WI 117   Fever/Cheer Up 10
63   Island WI 122   Get Ready/DON DRUMMOND: The Rocket 10
64   Island WI 167   Daddy/It's You 10
64   Black Swan WI 423   Down By The Riverside/This Way 10
64   Black Swan WI 428   Treat Me Bad/Sitting On Top 10
64   Black Swan WI 430   Come Into My Parlour/I Am In Love 10
     (see also Maytals)

VIKINGS
66   Alp 595 011   Bad News Feeling/What Can I Do 15

CLAUDIO VILLA
60s Cetra SP 4024   Addio ... Addio/Twist A Napoli (p/s) 5

VILLAGE
69   Head HDS 4002   Man In The Moon/Long Time Coming 25
     (see also Peter Bardens, Quiver)

VILLAGE IDIOTS
66   Piccadilly 7N 35282   Laughing Policeman/I Know An Old Lady 4

VILLAGE PEOPLE
77   DJM DJS 10817   San Francisco/Fire Island (12") 7

VILLAGE STOMPERS
63   Columbia DB 7123   Washington Square/Turkish Delight 6

CATERINA VILLALBA
60   Ember EMB S 104   Quando La Luna/Amore Fantastico (p/s) 5

JOE VINA
59   Top Rank JAR 251   Marina/That's Alright 4

R.A.E. VINCE & VINCENTS
64   Piccadilly 7N 35211   One Fine Day/Little Girl, I'm Sad 4

GENE VINCENT (& BLUE CAPS)
56   Capitol CL 14599   Be-Bop-A-Lula/Woman Love 18
56   Capitol CL 14599   Be-Bop-A-Lula/Woman Love (78) 10
56   Capitol CL 14628   Race With The Devil/Gonna Back Up Baby 65

Gene VINCENT

56	Capitol CL 14628	Race With The Devil/Gonna Back Up Baby (78)	20
56	Capitol CL 14637	Bluejean Bop/Who Slapped John?	45
56	Capitol CL 14637	Bluejean Bop/Who Slapped John? (78)	10
57	Capitol CL 14681	Jumps, Giggles And Shouts/Wedding Bells (Are Breaking ...)	80
57	Capitol CL 14681	Jumps, Giggles And Shouts/Wedding Bells (Are Breaking ...) (78)	20
57	Capitol CL 14693	Crazy Legs/Important Words	60
57	Capitol CL 14693	Crazy Legs/Important Words (78)	20
57	Capitol CL 14722	Five Days, Five Days/Bi-I-Bickey-Bi, Bo-Bo-Go	60
57	Capitol CL 14722	Five Days, Five Days/Bi-I-Bickey-Bi, Bo-Bo-Go (78)	20
57	Capitol CL 14763	Wear My Ring/Lotta Lovin'	30
57	Capitol CL 14763	Wear My Ring/Lotta Lovin' (78)	20
57	Capitol CL 14808	Dance To The Bop/I Got It	35
57	Capitol CL 14808	Dance To The Bop/I Got It (78)	25
58	Capitol CL 14830	Walkin' Home From School/I Got A Baby	25
58	Capitol CL 14830	Walkin' Home From School/I Got A Baby (78)	30
58	Capitol CL 14868	Baby Blue/True To You	25
58	Capitol CL 14908	Rocky Road Blues/Yes I Love You, Baby	25
58	Capitol CL 14935	Git It/Little Lover	25
59	Capitol CL 14974	Say Mama/Be Bop Boogie Boy	20
59	Capitol CL 15000	Who's Pushin' Your Swing/Over The Rainbow	15
59	Capitol CL 15035	Summertime/Frankie And Johnnie	15
59	Capitol CL 15053	Right Now/The Night Is So Lonely	15
59	Capitol CL 15099	Wild Cat/Right Here On Earth	12
60	Capitol CL 15115	I've Got To Get You Yet/My Heart	12
60	Capitol CL 15136	Pistol Packin' Mama (as Gene Vincent & Beat Boys)/Weeping Willow	12
60	Capitol CL 15169	Anna-Annabelle/Ac-Cent-Tchu-Ate The Positive	15
61	Capitol CL 15179	Maybe/Jezebel	15
61	Capitol CL 15185	If You Want My Lovin'/Mister Loneliness	15
61	Capitol CL 15202	She She Little Sheila/Hot Dollar	15
61	Capitol CL 15215	I'm Going Home (To See My Baby)/Love Of A Man	12
61	Capitol CL 15231	Unchained Melody/Brand New Beat	15
62	Capitol CL 15243	Baby Don't Believe Him/Lucky Star	15
62	Capitol CL 15264	Be-Bop-A-Lula/The King Of Fools	15
63	Capitol CL 15290	Held For Questioning/You're Still In My Heart	15
63	Capitol CL 15307	Rip It Up/High Blood Pressure (demo only)	150
63	Capitol CL 15307	Crazy Beat/High Blood Pressure	18
63	Columbia DB 7174	Temptation Baby/Where Have You Been All My Life	10
64	Columbia DB 7218	Humpity Dumpity/A Love 'Em And Leave 'Em Kinda Guy	12
64	Columbia DB 7293	La-Den-Da Den-Da-Da/The Beginning Of The End	12
64	Columbia DB 7343	Private Detective/You Are My Sunshine (as Gene Vincent & Shouts)	12
66	London HLH 10079	Bird Doggin'/Ain't That Too Much	15
66	London HLH 10099	Lonely Street/I've Got My Eyes On You	12
68	Capitol CL 15546	Be-Bop-A-Lula/Say Mama	7
69	Dandelion S 4596	Be-Bop-A-Lula '69/Ruby Baby	5
70	Dandelion S 4974	White Lightning/Scarlet Ribbons (For Her Hair)	5
70	Kama Sutra 2013 018	The Day The World Turned Blue/High On Life (some with large centre)	5
73	Spark SRL 1091	Story Of The Rockers/Pickin' Poppies (push-out or solid centre)	4
74	BBC BEEB 001	Roll Over Beethoven/Say Mama/Be-Bop-A-Lula '71 (push-out or solid centre)	6
77	Capitol CL 15906	Say Mama/Lotta Lovin'/Race With The Devil	6
58	Capitol EAP 1-985	HOT ROD GANG (EP)	35
58	Capitol EAP 1-1059	A GENE VINCENT RECORD DATE (EP)	30
58	Capitol EAP 3-1059	A GENE VINCENT RECORD DATE PART 3 (EP)	30
61	Capitol EAP 1-20173	IF YOU WANT MY LOVIN' (EP)	35
62	Capitol EAP 1-20354	RACE WITH THE DEVIL (EP)	35
63	Capitol EAP 1-20453	THE CRAZY BEAT OF GENE VINCENT PART 1 (EP)	35
64	Capitol EAP 2-20453	THE CRAZY BEAT OF GENE VINCENT PART 2 (EP)	35
64	Capitol EAP 3-20453	THE CRAZY BEAT OF GENE VINCENT PART 3 (EP)	35
63	Capitol EAP 1-20461	TRUE TO YOU (EP)	35
60s	Emidisc (no cat. no.)	GENE VINCENT FAN CLUB (EP, fan club issue, mail-order, 99 only)	150
79	Rollin' Danny RD 1	RAINY DAY SUNSHINE (EP)	10
81	Magnum Force MFEP 003	RAINY DAY SUNSHINE (EP, reissue)	10
56	Capitol T 764	BLUEJEAN BOP! (LP, originally with turquoise labels; later rainbow)	50/40
57	Capitol T 811	GENE VINCENT AND THE BLUECAPS (LP, turquoise or rainbow labels)	50/40
58	Capitol T 970	GENE VINCENT ROCKS! & THE BLUECAPS ROLL (LP, originally with turquoise labels, later rainbow labels)	50/40
59	Capitol T 1059	A GENE VINCENT RECORD DATE (LP)	40
59	Capitol T 1207	SOUNDS LIKE GENE VINCENT (LP)	45
60	Capitol T/ST 1342	CRAZY TIMES! (LP, mono/stereo)	40/60
63	Capitol T 20453	THE CRAZY BEAT OF GENE VINCENT (LP)	40
64	Columbia 33SX 1646	SHAKIN' UP A STORM (LP, as Gene Vincent & Shouts)	30
65	MFP MFP 1053	CRAZY TIMES (LP, reissue)	12
67	London HA-H 8333	GENE VINCENT (LP)	30
67	Capitol T 20957	THE BEST OF GENE VINCENT (LP)	15
68	Capitol ST 21144	THE BEST OF GENE VINCENT VOLUME 2 (LP)	18
70	Dandelion 63754	I'M BACK AND I'M PROUD (LP)	18
71	Kama Sutra 2316 005	THE DAY THE WORLD TURNED BLUE (LP, reissue)	12
72	Buddah 2361 009	IF YOU COULD ONLY SEE ME TODAY (LP)	15
72	Regal Starline SRS 5117	PIONEERS OF ROCK VOLUME 1 (LP)	10
74	Regal Starline SRS 5177	KING OF FOOLS: PIONEERS OF ROCK VOLUME 2 (LP)	10
81	Capitol E-ST 26223	THE SINGLES ALBUM (LP, with free EP [PSR 458])	10

VINCENT UNITS

81	Y Y 8	Carnival Song/Everything Is Going To Be All Wrong (p/s)	4
81	Y Y 8	Carnival Song/Everything Is Going To Be All Wrong (cassette)	8

CAROLE VINCI

78	EMI EMI 2801	Vivre/Souffire Et Sourire	12

JOEY VINE
65	Immediate IM 017	Down And Out/The Out Of Towner	15

VINEGAR JOE
72	Island WIP 6125	Never Met A Dog/Speed Queen Of Ventura	4
72	Island WIP 6148	Rock'n'Roll Gypsies/So Long	4
73	Island WIP 6174	Black Smoke From The Calumet/Long Way Round	4
72	Island ILPS 9183	VINEGAR JOE (LP)	15
72	Island ILPS 9214	ROCK AND ROLL GYPSIES (LP)	15
73	Island ILPS 9262	SIX STAR GENERAL (LP)	12

(see also Robert Palmer, Elkie Brooks)

EDDIE 'MR. CLEANHEAD' VINSON & HIS ORCHESTRA
51	Vogue V 2023	Queen Bee Blues/Jump And Grunt (78)	25

V. VINSTRICK & J.J. ALLSTARS
68	Doctor Bird DB 1167	Love Is Not A Game/CINDERELLA: The Way I See You	10

BOBBY VINTON
61	Fontana H 307	Little Lonely One/Corrine Corrina	4
62	London HLU 9592	I Love You The Way You Are/CHUCK & JOHNNY: You Are My Girl	4
62	Columbia DB 4878	Roses Are Red/You And I	4
62	Columbia DB 4900	Rain Rain Go Away/Over Over	4
63	Columbia DB 4961	Trouble Is My Middle Name/Let's Kiss And Make Up	4
63	Columbia DB 7015	Over The Mountain/Faded Pictures	4
63	Columbia DB 7052	Blue On Blue/Those Little Things	4
63	Columbia DB 7110	Blue Velvet/Is There A Place	4
63	Columbia DB 7179	There! I've Said It Again/The Girl With The Bow In Her Hair	4
64	Columbia DB 7240	My Heart Belongs To Only You/Warm And Tender	4
64	Columbia DB 7303	Tell Me Why/Remembering	4
64	Columbia DB 7348	Clinging Vine/Imagination Is A Magic Dream	4
64	Columbia DB 7422	Mr Lonely/The Bell That Couldn't Jingle	4
65	Columbia DB 7514	Long Lonely Nights/Satin	4
65	Columbia DB 7628	Don't Go Away Mad/Lonely Girl	4
65	Columbia DB 7731	What Colour Is A Man/Love Of Infatuation	4
66	Columbia DB 7808	Satin Pillows/Careless	4
66	Columbia DB 7922	Dum De Da/The Exodus Song	4
67	Columbia DB 8114	Coming Home Soldier/Don't Let My Mary Go Around	4
67	Columbia DB 8319	Please Love Me Forever/Miss America	4
68	Columbia DB 8346	Just As Much As Ever/Another Memory	4
62	Columbia SEG 8212	YOUNG IN HEART (EP)	8
64	Columbia SEG 8363	SONGS OF CHRISTMAS (EP)	12
63	Columbia 33SX 1517	SINGS THE BIG ONES (LP)	12
63	Columbia 33SX 1566	BLUE ON BLUE (LP)	12
65	Columbia 33SX 1649	TELL ME WHY (LP)	10

MATT VINYL
77	Housewife's Choice	Useless Tasks (p/s)	8

VIOLATORS
80	Violators FRS 002	NY Ripper/My Country (p/s)	8
82	No Future OI 9	Gangland/The Fugitive (p/s)	6
82	No Future OI 19	Summer Of '81/Live Fast Die Young (p/s)	5
83	Future FS 2	Life On The Red Line/Crossing The Sangsara (p/s)	4

VIOLENT FEMMES
84	Rough Trade RT 147	Ugly/Give Me A Car (p/s)	4
84	Rough Trade RTT 147	Ugly/Give Me A Car/Gone Daddy Gone/Good Feeling (12", p/s)	7
83	Rough Trade ROUGH 55	VIOLENT FEMMES (LP, with inner sleeve)	10

VIOLENTS
63	HMV POP 1130	Alpen Ros/Ghia	6

VIOLENT THIMBLE
67	Polydor 56217	Gentle People Pts 1 & 2	4

VIOLINSKI
79	Jet JET 136	Clog Dance/Time To Live (p/s, black vinyl)	4
79	Jet JET 136	Clog Dance/Time To Live (no p/s, white vinyl)	4
79	Jet SJET 146	Save Me/Cricket Bloody (p/s, blue vinyl)	4

(see also E.L.O.)

VIPERS (SKIFFLE GROUP)
56	Parlophone R 4238	Ain't You Glad/Pick A Bale Of Cotton	12
56	Parlophone R 4238	Ain't You Glad/Pick A Bale Of Cotton (78)	5
57	Parlophone R 4261	Don't You Rock Me Daddy-O/10,000 Years Ago	12
57	Parlophone R 4261	Don't You Rock Me Daddy-O/10,000 Years Ago (78)	5
57	Parlophone R 4286	Jim Dandy/Hi Liley, Liley Lo	12
57	Parlophone R 4286	Jim Dandy/Hi Liley, Liley Lo (78)	5
57	Parlophone R 4289	The Cumberland Gap/Maggie May	8
57	Parlophone R 4289	The Cumberland Gap/Maggie May (78)	5
57	Parlophone R 4308	Streamline Train/Railroad Steam Boat	7
57	Parlophone R 4308	Streamline Train/Railroad Steam Boat (78)	5
57	Parlophone R 4351	Homing Bird/Pay Me My Money Down	8
57	Parlophone R 4371	"Skiffle Party" Medley Pts. 1 & 2	8
57	Parlophone R 4371	"Skiffle Party" Medley Pts. 1 & 2 (78)	5
58	Parlophone R 4393	Baby Why?/No Other Baby (as Vipers)	8
58	Parlophone R 4393	Baby Why?/No Other Baby (as Vipers) (78)	5
58	Parlophone R 4435	Make Ready For Love/Nothing Will Ever Change (My Love ...) (as Vipers)	8
58	Parlophone R 4435	Make Ready For Love/Nothing Will Ever Change (My Love ...) (78)	5
58	Parlophone R 4484	Summertime Blues/Liverpool Blues (as Vipers)	20

VIPERS (SKIFFLE GROUP)

58	Parlophone R 4484	Summertime Blues/Liverpool Blues (as Vipers) (78)	5
57	Parlophone GEP 8615	SKIFFLE MUSIC VOL. 1 (EP)	12
57	Parlophone GEP 8626	SKIFFLE MUSIC VOL. 2 (EP)	12
57	Parlophone GEP 8655	SKIFFLING ALONG WITH THE VIPERS (EP)	15
57	Parlophone PMD 1050	COFFEE BAR SESSION (10" LP)	35

(see also Jet Harris & Tony Meehan, Shadows, Wally Whyton)

VIPERS
78	Mulligan LUNS 718	I've Got You/No Such Thing (p/s)	5

VIPPS
66	CBS 202031	Wintertime/Anyone	25

(see also V.I.P.s)

V.I.P.s
64	RCA RCA 1427	Don't Keep Shouting At Me/She's So Good	30
66	Island WI 3003	I Wanna Be Free/Don't Let It Go	25
67	Island WIP 6005	Straight Down To The Bottom/In A Dream	25

(see also Vipps, Art, Spooky Tooth, Felder's Orioles, Timebox, Patto)

V.I.P.s
78	Bust SOL 3	MUSIC FOR FUNSTERS (EP)	7
79	ROK V/VI	Can't Let You Go/URBAN DISTURBANCE: Wild Boys In Cortinas (co. sleeve)	5
80	Gem GEMS 43	I Need Somebody To Love (Could It Be You?)/One More Chance//Stuttgart Special/Who Knows/Janine (double pack, stickered p/s)	4

(see also Mood Six, Jed Dmochowski)

VIRGIL BROTHERS
69	Parlophone R 5787	Temptation 'Bout To Get Me/Look Away	6
69	Parlophone R 5802	Good Love/When You Walk Away	4

VIRGINIA TREE
75	Minstrel 0001	FRESH OUT (LP)	30

(see also Ghost, Shirley Kent)

VIRGINIA WOLVES
66	Stateside SS 563	Stay/B.L.T.	25

VIRGINIANS
63	Pye International 7N 25175	Limbo Baby/Greenback Dollar	6

VIRGIN PRUNES
81	Baby BABY 001	TWENTY TENS (EP)	15
81	Rough Trade RT 072	In The Greylight/War/Moments Of Mine (Despite Straight Lines) (1st issue in blue p/s with insert, later in black p/s without insert)	12/7
81	Rough Trade RT 089	A New Form Of Beauty Part One: Sandpaper Lullaby/Sleep/Fantasy Dreams (p/s)	7
81	Rough Trade RT 090	A New Form Of Beauty Part Two: Come To Daddy/Sweet Home Under White Clouds/Sad World (10", p/s, 33rpm)	8
81	Rough Trade RT 091T	A New Form Of Beauty Part Three: The Beast (Seven Bastard Suck)/The Slow Children (Abbagal)/Brain Damage/No Birds To Fly (12", p/s)	8
81	Rough Trade RT 089-091	A NEW FORM OF BEAUTY (7"/10"/12" box set)	25
82	Rough Trade RT 106	Pagan Love Song/Dave-id Is Dead (p/s)	10
82	Rough Trade RTT 106	Pagan Love Song (Vibe Akimbo)/Dave-id Is Dead (12", p/s)	8
82	Rough Trade RT 119	(What Shall We Do When) Baby Turns Blue/Yeo (p/s)	7
82	Rough Trade RTT 119	(What Shall We Do When) Baby Turns Blue/Yeo/Chance Of A Lifetime 12", p/s)	7
87	Baby BABY 011	HERESIE (10", double pack, gatefold p/s, 1st 1,000 on clear vinyl)	12/8
82	Rough Tapes COPY 007	A NEW FORM OF BEAUTY PART IV (cassette)	10

VIRGIN SLEEP
67	Deram DM 146	Love/Halliford House	25
68	Deram DM 173	Secret/Comes A Time	25

VIRTUES (U.S.)
59	HMV POP 621	Guitar Boogie Shuffle/Guitar In Orbit	10
59	HMV POP 637	Flippin' In/Shufflin' Along	12
59	HMV POP 637	Flippin' In/Shufflin' Along (78)	35

VIRTUES (Jamaica)
65	Island WI 196	Your Wife And Mother/Amen	8
68	Doctor Bird DB 1164	High Tide/RUPIE EDWARDS & VIRTUES: Burning Love	7

FRANK VIRTUOSO ROCKETS
56	Melodisc MEL 1386	Rollin' And Rockin'/Rock — Good Bye Mambo (78)	15
56	Melodisc MEL 1393	Toodle-Oo-Kangaroo/Hop-Skip-Jump Mambo (78)	6
58	Melodisc MEL 1386	Rollin' And Rockin'/Rock — Good Bye Mambo (triangular centre)	20

VISAGE
79	Radar ADA 48	Tar/Frequency 7	6
82	Polydor POSPP 441	Night Train/I'm Still Searching (picture disc)	6
82	Polydor POSPP 523	Pleasure Boys/The Anvil (picture disc)	6
82	Polydor POSPX 523	Pleasure Boys (Pleasure Mix)/The Anvil (12")	12
80s	Polydor	DANCE MIX (LP, promo only, stamped white sleeve)	10

(see also Steve Strange, Midge Ure, Ultravox, Rich Kids)

TONY VISCONTI
79	Regal Zonophone RZ 3089	I Remember Brooklyn/Sitting In A Field Of Heather	4

(see also Dib Cochran & Earwigs)

VISCOUNTS (U.S.)
59	Top Rank JAR 254	Harlem Nocturne/Dig	8
60	Top Rank JAR 388	The Touch (Le Grisbi)/Chug-A-Lug	10

60	Top Rank JAR 502	Night Train/Summertime	8
65	Stateside SS 468	Harlem Nocturne/Dig (reissue)	7
61	Top Rank JKP 3005	VISCOUNTS ROCK (EP)	40

VISCOUNTS (U.K.)

60	Pye 7N 15249	That's All Right/Rocking Little Angel	7
60	Pye 7N 15287	Fee-Fi-Fo-Fum/Shortnin' Bread	6
61	Pye 7N 15323	Money (Is The Root Of All Evil)/One Armed Bandit	6
61	Pye 7N 15344	Banned In Boston/Moonlight Promises	5
61	Pye 7N 15356	Joe Sweeney/Honey Come On And Dance With Me	4
61	Pye 7N 15379	Who Put The Bomp (In The Bomp, Bomp, Bomp)/What Am I Saying	5
62	Pye 7N 15414	Mama's Doin' The Twist/I'm Going But I'll Be Back	5
62	Pye 7N 15431	One Of The Guys/Dear Mary Brown	4
62	Pye 7N 15445	Everybody's Got A Ya Ya/Lot Of Livin' To Do	5
62	Pye 7N 15479	That Stranger Used To Be My Girl/Silent Night	4
63	Pye 7N 15510	Don't Let Me Cross Over/I'm Coming Home	4
63	Pye 7N 15536	It's You/I'll Never Get Over You	4
60	Pye NEP 24132	VISCOUNTS' HIT PARADE (EP)	15

(see also Gordon Mills)

VISIONS

69	Grape GR 3009	Captain Hook/The Girl	4

VISITORS

78	NRG SRTS/NRG 002	Take It Or Leave It/No Compromise (no p/s)	5
80	Departure RAPTURE 1	Empty Rooms/Orcadian Visitors (foldover p/s)	7
81	Rational RATE 2	Compatability/Poet's End (foldover p/s)	4

VISITORS

80s	Sha La La Ba Ba Ba-Ba Ba 8	Goldmining/MAGIC SHOP: It's True (flexidisc, p/s, free with 'Simply Thrilled' & other fanzines)	7/5

VITAL DISORDERS

85	Lowther International VD 3	Some People/Xmas Island Calypso (hand-screened p/s)	4

MIROSLAV VITOUS

79	Warner Bros K 17448	New York City/Basic Laws (12")	7

VIXEN

88	EMI MTS 48	Edge Of A Broken Heart/Charmed Life (p/s, with free backstage pass)	4
88	EMI MTSPD 48	Edge Of A Broken Heart/Love Made Me (live)/Cryin' (live) (12", pic disc)	7
88	EMI MTPPD 60	Crying/Desperate (shaped picture disc)	5
91	EMI MTS 66	Love Made Me (Remix)/Give It Away (p/s, with postcards)	4
91	EMI MTPD 66	Love Made Me (Remix)/Give It Away (shaped picture disc, with insert)	5

VLADO & ISOLDA

84	Ariola 106 500	Ciao Amore (English)/Ciao Amore (Croatian)	10

VOGUES (U.K.)

66	Columbia DB 7985	Younger Girl/Lies	10
66	King KG 1035	Magic Town/Humpty Dumpty	4

(see also Llan)

VOGUES (U.S.)

65	London HLU 9996	You're The One/Some Words	8
66	London HLU 10014	Five O'Clock World/Nothing To Offer You	8
68	Reprise RS 20766	My Special Angel/I Keep It Hid	5
68	Reprise RS 20686	Turn Around Look At Me/Then	5
69	London HLG 10247	Five O'Clock World/You're The One	6

VOICE

65	Mercury MF 905	Train To Disaster/Truth	80

(see also Karl Stuart & Profiles, Profile, Miller Anderson)

VOICE OF THE BEEHIVE

87	Food FOOD 9	Just A City/I Walk The Earth (p/s)	4
87	Food SNAK 9	Just A City/I Walk The Earth/7 Shocks (12", p/s)	7
87	London LON 151	I Say Nothing/Things You See When You Don't Have Your Gun (live) (p/s, shrinkwrapped with 3 badges)	4
88	London LONB 169	I Walk The Earth/This Weak/Jesus/No Green Blues ('Travel Pack' with poster & badge in envelope)	4
88	London LONP 175	Don't Call Me Baby/Jump This Way (picture disc)	4
88	London LONB 175	Don't Call Me Baby/Jump this Way/Goodbye Tonight (with poster & 2 badges in envelope)	4
88	London LONP 175	Don't Call Me Baby/Jump This Way (10", in foldout p/s)	5
88	London LONH 190	I Say Nothing/Things You See When You Don't Have Your Gun (live) (reissue, foldout 'Hanging Honeycomb' p/s)	4
88	London LONP 190	I Say Nothing/Things You See When You Don't Have Your Gun (live) (reissue, with 2 postcards & large sticker in envelope)	4
88	London LONB 206	I Walk The Earth/I Say Nothing/Don't Call Me Baby/This Weak (with poster & 2 badges in envelope)	4
88	London LONT 206	I Walk The Earth/This Weak/Tattoo Song/Everything I Had (10", clear vinyl, picture labels, PVC sleeve, numbered)	5

(see also Madness)

VOICEROYS

(see under Viceroys)

VOICES

56	Beltona BL 2667	"Rock And Roll Hit Parade" Medley Pts 1 & 2	8

VOICES OF EAST HARLEM

71	Elektra 2101 013	Right On Be Free/Gotta Be A Change Oh Yeah	6
71	Elektra 2101 018	No No No/Music In The Air	4

MINT VALUE £

70s	Elektra	RIGHT ON BE FREE (LP) 12

VOICES OF VICTORY
54	Vocalion V 1040	Trusting In Jesus?/Jesus Lifted Me (78) 12

VOIDS
66	Polydor BM 56073	Come On Out/I'm In A Fix 25

WES VOIGHT
59	Parlophone R 4586	I'm Movin' In/I'm Ready To Go Steady 50

VOIZ
77	Pilgrim Grapevine GRA 110	BOANERGES (LP, private pressing) 100

HOWARD VOKES COUNTRY BOYS
62	Starlite STEP 27	HOWARD VOKES COUNTRY BOYS (EP) 15
67	Starlite GRK 508	HOWARD VOKES COUNTRY BOYS (EP; reissue, with sleeve sticker over original catalogue number) 10
63	Starlite STEP 37	MOUNTAIN GUITAR (EP) 12

VOLCANOES
84	Volcanic VOLC 1	Strangers In The Night/Murder U.S.A. (p/s) 4

VOLCANOS
61	Philips PB 1098	Ruby Duby Du/Redhead 10
61	Philips PB 1113	Tightrope/Great Imposter 10
62	Philips PB 1246	Polaris/Scotch Mist 10
60	Philips BBE 12432	THE VOLCANOS (EP) 35

VOLUMES
62	Fontana 270 109TF	I Love You/Dreams 25
63	London HL 9733	Teenage Paradise/Sandra 20
68	Pama PM 755	I Just Can't Help Myself/One Way Lover (unreleased, test pressings only) 300

VOLUNTEERS
63	Parlophone R 5088	Father Along/Little David 4
	(see also Karol Keyes)	

VONTASTICS
66	Chess CRS 8043	Day Tripper/My Baby 10
67	Stateside SS 2002	Lady Love/When My Baby Comes Back Home 20

VON TRAPP FAMILY
80	Woronzow W 001	Brand New Thrill/Dreaming/No Reflexes (p/s) 30
	(see also Bevis Frond)	

VOOMINS
65	Polydor 56001	If You Don't Come Back/March Of The Voomins 8

VOW WOW
87	Arista RIS 38	Don't Leave Me Now/Nightless City (with John Wetton, poster p/s) 4
88	Arista VWWPK 1	Rock Me Now/Don'cha Wanna Come (poster p/s) 4
89	Arista VWW 3	I Feel The Power/Shot In The Dark (p/s, including transfer) 4
89	Arista VWWPP 3	I Feel The Power/Hurricane/You Know What I Mean (10" poster p/s) 5
	(see also Whitesnake)	

VOXPOPPERS
58	Mercury 7MT 202	The Last Drag/Wishing For Your Love 30
58	Mercury MEP 9533	VOXPOPPERS (EP) 50

V2
78	Bent SMALL BENT 1	Speed Freak/Nothing To Do/That's It (800 only, later reissued on red vinyl) 8
79	TJM TJM 1	Man In The Box/When The World Isn't There (12", p/s) 8
79	TJM TJM 6	Is Anybody Out There? (unissued)
70s	Groove	Gee Whiz It's You/Face In The Crowd (p/s, stamped white labels) 12

VULCANS
71	Trojan TRLS 53	STAR TREK (LP) 20
	(see also Second Hand)	

VULCAN'S HAMMER
73	Brown BVH 1	TRUE HEARTS AND SOUND BOTTOMS (LP, with insert) 450

VULTURES
80s	Rubber Connection SP 522	Time Let's Go/Is This A Man (p/s, with insert & sticker) 6

VULTURES
88	Narodnik NRK 006T	Good Thing/You're Not Scared/What I Say/Jack The Ripper (12", p/s) 7

VYE
80	Dead Good DEAD 8	Five Hours 'Til Tonight/Right Girl, Wrong Time/Til Dawn (p/s, with insert) 4

WACKERS
63	Oriole CB 1902	I Wonder Why/Why Can't It Happen To Me	7
64	Piccadilly 7N 35195	Love Or Money/Hooka Tooka	6
64	Piccadilly 7N 35210	The Girl Who Wanted Fame/You're Forgetting	6

ADAM WADE
60	Top Rank JAR 296	Tell Her For Me/Don't Cry, My Love	5
60	Top Rank JAR 370	Ruby/Too Far	5
60	HMV POP 764	I Can't Help It/I Had The Craziest Dream	5
60	HMV POP 787	Speaking Of Her/Blackout The Moon	5
60	HMV POP 807	In Pursuit Of Happiness/For The Want Of Your Love	6
61	HMV POP 843	Take Good Care Of Her/Sleepy Time Gal	5
61	HMV POP 896	Point Of No Return/The Writing On The Wall	5
61	HMV POP 913	As If I Didn't Know/Playin' Around	4
61	HMV POP 942	Tonight I Won't Be There/Linda	4
62	HMV POP 966	Cold Cold Winter/Preview Of Paradise	4
62	HMV POP 996	Prisoner's Song/Them There Eyes	5
60	HMV 7EG 8620	AND THEN CAME ADAM (EP)	10
64	Columbia SEG 8316	FOUR FILM SONGS (EP)	10
61	HMV CLP 1451	ADAM AND EVENING (LP)	15

JOHNNY WADE
60	HMV POP 757	Funny Thing/Shadow Love	4

MIKE WADE
68	Beacon BEA 3-104	Lovers/Two, Three, Four	4

WELLINGTON WADE
63	Oriole CB 1857	Let's Turkey Trot/It Ain't Necessarily So	8

(see also Ian & Zodiacs)

ADRIAN WAGNER
74	Atlantic K 50082	DISTANCES BETWEEN US (LP)	15

ROBERT WAGNER
57	London HLU 8491	Almost Eighteen/So Young	15

CHUCK WAGON
79	A&M AMS 7450	Rock 'n' Roll Won't Go Away/The Spy In My Face (p/s, purple vinyl)	6

(see also Dickies)

PORTER WAGONER
67	RCA RCA 1586	The Cold Hard Facts Of Life/You Can't Make A Heel Toe The Mark	5
64	RCA RCX 7157	A LITTLE SLICE OF LIFE (EP)	12
64	RCA RCX 7158	Y'ALL COME (EP)	10
65	RCA Victor RD 7693	THE BLUE GRASS STORY (LP)	15
65	RCA Camden CDN 5128	AN OLD LOG CABIN FOR SALE (LP)	12

WAH! (HEAT)
81	Inevitable INEV 001	Better Scream/Joe (wraparound p/s in poly bag)	6
81	Inevitable INEV 004	Seven Minutes To Midnight/Don't Step On The Cracks (p/s, diff. colour sleeves)	4
81	Eternal SLATE 1	Forget The Down!/The Checkmate Syndrome (p/s, as Wah!)	4
80s	WEA	OFFICIAL BOOTLEG (LP)	10

(see also Mighty Wah!, Pete Wylie, Faction)

WAILERS (U.S.)
59	London HL 8958	Tall Cool One/Road-Runner	15
59	London HL 8958	Tall Cool One/Road-Runner (78)	15
59	London HL 8994	Mau-Mau/Dirty Robber	75
59	London HL 8994	Mau-Mau/Dirty Robber (78)	25
64	London HL 9892	Tall Cool One/Road-Runner (reissue)	10

WAILERS (Jamaica)
(see under Bob Marley [& Wailers])

WAILING SOULS
70	Banana BA 305	Row Fisherman Row/Thou Shalt Not Steal	6
70	Banana BA 307	Back Out/Pack Your Things	6
71	Banana BA 335	Walk Walk Walk/KING SPORTY: Love Me Version (B-side actually by Denis Alcapone)	6
71	Green Door GD 4014	Harbour Shark/Harbour Shark Version	4

(see also Denis Alcapone)

CHERRY WAINER
58	Pye 7N 15161	Itchy Twitchy Feeling/Cerveza	8
58	Pye 7N 15170	Blue Cha Cha/Valancia	6
59	Pye 7N 15197	The Happy Organ/Spanish Marching Song	5
59	Pye 7N 15217	The Song Of Lotus Lee/Iced Coffee	5
59	Top Rank JAR 253	I'll Walk The Line/Saturday Night In Tia Juana	5
60	Columbia DB 4528	Happy Like A Bell (Ding Dong)/Money (That's What I Want)	15
63	Honey Hit TB 128	Sleepwalk/Red River Rock (p/s, as Cherry Wainer with Red Price Combo)	6
59	Pye NEP 24099	CHERRY WAINER (EP)	15
60	Top Rank BUY 042	WALTZES IN SPRINGTIME (LP)	10

(see also Red Price Combo)

PHIL WAINMAN
65	Columbia DB 7615	Hear Me A Drummer Man/Hear His Drums	10
68	Fontana TF 978	Going Going Gone/Hey Paradiddle	4

LOUDON WAINWRIGHT III
71	Atlantic K 40107	ALBUM I (LP, red label)	10
72	Atlantic K 40272	ALBUM II (LP, red label)	10

L.J. WAITERS & ELECTRIFIERS
76	Route RT 26	If You Ain't Gettin' Your Thing Parts 1 & 2	4

WAITING FOR THE SUN
70s	Profile	WAITING FOR THE SUN (LP, private pressing)	120

(see also After The Fire)

TOM WAITS
86	Island ISD 260	In The Neighbourhood/Singapore//Tango Till They're Sore/Rain Dogs (double pack)	4
73	Asylum SYL 9007	CLOSING TIME (LP)	10

WAKE
69	Pye 7N 17813	Angelina/So Happy	8
70	Carnaby CNS 4010	Live Today Little Girl/Days Of Emptiness	8
71	Carnaby CNS 4016	Noah/To Make You Happy	8
71	Carnaby 6151001	Linda/Got My Eyes On You	8
70	Carnaby CNLS 6005	23.59 (LP)	75

WAKE
82	Scan SCN 01	On Our Honeymoon/Give Up (p/s in bag)	15
84	Scan 45/Factory FAC 88	Talk About The Past/Everybody Works So Hard (p/s)	4
84	Scan 45/Factory FAC 88	Talk About The Past/Everybody Works So Hard (12", p/s)	7

JIMMY WAKELY
56	Coral Q 72125	Are You Mine? (with Ruth Ross)/Yellow Roses	12
56	Brunswick 05542	Are You Satisfied? (with Gloria Wood)/Mississippi Dreamboat	12
56	Brunswick 05563	Folsom Prison Blues/That's What The Lord Can Do	15
57	Brunswick LAT 8179	SANTA FE TRAIL (LP)	20

(see also Karen Chandler)

RICK WAKEMAN
73	A&M AMS 7061	Anne/Catherine	5
75	A&M AMS 7206	Love's Dream/Orpheus Song	5
75	A&M/Lyntone LYN 3176/7	Wagner's Dream/Love's Dream/Count Your Blessings (with Roger Daltrey, flexidisc free with '19' magazine)	7/5
79	A&M AMS 7435	Birdman Of Alcatraz/Flacons De Neige (p/s)	4
79	A&M AMS 7436	Animal Showdown/Sea Horses (p/s)	4
79	A&M AMS 7436	Animal Showdown/Yes We Have No Bananas/Sea Horses (picture disc)	5
80	WEA K 18354	Spider/Danielle (2,000 only)	4
71	Polydor 2460 135	PIANO VIBRATIONS (LP)	15

(see also Yes, Steve Howe, Jon Anderson, Bruford)

ANTON WALBROOK
53	Parlophone MSP 6002	La Rondo De L'Amour/BERLIN 'SYMPHONIKER' ORCHESTRA: The Blue Waltz	4
54	Parlophone MSP 6099	Always Young/If Only Took A Minute	4
54	Parlophone MSP 6100	Strike Another Match/Man Is Man	4

(see also Susan Swinford & Jeff Warren)

JERRY WALD
60	London HLU 8909	Sheba/Moon Over Miami (unissued)	

WALHAM GREEN E. WAPPING C.C.R.B.E. ASSOCIATION
68	Columbia DB 8426	Sorry Mr. Green/Death Of A Kind	30

BILLY WALKER (U.K.)
60	Philips PB 1001	Forever/Changed My Mind	6
64	Decca F 11917	My Heart Cries For You/Little On The Lonely Side	4
65	Columbia DB 7724	A Certain Girl/I Don't Wanna Fall In Love	6

BILLY WALKER (U.S.)
66	London HLU 10060	Million And One/Close To Linda	4

BOOTS WALKER
69	London HLP 10265	No One Knows/Geraldine	4

CLINT WALKER
60	Warner Bros WEP 6006	INSPIRATION (EP, also stereo WSEP 2006)	8/12

DAVID WALKER
68	RCA RCA 1664	Ring The Changes/Keep A Little Love	20

(see also Paradox)

GARY WALKER (& RAIN)
66	CBS 202036	You Don't Love Me/Get It Right	6
66	CBS 202081	Twinkie-Lee/She Makes Me Feel Better	5
68	Polydor 56237	Spooky/I Can't Stand To Lose You (as Gary Walker & Rain)	6
68	Philips BF 1740	Come In You'll Get Pneumonia/Francis (as Gary Walker & Rain)	25
74	United Artists UP 35742	Hello How Are You/Fran	4
66	CBS EPS 5742	HERE'S GARY (EP)	10

(see also Walker Brothers, Paul & Ritchie & Cryin' Shames, Badfinger, Universals)

JACKIE WALKER
58	London HLP 8588	Oh Lonesome Me/Only Teenagers Allowed	125
58	London HLP 8588	Oh Lonesome Me/Only Teenagers Allowed (78)	30

JOHN WALKER

67	Philips BF 1593	Anabella/You Don't Understand Me	4
67	Philips BF 1612	I Promise/I See Love In You	4
68	Philips BF 1655	I'll Be Your Baby Tonight/Open The Door Homer	4
68	Philips BF 1676	Kentucky Woman/I Cried All The Way Home	4
68	Philips BF 1724	Woman/Dream	4
69	Philips BF 1758	Yesterday's Sunshine/Little One	4
69	Carnaby CNS 4002	Everywhere Under The Sun/Traces Of Tomorrow	4
70	Carnaby CNS 4009	True Grit/Sun Comes Up	4
70	Carnaby CNS 4012	Cottonfields/Jamie	4
71	Carnaby CNS 4017	Over And Over Again/Sun Comes Up	4
67	Philips (S)BL 7829	IF YOU GO AWAY (LP)	25
69	Carnaby CNLS 6001	THIS IS JOHN WALKER (LP)	20

(see also Walker Brothers, John & Scott Walker)

JOHN & SCOTT WALKER

66	Philips BB 12597	SOLO JOHN — SOLO SCOTT (EP, 2 tracks each)	10

(see also Walker Brothers, Scott Walker, John Walker, Scott Engel)

JUNIOR WALKER & ALL STARS

65	Tamla Motown TMG 509	Shotgun/Hot'Cha	15
65	Tamla Motown TMG 520	Do The Boomerang/Tune Up	50
65	Tamla Motown TMG 529	Shake And Fingerpop/Cleo's Back	15
66	Tamla Motown TMG 550	Cleo's Mood/Baby You Know It Ain't Right	15
66	Tamla Motown TMG 559	Road Runner/Shoot Your Shot	10
66	Tamla Motown TMG 571	How Sweet It Is (To Be Loved By You)/Nothing But Soul (small print on label)	12
67	Tamla Motown TMG 571	How Sweet It Is (To Be Loved By You)/Nothing But Soul (later pressing)	6
66	Tamla Motown TMG 586	Money (That's What I Want) Pts 1& 2	10
67	Tamla Motown TMG 596	Pucker Up Buttercup/Any Way You Wannta	12
68	Tamla Motown TMG 637	Come See About Me/Sweet Soul	6
68	Tamla Motown TMG 667	Hip City Pts 1 & 2	5
69	Tamla Motown TMG 682	Home Cookin'/Mutiny	5
69	Tamla Motown TMG 691	Road Runner/Shotgun	4
69	Tamla Motown TMG 712	What Does It Take To Win Your Love/Brainwasher	4
70	Tamla Motown TMG 727	These Eyes/Got To Find A Way To Win Maria Back	4
66	Tamla Motown TME 2013	SHAKE AND FINGERPOP (EP)	20
65	Tamla Motown TML 11017	SHOTGUN (LP)	30
66	Tamla Motown TML 11029	SOUL SESSION (LP)	20
66	T. Motown (S)TML 11038	ROAD RUNNER (LP)	20
69	T. Motown (S)TML 11097	HOME COOKIN' (LP)	15
69	T. Motown (S)TML 11120	JUNIOR WALKER'S GREATEST HITS (LP)	10
70	T. Motown (S)TML 11140	THESE EYES (LP)	10
70	T. Motown STML 11152	LIVE (LP)	15
70	T. Motown STML 11167	A GASSSS! (LP)	12
72	T. Motown STML 11198	RAINBOW FUNK (LP)	10
72	T. Motown STML 11211	MOODY JUNIOR (LP)	10
73	T. Motown STML 11234	PEACE AND UNDERSTANDING IS HARD TO FIND (LP)	10

K. (Kent) WALKER & ALLSTARS

70s	Rymska RA 103	One Minute To Zero/Don't Come Back	6

KENT WALKER

68	Fab FAB 53	When You Going To Show Me How/Come Yah Come Yah	5

(see also K. Walker)

ROB WALKER

71	Upsetter US 366	Run Up Your Mouth (actually by Stranger Cole)/UPSETTERS: Version	5

RONNIE WALKER

69	Stateside SS 2151	It's A Good Feeling/Precious	8
75	Polydor 2006 578	Magic's In The Air/They Can't Say Hello	4

SCOTT WALKER

67	Philips BF 1628	Jackie/The Plague	5
68	Philips BF 1662	Joanna/Always Coming Back To You	5
69	Philips BF 1793	Lights of Cincinnati/Two Weeks Since You've Gone	4
72	Philips 6006 168	I Can Still See You/My This Way Home	4
71	Philips 6006 311	The Me I Never Knew/This Way Mary	4
73	CBS 1795	A Woman Left Lonely/Where Love Has Died	4
74	CBS 2521	Delta Dawn/We Had It All	4
67	Liberty LEP 2261	SCOTT ENGEL (EP)	20
67	Philips MCP 1006	GREAT SCOTT (cassette EP)	20
67	Philips (S)BL 7816	SCOTT (LP, mono/stereo)	15/20
68	Philips BL 7840	SCOTT 2 (LP, mono, originally with free signed portrait)	20/12
68	Philips SBL 7840	SCOTT 2 (LP, stereo, originally with free signed portrait)	25/15
68	Ember EMB LP 3393	LOOKING BACK WITH SCOTT WALKER (LP, mono or stereo)	18
69	Philips SBL 7882	SCOTT 3 (LP, gatefold sleeve)	30
69	Philips SBL 7900	SCOTT WALKER SINGS SONGS FROM HIS TV SERIES (LP)	15
69	Philips SBL 7910	THE BEST OF SCOTT WALKER VOL. 1 (LP)	12
69	Philips SBL 7913	SCOTT 4 (LP)	45
70	Philips 6308 035	'TIL THE BAND COMES IN (LP)	50
72	Philips 6308 127	THE MOVIEGOER (LP)	35
73	Philips 6308 148	ANY DAY NOW (LP)	35
73	CBS 65725	STRETCH (LP)	20
74	CBS 80254	WE HAD IT ALL (LP)	15
76	Philips 6625 017	SPOTLIGHT ON SCOTT WALKER (2-LP)	16
70s	Philips 6850 013	ROMANTIC SCOTT WALKER (LP)	30
70s	Philips 6850 022	TERRIFIC (LP, reissue of "Scott 2" with different cuts)	35

Scott WALKER

81	Zoo ZOO 2	FIRE ESCAPE IN THE SKY — THE GODLIKE GENIUS OF SCOTT WALKER (LP)	20

(see also Scott Engel, John & Scott Walker, Walker Brothers, Routers)

T-BONE WALKER

54	London HL 8087	The Hustle Is On/Baby Broke My Heart (78)	30
65	Liberty LIB 12018	Party Girl/Here In The Dark	12
63	London REP 1404	TRAVELLIN' BLUES (EP)	30
54	Capitol LC 6681	CLASSICS IN JAZZ (10" LP)	40
63	Capitol T 1958	T-BONE WALKER (LP)	20
65	MFP MFP 1043	THE BLUES OF T-BONE WALKER (LP)	20
68	MCA MUPS 331	THE TRUTH (LP)	10
68	Stateside S(S)L 10223	STORMY MONDAY BLUES (LP)	12
69	Stateside S(S)L 10265	FUNKY TOWN (LP)	15

WALKER BROTHERS

65	Philips BF 1401	Pretty Girls Everywhere/Doin' The Jerk	6
65	Philips BF 1409	Love Her/The Seventh Dawn	6
65	Philips BF 1428	Make It Easy On Yourself/But I Do	4
65	Philips BF 1454	My Ship Is Coming In/Don't Leave Me Now	4
66	Philips BF 1473	The Sun Ain't Gonna Shine Anymore/After The Lights Go Out	4
66	Philips BF 1497	(Baby) You Don't Have To Tell Me/My Love Is Growing	4
66	Philips BF 1537	Deadlier Than The Male/Archangel	5
66	Philips BF 1514	Another Tear Falls/The Saddest Night In The World	5
67	Philips BF 1548	Stay With Me Baby/Turn Out The Moon	5
67	Philips BF 1576	Walking In The Rain/Baby Make It The Last Time	5
76	GTO GT 67	Lines/First Day	4
77	GTO GT 78	We're All Alone/Have You Seen My Baby	4
78	GTO GT 230	The Electrician/Den Haague	4
66	Philips BE 12596	I NEED YOU (EP)	10
67	Philips BE 12603	THE WALKER BROTHERS (EP, probably unreleased)	30+
67	Philips MCP 1004	THE HITS OF THE WALKER BROTHERS & DUSTY SPRINGFIELD (cassette EP)	10
65	Philips BL 7691	TAKE IT EASY WITH THE WALKER BROTHERS (LP)	15
66	Philips BL 7732	PORTRAIT (LP, initially with photo insert)	18/12
67	Philips (S)BL 7770	IMAGES (LP)	12
67	Philips Intl. DBL 002	THE WALKER BROTHERS STORY (2-LP)	14
68	Wing WL 1188	THE FABULOUS WALKER BROTHERS (LP)	10
69	Philips SFL 13181	THE IMMORTAL WALKER BROTHERS (LP)	10

(see also Scott Walker, Scott Engel, John Walker, John & Scott Walker, Gary Walker [& Rain], Routers)

WALKIE TALKIES

79	Sire SIR 4023	Rich And Nasty/Summer In Russia	7

(see also Pauline Murray & Invisible Girls, Mission)

WALKING FLOORS

80s	My Death Telephone TEL1	No Next Time/Removal (foldover p/s)	4

WALKINGSEEDS

86	Probe Plus PP 19T	KNOW TOO MUCH (12" EP)	7
87	Moral Burro CEDE 2	Mark Chapman/Blathering Out (12", p/s)	7
90	Clawfist PIS 1	Reflection In A Tall Mirror/BEVIS FROND: Sexorcist (p/s, mail-order only)	6
90	Paperhouse PAPER 001	Gates Of Freedom/Astronomy Dominé (1,000 only)	4

(see also Bevis Frond)

FRED WALKING-STICK

61	Pye 7N 15390	When I Ask Yew/Ain't She Sweet	4

DENNIS WALKS

68	Amalgamated AMG 816	Having A Party/GROOVERS: Day By Day	8
68	Blue Cat BS 144	Belly Lick/DRUMBAGO & BLENDERS: The Game Song	8
69	Bullet BU 402	Heart Don't Leap/CLARENDONIANS: I Am Sorry	4
69	Bullet BU 408	Love Of My Life/Under The Shady Tree	4
71	Moodisc HM 101	Time Will Tell/Under The Shady Tree	4

WALL

79	Small Wonder SMALL 13	New Way/Suckers/Uniforms (p/s)	4

MAX WALL

73	York YR 203	The Fiddley Foodle Bird/Story Of The Fiddley Foodle Bird	4
75	DJM DJS 10352	Why Should I Care/Devil Bomb	4
77	Stiff BUY 12	England's Glory/Dream Tobacco (p/s)	4

REM WALL & HIS GREEN VALLEY BOYS

60	Top Rank JAR 324	Heartsick And Blue/One More Time	5

GIG WALLACE & HIS ORCHESTRA

60	Philips PB 981	Rockin' On The Railroad/Show Me The Way To Go Home	7
60	Philips PB 981	Rockin' On The Railroad/Show Me The Way To Go Home (78)	5

JERRY WALLACE

54	Polygon P 1133	Dixieanna/Runnin' After Love (78)	10
58	London HL 8719	With This Ring/How The Time Flies	12
58	London HL 8719	With This Ring/How The Time Flies (78)	20
58	London HL 7062	With This Ring/How The Time Flies (export issue)	6
59	London HLH 8943	Primrose Lane/By Your Side	6
60	London HLH 9040	Little Coco Palm/Mission Bell Blues	6
60	London HLH 9110	You're Singing Our Love Song To Somebody Else/King Of The Mountain	6
60	London HLH 9177	Swingin' Down The Lane/Teardrop In The Rain	5
61	London HLH 9264	There She Goes/Angel On My Shoulder	5
61	London HLH 9363	Life's A Holiday/I Can See An Angel	5
62	London HLH 9630	Shutters And Boards/Am I That Easy To Forget	5

| 64 | London HLH 9914 | Even The Bad Times Are Good/In The Misty Moonlight | 5 |
| 65 | Mercury MF 853 | Time/Rainbow | 4 |

SIPPIE WALLACE

| 67 | Storyville 671 198 | SIPPIE WALLACE SINGS THE BLUES (LP) | 15 |

WALLACE BROTHERS

64	Sue WI 334	Precious Words/You're Mine	10
65	Sue WI 355	Lover's Prayer/Love Me Like I Love You	15
67	Sue WI 4036	I'll Step Aside/Hold My Heart For A While	15
67	Sue ILP 950	SOUL CONNECTION (LP)	125

WALLACE COLLECTION

69	Parlophone R 5764	Daydream/Baby I Don't Mind	8
69	Parlophone R 5793	Love/Fly Me To The Earth	8
70	Parlophone R 5844	Serenade/Walk On Out	8
70	Parlophone PMC 7096	LAUGHING CAVALIER (LP, also stereo PCS 7096)	12
70	Parlophone PMC 7099	WALLACE COLLECTION (LP, also stereo PCS 7099)	10

'FATS' WALLER (& HIS RHYTHM)

50	HMV B 9935	I'm Gonna Sit Right Down And Write A Letter/Everybody Loves My Baby (78)	5
53	HMV 7M 128	My Very Good Friend The Milkman/Shortnin' Bread	8
53	HMV 7M 142	Honey Hush/You've Been Reading My Mail	8
53	HMV 7M 157	A Good Man Is Hard To Find/The Girl I Left Behind Me	7
54	HMV 7M 208	You've Been Taking Lessons In Love/I've Got A New Lease Of Life	7
54	HMV 7M 244	By The Light Of The Silvery Moon/Romance A La Mode (as Fats Waller & Deep River Boys)	10
60	RCA RCA 1189	Dinah/When Somebody Thinks You're Wonderful	4
54	HMV 7EG 8022	FATS WALLER AND HIS RHYTHM (EP)	7
54	HMV 7EG 8042	FATS WALLER AND HIS RHYTHM (EP)	7
54	HMV 7EG 8054	FATS WALLER AND HIS RHYTHM (EP)	7
55	HMV 7EG 8078	FATS WALLER AND HIS RHYTHM (EP)	7
55	HMV 7EG 8098	FATS WALLER (EP)	7
56	HMV 7EG 8148	FATS WALLER AND HIS RHYTHM (EP)	8
56	HMV 7EG 8191	SWINGING AT THE ORGAN (EP)	7
57	HMV 7EG 8212	FATS WALLER (EP)	7
57	HMV 7EG 8242	FATS WALLER AND HIS RHYTHM (EP)	7
57	HMV 7EG 8255	FATS WALLER AND HIS RHYTHM (EP)	8
58	HMV 7EG 8304	FATS WALLER IN LONDON NO. 1 (EP)	7
58	HMV 7EG 8341	FATS WALLER IN LONDON NO. 2 (EP)	7
59	RCA RCX 1010	FATS WALLER (EP)	8
59	RCA RCX 1053	YOUR FEET'S TOO BIG (EP)	10
60	HMV 7EG 8602	FATS WALLER IN LONDON NO. 3 (EP)	7
53	London AL 3507	REDISCOVERED FATS WALLER SOLOS (10" LP)	25
53	HMV DLP 1008	FAVOURITES (10" LP)	20
53	HMV DLP 1017	PLAYS AND SINGS (10" LP)	20
54	HMV DLP 1056	RHYTHM AND ROMANCE WITH FATS WALLER (10" LP)	20
54	London AL 3521	FATS AT THE ORGAN (10" LP)	20
54	London AL 3522	JIVIN' WITH FATS (10" LP)	20
55	HMV DLP 1082	FUN WITH FATS (10" LP)	15
55	HMV CLP 1036	THOMAS "FATS" WALLER NO. 1 (LP)	12
55	HMV CLP 1042	THOMAS "FATS" WALLER NO. 2 (LP)	12
56	HMV DLP 1111	YOUNG FATS WALLER (10" LP)	15
56	HMV DLP 1118	FAVOURITES NO. 2 (10" LP)	15
57	HMV DLP 1138	SPREADIN' RHYTHM AROUND (10" LP)	15
57	RCA RD 27047	FATS 1935-1937 (LP)	15
58	RCA RC 24004	FATS 1938-1942 (10" LP)	15
59	RCA Camden CDN 131	THE REAL FATS WALLER (LP)	12
60	RCA RD 27185	HANDFUL OF KEYS (LP)	10

GORDON (WALLER)

68	Columbia DB 8337	Rosecrans Boulevard/Red, Cream And Velvet	6
68	Columbia DB 8440	Every Day/Because Of A Woman	5
68	Columbia DB 8518	Weeping Annaleah/The Seventh Hour	5
69	Bell BLL 1059	I Was A Boy When You Needed A Man/Lady In The Window	4
70	Bell BLL 1106	You're Gonna Hurt Yourself/Sunshine	4
72	Vertigo 6360 069	GORDON (LP, as Gordon, gatefold sleeve, spiral label)	100

(see also Peter & Gordon)

BOB WALLIS & HIS STORYVILLE JAZZMEN

60	Top Rank JAR 331	Bluebird/Captain Morgan	4
60	Top Rank JAR 365	Madison Time/Bonne Nuit, Ma Cherie	4
60	Pye Jazz 7NJ 2039	Jingle Bells/Chinatown, My Chinatown	4
60	Pye Jazz NJE 1079	BOB WALLIS STORYVILLE JAZZMEN (EP)	7
60	Pye Jazz NJE 1085	BOB WALLIS PLAYS (EP)	7
62	Storyville SEP 368	BOB WALLIS STORYVILLE JAZZMEN (EP)	7
60	Top Rank BUY 023	EVERYBODY LOVES SATURDAY NIGHT (LP)	10
61	Pye Jazz NJL 27	OLE MAN RIVER (LP)	10
61	Pye Jazz NJL 30	TRAVELLIN' BLUES (LP)	10
62	Pye Jazz NJL 41	THE WALLIS COLLECTION (LP)	10

BOB WALLIS & SANDY BROWN

| 62 | Pye Jazz 7NJ 2060 | Oh Didn't It Rain/In A Little Spanish Town | 4 |

LARRY WALLIS

| 77 | Stiff BUY 22 | Police Car/On Parole (die-cut company sleeve) | 4 |

(see also Pink Fairies, Peter Wyngarde)

SHANI WALLIS

| 60 | Philips PB 1019 | Sixteen Reasons (Why I Love You)/Forever, Forever | 4 |
| 60 | Philips PB 1076 | Where's The Boy/And Now | 4 |

MINT VALUE £

67	London HLR 10125	Look Of Love/Let Your Love Come Through	4
68	London HLR 10225	As Long As He Needs Me/Where Is Love	4
67	London HA-R 8324	I'M A GIRL (LP)	10
67	London HA-R/SH-R 8338	LOOK TO LOVE (LP)	10

(see also Kirchin Band)

WALL OF VOODOO
| 82 | Illegal ILS 0031 | On Interstate 15/There's Nothing On This Side (p/s) | 4 |

WALRUS
70	Deram DM 308	Who Can I Trust?/Tomorrow Never Comes	4
71	Deram DM 323	Never Let My Body Touch Ground/Why	4
71	Deram SML 1072	WALRUS (LP)	25

JOE WALSH
| 73 | Probe PRO 600 | Rocky Mountain Way/(Daydream) Prayer | 4 |
| 74 | Probe PRO 611 | Meadows/Book Ends | 4 |

(see also James Gang)

SHEILA WALSH & CLIFF RICHARD
83	DJM SHEIL 1	Drifting/It's Lonely When The Lights Go Out (p/s)	4
83	DJM SHEIL 100	Drifting/It's Lonely When The Lights Go Out (picture disc)	8
83	DJM SHEILT 1	Drifting/It's Lonely When The Lights Go Out (12", p/s)	7
83	DJM SHEILT 100	Drifting/It's Lonely When The Lights Go Out (12" picture disc)	10

(see also Cliff Richard)

WALTER MITTY'S LITTLE WHITE LIES
| 81 | Hip HIP 2 | Brave New England/Good Boys From The South (p/s) | 4 |

BURT WALTERS
| 68 | Trojan TR 636 | Honey Love/KING CANNONBALL BRYAN: Thunderstorm | 7 |

DAVE WALTON
66	CBS 202057	Love Ain't What It Used To Be/Tell Me A Lie	8
66	CBS 202098	Every Window In The City/I've Left The Troubled Ground	4
67	CBS 202508	After You There Can Be Nothing/Can I Get It From You	4

WALTONES
87	Medium Cool MC 004	Downhill/Closest To	4
88	Medium Cool MC 016	I Dig You The Deepest/Fall In Love	4
80s	Zine 10	She Looks Right Through Me (Demo Version)/HEPBURNS: Where You Belong (flexidisc with 'Zine' fanzine, issue 10)	6/5

TRAVIS WAMMACK
65	Atlantic AT 4017	Scratchy/Fire Fly	20
72	United Artists UP 35412	What Ever Turns You On/Slip Away	4
72	United Artists UP 35468	So Good/Darling, You're All That I Need	4

WANDERER
| 59 | Top Rank JAR 183 | The Happy Hobo/True True Loneliness | 4 |
| 59 | Top Rank JAR 183 | The Happy Hobo/True True Loneliness (78) | 18 |

WANDERERS (U.S.)
60	MGM MGM 1102	I Could Make You Mine/I Need You More	20
61	MGM MGM 1169	As Time Goes By/There Is No Greater Love	15
64	United Artists UP 1020	Run Run Senorita/After He Breaks Your Heart	15

(see also Ray Pollard)

WANDERERS (Jamaica)
| 69 | Trojan TR 7721 | Wiggle Waggle/Jaga Jaga War | 5 |

WANDERERS (U.K.)
81	Polydor POSP 239	Ready To Snap/Beyond The Law	6
81	Polydor POSP 284	The Times They Are A'Changin'/Little Bit Frightening	6
81	Polydor POLS 1028	ONLY LOVERS LEFT (LP)	12

(see also Lords Of The New Church, Stiv Bators, Dead Boys)

WANGLERS
| 70s | Matchbox Classics MC 5 | KICKIN' OUT FOR THE COAST (EP, white label, yellow or red stickered foldover p/s) | 4 |

DEXTER WANSEL
| 78 | Phil. Intl. PIR 82786 | VOYAGER (LP) | 30 |
| 86 | Streetwave SWAVE 9 | Life On Mars Parts 1 & 2 (12", p/s) | 10 |

WAR
71	Liberty LBF 15443	Sun Oh Son/Lonely Feelin'	4
71	United Artists UP 35281	All Day Music/Get Down	5
72	United Artists UP 35327	Slipping Into Darkness/Nappy Head	4
72	United Artists UP 35469	The World Is A Ghetto/Four Cornered Room	4
73	United Artists UP 35521	Cisco Kid/Beetles In The Bog	4
73	United Artists UP 35576	Gypsy Man/Deliver The Word	4
74	United Artists UP 35623	Me And Baby Brother/In Your Eyes	4
75	United Artists UP 35836	Why Can't We Be Friends/In Mazatlan	4
77	MCA 12MCA 339	Galaxy Parts 1 & 2	7
71	Liberty LBG 83478	WAR (LP)	12
72	United Artists UAS 29269	ALL DAY MUSIC (LP)	12
73	United Artists UAS 29400	THE WORLD IS A GHETTO (LP)	10
73	United Artists UAG 29521	DELIVER THE WORD (LP)	10
75	United Artists UAG 29843	WHY CAN'T WE BE FRIENDS (LP)	10

(see also Eric Burdon & War)

BILLY WARD & HIS DOMINOES
| 53 | Parlophone R 3789 | Don't Thank Me/Rags To Riches (78) | 30 |
| 54 | Parlophone MSP 6112 | Three Coins In The Fountain/Lonesome Road | 90 |

MINT VALUE £

54	Parlophone R 3882	Three Coins In The Fountain/Lonesome Road (78)	35
56	Brunswick 05599	St. Therese Of The Roses/Home Is Where You Hang Your Heart	22
56	Brunswick 05599	St. Therese Of The Roses/Home Is Where You Hang Your Heart (78)	5
57	Brunswick 05656	Evermore/Half A Love (Is Better Than None)	18
57	Brunswick 05656	Evermore/Half A Love (Is Better Than None) (78)	5
57	London HLU 8465	Stardust/Lucinda	18
57	London HLU 8465	Stardust/Lucinda (78)	5
57	London HLU 8502	Deep Purple/Do It Again	18
57	London HLU 8502	Deep Purple/Do It Again (78)	5
58	London HLU 8634	Jennie Lee/Music, Maestro, Please	20
58	London HLU 8634	Jennie Lee/Music, Maestro, Please (78)	15
59	London HLU 8883	Please Don't Say 'No'/Behave, Hula Girl	12
59	London HLU 8883	Please Don't Say 'No'/Behave, Hula Girl (78)	5
58	London REU 1114	BILLY WARD AND HIS DOMINOES (EP)	100
58	Parlophone PMD 1061	BILLY WARD AND HIS DOMINOES FEATURING CLYDE McPHATTER (10" LP)	450
58	London HA-U 2116	YOURS FOREVER (LP)	40

(see also Dominoes, Clyde McPhatter, Jackie Wilson)

CHRISTINE WARD
| 66 | Decca F 12339 | The Face Of Empty Me/Girl I Used To Know | 10 |

CLARA WARD & HER SINGERS
| 65 | Stateside SS 474 | Gonna Build A Mountain/God Bless The Child | 4 |

CLIFFORD T. WARD
| 72 | Dandelion 2310 216 | SINGER SONGWRITER (LP) | 10 |

(see also Secrets, Simon's Secrets, Martin Raynor & Secrets)

DALE WARD
| 64 | London HLD 9835 | Oh Julie/Letter From Sherry | 8 |

HEDLEY WARD TRIO
| 56 | Melodisc MEL 1387 | Steamboat Rock/My Baby's Got Such Lovin' Ways (78) | 20 |

ROBIN WARD
| 63 | London HLD 9821 | Wonderful Summer/Dream Boy | 8 |

TERRY WARD with BUMBLIES
| 65 | Fontana TF 558 | Gotta Tell/When I Come To You | 4 |

WARD SINGERS
| 56 | London Jazz LZ-C 14013 | THE FAMOUS WARD SINGERS (10" LP) | 15 |

SHEELAGH WARDE
| 59 | Top Rank JAR 131 | Let Mr. Maguire Sit Down//The Golden Jubilee | 4 |

WARDENS
| 70s | SNO PEAS TIC 001 | Lust Like This/Do So Well (with insert, no p/s) | 4 |

WARDS OF COURT
| 67 | Deram DM 127 | All Night Girl/How Could Say One Thing | 8 |

LEON WARE
| 77 | Motown STML 12050 | MUSICAL MASSAGE (LP) | 18 |

WARHORSE
70	Vertigo 6059 027	St. Louis/No Chance	8
70	Vertigo 6360 015	WARHORSE (LP, spiral label, gatefold sleeve)	30
72	Vertigo 6360 066	RED SEA (LP, spiral label, gatefold sleeve)	45

(see also Deep Purple)

FRED WARING & HIS PENNSYLVANIANS
59	Capitol CL 14981	Dry Bones/Way Back Home	4
55	Brunswick OE 9194	THE BALLAD OF DAVY CROCKETT (EP)	10
51	Brunswick LAT 8011	LISTENING TIME (LP)	12
53	Brunswick LA 8625	WALT DISNEY FILM SONGS (10" LP)	12
54	Brunswick LA 8651	A SONG OF EASTER (10" LP)	10
54	Brunswick LA 8678	SONGS OF INSPIRATION (10" LP)	10
54	Brunswick LA 8693	'TWAS THE NIGHT BEFORE CHRISTMAS (10" LP)	10
55	Brunswick LA 8704	HARMONIZIN' THE OLD SONGS (10" LP)	10
55	Brunswick LAT 8068	FOR LISTENING ONLY (LP)	10

RAY WARLEIGH
| 69 | Philips SBL 7881 | RAY WARLEIGH'S FIRST ALBUM (LP) | 22 |

(see also John Mayall's Blues Breakers)

OZZIE WARLOCK & WIZARDS
| 59 | HMV POP 635 | Juke Box Fury/Wow! | 8 |

WARM
78	Warm 2001	It's The Kooler/Teenage Space Queen (p/s)	5
78	Warm SMS 001/2001/S	THE DEMO TAPES (EP, double pack)	10
78	Warm WARM 2003	Floosie/Chewing Gum Sue/Bye Bye It's Blues/Sometimes (p/s)	4

WARM DUST
70	Trend 6099 002	It's A Beautiful Day/Worm Dance	6
70	Trend TNLS 700	AND IT CAME TO PASS (2-LP)	20
71	Trend 6480 001	PEACE FOR OUR TIME (LP, white or black vinyl)	20/15

WARM EXPRESSION
| 70 | Columbia DB 8672 | Let No Man Put Asunder/The Holy City | 7 |

WARM JETS
| 79 | RSO RSO 47 | Big City Boys/Mr Natural (p/s) | 4 |
| 81 | Bridgehouse BHS 1 | Sticky Jack/Shell Shock (p/s) | 5 |

WARM SENSATION
| 69 | Columbia DB 8568 | I'll Be Proud Of You/The Clown | 4 |

(see also Ivy League)

WARM SOUNDS
67	Immediate IM 058	Sticks And Stones/Angeline	6
67	Deram DM 120	The Birds And Bees/Doo-Dah	6
68	Deram DM 174	Nite Is A-Comin'/Smeta Mergaty	20

(see also Denny Gerrard, Tuesday's Children)

JOHNNY WARMAN
| 78 | Ring O' 2017 112 | Head On Collision/London's Burning/Mind Games (die-cut company sleeve) | 4 |
| 81 | Rocket TRAIN 17 | WALKING INTO MIRRORS (LP) | 10 |

HERB & BETTY WARNER
| 59 | Felsted AF 114 | Slowly/'BUGS' BOWER GROUP: Slowly | 4 |

JACK WARNER with TOMMY REILLY
| 58 | Oriole CB 1426 | An Ordinary Copper/On The Way Up | 5 |

FLORENCE WARNER
73	Epic EPC 1626	For No Good Reason/Remember	4
75	Epic EPC 3817	Anyway I Love You/Dreamer	4
73	Epic EPC 80077	FLORENCE WARNER (LP)	15

GALE WARNING
| 56 | Pye N 15061 | Heartbreak Hotel/Met Rock (78) | 8 |
| 56 | Oriole CB 1349 | Rock Those Crazy Skins/I Need Your Love (78) | 10 |

WARP
| 70s | Warped WPD 001 | Do The Warp/ECT: (Here In Britain)/Fable/White (p/s) | 5 |

WARP NINE
| 75 | Stax STXS 2030 | Theme From 'Star Trek'/Para Song One | 4 |

ALMA WARREN
| 56 | Parlophone MSP 6200 | Stealin'/Now And Forever | 6 |

GUY WARREN
59	Brunswick 05791	Monkies And Butterflies/An African's Prayer (with Rod Saunders)	4
69	Columbia SCX 6340	AFRO-JAZZ (LP, as Guy Warren Of Ghana)	25
72	Regal Zono. SLRZ 1031	THE AFRICAN SOUNDS OF GUY WARREN (LP)	25

WARRIOR
| 84 | Warrior W 002 | BREAKOUT (7" EP, paper sleeve) | 10 |
| 83 | Warrior W 001 | FOR EUROPE ONLY (mini-LP) | 15 |

WARRIORS
| 64 | Decca F 11926 | You Came Along/Don't Make Me Blue | 35 |

(see also Yes)

WARRIORS
| 79 | Object OM 07 | Martial Time/Martial Law (p/s) | 4 |

WARSAW/JOY DIVISION
| 81 | Enigma PSS 138 | THE IDEAL BEGINNING (EP, poster p/s, semi-official release) | 15 |
| 81 | Enigma PSS 138 | THE IDEAL BEGINNING (12" EP, alternate tracks, semi-official release) | 15 |

(see also Joy Division)

WARSAW PAKT
| 78 | Island PAKT 1 | Safe And Warm/Sick And Tired (a few with p/s) | 40/10 |
| 77 | Island ILPS 9515 | NEEDLE TIME (LP, numbered stamped mailer p/s, with insert) | 20 |

DEE DEE WARWICK
65	Mercury MF 860	Do It With All Your Heart/Happiness	5
65	Mercury MF 867	We're Doin' Fine/You Don't Know	5
65	Mercury MF 890	Gotta Get A Hold Of Myself/Another Lonely Saturday	6
66	Mercury MF 909	A Lover's Chant/Worth Every Tear I Cry	18
65	Mercury MF 937	I Want To Be With You/Alfie	4
65	Mercury MF 953	Yours Till Tomorrow/I'm Gonna Make You Love Me	5
67	Mercury MF 974	When Love Slips Away/House Of God	6
68	Mercury MF 1061	I'll Be Better Off (Without You)/Monday, Monday	8
69	Mercury MF 1084	Foolish Heart/Thank God	4
69	Mercury MF 1125	That's Not Love/It's Not Fair	4
70	Atlantic 2091 011	She Didn't Know (She Kept On Talking)/Make Love To Me	5
70	Atlantic 2091 037	If This Was The Last Song/I'm Only Human	4
71	Atlantic 2091 057	Cold Night In Georgia/Searching	4
71	Atlantic 2091 092	Suspicious Minds/I'm Glad I'm A Woman	4
75	Private Stock PVT 13	Get Out Of My Life/Funny How Places Change	4
66	Mercury 10036 MCE	WE'RE DOING FINE (EP)	10

DIONNE WARWICK
63	Stateside SS 157	Don't Make Me Over/I Smiled Yesterday	7
63	Stateside SS 191	This Empty Place/Wishin' And Hopin'	7
63	Stateside SS 222	Please Let Him Love Me/Make The Music Play	10
63	Warner Bros WB 16530	Take It From Me/Sure Thing	5
63	Pye International 7N 25223	Please Let Him Love Me/Make The Music Play (reissue)	5
64	Pye International 7N 25234	Anyone Who Had A Heart/The Love Of A Boy	4
64	Pye International 7N 25241	Walk On By/Anytime Of Day	4
64	Pye International 7N 25256	You'll Never Get To Heaven/A House Is Not A Home	4
64	Pye International 7N 25265	Reach Out For Me/How Many Days Of Sadness	4
65	Pye International 7N 25290	You Can Have Him/Don't Say I Didn't Tell You	4
65	Pye International 7N 25302	Who Can I Turn To/That's Not The Answer	4
65	Pye International 7N 25310	(Here I Go Again) Looking With My Eyes/Only The Strong, Only The Brave	4

65	Pye International 7N 25316	Here I Am/They Long To Be Close To You	4
65	Pye International 7N 25338	Are You There (With Another Girl)/If I Ever Make You Cry	4
66	Pye International 7N 25357	In Between The Heartaches/Long Day, Short Night	4
66	Pye International 7N 25368	A Message To Michael/Here Where There Is Love	4
66	Pye International 7N 25378	Trains And Boats And Planes/Don't Go Breaking My Heart	4
66	Pye International 7N 25395	Another Night/Go With Love	4
67	Pye International 7N 25424	Alfie/The Beginning Of Loneliness	4
67	Pye International 7N 25428	The Windows Of The World/Walk Little Dolly	4
67	Pye International 7N 25435	I Say A Little Prayer/Window Wishin'	4
68	Pye International 7N 25445	(Theme From) The Valley Of The Dolls/Zip-A-Dee-Doo-Dah	4
68	Pye International 7N 25457	Do You Know The Way To San Jose?/Let Me Be Lonely	4
68	Pye International 7N 25474	Who Is Gonna Love Me?/(There's) Always Something There To Remind Me	4
64	Pye Intl. NEP 44024	IT'S LOVE THAT REALLY COUNTS (EP)	7
64	Pye Intl. NEP 44026	DON'T MAKE ME OVER (EP)	7
65	Pye Intl. NEP 44039	WISHIN' AND HOPIN' (EP)	7
65	Pye Intl. NEP 44044	DIONNE (EP)	7
65	Pye Intl. NEP 44046	FOREVER MY LOVE (EP)	7
65	Pye Intl. NEP 44049	WHO CAN I TURN TO? (EP)	7
66	Pye Intl. NEP 44051	HERE I AM (EP)	7
66	Pye Intl. NEP 44067	MESSAGE TO MICHAEL (EP)	7
66	Pye Intl. NEP 44073	WINDOW WISHIN' (EP)	7
66	Pye Intl. NEP 44077	I JUST DON'T KNOW WHAT TO DO WITH MYSELF (EP)	7
67	Pye Intl. NEP 44083	I LOVE PARIS (EP)	7
68	Pye Intl. NEP 44024	DO YOU KNOW THE WAY TO SAN JOSE? (EP)	7
64	Pye Intl. NPL 28037	PRESENTING DIONNE WARWICK (LP)	12
64	Pye Intl. NPL 28046	MAKE WAY FOR DIONNE WARWICK (LP)	10
65	Pye Intl. NPL 28055	THE SENSITIVE SOUND OF DIONNE WARWICK (LP)	10
66	Pye Intl. NPL 28071	HERE I AM (LP)	10
66	Pye Intl. NPL 28076	DIONNE WARWICK IN PARIS (LP)	10
67	Pye Intl. NPL 28096	HERE WHERE THERE IS LOVE (LP)	10
68	Pye Intl. N(S)PL 28114	VALLEY OF THE DOLLS (LP)	10
75	Warner Bros K 56178	TRACK OF THE CAT (LP)	10

WASHBOARD RHYTHM KINGS
| 56 | HMV 7EG 8101 | WASHBOARD RHYTHM KINGS (EP) | 12 |

WASHBOARD SAM
| 72 | RCA RD 8274 | FEELING LOWDOWN (LP) | 12 |

ALBERT WASHINGTON & KINGS
67	President PT 13	Doggin' Me Around/A Woman Is A Funny Thing	5
69	President PT 242	Turn On The Bright Lights/Lonely Mountain	6
68	President PT 182	I'm The Man/These Arms Of Mine	5
69	President PT 227	Woman Love/Bring It On Up	6
73	President PT 391	Rome Georgia/Telling All Your Friends	4

BABY WASHINGTON
64	Sue WI 302	That's How Heartaches Are Made/Doodlin'	20
64	Sue WI 321	I Can't Wait Until I See My Baby/Who's Gonna Take Care Of Me	20
65	London HLC 9987	Only Those In Love/Ballad Of Bobby Dawn	6
68	United Artists UP 2247	Get A Hold Of Yourself/Hurt So Bad	15
69	Atlantic 584 299	I Don't Know/I Can't Afford To Lose Him	7
70	Atlantic 584 316	Breakfast In Bed/What Becomes Of A Broken Heart	4
73	People PEO 105	Just Can't Get You Out Of My Mind/You're Just A Dream	4
74	People PEO 107	I've Got To Break Away/Can't Get Over You	4
66	London HA-C 8260	THAT'S HOW HEARTACHES ARE MADE (LP)	20
66	London HA-C 8292	ONLY THOSE IN LOVE (LP)	20

(see also Wilbert Harrison & Baby Washington)

BABY WASHINGTON & DON GARDNER
| 74 | People PEO 101 | Forever/Baby Let Me Get Close To You | 4 |
| 74 | People PLEO 13 | LAY A LITTLE LOVIN' (LP) | 10 |

(see also Don Gardner & Dee Dee Ford)

DINAH WASHINGTON
50s	Oriole CB 1130	Mad About The Boy/I Can't Face The Music (78)	15
50s	Oriole CB 1266	My Man's An Undertaker/Since My Man Has Gone And Went (78)	12
50s	Oriole CB 1279	Fat Daddy/TV Is The Thing (78)	12
59	Mercury AMT 1051	What A Diff'rence A Day Made/Come On Home	6
59	Mercury AMT 1069	Unforgettable/Nothing In The World	4
60	Mercury AMT 1105	This Bitter Earth/I Understand	4
60	Mercury AMT 1119	Love Walked In/I'm In Heaven Tonight	4
61	Mercury AMT 1125	We Have Love/Looking Back	4
61	Mercury AMT 1162	September In The Rain/Wake The Town And Tell The People	4
56	Emarcy EJT 501	AFTER HOURS WITH MISS D. (10" LP)	18
57	Emarcy EJL 1255	DINAH (LP)	15
57	Mercury MPL 6519	SINGS THE BEST IN BLUES (LP)	12
59	Top Rank RX 3006	THE BLUES (LP, with Betty Roche)	10
60	Mercury MMC 14030	WHAT A DIFF'RENCE A DAY MADE (LP)	12
60	Mercury MMC 14048	UNFORGETTABLE DINAH WASHINGTON (LP)	12
61	Mercury MMC 14063	I CONCENTRATE ON YOU (LP, also stereo CMS 18043)	12/14
65	Fontana FJL 125	DINAH! (LP)	10

(see also Brook Benton & Dinah Washington)

ELLA WASHINGTON
| 69 | Monument MON 1030 | He Called Me Baby/You're Gonna Make Me Cry Cry Cry | 6 |

GENO WASHINGTON & RAM JAM BAND
| 66 | Piccadilly 7N 35312 | Water/Understanding | 6 |
| 66 | Piccadilly 7N 35329 | Hi! Hi! Hazel/Beach Bash | 5 |

Geno WASHINGTON & RAM JAM BAND

66	Piccadilly 7N 35346	Que Sera Sera/All I Need	5
66	Piccadilly 7N 35359	Michael/Hold On To My Love	5
67	Piccadilly 7N 35392	She Shot A Hole In My Soul/I've Been Hurt By Love	7
67	Piccadilly 7N 35403	Tell It Like It Is/Girl I Want To Marry	6
67	Pye 7N 17425	Different Strokes/You Got Me Hummin'	4
68	Pye 7N 17570	I Can't Quit Her/Put Out The Fire Baby	4
68	Pye 7N 17649	I Can't Let You Go/Bring It To Me Baby	7
70	Pye 7N 45019	Alison Please/Each And Every Part Me	4
68	Pye NEP 24293	DIFFERENT STROKES (EP)	12
68	Pye NEP 24302	SMALL PACKAGE OF HIPSTERS (EP)	12
66	Piccadilly NEP 34054	HI (EP)	10
66	Piccadilly NPL 38026	HAND CLAPPIN', FOOT STOMPIN', FUNKY-BUTT . . . LIVE! (LP)	12
67	Piccadilly N(S)PL 38032	HIPSTERS, FLIPSTERS, FINGER-POPPIN' DADDIES! (LP)	10
68	Piccadilly N(S)PL 38029	SHAKE A TAIL FEATHER! (LP)	10
68	Pye N(S)PL 18219	LIVE! — RUNNING WILD (LP)	10

(see also Ram Jam Band)

GEORGE E. WASHINGTON

64	Fontana TF 510	Spare A Thought For Me/Words Of Love	4

GROVER WASHINGTON JR.

73	Kudu KUS 4001	Inner City Blues/Ain't No Sunshine	4
75	Kudu KUDU 924	Mister Magic/Black Frost	4
76	Kudu KUDU 930	Knucklehead Pts 1 & 2	4
73	Kudu KUL 1	INNER CITY BLUES (LP)	12
73	Kudu KUL 5	ALL THE KING'S HORSES (LP, original issue)	12
73	Kudu KULD 501	SOUL BOX (LP)	10
74	Kudu KU 07	ALL THE KING'S HORSES (LP, reissue)	10
75	Kudu KU 20	MISTER MAGIC (LP)	10
75	Kudu KU 24	FEELS SO GOOD (LP)	10
76	Kudu KU 32	A SECRET PLACE (LP)	10
77	Kudu SOULD 32	LIVE AT THE BIJOU (2-LP)	14

JERRY WASHINGTON

75	Contempo CS 2040	Right Here Is Where You Belong/In My Life I Haved Loved	4
75	Contempo CLP 517	RIGHT HERE IS WHERE YOU BELONG (LP)	10

KENNETH WASHINGTON & CHRIS BARBER BAND

67	CBS 202494	If I Had A Ticket/They Kicked Him Out Of Heaven (as Kenneth Washington with Chris Barber & T-Bones)	10
67	CBS 202592	Gimme That Old Time Religion/Just A Closer Walk With Thee	4

(see also Chris Barber)

NORMAN T. WASHINGTON

68	Pama PM 730	Sing Sing All Over/You've Been Cheating	4

SHERI WASHINGTON & BAND

57	Vogue V 9070	I Got Plenty/Ain't I Talkin' To You Baby	100
57	Vogue V 9070	I Got Plenty/Ain't I Talkin' To You Baby (78)	30

SISTER ERNESTINE B. WASHINGTON

50s	Melodisc MEL 1101	God's Amazing Grace/Where Could I Go But To The Lord (78)	10
55	Melodisc EPM 7-52	SISTER ERNESTINE WASHINGTON (EP)	10

TONY WASHINGTON (& HIS DC's)

64	Sue WI 327	Show Me How/Boof Ska	10
64	Fontana TF 478	Surely You Love Me/Man To Man	5
65	Black Swan WI 459	But I Do/Night Train (as Tony Washington & His DC's)	6
65	Black Swan WI 460	Dilly Dilly/Night Train (as Tony Washington & His DC's)	6

(see also Tony & Louise)

WASHINGTON DC's

64	Ember EMB S 190	Kisses Sweeter Than Wine/Where Did You Go	5
66	CBS 202226	32nd Floor/Whole Lot More	12
67	CBS 202464	Seek And Find/I Love Gerald Chevin The Great (some in p/s)	60/25
69	Domain D 9	I've Done It All Wrong/Anytime	8

WASP

75	EMI EMI 2253	Melissa/Little Miss Bristol	15

(see also Brian Bennett, Shadows)

W.A.S.P.

84	Music For Nations PKUT 109	Animal (Fuck Like A Beast)/Show No Mercy (shaped picture disc, 2 different designs)	12
84	M. F. Nations 12KUT 109	Animal (Fuck Like A Beast)/Show No Mercy (12", white vinyl)	20
84	Capitol 12CLP 336	I Wanna Be Somebody/Tormentor (Rageways) (12", picture disc)	12
84	Capitol CL 344	Schooldaze/Paint It Black (poster p/s)	4
84	Capitol 12CL 344	Schooldaze/Paint It Black (12", p/s)	10
85	M. For Nations PIG 109	Animal (Fuck Like A Beast)/Show No Mercy (12", picture disc)	7
85	Capitol CLP 374	Blind In Texas/Savage (shaped picture disc)	5
85	Capitol 12CLP 374	Blind In Texas/Savage/I Wanna Be Somebody (live) (12", picture disc)	7
86	Capitol CLD 388	Wild Child/Mississippi Queen//On Your Knees/Hellion (double pack)	5
86	Capitol CLP 432	9.5 N.A.S.T.Y./Easy Living (shaped picture disc)	6
87	Capitol 12CLP 458	Scream Until You Like It/Shoot It From The Hip (live)/Sleeping (In The Fire) (12", picture disc)	7
87	Capitol CL 469	I Don't Need No Doctor/Widowmaker (live) (blood pack)	6
87	Capitol CLS 469	I Don't Need No Doctor/Widowmaker (live) (poster p/s)	5
87	Capitol CLS 469	I Don't Need No Doctor/Widowmaker (live) (p/s, coloured vinyl)	4
87	Capitol CLP 469	I Don't Need No Doctor/Widowmaker (live) (shaped picture disc)	4
87	Capitol CLB 469	I Don't Need No Doctor/Widowmaker (live) (p/s, with backstage pass)	4
87	Capitol 12CLP 469	I Don't Need No Doctor/Widowmaker (live)/Sex Drive (12", poster p/s)	7
89	Capitol CLP 521	Mean Man/Locomotive Breath (picture disc)	4

89	Capitol CLM 521	Mean Man/Locomotive Breath (purple vinyl 'Means Test Pack' with badge) 4
89	Capitol CLPD 534	The Real Me/The Lake Of Fools (picture disc) 4

WASPS
77	NEMS NES 115	Can't Wait 'Til '78/MEAN STREET: Bunch Of Stiffs (p/s) 8
78	RCA PB 5137	Rubber Cars/This Time (p/s) 4
80	4-Play FOUR 001	Teenage Treats/She Made More Magic (p/s) 5

WASTED YOUTH
81	Bridgehouse BHS 5	Jealousy/Baby (p/s, clear vinyl) 4
81	Bridgehouse BHS 10	I'll Remember You/My Friends Are Dead (p/s) 4
82	Bridgehouse BHS 12	Rebecca's Room/Things Never Seem The Same As They Did (p/s) 4
82	Bridgehouse BHS 13	Wildlife/Games (p/s) 4
82	Bridgehouse BHS 14	Reach Out/Gone Midnight (p/s) 4
81	Bridgehouse BHLP 007	THE BEGINNING OF THE END (LP, 1st 5,000 with free 1-sided single "[Do The] Caveman [live]" [BHFNEE 1]) 12
80s	Wasted Youth WY 100	LIVE (LP) 10

(see also Tom Lucy)

WASTELAND
79	Ellie Jay EJSP 9261	WANT NOT (EP, also credits Disaster label, 2,000 only) 15
79	Invicta INV 014	Friends, Romans, Countrymen/Leave Me Alone (p/s) 15

WATCH COMMITTEE
68	Philips BF 1695	Throw Another Penny In The Well/Now I Think The Other Way 5

WATERBOYS
83	Chicken Jazz CJ 1	A Girl Called Johnny/The Late Train To Heaven (p/s) 7
83	Chicken Jazz CJT 1	A Girl Called Johnny/Ready For The Monkey House/Somebody Might Wave Back/Out Of Control (Another Pretty Face John Peel session) (12", p/s) 12
84	Ensign ENY 506	December/Where Are You Now When I Need You (p/s) 6
84	Ensign 12 ENY 506	December/Red Army Blues/The Three Day Man (Peter Powell session) (12", p/s) 12
84	Ensign ENY 508	The Big Music/The Earth Only Endures (p/s) 6
84	Ensign 12 ENY 508	The Big Music/Bury My Heart/The Earth Only Endures (12", p/s) 12
85	Ensign ENY 520	The Whole Of The Moon/Medicine Jack (p/s, later die-cut sleeve) 10/7
85	Ensign 12 ENY 520	The Whole Of The Moon (Extended)/Medicine Jack/Spirit (Extended)/ The Girl In The Swing (live) (12", p/s, later die-cut sleeve) 12/8

(see also DNV, Another Pretty Face, Funhouse, Last Chant, World Party)

WATERFALL
81	Gun Dog GUN 003LP	BENEATH THE STARS (LP, private pressing) 40
80s	Bob FRR 001	FLIGHT OF THE DAY (LP, private pressing) 50

WATER INTO WINE BAND
73	Myrrh MYR 1004	HILL CLIMBING FOR BEGINNERS (LP, brown or white cover, with insert) 85
76	CJT 002	HARVEST TIME (LP, private press) 200

WATERLOO & ROBINSON
76	Cube BUG 67	My Little World/Carry On 5

WATER PISTOLS
76	State 38	Gimme That Punk Junk/Soft Punk 10

WATERPROOF CANDLE
68	RCA RCA 1717	Electronically Heated Child/Saturday Morning Repentance 8

ETHEL WATERS
40s	Columbia DB 5534	Birmingham Bertha/Am I Blue? (78) 20
40s	Columbia DB 5663	Long Lean Lanky Mama/Better Keep An Eye On Your Man (78) 20
40s	Columbia DB 5664	Second-Handed Man/Waiting At The End Of The Road (78) 20
40s	Columbia DB 5648	True Blue Lou/Trav'lin All Alone (78) 20
40s	Columbia DB 5690	Do I Know What I'm Doing?/Shoo Shoo Boogie Boo (78) 20
40s	Columbia DB 8928	Heebie Jeebies/Ev'rybody Mess Aroun' (78) 20
60s	World Record Club T 949	ETHEL WATERS (LP) 12

FREDDIE WATERS
71	Buddah 2011 059	Singing A Song/I Love You I Love You I Love You 4
75	Mint CHEW 2	Groovin' On My Baby's Love/Kung Fu And You Too 4

MUDDY WATERS
53	Vogue V 2101	Walkin' Blues/Rollin' Stone Blues (78) 30
54	Vogue V 2273	Hello Little Girl/Long Distance Call (78) 30
55	Vogue V 2372	Honey Bee/Too Young To Know (78) 30
65	Chess CRS 8001	My John The Conquer Root/Short Dress Woman 12
65	Chess CRS 8019	I Got A Rich Man's Woman/My Dog Can't Bark 10
69	Chess CRS 8083	Let's Spend The Night Together/I'm A Man 7
69	Python P04	Country Boy/All Night Long 25
55	Vogue EPV 1046	MUDDY WATERS WITH LITTLE WALTER (EP) 75
56	London RUE 1060	MISSISSIPPI BLUES (EP) 75
63	Pye Intl. NEP 44010	MUDDY WATERS (EP) 15
65	Chess CRE 6006	I'M READY (EP) 20
66	Chess CRE 6022	THE REAL FOLK BLUES VOL. 4 (EP) 18
59	London Jazz LJZM 15152	THE BEST OF MUDDY WATERS (LP) 35
61	Pye Jazz NJL 34	AT NEWPORT (LP) 22
64	Pye Intl. NPL 28038	MUDDY WATERS — FOLK SINGER (LP) 20
64	Pye Intl. NPL 28040	THE BEST OF MUDDY WATERS (LP) 25
64	Pye Intl. NPL 28048	MUDDY SINGS BIG BILL (LP) 18
65	Chess CRL 4513	AT NEWPORT (LP, reissue) 18
66	Chess CRL 4515	THE REAL FOLK BLUES (LP) 18
67	Chess CRL 4525	MUDDY, BRASS AND THE BLUES (LP) 18

Muddy WATERS

67	Marble Arch MAL 661	AT NEWPORT (LP, 2nd reissue)	10
67	Chess CRL 4529	SUPER BLUES (LP, with Little Walter & Bo Diddley)	15
67	Marble Arch MAL 723	MUDDY SINGS BIG BILL (LP, reissue)	10
68	Chess CRL 4537	THE SUPER SUPER BLUES BAND (LP, with Howlin' Wolf & Bo Diddley)	20
68	Bounty BY 6031	DOWN ON STOVALL'S PLANTATION (LP)	15
69	Chess CRL 4542	ELECTRIC MUD (LP)	15
69	Chess CRL 4553	AFTER THE RAIN (LP)	18
69	Chess CRL 4556	FATHERS AND SONS (LP)	18
69	Polydor 236 574	BLUES MAN (LP)	12
69	Python PLP 12	MUDDY WATERS (LP)	25
69	Python PLP 18	MUDDY WATERS VOLUME 2 (LP)	25
69	Python PLP 19	MUDDY WATERS VOLUME 3 (LP)	25
69	Transatlantic TRA 188	MUDDY WATERS BLUES BAND WITH LUTHER JOHNSON (LP)	15
70	Sunnyland KS 100	VINTAGE MUDDY WATERS (LP, gatefold sleeve with inserts)	25
70	Syndicate Chapter LP 1/2	BACK IN THE EARLY DAYS (2-LP)	25
70	Syndicate Chapter LP 2	GOOD NEWS (LP)	20
71	Chess 6671 001	McKINLEY MORGANFIELD AKA MUDDY WATERS (LP)	12
72	Black Bear LP 901	RARE LIVE RECORDINGS VOL. 1 (LP)	20
72	Black Bear LP 902	RARE LIVE RECORDINGS VOL. 2 (LP)	20
72	Black Bear LP 903	RARE LIVE RECORDINGS VOL. 3 (LP)	20
72	Chess 6310 121	THE LONDON SESSIONS (LP)	10
74	Chess 6310 129	CAN'T GET NO GRINDIN' (LP)	10

(see also Little Walter, Howlin' Wolf, Bo Diddley, Luther Johnson)

ROGER WATERS

84	Harvest HAR 5528	5.01 AM (The Pros And Cons Of Hitch-Hiking)/4.30 AM (Apparently They Were Travelling Abroad) (p/s)	4
84	Harvest 12HAR 5528	5.01 AM (The Pros And Cons Of Hitch-Hiking)/4.30 AM (Apparently They Were Travelling Abroad)/4.33 AM (Running Shoes) (12", p/s)	7
84	Harvest HAR 5230	5.06 AM (Every Stranger's Eyes)/4.39 AM (For The First Time Today)	10
87	EMI CDEM 6	Radio Waves (Remix)/Going To Live In L.A. (demo)/Radio Waves (7" Version) (CD)	10
87	EMI EM 20	Sunset Strip/Money (live) (p/s)	10
87	EMI CDEM 37	The Tide Is Turning (After Live Aid)/Money ('live')/Get Back To Radio (demo recording) (CD)	7
70	Harvest SHSP 4008	MUSIC FROM THE FILM "THE BODY" (LP, as Roger Waters & Ron Geesin)	10

(see also Pink Floyd, Ron Geesin)

LAL & MIKE WATERSON

| 73 | Trailer LER 2076 | BRIGHT PHOEBUS (LP) | 15 |

WATERSONS

65	Topic 12T 125	NEW VOICES (LP, as Watersons with Harry Boardman & Maureen Craik)	12
65	Topic 12T 136	FROST AND FIRE (LP)	12
66	Topic 12T 142	WATERSONS (LP)	12
66	Topic 12T 167	A YORKSHIRE GARLAND (LP)	18

EARL WATSON

| 61 | Ember EMB S 129 | Nightmare/That Old Black Magic | 4 |

JOHN L. WATSON (& HUMMELFLUGS)

64	Pye 7N 15746	Looking For You/Dance With You	4
65	Piccadilly 7N 35233	Standing By/I'll Make It Worth Your While	4
70	Deram DM 285	A Mother's Love/Might As Well Be Gone (solo)	6
70	Deram SML 1061	WHITE HOT BLUE BLACK (LP)	20

(see also Web)

JOHNNY WATSON & KAMPAI KINGS

| 60 | Oriole CB 1532 | Moshi, Moshi, Anone! (Hello ...)/ABDULLA: Fatima's Theme | 4 |

JOHNNY 'GUITAR' WATSON

| 76 | Fantasy FTC 124 | I Don't Need A Lone Ranger/You Can Stay But The Noise Must Go | 4 |

WAH WAH WATSON

| 76 | CBS 4691 | Love Ain't Something You Get For Free/Bubbles | 5 |
| 76 | CBS 81582 | ELEMENTARY (LP) | 12 |

(see also Larry Williams & Johnny 'Guitar' Watson)

BEN WATT

81	Cherry Red CHERRY 25	Can't/Tower Of Silence/Saubade (p/s)	5
83	Cherry Red CHERRY 55	Some Things Don't Matter/On Box Hill (p/s)	4
82	Cherry Red 12CHERRY 36	SUMMER INTO WINTER (12" EP with Robert Wyatt, p/s)	7

(see also Everything But The Girl)

TOMMY WATT ORCHESTRA

| 56 | Parlophone MSP 6213 | Tender Trap/Who Done It | 4 |
| 56 | Parlophone MSP 6213 | Tender Trap/Who Done It (78) | 5 |

LU WATTERS & AND HIS YERAB BUENA JAZZ BAND

56	Vogue V 2125	Muskrat Rumble/Frankie And Johnny	4
56	Vogue V 2315	High Society/Aunt Hagar's Blues	4
52	Vogue LDE 009	LU WATTERS AND HIS JAZZ BAND (10" LP)	12
53	Good Time Jazz LP 8	LU WATTERS YERBA BUENA BAND VOL. 1 (10" LP)	15
54	Good Time Jazz LDG 038	LU WATTERS JAZZ BAND VOL. 1 (10" LP)	10
55	Columbia Clef 33C 9004	LU WATTERS AND HIS YERBA BUENA JAZZ BAND (10" LP)	12
56	London HB-U 1061	LU WATTERS — 1947 (10" LP)	10
57	Columbia Clef 33C 9036	DIXIELAND JAMBOREE (10" LP)	10

WATTS 103rd STREET RHYTHM BAND

| 69 | Warner Bros WB 7298 | Till You Get Enough/Light My Fire | 4 |
| 70 | Warner Bros WB 7365 | Love Land/Sorry Charlie | 4 |

| 70 | Warner Bros WB 7417 | Express Yourself/Living On Borrowed Time | 5 |
| 73 | Jay Boy BOY 71 | Spreadin' Honey/Charley | 8 |

(see also Charles Wright & Watts 103rd Street Rhythm Band)

CHARLIE WATTS

| 86 | CBS 450 253-1 | LIVE AT FULHAM HALL (LP, as Charlie Watts & His Orchestra) | 10 |

(see also Rolling Stones, People's Band)

NOBLE 'THIN MAN' WATTS (& HIS BAND)

58	London HLU 8627	Hard Times (The Slop)/Midnight Flight (with His Rhythm Sparks)	40
58	London HLU 8627	Hard Times (The Slop)/Midnight Flight (with His Rhythm Sparks) (78)	15
64	Sue WI 347	Noble's Theme/JUNE BATEMAN: I Don't Wanna	20
60s	XX MIN 717	NOBLE 'THIN MAN' WATTS AND WILD JIMMY SPURRILL (EP)	10

WATUSI WARRIORS

| 59 | London HL 8866 | Wa-Chi-Bam-Ba/Kalahari | 10 |
| 59 | London HL 8866 | Wa-Chi-Bam-Ba/Kalahari (78) | 5 |

WAVES

| 82 | Armageddon AS 021 | Nightmare/Hey War Pig (p/s) | 4 |
| 82 | Albion ION 1037 | Brown Eyed Son/She Loves To Groove (p/s) | 4 |

(see also Kimberley Rew)

NANCY WAYBURN

| 65 | Warner Bros WB 5646 | The World Goes On Without Me/Listen To My Heart | 8 |

ALVIS WAYNE

| 63 | Starlite ST45 104 | Don't Mean Maybe, Baby/I'd Rather Be With You | 250 |

BOBBY WAYNE

| 65 | Pye International 7N 25315 | Ballad Of A Teenage Queen/River Man | 8 |

CARL WAYNE (& VIKINGS)

64	Pye 7N 15702	What's A Matter Baby/Your Loving Ways (as Carl Wayne & Vikings)	25
65	Pye 7N 15824	This Is Love/You Could Be Fun (as Carl Wayne & Vikings)	25
70	RCA RCA 2032	Maybe God's Got Something Up His Sleeve/Rosanna	5
72	RCA RCA 2177	Imagine/Sunday Kind Of Love	4
72	RCA RCA 2257	Take My Hands For A While/Sweet Seasons	4
71	RCA SF 8239	CARL WAYNE (LP)	10

(see also Charlie Wayne, Move, Ace Kefford Stand, Keith Powell)

CHARLIE WAYNE

| 82 | Jet JET 7022 | Colourful Lady/THE MOVE: Aerial Pictures (p/s) | 4 |

CHRIS WAYNE & ECHOES

| 60 | Decca F 11231 | Lonely/Counting Girls | 5 |

JERRY WAYNE

| 60 | Vogue V 9169 | Half-Hearted Love/Ten Thousand Miles | 15 |

PAT WAYNE (& BEACHCOMBERS)

63	Columbia DB 7121	Go Back To Daddy/Jambalaya	10
63	Columbia DB 7182	Roll Over Beethoven/Is It Love?	10
64	Columbia DB 7262	Bye Bye Johnny/Strictly For The Birds	10
64	Columbia DB 7417	Brand New Man/Nobody's Child	7
65	Columbia DB 7603	Come Dance With Me/I Don't Want To Cry (solo)	5
65	Columbia DB 7739	My Friend/Tomorrow Mine (solo)	4
66	Columbia DB 7944	The Night Is Over/Hombre (solo)	5

RICK(Y) WAYNE

60	Triumph RGM 1009	Hot Chick A'roo/Don't Pick On Me (with Fabulous Flee-Rakkers)	35
60	Top Rank JAR 432	Hot Chick A'roo/Don't Pick On Me (unreleased)	
60	Pye 7N 15289	Make Way Baby/Goodness Knows Why (as Ricky Wayne & Off-Beats)	12
65	Oriole CB 306	Say You're Gonna Be My Own/It's A Crying Shame (as Rick Wayne)	7
65	CBS 201764	In My Imagination/Don't Ever Share Your Love (as Rick Wayne)	5

(see also Flee-Rekkers)

TERRY WAYNE

57	Columbia DB 4002	Matchbox/Your True Love	18
57	Columbia DB 4002	Matchbox/Your True Love (78)	5
57	Columbia DB 4035	Plaything/Slim Jim Tie	15
57	Columbia DB 4035	Plaything/Slim Jim Tie (78)	8
58	Columbia DB 4067	All Mama's Children/Forgive Me	15
58	Columbia DB 4067	All Mama's Children/Forgive Me (78)	8
58	Columbia DB 4112	Oh! Lonesome Me/There's Only One You	10
58	Columbia DB 4112	Oh! Lonesome Me/There's Only One You (78)	5
58	Columbia DB 4205	Little Brother/Where My Baby Goes	8
58	Columbia DB 4205	Little Brother/Where My Baby Goes (78)	5
59	Columbia DB 4312	Brooklyn Bridge/She's Mine	8
58	Columbia SEG 7758	TERRIFIC (EP)	60

THOMAS WAYNE

59	London HLU 8846	Tragedy/Saturday Date	35
59	London HLU 8846	Tragedy/Saturday Date (78)	20
59	London HL 7075	Tragedy/Saturday Date (export issue)	15

WAY OF THE WEST

| 81 | Lyntone LYN 10138/9 | Monkey Love/GRAHAM BONNET: Night Games/POLECATS: We Say Yeah/THIN LIZZY: Song For Jimmy (orange flexi with 'Flexipop' magazine, issue 10) | 5/4 |

WAYS & MEANS

| 66 | Columbia DB 7907 | Little Deuce Coupe/The Little Old Lady From Pasadena | 8 |
| 66 | Pye 7N 17217 | Sea Of Faces/Make The Radio A Little Louder | 15 |

MINT VALUE £

68	Trend TRE 1005	Breaking Up A Dream/She	4

WAYSTED
83	Chysalis CHS 2736	Women In Chains/Can't Take That Love Away (picture disc)	4

WAY WE LIVE
71	Dandelion DAN 8004/	A CANDLE FOR JUDITH (LP, gatefold sleeve, also listed as K 49004)	85

(see also Tractor)

WEAPON
80	Weapon	It's A Mad Mad World (p/s)	8
81	Weapon	It's A Mad Mad World (12", p/s)	15

WEAPONS GRADE PLUTONIUM
92	Over The Top OTT 002	Super-Gun Affair/Sod Off, Saddam (numbered p/s with petition insert)	8
92	Over The Top OTT 003	Turquoise Apples/Ewan Is King (turquoise vinyl, red or blue p/s)	4/5

WE ARE GOING TO EAT YOU
87	All The Madmen MADT 16	I Wish I Knew/Let's Fly/Fine Days/Let's Fly (Greedy Mix) (12", p/s)	7

WEATHERMAN & FRIENDS
82	Pre PRE 21	Life/Borderline (p/s)	4
82	Pre PRE 2112	Life/Borderline (12", p/s)	7

(see also Manicured Noise)

WEATHER PROPHETS
86	Creation CRE 029D	Almost Prayed/Your Heartbeat Breathes Life Into Me//Stones In My Passway/Downbound Train (double pack)	6
88	Creation CRELP 033	JUDGES, JURIES AND HORSEMEN (LP, with free 7" in plain sleeve: "Stepping Lightly On The Ancient Path"/"Odds And Ends" [CREFRE 2])	12
88	Creation CRELP 033	JUDGES, JURIES AND HORSEMEN (LP, autographed sleeve)	10

(see also Loft)

WEATHER REPORT
70s	CBS 64521	WEATHER REPORT (LP)	10
70s	CBS 64943	I SING THE BODY ELECTRIC (LP)	10
73	CBS 65532	SWEETNIGHTER (LP)	10
74	CBS 80027	MYSTERIOUS TRAVELLER (LP)	10

WEAVERS
59	Top Rank JAR 120	Wild Goose Grasses/Meet The Johnson Boys	4
57	Vanguard PPL 11006	AT THE CARNEGIE HALL (LP)	10
57	Vanguard PPL 11011	ON TOUR (LP)	10
59	Top Rank RX 3008	AT HOME (LP)	10
61	Brunswick LAT 8357	BEST OF THE WEAVERS (LP)	10

(see also Pete Seeger)

WEB
68	Deram DM 201	Hatton Mill Morning/Conscience	8
68	Deram DM 217	Baby Won't You Leave Me Alone/McVernon Street	6
69	Deram DM 253	Monday To Friday/Harold Dubbleyew	6
68	Deram SML 1025	FULLY INTERLOCKING (LP)	25
70	Deram SML 1058	THERAPHOSA BLONDI (LP)	25

(see also John L. Watson [& Hummleflugs])

WEB
70	Polydor 2383 024	I SPIDER (LP)	100

(see also Greenslade, Samurai)

DEAN WEBB
59	Parlophone R 4549	Warm Your Heart/Hey Miss Fannie	15
59	Parlophone R 4587	The Rough And The Smooth/Streamline Baby	15

DON WEBB
60	Coral Q 72385	Little Ditty Baby/I'll Be Back Home	100

GEORGE WEBB DIXIELANDERS
50s	Melodisc EPM7 70	THE GEORGE WEBB DIXIELANDERS (EP)	10

JILLA WEBB
56	MGM SP 1180	You Gotta Love Me Now/What Do You Think It Does To Me?	4

JIM(MY) WEBB
68	CBS 3672	I Keep It Hid/I Need You (as Jim Webb)	10
68	CBS (S) 63335	JIM WEBB SINGS JIM WEBB (LP, as Jim Webb)	15
70	Reprise K 44134	AND SO ON (LP)	10
74	Asylum SYL 9014	LAND'S END (LP, as Jimmy Webb)	10

JOHN WEBB
86	Numa NU 14	The Experiment Of Love/Cry Of The Sea (p/s)	4
86	Numa NUM 14	The Experiment Begins/Cry Of The Sea/The Experiment Of Love (12", p/s)	8

JOHNNY WEBB
56	Columbia DB 3805	Dig/Glendora	6
57	Columbia DB 3904	The Song Of The Moon/Give Me More	4
60s	Melodisc MEL 1617	Travelin' Man/Hold Back The Town (p/s)	4

LIZBETH WEBB
53	HMV 7M 140	I've Never Been In Love Before/If I Were A Bell	4

PETA WEBB
73	Topic 12TS 223	I HAVE WANDERED IN EXILE (LP)	40

(see also Oak)

ROGER WEBB & HIS TRIO
64	Parlophone PMC 1233	JOHN, PAUL AND ALL THAT JAZZ (LP)	10

SKEETER WEBB

55	Parlophone CMSP 32	Was It A Bad Dream/Your Secret's Not A Secret Anymore (export issue)	8

SONNY WEBB & CASCADES

64	Oriole CB 1873	You've Got Everything/Border Of The Blues	15
60s	Polydor NH 52158	You've Got Everything/Border Of The Blues (reissue)	8

MARLENE WEBBER

70	Bamboo BAM 33	My Baby/BRENTFORD ALLSTARS: You Gonna Hold Me (Version)	5
71	Ackee ACK 120	Natengula/Natengula Kera	4
71	Ackee ACK 122	Cumbaya/Hail Hi Freedom	4

(see also Webber Sisters, Tonettes)

WEBBER SISTERS

67	Island WI 3109	My World/ALVA LEWIS: Lonely Still	10

WEBS

68	London HLU 10188	This Thing Called Love/Tomorrow	4

CHASE WEBSTER

64	Hickory 45-1283	Life Can Have Meaning/Where Is Your Heart	4

DEENA WEBSTER

68	Parlophone R 5699	You're Losing/Wish You Were Here	8
68	Parlophone R 5721	Your Heart Is Free Just Like The Wind/Queen Merka And Me	4
68	Parlophone R 5738	Scarborough Fair/The Water Is Wide	4
69	Parlophone R 5798	Joey/It's Alright With Me	4
68	Parl. PMC/PCS 7052	TUESDAY'S CHILD (LP)	10

WEDDING PRESENT

85	Reception REC 001	Go Out And Get 'Em Boy/(The Moment Before) Everything's Spoiled Again (p/s, 500 only)	50
85	City Slang CSL 001	Go Out And Get 'Em Boy/(The Moment Before) Everything's Spoiled Again (reissue, different foldout p/s, 1,000 only)	35
86	Reception REC 002	Once More/At The Edge Of The Sea (p/s, 3,500 only)	20
86	Reception REC 002/12	DON'T TRY AND STOP ME MOTHER (12" EP, combines REC 001 & 002)	15
86	Reception REC 003	This Boy Can Wait/You Should Always Keep In Touch With Your Friends (p/s, matrix numbers 003 A2 & 003 B1)	10
86	Reception REC 003	This Boy Can Wait/You Should Always Keep In Touch With Your Friends (p/s, mispress both sides play B-side, matrix numbers 003 A1 & 003 A2)	10
86	Reception REC 003/12	This Boy Can Wait (Extended)/You Should Always Keep In Touch With Your Friends/Living And Learning (12", p/s)	12
87	Reception REC 005	My Favourite Dress/Every Mother's Son/Never Said (p/s, white vinyl, 3,000 only, 2,000 of which free with "George Best" LP)	10
87	Reception REC 005	My Favourite Dress/Every Mother's Son/Never Said (p/s)	5
87	Reception REC 005/12	My Favourite Dress (Long)/Every Mother's Son/Never Said (12", p/s)	7
87	Reception	A Million Miles/What Did Your Last Servant Die Of? (DJ promo, 200 only)	30
87	Reception REC 006	Anyone Can Make A Mistake/All About Eve	4
87	Reception REC 006/C	Anyone Can Make A Mistake/All About Eve/Getting Nowhere Fast (cassette, shrinkwrapped with badge)	7
88	Reception REC 009	Nobody's Twisting Your Arm/I'm Not Always So Stupid (g/fold p/s, 8,000 only)	4
88	Reception REC 010X	Davni Chasy/Katrusya (promo-only)	15
88	Reception REC 011C	Why Are You Being So Reasonable Now?/Not From Where I'm Standing/Give My Love To Kevin (Acoustic)/Pourquoi Es Tu Devenue Si Raisonable? (cassette)	4
88	Sounds WAVES 3	WAVES 3 (p/s, with other artists, free with 'Sounds' magazine)	4
88	House Of Dolls HOD 4	HOUSE OF DOLLS (EP with other artists, free with 'House Of Dolls' magazine)	6/4
89	RCA	Davni Chasy/Katrusya (promo-only)	15
90	RCA PB 43403	Brassneck/Don't Talk, Just Kiss (custom hand-painted p/s, 3,000 only)	10
90	RCA PJ 44022	3 SONGS (10" EP)	6
91	RCA PJ 44495	Dalliance/Niagara/She's My Best Friend/What Have I Said Now? (live) (10", numbered p/s)	5
92	RCA PB 45185	Blue Eyes/Cattle And Cane (p/s)	12
92	RCA PB 45183	Go Go Dancer/Don't Cry No Tears (p/s)	10
92	RCA PB 45181	Three/Think That It Might (p/s)	8
92	RCA PB 45311	Silver Shorts/Falling (p/s)	8
92	RCA PB 45313	Come Play With Me/Pleasant Valley Sunday (p/s)	8
92	RCA PB 45315	California/Let's Make Some Plans (p/s)	6
92	RCA PB 10115	Flying Saucer/Rocket (p/s)	6
92	RCA PB 10117	Boing/The Theme From Shaft (p/s)	5
92	RCA PB 10116	Loveslave/Chant Of The Ever Growing Skeletal Family (p/s)	5
92	RCA PB 11691	Sticky/Go Wild In The Country (p/s)	5
92	RCA PB 11692	The Queen Of Outer Space/UFO (p/s)	5
92	RCA PB 11693	No Christmas/Step Into Christmas (p/s, red vinyl with postcard)	5
87	Reception LEEDS 1	GEORGE BEST (LP, 2,000 only with white vinyl 7": "My Favourite Dress"/ "Every Mother's Son"/"Never Said" [REC 005] & inner sleeve, or with free black vinyl 7" or 12" edition)	15
87	Reception LEEDS 1	GEORGE BEST (LP, in 'George Best' carrier bag & inner sleeve)	10
88	Reception LEEDS 2	TOMMY (LP, 1,000 signed by band, with poster & inner sleeve)	20
88	Reception REC 010	UKRAINSKI VISTUPI V JOHNA PEELA (10" mini-LP, withdrawn)	12
93	Reception PL 74321	HIT PARADE 2 (LP, with free sessions LP)	10

WEDGEWOODS

64	Pye 7N 15642	September In The Rain/Gone Gone Away	4
65	Pye 7N 15846	Peace/Summer Love	4

BUDDY WEED & HIS ORCHESTRA

57	Vogue V 9075	The Kent Song/For Love	20

BERT WEEDON

55	Parlophone R 4113	China Boogie/Stranger Than Fiction (The Big Guitar) (78)	6

Bert WEEDON

56	Parlophone MSP 6242	The Boy With The Magic Guitar/Flannel-Foot	12
56	Parlophone R 4178	The Boy With The Magic Guitar/Flannel-Foot (78)	5
57	Parlophone R 4256	Theme From ITV's "$64,000 Question"/Twilight Time	10
57	Parlophone R 4256	Theme From ITV's "$64,000 Question"/Twilight Time (78)	5
57	Parlophone R 4315	The Jolly Gigolo/Soho Fair	10
57	Parlophone R 4315	The Jolly Gigolo/Soho Fair (78)	5
57	Parlophone R 4381	Play That Big Guitar/Quiet, Quiet, Ssh!	8
57	Parlophone R 4381	Play That Big Guitar/Quiet, Quiet, Ssh! (78)	5
58	Parlophone R 4446	Big Note Blues/Rippling Tango	8
58	Parlophone R 4446	Big Note Blues/Rippling Tango (78)	5
59	Saga SAG 2906	Fifi/Cat On A Hot Tin Roof (as Bert Weedon & Rag Pickers)	10
59	Top Rank JAR 117	Guitar Boogie Shuffle/Bert's Boogie	6
59	Top Rank JAR 117	Guitar Boogie Shuffle/Bert's Boogie (78)	7
59	Top Rank JAR 121	Sing Little Birdie/The Lady Is A Tramp	4
59	Top Rank JAR 122	Petite Fleur/My Happiness	4
59	Top Rank JAR 123	Charmaine/It's Time To Say Goodnight	4
59	Top Rank JAR 136	Teenage Guitar/Blue Guitar	6
59	Top Rank JAR 210	Jealousy/Tango, Tango	4
59	Top Rank JAR 211	Stardust/Summertime	4
59	Top Rank JAR 221	Nashville Boogie/King Size Guitar	5
59	Top Rank JAR 221	Nashville Boogie/King Size Guitar (78)	5
60	Top Rank JAR 300	Big Beat Boogie/Theme From "A Summer Place"	5
60	Top Rank JAR 360	Twelfth Street Rag/Querida	4
60	Top Rank JAR 415	Apache/Lonely Guitar	5
60	Top Rank JAR 517	Sorry Robbie/Easy Beat	5
61	Top Rank JAR 537	Ginchy/Yearning	4
61	Top Rank JAR 559	Mr. Guitar/Eclipse	4
61	Top Rank JAR 582	Ghost Train/Fury	4
61	HMV POP 946	China Doll/Red Guitar	4
62	HMV POP 989	Twist A Napoli/Twist Me Pretty Baby	4
62	HMV POP 1043	Some Other Love/Tune For Two	4
62	HMV POP 1077	South Of The Border/Poinciana	4
63	HMV POP 1141	Night Cry/Charlie Boy	10
63	HMV POP 1216	Dark Eyes/Black Jackets	4
64	HMV POP 1248	It Happened In Monterey/Lonely Night	4
64	HMV POP 1302	Gin Mill Guitar/Can't Help Falling In Love	4
64	HMV POP 1355	Tokyo Melody/Theme From "Limelight"	4
65	HMV POP 1485	High Steppin'/East Meets West	4
66	HMV POP 1535	Kick Off/McGregor's Leap	4
60s	Grovesnor GRS 1015	Watch Your Step/Safe And Sound (as Bert Weedon Quartet with Roy Edwards)	4
56	Esquire EP 56	WAXING THE WINNERS (EP)	10
59	Selmer amplifiers	DEMONSTRATION RECORD WITH DAVID GELL (EP)	7
61	Top Rank JKP 3008	WEEDON WINNERS (EP)	12
64	HMV 7EG 8856	GUITAR MAN (EP)	10
60	Top Rank BUY 026	KINGSIZE GUITAR (LP)	30
61	Top Rank 35/101	HONKY TONK GUITAR (LP)	25
70	Fontana 6438 009	THE ROMANTIC GUITAR OF BERT WEEDON (LP)	10
70	Fontana 6438 031	ROCKIN' AT THE ROUNDHOUSE (LP)	10

(see also George Chisholm)

WEE THREE

73	People PEO 104	Get On Board/Get On Board (Instrumental)	4

WEE WILLIE & WINNERS

74	Action ACT 4624	Get Some/A Plan For The Man	8
74	People PEO 116	I Don't Know What You Got But I Know Pts 1 & 2	4

WE FIVE

65	Pye International 7N 25314	You Were On My Mind/Small World	4
66	Pye International 7N 25346	Let's Get Together/Cast Your Fate To The Wind	5
66	Pye International NEP 44056	LET'S GET TOGETHER (EP)	7

WE 4

67	HMV POP 1603	Pretty Flowers/I'll Make You A Miracle	4

WE FREE KINGS

86	How! WOOF 1	Death Of The Wild Colonial Boy/Love Is In The Air (foldover p/s)	4

BOB WEIR

72	Warner Bros WB 7611	One More Saturday Night/Cassidy	4
72	Warner Bros K 46165	ACE (LP)	10

(see also Grateful Dead, Kingfish)

FRANK WEIR & HIS ORCHESTRA

54	Decca F 10271	The Happy Wanderer/From Your Lips	5
54	Decca F 10291	The Bandit/By Candlelight	5
55	Decca F 10384	The Cuckoo Cries/Misty Islands Of The Horizons	5
55	Decca F 10435	Theme From "Journey Into Space"/Serenade To An Empty Room	6
55	Decca F 10646	I'm A Little Echo (with Eula Parker)/Castles In The Air	4
60	Oriole CB 1559	Carribean Honeymoon/Farewell My Love	4
63	Philips 326 560 BF	Manhunt/Chant Of The Jungle (as Frank Weir & Werewolves)	4
55	Decca LF 1208	PRESENTING FRANK WEIR AND HIS SAXOPHONE (10" LP)	10

(see also Bill Darnell, Vera Lynn, Janie Marden)

NORRIS WEIR (& JAMAICANS)

70	Duke DU 85	Hard On Me (with Jamaicans)/TOMMY COWAN & JAMAICANS: Please Stop The Wedding	4
74	Dragon DRA 1030	Reggay Revolution/Version	6
75	Horse HOSS 81	Dr. Honey/Honey Dub	4

(see also Jamaicans)

WEIRD STRINGS

80	Velvet Moon VM 1	Oscar Mobile/Ancient Square (foldover p/s)	10
80	Ace ACE 009	Criminal Cage/Mi££ionaire (p/s)	8

(see also Paul Roland, Beau Brummel, Midnight Rags)

BRUCE WELCH

74	EMI EMI 2141	Please Mr. Please/Song Of Yesterday	80

(see also Shadows, Cliff Richard)

ELIZABETH WELCH

80	Industrial IR 002	Stormy Weather/Ya're Blase	10

HONEE WELCH

69	London HLU 10288	I'm Gonna Try/It's My Girl	4

LENNY WELCH

60	London HLA 9094	You Don't Know Me/I Need Someone	4
62	London HLA 9601	Taste Of Honey/Old Cathedral	5
63	London HLA 9810	Since I Fell For You/Are You Sincere	4
64	London HLA 9880	Ebb Tide/Congratulations Baby	4
64	London HLR 9910	If You See My Love/Father Sebastian	4
65	London HLR 9981	Darling Take Me Back/Time After Time	8
65	London HLR 9991	Two Different Worlds/I Was There	4
65	London HLR 10010	Run To My Lovin' Arms/Coronet Blue	10
66	London HLR 10031	Rags To Riches/I Want You To Worry	4
70	Major Minor MM 707	Breaking Up Is Hard To Do/Got To See If I Can Get My Mommy To Come Back Home	4
75	Mainstream MSS 307	When There's No Such Thing As Love/The Minx	5
66	London HA-R/SH-R 8267	TWO DIFFERENT WORLDS (LP)	10
66	London HA-R 8290	RAGS TO RICHES (LP)	10

TIM WELCH

60	Columbia DB 4529	Weak In The Knees/A Boy And A Girl In Love	6

WELFARE STATE

70s	Look LKLP 6347	WELFARE STATE SONGS (LP)	50

LAWRENCE WELK ORCHESTRA

56	Coral Q 72141	The "Threepenny Opera" Theme/Rock And Roll Waltz	5
57	Coral Q 72256	Around The World In 80 Days/Ten Little Trees	5
64	Dot DS 16697	The "Addams Family" Theme/Apples And Bananas	4

ORSON WELLES

59	Top Rank TR 5001	The Courtroom Scene From The Film "Compulsion" (both sides)	4

NICK WELLINGS & SECTION

77	The Label TLR 011	You Better Move On/Punk Funk	6

BOBBY WELLS

68	Beacon 3-102	Let's Copp A Groove/Recipe For Love (yellow or white label)	6/4
79	Grapevine GRP 124	Be's That Way Sometimes/Recipe For Love	4

HOUSTON WELLS (& MARKSMEN)

62	Parlophone R 4955	This Song Is Just For You/Paradise	10
62	Parlophone R 4980	North Wind/Shutters And Boards	10
63	Parlophone R 5031	Only The Heartaches/Can't Stop Pretending	10
63	Parlophone R 5069	Blowing Wild (The Ballad Of Black Gold)/Crazy Dreams	10
64	Parlophone R 5099	Anna Marie/Moon Watch Over My Baby	10
64	Parlophone R 5141	Galway Bay/Livin' Alone (as Houston Wells & Outlaws)	10
65	Parlophone R 5226	Coming Home/Blue Of The Night (solo)	6
68	CBS 3572	Teach Me Little Children/Does My Ring Hurt Your Finger	4
63	Parlophone GEP 8878	JUST FOR YOU (EP)	25
64	Parlophone GEP 8914	RAMONA (EP)	35
63	Parlophone PMC 1215	WESTERN STYLE (LP)	50

(see also Marksmen, Outlaws)

JEAN WELLS

71	Mojo 2092 023	After Loving You/Puttin' The Best On The Outside	20

JOHNNY WELLS

59	Columbia DB 4377	Lonely Moon/The One And Only One	8
67	Parlophone R 5559	Wondering Why/Guess I'm Dumb	5

JUNIOR WELLS

66	Delmark DS 9612	Hoodoo Man Blues (blue label)	20
66	Delmark DS 628	Southside Blues Jam (blue label)	10
68	Mercury MF 1056	Girl You Lit My Fire/It's A Man Down There	4
66	Delmark DJB 1	BLUES WITH A BEAT (EP)	20
60s	XX MIN 715	JUNIOR WELLS (EP)	12
68	Fontana (S)TFL 6084	IT'S MY LIFE BABY (LP)	18
68	Vanguard SVRL 19011	COMING AT YOU (LP)	15
68	Vanguard SVRL 19028	IT'S MY LIFE BABY (LP, reissue)	10
68	Mercury SMCL 20130	YOU'RE TUFF ENOUGH (LP)	12

(see also Buddy Guy)

KITTY WELLS

64	Brunswick 05920	I Gave My Wedding Dress Away/I've Thought Of Leaving You	6
55	Brunswick OE 9149	KITTY SINGS (EP)	15
61	Brunswick LAT 8361	KITTY'S CHOICE (LP)	15
64	Brunswick LAT 8575	QUEEN OF COUNTRY MUSIC (LP)	10
65	Brunswick LAT 8601	ESPECIALLY FOR YOU (LP)	10
65	Brunswick LAT 8621	LONESOME SAD AND BLUE (LP)	10
66	Brunswick LAT/STA 8646	SINGS SONGS MADE FAMOUS BY JIM REEVES (LP, mono/stereo)	10/12

| 66 | Brunswick LAT 8659 | COUNTRY ALL THE WAY (LP, mono/stereo) | 10/12 |
| 67 | Brunswick LAT 8683 | LOVE MAKES THE WORLD GO ROUND (LP) | 10 |

MARY WELLS

62	Oriole CBA 1762	You Beat Me To The Punch/Old Love	35
63	Oriole CBA 1796	Two Lovers/Operator	30
63	Oriole CBA 1829	Laughing Boy/Two Wrongs Don't Make A Right	40
63	Oriole CBA 1847	Your Old Standby/What Love Has Joined Together	30
63	Stateside SS 242	You Lost The Sweetest Boy/What's Easy For Two Is So Hard For One	16
64	Stateside SS 288	My Guy/Oh Little Boy	6
64	Stateside SS 316	Once Upon A Time (with Marvin Gaye)/What's The Matter With You, Baby	18
65	Stateside SS 372	Ain't That The Truth/Stop Takin' Me For Granted	10
65	Stateside SS 396	Use Your Head/Everlovin' Boy	8
65	Stateside SS 415	Never Never Leave Me/Why Don't You Let Yourself Go	8
65	Stateside SS 439	He's A Lover/I'm Learnin'	8
65	Stateside SS 463	Me Without You/I'm Sorry	8
68	Stateside SS 2111	The Doctor/Two Lovers' History	5
66	Atlantic AT 4067	Dear Lover/Can't You See You're Losing Me	15
66	Atlantic 584 054	Me And My Baby/Such A Sweet Thing	7
67	Atlantic 584 104	Hey You Set My Soul On Fire/Coming Home	5
70	Direction 58-4816	Dig The Way I Feel/Love Shooting Bandit	4
72	Atlantic K 10254	Dear Lover/Can't You See	5
65	T. Motown TME 2007	MARY WELLS (EP)	25
63	Oriole PS 40045	TWO LOVERS (LP)	50
63	Oriole PS 40051	BYE BYE BABY (LP)	60
64	Stateside SL 10095	SINGS MY GUY (LP)	35
65	Stateside SL 10133	MARY WELLS (LP)	20
65	Tamla Motown TML 11006	MY BABY JUST CARES FOR ME (LP)	25
66	Stateside SL/SSL 10171	LOVE SONGS TO THE BEATLES (LP)	15
66	Tamla Motown TML 11032	GREATEST HITS (LP)	16
68	Stateside SL/SSL 10266	SERVIN' UP SOME SOUL (LP)	10
68	Atlantic 587 049	THE TWO SIDES OF MARY WELLS (LP)	12

(see also Marvin Gaye)

TERRI WELLS

| 83 | Philly World PWS 111 | You Make It Heaven/You Make It Heaven (Instrumental) | 4 |

ALEX WELSH & DIXIELANDERS

55	Decca F 10538	I'll Build A Stairway To Paradise/Eccentric	4
55	Decca F 10557	Blues My Naughtie Sweetie Gives To Me/Shoe Shiner's Blues	4
55	Decca F 10607	As Long As I Live/New Orleans Stomp	4
55	Decca F 10651	Sugar/Smiles	4
55	Decca F 10652	What Can I Say After I Say I'm Sorry/Hard Hearted Hannah	4

DANNY WELTON

| 60 | Coral Q 72409 | Boogie Woogie/To Each His Own | 4 |

WENDY & LEMMY

| 82 | Bronze BRO 151 | Stand By Your Man/No Class/Masterplan (p/s) | 4 |

(ses also Plasmatics, Motorhead)

WE'RE TIRED

77	Deadline DEADS 8	My Life's On The Line/Against All Odds (p/s)	20
77	Deadline DEADS 11	Guide Me Through Hell/Time Is Against Me (p/s)	25
78	Deadline DEADS 15	Over The Edge/Anal-Retentive (p/s, as We're Tired & We're Proud)	8
77	Deadline DEADLP 2	FIND THE PRICE IN TIME (LP)	50

WERLWINDS

| 61 | Columbia DB 4650 | Winding It Up/Dig Deep | 12 |

HOWARD WERTH & MOONBEAMS

| 74 | Charisma CB 225 | Lucinda/Johan | 4 |
| 75 | Charisma CAS 11004 | KING BRILLIANT (LP) | 10 |

(see also Audience)

BRIAN WESKE

| 62 | Oriole CB 1723 | In The Midst Of The Crowd/All Mine Alone | 4 |

FRED WESLEY & J.B.s

73	Polydor 2066 322	Doing It To Death/Everybody Got Soul (with J.B.s)	6
74	Mojo 2093 025	J.B. Shout/Back Stabbers (with J.B.s)	6
80	RSO RSO 67	Houseparty/I Make Music (solo)	8
80	RSO RSO 67	Houseparty/I Make Music (12", solo)	15
73	Polydor 2391 125	EXORCIST — DAMN RIGHT, I AM SOMEBODY (LP, with J.B.s)	40
74	Polydor 2391 161	BREAKIN' BREAD (LP, with J.B.s)	30

(see also James Brown, JBs)

ADAM 'BATMAN' WEST

| 76 | Target TCT 111 | Batman And Robin/The Story Of Batman | 5 |

DODIE WEST

64	Decca F 12046	Goin' Out Of My Head/Is He Feeling Blue	4
65	Piccadilly 7N 35239	In The Deep Of The Night/Rovin' Boy (p/s)	6
65	Piccadilly 7N 35261	Thinking Of You/And Love Will Come	4
66	Piccadilly 7N 35287	Make The World Go Away/Who Does He Think He Is	5
68	Philips BF 1698	Living In Limbo/Birde Told Me	4

KEITH WEST

67	Parlophone R 5623	Excerpt From "A Teenage Opera"/MARK WIRTZ ORCHESTRA: Theme From "A Teenage Opera"	4
67	Parlophone R 5651	Sam (From "A Teenage Opera")/MARK WIRTZ'S MOOD MOSAIC: Thimble Full Of Puzzles	6
68	Parlophone R 5713	The Kid Was A Killer/On A Saturday	25

72	Parlophone R 5957	Excerpt From "A Teenage Opera"/Sam (From "A Teenage Opera")	4
73	Deram DM 402	Riding For A Fall/Days About To Rain	4
74	Deram DM 410	Havin' Someone/Know There's No Livin' Without You	4

(see also Tomorrow, Mark Wirtz, Mood Mosaic, Four Plus One, In Crowd, Philwit & Pegasus)

MAE WEST

67	Stateside SS 2021	Twist And Shout/Day Tripper	12
73	MGM 2006 203	Great Balls Of Fire/Men	5
56	Brunswick LAT 8082	THE FABULOUS MAE WEST (LP)	20
67	Stateside (S)SL 10197	WAY OUT WEST (LP)	15
70s	Polydor 2315 207	GREAT BALLS OF FIRE (LP)	10

SPEEDY WEST & JIMMY BRYANT

55	Capitol EAP1 520	TWO GUITARS COUNTRY STYLE PT. 1 (EP)	15
55	Capitol EAP2 520	TWO GUITARS COUNTRY STYLE PT. 2 (EP)	15
53	Capitol LC 6619	CAPITOL PRESENTS SPEEDY WEST & JIMMY BRYANT (10" LP)	25
55	Capitol LC 6694	TWO GUITARS COUNTRY STYLE (10" LP)	25

TABBY WEST

| 58 | Capitol CL 14861 | All That I Want/If You Promise Not To Tell | 5 |

WEST AFRICAN RHYTHM BOYS

60s	Melodisc HI 1	Calar O/Y B Club	4
60s	Melodisc HI 2	Iwa D'arekere/Ero Ya Kowawo	4
60s	Melodisc M 1505	Ominira/Gbonimawo	4
60s	Melodisc M 1513	We Have It In Africa/Aye Wa Adara	4
60s	Melodisc M 1567	Nigeria Odowoyin/Asikoloto	4
60s	Melodisc M 1568	Nigeria Koniset/Jekafo Ju Agbawo	4

MIKE WESTBROOK (CONCERT BAND)

69	Deram DM 234	A Life Of Its Own/Can't Get It Out Of My Mind	6
70	Deram DM 286	Requiem/Horray	6
70	Deram DM 311	Magic Garden/Original Peter (with Norma Winstone)	6
67	Deram DML 1013	CELEBRATION (LP)	45
68	Deram DML/SML 1031	RELEASE (LP)	30
69	Deram SML 1047	MARCHING SONG VOL. 1 (LP)	30
69	Deram SML 1048	MARCHING SONG VOL. 2 (LP)	30
70	Deram SML 1069	LOVE SONGS (LP)	30
71	RCA SER 5612	TYGER (LP, with insert)	25
71	RCA Neon NE 10	METROPOLIS (LP, gatefold sleeve)	40
72	Cadillac SGC 1001	LIVE (LP, private press)	18
75	RCA SF 8433	CITADEL/ROOM 315 (2-LP, with John Surman)	18
75	Transatlantic TRA 323	LOVE/DREAM & VARIATIONS (LP)	12

(see also Solid Gold Cadillac, John Surman)

WEST, BRUCE & LAING

72	CBS 65314	WHY DONTCHA (LP)	12
73	RSO 2394 107	WHATEVER TURNS YOU ON (LP)	12
74	RSO 2394 128	LIVE 'N' KICKIN' (LP)	15

(see also Jack Bruce, Mountain, Cream)

WEST COAST CONSORTIUM

| 67 | Pye 7N 17352 | Some Other Someday/Looking Back | 6 |
| 68 | Pye 7N 17482 | Colour Sergeant Lillywhite/Lady From Baltimore | 15 |

WEST COAST DELEGATION

| 67 | Deram DM 113 | Reach The Top/Mr. Personality Man | 8 |

WEST COAST KNACK

| 67 | Capitol CL 15497 | I'm Aware/Time Waits For No One | 12 |

WEST COAST POP ART EXPERIMENTAL BAND

| 68 | Reprise RSLP 6298 | A CHILD'S GUIDE TO GOOD AND EVIL (LP) | 40 |

WEST END (Austria)

| 83 | Epic A 3388 | Hurricane (English)/Hurricane (German) (promos only) | 4 |

WEST END (U.K.)

| 80s | Continental TIN 001 | The Servant/Fiction (p/s) | 4 |

JOHNNY WESTERN

| 60 | Philips PB 1030 | The Ballad Of Paladin/The Guns Of Rio Muerto (B-side with Richard Boone) | 5 |

WESTERNAIRES ORCHESTRA with CURLY WILLIAMS

| 57 | Brunswick 05692 | Walking Alone In A Crowd/Sweet Talk (Won Her Loving ...) | 4 |

WEST FIVE

65	HMV POP 1396	Congratulations/She Mine	20
65	HMV POP 1428	Someone Ain't Right/Just Like Romeo And Juliet	10
66	HMV POP 1513	If It Don't Work Out/Back To Square One	7

(see also Four, Ferris Wheel)

WEST INDIANS

68	Doctor Bird DB 1121	Right On Time/Hokey Pokey	10
68	Doctor Bird DB 1127	Falling In Love/I Mean It	10
69	Camel CA 16	Strange Whisperings/CARL DAWKINS: Hard To Handle	5
71	Dynamic DYN 413	Never Gonna Give You Up/REBELLIOUS SUBJECTS: Version	5

CLIVE WESTLAKE

| 68 | Fontana TF 940 | 199 Days/From The Beginning To The End | 4 |

KEVIN WESTLAKE & GARY FARR

| 68 | Marmalade 598 007 | Everyday/Green | 6 |

(see also Gary Farr & T-Bones, T-Bones)

WESTMINSTER FIVE

| 64 | Carnival CV 7017 | Shakin' The Blues/Railroad Blues | 8 |
| 65 | Carnival CV 7019 | Sticks And Stones/Mickey's Monkey (as Wes Minster Five) | 8 |

(see also Maynell Wilson)

GLEN WESTON

| 68 | Columbia DB 8328 | With This Ring/Liane | 4 |

KIM WESTON

64	Stateside SS 359	A Little More Love/Go Ahead And Laugh	60
65	Tamla Motown TMG 511	I'm Still Loving You/Just Loving You	80
65	Tamla Motown TMG 538	Take Me In Your Arms (Rock Me A Little While)/ Don't Compare Me With Her	35
66	Tamla Motown TMG 554	Helpless/A Love Like Yours	30
67	MGM MGM 1338	I Got What You Need/Someone Like You	10
67	MGM MGM 1357	That's Groovy/Land Of Tomorrow	6
68	MGM MGM 1382	Nobody/You're Just The Kind Of Guy	8
69	Major Minor MM 619	From Both Sides Now/We Try Harder	4
70	Major Minor MM 683	Danger Heartbreak Dead Ahead/I'll Be Thinking	4
65	Tamla Motown TME 2005	KIM WESTON (EP)	60
66	Tamla Motown TME 2015	ROCK ME A LITTLE WHILE (EP)	100
67	MGM C(S) 8055	FOR THE FIRST TIME (LP)	30

(see also Johnny Nash)

PETE WESTON

| 70 | Gas GAS 146 | Something Sweet/BIM & BAM: Love Letters | 4 |

WEST ONE

| 88 | Que Q 9 | California '69/Eurotrash (gig freebie, white label) | 12 |
| 80s | private cassette | WEST ONE (cassette) | 10 |

WEST POINT SUPERNATURAL

| 67 | Reaction 591 013 | Time Will Tell/Night Train | 10 |

WESTSIDE

| 74 | People PEO 111 | Running In And Out Of My Life/Highway Demon | 5 |

WESTWIND

| 73 | Penny Farthing PELS 505 | LOVE IS (LP) | 180 |

WEST WON

| 92 | Fun After All 12FAA 116D | Control (De-Code Mixes) (12", p/s) | 7 |
| 92 | Fun After All 12FAA 116D | Control (De-Code Mixes) (CD, 4-track) | 7 |

(see also Gary Numan)

WESTWORLD

| 86 | private pressing | Sonic Boom Boy/Sonic Boom Beat/Mix Me Up (12", hand screen-printed sleeve, handwritten label) | 10 |

WE THE PEOPLE

| 66 | London HLH 10089 | He Doesn't Go About It Right/You Burn Me Up And Down | 75 |

WE THREE TRIO

| 65 | London HLA 9966 | Baby The Rain Must Fall/Shine For Me | 5 |
| 67 | Fontana TL 5308 | THE WE THREE TRIO (LP) | 10 |

WET WET WET

87	Precious JEWEL 312	Wishing I Was Lucky (Metal Remix)/Words Of Wisdom/Still Can't Remember Your Name (12", p/s)	8
87	Precious JWLD 3	Wishing I Was Lucky (Remix)/Words Of Wisdom/Wishing I Was Lucky (Metal Mix)/I Still Can't Remember Your Name (12", double pack)	18
87	Precious JWLS 4	Sweet Little Mystery/Don't Let Me Be Lonely Tonight (shaped picture disc)	8
87	Precious JEWEL 412	SWEET LITTLE MYSTERY EP (12", 'wet cover')	15
87	Precious JEWEL 5	I Remember/I Don't Believe (withdrawn)	10
87	Precious JEWEL 512	I Remember/I Don't Believe (12", p/s, withdrawn)	15
87	Precious JEWEL 6	Angel Eyes (Home And Away)/We Can Love (box set with calendar)	6
87	Precious JWLMC 6	Angel Eyes (Home And Away)/We Can Love/Angel Eyes (Extended) (cassette)	4
88	Precious JEWEL 777	Temptation/Bottled Emotions (Keen For Loving) (gatefold/booklet p/s)	4
88	Precious JWLCD 7	Temptation (Extended)/Bottled Emotions/I Remember (Extended)/ Heaven Helps Us All (CD)	7
88	Lyntone/No. 1	Sweet Little Mystery/Interview With 'No. 1' magazine (flexidisc)	4
89	Precious JWL M/T/G/N 9	Sweet Surrender/This Time (live) (poster pack of each member)	each 5
89	Precious JWLMC 6	Sweet Surrender/This Time (live) (cassette)	4
89	Precious JWPD 10	Broke Away/You've Had It/And Now For Something Completely Different (picture disc)	5
90	Precious JWLM 11	Hold Back The River/Keys To Your Heart (Marti Pellow p/s)	4
90	Lyntone/Jamming!	I Can Give You Everything/FLOOR: Hold On (flexidisc free with 'Jamming!' magazine)	15/10

WE UGLY DOGS

| 67 | BT Puppy BTS 45537 | First Spring Rain/Poor Man | 4 |

WE'VE GOT A FUZZBOX & WE'RE GOING TO USE IT

| 86 | Vindaloo UGH 11 | XX Sex/Rules And Regulations/Do I Want To?/She/Aaarrrgghhh! (p/s, blue vinyl) | 5 |
| 86 | Vindaloo UGH 11T | XX Sex/Rules And Regulations (Splendiferous Mix)/Do I Want To?/She/ Aaarrrgghhh! (12", p/s, 1 side etched) | 7 |

W. GIMMICS

| 65 | Polydor EPH 27 125 | HOT RODS (EP) | 15 |

WHALE FEATHERS

| 71 | Blue Horizon 2431 009 | WHALE FEATHERS (LP) | 30 |

WHAM!

82	Innervision IVLA 2442	Wham Rap! (Enjoy What You Do) (Social Mix)/(Unsocial Mix) (p/s)	4
82	Innervision IVLA 13 2442	Wham Rap! (Enjoy What You Do) (Social Mix)/(Unsocial Mix) (12", p/s)	15
83	Innervision IVL 3143	Bad Boys/Bad Boys (Instrumental) (poster p/s)	8
83	Innervision IVL 3143	Bad Boys/Bad Boys (Instrumental) (picture disc)	15
83	Innervision IVL 3613	Club Tropicana/Blue (Armed With Love) (picture disc)	15
84	Epic KELL 4	Club Tropicana (free with 'Rice Krispies' offer)	4
84	Epic TA 4440	Wake Me Up Before You Go-Go/Wake Me Up (Instrumental)/A Ray Of Sunshine (12" poster p/s)	15
84	Epic QA/WA 4743	Freedom/Freedom (Instrumental) (George Michael or Andrew Ridgeley-shaped picture disc in wallet)	12/10
84	Epic GA 4949	Last Christmas/Everything She Wants (gatefold p/s)	7
84	Epic GTA 4949	Last Christmas/Everything She Wants (12", gatefold p/s)	8
85	Epic WTA 6716	I'm Your Man/Do It Right/I'm Your Man (12", picture disc)	7
86	Epic FIN 1	The Edge Of Heaven/Battlestations//Where Did Your Heart Go/Wham! Rap '86 (double pack)	4
80s	Epic	Fan Club Christmas single	10
86	Epic WHAM 2	THE FINAL (2-LP, box set, gold vinyl, with various pieces of memorabilia)	15
86	Epic EPC 450 125-4	THE 12" TAPE (cassette)	7

(see also George Michael)

PEETIE WHEATSTRAW

| 69 | Matchbox SDR 191 | THE DEVIL'S SON IN LAW (LP) | 12 |
| 69 | Matchbox SDR 192 | THE HIGH SHERIFF FROM HELL (LP) | 12 |

KENNY WHEELER & JOHN DANKWORTH ORCHESTRA

| 68 | Fontana STL 5494 | WINDMILL TILTER (LP) | 35 |

(see also Johnny Dankworth)

WHEELS

65	Columbia DB 7682	Gloria/Don't You Know	80
66	Columbia DB 7827	Bad Little Woman/Road Block (mispressing, demos & a few issues play "Call My Name" on B-side)	70
66	Columbia DB 7827	Bad Little Woman/Road Block	175
66	Columbia DB 7981	Kicks/Call My Name	75

(see also James Brothers, Yellow Dog, Demick & Armstrong)

WHEELS OF TIME

| 67 | Spin 62008 | 1984/So Long | 35 |

WHERE FORTUNE SMILES

| 71 | Dawn DNLS 3018 | WHERE FORTUNE SMILES (LP, with poster insert) | 15 |

(see also John Surman, John McLaughlin)

WHERE'S LISSE

| 81 | Glass GLASS 008 | Talk Takes Too Long/You Stole My Gun (p/s) | 5 |
| 82 | Glass GLASS 014 | Tutorial Single (p/s) | 4 |

WHICHWHAT

69	Beacon BEA 127	Gimme Gimme Good Lovin'/Wonderland Of Love	4
69	Beacon BEA 131	Why Do Lovers Break Each Other's Heart/When I See Her Smile	4
69	Beacon BEA 133	In The Year 2525/Parting	4
69	Beacon BEA 144	I Wanna Be Free/It's All Over Again	4
70	Beacon BEA 169	Vietnam Rose/Shame And Solution	5
70	Beacon BEAS 14	WHICHWHAT'S FIRST (LP)	40

WHIPPING BOY

| 80s | Liquid LQ 4 | Favourite Sister/Safari (no p/s) | 4 |

WHIRL

| 87 | Playroom Discs PLAYD 112 | Heaven Forbid/Mister Strikes Back/As Soon As/In A Dream (12", p/s) | 7 |
| 89 | The Sound Of Spasm 2 | Bizarre Love Triangle/CROCODILE RIDE: Shimmer (33rpm flexi, foldover p/s) | 4 |

WHIRLWIND

77	Pye International 7N 25733	Full Time Thing/Don't Let Him Get The Best Of You	5
78	Chiswick NS 25	Hang Loose/Together Forever	4
80	Chiswick CHIS 103	I Only Wish/Ducktails	4
80	Chiswick CHIS 122	Heaven Knows/Cruisin Around (p/s)	4
78	Chiswick WIK 7	BLOWING UP A STORM (10" mini-LP)	8
80	Chiswick CWK 3012	MIDNIGHT BLUE (10" mini-LP)	8

WHIRLWINDS

| 64 | HMV POP 1301 | Look At Me/Baby Not Like Me | 25 |

(see also Mockingbirds, Graham Gouldman, 10cc)

NANCY WHISKEY (& HER SKIFFLERS)

57	Oriole CB 1394	He's Solid Gone/Ella Speed (as Nancy Whiskey & Her Skifflers)	8
58	Oriole CB 1452	I Know Where I'm Goin'/Hillside In Scotland	6
59	Oriole CB 1485	Johnny Blue/The Old Grey Goose	6
65	Fontana TF 612	Bowling Green/I'm Leaving Today	6
50s	Topic T 7	NANCY WHISKEY (8" LP)	20

(see also Chas McDevitt Skiffle Group)

WHISPERS

72	Polydor 2916 003	THE WHISPERS (LP)	10
74	Contempo CRM 106	THE WHISPERS (LP)	10
74	Janus 9104 400	WHISPERS GETTIN' LOUDER (LP)	10

WHISTLER

| 71 | Deram SML 1083 | HO-HUM (LP) | 25 |

Ian WHITCOMB

IAN WHITCOMB

65	Capitol CL 15382	This Sporting Life/Fizz 4
65	Capitol CL 15395	You Turn Me On/Poor But Honest 7
65	Capitol CL 15418	N-N-Nervous!/The End 4
66	Capitol CL 15431	Good Hard Rock/High Blood Pressure 5
67	Ember NR 5065	YOU TURN ME ON (LP, with Jimmy Page & John Paul Jones) 20

BARRY WHITE

67	President PT 139	All In The Run Of A Day/Don't Take Your Love From Me 5

BUKKA WHITE

66	Fontana 688 804 ZL	SKY SONGS (LP, with Big Willie) 15
66	CBS Realm 52629	BUKKA WHITE (LP) 35
69	Blue Horizon 7-63229	MEMPHIS HOT SHOTS (LP) 35

DANNY WHITE

67	Sue WI 4031	Keep My Woman Home/I Am Dedicating My Life 22
74	MCA MU 155	Cracked Up Over You/Taking Inventory 6

DUKE WHITE

63	Island WI 084	It's Over/Forever 10
65	Black Swan WI 444	Sow Good Seeds/BABA BROOKS BAND: Bus Strike 10

GEORGIA WHITE

54	Vocalion V 1038	Was I Drunk?/Moonshine Blues (78) 20

IAN WHITE

70	private pressing	IAN WHITE (LP) 25

JEANETTE WHITE

69	A&M AMS 761	Music/No Sunshine 20

JOE WHITE

64	R&B JB 137	Sinners (as Joe White & Maytals)/ROLAND ALPHONSO: King Solomon 10
64	Ska Beat JB 180	Punch You Down (with Chuck)/TOMMY McCOOK: Cotton Tree 10
64	Island WI 145	When Are You Young/Wanna Go Home 10
64	Island WI 159	Hog In A Co Co/ROLAND ALPHONSO & SKATALITES: Sandy Gully 10
64	Island WI 166	Downtown Girl/DON DRUMMOND: Cool Smoke 8
65	Island WI 201	Low Minded People (as Joe White & Chuck)/Irene 10
66	Doctor Bird DB 1001	Every Night (with Chuck)/BABA BROOKS & HIS BAND: First Session 10
66	Doctor Bird DB 1024	My Love For You/SAMMY ISMAY & BABA BROOKS BAND: Cocktails For Two 10
66	Doctor Bird DB 1043	So Close (as Joe White & Della)/BABA BROOKS & HIS BAND: Eighth Games ...10
67	Doctor Bird DB 1069	Rudies All Around/Bad Man 10
67	Doctor Bird DB 1080	Lonely Nights/I Need You 10
67	Doctor Bird DB 1090	I Need A Woman/Hot Hops 10
68	Blue Cat BS 108	Way Of Life (actually by Lyn Tait & Jets)/I'm So Proud 8
68	Blue Cat BS 119	Try A Little Tenderness/LYN TAITT & CARL BRYAN: Tender Arms 8
68	Blue Cat BS 130	Pretty Girl/DERMOTT LYNCH: You Went Away 8
70	Sugar SJ 103	Yesterday/I Am Free 4
70	Trojan TR 7742	So Much Love/Maybe Now 4
70	Trojan TR 7768	I'm Going To Get There/RUPIE EDWARDS ALLSTARS: Kinky Funky Reggae 4
70	Big BG 301	This Is The Time/The Other Day 4
71	Big BG 309	Baby I Care/Ain't Misbehavin' 4
72	Songbird SB 1072	Trinity/SCOTTY: Monkey Drop 4
72	Dynamic DYN 440	Kenyatta/RECORDING BAND: Version 5
73	Gayfeet GS 202	If It Don't Work Out/BABA BROOKS BAND: Ki Salaboca 5
70s	Ultra PFU 1002	Give And Take/Roots Dub 4
70s	Magnet MGT 006	SINCE THE OTHER DAY (LP) 15

JOSH WHITE

50	London L 739	Take A Gal Like You/Wanderings (78) 5
50	London L 810	Like A Natural Man/The Foggy, Foggy Dew (78) 5
50	London L 828	I'm Gonna Move To The Outskirts Of Town/Hard Time Blues (78) 5
50	London L 907	Molly Malone/T.B. Blues (78) 5
51	London L 1028	On Top Of Old Smoky/Black Girl (with Bill Hill's Orchestra & Stargazers) (78) 5
51	London L 1138	Barbara Allen/The Lass With The Delicate Air (78) 5
52	London L 1142	Lonesome Road/He Never Said A Mumblin' Word (78) 5
52	London L 1143	Call Me Darling/I Want You, I Need You (78, export issue) 5
52	London L 1144	Waltzing Landing/Apples, Peaches And Cherries (78, export issue) 5
52	London L 1161	Free And Equal Blues Parts 1 & 2 (78) 6
57	Pye NJE 1057	BLUES AND ... PART 1 (EP) 8
57	Pye NJE 1058	BLUES AND ... PART 2 (EP) 8
57	Pye NJE 1059	BLUES AND ... PART 3 (EP) 8
58	Mercury YEP 9504	SOUTHERN BLUES (EP) 8
64	Storyville SEP 388	STORYVILLE BLUES ANTHOLOGY VOL. 8 (EP) 8
64	Mercury 10006MCE	JOSH WHITE (EP) 8
51	London H-APB 1005	A JOSH WHITE PROGRAM (10" LP) 15
52	Brunswick LA 8562	BALLADS AND BLUES (10" LP) 15
54	Brunswick LA 8653	BALLADS AND BLUES VOL. 2 (10" LP) 15
54	London H-APB 1032	JOSH WHITE SINGS — VOL. 2 (10" LP) 15
54	Mercury MG 25014	SONGS BY JOSH WHITE (10" LP) 15
55	London H-APB 1038	JOSH COMES A-VISITIN' (10" LP) 15
56	Nixa Jazz Today NJL 2	BLUES AND ... (LP) 12
58	HMV CLP 1159	JOSH WHITE STORIES VOLUME 1 (LP) 10
58	HMV CLP 1175	JOSH WHITE STORIES VOLUME 2 (LP) 10
62	Storyville SLP 123	JOHN HENRY, BALLADS, BLUES AND OTHER SONGS (LP) 10
62	Mercury MMC 14102	AT THE TOWN HALL (LP) 10
62	HMV CLP 1588	JOSH WHITE LIVE! (LP) 10
64	Mercury 20039 MCL	THE BEGINNING (LP) 15

| 64 | Ace Of Hearts AH 65 | JOSH WHITE (LP) | 10 |

(see also Teddy Moss/Josh White)

JOSH & BEVERLEY WHITE
| 64 | Realm REP 4003 | BEVERLEY & JOSH WHITE JNR (EP) | 7 |

K.C. WHITE
| 72 | Dynamic DYN 434 | Man No Dead/Version | 4 |
| 73 | Technique TE 929 | Anywhere But Nowhere/Bush In Session | 4 |

KITTY WHITE (& DAVE HOWARD)
| 54 | London HL 8102 | Jesse James/Scratch My Back (B-side with Dave Howard) | 25 |

LENNY WHITE
| 75 | Atlantic K 50213 | VENUSIAN SUMMER (LP) | 10 |

LOUISIANA JANE WHITE
| 69 | Philips BF 1810 | When The Battle Is Over/Blue Ribbons | 8 |

SNOWY WHITE
| 84 | Towerbell TOWX 52 | Peace On Earth/Broken Promises (picture disc) | 4 |

TAM WHITE
67	Decca F 12711	World Without You/Someone You Should Know (unreleased)	
68	Decca F 12849	Waiting Till The Night Comes Around/Girl Watcher	4
69	Deram DM 261	That Old Sweet Roll/Don't Make Promises	6
70	Middle Earth MDS 104	Lewis Carroll/Future Thoughts	6
70	Middle Earth MDLS 304	TAM WHITE (LP)	20

TERRY WHITE & TERRIERS
| 59 | Decca F 11133 | Rock Around The Mailbag/Blackout | 25 |

TONY JOE WHITE
68	Monument MON 1024	Soul Francisco/Whompt Out On You	4
69	Monument MON 1031	Polk Salad Annie/Aspen Colorado	4
68	Monument SMO 5027	BLACK AND WHITE (LP)	10
69	Monument SMO 5035	CONTINUED (LP)	10
70s	Warner Bros K 46068	TONY JOE WHITE (LP)	10
75	Warner Bros K 46147	THE TRAIN I'M ON (LP)	10
75	Warner Bros K 56149	BEST OF TONY JOE WHITE (LP)	10
70s	Warner Bros K 46229	HOME MADE ICE CREAM (LP)	10

WHITE DUCK
| 72 | Uni UN 541 | Billy Goat/Really | 5 |
| 73 | Uni UN 555 | Honey, You'll Be Alright/Carry Love | 4 |

WHITE ELEPHANT
| 70s | White Elephant RIOCH 1 | CITY WALLS (LP, with other artists) | 10 |

WHITE HEAT
80	Vallium VAL 1	Nervous Breakdown/Sammy Sez (p/s)	7
80	Vallium VAL 02	Finished With The Fashions/Ordinary Joe (p/s, with insert)	7
81	Vallium VAL 03	City Beat/It's No Use (p/s)	5
80	Valium	WHITE HEAT (LP)	15

WHITEHOUSE
80	Come Org. WDC 881004	BIRTHDEATH EXPERIENCE (LP)	100
80	Come Org. WDC 881005	TOTAL SEX (LP)	100
80	Come Org. WDC 881007	ERECTOR (LP, different coloured vinyls)	80
81	Come Org. WDC 881010	DEDICATED TO PETER KURTEN, SADIST AND MASS SLAYER (LP, some on coloured vinyl, some in custom sleeve)	80
81	Come Org. WDC	GREAT WHITE DEATH (LP)	65
81	Come Org. WDC 881013	BUCHENWALD (LP)	70
82	Come Org. WDC 881017	NEW BRITAIN (LP)	100
81	Come Org. WDC 881020	LIVE ACTION 1 (cassette)	20
80s	Come Org. WDC 881022	LIVE ACTION 2 (cassette)	20
80s	Come Org. WDC 881027	PSYCHOPATHIA SEXUALIS (LP, clear or black vinyl)	120
80s	Come Org. WDC 883033	RIGHT TO KILL — DEDICATED TO DENNIS ANDREW NEILSEN (LP, with inserts)	70
80s	Come Org.	150 MURDEROUS PASSIONS (LP)	60

(Many of the above LPs came in customised white card sleeves & were later available in a generic 'Peter Kurten' sleeve originally used for the 2nd pressing of the "Peter Kurten" LP. This latter design was also used for counterfeits. There may also be various coloured vinyl variations of the above LPs, worth around the same value. Below are cassettes, which may sell for more if complete with inserts or magazine. Some of the Live Action releases were videos.)

80s	Come Org. WDC 883044	RADIO INTERVIEWS/LIVE ACTION 9 USA VOL. I	12
80s	Come Org. WDC 883046	LIVE ACTION 13 USA VOL. III	12
80s	Come Org. WDC 883047	LIVE ACTION 14 USA VOL. IV	12
80s	Come Org. WDC 883048	LIVE ACTION 15/LIVE ACTION 16 USA VOL. V	12
80s	Come Org. WDC 883049	LIVE ACTION 20 USA VOL. VI	12
80s	Come Org. WDC 883050	LIVE ACTION 22/LIVE ACTION 23	12
80s	Come Org. WDC 883052	USA REHEARSAL	12
80s	Come Org. WDC 883053	LIVE ACTION 24/LIVE ACTION 25	12
80s	Come Org. WDC 883055	LIVE ACTION 26	12
80s	Susan Lawley 1	CREAM OF THE SECOND COMING (2-LP)	15

(see also Come, Nurse With Wound, New Order, Skullflower, Konstruktivits)

WHITE NOISE
| 60 | Island ILPS 9099 | AN ELECTRIC STORM (LP, pink label) | 15 |
| 75 | Virgin V 2032 | WHITE NOISE 2 (LP) | 10 |

WHITE PLAINS
| 70 | Deram SML 1067 | WHITE PLAINS (LP) | 15 |
| 71 | Deram SML 1092 | WHEN YOU ARE A KING (LP) | 15 |

(see also Carter-Lewis & Southerners, Ivy League, Kestrels, Flowerpot Men, Edison Lighthouse)

WHITESNAKE

78	EMI International INEP 751	SNAKEBITE (EP, white vinyl p/s; later black vinyl, no p/s) 10/7
78	EMI International INT 568	Lie Down/Don't Mess With Me (p/s) 5
79	EMI International INT 578	The Time Is Right For Love/Come On (live) (p/s) 4
79	United Artists BP 324	Long Way From Home/Trouble (live)/Ain't No Love In The Heart Of The City (live) (p/s) 4
80	United Artists BP 352	Fool For Your Loving/Mean Business/Don't Mess With Me (some in luminous p/s) 8/4
80	United Artists BP 381	Ain't No Love In The Heart Of The City (live)/Take Me With You (live) (p/s) 4
80	United Artists 12BP 381	Ain't No Love In The Heart Of The City (live)/Take Me With You (live) (12", p/s) ...7
82	Liberty BP 416	Here I Go Again/Bloody Luxury (picture disc) 8
82	Liberty BPP 418	Love An' Affection/Victim Of Love (withdrawn) 25
83	Liberty BPP 420	Guilty Of Love/Gambler (shaped picture disc) 10
84	Liberty BPP 423	Standing In The Shadows/All Or Nothing (US Mix) (p/s, with patch) 4
84	Liberty BPP 423	Standing In The Shadows/All Or Nothing (US Mix) (picture disc) 5
85	Liberty BP 424	Love Ain't No Stranger (US Album Mix)/Slow 'N' Easy (US Album Mix) (p/s) ... 5
85	Liberty BP 12 424	Love Ain't No Stranger (US Album Mix)/Slow 'N' Easy (US Album Mix) (12", p/s) ..8
87	EMI EMIW 5605	Still Of The Night/Here I Go Again (white vinyl, p/s, with poster) 10
87	EMI 12 EMIS 5605	Still Of The Night (Extended)/Here I Go Again '87/You're Gonna Break My Heart Again (12", p/s, with sticker) 7
87	EMI 12 EMIP 5605	Still Of The Night/Here I Go Again/You're Gonna Break My Heart Again (12", picture disc) 10
87	EMI EMP 3	Is This Love/Standing In The Shadows '87/Need Your Love So Bad '87 (shaped picture disc, with free white label 7") 7
87	EMI EMP 3	Is This Love/Standing In The Shadows '87/Need Your Love So Bad '87 (shaped picture disc, mispress, without "Need Your Love So Bad '87") 7
87	EMI EMX 3	Is This Love/Standing In The Shadows '87/Need Your Love So Bad '87 (poster p/s) 4
87	EMI 12EMW 3	Is This Love/Standing In The Shadows '87/Need Your Love So Bad '87 (12", p/s, white vinyl) 8
87	EMI EMP 35	Here I Go Again '87 US (1-sided, B-side etched, poster p/s) 5
87	EMI 10EMI 35	Here I Go Again '87 US/Guilty Of Love (10", p/s, white vinyl) 10
88	EMI 12EM 23	Give Me All Your Love/Fool For Your Loving (white vinyl, p/s, with insert) 5
88	EMI 12EM 23	Give Me All Your Love/Fool For Your Loving/Don't Break My Heart Again (12", p/s, white vinyl) 10
88	EMI 12EMP 23	Give Me All Your Love/Fool For Your Loving/Don't Break My Heart Again (12", picture disc) 10
89	EMI EMP 123	Fool For Your Loving (7" Version)/Slow Poke Music (p/s, with poster) 4
89	EMI 12EMS 123	Fool For Your Loving/Slow Poke Music/Walking In The Shadows Of The Blues (live) (12", p/s, white vinyl) 7
90	EMI EMPD 128	The Deeper The Love/Judgement Day (picture disc) 5
90	EMI 12EMS 128	The Deeper The Love/Judgement Day/Sweet Lady Luck (12" p/s, white vinyl) 7
90	EMI EMPD 150	Now You're Gone (Remix)/Wings Of The Storm (shaped picture disc w/ plinth) ...7
90	EMI 12EMS 150	Now You're Gone (Remix)/Kittens Got Claws/Cheap And Nasty (12", gatefold p/s, with booklet) 7
78	EMI Intl. INS 3022	TROUBLE (LP, 2 different inner sleeves) 12
82	Liberty LBGP 30354	SAINTS AN' SINNERS (LP, picture disc) 10
84	Liberty LBGP 240000 0	SLIDE IT IN (LP, picture disc, U.S. mixes) 12
87	EMI EMC 3528	WHITESNAKE 1987 (LP, embossed sleeve) 10
87	EMI EMC 3528	WHITESNAKE 1987 (LP, picture disc) 12

(see also David Coverdale's Whitesnake, Deep Purple, Roger Glover, Bernie Marsden, Jon Lord, Phenomena, Cozy Powell)

WHITE SPIRIT

80	Neat NEAT 05	Back To The Grind/Cheetah (p/s) 6
81	MCA MCA 638	Midnight Chaser/Suffragettes (p/s) 10
81	MCA MCA 652	High Upon High/No Reprieve (no p/s) 4
81	MCA MCF 3079	WHITE SPIRIT (LP) 12

(see also Gillan, Iron Maiden)

WHITE SS

| 78 | White SS CIA 72 | Mercy Killing/I'm Not One (live) (p/s) .... 15 |

WHITE TRASH

(see under Trash)

DAVID WHITFIELD

54	Decca F 10242	The Book/Heartless 15
54	Decca F 10327	Cara Mia/Love, Tears And Kisses (with Mantovani Orchestra) 15
54	Decca F 10355	Smile/How, When Or Where (B-side with Mantovani Orchestra) 8
54	Decca F 10399	Santo Natale/Adeste Fideles 10
55	Decca F 10458	Beyond The Stars/Open Up Your Heart (with Mantovani Orchestra) 12
55	Decca F 10515	Ev'rywhere/Mama 12
55	Decca F 10562	The Lady/Santa Rose Lea Rose 6
55	Decca F 10596	I'll Never Stop Loving You/Lady Of Madrid 6
55	Decca F 10627	When You Lose The One You Love/Angelus (with Mantovani Orchestra) 8
56	Decca F 10690	My September Love/The Rudder And The Rock 8
56	Decca F 10769	My Son John/My Unfinished Symphony 8
57	Decca F 10833	The Adoration Waltz/If I Lost You 8
57	Decca F 10864	I'll Find You/I'd Give You The World 8
57	Decca F 10890	Without Him/Dream Of Paradise 4
57	Decca F 10931	Ev'rything/Martinella 4
58	Decca F 10978	Cry My Heart/My One True Love (with Mantovani Orchestra) 4
58	Decca F 11018	On The Street Where You Live/Afraid 4
58	Decca F 11039	The Right To Love/That's When Your Heartaches Begin 4
58	Decca F 11079	This Is Lucia/Love Is A Stranger 4
59	Decca F 11101	Willingly/William Tell 4
61	Decca F 11336	Scottish Soldier/Scotland The Brave (unreleased)
55	Decca DFE 6225	CARA MIA (EP) 12

THE WHO

David WHITFIELD

56	Decca DFE 6342	DAVID WHITFIELD No. 1 (EP)	7
57	Decca DFE 6400	DAVID WHITFIELD No. 2 (EP)	7
58	Decca DFE 6434	DAVID WHITFIELD No. 3 (EP)	7
62	Decca STO 158	ALONE (EP, stereo)	8
54	Decca LF 1165	YOURS FROM THE HEART (10" LP)	16
58	Decca LK 4242	WHITFIELD FAVOURITES (LP)	12
58	Decca LK 4270	FROM DAVID WITH LOVE (LP)	12
60	Decca LK 4348/SKL 4094	MY HEART AND I (LP, mono/stereo)	10/12
61	Decca LK 4384/SKL 4126	ALONE (LP, mono/stereo)	10/12

WILBUR WHITFIELD

57	Vogue V 9078	P.B. Baby/The One I Love	125
57	Vogue V 9078	P.B. Baby/The One I Love (78)	50

(see also Little Wilbur & Pleasers)

LEONARD WHITING

65	Pye 7N 15943	Piper/That's What Mama Say	10

MARGARET WHITING

55	Capitol CL 14213	My Own True Love/Can This Be Love (triangular centre)	8
55	Capitol CL 14242	Heat Wave/Come Rain Or Shine (triangular centre)	8
55	Capitol CL 14307	Stowaway/All I Want Is All There Is And Then Some (triangular centre)	8
55	Capitol CL 14348	A Man/Mama's Pearls (triangular centre)	8
55	Capitol CL 14375	Lover, Lover/I Kiss You A Million Times (triangular centre)	8
56	Capitol CL 14527	I Love A Mystery/Bidin' My Time	6
56	Capitol CL 14591	Old Enough/Day In — Day Out	5
56	Capitol CL 14647	True Love/Haunting Love	5
57	Capitol CL 14685	The Money Tree/Maybe I Love Him	5
57	London HLD 8451	Kill Me With Kisses/Speak For Yourself John	6
58	London HLD 8562	I Can't Help (If I'm Still In Love With You)/That's Why I Was Born	6
58	London HLD 8662	Hot Spell/I'm So Lonesome I Could Cry	6
66	London HLD 10078	Nothing Lasts Forever/The Wheel Of Hurt	5
67	London HLD 10114	Just Like A Man/The World Inside Your Arms	6
68	London HLD 10196	Faithfully/Am I Losing You	4
53	Capitol LC 6585	CAPITOL PRESENTS MARGARET WHITING (10" LP)	15
56	Capitol LC 6811	MARGARET WHITING (10" LP)	15
58	London HA-D 2109	GOIN' PLACES (LP)	15
61	HMV CLP 1418/CSD 1339	SINGS THE JEROME KERN SONGBOOK VOL. ONE (LP, mono/stereo)	10/12
61	HMV CLP 1419/CSD 1340	SINGS THE JEROME KERN SONGBOOK VOL. TWO (LP, mono/stereo)	10/12
61	London HA-D 2321	JUST A DREAM (LP)	15
67	London HA-U/SH-U 8317	THE WHEEL OF HURT (LP)	15
67	London HA-U 8332	MAGGIE ISN'T MARGARET ANYMORE (LP)	15

RAY WHITLEY

65	HMV POP 1473	I've Been Hurt/There Is One Boy	40

BOBBY WHITLOCK

72	CBS 65109	BOBBY WHITLOCK (LP)	10
72	CBS 65301	RAW VELVET (LP)	12

(see also Derek & Dominoes)

SLIM WHITMAN

52	London L 1149	Indian Love Call/China Doll (78)	5
53	London L 1186	How Can I Tell/Love Song Of The Waterfall (78)	6
53	London L 1191	My Love Is Growing Stale/Bandera Waltz (78)	6
53	London L 1194	Restless Heart/Song Of The Old Water Wheel (78)	6
53	London L 1206	My Heart Is Broken In Three/Cold Empty Arms (78)	6
54	London L 1214	There's A Rainbow In Every Teardrop/Danny Boy (78)	5
54	London L 1226	North Wind/Darlin' Don't Cry (78)	5
54	London L 1149	Indian Love Call/China Doll	35
54	London HL 1149	Indian Love Call/China Doll (re-pressing with different prefix)	20
54	London L 1214	There's A Rainbow In Every Teardrop/Danny Boy	35
54	London HL 1214	There's A Rainbow In Every Teardrop/Danny Boy (re-pressing)	25
54	London L 1226	North Wind/Darlin' Don't Cry	40
54	London HL 1226	North Wind/Darlin' Don't Cry (re-pressing with different prefix)	30
54	London HL 8018	Stairway To Heaven/Lord, Help Me To Be As Thou	45
54	London HL 8039	Secret Love/Why	35
54	London HL 8061	Rose Marie/We Stood At The Altar	18
54	London HL 8080	Beautiful Dreamer/Ride Away	25
54	London HL 8091	The Singing Hills/I Hate To See You Cry	25
55	London HL 8125	When I Grow Too Old To Dream/Cattle Call	25
55	London HL 8141	Haunted Hungry Heart/Roll On Silvery Moon	25
55	London HLU 8167	I'll Never Stop Loving You/I'll Never Take You Back Again	25
55	London HLU 8196	Song Of The Wild/You Have My Heart	25
56	London HLU 8230	Tumbling Tumbleweeds/Tell Me	22
56	London HLU 8252	I'm A Fool/My Heart Is Broken In Three	22
56	London HLU 8287	Serenade/I Talk To The Waves	20
56	London HLU 8327	Dear Mary/Whiffenpoof Song	25
56	London HLU 8350	I'm Casting My Lasso Towards The Sky/There's A Love Knot In My Lariat	20
57	London HLP 8403	I'll Take You Home Again Kathleen/Careless Love	15

(the above 45s originally had gold labels & tri-centres, later round-centre &/or silver label reissues are worth half the value)

57	London HLP 8416	Curtain Of Tears/Smoke Signals (silver label)	12
57	London HLP 8420	Gone/An Amateur In Love (gold label)	25
57	London HLP 8434	Many Times/Warm, Warm Lips	12
57	London HLP 8459	Lovesick Blues/Forever	12
57	London HLP 8518	Unchain My Heart/Hush-A-Bye	12
58	London HLP 8590	A Very Precious Love/Careless Hands	12
58	London HLP 8642	Candy Kisses/Tormented	10
58	London HLP 8708	Wherever You Are/At The End Of Nowhere	10

59	London HLP 8835	I Never See Maggie Alone/The Letter Edged In Black	8
59	London HLP 8896	What Kind Of God (Do You Think You Are)/A Tree In The Meadow (unissued)	
60	London HLP 9103	Roll, River, Roll/Twilla Lee	6
61	London HLP 9302	Vaya Con Dios/Ramona	6
64	Liberty LIB 66040	I'll Hold You In My Heart/No Other Arms, No Other Lips	5
65	Liberty LIB 66103	Reminiscing/Mansion On The Hill	5
65	Liberty LIB 12013	Remember Me (I'm The One Who Loves You)/Virginia	5
65	Liberty LIB 12020	More Than Yesterday/Broken Down Merry-Go-Round	5
66	Liberty LIB 66181	A Travelin' Man/I Remember You	5
66	Liberty LIB 66212	One Dream/Jerry	5
66	Liberty LIB 66226	What's The World A-Comin' To/You Bring Out The Best In Me	5
54	London RE-P 1006	SLIM WHITMAN AND HIS SINGING GUITAR (EP, different colour sleeves)	15
55	London RE-P 1042	SONG OF THE WILD (EP)	15
56	London RE-P 1064	SLIM WHITMAN VOL. 2 PT. 1 (EP)	12
56	London RE-P 1070	SLIM WHITMAN VOL. 2 PT. 2 (EP)	12
57	London RE-P 1100	SLIM WHITMAN VOL. 2 PT. 3 (EP)	12
59	London RE-P 1199	SLIM WHITMAN SINGS (EP)	12
60	London RE-P 1258	SLIM WHITMAN SINGS No. 2 (EP)	12
63	London RE-P 1360	WAYWARD WIND (EP)	15
64	Liberty LEP 4018	IRISH LOVE SONGS THE SLIM WHITMAN WAY (EP)	10
65	Liberty LEP 4027	SLIM WHITMAN SINGS MORE IRISH SONGS (EP)	10
66	Liberty LEP 4046	SATISFIED MAN (EP)	12
54	London H-APB 1015	SLIM WHITMAN & HIS SINGING GUITAR (10" LP, gold or silver labels)	45/35
56	London HA-U 2015	SLIM WHITMAN & HIS SINGING GUITAR VOL. 2 (LP)	35
58	London HA-P 2139	SLIM WHITMAN SINGS (LP)	20
59	London HA-P 2199	SLIM WHITMAN SINGS VOL. 2 (LP)	20
60	London HA-P 2343	SLIM WHITMAN (LP)	20
61	London HA-P 2392	JUST CALL ME LONESOME (LP)	20
62	London HA-P 2443	SLIM WHITMAN SINGS VOL. 3 (LP, also stereo SAH-P 6232)	20/25
62	London HA-P 8013	SLIM WHITMAN SINGS VOL. 4 (LP)	20
63	London HA-P 8059	HEART SONGS AND LOVE SONGS (LP)	20
63	London HA-P 8093	I'M A LONELY WANDERER (LP)	20
64	Liberty LBY 3032	YODELING (LP)	15
65	Liberty LBY 3034	COUNTRY SONGS, CITY HITS (LP)	15
65	Liberty LBY 3054	THE BEST OF SLIM WHITMAN VOL. 1 (LP)	10
66	Liberty LBY 3060	THE BEST OF SLIM WHITMAN VOL. 2 (LP)	15
66	Liberty LBY 3067	REMINISCING (LP)	12
66	Liberty LBY 3003	IRISH SONGS (LP)	12
67	Liberty (S)LBY 3079	A TRAVELIN' MAN (LP)	12
67	Liberty (S)LBY 3086	A TIME FOR LOVE (LP)	12
67	Liberty LBY 3092	THE BEST OF SLIM WHITMAN VOL. 3 (LP)	20
67	Liberty LBY 83019	IRISH SONGS (LP, reissue)	10
67	Liberty LBL 83021	YODELING (LP, reissue)	10
67	Liberty LBL 83022	COUNTRY SONGS, CITY HITS (LP, reissue)	10
67	Liberty LBL/LBS 83029	A TRAVELIN' MAN (LP, reissue)	10
67	Liberty LBL/LBS 83035	A TIME FOR LOVE (LP, reissue)	10
67	Liberty LBL/LBS 83039	15TH ANNIVERSARY (LP)	10
68	Liberty LBL/LBS 83064	GREAT PERFORMANCES (LP)	10
68	Liberty LBL/LBS 83093	COUNTRY MEMORIES (LP)	10
68	Liberty LBL/LBS 83109	COOL WATER (LP)	12
68	Liberty LBL/LBS 83113	IN LOVE THE WHITMAN WAY (LP)	12
70	Liberty LBS 83390	TOMORROW NEVER COMES (LP)	10

MARVA WHITNEY

72	Mojo 2092 041	Daddy Don't Know About The Sugar Beat/We Need More But Somebody	8
70	Polydor 2001 036	This Girl's In Love With You/He's The One	15
69	Polydor 583 767	IT'S MY THING (LP)	125

(see also James Brown)

TIM WHITSETT

| 64 | Sue WI 318 | Macks By The Tracks/Shine | 10 |

TIM WHITSETT/STICKS HERMAN

| 60s | Range JRE 7002 | RHYTHM & BLUES (EP) | 15 |

PAUL WHITSUN JONES & WALLAS EATON & HOLLAND

| 65 | Oriole CB 1991 | Shake It Baby/Instant Marriage | 4 |

WHITSUNTIDE EASTER

| 77 | Pilgrim/Grapevine GRA 109 | NEXT TIME YOU PLAY A WRONG NOTE ... MAKE IT A SHORT ONE (LP, gatefold sleeve) | 150 |

ROG WHITTAKER (& COMPANIONS)

62	Fontana H 358	The Charge Of The Light Brigade/Keep It A Secret	4
62	Fontana 267 217TF	Steel Men/After The Laughter	4
63	Fontana 267 258TF	Butterfly/Times Is Tough	4
63	Fontana TF 393	The Sinner/Settle Down (as Rog Whittaker & Companions)	4
64	Fontana TF 437	Mud Puddle/Acre Of Wheat (as Rog Whittaker & His Companions)	4

(see also Hank & Mellowmen)

TOMMY WHITTLE (& HIS QUARTET)

57	HMV POP 379	The Finisher/Cabin In The Sky (as Tommy Whittle & His Quartet)	4
54	Esquire 20-028	WAXING WITH WHITTLE (LP)	15
60	Tempo TAP 27	NEW HORIZONS (LP)	10

WHIZZ KIDS

| 79 | Dead Good DEAD SIX | P.A.Y.E./99% Proof/National Assistance/Cheek To Cheek (p/s) | 6 |
| 80 | Ovation OVS 1213 | Suspect No. 1/Coma Life (ps) | 5 |

WHO

65	Brunswick 05926	I Can't Explain/Bald Headed Woman	10
65	Brunswick 05935	Anyway Anyhow Anywhere/Daddy Rolling Stone	15
65	Brunswick 05944	My Generation/Shout And Shimmy	8
66	Brunswick 05951	Circles/Instant Party (unreleased)	
66	Reaction 591 001	Substitute/Instant Party (withdrawn)	12
66	Reaction 591 001	Substitute/Circles	12
66	Reaction 591 001	Substitute/WHO ORCHESTRA: Waltz For A Pig (B-side actually by Graham Bond Organisation)	10
66	Brunswick 05956	A Legal Matter/Instant Party	15
66	Brunswick 05956	The Kids Are Alright/The Ox (mispressing, wrong catalogue number)	20
66	Brunswick 05965	The Kids Are Alright/The Ox	15
66	Reaction 591 004	I'm A Boy/In The City	6
66	Brunswick 05968	La-La-La-Lies/The Good's Gone	20
66	Reaction 591 010	Happy Jack/I've Been Away	6
67	Track 604 002	Pictures Of Lily/Doctor, Doctor	5
67	Track 604 006	Under My Thumb/The Last Time	20
67	Track 604 011	I Can See For Miles/Someone's Coming	6
68	Track 604 023	Dogs/Call Me Lightning	8
68	Track 604 024	Magic Bus/Dr. Jekyll And Mr Hyde	6
69	Track 604 027	Pinball Wizard/Dogs Part Two	4
70	Track 604 036	The Seeker/Here For More	5
70	Track 2094 002	Summertime Blues/Heaven And Hell	6
70	Track 2094 004	See Me, Feel Me/Overture From "Tommy" (withdrawn)	12
71	Track 2094 009	Won't Get Fooled Again/Don't Know Myself (p/s)	10
71	Track 2094 009	Won't Get Fooled Again/Don't Know Myself (white label, different matrix number)	4
71	Track 2094 012	Let's See Action/When I Was A Boy (black label)	5
72	Track 2094 102	Join Together/Baby Don't You Do It (black label)	5
72	Track 2094 106	Relay/Waspman	4
73	Track 2094 115	5.15/Water	4
75	Polydor 2001 561	Overture/See Me Feel Me/Listening To You (from "Tommy" soundtrack, p/s)	4
76	Polydor 2058 803	Substitute/I'm A Boy/Pictures Of Lily (12", company sleeve)	7
78	Polydor WHO 1	Who Are You?/Had Enough (paper label, p/s)	4
79	Polydor WHO 2	Long Live Rock/I'm The Face/My Wife (withdrawn, blank run-off groove)	5
79	Polydor WHO 2	Long Live Rock/I'm The Face/My Wife ('Strawberry' etch on run-off groove)	5
80	Polydor WHO 3	5.15/I'm One (p/s)	4
82	Polydor WHOP 6	Athena/A Man Is A Man (picture disc)	5
82	Polydor WHOPX 6	Athena/A Man Is A Man/Won't Get Fooled Again (12", picture disc)	7
82	Polydor WHOPX 6	Athena/A Man Is A Man/Won't Get Fooled Again (12", picture disc, mispress, plays "Why Did I Fall For That")	15
66	Brunswick 05956	A Legal Matter/Instant Party (export issue with Scandanavian p/s)	100
72	Track 2094 102	Join Together/Baby Don't You Do It (p/s, for Spanish export)	15
68	Decca AD 1001	My Generation/Shout And Shimmy (export issue, some in p/s)	100/50
68	Decca AD 1002	A Legal Matter/Instant Party (export issue)	40
69	Track PRO 1	I'm Free/1921 (promo)	30
69	Track PRO 2	Go To The Mirror/Sally Simpson (promo)	30
69	Track PRO 3	The Acid Queen/We're Not Gonna Take It (promo)	30
69	Track PRO 4	Christmas/Overture (promo)	30
69	Track	TOMMY (box set of above 4 promo-only singles)	200
66	Reaction 592 001	READY STEADY WHO (EP)	30
70	Track 2252 001	EXCERPTS FROM "TOMMY" (EP, 33rpm)	10
65	Brunswick LAT 8616	MY GENERATION (LP)	30
66	Reaction 593 002	A QUICK ONE (LP)	22
67	Track 612/613 002	THE WHO SELL OUT (LP, some with stickered sleeve & poster)	35/20
68	Track 612/613 006	DIRECT HITS (LP)	20
69	Track 613 013/014	TOMMY (2-LP, with numbered 12-page booklet)	20
70	Track 2406 001	LIVE AT LEEDS (LP, in foldout sleeve, with 12 inserts including poster; blue or red print on sleeve)	10
70	Track 2406 007	TOMMY PART ONE (LP)	15
70	Track 2406 008	TOMMY PART TWO (LP)	15
70	Track 2407 008	BACKTRACK 8 (LP, mono reissue Of "A Quick One")	10
70	Track 2407 009	BACKTRACK 9 (LP, stereo reissue of "The Who Sell Out")	10
70	Track 2407 014	BACKTRACK 14: THE OX (LP)	15
71	Track 2408 102	WHO'S NEXT (LP)	10
71	Track 2406 006	MEATY, BEATY, BIG AND BOUNCY (LP, gatefold sleeve, mispressed, plays "The Seeker" instead of "Magic Bus")	10
71	Track 2856 001	WHO DID IT? (LP, mail-order only, withdrawn)	250
73	Track 2657 013	QUADROPHENIA (2-LP, original with 22-page photo booklet)	14
74	Track 2406 116	ODDS AND SODS (LP, cut-away braille sleeve, with poster & lyric sheet)	10
75	Polydor 2490 129	THE WHO BY NUMBERS (LP, numbered sleeve)	10
81	Polydor 2675 216	PHASES (9-LP box set, stickered cover)	50

(see also High Numbers, Pete Townshend, Keith Moon, Roger Daltrey, John Entwistle)

WHO'S GEORGE

80	Impact ACT 1	Didn't Catch Your Name/Stand Up (p/s)	5
85	Impact ACT 2	Shu Shu/I'm Not Leaving (p/s)	4
86	Impact ACT 3	Who's George/Forever (poster p/s)	4

WALLY WHYTON (& VIPERS)

59	Parlophone R 4585	Don't Tell Me Your Troubles/It's All Over You	8
60	Parlophone R 4630	All Over This World/Got Me A Girl	6
60	Pye 7N 15304	It's A Rat Race/Marriage Of Convenience/95% Of Me Loves You (with Sally Miles)/You're Going To Be Caught (as Wally Whyton & Vipers)	6
61	Piccadilly 7N 35089	Little Red Pony/Christmas Land	6
68	Fontana TF 960	Gentle On My Mind/Ballad Of The Bol Weevil	4

Rare Record Price Guide

68	Fontana TF 994	Wichita Lineman/Leave Them A Flower	4
69	Fontana TF 1030	Jig Alone/Out On The Road	4
68	Fontana STL 5476	IT'S ME, MUM (LP)	10
69	Fontana STL 5535	LEAVE THEM A FLOWER (LP)	10

(see also Vipers, Sharkey Todd & Monsters)

INIA TE WIATA
57	HMV POP 301	Banana Boat Song/Call Of The Sea	4

WICHITA FALL
69	Liberty LBS 83208	LIFE IS BUT A DREAM (LP)	10

WICHITA TRAIN WHISTLE
68	Dot (S)LPD 516	MICHAEL NESMITH PRESENTS THE WICHITA TRAIN WHISTLE SINGS (LP)	25

(see also Michael Nesmith)

WIDOWMAKER
76	Jet 2310 432	WIDOWMAKER (LP)	10
77	United Artists UAG 30038	TOO LATE TO CRY (LP)	12

(see also Luther Grosvenor, Spooky Tooth, Love Affair)

JANE WIEDLIN
88	Manhattan MTP 36	Rush Hour/The End Of Love (picture disc)	4

(see also Go-Go's)

PERCY WIGGINS
67	Atlantic 584 113	Book Of Memories/Can't Find Nobody	10

SPENCER WIGGINS
67	Stateside SS 2024	Uptight Good Woman/Anything You Do Is Alright	8
70	Pama PM 794	I'm A Poor Man's Son/That's How Much I Love You	10

WIGGONS
61	Blue Beat BB 29	Rock Baby/Let's Sing The Blues	10

WILBURN BROTHERS
59	Brunswick 05799	The Silver Haired Daddy Of Mine/A Boy's Faithful Friend	7
59	Brunswick LAT 8291	SIDE BY SIDE (LP)	12
67	Brunswick LAT 8686	COOL COUNTRY (LP)	10

WILD & WANDERING
86	Iguana VYK 14	2000 LIGHT ALES FROM HOME (12" EP, with insert)	45

(see also Pop Will Eat Itself)

WILD ANGELS
68	Major Minor MM 569	Nervous Breakdown/Watch The Wheels Go Round	15
70	B&C CB 114	Buzz Buzz/Please Don't Touch	8
70	B&C CB 123	Sally Ann/Wrong Number Try Again	7
71	B&C CB 145	Three Night A Week/Time To Kill	6
72	Decca F 13308	Jo Jo Ann/My Way	5
72	Decca F 13356	Beauty School Dropout/Midnight Rider	5
73	Decca F 13374	Running Bear/Sussin'	4
73	Decca F 13412	Greased Lightning/Born To Hand-Jive	4
73	Decca F 13456	Clap Your hands And Stamp Your Feet/Wild Angels Rock'n'Roll	4
70	B&C BCM 101	LIVE AT THE REVOLUTION (LP)	10
70	B&C BCM 102	RED HOT 'N' ROCKIN' (LP)	10
72	Decca SKL 5134	OUT AT LAST (LP)	10

WILD BEASTS
79	Fried Egg EGG 2	Minimum Maximum/Another Noun (p/s)	4
80	Ring Piece CUS 886	Last One Of The Boys/We're Only Monsters (p/s)	5
81	Warped BEND 1	Life Is A Bum/Mary Lou/The Limit (p/s)	5

WILD-CATS
59	London HLT 8787	Gazachstahagen/Billy's Cha Cha	10
59	London HLT 8787	Gazachstahagen/Billy's Cha Cha (78)	5
59	London HLT 8907	Dancing Elephants/King Size Guitar (unreleased)	

JACK WILDE
69	Elektra EKSN 45068	Apple Pie Mother And The Flag/Ballad Of Baby Browning	4

KIM WILDE
81	Rak RAK 334	Water On Glass/Boys (p/s)	4
83	Rak 12RAKS 360	Love Blonde/Can Your Hear It (12", p/s, some with poster)	8
83	Rak 12 RAK 365	Dancing In The Dark (Extended)/Dancing In The Dark/Back Seat Driver (12", p/s, with poster)	12
84	MCA KIMP 1	The Second Time/Lovers On A Beach (picture disc)	15
84	MCA KIMP 2	The Touch/Shangri-La (shaped picture disc)	12
85	MCA KIMP 3	Rage To Love/Putty In Your Hands (shaped picture disc)	12
87	MCA KIMC 6	Say You Really Want Me (Video Remix)/Don't Say Nothing's Changed (cassette)	4
87	MCA KIM 6	Say You Really Want Me/Don't Say Nothing's Changed (gatefold p/s)	5
87	MCA KIM 6	Say You Really Want Me/Don't Say Nothing's Changed (cassette)	4
87	MCA KIMX 6	Say You Really Want Me (Extended)/Say You Really Want Me (7" Version) Don't Say Nothing's Changed (12", p/s, stickered p/s, some with poster)	8/7
88	MCA DKIM 7	Hey Mr. Heartache (Extended)/Hey Mr. Heartache (LP Version)/ Tell Me Where You Are (CD)	10
88	MCA KIMB 8	You Came/Stone (box set)	5
88	MCA KIMX 8	You Came (Pettibone Remix)/You Came (Extended)/Stone (12", p/s)	7
88	MCA DIMX 8	You Came (Extended)/Stone/You Came (CD)	10
88	MCA KIMG 9	Never Trust A Stranger/Wotcha Gonna Do (gatefold p/s)	5
88	MCA DKIM 9	Never Trust A Stranger (Extended)/You Came (Pettibone)/Wotcha Gonna Do (CD)	8
88	MCA KIMB 10	Four Letter Word/She Hasn't Got Time For You (numbered box set)	5
89	MCA DKIMT 11	Love In The Natural Way (Extended)/Love In The Natural Way/ You'll Be The One Who'll Lose (CD, picture disc)	10

Kim WILDE

90	MCA DKIM 13	Time (Extended)/Someday/Time (CD)	8
90	MCA KIMB 14	I Can't Say Goodbye/Sanjazz Megamix (box set)	5
83	Rak SRAK 1654081	CATCH AS CATCH CAN (LP)	12
87	MCA MCF 3339	ANOTHER STEP (LP)	10

MARTY WILDE (& WILDCATS)

57	Philips JK 1028	Honeycomb/Wild Cat (as Marty Wilde & Wildcats) (jukebox issue)	40
57	Philips JK 1028	Honeycomb/Wild Cat (as Marty Wilde & Wildcats) (78)	6
58	Philips PB 781	Love Bug Crawl/Afraid Of Love (78)	8
58	Philips PB 804	Oh-Oh, I'm Falling In Love Again/Sing, Boy, Sing (with Wildcats)	25
58	Philips PB 804	Oh-Oh, I'm Falling In Love Again/Sing, Boy, Sing (with Wildcats) (78)	7
58	Philips PB 835	Endless Sleep/Her Hair Was Yellow (as Marty Wilde & Wildcats)	8
58	Philips PB 835	Endless Sleep/Her Hair Was Yellow (as Marty Wilde & Wildcats) (78)	7
58	Philips PB 850	My Lucky Love/Misery's Child (as Marty Wilde & Wildcats)	7
58	Philips PB 850	My Lucky Love/Misery's Child (as Marty Wilde & Wildcats) (78)	7
58	Philips PB 875	No One Knows/The Fire Of Love	8
58	Philips PB 875	No One Knows/The Fire Of Love (78)	7
59	Philips PB 902	Donna/Love-a, Love-a, Love-a	8
59	Philips PB 902	Donna/Love-a, Love-a, Love-a (78)	10
59	Philips PB 926	A Teenager In Love/Danny	7
59	Philips PB 926	A Teenager In Love/Danny (78)	10
59	Philips PB 959	Sea Of Love/Teenage Tears	6
59	Philips PB 959	Sea Of Love/Teenage Tears (78)	10
59	Philips PB 972	Bad Boy/It's Been Nice	6
59	Philips PB 972	Bad Boy/It's Been Nice (78)	10
60	Philips PB 1002	Johnny Rocco/My Heart And I	5
60	Philips PB 1002	Johnny Rocco/My Heart And I (78)	25
60	Philips PB 1022	The Fight/Johnny At The Crossroads	7
60	Philips PB 1037	I Wanna Be Loved By You/Angry	6
60	Philips PB 1078	Little Girl/Your Seventeenth Spring	5
61	Philips PB 1101	Rubber Ball/Like Makin' Love	5
61	Philips PB 1121	When Does It Get To Be Love/Your Loving Touch	5
61	Philips PB 1161	Hide And Seek/Crazy Dream	5
61	Philips PB 1191	Tomorrow's Clown/The Hellions	5
61	Philips PB 1206	Come Running/Ev'ryone	5
62	Philips PB 1240	Jezebel/Don't Run Away	5
62	Philips 326 546BF	Ever Since You Said Goodbye/Send Me The Pillow You Dream On	4
63	Columbia DB 4980	Lonely Avenue/Brand New Love	5
63	Philips 326 579BF	No! Dance With Me/Little Miss Happiness	5
63	Columbia DB 7145	Save Your Love For Me/Bless My Broken Heart	4
64	Columbia DB 7198	When Day Is Done/I Can't Help The Way I Feel	4
64	Columbia DB 7285	Kiss Me/My, What A Woman	4
64	Decca F 11979	The Mexican Boy/Your Kind Of Love	5
66	Philips PB 1490	I've Got So Used To Loving You/The Beginning Of The End	5
68	Philips BF 1632	By The Time I Get To Phoenix/Shutters And Boards	4
68	Philips PB 1669	Abergavenny/Alice In Blue	4
69	Philips PB 1815	Shelley/Jump On The Train (with Deke Leonard)	5
57	Philips BBE 12164	PRESENTING MARTY WILDE (EP)	30
58	Philips BBE 12200	MORE OF MARTY (EP)	20
59	Philips BBE 12327	SEA OF LOVE (EP)	20
60	Philips BBE 12385	VERSATILE MR. WILDE (EP)	20
60	Philips BBE 12422	MARTY WILDE FAVOURITES (EP)	18
62	Philips BBE 12517	COME RUNNING (EP)	15
63	Philips BE 433 638	MARTY (EP)	16
59	Philips BBL 7342	WILDE ABOUT MARTY (LP)	35
60	Philips BBL 7380	MARTY WILDE SHOWCASE (LP)	30
60	Philips BBL 7385	THE VERSATILE MR. WILDE (LP, also on stereo SBBL 570)	30/35
69	Philips SBL 7877	DIVERSIONS (LP)	10
70	Philips 6308 010	ROCK 'N' ROLL (LP)	10
74	Philips 6308 102	GOOD ROCKING — THEN AND NOW (LP)	10

(see also Wilde Three, Brian Bennett, Shadows, Keith Shields)

RICH WILDE

| 79 | Dead Good DEAD 5 | The Lady Wants To Be Alone/The Lady Wants To Be A Clone (p/s) | 4 |

WILDER BROTHERS

| 57 | HMV POP 365 | I Want You/Teenage Angel | 75 |
| 57 | HMV POP 365 | I Want You/Teenage Angel (78) | 40 |

WILDERNESS CHILDREN

| 88 | Choabie/Flexi DOSS 1 | There's A Good Time A-Comin'/On The West Coast (33rpm flexi, foldover p/s & Thrilled Skinny flexi, with 'Sowing Seeds' fanzine, issue 5, all in PVC bag) | 8/6 |

(see also Thrilled Skinny)

WILDERNESS ROAD

| 74 | Dawn DNLS 3057 | WILDERNESS ROAD (LP, unissued) | |

WILDE THREE

| 65 | Decca F 12131 | Since You've Gone/Just As Long | 20 |
| 65 | Decca F 12232 | I Cried/Well Who's That? | 30 |

(see also Marty Wilde, Justin Hayward, Vernons Girls)

WILDFIRE

| 84 | Mausoleum | Jerusalem (p/s) | 4 |

WILD FLOWERS

| 84 | No Future FS 11 | Melt Like Ice (p/s) | 8 |
| 84 | Reflex RE 2 | Things Have Changed (Which Should Have Stayed The Same)/Second Thought (p/s) | 7 |

(see also Mighty Lemon Drops)

WILD HONEY

72	MAM MAM 97	He's My Sugar/People Of The Universe	4

WILD HORSES

79	EMI Intl. INTS 599	Criminal Tendencies/The Rapist (p/s)	4
80	EMI EMI 5047	Face Down/Dealer (p/s)	4
80	EMI EMI 5078	Fly Away/Blackmail (p/s, white vinyl)	4
80	EMI 12EMI 5078	Fly Away/Blackmail (12", p/s, white vinyl)	7
81	EMI EMI 5199	Everlasting Love/The Axe (no p/s)	4
81	EMI EMI 5149	I'll Give You Love/Rocky Mountain Way//The Kid/On A Saturday Night (double pack, gatefold p/s)	5

(see also Thin Lizzy, Motorhead, Rainbow)

WILD INDIANS

84	Hullaballoo! HA! 001	Love Of My Life/The Biggest Man/Maybe (p/s)	5
80s	Having Fun IP 001	Stolen Courage/POP WALLPAPER: The Great Adventure (flexidisc, gatefold p/s)	4

WILD MAGNOLIAS

75	Barclay BAR 30	Smoke My Peace Pipe/Handa Wanda	6
75	Barclay BAR 34	They Call Us Wild/Jumalaka Boom Boom	8
75	Barclay 80 529	THE WILD MAGNOLIAS 1 (LP, gatefold sleeve)	20
75	Barclay 90 033	THEY CALL US WILD (LP, gatefold sleeve)	25

WILD OATS

63	Oak RGJ 117	WILD OATS (EP)	500

WILD ONES

64	Fontana TF 468	Bowie Man/Purple Pill Eater	35

WILD SILK

68	Polydor 56256	Poor Man/Stop Crying	4
69	Columbia DB 8534	(Vision In A) Plaster Sky/Toymaker	10
69	Columbia DB 8611	Help Me/Crimson And Gold	8

WILD SWANS

82	Zoo CAGE 009	The Revolutionary Spirit/God Forbid (7", unissued, stamped white label)	25
82	Zoo CAGE 009	The Revolutionary Spirit/God Forbid (12", p/s)	10
82	Zoo CAGE 009	The Revolutionary Spirit/God Forbid (12", p/s, with 'The Lament Of Icarus' painting in top right of front sleeve, withdrawn)	25

(see also Lotus Eaters)

WILD TCHOUPITOULAS

77	Island ILPS 9360	WILD TCHOUPITOULAS (LP)	10

WILD THING

69	Elektra EKSN 45076	Old Lady/Next To Me	4
71	Polydor 2410 003	PARTYIN' (LP)	12

WILD TURKEY

71	Chrysalis CHR 1002	BATTLE HYMN (LP, gatefold sleeve)	12
72	Chrysalis CHR 1010	TURKEY (LP)	12
	(see also Jethro Tull)		

WILD UNCERTAINTY

66	Planet PLF 120	Man With Money/Broken Truth	25

WILDWEEDS

67	Chess CRS 8065	It Was Fun While It Lasted/Sorrow's Anthem	6

MAJOR WILEY

72	De Wolfe	SEVENTH CHILD (LP, library issue)	10

WILFRED & MILLIE

65	Island WI 190	The Vow/I Never Believe In You	8
	(see also Jackie [Edwards] & Millie [Small])		

MIKE WILHELM

76	Zigzag/United Artists ZZ 1	MIKE WILHELM (LP, sold via 'Zigzag' magazine)	18
	(see also Charlatans)		

ROBERT WILKINS

60s	Piedmont PLP 13162	REV ROBERT WILKINS (LP)	25

ROGER WILKINS

70	Spokane SPL 1002	BEFORE THE REVERENCE (LP)	40

COLM C.T. WILKINSON

78	RSO RSO 009	Born To Sing/The Simple Things In Life	4

WILLETT FAMILY

62	Topic 12T 84	ROVING JOURNEYMAN (LP)	25

AL WILLIAMS

79	Grapevine GRP 136	I Am Nothing/Brand New Love	6

ANDY WILLIAMS

56	London HLA 8284	Walk Hand In Hand/Not Any More	20
56	London HLA 8315	Canadian Sunset/High Upon A Mountain (gold or silver lettering onlabels)	20/12
56	London HL 7013	Canadian Sunset/High Upon A Mountain (export issue)	7
56	London HLA 8360	Baby Doll (From The Film)/Since I've Found My Baby (gold or silver)	20/12
56	London HLA 8360	Baby Doll (From The Film)/Since I've Found My Baby (78)	5
57	London HLA 8399	Butterfly/It Doesn't Take Very Long	15
57	London HLA 8437	I Like Your Kind Of Love/Stop Teasin' Me	12
57	London HLA 8487	Lips Of Wine/Straight From My Heart	12
58	London HLA 8587	Are You Sincere/Be Mine Tonight	10

Andy WILLIAMS

58	London HL 7034	Are You Sincere/Be Mine Tonight (export issue)	5
58	London HLA 8710	Promise Me, Love/Your Hand, Your Heart, Your Love	10
59	London HLA 8784	Hawaiian Wedding Song/House Of Bamboo	8
59	London HLA 8957	Lonely Street/Summer Love	7
59	London HLA 9018	The Village Of St. Bernadette/I'm So Lonesome I Could Cry	6
60	London HLA 9099	Wake Me When It's Over/We Have A Date	6
60	London HLA 9241	Don't Go To Strangers/You Don't Want My Love	5
61	London HLA 9348	The Bilbao Song/How Wonderful To Know	5
63	CBS AAG 138	Can't Get Used To Losing You/The Days Of Wine And Roses	4
72	CBS 8197	(Love Theme From) The Godfather/In The Summertime (p/s)	4
57	London REA 1088	ANDY WILLIAMS' BIG HITS (EP)	15
57	London REA 1102	ANDY WILLIAMS' BIG HITS No. 2 (EP)	15
63	London REA 1394	ANDY WILLIAMS' BEST (EP)	12
57	London HA-A 2054	ANDY WILLIAMS SINGS STEVE ALLEN (LP)	18
58	London HA-A 2113	ANDY WILLIAMS SINGS RODGERS AND HAMMERSTEIN (LP)	16
59	London HA-A 2203	TWO TIME WINNERS (LP)	16
60	London HA-A 2238	LONELY STREET (LP)	14
62	London HA-A 8005	ANDY WILLIAMS' BEST (LP)	12
63	London HA-A 8090	UNDER PARIS SKIES (LP)	10
73	CBS CQ 30797	YOU'VE GOT A FRIEND (LP, quadrophonic)	10
73	CBS CQ 31303/Q 64869	LOVE THEME FROM "THE GODFATHER" (LP, quadrophonic)	10
73	CBS CQ 31625	ALONE AGAIN (NATURALLY) (LP, quadrophonic)	10

AUDREY WILLIAMS

56	MGM SP 1179	Ain't Nothing Gonna Be All Right No How/Livin' It Up And Havin' A Ball	12
56	MGM MGM 911	Ain't Nothing Gonna Be All Right No How/Livin' It Up And Havin' A Ball (78)	6

(see also Hank Williams)

BIG JOE WILLIAMS

60s	Jazz Collector JEN 3	A MAN SINGS THE BLUES (EP)	8
60s	Jazz Collector JEN 4	A MAN SINGS THE BLUES VOLUME 2 (EP)	8
67	Delmark DJB 4	ON THE HIGHWAY (EP)	8
60s	XX MIN 700	BIG JOE WILLIAMS (EP)	7
63	Esquire 32-191	BLUES ON HIGHWAY 51 (LP)	30
63	'77' LA 12-19	PINEY WOODS BLUES (LP)	20
64	CBS BPG 63813	CLASSIC DELTA BLUES (LP)	12
64	Storyville SLP 158	PORTRAITS IN BLUES VOLUME 4 (LP)	15
64	Storyville SLP 163	PORTRAITS IN BLUES VOLUME 7 (LP)	15
65	Fontana 688 800 ZL	TOUGH TIMES (LP)	15
66	Xtra XTRA 1033	BIG JOE WILLIAMS (LP)	20
66	Bounty BY 6018	BACK TO THE COUNTRY (LP)	20
69	Storyville 618011	DON'T YOU LEAVE ME HERE (LP)	15
69	Liberty LBL/LBS 83207	HAND ME DOWN MY OLD WALKING STICK (LP)	12
69	Xtra XTRA 5059	LIVE AT FOLK CITY (LP)	10
70	RCA Intl. INTS 1087	CRAWLIN' KING SNAKE (LP)	15

(see also Poor Joe Williams)

BILLY WILLIAMS (QUARTET)

54	Vogue Coral Q 2012	Sh'Boom/Whenever Wherever (78)	6
54	Vogue Coral Q 2039	The Honeydripper/Love Me (as Billy Williams Quartet)	12
54	Vogue Coral Q 2039	The Honeydripper/Love Me (as Billy Williams Quartet) (78)	10
56	Vogue Coral Q 72149	A Crazy Little Palace/Cry Baby (as Billy Williams Quartet)	12
56	Vogue Coral Q 72149	A Crazy Little Palace/Cry Baby (as Billy Williams Quartet) (78)	5
56	Vogue Coral Q 72180	Pray/You'll Reach Your Star	8
56	Vogue Coral Q 72180	Pray/You'll Reach Your Star (78)	5
57	Vogue Coral Q 72222	Follow Me/Shame, Shame, Shame (as Billy Williams Quartet)	10
57	Vogue Coral Q 72222	Follow Me/Shame, Shame, Shame (as Billy Williams Quartet) (78)	10
57	Vogue Coral Q 72241	Butterfly/The Pied Piper	10
57	Vogue Coral Q 72266	I'm Gonna Sit Right Down And Write A Letter/Date With The Blues	15
57	Vogue Coral Q 72295	Got A Date With An Angel/The Lord Will Understand	8
58	Coral Q 72303	Don't Let Go/Baby, Baby (as Billy Williams Quartet)	8
58	Coral Q 72303	Don't Let Go/Baby, Baby (as Billy Williams Quartet) (78)	5
58	Coral Q 72316	Steppin' Out Tonight/There I've Said It Again (as Billy Williams Quartet)	30
58	Coral Q 72331	I'll Get By/It's Prayin' Time	6
59	Coral Q 72359	Nola/Tied To The Strings Of Your Heart	6
59	Coral Q 72369	Goodnight Irene/Red Hot Love	6
59	Coral Q 72369	Goodnight Irene/Red Hot Love (78)	8
59	Coral Q 72377	Telephone Conversation/Go To Sleep, Go To Sleep, Go To Sleep (with Barbara McNair)	8
60	Coral Q 72402	I Cried For You/Lover Of All Lovers	6
60	Coral Q 72414	Begin The Beguine/For You	5
58	Coral LVA 9092	BILLY WILLIAMS (LP)	10
60	Coral LVA 9120	HALF SWEET HALF BEAT (LP)	10
61	Coral LVA 9139	THE BILLY WILLIAMS REVUE (LP)	10

(seee also Barbara McNair)

BOBBY WILLIAMS

68	Action ACT 4509	Baby I Need Your Love/Try It Again	12
73	Contempo C 17	Let's Jam/You're My Baby	10

CHRIS WILLIAMS & HIS MONSTERS

59	Columbia DB 4383	The Monster/The Eton Boating Song	15

CLARENCE WILLIAMS (& HIS WASHBOARD BAND)

54	Columbia SCM 5134	High Society/Left All Alone With The Blues	15
58	Fontana TFE 17053	TREASURE OF NORTH AMERICAN MUSIC VOLUME 3 (EP)	10
59	Parlophone GEP 8733	CLARENCE WILLIAMS' WASHBOARD BAND (EP)	10
64	Collector JEL 18	JAZZ ORIGINATORS (EP)	10
54	London AL 3526	CLARENCE WILLIAMS AND HIS ORCHESTRA (10" LP)	20

55	Columbia 33S 1067	BACK ROOM SPECIAL (10" LP) 20
57	London AL 3561	CLARENCE WILLIAMS AND HIS ORCHESTRA VOL. 2 (10" LP) 20
60	Fontana TFL 5087	SIDNEY BECHET MEMORIAL (LP) 15
62	Philips BBL 7521	CLARENCE WILLIAMS VOL. 1: 1927-1935 (LP) 15

CLIVE WILLIAMS
| 70s | Rock Steady Rev. REVR 6 | Take Good Care Of My Baby/RICO: In Loving Memory Of Don Drummond ....4 |

DAN WILLIAMS & HIS ORCHESTRA
| 55 | London CAY 110 | Donkey City/SHAW PARK CALYPSO BAND: Take Her To Jamaica ....8 |

DANNY WILLIAMS
59	HMV POP 624	Tall A Tree/I Look At You 6
59	HMV POP 655	So High — So Low/My Own True Love 6
59	HMV POP 703	Youthful Years/It Doesn't Matter 6
60	HMV POP 803	A Million To One/Call Me A Dreamer 5
61	HMV POP 839	We Will Never Be As Young As This Again/Passing Breeze 5
61	HMV POP 885	The Miracle Of You/Lonely 4
61	HMV POP 932	Moon River/A Weaver Of Dreams 3
62	HMV POP 968	Jeannie/It Might As Well Be Spring/Unchain My Heart 4
62	HMV POP 1002	The Wonderful World Of The Young/A Kind Of Loving 4
62	HMV POP 1035	Tears/Tiara Tahiti 5
63	HMV POP 1112	My Own True Love/Who Can Say? 4
63	HMV POP 1150	More/Rhapsody 4
63	HMV POP 1172	The Wild Wind/Once Upon A Time 4
63	HMV POP 1203	A Day Without You/Secret Love 4
63	HMV POP 1236	How Do You Keep From Crying?/Now The Day Is Over 4
63	HMV POP 1263	White On White/After You 6
64	HMV POP 1305	Today/Lonely In A Crowd 4
64	HMV POP 1325	The Seventh Dawn/The World Around Me 4
64	HMV POP 1372	Forget Her, Forget Her/Lollipops And Roses 8
65	HMV POP 1388	The Roundabout Of Love/I Wanna Be Around 4
65	HMV POP 1410	Go Away/Masquerade 6
65	HMV POP 1455	Lovely Is She/Gone And Forgotten 4
65	HMV POP 1487	And So We Meet Again/Violets For Your Furs 4
66	HMV POP 1522	Don't Just Stand There/Now And Then 4
66	HMV POP 1560	Rain (Falling From The Skies)/I'm So Lost 6
67	Deram DM 149	Never My Love/Whose Little Girl Are You (with inverted matrix, later re-pressed with matrix right way up) 10/4
62	HMV 7EG 8748	HITS OF DANNY WILLIAMS (EP) 8
62	HMV 7EG 8763	DANNY WILLIAMS SWINGS WITH TONY OSBORNE (EP) 8
63	HMV 7EG 8800	THE DAYS OF WINE AND ROSES (EP) 8
61	HMV CLP 1458/CSD 1369	DANNY WILLIAMS (LP, mono/stereo) 10/12
61	HMV CLP 1521	MOON RIVER (LP) 10
62	HMV CLP 1605/CSD 1471	SWINGING FOR YOU (LP, mono/stereo) 10/12
67	Deram DML 1017	DANNY WILLIAMS (LP) 10

EDDIE WILLIAMS & LITTLE SONNY WILLIS
| 60s | XX MIN 707 | GOING TO CALIFORNIA (EP) ....7 |

GEORGE WILLIAMS & HIS ORCHESTRA
| 55 | Vogue Coral Q 72053 | The Rompin' Stomper/Knock-Out Choo-Choo ....4 |

GRANVILLE WILLIAMS ORCHESTRA
| 67 | Island WI 3062 | Hi-Life/More ....6 |
| 67 | Island ILP 971 | HI-LIFE (LP) ....30 |

HANK WILLIAMS (& HIS DRIFTING COWBOYS)
50	MGM MGM 269	Lovesick Blues/Wedding Bells (78) 15
51	MGM MGM 381	Moanin' The Blues/The Blues Come Around (78) 15
51	MGM MGM 405	Dear John/Fly Trouble (78) 15
51	MGM MGM 454	Hey, Good Lookin'/Howlin' At The Moon (78) 15
51	MGM MGM 459	Cold, Cold Heart/I'm A Long Gone Daddy (78) 15
52	MGM MGM 471	I Can't Help It (If I'm Still In Love With You)/Baby, We're Really In Love (78) 15
52	MGM MGM 483	Why Don't You Love Me/I'd Still Want You (78) 15
52	MGM MGM 505	Honky-Tonk Blues/I'm Sorry For You, My Friend (78) 15
52	MGM MGM 527	Long Gone Lonesome Blues/Half As Much (78) 15
52	MGM MGM 553	Nobody's Lonesome For Me/Mind Your Own Business (78) 15
52	MGM MGM 566	Jambalaya (On The Bayou)/Settin' The Woods On Fire (78) 15
53	MGM MGM 585	I'll Never Get Out Of This World Alive/I Could Never Be Ashamed Of You (as Hank Williams & His Drifting Cowboys) (78) 12
53	MGM SP 1016	I'll Never Get Out Of This World Alive/I Could Never Be Ashamed Of You (as Hank Williams & His Drifting Cowboys) (78) 40
53	MGM MGM 609	Kaw-Liga/Take These Chains From My Heart (& His Drifting Cowboys) (78) ...12
53	MGM SP 1034	Kaw-Liga/Take These Chains From My Heart (& His Drifting Cowboys) 35
53	MGM MGM 630	I Saw The Light/ARTHUR 'GUITAR BOOGIE' SMITH: In Memory Of Hank Williams (78) 15
53	MGM MGM 652	Ramblin' Man/I Won't Be Home No More (78) 12
53	MGM SP 1049	Ramblin' Man/I Won't Be Home No More 30
53	MGM MGM 666	My Bucket's Got A Hole In It/Let's Turn Back The Years (78) 12
53	MGM SP 1048	My Bucket's Got A Hole In It/Let's Turn Back The Years 30
53	MGM MGM 678	Window Shopping/You Win Again (78) 15
54	MGM MGM 704	Weary Blues (From Waitin')/I Can't Escape From You (78) 12
54	MGM SP 1067	Weary Blues (From Waitin')/I Can't Escape From You 30
54	MGM MGM 733	There'll Be No Teardrops Tonight/Crazy Heart (78) 12
54	MGM SP 1085	There'll Be No Teardrops Tonight/Crazy Heart 30
54	MGM MGM 768	I'm Satisfied With You/I Ain't Got Nothin' But Time (78) 12
54	MGM SP 1102	I'm Satisfied With You/I Ain't Got Nothin' But Time 30
55	MGM MGM 799	I'm Gonna Sing/California Zephyr (78) 15

Hank WILLIAMS

56	MGM MGM 889	The First Fall Of Snow/Someday You'll Call My Name (78, unreleased)	
56	MGM SP 1163	The First Fall Of Snow/Someday You'll Call My Name (unreleased)	
56	MGM MGM 896	Your Cheatin' Heart/A Teardrop On A Rose (78)	15
56	MGM MGM 921	There's No Room In My Heart (For The Blues)/I Wish I Had A Nickel (78)	10
56	MGM MGM 921	There's No Room In My Heart (For The Blues)/I Wish I Had A Nickel	20
56	MGM MGM 931	Blue Love (In My Heart)/Singing Waterfall (78)	10
56	MGM MGM 931	Blue Love (In My Heart)/Singing Waterfall	20
57	MGM MGM 942	Low Down Blues/My Sweet Love Ain't Around (78)	10
57	MGM MGM 942	Low Down Blues/My Sweet Love Ain't Around	20
57	MGM MGM 957	Rootie Tootie/Lonesome Whistle (78)	10
57	MGM MGM 957	Rootie Tootie/Lonesome Whistle	18
57	MGM MGM 966	Leave Me Alone With The Blues/With Tears In My Eyes (78)	10
57	MGM MGM 966	Leave Me Alone With The Blues/With Tears In My Eyes	18
66	MGM MGM 1309	You Win Again/I'm So Lonesome I Could Cry	8
66	MGM MGM 1322	Kaw-Liga/Let's Turn Back The Tears	8
54	MGM MGM-EP 512	HANK WILLIAMS AND HIS DRIFTING COWBOYS (EP, company sleeve)	20
55	MGM MGM-EP 551	JUST WAITIN' (EP, as Luke The Drifter, company sleeve, later p/s)	25/15
56	MGM MGM-EP 569	I SAW THE LIGHT (No. 1) (EP, company sleeve, later p/s)	18/12
57	MGM MGM-EP 582	HONKY TONKIN' (EP)	18
57	MGM MGM-EP 608	I SAW THE LIGHT (No. 2) (EP)	18
57	MGM MGM-EP 614	HONKY TONK BLUES (EP)	16
58	MGM MGM-EP 639	SONGS FOR A BROKEN HEART (No. 1) (EP)	18
58	MGM MGM-EP 649	SONGS FOR A BROKEN HEART (No. 2) (EP)	18
58	MGM MGM-EP 675	HANK'S LAMENTS (EP)	18
60	MGM MGM-EP 710	THE UNFORGETTABLE HANK WILLIAMS (EP)	15
60	MGM MGM-EP 726	THE UNFORGETTABLE HANK WILLIAMS (No. 2) (EP)	15
60	MGM MGM-EP 732	THE UNFORGETTABLE HANK WILLIAMS (No. 3) (EP)	15
61	MGM MGM-EP 757	HANK WILLIAMS FAVOURITES (EP)	15
63	MGM MGM-EP 770	THE AUTHENTIC SOUND OF THE COUNTRY HITS (EP)	10
52	MGM MGM-D 105	HANK WILLIAMS SINGS (10" LP, company sleeve, later p/s)	35/50
53	MGM MGM-D 119	HANK WILLIAMS AS LUKE THE DRIFTER (10" LP, co. sleeve, later p/s)	30/40
55	MGM MGM-D 137	HANK WILLIAMS MEMORIAL ALBUM (10" LP)	30
56	MGM MGM-D 144	MOANIN' THE BLUES (10" LP)	40
58	MGM MGM-D 150	SING ME A BLUE SONG (10" LP)	40
58	MGM MGM-D 154	THE IMMORTAL HANK WILLIAMS (10" LP)	40
59	MGM MGM-C 784	THE UNFORGETTABLE HANK WILLIAMS (LP)	25
60	MGM MGM-C 811	THE LONESOME SOUND OF HANK WILLIAMS (LP)	25
60	MGM MGM-C 834	WAIT FOR THE LIGHT TO SHINE (LP)	22
62	MGM MGM-C 893	ON STAGE (LP)	18
63	MGM MGM-C 956	THE SPIRIT OF HANK WILLIAMS (LP)	20
66	MGM MGM-C 8019	MAY YOU NEVER BE ALONE (LP)	18
66	MGM MGM-C 8020	IN MEMORY OF HANK WILLIAMS (LP)	16
66	MGM MGM-C 8021	I'M BLUE INSIDE (LP)	18
66	MGM MGM-C 8022	LUKE THE DRIFTER (LP)	15
66	MGM MGM-C 8023	THE MANY MOODS OF HANK WILLIAMS (LP)	16
67	MGM MGM-C(S) 8031	THE LEGEND LIVES ANEW (LP)	12
67	MGM MGM-C(S) 8038	MORE HANK WILLIAMS AND STRINGS (LP)	12
67	MGM MGM-C 8040	LOVE SONGS, COMEDY AND HYMNS (LP)	18
68	MGM MGM-C(S) 8057	I WON'T BE HOME NO MORE (LP)	12
68	MGM MGM-C(S) 8075	HANK WILLIAMS AND STRINGS VOL. 3 (LP)	10
69	MGM MGM-CS 8114	THE ESSENTIAL HANK WILLIAMS (LP)	10
74	MGM 2683 046	ON STAGE VOLUMES 1 & 2 (2-LP)	14
76	MGM 2353 128	LIVE AT THE GRAND OL' OPRY (LP)	10
79	World Records SM 551-556	THE LEGENDARY HANK WILLIAMS (6-LP box set)	25

(see also Audrey Williams)

HANK WILLIAMS & HANK WILLIAMS Jr.

65	MGM MGM-C 1008	SINGING TOGETHER (LP)	15

HANK WILLIAMS Jr.

63	MGM MGM 1223	Long Gone Lonesome Blues/Doesn't Anybody Know My Name	6
63	MGM MGM 1242	Goin' Steady With The Blues/Guess What, That's Right, She's Gone	5
64	MGM MGM 1254	Endless Sleep/My Bucket's Got A Hole In It	5
65	MGM MGM 1276	Mule Skinner Blues/I Went To All That Trouble	5
66	MGM MGM 1294	You're Ruinin' My Life/Pecos Jail	4
66	MGM MGM 1299	Cold Cold Heart/Is It That Fun To Heart Someone	4
66	MGM MGM 1316	Standing In The Shadows/It's Written All Over Your Face	4
66	MGM MGM 1322	Kaw-Liga/Let's Turn Back The Tears	4
64	MGM MGM-C 996	YOUR CHEATIN' HEART (LP)	12
67	MGM MGM-C(S) 8049	MY OWN WAY (LP)	10
69	MGM MGM-CS 8116	LIVE AT COBO HALL, DETROIT (LP)	10

JABBO WILLIAMS

50s	Jazz Collector L 51	Jab Blues/Pratt City (78)	6

JEANETTE WILLIAMS

69	Action ACT 4534	Stuff/You Gotta Come Through	12
70	Action ACT 4557	Hound Dog/I Can Feel A Heartbreak	12

(LITTLE) JERRY WILLIAMS

62	Cameo Parkway C 100	Baby You're My Everything/Just What Do You Plan To Do About It (as Little Jerry Williams)	20
74	Pye Disco Demand DDS 102	If You Ask Me/Yvonne	4

JIMMY WILLIAMS

65	Atlantic AT 4042	Walking On Air/I'm So Lost	10

JOE WILLIAMS

59	Columbia SCD 2116	Party Blues Pts 1 & 2	4
60	Columbia DB 4560	Somebody/One Is A Lonesome Number	4

60	Columbia SEG 8001	EVERYDAY I HAVE THE BLUES (EP)	10
60	Columbia SEG 8016	JOE SINGS THE BLUES (EP)	10
56	London HB-C 1065	JOE WILLIAMS SINGS (10" LP)	15
57	HMV CLP 1109	THE GREATEST (LP)	20
58	Columbia 33SX 1087	A MAN AIN'T SUPPOSED TO CRY (LP)	20
60	Columbia 33SX 1229	JOE WILLIAMS SINGS ABOUT YOU (LP, also stereo SCX 3308)	10/12
60	Columbia 33SX 1253	THAT KIND OF WOMAN (LP, also stereo SCX 3325)	10/12

(see also Count Basie)

JOHN WILLIAMS (U.K.)

67	Columbia DB 8128	She's That Kind Of Woman/My Ways Are Set	5
67	Columbia DB 8251	Can't Find Time For Anything Now/Flowers In Your Hair	5
67	Columbia SX 6169	JOHN WILLIAMS (LP)	50

JOHN WILLIAMS (U.K.)

| 84 | Island IS 155 | Paul McCartney's Theme From "The Honourary Consul"/
Clara's Theme (p/s) | 6 |

JOHN WILLIAMS ORCHESTRA (U.S.)

76	MCA MCA 220	"Jaws" Theme Pts 1 & 2	4
78	Arista ARIST 177	"Close Encounters Of The Third Kind" Pts 1 & 2 (p/s)	4
82	MCA MCA 800	Theme From "ET"/Over The Moon (p/s)	4

JOHNNY WILLIAMS

| 73 | Epic EPC 1007 | Slow Motion/Shall We Be Gather By The Water | 4 |
| 73 | Contempo C 20 | Just A Little Misunderstanding/Your Love Controls My Mind | 5 |

KENNETH WILLIAMS

63	Decca DEF 8548	EXTRACTS FROM PIECES OF EIGHT AND ONE OVER THE EIGHT (EP)	7
66	Decca DFE 8671	KENNETH WILLIAMS IN SEASON (EP)	7
67	Decca LK 4856	ON PLEASURE BENT (LP)	10

(see also Rambling Syd Rumpo)

KENNY WILLIAMS

| 77 | Decca FR 13731 | You're Fabulous Babe/Give Me My Heart | 4 |

LARRY WILLIAMS

57	London HLN 8472	Short Fat Fannie/High School Dance	30
57	London HLN 8472	Short Fat Fannie/High School Dance (78)	8
58	London HLN 8532	Bony Moronie/You Bug Me Baby	25
58	London HLN 8532	Bony Moronie/You Bug Me Baby (78)	8
58	London HLU 8604	Dizzy Miss Lizzy/Slow Down	30
58	London HLU 8604	Dizzy Miss Lizzy/Slow Down (78)	20
59	London HLU 8844	She Said "Yeah"/Bad Boy	20
59	London HLU 8844	She Said "Yeah"/Bad Boy (78)	20
60	London HLU 8911	I Can't Stop Loving You/Steal A Little Kiss	20
60	London HLM 9053	Baby, Baby/Get Ready	20
65	Sue WI 371	Strange/Call On Me	12
65	Sue WI 381	Turn On Your Lovelight/Dizzy Miss Lizzy	15
68	MGM MGM 1447	Shake Your Body Girl/Love I Can't Seem To Find You	8
59	London RE-U 1213	LARRY WILLIAMS (EP)	50
65	Sue ILP 922	LARRY WILLIAMS ON STAGE (LP)	35

LARRY WILLIAMS & JOHNNY 'GUITAR' WATSON

65	Decca F 12151	Sweet Little Baby/Slow Down	15
67	Columbia DB 8140	Mercy, Mercy, Mercy/A Quitter Never Wins	30
76	Epic EPC 4421	Too Late/Two For The Price Of One	6
65	Decca LK 4691	THE LARRY WILLIAMS SHOW (LP, with Stormsville Shakers)	35

(see also Johnny 'Guitar' Watson)

LEONA WILLIAMS

| 74 | Fountain FB 303 | LEONA WILLIAMS AND HER DIXIE BAND (LP) | 12 |

LLOYD WILLIAMS

66	Doctor Bird DB 1051	Sad World/TOMMY McCOOK'S BAND: A Little Bit Of Heaven	10
68	Treasure Isle TI 7029	Funky Beat/Goodbye Baby	10
68	Doctor Bird DB 1135	Wonderful World (with Tommy McCook)/TOMMY McCOOK & SUPERSONICS: Mad Mad World	10
70	Bamboo BAM 41	I'm In Love With You/Little Girl	5

LORETTA WILLIAMS

| 66 | Atlantic 584 032 | Baby Cakes/I'm Missing You | 18 |

LUTHER WEE WILLIE WILLIAMS ORCHESTRA

| 60s | Limbo XL 101 | Early In The Morning/Little Vilma | 6 |

MARY LOU WILLIAMS

64	Sue WI 311	Chuck A Lunk Jug Pts 1 & 2	15
55	Vogue EPV 1042	DON CARLOS MEETS MARY LOU WILLIAMS (EP)	10
56	Parlophone GEP 8567	AT THE PIANO (EP)	8
56	Columbia SEG 7608	MARY LOU WILLIAMS (EP)	8
50s	Esquire EP 66	MARY LOU WILLIAMS QUARTET (EP)	12
53	Vogue LDE 022	PLAYS IN LONDON (10" LP)	15
54	Esquire 20-026	PIANO PANORAMA (10" LP)	20
55	Felsted EDL 87012	IN PARIS (10" LP)	15

MAURICE WILLIAMS (& ZODIACS)

60	Top Rank JAR 526	Stay/Do You Believe (as Maurice Williams & Zodiacs)	8
61	Top Rank JAR 550	I Remember/Always	8
61	Top Rank JAR 563	Come Along/Do I	12
61	Top Rank JKP 3006	STAY WITH MAURICE WILLIAMS & THE ZODIACS (EP)	40

MIKE WILLIAMS

| 66 | Atlantic 584 027 | Lonely Soldier/If This Isn't Love | 8 |

OTIS WILLIAMS & HIS CHARMS
55	Parlophone CMSP 36	Ivory Tower/In Paradise (export issue)	100
56	Parlophone MSP 6239	Ivory Tower/In Paradise	125
56	Parlophone R 4175	Ivory Tower/In Paradise (78)	15
56	Parlophone R 4210	One Night Only/It's All Over Now	120
57	Parlophone R 4293	Walkin' After Midnight/I'm Waiting Just For You	100
58	Parlophone R 4495	The Secret/Don't Wake Up The Kids	50
62	Parlophone R 4860	The Secret/Two Hearts	40

(see also Charms)

PAT WILLIAMS ORCHESTRA
74	Capitol CL 15797	Police Story Theme/Magician Theme	5

PAUL WILLIAMS
73	Sonet SNTF 654	DELTA BLUES SINGER (LP)	15

(see also Juicy Lucy)

PAUL WILLIAMS BIG ROLL BAND/SET
64	Columbia DB 7421	Gin House/Rockin' Chair (as Paul Williams Big Roll Band)	15
65	Columbia DB 7768	The Many Faces Of Love/Jumpback (as Paul Williams & Zoot Money Band)	15
68	Decca F 12844	My Sly Sadie/Stop The Wedding (as Paul Williams Set)	6

(see also Zoot Money's Big Roll Band, John Mayall's Blues Breakers, Alan Price Set)

PAULETTE WILLIAMS
77	Fantasy FTC 140	Dancin'/What's Left To Say	4

POOR JOE WILLIAMS
60	Collector JEN 3	A MAN SINGS THE BLUES (EP)	12
60	Collector JEN 4	A MAN SINGS THE BLUES VOL. 2 (EP)	12

(see also Big Joe Williams)

RITA WILLIAMS
58	Oriole CB 1417	Looking For Someone To Love/Love Me Forever	4

ROBERT PETE WILLIAMS
63	'77' LA 12-17	THOSE PRISON BLUES (LP)	20
70s	Blues Beacon 1932 101ST	SUGAR FARM (LP)	15
72	Saydisc AMS 2002	ROBERT PETE WILLIAMS (LP)	15
73	Sonet SNTF 649	LEGACY OF THE BLUES (LP)	10

ROBERT PETE WILLIAMS/ROOSEVELT SYKES
67	'77' LEU 12-50	BLUES FROM THE BOTTOM (LP)	15

(see also Roosevelt Sykes)

ROGER WILLIAMS
55	London HLU 8214	Autumn Leaves/Take Care	12
56	London HLU 8341	Two Different Worlds (with Jane Morgan)/I'll Always Walk With You	15
57	London HLU 8379	Anastasia/A Serenade For Joy	8
57	London HLR 8422	Almost Paradise/For The First Time I've Fallen In Love	7
57	London HLR 8516	Till/Big Town	6
58	London HLR 8572	Arrivederci Roma/The Sentimental Touch	6
58	London HLR 8643	Indiscreet/Young And Warm And Wonderful	5
58	London HLR 8690	Near You/The Merry Widow Waltz	5
58	London HLR 8758	The World Outside (Warsaw Concerto)/Piano Concerto No. 1 (Tchaikovsky)	4
59	London HLR 8820	The Key To The Kingdom/Dearer Than Dear	4
59	London HLR 8857	Mockin' Bird Hill/Memories Are Made Of This	4
59	London HLR 8986	Mary's Boy Child/O Mio Babbino Caro (Oh! My Beloved Father)	4
57	London HA-R 2057	SONGS OF THE FABULOUS FIFTIES VOL. 1 (LP)	12
57	London HA-R 2058	SONGS OF THE FABULOUS FIFTIES VOL. 2 (LP)	12
58	London HA-R 2089	THE BOY NEXT DOOR (LP)	10
58	London HA-R 2096	SONGS OF THE FABULOUS FORTIES VOL. 1 (LP, stereo SAH-R 6035)	10
58	London HA-R 2097	SONGS OF THE FABULOUS FORTIES VOL. 2 (LP, stereo SAH-R 6036)	10

(see also Jane Morgan)

SAM WILLIAMS
78	Grapevine GRP 116	Love Slipped Thru' My Fingers/TOWANDA BARNES: You Don't Mean It	4

SMITTY WILLIAMS
62	MGM MGM 1167	The Cure/Oh Seymour	5

SONNY WILLIAMS
59	London HLD 8931	Bye Bye Baby Goodbye/Lucky Linda	12
59	London HLD 8931	Bye Bye Baby Goodbye/Lucky Linda (78)	18

SPARKIE WILLIAMS (1958 Champion Talking Budgerigar)
58	Parlophone R 4475	Sparkie Williams — Jailbird/Sparkie The Fiddle	4

TEX WILLIAMS
50	Capitol CL 13424	Talking Boogie/Tamburitza Boogie (with His Western Caravan) (78)	8
54	Brunswick 05327	River Of No Return/Dawn In The Meadow	12
54	Brunswick 05341	This Ole House (with Rex Allen)/There Were Doin' The Mambo	12
55	Brunswick 05393	Money/If You'd Believe Me	10
56	Brunswick 05516	Be Sure You're Right (And Then Go Ahead)/Old Betsy	6
57	Brunswick 05684	Talkin' To The Blues/Every Night (with Anita Kerr Singers)	12
60	Top Rank JAR 330	The Keeper Of Boothill/Bummin' Around	8
55	Brunswick OE 9147	ALL THE GREATS (EP)	8
61	Capitol (S)T 1463	SMOKE, SMOKE, SMOKE! (LP)	15

TONY WILLIAMS
61	Reprise RS 20019	Sleepless Nights/Mandolino Mandolino	5
61	Reprise RS 20030	My Prayer/Miracle	5
62	Philips BF 1282	How Come/When I Had You	30
60	Mercury MMC 14027	A GIRL IS A GIRL IS A GIRL (LP)	15

(see also Platters, Lifetime)

TONY WILLIAMS
| 78 | CBS 83338 | JOY OF FLYING (LP) | 10 |

WINSTON WILLIAMS
| 70 | Jackpot JP 733 | D.J.'s Choice/SLIM SMITH: Can't Do Without It | 4 |
| 70 | Jackpot JP 743 | The People's Choice/BOBBY JAMES: Let Me Go Girl | 4 |

CLAUDE WILLIAMSON
| 54 | Capitol KC 65003 | All God's Chillun Got Rhythm/Woody 'N You | 5 |

DUDLEY WILLIAMSON
| 67 | Doctor Bird DB 1117 | Coming On The Scene/Anything You Want | 8 |

ROBIN WILLIAMSON
| 72 | Island HELP 2 | MYRRH (LP) | 10 |
| 78 | Criminal STEAL 4 | AMERICAN STONEHENGE (LP) | 10 |
(see also Incredible String Band)

SONNY BOY WILLIAMSON (I)
40s	HMV	Decoration Day No. 2/Million Years Blues (78, possibly unissued)	50
69	Matchbox SDR 169	SONNY BOY AND HIS PALS (LP)	15
70	RCA Intl. INTS 1088	BLUEBIRD BLUES (LP)	12

SONNY BOY WILLIAMSON (II)
63	Pye Intl. 7N 25191	Help Me/Bye Bye Bird	10
64	Pye Intl. 7N 25268	Lonesome Cabin/The Goat	10
65	Sue WI 365	No Nights By Myself/Boppin' With Sonny Boy	10
66	Chess CRS 8030	Bring It On Home/Down Child	8
66	Blue Horizon 45-1008	From The Bottom/Empty Bedroom	45
64	Pye Intl. NEP 44037	SONNY BOY WILLIAMSON (EP)	15
65	Chess CRE 6001	HELP ME (EP)	20
66	Chess CRE 6013	IN MEMORIAM (EP)	20
66	Chess CRE 6018	REAL FOLK BLUES VOL. 2 (EP)	15
64	Pye Intl. NPL 28036	DOWN AND OUT BLUES (LP)	20
64	Marble Arch MAL 662	DOWN AND OUT BLUES (LP, reissue)	10
65	Chess CRL 4510	IN MEMORIAM (LP)	20
66	Fontana 670 158	PORTRAITS IN BLUES, VOL. 4 (LP)	18
67	Storyville 671 170	THE BLUES OF SONNY BOY WILLIAMSON (LP)	15
68	Marmalade 607/608 004	DON'T SEND ME NO FLOWERS (LP, with Brian Auger & Jimmy Page)	30
74	Rarity RLP 1	THE LAST SESSIONS — 1963 (LP)	25
(see also Ottilie Patterson)

SONNY BOY WILLIAMSON (II) & YARDBIRDS
65	Fontana TL 5277	SONNY BOY WILLIAMSON & THE YARDBIRDS (LP)	60
68	Fontana SFJL 960	SONNY BOY WILLIAMSON & THE YARDBIRDS (LP, reissue, different sleeve)	20
71	Philips 6435 011	SONNY BOY WILLIAMSON & THE YARDBIRDS (LP, 2nd reissue)	12
(see also Yardbirds, Brian Auger)

STU WILLIAMSON
| 56 | London Jazz LZ-N 14030 | SAPPHIRE (10" LP) | 12 |

DORIS WILLINGHAM
| 69 | Jay Boy BOY 1 | You Can't Do That/Lost Again | 10 |

CHUCK WILLIS
57	London HLE 8444	C.C. Rider/Ease The Pain	40
57	London HLE 8444	C.C. Rider/Ease The Pain (78)	18
57	London HLE 8489	That Train Has Gone/Love Me Cherry	40
57	London HLE 8489	That Train Has Gone/Love Me Cherry (78)	18
58	London HLE 8595	Betty And Dupree/My Crying Eyes	30
58	London HLE 8595	Betty And Dupree/My Crying Eyes (78)	15
58	London HLE 8635	What Am I Living For/Hang Up My Rock And Roll Shoes	30
58	London HLE 8635	What Am I Living For/Hang Up My Rock And Roll Shoes (78)	20
58	London HL 7039	What Am I Living For/Hang Up My Rock And Roll Shoes (export issue)	15
59	London HLE 8818	My Life/Thunder And Lightning	30
59	London HLE 8818	My Life/Thunder And Lightning (78)	15
59	Fontana TFE 17138	CHUCK WILLIS WAILS (EP)	150
63	Atlantic 588 145	I REMEMBER CHUCK WILLIS (LP)	12

RALPH WILLIS
54	Esquire 10-370	Lazy Woman Blues/Goodbye Blues (78)	20
54	Esquire 10-380	Old Home Blues/Salty Dog (78)	20
70	Pressure Beat PB 5502	Mad Rooster/As Far As I Can See	5
61	Esquire EP 241	RALPH WILLIS (EP)	20
60s	XX MIN 703	RALPH WILLIS (EP)	8
60s	XX MIN 711	RALPH WILLIS (EP)	8

SLIM WILLIS
| 65 | R&B MRB 5004 | Running Around | 12 |

TIMMY WILLIS
| 72 | United Artists UP 35352 | Mr. Soul Satisfaction/I'm Wondering | 4 |

WILLIS BROTHERS
| 67 | London HLB 10132 | Bob/Show Her Lots Of Gold | 4 |

WILLOWS
| 56 | London HLU 8290 | Church Bells May Ring/Baby Tell Me | 600 |
| 56 | London HLU 8290 | Church Bells May Ring/Baby Tell Me (78) | 60 |

BOB WILLS & HIS TEXAS PLAYBOYS
| 51 | MGM MGM 455 | 'Tater Pie/Ida Red Likes The Boogie (78) | 8 |
| 53 | MGM MGM 613 | Snatchin' And Grabbin'/I Want To Be Wanted (78) | 7 |

Bob WILLS

BOB WILLS with TOMMY DUNCAN
60	London HL 7102	Heart To Heart Talk/What's The Matter With The Mill (export issue)	12

(see also Tommy Duncan)

MICK WILLS
88	Woronzow WOO 9	FERN HILL (LP)	10

VIOLA WILLS
68	President PT 108	Lost Without The Love Of My Guy/I Got Love	6
68	President PT 150	Together Forever/Don't Kiss Me Hello And Mean Goodbye	4
68	President PT 152	I've Got To Have All Of You/Night Scene	4
68	President PT 154	You're Out Of My Mind/Any Time	5
86	Streetwave MKHAN 66	Dare To Dream/Both Sides Now (12", p/s)	7
74	Goodear EARLH 5002	SOFT CENTRES (LP)	10

WILMER & DUKES
68	Action ACT 4500	Give Me One More Chance/Get It	7

ADA WILSON
79	Ellie Jay EJSP 9288	In The Quiet Of My Room/I'm In Control Here (p/s)	10
80	Barn BARN 012	In The Quiet Of My Room/I'm In Control Here (no p/s, reissue)	5
80	Rockburgh ROCS 224	Head In The Clouds/It Doesn't Have To Be (p/s, with Keeping Dark)	4
85	Thin Sliced TSR 5	In The Quiet Of My Room (New Version)/In The Quiet Of My Room (p/s)	4

AL WILSON
68	Liberty LBF 15044	Do What You Gotta Do/Now I Know What Love Is	10
68	Liberty LBF 15121	The Snake/Who Could Be Lovin' You	15
69	Liberty LBF 15236	Shake Me Wake Me/I Stand Accused	4
69	Liberty LBF 15257	Lodi/By The Time I Get To Phoenix	4
75	Bell BLL 1436	The Snake/Willoughby Brook	4
69	Soul City SCS 92006	SEARCHING FOR THE DOLPHINS (LP)	20
74	Bell BELLS 247	LA LA PEACE SONG (LP)	10

BRIAN WILSON (& MIKE LOVE)
66	Capitol CL 15438	Caroline, No/Summer Means New Love	12
67	Capitol CL 15513	Gettin' Hungry/Devoted To You (as Brian Wilson & Mike Love)	15

(see also Beach Boys)

CLIVE WILSON
64	R&B JB 144	Mango Tree/Midnight In Chicago	8

DELROY WILSON
63	Island WI 097	Naughty People/I Shall Not Remove	10
63	Island WI 103	One, Two, Three/Back Biter	10
63	Island WI 116	You Bend My Love/Can't You See	10
63	Blue Beat BB 172	Spit In The Sky/Tell Me What	8
63	R&B JB 108	Lion Of Judah/Joe Liges	10
63	R&B JB 128	Prince Pharoah/Don't Believe Him	10
63	R&B JB 132	Squeeze Your Toe/Sugar Pie	10
64	Black Swan WI 405	Spit In The Sky/Voodoo Man	10
64	Black Swan WI 420	Goodbye/Treat Me Good	8
64	R&B JB 148	Lover Mouth/Every Mouth Must Be Fed	10
64	R&B JB 168	Sammy Dead/CYNTHIA & ARCHIE: Every Beat	8
65	Island WI 205	Pick Up The Pieces/Oppression	10
66	Doctor Bird DB 1022	Give Me A Chance/(It's) Impossible	10
66	Island WI 3013	Dancing Mood/SOUL BROTHERS: More And More	10
67	Island WI 3033	Riding For A Fall/Got To Change Your Ways	10
67	Island WI 3037	Ungrateful Baby/ROY RICHARDS: Hopeful Village Ska	10
67	Island WI 3050	Get Ready/ROY RICHARDS: Port-O-Jam	10
67	Studio One SO 2009	Won't You Come Home Baby/PETER & HORTENSE: I've Been Lonely	15
67	Studio One SO 2019	Never Conquer/Run For Your Life	15
67	Studio One SO 2031	I'm Not A King/HEPTONES: Take Me (B-side actually by Soul Vendors)	15
68	Island WI 3099	This Old Heart Of Mine/GLEN ADAMS: Grab A Girl	10
68	Island WI 3127	Once Upon A Time/I Want To Love You	10
68	Coxsone CS 7064	True Believer/MARSHALL WILLIAMS: College Girl	15
68	Studio One SO 2040	Mr. DJ/HEPTONES: Tripe Girl	15
68	Studio One SO 2046	Rain From The Skies/How Can I Love Someone	15
68	Studio One SO 2057	Feel Good all Over/I Like The Way You Walk	15
68	High Note HS 011	Put Yourself In My Place/It Hurts	6
69	High Note HS 015	I'm The One Who Loves You/AFROTONES: If I'm In A Corner	6
69	High Note HS 022	Your Number One/I've Tried My Best	6
69	Studio One SO 2074	Easy Snappin'/WEBBER SISTERS: Come On	15
69	Camel CA 15	Sad Mood (actually by Ken Parker)/STRANGER COLE: Give It To Me	5
70	Smash SMA 2317	I Am Trying/COLLINS ALLSTARS: Version	4
70	Smash SMA 2318	Satisfaction/Satisfaction Version (B-side with Alton Ellis)	4
70	Trojan TR 7740	Show Me The Way/BEVERLEY'S ALLSTARS: Version	5
70	Trojan TR 7769	Gave You My Love/BEVERLEY'S ALLSTARS: Version	5
70	Summit SUM 8503	Got To Get Away/BEVERLEY'S ALLSTARS: Version	4
71	Jackpot JP 763	Better Must Come/BUNNY LEE ALLSTARS: Version	5
71	Jackpot JP 769	Cool Operator/I'm Yours	5
71	Jackpot JP 770	Try Again/AGGROVATORS: Version	5
71	Jackpot JP 780	Keep Your Love Strong/Nice To Be Near	5
71	Jackpot JP 781	Peace And Love/JEFF BARNES: Who's Your Brother	5
71	Banana BA 333	Just Because Of You/I Love You Madly	6
72	Spur SP 2	Adis Ababa/KEITH HUDSON: Rudie Hot Stuff	6
73	Downtown DT 501	Pretty Girl/JOE GIBBS & PROFESSIONALS: Face Girl	5
73	Green Door GD 4060	Ain't That Peculiar/What Is Man	4
74	Harry J. HJ 6667	What Will Happen To The Youth Of Today	4
64	R&B JBL 1112	I SHALL NOT REMOVE (LP)	80
68	Coxsone CSL 8016	GOOD ALL OVER (LP)	70

| 72 | Trojan TRLS 44 | BETTER MUST COME (LP) | 15 |
| 70s | Big Shot BILP 102 | CAPTIVITY (LP) | 15 |

(see also Hortense & Delroy)

DENNIS WILSON (& RUMBO)

70	Stateside SS 2184	Sound Of Free/Lady (as Dennis Wilson & Rumbo)	30
77	Caribou CRB 5663	River Song/Farewell My Friend	4
77	Caribou CRB 81672	PACIFIC OCEAN BLUE (LP)	10

(see also Beach Boys)

DOYLE WILSON with JIMMY LACEY & BAND

| 58 | Vogue Pop V 9117 | Hey-Hey/You're The One For Me | 150 |
| 58 | Vogue Pop V 9117 | Hey-Hey/You're The One For Me (78) | 50 |

EDDIE WILSON

| 69 | Action ACT 4536 | Shing A Ling Stroll/Don't Kick The Teenager Around | 10 |
| 70 | Action ACT 4555 | Get Out On The Street/Must Be Love | 5 |

EDITH WILSON

| 60s | Fountain FB 302 | 1921-1922 WITH JOHNNY DUNN'S JAZZHOUNDS (LP) | 15 |

ERNEST ('SOUL') WILSON

67	Studio One SO 2032	Money Worries/SOUL VENDORS: Pe Da Pa	15
68	Studio One SO 2058	If I Were A Carpenter/SOUL VENDORS: Frozen Soul	15
68	Coxsone CS 7044	Storybook Children (as Ernest 'Soul' Wilson)/LITTLE FREDDIE:	
		After Laughter (B-side actually by Freddie McGregor)	15
68	Coxsone CS 7059	Undying Love/SOUL VENDORS: Tropic Isle	15
69	Amalgamated AMG 837	Private Number/GLEN ADAMS: She's So Fine	6
69	Crab CRAB 9	Private Number/Another Chance	4
69	Crab CRAB 17	Freedom Train/STRANGER COLE: You Should Never Have To Come	5
69	Crab CRAB 21	Just Once In My Lfe (with Freddy)/GLEN ADAMS: Mighty Organ	4

(see also Tinga & Ernest)

FRANK WILSON

| 79 | Tamla Motown TMG 1170 | Do I Love You (Indeed I Do)/Sweeter As The Days Go By | 6 |

FRANK WILSON & CAVALIERS

| 64 | Fontana TF 505 | Last Kiss/That's How Much I Love You | 8 |

GARLAND WILSON

| 53 | HMV 7M 122 | Just You, Just Me/Sweet Georgia Brown | 4 |

JACK WILSON QUARTET

| 64 | London HA-K/SH-K 8170 | THE JACK WILSON QUARTET (LP, featuring Roy Ayers) | 20 |

(see also Roy Ayers)

JACKIE WILSON

57	Vogue Coral Q 72290	Reet Petite/By The Light Of The Silvery Moon	18
57	Coral Q 72290	Reet Petite/By The Light Of The Silvery Moon (2nd pressing)	10
57	Coral Q 72290	Reet Petite/By The Light Of The Silvery Moon (78)	10
58	Coral Q 72306	To Be Loved/Come Back To Me	12
58	Coral Q 72306	To Be Loved/Come Back To Me (78)	8
58	Coral Q 72332	I'm Wanderin'/As Long As I Live	12
58	Coral Q 72332	I'm Wanderin'/As Long As I Live (78)	12
58	Coral Q 72338	We Have Love/Singing A Song	12
58	Coral Q 72338	We Have Love/Singing A Song (78)	15
58	Coral Q 72347	Lonely Teardrops/In The Blue Of The Evening	15
58	Coral Q 72347	Lonely Teardrops/In The Blue Of The Evening (78)	20
59	Coral Q 72366	That's Why/Love Is All	10
59	Coral Q 72366	That's Why/Love Is All (78)	25
59	Coral Q 72372	I'll Be Satisfied/Ask	10
59	Coral Q 72372	I'll Be Satisfied/Ask (78)	25
59	Coral Q 72380	You Better Know It/Never Go Away	8
59	Coral Q 72380	You Better Know It/Never Go Away (78)	30
59	Coral Q 72384	Talk That Talk/Only You, Only Me	8
59	Coral Q 72384	Talk That Talk/Only You, Only Me (78)	30
60	Coral Q 72393	Doggin' Around/The Magic Of Love	10
60	Coral Q 72407	A Woman, A Lover, A Friend/(You Were Made For) All My Love	8
60	Coral Q 72412	Alone At Last/Am I The Man	8
61	Coral Q 72421	The Tear Of The Year/My Empty Arms (unreleased, demos only)	20
61	Coral Q 72424	The Tear Of The Year/Your One And Only Love	8
61	Coral Q 72430	Please Tell Me Why/(So Many) Cute Little Girls	8
61	Coral Q 72434	I'm Comin' On Back To You/Lonely Life	8
61	Coral Q 72439	You Don't Know What It Means/Years From Now	8
61	Coral Q 72444	The Way I Am/My Heart Belongs To Only You	8
62	Coral Q 72450	The Greatest Hurt/There'll Be No Next Time	8
62	Coral Q 72453	Sing (And Tell The Blues So Long)/I Found Love (B-side with Linda Hopkins)	8
62	Coral Q 72454	I Just Can't Help It/My Tale Of Woe	8
63	Coral Q 72460	Baby Workout/What Good Am I Without You	8
63	Coral Q 72464	Shake A Hand/Say I Do (as Jackie Wilson & Linda Hopkins)	8
63	Coral Q 72465	Shake! Shake! Shake!/He's A Fool	8
63	Coral Q 72467	Baby Get It/The New Breed	8
64	Coral Q 72474	Big Boss Line/Be My Girl	8
64	Coral Q 72476	Squeeze Her — Tease Her (But Love Her)/Give Me Back My Heart	8
65	Coral Q 72480	Yes Indeed!/When The Saints Go Marching In (as Jackie Wilson	
		& Linda Hopkins)	8
65	Coral Q 72481	No Pity (In The Naked City)/I'm So Lonely	10
65	Coral Q 72482	I Believe I'll Love On/Lonely Teardrops	10
66	Coral Q 72484	To Make A Big Man Cry/Be My Love	10
66	Coral Q 72487	Whispers/The Fairest Of Them All	10
67	Coral Q 72493	(Your Love Keeps Lifting Me) Higher And Higher/I'm The One To Do It	10

MINT VALUE £

67	Coral Q 72496	Since You Showed Me How To Be Happy/The Who Who Song 12
68	MCA MU 1014	For Your Precious Love/Uptight (Everything's Alright) (as Jackie Wilson & Count Basie) 5
68	Decca AD 1008	For Your Precious Love/Uptight (Everything's Alright) (export issue) 12
69	MCA Soul Bag BAG 2	(Your Love Keeps Lifting Me) Higher And Higher/Whispers (Gettin' Louder) 5
69	MCA Soul Bag BAG 7	Since You Showed Me How To Be Happy/Chain Gang 5
69	MCA MU 1104	Since You Showed Me How To Be Happy/The Who Who Song (reissue) 4
69	MCA MU 1105	Helpless/Do It The Right Way 4
70	MCA MU 1131	(Your Love Keeps Lifting Me) Higher And Higher/Whispers (Gettin' Louder) (reissue) 4
72	MCA MU 1160	I Get The Sweetest Feeling/Soul Galore 4
73	Brunswick BR 3	Beautiful Day/What'cha Gonna Do About Love 4
75	Brunswick BR 18	I Get The Sweetest Feeling/(Your Love Keeps Lifting Me) Higher And Higher 4
75	Brunswick BR 23	Whispers (Gettin' Louder)/Reet Petite 4
75	Brunswick BR 28	Don't Burnsk No Bridges/(Instrumental) (with Chi-Lites) 4
59	Coral FEP 2016	JACKIE WILSON (EP) 40
60	Coral FEP 2043	THE DYNAMIC JACKIE WILSON (EP) 35
58	Coral LVA 9087	HE'S SO FINE (LP) 75
59	Coral LVA 9108	LONELY TEARDROPS (LP) 75
60	Coral LVA 9121	SO MUCH (LP) 60
60	Coral LVA 9130	JACKIE SINGS THE BLUES (LP) 60
60	Coral LVA 9135	MY GOLDEN FAVOURITES (LP) 45
61	Coral LVA 9144	A WOMAN, A LOVER, A FRIEND (LP) 60
61	Coral LVA 9148	YOU AIN'T HEARD NOTHIN' YET (LP) 45
62	Coral LVA 9151	BY SPECIAL REQUEST (LP, also stereo SVL 3018) 45/55
62	Coral LVA 9202	BODY AND SOUL (LP) 35
63	Coral LVA/SVL 9209	JACKIE WILSON AT THE COPA (LP, mono/stereo) 35/40
63	Coral LVA/SVL 9214	THE WORLD'S GREATEST MELODIES (LP, mono/stereo) 35/40
66	Coral LVA 9231	SPOTLIGHT ON JACKIE WILSON (LP) 35
66	Coral LVA/SVL 9232	SOUL GALORE (LP, mono/stereo) 35/40
67	Coral LVA 9235	WHISPERS (LP) 30
68	MCA MUP(S) 304	HIGHER AND HIGHER (LP) 12
68	MCA MUP(S) 333	TWO MUCH (LP, with Count Basie & His Orchestra) 10
69	MCA MUPS 361	I GET THE SWEETEST FEELING (LP) 10
70	MCA MUPS 405	DO YOUR THING (LP) 20
73	Brunswick BRLS 3001	YOU GOT ME WALKIN' (LP) 10
75	Brunswick BRLS 3016	THE VERY BEST OF JACKIE WILSON (LP) 10

(see also Billy Ward & Dominoes, Clyde McPhatter, Count Basie)

JACKIE WILSON/CLYDE McPHATTER

| 62 | Ember JBS 705 | Tenderly/CLYDE McPHATTER: Harbour Lights ....175 |
| 62 | Ember NR 5001 | CLYDE McPHATTER AND JACKIE WILSON (LP, 1 side each) ....100 |

(see also Clyde McPhatter).

JOE WILSON

| 71 | Pye Intl. 7N 25550 | Sweetness/When A Man Cries ....5 |

MARI WILSON & IMAGINATIONS

80	GTO GT 274	Love Man/If That's What You Want (p/s) 6
81	Compact Org. PINK 1	Dance Card/She's Had Enough Of You (p/s) 4
82	Compact Org. ACT 4	Beat The Beat/Glamourpuss (p/s) 4

MARTY WILSON & STRAT-O-LITES

| 58 | Brunswick 05750 | Hey! Eula/Hedge-Hopper ....12 |
| 58 | Brunswick 05750 | Hey! Eula/Hedge-Hopper (78) ....5 |

MAYNELL WILSON & WESTMINSTER FIVE

| 64 | Carnival CV 7014 | Hey Hey Johnny/Baby ....5 |
| 67 | CBM CBM 001 | Motown Feeling/Mean Ole World ....5 |

(see also Westminster Five)

MURRY WILSON

| 67 | Capitol CL 15525 | Plumber's Tune/Love Won't Wait ....4 |
| 67 | Capitol (S)T 2819 | THE MANY MOODS OF MURRY WILSON (LP) ....12 |

(see also Beach Boys)

NANCY WILSON

65	Capitol CL 15412	Where Does That Leave Me/Gentle Is My Love 8
66	Capitol CL 15443	Power Of Love/Rain Sometimes 4
66	Capitol CL 15466	You've Got Your Troubles/Uptight (Everything's Alright) 12
67	Capitol CL 15508	Don't Look Over Your Shoulder/Mercy, Mercy, Mercy 8
68	Capitol CL 15536	You Don't Know Me/Ode To Billie Joe 4
68	Capitol CL 15547	Face It Girl It's Over/The End Of Our Love 22
75	Capitol CL 15810	You're Right As Rain/There'll Always Be Forever 4

NANCY WILSON & CANNONBALL ADDERLEY

| 63 | Capitol EAP4 1657 | NANCY WILSON & CANNONBALL ADDERLEY (EP) ....7 |

(see also Cannonball Adderley)

PEANUTS WILSON

58	Coral Q 72302	Cast Iron Arm/You've Got Love 250
58	Coral Q 72302	Cast Iron Arm/You've Got Love (78) 70
76	MCA MCA 240	Cast Iron Arm/You've Got Love (reissue) 4

PHIL WILSON

| 87 | Creation CRE 036D | Waiting For A Change/Even Now//Down In The Valley/Love In Vain (double pack) 5 |
| 89 | Caff CAFF 3 | Better Days/You Won't Speak (p/s, with insert, handwritten label) ....10 |

(see also June Brides)

REUBEN WILSON

| 74 | People PEO 109 | I'll Take You There/Cisco Kid ....7 |
| 76 | Chess 6078 700 | Got To Get Your Own Pts 1 & 2 ....10 |

MINT VALUE £

72	Blue Note BST 84295	ON BROADWAY (LP)	15
72	Blue Note BST 84317	LOVE BUG (LP)	10
72	Blue Note BST 84343	BLUE MODE (LP)	10
73	People PLEO 1	CISCO KID (LP)	15
74	People PLEO 20	THE SWEET LIFE (LP)	15

RON WILSON
| 68 | Island WI 3112 | Dread Saras/DAVID BROWN: All My Life | 10 |

SMILEY WILSON
| 60 | London HLG 9066 | Running Bear/Long As Little Birds Fly | 40 |

TIMOTHY WILSON
| 73 | Decca F 13432 | Phoney People/Shine | 6 |

TONY WILSON
| 77 | Bearsville K 15530 | Anything That Keeps You Satisfied/I Can't Leave It Alone | 4 |
| 76 | Bearsville K 55513 | I LIKE YOUR STYLE (LP) | 10 |

TREVOR WILSON
| 65 | Ska Beat JB 207 | You Couldn't Believe/You Told Me You Care | 8 |

WILSON-GALE & CO.
| 80 | Jet JET 156 | I Wanna Stay (p/s) | 4 |
| 80 | Jet JET LP 233 | GIFT-WRAPPED SET (LP, with insert) | 10 |
(see also E.L.O.)

JOHNNY WILTSHIRE & HIS TREBLETONES
| 59 | Oriole CB 1494 | If The Shoe Fits/Cha Cha Choo Choo | 20 |
| 59 | Oriole CB 1494 | If The Shoe Fits/Cha Cha Choo Choo (78) | 30 |

WIMPLE WINCH
66	Fontana TF 686	What's Been Done/I Really Love You	100
66	Fontana TF 718	Save My Soul/Everybody's Worried 'Bout Tomorrow	100
67	Fontana TF 781	Rumble On Mersey Square South/Typical British Workmanship	80
67	Fontana TF 781	Rumble On Mersey Square South/Typical British Workmanship (mispressing, B-side plays "Atmospheres")	175
(see also Just Four Men, Pacific Drift, Cheeter)

WIND
| 85 | Proto ENA 126 | For Everyone/Für Alle/Fire And Ice (p/s) | 4 |

WIND IN THE WILLOWS
| 68 | Capitol CL 15561 | Moments Spent/Friendly Lion | 15 |
| 68 | Capitol ST 2956 | WIND IN THE WILLOWS (LP) | 20 |
(see also Debbie Harry, Blondie)

KAI WINDING
| 64 | Verve VS 501 | Baby Elephant Walk/Experiment In Terror | 4 |
| 65 | Verve VS 512 | Comin' Home Baby/More | 6 |

WINDOWS
| 78 | Skeleton SKL 008 | Re-Arrange/Over Dub (p/s) | 4 |
| 81 | Skeleton SKULP-2 | UPPERS ON DOWNERS (LP, with inserts) | 10 |
(see also Mutants)

BARBARA WINDSOR
| 67 | Parlophone R 5629 | Don't Dig Twiggy/Swinging London | 4 |

WINGS
(see under Paul McCartney & Wings)

WINSTON
| 60s | Holyground | WINSTON SINGS (EP) | 7 |

WINSTON (Richards) & BIBBIE (Seaton)
| 63 | R&B JB 115 | Lover Man/LESTER STIRLING: Gravy Cool | 10 |

WINSTON (Francis) & CECEIL (Locke)
| 70 | Banana BA 306 | United We Stand/SOUND DIMENSION: Sweet Message | 5 |

WINSTON & GEORGE
| 66 | Pyramid PYR 6002 | Denham Town/Keep The Pressure On | 8 |

WINSTON & PAT (Rhoden)
| 68 | Trojan TR 605 | Pony Ride/Baby You Send Me | 6 |

WINSTON & ROY
| 62 | Blue Beat BB 80 | Babylon Gone/COUNT OSSIE & HIS WARRIKAS: First Gone | 10 |

WINSTON (Richards) & TONETTES
| 65 | Ska Beat JB 225 | You Make Me Cry/CHECKMATES: Invisible Ska | 10 |

JIMMY WINSTON (& HIS REFLECTIONS)
| 66 | Decca F 12410 | Sorry She's Mine/It's Not What You Do (But The Way That You Do It) | 60 |
| 76 | Nems NEMS 12 | Sun In The Morning/Just Wanna Smile (solo) | 4 |
(see also Small Faces, Winston's Fumbs, Spheres)

ERIC WINSTONE (& HIS) ORCHESTRA
| 55 | Polygon P 1173 | Rhythm And Blues/Opus One Mambo (78) | 5 |
| 64 | Pye 7N 15603 | "Dr. Who" Theme/Pony Express | 8 |

NORMA WINSTONE
| 71 | Argo ZDA 148 | EDGE OF TIME (LP) | 45 |
(see also Mike Westbrook, Michael Garrick)

WINSTONS
| 69 | Pye Intl. 7N 25493 | Colour Him Father/Amen, Brother | 8 |
| 69 | Pye Intl. 7N 25500 | Love Of The Common People/Wheel Of Fortune | 4 |

WINSTON'S FUMBS
67	RCA RCA 1612	Real Crazy Apartment/Snow White	120

(see also Small Faces, Jimmy Winston & His Reflections, Yes, Spheres)

EDGAR WINTER (GROUP)
70	CBS 64083	ENTRANCE (LP, as Edgar Winter)	10
71	CBS 64298	WHITE TRASH (LP)	10
72	CBS 67244	ROAD WORK (2-LP)	14
73	CBS EQ 31584/Q 65074	THEY ONLY COME OUT AT NIGHT (LP, quadrophonic)	12

JOHNNY WINTER
69	CBS 4386	I'm Yours And I'm Hers/I'll Drown In My Tears	4
69	CBS 63619	JOHNNY WINTER (LP)	15
69	Liberty LBS 83240	PROGRESSIVE BLUES EXPERIMENT (LP)	12
70	Buddah 2359 011	FIRST WINTER (LP)	10
70	CBS 66231	SECOND WINTER (2-LP)	15
71	CBS 64117	JOHNNY WINTER AND ... (LP)	10
71	CBS 64289	JOHNNY WINTER AND ... LIVE (LP)	10
73	CBS CQ 32188/Q 65484	STILL ALIVE AND WELL (LP, quadrophonic)	12

(see also Johnny & Jammers)

PAUL WINTER
69	A&M AMLS 942	WINTER CONSORT (LP)	10

HUGO WINTERHALTER ORCHESTRA
54	HMV 7M 273	Land Of Dreams/Song Of The Barefoot Contessa	5
56	HMV POP 241	Canadian Sunset/This Is Real (with Eddie Haywood)	6

DON WINTERS
60	Brunswick 05827	Someday Baby/That's All I Need	12

(see also Anglos)

LIZ WINTERS & BOB CORT SKIFFLE GROUP
57	Decca F 10878	Love Is Strange/Freight Train	10
57	Decca F 10899	Maggie May/Jessamine	6
57	Decca DFE 6409	LIZ WINTERS AND BOB CORT (EP)	12

(see also Bob Cort Skiffle Group)

LOIS WINTERS
56	London HLD 8266	Japanese Farewell Song/JAN GARBER & HIS ORCHESTRA: My Dear	18

MIKE & BERNIE WINTERS
57	Parlophone R 4384	How Do You Do?/Does My Baby?	12
59	Parlophone R 4538	For Me and My Gal/Your Own Home Town	4

RUBY WINTERS
68	Stateside SS 2090	I Want Action/Better	6
79	Creole CR 171	Baby Lay Down/Lovin' Me Is A Full Time Job	8
79	Creole CR 174	Back To Love/I've Been Waiting For You All My Life	8

WYOMA WINTERS
54	HMV 7M 222	Where Can I Go Without You?/Won't You Give A Repeat Performance	4
54	HMV 7M 260	Toy Balloon/Shish Kebab	4

STEVIE WINWOOD
77	Island	Time Is Running Out/Penultimate Zone (12", promo only, company sleeve)	8
80	Island IPR 2040	While You See A Chance/Vacant Chair (12", promo only, pre-release sleeve)	7
80	Island CWIP 6655	While You See A Chance/Vacant Chair (cassette, 5,000 only)	5
81	Island WIP 6680	Spanish Dancer/Home On (12", p/s)	7
81	Island WIP 6747	There's A River/Two Way Stretch (p/s)	4
86	Island IS 294	Freedom Overspill/Spanish Dancer (p/s, with free cassette of LP highlights & interview [SW 2])	5
86	Island 12 ISG 294	Freedom Overspill (Liberty Mix)/(LP Version)/Spanish Dancer//Low Spark Of High Heeled Boys/Gimme Some Lovin' (12", gatefold p/s, w/ test pressing 7")	7
87	Island	CHRONICLES (5 x 7" box set, promo, 500 only)	25

(see also Anglos, Spencer Davis Group, Traffic, Blind Faith, Airforce)

WIPEOUT
82	M&L MNL 2	Baby Please Don't Go/Two-O-Five/Crawdaddy/Should A' Know Better (p/s)	4

WIPERS
84	Psycho PSYCHO 22	IS THIS REAL? (LP, with lyric insert)	10
84	Psycho PSYCHO 23	YOUTH OF AMERICA (LP)	10

WIRE
77	Harvest HAR 5144	Mannequin/Feeling Called Love/12XU (p/s)	12
78	Harvest HAR 5151	I Am The Fly/Ex Lion Tamer (p/s)	8
78	Harvest HAR 5161	Dot Dash/Options R (p/s)	8
79	Harvest HAR 5172	Outdoor Miner/Practice Makes Perfect (p/s, some on white vinyl)	8/6
79	Harvest HAR 5187	A Question of Degree/Former Airline (p/s)	8
79	Harvest HAR 5192	Map Ref 41 N 93 W/Go Ahead (p/s)	6
79	Harvest SPSLP 299	154 (12" p/s, with insert, white label sampler)	40
81	Rough Trade RT 079	Our Swimmer/Midnight Bahnhof Cafe (p/s)	5
83	Rough Trade RTT 123	Crazy About Love/Second Length (Our Swimmer)/Catapult 30 (12", p/s, 2 different designs)	8
89	Mute MUTE 87	Eardrum Buzz/The Offer (p/s, clear vinyl)	15
77	Harvest SHSP 4076	PINK FLAG (LP, with lyric inner)	10
77	Harvest TC-SHSP 4076	PINK FLAG (cassette)	12
78	Harvest SHSP 4093	CHAIRS MISSING (LP, 1st 10,000 with lilac lyric inner)	10
78	Harvest TC-SHSP 4093	CHAIRS MISSING (cassette)	10
79	Harvest SHSP 4105	154 (LP, with inner lyric sleeve & free 7" EP: "Song 2"/"Get Down [Parts I & II]"/"Let's Panic"/"Later"/"Small Electric Piece" [PSR 444])	12
84	Rough Trade ROUGH 29	DOCUMENT AND EYEWITNESS (LP, with free 12" EP [ROUGH 2912])	15

Rare Record Price Guide

84	Rough Trade COPY 004	DOCUMENT AND EYEWITNESS (cassette, in special box)	15
84	Rough Trade COPY 004	DOCUMENT AND EYEWITNESS (cassette with 12" EP tracks)	10
86	Pink PINKY 7	PLAY POP (mini-LP)	8
89	Mute STUMM 66	IBTABA (IT'S BEGINNING TO AND BACK AGAIN) (LP, with 4 postcards & signed print)	12

(see also Colin Newman, Gilbert & Lewis, Snakes, A.C. Marias A.C.)

MARK WIRTZ (ORCHESTRA & CHORUS)

68	Parlophone R 5668	(He's Our Dear Old) Weatherman (From "A Teenage Opera")/ Possum's Dance	12
68	Parlophone R 5683	Mrs. Raven/Knickerbocker Glory	6
69	CBS 4306	My Daddie Is A Baddie/I Love You Because	4
69	CBS 4539	Caroline/Goody, Goody, Goody	5

(see also Mood Mosaic, Keith West, Sweet Shop, Philwit & Pegasus)

WISDOM

76	Crystal CR 026	Nefertiti/What-Cha-Gonna-Du- About You	8

NORMAN WISDOM

56	Columbia SCM 5222	Two Rivers/Boy Meets Girl (with Ruby Murray)	10
57	Columbia DB 3864	Up In The World/Me And My Imagination	7
57	Columbia DB 3903	The Wisdom Of A Fool/Happy Ending	8
59	Top Rank JAR 246	Follow A Star/Give Me A Night In June	4
61	Columbia SCD 2160	Narcissus (The Laughing Record)/I Don't 'Arf Love You (with Joyce Grenfell)	8
56	Columbia SEG 7612	NORMAN WISDOM (EP)	8
57	Columbia SEG 7687	NORMAN AND RUBY (EP, with Ruby Murray)	7
58	Columbia 33SX 1085	IN "WHERE'S CHARLY?" (LP)	10

(see also Ruby Murray)

WISE BOYS

60	Parlophone R 4693	Why, Why, Why/My Fortune	8

WISE GUYS

60	Top Rank JAR 271	(Little Girl) Big Noise/As Long As I Have You	6

MAC WISEMAN

55	London HLD 8174	The Kentuckian Song/Wabash Cannon Ball	40
55	London HLD 8174	The Kentuckian Song/Wabash Cannon Ball (78)	7
56	London HLD 8226	My Little Home In Tennessee/I Haven't Got The Right To Love You	35
56	London HLD 8226	My Little Home In Tennessee/I Haven't Got The Right To Love You (78)	8
56	London HLD 8259	Fire Ball Mail/When The Roses Bloom Again	40
56	London HLD 8259	Fire Ball Mail/When The Roses Bloom Again (78)	15
57	London HLD 8412	Step It Up And Go/Sundown	150
57	London HLD 8412	Step It Up And Go/Sundown (78)	20
59	London HL 7084	Jimmy Brown The Newsboy/I've Got No Use For Woman (export issue)	25
56	London RED 1056	SONGS FROM THE HILLS (EP)	20
58	London RED 1147	SONGS FROM THE HILLS VOL. 2 (EP)	20
60	London RED 1242	SONGS FROM THE HILLS VOL. 3 (EP)	20
56	London HB-D 1052	SONGS FROM THE HILLS (10" LP)	40
60	London HA-D 2217	GREAT FOLK BALLADS (LP)	40

WISHBONE ASH

70	MCA MK 5051	Blind Eye/Queen Of Torture	5
72	MCA MKS 5097	No Easy Road/Blowin' Free	5
79	MCA MCA 518	Come On/Fast Johnny (p/s)	4
80	MCA MCAT 577	Helpless/Blowin' Free (12", p/s)	7
82	AVM WISH 1	Engine Overheat	4
70	MCA MKPS 2014	WISHBONE ASH (LP)	15
71	MCA MDKS 8004	PILGRIMAGE (LP)	12
73	MCA MDKS 8011	FOUR (LP,with poster and lyrics)	10
78	MCA MCG 3528	NO SMOKE WITHOUT FIRE (LP, with free single "Come In From The Rain"/ "Lorelei" [PSR 431])	10
80	MCA MCG 4012	LIVE DATES VOLUME 2 (with limited edition bonus LP)	10
85	Neat NEATP 1027	RAW TO THE BONE (LP, picture disc)	35
85	Neat NEAT 1027	RAW TO THE BONE (LP)	20

WISHFUL THINKING

66	Decca F 12438	Turning Round/V.I.P.	6
66	Decca F 12499	Step By Step/Looking Around	4
67	Decca F 12598	Count To Ten/Hang Around Girl	5
67	Decca F 12627	Peanuts/Cherry Cherry	5
67	Decca F 22673	Meet The Sun/Easier Said Than Loving You	7
68	Decca F 22742	Alone/Vegetables (export issue)	7
68	Decca F 12760	It's So Easy/I Want You Girl	4
71	B&C CB 169	Lu La Le Lu/We're Gonna Change All This	4
72	B&C CB 184	Clear White Light/Hiroshima	4
67	Decca SKL 4900	LIVE VOL. 1 (LP)	30
71	B&C CAS 1038	HIROSHIMA (LP)	15

WISHING STONES

86	Head HEAD 2	Beat Girl/Two Steps Take Me Back (p/s)	6
87	Head HEAD 6	New Ways/House Is Not A Home (p/s)	4
87	Head HEAD 612	New Ways/Wildwood/Hold Up/A House Is Not A Home (12", p/s)	7

(see also Loft)

TREVOR WISHART

78	private pressing	RED BIRD: A POLITICAL PRISONER'S DREAM (LP, with insert)	30
79	private pressing	BEACH SINGULARITY AND MENAGERIE (LP, with insert)	30

WITCHFINDER GENERAL

81	Heavy Metal HEAVY 6	Burning A Sinner/Satan's Children (p/s)	8
82	Heavy Metal 12HM 17	Soviet Invasion/Rabies/R.I.P. (live) (12", p/s)	15

WITCHFINDER GENERAL

83	Heavy Metal HEAVY 21	Music/Last Chance (p/s)	7
83	Heavy Metal HMPD 21	Music/Last Chance (picture disc)	8
82	Heavy Metal HMRLP 8	DEATH PENALTY (LP, red vinyl)	12
82	Heavy Metal HMRPD 8	DEATH PENALTY (LP, picture disc)	12
82	Heavy Metal HMRLP 13	FRIENDS OF HELL (LP)	10

WITCHFYNDE

79	Rondelet ROUND 1	Give 'Em Hell/Gettin' Heavy (p/s)	5
80	Rondelet ROUND 4	In The Stars/Wake Up Screaming (p/s)	5
83	Expulsion OUT 3	I'd Rather Go Wild/Cry Wolf (p/s)	12
80	Rondelet ABOUT 1	GIVE 'EM HELL (LP)	10
80	Rondelet ABOUT 2	STAGE FRIGHT (LP)	10
83	Expulsion (P)EXIT 5	CLOAK AND DAGGER (LP, some on picture disc)	10

BILL WITHERS

71	A&M AMS 845	Everybody's Talking/Harlem	5
71	A&M AMS 858	Ain't No Sunshine/Harlem	4
72	A&M AMS 7004	Lean On Me/Better Off Dead	4
72	A&M AMS 7038	Use Me/Let Me In Your Life	6
73	A&M AMS 7055	Kissing My Love/I Don't Know	6
73	A&M AMS 7068	Look What I Found/The Lady Is Waiting	6
73	A&M AMS 7080	Ain't No Sunshine/Harlem/Grandma's Hands	6
72	A&M AMLH 68107	STILL BILL (LP)	12
71	A&M AMLS 65002	JUST AS I AM (LP)	10
73	A&M AMLD 3001	LIVE AT CARNEGIE HALL (2-LP)	14
74	A&M AMLH 68230	+ 'JUSTMENTS (LP)	10
75	Sussex LPSX 10	BEST OF BILL WITHERS (LP)	10

JIMMY WITHERSPOON

51	Vogue V 2060	Big Fine Girl/No Rollin' Blues (78)	20
54	Parlophone MSP 6125	It/Highway To Happiness	25
54	Parlophone R 3914	It/Highway To Happiness (78)	15
54	Parlophone MSP 6142	Oh Boy/I Done Told You	30
54	Parlophone R 3951	Oh Boy/I Done Told You (78)	15
54	Vogue V 2261	Failing By Degrees/New Orleans Woman (78)	20
54	Vogue V 2295	Who's Been Jivin' With You/Rain, Rain, Rain (78)	20
56	Vogue V 2356	Jump, Children/Take Me Back Baby (78)	20
56	Vogue V 2060	Big Fine Girl/No Rollin' Blues	20
62	Vogue V 2420	All That's Good/When The Lights Go Out	20
64	Stateside SS 304	Evenin'/Money Is Getting Cheaper	10
64	Stateside SS 325	I Will Never Marry/I'm Coming Down With The Blues	10
64	Stateside SS 362	You're Next/Happy Blues	10
65	Stateside SS 429	Come Walk With Me/Oh How I Love You	10
65	Stateside SS 461	Love Me Right/Make My Heart Smile Again	10
66	Stateside SS 503	If There Wasn't Any You/I Never Thought I'd See The Day	10
66	Verve VS 538	It's All Over But The Crying/If I Could Have You Back Again	7
67	Verve VS 553	Past Forty Blues/My Baby's Quit Me	5
75	Capitol CL 15828	Fool's Paradise/Reflections	4
60	Vogue EPV 1198	RHYTHM AND BLUES CONCERT (EP)	40
61	Vogue EPV 1269	JIMMY WITHERSPOON AT MONTEREY (EP)	25
61	Vogue EPV 1270	JIMMY WITHERSPOON AT MONTEREY No. 2 (EP)	25
64	Vocalion EPVH 1278	JIMMY WITHERSPOON (EP)	15
65	Vocalion EPVH 1284	OUTSKIRTS OF TOWN (EP)	15
66	Vocalion VEH 170158	FEELING THE SPIRIT VOL. 1 (EP)	15
66	Vocalion VEH 170159	FEELING THE SPIRIT VOL. 2 (EP)	15
59	London Jazz LTZ-K 15150	NEW ORLEANS BLUES (LP, with Wilbur De Paris)	20
60	Vogue LAE 12218	SINGIN' THE BLUES (LP)	15
61	Vogue LAE 12253	AT THE RENAISSANCE (LP)	15
64	Stateside SL 10088	EVENIN' BLUES (LP)	20
65	Stateside SL 10105	BLUES AROUND THE CLOCK (LP)	25
65	Fontana 688 005 ZL	THERE'S GOOD ROCKIN' TONIGHT (LP)	15
65	Stateside SL 10114	SOME OF MY BEST FRIENDS ARE BLUES (LP)	25
65	Stateside SL 10139	BLUE SPOON (LP)	20
65	Vogue VRL 3005	JIMMY WITHERSPOON IN PERSON (LP)	15
66	Ember EMB 3369	JIMMY WITHERSPOON (LP)	15
67	Fontana (S)TL 5382	'SPOON SINGS AND SWINGS (LP)	25
67	Verve (S)VLP 9156	BLUE POINT OF VIEW (LP)	15
67	Transatlantic PR 7300	EVENIN' BLUES (LP, reissue)	12
68	Transatlantic PR 7356	SOME OF MY BEST FRIENDS ARE THE BLUES (LP, reissue)	12
68	Stateside (S)SL 10232	LIVE (LP)	20
68	Verve (S)VLP 9181	BLUES IS NOW (LP, with Brother Jack McDuff)	15
68	Verve (S)VLP 9216	SPOONFUL OF SOUL (LP)	15
68	Transatlantic PR 7418	SPOON IN LONDON (LP)	15
68	Transatlantic PR 7475	BLUES FOR EASY LIVERS (LP)	12
69	Stateside SSL 10289	THE BLUES SINGER (LP)	15
69	Ember CJS 820	SINGS THE BLUES AT THE RENAISSANCE (LP, reissue)	12
69	Polydor Intl. 623 256	BACK DOOR BLUES (LP)	15

(see also Eric Burdon, Brother Jack McDuff)

WIZARD'S CONVENTION

76	RCA RS 1085	WIZARD'S CONVENTION (LP, with insert)	12

(see also Deep Purple, Roger Glover, Jon Lord, David Coverdale, Ray Fenwick)

WIZZARD

73	Warner Bros K 16336	I Wish It Could Be Christmas Every Day/Rob Roy's Nightmare (gatefold p/s, withdrawn)	10
73	Harvest HAR 5079	I Wish It Could Be Christmas Every Day/Rob Roy's Nightmare (reissue, gatefold p/s, Harvest sticker over Warner Bros logo)	4
74	Warner Bros K 16357	Rock'n'Roll Winter/Dream Of Unwin (gatefold p/s)	4

74	Warner Bros K 16434	This Is The Story Of My Love (Baby)/Nixture	4
75	Jet JET 758	Rattlesnake Roll/Can't Help My Feelings	5
76	Harvest HAR 5106	See My Baby Jive/Angel Fingers/Ball Park Incident	6
73	Harvest SHSP 4025	WIZZARD BREW (LP)	10
74	Warner Bros K 56029	WIZZARD INTRODUCING EDDY AND THE FALCONS (LP, gatefold sleeve with poster)	10

(see also Roy Wood, Balls, Idle Race)

WKGB
79	Fetish FET 002	Non-Stop/Ultra Marine (p/s)	6

JAH WOBBLE
82	Jah Wobble JAH 1	Fading/Nocturnal (p/s)	4

(see also Don Letts & Jah Wobble, Joolz, Public Image Ltd)

WOLF
82	Chrysalis CHS 2592	Head Contact/Rock'n'Roll (p/s, clear vinyl)	6
82	Chrysalis CHS 12 2592	Head Contact/Rock'n'Roll/Soul For The Devil (12", p/s)	12

(DARRYL WAY'S) WOLF
73	Deram SDL 14	CANIS LUPUS (LP, as Darryl Way's Wolf, gatefold sleeve)	15
73	Deram SML 1104	SATURATION POINT (LP, as Darryl Way's Wolf)	15
74	Deram SML 1116	NIGHT MUSIC (LP)	10
78	Island ILPS 9550	CONCERTO FOR ELECTRIC VIOLIN (LP)	10

(see also Curved Air)

CHARLES WOLFE
68	NEMS 56-3675	Dance Dance Dance/Home	6

(see also At Last The 1958 Rock & Roll Show)

RICHARD WOLFE & HIS ORCHESTRA
60	London HLR 9143	Banjo Boy/Voila	4

WOLFGANG PRESS
84	4AD BAD 409	SCARECROW (12" EP)	12
85	4AD BAD 502	WATER (12" EP)	10
85	4AD BAD 506	Sweatbox/Muted/Heart Of Stone/I'm Coming Home (Mama) (12", p/s)	7
87	4AD BAD 702C	Big Sex/The Wedding/The Great Leveller/That Heat/God's Number (cassette)	5

WOLFHOUNDS
86	Pink PINKY 8	Cut The Cake/L.A. Juice/Deadthink/Another Lazy Day On The Lazy 'A' (12", p/s)	8
86	Pink PINKY 14	The Anti-Midas Touch/Restless Spell (p/s)	5
86	Pink PINKY 14T	The Anti-Midas Touch/Midget Horror/One Foot Wrong/Slow Lokis/Restless Spell (12", p/s)	7
86	Legend LEG 100/ LYN 18042	Rats On A Raft/RAZORCUTS: Sad Kaleidoscope (flexidisc, free with 'The Legend' & other fanzines, 500 only)	6/5
87	Pink PINKY 18	Cruelty/I See You (p/s)	4
87	Pink PINKY 18T	Cruelty/I See You/Whale On The Beach (12", p/s, with insert)	7

WOOLY WOLSTENHOLME
80	Polydor 2374 165	MAESTRO (LP)	10

(see also Barclay James Harvest)

WOLVES
64	Pye 7N 15676	Journey Into Dreams/What Do You Mean	7
64	Pye 7N 15733	Now/This Year Next Year	20
65	Pye 7N 17013	At The Club/Distant Dreams	15
66	Parlophone R 5511	Lust For Life/My Baby Loves Them	40

BOBBY WOMACK
68	Minit MLF 11001	Broadway Walk/Somebody Special	12
68	Minit MLF 11005	What Is This?/What You Gonna Do	8
68	Minit MLF 11010	Fly Me To The Moon/Take Me	5
69	Minit MLF 11012	California Dreamin'/Baby You Oughta Think It Over	5
72	United Artists UP 35339	That's The Way I Feel About 'Cha/Come L'Amore	6
72	United Artists UP 35375	Woman's Got To Have It/If You Don't Want My Love	6
73	United Artists UP 35456	Harry Hippie/I Can Understand It	6
73	United Artists UP 35512	Across 110th Street/Hang On In There	6
73	United Artists UP 35565	Nobody Wants You When You're Down And Out/I'm Through Trying To Prove My Love For You	5
74	Jay Boy BOY 75	What Is This?/I Wonder	7
75	United Artists UP 35859	Check It Out/Interlude No. 2	4
76	United Artists UP 36042	Where There's A Will There's A Way/Everything's Gonna Be Alright	4
76	United Artists UP 36098	Daylight/Trust Me	4
79	Arista ARIST 284	How Could You Break My Heart/I Honestly Love You	5
87	Arista RIS 17	How Could You Break My Heart/Give It Up (p/s)	4
87	Arista RIST 17	How Could You Break My Heart/Give It Up/Mr. D.J. Don't Stop The Music (12", p/s)	7
72	United Artists UAG 29365	UNDERSTANDING (LP)	12
73	United Artists UAS 29451	ACROSS 110th STREET (LP)	15
73	United Artists UAS 29306	COMMUNICATION (LP)	12
73	United Artists UAG 29456	FACTS OF LIFE (LP)	12
74	United Artists UAG 29574	LOOKIN' FOR A LOVE AGAIN (LP)	10
75	United Artists UAG 29715	I CAN UNDERSTAND IT (LP)	10
75	United Artists UAG 29762	I DON'T KNOW WHAT THE WORLD IS COMING TO (LP)	10
76	United Artists UAS 29907	SAFETY ZONE (LP)	10
76	United Artists UAS 29979	BW GOES C&W (LP)	10
76	CBS 81693	HOME IS WHERE THE HEART IS (LP)	10
79	Arista ARTY 165	ROADS OF LIFE (LP)	35
82	Motown STML 12168	THE POET (LP)	10

(see also Valentinos)

MINT VALUE £

WOMB
70s	Dot DLP 25933	WOMB (LP)	10
70s	Dot DLP 25959	OVERDUB (LP)	10

GIRL WONDER
66	Doctor Bird DB 1015	Mommy Out Of The Light/Cutting Wood	10

(LITTLE) STEVIE WONDER
63	Oriole CBA 1853	Fingertips Pts 1 & 2	18
63	Stateside SS 238	Workout, Stevie, Workout/Monkey Talk	30
64	Stateside SS 285	Castles In The Sand/Thank You (For Loving Me All The Way)	25
64	Stateside SS 323	Hey, Harmonica Man/This Little Girl	22

(the above singles were credited to Little Stevie Wonder)

65	Tamla Motown TMG 505	Kiss Me Baby/Tears In Vain	22
65	Tamla Motown TMG 532	High Heel Sneakers/Music Talk	15
66	Tamla Motown TMG 545	Uptight (Everything's Alright)/Purple Raindrops	8
66	Tamla Motown TMG 558	Nothing's Too Good For My Baby/With A Child's Heart	20
66	Tamla Motown TMG 570	Blowin' In The Wind/Ain't That Asking For Trouble	12
66	Tamla Motown TMG 588	A Place In The Sun/Sylvia	12
67	Tamla Motown TMG 602	Travelin' Man/Hey Love	8
67	Tamla Motown TMG 613	I Was Made To Love Her/Hold Me	6
67	Tamla Motown TMG 626	I'm Wondering/Every Time I See You I Go Wild	5
68	Tamla Motown TMG 653	Shoo-Be-Doo-Be-Doo-Da-Day/Why Don't You Lead Me To Love	5
68	Tamla Motown TMG 666	You Met Your Match/My Girl	5
68	Tamla Motown TMG 679	For Once In My Life/Angie Girl	5
69	Tamla Motown TMG 690	I Don't Know Why I Love You/My Cherie Amour	4
70	Tamla Motown TMG 757	Heaven Help Us All/I Gotta Have A Song	4
71	Tamla Motown TMG 772	We Can Work It Out/Don't Wonder Why (some in p/s)	10/4
71	Tamla Motown TMG 779	Never Dreamed You'd Leave Me In Summer/If You Really Love Me	4
84	Tamla Motown TMGT 1368	Do I Do/I Ain't Gonna Stand For It (12", p/s)	8
64	Stateside SE 1014	I CALL IT PRETTY MUSIC BUT PEOPLE CALL IT THE BLUES (EP)	25
65	Tamla Motown TME 2006	STEVIE WONDER (EP)	25
63	Oriole PS 40049	TRIBUTE TO UNCLE RAY (LP)	60
63	Oriole PS 40050	THE TWELVE-YEAR-OLD GENIUS — LIVE (LP)	50
64	Stateside SL 10078	THE JAZZ SOUL OF LITTLE STEVIE WONDER (LP)	35

(the above EPs and LPs were credited to Little Stevie Wonder)

65	Stateside SL 10108	HEY, HARMONICA MAN (LP)	80
66	T. Motown (S)TML 11036	UPTIGHT (EVERYTHING'S ALRIGHT) (LP)	15
67	T. Motown (S)TML 11045	DOWN TO EARTH (LP)	20
68	T. Motown (S)TML 11059	I WAS MADE TO LOVE HER (LP)	15
68	T. Motown (S)TML 11075	GREATEST HITS (LP)	10
69	T. Motown (S)TML 11085	SOMEDAY AT CHRISTMAS (LP)	25
69	T. Motown (S)TML 11098	FOR ONCE IN MY LIFE (LP)	12
70	T. Motown (S)TML 11128	MY CHERIE AMOUR (LP)	10
70	T. Motown (S)TML 11150	STEVIE WONDER LIVE (LP)	12
70	T. Motown STML 11164	LIVE AT THE TALK OF THE TOWN (LP)	12

WONDER BOY
69	Jackpot JP 703	Sweeten My Coffee (actually by Slim Smith)/MISTER MILLER: Cherry Pink	4
69	Jackpot JP 705	Love Power (actually by Slim Smith)/PAT KELLY: Since You Are Gone	5

(see also Slim Smith)

WONDER BOY
75	Ackee ACK 546	Pressure Pts 1 & 2	4

WONDERLAND
68	Polydor 56539	Poochy/Moscow	7

ALICE WONDERLAND
63	London HLU 9783	He's Mine/Cha Linde	6

WONDER STUFF
87	Far Out GONE ONE	A Wonderful Day/It's Not True/Like A Merry Go Round/Down Here (EP, p/s)	70
87	Far Out GONE 002	Unbearable/Ten Trenches Deep (some with p/s)	25/8
87	Far Out GO BIG 002	Unbearable/Ten Trenches Deep/I Am A Monster/Frank (12", p/s)	8
88	Polydor GONE 3	Give Give Give Me More More More/A Song Without An End (p/s)	10
88	Polydor GONEX 3	Give Give Give Me More More More/A Song Without An End/Meaner Than Mean/Sell The Free World (12", p/s)	15
88	Polydor GONECD 3	Give Give Give Me More More More/A Song Without An End/Meaner Than Mean/Sell The Free World (CD)	15
88	Polydor GONE 4	A Wish Away/Jealousy (p/s)	6
88	Polydor GONEX 4	A Wish Away/Jealousy/Happy-Sad/Goodbye Fatman (12", p/s)	12
88	Polydor GONECD 4	A Wish Away/Jealousy/Happy-Sad/Goodbye Fatman (CD)	12
88	Polydor GONE 5	It's Yer Money I'm After Baby/Astley In The Noose/Ooh, She Said/Rave From The Grave (p/s, with inner p/s)	6
88	Polydor GONEX 5	It's Yer Money I'm After Baby/Astley In The Noose/Ooh, She Said/Rave From The Grave (12", p/s, with inner p/s)	10
88	Polydor GONECD 5	It's Yer Money I'm After Baby/Astley In The Noose/Ooh, She Said/Rave From The Grave (CD)	10
89	Polydor GONE 6	Who Wants To Be The Disco King?/Unbearable (live) (p/s, with inner p/s)	5
89	Polydor GONE 6	Who Wants To Be The Disco King?/(same) (promo-only, with dayglo p/s)	10
89	Polydor GONEX 6	Who Wants To Be The Disco King?/Unbearable (live)/No For The 13th Time (live)/Ten Trenches Deep (live) (12", p/s, with inner p/s)	10
89	Polydor GONECD 6	Who Wants To Be The Disco King?/Unbearable (live)/No For The 13th Time (live)/Ten Trenches Deep (live) (CD)	8
89	House Of Dolls HOD 011	Who Wants To Be The Disco King? (King Of Disco Mega Mix)/PRUDES: Christmas/SANDKINGS: Colourblind (free with 'House Of Dolls' fanzine)	6/4
89	Polydor GONE 7	Don't Let Me Down Gently/It Was Me (p/s, with inner p/s)	5
89	Polydor GONECS 7	Don't Let Me Down Gently/It Was Me (cassette)	6

89	Polydor GONEX 7	Don't Let Me Down Gently (Extended Version)/Don't Let Me Down Gently/ It Was Me (12", p/s, with inner p/s)	10
89	Polydor GONECD 7	Don't Let Me Down Gently (Extended Version)/Don't Let Me Down Gently/ It Was Me (CD)	7
89	Polydor GONE 8	Golden Green/Get Together (p/s, with inner p/s)	4
89	Polydor GONECS 8	Golden Green/Get Together (cassette)	4
89	Polydor GONEX 8	Golden Green/Get Together/Gimme Some Truth (12", p/s, with inner p/s)	8
89	Polydor GONECD 8	Golden Green/Get Together/Gimme Some Truth (CD)	7
90	Polydor GONE 10	Circlesquare/Our New Song (p/s, with inner p/s)	4
90	Polydor GONEX 10	Circlesquare/Our New Song (12", p/s, with inner p/s)	8
90	Polydor GONECD 10	Circlesquare/Our New Song (CD)	7
87	Far Out	A HANDFUL OF SONGS (private cassette)	15
88	Polydor GONECD 1	THE EIGHT LEGGED GROOVE MACHINE (CD, mispressed with "Wish Away" printed on front cover)	30

WONDER WHO

65	Philips BF 1440	Don't Think Twice, It's Alright/Sassy	6
66	Philips BF 1504	On The Good Ship Lollipop/You're Nobody Till Somebody Loves You	6
67	Philips BF 1600	Lonesome Road/FOUR SEASONS: Around And Around	6

(see also Four Seasons, Frankie Valli)

ROYCE WONG

64	Blue Beat BB 301	Everything's Gonna Be Alright/Hang Your Head And Cry	6

ANITA WOOD

62	London HLS 9585	I'll Wait Forever/I Can't Show You How I Feel	20
64	Sue WI 328	Dream Baby/This Has Happened Before	12

BOBBY WOOD

64	Pye Intl. 7N 25264	I'm A Fool For Loving You/My Heart Went Boing! Boing! Boing!	7

BRENTON WOOD

67	Philips BF 1579	Oogum Boogum Song/I Like The Way You Love Me	5
67	Liberty LBF 15021	Gimme Little Sign/I Think You Got Your Fools Mixed Up	5
68	Liberty LBF 15065	Baby You Got It/Catch You On The Rebound	4
68	Liberty LBF 15103	Some Got It, Some Don't/Me And You	4
67	Liberty LBL/LBS 83088E	GIMME LITTLE SIGN (LP)	10

CHUCK WOOD

67	Big T BIG 104	Seven Days Too Long/Soul Shing A Ling	8
68	Big T BIG 107	I've Got My Lovelight Shining/Baby You Win	5
71	Mojo 2092 010	Seven Days Too Long/Soul Shing A Ling (reissue)	4

DEL WOOD

54	London HL 8036	Ragtime Annie/Backroom Polka	25
54	London REP 1007	RAGTIME PIANO (EP)	10
57	RCA RD 27011	DOWN YONDER (LP)	10

RON WOOD

76	Atlantic K 50308	MAHONEY'S LAST STAND (LP, with Ronnie Lane)	10

(see also Faces, Rolling Stones, Jeff Beck)

ROY WOOD

72	Harvest HAR 5058	When Gran'ma Plays The Banjo/Wake Up	6
75	Jet JET 754	Oh What A Shame/Bengal Jig (cartoon p/s)	4
75	Jet JET 761	Look Thru' The Eyes Of A Fool/Strider	4
76	Jet JET 768	Indiana Rainbow/The Thing Is This (This Is The Thing) (as Roy Wood's Wizzard)	5
76	Jet JET 785	Any Old Time Will Do/The Rain Came Down On Everything	4
77	Warner Bros K 16961	The Stroll/Jubilee (p/s)	4
77	Warner Bros K 17028	I Never Believed In Love/Inside My Life (as Roy Wood & Annie Haslam)	7
79	Automatic K 17459P	(We're) On The Road Again/Saxmaniacs (picture disc)	5
80	Cheapskate CHEAP 6	Rock City/Givin' Your Heart Away (p/s, as Roy Wood's Helicopters)	4
80	Cheapskate CHEAP 12	Sing Out The Old/Watch This Space	5
81	EMI EMI 5156	Green Glass Windows/The Driving Song (p/s, as Roy Wood's Helicopters)	4
81	EMI EMI 5203	Down To Zero/Olympic Flyer (p/s)	6
82	Speed SPEED 5	O.T.T./Mystery Song	5
84	Harvest HAR 5173	I Wish It Could Be Christmas Every Day/WIZZARD: See My Baby Jive (g/f p/s)	4
87	Jet JET 7048	One-Two-Three/Oh What A Shame (gatefold p/s)	4
76	Harvest SHDW 408	THE ROY WOOD STORY (2-LP)	14
82	Speed SPEED 1000	THE SINGLES (LP, initially without "I Wish It Could Be Christmas Everyday")	10

(see also Wizzard, Gerry Levine & Avengers, Mike Sheridan, Danny King's Mayfair Set, Move, ELO, Renaissance, Rockers)

WOODEN HORSE

72	York SYK 526	Pick Up The Pieces/Wake Me In The Morning	8
73	York SYK 543	Wooden Horses/Typewriter And Guitar	8
72	York FYK 403	WOODEN HORSE (LP)	60
73	York FYK 413	WOODEN HORSE II (LP, withdrawn, some with sleeve)	175/125

(see also Fox)

WOODEN O

69	Middle Earth MDLS 301	A HANDFUL OF PLEASANT DELITES (LP)	80

WOODENTOPS

84	Food FOOD 002	Plenty/Have You Seen The Lights (p/s)	5
84	Food SNAK 002	Plenty/Have You Seen The Lights/Everybody (12", p/s)	7
86	Rough Trade RT 178D	Love Affair With Everyday Living/Why//Move Me/Well Well Well (double pack)	4

(see also Upset, Innocents)

KEN WOODMAN & HIS PICCADILLY BRASS

66	Strike JLH 101	THAT'S NICE (LP)	18

MINT VALUE £

WOODPECKERS
64	Decca F 11835	The Woodpecker/You Can't Sit Down	4
65	Oriole CB 311	Hey Little Girl/What's Your Name	8

STANLEY WOODRUFF & U.S. TRIO
77	Grapevine GRP 102	What Took You So Long/Now Is Forever	4

DONALD WOODS & EARL PALMER BAND
58	Vogue V 9107	Memories Of An Angel/That Much Of Your Love	150
58	Vogue V 9107	Memories Of An Angel/That Much Of Your Love (78)	50

GAY WOODS
84	Rewind REW 18	Something's Gotten Hold Of My Heart/Cellophane Rain (p/s)	4

(see also Gay & Terry Woods, Woods Band, Steeleye Span, Sweeney's Men)

GAY & TERRY WOODS
77	Polydor 2058 810	Save The Last Dance For Me/One More Time	6
78	Rockburgh ROCS 202	We Can Work This One Out/Piece Of Summer (p/s)	4
75	Polydor 2383 322	BACKWOODS (LP)	30
76	Polydor 2383 375	THE TIME IS RIGHT (LP)	30
76	Polydor 2383 406	RENOWNED (LP, with insert)	40
78	Rockburgh ROC 104	TENDER HOOKS (LP, with insert)	15

(see also Woods Band, Gay Woods, Steeleye Span, Sweeney's Men)

NICK WOODS
62	London HLU 9621	Ballad Of Billy Bud/Don't Let Me Down	6

WOODS BAND
71	Greenwich GSLP 1004	THE WOODS BAND (LP)	50
77	Rockburgh CREST 29	THE WOODS BAND (LP, reissue in different sleeve)	15

(see also Gay & Terry Woods)

MAGGIE WOODWARD
59	Vogue V 9148	Ali Bama/Zulu Warrior	8

SHEB WOOLEY
51	MGM MGM 439	Hoot Owl Boogie/Country Kisses (78)	8
54	MGM MGM 757	Panama Pete/Blue Guitar (78)	5
55	MGM SP 1130	38-24-35/I Flipped	12
55	MGM MGM 824	38-24-35/I Flipped (78)	5
58	MGM MGM 981	The Purple People Eater/I Can't Believe You're Mine	10
58	MGM MGM 981	The Purple People Eater/Recipe For Love (2nd pressing)	8
58	MGM MGM 981	The Purple People Eater/Recipe For Love (78)	10
58	MGM MGM 997	Santa And The Purple People Eater/Star Of Love	7
58	MGM MGM 997	Santa And The Purple People Eater/Star Of Love (78)	10
59	MGM MGM 1017	Sweet Chile/More	7
60	MGM MGM 1081	Luke The Spook/My Only Treasure	8
61	MGM MGM 1132	The Wayward Wind/Bars Across The Windows	7
61	MGM MGM 1147	Meet Mr. Lonely/That's My Pa	7
62	MGM MGM 1162	Laughing The Blues/Somebody Please	6
65	MGM MGM 1257	Hootenany Hoot/Old Joe Rag	6
65	MGM MGM 1263	Blue Guitar/Natchez Landing	5
56	MGM MGM-EP 540	JEST PLAIN, WILD AND WOOLEY (EP)	25
61	MGM MGM-C 859	SONGS FROM THE DAY OF RAWHIDE (LP)	12
62	MGM MGM-C 903	THAT'S MY PA AND THAT'S MY PA (LP)	12
63	MGM MGM-C 945	SPOOFING THE BIG ONES! (LP)	12
63	MGM MGM-C 955	TALES OF 'HOW THE WEST WAS WON' (LP)	15

WOOLIES
67	RCA RCA 1602	Who Do You Love?/Hey Girl	30

WOOLLY
72	RCA RCA 2297	Golden Golden	4
73	Mooncrest MOON 10	Sunshine Souvenirs/Living And Loving You	4

WORD
83	Word WORD 001	Colour It!/Recurring	4

WORK
81	Woof WOOF 2	I Hate America/Fingers & Toes/Duty (p/s, clear vinyl)	5
82	Recommended	SLOW CRIMES (LP)	12

(see also Art Bears)

JIMMY WORK
56	London HLD 8270	When She Said "You All"/There's Only One You	60
56	London HLD 8270	When She Said "You All"/There's Only One You (78)	10
56	London HLD 8308	You've Gotta Heart Like A Merry-Go-Round/Blind Heart	35
56	London HLD 8308	You've Gotta Heart Like A Merry-Go-Round/Blind Heart (78)	10
55	London RED 1039	COUNTRY SONGS — WORK STYLE (EP)	30

WORKFORCE
80s	WF WF 1	The Right To Work/Holy Moses (p/s)	4

WORKING WEEK
84	Virgin VS 684-12	Venceremos/Bottom End (12", p/s, with Tracey Thorn & Julie Tippett)	8

WORLD
70	Liberty LBF 15402	Angelina	6
70	Liberty LBG 83419	LUCKY PLANET (LP)	15

(see also Neil Innes, Bonzo Dog Band)

WORLD COLUMN
76	Capitol CL 15852	So Is The Sun/It's Not Right	5

WORLD DOMINATION ENTERPRISES
85	Karbon KAR 008	Asbestos Lead Asbestos/Beats Baby Hi (p/s)	8

WORLD OF OZ
68	Deram DM 187	The Muffin Man/Peter's Birthday	10
68	Deram DM 205	King Croesus/Jack	6
69	Deram DM 233	Willow's Harp/Like A Tear	10
69	Deram DML/SML 1034	THE WORLD OF OZ (LP)	50

WORLD PARTY
86	Ensign ENY 604	Private Revolution/Holy Water (p/s)	4
86	Ensign ENYX 604	Private Revolution/Holy Water (12", p/s)	7
87	Ensign ENY 606	Ship Of Fools/World Groove (Do The Mind Guerrila) (gatefold p/s)	4
90	Ensign ENY 631	Message In The Box (box set, numbered)	5
	(see also Waterboys)		

WORLD OF TWIST
92	Caff CAFF 16	The Sausage/Skidding Into Love/Space Rockit (p/s, with insert)	6

WORRYING KYNDE
67	Piccadilly 7N 35370	Call Out The Name/Got The Blame	30

WORTH SCHOOL CHOIR
71	Decca Nova SDN 23	WORTH SCHOOL CHOIR (LP)	20

JOHNNY WORTH
57	Columbia DB 3962	Let's Go/Just Because	6
57	Columbia DB 3962	Let's Go/Just Because (78)	10
59	Embassy WB 338	Mean Streak/Fort Worth Jail	4
60	Oriole CB 1545	Nightmare/Hold Me, Thrill Me, Kiss Me	6
62	Columbia DB 4811	You Know What I Mean/All These Things	4

MARION WORTH
60	London HL 7089	Are You Willing, Willie/This Heart Of Mine (export issue)	10
60	London HL 7097	That's My Kind Of Love/I Lost Johnny (export issue)	10

STAN WORTH ORCHESTRA
63	London HLU 9703	Roman Holiday/Wiggle Wobble Walkers	5

WRANGLERS
64	Parlophone R 5163	Liza Jane/It Just Won't Work	40

WRATHCHILD
83	Bullet PBOL 5	Do You Want My Love/Twist The Knife (picture disc)	5
83	Bullet	Stakheel Strut (12, p/s, red vinyl)	7

LINK WRAY (& HIS RAY MEN)
58	London HLA 8623	Rumble/The Swag (as Link Wray & His Ray Men)	20
58	London HLA 8623	Rumble/The Swag (as Link Wray & His Ray Men) (78)	25
63	Stateside SS 217	Jack The Ripper/The Black Widow	12
64	Stateside SS 256	The Sweeper/Weekend	10
65	Stateside SS 397	Good Rockin' Tonight/I'll Do Anything For You	12
71	Polydor 2066 120	Fire And Brimstone/Juke Box Mama	4
73	Polydor 2066 320	Lawdy Miss Clawdy/Shine The Light	4
73	Virgin VS 103	I'm So Glad, I'm So Proud/Shawnee Tribe	4
76	Virgin VS 142	I Know You're Leaving Me Now/Quicksand	4
78	Chiswick NS 32	Batman Theme/Hidden Charms (unissued, demos probably exist)	15
64	Stateside SE 1015	MR. GUITAR (EP)	30
71	Polydor 2489 029	LINK WRAY (LP)	12
71	Union Pacific UP 002	THERE'S GOOD ROCKIN' TONIGHT (LP)	15
73	Virgin V 2006	BEANS & FATBACK (LP)	10
73	Polydor 2391 063	BE WHAT YOU WANT TO (LP)	10
74	Polydor 2391 128	THE LINK WRAY RUMBLE (LP)	10

RAY WRAY QUARTET
62	Salvo SLO 1808	When Your Lover Has Gone/A Song Is Born	10

WRECKLESS ERIC
77	Stiff BUY 16	Whole Wide World/Semaphore Signals (p/s)	4
78	Stiff BUY 25	Reconnez Cherie/Rags And Tatters (p/s, yellow vinyl)	4
78	Stiff BUY 34	Take The Cash/Girlfriend (p/s)	4
79	Stiff S12 BUY 49	Hit And Miss Judy/I Need A Situation/Let's Go To The Pictures (12", orange vinyl, die-cut p/s)	7
78	Stiff SEEZ B6	WRECKLESS ERIC (10" LP, brown vinyl)	10
78	Stiff SEEZ 9	THE WONDERFUL WORLD OF WRECKLESS ERIC (LP, black vinyl)	10
78	Stiff SEEZ B9	THE WONDERFUL WORLD OF WRECKLESS ERIC (LP, green vinyl)	10
78	Stiff SEEZ P9	THE WONDERFUL WORLD OF WRECKLESS ERIC (LP, picture disc, with insert)	10

JENNY WREN
66	Fontana TF 672	Chasing My Dreams All Over Town/A Thought Of You	35
79	RK RK 1017	I've Danced With A Man/Bring Down The Curtain	4

BIG JOHN WRENCHER
75	Big Bear BB 4	BIG JOHN'S BOOGIE (LP)	12

WRIGGLERS
68	Giant GN 26	The Cooler/You Cannot Know	8
68	Blue Cat BS 106	Get Right/If I Did Look	8

BETTY WRIGHT
68	Atlantic 584 216	Girls Can't Do What The Guys Do/Sweet Lovin' Daddy	5
72	Atlantic K 10143	Clean Up Woman/I'll Love You Forever	5

Charles WRIGHT & WATTS 103rd STREET BAND

CHARLES WRIGHT & WATTS 103rd STREET BAND
70s Warner Bros   EXPRESS YOURSELF (LP) 20
(see also Watts 103rd Street Rhythm Band)

DALE WRIGHT
58	London HLD 8573	She's Neat/Say That You Care (as Dale Wright & Rock-Its)	120
58	London HLD 8573	She's Neat/Say That You Care (as Dale Wright & Rock-Its) (78)	25
59	Pye Intl. 7N 25022	That's Show Biz/That's My Gal (as Dale Wright & Wright Guys)	25
59	Pye Intl. N 25022	That's Show Biz/That's My Gal (as Dale Wright & Wright Guys) (78)	50

EARL WRIGHT
75   Capitol CL 15825   Thumb A Ride/Like A Rolling Stone 5

GARY WRIGHT('S WONDERWHEEL)
70	A&M AMLS 2004	EXTRACTION (LP)	12
71	A&M AMLS 64296	FOOTPRINT (LP)	12
72	A&M AMLH 64362	RING OF CHANGES (LP, as Gary Wright's Wonderwheel)	10

(see also Spooky Tooth, Wonderwheel)

GINNY WRIGHT (& TOM TALL)
55	London HL 8119	Indian Moon/Your Eyes Feasted Upon Her (solo)	30
55	London HL 8150	Are You Mine?/Boom Boom Boomerang (with Tom Tall)	25
55	London RE-U 1035	COUNTRY SONGS VOL. 2 (EP, with Tom Tall)	30

(see also T. Tommy Cutrer & Ginny Wright, Tom Tall)

MILTON WRIGHT & TERRA SHIRMA STRINGS
77   Grapevine GRP 103   I Belong To You/Gallop 4

NAT WRIGHT
59   HMV POP 629   Anything/For You My Love 30

OTIS WRIGHT
67	Doctor Bird DLM 5005	PEACE PERFECT PEACE (LP)	70
67	Doctor Bird DLM 5006	IT WILL SOON BE DONE (LP)	70
60s	Coxsone TLP 1001	OVER IN GLORYLAND (LP)	70

O.V. WRIGHT
65	Vocalion VP 9249	You're Gonna Make Me Cry/Monkey Dog	10
66	Vocalion VP 9255	Poor Boy/I'm In Your Corner	8
66	Vocalion VP 9272	Gone For Good/How Long Baby	8
67	London HLZ 10137	8 Men 4 Women/Fed Up With The Blues	7
68	Sue WI 4043	What About You/What Did You Tell This Girl Of Mine	15
68	Action ACT 4505	Oh Baby Mine/Working Your Game	12
69	Action ACT 4527	I Want Everyone To Know/I'm Gonna Forget About You	8
65	Vocalion VEP 170165	O.V. WRIGHT (EP)	35
68	Island ILP 975	8 MEN, 4 WOMEN (LP)	30

RICK WRIGHT
78	Harvest SHVL 818	WET DREAM (LP, gatefold stickered sleeve)	10
84	Harvest SHSP 24 0101 1	IDENTITY (LP, with inner bag, as Rick Wright with Zee)	10

(see also Pink Floyd)

RITA WRIGHT
68	Tamla Motown TMG 643	I Can't Give Back The Love I Feel For You/Something On My Mind	8
71	Tamla Motown TMG 791	I Can't Give Back The Love I Feel For You/Something On My Mind (reissue)	4
78	Jet UP 36382	Love Is All You Need/Touch Me, Take Me	12

RUBEN WRIGHT
66   Capitol CL 15460   Hey! Girl/I'm Walking Out On You 15

RUBY WRIGHT
53	Parlophone MSP 6025	Till I Waltz Again With You/When I Gave You My Love (with Charlie Gore)	20
54	Parlophone MSP 6073	Bimbo/Boy, You Got Yourself A Gal	20
54	Parlophone R 3816	Bimbo/Boy, You Got Yourself A Gal (78)	5
54	Parlophone MSP 6133	Santa's Little Sleigh Bells/Toodle Loo To You	15
55	Parlophone MSP 6150	What Have They Told You?/I Had The Funniest Feeling	12
56	Parlophone MSP 6209	I Fall In Love With You Ev'ry Day/Do You Believe?	12
59	Parlophone R 4556	Three Stars/I Only Have One Lifetime	12
59	Parlophone R 4556	Three Stars/I Only Have One Lifetime (78)	20
59	Parlophone R 4589	You're Just A Flower From An Old Bouquet/Sweet Night Of Love	7
59	Parlophone GEP 8785	THE THREE STARS GIRL (EP)	25

SAMUEL E. WRIGHT
73   Paramount PARA 3035   There's Something Funny Going On/300 Pounds Of Hunger 4

STEVE WRIGHT
59	London HLW 8891	Wild, Wild, Women/Love You	100
59	London HLW 8891	Wild, Wild, Women/Love You (78)	45

WINSTON WRIGHT
69	Doctor Bird DB 1308	Five Miles High/CARL DAWKINS: Only Girl	5
69	Trojan TR 7701	Moonlight (Lover) Groover/SENSATIONS: Everyday Is Just A Holiday	5
69	Trojan TR 7715	Moon Invader (with Tommy McCook)/RADCLIFF RUFFIN: You Got To Love Me	5
70	Trojan TR 7775	Meshwire (with Tommy McCook)/BARONS: Darling Please Return	5
70	Bamboo BAM 60	Reggae Feet/DON DRUMMOND: The Rocket	5
71	Upsetter US 378	Example/UPSETTER: Version	5

ZACHARIAH WRIGHT
70s   Bamboo BAM 403   Lumumba Limbo/Green, Red and Gold 8

WRIT
66   Decca F 12385   Did You Ever Have To Make Up Your Mind/Solid Golden Teardrops 5

WRITING ON THE WALL
69	Middle Earth MDS 101	Child On A Crossing/Lucifer Corpus	25
69	Middle Earth MDLS 303	THE POWER OF THE PICTS (LP)	150

WRITING ON THE WALL
73	Pye 7N 45251	Man Of Renown/Buffalo	4

W12 SPOTS
70s	Shepherds Bush SB 1	Sid Never Did/COSMIC PUNKS: 99 Years (no p/s)	12

WURZEL
87	GWR GWR 4	Bess/People Say I'm Crazy (p/s)	5
87	GWR GWT 4	Bess/People Say I'm Crazy/Midnight In London/E.S.P. (12", p/s)	8

JOHNNY WYATT
68	President PT 109	This Thing Called Love/To Whom It May Concern	7

ROBERT WYATT
74	Virgin VS 114	I'm A Believer/Memories	4
77	Virgin VS 115	Yesterday Man/Sonia	6
82	Rough Trade RT 115	Shipbuilding/Memories Of You (reissue, foldout p/s)	5
70	CBS 64189	THE END OF AN EAR (LP)	12
74	Virgin V 2017	ROCK BOTTOM (LP)	10
75	Virgin V 2034	RUTH IS STRANGER THAN RICHARD (LP)	10
82	Rough Trade ROUGH 35	NOTHING CAN STOP US (LP, early pressing without "Shipbuilding")	10

(see also Soft Machine, Matching Mole)

PETE WYLIE
86	MDM MDMD 7	Sinful/I Want The Moon Mother//Sophie's Sinful/Joy Of Being (double pack)	4

(see also Wah! Heat)

RICHARD ('POPCORN') WYLIE
63	Columbia DB 7012	Brand New Man/So Much Love In My Heart (as Richard Wylie)	20
77	Grapevine GRP 100	Rosemary What Happened Pts 1 & 2 (as Richard 'Popcorn' Wylie)	4

BILL WYMAN
74	Rolling Stones RS 19112	Monkey Grip Glue/What A Blow (custom sleeve)	4
74	Rolling Stones COC 59102	MONKEY GRIP (LP)	12
76	Rolling Stones COC 59105	STONE ALONE (LP)	12
81	A&M AMLSP 68540	BILL WYMAN (LP, picture disc)	10

(see also Rolling Stones)

MARTYN WYNDHAM-READ
70	Trailer LER 2009	NED KELLY AND THAT GANG (LP)	15
72	Trailer LER 2028	MARTYN WYNDHAM READ (LP)	12
73	Argo ZFB 82	HARRY THE HAWKER IS DEAD (LP)	25
75	Trailer LER 2092	MAYPOLES TO MISTLETOE (LP)	10

TAMMY WYNETTE
68	CBS 3594	D-I-V-O-R-C-E/Don't Make Me Now	4
73	CBS EQ 30658/Q 64502	WE SURE CAN LOVE EACH OTHER (LP, quadrophonic)	10

(see also George Jones & Tammy Wynette)

MISS WYNG
40s	Imperial IMP 2162	Go Down Moses/Scandalise My Name (78)	30

PETER WYNGARDE
70	RCA Victor RCA 1967	La Ronde De L'Amour/The Way I Cry Over You	6
70	RCA SF 8087	PETER WYNGARDE (LP, gatefold sleeve)	25

(see also Larry Wallis, Tyrannosaurus Rex)

SANDY WYNNS
65	Fontana TF 550	Touch Of Venus/Lovers' Quarrel	120

MARK WYNTER
60	Decca F 11263	Image Of A Girl/Glory Of Love	6
60	Decca F 11279	Kickin' Up The Leaves/That's What I Thought	6
61	Decca F 11323	Dream Girl/Two Little Girls	6
61	Decca F 11354	Exclusively Yours/Warm And Willing	6
61	Decca F 11380	Girl For Ev'ryday/The Best Time For Love	6
62	Decca F 11434	Heaven's Plan/In Your Heart	6
62	Decca F 11467	I Love Her Still/Angel Talk	6
62	Pye 7N 15466	Venus In Blue Jeans/Please Come Back To Me	4
62	Pye 7N 15492	Go Away Little Girl/That Kinda Talk	4
63	Pye 7N 15511	Aladdin's Lamp/It Can Happen Any Day	5
63	Pye 7N 15525	Shy Girl/Because Of You	4
63	Pye 7N 15554	Running To You/Don't Cry	5
63	Pye 7N 15577	It's Almost Tomorrow/Music To Midnight	4
64	Pye 7N 15595	The Boy You're Kissin'/I Learned A Lot From You	5
64	Pye 7N 15626	Only You/It's Love You Want	5
64	Pye 7N 15658	Answer Me/I Wish You Everything	5
64	Pye 7N 15686	Love Hurts/Can't Help Forgiving You	5
64	Pye 7N 15716	Forever And A Day/And I Love Her	5
65	Pye 7N 15771	Can I Get To Know You Better/Am I Living A Dream	5
65	Pye 7N 15861	Someday You'll Want Me To Want You/Here Comes Summer	5
65	Pye 7N 15994	Babe I'm Gonna Leave You/The Very Thought Of You	5
66	Pye 7N 17051	Before Your Time/Something About You	4
66	Pye 7N 17122	We'll Sing In The Sunshine/Pencil And Paper	4
66	Pye 7N 17214	You Made Me What I Am/Oh Girl	4
68	Pye 7N 17438	Please Love Me Tender/The Best Thing In My Life	4
68	Pye 7N 17651	She's A Woman/Bless Your Little Heart	4
60	Decca DFE 6674	MARK TIME (EP)	18
63	Pye NEP 24176	IT'S MARK TIME (EP)	15

Mark WYNTER

GAIL WYNTERS

XTC

XCALIBRES
65	CBS 201805	We Will Love/Swing That Chariot	4
65	Mercury MF 941	You'll Find Out/That's What Happens	4

X-CELLS
81	Snotty Snail NEL COL 4	Freedom Man/Nowhere TO Go (p/s)	4
81	Snotty Snail NEL COL 5	Schizoid (p/s)	4
81	Snotty Snail	SCHIZOID (LP)	10

X-CERPTS
64	CBS 201546	Undercover Agent/Beneath The Shades	4

X-CERTS
70s	Zama	Feeling The Groove (p/s)	8
81	Recreational PLAY 1	Together/Untogether (p/s, with lyric insert)	4

X-DREAMISTS
78	Good Vibrations GOT 5	Right Way Home/Dance Away Love (p/s)	5

X-E-CUTORS
80	Rok ROK 13/14	Too Far To Look Inside My Head/X-FILMS: After My Blood (die-cut co. sleeve)	5

X-EFFECTS
70s	Pre-Fab ZO-2	19 (French Gymnastics)/Female Pulse (p/s)	4

XERO
83	Brickyard XERO 1	Oh Baby/Hold On/Lone Wolf (p/s)	7
83	Brickyard XERO 1T	Oh Baby/Hold On/Lone Wolf (12", plain card sleeve with sticker, withdrawn)	15

(see also Bruce Dickinson, Iron Maiden)

XIT
72	Rare Earth RES 107	I Was Raised/End	4
73	Rare Earth RES 111	Reservation Of Education/Young Warrior	4
72	Rare Earth SREA 4002	PLIGHT OF THE RED MAN (LP)	10

XL5
63	HMV POP 1148	XL5 (Zero G)/Caviare	10

XL5/DON SPENCER
63	HMV 7EG 8802	FIREBALL AND OTHER TITLES (EP, 2 tracks each)	25

XL 5's
80	Fourplay FOUR 004	Fireball/Misirlou	5

X-MAL DEUTSCHLAND
86	4AD AD 311	Incubus Succubus II/Vito (p/s)	7

X-MEN
84	Creation CRE 006	Do The Ghost/Talk (foldaround p/s in bag, orange/blue or yellow/green p/s)	10
85	Creation CRE 013	Spiral Girl/Bad Girl (foldaround p/s in poly bag)	8

X-O-DUS
79	Factory FAC 11	English Black Boys/See Them A'Come (12", dark grey textured p/s)	8
79	Factory FAC 11	English Black Boys/See Them A'Come (12", dark grey textured p/s, 2nd pressing)	8

XPOZEZ
80s	Fight FIGHT 1	SYSTEMS KILL (EP)	6
82	Red Rhino RED 15	1000 Marching Feet/Terminal Case (p/s)	5
83	Sexual Phonograph SPH 2	(Be My) New York Doll/It's All Been Done Before (p/s)	4

X-RAYS
59	London HLR 8805	Chinchilla/Out Of Control	25
59	London HLR 8805	Chinchilla/Out Of Control (78)	5

X-RAY SPEX
77	Virgin VS 189	Oh Bondage, Up Yours/I Am A Cliche (p/s)	12
77	Virgin VS 189-12	Oh Bondage, Up Yours/I Am A Cliche (12", no p/s)	8
78	EMI International INT 553	The Day The World Turned Day-Glo/lama Poseur (p/s, 15,000 on orange vinyl)	6/4
78	EMI International INT 563	Identity/Let's Submerge (p/s, initially on pink vinyl)	6/4
78	EMI International INT 573	Germ Free Adolescents/Age (p/s)	5
79	EMI International INT 583	Highly Inflammable/Warrior In Woolworths (p/s, initially on red vinyl)	6/4
78	EMI Intl. INS 3023	GERM FREE ADOLESCENTS (LP, with lyric inner sleeve)	15
80s	EMI Intl. INS 3023	GERM FREE ADOLESCENTS (LP, orange vinyl reissue)	10

(see also Poly Styrene, Mari Elliott)

XS DISCHARGE
80	G. Marxist COMMINIQUE 3	Across The Border/Frustration (p/s)	6

XS ENERGY
78	World WRECK 1	Eighteen/Jenny's Alright/Horroscope! (numbered foldover yellow or green p/s, stamped white labels)	10
79	Dead Good DEAD 1	Eighteen/Jenny's Alright/Horroscope! ('National Souvenir Issue', different foldover p/s, stamped white labels)	6
79	Dead Good DEAD 1	Eighteen/Jenny's Alright/Horroscope! (no p/s, stamped white sleeve & yellow printed labels)	7
79	Dead Good DEAD 3	Use You/Imaginary (p/s)	5

XTC

77	Virgin VS 188	Science Friction/She's So Square (p/s, unreleased) 200
77	Virgin VS 188-12	3D EP (12" EP) 8
78	Virgin VS 201	Statue Of Liberty/Hang On To The Night (p/s) 6
78	Virgin VS 209	This Is Pop?/Heatwave (p/s) 6
78	Virgin VS 231	Are You Receiving Me/Instant Tunes (p/s) 5
79	Virgin VS 259	Life Begins At The Hop/Homo Safari (1st 30,000 on clear vinyl, PVC sleeve with insert) 6
79	Virgin VS 259	Life Begins At The Hop/Homo Safari (p/s) 4
79	Virgin VS 282	Making Plans For Nigel/Bushman President (Homo Safari Series No. 2)/ Pulsing, Pulsing (initially with game-board p/s with playing pieces) 6/4
79	Smash Hits HIT 002	Ten Feet Tall/SKIDS: The Olympian (33rpm red flexidisc with 'Smash Hits') 5/4
80	Virgin VS 322	Wait Till Your Boat Goes Down/Ten Feet Tall (U.S. version) (p/s) 5
80	Virgin VS 365	Generals And Majors/Don't Lose Your Temper (p/s) 4
80	Virgin VS 365	Generals And Majors/Don't Lose Your Temper//Smokeless Zone/The Somnambulist (double pack) 6
81	Virgin VS 372	Towers Of London/Set Myself On Fire (live) (p/s) 4
81	Virgin VS 372	Towers Of London/Set Myself On Fire (live)//Battery Brides (live)/ Scissor Man (double pack) 6
81	RSO RSO 71	Take This Town/RUTS: Babylon's Burning (p/s) 6
81	Virgin VS 384	Sgt. Rock (Is Going To Help Me)/Living Through Another Cuba/ Generals And Majors (1st 20,000 in poster p/s, with stickered PVC sleeve) 6/4
81	Virgin VS 407	Respectable Street/Strange Tales, Strange Tails/Officer Blue (p/s) 4
82	Virgin VS 462	Senses Working Overtime/Blame The Weather/Tissue Tigers (initially in poster p/s) 5/4
82	Virgin VS 462-12	Senses Working Overtime/Egyptian Solution (Homo Safari Series No. 3)/ Blame The Weather/Tissue Tigers (12", p/s) 7
82	Lyntone LYN 11032	Looking For Footprints (flexidisc free with 'Flexipop' magazine, issue 16; on red, blue, green or yellow vinyl; add £1 if with magazine) 4-5
82	Virgin VS 482	Ball And Chain/Punch And Judy/Heaven Is Paved With Broken Glass (p/s) 4
82	Virgin VS 482-12	Ball And Chain/Heaven Is Paved With Broken Glass/Punch And Judy/ Cockpit Dance Mixture (12", p/s) 7
82	Virgin VS 490	No Thugs In Our House/Chain Of Command/Limelight/Over Rusty Water (9" die-cut gatefold p/s) 7
83	Virgin VS 553	Great Fire/Gold (p/s, with outer p/s) 6
83	Virgin VSY 606	Wonderland/Jump (picture disc) 6
83	Virgin VS 613	Love On A Farmboy's Wages/In Loving Memory Of A Name//Desert Island/Toys (double pack) 7
84	Virgin VS 709	All You Pretty Girls/Washaway (p/s, with outer die-cut p/s) 5
84	Virgin VS 721	This World Over/Blue Overall (p/s, with postcards) 5
87	Virgin VSY 912	This Meeting Place/The Man Who Sailed Around His Soul (clear vinyl with printed PVC sleeve) 6
78	Virgin V 2095	WHITE MUSIC (LP, with black inner sleeve) 10
78	Virgin V 2108	GO 2 (LP, with insert, 1st 15,000 with free 12" EP: "Go +") 15
79	Virgin V 2129	DRUMS AND WIRES (LP, with gatefold insert, 1st 15,000 with free 7": "Chain Of Command"/"Limelight" [VDJ 30]) 12
80	Virgin V 2173	BLACK SEA (LP, with green paper outer sleeve & lyric insert) 10
84	Virgin V 2251	WAXWORKS (LP, with free LP, "Beeswax") 12
84	Virgin V 2325	THE BIG EXPRESS (LP, circular sleve & lyric inner) 10
88	Virgin CDVT 2581	ORANGES AND LEMONS (LP, as 3-CD single box set) 12

(see also Mr Partridge, Barry Andrews, Three Wise Men, Dukes Of Stratosphere, Johnny Japes & His Jesticles, Colonel, Spys)

XTRAVERTS

80s	Spike SRTS SP 001	Blank Generation/A-Lad-In-Sane (no p/s) 15
81	Xtraverts XTRA 001	Speed/1984 (foldout poster p/s, white labels) 6
80s	Rising Sun RS 1	Police State/PLASTIC PEOPLE: Demolition (p/s, multi-coloured vinyl) 6

Y

(see under Yen)

Y & T (Yesterday & Today)

| 83 | A&M AMP 135 | Mean Streak/Straight Thru The Heart (shaped picture disc) | 6 |

YACHTS

| 78 | Radar ADA 23 | Look Back In Love (Not In Anger)/I Can't Stay Long (p/s, blue vinyl) | 4 |
| 79 | Radar RAD 19 | THE YACHTS (LP, with live 7" "Suffice To Say"/"On And On" [SAM 98, p/s]) | 10 |

(see also Big In Japan/Chuddie Nuddies)

YA HO WA 13

| 83 | Psycho PSYCHO 2 | GOLDEN SUNRISE (LP, 319 copies only, different coloured vinyls, some on black vinyl without sleeve) | 50 |

YAKS

| 65 | Decca F 12115 | Yakety Yak/Back In '57 | 8 |

YAMASUKIS

| 71 | Dandelion DAN 7004 | Yamasuki/Aieaoa (p/s, also listed as K 19003) | 4 |

YANA

56	HMV POP 252	If You Don't Love Me/Climb Up The Wall	12
57	HMV POP 340	Mr. Wonderful/Too Close For Comfort	10
58	HMV POP 481	I Need You/I Miss You Mama	8
58	HMV POP 546	Papa And Mama/In The Morning	6

JIMMY YANCEY

40s	HMV B 9366	Yancey Stomp/Five O'Clock Blues (78)	15
40s	HMV B 9374	Slow And Easy Blues/The Mellow Blues (78)	10
40s	HMV B 9381	State Street Special/ Tell 'Em About Me (78)	12
54	HMV 7EG 8062	JIMMY YANCEY (EP)	15
55	HMV 7EG 8083	JIMMY YANCEY (EP)	15
58	Vogue EPV 1203	YANCEY'S PIANO (EP)	15
54	London AL 3525	JIMMY YANCEY — A LOST RECORDING DATE (10" LP)	25
50s	Gannet 5137	JIMMY AND MAMA YANCEY (LP)	12
68	Atlantic 590 018	LOWDOWN DIRTY BLUES (LP)	15

JIMMY YANCEY & FABER SMITH

| 40s | Parlophone R 2959 | I Received A Letter/East St. Louis Blues (78) | 12 |

MAMA YANCEY/DON EWELL

| 57 | Tempo LAP 7 | MAMA YANCEY-DON EWELL (10" LP) | 25 |

ZALMAN YANOVSKY

67	Kama Sutra KAS 209	As Long As You're Here/Ereh Er'uoy Sa Gnol Sa (unreleased)	
67	Pye Intl. 7N 25438	As Long As You're Here/Ereh Er'uoy Sa Gnol Sa	5
71	Kama Sutra 2316 003	ALIVE AND WELL IN ARGENTINA (LP)	12

(see also Mugwumps, Lovin' Spoonful)

YARDBIRDS

64	Columbia DB 7283	I Wish You Would/A Certain Girl	15
64	Columbia DB 7391	Good Morning Little Schoolgirl/I Ain't Got You	12
65	Columbia DB 7499	For Your Love/Got To Hurry	7
65	Columbia DB 7594	Heart Full Of Soul/Steeled Blues	5
65	Columbia DB 7706	Evil Hearted You/Still I'm Sad	5
66	Columbia DB 7848	Shapes Of Things/You're A Better Man Than I	6
66	Columbia DB 7848	Shapes Of Things/Still I'm Sad (mispressing)	40
66	Columbia DB 7928	Over, Under, Sideways, Down/Jeff's Boogie	12
66	Columbia DB 8024	Happenings Ten Years Time Ago/Psycho Daisies	20
67	Columbia DB 8165	Little Games/Puzzles	25
68	Columbia DB 8368	Goodnight Sweet Josephine/Think About It (unreleased; acetates only, £200)	
83	Edsel E 5005	Over, Under, Sideways, Down/Psycho Daisies (p/s)	4
84	Edsel E 5007	Rack My Mind/Jeff's Boogie (p/s)	4
64	Columbia SEG 8421	FIVE YARDBIRDS (EP)	50
67	Columbia SEG 8521	OVER UNDER SIDEWAYS DOWN (EP)	125
64	Columbia 33SX 1677	FIVE LIVE YARDBIRDS (LP, blue/black label, flipback sleeve)	40
69	Columbia 33SX 1677	FIVE LIVE YARDBIRDS (LP, later issue, black/white label, flipback sleeve)	15
66	Columbia SCXC 28	HAVING A RAVE UP WITH THE YARDBIRDS (LP, export issue)	70
66	Columbia S(C)X 6063	YARDBIRDS (LP, blue/black label, flipback sleeve, mono/stereo)	25/30
69	Columbia S(C)X 6063	YARDBIRDS (LP, later issue, black/white label, flipback sleeve)	10
71	Regal Starline SRS 5069	REMEMBER ... THE YARDBIRDS (LP)	10
84	Charly BOX 104	SHAPES OF THINGS (LP, box set)	30

(see also Eric Clapton, Jeff Beck, Jimmy Page, Keith Relf, Jim McCarty, Reign, Stairway, Sonny Boy Williamson & Yardbirds)

YARGO

| 86 | Skysaw SKY 6 | Get High (5.00)/Get High (6.00)/Get There/Get High (14.55) (12", p/s) | 7 |
| 88 | Bodybeat BODY 004 | Help/Carrying Mine Dub (p/s) | 4 |

MIKE YARWOOD

| 68 | Columbia DB 8334 | Saturday Night At The Crown/Harold | 4 |

TOM YATES

| 67 | CBS BPG 63094 | SECOND CITY SPIRITUAL (LP, as Thomas Yates) | 30 |

Tom YATES

72	President PTLS 1053	LOVE COMES WELL ARMED (LP, with booklet)	15
77	Satril SATL 4007	SONG OF THE SHIMMERING WAY (LP, with insert)	15

YAZOO
83	Mute L12 YAZ 003	Nobody's Diary/Situation (12", numbered p/s)	8

(see also Depeche Mode, Alison Moyet, Erasure)

YAZZ
89	Big Life BLBXLP 1	THE WANTED REMIXES (mini-LP, with insert, autographed, 50 only)	15

Y BLEW
67	Qualiton QSP 7001	Maes 'B'/Beth Sy'n Dod Rhyngom Ni (p/s)	10

YEAH YEAH NOH
84	In Tape IT 008	Cottage Industry/Bias Binding/Tommy Opposite (p/s)	5
84	In Tape IT 010	Beware The Weakling Lies/Startling Pillow Case And Why? (p/s)	4
85	In Tape IT 012	Prick Up Your Ears/Brown Shirt/TERRY & GERRY: Bias Binding (p/s)	4

YEAR ONE
69	Major Minor MM 660	Eli's Comin'/Will You Be Staying After Sunday	5

YEH YEH
	Berlin BRS 001	You Will Pay/7 Bells (grey p/s)	5

YELLO
80	Do It DUN 11	Bimbo/IT Splash (p/s)	5
82	Do It DUN 13	Bostich/She's Got A Gun (Instrumental) (p/s)	5
82	Do It DUN 18	She's Got A Gun/Bluehead (p/s)	4
82	Do It DUNIT 18	She's Got A Gun/Bluehead/The Evening's Young (12", p/s)	8
82	Do It DUN 23	Pinball Cha Cha/Smile On You (p/s)	4
82	Do It DUNIT 23	Pinball Cha Cha/Smile On You (12", p/s)	7
82	Take It!	Bimbo/RENALDO & LOAF: Honest Joe's Indian Gets The Goat On The Way To The Cowboy Conga (33rpm square blue flexidisc with 'Take It!' magazine)	8/6
83	Stiff BUYP 176	I Love You/Rubber Vest (3-D picture disc, with glasses)	6
83	Stiff BUYD 191	Lost Again/Base For Alec//Let Me Cry/She's Got A Gun (double pack)	6
86	Mercury MEDRP 218	Goldrush/She's Got A Gun//Pinball Cha Cha/Vicious Games (double pack)	6
86	Mercury MERXD 218	GOLDRUSH (12", double pack)	10
87	Mercury MERX 253	The Rhythm Divine (featuring Shirley Bassey)/Dr. Van Steiner (Instrumental)/Tool In Rose (12", p/s)	7
87	Mercury MERXR 253	The Rhythm Divine (Version 2)/Dr. Van Steiner (Instrumental)/The Rhythm Divine (Original 7" Version) (12", p/s, with Billy McKenzie)	30
88	Mercury YELLR 212	Tied Up In Life/Tied Up In Life (Tied Up In Red Mix) (12", p/s)	10
81	Do It RIDE 8	CLARO QUE SI! (LP, pink sleeve)	12

(see also Associates)

YELLOW BALLOON
67	Stateside SS 2008	Yellow Balloon/Noollab Wolley	8
68	Stateside SS 2124	Stained Glass Window/Can't Get Enough Of Your Love	5

YELLOW BELLOW ROOM BOOM
68	CBS 3205	Seeing Things Green/Easy Life	12

(see also 10cc)

YELLOW DOG
78	Virgin VS 224	Little Gods/Fat Johnny (luminous vinyl, printed PVC sleeve)	4

(see also Wheels)

YELLOW MAGIC ORCHESTRA
80	A&M JAPAN 2	Nice Age/Rydeen (p/s, yellow vinyl)	4
80	A&M AMS 7502	Computer Game/Firecracker/Technopolis (yellow vinyl, PVC sleeve)	4
80	A&M AMS 7559	Behind The Mask/Yellow Magic (p/s, yellow vinyl)	4

YELLOW PAGES
68	Page One POF 090	Here Comes Jane/Ring-A-Ding	5

YELLOW PAYGES
70	UNI UNS 516	Little Woman/Follow The Bouncing Ball	8
71	UNI UNS 534	Birds Of A Feather/Lady Friend	5

YELLOWSTONE & VOICE
72	Regal Zono. RZ 3065	Thinking About You And Me/Grandmother Says	4
73	Regal Zono. RZ 3073	Memories/Well Hello	4
72	Parlophone R 5965	The Flying Dutchman/Philosopher	4
72	Regal Zono. SRZA 8511	YELLOWSTONE & VOICE (LP)	15

YEMM & YEMEN
66	Columbia DB 8022	Black Is The Night/Do Blondes Really Have More Fun	10

YEN
87	Polydor POSP 817	Lonely/Many A Time (p/s, as Y)	5
87	Polydor POSPX 817	Lonely (Solitude Mix)/Many A Time/Lonely (7" Version) (12", p/s, as Y)	7
89	Index IND 1	Red Indians/Trigger (p/s)	7
89	IRS EIRS 130	Billie Holiday's Shoes/Escape (p/s)	4
89	IRS EIRST 130	Billie Holiday's Shoes/Escape (Rix Mix)/Escape (12", p/s)	7
90	IRS EIRS 136	Talk To Me/Air (p/s)	4
90	IRS EIRST 136	Talk To Me/Escape/Air On A Shoestring (12", p/s)	7
91	IRS EIRST 159	It's Unbelievable/It's Unbelievable (Epping Forest Mix) (12", no p/s, unreleased)	8
91	Polydor POSPX 963	Living/Believe/Index/Thoughts (7" Version) (12", p/s)	7

(see also N & Y)

YES
69	Atlantic 584 280	Sweetness/Something's Coming	30
69	Atlantic 584 298	Looking Around/Everydays (possibly unreleased; maybe demos only)	60+

70	Atlantic 584 323	Time And A Word/The Prophet	20
70	Atlantic 2091 004	Sweet Dreams/Dear Father	20
74	Atlantic K 10407	Roundabout/And You And I	5
77	Atlantic K 10985	Going For The One/Parallels (unreleased)	
77	Atlantic K 10999	Wondrous Stories/Parallels (12", blue vinyl, p/s)	7
77	Atlantic K 11047	Going For The One/Awaken Part I (12")	8
78	Atlantic K 11184	Don't Kill The Whale/Abilene	5
80	Atlantic K 11622	Into The Lens/Does It Really Happen?	4
83	Atco B 9817P	Owner Of A Lonely Heart/Our Song (black or grey shaped picture disc)	6/5
83	Atco B 9817C	Owner Of A Lonely Heart/Our Song (cassette)	6
70s	Lyntone LYN 2536	Interview/Five Songs (free with 80-page Yes songbook)	10
69	Atlantic 588 190	YES (LP, red/plum label with lyric insert)	15
70	Atlantic 2400 006	TIME AND A WORD (LP, red/plum label, with lyric insert)	12
71	Atlantic 2400 101	THE YES ALBUM (LP, red/plum label, gatefold sleeve)	10
71	Atlantic 2401 019	FRAGILE (LP, red/plum label, gatefold sleeve with booklet)	12
77	Atlantic DSK 50379	GOING FOR THE ONE (LP, as 3 x 12" singles)	18
80	Atlantic K 50842	CLASSIC YES (LP, with free 45 "Roundabout"/"Your Move" [SAM 141])	15

(see also Hans Christian, Jon Anderson, Syn, Syndicats, Winston's Fumbs, Federals, Warriors, Tomorrow, Peter Banks, Asia, Rick Wakeman, Steve Howe, Anderson Bruford Wakeman & Howe)

YOBS

77	NEMS NES 114	Run Rudolph Run/The Worm Song (p/s)	4
78	Yob YOB 79	Silent Night/Stille Nacht (p/s)	6
81	Safari YULE 1	Rub-A-Dum-Dum/Another Christmas (p/s)	5
82	Fresh FRESH 41	Yobs On 45/The Ballad Of Warrington (p/s)	5
80	Safari RUDE 1	CHRISTMAS ALBUM (LP)	10

(see also Boys)

MAHARISHI MAHESH YOGI

| 67 | Liberty LBS 83075E | MAHARISHI MAHESH YOGI (LP) | 15 |

YOLANDA

| 60 | Triumph RGM 1007 | With This Kiss/Don't Tell Me Not To Love You | 20 |

PETE YORK PERCUSSION BAND

| 73 | Decca TXS 109 | PERCUSSION BAND (LP, with Ian Paice, gatefold sleeve) | 20 |

(see also Spencer Davis Group, Hardin & York, Deep Purple)

RUSTY YORK

| 58 | Parlophone R 4398 | Peggy Sue/Shake 'Em Up Baby (unissued, demos only) | 350 |

(see also Bonnie Lou)

STEVE YORK'S CAMELO PARDALIS

| 73 | Virgin V 2003 | MANOR LIVE (LP) | 10 |

(see also Elkie Brooks, Boz Scaggs, Lol Coxhill, Graham Bond, Mike Patto)

YORK BROTHERS

54	Parlophone CMSP 5	Why Don't You Open The Door/You're My Every Dream Come True (export issue)	8
54	Parlophone CMSP 22	Strange Town/Three O'Clock Blues (export issue)	8
58	Parlophone GEP 8736	COUNTRY AND WESTERN (EP)	15
58	Parlophone GEP 8753	COUNTRY AND WESTERN NO. 2 (EP)	18

YOU KNOW WHO GROUP

| 65 | London HLR 9947 | Roses Are Red My Love/Playboy | 5 |

CHRIS YOULDEN

72	Deram DM 377	Nowhere Road/Standing On The Corner	4
73	Deram SML 1099	NOWHERE ROAD (LP)	15
74	Deram SML 1112	CITY CHILD (LP)	15

(see also Savoy Brown)

BILLY YOUNG

| 72 | Atlantic K 10277 | The Sloopy/Same Old Thing Again | 5 |
| 72 | Jay Boy BOY 55 | I'm Available/Sweet Woman | 6 |

BILLY YOUNG & JELLY ROLL MORTON

| 56 | HMV 7EG 8178 | THE BLUES THEY SANG (EP) | 12 |

BRETT YOUNG (& GHOST SQUAD)

| 63 | Pye 7N 15578 | Guess What/It Just Happened | 5 |
| 64 | Pye 7N 15641 | Never Again/You Can't Fool Me (as Brett Young & Ghost Squad) | 5 |

DARREN YOUNG

| 63 | Parlophone R 4919 | My Tears Will Turn To Laughter/I've Just Fallen For Someone | 10 |

(see also Johnny Gentle)

EVE YOUNG & SNOOKY LANSON

| 50 | London L 751 | Beloved, Be Faithful/I'm In The Middle Of A Riddle (with Eve Young) (78) | 5 |
| 50 | London L 800 | An Ordinary Broom/EVE YOUNG & STUART FOSTER: Sometime (78) | 5 |

(see also Snooky Lanson)

FARON YOUNG

55	Capitol CL 14336	Live Fast, Love Hard, Die Young/Forgive Me, Dear	20
56	Capitol CL 14574	If You Ain't Lovin' (You Ain't Livin')/All Right	15
56	Capitol CL 14655	I've Got Five Dollars And It's Saturday Night/You're Still Mine	15
57	Capitol CL 14735	The Shrine Of St. Cecilia/He Was There	10
57	Capitol CL 14762	Love Has Finally Come My Way/Moonlight Mountain	8
57	Capitol CL 14793	Vacation's Over/Honey Stop! (And Think Of Me)	12
58	Capitol CL 14822	Snowball/The Locket	8
58	Capitol CL 14860	I Can't Dance/Rosalie (Is Gonna Get Married)	12
58	Capitol CL 14891	Every Time I'm Kissing You/Alone With You	8
58	Capitol CL 14930	I Hate Myself/That's The Way I Feel	6
59	Capitol CL 14975	Last Night At A Party/A Long Time Ago	6

Faron YOUNG

59	Capitol CL 15004	That's The Way It's Gotta Be/We're Talking It Over	6
59	Capitol CL 15050	I Hear You Talkin'/Country Girl	6
59	Capitol CL 15093	Face To The Wall/Riverboat	5
60	Capitol CL 15133	I'll Be Alright (In The Morning)/Your Old Used To Be	5
60	Capitol CL 15151	Is She All You Thought She'd Be/There's Not Any Like You Left	5
60	Capitol CL 15173	Forget The Past/A World So Full Of Love	5
61	Capitol CL 15197	Hello Walls/Congratulations	5
62	Mercury AMT 1198	The Yellow Bandana/How Much I Must Have Loved You	5
57	Capitol EAP1 778	SWEETHEARTS OR STRANGERS PT. 1 (EP, with Country Deputies)	12
57	Capitol EAP2 778	SWEETHEARTS OR STRANGERS PT. 2 (EP, with Country Deputies)	12
58	Capitol EAP3 778	SWEETHEARTS OR STRANGERS PT. 3 (EP, with Country Deputies)	12
63	Capitol EAP1 1549	HELLO WALLS (EP)	12
58	Capitol T 1004	OBJECTS OF MY AFFECTION (LP)	15
59	Capitol T 1096	THIS IS FARON YOUNG (LP)	15
64	Mercury 20026MCL	STORY SONGS FOR COUNTRY FOLK (LP)	12
64	Mercury 20025MCL	COUNTRY DANCE FAVOURITES (LP)	12
65	Capitol (S)T 2037	YOUNG'S MEMORY LANE (LP)	12
66	Capitol (S)T 1876	ALL-TIME GREAT HITS OF FARON YOUNG (LP)	10

GEORGIE YOUNG & ROCKIN' BOCS

| 58 | London HLU 8748 | Nine More Miles/The Sneak | 8 |
| 58 | London HLU 8748 | Nine More Miles/The Sneak (78) | 10 |

HARRY YOUNG

| 65 | Dot DS 16756 | Show Me The Way/One Has My Name | 10 |

JESSE COLIN YOUNG

| 79 | Elektra K 12346 | Rave On/Slow And Easy | 4 |

(see also Youngbloods)

JIMMY YOUNG

54	Decca F 10232	A Baby Cried/Remember Me	10
54	Decca F 10406	Give Me Your Word/Lonely Nightingale	10
55	Decca F 10444	These Are The Things We'll Share/Don't Go To Strangers	8
55	Decca F 10483	If Anyone Finds This, I Love You/The Sand And The Sea	8
55	Decca F 10502	Unchained Melody/Help Me Forget	15
55	Decca F 10597	The Man From Laramie/No Arms Can Ever Hold You	15
55	Decca F 10640	Someone On Your Mind/I Look At You	12
56	Decca F 10694	Chain Gang/Capri In May	12
56	Decca F 10736	Rich Man, Poor Man/The Wayward Wind	10
56	Decca F 10774	More/I'm Gonna Steal You Away	10
57	Decca F 10842	Lovin' Baby/My Faith, My Hope, My Love	7
57	Decca F 10875	Round And Round/Walkin' After Midnight	7
57	Decca F 10925	Man On Fire/Love In The Afternoon	6
57	Decca F 10948	Deep Blue Sea/Harbour Of Desire	6
58	Columbia DB 4100	Love Me Again/A Very Precious Love	4
58	Columbia DB 4147	Her Hair Was Yellow/The State Of Happiness	4
58	Columbia DB 4176	Volare (Nel Blu Dipinto ...)/Beats There A Heart So True?	4
58	Columbia DB 4211	There! I've Said It Again/I Could Be A Mountain	4
55	Pye NEP 24004	JIMMY YOUNG SINGS (EP)	7
56	Decca DFE 6277	PRESENTING JIMMY YOUNG (EP)	7
57	Decca DFE 6404	JIMMY YOUNG (EP)	7
55	Decca LF 1200	PRESENTING JIMMY YOUNG (10" LP)	10
57	Decca LK 4219	THE NIGHT IS YOUNG (LP)	10
58	Columbia 33SX 1102	YOU (LP)	10

JOE E. YOUNG & TONIKS

| 68 | Toast TT 502 | Life Time Of Lovin'/Flower In My Hand | 5 |
| 68 | Toast (S)TLP 1 | SOUL BUSTER! (LP) | 10 |

JOHNNIE YOUNG

| 67 | Polydor BM 56186 | Craise Finton Kirk/I Am The World | 4 |
| 67 | Polydor BM 56199 | Every Christian/Epitaph To Mr. Simon Sir | 4 |

JOHNNY YOUNG

67	Decca F 22548	Step Back/Cara Lyn (as Johnny Young & Kompany)	8
67	Decca F 22636	Lady/Good Evening Girl	4
68	RCA RCA 1826	Always Thinking Of You/Dreaming Country (as Johnny Young Four)	4

JOHNNY YOUNG

| 70 | Blue Horizon 7-63852 | FAT MANDOLIN (LP) | 40 |

KAREN YOUNG

68	Major Minor MM 584	Too Much Of A Good Thing/You Better Sit Down	8
65	Mercury MF 943	Are You Kidding/I'm Yours, You're Mine	7
65	Pye 7N 15956	We'll Start The Party Again/Wonderful Summer	8

KATHY YOUNG & INNOCENTS

| 61 | Top Rank JAR 534 | A Thousand Stars/Eddie My Darling | 20 |
| 61 | Top Rank JAR 554 | Happy Birthday Blues/Someone To Love | 12 |

(see also Innocents)

LEON YOUNG STRINGS

| 64 | Pye 7N 15646 | Glad All Over/This Boy | 15 |

LESTER YOUNG (QUINTET)

56	Vogue V 2362	New Lester Leaps In/She's Funny That Way	4
56	Vogue V 2384	You're Driving Me Crazy/East Of The Sun	4
56	Vogue EPV 1127	LESTER YOUNG (EP)	10
55	Felsted EDL 87014	BATLE OF THE SAXES (10" LP)	15
55	Columbia Clef 33C 9001	LESTER YOUNG WITH THE OSCAR PETERSON TRIO (10" LP)	15
56	Columbia Clef 33C 9015	LESTER YOUNG (10" LP)	15

56	Columbia Clef 33CX 10031	THE PRESIDENT, LESTER YOUNG (LP)	12
56	Columbia Clef 33CX 10054	THE JAZZ GIANTS '56 (LP)	12
57	Columbia Clef 33CX 10070	PRES (LP)	12
58	London Jazz LTZ-C 15132	BLUE LESTER (LP)	15
59	HMV CLP 1302	PRES AND TEDDY (LP, with Teddy Wilson)	10
59	Fontana TFL 5064	LESTER YOUNG MEMORIAL ALBUM VOL. 1 (LP, with Count Basie)	12
60	Fontana TFL 5065	LESTER YOUNG MEMORIAL ALBUM VOL. 2 (LP, with Count Basie)	12
62	Stateside SL 10002	LESTER YOUNG & KANSAS CITY 5 (LP)	10
65	Fontana TL 5260	PREZ (LP)	10
66	Fontana FJL 128	LESTER YOUNG LEAPS AGAIN (LP)	10

(see also Count Basie, Coleman Hawkins & Lester Young)

LLOYD YOUNG

72	Bullet BU 500	Bread And Butter/SHALIMAR ALLSTARS: Version	4
72	Duke DU 135	Soup/J.J. ALLSTARS: Version	4
72	Green Door GD 4037	Shalimar Special/G. MAHTANI ALLSTARS: Version	4
72	Techniques TE 917	High Explosion/ANSELL COLLINS: Version	4

MIGHTY JOE YOUNG

| 72 | Sonet SNTF 633 | LEGACY OF THE BLUES VOL. 4 (LP) | 10 |
| 72 | Delmark DS 629 | BLUES WITH A TOUCH OF SOUL (LP, blue label) | 12 |

NEIL YOUNG

69	Reprise RS 23405	The Loner/Everybody Knows This Is Nowhere	6
69	Reprise RS 23462	Down By The River (Edit)/Cinnamon Girl (Alternate Mix)	5
70	Reprise RS 20861	Oh Lonesome Me (Long Version)/Sugar Mountain	5
70	Reprise RS 20958	Only Love Can Break Your Heart/Birds	4
74	Reprise K 14350	Southern Man/Till The Morning Comes/After The Goldrush/Heart Of Gold (special sleeve)	4
74	Reprise K 14360	Walk On/For The Turnstiles	4
76	Reprise K 14431	Don't Cry No Tears/Stupid Girl	5
83	Geffen GEF 2781	Little Thing Called Love/We R In Control (p/s)	4
83	Geffen GEF 3581	Wonderin'/Payola Blues (p/s)	4
86	Geffen GEF 7	Weight Of The World/Pressure (p/s)	4
69	Reprise RSLP 6317	NEIL YOUNG (LP, with/without name on sleeve)	12/20
69	Reprise RSLP 6349	EVERYBODY KNOWS THIS IS NOWHERE (LP)	10
70	Reprise RSLP 6383	AFTER THE GOLDRUSH (LP, gatefold sleeve, with lyric insert)	10
73	Reprise K 54010	TIME FADES AWAY (LP, with lyric insert)	10
74	Reprise K 54014	ON THE BEACH (LP, with inner sleeve)	12
75	Reprise K 54040	TONIGHT'S THE NIGHT (LP, with inner sleeve & insert)	10

(see also Buffalo Springfield, Crosby, Stills, Nash & Young)

PAUL YOUNG

82	CBS A 2751	Iron Out The Rough Spots/Behind Your Smile (p/s)	4
83	CBS PY 1	Love Of The Common People/Tender Trap (p/s)	4
83	CBS WA 3371	Wherever I Lay My Hat (That's My Home)/Broken Man (shaped picture disc)	5
83	CBS WA 3585	Love Of The Common People/Behind Your Smile (live) (picture disc)	4
83	CBS DA 3585	Love Of The Common People/Behind Your Smile (live)//Wherever I Lay My Hat (That's My Home)/Oh Women (double pack)	4
84	CBS WA 4786	I'm Gonna Tear Your Playhouse Down/One Step Forward (shaped picture disc)	4
84	CBS DA 4972	Everything Must Change/Give Me My Freedom//Everything Must Change (Instrumental Version)/Paul's Christmas Message/I Close My Eyes And Count To Ten (live) ('The Christmas Package' double pack, gatefold sleeve)	4
85	CBS DA 6321	Tomb Of Memories/Man In The Iron Mask//Bite The Hand That Feeds/No Parlez (double pack)	4

(see also Q-Tips)

RALPH YOUNG

55	Brunswick 05466	The Man From Laramie/The Bible Tells Me So	10
55	Brunswick 05500	Bring Me A Bluebird/A Room In Paris	6
56	Brunswick 05605	The Legend Of Wyatt Earp/Do You Know?	6

(see also Jack Pleis)

ROGER YOUNG

| 66 | Columbia DB 7869 | Sweet, Sweet Morning/Whatcha Gonna Give Me? | 8 |
| 66 | Columbia DB 8092 | Lady Be Good/It's Been Nice | 4 |

ROY YOUNG (BAND)

59	Fontana H 200	Just Keep It Up/Big Fat Mama	15
59	Fontana H 200	Just Keep It Up/Big Fat Mama (78)	6
59	Fontana H 215	Hey Little Girl/Just Ask Your Heart	10
59	Fontana H 215	Hey Little Girl/Just Ask Your Heart (78)	8
60	Fontana H 237	I Hardly Know Me/Gilee	12
60	Fontana H 247	Taboo/I'm In Love	8
61	Fontana H 290	Plenty Of Love/You Were Meant For Me (as Roy Young & Hunters)	10
61	Ember EMB S 128	Four And Twenty Thousand Kisses/Late Last Evening	8
70	RCA RCA 2031	Granny's Got A Painted Leg (as Roy Young Band)	4
70	RCA SF 8161	ROY YOUNG BAND (LP)	12

SUSANNAH YOUNG

| 67 | Philips BF 1559 | Lazy Afternoon/Here's That Rainy Day | 4 |
| 67 | Philips BL 7728 | SWEETEST SOUNDS (LP) | 10 |

TOMMIE YOUNG

| 73 | Contempo C 12 | Everybody's Got A Little Devil In Their Soul/Do You Still The Same Way | 4 |
| 73 | Contempo C 23 | She Don't Have To See You/That's All Part Of Loving Him | 4 |

VICKI YOUNG

54	Capitol CL 14144	Riot In Cell Block Number Nine/Honey Love (78)	5
55	Capitol CL 14228	Heart Of Stone/Tweedle Dee	15
55	Capitol CL 14281	Live Fast, Love Hard, Die Young/Zoom, Zoom, Zoom	12

56	Capitol CL 14528	Steel Guitar/Bye, Bye For Just A While	8
56	Capitol CL 14653	Spanish Main/Tell Me In Your Own Sweet Way (with Joe 'Fingers' Carr)	8
56	Capitol EAP1 593	VICKI YOUNG (EP)	20

(see also Joe 'Fingers' Carr)

VICTOR YOUNG & HIS SINGING STRINGS

54	Brunswick 05320	The High And The Mighty/The Song From "The Caine Mutiny" (I Can't Believe That You're In Love With Me)	4
54	Brunswick 05337	Lisa (The "Rear Window" Theme)/Smile (Theme From "Modern Times")	4
54	Brunswick 05350	Moonlight And Roses/Magnificent Obsession	4
55	Brunswick 05386	You My Love (From "Young At Heart")/Passion Tango (From "Passion")	4
55	Brunswick 05448	Cherry Pink And Apple Blossom White/The World Is Mine	6
55	Brunswick 05479	The Toy Tiger/Autumn Leaves	4
55	Brunswick 05498	Tall Men (adapted from "Cindy")/Theme From "The Left Hand Of God"	4
56	Brunswick 05579	Love Theme From "The Proud And Profane" (To Love You)/East Of Eden — Theme	4

YOUNG & MOODY BAND

| 81 | Bronze BRO 120 | These Eyes/I Won't Let Go (p/s) | 5 |
| 81 | Bronze BRO 130 | Don't Do That/How Can I Help You Tonight | 7 |

YOUNG BLOOD

68	Pye 7N 17495	Green Light/Don't Leave Me In The Dark	10
68	Pye 7N 17588	Just How Loud/Masquerade	8
68	Pye 7N 17627	Bang-Shan-A-Lang/I Can't Stop	8
69	Pye 7N 17696	Continuing Story Of Bungalow Bill/I Will	8

(see also Cozy Powell, Ace Kefford Stand)

YOUNG BLOOD

| 84 | Landslide LAND 1 | FIRST BLOOD (12", p/s) | 7 |

YOUNGBLOODS

69	RCA RCA 1821	Darkness Darkness/On Sir Francis Drake	6
69	RCA RCA 1877	Get Together/Beautiful	4
70	RCA RCA 1955	Darkness Darkness/On Sir Francis Drake (reissue)	4
69	RCA SF 8026	ELEPHANT MOUNTAIN (LP)	12
70	Warner Bros WS 1878	ROCK FESTIVAL (LP)	12
70	RCA LSA 3012	THE BEST OF THE YOUNGBLOODS (LP)	10
71	Warner Bros K 46100	RIDE THE WIND (LP)	12
71	RCA SF 8218	SUNLIGHT (LP)	12

(see also Jesse Colin Young)

YOUNG BUCKS

| 77 | Blueport BLU 1 | Get Your Feet Back On The Ground/Cold, Cold Morning (p/s) | 6 |

YOUNG DISCIPLES

| 90 | Talkin' Loud TLKX 2 | Get Yourself Together/Young Disciples Theme (12", p/s) | 10 |

YOUNGFOLK

| 68 | President PT 136 | Lonely Girl/Joey | 8 |

YOUNG GROWLER & CALYPSO RHYTHM KINGS

| 66 | Columbia DB 7870 | Amy The Sunbather/Sweet Trinidad | 4 |
| 66 | Columbia DB 7958 | "V" For Victory/Be Nice To Women | 4 |

YOUNG-HOLT TRIO

| 67 | Coral Q 72489 | Wack Wack/This Little Light Of Mine | 8 |

YOUNG-HOLT UNLIMITED

69	MCA MU 1053	Soulful Strut/Country Slicker Joe	8
72	MCA MU 1159	Just Ain't No Love/Love Makes A Woman	4
69	MCA MUPS 368	SOULFUL STRUT (LP)	20

(see also Ramsey Lewis Trio)

YOUNG IDEA

66	Columbia DB 7961	The World's Been Good To Me/It Can't Be	5
66	Columbia DB 8067	Gotta Get Out Of The Mess I'm In/Games Men Play	4
67	Columbia DB 8132	Peculiar Situation/Just Look At The Rain	4
67	Columbia DB 8205	With A Little Help From My Friends/Colours Of Darkness	4
67	Columbia DB 8284	Mister Lovin' Luggage Man/Room With A View	4
68	M. For Pleasure MFP 1225	WITH A LITTLE HELP FROM MY FRIENDS (LP)	10

YOUNG JESSIE

| 58 | London HLE 8544 | Shuffle In The Gravel/Make Believe | 175 |
| 58 | London HLE 8544 | Shuffle In The Gravel/Make Believe (78) | 25 |

YOUNG MARBLE GIANTS

80	Rough Trade RT 043	Final Day/Radio Silents/Cakewalking/(4th track uncredited) (p/s)	4
81	Rough Trade RT 059	TESTCARD (EP)	4
80	Rough Trade ROUGH 8	COLOSSAL YOUTH (LP, original issue)	10

(see also Weekend, Pedestrians, Jah Scouse)

YOUNG ONES

| 63 | Decca F 11705 | Baby That's It/How Do I Tell You | 8 |

YOUNG RASCALS

65	Atlantic AT 4059	I Ain't Gonna Eat My Heart Out Anymore/Slow Down	6
66	Atlantic AT 4082	Good Lovin'/Mustang Sally	5
66	Atlantic 584 024	You Better Run/Love Is A Beautiful Thing	10
66	Atlantic 584 050	Come On Up/What Is The Reason	10
66	Atlantic 584 067	Too Many Fish In The Sea/No Love To Give	5
67	Atlantic 584 081	I've Been Lonely Too Long/If You Knew	10
67	Atlantic 584 085	I Ain't Gonna Eat My Heart Out Anymore/Good Lovin'	4
67	Atlantic 584 111	Groovin'/Sueno	4

MINT VALUE £

67	Atlantic 584 128	A Girl Like You/It's Love	4
67	Atlantic 584 138	How Can I Be Sure/I Don't Love You Anymore	4
68	Atlantic 584 161	It's Wonderful/Of Course	7
66	Atlantic 587 012	THE YOUNG RASCALS (LP)	12
67	Atlantic 587 060	COLLECTIONS (LP)	10
67	Atlantic 587/588 074	GROOVIN' (LP)	12

(see also Rascals, Joey Dee & Starlighters)

YOUNG SISTERS
| 62 | London HLU 9610 | Casanova Brown/My Guy | 6 |

YOUNG SOULS
| 69 | Amalgamated AMG 844 | Why Did You Leave/Main A Wail | 6 |

YOUNG TRADITION
74	Argo AFW 115	The Boar's Head Carol/The Shepherd's Hymn	5
68	Transatlantic TRAEP 164	CHICKEN ON A RAFT (EP)	10
66	Transatlantic TRA 142	YOUNG TRADITION (LP)	20
67	Transatlantic TRA 155	SO CHEERFULLY ROUND (LP)	20
68	Transatlantic TRA 172	GALLERIES (LP, with Dave Swarbrick)	20
68	Transatlantic TRASAM 13	THE YOUNG TRADITION SAMPLER (LP)	15
73	Transatlantic TRASAM 30	GALLERIES REVISITED (LP, reissue)	15

(see also Dave Swarbrick, Peter Bellamy)

YOUNG WORLD SINGERS
| 64 | Brunswick 05916 | Ringo For President/A Boy Like That | 5 |

YOUTH
| 66 | Polydor 56121 | As Long As There Is Your Love/Your One And Only Love | 10 |

YOUTH
| 69 | Deram DM 226 | Meadow Of My Love/Love Me Or Leave Me | 4 |

YOUTH
| 84 | Illuminated JAMS 36 | THE EMPTY QUARTER (LP) | 18 |
| 85 | Illuminated JAMS 41 | YOUTH AT THE DIORAMA (LP) | 12 |

(see also Killing Joke, Brilliant)

JOHNNY YOUTH
| 69 | Grape GR 3002 | Darling It Won't/HIP CITY BOYS: Moon Train | 4 |

YOUTH VALLEY CHORALE
| 63 | London HLU 9818 | Do You Hear What I Hear/Little Bell | 4 |

YOU'VE GOT FOETUS ON YOUR BREATH
| 81 | Self Immolation WOMB 07 | Wash It All Off/333 | 25 |
| 81 | Self Imm. WOMB OYBL-1 | DEAF (LP) | 50 |

(see also Foetus, Philip & His Foetus Vibrations, Scraping Foetus Off The Wheel)

LES YPER SOUND
| 67 | Fontana TF 880 | Too Fortiche/Psyche Rock | 50 |

Y TRWYNAU COCH
70s	Record. Sqwar RSROC 1	WASTOD AR Y TU FAS (BANANAS) (EP)	8
78	Recordian Sqwar RSROC 002	Merched Dan 15 (I Often Think Of Girls Under 15)/Byw Ar Arian Fy Rhieni/ Mynd I'r Capel Mewn Levis/Ail Ddechre	8
80s	Record. Coch OCHR 2198	RHEDEG RHAG Y TORPIDOS (LP)	20

JOHNNY YUKON
| 60 | Top Rank JAR 347 | Made To Be Loved/Magnolia | 4 |

TIMI YURO
61	London HLG 9403	Hurt/I Apologise	8
62	London HLG 9484	Smile/JOHNNIE RAY: I Believe	8
62	Liberty LIB 55410	Satan Never Sleeps/Let Me Call You Sweetheart	6
62	Liberty LIB 55469	What's A-Matter Baby/Thirteenth Hour	15
63	Liberty LIB 55519	I Ain't Gonna Cry No More/Love Of A Boy	15
63	Liberty LIB 55587	Make The World Go Away/Look Down	7
63	Liberty LIB 55634	Gotta Travel On/Down In The Valley	5
64	Liberty LIB 10177	Hurt/Be Anything (But Be Mine)	6
64	Mercury MF 826	If/I'm Afraid The Masquerade Is Over	4
65	Mercury MF 848	You Can Have Him/Could This Be Magic	4
65	Mercury MF 859	Get Out Of My Life/Can't Stop Running Away	30
65	Mercury MF 903	Once A Day/Pretend	4
65	Mercury MF 949	Turn The World Around The Other Way/Just A Ribbon	4
66	Mercury MF 978	Cuttin' In/Why Not Now	4
68	Liberty LIB 15142	I Must Have Been Out Of My Mind/Interlude	15
68	Liberty LIB 15182	It'll Never Be Over For Me/As Long As There Is You	100
65	Liberty LEP 2214	TIMI YURO: SOUL! (EP)	12
66	Liberty LEP 2253	MAKE THE WORLD GO AWAY (EP)	12
62	London HA-G 2415	TIMI YURO (LP)	20
62	Liberty LBY 1042	SOUL! (LP)	16
63	Liberty (S)LBY 1154	WHAT'S A MATTER BABY (LP)	15
64	Liberty LBY 1192	MAKE THE WORLD GO AWAY (LP)	15
64	Mercury 20032 MCL	THE AMAZING YURO (LP)	12
65	Liberty LBY 1247	HURT (LP)	20
66	Liberty (S)LBY 1275	LET ME CALL YOU SWEETHEART (LP)	14
66	Liberty (S)LBY 1290	THE BEST OF TIMI YURO (LP)	12
68	Liberty LBL/LBS 83115	GREAT PERFORMANCES (LP)	10
68	Liberty LBL/LBS 83128	TIMI IN THE BEGINNING (LP)	12
69	Liberty LBS 83198E	SOMETHING BAD ON MY MIND (LP)	20
69	Mercury SMWL 21010	TALENTED TIMI (LP)	10

(see also Johnnie Ray)

MINT VALUE £

HELMUT ZACHARIAS
56	Polydor BM 6011	China Boogie/Slap Happy (as Helmut Zacharias & His Orchestra) (78) 5
57	Polydor BM 6058	Rock 'N' Roll "Roll-Mops" Rock/Barock 'N' Roll Rock (with Hot Club) (78) 5
64	Polydor NH 52341	Tokyo Melody/Teatime In Tokyo 4
65	Polydor 236 809	PLAYS THE HITS OF THE BEATLES (LP) 10

JOHN ZACHERLE
58	London HLU 8599	Dinner With Drac Pt 1/Dinner With Drac — Conclusion 20
58	London HLU 8599	Dinner With Drac Pt 1/Dinner With Drac — Conclusion (78) 12

ZAGER & EVANS
69	RCA SF 8056	2525 (LP) 10

ZAKARRIAS
71	Deram SML 1091	ZAKARRIAS (LP) 180

TOMMY ZANG
59	HMV POP 611	Break The Chain/I'll Put A String On Your Finger 6
62	Polydor NH 66955	I'm Gonna Slip You Offa My Mind/Every Hour, Every Day 6
62	Polydor NH 66957	Hey, Good Lookin'/With Love (For You) 8
62	Polydor NH 66960	Take These Chains From My Heart/Truly, Truly 6
62	Polydor NH 66977	I Can't Hold Your Letters (In My Arms)/She's Getting Married 6
62	Polydor NH 66980	Just Call My Name/I Love You Because 8

ZAPP
80	Warner K 17712	More Bounce To The Ounce/Brand New Player 4
80	Warner K 17712T	More Bounce To The Ounce/Brand New Player (12") 7

FRANK ZAPPA/MOTHERS OF INVENTION
66	Verve VS 545	It Can't Happen Here/How Could I Be Such A Fool (as Mothers Of Invention) ...35
67	Verve VS 557	Big Leg Emma/Why Don't You Do Me Right (as Mothers Of Invention) 35
71	Reprise K 14100	Tears Began To Fall/Junior Mintz Boogie (as Mothers Of Invention) 18
71	Reprise K 14120	Tears Began To Fall/Happy Together (as Mothers Of Invention) 6
71	United Artists UP 35319	What Will This Evening Bring Me This Morning?/Daddy Daddy Daddy 20
73	Discreet K 19201	Cosmic Debris/Uncle Remus 8
73	Discreet K 19202	Don't Eat The Yellow Snow/Camarillo Brillo 8
75	Discreet K 19205	Stink Foot/Du Bist Mein Sofa 6
79	CBS 7261	Dancin' Fool/Baby Snakes 4
80	CBS 7950	Joe's Garage/Catholic Girls 4
80	CBS 7950	Joe's Garage/BOB DYLAN: When You Gonna Wake Up (mispressing) 20
80	CBS 8625	I Don't Wanna Get Drafted/Ancient Armaments 4
81	CBS A 1622	You Are What You Is/Harder Than Your Husband (p/s) 4
81	CBS A 12 1622	You Are What You Is/Harder Than Your Husband (12" picture disc) 12
81	CBS XPS 147	Shut Up 'N' Play Yer Guitar/Variation On The C Santana Secret (p/s) 5
82	CBS A 2412	Valley Girl/Teenage Prostitute (p/s) 4
66	Verve (S)VLP 9154	FREAK OUT! (LP, as Mothers Of Invention) 35
67	Verve VLP 9174	ABSOLUTELY FREE (LP, as Mothers Of Invention) 25
67	Verve (S)VLP 9199	WE'RE ONLY IN IT FOR THE MONEY (LP, as Mothers Of Invention,
		some with insert) 35/25
68	Verve (S)VLP 9233	LUMPY GRAVY (LP, gatefold sleeve) 25
69	Verve SVLP 9237	CRUISIN' WITH RUBEN AND THE JETS (LP, as Mothers Of Invention, g/fold slv) 25
69	Verve (S)VLP 9239	MOTHERMANIA — THE BEST OF THE MOTHERS (LP, mono/stereo
		as Mothers Of Invention) 22/18
69	Transatlantic TRA 197	UNCLE MEAT (2-LP, as Mothers Of Invention, some with booklet) 35/25
69	Reprise RSLP 6356	HOT RATS (LP, 3- or 1-colour label, gatefold sleeve) 18/15
69	Reprise RSLP 6370	BURNT WEENY SANDWICH (LP, as Mothers Of Invention, gatefold
		sleeve, 3- or 1-colour label) 18/15
70	Reprise RSLP 2028	WEASELS RIPPED MY FLESH (LP, as Mothers Of Invention) 15
70	Reprise RSLP 2030	CHUNGA'S REVENGE (LP, green or red gatefold sleeve) 15/12
71	Reprise K 44019	WEASELS RIPPED MY FLESH (LP, reissue) 12
71	Reprise K 44020	CHUNGA'S REVENGE (LP, reissue, gatefold sleeve) 12
71	Reprise K 44078	HOT RATS (LP, reissue, gatefold sleeve) 12
71	Reprise K 44083	BURNT WEENY SANDWICH (LP, reissue, gatefold sleeve) 12
71	Reprise K 44150	FILLMORE EAST — JUNE 1971 (LP, as Mothers Of Invention) 12
71	United Artists UDF 50003	200 MOTELS (2-LP, with booklet & poster, as Frank Zappa & Mothers Of Invention) ...18
71	Verve/Polydor 2683 004	FREAK OUT (2-LP, reissue) 22
72	Verve/Polydor 2317 047	MOTHERMANIA (LP, reissue) 15
72	Reprise K 44179	JUST ANOTHER BAND FROM L.A. (LP, as Mothers Of Invention,
		gatefold sleeve) 12
72	Verve/Polydor 2317 035	ABSOLUTELY FREE (LP, reissue, gatefold sleeve) 12
72	Verve/Polydor 2317 034	WE'RE ONLY IN IT FOR THE MONEY (LP, reissue, gatefold sleeve) 15
72	Reprise K 44203	WAKA/JAWAKA: HOT RATS (LP) 12
72	Verve/Polydor 2317 046	LUMPY GRAVY (LP, reissue, gatefold sleeve) 15
73	Reprise K 44209	THE GRAND WAZOO (LP, gatefold sleeve) 15
73	Verve/Polydor 2352 017	MOTHERMANIA (LP, 2nd reissue) 15
73	Verve/Polydor 2626 002	MOTHER'S DAY (LP) 18
73	Verve/Polydor 2317 069	CRUISIN' WITH RUBEN AND THE JETS (LP, reissue, gatefold sleeve) 15
73	DiscReet K 41000	OVERNITE SENSATION (LP, as Mothers Of Invention) 10
73	DiscReet K 59201	APOSTROPHE (LP) 10

MINT VALUE £

74	DiscReet K 69201	ROXY AND ELSEWHERE (2-LP, as Mothers Of Invention)	15
74	DiscReet K 59207	ONE SIZE FITS ALL (LP, as Mothers Of Invention, gatefold sleeve)	12
75	Verve/Polydor 2352 057	ROCK FLASHBACKS (LP)	15
76	Warner Bros K 56298	ZOOT ALLURES (LP)	10
77	DiscReet K 69204	ZAPPA IN NEW YORK (LIVE) (2-LP, including "Punky's Whips")	40
77	DiscReet K 69204	ZAPPA IN NEW YORK (LIVE) (2-LP)	14
78	DiscReet K 59210	STUDIO TAN (LP)	10
78	DiscReet K 59211	SLEEP DIRT (LP)	10
79	DiscReet K 59212	ORCHESTRAL FAVOURITES (LP)	10
79	DiscReet K 64024	BURNT WEENY SANDWICH/WEASELS RIPPED MY FLESH (2-LP)	15
79	CBS 86101	JOE'S GARAGE ACT I (LP, with lyric sheet)	12
79	CBS 88475	JOE'S GARAGE ACTS II & III (2-LP, with lyric sheet)	14
81	CBS 66368	SHUT UP 'N' PLAY YER GUITAR (3-LP box set)	20
82	CBS 85804	SHIP ARRIVING TOO LATE TO SAVE A DROWNING WITCH (LP, with free 7" "Shut Up 'N' Play Yer Guitar" extracts [XPS 147])	12

(see also Flo & Eddie, Jeff Simmons, Wild Man Fischer, Captain Beefheart, John Lennon, Geronimo Black, Little Feat)

ZAP POW

| 74 | Island WIP 6181 | This Is Reggae Music/Break Down The Barriers | 4 |

PETE ZEAR

| 84 | no label credit/matrix: 22-1 | Tomorrow's World/Fast Food (stamped white label, with insert, numbered) | 10 |

(see also Ruts, Rat Scabies)

ZED

| 79 | Initial IRC 003 | VISIONS OF DUNE (LP) | 12 |

ZEITGEIST

| 80 | Enchaine ENC 1 | Shake-Rake/Sniper (p/s) | 4 |

ZENITH SIX

56	Tempo A 145	Climax Rag/The Chant	5
57	Tempo A 159	Mahogany Hall Stomp/Cannon Ball Blues	5
56	Decca DFE 6255	THE ZENITH SIX AT THE ROYAL FESTIVAL HALL (EP)	10
57	Tempo EXA 42	THE ZENITH SIX (EP)	10
57	Tempo EXA 58	THE ZENITH SIX (EP)	10

SI ZENTNER ORCHESTRA

| 62 | Liberty LIB 55374 | (Up A) Lazy River/Shufflin' Blues | 5 |
| 64 | Liberty LIB 10169 | The James Bond Theme/Bond's 007 Theme | 4 |

ZEPHYR

| 70 | Probe SPB 1006 | ZEPHYR (LP) | 25 |

(see also Tommy Bolin)

ZEPHYRS

63	Decca F 11647	What's All That About/Oriental Dream	20
64	Columbia DB 7199	Sweet Little Baby/I Can Tell	15
64	Columbia DB 7324	A Little Bit Of Soap/No Message	15
64	Columbia DB 7410	Wonder What I'm Gonna Do/Let Me Love You Baby	15
65	Columbia DB 7481	She's Lost You/There's Something About You	15
65	Columbia DB 7571	I Just Can't Take It/She Laughed	15

ZERO FIVE

| 65 | Columbia DB 7751 | Dusty/Just Like A Girl | 5 |

ZEROS

| 77 | Small Wonder SMALL 2 | Hungry/Radio Fun | 4 |
| 70s | Rok ROK 15/16 | What's Wrong With A Pop Group/ACTION REPLAY: Decisions (die-cut co. sleeve) | 5 |

ZERO ZERO SEVEN

| 80s | Scanlite BOND 1 | Message From Bond/James Bond Theme (p/s) | 4 |

ZERRA 1

| 84 | Lyntone LYN 15506 | Tumbling Down/The Other Side/I Know/Diaries/Rain (excerpts flexidisc) | 4 |

Z'EV

| 82 | Fetish FE 13 | Wipeout!/Element L (p/s) | 6 |

WARREN ZEVON

| 76 | Atlantic K 13060 | I'll Sleep When I'm Dead/Mohammed's Radio | 4 |
| 78 | Atlantic K 13111 | Werewolves Of London/Tenderness On The Block | 4 |

TUCKER ZIMMERMAN

69	Regal Zono. RZ 3020	The Red Wind/Moondog	4
69	Regal Zono. SLRZ 1010	TEN SONGS BY TUCKER ZIMMERMAN (LP)	15
72	Village Thing VTS 13	TUCKER ZIMMERMANN (LP)	15

ZIOR

71	Nepentha 6129 002	Za Za Za Zilda/She's A Bad Bad Woman	8
71	Nepentha 6129 003	Cat's Eyes/I Really Do	8
71	Nepentha 6437 005	ZIOR (LP, gatefold sleeve)	35

(see also Monument)

ZIPPERS

| 64 | Hickory 45-1252 | My Sailor Boy/Pretend Your Still Mine | 4 |

ZODIAC

| 68 | Elektra EKL 4009 | COSMIC SOUNDS (LP, also stereo EKS 74009) | 20 |

ZODIAC MINDWARP

| 88 | Mercury ZODS 3 | Planet Girl/Dog Face Driver (shaped picture disc) | 5 |

ZODIAC MOTEL

| 87 | Swordfish SWF 1 | The Story Of Roland Flagg (1-sided promo, white label, foldover p/s) | 12 |
| 87 | Swordfish SWF 004 | Sunshine Miner (p/s) | 10 |

87	Swordfish ZOMO 1	Sunshine Miner/Crescendo/Inside My Mind/Sugarblood (12", p/s) 8
87	Swordfish ZOMO 2	Crystal Injection/I Can Only Give You Everything/Destiny Ranch/
		Stephanie Blue (12", p/s) 7
87	Swordfish SWFLP 001	THE STORY OF ROLAND FLAGG (LP) 10

(see also Birdland)

ZODIACS
| 58 | Oriole CB 1432 | The Yum-Yum Song/Secrets .... 4 |

ZOMBIES
64	Decca F 11940	She's Not There/You Make Me Feel Good 5
64	Decca F 12004	Leave Me Be/Woman 6
65	Decca F 12072	Tell Her No/What More Can I Do 6
65	Decca F 12125	She's Coming Home/I Must Move 7
65	Decca F 12225	Whenever You're Ready/I Love You 7
65	Decca F 12296	Is This The Dream/Don't Go Away 7
66	Decca F 12322	Remember You/Just Out Of Reach 8
66	Decca F 12426	Indication/How We Were Before 8
66	Decca F 12495	Gotta Get A Hold Of Myself/The Way I Feel Inside 8
67	Decca F 12584	Goin' Out Of My Head/She Does Everything For Me 7
68	Decca F 12798	I Love You/The Way I Feel Inside 7
67	CBS 2960	Friends Of Mine/Beechwood Park 12
67	CBS 3087	Care Of Cell 44/Maybe After He's Gone 12
68	CBS 3380	Time Of The Season/I'll Call You Mine 12
65	Decca DFE 8598	THE ZOMBIES (EP) 30
65	Decca LK 4679	BEGIN HERE (LP) 60
68	CBS (S)BPG 63280	ODYSSEY AND ORACLE (LP) 35
73	Epic EPC 65728	TIME OF THE ZOMBIES (2-LP) 15
65	RCA RD 7791	BUNNY LAKE IS MISSING (LP, soundtrack) 35

(see also Unit Four Plus Two, Argent, Neil MacArthur, Colin Blunstone)

ZONES
| 78 | Zoom ZUM 4 | Stuck With You/No Angels (p/s) .... 4 |

(see also Slik, PVC 2)

ZOO
| 70 | Major Minor SMLP 74 | ZOO (LP) .... 12 |
| 71 | Barclay 521172 | ZOO (LP) .... 12 |

ZOOKIE
| 77 | DJM DJS 10796 | Judie Judie Hold On/I Couldn't Be You .... 8 |
| 78 | DJM DJS 10866 | Bubbles/Don't Rock Me .... 8 |

(see also Judie Tzuke, Tzuke & Paxo)

ZOOT
(see under Zoot Simms)

ZORRO
| 79 | Bridgehouse | 'Arrods Don't Sell 'Em .... 8 |

ZOSKIA
85	Temple TOPY 005	Be Like Me (12", p/s, transparent vinyl) 15
84	All The Madmen MAD 8	Rape/Thank You (p/s) 6
86	All The Madmen MADT 8	Rape/Black Action (12", p/s, reissue) 8

ZOSKIA MEETS SUGARDOG
| 84 | Temple TOPYS 021 | J.G. (unissued, white label promos only) .... 8 |

ZOUNDS
81	Crass 4219844/3	Can't Cheat Karma/War/Subvert (foldout poster p/s) 5
81	Rough Trade RT 069	Demystification/Great White Hunter (p/s) 6
82	Rough Trade RT 094	Dancing/True Love (p/s) 6
82	Not So Brave NSB 001	LA VACHE QUI RIT (EP, with poster) 7
82	Rough Trade RT 098	More Trouble Coming Every Day/Knife (p/s) 5
80s	Recommended RR 14.15	Manège (12.59) (1-sided, other side printed, foldout sleeve in
		PVC sleeve) 8

ZUIDERZEE
| 66 | CBS 202062 | (You're My) Soul And Inspiration/Please Don't Call Me .... 4 |
| 66 | CBS 202235 | Peace Of Mind/Provocative Child .... 6 |

ZYGOAT
| 74 | Polydor 2058 124 | Catching A Thief/Letitia's Song .... 4 |
| 74 | Polydor 2383 270 | ZYGOAT (LP) .... 13 |

ZZEBRA
74	Polydor 2058 446	Zardoz/Amusofi 4
75	Polydor 2058 579	Mr. J/Put The Light On Me 4
74	Polydor 2383 296	ZZEBRA (LP) 10
75	Polydor 2383 326	PANIC (LP) 10

(see also John McCoy, Gillan)

ZZ TOP
72	London HLU 10376	Francene/Down Brownie 10
74	London HLU 10458	Beer Drinkers And Hell Raisers/La Grange 10
75	London HLU 10475	La Grange/Just Got Paid 10
75	London HLU 10495	Tush/Blue Jean Blues 8
76	London HLU 10538	It's Only Love/Asleep In The Desert 8
77	London HLU 10547	Arrested For Driving While Blind/Neighbour, Neighbour 10
77	London HLU 10547	Arrested For Driving While Blind/Neighbour, Neighbour (mispress, B-side
		plays Ray Charles' "I Can See Clearly Now") 15
83	Warner Bros W 9693	Gimme All Your Lovin'/If I Could Only Flag Her Down (p/s) 4

83	Warner Bros W 9693P	Gimme All Your Lovin'/Jesus Just Left Chicago/Arrested For Driving While Blind/Heard It On The X (12", p/s) 7
83	Warner Bros W 9693T	Gimme All Your Lovin'/If I Could Only Flag Her Down (car-shaped picture disc) 15
84	Warner Bros W 9334T	T.V. Dinners (Full Length)/Cheap Sunglasses//Legs (Metal Mix)/A Fool For Your Stockings (12" double pack) 7
85	Warner Bros W 2001P	Sleeping Bag/Party On The Patio ('sphinx' shaped picture disc) 10
85	Warner Bros W 2001P	Sleeping Bag/Party On The Patio (interlocking jigsaw-shaped picture disc) 8
85	Warner Bros W 2001DP	Sleeping Bag/Party On The Patio ('sleeping bag'-shaped picture disc) 8
86	Warner Bros W 2002BP	Stages/Hi-Fi Mama (interlocking jigsaw-shaped picture disc) 8
86	Warner Bros W 2003FP	Rough Boy/Delirious (interlocking jigsaw-shaped picture disc) 8
86	Warner Bros W 2003FP	Rough Boy/Delirious (interlocking jigsaw-shaped picture disc, with free 12", shrinkwrapped) 10
74	Warner Bros W 8946	Beer Drinkers And Hell Raisers/I'm Bad, I'm Nationwide//Tush/ Got Me Under Pressure (double pack) 4
86	Warner Bros W 8515	Velcro Fly/Can't Stop Rockin' ('86 Remix)/Woke Up With Wood (with velcro zipper) 4
72	London SH-U 8433	RIO GRANDE MUD (LP, original) 10
73	London SH-U 8459	TRES HOMBRES (LP, original) 10
75	London SH-U 8482	FANDANGO! (LP, original) 10
76	London LDU 1	TEJAS (LP, , original fold-out sleeve) 12
83	Warner Bros W 3774P	ELIMINATOR (LP, picture disc) 12
87	Warner Bros 925 661-2	ZZ TOP'S FIRST ALBUM/RIO GRANDE MUD/TRES HOMBRES/FANDANGO/ TEJAS/EL LOCO (3-CD set of 1st 6 LPs, with booklet) 35

ZZY

| 89 | Zebedee MAGIC 03 | Thank God It's Over/Acid Haze (p/s, blank labels, dead groove on A-side) ...... 18 |
| 91 | Zebedee MAGICD 06 | Is This The Last Time?/Heading For The Light (Of The Soul) (CD) .... 12 |

ZZ TOP

Various Artists

VARIOUS ARTISTS — SINGLES
(alphabetical by title)

56	Decca F 10752	ALL STAR HIT PARADE (Dickie Valentine/Joan Regan/Winifred Atwell/ Dave King/Lita Roza/David Whitfield) 10
57	Decca F 10915	ALL STAR HIT PARADE No. 2 (Johnston Bros/Bill Cotton/Jimmy Young/ Max Bygraves/Beverley Sisters/Tommy Steele) 8
78	Good Vibrations GOT 7	BATTLE OF THE BANDS (double pack, numbered; Idiots/Outcasts/Rudi/ Spider) 6
80	Vinyl Drip DRIP 001	BLACKPOOL ROX (p/s; Membranes/Section 25/Syntax/Kenneth Turner Set) 6
79	Skeleton SKL 002	THE BLANK TAPES VOL. 1 (folded p/s; Attempted Moustache/Junk Act/ Geisha Girls/Zorkie Twins) 5
80	Crass 421984/5	BULLSHIT DETECTOR (12", p/s; A.P.F. Brigade/Alternative/Amebix/ Clockwork Criminals/Counter Attack/Crass/Frenzy Battalion/Fuck The CIA/ Icon/Reputations In Jeopardy/Sceptics/Sinyx/Speakers/Andy T.) 7
53	Columbia SCD 2008	COLUMBIA CAVALCADE (Marie Benson/Steve Conway/Beverley Sisters/ Teddy Johnson/Steve Race/Johnny Brandon/Ronnie Ronalde/Ensemble) 5
71	Dandelion DS 7001	DANDELION (die-cut sleeve; Principal Edwards Magic Theatre/Stackwaddy/ Siren/The Way We Live) 7
89	Decoy FART 3	DECOY (gig freebie; Mega City Four/Les Thugs/Hard-Ons/ Bomb Disneyland) 7
79	Fast Products FAST 9B	EARCOM 2 (12"; Joy Division/Thursdays/Basczax) 15
79	Fast Products FAST 9C	EARCOM 3 (double pack, gatefold p/s with colour postcard insert; D.A.F./Middle Class/Noh Mercy/Stupid Babies) 5
78	Stiff FREEBIE 2	EXCERPTS FROM STIFF'S GREATEST HITS (promo-only sampler, 33rpm) 10
91	Fontana FONT 1	THE FONTANA SINGLES BOX SET VOLUME 1 — HITS AND RARITIES (12-single box set, with 12 inserts) 30
91	Fontana FONT 2	THE FONTANA SINGLES BOX SET VOLUME 2 — HITS AND RARITIES (12-single box set, with 12 inserts) 30
79	Heartbeat PULSE 4	4 ALTERNATIVES (p/s; 48 Hours/Joe Public/Numbers/Z-Certs) 5
80s	Illuminated 12 PDS 85	GET THAT SNARE! (12", p/s; DAF/400 Blows) 7
80	Groucho Marxist COMMUNIQUE 2	HA! HA! FUNNY POLIS (PAISLEY ROCK AGAINST RACISM) (p/s; Defiant Pose/Fegs/Urban Enemies/XS Discharge) 5
88	House Of Dolls HOD 004	HOUSE OF DOLLS (Wedding Present/Trudy/Hunters Club/Claytown Troupe) (no p/s, free with 'House Of Dolls' magazine) 6/4
88	House Of Dolls HOD 009	HOUSE OF DOLLS (Pop Will Eat Itself/Wild Poppies/Blow Up/Godspeed) (no p/s, free with 'House Of Dolls' magazine) 6/4
86	Pink PINKY 11	IF IT SELLS IT SMELLS (12"; Jamie Wednesday/Wolfhounds/McCarthy/ Rumblefish; die-cut sleeve with inner & label insert) 10
83	Future FUTURE 1	THE INVISIBLE FRAME (Blitz/And Also The Trees & others) 7
60s	Lyntone LYN 765/6	KEELE RAG RECORD (flexidisc; Incas & others) 40
60s	Lyntone	KEELE RAG RECORD NO. 2 (flexidisc; Escorts/Lance Harvey & Kingpins/ Keele Row) 30
79	Decca FR 13864	THE LONDON BOYS (p/s; David Bowie/Small Faces/Birds/Dobie Gray) 7
60s	Mercury YARD 002	MUSIC FOR 5 AM (promo for Yardley; Hollies & others) 10
83	Gross Product OBCT 1	MUSIC FROM THE EAST ZONE (Railway Children/Screen 3/ Fire Hydrant Men) 8
80	EMI	MUTHA'S PRIDE (4-track) 12
85	Abstract 12 ABS 030	NEVER MIND THE JACKSONS, HERE'S THE POLLOCKS (12"; New Model Army & others) 10
80	Neutron NT 003	1980! THE FIRST FIFTEEN MINUTES (Vice Versa/Clock DVA/ I'm So Hollow/Stunt Kites) 8
82	Neat NEAT 25	ONE TAKE NO DUBS (12"; Black Rose/Hellanbach/Alien/Avenger) 8
81	Pop Pix No. 1	POP PIX (blue flexidisc with 'Pop Pix' magazine; Kim Carnes/ Gary U.S. Bonds./Our Daughters Wedding/Tubes) 4
82	Recommended RR-8.9	RECOMMENDED RECORDS SAMPLER (Peter Blegvad/Homosexuals/Faust/ R. Stevie Moore; 1-sided, foldout p/s, clear vinyl, silk-screened PVC cover) 8
80	Energy NRG 1	ROOM TO MOVE (p/s; Big Self/Outcasts/Shock Treatment/Vipers) 5
87	Barracuda Blue 12 UTA 10	SAVAGE AMUSEMENT (12"; Captain Sensible/John Asherton/Tigersharks) 7
88	Sniffin' Rock SR 006 A7	SNIFFIN' ROCK PRESENTS (no p/s; free with 'Sniffin' Rock' issue 9; Senseless Things/Crazyhead/Birdhouse) 7/5
87	Sounds SONIC 1	SONIC SOUNDS 1 (33rpm EP free with 'Sounds' mag; Pop Will Eat Itself/ Crazyhead/Jack Rubies/Georgia Satellites) 4
80s	Polydor 2659 027	SOUNDS PRESENTS "THE GUITAR ALBUM" (flexidisc with 'Sounds') 8/6
88	Sounds WAVES 3	SOUNDS WAVES 3 (p/s; Wedding Present & others; free with 'Sounds') 4
70s	Groucho Marxist WH 1	SPECTACULAR COMMODITY (Mental Errors/Mod Cons/Poems/Sneex/ XS Discharge) 5
70s	Stiff BUY 1-10	STIFF BOX SET NO. 1 (10 x 7" box set) 40
70s	Stiff BUY 11-20	STIFF BOX SET NO. 2 (10 x 7" box set) 20
88	Underground	STRUM DRUM (Wedding Present & others) (cassette with 'Underground' magazine, issue 13) 8/6
57	Parlophone R 4356	TOP TEN SPECIAL (Jim Dale/King Brothers/Vipers Skiffle Group) 8
86	Underground 7	UNDERGROUND RHYTHM AND NOISE (cassette with 'Underground' issue 7) 8/6
70s	Fuck Off FEP 001	WEIRD NOISE (white labels; Danny & Dressmakers/The Door & The Window/ Instant Automatons/012/Sell-Outs) 5

VARIOUS ARTISTS — EPs
(alphabetical by title)

A

63	Pye NEP 24168	ALL STAR HIT PARADE (Kenny Ball/Chris Barber Jazz Band/Joe Brown/ Lonnie Donegan Skiffle Group/Mary Wynter) 7
64	Pye NEP 24172	ALL STAR HIT PARADE VOL. 2 (Joe Brown/Petula Clark/Julie Grant/ Benny Hill/Mark Wynter) 7
64	Decca DFE 8571	AMERICAN COUNTRY JUBILEE NO. 1 (Ray Phillips/Autrey Inman/ Marvin McCullough/Billy Parker) 10

B

57	Philips BBE 12148	THE BELLS ARE RINGING (Tony Bennett/Vic Damone/De John Sisters/ Jo Stafford) 8
60s	Melodisc EPM7 115	BEST OF BLUEGRASS (COUNTRY STRINGS) (Bill Browning/Buzz Busby/ Country Gentlemen/Williams Brothers) 10
58	Philips BBE 12225	BEST WISHES FOR CHRISTMAS (Beverley Sisters/David Hughes Wally Scott Orchestra) 7
59	Mercury ZEP 10024	THE BIG BAND SOUND (Quincy Jones/Ralph Marterie Orchestra) 7
66	Fontana TF 17469	THE BIG FOUR (Dave Dee Dozy Beaky Mick & Tich/Spencer Davis Group/ Mindbenders/Pretty Things) 8
56	Philips BBE 12021	THE BIG FOUR (Roy Hamilton/Frankie Laine/Mitch Miller Orchestra/ Something Smith & Redheads) 12
56	Philips BBE 12040	THE BIG FOUR No. 2 (Mindy Carson/Don Cherry/Frankie Laine/Jo Stafford) 12
56	Philips BBE 12088	THE BIG FOUR No. 3 (Shirley Bassey/Ronnie Carroll/David Hughes/ Anne Shelton) 8
56	Philips BBE 12091	THE BIG FOUR No. 4 (Rosemary Clooney/Doris Day/Four Lads/Frankie Laine) .. 12
57	Philips BBE 12114	THE BIG FOUR No. 5 (Shirley Bassey/Ronnie Carroll/Anne Shelton/ Frankie Vaughan) 10
57	Philips BBE 12139	THE BIG FOUR No. 6 (Shirley Bassey/Ronnie Carroll/Kaye Sisters/ Frankie Vaughan) 8
57	Philips BBE 12145	THE BIG FOUR No. 7 (Tony Bennett/Doris Day/Guy Mitchell/Johnnie Ray) 12
57	Philips BBE 12158	THE BIG FOUR No. 8 (Shirley Bassey/Robert Earl/Kaye Sisters/Steve Martin) 8
58	Philips BBE 12165	THE BIG FOUR No. 9 (Robert Earl/Anne Shelton/Joyce Shock/ Frankie Vaughan & Kaye Sisters) 10
58	Philips BBE 12190	THE BIG FOUR No. 10 (Jimmy Lloyd/Robert Earl/Kaye Sisters/Anne Shelton) ... 10
59	Philips BBE 12288	THE BIG FOUR No. 11 (Shirley Bassey/Kaye Sisters/Frankie Vaughan/ Marty Wilde) 10
59	Philips BBE 12336	THE BIG FOUR No. 12 (Frankie Laine/G. Mitchell/Johnnie Ray/Leslie Uggams) .. 12
66	Philips BBE 12593	THE BIG FOUR (Roger Miller/Four Seasons/Dusty Springfield/Walker Brothers) .. 7
59	Collector JEL 8	BLIND LEMON JEFFERSON/BUDDY BOY HAWKINS 15
64	Fontana TFE 18010	BLOWING IN THE WIND (Bob Dylan/Joan Baez/Pete Seeger) 35
60s	Range JRE 7005	BLUEGRASS (Coney Carver/Freeman Ervin) 7
59	Fontana TFE 17081	THE BLUES (Danny Barker/Jimmy Giuffre/Jo Jones/Pee Wee Russell) 7
61	Pieces Of 8 PEP 605	THE BLUES (Big Bill Broonzy/Josh White) 10
64	Pye Intl. NEP 44029	THE BLUES VOL. 1 PT. 1 (John Lee Hooker/Muddy Waters/Sonny Boy Williamson/Jimmy Witherspoon) 15
64	Pye Intl. NEP 44035	THE BLUES VOL. 1 PT. 2 (Howling Wolf/Buddy Guy/Little Walter/Muddy Waters) 12
66	Chess CRE 6011	THE BLUES VOL. 2 PT. 1 (Otis Rush/Chuck Berry/John Lee Hooker/Little Walter) 15
64	Pye Intl. NEP 44038	BLUES FESTIVAL (Sugar Pie De Santo/Willie Dixon/Sonny Boy Williamson/ Howlin' Wolf) 20
63	Columbia SEG 8226	BLUES ON PARADE NO. 1 (Jimmy Cotton/Brownie McGhee/ Roosevelt Sykes/Sonny Terry) 12
56	HMV 7EG 8178	THE BLUES THEY SANG (Lizzie Miles/Billy Young & Jelly Roll Morton) 18
61	Pye NEP 24142	BYE BYE BIRDIE (Brook Brothers/Patti Brook/Joe Brown/Jimmy Justice/ Kids/Viscounts) 7
61	Philips BBE 12475	BYE BYE BIRDIE NO. 4 (Marty Wilde & others) 10

C

63	Cameo Parkway CPE 552	CAMEO BIG FOUR (Bobby Rydell/Chubby Checker/Dovells/Orlons) 10
56	Columbia 33S 1083	CABARET NIGHT IN PARIS 10
57	Columbia 33S 1099	CABARET NIGHT IN PARIS No. 4 10
57	Columbia 33S 1105	CABARET NIGHT IN PARIS No. 5 10
59	Mercury ZEP 10014	CHA CHA FOR NOW (Jan August/Sil Austin/Jerry Murad's Harmonicats) 7
62	Topic TOP 74	THE COLLIERS' RANT (Louis Killen/Johnny Handle/Colin Ross) 7
59	Mercury ZEP 10012	COUNTRY AND WESTERN (George Jones/Jimmie Skinner) 20
60s	Range JRE 7001	COUNTRY AND WESTERN (Jim Chriss/Bob Strack/Jimmy Strickland) 7
60s	Range JRE 7004	COUNTRY AND WESTERN (Gabe Dean/Jimmy Dry/Rex Dario) 7
60	Top Rank JKP 2055	COUNTRY AND WESTERN EXPRESS VOL. 1 (Bill Alex Dixie Drifters/ Jenny Herrill/Elmer Snodgrass/Musical Pioneers) 7
60	Top Rank JKP 2056	COUNTRY AND WESTERN EXPRESS VOL. 2 (Jack Chambers & Rainbow Boys/Ralph Hodge & Hodges Brothers Band) 7
60	Top Rank JKP 2063	COUNTRY AND WESTERN EXPRESS VOL. 4 (Claude Gray/Eddie Noack) 7
60	Top Rank JKP 2065	COUNTRY AND WESTERN EXPRESS VOL. 6 (Tony Douglas/James O'Gwynn) .. 15
63	CBS AGG 20033	COUNTRY AND WESTERN HITS VOL. 1 (Carl Butler/Lester Flatt & Earl Scruggs/Lefty Frizzell/Stonewall Jackson/Ray Price) 7
64	CBS AGG 20041	COUNTRY AND WESTERN HITS VOL. 2 (Johnny Cash/Lester Flatt & Earl Scruggs/Lefty Frizzell/Marty Robbins) 7
65	Hickory LPE 1505	COUNTRY AND WESTERN SHOWCASE VOL. 2 (Roy Acuff/Wilma Lee/ Stoney Cooper) 7
57	Philips BBE 12149	COUNTRY AND WESTERN SPECTACULAR (George Morgan/Ray Price/ Mel Tillis/Marty Robbins) 12
59	Mercury ZEP 10038	COUNTRY AND WESTERN TRAIL BLAZERS NO. 1 (Connie Hall/ James O'Gwynn/Jimmy Skinner/Charlie Walker) 10
60	Mercury ZEP 10052	COUNTRY AND WESTERN TRAIL BLAZERS NO. 2 (Bill Clifton & Dixie Mountain Boys/George Jones) 10

MINT VALUE £

60	Mercury ZEP 10080	COUNTRY AND WESTERN TRAIL BLAZERS NO. 3 (James O'Gwynn/ Connie Hall) 7
60s	Heritage 105	THE COUNTRY BLUES 20
58	RCA RCX 107	COUNTRY GUITAR VOL. 1 (Bonnie, Jim Edward & Maxine Brown/ Hank Locklin/Jim Reeves/Hank Snow) 7
58	RCA RCX 110	COUNTRY GUITAR VOL. 2 (Skeeter Davis/Don Gibson/Jim Reeves/Hank Snow) ..8
59	RCA RCX 127	COUNTRY GUITAR VOL. 5 (Eddy Arnold/Browns/Skeeter Davis/ Johnny & Jack/Hank Snow/Porter Wagoner) 7
59	RCA RCX 141	COUNTRY GUITAR VOL. 6 (Hank Locklin/Eddy Arnold/Browns/Hank Snow/ Porter Wagoner/Johnny & Jack) 7
59	RCA RCX 147	COUNTRY GUITAR VOL. 8 (Browns/Don Gibson/Hawkshaw Hawkins/ Johnny & Jack/Jim Reeves) 7
59	RCA RCX 159	COUNTRY GUITAR VOL. 9 (Hank Locklin/Gail Davis/Skeeter Davis/Jimmy Driftwood/Jim Reeves) 8
59	RCA RCX 176	COUNTRY GUITAR VOL. 10 (Hank Locklin/Skeeter Davis/Hawkshaw Hawkins/Johnny & Jack/Sons Of The Pioneers/Hank Snow) 8
59	RCA RCX 177	COUNTRY GUITAR VOL. 11 (Browns/Eddy Arnold/Jack Clement/Hank Snow) 7
60	RCA RCX 185	COUNTRY GUITAR VOL. 12 (Eddy Arnold/Hawkshaw Hawkins/Jim Reeves/ Hank Snow/Porter Wagoner) 7
62	RCA RCX 7105	COUNTRY GUITAR VOL. 16 (Bill Monroe & Blue Grass Boys/Monroe Bros) 10
63	Decca DFE 8522	COUNTRY JUBILEE VOL. 1 (Sonny Miller/Ray Phillips/Ott Stephens/ Sonny Williams) 7
63	Decca DFE 8523	COUNTRY JUBILEE VOL. 2 (Kendall Hayes/Margie Laffery/ Lonesome Pine Fiddlers/Marvin McCullough) 7

D

56	Mercury MEP 9509	DAMN YANKEES (Rusty Draper/Vic Damone/Patti Page/Sarah Vaughan) 8
54	Capitol EAP1 518	DANCE CRAZE (Ray Anthony/Pee Wee Hunt/Stan Kenton) 10
80	Sue 10WIP 6599	DANCE WHATCHA WANNA (10" die-cut sleeve; Donnie Elbert/Billy Preston/ Righteous Brothers/Bob & Earl/Owen Gray/Robert Parker) 7
60s	XX MIN 706	DARK MUDDY BOTTOM (Jimmy Slim/Good Jelly Bess/Lightning Leon/ Little Red Walters/Willie B.) 10
58	MGM MGM-EP 652	DEEP IN MY HEART Excerpts (Rosemary Clooney/Vic Damone/Tony Martin/ Jane Powell/Helen Traubel) 7
50s	Poydras 102	DEPRESSION BLUES 12
63	Decca DFE 8520	DISCS-A-GO GO (Karl Denver/Billy Fury/Jet Harris/Vernons Girls) 20
60s	Jan & Dil JR 450	DOWN HOME BLUES — SIXTIES STYLE (Lightning Leon/Jerry McCain/ Little Red Walters) 10
60s	XX MIN 709	DOWNHOME HARP (Kid Thomas/Eddie Hope/Jerry McCain) 7
59	Fontana TFE 17146	DRUMBEAT (Lana Sisters/Adam Faith/Bob Miller & Millermen/Sylvia Sands/ Roy Young) 18

E

65	Edinburgh S.C. ESC 02	EDINBURGH STUDENTS CHARITIES APPEAL (33rpm, die-cut paper p/s; Athenians/Avengers/Ray & Archie Fisher/Lynn & Kathy). 25
66	Edinburgh S.C. ESC 03	EDINBURGH STUDENTS CHARITIES APPEAL 25
60	Felsted ESD 3083	AN EVENING AT LA POUBELLE (Curly Hamner/Ben Dalida/Wackadous) 7
67	Philips P 160E	EXQUISITE FORM (freebie; Dave Dee, Dozy, Beaky, Mick & Tich/Herd/ Walker Brothers/Dusty Springfield) 7

F

78	Factory FAC 2	A FACTORY SAMPLE (double pack, some with 5 stickers; Joy Division/ Cabaret Voltaire/Durutti Column/John Dowie) 40/25
59	Collector JEL 2	FEMALE BLUES VOL. 1 (Ida Cox/Ma Rainey) 12
60	Collector JEL 14	FEMALE BLUES VOL. 2 (Bertha Henderson/Rosa Henderson) 12
60	Collector JEL 22	FEMALE BLUES VOL. 3 (Ma Rainey/Trixie Smith) 12
64	Pye Intl. NEP 44030	FESTIVAL OF THE BLUES NO. 1 (Willie Dixon/Buddy Guy/Muddy Waters/ Sonny Boy Williamson) 15
81	Pax PAX 1	5 MILES TO MIDNIGHT (12"; Brothers/Doormen/I Scream/Mortuary In Wax) 7
58	Parlophone GEP 8694	FLUTE COCKTAIL (Bill Doggett/Johnny Pate Quartet) 7
66	HMV 7EG 8911	FOLKSOUND OF BRITAIN (Cyril Tawney/Lewis Johns/John Steele) 7
89	Food 12FOODG 23	FOOD CHRISTMAS EP (Jesus Jones/Crazyhead/Diesel Park West) (12", g/fold p/s) 7
89	Food CDFOOD 23	FOOD CHRISTMAS EP (Jesus Jones/Crazyhead/Diesel Park West) (CD) 7
64	Ember EMB EP 4530	FOOL BRITANNIA (Peter Sellers/Dan Massey/Anthony Newley/Joan Collins/ Maureen Lipton) 8
79	Heartbeat PULSE 4	4 ALTERNATIVES (Numbers/X-Certs/Joe Public/48 Hours) 5
57	Philips BBE 12140	FOUR GREAT MOVIE THEMES (V. Damone/Hi-Los/Frankie Laine/Jerry Vale) 12
81	Albion FREEBIE 1	FREEBIE 1 (square flexi; Robyn Hitchcock/Cosmopolitans/ Motor Boys Motor/dB's) 7

G

72	Chess 6145 011	GENESIS — THE BEGINNINGS OF ROCK 10
59	MGM MGM-EP 703	GIRLS AND MORE GIRLS (June Allyson/Ava Gardner/Judy Garland/ Kathryn Grayson) 8
67	Down with the Game 202	GOD DON'T LIKE IT 15
67	Down with the Game 203	GOD DON'T LIKE IT VOLUME 2 15
60s	XX MIN 707	GOING TO CALIFORNIA (Little Sonny Willis/Eddie Williams) 8
59	Philips BBE 12318	GREAT COUNTRY AND WESTERN HITS (Johnny Cash/Johnny Horton/ Stonewall Jackson/Carl Smith) 10
66	Pye Intl. NEP 45054	THE GREATEST ON STAGE (Maxine Brown/Chuck Jackson/Shirelles/ Dionne Warwick) 10
67	CBS WEP 1131	GREAT SCREEN THEMES (John Barry/Percy Faith & His Orchestra) 7
70	Village Thing VTSX 1000	THE GREAT WHITE DAP (Wizz Jones/Sun Also Rises/Ian A. Anderson/ Pigsty Hill Light Orchestra) 20
63	London REU 1393	GROUP OF GOODIES (Marcie Blane/Kokomo/Bill Black's Combo/Ernie Maresca) 15
59	Mercury ZEP 10010	GROUPS GALORE (Del Vikings/Mark IV/Diamonds/Hi-Liters) 75
56	Philips BBE 12077	GUYS AND DOLLS (Frankie Laine/Rosemary Clooney/Jo Stafford/Jerry Vale) 8

H

64	Hickory LPE 1500	HICKORY SHOWCASE VOL. 1 (Roy Acuff/Wilma Lee/Stoney Cooper) 7
64	Hickory LPE 1501	HICKORY SHOWCASE VOL. 2 (Bobby Lord/Bob Luman) 12
64	Hickory LPE 1504	HICKORY SHOWCASE VOL. 3 (Bobby Lord/Bob Luman) 12
57	Capitol EAP1 852	HIT CALYPSOS (Andrews Sisters/Nat 'King' Cole/Stan Kenton/
		Lord Flea Calypsonians) 10
55	MGM MGM-EP 525	HIT THE DECK — SOUNDTRACK EXCERPTS (Tony Martin/Jane Powell/
		Debbie Reynolds) 7
55	MGM MGM-EP 526	HIT THE DECK — SOUNDTRACK EXCERPTS (Tony Martin/Jane Powell/
		Ane Miller/Vic Damone) 7
65	Pye NEP 24213	THE HITMAKERS NO. 1 (Searchers/Kenny Ball Jazzmen/Dixie Cups/
		Dionne Warwick) 7
65	Pye NEP 24214	THE HITMAKERS NO. 2 (Honeycombs/Tony Jackson/Kinks/Shangri-La's) 12
65	Pye NEP 24215	THE HITMAKERS NO. 3 (Chuck Berry/Julie Grant/Rockin' Berries/Sandie Shaw) . 7
66	Pye NEP 24241	THE HITMAKERS VOL. 1 (Ivy League/Tommy Quickly/Sandie Shaw/
		Sounds Orchestral) 7
66	Pye NEP 24242	THE HITMAKERS VOL. 2 (Chuck Berry/Kinks/Sue Thompson/Shangri-La's) 10
66	Pye NEP 24243	THE HITMAKERS VOL. 3 (Kinks/Lancastrians/Rockin' Berries/Searchers) 10
66	Pye Intl. NEP 44065	HITMAKERS INTERNATIONAL (Fontella Bass/James Brown/Petula Clark/
		Lovin' Spoonful) 7
57	Brunswick OE 9340	HIT PARADE (Rex Allen/Peggy Lee/Jeri Southern/Victor Young Orchestra) 7
58	Brunswick OE 9450	HIT PARADE NO. 2 (Carmen Cavallaro/Four Aces/Grandpa Jones/
		Jack Pleis & His Orchestra) 10
56	Mercury MEP 9003	HIT PARADE VOL. 1 (Georgia Gibbs/Platters/Crew Cuts/Patti Page) 15
56	Mercury MEP 9510	HIT PARADE VOL. 2 (Sarah Vaughan/Ralph Marterie/Patti Page/Crew Cuts) 15
65	Decca DFE 8648	HITS VOL. 1 (Chris Andrews/Fortunes/Hedgehoppers Anonymous/Jonathan King) 7
65	Decca DFE 8649	HITS VOL. 2 (Lulu/Chris Andrews/Marianne Faithfull/Fortunes) 10
65	Decca DFE 8653	HITS VOL. 3 (Pinkerton's Assorted Colours/St. Louis Union/Mexicans/
		Paul & Barry Ryan) 10
66	Decca DFE 8662	HITS VOL. 4 (Dave Berry/Val Doonican/Joy Marshall/Crispian St. Peters) 7
66	Decca DFE 8663	HITS VOL. 5 (Animals/Los Bravos/Alan Price Set/Small Faces) 10
66	Decca DFE 8667	HITS VOL. 6 (Jonathan King/Lulu/Alan Price Set/Small Faces) 10
67	Decca DFE 8675	HITS VOL. 7 (Ronnie Aldrich/Val Doonican/Bachelors/Small Faces) 10
55	Capitol EAP1 482	HITS FROM CAN CAN (Les Baxter Orchestra/Nat 'King' Cole/Gordon MacRae/
		Kay Starr) 8
62	Mercury ZEP 10133	HITSVILLE! (Brook Benton/Crew Cuts/Phil Philips/Diamonds) 20
59	Coral FEP 2034	HITSVILLE VOL. 1 (Buddy Holly/McGuire Sisters/Betty Madigan/Billy Williams) . 40
59	Coral FEP 2035	HITSVILLE VOL. 2 (Lennon Sisters/Art Lund/Teresa Brewer/Jackie Wilson) 18
65	Tamla Motown TME 2001	HITSVILLE U.S.A. NO. 1 (Marvin Gaye/Brenda Holloway/Carolyn Crawford/
		Eddie Holland) 50
66	Post War Blues 100	HOBOS AND DRIFTERS 15
75	Solid Sender SEP 100	HOUSTON JUMP (James Widemouth Brown & His Orchestra/Henry Hayes
		Four Kings & Carl Campbell/Goree Carter & Hepcats) 10

I

65	Chess CRE 6010	IN CROWD (Radiants/Ramsey Lewis Trio/Little Milton/Billy Stewart) 12
78	Radar SAM 88	INTERNATIONAL ARTISTS (13th Floor Elevators/Red Crayola/
		Lost & Found/Golden Dawn; Red Crayola Hope & Anchor gig freebie
		with 'Howdy From Texas The Lone Star State' magazine) 12/8
56	Mercury MEP 9503	ITEMS FROM GUYS AND DOLLS (Richard Hayes/Kitty Kallen/Frankie Laine/
		David Le Winter) 12
59	Mercury ZEP 10001	IT'S CHA CHA TIME (Jan August & Richard Hayman Orchestra/Jerry Murad's
		Harmonicats/Hi Liters/Ray Materie Orchestra) 12
56	Columbia SEG 7639	IT'S GREAT TO BE YOUNG — FILM TUNES (Ruby Murray/Coronets/
		Ray Martin Orchestra/Mr Dingle) 10
62	Pye Jazz NJE 1083	IT'S TRAD DAD — FILM SOUNDTRACK (Bob Wallis/Kenny Ball & His Jazzmen) . . 7

J

| 67 | Natchez NEP-701 | THE JUG BANDS VOLUME 1 . . . . 15 |
| 64 | Columbia SEG 8337 | JUST FOR YOU (Peter & Gordon/Freddie & Dreamers) . . . . 10 |

K

56	London REE 1047	THE KING AND QUEEN OF R&B (Ruth Brown/Joe Turner) 90
59	Top Rank 45-TR 5004	KING SIZE (maxi-single; Craig Douglas/Sheila Buxton/Bert Weedon) 7
61	RCA Victor RCX 203	KINGS OF THE BLUES VOL. 2 (Jazz Gillum/Big Maceo/Washboard Sam/
		Sonny Boy Williamson) 12
61	RCA Victor RCX 204	KINGS OF THE BLUES VOL. 3 (Arthur Big Boy Crudup/Furry Lewis/
		Poor Joe Williams) 12
55	Mercury EP-1 3160	KISMET (Vic Damone/Georgia Gibbs/Ross Bagdasarian) 7
60	Warner Bros WEP 6010	KOOKIE STAR OF SEVENTY SEVEN SUNSET STRIP
		(Joannie Sommers/Eddie Byrne/Connie Stevens) 10

L

66	Holyground HG 111	THE LAST THING ON MY MIND (EP, 99 copies only) 30
59	Top Rank JKR 8008	LET'S GO NO. 1 (Jimmy Lee/Johnny Hines/Treetoppers) 12
59	Top Rank JKR 8012	LET'S GO NO. 2 (Johnny Hines/Billy Mack/Victors/Ted & Ray) 15
61	Philips BBE 12414/	LET'S MAKE LOVE — FILM SOUNDTRACK (Yves Montand/Marilyn Monroe/
	SBBE 9031	Frankie Vaughan; mono/stereo) 18/25
57	London RED 1075	LONDON HIT PARADE NO. 1 (Tab Hunter/Hilltoppers/Pat Boone/
		Fontane Sisters) 12
57	London REP 1096	LONDON HIT PARADE NO. 2 (Fats Domino/Slim Whitman/Ken Copeland/
		Roy Brown) 40
58	London RED 1097	LONDON HIT PARADE NO. 3 (Pat Boone/Gale Storm/Tab Hunter/Jim Lowe) 12
58	London RED 1130	LONDON HIT PARADE NO. 4 (Pat Boone/Nick Todd/Bonnie Guitar/Hilltoppers) . 12
58	London RED 1145	LONDON HIT PARADE NO. 5 (Pat Boone/Fontane Sisters/Frank De Rosa) 12
63	Decca DFE 8538	A LONDON HOOTENANNY (Davy Graham/Thamesiders) 12
73	Ronco MR EP 001	LONG LIVE ROCK (no p/s; Billy Fury/Eugene Wallace/Wishful Thinking) 15

M

59	Collector JEL 2	MALE BLUES VOL. 1 (Georgia Slim/Walter Roland)	12
59	Collector JEL 4	MALE BLUES VOL. 3 (Blind Jake/Ramblin' Thomas)	10
59	Collector JEL 5	MALE BLUES VOL. 4 (Tall Tom/Pinewood Tom)	12
60	Collector JEL 10	MALE BLUES VOL. 6 (Hound Head Henry/Frankie Jaxon)	15
60	Collector JEL 13	MALE BLUES VOL. 7 (Blind Lemon Jefferson/Ed Bell)	10
60	Collector JEL 24	MALE BLUES VOL. 8 (Blind Lemon Jefferson/Huddie Leadbetter)	10
67	Piccadilly NEP 34100	MAXWELL HOUSE PRESENTS HITMAKERS (Kenny Ball/Petula Clark/Honeycombs/Anita Harris)	7
57	Decca DFE 6408	MERRY CHRISTMAS (Dave King/Mantovani Orchestra/Dickie Valentine/David Whitfield)	8
60	MGM MGM-EP 749	M.G.M. EVERGREENS (Billy Eckstine/Tommy Edwards/Lennie Hayton/Sam 'The Man' Taylor & Catmen)	8
64	RCA RCX 7159	MONTH'S BEST FROM THE COUNTRY AND WEST (Eddy Arnold/Bobby Bare/George Hamilton IV/Connie Smith)	7
64	RCA RCX 7162	MONTH'S BEST FROM THE COUNTRY AND WEST VOL. 2 (Skeeter Davis/Bobby Bare/Don Gibson/Jim Reeves/Hank Snow)	7
64	RCA RCX 7171	MONTH'S BEST FROM THE COUNTRY AND WEST VOL. 3 (Eddy Arnold/Archie Campbell/Porter Wagoner/Dottie West)	7
65	RCA RCX 7172	MONTH'S BEST FROM THE COUNTRY AND WEST VOL. 4 (Bobby Bare/Jim Edward Brown/Willie Nelson/Connie Smith)	7
65	RCA RCX 7178	MONTH'S BEST FROM THE COUNTRY AND WEST VOL. 5 (Bobby Bare/Norma Jean/Porter Wagoner/Connie Smith)	7
65	RCA RCX 7181	MONTH'S BEST FROM THE COUNTRY AND WEST VOL. 6 (Don Gibson/Bobby Bare/Carl Belew/George Hamilton IV/Hank Locklin/Dottie West)	7
67	RCA RCX 7186	MONTH'S BEST FROM THE COUNTRY AND WEST VOL. 7 (Waylon Jennings/Stu Phillips/Connie Smith/Dottie West)	7
60s	Jan & Dil TR 451	MORE DOWN HOME BLUES (Good Jelly Boss/Juke Boy Bonner/Papa Lightfoot/Snooky Prior)	10
60	Philips BBE 12348	MOST HAPPY FELLA HITS (Doris Day/Four Lads/Frankie Laine/Jo Stafford)	8
64	Stateside SE 1021	MOVIE MUSIC (John Barry/Artie Butler/Eddie Heywood/Bill Ramal Combo)	7

N

71	Eden	NAPTON FOLK CLUB (private pressing, 100 only)	50
56	Vogue EPV 1106	NEGRO SPIRITUALS (Original Five Blind Boys/Sensational Nightingales)	8
62	Vogue EPV 1271	NEGRO SPIRITUALS (Dixie Hummingbirds/Sensational Nightingales)	8
62	Vogue EPV 1276	NEGRO SPIRITUALS (Five Blind Boys/Spirits Of Memphis)	8
66	Tamla Motown TME 2014	NEW FACES FROM HITSVILLE (Jimmy Ruffin/Chris Clark & Lewis Sisters/Tammi Terrell/Monitors)	100
57	Pye NEP 24052	NIXA HIT PARADE NO. 1 (Gary Miller/Pet Clark/Lonnie Donegan/John Frazer)	10
58	Pye NEP 24064	NIXA HIT PARADE NO. 2 (Pearl Carr & Teddy Johnson/Petula Clark/Lonnie Donegan Skiffle Group/Colin Hicks & Cabin Boys)	12
58	Pye NEP 24071	NIXA HIT PARADE NO. 3 (Marion Ryan/Gary Miller/Lonnie Donegan/Edmund Hockridge)	10
58	Pye NEP 24078	NIXA HIT PARADE NO. 4 (Marion Ryan/Petula Clark/Joe Henderson/Gary Miller)	10
58	Pye NEP 24082	NIXA HIT PARADE NO. 5 (Petula Clark/Lonnie Donegan Skiffle Group/Marion Ryan/Bill Shepherd Orchestra)	7
58	Pye NEP 24090	NIXA HIT PARADE NO. 6 (Lita Roza/Petula Clark/Lonnie Donegan Skiffle Group/Joe Henderson)	7
59	Pye NEP 24100	NIXA HIT PARADE NO. 7 (Lita Roza/Petula Clark/Lonnie Donegan Skiffle Group/Edmund Hockridge)	7

O

65	Columbia SEG 8413	ON THE SCENE (Downliners Sect/Animals/Cherokees/Cheynes/Georgie Fame/Yardbirds)	25
63	MGM MGM-EP 787	ORIGINAL HITS (Tommy Edwards/Johnny Ferguson/Jimmy Jones/Conway Twitty)	20
63	London REK 1390	THE ORIGINAL HITS (Drifters/Richie Barrett/Coasters/Ben E. King)	12
65	Atlantic AET 6006	ORIGINAL HITS VOL. 2 (Barbara Lewis/Coasters/Solomon Burke/Drifters)	15
62	Ember EMB 4522	ORIGINAL RHYTHM AND BLUES HITS (Jesse Belvin/Ray Charles/Linda Hayes/Jimmy McCracklin/Johnny Moore Blazers)	30
55	Pye Jazz NJE 1043	ORIGINS OF SKIFFLE (Isla Cameron/Guy Carawan/Peggy Seeger)	12
57	Columbia SEG 7669	OUR CHOICE (Eddie Calvert/Michael Holliday/Ruby Murray)	10

P

55	London REA 1036	THE PAJAMA GAME (Archie Bleyer Orchestra/Stephen Douglas/Douglas & Dorothy Evans/Arthur Malvin)	8
55	Decca DFE 6147	PARADE OF STARS (Joan Regan/Edmundo Ros & Stargazers/Dickie Valentine/Stargazers)	10
58	Pye NEP 85000	POPS GO STEREO (Marion Ryan/Tony Osborne Orchestra/Bill Shepherd Orch.)	10

R

67	Action ACT 002 EP	RAG GOES MAD AT THE MOJO (33rpm, Joe Cocker's Blues Band & others, free with Sheffield University rag magazine 'Twikker')	50
78	Virgin VR 08 10274/SHOL 2550	RECORD MIRROR (no p/s; Tangerine Dream/XTC/Motors/U-Roy; with 2nd EP "The State Disco Party" & 'Record Mirror' magazine)	7
86	Record Mirror RM 6	FREE 5-TRACK EP (12"; Mighty Lemon Drops/Bodines/Westworld/World Party; with magazine)	7
56	Vogue EPV 1113	RHYTHM AND BLUES (Dominoes/Swallows)	120
60s	Range JRE 7002	RHYTHM AND BLUES (Sticks Herman/Tim Whitsett)	7
60s	Range JRE 7006	RHYTHM AND BLUES (Harry Lewis/Tommy Wills)	7
63	Stateside SE 1008	RHYTHM AND BLUES (Jimmy Reed/John Lee Hooker)	15
64	Stateside SE 1009	R&B CHARTMAKERS NO. 1 (Martha & Vandellas/Miracles/Marvin Gaye/Marvelettes)	40
64	Stateside SE 1018	R&B CHARTMAKERS NO. 2 (Miracles/Kim Weston/Supremes/Marvelettes)	40
64	Stateside SE 1022	R&B CHARTMAKERS NO. 3 (Marvin Gaye/Darnells/Eddie Holland/Martha & Vandellas)	40
64	Stateside SE 1025	R&B CHARTMAKERS NO. 4 (Supremes/Eddie Holland/Temptations/Contours)	40

62	Ember EMB EP 4522	RHYTHM & BLUES HITS (33rpm)	15
57	Vogue EPV 1198	RHYTHM AND BLUES CONCERT (Helen Humes/Jimmy Witherspoon)	20
64	Pye Intl. NEP 44021	RHYTHM AND BLUES SHOWCASE VOL. 1 (Don & Bob/Dale Hawkins/ Clarence Henty/Larry Williams)	15
64	Pye Intl. NEP 44022	RHYTHM AND BLUES SHOWCASE VOL. 2 (Jimmy McCracklin/ Muddy Waters/Little Walter/Howlin' Wolf)	15
57	Vogue VE1 70111	ROCK AND ROLL (Mister Google Eyes August/Louis Jones Rock & Roll Band/Walter Price Rock & Roll Band/Clarence Gatemouth Brown)	75
58	Embassy WEP 1004	ROCK 'N ROLL TIME (Rock'n'Rollers)	7
62	Capitol EAP1 20197	ROUND-UP (Tommy Collins/Farmer Boys/Ferlin Husky/Texas Bill Strength)	10
60	Top Rank JKP 2060	RUSHING FOR PERCUSSION (Preston Epps/Sandy Nelson)	15

S

63	Decca DFE 8541	SEA SHANTIES (FROM A LONDON HOOTENANNY) (Redd Sullivan/Lou Killen/Bob Davenport)	7
80	Statik 01 (X/80/CUS 675)	SECOND CITY STATIK — A GLASGOW COMPILATION (12", p/s; Alleged/Positive Noise/Restricted Code)	7
81	Springtime RARA 1001	THE SECRET POLICEMAN'S OTHER BALL (Sting/Phil Collins/Bob Geldof) (10", promo-only sampler)	15
55	Columbia SEG 7528	SHOUT FOR JOY (Pete Johnson/Albert Ammons/Meade Lux Lewis)	20
63	London REP 1403	SINGING THE BLUES (Ernie K-Doe/Showmen/Jesse Hill/Chris Kenner)	20
58	MGM MGM-EP 671	SINGING IN THE RAIN (Debbie Reynolds/Gene Kelly/Donald O'Connor)	7
58	Decca DFE 6485	SIX FIVE SPECIAL (Jackie Dennis/Joan Regan/Diane Todd/Dickie Valentine)	15
58	Pye NEP 24076	SIX HIT SONGS FROM MY FAIR LADY (Lita Roza/Petula Clark/Ray Ellington/ Gary Miller/Max Miller/Marion Ryan)	7
80s	Smash Hits	SMASH HITS INTERVIEW PACK (4 flexidiscs in envelope sleeve; Duran Duran/Spandau Ballet/Boy George/Frankie Goes To Hollywood)	8
62	Pye NEP 24158	SOME PEOPLE (Eagles/Valerie Mountain)	10
66	Lyntone LYN 995	THE SOUND OF THE STARS (flexidisc with 'Disc And Music Echo'; Beatles/ Pete Townshend/Hollies, etc; with/without mag & envelope/stamp)	20/10
65	Keele Rag/Lyntone LYN 951/952	SOUNDS OF SAVILE (Hipster Image/London Apprentices) Tom & Brennie; some in die-cut title sleeve)	50/40
55	Decca DFE 6147	STAR PARADE (Stargazers/Edmundo Ros Orchestra/Joan Regan & Squadronaires/Dickie Valentine)	10
60s	208 Radio Luxembourg	STAR SOUVENIR GREETINGS (flexidisc)	15
60	Mercury ZEP 10088	SURPRISE PACKAGE (Ben Hewitt/Diamonds)	50
59	Top Rank JKR 8007	SWEET BEAT (Lee Allen Band/Fred Parris/Cindy Mann/Mellokings)	20
58	Capitol EAP1 1026	SWINGIN' DRUMS (Billy May & His Orchestra/Earl Palmer & His Orchestra)	8

T

64	Oriole EP 7080	TAKE SIX (Mark Peters' Silhouettes/Ian & Zodiacs/Farons Flamingos/Earl Preston & T.T.'s/Rory Storm & Hurricanes/Sonny Wade & Cascades)	30
59	Mercury ZEP 10015	TEAR IT UP (Boyd Bennett Orchestra/Red Prysock/Hi-Liters)	80
57	Mercury MEP 9522	TEEN-AGE ROCK (Red Prysock/Rusty Draper/Chuck Miller/Crew Cuts)	65
58	RCA RCX 111	TEENAGE TOPS (Ray Peterson/Jimmy Dell/Marlin Greene/Barry De Vorzon)	25
64	Ember EMB 4540	TEEN SCENE '64 (Dave Clark Five/Ray Singer/Washington D.C.'s)	20
67	CBS Special Products WEP 1126	THEMES FROM JAMES BOND FILMS (John Barry Orchestra/Mertens Brothers Style/Percy Faith)	8
59	Brunswick OE 9425	THEY SOLD A MILLION NO. 9 (Jerry Lewis/Four Aces/Bobby Helms/Kitty Kallen)	15
59	Brunswick OE 9426	THEY SOLD A MILLION NO. 10 (Andrews Sisters/Four Aces/Ink Spots/ Mills Brothers)	8
59	Brunswick OE 9427	THEY SOLD A MILLION NO. 11 (Inkspots/Louis Jordan & His Tympany Five/ Mills Brothers/Weavers)	12
59	Brunswick OE 9431	THEY SOLD A MILLION NO. 15 (Four Aces/Bill Haley)	15
57	Decca DFE 6411	TOPS IN POPS NO. 1 (Beverley Sisters/Bob Cort Skiffle Group/Terry Dene/ Tommy Steele)	10
58	Decca DFE 6467	TOPS IN POPS NO. 3 (Jackie Dennis/D. King/Southlanders/David Whitfield)	10
59	Decca DFE 6583	TOPS IN POPS NO. 7 (Beverley Sisters/Ted Heath & His Music/ Lord Rockingham's XI/Tommy Steele)	8
63	Stateside SE 1004	TOP TEEN DANCES (Johnnie Morisette/Huey 'Piano' Smith & Clowns/ Al Brown's Tunetoppers/Spartans)	15
67	Pye NEP 24276	TOP T.V. THEMES (Cyril Stapleton/Ron Grainer Orchestra/Barry Gray Orchestra/Eliminators/Johnny Keating & Z Men)	8
60	Fontana TFE 17265	TREASURES OF NORTH AMERICAN NEGRO MUSIC VOL. 6 (Reverend J.C. Burnett/Reverend J.M. Gates/Reverend W. Mosley)	10
65	Century 21 MA 105	T.V. CENTURY 21 THEMES (David Graham/Sylvia Anderson/Peter Dyneley/ Barry Gray Orchestra/Gary Miller/Eric Winstone Orchestra)	12
64	Decca DEF 8585	T.V. THEMES (Andrew Oldham Orchestra/Ted Heath Music/ Ron Grainer Music/Cryil Stapleton Orchestra)	40
66	Decca DFE 8661	T.V. THEMES (Magicians/Frank Chacksfield Orchestra/Larry Page Orchestra)	7
66	Pye NEP 24244	T.V. THEMES 1966 (Laurie Johnson Orchestra/John Schroeder Orchestra/ Cyril Stapleton Orchestra)	12
62	Starlite STEP 31	TWIST OFF (Wayne Farmer/Medallions/Charles Perrywell/Piano Slim/ Teenbeats/Dellos)	50
62	Starlite STEP 29	TWIST ON (Mighty Trojans/Dee Dee Gaudet/Dixie Lee/ Percy & The Rocking Aces)	60

U-V

| 80s | Fierce FRIGHT/SFTRI 38 | AN UNHOLY MONTAGE (200 only, coloured vinyl with numbered insert) | 30 |
| 65 | Vogue VRE 5002 | VOGUE SURPRISE PARTIE (Petula Clark/Jean Jacques Debout/Francoise Hardy/Michel Paje) | 8 |

W

59	RCA RCX 128	WAGON TRAIN (Shorty Long/Prairie Chiefs/Sons Of The Pioneers)	7
69	Apple CT 1	WALLS ICE CREAM PRESENTS (Mary Hopkin/Iveys/Jackie Lomax/ James Taylor; with/without p/s)	40/15
65	Liberty LEP 4036	WE SING THE BLUES (Jesse Hill/Ernie K. Doe/Aaron Neville/Benny Spellman)	15
75	Solid Sender SEP 101	WEST SIDE CHICAGO	10

MINT VALUE £

84	Rather/Seventeen GEAR 17	WHAT A NICE WAY TO TURN SEVENTEEN NO. 2 (Swell Maps & others; with magazine) 12
64	Fontana TFE 18009	WITH GOD ON OUR SIDE (Bob Dylan/Joan Baez/Pete Seeger) 35
66	Chess CRE 6009	WITH THE BLUES (Eddie Boyd Blues Combo/Buddy Guy) 12

Y

64	Fontana TFE 18011	YE PLAYBOYS AND PLAYGIRLS (Bob Dylan/Joan Baez/Pete Seeger) 35
68	Chess CRE 6026	YOUR CHESS REQUESTS (Fontella Bass/Tony Clarke/Mitty Collier/Billy Stewart) 15
57	Mercury MEP 9525	YOUR CHOICE (Hal Mooney Orchestra/Chuck Miller/Sarah Vaughan/ Florian Zabach) 20
58	Mercury MEP 9532	YOUR CHOICE NO. 2 (Ralph Marterie Orch./Patti Page/Platters/Myoshi Umeki) ..12

UNTITLED EPs & SINGLES

73	Buddah 2011 164	(Shangri-La's/Tradewinds/Ad Libs) 5
60s	Coxsone SCE 1	(no p/s, 33rpm; Gaylads/Hugh Godfrey/Glen & Dave/Roy Richards/ Cables/Richard Ace) 25
71	Track 2094 011	(John's Children/Crazy World Of Arthur Brown/Thunderclap Newman/Jimi Hendrix; withdrawn blue sleeve crediting Pete Townshend as producer) 100
71	Track 2094 011	(John's Children/Crazy World Of Arthur Brown/Thunderclap Newman/Jimi Hendrix; red & white sleeve with press pack, also maroon & gold sleeve) 50/7

VARIOUS ARTISTS — LPs & COMPILATIONS
(alphabetical by title)

A

80	Absurd TAKE 1	ABSURD TAKE AWAY 10
88	Woronzow WOO 6	ACID JAM (LP) 12
69	Action ACLP 6005	ACTION PACKED SOUL 15
81	Adventures In Reality 1	ADVENTURES IN REALITY COMPILATION (cassette with booklet) 10
85	United Dairies UD 012	AN AFFLICTED MAN'S MUSICAL BOX (3 different editions, 1st in gatefold sleeve) 45/20
70	Pama PMP 2004	AFRICAN MELODY 15
71	Trojan TBL 166	AFRICA'S BLOOD 20
73	Polydor 2460 186	AMERICAN BLUES LEGENDS '73 12
74	Big Bear BEAR 1	AMERICAN BLUES LEGENDS 1974 10
75	Big Bear BEAR 8	AMERICAN BLUES LEGENDS 1975 10
66	Stateside SL 10172	AN ALBUM FULL OF SOUL 25
69	Key KL 002	ALIVE! 30
84	Creation CRELP 001	ALIVE IN THE LIVING ROOM 15
84	Whaam! BIG 8	ALL FOR ART ... AND ART FOR ALL 30
71	Utd. Artists UDX 201/202	ALL GOOD CLEAN FUN (2-LP) 15
58	Pye Nixa NJT 509	ALL THE WINNERS (10") 15
77	Riva RVLP 2	ALL THIS AND WORLD WAR TWO (2-LP, with booklet) 15
58	Parlophone PMD 1064	ALL TIME COUNTRY AND WESTERN HITS (10") 12
60s	Topic 12T 189	ALONG THE COALY TYNE (original sleeve) 12
63	Polydor LPHM 46 397	AMERICAN FOLK BLUES FESTIVAL (also stereo SLPHM 237 597) 15
70s	Rare Records 2	AMERICAN FOLK BLUES FESTIVAL 1962 15
64	Fontana TL 5204	AMERICAN FOLK BLUES FESTIVAL 1963 15
65	Fontana TL 5225	AMERICAN FOLK BLUES FESTIVAL 1964 15
66	Fontana TL 5286	AMERICAN FOLK BLUES FESTIVAL 1965 15
66	Fontana (S)TL 5389	AMERICAN FOLK BLUES FESTIVAL 1966 (mono/stereo) 15/20
70	CBS 63912	AMERICAN FOLK BLUES FESTIVAL 1969 12
70s	Lorimar/CBS 70172	AMERICATHON 10
70s	Skeleton SKLLP 1	AND THE DANCE GOES ON 10
80s	Pleasantly Surprised PS 2	THE ANGELS ARE COMING (2-cassette, with booklet) 25
80	Alt. Capitalists ACC 007	ANOTHER CRACK IN THE VOID (C60 cassette) 10
69	Immediate IMAL 03/04	ANTHOLOGY OF BRITISH BLUES VOLUME 1 (2-LP, gatefold sleeve) 18
69	Immediate IMAL 05/06	ANTHOLOGY OF BRITISH BLUES VOLUME 2 (2-LP, gatefold sleeve) 18
64	London HA-K/SH-K 8174	APOLLO SATURDAY NIGHT (mono/stereo) 30/40
60s	Atlantic 590 007	APOLLO SATURDAY NIGHT (reissue) 12
80s	Ram RAMLP 001	THE ART OF SOLVING PROBLEMS (with insert) 10
74	Ashanti SHAN 106	ASHANTI SHOWCASE 10
64	Decca LK 4597	AT THE CAVERN 35
65	Atlantic ATL 5020	ATLANTIC DISCOTHEQUE 12
60s	Atlantic AP 2	ATLANTIC IS SOUL 15
60s	Atlantic AC 3	ATLANTICLASSICS 25
74	Horse HRLP 705	ATLANTIC ONE 10
67	Pye NPL 18198	AT LAST THE 1948 SHOW 12
80s	Sweatbox AMO 5	AUDIO VISUAL — AUDIO MAGAZINE NO. 5 (printed PVC sleeve) 15
80s	Sweatbox SAM 006	AUDIO VISUAL — AUDIO MAGAZINE NO. 6 (printed PVC sleeve, w/ inner & booklet) 15
80	Aura BAUL 601	AURAL WAX 10
60s	Beacon SBEAB 9	AUTHENTIC CHICAGO BLUES 15
72	Windmill WMD 124	AUTHENTIC CHICAGO BLUES 15
64	Stateside SL 10107	AUTHENTIC SKA 25
64	Stateside SL 10068	AUTHENTIC RHYTHM AND BLUES 25
79	Heartbeat HB 1	AVON CALLING — THE BRISTOL COMPILATION (with poster) 10
80s	Flaccid FLAC 1	AYLESBURY GOES FLACCID 12

B

67	Fontana FJL 135	BACK TO BACK 10
70s	Weird	BACK TO SING FOR FREE AGAIN SOON (C90 cassette) 10
70	Track 2407 001	BACKTRACK ONE 10
70	Track 2407 002	BACKTRACK TWO 10
70	Track 2407 006	BACKTRACK SIX 15
70	Track 2407 007	BACKTRACK SEVEN 10

54	London AL 3535	BACKWOODS BLUES (10")	30
62	Fontana 688 200 ZL	BALLIN'	15
68	Pama PMLP 4	BANG BANG LULU	25
60	Melodisc 12-115	BANJO BREAKDOWN	10
64	Storyville 670 155	BARRELHOUSE BLUES AND BOOGIE-WOOGIE VOLUME 1	12
65	Storyville 670 183	BARRELHOUSE BLUES AND BOOGIE-WOOGIE VOLUME 2	12
59	Fontana TFR 6018	BARRELHOUSE, BOOGIE WOOGIE AND BLUES (10")	15
58	Vogue Coral LRA 10022	BARRELHOUSE PIANO (10" LP)	20
59	Vogue Coral LRA 10023	BARRELHOUSE PIANO VOLUME 2 (10" LP)	20
83	London CAVE 1	THE BATCAVE — YOUNG LIMBS AND NUMB HYMNS	10
71	Trojan TBL 167	BATTLE AXE	20
71	B&C BCM 103	BATTLE OF THE BANDS	10
60s	Melodisc 12-192	BATTLE OF THE GIANTS	15
53	MGM MGM-D 115	A BATTLE OF JAZZ: HOT VERSUS COOL (10")	12
69	Beacon BEAB 1	BEACON BRINGS IT TO YOU	10
70s	Revival RVS 1004	BEALE STREET MESSAROUND	12
87	Pink PINKY 15	BEAUTY	10
80s	Porrit's Hill PHEW 2	BECKET HOUSE	12
68	Elektra EUK 262	BEGIN HERE (also stereo EUKS 7262)	10
80s	Rip Off ROLP 1	BELFAST ROCKS	15
68	Bell MBLL 102	BELL'S CELLAR OF SOUL VOLUME 1	12
69	Bell MBLL 107	BELL'S CELLAR OF SOUL VOLUME 2	12
69	Bell MBLL 117	BELL'S CELLAR OF SOUL VOLUME 3	12
69	Bell MBLL/SBLL 111	THE BEST FROM BELL	10
69	Bell MBLL/SBLL 124	THE BEST FROM BELL VOLUME 2	10
78	Stiff ODD 2	BE STIFF	10
70s	Storyville 671 188	THE BEST OF THE BLUES	12
67	United Artists LAS 29021	THE BEST OF BOND (mono)	10
69	United Ariists UAS 29021	THE BEST OF BOND (stereo)	10
85	Kamaflage	BEST OF BRITISH	10
65	Xtra XTRA 1031	THE BEST OF BRITISH FOLK	10
69	Pama SECO 18	THE BEST OF CAMEL	15
69	President PTL 1016	THE BEST OF PRESIDENT VOLUME 1	10
62	Parlophone PMC 1145	BEYOND THE FRINGE	15
87	Imaginary ILLUSION 001	BEYOND THE WILDWOOD — A TRIBUTE TO SYD BARRETT	10
73	Attack ATLP 1011	BIG BAMBOO	10
60	Fontana TFL 5080	THE BIG BEAT!	20
64	London HA-B 8199	THE BIG 'D' JAMBOREE	15
69	Minit 40007E	THE BIG ONE	15
70	Pama SECO 32	BIRTH CONTROL	15
70	Matchbox SDX 207/8	BLACK DIAMOND EXPRESS TO HELL (2-LP)	20
60	Columbia 33SX 1244	BLACKPOOL NIGHTS	20
58	HMV CLP 1167	BLACK SLACKS AND BOBBY SOCKS	30
70	Ember SE 8009	BLACK SOUL EXPLOSION	10
70	CBS 52796	BLACK WHITES AND BLUES	15
68	Coxsone CSP 1	BLUE BEAT SPECIAL	25
66	RCA Victor RD 7786	BLUEBIRD BLUES	15
63	Stateside SL 10021	THE BLUEGRASS HALL OF FAME	10
65	London HA-B 8227	BLUEGRASS HALL OF FAME VOL. 2	10
64	London HA-B 8118	BLUEGRASS SPECTACULAR	10
62	Columbia 33SX 1417	THE BLUES	30
68	Marble Arch MAL 804	THE BLUES	10
64	Chess CRL 4003	BLUES PART 4	15
64	Pye Intl. NPL 28030	BLUES VOL. 1	12
64	Pye Intl. NPL 28035	BLUES VOL. 2	12
64	Pye Intl. NPL 28045	BLUES VOL. 3	12
67	Marble Arch MAL 664	BLUES & SOUL	12
68	Immediate IMLP 014	BLUES ANYTIME VOL. 1	15
68	Immediate IMCP 015	BLUES ANYTIME VOL. 2	15
68	Immediate IMLP 019	BLUES ANYTIME VOL. 3	15
66	London HA-S 8265	THE BLUES CAME DOWN FROM MEMPHIS	30
73	Flyright LP 504	BLUES CAME TO CHAPEL HILL	12
65	Storyville SLP 176	BLUESCENE USA: VOLUME 1 — CHICAGO	15
65	Storyville SLP 177	BLUESCENE USA: VOLUME 2 — LOUISIANA BLUES	15
65	Storyville SLP 181	BLUESCENE USA: VOLUME 3 — BLUES ALL AROUND MY BED	15
67	Storyville SLP 180	BLUESCENE USA: VOLUME 4 — MISSISSIPPI BLUES	15
60	Philips BBL 7369	BLUES FELL THIS MORNING	40
73	Polydor 2383 257	BLUES FOR MR. CRUMP	25
70	Pye NPL 28142	BLUES FROM THE BAYOU	15
69	Python PLP 6	BLUES FROM CHICAGO	25
70	Python PLP 9	BLUES FROM CHICAGO VOL. 2	25
71	Python PLP 15	BLUES FROM CHICAGO VOL. 3	25
60s	Heritage 1004	BLUES FROM MAXWELL STREET	30
71	Python PLP 21	BLUES FROM THE WINDY CITY	25
77	Flyright LP 4713	BLUES FROM THE WINDY CITY	12
60s	Sunflower (no cat. no.)	BLUES IS MY COMPANION	25
60s	Sunflower (no cat. no.)	BLUES KEEP FALLING	25
69	Blue Horizon 7-66227	BLUES JAM AT CHESS (2-LP)	40
69	Immediate IMLP 024	BLUES LEFTOVERS	12
67	Saydisc Match. SDM 142	BLUES LIKE SHOWERS OF RAIN	50
68	Saydisc Match. SDM 167	BLUES LIKE SHOWERS OF RAIN VOLUME 2	50
65	Decca LK 4681	BLUES NOW	30
72	Blues Obscurities	BLUES OBSCURITIES VOL. 1: SOUTHERN BLUES/DARK MUDDY BOTTOM	30
72	Blues Obscurities	BLUES OBSCURITIES VOL. 2: LONESOME HARMONICA	30
72	Blues Obscurities	BLUES OBSCURITIES VOL. 3: WEST COAST BLUES	30
72	Blues Obscurities	BLUES OBSCURITIES VOL. 4: ONE RAINY MORNING	30

Various Artists: LPs

72	Blues Obscurities	BLUES OBSCURITIES VOL. 5: SOMETHING'S GONE WRONG	30
72	Blues Obscurities	BLUES OBSCURITIES VOL. 6: COMING BACK HOME	30
72	Blues Obscurities	BLUES OBSCURITIES VOL. 7	30
72	Blues Obscurities	BLUES OBSCURITIES VOL. 8	30
72	Blues Obscurities	BLUES OBSCURITIES VOL. 9	30
72	Blues Obscurities	BLUES OBSCURITIES VOL. 10	30
74	London HA-U 8454	BLUES OBSCURITIES VOL. 1: DARK MUDDY BOTTOM (reissue)	15
74	London HA-U 8455	BLUES OBSCURITIES VOL. 2: LONESOME HARMONICA (reissue)	15
74	London HA-U 8456	BLUES OBSCURITIES VOL. 3: STRETCHIN' OUT	15
69	Mercury SMXL 77	BLUES PACKAGE '69	10
69	Highway 51 H 102	BLUES PEOPLE	50
68	Matchbox SDR 146	BLUES PIANO	12
72	Atlantic K 40404	BLUES PIANO — CHICAGO PLUS	20
68	Kokomo K 1001	A BLUES POTPOURRI	50
71	Rarities (Tony's Records)	BLUES RARITIES VOL. 1 (2-LP)	25
69	Atlantic Special 590 019	BLUES ROLL ON	15
70s	Poppy	BLUES ROOTS VOLUME ONE	20
66	Decca LK 4748	BLUES SOUTHSIDE CHICAGO	25
71	Python PLP 16	BLUES TODAY — SOUTHERN STYLE	25
60s	Topic 12T 128	BONNY LASS COME O'ER THE BURN	10
70s	Milestone MLP 2009	BOOGIE WOOGIE RARITIES	15
55	London AL 3544	BOOGIE WOOGIE WITH THE BLUES (10")	15
69	Pama SECO 17	BOSS REGGAE	40
80	Aardvark STEAL 2	BOUQUET OF STEEL (blue vinyl with 27-page booklet)	15
70s	Bradley's BRADB 4001	BRADLEY'S ROADSHOW	10
63	Parlophone PMC 1190	BRIDGE ON THE RIVER WYE (also stereo PCS 3036)	15
87	GWR GBS 1	BRISTOL CUSTOM BIKE SHOW 1986 (some with poster)	15/10
70s	Bristol Recorder BR 002	THE BRISTOL RECORDER VOL. 2 (LP, some with magazine)	25/15
70s	Bristol Recorder BR 003	THE BRISTOL RECORDER VOL. 3 (LP, with magazine)	10
68	Island ILP 966/ILPS 9066	BRITISH BLUE-EYED SOUL	40
67	Tamla Motown TML 11055	BRITISH MOTOWN CHARTBUSTERS (mono)	12
69	T. Motown STML 11055	BRITISH MOTOWN CHARTBUSTERS (stereo)	12
68	T. Motown (S)TML 11082	BRITISH MOTOWN CHARTBUSTERS VOL. 2	10
70	Trojan TBL 106	BRIXTON CAT	12
60s	Dial DLP 1	BRUM BEAT	60
79	Big Bear BRUM 1	BRUM BEAT — LIVE AT THE BARREL ORGAN (2-LP, with inserts)	20
72	Flyright LP 106	BULL CITY BLUES	12
66	Decca LK 4734	BUMPER BUNDLE	20
79	Cherry Red ARED 2	BUSINESS UNUSUAL (with 'Zig Zag' small labels catalogue)	10
81	Autumn AU 2	BUSTED AT OZ	20

C

71	Trojan TBL 171	CARIBBEAN DANCE FESTIVAL	10
73	Flyright LP 505	CAROLINA COUNTRY BLUES	15
81	Rough Trade/NME COPY 1	C-81 (mail-order cassette via 'NME')	10
86	NME 022	C-86 (mail-order cassette via 'NME')	10
80s	Cerne CERNE 123	THE CERNE BOX SET (3-LP box set; Nurse With Wound/Current 93/ Sol Invictus; with 3 inserts)	40
60	Chappell 672-677	CHAPPELL RECORDED MUSIC (library issue)	20
60	Chappell 678-682	CHAPPELL RECORDED MUSIC (library issue)	20
60s	Columbia	CHARTBUSTERS USA	25
73	Checker 6445 150	CHESS GOLDEN DECADE VOL. 1: THE EARLY 50's	12
73	Checker 6445 150	CHESS GOLDEN DECADE VOL. 2: 1956 TAKE IT EASY GREASY	12
73	Checker 6445 150	CHESS GOLDEN DECADE VOL. 3: 1957 DIME STORE PONY TAIL	12
74	Checker 6445 150	CHESS GOLDEN DECADE VOL. 4: 1958-1959 BOOK OF LOVE	12
74	Checker 6445 150	CHESS GOLDEN DECADE VOL. 5: 1959-1961 GOOD MORNING LITTLE SCHOOLGIRL	12
70s	Chess	CHESS STORY VOL. 1	10
70s	Delmark DS 624	CHICAGO AIN'T NOTHING BUT A BLUES BAND	12
60s	Vanguard VSD 79217	CHICAGO BLUES VOLUME 2	10
66	Fontana TFL 6068	CHICAGO/THE BLUES/TODAY	15
66	Fontana TFL 6069	CHICAGO/THE BLUES/TODAY VOLUME 2	15
66	Fontana TFL 6070	CHICAGO/THE BLUES/TODAY VOLUME 3	15
69	Vanguard SVRL 19020	CHICAGO/THE BLUES/TODAY VOLUME 1	20
69	Vanguard SVRL 19021	CHICAGO/THE BLUES/TODAY VOLUME 2	20
69	Vanguard SVRL 19022	CHICAGO/THE BLUES/TODAY VOLUME 3	15
68	Sunflower ET 1401	THE CHICAGO HOUSE BANDS	25
70s	JSP 1004	CHICAGO JUMP	12
69	Kokomo K 1005	CHICAGO SESSIONS VOLUME 1	40
70	Flyright LP 4700	CHICKEN STUFF	15
58	Philips BBR 8112	CHRISTMAS (10")	15
73	United Artists UDX 205/6	CHRISTMAS AT THE PATTI (2 x 10")	18
68	Chess CRLS 4541	CHRISTMAS DEDICATION	15
81	Ze ILPS 7071/2	A CHRISTMAS RECORD (white or black vinyl, different track listings)	10
63	London HA-U 8141	A CHRISTMAS GIFT FOR YOU	30
72	Speciality SNTF 5015	CITY BLUES	10
80s	White Elephant RIOCH 1	CITY WALLS — A SOUTHAMPTON COMPILATION (with insert)	10
55	London AL 3559	CLASSIC JAZZ PIANO (10")	25
52	Capitol LC 6559	CLASSICS IN JAZZ: PIANO ITEMS (10")	15
52	Capitol LC 6561	CLASSICS IN JAZZ: THE MODERN IDIOM (10")	15
52	Capitol LC 6562	CLASSICS IN JAZZ: DIXIELAND STYLE (10")	10
52	Capitol LC 6563	CLASSICS IN JAZZ: SMALL COMBOS (10")	12
53	Capitol LC 6579	CLASSICS IN JAZZ: TRUMPET STYLISTS (10")	15
53	Capitol LC 6598	CLASSICS IN JAZZ: SAX STYLISTS (10")	15
53	Capitol LC 6598	CLASSICS IN JAZZ: COOL AND QUIET (10")	15
70s	Waldo's DS 005	CLEANING UP THE MUSIC BIZ	10
72	Pegasus PS 1	CLOGS (FOLK SAMPLER)	10

MINT VALUE £

72	Pegasus PS 2	CLUB FOLK VOLUME ONE	10
72	Pegasus PS 3	CLUB FOLK VOLUME TWO	10
70	Trojan TBL 159	CLUB REGGAE VOLUME ONE	10
71	Trojan TBL 164	CLUB REGGAE VOLUME TWO	10
71	Trojan TBL 178	CLUB REGGAE VOLUME THREE	10
72	Trojan TBL 188	CLUB REGGAE VOLUME FOUR	10
68	Island ILP 965	CLUB ROCK STEADY '68	50
70	Trojan TTL 54	CLUB ROCK STEADY	20
67	Island ILP 948	CLUB SKA '67	50
67	Island ILP 956	CLUB SKA '67 VOL. 2	50
70	Trojan TTL 48	CLUB SKA VOLUME ONE	15
70	Trojan TTL 51	CLUB SKA VOLUME ONE	20
68	Island ILP 964	CLUB SOUL	30
60s	Gallojazz	COLD CASTLE JAZZ FESTIVAL	80
66	Elektra EUK 253	A COLD WIND BLOWS	10
65	Tamla Motown TML 11001	A COLLECTION OF 16 TAMLA MOTOWN HITS	30
67	Tamla Motown TML 11043	A COLLECTION OF 16 ORIGINAL BIG HITS VOL. 4	20
67	Tamla Motown TML 11050	A COLLECTION OF 16 ORIGINAL BIG HITS VOL. 5	15
68	T. Motown (S)TML 11074	A COLLECTION OF 16 BIG HITS VOL. 6	15
69	T. Motown (S)TML 11092	A COLLECTION OF BIG HITS VOL. 7	12
70	T. Motown (S)TML 11130	A COLLECTION OF 16 BIG HITS VOL. 8	10
75	Chicago 202	COLLECTORS BLUES SERIES VOL. 1	20
75	Chicago 205	COLLECTORS BLUES SERIES VOL. 2	20
75	Chicago 210	COLLECTORS BLUES SERIES VOL. 3	20
75	Chicago 212	COLLECTORS BLUES SERIES VOL. 4	20
75	Chicago 213	COLLECTORS BLUES SERIES VOL. 5	20
54	London AL 3514	COLLECTORS' ITEMS VOLUME ONE (10")	15
54	London AL 3533	COLLECTORS' ITEMS VOLUME TWO (10")	15
56	London AL 3550	COLLECTORS' ITEMS VOLUME THREE (10")	15
64	Blue Beat BBLP 803	COME FLY WITH ME	70
84	TPSU TPSU 0001	COMMUNICATE!!!! LIVE AT THAMES POLY (2-LP, with booklet)	15
72	Apple STCX 3385	THE CONCERT FOR BANGLA DESH (3-LP box set, with booklet)	22
64	Decca LK 4664	CONVERSATION WITH THE BLUES	50
57	Tempo TAP 10	COOL MUSIC FOR A HOT NIGHT - MOOD MUSIC IN THE MODERN MANNER	25
72	Wicksteed WCKLP 02	CORBY CATCHMENT AREA (private pressing)	175
80s	Third Mind TMLP 09	COULD YOU WALK ON THE WATER	10
66	Stateside SL 10170	COUNTRY COUSINS	10
64	London HA-B 8145	COUNTRY & WESTERN GOLDEN HIT PARADE VOL. 1	15
64	London HA-B 8146	COUNTRY & WESTERN GOLDEN HIT PARADE VOL. 2	15
60	Philips BBL 7410	COUNTRY AND WESTERN REQUESTS	10
73	Speciality SNTF 5014	COUNTRY BLUES	10
60s	Saydisc Roots RL 334	COUNTRY BLUES OBSCURITIES VOLUME 1	12
56	Brunswick LA 8729	COUNTRY FAVOURITES VOL. ONE (10")	15
65	London HA-B 8243	COUNTRY GUITAR HALL OF FAME	15
64	London HA-B 8198	THE COUNTRY MUSIC FESTIVAL	12
66	London HA-B 8263	COUNTRY MUSIC FESTIVAL VOL. 2	10
66	London HA-B 8287	COUNTRY MUSIC FESTIVAL VOL. 3	10
63	Stateside SL 10017	THE COUNTRY MUSIC HALL OF FAME	10
63	London HA-B 8076	COUNTRY MUSIC HALL OF FAME VOL. 1	12
63	London HA-B 8077	COUNTRY MUSIC HALL OF FAME VOL. 2	12
64	London HA-B 8156	COUNTRY MUSIC HALL OF FAME VOL. 3	12
64	London HA-B 8157	COUNTRY MUSIC HALL OF FAME VOL. 4	12
65	London HA-B 8216	COUNTRY MUSIC HALL OF FAME VOL. 5	12
65	London HA-B 8217	COUNTRY MUSIC HALL OF FAME VOL. 6	12
66	London HA-B 8283	COUNTRY MUSIC HALL OF FAME VOL. 7	12
66	London HA-B 8284	COUNTRY MUSIC HALL OF FAME VOL. 8	12
67	London HA-B 8328	COUNTRY MUSIC HALL OF FAME VOL. 9	10
67	London HA-B 8329	COUNTRY MUSIC HALL OF FAME VOL. 10	10
68	London HA-B 8354	COUNTRY MUSIC HALL OF FAME VOL. 11	10
68	London HA-B 8355	COUNTRY MUSIC HALL OF FAME VOL. 12	10
65	London HA-B 8206	THE COUNTRY MUSIC MEMORIAL ALBUM	10
62	Stateside SL 10003	COUNTRY MUSIC SPECTACULAR	10
64	London HA-B 8185	COUNTRY MUSIC U.S.A.	10
65	London HA-B 8224	COUNTRY MUSIC WHO'S WHO	10
59	Capitol T 1179	THE COUNTRY'S BEST	10
69	Pama ECO 2	CRAB — GREATEST HITS	20
80	Rabid/Absurd LAST 1	THE CRAP STOPS HERE	10
60	Fontana TFL 5103	THE CREAM OF 'TAKE IT FROM HERE' (also stereo SFL 534)	10
60s	Saydisc Roots RL 332	CREAM OF THE CROP	12

D

90	Wau! Mr Modo WAMLP002	DANCEBUSTERS VOLUME ONE	10
90	Wau! Mr M. WAMCD002	DANCEBUSTERS VOLUME ONE (CD)	15
68	High Note/Big Shot BSLP 5002	DANCING DOWN ORANGE STREET	40
76	Dark Horse DH1	DARK HORSE RECORDS '76 (promo-only sampler)	25
79	Dead Good DEAD 4	DEAD GOOD'S DEAD GOODS	10
78	Virgin VD 2508	DEAD ON ARRIVAL (glow-in-dark vinyl with poster)	10
80s	Debut LPMAG 6	DEBUT — ISSUE 6 (LP, gatefold sleeve with magazine)	10
66	Highway 51 H 100	DECADE OF THE BLUES — THE 1950'S	50
66	Highway 51 H-104	DECADE OF THE BLUES — THE 1950'S VOLUME 2	40
54	Decca LF 1160	DECCA SHOWCASE VOL. 3 (10")	12
55	Decca LF 1265	DECCA SHOWCASE VOL. 5 (10")	12
65	London HA-B 8249	DECK OF CARDS	10
69	Topic 12T 188	DEEP LANCASHIRE	10
70	Stax SXATS 1037	THE DEEP SOUL OF STAX	10
71	Flyright LP 102	DEEP SOUTH COUNTRY BLUES	12

MINT VALUE £

80s	NME	DEPARTMENT OF ENJOYMENT (cassette, mail-order only via 'NME' mag)	10
67	Island ILP 955	DERRICK HARRIOTT'S ROCKSTEADY PARTY	80
72	Trojan TTL 50	DERRICK HARRIOTT'S ROCKSTEADY PARTY (reissue)	35
80s	Yankhi 01	DEVASTATE TO LIBERATE	15
80	DinDisc DONE 1	DINDISC 1980 (with free 20" x 20" game)	10
69	Minit MLL/MLS 40005	DIRT BLUES	20
70	BBC	DISC A DAWN	30
67	Island ILP 943	DOCTOR SOUL	40
70s	Pleasantly Surprised PS12	DOCUMENT (cassette)	18
79	Object Music OBJ 014	DO THE MARU	10
80s	Compact Org. PACT 6	DO THEY MEAN US (2-LP with inserts & poster)	14
89	EMI EE 3530	THE DOTTED LINE (HERE)	10
89	EMI TCEE 3530	THE DOTTED LINE (HERE) (cassette)	10
89	EMI EE 3531	THE DOTTED LINE (THERE)	10
89	EMI TCEE 3531	THE DOTTED LINE (THERE) (cassette)	10
70	Python PLP	DOWNHOME BLUES	25
70	Python PLP 14	DOWNHOME BLUES VOLUME 2	25
71	Python PLP 22	DOWNHOME BLUES VOLUME 3	25
73	Speciality SNTF 5024	DOWN HOME BLUES	10
71	Flyright LP 4703	DOWN IN HOGAN'S ALLEY	15
67	Down With The Game 200	DOWN WITH THE GAME VOLUME 1	30
67	Down With The Game 201	DOWN WITH THE GAME VOLUME 2	30
68	Down With The Game 203	DOWN WITH THE GAME VOLUME 3	30
68	Down With The Game 204	DOWN WITH THE GAME VOLUME 4	30
68	Down With The Game 205	DOWN WITH THE GAME VOLUME 5	30
68	Down With The Game 206	DOWN WITH THE GAME VOLUME 6	30
67	Island ILP 954	DR. KITCH	30
82	Beggars Banquet BEGA 35	DR. RHINO AND MR HYDE	12
69	Pama PMLP 11	A DREAM (LP)	10
80s	Pleasantly Surprised PS 6	DREAMS AND DESIRES (cassette, in bag)	15
59	Parlophone PMC 1101	DRUMBEAT	30
68	Island ILP 976	THE DUKE AND THE PEACOCK	40
69	Trojan TTL 8	DUKE REID'S GOLDEN HITS	15
67	Island ILP 958	DUKE REID'S ROCK STEADY	70
70	Trojan TTL 53	DUKE REID'S ROCK STEADY	35

E

70	Matchbox SDR 199	EARLY BLUES VOLUME 1: SKOODLE-UM-SKOO	15
70	Matchbox SDR 206	EARLY BLUES VOLUME 2: HOMETOWN SKIFFLE	15
70	Middle Earth MDLS 20	EARTHED	50
80	Dead Good GOOD 1	EAST (with inner & stickered sleeve)	20
73	Southern Sound SD 200	EAST VERNON BLUES	30
63	Decca LK 4546	EDINBURGH FOLK FESTIVAL VOLUME 1	25
63	Decca LK 4563	EDINBURGH FOLK FESTIVAL VOLUME 2	25
80s	Fried Egg FRY 2	E(GG)CLECTIC 1	10
55	Philips BBR 8046	EIGHT EVERGREENS (10")	12
75	Island/Transatlantic FOLK 1001	ELECTRIC MUSE — THE STORY OF FOLK INTO ROCK (4-LP box set with booklet)	45
80s	Push PUSH 001	ELEGANCE, CHARM AND DEADLY DANGER	15
80s	Extract XX 001	ELEPHANT TABLE ALBUM	10
57	Brunswick LAT 8166	ENCYCLOPAEDIA OF JAZZ ON RECORDS VOL. 1	12
57	Brunswick LAT 8167	ENCYCLOPAEDIA OF JAZZ ON RECORDS VOL. 2	12
57	Brunswick LAT 8168	ENCYCLOPAEDIA OF JAZZ ON RECORDS VOL. 3	12
57	Brunswick LAT 8169	ENCYCLOPAEDIA OF JAZZ ON RECORDS VOL. 4	12
83	Psycho PSYCHO 1	ENDLESS JOURNEY VOL. 1 (numbered)	25
83	Psycho PSYCHO 3	ENDLESS JOURNEY VOL. 2 (numbered)	20
83	Psycho PSYCHO 19	ENDLESS JOURNEY VOL. 3 (numbered)	20
83	Essence Rare	ESSENCE RARE (C60 cassette)	10
89	Gee Street GEE A 002	ETERNITY PROJECT ONE	20
89	Gee Street GEE ACD 002	ETERNITY PROJECT ONE (CD)	25
67	Speciality SPE/LP 6601	EVERYDAY I HAVE THE BLUES	15
72	Blue Horizon 2683 007	THE EXCELLO STORY (2-LP)	70
68	Amal. AMGLP 2002	EXPLOSIVE ROCKSTEADY	30

F

80s	Facet	FACET 1 (C60 cassette with magazine)	10
67	Elektra EUK 259	FANTASTIC FOLK	12
78	Lightning LIP 2	FAREWELL TO THE ROXY	10
80s	Come Org. WDC 881021	FASHIONED TO A DEVICE BEHIND A TREE	80
63	Pye Intl. NPL 28033	FESTIVAL OF THE BLUES	20
67	Marble Arch MAL 724	FESTIVAL OF THE BLUES (reissue)	10
61	Melodisc 12-116	FIDDLIN' COUNTRY STYLE	10
89	Fire FIRE CD 19	15 FLAMING GROOVIES (CD, promo-only)	15
60s	Melodisc MS 4	15 OLDIES BUT GOODIES	15
65	Sue ILP 920	50 MINUTES & 24 SECONDS OF RECORDED DYNAMITE	40
72	Warner Bros K 66013	FILLMORE: THE LAST DAYS (3-LP box set with poster & booklet)	30
72	CBS 63816	FILLMORE WEST	10
65	London HA-B 8205	FINGERS ON FIRE	15
60	HMV CLP 1358/CSD 1298	FINGS AIN'T WOT THEY USED TO BE	20
64	London HA-B 8117	FIRE ON THE STRINGS	10
69	Spark SRLM 2003	FIREPOINT — A COLLECTION OF FOLK BLUES	25
71	CBS 66311	THE FIRST GREAT ROCK FESTIVALS OF THE 70s: ISLE OF WIGHT AND ATLANTA (3-LP)	25
56	Mercury MPT 7512	FIRST ROCK 'N' ROLL PARTY (10")	20
57	Esquire 20-089	THE FIRST NATIONAL SKIFFLE CONTEST (10")	20
80s	Alt. Tentacles VIRUS 22	FLEX YOUR HEAD	10
76	Flams Ltd/Wounded	FOLK AT THE CHEQUERS (private pressing)	15

66	Elektra EUK 251/2	FOLK BOX (2-LP)	15
66	Waverley ZLP 2067	FOLK FAVOURITES	10
60	Top Rank 35/070	FOLK FESTIVAL AT NEWPORT 1959 VOLUME 1	10
60	Top Rank 35/071	FOLK FESTIVAL AT NEWPORT 1959 VOLUME 2	10
60	Top Rank 35/072	FOLK FESTIVAL AT NEWPORT 1959 VOLUME 3	10
62	Fontana TFL 6000	FOLK FESTIVAL AT NEWPORT (VOL. 1)	10
62	Fontana TFL 6004	FOLK FESTIVAL AT NEWPORT (VOL. 2)	10
62	Fontana TFL 6009	FOLK FESTIVAL AT NEWPORT (VOL. 4)	10
60s	Decca	FOLK NOW	15
69	Topic 12T 159	THE FOLK SONGS OF BRITAIN — JACK OF ALL TRADES	10
69	Topic 12T 160	THE FOLK SONGS OF BRITAIN VOL. 4 — CHILD BALLADS 1	10
60s	Caedmon TC 1142	THE FOLK SONGS OF BRITAIN — SONGS OF COURTSHIP	10
60s	Caedmon TC 1143	THE FOLK SONGS OF BRITAIN — SONGS OF SEDUCTION	10
60s	Caedmon TC 1144	THE FOLK SONGS OF BRITAIN — JACK OF ALL TRADES	10
60s	Caedmon TC 1145	THE FOLK SONGS OF BRITAIN VOL. 4 — CHILD BALLADS 1	10
60s	Caedmon TC 1146	THE FOLK SONGS OF BRITAIN — CHILD BALLADS 2	10
60s	Caedmon TC 1162	THE FOLK SONGS OF BRITAIN — SAILORMEN AND SERVINGMAIDS	10
60s	Caedmon TC 1163	THE FOLK SONGS OF BRITAIN — FAIR GAME AND FOUL	10
60s	Caedmon TC 1164	THE FOLK SONGS OF BRITAIN — A SOLDIER'S LIFE FOR ME	10
60s	Caedmon TC 1224	THE FOLK SONGS OF BRITAIN — SONGS OF CEREMONY	10
60s	Caedmon TC 1225	THE FOLK SONGS OF BRITAIN — SONGS OF ANIMAL & OTHER MARVELS	10
57	HMV DLP 1143	FOLK SONG TODAY (10")	20
65	HMV CLP 1910	FOLKSOUND OF BRITAIN	15
63	Ember CEL 902	FOOL BRITANNIA	10
80s	Martyrwell M. MARY 141	FOOLS RUSH IN WHERE ANGELS DARE TO TREAD	10
80	Rocket DIAL 1	499 2139 (with inner sleeve)	10
65	Decca LK 4695	FOURTEEN — THE LORD'S TAVERNERS' ALBUM	25
80	Defensive PACT 1	FOUR WAYS OUT (LP)	10
70	Bamboo BLP 205	FREEDOM SOUNDS	40
81	Fresh FRESH LP 8	A FRESH SELECTION	10
72	Trojan TRL 51	FROM BAM BAM TO CHERRY OH BABY	10
80s	New European BADVC 666	FROM TORTURE TO CONSCIENCE (with insert)	20
69	Liberty LBS 83278	FROM THE VAULTS	10
70	Trojan TBL 137	FUNKY CHICKEN	15
80s	Urban	(JAMES BROWN'S) FUNKY PEOPLE VOL. 1	10
80s	Urban URBLP 14	(JAMES BROWN'S) FUNKY PEOPLE VOL. 2	10
70	Bamboo BLP 206	FUNKY REGGAE	40
82	Come Org. WDC 881021	FÜR ILSE KOCH (some on red vinyl)	80/60
70	Ember Explosion	FUTURE STAR EXPLOSION	10
80s	Third Mind TMLP 15	FUTURE TENSE VOL. 1	10

G

69	Pama ECO 4	GAS — GREATEST HITS	20
66	Doctor Bird DLM 5001	GAYFEET	70
52	Brunswick LA 8544	GEMS OF JAZZ VOL. 1 (10")	12
52	Brunswick LA 8561	GEMS OF JAZZ VOL. 1 (10")	12
55	HMV DLP 1039	GENE NORMAN PRESENTS JUST JAZZ (10")	20
72	Chess 6641 047	GENESIS — THE BEGINNINGS OF ROCK (4-LP, box set with booklet)	50
73	Chess 6641 125	GENESIS — MEMPHIS TO CHICAGO (4-LP, box set with booklet)	50
75	Chess 6641 174	GENESIS — SWEET HOME CHICAGO (4-LP, box set with booklet)	50
71	Revival RVS 1007	GEORGIA BLUES	12
69	Kokomo K 1004	GEORGIA GUITARS 1927-1938	40
67	Coxsone CSL 8007	GET READY ROCK STEADY	70
69	Pama SECO 20	A GIFT FROM PAMA	15
66	Columbia SX 6062	GO!	35
80s	Touch & Go TG 11	GOD'S FAVOURITE DOG	20
72	Flyright LP 103	GOIN' AWAY WALKING	15
70	Python LP 1	GOIN' BACK TO CHICAGO	25
60s	Heritage 1003	GOING TO CALIFORNIA	30
68	Decca LK 4931	GOIN' UP COUNTRY	10
74	Chess 6445 203	GOLDEN DECADE VOL. 7 1963-1965 HIGH HEEL SNEAKERS (gatefold sl.)	15
69	Roulette RCP 1000	GOLDEN GOODIES VOL. 1	10
69	Roulette RCP 1001	GOLDEN GOODIES VOL. 2	10
59	Philips BBL 7331	GOLDEN HITS	18
60	Philips BBL 7422	GOLDEN HITS VOL. 2	15
61	Philips BBL 7581	GOLDEN HITS VOL. 3	18
57	Capitol T 830	THE GOLD RECORD (blue label)	12
88	53rd & 3rd AGAS 3	GOOD FEELINGS	10
70s	Eron 004	GOOD FOLK OF KENT	60
65	Atlantic ATL 5004	GOOD OLD FIFTIES	25
68	Elek. EUK 260/EUKS 7260	GOOD TIME MUSIC (U.K. version of "What's Shakin'", gold or red label)	35/25
72	CBS 67234	GOSPEL SOUND (2-LP)	20
59	Brunwick LAT 8290	GOSPEL TRAIN	12
64	London HA-B 8172	GRAND OLE OPRY SPECTACULAR VOL. 1	12
64	London HA-B 8173	GRAND OLE OPRY SPECTACULAR VOL. 2	12
73	United Artists UDX 203/4	GREASY TRUCKERS PARTY (2-LP, gatefold sleeve)	22
73	Greasy Truckers GT 4997	GREASY TRUCKERS LIVE AT DINGWALLS (2-LP with insert)	18
73	Vanguard VSD 25/26	GREAT BLUESMEN (2-LP)	15
54	London AL 3530	THE GREAT BLUES SINGERS (10")	25
60s	Riverside RLP 12-121	THE GREAT BLUES SINGERS	20
80s	Direct DH 1005	THE GREAT BRITISH BEAT VOL. 2 (cassette via Direct Hits fan club)	10
75	D. Demand DDDDLP 5002	GREAT DISCO DEMANDS	10
55	HMV DLP 1025	GREAT ELLINGTON SOLOISTS (10")	25
70	Trojan TBL 111	GREATER JAMAICA	20
75	Brunswick BRLS 3006	GREATEST HITS	10
81	Street Level/Fuck Off	THE GREATEST HITS (MUSIC 4 PLEASURE) (cassette)	10
64	Stateside SL 10075	THE GREATEST GOSPEL SONGS OF OUR TIME	10

Various Artists: LPs

67	Doctor Bird DLM 5009	GREATEST JAMAICAN BEAT	70
66	Pye Intl. NPL 28052	THE GREATEST ON STAGE	10
54	HMV DLP 1054	GREAT TRUMPET SOLOISTS (10")	25
60	Columbia 33SX 1296	GRETSCH DRUM NIGHT AT BIRDLAND (also stereo SCX 3359)	10
71	Bamboo BDLP 215	GROOVING WITH BAMBOO	40
69	Direction 8-63452	GROOV'Y BABY	10
63	Realm RM 149	GROUP BEAT '63	20
63	London HA-U 8086	GROUP OF GOODIES	20
78	Virgin VCL 5001	GUILLOTINE (10" mini-LP, with inner sleeve)	8
71	Sunnyland KS 102	GULF COAST BLUES	25
68	Instant INLP 003	GULLIVER'S TRAVELS	40
80s	Situation Two SITU 17	GUNFIRE AND PIANOS (with inner)	12
80s	Situation Two SITC 17	GUNFIRE AND PIANOS (cassette)	10
69	Trojan TTL 16	GUNS OF NAVARONE	20
69	Liberty LBX 3	GUTBUCKET	10
60s	Reprise R 2016	GUYS AND DOLLS	12
68	Island ILP 977	GUY STEVENS' TESTAMENT OF ROCK'N'ROLL	25

H

50s	Oriole MG 20033	HAIL VARIETY!	10
68	Immediate IMLYIN 2	HAPPY TO BE PART OF THE INDUSTRY OF HUMAN HAPPINESS	10
77	VJM VLP 40	HARD LUCK BLUES	12
77	Revival RVS 1009	HARD TIMES BLUES	12
74	Decca DPA 3009/10	HARD UP HEROES 1963-68 (2-LP, gatefold sleeve)	15
56	London AL 3553	HARLEM PIANO ROLL (10")	20
69	Harvest SPSLP 118	HARVEST SAMPLER OF THE INITIAL FOUR JUNE RELEASES (promo-only)	80
71	Sunnyland KS 101	HAVIN' A GOOD TIME — CHICAGO BLUES ANTHOLOGY	25
66	Polydor 582 701	HEADLINE NEWS	15
87	Play Hard	HEAD OVER EARS (with 'Debris' magazine)	12/10
71	Vertigo 6360 045	HEADS TOGETHER, FIRST ROUND (2-LP, gatefold sleeve, spiral label)	15
81	Heavy Metal	HEAVY METAL HEROES VOLUME I	15
82	Heavy Metal	HEAVY METAL HEROES VOLUME II	10
68	Trojan TRL 6	HERE COMES THE DUKE	35
65	Pye NPL 18121	HERE COME THE GIRLS	15
80s	Temps Modernes LTMV:XI	HEURES SANS SOLEIL	25
69	Pama PSP 1002	HEY BOY HEY GIRL	25
80	Rockburgh ROC 111	HICKS FROM THE STICKS	12
59	Parlophone PMD 1085	HIGHWAY TO HEAVEN (10")	15
68	Atlantic 587 094	HISTORY OF RHYTHM AND BLUES — VOL. 1, THE ROOTS 1947-52	10
68	Atlantic 587 095	HISTORY OF RHYTHM AND BLUES — VOL. 2, THE GOLDEN YEARS 1953-55	10
68	Atlantic 587 096	HISTORY OF RHYTHM AND BLUES — VOL. 3, ROCK 'N' ROLL 1956-57	10
68	Atlantic 587 097	HISTORY OF RHYTHM AND BLUES — VOL. 4, THE BIG BEAT 1958-60	10
68	Atlantic 587 140	HISTORY OF RHYTHM AND BLUES — VOL. 5	10
68	Atlantic 587 141	HISTORY OF RHYTHM AND BLUES — VOL. 6	10
69	Bamboo BDLP 203	HISTORY OF SKA VOLUME ONE	40
69	Marble Arch MAL 1259	HITMAKERS	15
57	Pye Nixa NPT 19015	HIT PARADE OF 1956 (10")	18
59	Pye Nixa NPT 19032	HIT PARADE OF 1958	10
80s	Hits & Corruption HAC 1	HITS AND CORRUPTION (with cassette)	10
66	Marble Arch MAL 650	HITS FROM THE IVY LEAGUE, THE ROCKIN' BERRIES & THE SORROWS	12
77	Stiff FIST 1	HITS GREATEST STIFFS (with 7", Max Wall's "England's Glory" [BUY 12])	10
65	Tamla Motown TML 11019	HITSVILLE U.S.A.	30
67	Stax 589 005	HIT THE ROAD STAX	12
81	United Dairies UD 05	HOISTING THE BLACK FLAG	60
81	Interior Music IM 011	HOMMAGE A DURAS	10
60s	Melodisc 12-216	HONEYS	15
52	Capitol LC 6544	HONKY TONK PIANO (10")	12
60s	Riverside RLP 8806	HONKY TONK TRAIN	20
64	Stateside SL 10079	HOOTENANNY AT THE TROUBADOUR	10
63	Decca LK 4544	HOOTENANNY IN LONDON	20
78	Warner Bros K 66077	THE HOPE AND ANCHOR FRONT ROW FESTIVAL (2-LP)	14
71	Pama PMP 2006	HOT NUMBERS	15
71	Pama PMP 2009	HOT NUMBERS VOLUME TWO	15
70	Trojan TBL 128	HOT SHOTS OF REGGAE	15
70	Track 613 016	THE HOUSE THAT TRACK BUILT (gatefold sleeve)	20
69	Blue Horizon PR 45/46	HOW BLUE CAN WE GET (2-LP, gatefold sleeve with insert)	30

I

69	Liberty LBS 83252	I ASKED FOR WATER … AND SHE GAVE ME GASOLINE	70
80	TJM TJM 11	IDENTITY PARADE	12
80s	EMI TAPE 1/ EJ26 0663 1	IF YOU CAN'T PLEASE YOURSELF, YOU CAN'T PLEASE YOUR SOUL (with inner sleeve, insert & file)	10
69	Immediate IMLYIN 1	IMMEDIATE LETS YOU IN	10
67	Parlophone PMC 7024	I'M SORRY I'LL READ THAT AGAIN	15
70	Highway 51 H-104	I'M YOUR COUNTRY MAN	40
66	CBS/Denson Shoes	THE IN CROWD (shoe offer compilation)	25
69	Trojan TTL 15	INDEPENDENT JAMAICA	20
67	Fontana TL 5426	INDIAN MUSIC	10
79	Object Music OBJ 002	INDISCRETE MUSIC — DUBIOUS COLLABORATION (500 only)	10
84	Illuminated JAMS 39	THE INDUSTRIAL RECORDS STORY	20
80s	United Dairies UD 015	IN FRACTURED SILENCE	35
69	T. Motown (S)TML 11124	IN LOVING MEMORY	45
69	Blue Horizon PR 37	IN OUR OWN WAY (OLDIES BUT GOODIES)	20
64	Decca LK 4633	IRISH FOLK NIGHT	15
60s	Topic 12T 86	IRON MUSE	12
61	Oriole MG 20046	IT'S ALL HAPPENING HERE	10

J

58	Parlophone PMC 1072	JACK GOOD'S 'OH BOY!'	25
69	Amalgamated CSP 3	JACKPOT OF HITS	20
77	Policy Wheel PW 4593	JACKSON BLUES BOYS	12
61	Blue Beat BBLP 801	JAMAICAN BLUES	90
68	Blue Cat BCL 1	JAMAICAN MEMORIES	40
68	Atlantic 587 075	JAMAICA SKA	40
68	Flyright LP 3502	JAMBALAYA ON THE BAYOU — VOLUME 1	20
69	Flyright LP 3503	JAMBALAYA ON THE BAYOU — VOLUME 2	20
72	Utd. Artists UAS 60027/8	JAMES BOND COLLECTION (2-LP with booklet)	18
72	Rolling Stones COC 39100	JAMMING WITH EDWARD	10
55	Columbia Clef 33CX 10008	JAM SESSION	10
56	Tempo TAP 5	JAZZ AT THE FLAMINGO	25
50s	Columbia SLJS 1	JAZZ EXPLOSION	10
72	Decca ECS 2114	JAZZ IN BRITAIN 1968-1969	25
84	Streetsounds MUSIC 1	JAZZ JUICE	30
85	Streetsounds SOUND 1	JAZZ JUICE (reissue)	25
86	Streetsounds SOUND 4	JAZZ JUICE 2	20
86	Streetsounds SOUND 5	JAZZ JUICE 3	20
86	Streetsounds SOUND 6	JAZZ JUICE 4	20
87	Streetsounds SOUND 8	JAZZ JUICE 5	18
87	Streetsounds SOUND 9	JAZZ JUICE 6	18
87	Streetsounds CDSND 9	JAZZ JUICE 6 (CD)	15
88	Streetsounds SOUND 10	JAZZ JUICE 7	18
88	Streetsounds CDSND 10	JAZZ JUICE 7 (CD)	15
88	Streetsounds SOUND 11	JAZZ JUICE 8	15
88	Streetsounds CDSND 11	JAZZ JUICE 8 (CD)	15
88	Streetsounds SOUND 12	JAZZ JUICE 9	15
88	Streetsounds CDSND 12	JAZZ JUICE 9 (CD)	15
57	London AL 3562	JAZZ OF THE ROARING TWENTIES VOLUME TWO (10")	15
57	London AL 3565	JAZZ PIANO RARITIES (10")	20
55	Columbia Clef 33C 9007	JAZZ SCENE (10")	15
55	Columbia Clef 33C 9008	JAZZ SCENE VOL. 2 (10")	15
62	Parlophone PMC 1177	JAZZ SOUNDS OF THE 20s VOL. 4: BLUES SINGERS & ACCOMPANISTS	15
56	Vogue LAE 12038	JAZZ WEST COAST	12
57	Vogue LAE 12061	JAZZ WEST COAST VOLUME 2	12
58	Vogue LAE 12115	JAZZ WEST COAST VOLUME 3	12
61	Vogue LAE 12235	JAZZ WEST COAST VOLUME 5	12
77	Decca DPA 3035/3036	THE JOE MEEK STORY (2-LP)	16
60	Top Rank 35/064	JOHN HAMMOND'S SPIRITUALS TO SWING VOLUME 1	10
60	Top Rank 35/065	JOHN HAMMOND'S SPIRITUALS TO SWING VOLUME 2	10
69	BBC REC 52S	JOHN PEEL PRESENTS TOP GEAR	30
60	HMV CLP 1327	A JUG OF PUNCH	15
60s	Ace Of Hearts AH 163	JUGS AND WASHBOARDS	15
67	RCA Victor RD 7893	JUGS WASHBOARDS AND KAZOOS	15
70s	Eric's ERICS 008	JUKEBOX AT ERIC'S	10
76	RCA RS 1066	JUMPING AT THE GO GO	18
77	Policy Wheel PW 459-1	JUMPING ON THE HILL	12
64	R&B JBL 1111	JUMP JAMAICA JUMP	75
69	RCA Intl. INT 1014	JUST A LITTLE BIT OF SOUL	10
79	Kick KK 1	JUST FOR KICKS	25
80s	Quiet QLP 1	JUST WHEN YOU THOUGHT IT WAS ... QUIET!	10

K

81	White Witch	KENT ROCKS (500 only)	10
54	HMV DLP 1048	KEYBOARD KINGS OF JAZZ (10")	25
72	Key	KEY COLLECTION (with insert)	15
70	Trojan TBL 140	KING SIZE REGGAE	20
60s	Gryphon 13159	KINGS OF THE TWELVE STRING GUITAR	20
71	Flyright LP 101	KINGS OF THE TWELVE STRING GUITAR (reissue)	15
60s	Saydisc Roots RL 333	KINGS OF MEMPHIS TOWN 1927-1930	15

L

79	The Label TRLP 002	THE LABEL — SOFA	10
79	The Label TRLP 002 S	THE LABEL — SOFA ('special defractor' 3D picture disc, stickered PVC sl.)	35
79	Cherry Red ARED 4	LABELS UNLIMITED	10
80s	Fetish FR 2011	THE LAST TESTAMENT (with inner, stickered sleeve)	20
68	Island ILP 986	LEAPING WITH MR LEE (by Bunny Lee All Stars)	60
66	Blue Horizon LP 2	LET ME TELL YOU ABOUT THE BLUES	250
60s	Polydor SLPHM 237 622	LET'S DO THE TWIST, HULLY GULLY, SLOP, SURF, LOCOMOTION, MONKEY	20
66	Neshoba N 11	LET'S GO DOWN SOUTH	40
58	Brunswick LAT 8271	LET'S HAVE A PARTY	15
60	Philips BBL 7414	LET'S MAKE LOVE	10
81	Alt. Tentacles VIRUS 4	LET THEM EAT JELLYBEANS (with lyric poster)	10
80s	Third Mind/Abstract	LIFE AT THE TOP	25
77	NEMS NEL 6013	LIVE AT THE VORTEX	15
65	Fontana TL 5240	LIVE AT THE WHISKEY A-GO-GO	10
68	Big Shot BBTL 4000	LIVE IT UP	60
64	Embassy WLP 6065	LIVERPOOL BEAT	12
60s	CBS Realm RM 209	LIVIN' WITH THE BLUES	12
70	Trojan TBL 135	LOCH NESS MONSTER	15
50s	Parlophone	LONDON'S GIRL FRIENDS	15
87	4AD CAD 703D	LONELY IS AN EYESORE (cardboard pack with book)	12
87	4AD CADX 703	LONELY IS AN EYESORE (wooden box with etching, screen print, CD, video & cassette, 200 only)	200
78	Chiswick CH 5	LONG SHOTS, DEAD CERTS & ODDS ON FAVORITES — CHISWICK CHARTBUSTERS VOL. 2	10

Various Artists: LPs

| 69 | Pama PSP 1001 | A LOVELY DOZEN | 25 |

M

58	Pye Nixa Jazz NJL 13	MAD THAD	10
70s	Object Music OBJ 003	A MANCHESTER COLLECTION	10
88	Bop BC V001	MANCHESTER, NORTH OF ENGLAND (white labels only)	10
70	Trojan TBL 129	MAN FROM CAROLINA	15
70	CBS 52798	MA RAINEY AND THE CLASSIC BLUES SINGERS	15
60s	Marmalade 643 314	MARMALADE 100% PROOF	12
68	President PTL 1002	MAR-V-LUS SOUND OF R&B AND SOUL MUSIC	10
72	Village Thing VTSAM 16	MATCHBOX DAYS	20
70s	Liberty LBL/LBS 83190	ME AND THE DEVIL	18
64	London HA 8129	MEMORIES ARE MADE OF HITS VOL. 1	15
64	London HA 8130	MEMORIES ARE MADE OF HITS VOL. 2	15
64	London HA 8131	MEMORIES ARE MADE OF HITS VOL. 3	15
64	London HA 8138	MEMORIES ARE MADE OF HITS VOL. 4	15
64	London HA 8148	MEMORIES ARE MADE OF HITS VOL. 5	15
64	London HA 8171	MEMORIES ARE MADE OF HITS VOL. 6	15
64	London HA 8189	MEMORIES ARE MADE OF HITS VOL. 7	15
65	London HA 8213	MEMORIES ARE MADE OF HITS VOL. 8	15
54	Vogue Coral LVC 10008	MERRY CHRISTMAS (10")	10
69	T. Motown (S)TML 11126	MERRY CHRISTMAS FROM MOTOWN	10
60s	Capitol T 9030	MERRY CHRISTMAS TO YOU	10
80	BBC	METAL EXPLOSION	10
84	Roadrunner	METAL MACHINE	10
81	Virgin OVEDC 5	METHODS OF DANCE (cassette with 5 extra tracks)	10
56	Nixa Jazz Today NJL 3	MIDNIGHT AT NIXA	10
66	Atlantic 587 021	MIDNIGHT SOUL	10
62	Brunswick LAT 8401	MIDNIGHT JAMBOREE (also stereo STA 3061)	12
56	London AL 3554	MIDWESTERN JAZZ (10")	15
72	Polydor	MILL VALLEY JAM SESSION	12
60	Coral LVA 9126	MILLION-AIRS	15
80	Pipe PIPE 2	MINIATURES (with poster insert, 500 only)	15
80	Pipe PIPE 2	MINIATURES (cassette with mini-booklet insert, 100 only)	30
71	Trojan TBL 174	MISS LABBA LABBA REGGAE	15
60	Top Rank BUY 028	MR. BLUE	25
60s	Bounty BY 6025	MODERN CHICAGO BLUES	25
55	HMV DLP 1022	MODERN JAZZ PIANO (10")	20
56	Tempo TAP 2	MODERN JAZZ SCENE 1956	20
53	Esquire 20-011	MODERN MIXTURE VOLUME ONE (10")	10
79	Bridgehouse BHLP 003	MODS MAYDAY '79 (original issue)	10
73	Stax STX 1029	MONTREUX FESTIVAL 1973	12
74	Mooncrest CREST 17	RAVE ON	10
70	Trojan TTL 31	MOONLIGHT GROOVER	20
80	Danceville	THE MOONLIGHT TAPES	12
62	HMV CLP 1583	MORE OF YOUR FAVOURITE TV AND RADIO THEMES	12
68	Marble Arch MAL 813	MORE RHYTHM AND BLUES	10
65	private pressing	MORE SONGS AT THE COUNT HOUSE	50
81	cassette	MORROCCI KLUNG! (cassette in printed 5" x 9" mailing envelope)	10
86	Iguana VYK LP 11	MOTOR CITY 9 (with booklet)	15
65	Tamla Motown TML 11007	THE MOTORTOWN REVUE	50
66	Tamla Motown TML 11027	THE MOTORTOWN REVUE IN PARIS	50
70	T. Motown (S)TML 11127	THE MOTORTOWN REVUE LIVE	10
74	T. Motown STML 11270	MOTOWN CHARTBUSTERS VOL. 9 (green vinyl)	10
66	Tamla Motown TML 11030	MOTOWN MAGIC	30
68	Tamla Motown TML 11064	MOTOWN MEMORIES	25
68	Tamla Motown TML 11077	MOTOWN MEMORIES VOL. 2	20
70	T. Motown STML 11143	MOTOWN MEMORIES VOL. 3	25
72	Tamla Motown TMSP 1130	THE MOTOWN STORY (box set)	25
83	Tamla Motown TMSP 6019	THE MOTOWN STORY — THE FIRST 25 YEARS (box set)	20
53	London AL 3503	MUGGY, TESCH AND THE CHICAGOANS (10")	15
57	Pye NJL 11	MURDERER'S HOME	15
71	Mushroom 100 MR 16	THE MUSHROOM FOLK SAMPLER	60
57	Brunswick LAT 8201	MUSIC FOR THE BOY FRIEND — HE REALLY DIGS ROCK'N'ROLL	25
73	Charisma CADS 101	MUSIC FROM FREE CREEK (2-LP)	14
69	Polydor 583 728	MUSIC FROM THE TWISTED NERVE AND LES BICYCLETTES DE BELSIZE	50
71	Trojan TBL 170	MUSIC HOUSE	10
71	Trojan TBL 177	MUSIC HOUSE VOLUME TWO	10
81	Ze ISSP 4001	MUTANT DISCO (3 x 12" box set, numbered, 2,000 only)	10

N

62	London HA-B 8003	NASHVILLE SATURDAY NIGHT	12
63	London HA-B 8028	NASHVILLE STEEL GUITAR	10
69	Bamboo BLP 201	NATURAL REGGAE VOLUME ONE	40
70	Bamboo BLP 204	NATURAL REGGAE VOLUME TWO	40
81	4AD CAD 117	NATURES MORTES — STILL LIVES (export issue)	60
80s	Musique Brut BRV 002	NECROPOLIS, AMPHIBIANS AND REPTILES — THE MUSIC OF ADOLF WOLFLI	20
70s	Bounty BY 6012	NEGRO FOLKLORE FROM TEXAS STATE PRISON	20
57	Vogue LAE 12033	NEGRO SPIRITUALS	20
81	Logo	NEW ELECTRIC WARRIORS	10
53	London AL 3509	NEW ORLEANS HORNS (10")	15
56	London AL 3557	NEW ORLEANS HORNS VOLUME 2 (10")	12
74	Flyright LP 4708	NEW ORLEANS R&B VOLUME 1	15
74	Flyright LP 4709	NEW ORLEANS R&B VOLUME 2	15
60s	'77' 77LA 12/16	NEW ORLEANS TODAY	10
60s	'77' 77LA 12/29	NEW ORLEANS TODAY VOL. 2	10
65	Fontana TFL 6038	NEWPORT BROADSIDE	25

65	Fontana TFL 6050	NEWPORT FOLK FESTIVAL VOL. 1	12
65	Fontana TFL 6041	NEWPORT FOLK FESTIVAL EVENING CONCERT VOL. 1	25
57	Philips BBL 7147	NEWPORT JAZZ FESTIVAL	10
57	Philips BBL 7152	NEWPORT JAZZ FESTIVAL	10
80s	Lakeland	NEW SONGS FOR MUTANTS: A LAKELAND COMPILATION	10
72	Flyright LP 4706	NEW YORK CITY BLUES	15
55	London AL 3541	NEW YORK JAZZ OF THE ROARING TWENTIES (10")	15
72	Flyright LP 4707	NEW YORK RHYTHM AND BLUES	15
57	Vanguard PPL 11004	A NIGHT AT THE APOLLO	15
69	Blue Horizon 7-63210	1968 MEMPHIS COUNTRY BLUES FESTIVAL	25
80s	NMX	NMX: LIVE AT SHEFFIELD (cassette)	10
68	Spark SRLM 107	NO INTRODUCTION (LP)	20
82	ZG Music No. 5	NOISE FEST (cassette)	12
69	Trojan TTL 14	NO MORE HEARTACHES	15
69	Regal Starline SRS 5013	NO ONE'S GONNA CHANGE OUR WORLD	10
60	Fontana TFL 5123	NOTHIN' BUT THE BLUES	15
71	CBS 66278	NOTHING BUT THE BLUES (2-LP, Blue Horizon pressings may also exist)	25
70	Decca Nova SPA 72	NOVA SAMPLER	12
70s	Warm PFLP 201	NOVA-VAGA	15
79	A&M AMLE 68505	NO WAVE (pizza picture disc)	12
79	A&M AMLE 68505	NO WAVE (orange, mauve or blue vinyl)	10
69	Pama ECO 6	NU BEAT — GREATEST HITS	20
72	Elektra K 62012	NUGGETS (2-LP, gatefold sleeve)	35
80s	Numa NUMA 1004	NUMA RECORDS YEAR 1 (with free Italian 12" "My Dying Machine")	15

O

69	Liberty LBS 83234	OAKLAND BLUES	15
80	Object Music OBJ 006	OBJECTIVITY	10
70s	Rok ROK 001	ODDS, BODS, MODS AND SODS	12
78	Raw RAWLP 2	OH NO IT'S MORE FROM RAW	15
64	Stateside SL 10094	OLDIES R & B	20
68	Big Shot BBTL 4001	ONCE MORE	60
73	Charisma CLASS 3	ONE MORE CHANCE	10
63	Columbia 33SX 1536	ONE NIGHT STAND	25
61	Decca LK 4393	ONE OVER THE EIGHT	12
63	Stateside SL 10065	ON STAGE	35
69	Atco 228 009/010	ON STAGE — LIVE (2-LP)	15
73	Xtra XTRA 1133	ON THE ROAD AGAIN	25
64	Columbia 33SX 1662	ON THE SCENE	50
80s	Interior Music IM 005	OPERATION TWILIGHT	10
63	Stateside SL 10024	OPRY TIME IN TENNESSEE	10
67	Polydor 236 216	ORIGINAL AMERICAN FOLK BLUES FESTIVAL	12
64	Rio RLP 1	THE ORIGINAL COOL JAMAICAN SKA	50
70	Mercury SMCL 20182	ORIGINAL GOLDEN HITS OF THE GREAT BLUES SINGERS	10
73	Prince Buster PB 10	ORIGINAL GOLDEN OLDIES VOLUME 2	18
70	Mercury SMCL 20183	ORIGINAL GOLDEN RHYTHM AND BLUES HITS VOLUME 1	10
60	London HA-G 2308	THE ORIGINAL HITS	30
61	London HA-G 2339	THE ORIGINAL HITS VOL. 2	30
67	Ember SPE/LP 6602	THE ORIGINAL SOUND OF DETROIT	10
52	Vogue LDE 006	ORIGINATORS OF MODERN JAZZ (10")	12
62	London HA-U 2404	OUR SIGNIFICANT HITS	35
60s	Ace Of Hearts AH 72	OUT CAME THE BLUES	15
67	Ace Of Hearts AH 158	OUT CAME THE BLUES VOLUME 2	15
60s	Coral CP 58	OUT CAME THE BLUES (reissue)	10
70s	ABC ABCL 5192	OUT ON THE STREETS AGAIN	12

P

64	Golden Guinea GGL 0268	PACKAGE TOUR	18
65	Blue Beat BBLP 804	PAIN IN MY BELLY	70
55	London HA-A 2001	THE PAJAMA GAME	10
67	Island ILP 945	PAKISTANI SOUL SESSION	15
61	Parlophone PMC 1134	PARADE OF THE POPS	10
68	Studio One SOL 9009	PARTY TIME IN JAMAICA	70
81	Cherry Red BRED 15	PERSPECTIVES AND DISTORTION (gatefold sleeve)	15
86	Streetsounds PHST 1986	THE PHILADELPHIA YEARS (14-LP box set)	80
72	Apple APCOR 24	PHIL SPECTOR'S CHRISTMAS ALBUM	15
75	Warner Bros K 59010	PHIL SPECTOR'S CHRISTMAS ALBUM (reissue)	10
80	Phil Spector Intl. 2307 015	PHIL SPECTOR '74/'79	10
67	Riverside RLP 8809	PIANO BLUES 1927-1933	20
70s	Storyville 671 187	PIANO BLUES	12
77	Magpie PY 4401	PIANO BLUES VOLUME 1: PARAMOUNT 1929-30	10
77	Magpie PY 4402	PIANO BLUES VOLUME 2: BRUNSWICK 1928-30	10
77	Magpie PY 4403	PIANO BLUES VOLUME 3: VOCALION 1928-30	10
77	Magpie PY 4404	PIANO BLUES VOLUME 4: THOMAS FAMILY 1925-1929	10
78	Magpie PY 4405	PIANO BLUES VOLUME 5: POSTSCRIPT 1927-1933	10
78	Magpie PY 4406	PIANO BLUES VOLUME 6: WALTER ROLAND 1933-1935	10
78	Magpie PY 4407	PIANO BLUES VOLUME 7: LEROY CARR 1930-1935	10
78	Magpie PY 4408	PIANO BLUES VOLUME 8: TEXAS SEAPORT 1934-1937	10
79	Magpie PY 4409	PIANO BLUES VOLUME 9: LOFTON/NOBLE 1935-36	10
79	Magpie PY 4410	PIANO BLUES VOLUME 10: TERRITORY BLUES 1934-41	10
80	Magpie PY 4411	PIANO BLUES VOLUME 11: TEXAS SANTA FE 1934-1937	10
80	Magpie PY 4412	PIANO BLUES VOLUME 12: THE BIG FOUR 1933-1941	10
80	Magpie PY 4413	PIANO BLUES VOLUME 13: CENTRAL HIGHWAY 1933-1941	10
80	Magpie PY 4414	PIANO BLUES VOLUME 14: THE ACCOMPANISTS 1933-41	10
81	Magpie PY 4415	PIANO BLUES VOLUME 15: DALLAS 1927-1929	10
81	Magpie PY 4416	PIANO BLUES VOLUME 16: CHARLIE SPAND 1929-1931	10
82	Magpie PY 4417	PIANO BLUES VOLUME 17: PARAMOUNT VOL. 2 1927-32	10

Various Artists: LPs

82	Magpie PY 4420	PIANO BLUES VOLUME 20: BARRELHOUSE YEARS 1928-33 10
82	Magpie PY 4421	PIANO BLUES VOLUME 21: UNISSUED BOOGIE 1938-1945 10
56	Vogue Coral LVA 9069	PIANO JAZZ — BARRELHOUSE AND BOOGIE WOOGIE 15
70s	Horse HRLP 704	PICK HITS 10
70	Harvest SHSS 1/2	PICNIC (2-LP) 14
72	Flyright LP 104	PIEDMONT BLUES 15
82	Cherry Red PZRED 41	PILLOWS AND PRAYERS (picture disc in printed PVC sleeve) 10
60	HMV CLP 1362	A PINCH OF SALT 20
53	London AL 3506	PIONEERS OF BOOGIE WOOGIE (10") 30
54	London AL 3537	PIONEERS OF BOOGIE WOOGIE VOLUME TWO (10") 30
73	Trojan TBL 203	PIPELINE 15
70s	Flyright LP 4711	PLAY MY JUKEBOX 12
80s	Pleasantly Surprised PS 1	PLEASANTLY SURPRISED (cassette, in bag with inserts) 18
56	Mercury MPT	POP PARADE VOL. 1 (10") 15
56	Mercury MPT	POP PARADE VOL. 2 (10") 15
57	Mercury MPT 7519	POP PARADE VOL. 3 (10") 15
57	Mercury MPT 7523	POP PARADE VOL. 4 (10") 15
57	Mercury MPT 7525	POP PARADE VOL. 5 (10") 25
65	Post War Blues PWB 1	POST WAR BLUES: CHICAGO 30
66	Post War Blues PWB 2	POST WAR BLUES: MEMPHIS ON DOWN 30
67	Post War Blues PWB 3	POST WAR BLUES: EASTERN AND GULF COAST STATES 30
68	Post War Blues PWB 4	POST WAR BLUES: TEXAS 30
68	Post War Blues PWB 5	POST WAR BLUES: DETROIT 30
60s	Post War Blues PWB 6	POST WAR BLUES: WEST COAST 30
60s	Post War Blues PWB 7	POST WAR BLUES: THE DEEP SOUTH 30
69	Python PWBC 1	POST WAR COLLECTOR SERIES VOL. 1 25
63	Stateside SL 10046	PREACHIN' THE BLUES 15
80	4AD BAD 11	PRESAGES (mini-LP, green/pink or brown sleeve) 15/20
70	Kokomo K 1006	PRE-WAR TEXAS BLUES 40
60s	Jazz Collector JGN 1001	PRIMITIVE PIANO 20
87	A&M AMA 3906	PRINCE'S TRUST 10TH ANNIVERSARY BIRTHDAY PARTY (2-LP, with Paul McCartney 7": "Long Tall Sally"/"I Saw Her Standing There" [p/s, FREE 21]) 14
63	London HA-B 8062	PRISONERS' SONGS 10
79	Blueprint BLUSP 1	PROTOTYPES 10
80s	United Dairies UD 134	PSILOTRIPITAKA (3-LP [UD 01, 03 & 04], with free disc "Registered Nurse Second Coming" [UD 00], 1,000 only, 25 in 'leather bondage bag') 150/75
80s	United Dairies UD 134CD	PSILOTRIPITAKA (3-CD [UD 01, 03 & 04], with free CD "Registered Nurse Second Coming" [UD 00CD], 1,000 only, 25 in 'leather bondage bag') 150/75
65	Sue ILP 919	PURE BLUES VOL. 1 20
68	Island ILP 978	PUT IT ON — IT'S ROCK STEADY 35
71	Pye PSA 6	PYE SALES SAMPLER (LP; sampler for Dawn/Pye releases; 99 copies only, with release sheet) 20

Q

68	Stateside S(S)L 10209	A QUARTET OF SOUL 12
70	Trojan TBL 136	QUEEN OF THE WORLD 15
81	Bronze	A QUIET NIGHT IN 10
50s	Vogue LAE 12031	THE QUINTET OF THE YEAR 10

R

60s	Minit	R&B CLASSICS 12
60s	Mercury MCL 20019	R&B PARTY 15
85	Rouska RANT 001	RAGING SUN 10
69	Polydor 236 514	RAGS, REELS AND AIRS 10
54	London AL 3515	RAGTIME PIANO ROLL (10") 20
54	London AL 3523	RAGTIME PIANO ROLL VOLUME 2 (10") 20
55	London AL 3542	RAGTIME PIANO ROLL VOLUME 3 (10") 20
57	London AL 3563	RAGTIME PIANO ROLL VOLUME 4 (10") 20
84	Womad WOMAD 001	RAINDROPS PATTERING ON BANANA LEAVES 10
70s	Phil Spector Intl. 2307 008	RARE MASTERS VOL. 1 10
70s	Phil Spector Intl. 2307 009	RARE MASTERS VOL. 2 10
73	Attack ATLP 1012	RAVE ON BROTHER 10
67	Ace Of Clubs ACL 1220	RAW BLUES (also stereo SCL 1220) 15
77	Raw RAWLP 1	RAW DEAL (black & white sleeve & red/blue label) 12
79	Raw RAWLP 1	RAW DEAL (reissue, yellow/black sleeve & green/white label) 10
73	GM GML 1008	READING FESTIVAL '73 10
82	Mean	READING FESTIVAL '82 15
64	Decca LK 4577	READY, STEADY, GO! 25
68	Pama PMLP 3	READY STEADY GO ROCKSTEADY 30
64	Decca LK 4634	READY, STEADY, WIN 30
80s	Weird	REALLY WEIRD (C90 cassette) 10
65	Stateside SL 10112	THE REAL R & B 15
80s	Recloose Org. LOOSE 12	R.O. (RECLOOSE ORGANISATION) (picture disc with insert) 20
82	Recommended 104	RECOMMENDED SAMPLER 15
79	Destiny DS 10001	THE RECORD COLLECTOR 20
70	CBS 52797	RECORDING THE BLUES 15
65	Red Bird RB 20-102	RED BIRD GOLDIES 25
69	Trojan TTL 11	RED, RED WINE VOL. 1 10
69	Trojan TTL 11	RED, RED WINE VOL. 1 (pink Island label, different track listing & sleeve) .....40+
70	Trojan TBL 116	RED, RED WINE 10
70	Trojan TBL 105	REGGAE CHARTBUSTERS 10
71	Trojan TBL 169	REGGAE CHARTBUSTERS 10
70	Trojan TBL 147	REGGAE CHARTBUSTERS VOLUME TWO 10
70	Trojan TBL 115	REGGAE FLIGHT 404 15
68	Big Shot BIL 3000	REGGAE GIRL 40
69	Pama ECO 3	REGGAE HITS '69 VOL. 1 20
69	Pama ECO 11	REGGAE HITS VOL. 2 20

69	Pama PTP 1001	REGGAE HIT THE TOWN	20
68	Studio One SOL 9007	REGGAE IN THE GRASS	70
71	Trojan TBL 181	REGGAE JAMAICA	10
71	Bamboo BDLP 208	REGGAEMATIC SOUNDS	40
70	Trojan TBL 144	REGGAE MOVEMENT	15
72	Trojan TBL 189	REGGAE POWER VOLUME TWO	10
70	Trojan TBL 130	REGGAE REGGAE REGGAE	15
71	Trojan TBL 176	REGGAE REGGAE REGGAE VOLUME TWO	10
70	London HA-J 8411	REGGAE REVOLUTION (unissued)	
69	Coxsone CSP 2	REGGAE SPECIAL	25
70	Trojan TBL 151	REGGAE STEADY GO	10
68	Coxsone CSL 8017	REGGAE TIME	70
72	Ashanti ANB 201	REGGAE TIME	10
71	Pama PMP 2012	REGGAE TO REGGAE	25
69	Pama PSP 1004	REGGAE TO UK WITH LOVE	20
80s	Ré 0101	RE RECORDS QUARTERLY VOL. No. 1 (with printed book)	15
71	Revelation REV 1/2/3	REVELATIONS — A MUSICAL ANTHOLOGY FOR GLASTONBURY FAYRE (3-LP, poster sleeve with booklets, pyramid & printed polythene bag)	80
84	Anagram GRAM 17	REVENGE OF THE KILLER PUSSIES (BLOOD ON THE CATS # 2) (multi-coloured pink vinyl)	10
64	Decca LK 4616	RHYTHM AND BLUES	40
67	Marble Arch MAL 726	RHYTHM AND BLUES	12
69	Liberty LBL 83216	RHYTHM AND BLUES VOLUME 1: END OF AN ERA	15
69	Liberty LBL 83328	RHYTHM AND BLUES VOLUME 2: SWEET 'N' GREASY	15
63	CBS Realm RM 101	R&B GREATS VOLUME 1	20
64	CBS Realm RM 175	R&B GREATS VOLUME 2	20
64	Mercury MCL 20019	RHYTHM AND BLUES PARTY	25
76	Philips 643 6028	RHYTHM AND BLUES PARTY (reissue)	15
73	T. Motown STML 11232	RIC TIC RELICS	18
68	Coxsone CSL 8015	RIDE ME DONKEY	70
69	Trojan TTL 18	RIDE YOUR DONKEY	20
81	A&M NUKE 1	RIGHT AFTER THIS . . . ALRIGHT? (promo-only)	10
55	Vogue Coral LRA 10023	RIVERBOAT JAZZ (10" LP)	15
71	London SHU 8245	RIVERTOWN BLUES	15
61	London HA-A 2338	ROCK-A-HITS	40
57	London HB-C 1067	ROCK 'N' ROLL (10")	40
59	London HA-E 2180	ROCK AND ROLL FOREVER	50
60	HMV DLP 1204	ROCKET ALONG — NEW BALLADS ON OLD LINES (10" LP)	15
70s	Flynight FLY 662	ROCKIN' ACCORDION	10
58	Decca LF 1300	ROCKIN' AT THE '2 I'S' (10")	40
59	London HA-E 2167	ROCKIN' TOGETHER	45
60s	Decca LK 5002	ROCK STEADY	10
69	Pama PMLP 7	ROCKSTEADY COOL	30
68	Coxsone CSL 8013	ROCKSTEADY COXSONE STYLE	70
68	Atlantic Special 590 019	ROOTS OF THE BLUES	12
77	Harvest SHSP 4069	THE ROXY LONDON W.C.2 (JAN - APR 77) (with inner bag)	12
77	Harvest TC-SHSP 4069	THE ROXY LONDON W.C.2 (JAN - APR 77) (cassette)	10
81	Naive NAIVE 2	RUPERT PREACHING AT A PICNIC (handmade sleeve)	15
69	XTRA 1035	RURAL BLUES (2-LP)	20
69	Liberty LBL 83213	RURAL BLUES VOLUME 1: GOIN' UP THE COUNTRY	15
69	Liberty LBL 83214	RURAL BLUES VOLUME 2: SATURDAY NIGHT FRICTION	15
69	Liberty LBL 83329	RURAL BLUES VOLUME 3: DOWN HOME STOMP	15

S

70	Transworld SPLP 101	SAMANTHA PROMOTIONS (purple cover, private pressing with poster)	700
70	Transworld SPLP 102	SAMANTHA PROMOTIONS (orange cover, private pressing with poster)	800
60	Parlophone PMC 1130	SATURDAY CLUB	30
64	Decca LK 4583	SATURDAY CLUB	25
67	Atlantic 590 007	SATURDAY NIGHT AT THE APOLLO	12
63	Brunswick LAT/STA 8520	SATURDAY NIGHT AT THE GRAND OLE OPRY	12
70	CBS 52799	SAVANNAH SYNCOPATORS	12
69	Pama ECO 8	SCANDAL IN BRIXTON MARKET	18
65	Columbia 33SX 1730	SCENE '65	45
69	Bamboo BDLP 202	A SCORCHA FROM BAMBOO	40
80s	Barc. Towers SUPLP 2004	SCOTTISH KULTCHUR	12
78	Polydor 2480 429	SCOUSE THE MOUSE (stickered sleeve with printed competition insert)	80
78	Polydor 3194 429	SCOUSE THE MOUSE (cassette)	25
68	CBS 66288	SCREENING THE BLUES (2-LP)	20
81	Airship AP 342	SEASIDE ROCK (2-LP)	20
80	Statik 01	SECOND CITY STATIK — A GLASGOW COMPILATION	10
92	Imaginary ILLUSION 34	SECONDS OUT ROUND ONE — LIVE HIT THE NORTH SESSIONS (with free promo 12" [FREE 004])	10
80s	Come Org. WDC 881008	THE SECOND COMING (various coloured vinyls)	60
80s	Davies LP-D2 VOR 8	A SECRET LIVERPOOL (1-sided cardboard sleeve; later 2-sided normal sleeve)	15/12
68	Elektra EUK 261	SELECT ELEKTRA (also stereo EUKS 7261)	15
80s	Uniton UO 28	A SENSE OF BEAUTY	10
80	Kathedral KATH 1	SENT FROM COVENTRY (with booklet)	12
68	Atlantic 587 109	SHAKE, RATTLE AND ROLL	12
81	Albion/Shake SHAKE 1	SHAKE TO DATE	10
80s	In Phaze	SHED SOUNDS SAMPLER (cassette)	10
78	Virgin VCL 5003	SHORT CIRCUIT — LIVE AT THE ELECTRIC CIRCUS (10"; orange, yellow, blue or black vinyl)	100/30/15/8
78	Virgin VCL 5003	SHORT CIRCUIT — LIVE AT THE ELECTRIC CIRCUS (10"; black vinyl with free John Dowie EP [VED 1004])	12
60s	Chess CRL 4519	SING A SONG OF SOUL	15
57	Camden CDN 147	SINGIN' THE BLUES	10

Year	Label/Cat No	Title	Value
79	Sire SMP 1	THE SIRE MACHINE TURNS YOU UP	12
57	Parlophone PMC 1047	SIX-FIVE SPECIAL	25
71	Pama PMP 2015	16 DYNAMIC REGGAE HITS	15
72	Trojan TBL 191	16 DYNAMIC REGGAE HITS	10
66	Island ILP 930	SKA AT THE JAMAICAN PLAYBOY CLUB	60
67	Coxsone CSL 8003	SKA-AU-GO-GO	70
66	Doctor Bird DLM 5000	SKA BOO DA BA	70
65	Blue Beat BBLP 805	SKA-LYP-SOUL	70
67	Studio One SOL 9000	SKA TO ROCKSTEADY	70
68	Ace Of Clubs ACL 1250	SKIFFLE	20
81	Beggars Banquet BEGA 31	SLIPSTREAM — THE BEST OF BRITISH JAZZ FUNK (2-LP)	14
80s	Inevitable INEVLP 1	SMALL HITS AND NEAR MISSES	10
82	RSB 1	THE SNOOPIES ALBUM (THE LAST REMAINS OF A RICHMOND VENUE) (numbered with inserts, 1,000 only)	12
67	Polydor 583 064	SOCK IT TO 'EM	12
60s	Solar	THE SOLAR BOX SET	40
70s	United Artists LBR 1007	SOLD ON SOUL	15
71	Bamboo BDLP 212	SOLID GOLD	40
66	Atlantic ATL 5048	SOLID GOLD SOUL	12
60s	Atlantic 587 058	SOLID GOLD SOUL VOL. 2	12
70s	Disco Demand DDLP 5002	SOLID SOUL SENSATIONS	12
81	Some Bizzare BZLP 1	THE SOME BIZZARE ALBUM	12
72	South. Preservation SPR 1	SOME COLD RAINY DAY	25
75	Flyright LP 114	SOME COLD RAINY DAY (reissue)	15
65	Lestar	SOME FOLK IN LEICESTER (private pressing)	50
70	Pama PMP 2003	SOMETHING SWEET FROM THE LADY	15
84	EMI TOPCAT 1	SOMETIMES A GREAT NOTION	10
60	Topic 12001	SONGS AGAINST THE BOMB	12
69	Liberty LBX 4	SON OF GUTBUCKET	10
72	Probe SPB 1061	SOUL BIBLE	10
69	Direction (S)PR 28	SOUL DIRECTION	12
69	Polydor 584 163	SOUL FEVER	10
60s	Minit MLL 40011E	SOUL FOOD	18
60s	Soul City SCB 1	SOUL FROM THE CITY	20
60s	Ember SPE/LP 6606	SOUL FROM THE VAULTS	12
74	Trojan TRL 65	SOULFUL REGGAE	10
68	Trojan TRL 3	SOUL OF JAMAICA	35
68	Polydor Special 236 213	SOUL PARTY	10
69	Pama PMLP 8	SOUL SAUCE FROM PAMA	20
69	Polydor 236 554	SOUL SELLER	15
70s	United Artists UAL 229018	SOUL SENSATION	12
66	Stateside SL 10186	SOUL SIXTEEN	18
66	Sue ILP 934	SOUL '66	35
60s	CBS BPG 62965	SOUL SOUNDS	10
67	HMV CLP 3617	SOUL SOUNDS OF THE 60s	25
67	Stateside SL 10203	SOUL SUPPLY	25
65	Pye Intl. NPL 28061	THE SOUND OF BACHARACH	12
68	President PTL 1008	THE SOUND OF SOUL	10
64	Stateside SL 10077	THE SOUND OF THE R&B HITS	35
70s	Grapevine GRAL 1001	SOUND OF THE GRAPEVINE	20
69	Joy JOY 125	SOUNDS LIKE SKA	10
70s	Sonet SNTF 806	SOUTHEND ROCK	10
60s	Saydisc Roots RL 328	SOUTHERN SANCTIFIED SINGERS	15
61	London Jazz LTZ-K 15209	SOUTHERN FOLK HERITAGE VOLUME 1: SOUNDS OF THE SOUTH	10
61	London Jazz LTZ-K 15210	SOUTHERN FOLK HERITAGE VOLUME 2: BLUE RIDGE MOUNTAIN MUSIC	10
61	London Jazz LTZ-K 15211	SOUTHERN FOLK HERITAGE VOLUME 3: ROOTS OF THE BLUES	10
61	London Jazz LTZ-K 15209	SOUTHERN FOLK HERITAGE VOLUME 7: THE BLUES ROLL ON	10
54	London AL 3529	SOUTHSIDE CHICAGO JAZZ (10")	15
71	Python PLP 10	SOUTHSIDE CHICAGO	25
58	Tempo TAP 17	SPEAK LOW — MORE MUSIC IN THE MODERN MANNER	25
57	Pye Nixa NPT 19019	SPIN WITH THE STARS — SELECTION NO. 2 (10")	18
57	Pye Nixa NPT 19021	SPIN WITH THE STARS — SELECTION NO. 3 (10")	18
65	Fontana TL 5243	SPIRITUAL AND GOSPEL FESTIVAL	10
59	Top Rank 35/064	SPIRITUALS TO SWING VOLUME 1	20
59	Top Rank 35/065	SPIRITUALS TO SWING VOLUME 2	20
82	WEA K 85415	A SPLASH OF COLOUR	12
69	RCA RD 7921/2	THE STARS OF THE GRAND OLE OPRY (2-LP)	15
62	Liberty LBY 1001	THE STARS OF LIBERTY	25
57	Decca LF 1299	STARS OF THE 6.5 SPECIAL (10")	35
66	London HA-B 8269	STARS OF THE STEEL GUITAR	10
80s	Pleasantly Surprised PS 3	STATE OF AFFAIRS (cassette, in bag with inserts)	15
85	Statik POL 274	STATIK COMPILATION ONE (2-LP)	20
60s	Stax XATS 1007	STAX SOUL EXPLOSION	10
70s	Stax STXH 5004	THE STAX STORY (VOL. 1)	10
70s	Stax STXH 5005	THE STAX STORY (VOL. 1)	10
67	Stax 589 010	THE STAX/VOLT SHOW VOL. 1	12
67	Stax 589 011	THE STAX/VOLT SHOW VOL. 2	12
60	Topic 10T59	STILL I LOVE HIM	10
69	CBS 66218	STORY OF THE BLUES (2-LP)	15
70	CBS 66232	STORY OF THE BLUES VOLUME 2 (2-LP)	20
70	Pama PMP 2002	STRAIGHTEN UP	15
71	Pama PMP 2007	STRAIGHTEN UP VOLUME TWO	15
71	Pama PMP 2014	STRAIGHTEN UP VOLUME THREE	15
72	Pama PMP 2017	STRAIGHTEN UP VOLUME FOUR	15
77	Beggars Banquet BEGA 1	STREETS	12
80s	Streetsound	STREETSOUND ELECTRO (box set)	60

83	Streetsounds ELCST 1	STREETSOUND ELECTRO 1	10
83	Streetsounds ELCST 2	STREETSOUND ELECTRO 2	10
84	Streetsounds ELCST 3	STREETSOUND ELECTRO 3	10
84	Streetsounds ELCST 4	STREETSOUND ELECTRO 4	10
79	Open Eye OE LP 501	STREET TO STREET — A LIVERPOOL COMPILATION	20
81	Open Eye OE LP 502	STREET TO STREET — A LIVERPOOL COMPILATION VOL. 2	10
80s	Chick CHR 001	SUBWAY (clear vinyl)	20
80s	INST-4	SUCK	12
65	Sue ILP 925	THE SUE STORY	35
66	Sue ILP 933	THE SUE STORY VOL. 2	35
66	Sue ILP 939	THE SUE STORY VOL. 3	30
65	London HA-C 8239	THE 'SUE' STORY	30
60s	Reprise R 5031	THE SUMMIT	25
70s	Sun BOX 105	SUN RECORDS: THE BLUES YEARS (9-LP box with booklet)	50
80s	Sunset Gun	SUNSET GUN (cassette with 'Sunset Gun' fanzine)	10
60s	Ember NR 5038	SUNSTROKE	15
73	Philips 6369 416	SUPER BLACK BLUES	12
81	Stuff S4	SUPERCOMPILATION (cassette)	10
70s	Blue Horizon PR 31	SUPER DUPER BLUES	15
68	Pye Intl. NPL 28107	SUPER SOUL	15
70	Blue Horizon 7-66263	SWAMP BLUES (2-LP)	45
68	Stateside S(S)L 10243	SWEET SOUL SOUNDS	20
68	Coxsone CSL 8018	SWING EASY	60
68	Saga	SWINGING SAGA	10
58	Tempo TAP 21	SWINGIN' THE BLUES	20

T

60	Fontana TFL 5103	TAKE IT FROM HERE (excerpts from radio show, also stereo STFL 534)	10
71	Rubber LP 001	TAKE OFF YOUR HEAD AND LISTEN	10
80s	Subway Org. SUBORG 001	TAKE THE SUBWAY TO YOUR SUBURB (mini-LP, red or yellow sleeve)	8
70s	Grapevine GRAL 1000	TALK OF THE GRAPEVINE	15
65	London HA-B 8250	THE TALL 12	12
67	London HA-B 8315	THE TALL 12 VOL. 2	12
70s	REL RELP 466	TARTAN ALBUM (tartan picture disc)	10
58	Capitol T 1009	TEENAGE ROCK (turquoise or 'rainbow' label)	35/30
63	Stateside SL 10020	TENNESSEE GUITAR	15
56	Nixa Jazz Today NJL 4	TENORAMA	12
70s	Fountain FV 205	TEXAS BLUES	15
69	Highway 51 H 103	TEXAS-LOUISIANA BLUES	50
62	Ace Of Clubs ACL 1108	THANK YOUR LUCKY STARS	20
63	Golden Guinea GGL 0190	THANK YOUR LUCKY STARS	10
63	Decca LK 4554	THANK YOUR LUCKY STARS VOLUME 2	25
60s	Parlophone PMC 1197	THAT WAS THE WEEK THAT WAS (also stereo PCS 3040)	10
70s	Dandelion 2485 021	THERE IS SOME FUN GOING FORWARD (some with poster)	15/10
69	Action ACLP 6009	THESE KIND OF BLUES VOL. 1	15
81	TTFTC 001	THE THING FROM THE CRYPT (I NEARLY DIED LAUGHING)	10
80s	Come Org. WDC 881021	33 FUR ILSE KOCH (some on red vinyl)	60
68	Minit MLL/MLS 40002	THIRTY-THREE MINITS OF BLUES AND SOUL	12
80s	2-Tone CHR TT 5007	THIS ARE 2-TONE (with free poster)	10
64	Island ILP 910	THIS IS BLUE BEAT (unreleased, white labels may exist)	100+
69	Chess CRL 4540	THIS IS CHESS	12
60s	Island IWP 5	THIS IS THE BLUES	25
63	Oriole PS 40047	THIS IS MERSEYBEAT VOL. 1	40
63	Oriole PS 40048	THIS IS MERSEYBEAT VOL. 2	40
70s	Grapevine GRAL 1002	THIS IS NORTHERN SOUL	20
69	Pama PSP 1003	THIS IS REGGAE	20
71	Pama PMP 2005	THIS IS REGGAE VOLUME TWO	15
71	Pama PMP 2008	THIS IS REGGAE VOLUME THREE	15
72	Pama PMP 2016	THIS IS REGGAE VOLUME FOUR	15
60s	Island IWP 3	THIS IS SUE!	20
60	Philips BBL 7356	THIS WONDERFUL WORLD OF JAZZ	10
63	RCA RD/SF 7608	THE THREE GREAT GUYS (Paul Anka, Sam Cooke & Neil Sedaka)	15
70	Saydisc Matchbox SDR182	THOSE CAKEWALKIN' BABIES FROM HOME	15
80s	Extract XX 002	THREE MINUTE SYMPHONIE	10
69	Trojan TTL 1	TIGHTEN UP	15
69	Trojan TTL 7	TIGHTEN UP VOLUME TWO	10
69	Trojan TTL 7	TIGHTEN UP VOLUME TWO (pink Island label with diff. track listing & sl.)	40+
70	Trojan TBL 120	TIGHTEN UP	10
70	Trojan TBL 131	TIGHTEN UP VOLUME TWO	10
70	Trojan TBL 145	TIGHTEN UP VOLUME THREE	10
71	Trojan TBL 163	TIGHTEN UP VOLUME FOUR	10
71	Trojan TBL 165	TIGHTEN UP VOLUME FIVE	10
72	Trojan TBL 185	TIGHTEN UP VOLUME SIX	10
60s	Ember FA 2018	TOP OF THE POPS	10
63	Golden Guinea GGL 0196	TOP TV THEMES	12
82	Zoo ZOO 4	TO THE SHORES OF LAKE PLACID (gatefold sleeve with 4-page booklet)	15
70s	Ode 99001	TOMMY (2-LP box set)	15
55	Decca LK 4088	TRADITIONAL JAZZ AT THE ROYAL FESTIVAL HALL	20
55	Decca LK 4100	TRADITIONAL JAZZ AT THE ROYAL FESTIVAL HALL VOL. 2	15
56	Tempo TAP 1	TRADITIONAL JAZZ SCENE 1956	10
72	United Artists	THE TRANSPORTS (2-LP, with book)	60
70	RCA Intl. INTS 1175	TRAVELLING THIS LONESOME ROAD	15
65	'77' LA 12-2	A TREASURY OF FIELD RECORDINGS VOLUME 1	20
65	'77' LA 12-3	A TREASURY OF FIELD RECORDINGS VOLUME 2	20
60s	Embassy WLP 6041	TRIBUTE TO CLIFF	12
60s	Embassy	TRIBUTE TO ELVIS	10
64	Columbia 33SX 1635	TRIBUTE TO MICHAEL HOLLIDAY	25

Various Artists: LPs

72	CBS 64861	TRIBUTE TO WOODY GUTHRIE PART 1 (gatefold sleeve)	10
80	Skeleton SKL LP 1	A TRIP TO THE DENTIST (with insert)	15
61	Parlophone PMC 1139	TRIPLE TREAT	20
71	Trojan TBL 172	TROJAN REGGAE PARTY	10
71	Trojan TBL 180	TROJAN'S GREATEST HITS	10
72	Trojan TBL 190	TROJAN'S GREATEST HITS VOLUME TWO	10
80s	K-Tel NE 1261	THE TUBE	10
67	Riverside RLP 8802	TUB JUG WASHBOARD BANDS	20
60s	Melodisc 12-193	12 BIG HITS	15
60s	Melodisc 12-217	12 CARAT GOLD	15
66	London HA-F/SH-F 8285	THE TWELVE-STRING STORY — GUITAR SOLOS	10
73	Dragon DRLS 5003	20 DRAGON HITS	10
63	Philips BL 7578	TWIST AT THE STAR-CLUB, HAMBURG	35

U-V

88	Link LINKLP 053	UNDERGROUND ROCKERS	10
80s	Link LINKLP	UNDERGROUND ROCKERS VOL. 2	10
69	Island ILP 993/ILPS 9093	THE UNFOLDING OF THE BOOK OF LIFE VOL. 1	18
69	Island ILP 994/ILPS 9094	THE UNFOLDING OF THE BOOK OF LIFE VOL. 2	18
70s	Flyright FLY 577	UNISSUED CHICAGO BLUES	10
69	Pama ECO 7	UNITY'S GREATEST	20
80	Safari UPP 1	UPPERS ON THE SOUTH DOWNS (original issue)	10
68	Atlantic 588 122	UPTOWN SOUL	10
77	Speciality SNTF 5023	URBAN BLUES	12
69	Liberty LBL 83215	URBAN BLUES VOLUME 1: BLUES UPTOWN	15
69	Liberty LBL 83327	URBAN BLUES VOLUME 2: NEW ORLEANS BOUNCE	15
80s	Pungent PUN 1	URBAN DEVELOPMENT (cassette)	12
72	Village Thing VTSAM 15	US	10
50s	Audubon AAM	VAUDEVILLE (10")	20
70	VJM VLP 30	VAUDEVILLE BLUES	15
78	Attrix RB 03	VAULTAGE '78 (TWO SIDES OF BRIGHTON) (originally hand-screened sleeve, later with insert)	12/10
71	Trojan TBL 175	VERSION GALORE VERSION TWO	15
73	Trojan TBL 200	VERSION GALORE VERSION THREE	15
72	Trojan TBL 182	VERSION TO VERSION	15
73	Trojan TBL 206	VERSION TO VERSION VOLUME THREE	15
70	Vertigo 6499 407/8	VERTIGO ANNUAL 1970 (2-LP, set no.: 6657 001)	14
55	Philips BBR 8071	VISIT TO JAZZLAND (10")	10
80s	Recommended RM 01	VOICES, NOTES AND NOISE	15

W

70s	Object Music OBJ 007	WAITING ROOM	10
62	Columbia 33SX 1385	WAKEY WAKEY	25
80s	Psycho PSYCHO 35	THE WAKING DREAM	10
64	Pye Intl. NPL 28041	WALKING BY MYSELF	25
64	Pye Intl. NPL 28044	WALKING THE BLUES	20
73	Flyright LP 503	THE WALKING VICTROLA	12
81	Phil Spector Intl. WOS 001	WALL OF SOUND (9-LP box set)	40
60s	Ace Of Hearts AH 55	WASHBOARD RHYTHM	15
70s	Polydor 218 006	WAY INTO THE 70'S	10
78	Bridgehouse BHLP 001	A WEEKEND AT THE BRIDGE E16 (with free 12" EP)	10
59	Coral LVA 9096	WE LIKE GIRLS	20
59	Coral LVA 9098	WE LIKE GUYS	20
63	London HA-P 8061	WE SING THE BLUES	30
60s	Liberty LBY 3051	WE SING THE BLUES	25
65	Sue ILP 921	WE SING THE BLUES!	30
70	Trojan TTL 34	WHAT AM I TO DO	15
80s	Rather/17 RATHER 13	WHAT A NICE WAY TO TURN SEVENTEEN NO. 3 (with magazine)	10
80s	Seventeen SEVENTEEN 6	WHAT A NICE WAY TO TURN SEVENTEEN NO. 6 (with magazine)	10
68	Elektra EKS 7304	WHAT'S SHAKIN' (reissue of "Good Time Music")	15
81	S&T	WHERE THE HELL IS LEICESTER?	10
87	Sunrise A 40111 M	WHERE WOULD YOU RATHER BE TONIGHT?	10
79	London Bomp DHS-Z 3	WHO PUT THE BOMP? (2-LP, gatefold sleeve)	15
70	Trojan TBL 131	WHO YOU GONNA RUN TO	20
72	private pressing	WHOLLY GRAIL	25
61	Philips BBL 7430	WINNERS OF DOWN BEAT'S INTERNATIONAL CRITICS' POLL 1960	10
66	Dot DLP 3535	WIPE OUT	12
76	RCA RS 1085	WIZARD'S CONVENTION (with insert)	10
67	RCA Victor RD 7840	WOMEN OF THE BLUES	20
81	Glass GLASS 010	THE WONDERFUL WORLD OF GLASS	15
70s	Readers Digest RDS 6704	WONDERLAND OF SOUND (10-LP set)	30
70	Atlantic 2663 001	WOODSTOCK (3-LP)	18
71	Atlantic 2657 003	WOODSTOCK II (2-LP)	14
63	London HA-P 8099	A WORLD OF BLUES	30
69	Decca (S)PA-R 14	THE WORLD OF BLUES POWER	10
73	Decca SPA 263	WORLD OF BLUES POWER VOLUME 3	15
69	Pama SECO 19	A WORLD OF BULLET	15
71	Argo SPA 132	THE WORLD OF FOLK	20
69	Decca (S)PA 34	WOWIE ZOWIE — THE WORLD OF PROGRESSIVE MUSIC	10
84	Creation CRELP 002	WOW, WILD SUMMER! (original with £2.99 price & white background)	10

Y-Z

70	Trojan TBL 142	YOU CAN'T WINE	15
69	Trojan TTL 9	YOU LEFT ME STANDING	20
78	Stiff DEAL 1	YOU'RE EITHER ON THE TRAIN OR OFF THE TRAIN (promo-only, with booklet)	12
62	HMV CLP 1565	YOUR FAVOURITE TV AND RADIO THEMES	10

63	HMV CLP 1676	YOUR FAVOURITE TV AND RADIO THEMES (VOL. 3) 10
66	HMV CSD 3521	YOUR FAVOURITE TV AND RADIO THEMES VOL. 5 10
71	Bamboo BDLP 211	YOUR JAMAICAN GIRL 40
84	Zulu ZULU 6	THE ZULU COMPILATION 15
80s	Relentless R 101	!!?! ... A TASTER 12

TV & SOUNDTRACK LPs
(alphabetical by title)
A

70	Paramount SPFL 260	THE ADVENTURERS 15
54	Philips BBL 7005	AFTER THE BALL 10
60	Philips BBL 7429	THE ALAMO (also stereo SBBL 599) 10/12
56	Nixa NPT 19010	ALEXANDER THE GREAT 10
69	MGM	ALFRED THE GREAT 75
74	WEA K 56009	ALICE'S ADVENTURES IN WONDERLAND (2-LP) 14
61	Fontana STFL 591	ALL NIGHT LONG 15
71	Buddah 2318 034	ALL THE RIGHT NOISES 12
50s	MGM CD 1	ANNIE GET YOUR GUN (musical) (10") 10
56	Brunswick LAT 8118	ANYTHING GOES 12
60	London HA-T 2287	THE APARTMENT 10
58	London HA-D 2078	APRIL LOVE 12
66	RCA Victor RD 7817	ARABESQUE 10
57	Brunswick LAT 8185	AROUND THE WORLD IN EIGHTY DAYS 10

B

67	Fontana TL 5306	BABY, THE RAIN MUST FALL 10
77	Sire SRK 6026	BANJOMAN 10
68	Stateside (S)SL 10260	BARBARELLA 30
67	London HA-D 8337	BAREFOOT IN THE PARK 10
66	Stateside S(S)L 10179	BATMAN 15
60	Columbia 33SX 1125	BEAT GIRL 30
64	RCA Victor RD 7679	BECKET 10
68	Decca LK/SKL 4923	BEDAZZLED 15
73	Ronco RR 2006	THE BELSTONE FOX (gatefold sleeve) 15
60	MGM MGM-C 802	BEN-HUR (also stereo CS 6006) 10
57	London HA-U 1069	THE BEST THINGS IN LIFE ARE FREE 10
71	Stateside SSL 10311	BEYOND THE VALLEY OF THE DOLLS 18
66	Stateside S(S)L 10188	THE BIBLE 10
59	London HA-T 2142	THE BIG COUNTRY 10
67	United Artists SULP 1183	BILLION DOLLAR BRAIN 15
68	Dot (S)LPD 508	BLUE 10
61	RCA RD 27238/SF 5115	BLUE HAWAII (mono/stereo) 15/25
69	MCA MUPS 360	BOOM! 75
72	Bell BELLS 209	BURGLARS 10
66	RCA RD 7791	BUNNY LAKE IS MISSING 40
70	A&M AMLS 963	BUTCH CASSIDY AND THE SUNDANCE KID 10
63	RCA Victor RD 7580	BYE BYE BIRDIE (musical) 10

C

66	RCA Victor RD/SF 7820	CALIFORNIA HOLIDAY (mono/stereo) 17/22
53	Brunswick LA 8603	CALL ME MADAM (10") 12
69	Stateside (S)SL 10276	CANDY 12
56	Capitol (S)LCT 6105	CAROUSEL 10
64	MGM MGM-C 984	THE CARPETBAGGERS 15
64	London HA-A/SH-A 8219	THE CARPETBAGGERS 15
67	RCA RD/SF 7874	CASINO ROYALE 30/35
71	Polydor 2383 035	CATCH MY SOUL 10
62	Warner Bros WS 8117	THE CHAPMAN REPORT 15
68	United Artists	THE CHARGE OF THE LIGHT BRIGADE 10
66	CBS (S)BPG 62665	THE CHASE 15
67	Fontana TL 5417	CHIMES AT MIDNIGHT 30
50s	Columbia OL 5190	CINDERELLA (also stereo OS 2005) 12
50s	Columbia OL 6330	CINDERELLA (remake, also stereo OS 2730) 12
68	RCA Victor RD/SF 7917	CLAMBAKE (mono/stereo) 15/18
81	CBS 73588	CLASH OF THE TITANS 10
63	Stateside SL/SSL 10044	CLEOPATRA 10
65	Fontana TL 5259	THE COLLECTOR 20
78	MGM 2315 398	COMA 10
62	Parlophone PMC 1194	THE COOL MIKADO 50
74	EMI EMA 782	CROSS OF IRON (gatefold sleeve) 15
68	Stateside (S)SL 10222	CUSTER OF THE WEST 20

D

62	Fontana TFL 5184	DANGEROUS FRIENDSHIPS 15
67	Stateside (S)SL 10217	THE DAY THE FISH CAME OUT 10
68	Stateside (S)SL 10263	DEADFALL 20
79	EMI EMC 3256	DEATH ON THE NILE 10
68	Stateside (S)SL 10259	DECLINE AND FALL ... OF A BIRDWATCHER 30
58	London HA-D 2111	DESIRE UNDER THE ELMS 12
71	United Artists UAS 29216	DIAMONDS ARE FOREVER 12
59	Top Rank RX 3016	THE DIARY OF ANNE FRANK 20
67	Stateside SL/SSL 102143	DOCTOR DOLITTLE (2-LP) 4
62	Columbia 33SX 1446	DON'T KNOCK THE TWIST 15
67	RCA Victor RD/SF 7892	DOUBLE TROUBLE (mono/stereo) 15/18
63	United Artists (S)ULP 1097	DR NO (mono/stereo) 15/18
77	RCA RD/SF 7846	DROP DEAD ... DARLING 10
60	HMV CLP 1352/CSD 1296	DRUM CRAZY (THE GENE KRUPA STORY) (mono/stereo) 12/15

Various Artists: T.V. & Soundtrack LPs

| 58 | Decca LF 1308 | THE DUKE WORE JEANS (10") ....15 |

E

70	Stateside SSL 5018	EASY RIDER 10
69	RCA Victor RD 8011	ELVIS ("TV Special" Soundtrack) 12
78	Astoria 1	ELVIS (sold at performances of "Elvis" show) 30
63	Parlophone PMC 1198	THE ESTABLISHMENT 12
81	Island ILPS 9682	EXCALIBUR 10
61	London HA-T 2362	EXODUS 10

F

57	Capitol LCT 6139	A FACE IN THE CROWD (10") 20
67	Decca LK/SKL 4847	THE FAMILY WAY 60
60	Top Rank 30/003/004/005	FANTASIA (3-LP) 20
67	MGM C(S) 8053	FAR FROM THE MADDING CROWD 20
67	Stateside S(S)L 10213	FATHOM 10
68	Zeus CF 201	FESTIVAL AT TOWERSEY (private pressing, 99 only) 50
63	CBS SBPG 62148	55 DAYS AT PEKING 15
66	Columbia S(C)X 6079	FINDERS KEEPERS (with inner sleeve, mono/stereo) 15/20
60s	Reprise F(S) 2015	FINIAN'S RAINBOW 20
68	Warner Bros WF(S) 2550	FINIAN'S RAINBOW 18
59	London HA-U 2189	THE FIVE PENNIES (also stereo SH-U 6044) 10
65	RCA Victor RD 7723	FLAMING STAR AND SUMMER KISSES (black or orange 1969 label) 50/60
68	Stateside (S)SL 10253	A FLEA IN HER EAR 10
61	Golden Guinea GGL 0092	THE FLINTSTONES 15
62	Brunswick LAT 8392	FLOWER DRUM SONG (also stereo STA 3054) 12
66	RCA Victor RD/SF 7793	FRANKIE AND JOHNNY (mono/stereo) 15/20
71	Paramount SPFL 269	FRIENDS 10
63	United Artists (S)ULP 1052	FROM RUSSIA WITH LOVE (mono/stereo) 15/18
60	London HA-T 2257	THE FUGITIVE KIND 10
63	RCA Victor RD/SF 7609	FUN IN ACAPULCO (mono/stereo) 15/20
70	CBS 70044	FUNNY GIRL (gatefold sleeve) 10

G

65	Liberty (S)LBY 1261	GENGHIS KHAN (mono/stereo) 15
53	MGM MGM-D 116	GENTLEMEN PREFER BLONDES (10") 50
70s	Pye	GET CARTER 18
57	Capitol LCT 6122	GIANT 15
60	RCA RD 27192/SF 5078	G.I. BLUES (mono/stereo) 15/30
65	RCA Victor RD/SF 7714	GIRL HAPPY (mono/stereo) 15/20
63	RCA Victor RD/SF 7534	GIRLS! GIRLS! GIRLS! (mono/stereo) 15/20
54	Brunswick LA 8647	GLENN MILLER STORY (10") 10
58	London HA-T 2125	GOD'S LITTLE ACRE 12
73	United Artists UAS 29576	THE GOLDEN VOYAGE OF SINBAD 10
64	United Artists (S)ULP 1076	GOLDFINGER (mono/stereo) 12/15
64	Decca LK 4673	GONKS GO BEAT 70
65	Stateside SL 10126	GOODBYE CHARLIE 10
69	Warner Bros W(S) 1786	GOODBYE COLUMBUS 10
84	Warner Bros K 925 120-1	GREYSTOKE THE LEGEND OF TARZAN LORD OF THE APES 12
63	Philips BBL 7500	THE GUNS OF NAVARONE 10
62	Warner Bros WM/WS 8120	GYPSY 10

H

65	RCA Victor RD/SF 7767	HAREM HOLIDAY (mono/stereo) 15/20
66	United Artists (S)ULP 1154	HAWAII 10
80s	PRT/Chips CHILP 1	HAWK THE SLAYER (gatefold sleeve) 10
70	Stateside SSL 10292	HELLO DOLLY! 10
70	Stateside SSL 10309	HELLO-GOODBYE 10
74	Tamla Motown SSL11260	HELL UP IN HARLEM (Edwin Starr & Others) 15
67	United Artists (S)ULP 1186	HERE WE GO ROUND THE MULBERRY BUSH 18
59	Capitol T 1160	HEY BOY! HEY GIRL! 20
62	Columbia 33SX 1421	HEY, LET'S TWIST 12
56	Capitol (S)LCT 6116	HIGH SOCIETY 10
70	Polydor 2400 137	HOMER 10
66	Stateside SL/SSL 10187	HOW TO STEAL A MILLION 20
61	Golden Guinea GGL 0069	HUCKLEBERRY HOUND 10
67	RCA Victor RD 7877	HURRY SUNDOWN 10

I

67	Stateside SL/SSL 10207	IN LIKE FLINT 15
66	CBS BPG 62530	THE IPCRESS FILE 25
69	Paramount SPFL 256	THE ITALIAN JOB 10
63	RCA Victor RD/SF 7565	IT HAPPENED AT THE WORLD'S FAIR (mono/stereo) 15/20
63	Columbia 33SX 1533	IT'S ALL HAPPENING (also stereo SCX 3486) 12/15
63	Philips BL 7609	IT'S ALL OVER TOWN 10
62	Columbia 33SX 1412	IT'S TRAD, DAD! 15

J

57	Capitol LCT 6140	THE JAMES DEAN STORY 25
69	Stateside (S)SL 10264	JOANNA 10
74	RSO 2394 141	JOHN, PAUL, GEORGE, RINGO AND BERT (London cast recording, with Barbara Dickson) 10
77	Polydor/EG 2302 079	JUBILEE 10
63	Decca LK 4524	JUST FOR FUN 30
64	Decca	JUST FOR YOU 25

K

72	Polydor 2383 102	KIDNAPPED 12
58	RCA RD 27088	KING CREOLE 35
58	Capitol LCT 6165	KINGS GO FORTH 10
66	Fontana (S)TL 5302	KING RAT 10

60s	Reprise F(S) 2017	KISS ME KATE	12
64	RCA Victor RD/SF 7645	KISSIN' COUSINS (LP, mono/stereo)	15/20
69	Stateside (S)SL 10227	KRAKATAO: EAST OF JAVA	15

L

61	RCA RD 27202	LA DOLCE VITA	15
72	HMV CSD 3728	LADY CAROLINE LAMB	15
69	Stateside S(S)L 10267	LADY IN CEMENT	10
71	United Artists UAS 29120	THE LANDLORD	10
71	Probe SPB 1027	THE LAST VALLEY (some with insert)	35/30
64	Stateside S(S)L 10058	THE LEOPARD	10
60	Philips BBL 7414	LET'S MAKE LOVE	35
64	Stateside S(S)L 10057	LIGHT FANTASTIC	10
68	CBS 70049	THE LION IN WINTER	15
87	Warner Bros 925 616-2	THE LIVING DAYLIGHTS (CD)	15
Decca LK 4320		LOCK UP YOUR DAUGHTERS	10
76	MGM 2315 376	LOGAN'S RUN	15
73	Reflection	LONESOME STONE (stage production recording)	18
63	Stateside S(S)L 10045	THE LONGEST DAY	10
65	Colpix PXL 521	LORD JIM	15

M

69	Warner Bros WS 1805	THE MADWOMAN OF CHAILLOT	15
70	Pye Intl. NSPL 28133	THE MAGIC CHRISTIAN	30
65	Stateside SL 10136	THOSE MAGNIFICENT MEN IN THEIR FLYING MACHINES	10
54	Brunswick LAT 8045	MAGNIFICENT OBSESSION	12
66	CBS SBPG 62525	MAJOR DUNDEE	15
66	RCA	A MAN FOR ALL SEASONS (2-LP)	25
59	Top Rank 35/043	MAN FROM INTERPOL (TV series music)	20
66	RCA RD 7758	THE MAN FROM U.N.C.L.E.	20
64	Stateside S(S)L 10087	MAN IN THE MIDDLE	30
63	Stateside S(S)L 10048	MARILYN (mono/stereo)	15/18
56	Brunswick LAT 8101	THE MAN WITH THE GOLDEN ARM	15
74	United Artists UAS 29671	THE MAN WITH THE GOLDEN GUN	12
70	Polydor 2383 043	MELODY	10
57	London HA-P 2076	MEN IN WAR	12
76	EMI SLCW 1033	THE MESSAGE (gatefold sleeve)	12
66	Fontana TL 5347	MODESTY BLAISE	20
69	Paramount SPFL 252	MORE MISSION: IMPOSSIBLE	18
60	MGM MGM-C 857	MORE MUSIC FROM BEN-HUR	15
66	RCA RD 7832	MORE MUSIC FROM THE MAN FROM U.N.C.L.E.	25
60	EMI EMC 3054	MURDER ON THE ORIENT EXPRESS	10
68	Dot (S)LPD 503	MUSIC FROM 'MISSION: IMPOSSIBLE' TV SERIES	18
50s	Capitol W 990	THE MUSIC MAN (original Broadway cast recording)	25
64	Stateside SL 10073	MY PEOPLE	10

N

70	United Artists UAS 5213	NED KELLY	15
60	London HA-T 2309	NEVER ON SUNDAY	10
72	Bell BELLS 202	NICHOLAS AND ALEXANDRA	15
68	Dot (S)LPD 507	NO WAY TO TREAT A LADY	10

O

83	A&M 394 967-2	OCTOPUSSY (CD)	18
60	London HA-T 2220	ODDS AGAINST TOMORROW	10
75	MCA MCF 2591	ODESSA FILE	10
64	Stateside SL/SSL 10056	OF LOVE AND DESIRE	10
69	Paramount SPFL 251	OH! WHAT A LOVELY WAR	10
50	Brunswick LAT 8001	OKLAHOMA (original cast recording)	15
60	Decca LK 4359	OLIVER! (original cast recording)	20
61	HMV CLP 1459/CSD 1370	OLIVER! (mono/stereo)	40/50
60s	World Records TP 151	OLIVER!	10
70	CBS 70075	ON A CLEAR DAY YOU CAN SEE FOREVER (gatefold sleeve)	10
80s	Illuminated JAMS 35	ONCE UPON A TIME	12
61	Decca LK 4393	ONE OVER THE EIGHT	12
69	United Artists UAS 29020	ON HER MAJESTY'S SECRET SERVICE	20
60	London HA-T 2222	ON THE BEACH/FILMS THEMES FROM HOLLYWOOD	10
61	Decca LK 4395	ON THE BRIGHTER SIDE	12
54	HMV DLP 1059	ORCHESTRA WIVES (10")	12
66	Stateside SL 10174	OUR MAN FLINT	12

P

69	Paramount SPFL 257	PAINT YOUR WAGON	10
57	Capitol LCT 6148	PAL JOEY	10
66	RCA Victor RD/SF 7810	PARADISE, HAWAIIAN STYLE (mono/stereo)	15/18
59	London HA-T 2143	PARIS HOLIDAY	10
70	Stateside SSL 10302	PATTON	10
66	Philips (S)BL 7782	THE PEKING MEDALLION	15
61	Pye Intl. NPL 28015	PEPE	12
70	Warner Bros WS 2554	PERFORMANCE	15
71	CBS 64816	THE PERSUADERS	10
59	RCA RD 27123/SF 5033	PETER GUNN	12
55	Philips BBL 7059	PETE KELLY'S BLUES	10
71	CBS 64816	THE PERSUADERS	10
59	Decca LK 4337	PIECES OF EIGHT	12
69	Stateside (S)SL 10278	THE PRIME OF MISS JEAN BRODIE	10
86	Bam Caruso WEBA 066	THE PRISONER (fan club issue, gatefold sleeve, inner sleeve, booklet, membership form, map & poster)	20
86	Bam Caruso KIRI 66	THE PRISONER (reissue)	10
69	RCA SF 8072	THE PRODUCERS	10

| 61 | Contemporary LAC 12293 | THE PROPER TIME | 12 |
| 68 | Stateside (S)SL 10248 | PRUDENCE AND THE PILL | 10 |

R

71	Columbia SCX 6447	THE RAGING MOON	10
66	Polydor	RED AND BLUE	25
72	Paramount SPFL 275	THE RED TENT	10
70s	RCA Red Seal RS 1010	THE RETURN OF THE PINK PANTHER	10
70	United Artists (S)ULP 1156	RETURN OF THE SEVEN	10
68	United Artists UAS 29069	REVOLUTION	12
68	MGM C(S) 8079	THE RISE AND FALL OF THE THIRD REICH	10
53	Brunswick LA 8578	ROAD TO BALI (10")	12
60s	Reprise R 2021	ROBIN AND THE SEVEN HOODS	25
57	Mercury MPT 7527	ROCK ALL NIGHT (10")	125
57	Brunswick LAT 8162	ROCK, PRETTY BABY	75
75	UK UKAL 1015	THE ROCKY HORROR SHOW (Original London Cast)	15
75	UK UKMC 1015	THE ROCKY HORROR SHOW (cassette, Original London Cast)	10
74	Ode ODE 77026	THE ROCKY HORROR SHOW (Original Roxy Cast)	15
75	Ode ODE 78332	THE ROCKY HORROR PICTURE SHOW (Original Soundtrack)	15
75	Ode OPD 91653/ OSV 21653	THE ROCKY HORROR PICTURE SHOW (picture disc, 2 pressings)	15
70	Paramount SPFL 263	ROSALINO	10
68	Dot (S)LPD 519	ROSEMARY'S BABY	12
65	Parlophone PMC 1262	ROTTEN TO THE CORE	10
64	RCA Victor RD/SF 7678	ROUSTABOUT (mono/stereo)	15/20
70s	MGM 2315 028	RYAN'S DAUGHTER (gatefold sleeve)	10

S

53	Brunswick LA 8604	SALOME (10")	12
67	Stateside S(S)L 10198	THE SAND PEBBLES	10
58	Philips BBL 7216	SATCHMO THE GREAT	12
70	CBS 70077	SCROOGE (musical, gatefold sleeve)	12
80	EMI EMC 3340	THE SEA WOLVES	10
78	A&M AMLZ 666000	SGT PEPPER'S LONELY HEARTS CLUB BAND (2-LP, pink vinyl, gatefold sleeve with inners & poster)	14
73	Probe SPB 1077	SHAFT IN AFRICA	15
74	ABC ABCL 5035	SHAFT IN AFRICA (reissue)	10
70	Stateside SSL 10307	THE SICILIAN CLAN	10
65	Columbia 33SX 1602	SIBERIAN SHOOT-OUT	10
68	Columbia SAX 9001	SIGHTS & SOUNDS OF LONDON	10
58	Capitol T 929	SING, BOY, SING	35
78	Charisma CAS 1139	SIR HENRY AT RAWLINSON END (with insert)	10
73	Polydor 2391 084	SLAUGHTER'S BIG RIP-OFF	25
59	Top Rank RX 3022	SLEEPING BEAUTY	10
68	Stateside S(S)L 10224	SMASHING TIME	20
60	London HA-T 2221	SOLOMON AND SHEBA	10
59	Capitol LCT 6180	SOME COME RUNNING	10
59	London HA-T 2176	SOME LIKE IT HOT (also stereo SAH-T 6040)	45/50
66	CBS BPG 62558	THE SONS OF KATIE ELDER	15
69	RCA Victor SF 8024	THE SOUTHERN STAR	10
58	London HA-D 2079	SPANISH AFFAIR	10
68	RCA Victor RD/SF 7957	SPEEDWAY (mono/stereo)	18/25
77	United Artists UAG 30098	THE SPY WHO LOVED ME	10
66	Fontana TL 5354	STAGECOACH	10
68	Stateside S(S)L 10233	STAR!	10
62	London HA-D 2453	STATE FAIR (musical, also stereo SAH-D 6241)	12/15
63	Columbia 33SX 1472	SUMMER HOLIDAY (with inner sleeve, mono)	15
63	Columbia SCX 3462	SUMMER HOLIDAY (stereo, initially issued with green labels, later with blue/black labels)	30/20
57	London HA-R 2077	THE SUN ALSO RISES	10
72	Buddah 2318 065	SUPERFLY	10
73	Buddah 2318 087	SUPER FLY T.N.T.	10
64	Stateside SL 10089	SURF PARTY	20
57	Brunswick LAT 8195	SWEET SMELL OF SUCCESS	10
68	Stateside S(S)L 10250	THE SWEET RIDE	10
70	CBS 70043	THE SWIMMER	10
66	Mercury 20057 SMCL	SYLVIA	10

T

69	HMV CSD 3690	TALES OF BEATRICE POTTER	10
57	Vogue Coral LVA 9070	TAMMY	10
71	RCA Victor SF 8162	THAT'S THE WAY IT IS	10
58	London HA-D 2074-5	THE TEN COMMANDMENTS (2-LP)	20
73	Ronco MR 2002/3	THAT'LL BE THE DAY (2-LP)	14
63	Parlophone PMC 1197	THAT WAS THE WEEK THAT WAS (also stereo PCS 3040)	15
55	Brunswick LAT 8059	THERE'S NO BUSINESS LIKE SHOW BUSINESS	10
70	Stateside SSL 10305	THEY SHOOT HORSES, DON'T THEY?	10
65	United Artists (S)ULP 1110	THUNDERBALL (mono/stereo)	12/14
66	United Artists (S)ULP 1159	THUNDERBIRDS ARE GO! (mono/stereo)	70/80
67	Pye NPL 18154	TILL DEATH DO US PART	10
80	RSO 2685 145	TIMES SQUARE	10
59	MGM MGM-C 772	TOM THUMB	10
68	Instant INLP 002	TONITE LET'S ALL MAKE LOVE IN LONDON	50
67	Fontana (S)TL 5446	TO SIR, WITH LOVE	12
69	Stateside (S)SL 10271	THE TOUCHABLES	15
66	Polydor	THE TRAP	20
60	Pye Nonsuch PPLD 206	THE TRIAL OF LADY CHATTERLEY (drama/documentary)	10
68	Polydor	TWISTED NERVE/LES BICYCLETTES DE BELSIZE	60
72	Decca SKL 5345	THE TWISTER	20

U

60	London HA-T 2258	THE UNFORGIVEN	10
68	Fontana (S)TL 5460	UP THE JUNCTION — ORIGINAL SOUNDTRACK RECORDING	15
69	Stax (S)XATS 1005	UPTIGHT	12

V

68	Stateside (S)SL 10228	VALLEY OF THE DOLLS	12
71	London SH-U 8420	VANISHING POINT	10
58	London HAT 2118	THE VIKINGS	25

W

73	Charisma DCS 10	WAR OF THE WORLDS	10
66	Brunswick STA 8636	THE WAR LORD	20
68	Philips BL 7833	WATERHOLE # 3	10
64	Piccadilly N(S)PL 38011	WHAT A CRAZY WORLD	15
64	Golden Guinea GGL 0272	WHAT A CRAZY WORLD (reissue)	10
64	Stateside SL 10090	WHAT A WAY TO GO!	10
58	RCA RD 27103	WHATEVER LOLA WANTS	10
65	United Artists ULP 1096	WHAT'S NEW PUSSYCAT?	15
69	MGM CS 8102	WHERE EAGLES DARE	10
69	Paramount SPFL 254	WHERE'S JACK?	18
66	United Artists (S)ULP 1166	WHIPLASH WILLIE	10
57	London HA-N 2023	WILD BILL HICKOK AND JINGLES ON THE SANTA FEY TRAIL	15
69	Warner Bros	WILD BUNCH	20
75	Arista ARTY 111	THE WIND AND THE LION	15
57	MGM MGM-C 757	THE WIZARD OF OZ	25

Y

61	Golden Guinea GGL 0081	YOGI BEAR TV SERIES	10
69	CBS 70045	YOU ARE WHAT YOU EAT	12
61	Columbia 33SX 1384	THE YOUNG ONES (with inner, also stereo SCX 3397)	18/35
72	HMV CSDA 9002	YOUNG WINSTON	10
67	United Artists (S)ULP 1171	YOU ONLY LIVE TWICE	16
67	Kama Sutra KLP 402	YOU'RE A BIG BOY NOW	12

Z

71	Probe SPB 1026	ZACHARIAH	10
65	Stateside SL 10127	ZORBA THE GREEK	10
64	Ember NR 5012	ZULU	15

ORIGINAL CAST RECORDING LPs
(alphabetical by title)

64	Col. SX 1676/SCX 3522	ALADDIN AND HIS WONDERFUL LAMP (gatefold sleeve, mono/stereo)	15/18
70	Argo ZTA 501-2	ALICE IN WONDERLAND (2-LP)	40
70	CBS 70053	ANNE OF GREEN GABLES	15
50	Brunswick LAT 8002	ANNIE GET YOUR GUN	15
66	Columbia S(C)X 6009	BABES IN THE WOOD (mono/stereo)	12/15
64	Capitol (S)W 2191	BEN FRANKLIN IN PARIS	10
74	CBS 70133	BILLY (gatefold sleeve)	12
50s	HMV	THE BOYFRIEND (10")	20
50s	Philips ABL 3383	BYE BYE BIRDIE — LONDON CAST (also stereo)	20
50s	Columbia KOS 3040	CABARET	20
60s	Encore	CAN CAN	40
50	Brunswick LAT 8006	CAROUSEL	15
66	CBS 62627	CHARLIE GIRL	12
67	Columbia S(C)X 6103	CINDERELLA	25
70	CBS 70063	DAMES AT SEA	20
57	HMV CLP 1108	DAMN YANKEES	10
58	Pye NPL 18016	EXPRESSO BONGO	15
50s	Oriole MG 20016	FREE AS AIR	15
50s	Columbia SCXA 9252	GONE WITH THE WIND (gatefold sleeve)	12
53	Brunswick LAT 8022	GUYS AND DOLLS	15
70s	RCA Red Seal SER 5686	GYPSY (gatefold sleeve)	10
63	Decca SKL 4521	HALF A SIXPENCE	10
65	RCA Victor SF 7768	HELLO, DOLLY!	20
70	CBS BRG 70027	HOUDINI — MAN OF MAGIC	15
68	RCA Victor RD 7938	I DO! I DO!	15
76	EMI EMC 3139	IRENE	15
66	HMV CLP/CSD 3591	JORROCKS	15
53	Brunswick LAT 8026	THE KING AND I (original cast recording)	15
62	HMV CLP 1569/CSD 1441	LIONEL BART'S BLITZ!	12
72	Columbia SCX 6504	MAID OF THE MOUNTAINS	10
68	London HA-R/SH-R 8362	MAN OF LA MANCHA	10
60	HMV CLP 1365	THE MOST HAPPY FELLA!	20
60s	CBS 70048	MR & MRS	12
60	London HA-T 2286	ONCE UPON A MATTRESS	15
80	Warner Bros K 56850	ONE MO' TIME	10
60s	Philips SAL 3431	PICKWICK (gatefold sleeve)	15
78	EMI EMC 3233	PRIVATES ON PARADE	15
60s	Philips 632 303 BL	SPACE IS SO STERLING	15
73	Decca SKL 5137	TOM BROWNE'S SCHOOLDAYS	15
54	Parlophone PMD 1011	WEDDING PARIS (10")	25
61	HMV CLP 1467	WILDEST DREAMS	12
56	HMV DLP 1125	WILD GROWS THE HEATHER (10")	30
68	RCA SB 6792	THE YOUNG VISITORS	20

RECORD COLLECTOR'S
BACK ISSUES

A COMPLETE INDEX TO ALL ARTISTS
FEATURED IN PREVIOUS ISSUES

THE ARTISTS, SUBJECTS AND LABELS COVERED IN PREVIOUS ISSUES OF **RECORD COLLECTOR** ARE LISTED IN ALPHABETICAL ORDER BELOW.

Indexes to the U.K. SOUL SINGLES, SPECIAL PRESSINGS and COLLECTABLE INDIE SINGLES listings are printed on page 1149. The issue in which each feature appeared is shown by the number in brackets. Please quote the NUMBER of the issue(s) you require when ordering.

All discographies are U.K. RELEASES only unless stated otherwise. Discographies include values current at the time each issue was published. (*) indicates the discography is unpriced.

Issues up to and including No. 46 are A5 size, and issues from No. 47 are A4 size. Binders are available for the A4 issues — please see the latest issue of **RECORD COLLECTOR** for details.

NOTE: ISSUES 1-31, 33 and 34 ARE ALL OUT-OF-PRINT!

THE PRICES LISTED HERE APPLY UNTIL <u>SEPTEMBER 1994</u>

COST PER ISSUE: U.K. — £3.50; EUROPE — £4.20. Both rates are for SURFACE MAIL. If you want us to rush you your Back Issues and don't mind paying the extra postal charges, the AIRMAIL rate for EUROPE is £5.30.

READERS IN U.S.A., CANADA, AUSTRALIA, NEW ZEALAND AND JAPAN. We regret that we cannot accept orders for single issues paid in your currency due to high banking charges for foreign cheque transactions. Instead, we are offering a **FOUR-ISSUE SELECTION** at the following rates: U.S.A. – US $27.00 Surface (US $46.00 Airmail); Canada – Can. $31.00 Surface (Can. $53.00 Airmail); Australia – Aus. $37.00 Surface (Aus. $70.00 Airmail); New Zealand – NZ $48.50 Surface (NZ $93.00 Airmail); Japan — ¥ 2500 Surface (¥ 4000 Airmail).

TO ORDER: UK — send a crossed cheque or Postal Order, payable to 'Parker Publishing'. Overseas, send £ Eurocheque, IMO, Bank Draft or cash (Registered Mail). Please state clearly which issue number(s) you require, and print your NAME & ADDRESS clearly in CAPITAL LETTERS. Send your order and payment to:

**THE PRODUCTION MANAGER,
RECORD COLLECTOR, 45 ST. MARY'S ROAD,
EALING, LONDON W5 5RQ.**

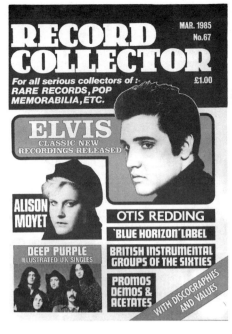

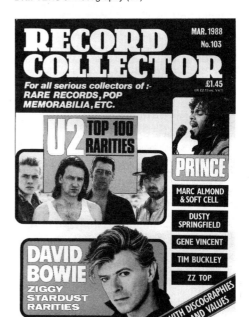

1139

RECORD COLLECTOR

OCT. 1990
No.134

For all serious collectors of:
RARE RECORDS, CDs,
POP MEMORABILIA, etc.

£1.95

MADONNA

JOHN LENNON
50th ANNIVERSARY
CELEBRATIONS

HENDRIX
THE STUDIO YEARS

JOE MEEK

GARY NUMAN
1984-90

JIM McCARTY
& THE YARDBIRDS

JEAN-MICHEL
JARRE

THE PRIMITIVES

WITH DISCOGRAPHIES
AND VALUES

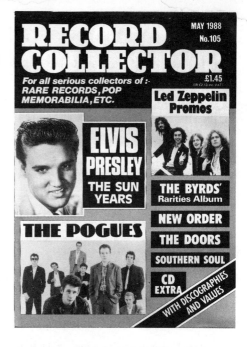

RECORD COLLECTOR
MAY 1988
No.105
For all serious collectors of :-
**RARE RECORDS, POP
MEMORABILIA, ETC.**
£1.45
(IR £2.13 inc VAT)

Led Zeppelin
Promos
ELVIS PRESLEY
THE SUN YEARS
THE BYRDS'
Rarities Album
THE POGUES
NEW ORDER
THE DOORS
SOUTHERN SOUL
CD EXTRA
WITH DISCOGRAPHIES AND VALUES

1147

U.K. SOUL RELEASES

This series of collectable soul singles on U.K. labels is in alphabetical order. Each month, the feature contains a brief guide to the most valuable records on the respective label(s). The issue number is in brackets before the label name.

(20) Columbia; (31) Hot Wax, Invictus; (32) Jay Boy Pt 1; (35) London Pt 1; (36) London Pt 2; (37) London Pt 3; (38) London Pt 4; (39) Major Minor; MCA; (40) Mercury; (41) MGM; (42) Minit; (43) Mojo; (44) Monument; (45) Mowest, Now; (46) Oriole; (47) Page One, Pama, Paramount; (48) Parlophone; (49) People; (50) Philips; (51) Philadelphia Intl Pt 1; (52) Philadelphia Intl Pt 2; (53) Piccadilly, Planet; (54) Polydor Pt 1; (55) Polydor Pt 2; (56) President; (57) Power Exchange; (58) Probe; (59) Pye, Pye Intl Pt 1; (60) Pye Intl Pt 2; (61) Pye Intl Pt 3; (62) RCA; (63) Red Bird; (64) Regal Zonophone, Reprise, Right On!; (65) Riverside, R&B, Roulette, Route; (66) S&B, Salsoul, Santa Ponsa; (67) Seville; (68) Soul City; (69) Spark, Specialty, Stateside Pt 1; (70) Stateside Pt 2; (71) Stateside Pt 3; (72) Stax Pt 1; (73) Stax Pt 2; (74) Sue Pt 1; (75) Sue Pt 2; (76) Surrey, Sussex, Tamla Motown Pt 1; (77) Tamla Motown Pt 2; (78) Tangerine, Toast, Top Rank; (79) Track, 20th Century; (80) Transatlantic, Trojan, UK; (81) Utd Artists Pt 1; (82) Utd Artists Pt 2; (83) Uni, UPC, Upfront, Vanguard, Vertigo, Verve; (84) Vogue Pt 1; (85) Vogue/Vocalion Pt 2; (86) Wand; (87) Warner Bros; (88) Westbound, WWA, Youngblood

COLLECTABLE INDIE SINGLES GUIDE

This series of collectable U.K. independent singles is in alphabetical order. The coverage is as follows:

SPECIAL PRESSINGS GUIDE

This list of collectable items is in alphabetical artist order. The coverage is as follows:

RECORD COLLECTOR'S GRADING SYSTEM

In order to assist everyone who buys and sells rare discs, Record Collector magazine has originated a set of standards for the condition of second-hand records. Anyone buying or selling records through the magazine should use our conditions to state what amount of wear and tear the disc, its sleeve and/or contents have been subject to. The seven standard condition categories and a description of what each one means are listed below:

MINT: The record itself is in brand new condition with no surface marks or deterioration in sound quality. The cover and any extra items such as the lyric sheet, booklet or poster are in perfect condition.

EXCELLENT: The record shows very slight signs of having been played, but there is no lessening in sound quality and the cover and packaging are as new.

VERY GOOD: The record has obviously been played a few times, but displays no major deterioration in sound quality. A slight amount of wear and tear on the cover or extra items is acceptable.

GOOD: The record still produces a reasonable sound but has obviously been played a lot. Although showing wear and tear, neither the record, cover nor contents display any major defects.

FAIR: It is noticeable that the record has been played so much that the sound quality has deteriorated quite a bit. The cover and contents are showing signs of folding, scuffing of edges, etc.

POOR: The record is still just about playable but has not been cared for properly and displays considerable surface noise and other deterioration in sound quality.

BAD: The record will not play properly due to scratches, bad surface noise, etc. The cover and contents will be torn, stained, defaced or even missing.

CDs & CASSETTES: As a general rule, CDs and cassettes either play perfectly — in which case they are in Mint condition — or they don't, in which case their value is minimal. Cassette tape is liable to deteriorate with age, even if it remains unplayed, so care should be taken when purchasing cassettes that are more than 15 or so years old. CDs are difficult to grade visually: they can look perfect but actually be faulty, while in other cases they may appear scratched or dented but still play without any problems or deterioration in sound quality. Cassette and CD inlays and booklets should be graded in the same way as record covers and sleeves; in general, the plastic containers for cassettes and CDs can easily be replaced if they are broken or scratched.

RECORD COLLECTOR'S GRADING READY RECKONER

This Ready Reckoner will help you work out the value of a record in any condition. For example, if you see a disc which is valued at £10 in Mint condition, but which you consider to be in only Very Good condition, then you can consult the Ready Reckoner and find out the appropriate price for the record — in this case, £6.50. As very few collectors are interested in records in Poor or Bad condition, we consider that any disc worth less than £10 in Mint condition is virtually worthless in Poor or Bad condition.

Mint	EX	VG	Good	Fair	Poor	Bad
500	400	325	250	150	75	25
300	240	190	155	90	45	15
250	200	160	125	75	35	12
200	160	130	100	60	30	10
150	120	100	75	45	25	8
125	100	80	65	40	20	7
100	80	65	50	30	15	5
75	60	50	35	22	10	4
50	40	33	25	15	8	3
40	32	26	20	10	6	2.50
30	25	20	15	9	4.50	2
25	20	17	12	8	4	1.75
20	16	13	10	6	3	1.50
15	12	10	7	4.50	2	1
12	10	8	6	3.50	1	50p
10	8	6.50	4.50	2	75p	—
9	7	5.75	4	1.75	—	—
8	6	4.50	3.50	1.50	—	—
7	5	3.75	3	1.50	—	—
6	4.50	3.50	2.50	1.25	—	—
5	4	3	2	1.25	—	—
4	3.25	2.50	1.75	1	—	—
3	2.50	2	1.50	75p	—	—
2	1.75	1.30	1	50p	—	—

ABBREVIATIONS USED IN THIS PRICE GUIDE

alt.	alternative	no.	number
b&w	black and white	no'd	numbered
cass.	cassette	p/s	picture sleeve
cat. no.	catalogue number	pic disc	picture disc
CD	compact disc	pt(s)	part(s)
co.	company	stkr	sticker
d/pack	double pack	sl.	sleeve
dble.	double	st.	stereo
diff.	different	t/p	test pressing
edn.	edition	vers.	version
ext.	extended	vol.	volume
flexi	flexidisc	w/	with
g/f(old)	gatefold sleeve	w/l	white label
intl.	international	2-CD	double CD
m/s	mono/stereo	2-LP	double LP
mag.	magazine	3-LP	triple LP

OTHER IMPORTANT TERMS

company sleeve	standard non-picture cover bearing the company name or logo, used by a label for its single releases
demo	demonstration record not commercially available to the public
die-cut sleeve	sleeve with circular hole cut into the centre
double pack	two singles issued together as one package
gatefold sleeve	double-size sleeve that opens out like a book
private pressing	record issued and distributed by private individuals rather than a company
promo	promotional record or item sent out to the media to publicise a new release
stickered	record issued with a small sticker on the cover, sleeve or wrapping
test pressing	manufacturer's sample record, pressed for quality control purposes
tri-centre	push-out triangular centre found on some 1950s singles and EPs
tri-fold	triple fold-out sleeve
withdrawn	record deliberately removed from sale by its manufacturer

For full details of how to use the guide, see the "Using The Guide" section on pages 12-15, or the brief summary on page 18.